Periodic Table of the Elements

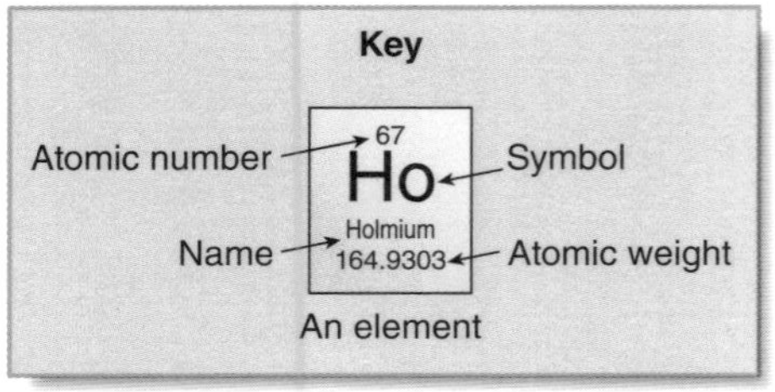
Key
Atomic number
67
Ho
Holmium
164.9303
Symbol
Name
Atomic weight
An element

Period number	Group number → 1A	2A	3B	4B	5B	6B	7B	8B	8B	8B	1B	2B	3A	4A	5A	6A	7A	8A	
1	1 H Hydrogen 1.0079																	2 He Helium 4.0026	1
2	3 Li Lithium 6.941	4 Be Beryllium 9.0122											5 B Boron 10.811	6 C Carbon 12.011	7 N Nitrogen 14.0067	8 O Oxygen 15.9994	9 F Fluorine 18.9984	10 Ne Neon 20.1797	2
3	11 Na Sodium 22.9898	12 Mg Magnesium 24.3050											13 Al Aluminum 26.9815	14 Si Silicon 28.0855	15 P Phosphorus 30.9738	16 S Sulfur 32.066	17 Cl Chlorine 35.4527	18 Ar Argon 39.948	3
4	19 K Potassium 39.0983	20 Ca Calcium 40.078	21 Sc Scandium 44.9559	22 Ti Titanium 47.88	23 V Vanadium 50.9415	24 Cr Chromium 51.9961	25 Mn Manganese 54.9380	26 Fe Iron 55.845	27 Co Cobalt 58.9332	28 Ni Nickel 58.693	29 Cu Copper 63.546	30 Zn Zinc 65.41	31 Ga Gallium 69.723	32 Ge Germanium 72.64	33 As Arsenic 74.9216	34 Se Selenium 78.96	35 Br Bromine 79.904	36 Kr Krypton 83.80	4
5	37 Rb Rubidium 85.4678	38 Sr Strontium 87.62	39 Y Yttrium 88.9059	40 Zr Zirconium 91.224	41 Nb Niobium 92.9064	42 Mo Molybdenum 95.94	43 Tc Technetium (98)	44 Ru Ruthenium 101.07	45 Rh Rhodium 102.9055	46 Pd Palladium 106.42	47 Ag Silver 107.8682	48 Cd Cadmium 112.411	49 In Indium 114.82	50 Sn Tin 118.710	51 Sb Antimony 121.760	52 Te Tellurium 127.60	53 I Iodine 126.9045	54 Xe Xenon 131.29	5
6	55 Cs Cesium 132.9054	56 Ba Barium 137.327	57 La Lanthanum 138.9055	72 Hf Hafnium 178.49	73 Ta Tantalum 180.9479	74 W Tungsten 183.84	75 Re Rhenium 186.207	76 Os Osmium 190.2	77 Ir Iridium 192.22	78 Pt Platinum 195.08	79 Au Gold 196.9665	80 Hg Mercury 200.59	81 Tl Thallium 204.3833	82 Pb Lead 207.2	83 Bi Bismuth 208.9804	84 Po Polonium (209)	85 At Astatine (210)	86 Rn Radon (222)	6
7	87 Fr Francium (223)	88 Ra Radium (226)	89 Ac Actinium (227)	104 Rf Rutherfordium (267)	105 Db Dubnium (268)	106 Sg Seaborgium (271)	107 Bh Bohrium (272)	108 Hs Hassium (270)	109 Mt Meitnerium (276)	110 Ds Darmstadtium (281)	111 Rg Roentgenium (280)	112 Cn Copernicium (285)	113 — — (284)	114 Fl Flerovium (289)	115 — — (288)	116 Lv Livermorium (293)	117 — — (294)	118 — — (294)	7

Lanthanides	6	58 Ce Cerium 140.115	59 Pr Praseodymium 140.9076	60 Nd Neodymium 144.24	61 Pm Promethium (145)	62 Sm Samarium 150.36	63 Eu Europium 151.964	64 Gd Gadolinium 157.25	65 Tb Terbium 158.9253	66 Dy Dysprosium 162.50	67 Ho Holmium 164.9303	68 Er Erbium 167.26	69 Tm Thulium 168.9342	70 Yb Ytterbium 173.04	71 Lu Lutetium 174.967	6
Actinides	7	90 Th Thorium 232.0381	91 Pa Protactinium 231.0359	92 U Uranium 238.0289	93 Np Neptunium (237)	94 Pu Plutonium (244)	95 Am Americium (243)	96 Cm Curium (247)	97 Bk Berkelium (247)	98 Cf Californium (251)	99 Es Einsteinium (252)	100 Fm Fermium (257)	101 Md Mendelevium (258)	102 No Nobelium (259)	103 Lr Lawrencium (260)	7

COMMON FUNCTIONAL GROUPS

Type of Compound	General Structure	Example	Functional Group
Acid chloride	$R-C(=\ddot{O})-\ddot{Cl}:$	$CH_3-C(=\ddot{O})-\ddot{Cl}:$	$-COCl$
Alcohol	$R-\ddot{O}H$	$CH_3-\ddot{O}H$	$-OH$ hydroxy group
Aldehyde	$R-C(=\ddot{O})-H$	$CH_3-C(=\ddot{O})-H$	$C=O$ carbonyl group
Alkane	$R-H$	CH_3CH_3	– –
Alkene	$>C=C<$	$H_2C=CH_2$	double bond
Alkyl halide	$R-\ddot{X}:$ (X = F, Cl, Br, I)	$CH_3-\ddot{Br}:$	$-X$ halo group
Alkyne	$-C\equiv C-$	$H-C\equiv C-H$	triple bond
Amide	$R-C(=\ddot{O})-\ddot{N}(H \text{ (or R)})-H \text{ (or R)}$	$CH_3-C(=\ddot{O})-\ddot{N}H_2$	$-CONH_2$, $-CONHR$, $-CONR_2$
Amine	$R-\ddot{N}H_2$ or $R_2\ddot{N}H$ or $R_3\ddot{N}$	$CH_3-\ddot{N}H_2$	$-NH_2$ amino group
Anhydride	$R-C(=\ddot{O})-\ddot{O}-C(=\ddot{O})-R$	$CH_3-C(=\ddot{O})-\ddot{O}-C(=\ddot{O})-CH_3$	$-C(=O)-O-C(=O)-$

Type of Compound	General Structure	Example	Functional Group
Aromatic compound	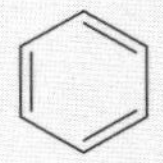	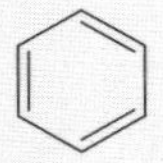	phenyl group
Carboxylic acid	$R-C(=\ddot{O})-\ddot{O}H$	$CH_3-C(=\ddot{O})-\ddot{O}H$	$-COOH$ carboxy group
Ester	$R-C(=\ddot{O})-\ddot{O}R$	$CH_3-C(=\ddot{O})-\ddot{O}CH_3$	$-COOR$
Ether	$R-\ddot{O}-R$	$CH_3-\ddot{O}-CH_3$	$-OR$ alkoxy group
Ketone	$R-C(=\ddot{O})-R$	$CH_3-C(=\ddot{O})-CH_3$	$C=O$ carbonyl group
Nitrile	$R-C\equiv N:$	$CH_3-C\equiv N:$	$-C\equiv N$ cyano group
Sulfide	$R-\ddot{S}-R$	$CH_3-\ddot{S}-CH_3$	$-SR$ alkylthio group
Thiol	$R-\ddot{S}H$	$CH_3-\ddot{S}H$	$-SH$ mercapto group
Thioester	$R-C(=\ddot{O})-\ddot{S}R$	$CH_3-C(=\ddot{O})-\ddot{S}CH_3$	$-COSR$

Mc Graw Hill connect™

Student Quick Tips

Use this Student Quick Tips guide for a quick and easy start with McGraw-Hill Connect. You'll get valuable tips on registering, doing assignments, and accessing resources, as well as information about the support center hours.

Getting Started

TIP: To get started in Connect, you will need the following:

- Your instructor's Connect Web Address

  Sample of Connect Web Address:
  http://www.mcgrawhillconnect.com/class/instructorname_section_name

- Connect Access Code

TIP: If you do not have an access code or have not yet secured your tuition funds, you can click "Free Trial" during registration. This trial will provide temporary Connect access (typically three weeks) and will remind you to purchase online access before the end of your trial.

Registration and Sign In

1. Go to the Connect Web Address provided by your instructor
2. Click on **Register Now**
3. Enter your email address

TIP: If you already have a McGraw-Hill account, you will be asked for your password and will not be required to create a new account.

4. Enter a registration code or choose **Buy Online** to purchase access online

(Continued: **Registration and Sign In**)

5. Follow the on-screen directions

TIP: Please choose your Security Question and Answer carefully. We will ask you for this information if you forget your password.

6. When registration is complete, click on **Go to Connect Now**
7. You are now ready to use **Connect**

Trouble Logging In?

- Ensure you are using the same email address you used during registration
- If you have forgotten your password, click on the "Forgot Password?" link at your Instructor's Connect Course Web Address
- When logged into Connect, you can update your account information (e.g. email address, password, and security question/answer) by clicking on the *"My Account"* link located at the top-right corner

Home (Assignments)

TIP: If you are unable to begin an assignment, verify the following:

- The assignment is available (start and due dates)
- That you have not exceeded the maximum number of attempts
- That you have not achieved a score of 100%
- If your assignment contains questions that require manual grading, you will not be able to begin your next attempt until your instructor has graded those questions

(Continued: **Home Assignments**)

TIP: Based on the assignment policy settings established by your Instructor, you may encounter the following limitations when working on your assignment(s):

- Ability to Print Assignment
- Timed assignments – once you begin a "*timed assignment*," the timer will not stop by design

TIP: "*Save & Exit*" vs. "*Submit*" button

- If you are unable to complete your assignment in one sitting, utilize the "*Save & Exit*" button to save your work and complete it at a later time
- Once you have completed your assignment, utilize the "*Submit*" button in order for your assignment to be graded

Library

TIP: The *Library* section of your Connect account provides shortcuts to various resources.

- If you purchased ConnectPlus, you will see an *eBook* link, which can also be accessed from the section information widget of the *Home* tab
- *Recorded Lectures* can be accessed if your instructor is using *Tegrity Campus* to capture lectures. You may also access recorded lectures when taking an assignment by clicking on the projector icon in the navigation bar
- Many McGraw-Hill textbooks offer additional resources such as narrated slides and additional problems, which are accessible through the *Student Resources* link

Reports

TIP: Once you submit your assignment, you can view your available results in the *Reports* tab.

- If you see a dash (-) as your score, your instructor has either delayed or restricted your ability to see the assignment feedback
- Your instructor has the ability to limit the amount of information (e.g. questions, answers, scores) you can view for each submitted assignment

Need More Help?

CONTACT US ONLINE

Visit us at:

www.mcgrawhillconnect.com/support

Browse our support materials including tutorial videos and our searchable Connect knowledge base. If you cannot find an answer to your question, click on "Contact Us" button to send us an email.

GIVE US A CALL

Call us at:

1-800-331-5094

Our live support is available:

Mon-Thurs:	8 am – 11 pm CT
Friday:	8 am – 6 pm CT
Sunday:	6 pm – 11 pm CT

CHEM

2310 – 2320

Janice Gorzynski Smith

University of Hawai'i at Mānoa

University of Utah

McGraw Hill Education

1 2 3 4 5 6 7 8 9 0 KNG KNG 15 14 13

ISBN-13: 978-1-259-12545-4
ISBN-10: 1-259-12545-9

Learning Solutions Representative: James Doepke
Associate Project Manager: Mark Bodensteiner
Cover Photo Credit: 009463.mod.tif © Creatas/PunchStock

About the Author

Janice Gorzynski Smith was born in Schenectady, New York. She became interested in chemistry in high school and went on to major in chemistry at Cornell University, where she received an A.B. degree *summa cum laude*. Jan earned a Ph.D. in Organic Chemistry from Harvard University under the direction of Nobel Laureate E. J. Corey, and she also spent a year as a National Science Foundation National Needs Postdoctoral Fellow at Harvard. During her tenure with the Corey group, she completed the total synthesis of the plant growth hormone gibberellic acid.

Following her postdoctoral work, Jan joined the faculty of Mount Holyoke College, where she was employed for 21 years. During this time she was active in teaching organic chemistry lecture and lab courses, conducting a research program in organic synthesis, and serving as department chair. Her organic chemistry class was named one of Mount Holyoke's "Don't-miss courses" in a survey by *Boston* magazine. After spending two sabbaticals amidst the natural beauty and diversity in Hawai'i in the 1990s, Jan and her family moved there permanently in 2000. She is currently a faculty member at the University of Hawai'i at Mānoa, where she teaches the two-semester organic chemistry lecture and lab courses. In 2003, she received the Chancellor's Citation for Meritorious Teaching.

Jan resides in Hawai'i with her husband Dan, an emergency medicine physician. She has four children and one grandchild. When not teaching, writing, or enjoying her family, Jan bikes, hikes, snorkels, and scuba dives in sunny Hawai'i, and time permitting, enjoys travel and Hawaiian quilting.

For Megan Sarah

Contents in Brief

Prologue 1
1 Structure and Bonding 7
2 Acids and Bases 58
3 Introduction to Organic Molecules and Functional Groups 86
4 Alkanes 120
5 Stereochemistry 166
6 Understanding Organic Reactions 205
7 Alkyl Halides and Nucleophilic Substitution 238
8 Alkyl Halides and Elimination Reactions 288
9 Alcohols, Ethers, and Epoxides 324
10 Alkenes 372
11 Alkynes 416
12 Oxidation and Reduction 444
13 Mass Spectrometry and Infrared Spectroscopy 483
14 Nuclear Magnetic Resonance Spectroscopy 514
15 Radical Reactions 558
16 Conjugation, Resonance, and Dienes 593
17 Benzene and Aromatic Compounds 630
18 Reactions of Aromatic Compounds 665
19 Carboxylic Acids and the Acidity of the O–H Bond 718
20 Introduction to Carbonyl Chemistry; Organometallic Reagents; Oxidation and Reduction 753
21 Aldehydes and Ketones—Nucleophilic Addition 807
22 Carboxylic Acids and Their Derivatives—Nucleophilic Acyl Substitution 859
23 Substitution Reactions of Carbonyl Compounds at the α Carbon 915
24 Carbonyl Condensation Reactions 954
25 Amines 988
26 Carbon–Carbon Bond-Forming Reactions in Organic Synthesis 1042
27 Pericyclic Reactions 1069
28 Carbohydrates 1098
29 Amino Acids and Proteins 1148
30 Lipids 1194
31 Synthetic Polymers 1225
Appendices A-1
Glossary G-1
Credits C-1
Index I-1

Contents

Preface xiii

Acknowledgments xxi

List of *How To's* xxiv

List of Mechanisms xxvi

List of Selected Applications xxix

Prologue 1

What Is Organic Chemistry? 1

Some Representative Organic Molecules 2

Organic Chemistry in the Marine Environment 4

1 Structure and Bonding 8

1.1 The Periodic Table 8

1.2 Bonding 11

1.3 Lewis Structures 13

1.4 Isomers 18

1.5 Exceptions to the Octet Rule 18

1.6 Resonance 19

1.7 Determining Molecular Shape 24

1.8 Drawing Organic Structures 29

1.9 Hybridization 34

1.10 Ethane, Ethylene, and Acetylene 38

1.11 Bond Length and Bond Strength 43

1.12 Electronegativity and Bond Polarity 45

1.13 Polarity of Molecules 47

1.14 L-Dopa—A Representative Organic Molecule 48

Key Concepts 49

Problems 51

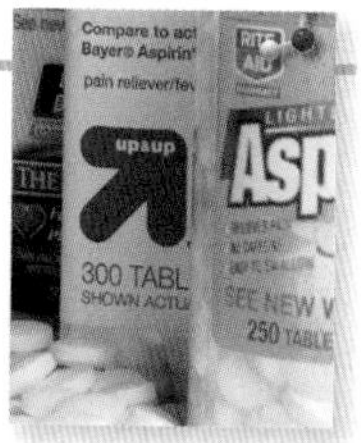

2 Acids and Bases 58

2.1 Brønsted–Lowry Acids and Bases 59

2.2 Reactions of Brønsted–Lowry Acids and Bases 60

2.3 Acid Strength and pK_a 62

2.4 Predicting the Outcome of Acid–Base Reactions 65

2.5 Factors That Determine Acid Strength 66

2.6 Common Acids and Bases 76

2.7 Aspirin 76

2.8 Lewis Acids and Bases 77

Key Concepts 79

Problems 80

3 Introduction to Organic Molecules and Functional Groups 86

3.1 Functional Groups 87

3.2 An Overview of Functional Groups 88

3.3 Intermolecular Forces 92

3.4 Physical Properties 96

3.5 Application: Vitamins 102

3.6 Application of Solubility: Soap 104

3.7 Application: The Cell Membrane 105

3.8 Functional Groups and Reactivity 108

3.9 Biomolecules 110

Key Concepts 111

Problems 113

4 Alkanes 120

4.1 Alkanes—An Introduction 121

4.2 Cycloalkanes 125

4.3 An Introduction to Nomenclature 125

4.4 Naming Alkanes 126

4.5 Naming Cycloalkanes 132

4.6 Common Names 134

4.7 Fossil Fuels 135

4.8 Physical Properties of Alkanes 136

4.9 Conformations of Acyclic Alkanes—Ethane 137

4.10 Conformations of Butane 141

4.11 An Introduction to Cycloalkanes 144

4.12 Cyclohexane 145

4.13 Substituted Cyclohexanes 148

4.14 Oxidation of Alkanes 154

4.15 Lipids—Part 1 156

Key Concepts 158

Problems 160

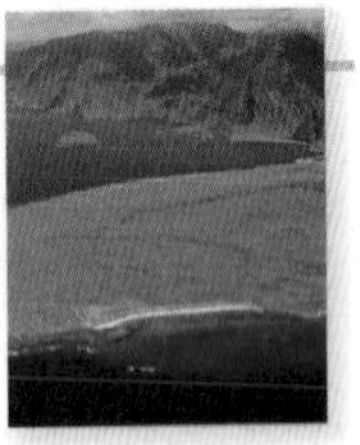

5 Stereochemistry 166

5.1 Starch and Cellulose 167
5.2 The Two Major Classes of Isomers 169
5.3 Looking Glass Chemistry—Chiral and Achiral Molecules 170
5.4 Stereogenic Centers 173
5.5 Stereogenic Centers in Cyclic Compounds 176
5.6 Labeling Stereogenic Centers with *R* or *S* 178
5.7 Diastereomers 183
5.8 Meso Compounds 185
5.9 *R* and *S* Assignments in Compounds with Two or More Stereogenic Centers 187
5.10 Disubstituted Cycloalkanes 187
5.11 Isomers—A Summary 189
5.12 Physical Properties of Stereoisomers 190
5.13 Chemical Properties of Enantiomers 195
Key Concepts 197
Problems 198

6 Understanding Organic Reactions 205

6.1 Writing Equations for Organic Reactions 206
6.2 Kinds of Organic Reactions 207
6.3 Bond Breaking and Bond Making 209
6.4 Bond Dissociation Energy 212
6.5 Thermodynamics 216
6.6 Enthalpy and Entropy 218
6.7 Energy Diagrams 220
6.8 Energy Diagram for a Two-Step Reaction Mechanism 222
6.9 Kinetics 225
6.10 Catalysts 228
6.11 Enzymes 229
Key Concepts 230
Problems 232

7 Alkyl Halides and Nucleophilic Substitution 238

7.1 Introduction to Alkyl Halides 239
7.2 Nomenclature 240
7.3 Physical Properties 241
7.4 Interesting Alkyl Halides 242
7.5 The Polar Carbon–Halogen Bond 244
7.6 General Features of Nucleophilic Substitution 245
7.7 The Leaving Group 246
7.8 The Nucleophile 248
7.9 Possible Mechanisms for Nucleophilic Substitution 252
7.10 Two Mechanisms for Nucleophilic Substitution 253
7.11 The S_N2 Mechanism 254
7.12 Application: Useful S_N2 Reactions 260
7.13 The S_N1 Mechanism 262
7.14 Carbocation Stability 266
7.15 The Hammond Postulate 268
7.16 Application: S_N1 Reactions, Nitrosamines, and Cancer 271
7.17 When Is the Mechanism S_N1 or S_N2? 272
7.18 Vinyl Halides and Aryl Halides 277
7.19 Organic Synthesis 278
Key Concepts 280
Problems 281

8 Alkyl Halides and Elimination Reactions 288

8.1 General Features of Elimination 289
8.2 Alkenes—The Products of Elimination Reactions 291
8.3 The Mechanisms of Elimination 294
8.4 The E2 Mechanism 295
8.5 The Zaitsev Rule 299
8.6 The E1 Mechanism 301
8.7 S_N1 and E1 Reactions 304
8.8 Stereochemistry of the E2 Reaction 305
8.9 When Is the Mechanism E1 or E2? 309
8.10 E2 Reactions and Alkyne Synthesis 310
8.11 When Is the Reaction S_N1, S_N2, E1, or E2? 311
Key Concepts 315
Problems 317

9 Alcohols, Ethers, and Epoxides 324

9.1 Introduction 325
9.2 Structure and Bonding 326
9.3 Nomenclature 327

9.4 Physical Properties 330
9.5 Interesting Alcohols, Ethers, and Epoxides 331
9.6 Preparation of Alcohols, Ethers, and Epoxides 334
9.7 General Features—Reactions of Alcohols, Ethers, and Epoxides 336
9.8 Dehydration of Alcohols to Alkenes 338
9.9 Carbocation Rearrangements 341
9.10 Dehydration Using $POCl_3$ and Pyridine 344
9.11 Conversion of Alcohols to Alkyl Halides with HX 345
9.12 Conversion of Alcohols to Alkyl Halides with $SOCl_2$ and PBr_3 349
9.13 Tosylate—Another Good Leaving Group 352
9.14 Reaction of Ethers with Strong Acid 355
9.15 Reactions of Epoxides 357
9.16 Application: Epoxides, Leukotrienes, and Asthma 361
9.17 Application: Benzo[*a*]pyrene, Epoxides, and Cancer 363
Key Concepts 363
Problems 365

10 Alkenes 372

10.1 Introduction 373
10.2 Calculating Degrees of Unsaturation 374
10.3 Nomenclature 376
10.4 Physical Properties 380
10.5 Interesting Alkenes 380
10.6 Lipids—Part 2 382
10.7 Preparation of Alkenes 384
10.8 Introduction to Addition Reactions 385
10.9 Hydrohalogenation—Electrophilic Addition of HX 386
10.10 Markovnikov's Rule 389
10.11 Stereochemistry of Electrophilic Addition of HX 391
10.12 Hydration—Electrophilic Addition of Water 394
10.13 Halogenation—Addition of Halogen 395
10.14 Stereochemistry of Halogenation 396
10.15 Halohydrin Formation 398
10.16 Hydroboration–Oxidation 401
10.17 Keeping Track of Reactions 406
10.18 Alkenes in Organic Synthesis 407
Key Concepts 409
Problems 410

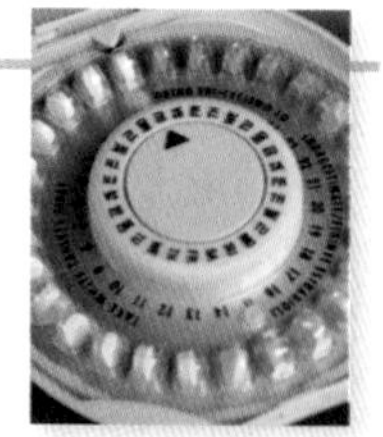

11 Alkynes 416

11.1 Introduction 417
11.2 Nomenclature 418
11.3 Physical Properties 419
11.4 Interesting Alkynes 420
11.5 Preparation of Alkynes 421
11.6 Introduction to Alkyne Reactions 422
11.7 Addition of Hydrogen Halides 424
11.8 Addition of Halogen 426
11.9 Addition of Water 427
11.10 Hydroboration–Oxidation 429
11.11 Reaction of Acetylide Anions 431
11.12 Synthesis 434
Key Concepts 437
Problems 438

12 Oxidation and Reduction 444

12.1 Introduction 445
12.2 Reducing Agents 446
12.3 Reduction of Alkenes 447
12.4 Application: Hydrogenation of Oils 450
12.5 Reduction of Alkynes 452
12.6 The Reduction of Polar C–X σ Bonds 455
12.7 Oxidizing Agents 456
12.8 Epoxidation 458
12.9 Dihydroxylation 461
12.10 Oxidative Cleavage of Alkenes 463
12.11 Oxidative Cleavage of Alkynes 465
12.12 Oxidation of Alcohols 466
12.13 Green Chemistry 469
12.14 Application: The Oxidation of Ethanol 470
12.15 Sharpless Epoxidation 471
Key Concepts 474
Problems 476

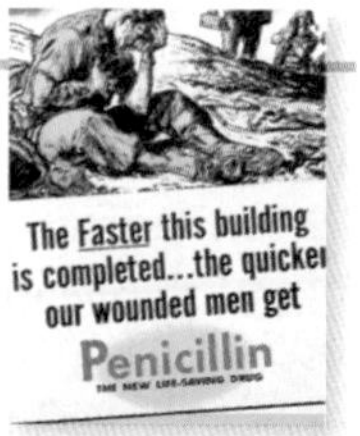

13 Mass Spectrometry and Infrared Spectroscopy 483

13.1 Mass Spectrometry 484
13.2 Alkyl Halides and the M + 2 Peak 488
13.3 Fragmentation 489
13.4 Other Types of Mass Spectrometry 492

13.5 Electromagnetic Radiation 494
13.6 Infrared Spectroscopy 496
13.7 IR Absorptions 498
13.8 IR and Structure Determination 505
Key Concepts 507
Problems 508

14 Nuclear Magnetic Resonance Spectroscopy 514

14.1 An Introduction to NMR Spectroscopy 515
14.2 ^{1}H NMR: Number of Signals 518
14.3 ^{1}H NMR: Position of Signals 522
14.4 The Chemical Shift of Protons on *sp*^{2} and *sp* Hybridized Carbons 525
14.5 ^{1}H NMR: Intensity of Signals 527
14.6 ^{1}H NMR: Spin–Spin Splitting 529
14.7 More Complex Examples of Splitting 533
14.8 Spin–Spin Splitting in Alkenes 536
14.9 Other Facts About ^{1}H NMR Spectroscopy 538
14.10 Using ^{1}H NMR to Identify an Unknown 541
14.11 ^{13}C NMR Spectroscopy 543
14.12 Magnetic Resonance Imaging (MRI) 547
Key Concepts 548
Problems 549

15 Radical Reactions 558

15.1 Introduction 559
15.2 General Features of Radical Reactions 560
15.3 Halogenation of Alkanes 562
15.4 The Mechanism of Halogenation 563
15.5 Chlorination of Other Alkanes 566
15.6 Chlorination Versus Bromination 566
15.7 Halogenation as a Tool in Organic Synthesis 570
15.8 The Stereochemistry of Halogenation Reactions 570
15.9 Application: The Ozone Layer and CFCs 573
15.10 Radical Halogenation at an Allylic Carbon 574
15.11 Application: Oxidation of Unsaturated Lipids 577
15.12 Application: Antioxidants 578
15.13 Radical Addition Reactions to Double Bonds 579
15.14 Polymers and Polymerization 582
Key Concepts 585
Problems 586

16 Conjugation, Resonance, and Dienes 593

16.1 Conjugation 594
16.2 Resonance and Allylic Carbocations 596
16.3 Common Examples of Resonance 597
16.4 The Resonance Hybrid 599
16.5 Electron Delocalization, Hybridization, and Geometry 600
16.6 Conjugated Dienes 601
16.7 Interesting Dienes and Polyenes 602
16.8 The Carbon–Carbon σ Bond Length in 1,3-Butadiene 603
16.9 Stability of Conjugated Dienes 604
16.10 Electrophilic Addition: 1,2- Versus 1,4-Addition 606
16.11 Kinetic Versus Thermodynamic Products 608
16.12 The Diels–Alder Reaction 610
16.13 Specific Rules Governing the Diels–Alder Reaction 612
16.14 Other Facts About the Diels–Alder Reaction 616
16.15 Conjugated Dienes and Ultraviolet Light 619
Key Concepts 621
Problems 623

17 Benzene and Aromatic Compounds 630

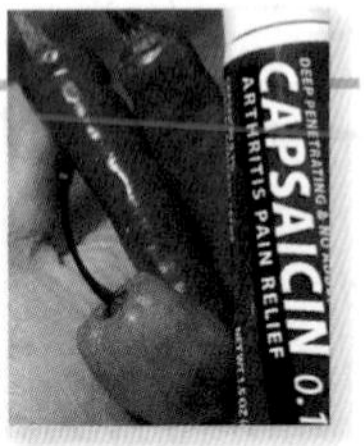

17.1 Background 631
17.2 The Structure of Benzene 632
17.3 Nomenclature of Benzene Derivatives 634
17.4 Spectroscopic Properties 636
17.5 Interesting Aromatic Compounds 637
17.6 Benzene's Unusual Stability 639
17.7 The Criteria for Aromaticity—Hückel's Rule 640
17.8 Examples of Aromatic Compounds 643
17.9 What Is the Basis of Hückel's Rule? 650
17.10 The Inscribed Polygon Method for Predicting Aromaticity 653
17.11 Buckminsterfullerene—Is it Aromatic? 655
Key Concepts 656
Problems 657

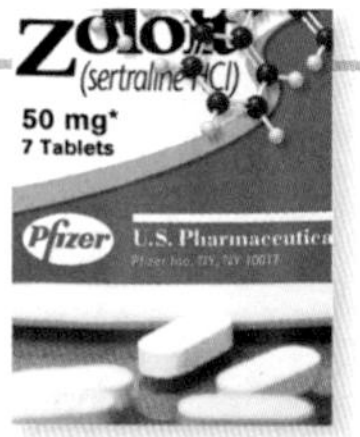

18 Reactions of Aromatic Compounds 665

18.1 Electrophilic Aromatic Substitution 666
18.2 The General Mechanism 667
18.3 Halogenation 669
18.4 Nitration and Sulfonation 670
18.5 Friedel–Crafts Alkylation and Friedel–Crafts Acylation 672
18.6 Substituted Benzenes 678
18.7 Electrophilic Aromatic Substitution of Substituted Benzenes 681
18.8 Why Substituents Activate or Deactivate a Benzene Ring 684
18.9 Orientation Effects in Substituted Benzenes 686
18.10 Limitations on Electrophilic Substitution Reactions with Substituted Benzenes 690
18.11 Disubstituted Benzenes 692
18.12 Synthesis of Benzene Derivatives 694
18.13 Nucleophilic Aromatic Substitution 695
18.14 Halogenation of Alkyl Benzenes 699
18.15 Oxidation and Reduction of Substituted Benzenes 701
18.16 Multistep Synthesis 705
Key Concepts 708
Problems 710

19 Carboxylic Acids and the Acidity of the O–H Bond 718

19.1 Structure and Bonding 719
19.2 Nomenclature 720
19.3 Physical Properties 723
19.4 Spectroscopic Properties 724
19.5 Interesting Carboxylic Acids 725
19.6 Aspirin, Arachidonic Acid, and Prostaglandins 726
19.7 Preparation of Carboxylic Acids 728
19.8 Reactions of Carboxylic Acids—General Features 729
19.9 Carboxylic Acids—Strong Organic Brønsted–Lowry Acids 730
19.10 Inductive Effects in Aliphatic Carboxylic Acids 734
19.11 Substituted Benzoic Acids 735
19.12 Extraction 738
19.13 Sulfonic Acids 741
19.14 Amino Acids 741
Key Concepts 744
Problems 745

20 Introduction to Carbonyl Chemistry; Organometallic Reagents; Oxidation and Reduction 753

20.1 Introduction 754
20.2 General Reactions of Carbonyl Compounds 755
20.3 A Preview of Oxidation and Reduction 758
20.4 Reduction of Aldehydes and Ketones 760
20.5 The Stereochemistry of Carbonyl Reduction 762
20.6 Enantioselective Carbonyl Reductions 763
20.7 Reduction of Carboxylic Acids and Their Derivatives 766
20.8 Oxidation of Aldehydes 771
20.9 Organometallic Reagents 771
20.10 Reaction of Organometallic Reagents with Aldehydes and Ketones 775
20.11 Retrosynthetic Analysis of Grignard Products 778
20.12 Protecting Groups 781
20.13 Reaction of Organometallic Reagents with Carboxylic Acid Derivatives 783
20.14 Reaction of Organometallic Reagents with Other Compounds 786
20.15 α,β-Unsaturated Carbonyl Compounds 788
20.16 Summary—The Reactions of Organometallic Reagents 791
20.17 Synthesis 792
Key Concepts 795
Problems 798

21 Aldehydes and Ketones—Nucleophilic Addition 807

21.1 Introduction 808
21.2 Nomenclature 809
21.3 Physical Properties 812
21.4 Spectroscopic Properties 813
21.5 Interesting Aldehydes and Ketones 815
21.6 Preparation of Aldehydes and Ketones 816

21.7 Reactions of Aldehydes and Ketones—General Considerations 818
21.8 Nucleophilic Addition of H^- and R^-—A Review 821
21.9 Nucleophilic Addition of ^-CN 823
21.10 The Wittig Reaction 825
21.11 Addition of 1° Amines 830
21.12 Addition of 2° Amines 833
21.13 Addition of H_2O—Hydration 835
21.14 Addition of Alcohols—Acetal Formation 837
21.15 Acetals as Protecting Groups 841
21.16 Cyclic Hemiacetals 842
21.17 An Introduction to Carbohydrates 845
Key Concepts 846
Problems 849

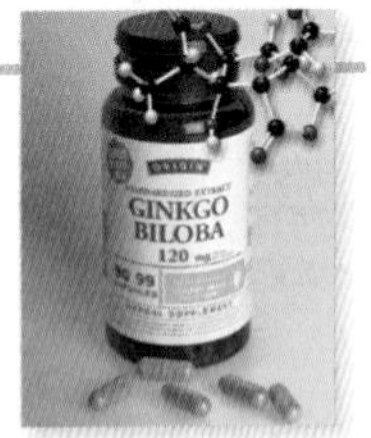

22 Carboxylic Acids and Their Derivatives—Nucleophilic Acyl Substitution 859

22.1 Introduction 860
22.2 Structure and Bonding 862
22.3 Nomenclature 864
22.4 Physical Properties 868
22.5 Spectroscopic Properties 869
22.6 Interesting Esters and Amides 871
22.7 Introduction to Nucleophilic Acyl Substitution 873
22.8 Reactions of Acid Chlorides 876
22.9 Reactions of Anhydrides 878
22.10 Reactions of Carboxylic Acids 880
22.11 Reactions of Esters 885
22.12 Application: Lipid Hydrolysis 887
22.13 Reactions of Amides 890
22.14 Application: The Mechanism of Action of β-Lactam Antibiotics 891
22.15 Summary of Nucleophilic Acyl Substitution Reactions 892
22.16 Natural and Synthetic Fibers 893
22.17 Biological Acylation Reactions 895
22.18 Nitriles 897
Key Concepts 902
Problems 905

23 Substitution Reactions of Carbonyl Compounds at the α Carbon 915

23.1 Introduction 916
23.2 Enols 917
23.3 Enolates 919
23.4 Enolates of Unsymmetrical Carbonyl Compounds 925
23.5 Racemization at the α Carbon 927
23.6 A Preview of Reactions at the α Carbon 928
23.7 Halogenation at the α Carbon 928
23.8 Direct Enolate Alkylation 933
23.9 Malonic Ester Synthesis 936
23.10 Acetoacetic Ester Synthesis 940
Key Concepts 943
Problems 945

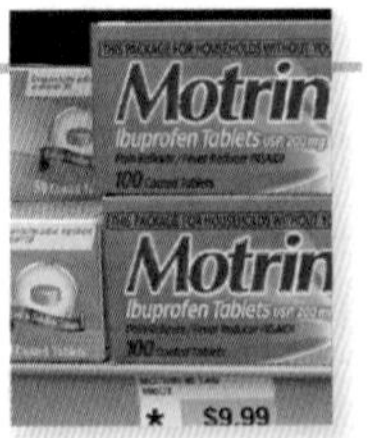

24 Carbonyl Condensation Reactions 954

24.1 The Aldol Reaction 955
24.2 Crossed Aldol Reactions 960
24.3 Directed Aldol Reactions 963
24.4 Intramolecular Aldol Reactions 965
24.5 The Claisen Reaction 967
24.6 The Crossed Claisen and Related Reactions 969
24.7 The Dieckmann Reaction 971
24.8 The Michael Reaction 972
24.9 The Robinson Annulation 974
Key Concepts 978
Problems 979

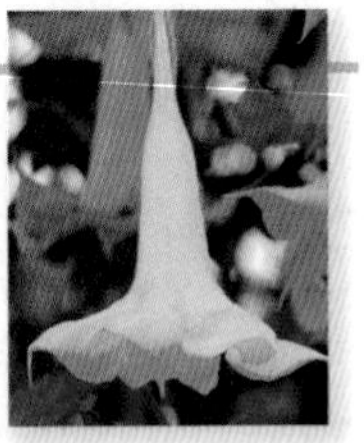

25 Amines 988

25.1 Introduction 989
25.2 Structure and Bonding 989
25.3 Nomenclature 991
25.4 Physical Properties 993
25.5 Spectroscopic Properties 994
25.6 Interesting and Useful Amines 995
25.7 Preparation of Amines 998
25.8 Reactions of Amines—General Features 1005
25.9 Amines as Bases 1005

25.10 Relative Basicity of Amines and Other Compounds 1007
25.11 Amines as Nucleophiles 1014
25.12 Hofmann Elimination 1016
25.13 Reaction of Amines with Nitrous Acid 1020
25.14 Substitution Reactions of Aryl Diazonium Salts 1022
25.15 Coupling Reactions of Aryl Diazonium Salts 1026
25.16 Application: Synthetic Dyes 1028
25.17 Application: Sulfa Drugs 1030
Key Concepts 1031
Problems 1034

26 Carbon–Carbon Bond-Forming Reactions in Organic Synthesis 1042

26.1 Coupling Reactions of Organocuprate Reagents 1043
26.2 Suzuki Reaction 1046
26.3 Heck Reaction 1050
26.4 Carbenes and Cyclopropane Synthesis 1052
26.5 Simmons–Smith Reaction 1055
26.6 Metathesis 1056
Key Concepts 1061
Problems 1062

27 Pericyclic Reactions 1069

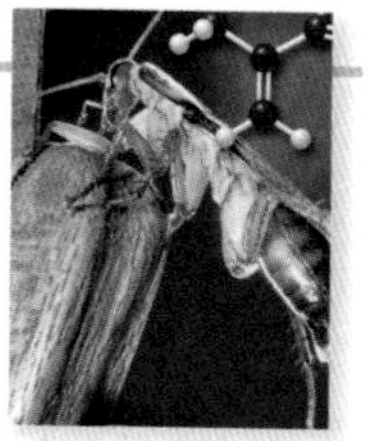

27.1 Types of Pericyclic Reactions 1070
27.2 Molecular Orbitals 1071
27.3 Electrocyclic Reactions 1074
27.4 Cycloaddition Reactions 1081
27.5 Sigmatropic Rearrangements 1085
27.6 Summary of Rules for Pericyclic Reactions 1090
Key Concepts 1091
Problems 1092

28 Carbohydrates 1098

28.1 Introduction 1099
28.2 Monosaccharides 1100
28.3 The Family of D-Aldoses 1106
28.4 The Family of D-Ketoses 1108
28.5 Physical Properties of Monosaccharides 1108
28.6 The Cyclic Forms of Monosaccharides 1109
28.7 Glycosides 1115
28.8 Reactions of Monosaccharides at the OH Groups 1119
28.9 Reactions at the Carbonyl Group—Oxidation and Reduction 1120
28.10 Reactions at the Carbonyl Group—Adding or Removing One Carbon Atom 1123
28.11 The Fischer Proof of the Structure of Glucose 1126
28.12 Disaccharides 1129
28.13 Polysaccharides 1132
28.14 Other Important Sugars and Their Derivatives 1134
Key Concepts 1139
Problems 1141

29 Amino Acids and Proteins 1148

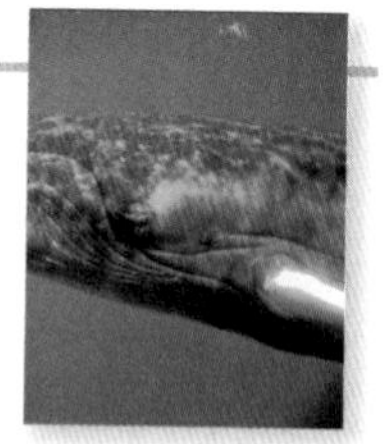

29.1 Amino Acids 1149
29.2 Synthesis of Amino Acids 1152
29.3 Separation of Amino Acids 1155
29.4 Enantioselective Synthesis of Amino Acids 1159
29.5 Peptides 1160
29.6 Peptide Sequencing 1165
29.7 Peptide Synthesis 1168
29.8 Automated Peptide Synthesis 1173
29.9 Protein Structure 1175
29.10 Important Proteins 1182
Key Concepts 1185
Problems 1187

30 Lipids 1194

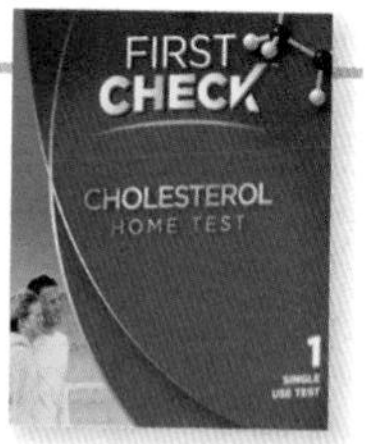

30.1 Introduction 1195
30.2 Waxes 1196
30.3 Triacylglycerols 1197
30.4 Phospholipids 1201
30.5 Fat-Soluble Vitamins 1204
30.6 Eicosanoids 1205
30.7 Terpenes 1208
30.8 Steroids 1214
Key Concepts 1219
Problems 1220

31 Synthetic Polymers 1225

31.1 Introduction 1226
31.2 Chain-Growth Polymers—Addition Polymers 1227
31.3 Anionic Polymerization of Epoxides 1234
31.4 Ziegler–Natta Catalysts and Polymer Stereochemistry 1235
31.5 Natural and Synthetic Rubbers 1237
31.6 Step-Growth Polymers—Condensation Polymers 1238
31.7 Polymer Structure and Properties 1243
31.8 Green Polymer Synthesis 1244
31.9 Polymer Recycling and Disposal 1247
Key Concepts 1250
Problems 1251

Appendix A pK_a Values for Selected Compounds A-1
Appendix B Nomenclature A-3
Appendix C Bond Dissociation Energies for Some Common Bonds [A–B → A• + •B] A-7
Appendix D Reactions that Form Carbon–Carbon Bonds A-8
Appendix E Characteristic IR Absorption Frequencies A-9
Appendix F Characteristic NMR Absorptions A-10
Appendix G General Types of Organic Reactions A-12
Appendix H How to Synthesize Particular Functional Groups A-14

Glossary G-1
Credits C-1
Index I-1

Preface

My goal in writing *Organic Chemistry* was to create a text that showed students the beauty and logic of organic chemistry by giving them a book that they would *use*. This text is based on lecture notes and handouts that were developed in my own organic chemistry courses over my 30-year teaching career. I have followed two guiding principles: use relevant and interesting applications to illustrate chemical phenomena, and present the material in a student-friendly fashion using bulleted lists, solved problems, and extensive illustrations and summaries. *Organic Chemistry* is my attempt to simplify and clarify a course that intimidates many students—to make organic chemistry interesting, relevant, and accessible to *all* students, both chemistry majors and those interested in pursuing careers in biology, medicine, and other disciplines, without sacrificing the rigor they need to be successful in the future.

"As an organic chemistry instructor and a practicing chemistry education researcher, I try to sew together my teaching and research interests so they inform one another. For all the research literature I have read on student concept attainment in the sciences, it seems like Janice Smith has read most of it too, because it is put into practice in her textbook. The illustrations are well constructed and pertinent to the topics covered in textual format, the problems are written to provide students a clearer understanding of the best solution strategies, and the applications to biological and medicinal careers are unparalleled. Since reading and teaching from Smith's 1st edition, I believe that textbook pedagogy and student learning style are as closely merged as possible in her work; for this my students and I are most appreciative!"

—David P. Cartrette, South Dakota State University

The Basic Features

"Smith reads more like a web page than a conventional textbook. Today's students seem to do better with that format than with a traditional format with long text paragraphs."
—Nolan K. Carter, University of Central Arkansas

- **Style** This text is different—by design. Today's students rely more heavily on visual imagery to learn than ever before. The text uses less prose and more diagrams, equations, tables, and bulleted summaries to introduce and reinforce the major concepts and themes of organic chemistry.
- **Content** *Organic Chemistry* accents basic themes in an effort to keep memorization at a minimum. Relevant examples from everyday life are used to illustrate concepts, and this material is integrated throughout the chapter rather than confined to a boxed reading. Each topic is broken down into small chunks of information that are more manageable and easily learned. Sample problems are used as a tool to illustrate stepwise problem solving. Exceptions to the rule and older, less useful reactions are omitted to focus attention on the basic themes.
- **Organization** *Organic Chemistry* uses functional groups as the framework within which chemical reactions are discussed. Thus, the emphasis is placed on the reactions that different functional groups undergo, not on the reactions that prepare them. Moreover, similar reactions are grouped together so that parallels can be emphasized. These include acid–base reactions (Chapter 2), oxidation and reduction (Chapters 12 and 20), radical reactions (Chapter 15), and reactions of organometallic reagents (Chapter 20).

"Many students like to highlight their textbooks . . . they are looking for the key concepts. Smith does some of the heavy lifting for them by pulling the concepts out as bulleted lists. I like the style."
—Ronald K. Castellano, University of Florida

By introducing one new concept at a time, keeping the basic themes in focus, and breaking complex problems down into small pieces, I have found that many students find organic chemistry an intense but learnable subject. Many, in fact, end the year-long course surprised that they have actually *enjoyed* their organic chemistry experience.

Organization and Presentation

For the most part, the overall order of topics in the text is consistent with the way most instructors currently teach organic chemistry. There are, however, some important differences in the way topics are presented to make the material logical and more accessible. This can especially be seen in the following areas.

- **Review material** Chapter 1 presents a healthy dose of review material covering Lewis structures, molecular geometry and hybridization, bond polarity, and types of bonding. While many of these topics are covered in general chemistry courses, they are presented here from an organic chemist's perspective. I have found that giving students a firm grasp of these fundamental concepts helps tremendously in their understanding of later material.
- **Acids and bases** Chapter 2 on acids and bases serves two purposes. It gives students experience with curved arrow notation using some familiar proton transfer reactions. It also illustrates how some fundamental concepts in organic structure affect a reaction, in this case an acid–base reaction. Since many mechanisms involve one or more acid–base reactions, I emphasize proton transfer reactions early and come back to this topic often throughout the text.
- **Functional groups** Chapter 3 uses the functional groups to introduce important properties of organic chemistry. Relevant examples—PCBs, vitamins, soap, and the cell membrane—illustrate fundamental solubility concepts. In this way, practical topics that are sometimes found in the last few chapters of an organic chemistry text (and thus often omitted because instructors run out of time) are introduced early so that students can better grasp why they are studying the discipline.

> *"[Smith] explains everything very well, shows a lot of examples and step-by-step approaches. The building-up of each chapter is very logical and helps students to understand the concepts. It is a great book!"*
>
> *—Claudia Taenzler, University of Texas at Dallas*

- **Stereochemistry** Stereochemistry (the three-dimensional structure of molecules) is introduced early (Chapter 5) and reinforced often, so students have every opportunity to learn and understand a crucial concept in modern chemical research, drug design, and synthesis.
- **Modern reactions** While there is no shortage of new chemical reactions to present in an organic chemistry text, I have chosen to concentrate on new methods that introduce a particular three-dimensional arrangement in a molecule, so-called asymmetric or enantioselective reactions. Examples include Sharpless epoxidation (Chapter 12), CBS reduction (Chapter 20), and enantioselective synthesis of amino acids (Chapter 29).
- **Grouping reactions** Since certain types of reactions have their own unique characteristics and terminology that make them different from the basic organic reactions, I have grouped these reactions together in individual chapters. These include acid–base reactions (Chapter 2), oxidation and reduction (Chapters 12 and 20), radical reactions (Chapter 15), and reactions of organometallic reagents (Chapter 20). I have found that focusing on a group of reactions that share a common theme helps students to better see their similarities.
- **Synthesis** Synthesis, one of the most difficult topics for a beginning organic student to master, is introduced in small doses, beginning in Chapter 7 and augmented with a detailed discussion of retrosynthetic analysis in Chapter 11. In later chapters, special attention is given to the retrosynthetic analysis of compounds prepared by carbon–carbon bond-forming reactions (for example, Sections 20.11 and 21.10C).
- **Spectroscopy** Since spectroscopy is such a powerful tool for structure determination, four methods are discussed over two chapters (Chapters 13 and 14).
- **Key Concepts** End-of-chapter summaries succinctly summarize the main concepts and themes of the chapter, making them ideal for review prior to working the end-of-chapter problems or taking an exam.

New to the Fourth Edition

- A new Chapter 27 (Pericyclic Reactions) has been added to the fourth edition. The study of pericyclic reactions and sigmatropic rearrangements provides students with a set of rules for predicting the identity and stereochemistry of products formed, and thus tools for synthesizing organic molecules. This new chapter also provides additional study of molecular orbitals.
- A new Section 18.13 (Nucleophilic Aromatic Substitution) with accompanying illustrations and problems has been added to the fourth edition text to provide students with additional information on substitution reactions involving aryl halides.
- Also in response to reviewer feedback, new material has been added on resonance structures (Section 1.6B); glucose metabolism and entropy (Section 6.6); marine natural products (Section 7.4); green chemistry (Section 12.13); juvenile hormones (Section 20.10C); and regioselectivity (Section 23.8B). In addition, sections on hydroboration–oxidation of terminal alkynes (Section 11.10), the reactivity–selectivity principle (Section 15.6), and terpenes (Section 30.7) have been rewritten to clarify and update the material.
- Over eighty new problems incorporating molecular art to help students visualize structures in a three-dimensional manner have been included in the fourth edition. Additionally, more than 200 other new problems have also been added to the new edition, increasing the number of more complex, challenging problems.
- New *How To*'s, Sample Problems, and micro-to-macro illustrations have also been added throughout the new edition to clarify topics and enhance the student learning experience.
- In order to address reviewer concerns, the page layout for the fourth edition has been made more flexible, allowing figures to fall at the end of paragraphs containing figure references—thus placing figures closer to their text call-outs.

Tools to Make Learning Organic Chemistry Easier

Illustrations

Organic Chemistry is supported by a well-developed illustration program. Besides traditional skeletal (line) structures and condensed formulas, there are numerous ball-and-stick molecular models and electrostatic potential maps to help students grasp the three-dimensional structure of molecules (including stereochemistry) and to better understand the distribution of electronic charge.

Figure 21.9 The key reaction in the chemistry of vision

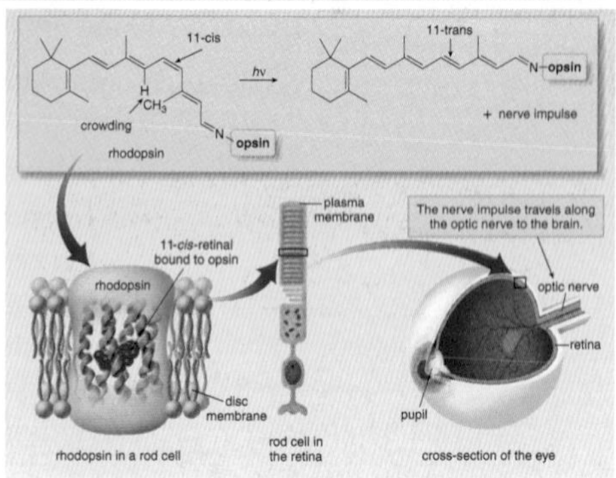

- Rhodopsin is a light-sensitive compound located in the membrane of the rod cells in the retina of the eye. Rhodopsin contains the protein opsin bonded to 11-*cis*-retinal via an imine linkage. When light strikes this molecule, the crowded 11-cis double bond isomerizes to the 11-trans isomer, and a nerve impulse is transmitted to the brain by the optic nerve.

"I believe that dissecting the text gives students time to understand and to digest, step-by-step, each concept presented, rather than memorize them. This helps students in achieving better results faster. . . . The quality of the illustrations is very good, without unnecessary explanations that could make them confusing. The language is easy to follow, the concept easy to understand."
—Camelia Gogonea, Cleveland State University

Micro-to-Macro Illustrations

Unique to *Organic Chemistry* are micro-to-macro illustrations, where line art and photos combine with chemical structures to reveal the underlying molecular structures giving rise to macroscopic properties of common phenomena. Examples include starch and cellulose (Chapter 5), adrenaline (Chapter 7), partial hydrogenation of vegetable oil (Chapter 12), and dopamine (Chapter 25).

Figure 12.4 Partial hydrogenation of the double bonds in a vegetable oil

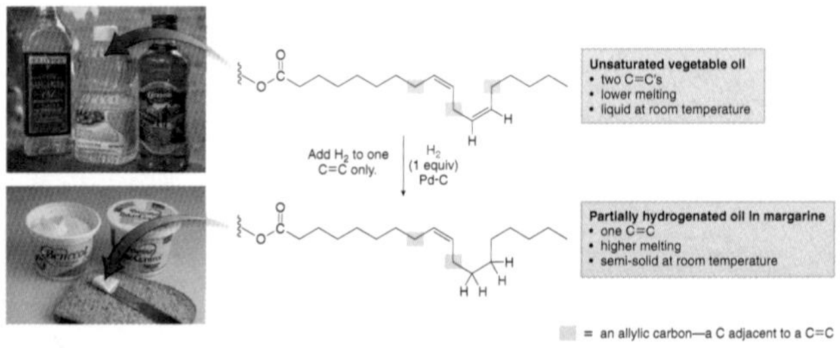

- **Decreasing** the number of degrees of unsaturation **increases** the melting point. Only one long chain of the triacylglycerol is drawn.
- When an oil is *partially* hydrogenated, some double bonds react with H_2, whereas some double bonds remain in the product.
- Partial hydrogenation **decreases** the number of allylic sites (shown in blue), making a triacylglycerol **less** susceptible to oxidation, thereby increasing its shelf life.

Spectra

Over 100 spectra created specifically for *Organic Chemistry* are presented throughout the text. The spectra are color-coded by type and generously labeled. Mass spectra are green; infrared spectra are red; and proton and carbon nuclear magnetic resonance spectra are blue.

Figure 13.5 Identifying fragments in the mass spectrum of hexane

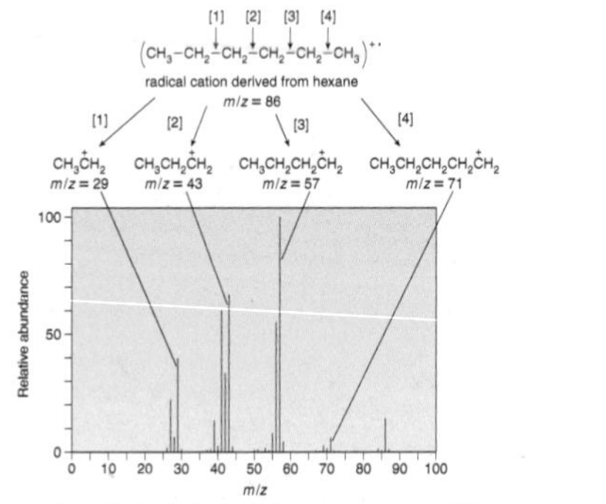

- Cleavage of C–C bonds (labeled [1]–[4]) in hexane forms lower molecular weight fragments that correspond to lines in the mass spectrum. Although the mass spectrum is complex, possible structures can be assigned to some of the fragments, as shown.

Mechanisms

Curved arrow notation is used extensively to help students follow the movement of electrons in reactions. Where appropriate, mechanisms are presented in parts to promote a better conceptual understanding.

Mechanism 9.2 Dehydration of a 1° ROH—An E2 Mechanism

Step [1] The O atom is protonated.

Step [2] The C–H and C–O bonds are broken and the π bond is formed.

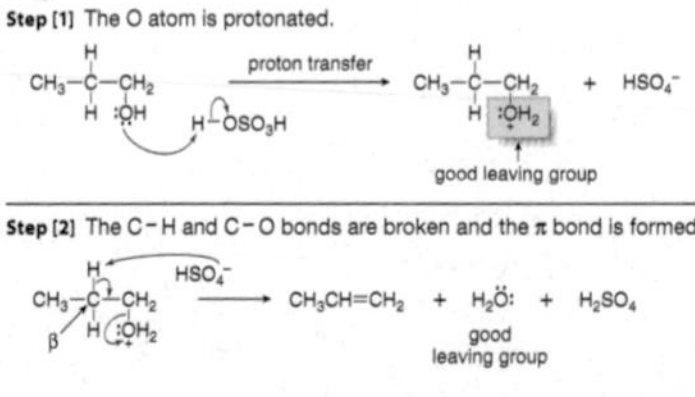

- **Protonation of the oxygen atom** of the alcohol converts a poor leaving group (^-OH) into a good leaving group (H_2O).
- **Two bonds are broken and two bonds are formed in a single step:** the base (HSO_4^- or H_2O) removes a proton from the β carbon; the electron pair in the β C–H bond forms the new π bond; the leaving group (H_2O) comes off with the electron pair in the C–O bond.

Problem Solving

Sample Problems

Sample Problems show students how to solve organic chemistry problems in a logical, stepwise manner. More than 800 follow-up problems are located throughout the chapters to test whether students understand concepts covered in the Sample Problems.

"... [T]he sample problems and examples are well matched within the context of the material. They match well with the exercises in the chapter and show a very clear way of attacking the problems.... [T]he problems are very concise and don't get bogged down in fluff."
—Nathan C. Tice, Eastern Kentucky University

Sample Problem 2.2 Label the acid and base, and the conjugate acid and base in the following reaction. Use curved arrow notation to show the movement of electron pairs.

Solution

CH_3^- is the base because it accepts a proton, forming its conjugate acid, CH_4. H_2O is the acid because it donates a proton, forming its conjugate base, ^-OH. Two curved arrows are needed. One shows that the lone pair on CH_3^- bonds to a proton of H_2O, and the second shows that the electron pair in the O – H bond remains on O.

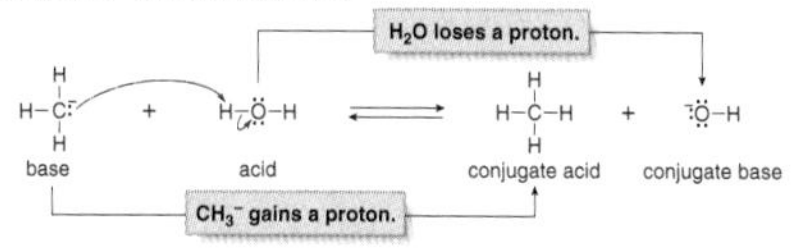

How To's

How To's provide students with detailed instructions on how to work through key processes.

How To Name an Ester (RCO_2R') Using the IUPAC System

Example Give a systematic name for each ester:

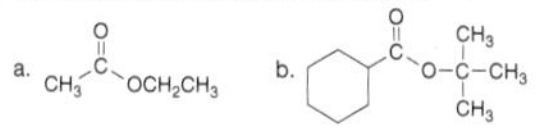

Step [1] Name the R' group bonded to the oxygen atom as an alkyl group.

- The name of the alkyl group, ending in the suffix *-yl*, becomes the *first* part of the ester name.

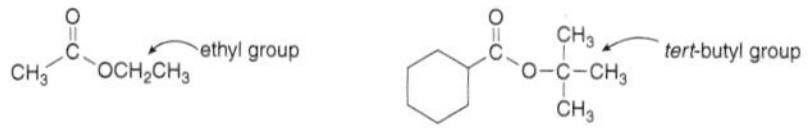

Step [2] Name the acyl group (RCO–) by changing the *-ic acid* ending of the parent carboxylic acid to the suffix *-ate*.

- The name of the acyl group becomes the *second* part of the name.

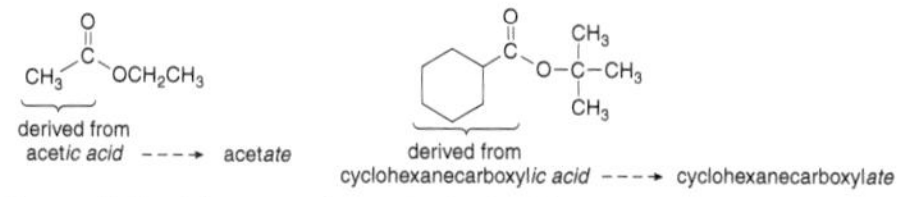

Answer: ethyl acetate **Answer: *tert*-butyl cyclohexanecarboxylate**

"Overall, this is one of the best problem sets in any text in terms of the correspondence between the problems and the concepts being taught. There are always multiple problems for each example."
—T. Keith Hollis, The University of Mississippi

Applications and Summaries

Key Concept Summaries

Succinct summary tables reinforcing important principles and concepts are provided at the end of each chapter.

KEY CONCEPTS

Alkenes

General Facts About Alkenes

- Alkenes contain a carbon–carbon double bond consisting of a stronger σ bond and a weaker π bond. Each carbon is sp^2 hybridized and trigonal planar (10.1).
- Alkenes are named using the suffix ***-ene*** (10.3).
- Alkenes with different groups on each end of the double bond exist as a pair of diastereomers, identified by the prefixes *E* and *Z* (10.3B).
- Alkenes have weak intermolecular forces, giving them low mp's and bp's, and making them water insoluble. A cis alkene is more polar than a trans alkene, giving it a slightly higher boiling point (10.4).
- Because a π bond is electron rich and much weaker than a σ bond, alkenes undergo addition reactions with electrophiles (10.8).

Stereochemistry of Alkene Addition Reactions (10.8)

A reagent XY adds to a double bond in one of three different ways:

- **Syn addition**—X and Y add from the same side.

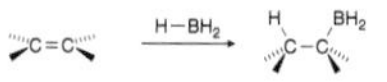

- Syn addition occurs in **hydroboration.**

- **Anti addition**—X and Y add from opposite sides.

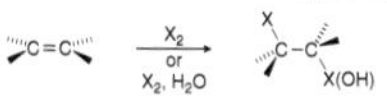

- Anti addition occurs in **halogenation** and **halohydrin formation.**

- **Both syn and anti addition** occur when carbocations are intermediates.

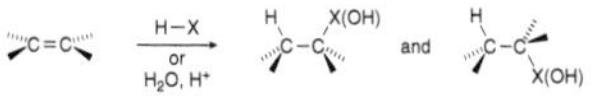

- Syn and anti addition occur in **hydrohalogenation** and **hydration.**

Addition Reactions of Alkenes

[1] Hydrohalogenation—Addition of HX (X = Cl, Br, I) (10.9–10.11)

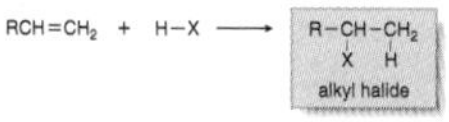

- The mechanism has two steps.
- Carbocations are formed as intermediates.
- Carbocation rearrangements are possible.
- Markovnikov's rule is followed. H bonds to the less substituted C to form the more stable carbocation.
- Syn and anti addition occur.

[2] Hydration and related reactions (Addition of H_2O or ROH) (10.12)

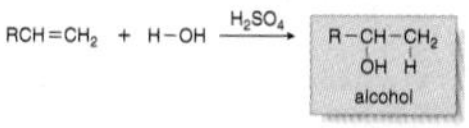

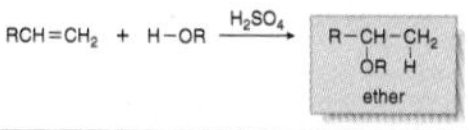

For both reactions:
- The mechanism has three steps.
- Carbocations are formed as intermediates.
- Carbocation rearrangements are possible.
- Markovnikov's rule is followed. H bonds to the less substituted C to form the more stable carbocation.
- Syn and anti addition occur.

Margin Notes

Margin notes are placed carefully throughout the chapters, providing interesting information relating to topics covered in the text. Some margin notes are illustrated with photos to make the chemistry more relevant.

Canola, soybeans, and flaxseed are excellent dietary sources of linolenic acid, an essential fatty acid. Oils derived from omega-3 fatty acids (Problem 10.11) are currently thought to be especially beneficial for individuals at risk of developing coronary artery disease.

Learning Resources for Instructors and Students

The following items may accompany this text. Please consult your McGraw-Hill representative for policies, prices, and availability as some restrictions may apply.

Student Study Guide/Solutions Manual

Written by Janice Gorzynski Smith and Erin Smith Berk, the Student Study Guide/Solutions Manual provides step-by-step solutions to all in-chapter and end-of-chapter problems. Each chapter begins with an overview of key concepts and includes a short-answer practice test on the fundamental principles and new reactions.

McGraw-Hill Connect® Chemistry

www.mcgrawhillconnect.com/chemistry

McGraw-Hill Connect® Chemistry is a web-based assignment and assessment platform that gives students the means to better connect with their coursework, with their instructors, and with the important concepts that they will need to know for success now and in the future. The chemical drawing tool found within Connect Chemistry is PerkinElmer® ChemDraw, which is widely considered the "gold standard" of scientific drawing programs and the cornerstone application for scientists who draw and annotate molecules, reactions, and pathways. This collaboration of Connect and ChemDraw features an easy-to-use, intuitive, and comprehensive course management and homework system with professional-grade drawing capabilities.

"The Connect assignments are great in the fact that you have so many ways to customize and change the settings in terms of assignment and individual question attempts and scoring. The eBook is very well done and I appreciate the note and highlighting abilities."
—*Jason Dunham, Bass State University*

"Retrosynthesis! Synthesis is so difficult. . . . [T]his was awesome! The conceptual development of chirality was exceptional. The references to page numbers within the text was great as it would make students actually look in the book!"
—*Jenny VanWyk, Southwestern Illinois College*

With Connect Chemistry, instructors can deliver assignments, quizzes, and tests online. Questions from the text are presented in an auto-gradable format and tied to the text's learning objectives. Instructors can edit existing questions and author entirely new problems. They also can track individual student performance—by question, assignment, or in relation to the class overall—with detailed grade reports; integrate grade reports easily with Learning Management Systems (LMS) such as WebCT and Blackboard; and much more.

By choosing Connect Chemistry, instructors are providing their students with a powerful tool for improving academic performance and truly mastering course material. Connect Chemistry allows students to practice important skills at their own pace and on their own schedule. Importantly, students' assessment results and instructors' feedback are all saved online—so students can continually review their progress and plot their course to success.

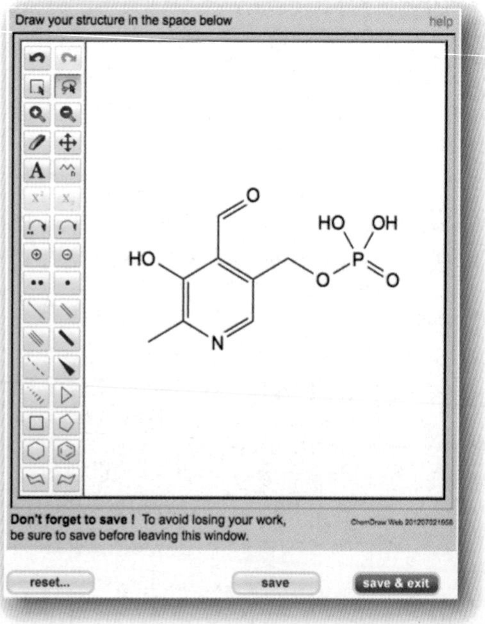

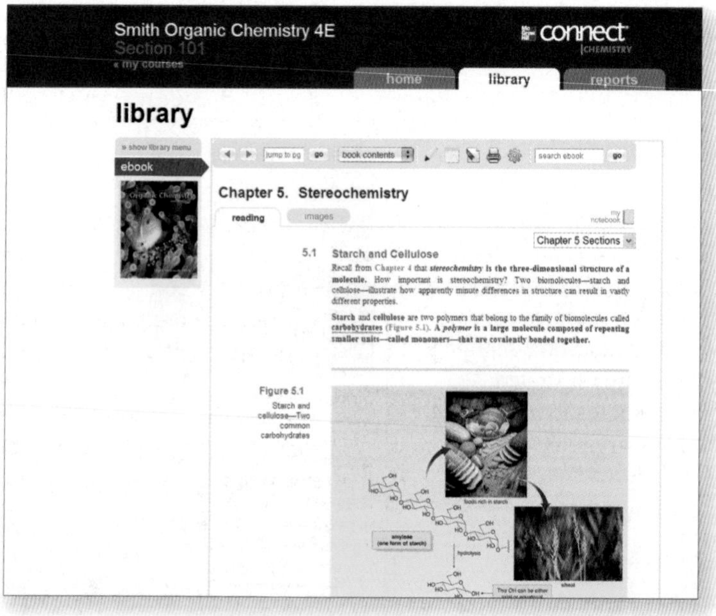

McGraw-Hill ConnectPlus® Chemistry

connect plus+ |chemistry

Featuring PerkinElmer® ChemDraw

Like Connect Chemistry, **McGraw-Hill ConnectPlus® Chemistry** provides students with online assignments and assessments, plus 24/7 online access to an eBook—an online edition of the text—to aid them in successfully completing their work, wherever and whenever they choose.

McGraw-Hill LearnSmart™

"I just want to say that I really like LearnSmart and retrosynthesis, the feedback and several choices of reagents and substrates for the synthetic sequences."
—Hector Palencia, University of Nebraska–Kearney

McGraw-Hill LearnSmart™ is available as a stand-alone product as well as an integrated feature of McGraw-Hill Connect® Chemistry. It is an adaptive learning system designed to help students learn faster, study more efficiently, and retain more knowledge for greater success. LearnSmart assesses a student's knowledge of course content through a series of probes, pinpointing concepts the student does not understand. This innovative study tool also has features that allow instructors to see exactly what students have accomplished and a built-in assessment tool for graded assignments. Visit the following site for a demonstration. **www.mhlearnsmart.com.**

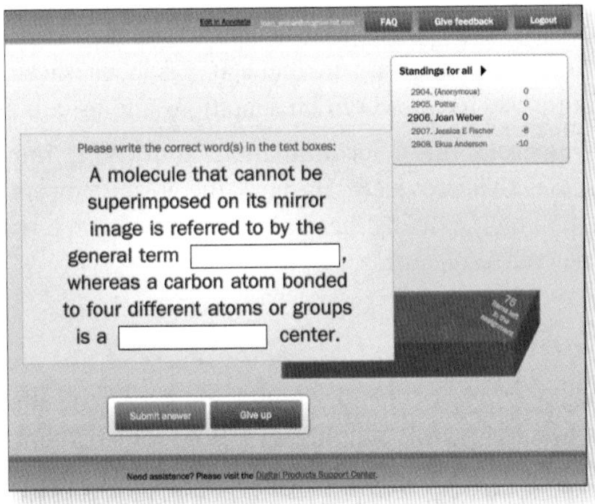

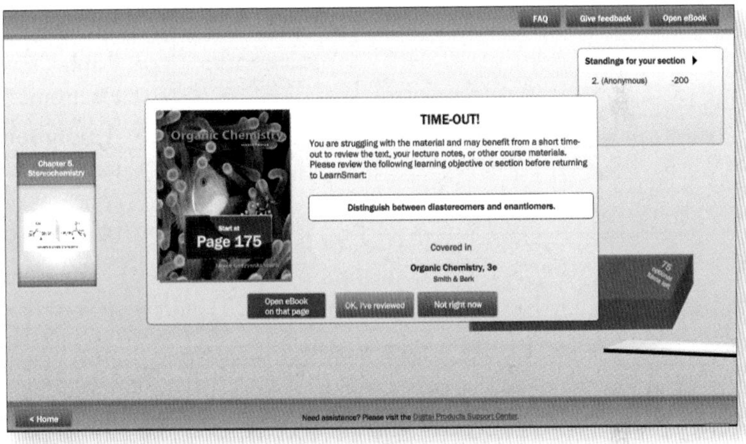

"LearnSmart was great and fun for the students. It was game-like and they thought it would be very helpful. . . . The thing that was the best was that when I showed it to my students they stayed after class and tested it. They said that studying was better when it was fun, and LearnSmart was fun for them."
—Stacey Thomson, Pasco-Hernando Community College–West Campus

Customizable Textbooks: McGraw-Hill Create™

Create what you've only imagined. Introducing McGraw-Hill Create™—a new, self-service website that allows you to create custom course materials (print and eBooks) by drawing upon McGraw-Hill's comprehensive, cross-disciplinary content. Add your own content quickly and easily. Tap into other rights-secured third party sources as well. Then, arrange the content in a way that makes the most sense for your course, and if you wish, personalize your book with your course name and information. Choose the best delivery format for your course: color print, black-and-white print, or eBook. The eBook is now viewable for the iPad! And when you are finished customizing, you will receive a free PDF review copy in just minutes! Visit McGraw-Hill Create (**www.mcgrawhillcreate.com**) today and begin building your perfect book.

Presentation Tools

Within the Instructor's Presentation Tools, instructors have access to editable PowerPoint lecture outlines, which appear as ready-made presentations that combine art and lecture notes for each chapter of the text. For instructors who prefer to create their lecture notes from scratch, all illustrations, photos, tables, *How To*'s, and Sample Problems are pre-inserted by chapter into a separate set of PowerPoint slides. They are also available as individual .jpg files.

An online digital library contains photos, artwork, animations, and other media types that can be used to create customized lectures, visually enhanced tests and quizzes, compelling course websites, or attractive printed support materials. All assets are copyrighted by McGraw-Hill Higher Education, but can be used by instructors for classroom purposes. The visual resources in this collection include:

- **Art** Full-color digital files of all illustrations in the book can be readily incorporated into lecture presentations, exams, or custom-made classroom materials.
- **Photos** The photo collection contains digital files of photographs from the text, which can be reproduced for multiple classroom uses.
- **Tables** Every table that appears in the text has been saved in electronic form for use in classroom presentations and/or quizzes.
- **Animations** Numerous full-color animations illustrating important processes are also provided. Harness the visual impact of concepts in motion by importing these files into classroom presentations or online course materials.

Brownstone's Diploma Testing Software

Serves up over 1,200 test questions to accompany *Organic Chemistry*. Diploma's software allows you to quickly create a customized test using McGraw-Hill's supplied questions, or by authoring your own questions. Diploma is a downloadable application that allows you to create your tests without an Internet connection—just download the software and question files directly to your computer.

Digital Lecture Capture: Tegrity®

McGraw-Hill Tegrity® records and distributes your lecture with just a click of a button. Students can view anytime/anywhere via computer, iPod, or mobile device. Tegrity indexes as it records your slideshow presentations and anything shown on your computer, so students can use keywords to find exactly what they want to study.

Acknowledgments

When I started working on the first edition of *Organic Chemistry* in the fall of 1999, I had no sense of the magnitude of the task, or any idea of just how many people I would rely upon to complete it. Fortunately, I have had the steadfast support of a dedicated team of publishing professionals at McGraw-Hill.

I am especially thankful for the opportunity to work with Senior Developmental Editor Mary Hurley, who skillfully and efficiently guided me through the process of updating this fourth edition. I am grateful to once again work with Senior Project Manager Jayne Klein, who managed the production of the text in a manner that allowed for a large family get-together and an extended vacation. *Organic Chemistry* has also benefited greatly from the expertise and market-based feedback provided by Executive Marketing Manager Tami Hodge.

Special thanks go out to Brand Manager Todd Turner, who gave me the day-to-day editorial support crucial in producing a revision of *Organic Chemistry.* Thanks also to Publisher Thomas Timp, who efficiently directed the editorial team that produced this revision. I also appreciate the work of Laurie Janssen (Designer) and Carrie Burger (Photo Researcher) who are responsible for the visually pleasing appearance of this edition. Thanks are again due to freelance Developmental Editor John Murdzek for his meticulous editing and humorous insights on my project.

Organic Chemistry is complemented with useful supplements prepared by qualified and dedicated individuals. Special thanks go to Felix Ngassa of Grand Valley State University who authored the instructor's test bank, and Layne Morsch of The University of Illinois, Springfield who prepared the PowerPoint lecture outlines and clicker questions. I am also grateful for the keen eyes of Susan Odom of the University of Kentucky for her careful accuracy checking of the Test Bank and online quizzes to accompany this text.

Organic Chemistry is also complemented by the exemplary digital products Connect® and LearnSmart™. We are extremely appreciative of the talents of the following individuals who played important roles in the authoring and content development for our digital products.

Kim Albizati, *University of California–San Diego*
Neil Allison, *University of Arkansas*
Susan Bane, *Binghamton University*
Chad J. Booth, *Texas State University*
John Bougher, *University of Ohio*
Chloe Brennan, *St. Olaf University*
Kelly B. Butzler, *Pennsylvania College of Technology*
David P. Cartrette, *South Dakota State University*
Ronald K. Castellano, *University of Florida*
Claire Cohen, *University of Toledo*
Greg Cook, *North Dakota State University*
Tammy Davidson, *University of Florida*
Peter de Lijser, *California State University–Fullerton*
Amy Deveau, *University of New England*
Matthew R. Dintzner, *Western New England University*
Mike Evans, *University of Illinois at Urbana–Champaign*
Tiffany Gierasch, *University of Maryland–Baltimore County*
Allison D. Goldberg, *Hunter College of CUNY*
Sara Hein, *Winona State University*
Shirley Hino, *Santa Rosa Junior College*
Phil Janowicz, *California State University–Fullerton*
David G. Jones, *North Carolina Central University*
Eric Kantorowski, *California Polytechnic State University*
Adam I. Keller, *Columbus State Community College*
Julia Keller, *Florida State College*
Jens Kuhn, *Santa Barbara City College*
Amy Lane, *University of North Florida*
Margaret Ruth Leslie, *Kent State University*
Michael Lewis, *Saint Louis University*
Eric Masson, *Ohio University*
Mark McMills, *Ohio University*
Layne A. Morsch, *University of Illinois–Springfield*
John S. Murdzek
Thomas W. Nalli, *Winona State University*
Massimo Pacilli, *DePaul University*
Andrea Pellerito, *Indiana University–Bloomington*
Karen E. S. Phillips, *Hunter College of CUNY*
Danaè R. Quirk–Dorr, *Minnesota State University–Mankato*
Paul D. Root, *Henry Ford Community College*
Rebecca J. Rowe, *University of New England*
Jason R. Schmink, *Bryn Mawr College*
Jacob Schroeder, *Clemson University*
Alexander J. Seed, *Kent State University*
Chad Stearman, *Missouri State University*
Brent Sumerlin, *Southern Methodist University*
Emily Tansey, *Otterbein University*
John T. Tansey, *Otterbein University*
Yitzhak Tor, *University of California–San Diego*
David Tramontozzi, *Macomb Community College*
Khoi N. Van, *Texas A&M University*
Haim Weizman, *University of California–San Diego*
Erin Whitteck
Ronald Wikholm, *University of Connecticut*
Gregory M. Williams, *University of Oregon*
Regina Zibuck, *Wayne State University*

My immediate family has experienced the day-to-day demands of living with a busy author. Thanks go to my husband Dan and my children Erin, Jenna, Matthew, and Zachary, all of whom keep me grounded during the time-consuming process of writing and publishing a textbook.

Among the many others that go unnamed but who have profoundly affected this work are the thousands of students I have been lucky to teach over the last 30 years. I have learned so much from my daily interactions with them, and I hope that the wider chemistry community can benefit from this experience by the way I have presented the material in this text.

This fourth edition has evolved based on the helpful feedback of many people who reviewed the third edition text and digital products, class-tested the book, and attended focus groups or symposiums. These many individuals have collectively provided constructive improvements to the project.

Dragos Albinescu, *Northeastern State University*
Neil Allison, *University of Arkansas*
Jeff Arterburn, *New Mexico State University*
Anne Baranger, *University of Illinois at Urbana–Champaign*
Michael Berg, *Virginia Polytechnic Institute and State University*
Kenneth Darrell Berlin, *Oklahoma State University*
Narayan G. Bhat, *The University of Texas–Pan American*
Ned Barry Bowden, *University of Iowa*
Peter Bridson, *University of Memphis*
David Brook, *San Jose State University*
Matthew Brooker, *Trident Technical College*
Banita White Brown, *University of North Carolina at Charlotte*
David P. Brown, *St. John's University*
Scott Bur, *Gustavus Adolphus College*
K. Nolan Carter, *University of Central Arkansas*
David P. Cartrette, *South Dakota State University*
Ronald K. Castellano, *University of Florida*
Steven L. Castle, *Brigham Young University–Provo*
Judy Chen, *Columbia University*
E. A. Cioffi, *University of South Alabama*
Edward L. Clennan, *University of Wyoming*
Tom Cole, *San Diego State University*
Greg Cook, *North Dakota State University*
Sergio Cortes, *University of Texas at Dallas*
Peter de Lijser, *California State University–Fullerton*
Cristina De Meo, *Southern Illinois University–Edwardsville*
Amy Deveau, *University of New England*
Matthew R. Dintzner, *Western New England University*
Marion T. Doig III, *College of Charleston*
William A. Donaldson, *Marquette University*
Phil Egan, *Texas A&M University–Corpus Christi*
Ihsan Erden, *San Francisco State University*
Markus Etzkorn, *University of North Carolina at Charlotte*
Mike Evans, *University of Illinois at Urbana–Champaign*
Conrad R. Fjetland, *University of Texas at Austin*
Maryam Foroozesh, *Xavier University of Louisiana*
Joseph M. Fortunak, *Howard University*
Andrew Frazer, *University of Central Florida–Orlando*
Lee Friedman, *University of Maryland–College Park*
Tiffany Gierasch, *University of Maryland–Baltimore County*
Camelia Baleanu Gogonea, *Cleveland State University*
Julie Goll, *University of Waterloo*
Galina Z. Goloverda, *Xavier University of Louisiana*
Joseph Grabowski, *University of Pittsburgh*
Dennis Gravert, *Los Medanos College*
Nathaniel Grove, *Clemson University*
Fathi Halaweish, *South Dakota State University*
Michael M. Haley, *University of Oregon*
Gregory H. Hanson, *Otterbein University*
Sara Hein, *Winona State University*
Rick Heldrich, *College of Charleston*
T. Keith Hollis, *The University of Mississippi*
David Hunt, *The College of New Jersey*
Tom Ippoliti, *University of St. Thomas*
Jennifer A. Irvin, *Texas State University–San Marcos*
Phil Janowicz, *California State University–Fullerton*
Thomas C. Jempty, *Austin Community College*
Michael Jennings, *The University of Alabama*
Eric Kantorowski, *California Polytechnic State University*
Mohammad R. Karim, *Tennessee State University*
Kristopher Keuseman, *Mount Mercy University*
James J. Kiddle, *Western Michigan University*
Kathleen Kilway, *University of Missouri–Kansas City*
Rebecca Kissling, *Binghamton University*
Mike Koerner, *University of Arizona*
Jens Kuhn, *Santa Barbara City College*
T. Randall Lee, *University of Houston*
Jeanne Leslie, *University of Tampa*
Michael Lewis, *Saint Louis University*
Janis Louie, *University of Utah*
Scott Luaders, *Quincy University*
Frederick Luzzio, *University of Louisville*
Javier Macossay, *The University of Texas–Pan American*
Robert Maleczka, *Michigan State University*
Ned H. Martin, *University of North Carolina–Wilmington*
Luis Martinez, *Brevard Community College–Palm Bay*
Eric Masson, *Ohio University*
Dominic McGrath, *University of Arizona*
Mark McMills, *Ohio University*
G. Patrick Meier, *Washington State University*
Ognjen Miljanic, *University of Houston*
Chammi Miller, *Blinn College*
Deb Mlsna, *Mississippi State University*
Layne Alan Morsch, *University of Illinois–Springfield*
Joan Mutanyatta–Comar, *Georgia State University*
Jennifer Muzyka, *Centre College*
Felix N. Ngassa, *Grand Valley State University*
Jacqueline Nikles, *University of Alabama at Birmingham*
James S. Norwick, *University of California–Irvine*
Krzysztof Ochwat, *Wilbur Wright College*
George O'Doherty, *West Virginia University*
Susan Odom, *University of Kentucky*
Hector Palencia, *University of Nebraska–Kearney*

Yi Pang, *University of Akron*
Cyril Párkányi, *Florida Atlantic University*
Jon Parquette, *The Ohio State University*
Keith O. Pascoe, *Georgia State University*
Matt A. Peterson, *Brigham Young University*
Christine Ann Pruis, *Arizona State University*
Michael William Rathke, *Michigan State University*
Cynthia Robledo, *University of Puerto Rico at Mayaguez*
Harold R. Rogers, *California State University–Fullerton*
Suzanne Ruder, *Virginia Commonwealth University*
Rob Sammelson, *Ball State University*
Elke Schoffers, *Western Michigan University*
Jacob Schroeder, *Clemson University*
Daniel S. Sem, *Marquette University*
Buchang Shi, *Eastern Kentucky University*
Joel L. Shulman, *University of Cincinnati*
Joseph C. Sloop, *Georgia Gwinnett College*
Richard Steiner, *University of Utah*
Wesley Stites, *University of Arkansas*
Brent Sumerlin, *Southern Methodist University*
Chris Switzer, *University of California–Riverside*
Claudia Taenzler, *University of Texas–Dallas*
Richard M. Tarkka, *University of Central Arkansas*
Carol Taylor, *Louisiana State University*
Stacey Thomson, *Pasco-Hernando Community College–West Campus*
Nathan C. Tice, *Eastern Kentucky University*
Yitzhak Tor, *University of California–San Diego*
Amber Tuten, *Thomas University*
Jenny VanWyk, *Southwestern Illinois College*
Chrysoula Vasileiou, *Michigan State University*
Peter Wade, *Drexel University*
Kevin D. Walker, *Michigan State University*
Martin Walker, *State University of New York at Potsdam*
Haim Weizman, *University of California–San Diego*
Christine Whitlock, *Georgia Southern University*
Ron Wikholm, *University of Connecticut*
Randy Winchester, *Grand Valley State University*
Jane Wissinger, *University of Minnesota*
Catherine Woytowicz, *The George Washington University*
Regina Zibuck, *Wayne State University*

Although every effort has been made to make this text and its accompanying Student Study Guide/Solutions Manual as error-free as possible, some errors undoubtedly remain and, for them, I am solely responsible. Please feel free to email me about any inaccuracies, so that subsequent editions may be further improved.

With much aloha,

Janice Gorzynski Smith
jgsmith@hawaii.edu

List of *How To's*

How To boxes provide detailed instructions for key procedures that students need to master. Below is a list of each *How To* and where it is presented in the text.

Chapter 1 Structure and Bonding
How To Draw a Lewis Structure 14
How To Interpret a Skeletal Structure 31

Chapter 2 Acids and Bases
How To Determine Relative Acidity of Protons 73

Chapter 4 Alkanes
How To Name an Alkane Using the IUPAC System 128
How To Name a Cycloalkane Using the IUPAC System 132
How To Draw a Newman Projection 139
How To Draw the Chair Form of Cyclohexane 146
How To Draw the Two Conformations for a Substituted Cyclohexane 149
How To Draw Two Conformations for a Disubstituted Cyclohexane 152

Chapter 5 Stereochemistry
How To Assign *R* or *S* to a Stereogenic Center 179
How To Find and Draw All Possible Stereoisomers for a Compound with Two Stereogenic Centers 183

Chapter 7 Alkyl Halides and Nucleophilic Substitution
How To Name an Alkyl Halide Using the IUPAC System 240

Chapter 9 Alcohols, Ethers, and Epoxides
How To Name an Alcohol Using the IUPAC System 327

Chapter 10 Alkenes
How To Name an Alkene 376
How To Assign the Prefixes *E* and *Z* to an Alkene 378

Chapter 11 Alkynes
How To Develop a Retrosynthetic Analysis 435

Chapter 13 Mass Spectrometry and Infrared Spectroscopy
How To Use MS and IR for Structure Determination 506

Chapter 14 Nuclear Magnetic Resonance Spectroscopy
How To Determine the Number of Protons Giving Rise to an NMR Signal 528
How To Use ^{1}H NMR Data to Determine a Structure 541

Chapter 16 Conjugation, Resonance, and Dienes
How To Draw the Product of a Diels–Alder Reaction 611

Chapter 17 Benzene and Aromatic Compounds
How To Use the Inscribed Polygon Method to Determine the Relative Energies of MOs for Cyclic, Completely Conjugated Compounds 653

Chapter 18 Reactions of Aromatic Compounds
How To Determine the Directing Effects of a Particular Substituent 686

Chapter 21 Aldehydes and Ketones—Nucleophilic Addition
How To Determine the Starting Materials for a Wittig Reaction Using Retrosynthetic Analysis 828

Chapter 22 Carboxylic Acids and Their Derivatives—Nucleophilic Acyl Substitution
How To Name an Ester (RCO_2R') Using the IUPAC System 865
How To Name a 2° or 3° Amide 866

Chapter 24 **Carbonyl Condensation Reactions**
How To Synthesize a Compound Using the Aldol Reaction 959
How To Synthesize a Compound Using the Robinson Annulation 977

Chapter 25 **Amines**
How To Name 2° and 3° Amines with Different Alkyl Groups 991

Chapter 28 **Carbohydrates**
How To Draw a Haworth Projection from an Acyclic Aldohexose 1111

Chapter 29 **Amino Acids and Proteins**
How To Use (*R*)-α-Methylbenzylamine to Resolve a Racemic Mixture of Amino Acids 1157
How To Synthesize a Dipeptide from Two Amino Acids 1169
How To Synthesize a Peptide Using the Merrifield Solid Phase Technique 1174

List of Mechanisms

Mechanisms are the key to understanding the reactions of organic chemistry. For this reason, great care has been given to present mechanisms in a detailed, step-by-step fashion. The list below indicates when each mechanism in the text is presented for the first time.

Chapter 7 Alkyl Halides and Nucleophilic Substitution
- 7.1 The S_N2 Mechanism 255
- 7.2 The S_N1 Mechanism 263

Chapter 8 Alkyl Halides and Elimination Reactions
- 8.1 The E2 Mechanism 295
- 8.2 The E1 Mechanism 301

Chapter 9 Alcohols, Ethers, and Epoxides
- 9.1 Dehydration of 2° and 3° ROH—An E1 Mechanism 339
- 9.2 Dehydration of a 1° ROH—An E2 Mechanism 340
- 9.3 A 1,2-Methyl Shift—Carbocation Rearrangement During Dehydration 342
- 9.4 Dehydration Using $POCl_3$ + Pyridine—An E2 Mechanism 344
- 9.5 Reaction of a 1° ROH with HX—An S_N2 Mechanism 346
- 9.6 Reaction of 2° and 3° ROH with HX—An S_N1 Mechanism 347
- 9.7 Reaction of ROH with $SOCl_2$ + Pyridine—An S_N2 Mechanism 349
- 9.8 Reaction of ROH with PBr_3—An S_N2 Mechanism 350
- 9.9 Mechanism of Ether Cleavage in Strong Acid—
  $(CH_3)_3COCH_3 + HI \rightarrow (CH_3)_3CI + CH_3I + H_2O$ 356

Chapter 10 Alkenes
- 10.1 Electrophilic Addition of HX to an Alkene 388
- 10.2 Electrophilic Addition of H_2O to an Alkene—Hydration 394
- 10.3 Addition of X_2 to an Alkene—Halogenation 396
- 10.4 Addition of X and OH—Halohydrin Formation 399
- 10.5 Addition of H and BH_2—Hydroboration 402

Chapter 11 Alkynes
- 11.1 Electrophilic Addition of HX to an Alkyne 425
- 11.2 Addition of X_2 to an Alkyne—Halogenation 426
- 11.3 Tautomerization in Acid 428
- 11.4 Hydration of an Alkyne 428

Chapter 12 Oxidation and Reduction
- 12.1 Addition of H_2 to an Alkene—Hydrogenation 448
- 12.2 Dissolving Metal Reduction of an Alkyne to a Trans Alkene 454
- 12.3 Reduction of RX with $LiAlH_4$ 456
- 12.4 Epoxidation of an Alkene with a Peroxyacid 458
- 12.5 Oxidation of an Alcohol with CrO_3 467
- 12.6 Oxidation of a 1° Alcohol to a Carboxylic Acid 468

Chapter 15 Radical Reactions
- 15.1 Radical Halogenation of Alkanes 564
- 15.2 Allylic Bromination with NBS 575
- 15.3 Radical Addition of HBr to an Alkene 581
- 15.4 Radical Polymerization of $CH_2{=}CHZ$ 584

Chapter 16 Conjugation, Resonance, and Dienes
- 16.1 Electrophilic Addition of HBr to a 1,3-Diene—1,2- and 1,4-Addition 607

Chapter 18 Reactions of Aromatic Compounds
- 18.1 General Mechanism—Electrophilic Aromatic Substitution 668
- 18.2 Bromination of Benzene 669
- 18.3 Formation of the Nitronium Ion ($^+NO_2$) for Nitration 670
- 18.4 Formation of the Electrophile $^+SO_3H$ for Sulfonation 671
- 18.5 Formation of the Electrophile in Friedel–Crafts Alkylation—Two Possibilities 673

18.6 Friedel–Crafts Alkylation Using a 3° Carbocation 673
18.7 Formation of the Electrophile in Friedel–Crafts Acylation 674
18.8 Friedel–Crafts Alkylation Involving Carbocation Rearrangement 675
18.9 A Rearrangement Reaction Beginning with a 1° Alkyl Chloride 676
18.10 Nucleophilic Aromatic Substitution by Addition–Elimination 696
18.11 Nucleophilic Aromatic Substitution by Elimination–Addition: Benzyne 698
18.12 Benzylic Bromination 700

Chapter 20 Introduction to Carbonyl Chemistry; Organometallic Reagents; Oxidation and Reduction
20.1 Nucleophilic Addition—A Two-Step Process 756
20.2 Nucleophilic Substitution—A Two-Step Process 757
20.3 $LiAlH_4$ Reduction of RCHO and $R_2C{=}O$ 761
20.4 Reduction of RCOCl and RCOOR' with a Metal Hydride Reagent 767
20.5 Reduction of an Amide to an Amine with $LiAlH_4$ 769
20.6 Nucleophilic Addition of R"MgX to RCHO and $R_2C{=}O$ 775
20.7 Reaction of R"MgX or R"Li with RCOCl and RCOOR' 784
20.8 Carboxylation—Reaction of RMgX with CO_2 787
20.9 1,2-Addition to an α,β-Unsaturated Carbonyl Compound 789
20.10 1,4-Addition to an α,β-Unsaturated Carbonyl Compound 790

Chapter 21 Aldehydes and Ketones—Nucleophilic Addition
21.1 General Mechanism—Nucleophilic Addition 819
21.2 General Mechanism—Acid-Catalyzed Nucleophilic Addition 819
21.3 Nucleophilic Addition of ^{-}CN—Cyanohydrin Formation 824
21.4 The Wittig Reaction 827
21.5 Imine Formation from an Aldehyde or Ketone 831
21.6 Enamine Formation from an Aldehyde or Ketone 833
21.7 Base-Catalyzed Addition of H_2O to a Carbonyl Group 836
21.8 Acid-Catalyzed Addition of H_2O to a Carbonyl Group 836
21.9 Acetal Formation—Part [1] Formation of a Hemiacetal 839
21.10 Acetal Formation—Part [2] Formation of the Acetal 839
21.11 Acid-Catalyzed Cyclic Hemiacetal Formation 843
21.12 A Cyclic Acetal from a Cyclic Hemiacetal 844

Chapter 22 Carboxylic Acids and Their Derivatives—Nucleophilic Acyl Substitution
22.1 General Mechanism—Nucleophilic Acyl Substitution 873
22.2 Conversion of Acid Chlorides to Anhydrides 877
22.3 Conversion of Acid Chlorides to Carboxylic Acids 878
22.4 Conversion of an Anhydride to an Amide 879
22.5 Conversion of Carboxylic Acids to Acid Chlorides 881
22.6 Fischer Esterification—Acid-Catalyzed Conversion of Carboxylic Acids to Esters 882
22.7 Conversion of Carboxylic Acids to Amides with DCC 884
22.8 Acid-Catalyzed Hydrolysis of an Ester to a Carboxylic Acid 886
22.9 Base-Promoted Hydrolysis of an Ester to a Carboxylic Acid 886
22.10 Amide Hydrolysis in Base 890
22.11 Hydrolysis of a Nitrile in Base 899
22.12 Reduction of a Nitrile with $LiAlH_4$ 900
22.13 Reduction of a Nitrile with DIBAL-H 901
22.14 Addition of Grignard and Organolithium Reagents (R–M) to Nitriles 901

Chapter 23 Substitution Reactions of Carbonyl Compounds at the α Carbon
23.1 Tautomerization in Acid 918
23.2 Tautomerization in Base 918
23.3 Acid-Catalyzed Halogenation at the α Carbon 929
23.4 Halogenation at the α Carbon in Base 930
23.5 The Haloform Reaction 931

Chapter 24 Carbonyl Condensation Reactions
24.1 The Aldol Reaction 956
24.2 Dehydration of β-Hydroxy Carbonyl Compounds with Base 958
24.3 The Intramolecular Aldol Reaction 965
24.4 The Claisen Reaction 968

24.5 The Dieckmann Reaction 972
24.6 The Michael Reaction 973
24.7 The Robinson Annulation—Part [A] Michael Addition to Form a 1,5-Dicarbonyl Compound 975
24.8 The Robinson Annulation—Part [B] Intramolecular Aldol Reaction to Form a 2-Cyclohexenone 976

Chapter 25 Amines
25.1 The E2 Mechanism for the Hofmann Elimination 1017
25.2 Formation of a Diazonium Salt from a 1° Amine 1020
25.3 Formation of an *N*-Nitrosamine from a 2° Amine 1021
25.4 Azo Coupling 1026

Chapter 26 Carbon–Carbon Bond-Forming Reactions in Organic Synthesis
26.1 Suzuki Reaction 1048
26.2 Heck Reaction 1052
26.3 Formation of Dichlorocarbene 1053
26.4 Addition of Dichlorocarbene to an Alkene 1054
26.5 Simmons–Smith Reaction 1056
26.6 Olefin Metathesis: $2\ RCH{=}CH_2 \rightarrow RCH{=}CHR + CH_2{=}CH_2$ 1058

Chapter 28 Carbohydrates
28.1 Glycoside Formation 1116
28.2 Glycoside Hydrolysis 1117

Chapter 29 Amino Acids and Proteins
29.1 Formation of an α-Amino Nitrile 1154
29.2 Edman Degradation 1166

Chapter 30 Lipids
30.1 Biological Formation of Geranyl Diphosphate 1211
30.2 Biological Formation of Farnesyl Diphosphate 1212
30.3 Isomerization of Geranyl Diphosphate to Neryl Diphosphate 1213

Chapter 31 Synthetic Polymers
31.1 Radical Polymerization of $CH_2{=}CHPh$ 1228
31.2 Forming Branched Polyethylene During Radical Polymerization 1230
31.3 Cationic Polymerization of $CH_2{=}CHZ$ 1231
31.4 Anionic Polymerization of $CH_2{=}CHZ$ 1233
31.5 Ziegler–Natta Polymerization of $CH_2{=}CH_2$ 1236

List of Selected Applications

Applications make any subject seem more relevant and interesting—for nonmajors and majors alike. The following is a list of the most important biological, medicinal, and environmental applications that have been integrated throughout *Organic Chemistry*. Each chapter opener showcases an interesting and current application relating to the chapter's topic. (Code: G = general; M = medicinal; B = biological; E = environmental)

Prologue

G, E	Examples of simple organic compounds—methane, a component in natural gas; ethanol, the alcohol in beer and wine; and trichlorofluoromethane, a refrigerant and aerosol propellant implicated in ozone destruction
M	Some complex organic compounds that are useful drugs—the antibiotic amoxicillin, the antidepressant fluoxetine (Prozac), and AZT, a drug used to treat HIV
B	The neurotoxin tetrodotoxin
M	Trabectedin (Yondelis), a drug used to treat ovarian cancer and soft tissue carcinoma

Chapter 1 Structure and Bonding

M	L-Dopa, the drug of choice for the treatment of Parkinson's disease (Opener, Section 1.14)
M	Fosamax, a drug used to prevent bone loss in women (Section 1.5)
B	Enanthotoxin, a poisonous compound isolated from hemlock water dropwort (Section 1.7)
M	Structures of active ingredients in common sunscreens (Section 1.8B)

Chapter 2 Acids and Bases

M	The acid–base chemistry of aspirin, the most widely used over-the-counter drug (Opener, Section 2.7)
M	The acid–base chemistry of morphine (Section 2.1)
M	Pseudoephedrine, the nasal decongestant in Sudafed (Section 2.5, Problem 2.16)
M	Glycolic acid, an α-hydroxy acid used in skin care products (Section 2.5, Problem 2.18)
E	Sulfuric acid, a major contributor to acid rain (Section 2.6)

Chapter 3 Introduction to Organic Molecules and Functional Groups

B	Vitamin C, a water-soluble vitamin needed in the formation of the protein collagen (Opener)
E	Hemibrevetoxin B, a neurotoxin produced by algal blooms ("red tides") (Section 3.2B)
M	Atenolol, a β blocker used to treat high blood pressure, and donepezil, used to treat Alzheimer's disease (Section 3.2C)
M	Identifying functional groups in Tamiflu, an antiviral drug used to treat influenza (Section 3.2C, Problem 3.2)
B	How geckos stick to walls and ceilings (Section 3.3B)
E	Solubility principles and the pollutants MTBE and PCBs in the environment (Section 3.4C)
B	How structure explains the fat solubility of vitamin A and the water solubility of vitamin C (Section 3.5)
G	How soap cleans away dirt (Section 3.6)
B	The structure of the cell membrane (Section 3.7A)
M	How ionophores like the antibiotic valinomycin transport ions across a cell membrane (Section 3.7B)
B	Hydrogen bonding in DNA, deoxyribonucleic acid, the high molecular weight compound that stores the genetic information of an organism (Section 3.9)

Chapter 4 Alkanes

G	Alkanes, the major constituents of petroleum, which is refined to produce gasoline, diesel fuel, and home heating oil (Opener, Section 4.7)
B	The cockroach pheromone undecane (Section 4.1)
B	Classifying carbon atoms in bilobalide, a compound isolated from *Ginkgo biloba* extracts (Section 4.1A, Problem 4.4)
E	The combustion of alkanes, the concentration of atmospheric carbon dioxide, and climate change (Section 4.14B)
B	An introduction to lipids, biomolecules whose properties can be explained by understanding alkane chemistry; cholesterol in the cell membrane; waxes (Section 4.15)

Chapter 5 Stereochemistry

M	The three-dimensional structure of thalidomide, the anti-nausea drug that caused catastrophic birth defects (Opener, Section 5.5)
B	How differences in the three-dimensional structure of starch and cellulose affect their shape and function (Section 5.1)
M, B	Identifying stereogenic centers in Darvon (an analgesic), ephedrine (a decongestant), albuterol (a bronchodilator), and chloramphenicol (an antibiotic) (Section 5.4A)

M Identifying stereogenic centers in taxol (anticancer agent), gabapentin (drug used for seizures, chronic pain), and Zocor (cholesterol-lowering drug) (Section 5.5)

M Assigning *R* and *S* configurations in the drugs Plavix and Zestril (Section 5.6, Problems 5.14 and 5.15)

M The importance of the three-dimensional structure in the pain reliever (*S*)-naproxen (Section 5.13A)

M How mirror image isomers can have drastically different properties—the analgesic ibuprofen, the antidepressant fluoxetine, and the anti-inflammatory agent naproxen (Section 5.13)

B The sense of smell—How mirror image isomers can smell differently (Section 5.13)

Chapter 6 Understanding Organic Reactions

B Energy changes in the metabolism of glucose and the combustion of isooctane, a high-octane component of gasoline (Opener, Section 6.4)

B Entropy changes in the metabolism of glucose (Section 6.5)

B Enzymes, biological catalysts (Section 6.11)

Chapter 7 Alkyl Halides and Nucleophilic Substitution

B Organic halides produced by marine organisms for self-defense or feeding deterrents (Opener, Section 7.4)

E CFCs and DDT, two polyhalogenated compounds once widely used, now discontinued because of adverse environmental effects (Section 7.4)

B The biological synthesis of adrenaline, the hormone secreted in response to a strenuous or challenging activity (Section 7.12)

M Nucleophilic substitutions that are key steps in the synthesis of Myambutol (used to treat tuberculosis) and Prozac (an antidepressant) (Section 7.12)

B *S*-Adenosylmethionine (SAM), a nutritional supplement used by the cell in key nucleophilic substitutions that synthesize amino acids, hormones, and neurotransmitters (Section 7.12)

B How nitrosamines, compounds formed in cured meats preserved with sodium nitrite, are thought to be cancer-causing (Section 7.16)

M The importance of organic synthesis in preparing useful drugs such as aspirin (Section 7.19)

Chapter 8 Alkyl Halides and Elimination Reactions

E DDE, a degradation product of the pesticide DDT (Opener, Section 8.1)

B, M Elimination reactions in the synthesis of a prostaglandin, an antimalarial drug, and a female sex hormone (Section 8.4)

Chapter 9 Alcohols, Ethers, and Epoxides

B Palytoxin, a toxic component isolated from marine soft corals of the genus *Palythoa* (Opener)

M Dexamethasone, a synthetic steroid used to treat some forms of arthritis, skin conditions, and asthma (Section 9.1, Problem 9.2)

G, E Ethanol, a gasoline additive and renewable fuel source that can be produced from the fermentation of carbohydrates in grains (Section 9.5)

G Dehydration reactions in the syntheses of vitamin A and patchouli alcohol (used in perfumery) (Section 9.10)

M Epoxides, useful intermediates in the syntheses of salmeterol and albuterol (two bronchodilators) (Section 9.15)

M The design of asthma drugs that block the synthesis of leukotrienes, highly potent molecules that contribute to the asthmatic response (Section 9.16)

B The metabolism of polycyclic aromatic hydrocarbons (PAHs) to carcinogens that disrupt normal cell function resulting in cancer or cell death (Section 9.17)

Chapter 10 Alkenes

B Fats and oils—the properties of saturated and unsaturated fatty acids (Opener, Section 10.6)

B 11-*cis*-Retinal, the light-sensitive aldehyde involved in the vision of all vertebrates, arthropods, and mollusks (Section 10.3B, Problem 10.7)

B The naturally occurring alkenes β-carotene, zingiberene, (*R*)-limonene, and α-farnesene (Section 10.5)

G Ethylene, the starting material for preparing the polymer polyethylene and many other simple compounds used to make a variety of other polymers (Section 10.5)

B Triacylglycerols, fatty acids, fats, and oils (Section 10.6)

B Omega-3 fatty acids, highly unsaturated fatty acids thought to be beneficial for individuals at risk of developing coronary artery disease (Section 10.6, Problem 10.11)

B The synthesis of the female sex hormone estrone (Section 10.15B)

M The synthesis of artemisinin, an antimalarial drug isolated from qinghao, a Chinese herbal remedy (Section 10.16)

Chapter 11	**Alkynes**
M	Oral contraceptives (Opener, Section 11.4)
M	Synthetic hormones mifepristone and Plan B, drugs that prevent pregnancy (Section 11.4)
B	Histrionicotoxin, a diyne isolated from the skin of a frog, used as a poison on arrow tips by the Choco tribe of South America (Section 11.4)
B	Acetylide anion reactions used in the synthesis of two marine natural products (Section 11.11)
Chapter 12	**Oxidation and Reduction**
B	The metabolism of ethanol, the alcohol in alcoholic beverages (Opener, Section 12.14)
B	The partial hydrogenation of vegetable oils and the formation of "trans fats" (Section 12.4)
B	The use of disparlure, a sex pheromone, in controlling the spread of gypsy moths (Section 12.8)
G	Blood alcohol screening (Section 12.12)
E	Green chemistry—environmentally benign oxidation reactions (Section 12.13)
B	The synthesis of insect pheromones using asymmetric epoxidation (Section 12.15)
Chapter 13	**Mass Spectrometry and Infrared Spectroscopy**
M	Infrared spectroscopy and the structure determination of penicillin (Opener, Section 13.8)
M	Using instrumental analysis to detect THC, the active component in marijuana, and other drugs (Section 13.4B)
B	Mass spectrometry and high molecular weight biomolecules (Section 13.4C)
Chapter 14	**Nuclear Magnetic Resonance Spectroscopy**
B	Modern spectroscopic methods and the structure of palau'amine, a complex natural product isolated from a sea sponge (Opener, Problem 14.22)
B	Esters of chrysanthemic acid (from chrysanthemum flowers) as insecticides (Section 14.11, Problem 14.28)
M	Magnetic resonance imaging (MRI) and medicine (Section 14.12)
Chapter 15	**Radical Reactions**
G	Polystyrene, a common synthetic polymer used in packaging materials and beverage cups (Opener)
E	Ozone destruction and CFCs (Section 15.9)
B	The oxidation of unsaturated lipids by radical reactions (Section 15.11)
M, B	Two antioxidants—naturally occurring vitamin E and synthetic BHT (Section 15.12)
G	The formation of useful polymers from monomers by radical reactions (Section 15.14)
Chapter 16	**Conjugation, Resonance, and Dienes**
M	The laboratory synthesis of morphine by a Diels–Alder reaction (Opener)
M	Simvastatin (Zocor) and calcitriol (Rocaltrol), two drugs with conjugated double bonds (Section 16.7)
M	Lycopene, a highly unsaturated red pigment found in tomatoes, watermelon, and other fruits (Sections 16.7 and 16.15A)
B	The Diels–Alder reaction and the synthesis of tetrodotoxin, a toxin isolated from the puffer fish (Section 16.12)
M	The synthesis of steroids by Diels–Alder reactions (Section 16.14C)
G	Why lycopene and other highly conjugated compounds are colored (Section 16.15A)
G	How sunscreens work (Section 16.15B)
Chapter 17	**Benzene and Aromatic Compounds**
B, M	Capsaicin, the spicy component of hot peppers and active ingredient in topical creams for the treatment of chronic pain (Opener)
G	Polycyclic aromatic hydrocarbons (PAHs), constituents of cigarette smoke and diesel exhaust (Section 17.5)
M	Examples of common drugs that contain an aromatic ring—Zoloft, Valium, Novocain, Viracept, Viagra, and Claritin (Section 17.5)
B	Histamine and scombroid fish poisoning (Section 17.8)
M	Quinine, an antimalarial drug (Section 17.8, Problem 17.13)
G	Diamond, graphite, and buckminsterfullerene (Section 17.11)
Chapter 18	**Reactions of Aromatic Compounds**
M, E	Examples of biologically active aryl chlorides—the drugs bupropion and chlorpheniramine, and 2,4-D and 2,4,5-T, herbicide components of the defoliant Agent Orange (Section 18.3)
M	The synthesis of sertraline (Zoloft), an SSRI antidepressant (Opener, Section 18.5D)
M	The synthesis of the hallucinogen LSD (Section 18.5D)
M	Benzocaine, the active ingredient in the over-the-counter topical anesthetic Orajel (Section 18.15C)

Chapter 19 Carboxylic Acids and the Acidity of the O–H Bond

- G Hexanoic acid, the foul-smelling carboxylic acid in ginkgo seeds (Opener, Problem 19.51)
- B GHB (4-hydroxybutanoic acid), an illegal recreational intoxicant used as a "date rape" drug (Section 19.5)
- M, B How NSAIDs block the synthesis of prostaglandins to prevent inflammation (Section 19.6)
- M Urushiol, an irritant in poison ivy (Section 19.11, Problem 19.18)
- B An introduction to amino acids, the building blocks of proteins; why vegetarians must have a balanced diet (Section 19.14)

Chapter 20 Introduction to Carbonyl Chemistry; Organometallic Reagents; Oxidation and Reduction

- B The use of a reduction reaction to synthesize the marine neurotoxin ciguatoxin CTX3C (Opener, Section 20.7A)
- B, M Reduction reactions in the synthesis of the analgesic ibuprofen and the perfume component muscone (Section 20.4)
- M The synthesis of the long-acting bronchodilator salmeterol (Section 20.6A)
- M The use of CBS reagents to synthesize cholesterol-lowering drugs (Section 20.6A, Problem 20.9)
- B Biological oxidation–reduction reactions with the coenzymes NADH and NAD^+ (Section 20.6B)
- M The use of organometallic reagents to synthesize the oral contraceptive ethynylestradiol (Section 20.10C)
- B The use of juvenile hormone mimics to control certain insect populations; the use of organometallic reagents to synthesize the C_{18} juvenile hormone (Section 20.10C)

Chapter 21 Aldehydes and Ketones—Nucleophilic Addition

- M Digoxin, a naturally occurring drug isolated from the woolly foxglove plant and used to treat congestive heart failure (Opener, Problem 21.36)
- B Examples of naturally occurring aldehydes—vanillin, citronellal, cinnamaldehyde, and geranial (Section 21.5)
- M Cortisone and prednisone, steroids that contain ketones (Section 21.5)
- B Naturally occurring cyanohydrin derivatives—linamarin, from cassava root; and amygdalin, often called laetrile, from apricot, peach, and wild cherry pits (Section 21.9B)
- B The use of the Wittig reaction in the synthesis of β-carotene, the orange pigment in carrots (Section 21.10B)
- B The role of rhodopsin in the chemistry of vision (Section 21.11B)

Chapter 22 Carboxylic Acids and Their Derivatives—Nucleophilic Acyl Substitution

- B, M Ginkgolide B, a major constituent of the extracts of the ginkgo tree, *Ginkgo biloba* (Opener, Problem 22.21)
- M, B Compounds that contain an ester—vitamin C and cocaine (Section 22.6)
- M, B Useful amides—proteins, the polyamide met-enkephalin, the anticancer drug Gleevec, the penicillin antibiotics, and the cephalosporin antibiotics (Section 22.6)
- G The synthesis of the insect repellent DEET (Section 22.8)
- B Blattellaquinone, the sex pheromone of the female German cockroach (Section 22.8, Problem 22.13)
- M The use of acylation in the synthesis of aspirin, acetaminophen (the active ingredient in Tylenol), and heroin (Section 22.9)
- B The hydrolysis of triacylglycerols in the metabolism of lipids (Section 22.12A)
- G Olestra, a fake fat (Section 22.12A)
- G The synthesis of soap (Section 22.12B)
- M The mechanism of action of β-lactam antibiotics like penicillin (Section 22.14)
- G Natural and synthetic fibers—nylon and polyesters (Section 22.16)
- B Biological acylation reactions (Section 22.17)
- M Cholesteryl esters in plaque, the deposits that form on the walls of arteries (Section 22.17)

Chapter 23 Substitution Reactions of Carbonyl Compounds at the α Carbon

- M The synthesis of tamoxifen, an anticancer drug used in the treatment of breast cancer (Opener, Section 23.8C)
- M The synthesis of the antimalarial drug quinine by an intramolecular substitution reaction (Section 23.7C)
- M The use of the acetoacetic ester synthesis in the synthesis of illudin-S, an antitumor agent (Section 23.10, Problem 23.28)

Chapter 24 Carbonyl Condensation Reactions

- M The synthesis of the anti-inflammatory agent ibuprofen (Opener, Problem 24.19)
- B The synthesis of periplanone B, sex pheromone of the female American cockroach (Section 24.3)
- B Synthesis of *ar*-turmerone, a component of turmeric, a principal ingredient in curry powder (Section 24.3)
- M The synthesis of the drug donepezil (for treating dementia) using a directed aldol reaction (Section 24.3, Problem 24.11)
- B The synthesis of the steroid progesterone by an intramolecular aldol reaction (Section 24.4)
- M Avobenzone, a common ingredient in commercial sunscreens (Section 24.6A, Problem 24.17)
- B The synthesis of the female sex hormone estrone by a Michael reaction (Section 24.8)

Chapter 25	**Amines**
M	Scopolamine, an alkaloid used to treat nausea and vomiting associated with motion sickness (Opener)
M	Histamine, antihistamines, and antiulcer drugs like Tagamet (cimetidine) (Section 25.6B)
B	Naturally occurring alkaloids—atropine from the poisonous nightshade plant, nicotine from tobacco, and coniine from hemlock (Section 25.6A)
B, M	Biologically active derivatives of 2-phenylethylamine—adrenaline, noradrenaline, methamphetamine, mescaline, and dopamine (Section 25.6C)
B, M	The neurotransmitter serotonin and widely used antidepressants called SSRIs (selective serotonin reuptake inhibitors) (Section 25.6C)
B	Bufotenin and psilocin, naturally occurring hallucinogens (Section 25.6)
M	The synthesis of methamphetamine (Section 25.7C)
M	Drugs such as the antihistamine diphenhydramine, sold as water-soluble ammonium salts (Section 25.9)
M	Acid–base properties of the drugs chloroquine, tacrine, quinine, and brompheniramine (Section 25.10F, Problem 25.25)
G	Azo dyes (Section 25.15)
G	Perkin's mauveine and synthetic dyes (Section 25.16A)
G	How dyes bind to fabric (Section 25.16B)
M	Sulfa drugs (Section 25.17)
Chapter 26	**Carbon–Carbon Bond-Forming Reactions in Organic Synthesis**
B, E	Bombykol, the sex pheromone of the female silkworm moth (Opener, Section 26.2B)
E	Pyrethrin I, a biodegradable insecticide isolated from chrysanthemums (Section 26.4, Problem 26.35)
M	Ring-closing metathesis and the synthesis of epothilone A, an anticancer drug, and Sch38516, an antiviral agent (Section 26.6)
Chapter 27	**Pericyclic Reactions**
B	Pericyclic reactions in the synthesis of periplanone B (sex pheromone of the female American cockroach) (Opener, Problem 27.22)
B	The role of photochemical electrocyclic ring opening and sigmatropic rearrangements in the formation of vitamin D_3 from 7-dehydrocholesterol (Section 27.3C, Problem 27.9)
M	The synthesis of the alkaloid reserpine using a [4 + 2] cycloaddition reaction (Section 27.4B, Problem 27.15)
M	Garsubellin A, a natural product that stimulates the synthesis of the neurotransmitter acetylcholine (Section 27.5, Problem 27.24)
Chapter 28	**Carbohydrates**
B	Lactose, the carbohydrate in milk (Opener, Section 28.12)
B	Glucose, the most common simple sugar (Section 28.6)
B, M	Naturally occurring glycosides—salicin from willow bark and solanine, isolated from the deadly nightshade plant (Section 28.7C)
G	Rebaudioside A (trade name Truvia), a sweet glycoside from the stevia plant (Section 28.7C)
B	Common disaccharides—maltose from malt, lactose from milk, and sucrose, table sugar (Section 28.12)
G	Artificial sweeteners (Section 28.12C)
B	Common polysaccharides—cellulose, starch, and glycogen (Section 28.13)
B, M	Glucosamine, an over-the-counter remedy used for osteoarthritis, and chitin, the carbohydrate that gives rigidity to crab shells (Section 28.14A)
B	*N*-Glycosides and the structure of DNA (Section 28.14B)
Chapter 29	**Amino Acids and Proteins**
B	Myoglobin, the protein that stores oxygen in tissues (Opener, Section 29.10C)
B	The naturally occurring amino acids (Section 29.1)
B	The structures of the hormones bradykinin, oxytocin, and vasopressin (Section 29.5C)
B	The artificial sweetener aspartame (Section 29.5C)
B	The structure of glutathione, a powerful antioxidant in cells (Section 29.5C, Problem 29.17)
B	The preparation of polypeptides and proteins using automated peptide synthesis—the Merrifield method (Section 29.8)
B	The structure of spider silk (Section 29.9B)
M	The structure of insulin (Section 29.9C)
B	β-Keratin, the protein in hair (Section 29.10A)
B	Collagen, the protein in connective tissue (Section 29.10B)
B	The globular protein hemoglobin; the structure of sickle cell hemoglobin (Section 29.10C)

Chapter 30 Lipids

B Cholesterol, the most prominent steroid (Opener, Section 30.8B)
B Structure of spermaceti wax (Section 30.2)
B Waxes obtained from jojoba seeds, which are used in cosmetics and personal care products (Section 30.2, Problem 30.1)
B Triacylglycerols, the components of fats and oils (Section 30.3)
B Energy storage and the metabolism of fats (Section 30.3)
B The phospholipids in cell membranes (Section 30.4)
B Fat-soluble vitamins—A, D, E, and K (Section 30.5)
B The eicosanoids, a group of biologically active lipids that includes the prostaglandins and leukotrienes (Section 30.6)
M Misoprostol, an analogue of PGE_1, used to prevent gastric ulcers (Section 30.6)
M NSAIDs like aspirin and ibuprofen, drugs that inactivate COX-1 and COX-2 enzymes (Section 30.6)
M Vioxx, Bextra, and Celebrex—anti-inflammatory drugs (Section 30.6)
B Essential oils (Section 30.7)
B Biformene, a terpenoid in amber (Section 30.7, Problem 30.13)
B, M The structure of steroids—cholesterol, female sex hormones, male sex hormones, adrenal cortical steroids, anabolic steroids, and oral contraceptives (Section 30.8)
M Cholesterol and cholesterol-lowering drugs atorvastatin (Lipitor) and simvastatin (Zocor) (Section 30.8B)

Chapter 31 Synthetic Polymers

G Polyethylene terephthalate, an easily recycled synthetic polymer used in transparent soft drink containers (Opener, Sections 31.6B and 31.9A)
G Polyethylene, the plastic in milk jugs and plastic bags, and other chain-growth polymers (Section 31.2)
G Using Ziegler–Natta catalysts to make high-density polyethylene (Section 31.4)
G Dyneema, a strong fiber made of ultra high-density polyethylene (Section 31.4)
B Natural and synthetic rubber (Section 31.5)
G The synthesis of step-growth polymers—polyamides such as nylon and Kevlar, polyesters such as Dacron, polyurethanes such as spandex, and polycarbonates such as Lexan (Section 31.6)
M Dissolving sutures (Section 31.6B)
G Epoxy resins (Section 31.6E)
E Green polymer synthesis—environmentally benign methods for preparing polymers (Section 31.8)
E Polymer recycling (Section 31.9A)
E Biodegradable polymers (Section 31.9B)

Prologue

What is organic chemistry?
Some representative organic molecules
Organic chemistry in the marine environment

Organic chemistry. You might wonder how a discipline that conjures up images of eccentric old scientists working in basement laboratories is relevant to you, a student in the twenty-first century.

Consider for a moment the activities that occupied your past 24 hours. You likely showered with soap, drank a caffeinated beverage, ate at least one form of starch, took some medication, read a newspaper, listened to a CD, and traveled in a vehicle that had rubber tires and was powered by fossil fuels. If you did any *one* of these, your life was touched by organic chemistry.

What Is Organic Chemistry?

- **Organic chemistry is the chemistry of compounds that contain the element carbon.**

It is one branch in the entire field of chemistry, which encompasses many classical subdisciplines including inorganic, physical, and analytical chemistry, and newer fields such as bioinorganic chemistry, physical biochemistry, polymer chemistry, and materials science.

Organic chemistry was singled out as a separate discipline for historical reasons. Originally, it was thought that compounds in living things, termed ***organic compounds,*** were fundamentally different from those in nonliving things, called ***inorganic compounds.*** Although we have known for more than 150 years that this distinction is artificial, the name *organic* persists. Today the term refers to the study of the compounds that contain carbon, many of which, incidentally, are found in living organisms.

It may seem odd that a whole discipline is devoted to the study of a single element in the periodic table, when more than 100 elements exist. It turns out, though, that there are far more organic compounds than any other type. **Organic chemicals affect virtually every facet of our lives, and for this reason, it is important and useful to know something about them.**

Clothes, foods, medicines, gasoline, refrigerants, and soaps are composed almost solely of organic compounds. Some, like cotton, wool, or silk are naturally occurring; that is, they can be isolated directly from natural sources. Others, such as nylon and polyester, are synthetic, meaning they are produced by chemists in the laboratory. By studying the principles and concepts of organic chemistry, you can learn more about compounds such as these and how they affect the world around you.

Realize, too, what organic chemistry has done for us. Organic chemistry has made available both comforts and necessities that were previously nonexistent, or reserved for only the wealthy. We have seen an enormous increase in life span, from 47 years in 1900 to over 70 years currently. To a large extent this is due to the isolation and synthesis of new drugs to fight infections and the availability of vaccines for childhood diseases. Chemistry has also given us the tools to control insect populations that spread disease, and there is more food for all because of fertilizers, pesticides, and herbicides. Our lives would be vastly different today without the many products that result from organic chemistry (Figure 1).

Figure 1
Products of organic chemistry used in medicine

a. Oral contraceptives

b. Plastic syringes

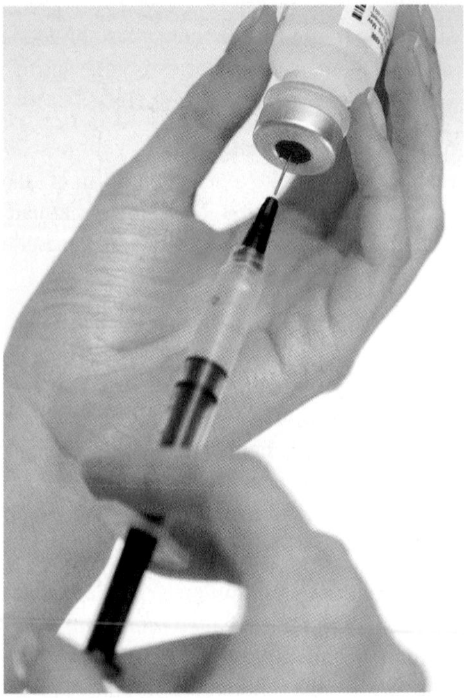

c. Antibiotics

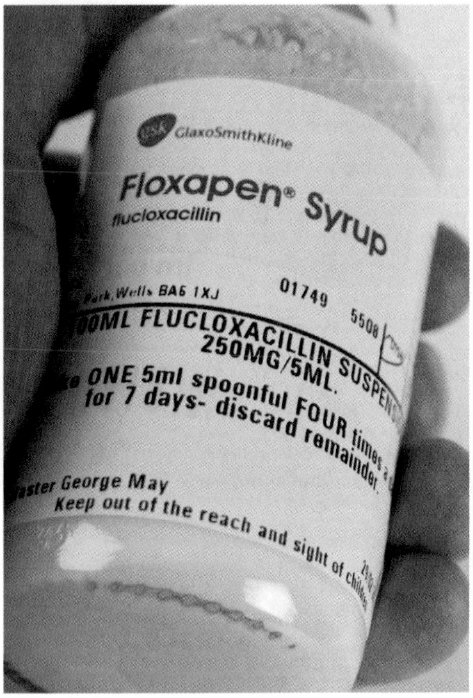

d. Synthetic heart valves

- Organic chemistry has given us contraceptives, plastics, antibiotics, and the knitted material used in synthetic heart valves.

Some Representative Organic Molecules

Perhaps the best way to appreciate the variety of organic molecules is to look at a few. Three simple organic compounds are **methane, ethanol,** and **trichlorofluoromethane.**

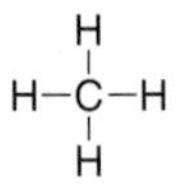

methane

- **Methane,** the simplest of all organic compounds, contains one carbon atom. Methane—the main component of natural gas—occurs widely in nature. Like other hydrocarbons—organic compounds that contain only carbon and hydrogen—**methane is combustible;** that is, it burns in the presence of oxygen. Methane is the product of the anaerobic (without air) decomposition of organic matter by bacteria. The natural gas we use today was formed by the decomposition of organic material millions of years ago. Hydrocarbons such as methane are discussed in Chapter 4.

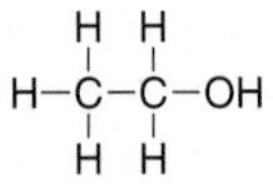

ethanol

- **Ethanol,** the alcohol present in beer, wine, and other alcoholic beverages, is formed by the fermentation of sugar, quite possibly the oldest example of organic synthesis. Ethanol can also be made in the lab by a totally different process, but **the ethanol produced in the lab is identical to the ethanol produced by fermentation.** Alcohols including ethanol are discussed in Chapter 9.

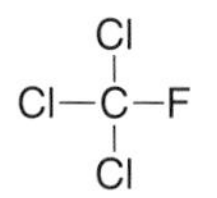
Cl
Cl—C—F
Cl
trichlorofluoromethane

- **Trichlorofluoromethane** is a member of a class of molecules called **c**hloro**f**luoro**c**arbons or **CFCs,** which contain one or two carbon atoms and several halogens. Trichlorofluoromethane is an unusual organic molecule in that **it contains no hydrogen atoms.** Because it has a low molecular weight and is easily vaporized, trichlorofluoromethane has been used as an aerosol propellant and refrigerant. It and other CFCs have been implicated in the destruction of the stratospheric ozone layer, as is discussed in Chapter 15.

Because more complicated organic compounds contain many carbon atoms, organic chemists have devised a shorthand to draw them. Keep in mind the following when examining these structures:

- **Each solid line represents a two-electron covalent bond.**
- **When no atom is drawn at the corner of a ring, an organic chemist assumes it to be carbon.**

For example, in the six-membered ring drawn, there is one carbon atom at each corner of the hexagon.

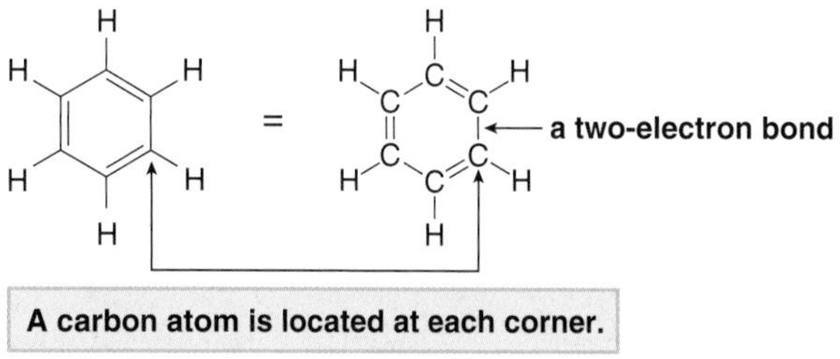
a two-electron bond
A carbon atom is located at each corner.

Three complex organic molecules that are important medications are **amoxicillin, fluoxetine,** and **AZT.**

- **Amoxicillin** is one of the most widely used antibiotics in the penicillin family. The discovery and synthesis of such antibiotics in the twentieth century have made routine the treatment of infections that were formerly fatal. You were likely given some amoxicillin to treat an ear infection when you were a child. The penicillin antibiotics are discussed in Chapter 22.

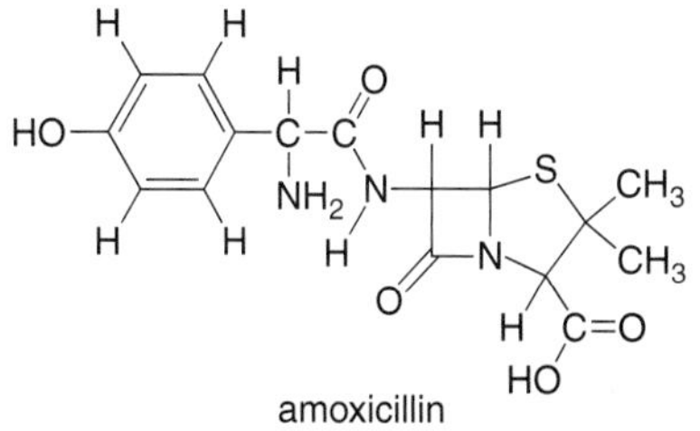
amoxicillin

- **Fluoxetine** is the generic name for the antidepressant **Prozac.** Prozac was designed and synthesized by chemists in the laboratory, and is now produced on a large scale in chemical factories. Because it is safe and highly effective in treating depression, Prozac is widely prescribed. Over 40 million individuals worldwide have used Prozac since 1986.

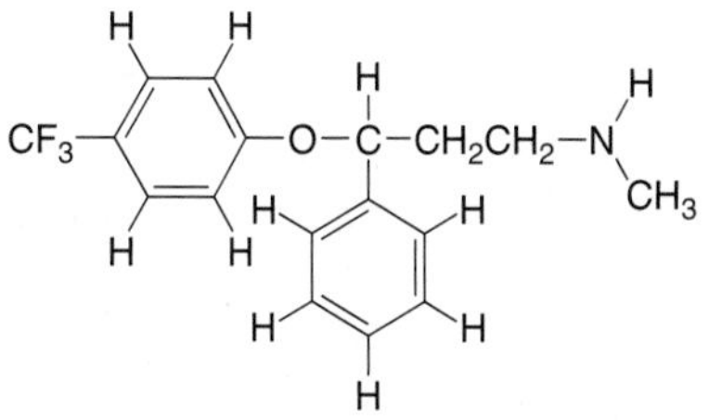
fluoxetine

- **AZT, az**idodeoxy**t**hymidine, is a drug that treats human immunodeficiency virus (HIV), the virus that causes acquired immune deficiency syndrome (AIDS). Also known by its generic name **zidovudine,** AZT represents a chemical success to a different challenge: synthesizing agents that combat viral infections.

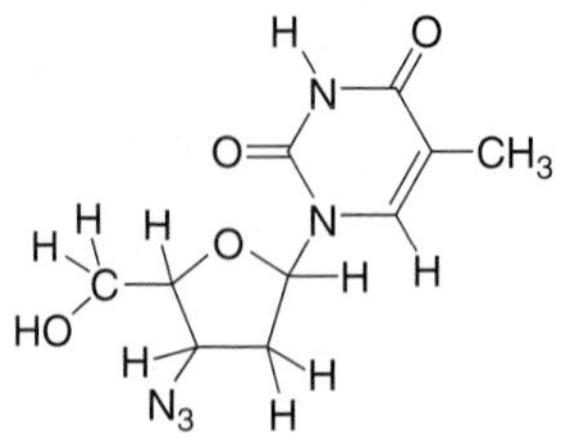

AZT

Other complex organic compounds having interesting properties are **capsaicin** and **DDT.**

- **Capsaicin,** one member of a group of compounds called *vanilloids,* is responsible for the characteristic spiciness of hot peppers. It is the active ingredient in pepper sprays used for personal defense and topical creams used for pain relief.

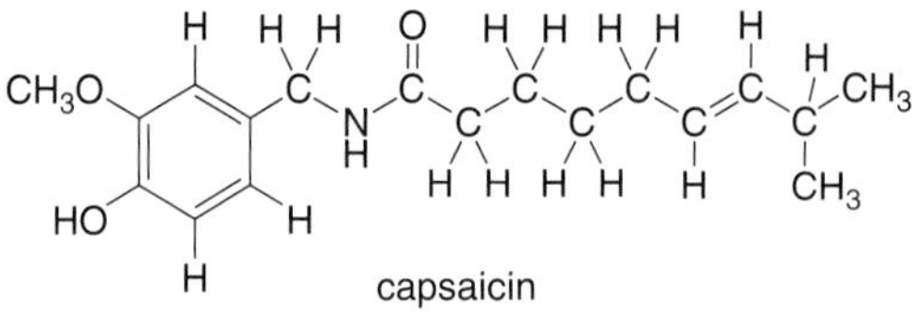

capsaicin

- **DDT, d**ichloro**d**iphenyl**t**richloroethane, is a pesticide once called "miraculous" by Winston Churchill because of the many lives it saved by killing disease-carrying mosquitoes. DDT use is now banned in the United States and many developed countries because it is a nonspecific insecticide that persists in the environment.

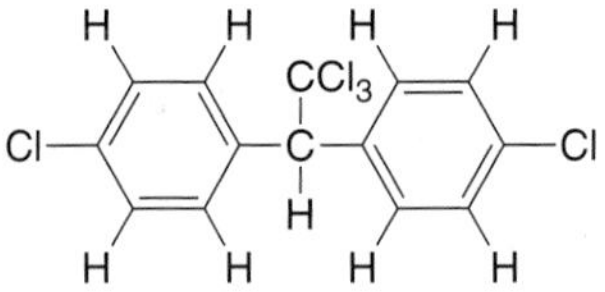

DDT

What are the common features of these organic compounds?

- All organic compounds contain carbon atoms and most contain hydrogen atoms.
- All the carbon atoms have four bonds. A stable carbon atom is said to be *tetravalent*.
- Other elements may also be present. Any atom that is not carbon or hydrogen is called a *heteroatom*. Common heteroatoms include N, O, S, P, and the halogens.
- Some compounds have chains of atoms and some compounds have rings.

These features explain why there are so many organic compounds: **Carbon forms four strong bonds with itself and other elements. Carbon atoms combine together to form rings and chains.**

Organic Chemistry in the Marine Environment

Nature has generously supplied the organic chemist with a wide variety of complex molecules, biologically active drugs, and curious ecological adaptations. In the past 40 years, the chemistry of the marine environment has proven to be especially fruitful in producing unique chemical compounds and unusual behaviors.

For example, two complex molecules isolated from marine organisms are tetrodotoxin and trabectedin (Figure 2).

Figure 2

Tetrodotoxin and trabectedin, natural products from marine sources

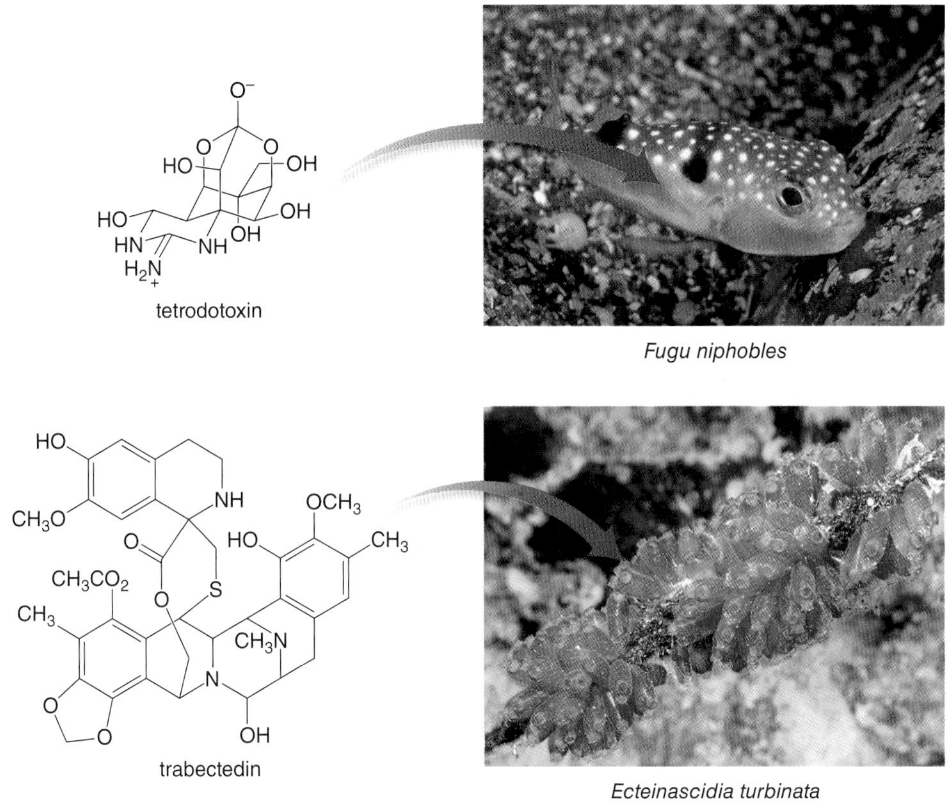

- Hydrogen atoms bonded to ring carbons are omitted in the structures of tetrodotoxin and trabectedin, a convention described in Section 1.8.

- **Tetrodotoxin,** a neurotoxin, is found in puffer fish of the genus *Fugu.* Puffer fish, a culinary delicacy in Japan, must be carefully prepared to remove organs such as the liver and ovaries that contain unsafe levels of this potent poison.
- **Trabectedin,** isolated from the sea squirt *Ecteinascidia turbinata,* is a novel anticancer drug recently approved in Europe for the treatment of ovarian cancer and soft tissue carcinoma. Trabectedin, also known as ecteinascidin 743, is marketed under the trade name Yondelis.

Finally, the complex chemistry that allows an anemonefish to live among the stinging tentacles of a sea anemone has attracted the attention of chemists, biochemists, and chemical biologists (Figure 3). Over the last 25 years, it has been shown that anemonefish are covered in a mucous

Figure 3

The attractant amphikuemin, secreted by the sea anemone *Heteractis crispa*

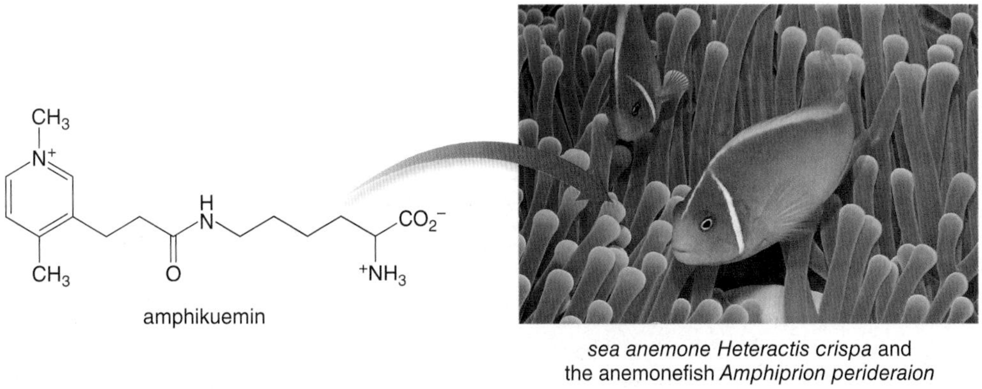

- Hydrogen atoms bonded to carbon are omitted on the ring carbons and carbon chain in the structure of amphikuemin (Section 1.8).

coating that protects them from the protein neurotoxin used by the sea anemone to ward off predators and kill prey. Moreover, the symbiosis between the sea anemone *Heteractis crispa* and the pink anemonefish *Amphiprion perideraion* is initiated by the secretion of **amphikuemin,** a compound of molecular formula $C_{16}H_{26}N_3O_3$ derived from the amino acid lysine (Chapter 29). The details of many of the chemical phenomena in this intricate biological system are as yet unknown and awaiting discovery.

In this introduction, we have seen a variety of molecules that have diverse structures. They represent a miniscule fraction of the organic compounds currently known and the many thousands that are newly discovered or synthesized each year. The principles you learn in organic chemistry will apply to all of these molecules, from simple ones like methane and ethanol, to complex ones like capsaicin and trabectedin. It is these beautiful molecules, their properties, and their reactions that we will study in organic chemistry.

WELCOME TO THE WORLD OF ORGANIC CHEMISTRY!

Structure and Bonding

1

1.1 The periodic table
1.2 Bonding
1.3 Lewis structures
1.4 Isomers
1.5 Exceptions to the octet rule
1.6 Resonance
1.7 Determining molecular shape
1.8 Drawing organic structures
1.9 Hybridization
1.10 Ethane, ethylene, and acetylene
1.11 Bond length and bond strength
1.12 Electronegativity and bond polarity
1.13 Polarity of molecules
1.14 L-Dopa—A representative organic molecule

L-Dopa, also called levodopa, was first isolated from seeds of the broad bean plant *Vicia faba* in 1913. Since 1967 it has been the drug of choice for the treatment of Parkinson's disease, a debilitating illness that results from the degeneration of neurons that produce the neurotransmitter dopamine in the brain. L-Dopa is an oral medication that is transported to the brain by the bloodstream, where it is converted to dopamine. Since L-dopa must be taken in large doses with some serious side effects, today it is often given with other drugs that lessen its negative impact on an individual. In Chapter 1, we learn about the structure, bonding, and properties of organic molecules like L-dopa.

Before examining organic molecules in detail, we must review some important features about structure and bonding learned in previous chemistry courses. We will discuss these concepts primarily from an organic chemist's perspective, and spend time on only the particulars needed to understand organic compounds.

Important topics in Chapter 1 include drawing Lewis structures, predicting the shape of molecules, determining what orbitals are used to form bonds, and how electronegativity affects bond polarity. Equally important is Section 1.8 on drawing organic molecules, both shorthand methods routinely used for simple and complex compounds, as well as three-dimensional representations that allow us to more clearly visualize them.

1.1 The Periodic Table

All matter is composed of the same building blocks called **atoms.** There are two main components of an atom.

- The **nucleus** contains positively charged **protons** and uncharged **neutrons.** Most of the mass of the atom is contained in the nucleus.
- The **electron cloud** is composed of negatively charged **electrons.** The electron cloud comprises most of the volume of the atom.

Schematic of an atom

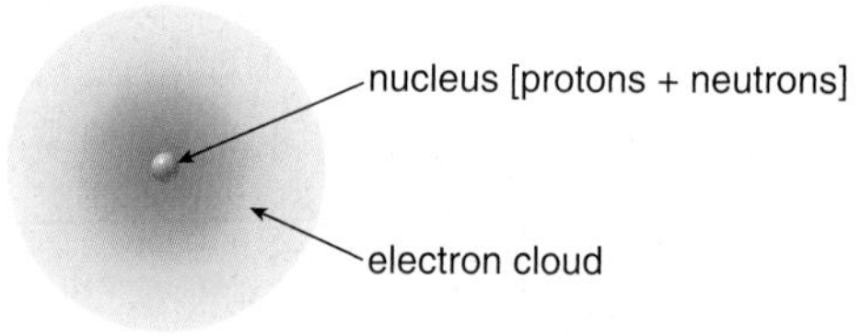
nucleus [protons + neutrons]
electron cloud

The charge on a proton is equal in magnitude but opposite in sign to the charge on an electron. In a neutral atom, the **number of protons in the nucleus equals the number of electrons.** This quantity, called the **atomic number,** is unique to a particular element. For example, every neutral carbon atom has an atomic number of six, meaning it has six protons in its nucleus and six electrons surrounding the nucleus.

In addition to neutral atoms, we will also encounter **charged ions.**

- A *cation* is positively charged and has fewer electrons than its neutral form.
- An *anion* is negatively charged and has more electrons than its neutral form.

The number of neutrons in the nucleus of a particular element can vary. **Isotopes** are two atoms of the same element having a different number of neutrons. The **mass number** of an atom is the total number of protons and neutrons in the nucleus. Isotopes have different mass numbers.

Isotopes of carbon and hydrogen are sometimes used in organic chemistry, as we will see in Chapter 14.

- The most common isotope of hydrogen has one proton and no neutrons in the nucleus, but 0.02% of hydrogen atoms have one proton and one neutron. This isotope of hydrogen is called **deuterium,** and is sometimes symbolized by the letter **D.**
- Most carbon atoms have six protons and six neutrons in the nucleus, but 1.1% have six protons and seven neutrons.

The **atomic weight** is the weighted average of the mass of all isotopes of a particular element, reported in atomic mass units (amu).

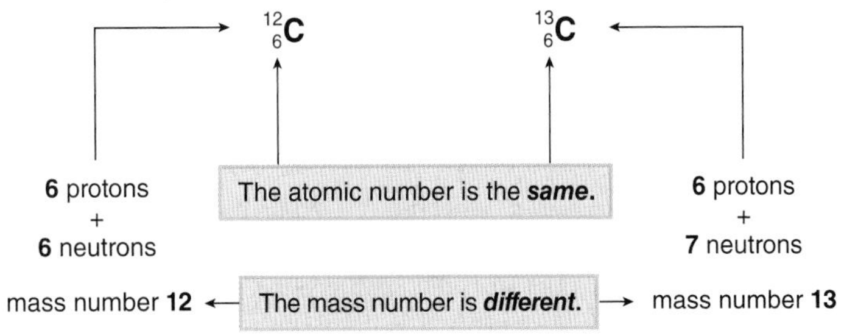

Figure 1.1
A comparison of two isotopes of the element carbon

Each atom is identified by a one- or two-letter abbreviation that is the characteristic symbol for that element. Carbon is identified by the single letter **C.** Sometimes the atomic number is indicated as a subscript to the left of the element symbol, and the mass number is indicated as a superscript, as shown in Figure 1.1.

Long ago it was realized that groups of elements have similar properties, and that these atoms could be arranged in a schematic way called the **periodic table.** There are more than 100 known elements, arranged in the periodic table in order of increasing atomic number. The periodic table is composed of rows and columns.

A **row** in the periodic table is also called a ***period,*** and a **column** is also called a ***group.*** A periodic table is located on the inside front cover for your reference.

- **Elements in the same row are similar in *size.***
- **Elements in the same column have similar *electronic and chemical properties.***

Each column in the periodic table is identified by a **group number,** an Arabic (1 to 8) or Roman (I to VIII) numeral followed by the letter A or B. For example, carbon is located in group **4A** in the periodic table in this text.

Carbon's entry in the periodic table:

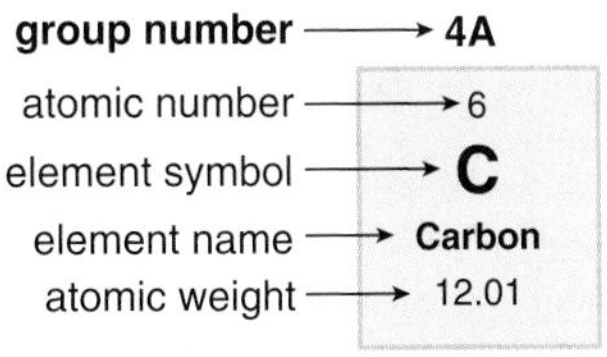

Although more than 100 elements exist, most are not common in organic compounds. Figure 1.2 contains a truncated periodic table, indicating the handful of elements that are routinely seen in this text. **Most of these elements are located in the first and second rows of the periodic table.**

Across each row of the periodic table, electrons are added to a particular shell of orbitals around the nucleus. The shells are numbered 1, 2, 3, and so on. Adding electrons to the first shell forms the first row. Adding electrons to the second shell forms the second row. **Electrons are first added to the shells closest to the nucleus.** These electrons are held most tightly.

Each shell contains a certain number of subshells called **orbitals.** An orbital is a region of space that is high in electron density. There are four different kinds of orbitals, called ***s, p, d,*** and ***f.*** The first shell has only one orbital, called an *s* orbital. The second shell has two kinds of orbitals, *s* and ***p,*** and so on. Each type of orbital occupies a certain space and has a particular shape.

Figure 1.2
A periodic table of the common elements seen in organic chemistry

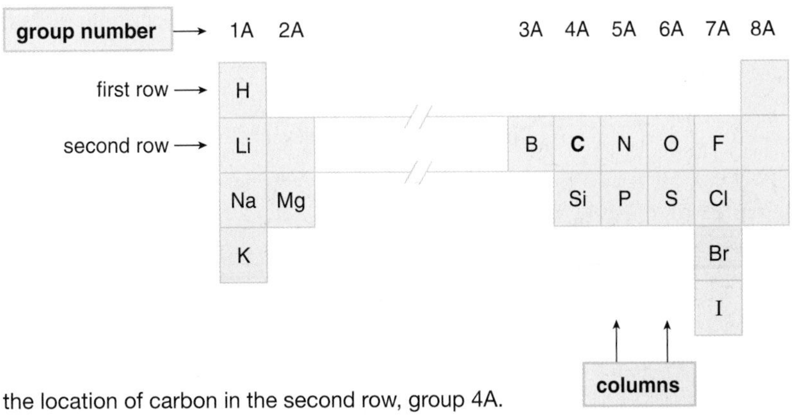

- Note the location of carbon in the second row, group 4A.

For the first- and second-row elements, we must deal with only ***s* orbitals** and ***p* orbitals.**

- An ***s* orbital** has a **sphere of electron density.** It is ***lower in energy*** than other orbitals of the same shell, because electrons are kept close to the positively charged nucleus. An *s* orbital is filled with electrons before a *p* orbital in the same shell.
- A ***p* orbital** has a **dumbbell shape.** It contains a **node of electron density** at the nucleus. A node means there is no electron density in this region. A *p* orbital is ***higher in energy*** than an *s* orbital (in the same shell) because its electron density is farther away from the nucleus. A *p* orbital is filled with electrons only after an *s* orbital of the same shell is full.

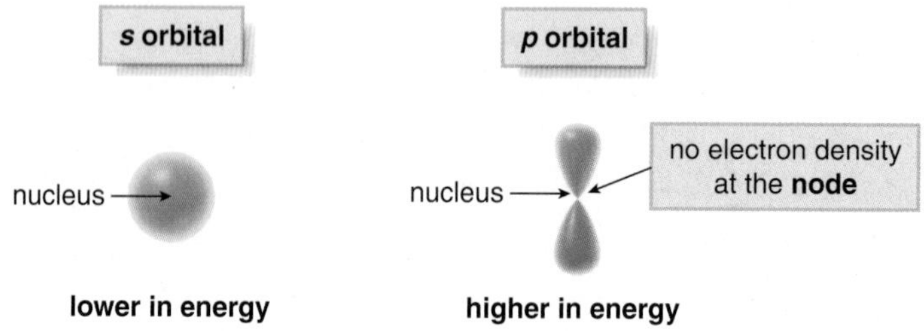

Let's now look at the elements in the first and second rows of the periodic table.

1.1A The First Row

The first row of the periodic table is formed by adding electrons to the first shell of orbitals around the nucleus. There is only one orbital in the first shell, called the **1*s* orbital.**

- **Remember: Each orbital can have a maximum of two electrons.**

As a result, there are **two elements in the first row,** one having one electron added to the 1*s* orbital, and one having two. The element hydrogen (H) has what is called a $1s^1$ configuration with one electron in the 1*s* orbital, and helium (He) has a $1s^2$ configuration with two electrons in the 1*s* orbital.

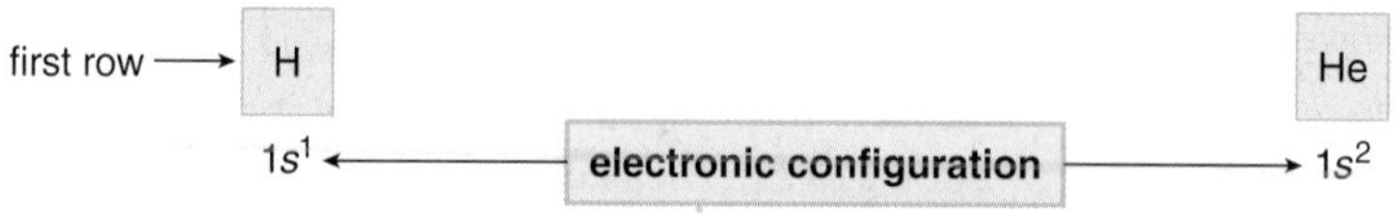

1.1B The Second Row

Every element in the second row has a filled first shell of electrons. Thus, all second-row elements have a $1s^2$ configuration. These electrons in the inner shell of orbitals are called **core electrons,** and are not usually involved in the chemistry of a particular element.

Each element in the second row of the periodic table has four orbitals available to accept additional electrons:

- **one 2*s* orbital,** the *s* orbital in the second shell
- **three 2*p* orbitals,** all dumbbell-shaped and perpendicular to each other along the *x*, *y*, and *z* axes

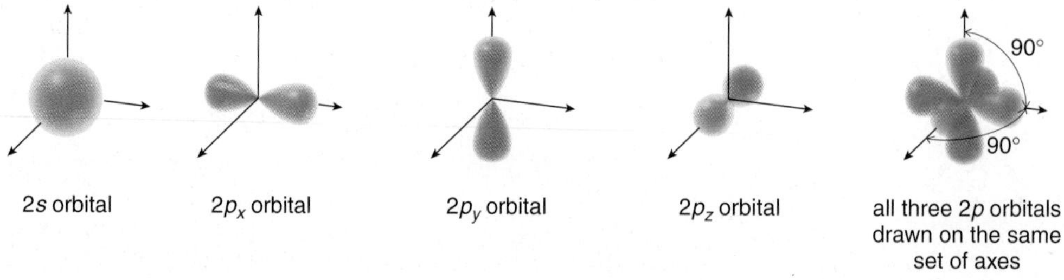

Because each of the four orbitals in the second shell can hold two electrons, there is a **maximum capacity of *eight* electrons** for elements in the second row. The second row of the periodic table consists of eight elements, obtained by adding electrons to the 2*s* and three 2*p* orbitals.

group number	1A	2A	3A	4A	5A	6A	7A	8A
second row	Li	Be	B	**C**	N	O	F	Ne
number of valence electrons	1	2	3	4	5	6	7	8

The outermost electrons are called **valence electrons.** The valence electrons are more loosely held than the electrons closer to the nucleus, and as such, they participate in chemical reactions. **The group number of a second-row element reveals its number of valence electrons.** For example, carbon in group 4A has four valence electrons, and oxygen in group 6A has six.

Problem 1.1 While the most common isotope of nitrogen has a mass number of 14 (nitrogen-14), a radioactive isotope of nitrogen has a mass number of 13 (nitrogen-13). Nitrogen-13 is used in PET (positron emission tomography) scans by physicians to monitor brain activity and diagnose dementia. For each isotope, give the following information: (a) the number of protons; (b) the number of neutrons; (c) the number of electrons in the neutral atom; and (d) the group number.

1.2 Bonding

Until now our discussion has centered on individual atoms, but it is more common in nature to find two or more atoms joined together.

- ***Bonding*** **is the joining of two atoms in a stable arrangement.**

Bonding may occur between atoms of the same or different elements. Bonding is a favorable process because it always leads to ***lowered energy and increased stability.*** Joining two or more elements forms **compounds.** Although only about 100 elements exist, more than 50 million compounds are known. Examples of compounds include hydrogen gas (H_2), formed by joining two hydrogen atoms, and methane (CH_4), the simplest organic compound, formed by joining a carbon atom with four hydrogen atoms.

One general rule governs the bonding process.

- **Through bonding, atoms attain a complete outer shell of valence electrons.**

Alternatively, because the noble gases in group 8A of the periodic table are especially stable as atoms having a filled shell of valence electrons, the general rule can be restated.

- **Through bonding, atoms attain a stable noble gas configuration of electrons.**

What does this mean for first- and second-row elements? **A first-row element like hydrogen can accommodate *two electrons* around it.** This would make it like the noble gas helium at the end of the same row. **A second-row element is most stable with *eight valence electrons* around it** like neon. Elements that behave in this manner are said to follow the **octet rule.**

There are two different kinds of bonding: **ionic bonding** and **covalent bonding.**

- ***Ionic bonds*** **result from the *transfer* of electrons from one element to another.**
- ***Covalent bonds*** **result from the *sharing* of electrons between two nuclei.**

The type of bonding is determined by the location of an element in the periodic table. An ionic bond generally occurs when elements on the **far left** side of the periodic table combine with elements on the **far right** side, ignoring the noble gases, which form bonds only rarely. **The resulting ions**

are held together by extremely strong electrostatic interactions. A positively charged cation formed from the element on the left side attracts a negatively charged anion formed from the element on the right side. The resulting **salts** are seen in many of the inorganic compounds with which you are familiar. Sodium chloride (NaCl) is common table salt, and potassium iodide (KI) is an essential nutrient added to make iodized salt.

Atoms readily form ionic bonds when they can attain a noble gas configuration by gaining or losing just one or two electrons. NaCl and KI are ionic compounds.

Ionic compounds form extended crystal lattices that maximize the positive and negative electrostatic interactions. In NaCl, each positively charged Na^+ ion is surrounded by six negatively charged Cl^- ions, and each Cl^- ion is surrounded by six Na^+ ions.

NaCl—An ionic crystalline lattice

Lithium fluoride, LiF, is an example of an ionic compound.

- The element **lithium,** located in group 1A of the periodic table, has just one valence electron in its second shell. If this electron is lost, lithium forms the cation Li^+ having no electrons in the second shell. However, it will have a stable electronic arrangement with two electrons in the first shell like helium.
- The element **fluorine,** located in group 7A of the periodic table, has seven valence electrons. By gaining one it forms the anion F^-, which has a filled valence shell (an octet of electrons), like neon.
- Thus, lithium fluoride is a stable ionic compound.

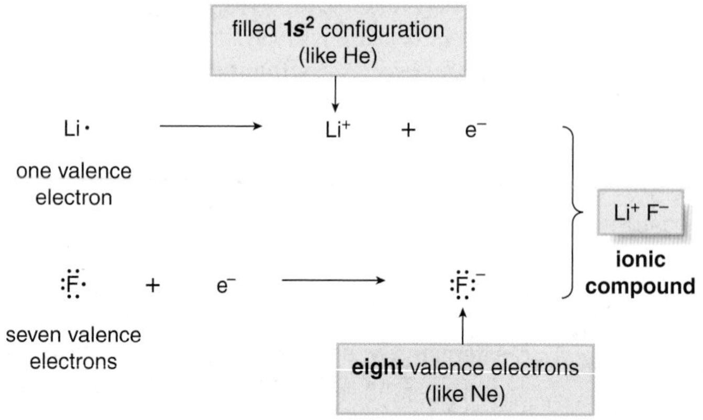

- **The transfer of electrons forms stable salts composed of cations and anions.**

A **compound** may have either ionic or covalent bonds. A **molecule** has only covalent bonds.

The second type of bonding, **covalent bonding,** occurs with elements like carbon in the middle of the periodic table, which would otherwise have to gain or lose several electrons to form an ion with a complete valence shell. **A covalent bond is a two-electron bond,** and a compound with covalent bonds is called a **molecule.** Covalent bonds also form between two elements from the same side of the table, such as two hydrogen atoms or two chlorine atoms. H_2, Cl_2, and CH_4 are all examples of covalent molecules.

Problem 1.2 Label each bond in the following compounds as ionic or covalent.

a. F_2 b. LiBr c. CH_3CH_3 d. $NaNH_2$

How many covalent bonds will a particular atom typically form? As you might expect, it depends on the location of the atom in the periodic table. In the first row, **hydrogen forms one covalent bond** using its one valence electron. When two hydrogen atoms are joined in a bond, each has a filled valence shell of two electrons.

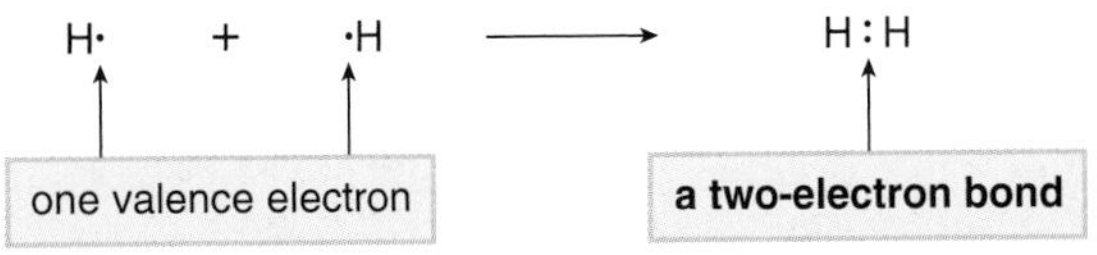

Second-row elements can have no more than eight valence electrons around them. For neutral molecules, two consequences result.

- **Atoms with one, two, three, or four valence electrons form one, two, three, or four bonds,** respectively, in neutral molecules.
- **Atoms with five or more valence electrons** form enough bonds to give an octet. This results in the following simple equation:

predicted number of bonds = 8 − **number of valence electrons**

For example, B has three valence electrons, so it forms three bonds, as in BF_3. N has five valence electrons, so it also forms three bonds (8 – 5 = 3 bonds), as in NH_3.

Nonbonded pair of electrons = unshared pair of electrons = lone pair

These guidelines are used in Figure 1.3 to summarize the usual number of bonds formed by the common atoms in organic compounds. Notice that when second-row elements form fewer than four bonds their octets consist of both **bonding (shared) electrons** and **nonbonding (unshared) electrons.** Unshared electrons are also called **lone pairs.**

Problem 1.3 How many covalent bonds are predicted for each atom?

a. O b. Al c. Br d. Si

Figure 1.3
Summary: The usual number of bonds of common neutral atoms

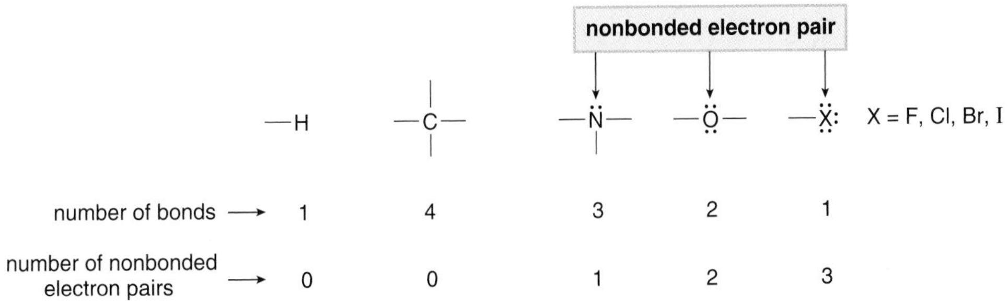

1.3 Lewis Structures

***Lewis structures* are electron dot representations for molecules.** There are three general rules for drawing Lewis structures.

1. Draw only the valence electrons.
2. Give every second-row element no more than eight electrons.
3. Give each hydrogen two electrons.

The letter **X** is often used to represent one of the halogens in group 7A: F, Cl, Br, or I.

To draw a Lewis structure for a diatomic molecule like **HF,** recall that hydrogen has one valence electron and fluorine has seven. H and F each donate one electron to form a two-electron bond. The resulting molecule gives both H and F a filled valence shell.

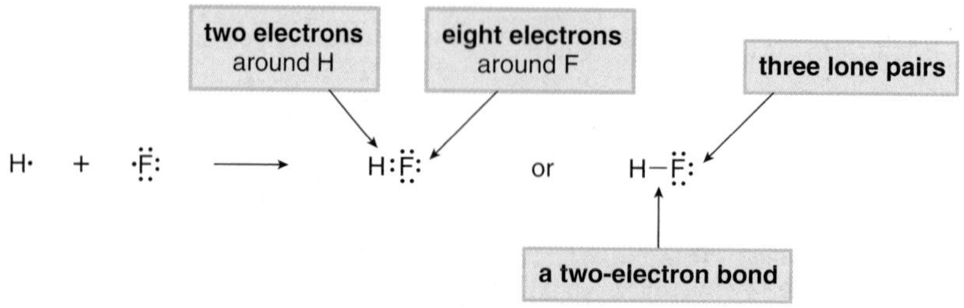

In a Lewis structure, **a *solid line* indicates a two-electron covalent bond.**

1.3A A Procedure for Drawing Lewis Structures

Drawing a Lewis structure for larger molecules is easier if you follow a stepwise procedure.

How To Draw a Lewis Structure

Step [1] Arrange atoms next to each other that you think are bonded together.

- Always place hydrogen atoms and halogen atoms on the periphery because H and X (X = F, Cl, Br, and I) form only one bond each.

For $\mathbf{CH_4}$:

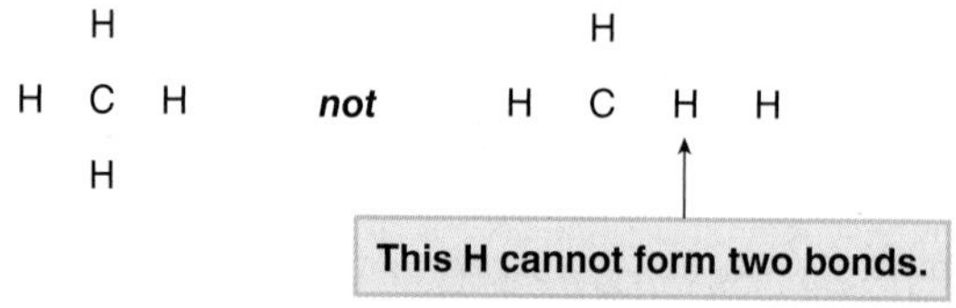

- As a first approximation, place no more atoms around an atom than the number of bonds it usually forms.

For $\mathbf{CH_5N}$:

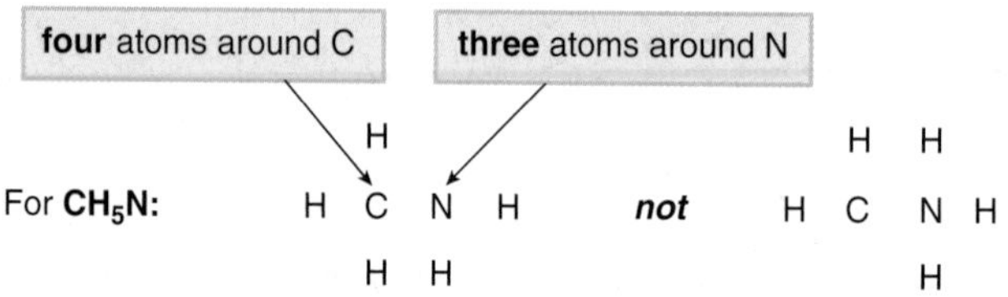

- In truth, the proper arrangement of atoms may not be obvious, or more than one arrangement may be possible (Section 1.4). Even in many simple molecules, the connectivity between atoms must be determined experimentally.

Step [2] Count the electrons.

- Count the number of valence electrons from all atoms.
- Add one electron for each negative charge.
- Subtract one electron for each positive charge.
- This sum gives the total number of electrons that must be used in drawing the Lewis structure.

Step [3] Arrange the electrons around the atoms.

- Place a bond between every two atoms, giving two electrons to each H and no more than eight to any second-row atom.
- Use all remaining electrons to fill octets with lone pairs.
- If all valence electrons are used and an atom does not have an octet, form multiple bonds, as shown in Sample Problem 1.2.

Step [4] Assign formal charges to all atoms.

- Formal charges are discussed in Section 1.3C.

Sample Problem 1.1 illustrates how to draw a Lewis structure of a simple organic molecule.

Sample Problem 1.1 Draw a Lewis structure for methanol, a compound with molecular formula CH_4O.

Solution

Step [1] Arrange the atoms.

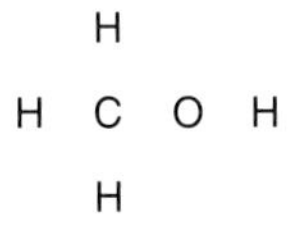

- Place the second-row elements, C and O, in the middle.
- Place three H's around C to surround C by four atoms.
- Place one H next to O to surround O by two atoms.

Step [2] Count the electrons.

$$\begin{aligned} 1\,C \times 4\,e^- &= 4\,e^- \\ 1\,O \times 6\,e^- &= 6\,e^- \\ 4\,H \times 1\,e^- &= \underline{4\,e^-} \\ &\mathbf{14\,e^-\ total} \end{aligned}$$

Step [3] Add the bonds and lone pairs.

- Add five two-electron bonds to form the C–H, C–O, and O–H bonds, using 10 of the 14 electrons.
- Place two lone pairs on the O atom to use the remaining four electrons and give the O atom an octet.

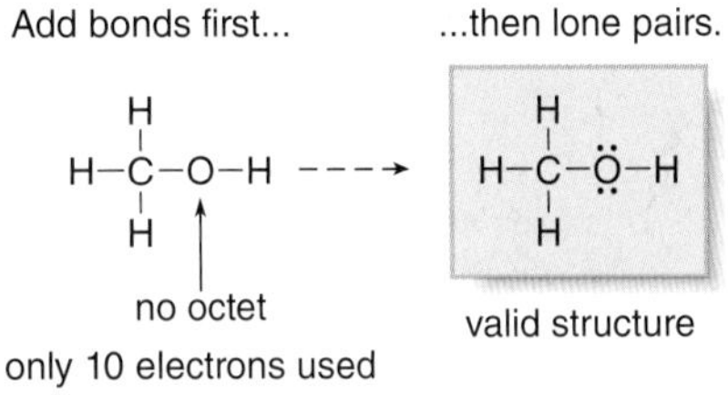
Add bonds first...
...then lone pairs.
no octet
only 10 electrons used
valid structure

To check if a Lewis structure is valid, we must answer YES to three questions.

- Have all the electrons been used?
- Is each H surrounded by two electrons?
- Is each second-row element surrounded by no more than eight electrons?

Since the answer to all three questions is YES, we have drawn a valid Lewis structure for CH_4O.

Problem 1.4 Draw a valid Lewis structure for each species:

a. CH_3CH_3 b. CH_5N c. CH_3^- d. CH_3Cl

1.3B Multiple Bonds

Sample Problem 1.2 illustrates two examples of when multiple bonds are needed in Lewis structures.

Sample Problem 1.2 Draw a Lewis structure for each compound. Assume the atoms are arranged as follows:

a. ethylene, C_2H_4 b. acetylene, C_2H_2

H C C H H C C H
H H

Solution

a. **Ethylene, C_2H_4:** Follow Steps [1] to [3] to draw a Lewis structure. After placing five bonds between the atoms and adding the two remaining electrons as a lone pair, one C still has no octet.

Step [2] Count the electrons.

$$\begin{aligned} 2\,C \times 4\,e^- &= 8\,e^- \\ 4\,H \times 1\,e^- &= \underline{4\,e^-} \\ &\mathbf{12\,e^-\ total} \end{aligned}$$

Step [3] Add the bonds and lone pairs.

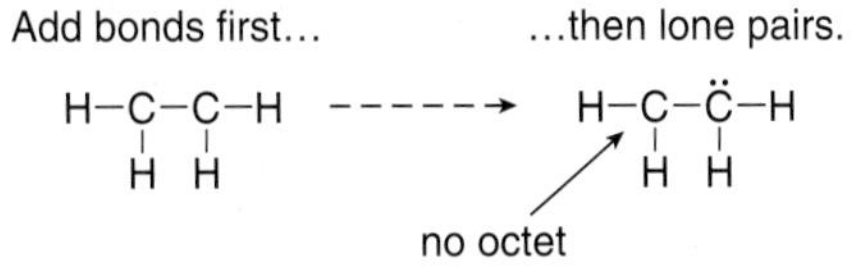
Add bonds first...
...then lone pairs.
no octet

To give both C's an octet, **change *one* lone pair into *one* bonding pair of electrons between the two C's, forming a double bond.**

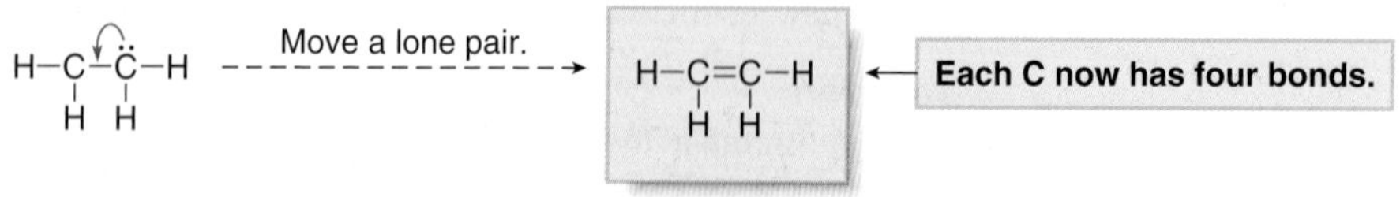
Move a lone pair.
Each C now has four bonds.

ethylene
a valid Lewis structure

This uses all 12 electrons, each C has an octet, and each H has two electrons. The Lewis structure is valid. **Ethylene contains a carbon–carbon double bond.**

b. **Acetylene, C_2H_2:** A similar phenomenon occurs with acetylene. Placing the 10 valence electrons gives a Lewis structure in which one or both of the C's lack an octet.

Step [2] Count the electrons.

$2\ C \times 4\ e^- = 8\ e^-$
$2\ H \times 1\ e^- = 2\ e^-$
$10\ e^-$ total

Step [3] Add the bonds and lone pairs.

Add bonds first... ...then lone pairs.

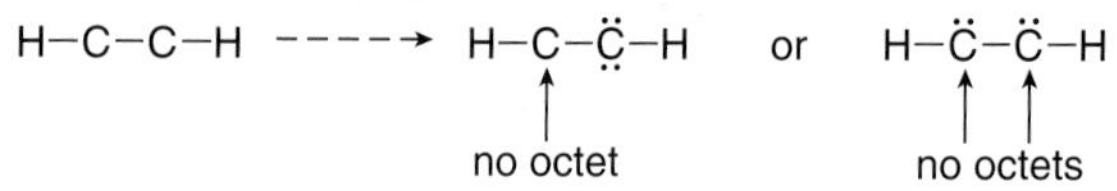
no octet
or
no octets

Carbon always forms four bonds in stable organic molecules. Carbon forms single, double, and triple bonds to itself and other elements.

For a second-row element in a stable molecule:

number of bonds
\+ number of lone pairs
= 4

In this case, **change *two* lone pairs into *two* bonding pairs of electrons, forming a triple bond.**

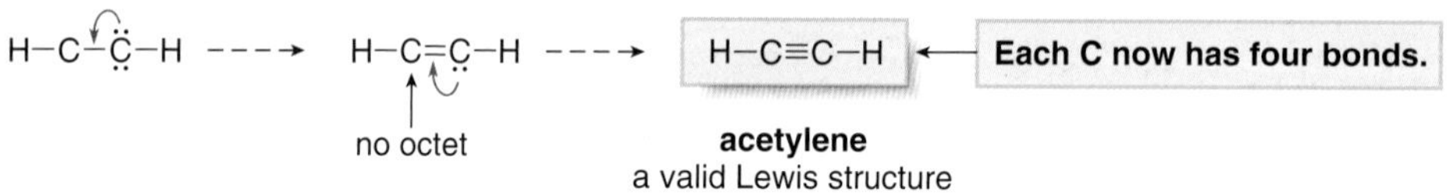
no octet
Each C now has four bonds.

acetylene
a valid Lewis structure

This uses all 10 electrons, each C has an octet, and each H has two electrons. The Lewis structure is valid. **Acetylene contains a carbon–carbon triple bond.**

- **After placing all electrons in bonds and lone pairs, use a lone pair to form a multiple bond if an atom does not have an octet.**

You must change *one* lone pair into *one* new bond for each *two* electrons needed to complete an octet. In acetylene, for example, four electrons were needed to complete an octet, so two lone pairs were used to form two new bonds, forming a triple bond.

Problem 1.5 Draw an acceptable Lewis structure for each compound, assuming the atoms are connected as arranged. Hydrogen cyanide (HCN) is a poison, formaldehyde (H_2CO) is a preservative, and glycolic acid ($HOCH_2CO_2H$) is used to make dissolving sutures.

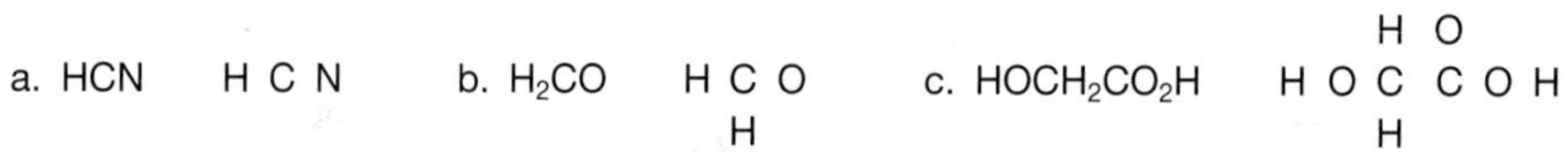
a. HCN
H C N
b. H2CO
H C O
H
c. HOCH2CO2H
H O
H O C C O H
H

1.3C Formal Charge

To manage electron bookkeeping in a Lewis structure, organic chemists use **formal charge.**

- ***Formal charge* is the charge assigned to individual atoms in a Lewis structure.**

By calculating formal charge, we determine how the number of electrons around a particular atom compares to its number of valence electrons. Formal charge is calculated as follows:

formal charge = **number of valence electrons** – **number of electrons an atom "owns"**

The number of electrons "owned" by an atom is determined by its number of bonds and lone pairs.

- **An atom "owns" *all* of its unshared electrons and *half* of its shared electrons.**

$$\textbf{number of electrons owned} = \textbf{number of unshared electrons} + \frac{1}{2}\left[\textbf{number of shared electrons}\right]$$

The number of electrons "owned" by different carbon atoms is indicated in the following examples:

- C shares eight electrons.
- C "owns" **four** electrons.

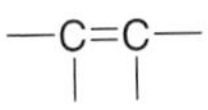

- Each C shares eight electrons.
- Each C "owns" **four** electrons.

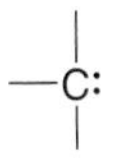

- C shares six electrons.
- C has two unshared electrons.
- C "owns" **five** electrons.

Sample Problem 1.3 illustrates how formal charge is calculated on the atoms of a polyatomic ion. **The sum of the formal charges on the individual atoms equals the net charge on the molecule or ion.**

Sample Problem 1.3 Determine the formal charge on each atom in the ion H_3O^+.

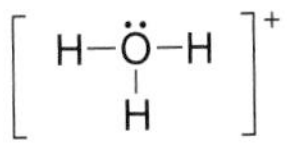

Solution

For each atom, two steps are needed:

Step [1] Determine the number of electrons an atom "owns."

Step [2] Subtract this sum from its number of valence electrons.

O atom	H atoms
[1] number of electrons "owned" by O $2 + \frac{1}{2}(6) = 5$	[1] number of electrons "owned" by each H $0 + \frac{1}{2}(2) = 1$
[2] formal charge on O 6 − 5 = **+1**	[2] formal charge on each H 1 − 1 = **0**

The formal charge on each H is 0. The formal charge on oxygen is +1. The overall charge on the ion is the sum of all of the formal charges; 0 + 0 + 0 + 1 = **+1.**

Problem 1.6 Calculate the formal charge on each second-row atom:

a. 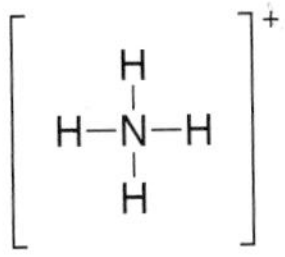

b. 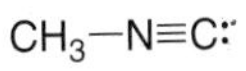

c. 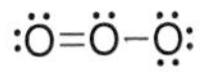

Problem 1.7 Draw a Lewis structure for each ion:

a. CH_3O^- b. HC_2^- c. $(CH_3NH_3)^+$ d. $(CH_3NH)^-$

Sometimes it is easier to count bonds, rather than shared electrons when determining formal charge.

$\frac{1}{2}$[number of shared electrons] = number of bonds

A shortcut method to determine the number of bonds in a Lewis structure is given in the *Student Study Guide/Solutions Manual* (page 1–4).

When you first add formal charges to Lewis structures, use the procedure in Sample Problem 1.3. With practice, you will notice that certain bonding patterns always result in the same formal charge. For example, any N atom with four bonds (and, thus no lone pairs) has a +1 formal charge. Table 1.1 lists the bonding patterns and resulting formal charges for carbon, nitrogen, and oxygen.

Table 1.1 Formal Charge Observed with Common Bonding Patterns for C, N, and O

Atom	Number of valence electrons	Formal charge +1	Formal charge 0	Formal charge –1
C	4	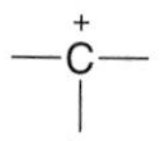		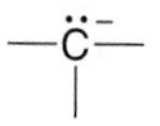
N	5		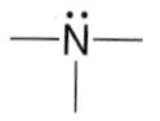	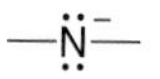
O	6	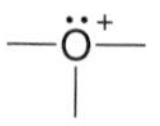	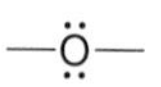	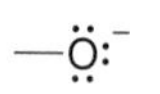

1.4 Isomers

In drawing a Lewis structure for a molecule with several atoms, sometimes more than one arrangement of atoms is possible for a given molecular formula. For example, there are two acceptable arrangements of atoms for the molecular formula C_2H_6O.

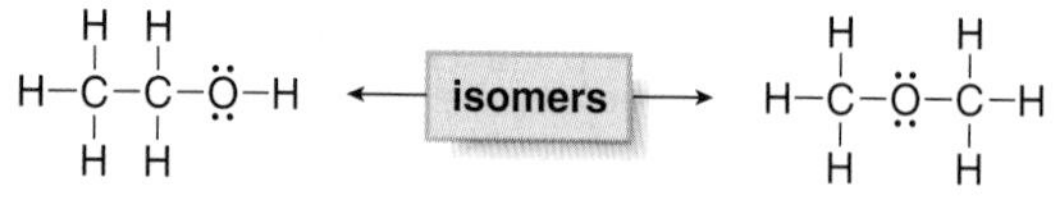

ethanol dimethyl ether

same molecular formula
C_2H_6O

Both are valid Lewis structures, and both molecules exist. One is called ethanol, and the other, dimethyl ether. These two compounds are called **isomers.**

- ***Isomers* are different molecules having the same molecular formula.**

Ethanol and dimethyl ether are **constitutional isomers** because they have the same molecular formula, but the ***connectivity of their atoms is different.*** For example, ethanol has one C–C bond and one O–H bond, whereas dimethyl ether has two C–O bonds. A second class of isomers, called **stereoisomers,** is introduced in Section 4.13B.

Problem 1.8 Draw Lewis structures for each molecular formula.

a. $C_2H_4Cl_2$ (two isomers) b. C_3H_8O (three isomers) c. C_3H_6 (two isomers)

1.5 Exceptions to the Octet Rule

Most of the common elements in organic compounds—**C, N, O, and the halogens**—follow the octet rule. Hydrogen is a notable exception, because it accommodates only two electrons in bonding. Additional exceptions include boron and beryllium (second-row elements in groups 3A and 2A, respectively), and elements in the third row (particularly phosphorus and sulfur).

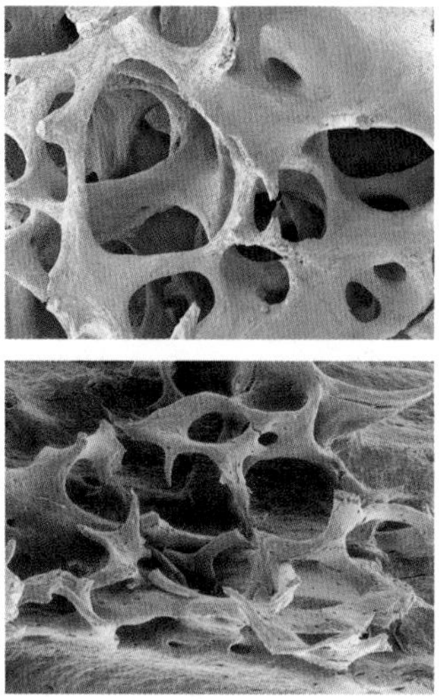

Alendronic acid, sold as a sodium salt under the trade name of **Fosamax,** is used to prevent osteoporosis in women. Osteoporosis decreases bone density, as shown by comparing normal bone (top) with brittle bone (bottom).

Elements in groups 2A and 3A of the periodic table, such as beryllium and boron, do not have enough valence electrons to form an octet in a neutral molecule. Lewis structures for BeH_2 and BF_3 show that these atoms have only four and six electrons, respectively, around the central atom. There is nothing we can do about this! There simply aren't enough electrons to form an octet.

four electrons around Be

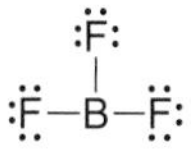

six electrons around B

Because the Be and B atoms each have less than an octet of electrons, these molecules are highly reactive.

A second exception to the octet rule occurs with some elements located in the third row and later in the periodic table. These elements have empty *d* orbitals available to accept electrons, and thus they may have ***more than eight*** **electrons** around them. For organic chemists, the two most common elements in this category are **phosphorus** and **sulfur,** which can have 10 or even 12 electrons around them. Examples of these phosphorus and sulfur compounds include the following:

10 electrons around S

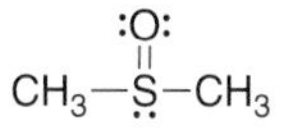

dimethyl sulfoxide (abbreviated as DMSO)

12 electrons around S

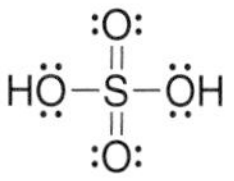

sulfuric acid

10 electrons around each P

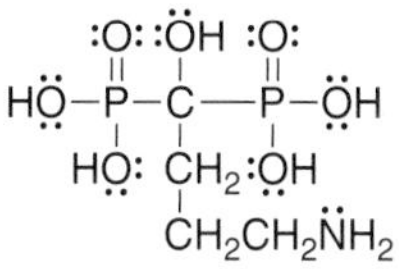

alendronic acid

1.6 Resonance

Some molecules can't be adequately represented by a single Lewis structure. For example, two valid Lewis structures can be drawn for the anion $(HCONH)^-$. One structure has a negatively charged N atom and a C–O double bond; the other has a negatively charged O atom and a C–N double bond. These structures are called **resonance structures** or **resonance forms.** A **double-headed arrow** is used to separate two resonance structures.

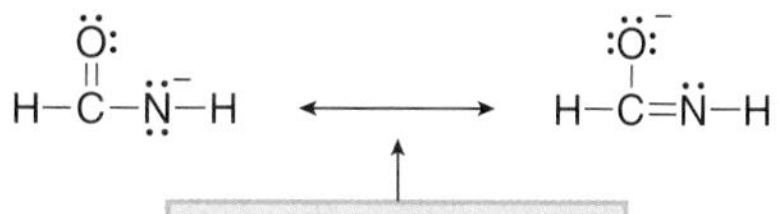

double-headed arrow

- *Resonance structures* are two Lewis structures having the *same* placement of atoms but a *different* arrangement of electrons.

Which resonance structure is an accurate representation for $(HCONH)^-$? **The answer is *neither* of them.** The true structure is a composite of both resonance forms, and is called a **resonance hybrid.** The hybrid shows characteristics of ***both*** resonance structures.

Each resonance structure implies that electron pairs are localized in bonds or on atoms. In actuality, resonance allows certain electron pairs to be ***delocalized*** over two or more atoms, and this delocalization of electron density adds stability. **A molecule with two or more resonance structures is said to be *resonance stabilized.*** We will return to the resonance hybrid in Section 1.6C. First, however, we examine the general principles of resonance theory and learn how to interconvert two or more resonance structures.

1.6A An Introduction to Resonance Theory

Keep in mind the following basic principles of resonance theory.

- **Resonance structures are not real. An individual resonance structure does not accurately represent the structure of a molecule or ion. Only the hybrid does.**
- **Resonance structures are *not* in equilibrium with each other. There is no movement of electrons from one form to another.**
- **Resonance structures are *not* isomers. Two isomers differ in the arrangement of *both* atoms and electrons, whereas resonance structures differ *only* in the *arrangement of electrons.***

Resonance structures are different ways of drawing the same compound. Two resonance structures are *not* different compounds.

For example, ions **A** and **B** are resonance structures because the atom position is the same in both compounds, but the location of an electron pair is different. In contrast, compounds **C** and **D** are isomers since the atom placement is different; **C** has an O–H bond, and **D** has an additional C–H bond.

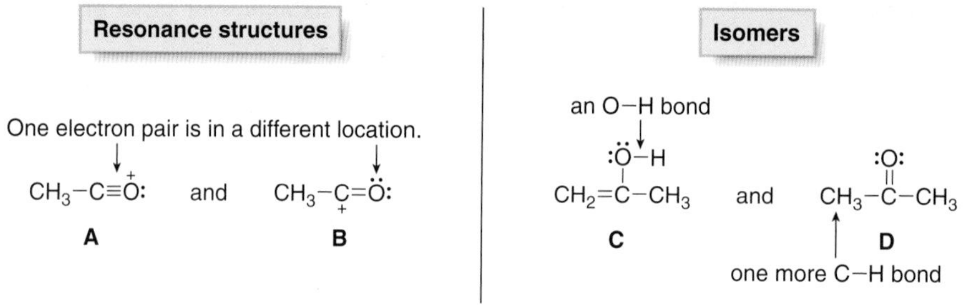

Problem 1.9 Classify each pair of compounds as isomers or resonance structures.

Problem 1.10 Considering structures **A–D**, classify each pair of compounds as isomers, resonance structures, or neither: (a) **A** and **B;** (b) **A** and **C;** (c) **A** and **D;** (d) **B** and **D.**

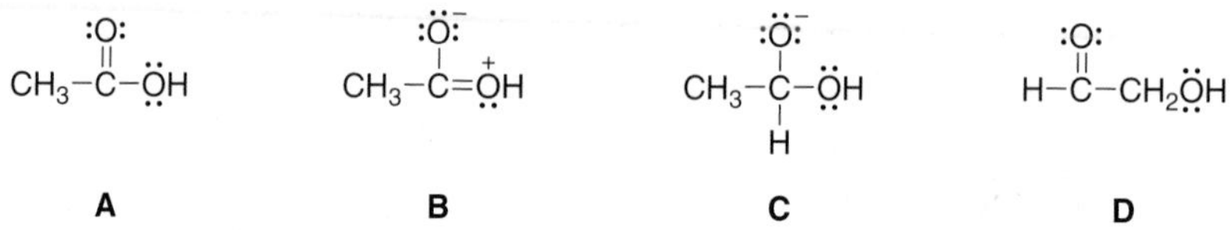

1.6B Drawing Resonance Structures

To draw resonance structures, use the three rules that follow:

Rule [1] **Two resonance structures differ in the position of multiple bonds and nonbonded electrons. The placement of atoms and single bonds always stays the same.**

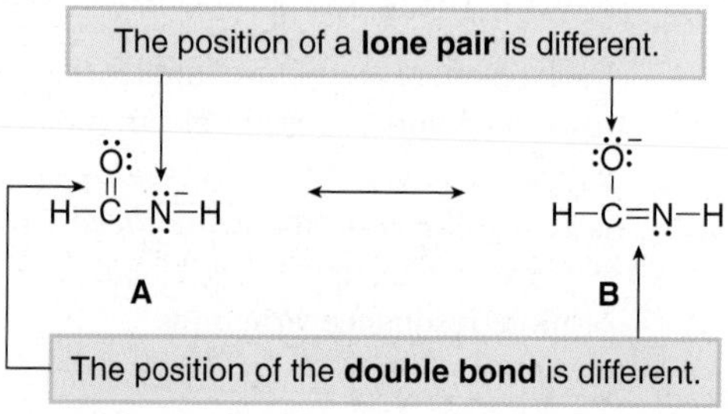

Rule [2] **Two resonance structures must have the same number of unpaired electrons.**

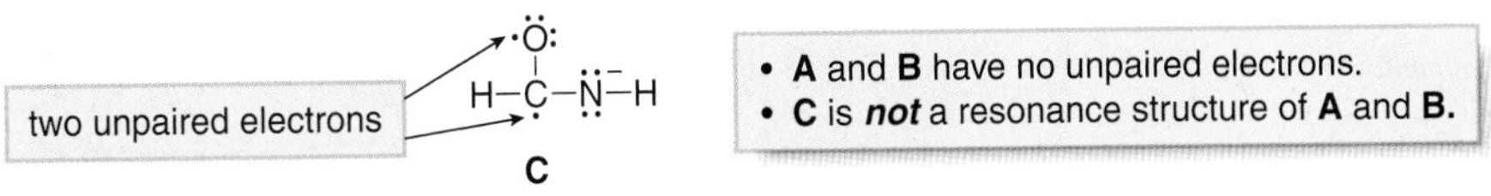

Rule [3] **Resonance structures must be valid Lewis structures. Hydrogen must have two electrons and no second-row element can have more than eight electrons.**

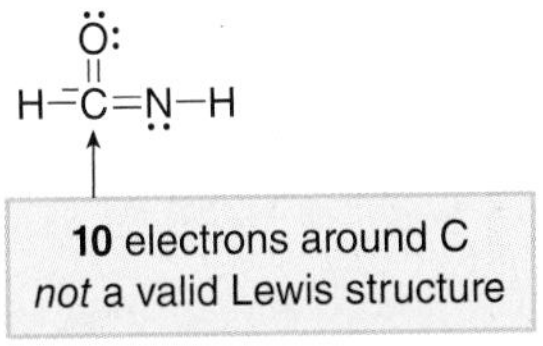

Curved arrow notation is a convention that shows how electron position differs between the two resonance forms.

- ***Curved arrow notation shows the movement of an electron pair.*** **The tail of the arrow always begins at an electron pair, either in a bond or lone pair. The head points to where the electron pair "moves."**

A curved arrow always begins at an electron pair. It ends at an atom or a bond.

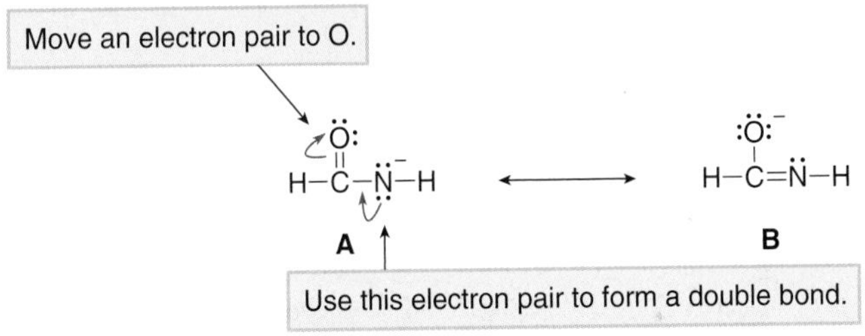

Resonance structures **A** and **B** differ in the location of two electron pairs, so two curved arrows are needed. To convert **A** to **B,** take the lone pair on N and form a double bond between C and N. Then, move an electron pair in the C – O double bond to form a lone pair on O. Curved arrows thus show how to reposition the electrons in converting one resonance form to another. **The electrons themselves do not actually move.** Sample Problem 1.4 illustrates the use of curved arrows to convert one resonance structure to another.

Sample Problem 1.4 Follow the curved arrows to draw a second resonance structure for each ion.

Solution

a. The curved arrow tells us to move **one** electron pair in the double bond to the adjacent C – C bond. Then determine the formal charge on any atom whose bonding is different.

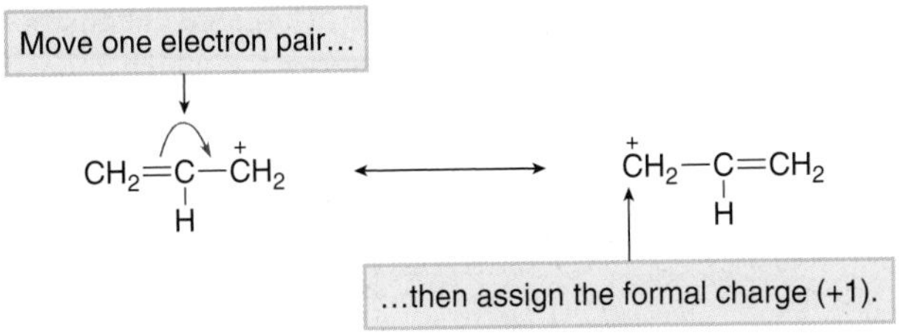

Positively charged carbon atoms are called **carbocations.** Carbocations are unstable intermediates because they contain a carbon atom that is lacking an octet of electrons.

b. **Two** curved arrows tell us to move **two** electron pairs. The second resonance structure has a formal charge of (–1) on O.

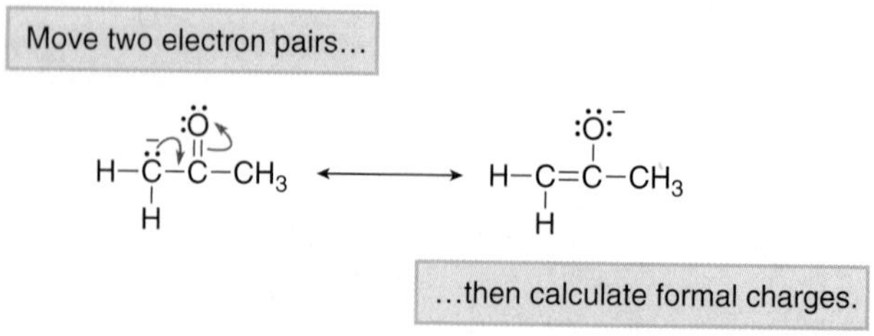

This type of resonance-stabilized anion is called an **enolate anion.** Enolates are important intermediates in many organic reactions, and all of Chapters 23 and 24 is devoted to their preparation and reactions.

Problem 1.11 Follow the curved arrows to draw a second resonance structure for each species.

a. 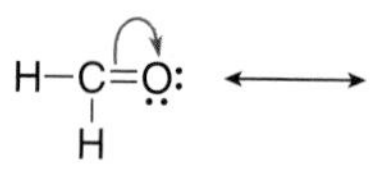

b. 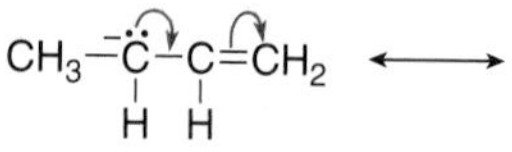

Problem 1.12 Use curved arrow notation to show how the first resonance structure can be converted to the second.

a. 

b. 

Two resonance structures can have exactly the same kinds of bonds, as they do in the carbocation in Sample Problem 1.4a, or they may have different types of bonds, as they do in the enolate in Sample Problem 1.4b. Either possibility is fine as long as the individual resonance structures are valid Lewis structures.

A resonance structure can have an atom with *fewer* than eight electrons around it. **B** is a resonance structure of **A** even though the carbon atom is surrounded by only six electrons.

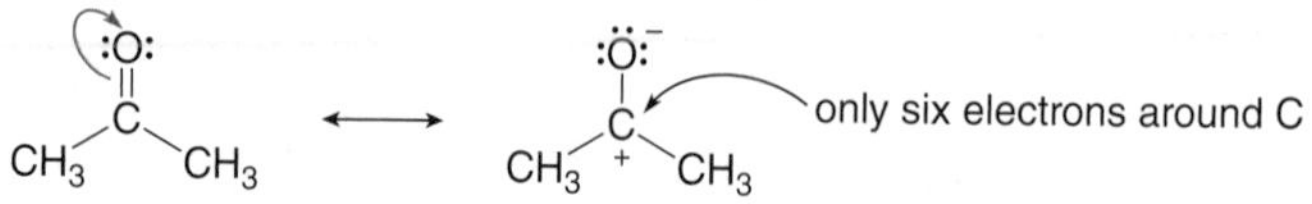

A **B**

a valid resonance structure

In contrast, a resonance structure can *never* have a second-row element with more than eight electrons. **C** is *not* a resonance structure of **A** because the carbon atom is now surrounded by 10 electrons.

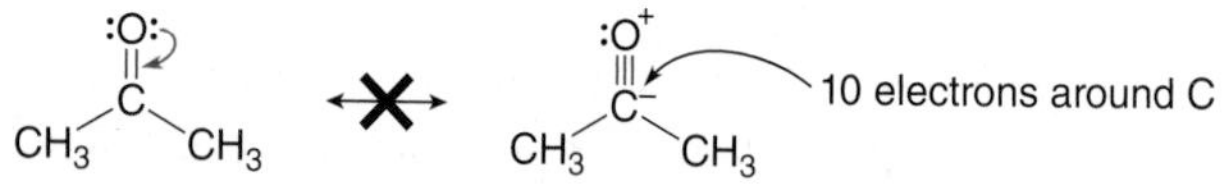

A **C**

not a valid resonance structure

We will learn much more about resonance in Chapter 16.

The ability to draw and manipulate resonance structures is an important skill that will be needed throughout your study of organic chemistry. With practice, you will begin to recognize certain common bonding patterns for which more than one Lewis structure can be drawn. For now, notice that:

- **A second resonance structure can be drawn when a lone pair is located on an atom directly bonded to a multiple bond.**

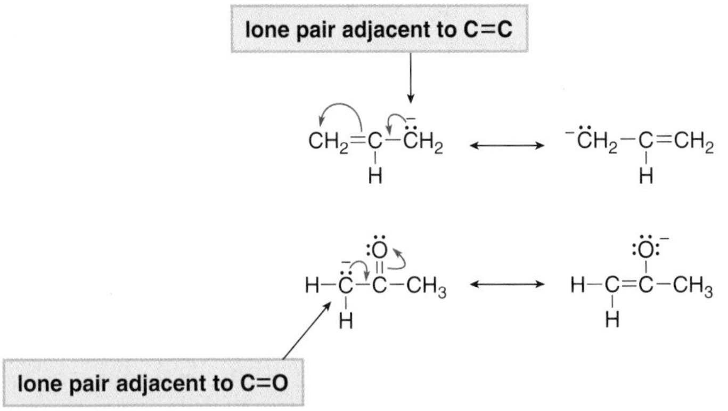
lone pair adjacent to C=C
lone pair adjacent to C=O

- **A second resonance structure can be drawn when an atom bearing a (+) charge is bonded to either a multiple bond or an atom with a lone pair.**

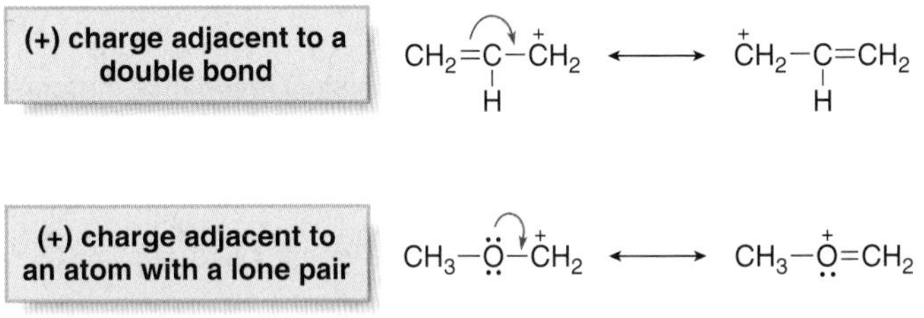
(+) charge adjacent to a double bond
(+) charge adjacent to an atom with a lone pair

Problem 1.13 Draw a second resonance structure for each species.

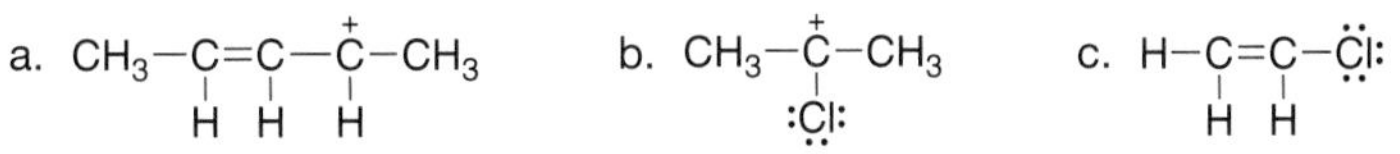

1.6C The Resonance Hybrid

The **resonance hybrid** is the composite of all possible resonance structures. In the resonance hybrid, the electron pairs drawn in different locations in individual resonance structures are ***delocalized.***

- **The resonance hybrid is more stable than any resonance structure because it delocalizes electron density over a larger volume.**

What does the hybrid look like? When all resonance forms are identical, as they were in the carbocation in Sample Problem 1.4a, each resonance form contributes **equally** to the hybrid.

When two resonance structures are different, the hybrid looks more like the "better" resonance structure. The "better" resonance structure is called the **major contributor** to the hybrid, and all others are **minor contributors.** The hybrid is the weighted average of the contributing resonance structures. What makes one resonance structure "better" than another? There are many factors, but for now, we will learn just two.

- A "better" resonance structure is one that has *more bonds* and *fewer charges.*

X more bonds fewer charges — **major contributor**

Y — **minor contributor**

Comparing resonance structures **X** and **Y, X** is the major contributor because it has more bonds and fewer charges. Thus, the hybrid looks more like **X** than **Y.**

How can we draw a hybrid, which has delocalized electron density? First, we must determine what is different in the resonance structures. Two differences commonly seen are the **position of a multiple bond** and the **site of a charge.** The anion $(HCONH)^-$ illustrates two conventions for drawing resonance hybrids.

A **B**

individual resonance structures

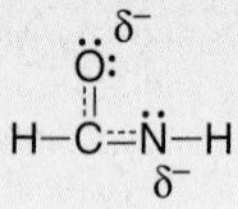

resonance *hybrid*

Common symbols and conventions used in organic chemistry are listed on the inside back cover.

- **Double bond position.** Structure **A** has a C–O double bond, whereas structure **B** has a C–N double bond. A dashed line in the hybrid indicates partial double bond character between these atoms.
- **Location of the charge.** A negative charge resides on different atoms in **A** and **B.** The symbol δ^- (for a partial negative charge) indicates that the charge is delocalized on the N and O atoms in the hybrid.

This discussion of resonance is meant to serve as an introduction only. You will learn many more facets of resonance theory in later chapters. In Chapter 2, for example, the enormous effect of resonance on acidity is discussed.

Problem 1.14 Label the resonance structures in each pair as major, minor, or equal contributors to the hybrid. Then draw the hybrid.

a. 

b. 

Problem 1.15 Draw a second resonance structure for nitrous acid. Label each resonance structure as a major, minor, or equal contributor to the hybrid. Then draw the resonance hybrid.

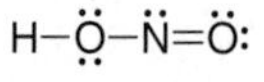

nitrous acid

1.7 Determining Molecular Shape

We can now use Lewis structures to determine the shape around a particular atom in a molecule. Consider the H_2O molecule. The Lewis structure tells us only which atoms are connected to each other, but it implies nothing about the geometry. What does the overall molecule look like? Is H_2O a bent or linear molecule? Two variables define a molecule's structure: **bond length** and **bond angle.**

1.7A Bond Length

Although the SI unit for bond length is the picometer (pm), the angstrom (Å) is still widely used in the chemical literature; 1 Å = 10^{-10} m. As a result, 1 pm = 10^{-2} Å, and 95.8 pm = 0.958 Å.

***Bond length* is the average distance between the centers of two bonded nuclei.** Bond lengths are typically reported in picometers (pm), where 1 pm = 10^{-12} m. For example, the O–H bond length in H_2O is 95.8 pm. Average bond lengths for common bonds are listed in Table 1.2.

- **Bond length *decreases* across a row of the periodic table as the size of the atom *decreases.***

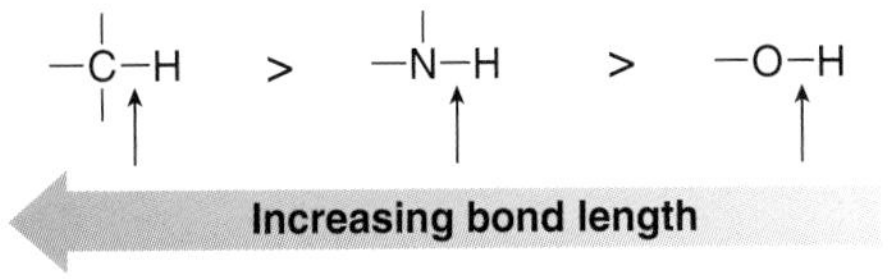

- **Bond length *increases* down a column of the periodic table as the size of an atom *increases.***

H–F < H–Cl < H–Br

Increasing bond length

Learn these general trends. Often, knowing such trends is more useful than learning a set of exact numbers, because we are usually interested in comparisons rather than absolute values.

Table 1.2 Average Bond Lengths

Bond	Length (pm)	Bond	Length (pm)	Bond	Length (pm)
H–H	74	H–F	92	C–F	133
C–H	109	H–Cl	127	C–Cl	177
N–H	101	H–Br	141	C–Br	194
O–H	96	H–I	161	C–I	213

1.7B Bond Angle

Bond angle determines the shape around any atom bonded to two other atoms. To determine the bond angle and shape around a given atom, we must first determine how many groups surround the atom. **A group is either an atom or a lone pair of electrons.** Then we use the **valence shell electron pair repulsion (VSEPR) theory** to determine the shape. VSEPR is based on the fact that electron pairs repel each other; thus:

- **The most stable arrangement keeps these groups as far away from each other as possible.**

A second-row element has only three possible arrangements, defined by the number of groups surrounding it.

To determine geometry: [1] Draw a valid Lewis structure; [2] count groups around a given atom.

Number of groups	Geometry	Bond angle
• two groups	linear	180°
• three groups	trigonal planar	120°
• four groups	tetrahedral	109.5°

Let's examine several molecules to illustrate this phenomenon. In each example, we first need a valid Lewis structure, and then we merely count groups around a given atom to predict its geometry.

Two Groups Around an Atom

Any atom surrounded by only two groups is linear and has a bond angle of 180°. Two examples illustrating this geometry are $\mathbf{BeH_2}$ (beryllium hydride) and **HC≡CH** (acetylene). We consider each carbon atom in acetylene *separately.* Because each C is surrounded by two atoms and no lone pairs, each H–C–C bond angle in acetylene is 180°, and therefore all four atoms are linear.

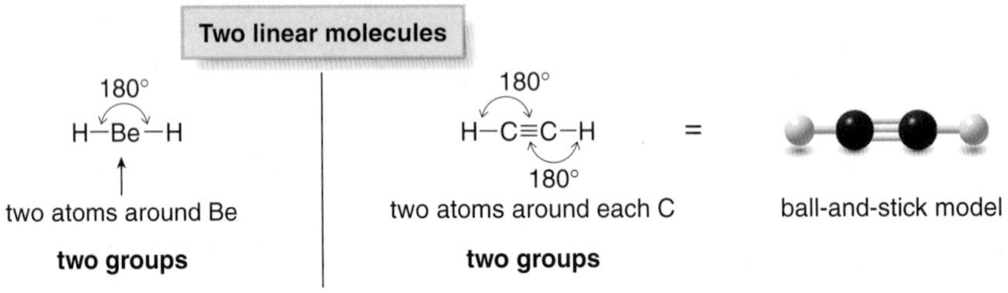

Acetylene illustrates another important feature: ***ignore multiple bonds in predicting geometry.* Count only atoms and lone pairs.**

Most students in organic chemistry find that building models helps them visualize the shape of molecules. Invest in a set of models *now*.

Common element colors are also shown on the inside back cover.

We will begin to represent molecules with models having balls for atoms and sticks for bonds, as in the ball-and-stick model of acetylene just shown. These representations are analogous to a set of molecular models. Balls are color-coded using accepted conventions: carbon (black), hydrogen (white or gray), oxygen (red), and so forth, as shown.

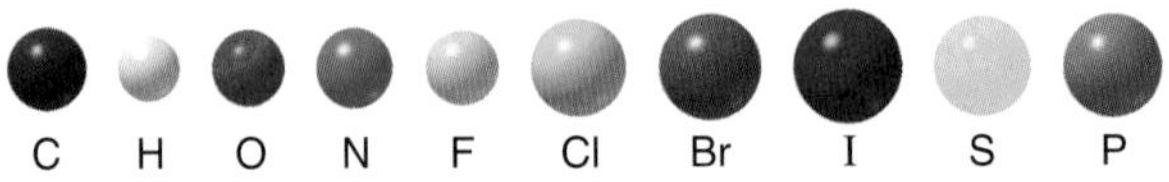

Three Groups Around an Atom

Any atom surrounded by three groups is trigonal planar and has bond angles of 120°. Two examples illustrating this geometry are $\mathbf{BF_3}$ (boron trifluoride) and $\mathbf{CH_2{=}CH_2}$ (ethylene). *Each* carbon atom of ethylene is surrounded by three atoms and no lone pairs, making *each* H–C–C bond angle 120°.

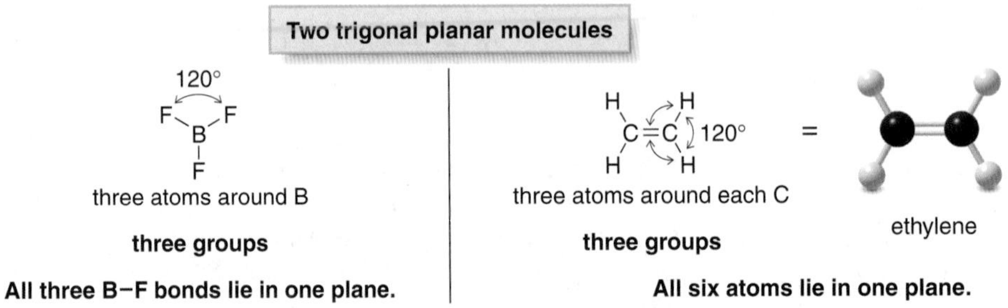

Four Groups Around an Atom

Any atom surrounded by four groups is tetrahedral and has bond angles of approximately 109.5°. For example, the simple organic compound methane, $\mathbf{CH_4}$, has a central carbon atom with bonds to four hydrogen atoms, each pointing to a corner of a tetrahedron. This arrangement keeps four groups farther apart than a square planar arrangement in which all bond angles would be only 90°.

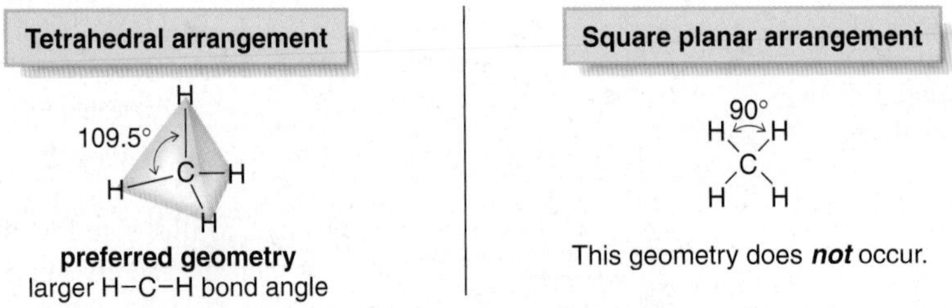

How can we represent the three-dimensional geometry of a tetrahedron on a two-dimensional piece of paper? **Place two of the bonds in the plane of the paper, one bond in front and one bond behind,** using the following conventions:

- A *solid line* is used for a bond *in* the plane.
- A *wedge* is used for a bond in *front* of the plane.
- A *dashed line* is used for a bond *behind* the plane.

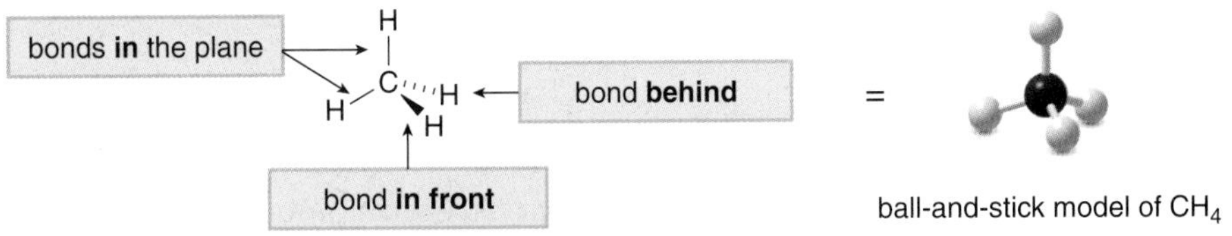

This is just one way to draw a tetrahedron for CH_4. We can turn the molecule in many different ways, generating many equivalent representations. For example, all of the following are acceptable drawings for CH_4.

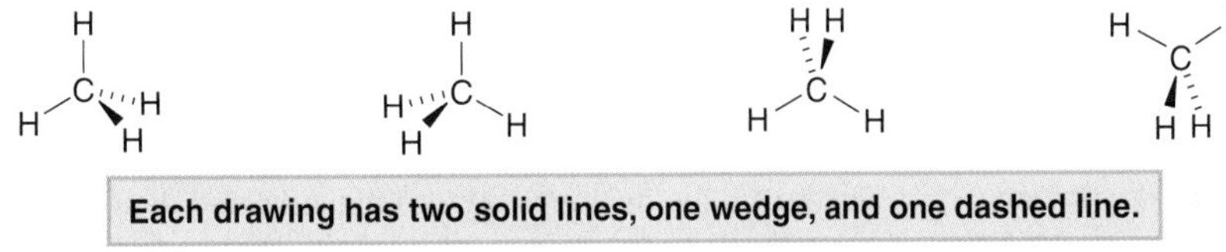

Finally, **wedges and dashes are used for groups that are really *aligned one behind another.*** It does not matter in the following two drawings whether the wedge or dash is skewed to the left or right, because the two H atoms are really aligned as shown in the three-dimensional model.

All carbons in stable molecules are ***tetravalent,*** but the geometry varies with the number of groups around the particular carbon.

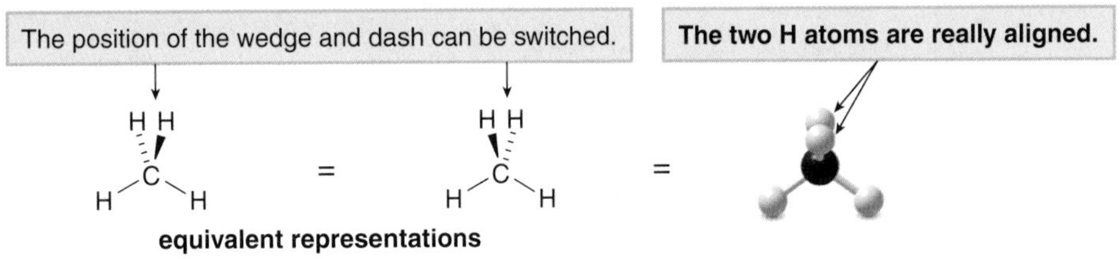

Problem 1.16 Draw two different three-dimensional representations for CH_2Cl_2 (dichloromethane) using wedges and dashes.

Ammonia (NH_3) and water (H_2O) both have atoms surrounded by four groups, some of which are lone pairs. In $\mathbf{NH_3}$, the three H atoms and one lone pair around N point to the corners of a tetrahedron. The H–N–H bond angle of 107° is close to the theoretical tetrahedral bond angle of 109.5°. This molecular shape is referred to as a **trigonal pyramid,** because one of the groups around the N is a nonbonded electron pair, not another atom.

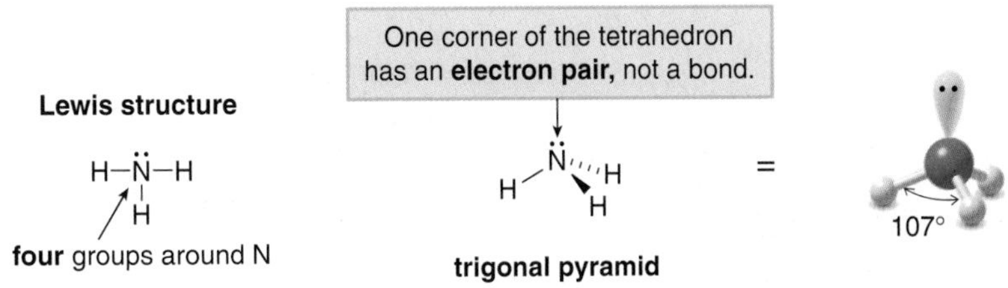

In $\mathbf{H_2O}$, the two H atoms and two lone pairs around O point to the corners of a tetrahedron. The H–O–H bond angle of 105° is close to the theoretical tetrahedral bond angle of 109.5°. Water has a **bent** molecular shape, because two of the groups around oxygen are lone pairs of electrons.

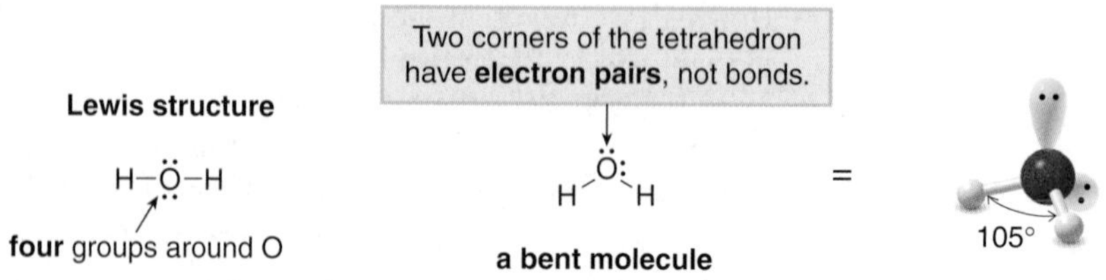
Lewis structure
H–Ö–H
four groups around O
Two corners of the tetrahedron have electron pairs, not bonds.
a bent molecule
=
105°

In both NH_3 and H_2O the bond angle is somewhat smaller than the theoretical tetrahedral bond angle because of repulsion of the lone pairs of electrons. The bonded atoms are compressed into a smaller space with a smaller bond angle.

Predicting geometry based on counting groups is summarized in Table 1.3.

Table 1.3 Summary: Determining Geometry Based on the Number of Groups

Number of groups around an atom	Geometry	Bond angle	Examples
2	linear	180°	BeH_2, HC≡CH
3	trigonal planar	120°	BF_3, $CH_2{=}CH_2$
4	tetrahedral	109.5°	CH_4, NH_3, H_2O

Sample Problem 1.5

Determine the geometry around the indicated atom in each species.

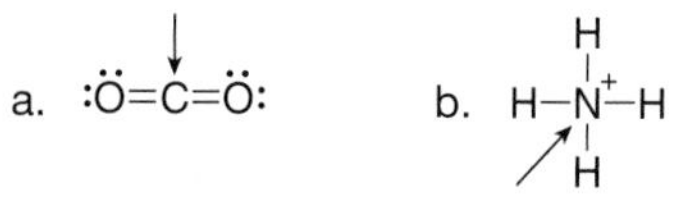

Solution

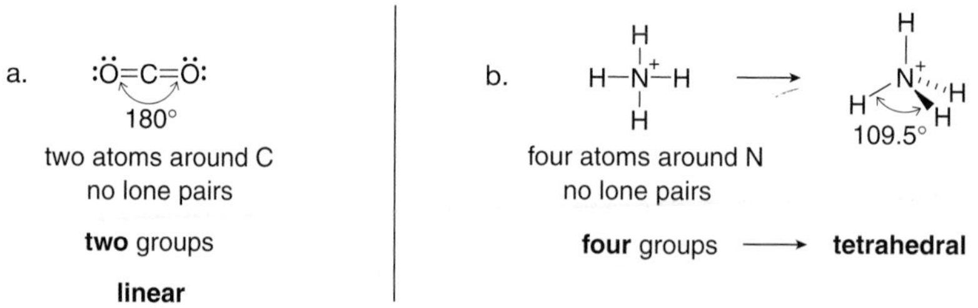
a.
180°
two atoms around C
no lone pairs
two groups
linear
b.
109.5°
four atoms around N
no lone pairs
four groups
tetrahedral

Problem 1.17 Determine the geometry around all second-row elements in each compound.

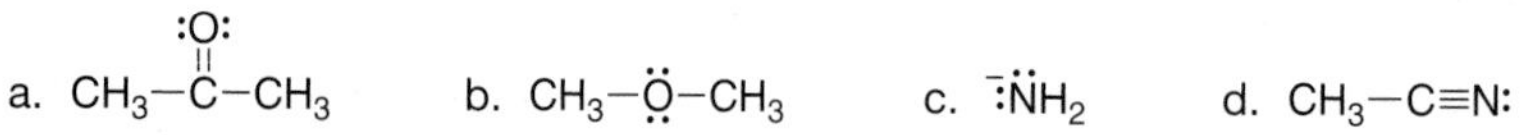

Problem 1.18 Predict the indicated bond angles in each compound.

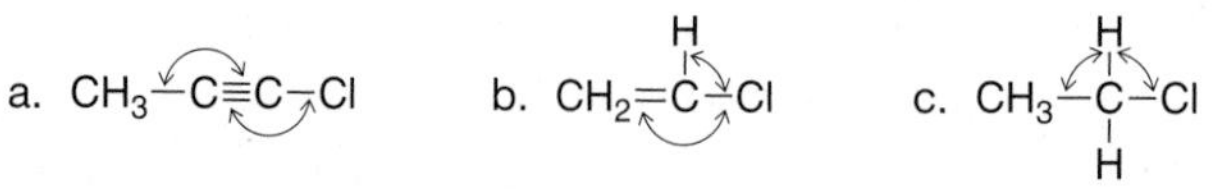

Problem 1.19 Using the principles of VSEPR theory, you can predict the geometry around any atom in any molecule, no matter how complex. Enanthotoxin is a poisonous compound isolated from a common variety of hemlock grown in England. Predict the geometry around the indicated atoms in enanthotoxin.

The hemlock water dropwort is the source of the poison enanthotoxin.

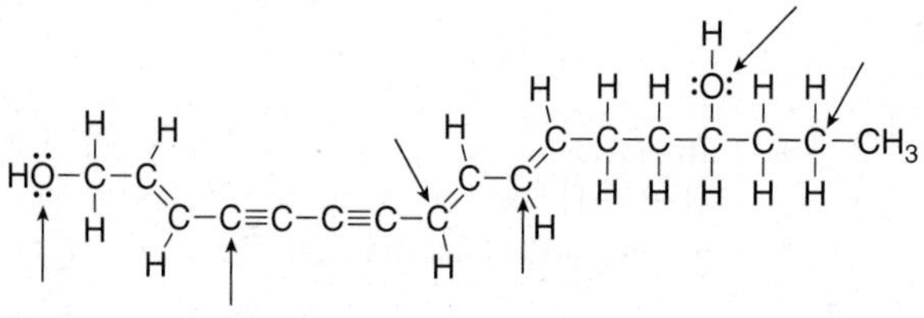

enanthotoxin

1.8 Drawing Organic Structures

Drawing organic molecules presents a special challenge. Because they often contain many atoms, we need shorthand methods to simplify their structures. The two main types of shorthand representations used for organic compounds are **condensed structures** and **skeletal structures.**

1.8A Condensed Structures

Condensed structures are most often used for compounds having a chain of atoms bonded together, rather than a ring. The following conventions are used:

- **All of the atoms are drawn in, but the two-electron bond lines are generally omitted.**
- **Atoms are usually drawn next to the atoms to which they are bonded.**
- **Parentheses are used around similar groups bonded to the same atom.**
- **Lone pairs are omitted.**

To interpret a condensed formula, it is usually best to start at the **left side** of the molecule and remember that the ***carbon atoms must be tetravalent.*** A carbon bonded to three H atoms becomes CH_3; a carbon bonded to two H atoms becomes CH_2, and so forth. Two examples of condensed formulas for compounds having only carbon and hydrogen are given below.

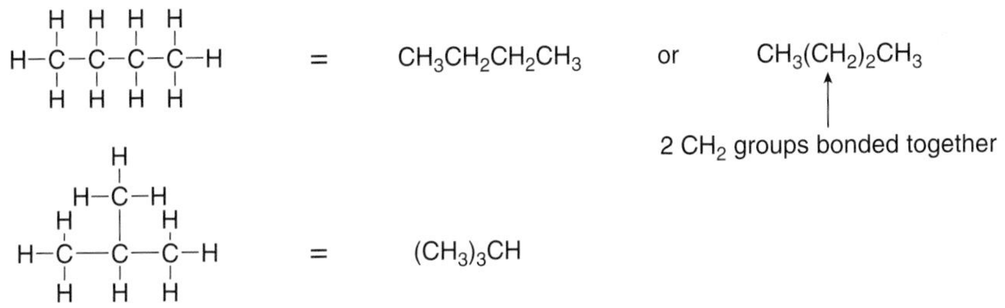
= $CH_3CH_2CH_2CH_3$ or $CH_3(CH_2)_2CH_3$
2 CH_2 groups bonded together
= $(CH_3)_3CH$

Recall from the prologue: A **heteroatom** is any atom that is not C or H.

Other examples of condensed structures with heteroatoms and carbon–carbon multiple bonds are given in Figure 1.4. You must learn how to convert a Lewis structure to a condensed structure, and vice versa.

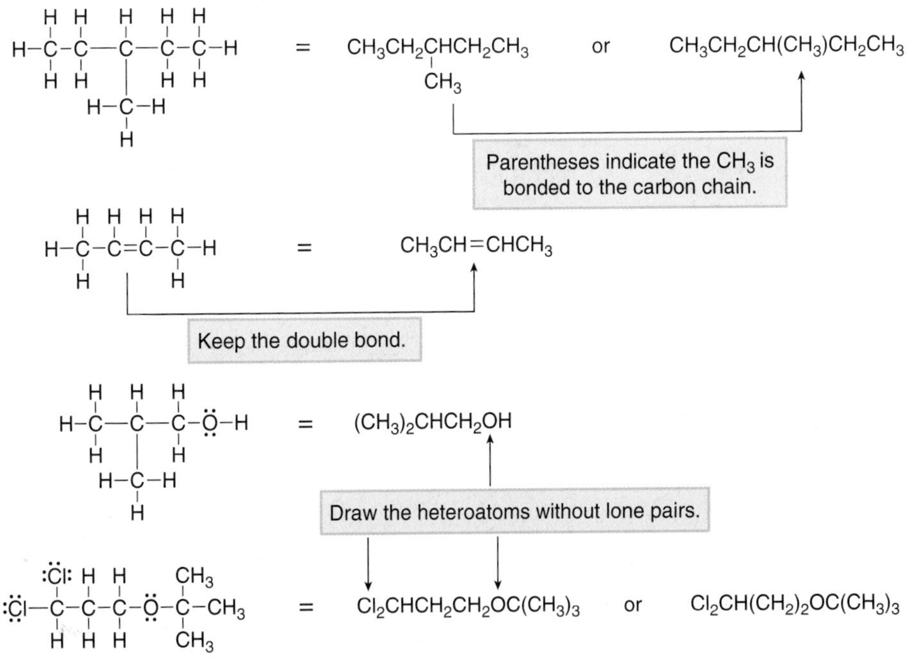
= $CH_3CH_2CHCH_2CH_3$ (with CH_3 below) or $CH_3CH_2CH(CH_3)CH_2CH_3$
Parentheses indicate the CH_3 is bonded to the carbon chain.
= $CH_3CH{=}CHCH_3$
Keep the double bond.
= $(CH_3)_2CHCH_2OH$
Draw the heteroatoms without lone pairs.
= $Cl_2CHCH_2CH_2OC(CH_3)_3$ or $Cl_2CH(CH_2)_2OC(CH_3)_3$

Figure 1.4 Examples of condensed structures

Figure 1.5
Condensed structures containing a C–O double bond

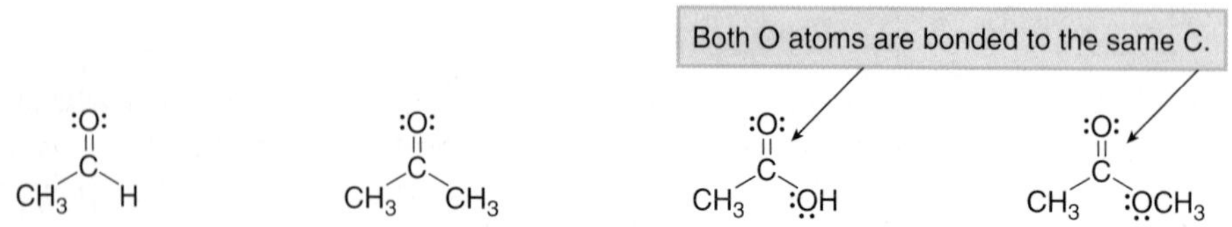
Both O atoms are bonded to the same C.

CH_3CHO CH_3COCH_3 CH_3CO_2H $CH_3CO_2CH_3$

- Take special note of condensed structures with oxygen atoms. In these examples, the only way for all atoms to have an octet is by having a carbon–oxygen double bond.

Translating some condensed formulas is not obvious, and it will come only with practice. This is especially true for compounds containing a carbon–oxygen double bond. Some noteworthy examples in this category are given in Figure 1.5. While carbon–carbon double bonds are generally drawn in condensed structures, carbon–oxygen double bonds are usually omitted.

Sample Problem 1.6 Convert each condensed formula to a Lewis structure.

a. $(CH_3)_2CHOCH_2CH_2CH_2OH$ b. $CH_3(CH_2)_2CO_2C(CH_3)_3$

Solution

Start at the left and proceed to the right, making sure that each carbon has four bonds. Give any heteroatom enough lone pairs to have an octet.

a. $(CH_3)_2CHOCH_2CH_2CH_2OH$

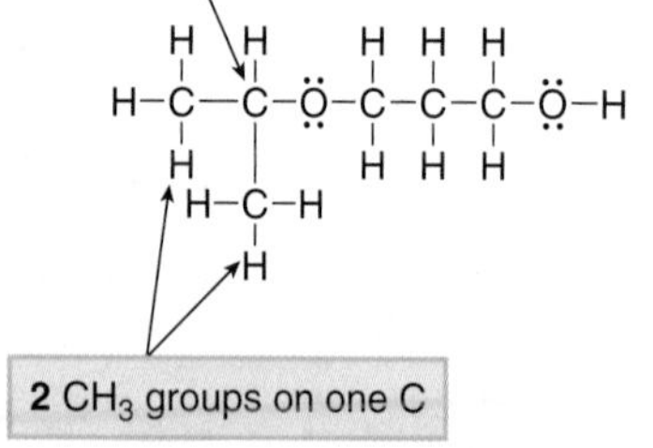
2 CH3 groups on one C

b. $CH_3(CH_2)_2CO_2C(CH_3)_3$

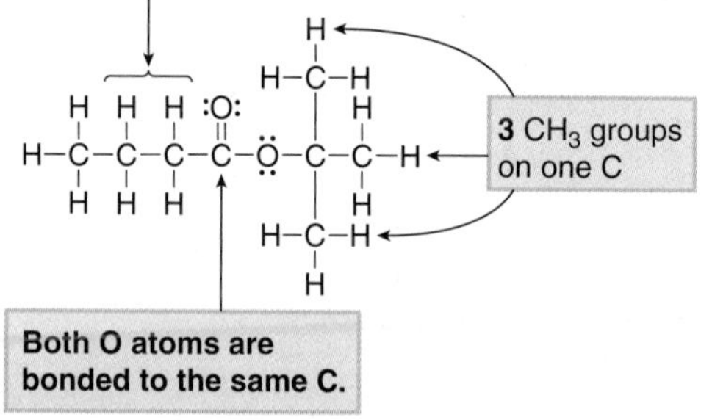
3 CH3 groups on one C
Both O atoms are bonded to the same C.

Problem 1.20 Convert each condensed formula to a Lewis structure.

a. $CH_3(CH_2)_4CH(CH_3)_2$
b. $(CH_3)_2CHCH(CH_2CH_3)_2$
c. $(CH_3)_3CCH(OH)CH_2CH_3$
d. $(CH_3)_2CHCHO$

Problem 1.21 Simplify each condensed structure by using parentheses around similar groups.

a. $CH_3CH_2CH_2CH_2CH_2Cl$

b. 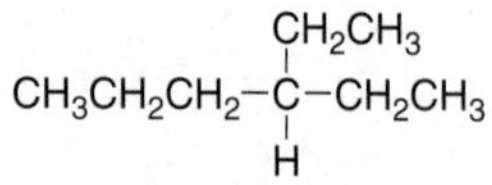

c. 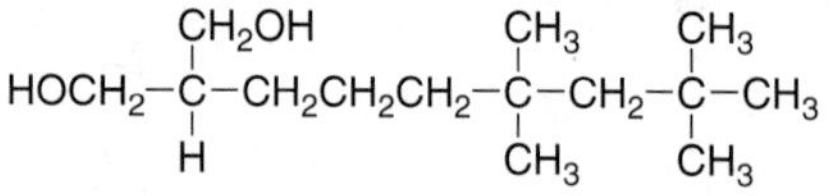

Problem 1.22 During periods of strenuous exercise, the buildup of lactic acid [$CH_3CH(OH)CO_2H$] causes the aching feeling in sore muscles. Convert this condensed structure to a Lewis structure of lactic acid.

1.8B Skeletal Structures

Skeletal structures are used for organic compounds containing both rings and chains of atoms. Three important rules are used to draw them:

- **Assume there is a carbon atom at the junction of any two lines or at the end of any line.**
- **Assume there are enough hydrogens around each carbon to make it tetravalent.**
- **Draw in all heteroatoms and the hydrogens directly bonded to them.**

Carbon chains are drawn in a zigzag fashion, and rings are drawn as polygons, as shown for hexane and cyclohexane.

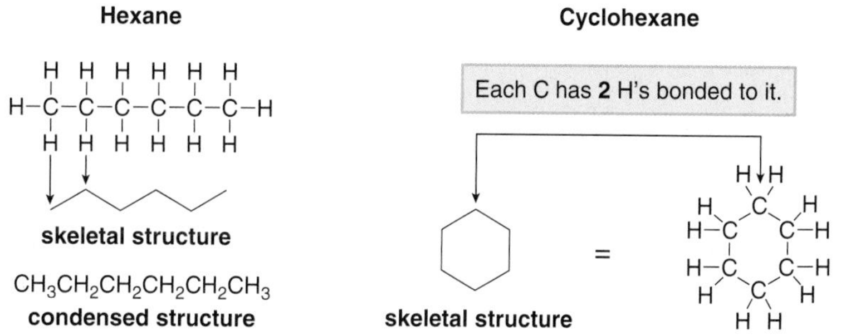

How To Interpret a Skeletal Structure

Example Draw in all C atoms, H atoms, and lone pairs in the following molecule:

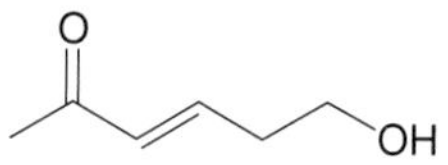

Step [1] **Place a C atom at the intersection of any two lines and at the end of any line.**

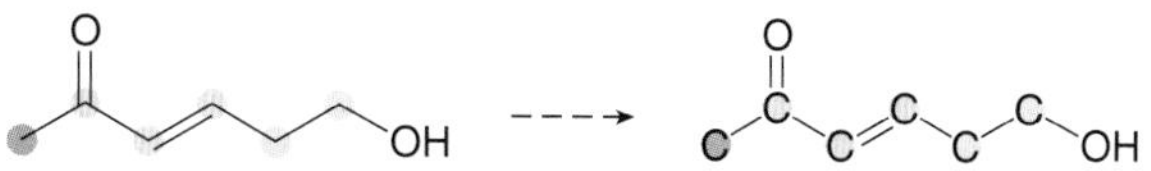

- This molecule has six carbons, including the C labeled in red at the left end of the chain.
- There are two C's (labeled in green) between the C=C and the OH group.

Step [2] **Add enough H's to make each C tetravalent.**

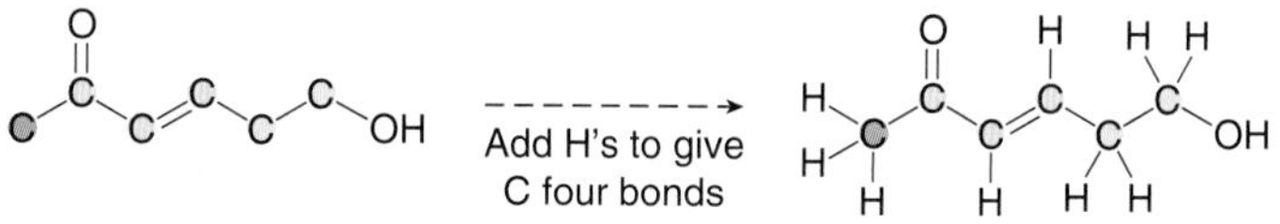

- The end C labeled in red needs three H's to be tetravalent.
- Each C on the C=C has three bonds already, so only one H must be drawn.
- There are two CH_2 groups between the C=C and the OH group.

Step [3] **Add lone pairs to give each heteroatom an octet.**

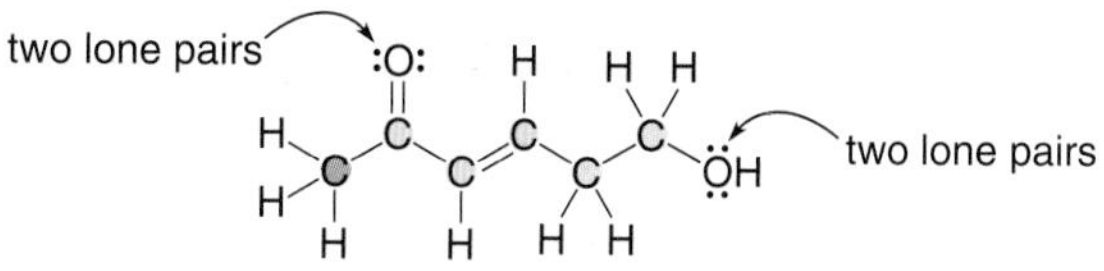

Each O needs **two** lone pairs for an octet.

Figure 1.6
Interpreting skeletal structures

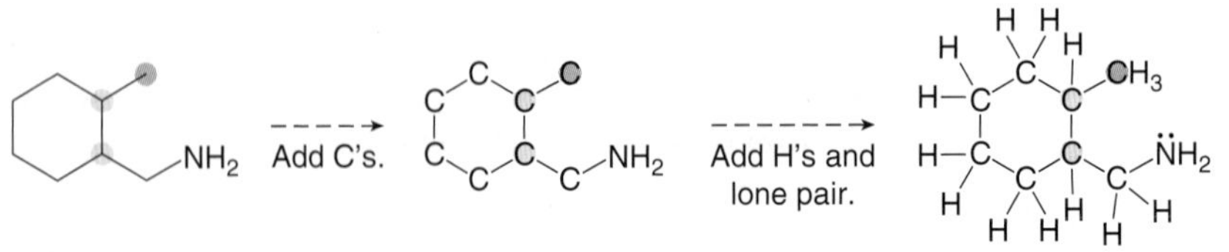
Add C's.
Add H's and lone pair.

- C labeled in red needs 3 H's.
- C's labeled in blue need 1 H.
- All other C's need 2 H's.
- N needs one lone pair.

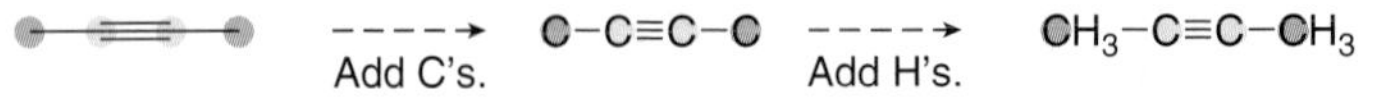
Add C's.
Add H's.

- C's labeled in red need 3 H's.
- C's labeled in green have four bonds to C.

Figure 1.6 shows other examples of skeletal structures, and Sample Problem 1.7 illustrates how to interpret the skeletal structure for a more complex cyclic compound.

Sample Problem 1.7

Draw a complete structure for vanillin showing all C atoms, H atoms, and lone pairs. Vanillin is the principal component of the extract of the vanilla bean.

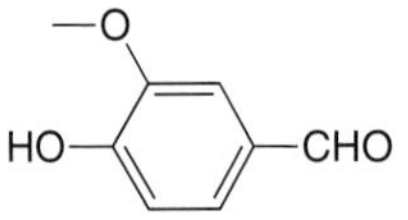

vanillin

vanilla bean

Solution

Skeletal structures have a C atom at the junction of any two lines and at the end of any line. Each C must have enough H's to make it tetravalent. In structures that contain a –CHO group, the C atom is doubly bonded to the O atom and singly bonded to H. Each O atom needs two lone pairs to have a complete octet.

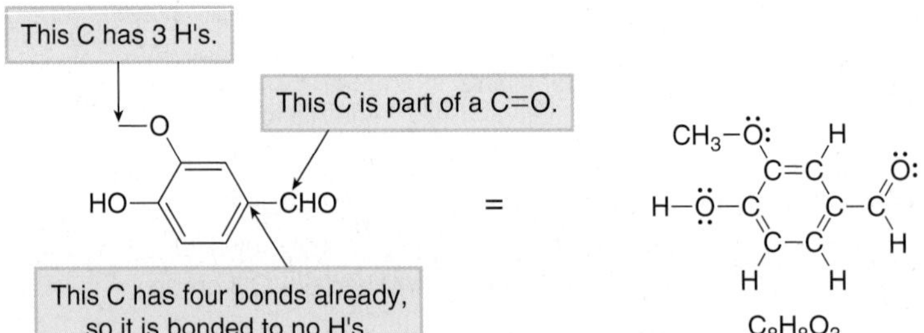
This C has 3 H's.
This C is part of a C=O.
This C has four bonds already, so it is bonded to no H's.

$C_8H_8O_3$

Problem 1.23 How many hydrogen atoms are present around each indicated carbon atom in the following molecules? What is the molecular formula for each molecule? Both compounds are active ingredients in some common sunscreens.

a. 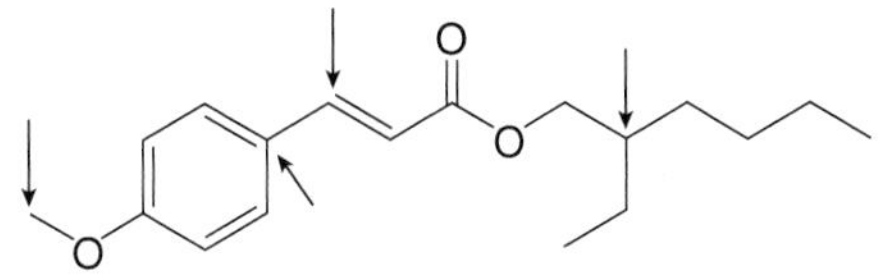

octinoxate
(2-ethylhexyl 4-methoxycinnamate)

b. 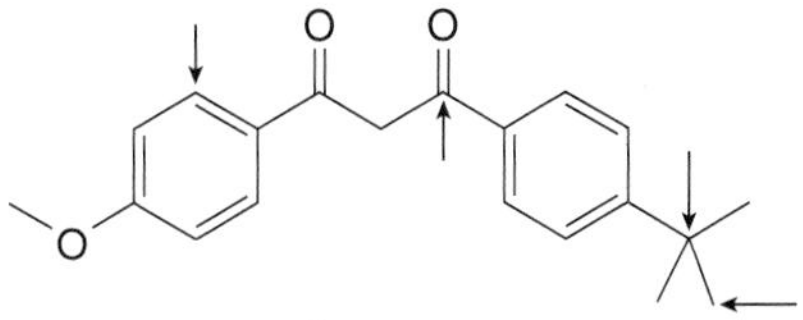

avobenzone

Water BABIES
Coppertone
45
BANANA BOAT
KIDS
15 plus
SUNBLOCK

Problem 1.24 Convert each skeletal structure to a complete structure with all C's, H's, and lone pairs drawn in.

a.  b.  c. 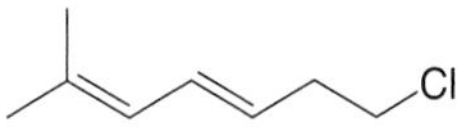 d. 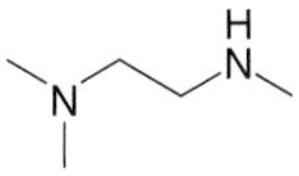

When heteroatoms are bonded to a carbon skeleton, the heteroatom is joined *directly* to the carbon to which it is bonded, with no H atoms in between. Thus, an OH group is drawn as OH or HO depending on where the OH is located. In contrast, when carbon appendages are bonded to a carbon skeleton, the H atoms will be drawn to the *right* of the carbon to which they are bonded regardless of the location.

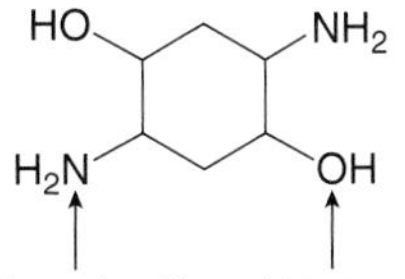
HO
NH_2
H_2N
OH

Place the O and N atoms directly joined to the ring.

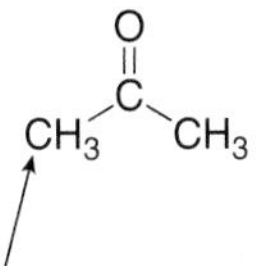
O
C
CH_3
CH_3

This C is bonded to the C=O.

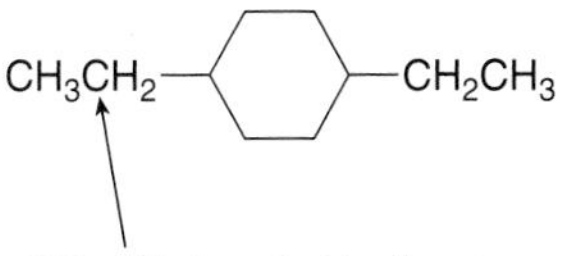
CH_3CH_2
CH_2CH_3

This C is bonded to the ring.

1.8C Skeletal Structures with Charged Carbon Atoms

Take care in interpreting skeletal structures for positively and negatively charged carbon atoms, because *both* the hydrogen atoms *and* the lone pairs are omitted. Keep in mind the following:

- **A charge on a carbon atom takes the place of one hydrogen atom.**
- **The charge determines the number of lone pairs. Negatively charged carbon atoms have one lone pair and positively charged carbon atoms have none.**

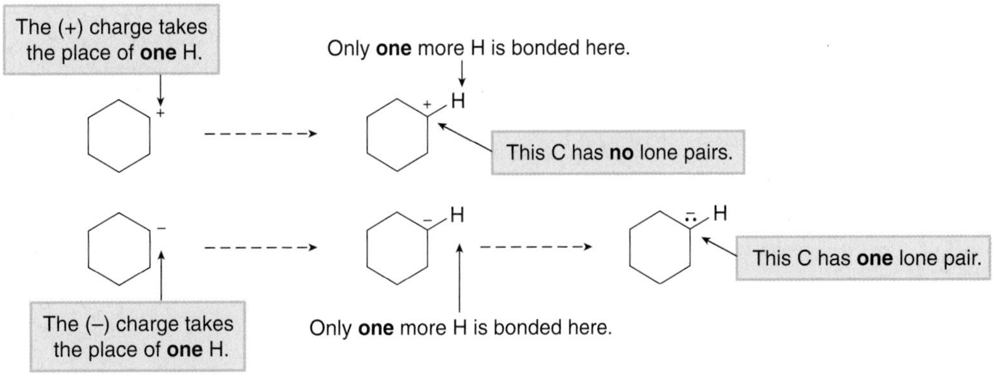
The (+) charge takes the place of **one** H.
Only **one** more H is bonded here.
This C has **no** lone pairs.
This C has **one** lone pair.
The (–) charge takes the place of **one** H.
Only **one** more H is bonded here.

Skeletal structures often leave out lone pairs on heteroatoms, but *don't forget about them.* Use the formal charge on an atom to determine the number of lone pairs. For example, a neutral O atom with two bonds needs two additional lone pairs, and a positively charged O atom with three bonds needs only one lone pair.

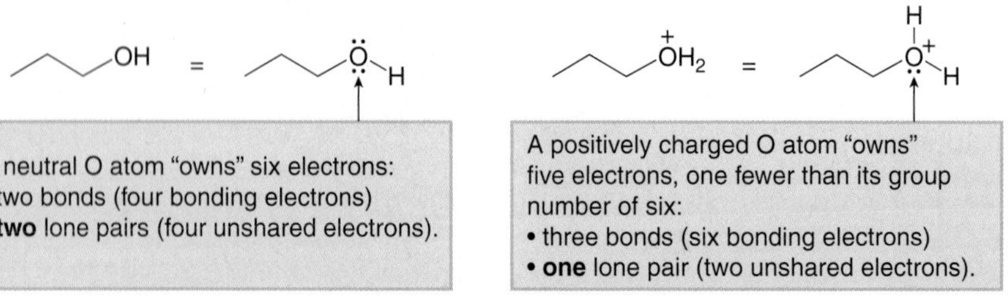
OH
H
A neutral O atom "owns" six electrons:
• two bonds (four bonding electrons)
• **two** lone pairs (four unshared electrons).
OH2
A positively charged O atom "owns" five electrons, one fewer than its group number of six:
• three bonds (six bonding electrons)
• **one** lone pair (two unshared electrons).

Problem 1.25 Draw in all hydrogens and lone pairs on the charged carbons in each ion.

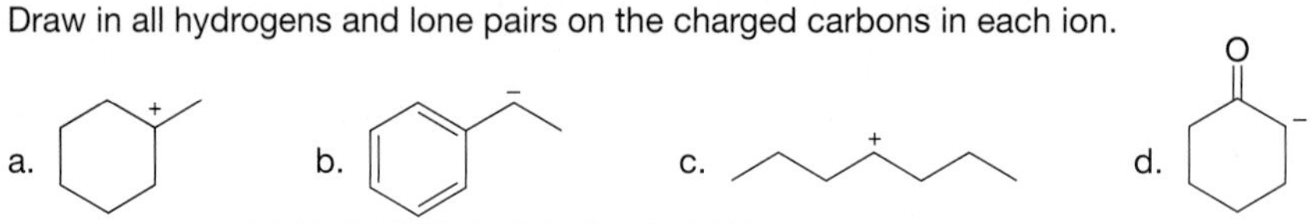
a.
b.
c.
d.

Problem 1.26 Draw a skeletal structure for the molecules in parts (a) and (b), and a condensed structure for the molecules in parts (c) and (d).

a. $(CH_3)_2C{=}CH(CH_2)_4CH_3$

c. 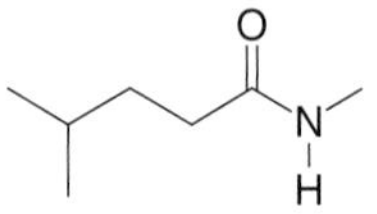

b. 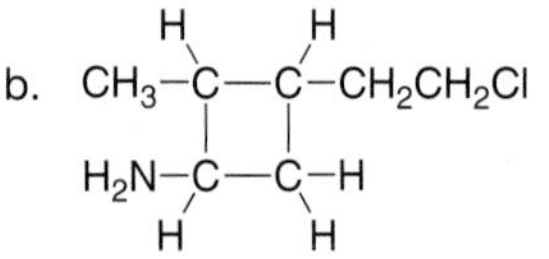
CH3
CH2CH2Cl
H2N

d. 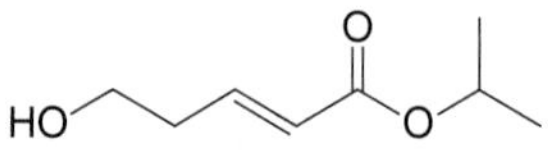
HO

1.9 Hybridization

What orbitals do the first- and second-row atoms use to form bonds? Let's begin with hydrogen and then examine the orbitals used for bonding by atoms in the second row.

1.9A Hydrogen

Recall from Section 1.2 that two hydrogen atoms share each of their electrons to form H_2. Thus, the 1*s* orbital on one H overlaps with the 1*s* orbital on the other H to form a bond that concentrates electron density between the two nuclei. This type of bond, called a **σ** (sigma) **bond,** is cylindrically symmetrical because the electrons forming the bond are distributed symmetrically about an imaginary line connecting the two nuclei.

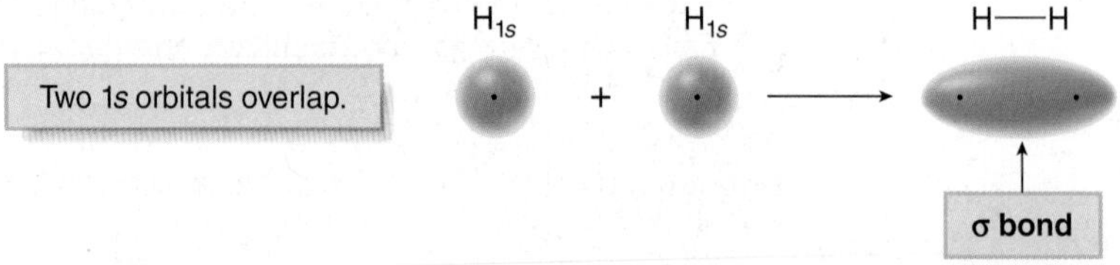
Two 1s orbitals overlap.
H1s
H1s
H—H
σ bond

- **A σ bond concentrates electron density on the axis that joins two nuclei. All single bonds are σ bonds.**

1.9B Bonding in Methane

To account for the bonding patterns observed in more complex molecules, we must take a closer look at the 2*s* and 2*p* orbitals of atoms of the second row. Let's illustrate this with methane, CH_4.

Carbon has two core electrons, plus **four valence electrons.** To fill atomic orbitals in the most stable arrangement, electrons are placed in the orbitals of lowest energy. For carbon, this places two in the 2*s* orbital and one each in two 2*p* orbitals.

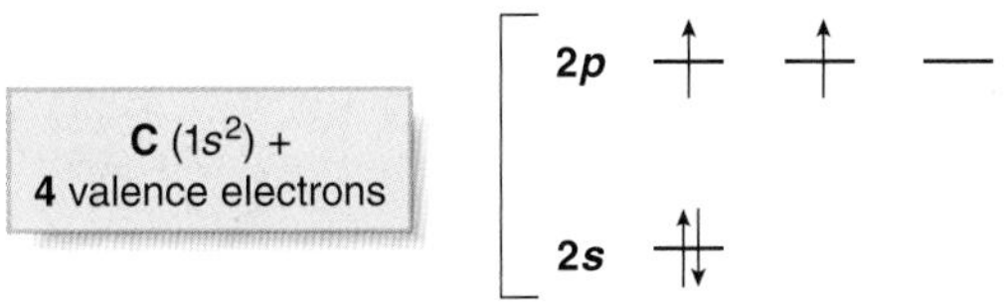
C (1s²) +
4 valence electrons
2p
2s

- **This lowest energy arrangement of electrons for an atom is called its ground state.**

In this description, **carbon should form *only two bonds*** because it has only two unpaired valence electrons, and CH_2 should be a stable molecule. In reality, however, CH_2 is a highly reactive species that cannot be isolated under typical laboratory conditions. In CH_2, carbon would not have an octet of electrons.

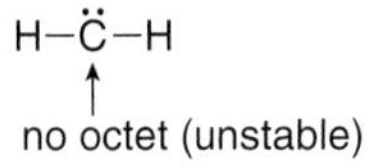
H–C̈–H
no octet (unstable)

There is a second possibility. Promotion of an electron from a 2*s* to a vacant 2*p* orbital would form **four** unpaired electrons for bonding. This process requires energy because it moves an electron to a higher energy orbital. This higher energy electron configuration is called an electronically **excited state.**

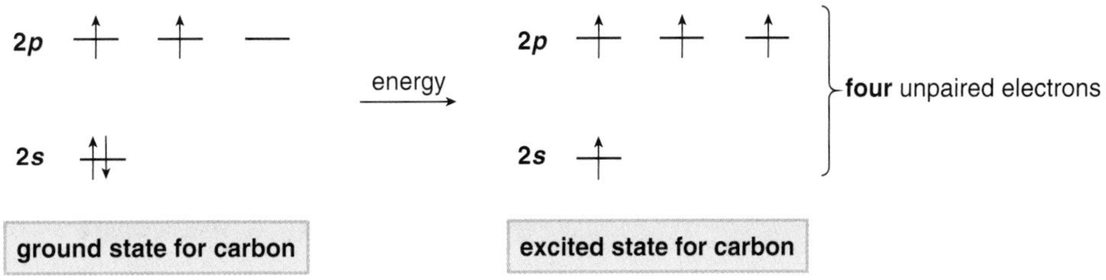
2p
2s
energy
2p
2s
four unpaired electrons
ground state for carbon
excited state for carbon

This description is still not adequate. Carbon would form two different types of bonds: three with 2*p* orbitals and one with a 2*s* orbital. **But experimental evidence points to carbon forming *four identical bonds* in methane.**

To solve this dilemma, chemists have proposed that atoms like carbon do not use pure *s* and pure *p* orbitals in forming bonds. Instead, atoms use a set of new orbitals called **hybrid orbitals.** The mathematical process by which these orbitals are formed is called **hybridization.**

- ***Hybridization* is the combination of two or more atomic orbitals to form the same number of hybrid orbitals, each having the same shape and energy.**

Hybridization of one 2*s* orbital and three 2*p* orbitals for carbon forms four hybrid orbitals, each with one electron. These new hybrid orbitals are intermediate in energy between the 2*s* and 2*p* orbitals.

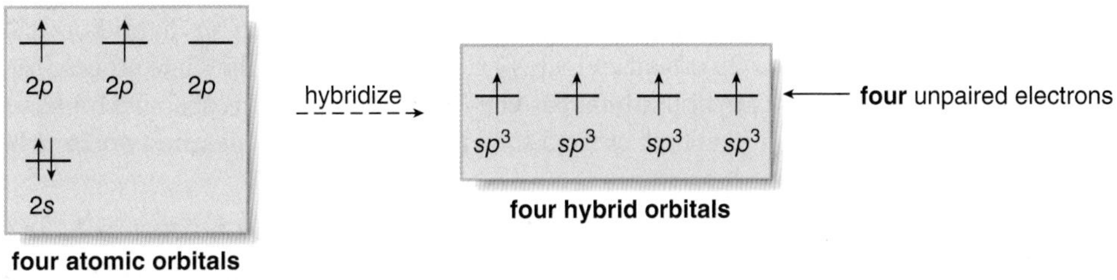
2p 2p 2p
2s
four atomic orbitals
hybridize
sp³ sp³ sp³ sp³
four hybrid orbitals
four unpaired electrons

- **These hybrid orbitals are called *sp*^{3} *hybrids* because they are formed from *one* s orbital and *three p* orbitals.**

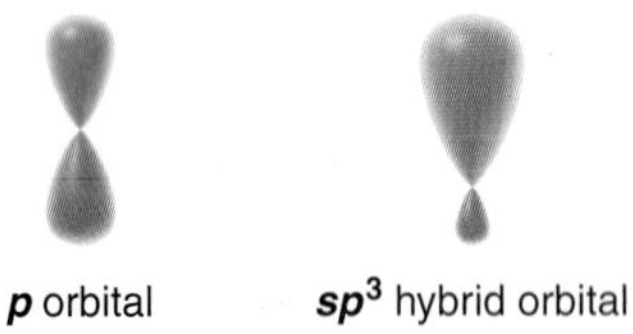

What do these new hybrid orbitals look like? Mixing a spherical 2*s* orbital and three dumbbell-shaped 2*p* orbitals together produces four orbitals having one large lobe and one small lobe, oriented toward the corners of a tetrahedron. Each large lobe concentrates electron density in the bonding direction between two nuclei. This makes bonds formed from hybrid orbitals ***stronger*** than bonds formed from pure *p* orbitals.

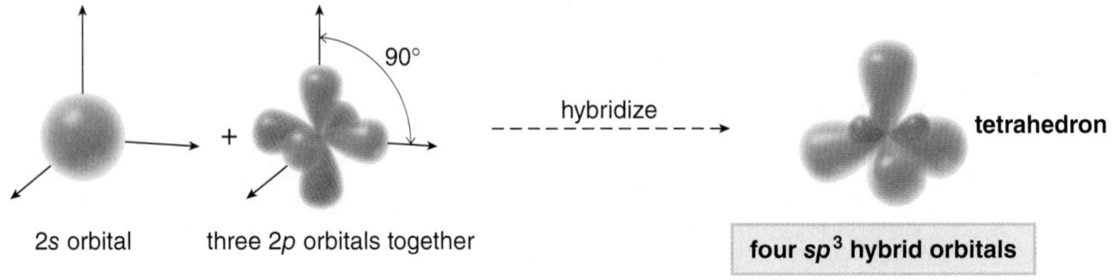

The four hybrid orbitals form four equivalent bonds. We can now explain the observed bonding in CH_4.

- **Each bond in CH_4 is formed by overlap of an *sp*^{3} hybrid orbital of carbon with a 1*s* orbital of hydrogen. These four bonds point to the corners of a tetrahedron.**

All four C–H bonds in methane are **σ bonds,** because the electron density is concentrated on the axis joining C and H. An orbital picture of the bonding in CH_4 is given in Figure 1.7.

Problem 1.27 What orbitals are used to form each of the C–C and C–H bonds in $CH_3CH_2CH_3$ (propane)? How many σ bonds are present in this molecule?

Figure 1.7
Bonding in CH_4 using *sp*^{3} hybrid orbitals

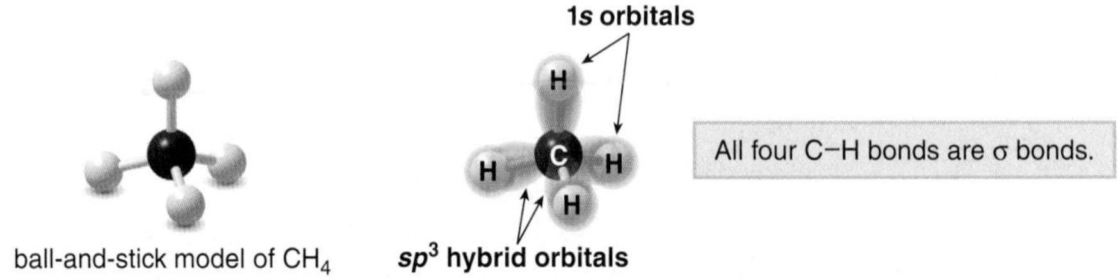

1.9C Other Hybridization Patterns—*sp* and *sp*^{2} Hybrid Orbitals

Forming *sp*^{3} hybrid orbitals is just one way that 2*s* and 2*p* orbitals can hybridize. In fact, three common modes of hybridization are seen in organic molecules. The number of orbitals is always conserved in hybridization; that is, a **given number of atomic orbitals hybridize to form an equivalent number of hybrid orbitals.**

- **_One_ 2*s* orbital and _three_ 2*p* orbitals form _four sp_^{3} hybrid orbitals.**
- **_One_ 2*s* orbital and _two_ 2*p* orbitals form _three sp_^{2} hybrid orbitals.**
- **_One_ 2*s* orbital and _one_ 2*p* orbital form _two sp_ hybrid orbitals.**

We have already seen pictorially how four *sp*^{3} hybrid orbitals are formed from one 2*s* and three 2*p* orbitals. Figures 1.8 and 1.9 illustrate the same process for *sp* and *sp*^{2} hybrids. Each *sp* and *sp*^{2} hybrid orbital has one large and one small lobe, much like an *sp*^{3} hybrid orbital. Note, however, that both *sp*^{2} and *sp* hybridization **leave one and two 2*p* orbitals *unhybridized,*** respectively, on each atom.

To determine the hybridization of an atom in a molecule, we count groups around the atom, just as we did in determining geometry. **The number of groups (atoms and nonbonded electron**

Figure 1.8
Forming two *sp* hybrid orbitals

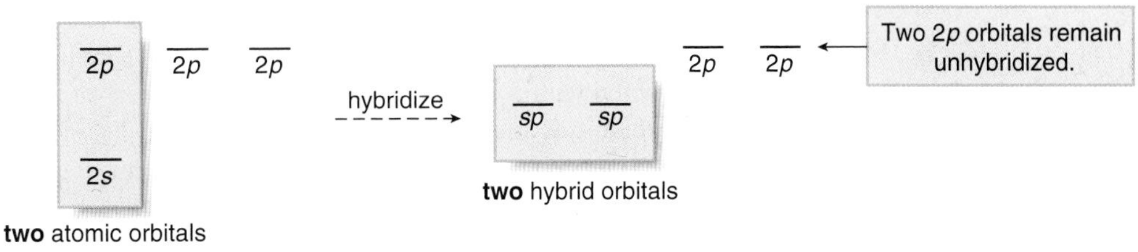

- Forming **two *sp* hybrid orbitals** uses **one 2*s*** and **one 2*p* orbital,** leaving **two 2*p* orbitals *unhybridized.***

Figure 1.9
Forming three sp^2 hybrid orbitals

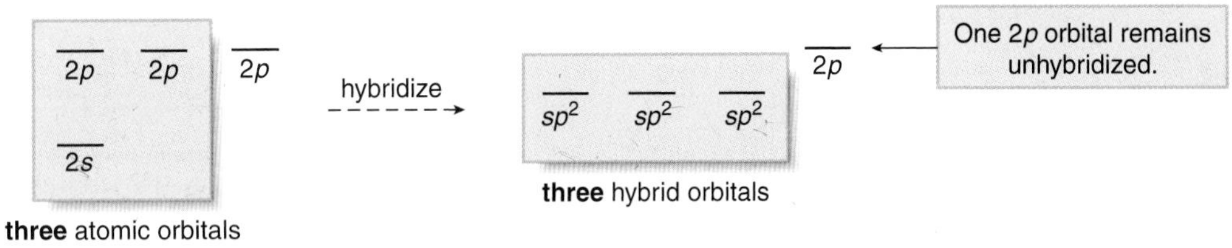

- Forming **three sp^2 hybrid orbitals** uses **one 2*s*** and **two 2*p* orbitals,** leaving **one 2*p* orbital *unhybridized.***

The **superscripts** for hybrid orbitals correspond to the **number of atomic orbitals** used to form them. The number "1" is understood.

For example: $sp^3 = s^1p^3$

one 2*s* + **three** 2*p* orbitals used to make each hybrid orbital

pairs) corresponds to the number of atomic orbitals that must be hybridized to form the hybrid orbitals.

number of groups around an atom	number of orbitals used	type of hybrid orbital
2	2	**two *sp*** hybrid orbitals
3	3	**three sp^2** hybrid orbitals
4	4	**four sp^3** hybrid orbitals

Let's illustrate this phenomenon with BeH_2, BF_3, NH_3, and H_2O. We already determined the geometry in these molecules by counting groups in Section 1.7.

In **BeH_2,** the **Be atom is *sp* hybridized** because it is surrounded by two groups (two H atoms). Each Be–H bond is formed by overlap of an *sp* hybrid orbital from Be and a 1*s* orbital from H. The *sp* hybrid orbitals are oriented 180° away from each other.

In **BF_3,** the **B atom is sp^2 hybridized** because it is surrounded by three groups (three F atoms). Each B–F bond is formed by overlap of an sp^2 hybrid orbital from B and a 2*p* orbital from F. The sp^2 hybrid orbitals all lie in a plane, and are oriented 120° apart. The B atom also has a vacant unhybridized 2*p* orbital. This orbital is located ***above and below the plane*** of the BF_3 molecule.

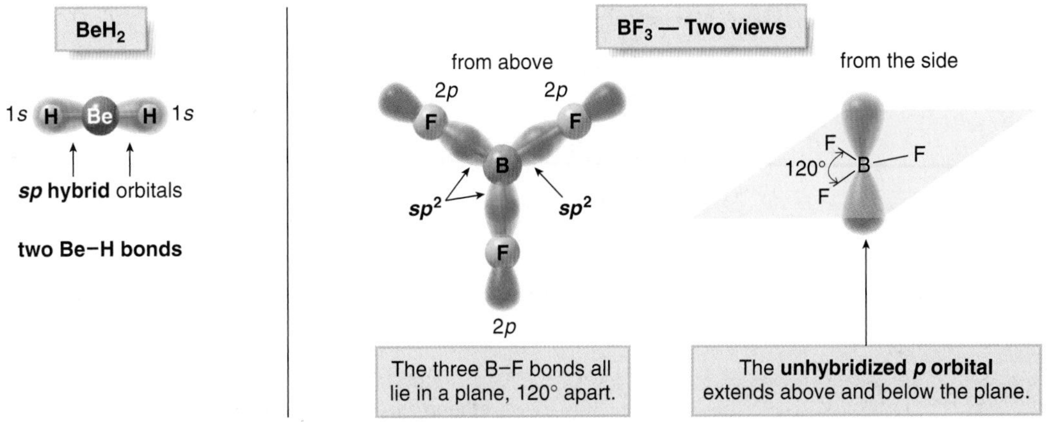

The N atom in NH_3 and the O atom in H_2O are both surrounded by four groups, making them sp^3 hybridized. Each N–H and O–H bond in these molecules is formed by overlap of an sp^3 hybrid orbital with a 1*s* orbital from H. The lone pairs of electrons on N and O also occupy sp^3 hybrid orbitals, as shown in Figure 1.10.

Figure 1.10
Hybrid orbitals of NH_3 and H_2O

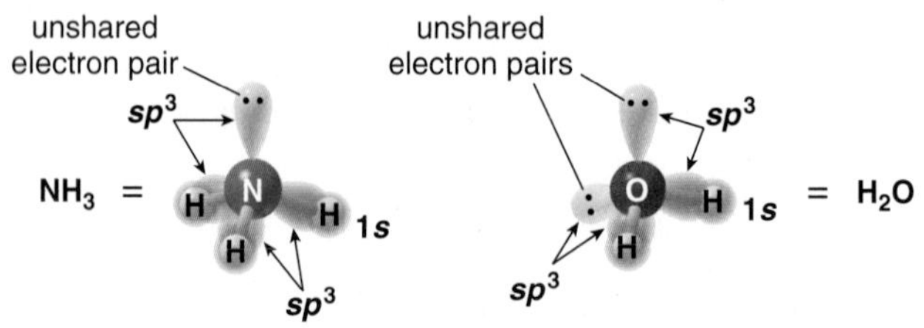

Sample Problem 1.8 What orbitals are used to form each bond in methanol, CH_3OH?

Solution

To solve this problem, draw a valid Lewis structure and count groups around each atom. Then, use the rule to determine hybridization: two groups = *sp*, three groups = sp^2, and four groups = sp^3.

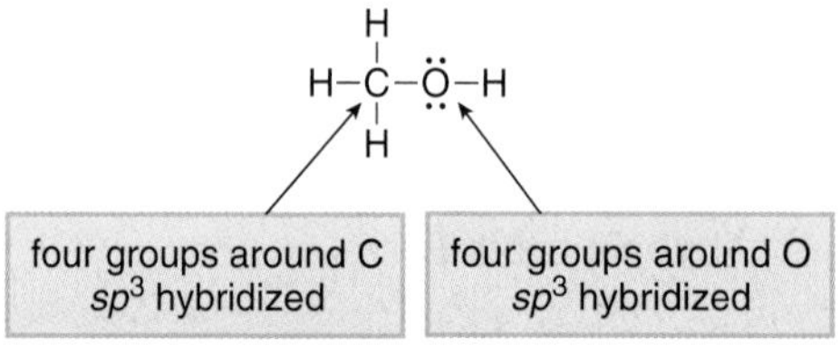

- All C–H bonds are formed from $C_{sp^3}–H_{1s}$.
- The C–O bond is formed from $C_{sp^3}–O_{sp^3}$.
- The O–H bond is formed from $O_{sp^3}–H_{1s}$.

Problem 1.28 What orbitals are used to form each bond in the following molecules?

a. CH_3BeH b. $(CH_3)_3B$ c. CH_3OCH_3

1.10 Ethane, Ethylene, and Acetylene

Let's now use the principles of hybridization to determine the type of bonds in **ethane, ethylene,** and **acetylene.**

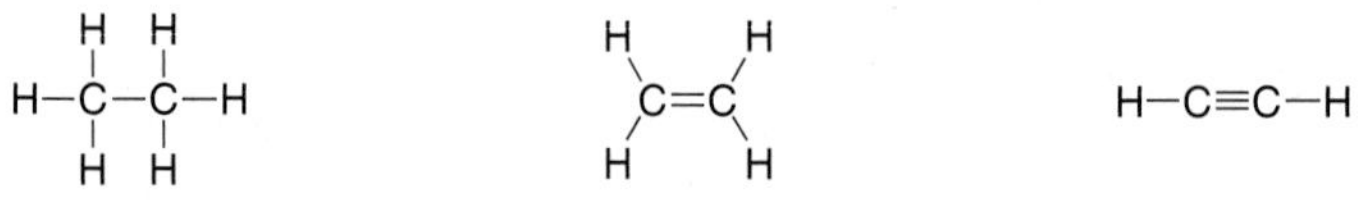

ethane ethylene acetylene

1.10A Ethane—CH_3CH_3

According to the Lewis structure for **ethane, CH_3CH_3,** each carbon atom is singly bonded to four other atoms. As a result:

- **Each carbon is tetrahedral.**
- **Each carbon is sp^3 hybridized.**

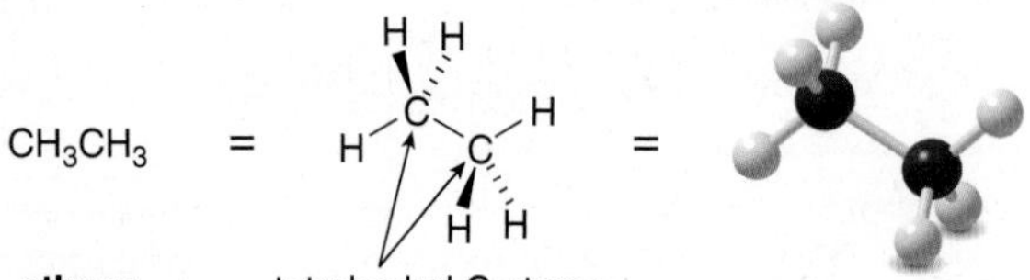

ethane tetrahedral C atoms

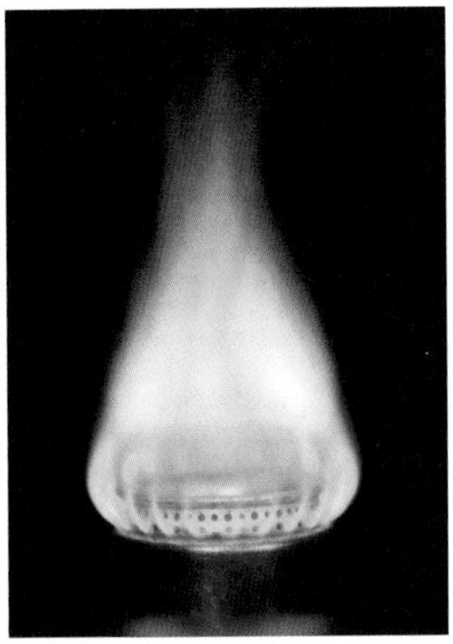

Ethane is a constituent of natural gas.

All of the bonds in ethane are σ bonds. The C–H bonds are formed from the overlap of one of the three sp^3 hybrid orbitals on each carbon atom with the 1*s* orbital on hydrogen. The C–C bond is formed from the overlap of an sp^3 hybrid orbital on each carbon atom.

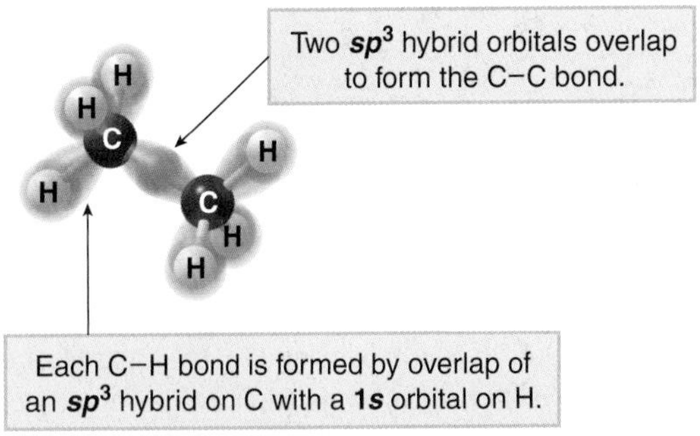
Two **sp³** hybrid orbitals overlap to form the C–C bond.
Each C–H bond is formed by overlap of an **sp³** hybrid on C with a **1s** orbital on H.

Finally, a model of ethane shows that **rotation can occur around the central C–C σ bond.** Note how the relative position of the H atoms on the adjacent CH_3 groups changes from one representation to another. This process is discussed in greater detail in Chapter 4.

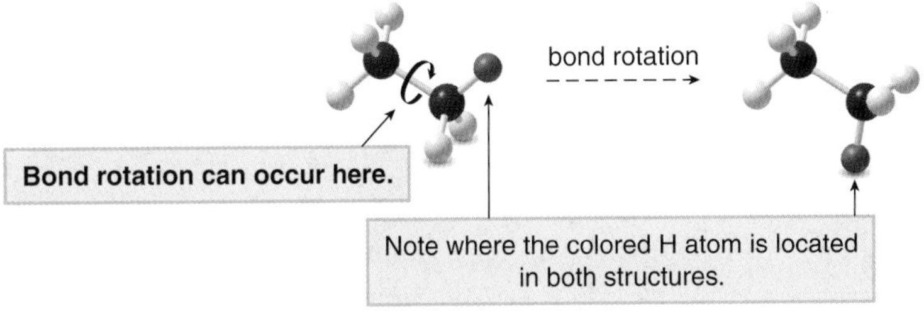
bond rotation
Bond rotation can occur here.
Note where the colored H atom is located in both structures.

1.10B Ethylene—C_2H_4

Ethylene is an important starting material in the preparation of the plastic polyethylene.

Based on the Lewis structure of **ethylene, $CH_2{=}CH_2$,** each carbon atom is singly bonded to two H atoms and doubly bonded to the other C atom, so each C is surrounded by three groups. As a result:

- **Each carbon is trigonal planar (Section 1.7B).**
- **Each carbon is sp^2 hybridized.**

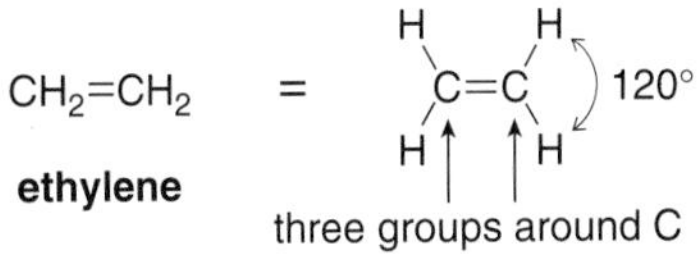
CH₂=CH₂
ethylene
120°
three groups around C

What orbitals are used to form the two bonds of the C–C double bond? Recall from Section 1.9 that **sp^2 hybrid orbitals** are formed from **one 2*s* and two 2*p* orbitals,** leaving one **2*p* orbital unhybridized.** Because carbon has four valence electrons, **each of these orbitals has one electron** that can be used to form a bond.

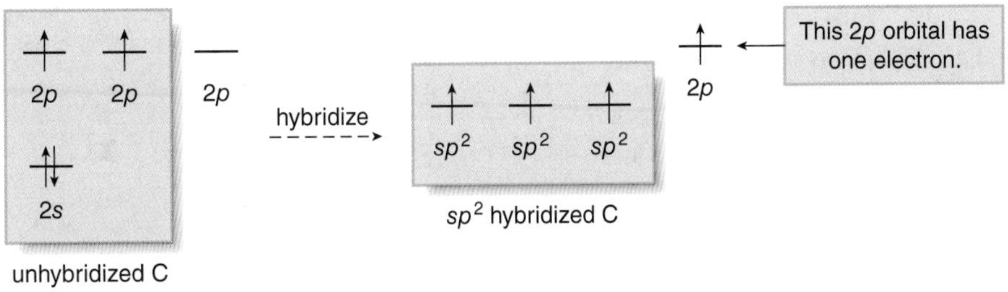
2p
2p
2p
2s
unhybridized C
hybridize
sp²
sp²
sp²
sp² hybridized C
2p
This 2p orbital has one electron.

Each C−H bond results from the end-on overlap of an sp^2 hybrid orbital on carbon and the 1*s* orbital on hydrogen. Similarly, one of the C−C bonds results from the end-on overlap of an sp^2 hybrid orbital on each carbon atom. Each of these bonds is a **σ bond.**

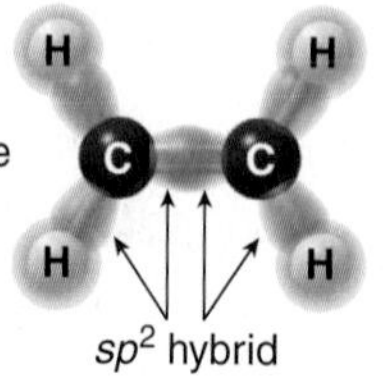

- Each C has three sp^2 hybrid orbitals.
- The C−H bonds and the C−C bond are σ bonds.

The second C−C bond results from the side-by-side overlap of the 2*p* orbitals on each carbon. Side-by-side overlap creates an area of electron density above and below the plane containing the sp^2 hybrid orbitals (that is, the plane containing the six atoms in the σ bonding system).

Overlap of the 2*p* orbitals forms the second C−C bond.

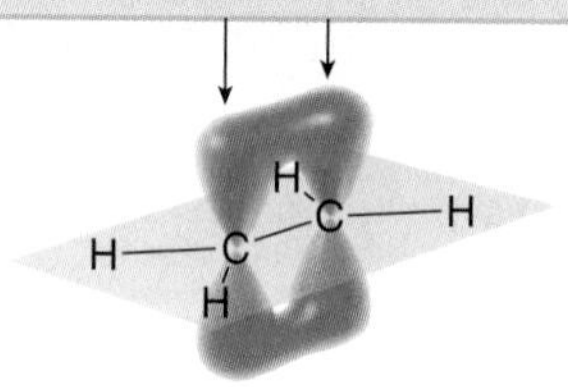

In this second bond, the electron density is ***not*** concentrated on the axis joining the two nuclei. This new type of bond is called a **π bond.** Because the electron density in a π bond is farther from the two nuclei, **π bonds are usually weaker and therefore more easily broken than σ bonds.**

Thus, a carbon–carbon double bond has two components:

- **a σ bond, formed by end-on overlap of two sp^2 hybrid orbitals;**
- **a π bond, formed by side-by-side overlap of two 2*p* orbitals.**

Figure 1.11 summarizes the bonding observed in ethylene.

Unlike the C−C single bond in ethane, rotation about the C−C double bond in ethylene is **restricted.** It can occur only if the π bond first breaks and then re-forms, a process that requires considerable energy.

All double bonds are composed of one σ and one π bond.

Rotation around a C=C bond does *not* occur.

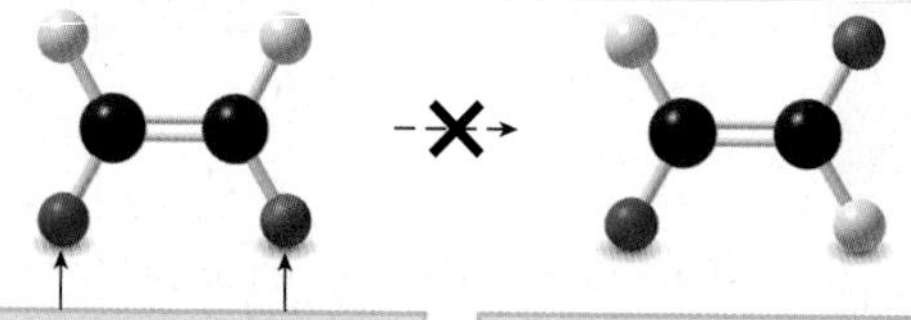

labels on the **same side** of the C=C

labels on **opposite sides** of the C=C

Figure 1.11
Summary: The σ and π bonds in ethylene

The five σ bonds are labeled.

The π bond extends **above and below the plane** of the molecule.

Overlap of the two sp^2 hybrid orbitals forms the C−C σ bond.

Overlap of the two 2*p* orbitals forms the C−C π bond.

1.10C Acetylene—C_2H_2

Based on the Lewis structure of **acetylene, HC≡CH,** each carbon atom is singly bonded to one hydrogen atom and triply bonded to the other carbon atom, so each carbon atom is surrounded by two groups. As a result:

- **Each carbon is linear (Section 1.7B).**
- **Each carbon is *sp* hybridized.**

Because acetylene produces a very hot flame on burning, it is often used in welding torches. The fire is very bright, too, so it was once used in the lamps worn by spelunkers—people who study and explore caves.

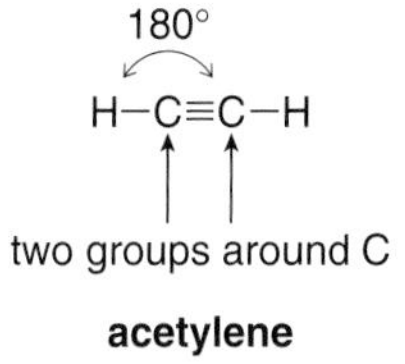

What orbitals are used to form the bonds of the C−C triple bond? Recall from Section 1.9 that ***sp* hybrid orbitals** are formed from **one 2*s* and one 2*p* orbital,** leaving **two 2*p* orbitals unhybridized.** Because carbon has four valence electrons, **each of these orbitals has one electron** that can be used to form a bond.

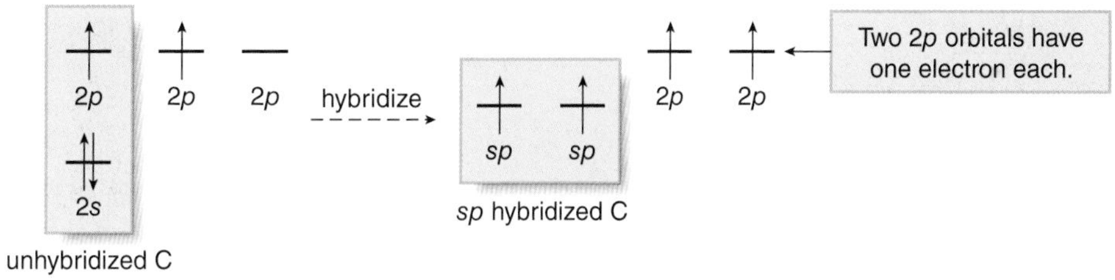

Each C−H bond results from the end-on overlap of an *sp* hybrid orbital on carbon and the 1*s* orbital on hydrogen. Similarly, one of the C−C bonds results from the end-on overlap of an *sp* hybrid orbital on each carbon atom. Each of these bonds is a **σ bond.**

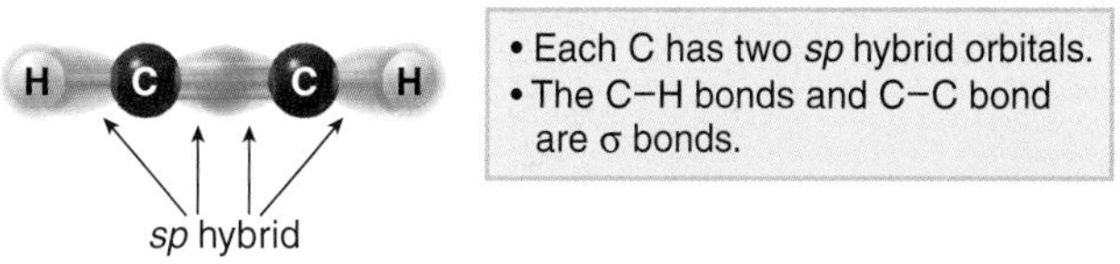

Each carbon atom also has two **unhybridized 2*p* orbitals** that are perpendicular to each other and to the *sp* hybrid orbitals. Side-by-side overlap between the two 2*p* orbitals on one carbon with the two 2*p* orbitals on the other carbon creates the second and third bonds of the C−C triple bond. The electron density from one of these two bonds is above and below the axis joining the two nuclei, and the electron density from the second of these two bonds is in front of and behind the axis, so both of these bonds are **π bonds.**

The side-by-side overlap of two *p* orbitals always forms a π bond.

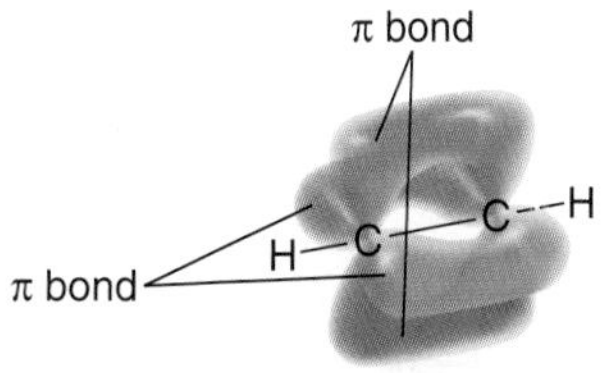

Thus, a carbon–carbon triple bond has three components:

All triple bonds are composed of one σ and two π bonds.

- **a σ bond, formed by end-on overlap of two *sp* hybrid orbitals;**
- **two π bonds, formed by side-by-side overlap of two sets of 2*p* orbitals.**

Figure 1.12 summarizes the bonding observed in acetylene. Table 1.4 summarizes the three possible types of bonding in carbon compounds.

Figure 1.12
Summary: The σ and π bonds in acetylene

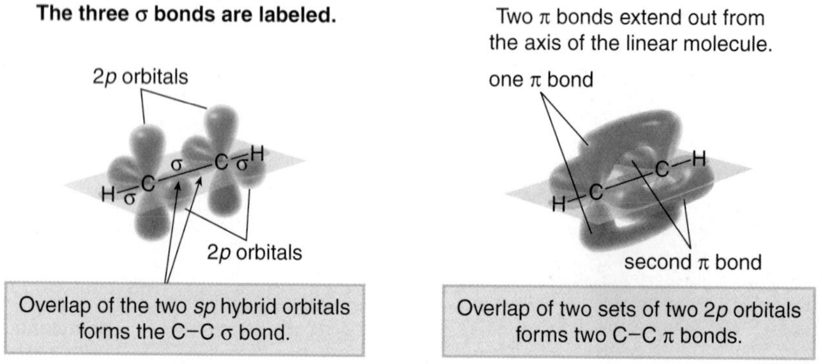
The three σ bonds are labeled.
2p orbitals
H σ C σ C σ H
2p orbitals
Overlap of the two sp hybrid orbitals forms the C–C σ bond.
Two π bonds extend out from the axis of the linear molecule.
one π bond
H–C–C–H
second π bond
Overlap of two sets of two 2p orbitals forms two C–C π bonds.

Table 1.4 A Summary of Covalent Bonding Seen in Carbon Compounds

Number of groups bonded to C	Hybridization	Bond angle	Example	Observed bonding
4	sp^3	109.5°	CH_3CH_3 ethane	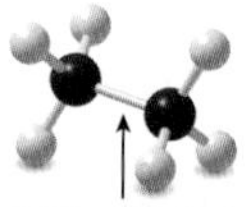 one σ bond; C_{sp^3}–C_{sp^3}
3	sp^2	120°	$CH_2{=}CH_2$ ethylene	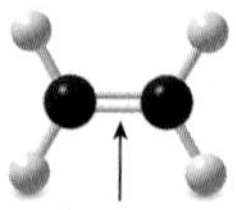 one σ bond + one π bond; C_{sp^2}–C_{sp^2}; C_{2p}–C_{2p}
2	sp	180°	HC≡CH acetylene	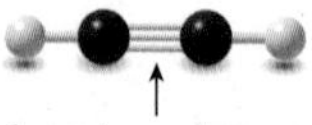 one σ bond + two π bonds; C_{sp}–C_{sp}; C_{2p}–C_{2p}, C_{2p}–C_{2p}

Sample Problem 1.9 Answer each question for the molecule acetone, drawn below:

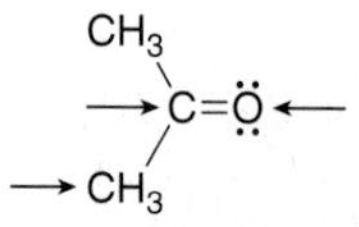
CH3
C=O
CH3
acetone

a. Determine the hybridization of the indicated atoms.
b. What orbitals are used to form the C–O double bond?
c. In what type of orbital does each lone pair reside?

Solution

a.

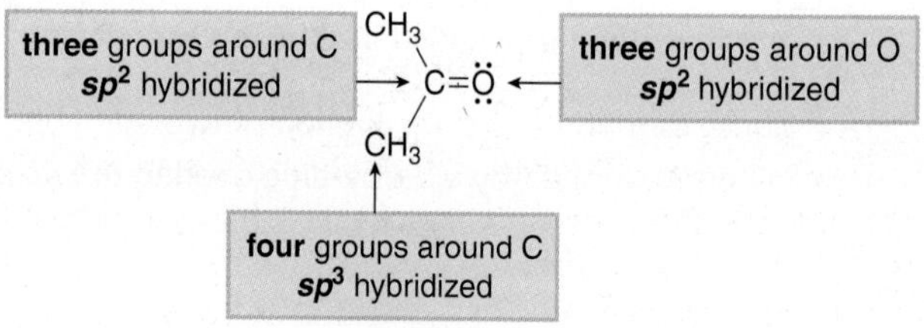
three groups around C
sp² hybridized
CH3
C=O
CH3
three groups around O
sp² hybridized
four groups around C
sp³ hybridized

b. • The σ bond is formed from the end-on overlap of $C_{sp^2}-O_{sp^2}$.
   • The π bond is formed from the side-by-side overlap of $C_{2p}-O_{2p}$.

c. The O atom has three sp^2 hybrid orbitals.
   • One is used for the σ bond of the double bond.
   • The remaining two sp^2 hybrids are occupied by the lone pairs.

Problem 1.29 Determine the hybridization around the indicated atoms in the following molecules:

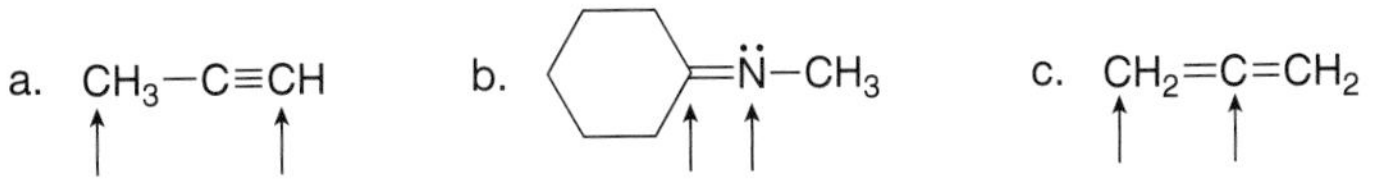

Problem 1.30 Classify each bond in the following molecules as σ or π:

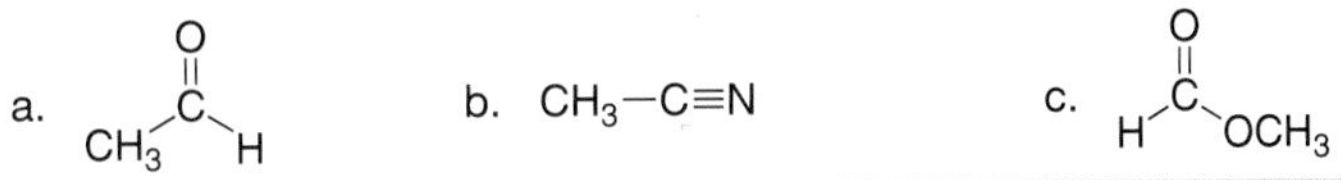

1.11 Bond Length and Bond Strength

Let's now examine the relative bond length and bond strength of the C–C and C–H bonds in ethane, ethylene, and acetylene.

1.11A A Comparison of Carbon–Carbon Bonds

While the SI unit of energy is the **joule** (J), organic chemists often report energy values in **calories** (cal). For this reason, energy values in the tables in this text are reported in joules, followed by the number of calories in parentheses.
1 cal = 4.18 J

Note the inverse relationship between bond length and bond strength. The shorter the bond, the closer the electron density is kept to the nucleus, and the harder the bond is to break. ***Shorter* bonds are *stronger* bonds.**

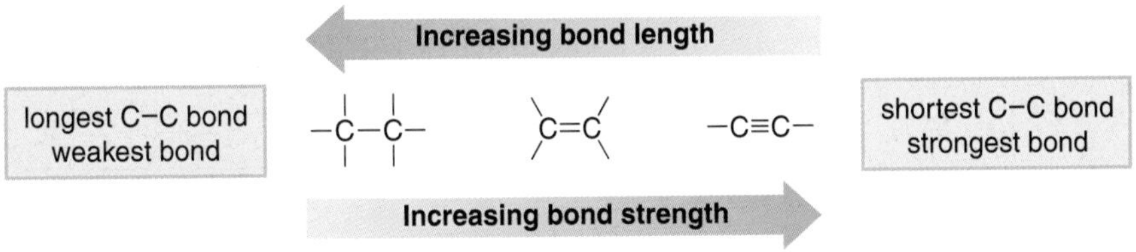

- **As the number of electrons between two nuclei *increases*, bonds become shorter and stronger.**
- **Thus, triple bonds are shorter and stronger than double bonds, which are shorter and stronger than single bonds.**

Values for bond lengths and bond strengths for CH_3CH_3, $CH_2{=}CH_2$, and HC≡CH are listed in Table 1.5. Be careful not to confuse two related but different principles regarding multiple bonds such as C–C double bonds. **Double bonds, consisting of both a σ and a π bond, are *strong*.** The **π component** of the double bond, however, is usually much ***weaker* than the σ component.** This is a particularly important consideration when studying alkenes in Chapter 10.

1.11B A Comparison of Carbon–Hydrogen Bonds

The length and strength of a C–H bond vary slightly depending on the hybridization of the carbon atom.

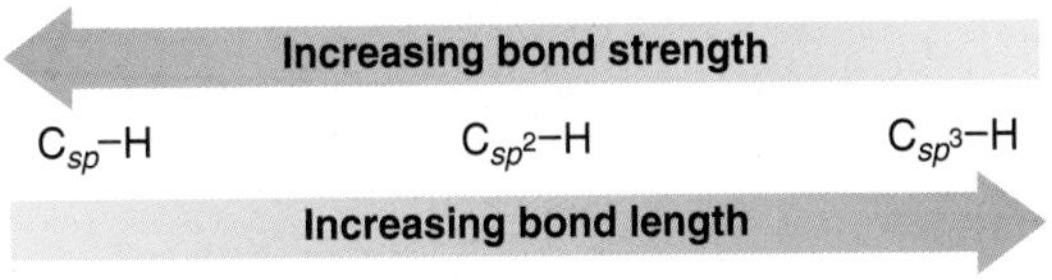

To understand why this is so, we must look at the atomic orbitals used to form each type of hybrid orbital. A single 2*s* orbital is always used, but the number of 2*p* orbitals varies with the type of

Table 1.5 Bond Lengths and Bond Strengths for Ethane, Ethylene, and Acetylene

Compound	C–C bond length (pm)	Bond strength kJ/mol (kcal/mol)
$CH_3{-}CH_3$	153	368 (88)
$CH_2{=}CH_2$	134	635 (152)
$HC{\equiv}CH$	121	837 (200)
	Increasing bond length ↑	Increasing bond strength ↓

Compound	C–H bond length (pm)	Bond strength kJ/mol (kcal/mol)
$CH_3CH_2{-}H$	111	410 (98)
$CH_2{=}C(H){-}H$	110	435 (104)
$HC{\equiv}C{-}H$	109	523 (125)
	Increasing bond length ↑	Increasing bond strength ↓

hybridization. A quantity called **percent *s*-character** indicates the fraction of a hybrid orbital due to the 2*s* orbital used to form it.

$$sp \text{ hybrid} \quad \frac{\text{one 2s orbital}}{\text{two hybrid orbitals}} = 50\%\ s\text{-character}$$

$$sp^2 \text{ hybrid} \quad \frac{\text{one 2s orbital}}{\text{three hybrid orbitals}} = 33\%\ s\text{-character}$$

$$sp^3 \text{ hybrid} \quad \frac{\text{one 2s orbital}}{\text{four hybrid orbitals}} = 25\%\ s\text{-character}$$

Why should the percent *s*-character of a hybrid orbital affect the length of a C–H bond? A 2*s* orbital keeps electron density closer to a nucleus compared to a 2*p* orbital. As the **percent *s*-character increases,** a hybrid orbital holds its electrons closer to the nucleus, and the **bond becomes shorter and stronger.**

Increased percent *s*-character ⟶ Increased bond strength ⟶ Decreased bond length

Problem 1.31 Which of the indicated bonds in each pair of compounds is shorter?

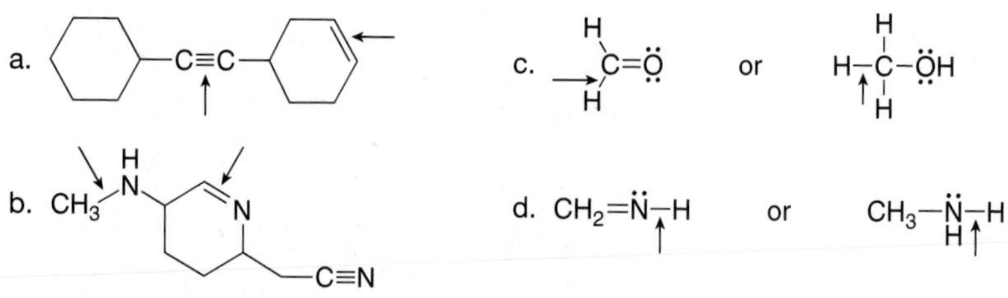

a.
C≡C
b. CH3
H
N
N
C≡N
c.
H
C=O
H
or
H
H–C–OH
H
d. CH2=N–H
or
CH3–N–H
H

1.12 Electronegativity and Bond Polarity

***Electronegativity* is a measure of an atom's attraction for electrons in a bond.** Thus, electronegativity indicates how much a particular atom "*wants*" electrons. The following trends in electronegativity are observed in the periodic table:

- **Electronegativity *increases* across a row of the periodic table as the nuclear charge increases (excluding the noble gases).**
- **Electronegativity *decreases* down a column of the periodic table as the atomic radius increases, pushing the valence electrons farther from the nucleus.**

As a result, the *most* electronegative elements are located at the **upper right-hand corner** of the periodic table, and the *least* electronegative elements in the **lower left-hand corner.** A scale has been established to represent electronegativity values arbitrarily, from 0 to 4, as shown in Figure 1.13.

Electronegativity values are relative, so they can be used for comparison purposes only. When comparing two different elements, one is **more electronegative** than the other if it attracts electron density toward itself. One is less electronegative—**more electro*positive***—if it gives up electron density to the other element.

Problem 1.32 Rank the following atoms in order of increasing electronegativity. Label the most electronegative and most electropositive atom in each group.

a. Se, O, S b. P, Na, Cl c. Cl, S, F d. O, P, N

Electronegativity values are used as a guideline to indicate whether the electrons in a bond are **equally shared** or **unequally shared** between two atoms. For example, whenever two identical atoms are bonded together, each atom attracts the electrons in the bond to the same extent. The electrons are equally shared, and the **bond is *nonpolar.*** Thus, a **carbon–carbon bond is nonpolar.** The same is true whenever two different atoms having similar electronegativities are bonded together. **C – H bonds are considered to be nonpolar,** because the electronegativity difference between C (2.5) and H (2.2) is small.

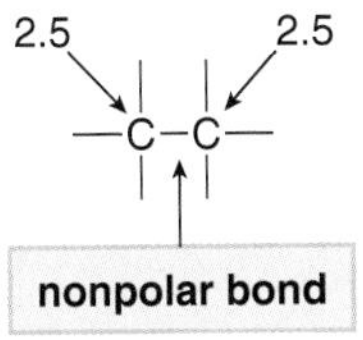

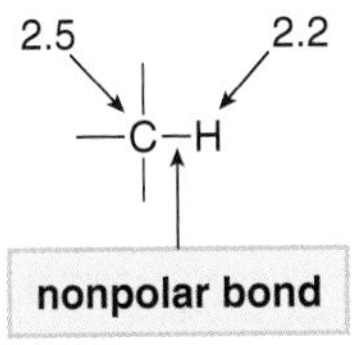

The small electronegativity difference between C and H is ignored.

Figure 1.13 Electronegativity values for some common elements

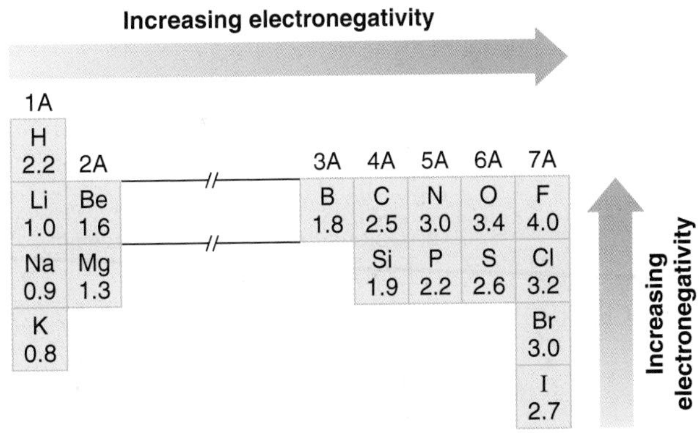

Bonding between atoms of different electronegativity values results in the **unequal sharing** of electrons. For example, in a C–O bond, the electrons are pulled away from C (2.5) toward O (3.4), the element of higher electronegativity. **The bond is *polar,* or *polar covalent.*** The bond is said to have a **dipole;** that is, **a separation of charge.**

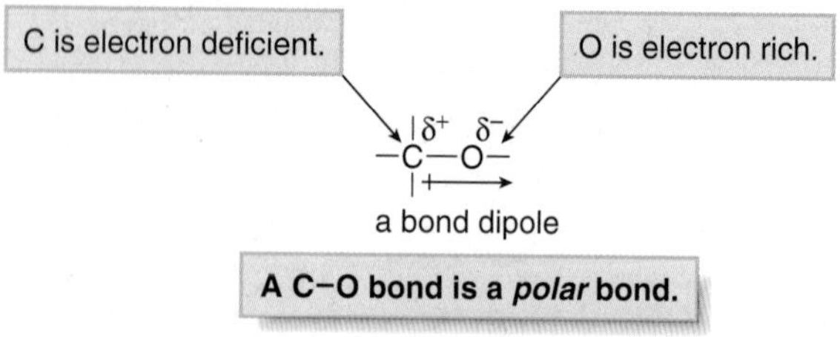

The direction of polarity in a bond is often indicated by an arrow, with the head of the arrow pointing toward the more electronegative element. The tail of the arrow, with a perpendicular line drawn through it, is positioned at the less electronegative element. Alternatively, the symbols δ^+ and δ^- indicate this unequal sharing of electron density.

- **δ^+ means an atom is electron deficient (has a partial positive charge).**
- **δ^- means the atom is electron rich (has a partial negative charge).**

Problem 1.33 Show the direction of the dipole in each bond. Label the atoms with δ^+ and δ^-.

a. H–F

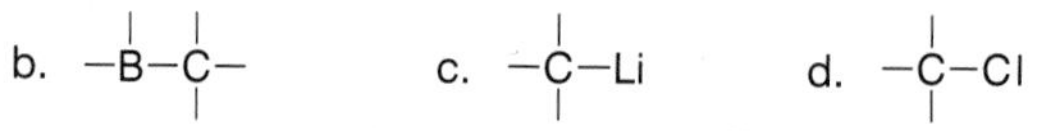

Students often wonder how large an electronegativity difference must be to consider a bond polar. That's hard to say. We will set an arbitrary value for this difference and use it as an *approximation.* **Usually, a polar bond will be one in which the electronegativity difference between two atoms is ≥ 0.5 units.**

The distribution of electron density in a molecule can be shown using an **electrostatic potential map.** These maps are color coded to illustrate areas of high and low electron density. Electron-rich regions are indicated in red, and electron-deficient sites are indicated in blue. Regions of intermediate electron density are shown in orange, yellow, and green.

For example, an electrostatic potential map of CH_3Cl clearly indicates the polar nature of the C–Cl bond (Figure 1.14). The more electronegative Cl atom pulls electron density toward it, making it electron rich. This is indicated by the red around the Cl in the plot. The carbon is electron deficient, and this is shown with blue.

When comparing two maps, the comparison is useful only if they are plotted *using the same scale* of color gradation. For this reason, whenever we compare two plots in this text, they will be drawn side by side using the same scale. It will be difficult to compare two plots in different parts of the book, because the scale may be different. Despite this limitation, an electrostatic potential plot is a useful tool for visually evaluating the distribution of electron density in a molecule, and with care, comparing the electron density in two different molecules.

Figure 1.14 Electrostatic potential plot of CH_3Cl

a. Color scheme used for electron density

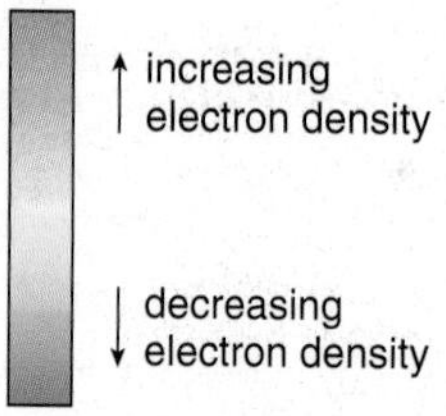

b. Electrostatic potential plot

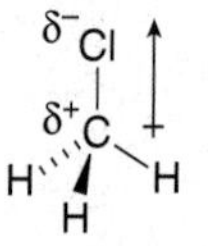

1.13 Polarity of Molecules

A **polar molecule** has either one polar bond, or two or more bond dipoles that reinforce. A **nonpolar molecule** has either no polar bonds, or two or more bond dipoles that cancel.

Whenever C or H is bonded to N, O, and all halogens, the bond is ***polar.*** Thus, the C–I bond is considered polar even though the electronegativity difference between C and I is small. Remember, electronegativity is just an approximation.

Thus far, we have been concerned with the polarity of one bond. To determine whether a molecule has a net dipole, use the following two-step procedure:

[1] Use electronegativity differences to **identify all of the polar bonds and the directions of the bond dipoles.**

[2] **Determine the geometry** around individual atoms by counting groups, and decide if individual dipoles **cancel** or **reinforce each other in space.**

The two molecules H_2O and CO_2 illustrate different outcomes of this process. In H_2O, each O–H bond is polar because the electronegativity difference between O (3.4) and H (2.2) is large. Since H_2O is a **bent** molecule, the two dipoles reinforce (both point *up*). Thus, **H_2O has a net dipole, making it a polar molecule.** CO_2 also has polar C–O bonds because the electronegativity difference between O (3.4) and C (2.5) is large. However, CO_2 is a **linear** molecule, so the two dipoles, which are equal and opposite in direction, **cancel.** Thus, CO_2 is a **nonpolar molecule** with **no net dipole.**

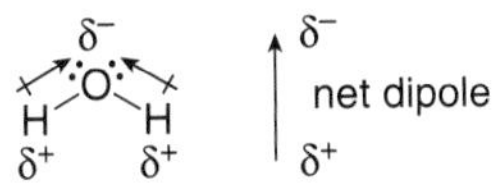

The net dipole bisects the H–O–H bond angle.
The two individual dipoles reinforce.

H_2O is a polar molecule.

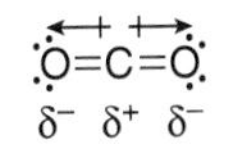

no net dipole
The two dipoles cancel.

CO_2 is a nonpolar molecule.

Electrostatic potential plots for H_2O and CO_2 appear in Figure 1.15. Additional examples of polar and nonpolar molecules are given in Figure 1.16.

Problem 1.34 Indicate which of the following molecules is polar because it possesses a net dipole. Show the direction of the net dipole if one exists.

a. CH_3Br b. CH_2Br_2 c. CF_4 d. 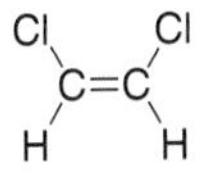 e. 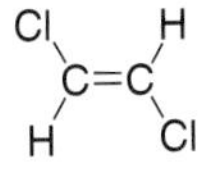

Figure 1.15 Electrostatic potential plots for H_2O and CO_2

- The electron-rich (red) region is concentrated on the electronegative O atom. Both H atoms are electron deficient (blue-green).
- Both electronegative O atoms are electron rich (red) and the central C atom is electron deficient (blue).

Figure 1.16 More examples of polar and nonpolar molecules

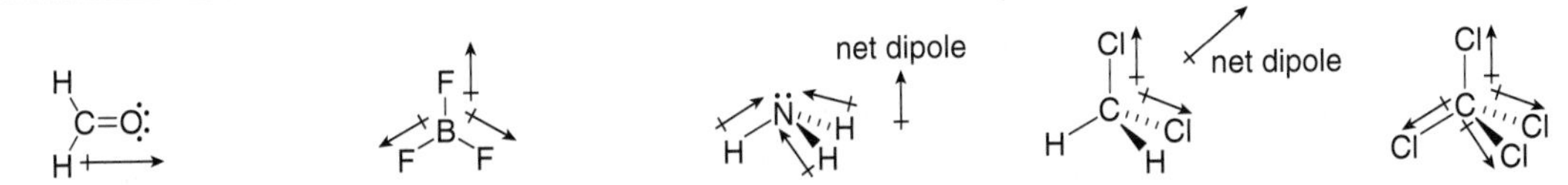

one polar bond	three polar bonds All dipoles cancel. **no** net dipole	three polar bonds All dipoles reinforce.	two polar bonds Both dipoles reinforce.	four polar bonds All dipoles cancel. **no** net dipole
a **polar** molecule	a **nonpolar** molecule	a **polar** molecule	a **polar** molecule	a **nonpolar** molecule

1.14 L-Dopa—A Representative Organic Molecule

The principles learned in this chapter apply to all organic molecules regardless of size or complexity. For example, we now know a great deal about the structure of **L-dopa,** a drug used to treat Parkinson's disease described in the chapter opener.

Sample Problem 1.10 Answer each question about L-dopa.

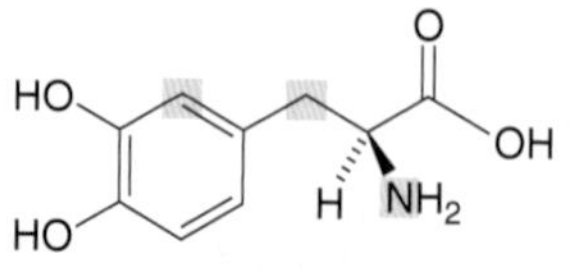

L-dopa

a. Convert the skeletal structure to a Lewis structure.
b. What is the hybridization and geometry around each labeled atom?
c. Label three polar bonds.

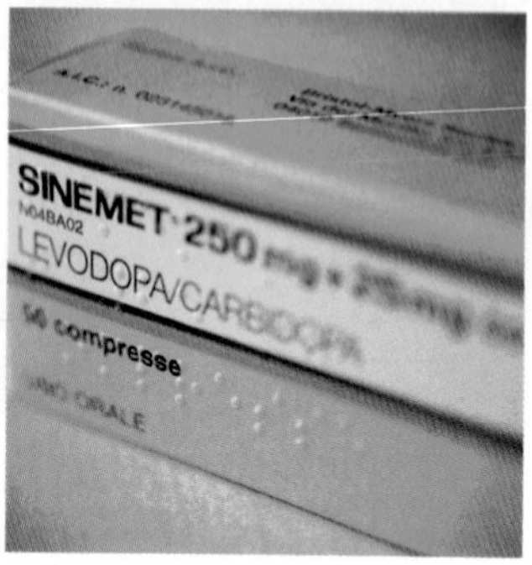
SINEMET 250
LEVODOPA/CARBIDOPA
compresse

Sinemet, the trade name of a drug used to treat Parkinson's disease, contains a combination of L-dopa (Sample Problem 1.10) and carbidopa (Problem 1.36). Carbidopa increases the effectiveness of L-dopa by inhibiting its metabolism prior to crossing the blood–brain barrier and entering the brain.

Solution

a, b. Convert the skeletal structure to a Lewis structure as in Sample Problem 1.7. Each O atom needs two lone pairs and each N atom needs one for an octet. Count groups around an atom to determine hybridization and shape.

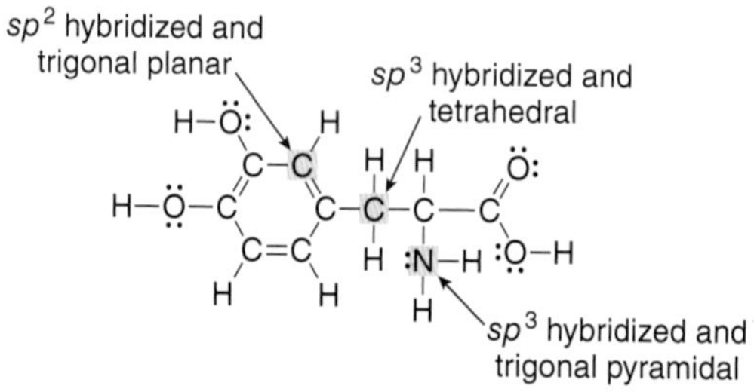
sp^2 hybridized and trigonal planar
sp^3 hybridized and tetrahedral
sp^3 hybridized and trigonal pyramidal

Lewis structure of L-dopa

c. All C–O, O–H, N–H, and C–N bonds are polar because the electronegativity difference between the atoms is large.

Problem 1.35 Provide the following information about L-dopa.

a. Label all sp^3 hybridized C atoms.
b. Label all H atoms that bear a partial positive charge (δ^+).
c. Draw another resonance structure.

Sample Problem 1.11 illustrates how to derive structural information from a ball-and-stick model.

Sample Problem 1.11 Use the ball-and-stick model of vitamin B_6 to answer each question.

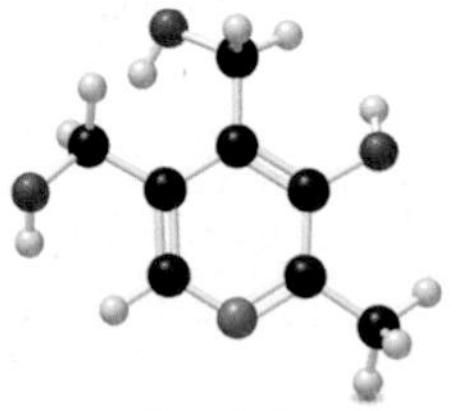

vitamin B_6

a. Draw a skeletal structure of vitamin B_6.
b. How many sp^2 hybridized carbons are present?
c. What is the hybridization of the N atom in the ring?

Solution

Use the element colors shown in Section 1.7B to convert the 3-D model to a skeletal structure [black (C), gray (H), red (O), blue (N)]. H atoms on carbon are omitted, but H atoms on heteroatoms are drawn in. Count groups to determine hybridization. Each O atom needs two lone pairs and each N needs one to give an octet of electrons.

a. 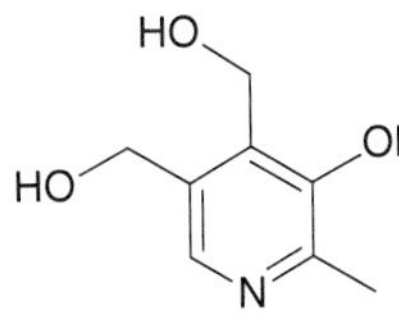

skeletal structure of vitamin B_6

b, c. 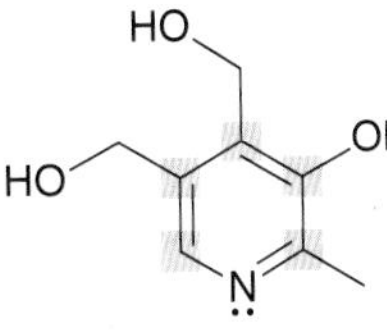

- Each C labeled in blue is sp^2 hybridized.
- The N atom is surrounded by three groups (two atoms and one lone pair), making it sp^2 hybridized.

Problem 1.36 Use the ball-and-stick model to answer each question about carbidopa, a drug used in combination with L-dopa to treat Parkinson's disease

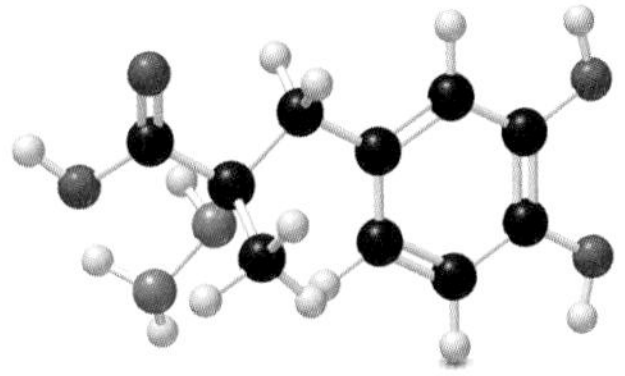

carbidopa

a. Draw a skeletal structure of carbidopa.
b. Determine the hybridization around each carbon atom.
c. What is the hybridization and geometry around each N atom?
d. How many polar bonds are present?

KEY CONCEPTS

Structure and Bonding

Important Facts

- **The general rule of bonding:** Atoms "strive" to attain a complete outer shell of valence electrons (Section 1.2). H "wants" two electrons. Second-row elements "want" eight electrons.
- **Formal charge** is the difference between the number of valence electrons of an atom and the number of electrons it "owns" (Section 1.3C). See Sample Problem 1.3 for a stepwise example.
- **Curved arrow notation** shows the movement of an electron pair. The tail of the arrow always begins at an electron pair, either in a bond or a lone pair. The head points to where the electron pair "moves" (Section 1.6).
- **Electrostatic potential plots** are color-coded maps of electron density, indicating electron-rich and electron-deficient regions (Section 1.12).

The Importance of Lewis Structures (Sections 1.3–1.5)

A properly drawn Lewis structure shows the number of bonds and lone pairs present around each atom in a molecule. In a valid Lewis structure, each H has two electrons, and each second-row element has no more than eight. This is the first step needed to determine many properties of a molecule.

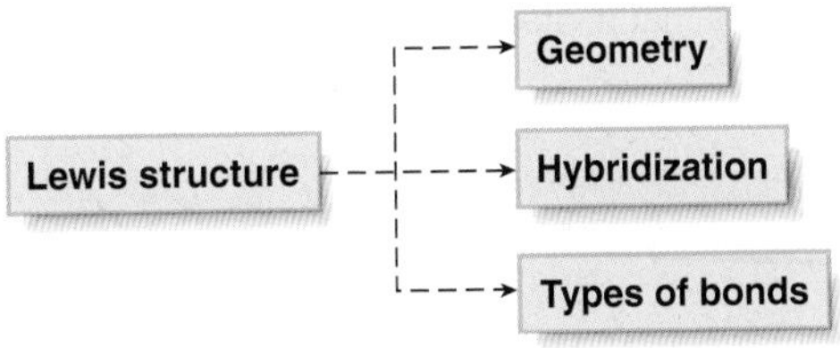

[linear, trigonal planar, or tetrahedral] (Section 1.7)

[*sp*, sp^2, or sp^3] (Section 1.9)

[single, double, or triple] (Sections 1.3, 1.10)

Resonance (Section 1.6)

The basic principles:

- Resonance exists when a compound cannot be represented by a single Lewis structure.
- Resonance structures differ in the position of only nonbonded electrons and π bonds, not atoms.
- The resonance hybrid is the only accurate representation for a resonance-stabilized compound. A hybrid represents the compound better than any single resonance structure because electron density is delocalized.

The difference between resonance structures and isomers:

- Two **isomers** differ in the arrangement of *both* atoms and electrons.
- **Resonance structures** differ *only* in the arrangement of electrons.

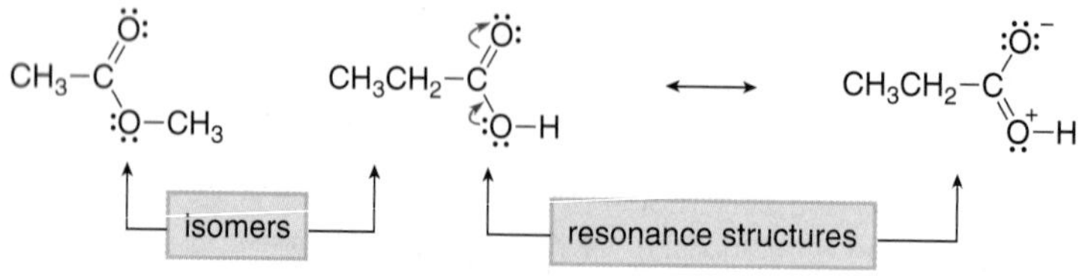

Geometry and Hybridization

The number of groups around an atom determines both its geometry (Section 1.7) and hybridization (Section 1.9).

Number of groups	Geometry	Bond angle (°)	Hybridization
2	linear	180	*sp*
3	trigonal planar	120	sp^2
4	tetrahedral	109.5	sp^3

Drawing Organic Molecules (Section 1.8)

- Shorthand methods are used to abbreviate the structure of organic molecules.

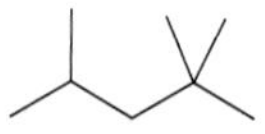 = 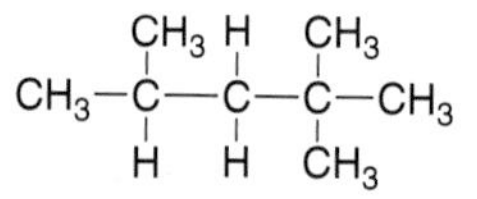 = $(CH_3)_2CHCH_2C(CH_3)_3$

skeletal structure | isooctane | condensed structure

- A carbon bonded to four atoms is tetrahedral. The best way to represent a tetrahedron is to draw two bonds in the plane, one bond in front, and one bond behind.

Bond Length

- Bond length decreases across a row and increases down a column of the periodic table (Section 1.7A).
- Bond length decreases as the number of electrons between two nuclei increases (Section 1.11A).
- Bond length decreases as the percent *s*-character increases (Section 1.11B).
- Bond length and bond strength are inversely related. In general, shorter bonds are stronger bonds (Section 1.11).
- Sigma (σ) bonds are generally stronger than π bonds (Section 1.10).

Electronegativity and Polarity (Sections 1.12, 1.13)

- Electronegativity increases across a row and decreases down a column of the periodic table.
- A polar bond results when two atoms of different electronegativity values are bonded together. Whenever C or H is bonded to N, O, or any halogen, the bond is polar.
- A polar molecule has either one polar bond, or two or more bond dipoles that reinforce.

PROBLEMS

Problems Using Three-Dimensional Models

1.37 Citric acid is responsible for the tartness of citrus fruits, especially lemons and limes.

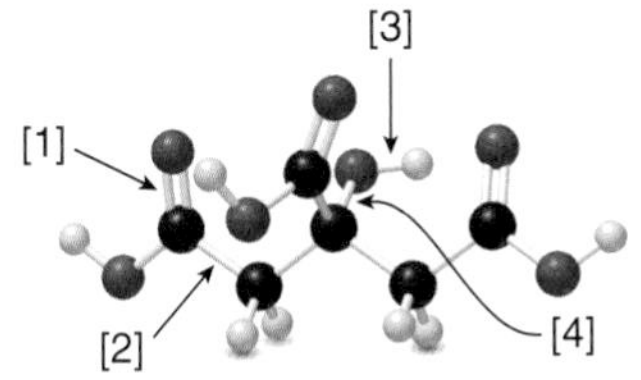

citric acid

a. What is the molecular formula for citric acid?
b. How many lone pairs are present?
c. Draw a skeletal structure.
d. How many sp^2 hybridized carbons are present?
e. What orbitals are used to form each indicated bond ([1]–[4])?

1.38 Zingerone gives ginger its pungent taste.

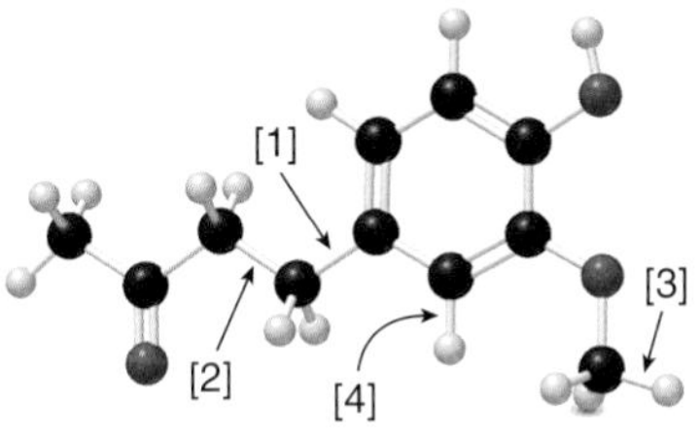

zingerone

a. What is the molecular formula for zingerone?
b. How many lone pairs are present?
c. Draw a skeletal structure.
d. How many sp^2 hybridized carbons are present?
e. What orbitals are used to form each indicated bond ([1]–[4])?

Atomic Structure, Ionic Bonding, and Covalent Bonding

1.39 Two radioactive isotopes of iodine used for the diagnosis and treatment of thyroid disease have mass numbers of 123 and 131. For each isotope, give the following information: (a) the number of protons; (b) the number of neutrons; (c) the number of electrons in the neutral atom; (d) the group number.

1.40 Label each bond in the following compounds as ionic or covalent.
a. NaI b. BrCl c. HCl d. CH_3NH_2 e. $NaOCH_3$

Lewis Structures and Formal Charge

1.41 Assign formal charges to each carbon atom in the given species. All lone pairs have been drawn in.

a. $CH_2{=}\ddot{C}H$ b. $H{-}\ddot{C}{-}H$ c. $H{-}\dot{C}{-}H$ (with H below C) d. $H{-}C{-}\dot{C}$ (each C bearing H above and H below)

1.42 Assign formal charges to each N and O atom in the given molecules. All lone pairs have been drawn in.

a. $CH_3{-}\ddot{N}{-}CH_3$ c. $CH_3{-}N{\equiv}N{:}$ e. $CH_3{-}\ddot{O}{\cdot}$

b. $:\ddot{N}{=}N{=}\ddot{N}:$ d. $CH_3{-}C({=}\ddot{O}H){-}CH_3$ f. $CH_3{-}\ddot{N}{=}\ddot{O}$

1.43 Draw one valid Lewis structure for each compound. Assume the atoms are arranged as drawn.

a. CH_2N_2 H C N N (H below C)
b. CH_3NO_2 H C N O (H above C; H O below C N)
c. CH_3CNO H C C N O (H above and below the first C)
d. HCO_2^- H C O (O above C)
e. HCO_3^- H O C O (O above C)
f. $^-CH_2CN$ H C C N (H below the first C)

1.44 Draw a valid Lewis structure for each compound.
a. N_2 b. $(CH_3OH_2)^+$ c. $(CH_3CH_2)^-$ d. HNNH e. H_6BN

1.45 Draw an acceptable Lewis structure from each condensed structure, such that all atoms have zero formal charge.
a. diethyl ether, $(CH_3CH_2)_2O$, the first general anesthetic used in medical procedures
b. acrylonitrile, CH_2CHCN, starting material used to manufacture synthetic Orlon fibers
c. dihydroxyacetone, $(HOCH_2)_2CO$, an ingredient in sunless tanning products
d. acetic anhydride, $(CH_3CO)_2O$, a reagent used to synthesize aspirin

Isomers and Resonance Structures

1.46 Creatine is a dietary supplement used by some athletes to boost their athletic performance. (a) Draw in all lone pairs in creatine. (b) Draw two additional resonance structures showing all lone pairs and formal charges.

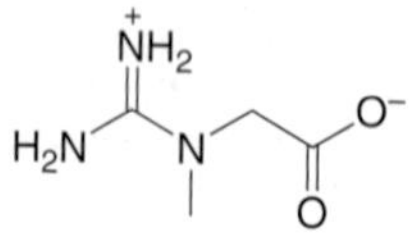

creatine

1.47 Draw all possible isomers for each molecular formula.

a. C_3H_7Cl (two isomers) b. C_2H_4O (three isomers) c. C_3H_9N (four isomers)

1.48 Draw Lewis structures for the nine isomers having molecular formula C_3H_6O, with all atoms having a zero formal charge.

1.49 With reference to compound **A** drawn below, label each compound as an isomer, a resonance structure, or neither.

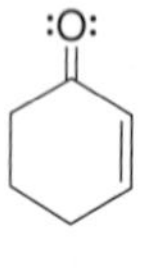

A

a. 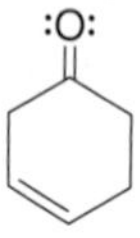 b. 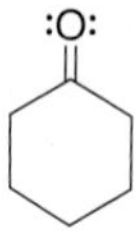 c. 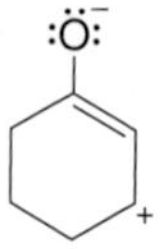 d. 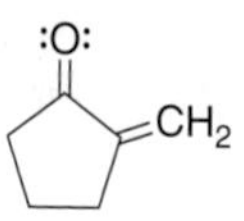

1.50 With reference to cation **B**, label each species as an isomer, a resonance structure, or neither.

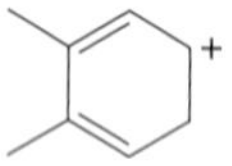

B

a. 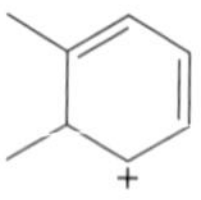 b. 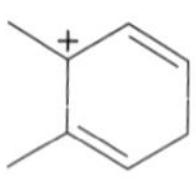 c. 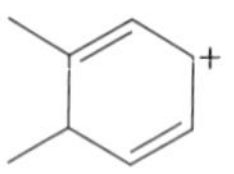 d. 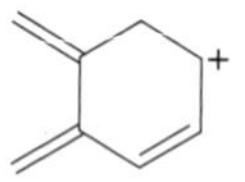

1.51 How are the molecules or ions in each pair related? Classify them as resonance structures, isomers, or neither.

a. $CH_3-\ddot{O}-CH_2CH_3$ and $CH_3-C(CH_3)(H)-\ddot{O}H$

b.  and $CH_3-C(H)=C(H)-CH_3$

c. 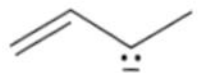 and 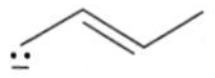

d. $CH_3CH_2CH_3$ and $CH_3CH_2\ddot{C}H_2$

1.52 Add curved arrows to show how the first resonance structure can be converted into the second.

a. $CH_3-\overset{+}{C}(H)-\ddot{N}(H)-CH_3 \longleftrightarrow CH_3-C(H)=\overset{+}{N}(H)-CH_3$

b. $H-C(=\ddot{O}:)-\ddot{N}H_2 \longleftrightarrow H-C(-\ddot{O}:^-)=\overset{+}{N}H_2$

c. 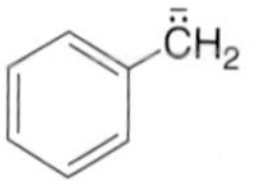 ⟷ 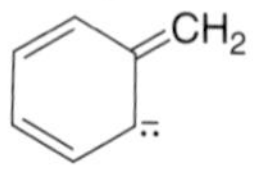

1.53 Follow the curved arrows to draw a second resonance structure for each species.

a. $CH_3-\overset{+}{N}\equiv N:$ ⟷

b. $CH_3-C(-\ddot{O}:^-)=CH-\overset{+}{C}H_2$ ⟷

c. 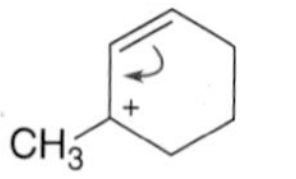 ⟷

d. 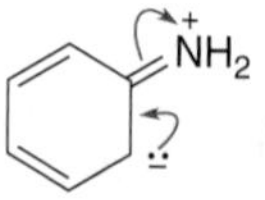 ⟷

1.54 Draw a second resonance structure for each ion. Then, draw the resonance hybrid.

a. $CH_3-C(=\ddot{O}:)-\ddot{O}:^-$

b. $CH_2=\overset{+}{N}H_2$

c. 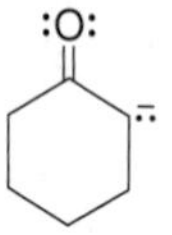

d. $H-C(=\overset{+}{\ddot{O}}H)-H$

1.55 Draw all reasonable resonance structures for each species.

a. O_3

b. NO_3^- (a central N atom)

c. N_3^-

d. $CH_3-C(=\ddot{O}:)-\ddot{C}H-C(=\ddot{O}:)-CH_3$

e. 

f. $CH_2=CH-\ddot{C}H-CH=CH_2$

g. 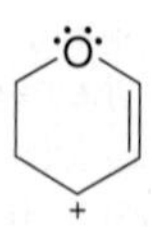

1.56 Draw four additional resonance structures for the following cation. Then draw the resonance hybrid.

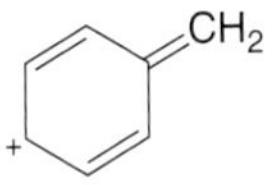

1.57 Rank the resonance structures in each group in order of increasing contribution to the resonance hybrid. Label the resonance structure that contributes the most as **3** and the resonance structure that contributes the least as **1.** Label the intermediate contributor as **2.**

a. 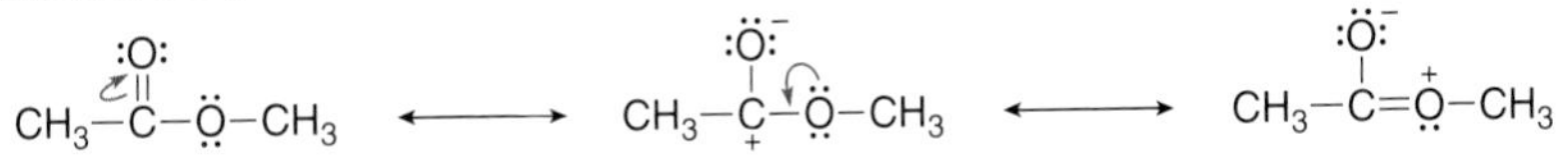

b. 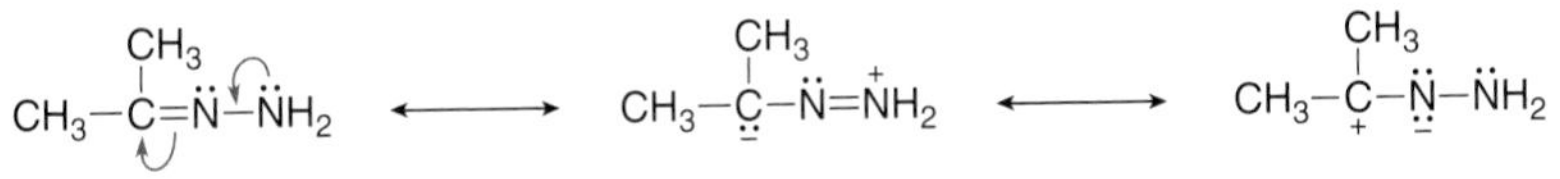

1.58 Consider the compounds and ions with curved arrows drawn below. When the curved arrows give a second valid resonance structure, draw the resonance structure. When the curved arrows generate an invalid Lewis structure, explain why the structure is unacceptable.

a. 

b. 

c. 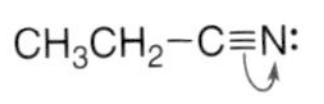

d. 

Geometry

1.59 Predict all bond angles in each compound.

a. CH_3Cl b. NH_2OH c. $CH_2{=}NCH_3$ d. $HC{\equiv}CCH_2OH$ e. 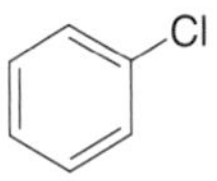

1.60 Predict the geometry around each indicated atom.

a. $CH_3CH_2CH_2CH_3$

b. $(CH_3)_2N^-$

c. 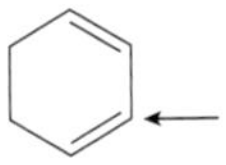

d. BF_4^-

e. 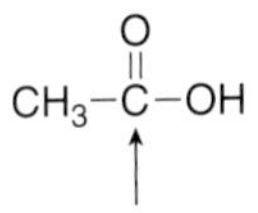

f. $(CH_3)_3N$

1.61 Draw the structure of halothane, $CF_3CHClBr$, in three dimensions, using solid lines, wedges, and dashes to illustrate the position of atoms. Halothane is a safe and widely used general anesthetic.

Drawing Organic Molecules

1.62 How many hydrogens are present around each carbon atom in the following molecules?

a. 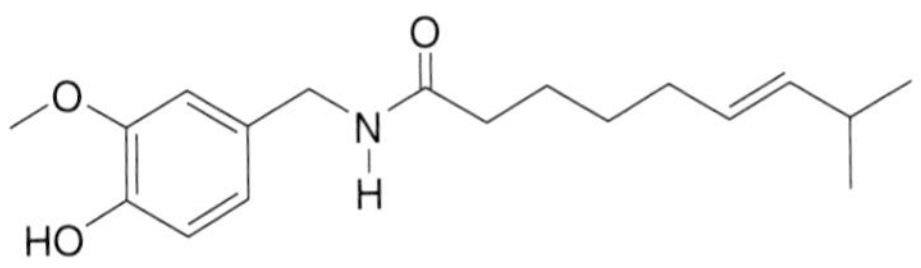

capsaicin
(spicy component of hot peppers)

b. 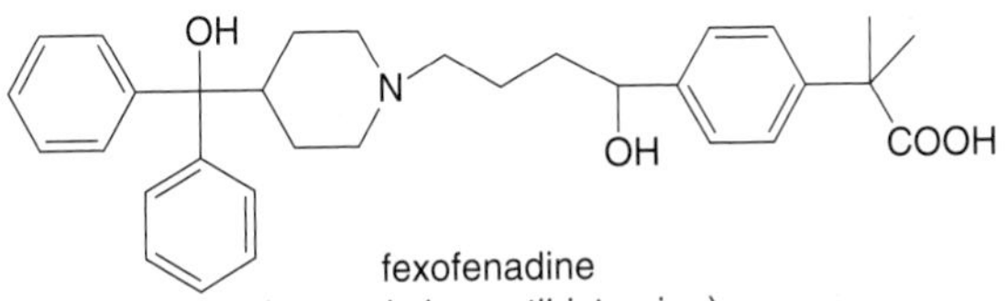

fexofenadine
(nonsedating antihistamine)

1.63 Draw in all the carbon and hydrogen atoms in each molecule.

a. 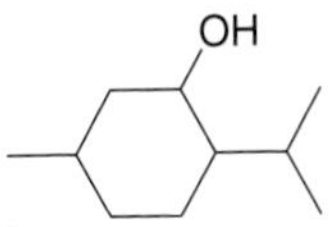

menthol
(isolated from peppermint oil)

b. 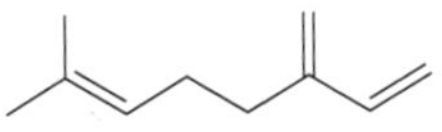

myrcene
(isolated from bayberry)

c. 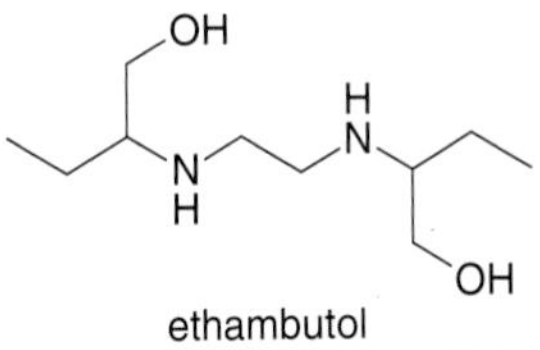

ethambutol
(drug used to treat tuberculosis)

d. 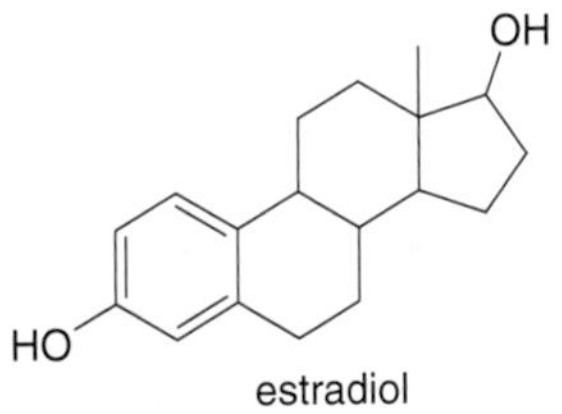

estradiol
(a female sex hormone)

1.64 Convert each molecule into a skeletal structure.

a. $(CH_3)_2CHCH_2CH_2CH(CH_3)_2$

b. $CH_3CH(Cl)CH(OH)CH_3$

c. $(CH_3)_3C(CH_2)_5CH_3$

d. 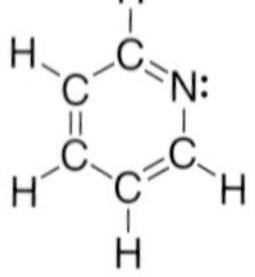

e. 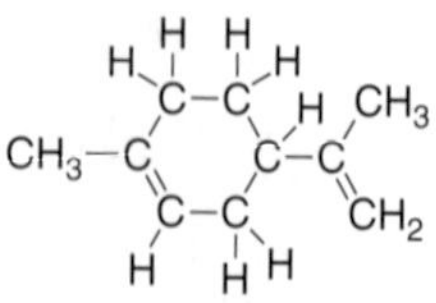

limonene
(oil of lemon)

f. $CH_3(CH_2)_2C(CH_3)_2CH(CH_3)CH(CH_3)CH(Br)CH_3$

1.65 Convert the following condensed formulas into Lewis structures.

a. CH_3CH_2COOH
b. $CH_3CONHCH_3$
c. CH_3COCH_2Br
d. $(CH_3)_3COH$
e. $(CH_3)_3CCHO$
f. CH_3COCl
g. $CH_3COCH_2CO_2H$
h. $HO_2CCH(OH)CO_2H$

1.66 Draw in all the hydrogen atoms and nonbonded electron pairs in each ion.

a. 
b. 
c. 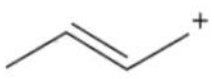
d. 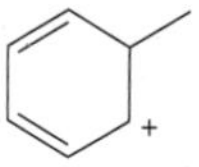

1.67 Draw in all H atoms and lone pairs in each ion.

a. 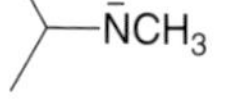
b. 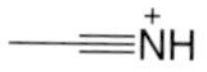
c. 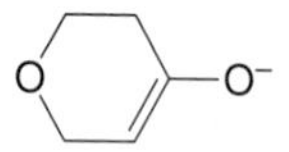
d. 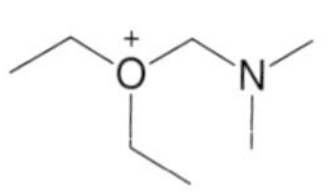

1.68 Each of the following condensed or skeletal structures is an incorrect representation of a molecule or ion. Explain what is wrong in each structure.

a. $CH_3CH{=}CH{=}CHCH_3$
b. $(CH_3)_3CHCH_2CH_2CH_3$
c. 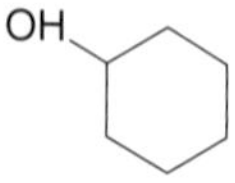
d. 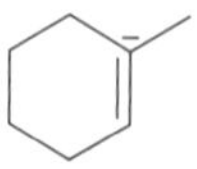
e. 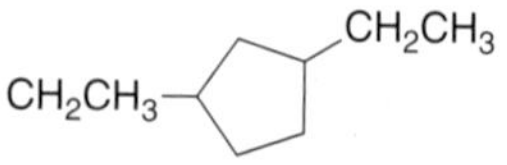

Hybridization

1.69 Predict the hybridization and geometry around each indicated atom.

a. CH_3CH_2 (arrow at second C)
b. 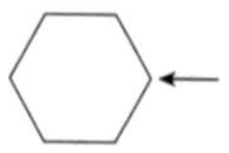
c. $(CH_3)_3O^+$ (arrow at O)
d. 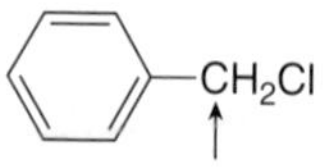
e. $CH_3{-}C{\equiv}C{-}H$ (arrow at C)
f. $CH_2{=}NOCH_3$ (arrow at N)
g. $CH_3CH{=}C{=}CH_2$ (arrows at CH and C)

1.70 What orbitals are used to form each indicated bond? For multiple bonds, indicate the orbitals used in individual bonds.

a. 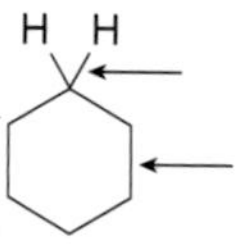
b. 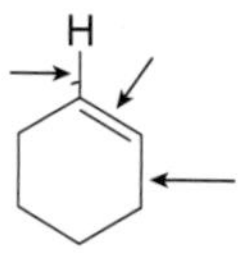
c. 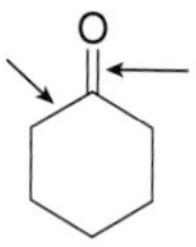
d. 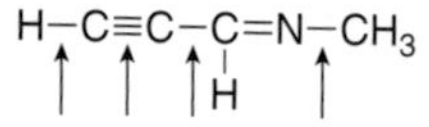

1.71 Ketene, $CH_2{=}C{=}O$, is an unusual organic molecule that has a single carbon atom doubly bonded to two different atoms. Determine the hybridization of both C atoms and the O in ketene. Then, draw a diagram showing what orbitals are used to form each bond (similar to Figures 1.11 and 1.12).

1.72 Consider the unstable cation and anion drawn below.

$CH_2{=}\overset{+}{C}H$ $\quad$ $CH_2{=}\ddot{C}H$

a. What is the hybridization of each carbon atom in these ions?
b. What orbitals are used to form both bonds in each carbon–carbon double bond?

Bond Length and Strength

1.73 Rank the following bonds in order of *increasing* bond length.

a. 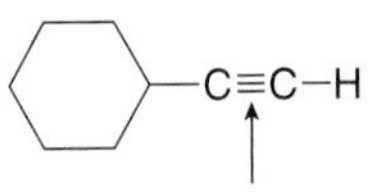 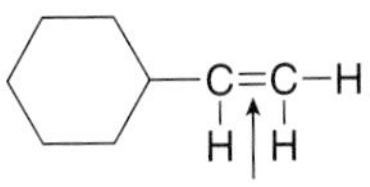 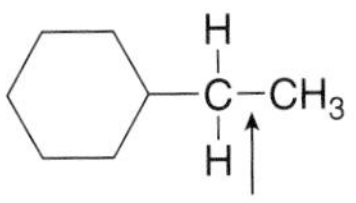

b. 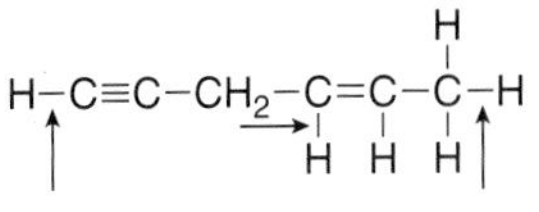

1.74 Answer the following questions about compound **A**.

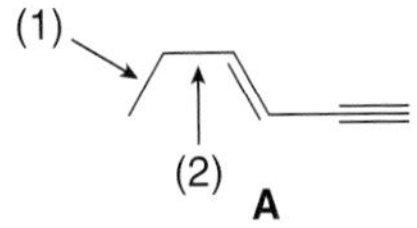

A

a. Label the shortest C–C single bond.
b. Label the longest C–C single bond.
c. Considering all the bonds, label the shortest C–C bond.
d. Label the weakest C–C bond.
e. Label the strongest C–H bond.
f. Explain why bond (1) and bond (2) are different in length, even though they are both C–C single bonds.

1.75 Two useful organic compounds that contain Cl atoms are drawn below. Vinyl chloride is the starting material used to prepare poly(vinyl chloride), a plastic used in insulation, pipes, and bottles. Chloroethane (ethyl chloride) is a local anesthetic. Why is the C–Cl bond of vinyl chloride stronger than the C–Cl bond in chloroethane?

$CH_2{=}CHCl$	CH_3CH_2Cl
vinyl chloride	chloroethane (ethyl chloride)

Bond Polarity

1.76 Use the symbols δ⁺ and δ⁻ to indicate the polarity of the labeled bonds.

a. Br–Cl   b. NH_2–OH   c. CH_3–NH_2 d. 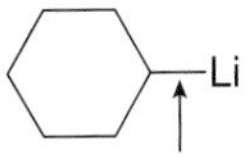

1.77 Label the polar bonds in each molecule. Indicate the direction of the net dipole (if there is one).

a. $CHBr_3$
b. $CH_3CH_2OCH_2CH_3$
c. CBr_4

d. 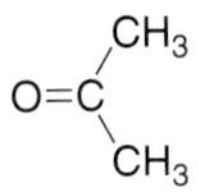

e. 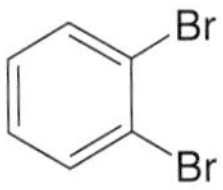

f. 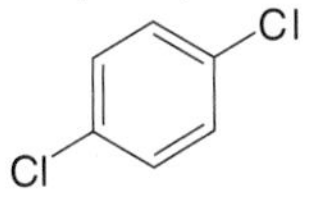

General Questions

1.78 Answer the following questions about acetonitrile ($CH_3C{\equiv}N$:).

a. Determine the hybridization of both C atoms and the N atom.
b. Label all bonds as σ or π.
c. In what type of orbital does the lone pair on N reside?
d. Label all bonds as polar or nonpolar.

1.79 Benzene is the simplest member of a whole class of compounds called aromatic hydrocarbons.

benzene

a. How is each carbon atom hybridized?
b. What is the geometry around each carbon atom? What is the overall geometry of the benzene ring?
c. Draw a diagram showing the orbitals used to join the carbon atoms of the ring.
d. Follow the indicated curved arrow notation to draw a second resonance structure.

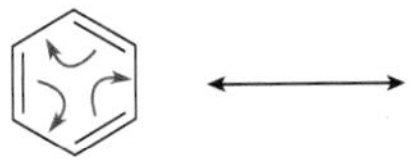

e. Benzene and other aromatic hydrocarbons are shown in Chapter 17 to be very stable. Offer an explanation.

1.80 The principles of this chapter can be applied to organic molecules of any size. Answer the following questions about amoxicillin, an antibiotic from the penicillin family.

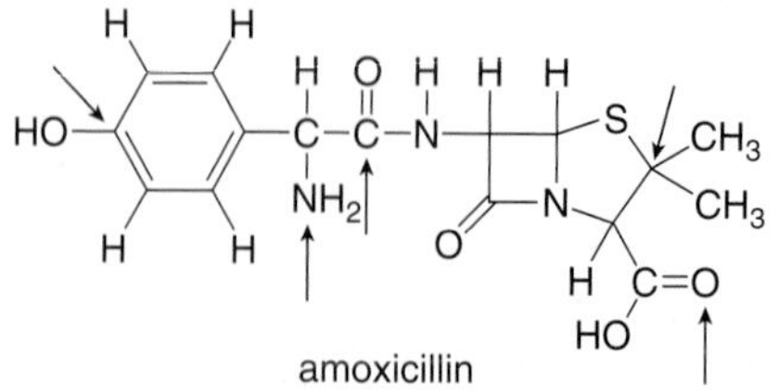

amoxicillin

a. Predict the hybridization and geometry around each indicated atom.
b. Label five polar bonds using the symbols δ^+ and δ^-.
c. Draw a skeletal structure.
d. How many π bonds does amoxicillin have? Label them.
e. Find a C–H bond containing a carbon atom having a hybrid orbital with 33% *s*-character.

1.81

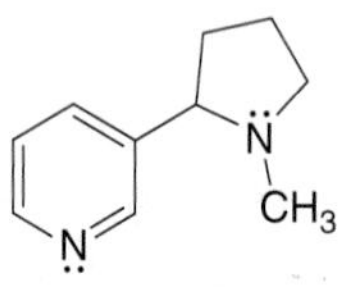

nicotine

a. What is the hybridization of each N atom in nicotine?
b. What is the geometry around each N atom?
c. In what type of orbital does the lone pair on each N atom reside?
d. Draw a constitutional isomer of nicotine.
e. Draw a resonance structure of nicotine.

1.82 Stalevo is the trade name for a medication used for Parkinson's disease, which contains L-dopa, carbidopa, and entacapone.

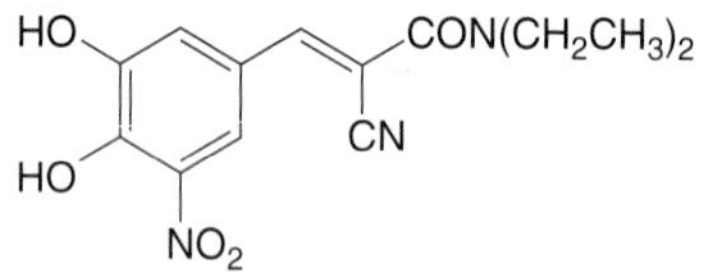

entacapone

a. Draw a Lewis structure for entacapone.
b. Which C–C bond in entacapone is the longest?
c. Which C–C single bond is the shortest?
d. Which C–N bond is the longest?
e. Which C–N bond is the shortest?
f. Use curved arrows to draw a resonance structure that is an equal contributor to the resonance hybrid.
g. Use curved arrows to draw a resonance structure that is a minor contributor to the resonance hybrid.

1.83 CH_3^+ and CH_3^- are two highly reactive carbon species.
a. What is the predicted hybridization and geometry around each carbon atom?
b. Two electrostatic potential plots are drawn for these species. Which ion corresponds to which diagram and why?

A B

Challenge Problems

1.84 The N atom in CH_3CONH_2 (acetamide) is *sp*^{2} hybridized, even though it is surrounded by four groups. Using this information, draw a diagram that shows the orbitals used by the atoms in the $-CONH_2$ portion of acetamide, and offer an explanation as to the observed hybridization.

1.85 Use the observed bond lengths to answer each question. (a) Why is bond [1] longer than bond [2]? (b) Why are bonds [3] and [4] equal in length, and shorter than bond [2]?

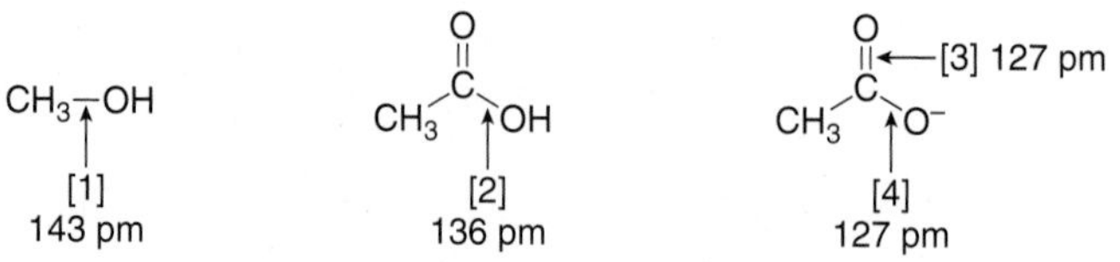
[1] 143 pm
[2] 136 pm
[3] 127 pm
[4] 127 pm

1.86 Draw at least 10 more resonance structures for acetaminophen, the active pain reliever in Tylenol.

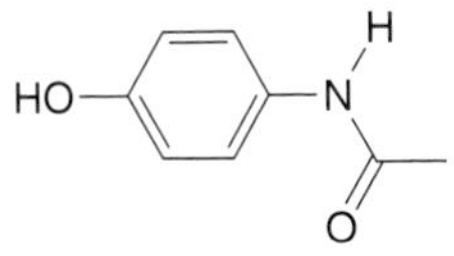

acetaminophen

1.87 When two carbons having different hybridization are bonded together, the C – C bond contains a slight dipole. In a $C_{sp^2} - C_{sp^3}$ bond, what is the direction of the dipole? Which carbon is considered more electronegative?

1.88 Draw all possible isomers having molecular formula C_4H_8 that contain one π bond.

1.89 Use the principles of resonance theory to explain why carbocation **A** is more stable than carbocation **B.**

A **B**

1.90 The curved arrow notation introduced in Section 1.6 is a powerful method used by organic chemists to show the movement of electrons not only in resonance structures, but also in chemical reactions. Since each curved arrow shows the movement of two electrons, following the curved arrows illustrates what bonds are broken and formed in a reaction. Consider the following three-step process. (a) Add curved arrows in Step [1] to show the movement of electrons. (b) Use the curved arrows drawn in Step [2] to identify the structure of **X. X** is converted in Step [3] to phenol and HCl.

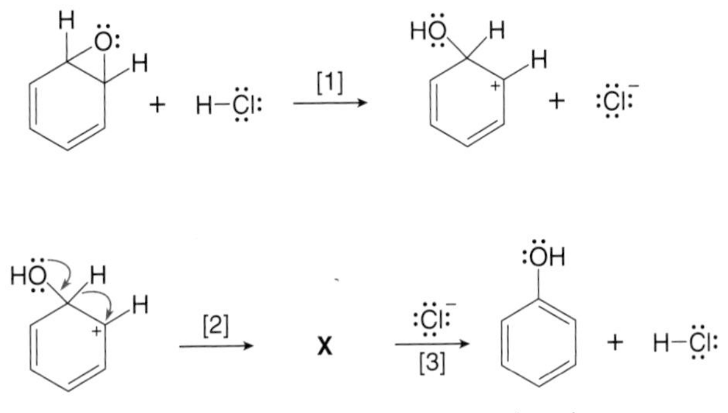

2 Acids and Bases

2.1 Brønsted–Lowry acids and bases
2.2 Reactions of Brønsted–Lowry acids and bases
2.3 Acid strength and pK_a
2.4 Predicting the outcome of acid–base reactions
2.5 Factors that determine acid strength
2.6 Common acids and bases
2.7 Aspirin
2.8 Lewis acids and bases

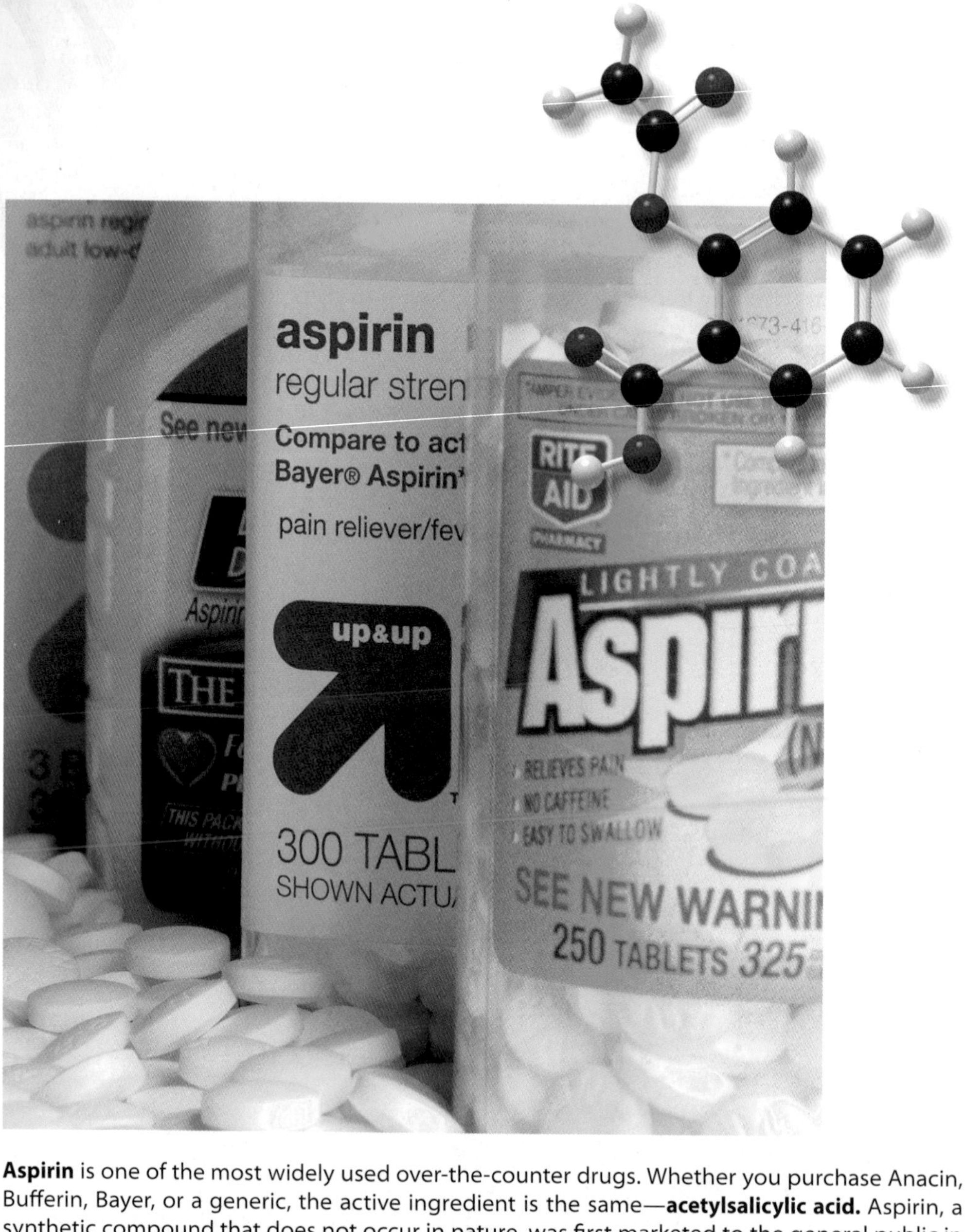

Aspirin is one of the most widely used over-the-counter drugs. Whether you purchase Anacin, Bufferin, Bayer, or a generic, the active ingredient is the same—**acetylsalicylic acid.** Aspirin, a synthetic compound that does not occur in nature, was first marketed to the general public in 1899, and is now used regularly by over 100 million people throughout the world. Like many drugs, aspirin undergoes a proton transfer reaction after ingestion. In Chapter 2, we learn about acidity and the role of acid–base reactions in aspirin's chemistry.

Chemical terms such as *anion* and *cation* may be unfamiliar to most nonscientists, but *acid* has found a place in everyday language. Commercials advertise the latest remedy for the heartburn caused by excess stomach *acid.* The nightly news may report the latest environmental impact of *acid* rain. Wine lovers know that wine sours because its alcohol has turned to *acid. Acid* comes from the Latin word *acidus,* meaning sour, because when tasting compounds was a routine method of identification, these compounds were sour.

In Chapter 2, we will concentrate on two definitions of acids and bases: the **Brønsted–Lowry** definition, which describes acids as ***proton donors*** and bases as ***proton acceptors,*** and the **Lewis** definition, which describes acids as ***electron pair acceptors*** and bases as ***electron pair donors.***

2.1 Brønsted–Lowry Acids and Bases

The general words "acid" and "base" usually mean a *Brønsted–Lowry* acid and *Brønsted–Lowry* base.

H^+ = proton

H–A = general Brønsted–Lowry acid. **B:** = general Brønsted–Lowry base.

The Brønsted–Lowry definition describes acidity in terms of protons: positively charged **hydrogen ions, H^+.**

- A Brønsted–Lowry acid is a *proton donor.*
- A Brønsted–Lowry base is a *proton acceptor.*

A Brønsted–Lowry acid must contain a *hydrogen* atom. This definition of an acid is often familiar to students, because many inorganic acids in general chemistry are Brønsted–Lowry acids. The symbol **H–A** is used for a general Brønsted–Lowry acid.

A Brønsted–Lowry base must be able to form a bond to a proton. Because a proton has no electrons, **a base must contain an "available" electron pair** that can be easily donated to form a new bond. These include **lone pairs** or electron pairs in **π bonds.** The symbol **B:** is used for a general Brønsted–Lowry base.

Examples of Brønsted–Lowry acids and bases are given in Figure 2.1.

Charged species such as ^-OH and $^-NH_2$ are used as **salts,** with cations such as Li^+, Na^+, or K^+ to balance the negative charge. These cations are called **counterions** or **spectator ions,** and their **identity is usually inconsequential.** For this reason, the counterion is often omitted.

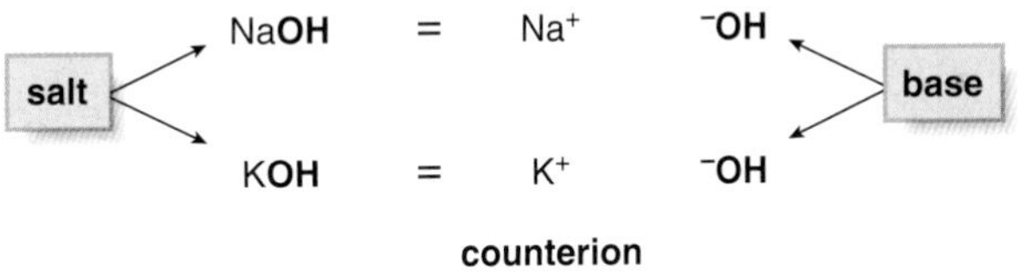
salt
NaOH = Na+ -OH
KOH = K+ -OH
base
counterion

Compounds like H_2O and CH_3OH that contain both hydrogen atoms and lone pairs may be either an acid or a base, depending on the particular reaction. These fundamental principles are true no matter how complex the compound. For example, the addictive pain reliever **morphine** is a

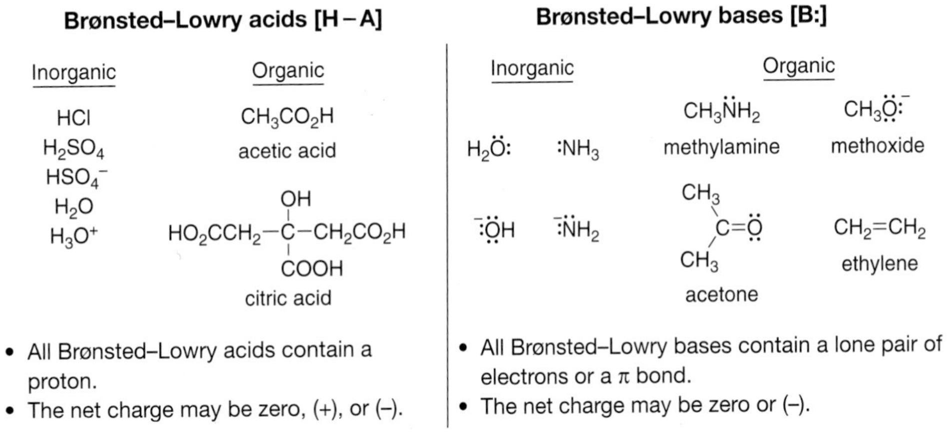
Brønsted–Lowry acids [H–A]
Inorganic
HCl
H2SO4
HSO4−
H2O
H3O+
Organic
CH3CO2H
acetic acid
OH
HO2CCH2–C–CH2CO2H
COOH
citric acid
All Brønsted–Lowry acids contain a proton.
The net charge may be zero, (+), or (–).
Brønsted–Lowry bases [B:]
Inorganic
H2O:
:NH3
−:OH
−:NH2
Organic
CH3NH2
methylamine
CH3O:−
methoxide
CH3
C=O
CH3
acetone
CH2=CH2
ethylene
All Brønsted–Lowry bases contain a lone pair of electrons or a π bond.
The net charge may be zero or (–).

Figure 2.1 Examples of Brønsted–Lowry acids and bases

Morphine is obtained from the opium poppy.

Brønsted–Lowry acid because it contains many hydrogen atoms. It is also a Brønsted–Lowry base because it has lone pairs on O and N, and four π bonds.

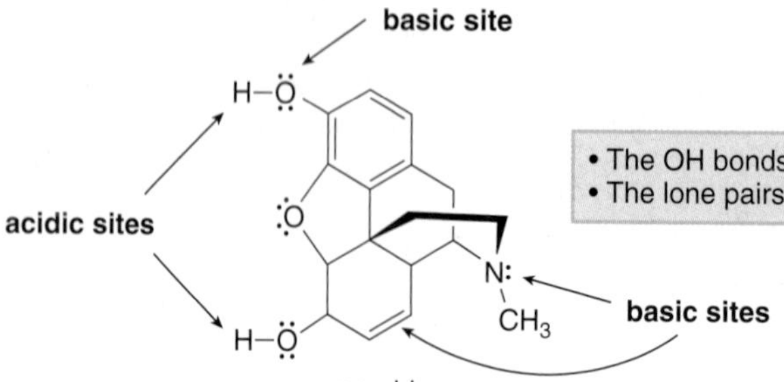
basic site
acidic sites
basic sites
H–O
O
N:
CH3
H–O

morphine

- The OH bonds make morphine an acid.
- The lone pairs and π bonds make morphine a base.

Problem 2.1 a. Which compounds are Brønsted–Lowry acids: HBr, NH_3, CCl_4?

b. Which compounds are Brønsted–Lowry bases: CH_3CH_3, $(CH_3)_3CO^-$, HC≡CH?

c. Classify each compound as an acid, a base, or both: CH_3CH_2OH, $CH_3CH_2CH_2CH_3$, $CH_3CO_2CH_3$.

2.2 Reactions of Brønsted–Lowry Acids and Bases

A Brønsted–Lowry acid–base reaction results in transfer of a proton from an acid to a base. These acid–base reactions, also called ***proton transfer reactions,*** are fundamental to the study of organic chemistry.

Consider, for example, the reaction of the acid H–A with the base :B. **In an acid–base reaction, one bond is broken and one is formed.**

- **The electron pair of the base B: forms a new bond to the proton of the acid.**
- **The acid H–A loses a proton, leaving the electron pair in the H–A bond on A.**

Recall from Section 1.6 that a curved arrow shows the movement of an **electron pair.** The tail of the arrow always begins at an electron pair and the head points to where that electron pair "moves."

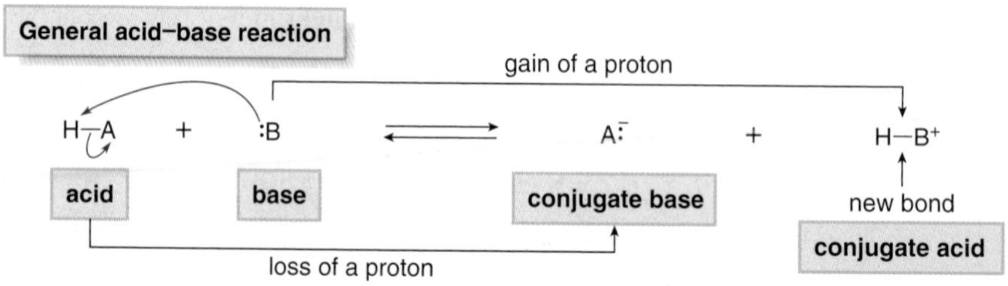
General acid–base reaction
gain of a proton
H–A
+
:B
A:⁻
+
H–B+
acid
base
conjugate base
new bond
conjugate acid
loss of a proton

This "movement" of electrons in reactions can be illustrated using curved arrow notation. Because **two electron pairs** are involved in this reaction, **two curved arrows** are needed. Two products are formed.

- Loss of a proton from an acid forms its *conjugate base.*
- Gain of a proton by a base forms its *conjugate acid.*

Keep in mind two other facts about this general reaction:

- The **net charge must be the same** on both sides of any equation. In this example, the net charge on each side is zero. Individual charges can be calculated using formal charges.
- **A double reaction arrow** is used between starting materials and products to indicate that the reaction can proceed in the forward and reverse directions. These are **equilibrium arrows.**

Two examples of proton transfer reactions are drawn here with curved arrow notation.

A double reaction arrow indicates equilibrium.

equilibrium arrows

Remove H⁺ from an acid to form its conjugate base. Add H⁺ to a base to form its conjugate acid.

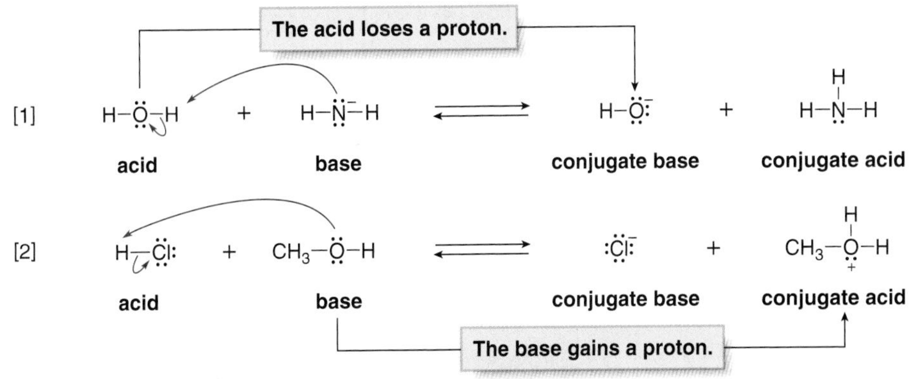

- **Brønsted–Lowry acid–base reactions always result in the transfer of a proton from an acid to a base.**

The ability to identify and draw a conjugate acid or base from a given starting material is illustrated in Sample Problems 2.1 and 2.2.

Sample Problem 2.1

a. What is the conjugate acid of CH_3O^-?
b. What is the conjugate base of NH_3?

Solution

a. **Add H⁺ to CH_3O^- to form its conjugate acid.**

Add a proton to a lone pair.

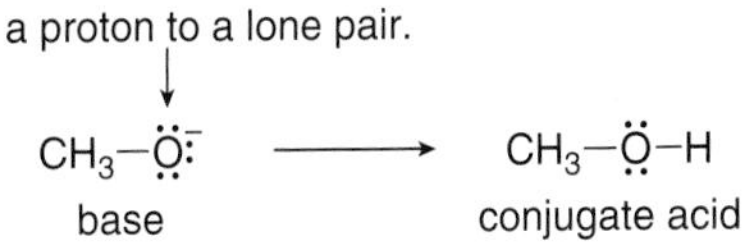

b. **Remove H⁺ from NH_3 to form its conjugate base.**

Leave the electron pair on N.

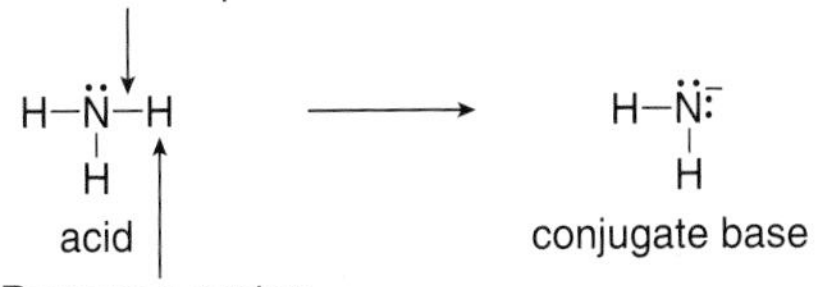

Problem 2.2

a. Draw the conjugate acid of each base: NH_3, Cl^-, $(CH_3)_2C{=}O$.
b. Draw the conjugate base of each acid: HBr, HSO_4^-, CH_3OH.

Sample Problem 2.2

Label the acid and base, and the conjugate acid and base in the following reaction. Use curved arrow notation to show the movement of electron pairs.

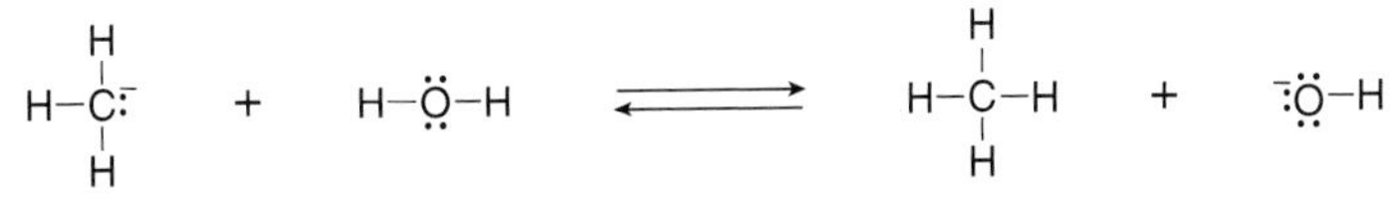

Solution

CH_3^- is the base because it accepts a proton, forming its conjugate acid, CH_4. H_2O is the acid because it donates a proton, forming its conjugate base, ^-OH. Two curved arrows are needed. One shows that the lone pair on CH_3^- bonds to a proton of H_2O, and the second shows that the electron pair in the O–H bond remains on O.

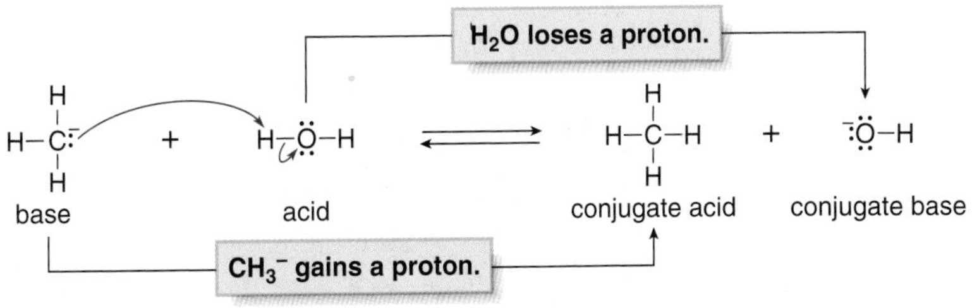

Problem 2.3 Label the acid and base, and the conjugate acid and base in the following reactions. Use curved arrows to show the movement of electron pairs.

a. $HCl + H_2O \rightleftharpoons Cl^- + H_3O^+$

b. 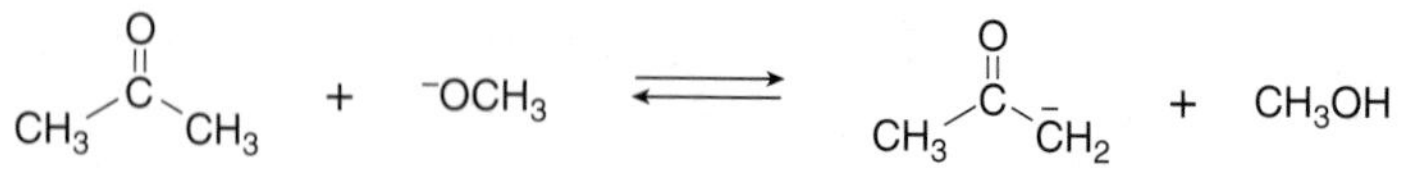
O
CH3 C CH3
+ ⁻OCH3
O
CH3 C CH2
+ CH3OH

In all proton transfer reactions, the **electron-rich base** donates an electron pair to the acid, which usually has a polar H–A bond. Thus, the H of the acid bears a partial positive charge, making it **electron deficient.** This is the first example of a general pattern of reactivity.

- **Electron-rich species react with electron-deficient ones.**

Given two starting materials, how do you know which is the acid and which is the base in a proton transfer reaction? The following generalizations will help to decide this in many reactions:

[1] Common acids and bases introduced in general chemistry will often be used in the same way in organic reactions. HCl and H_2SO_4 are strong acids, and ^-OH is a strong base.

[2] When only one starting material contains a hydrogen, it must be the acid. If only one starting material has a lone pair or a π bond, it must be the base.

[3] A starting material with a net positive charge is usually the acid. A starting material with a negative charge is usually the base.

Problem 2.4 Draw the products of each proton transfer reaction.

a. $CCl_3CO_2H + {}^-OCH_3 \rightleftharpoons$

b. $H-C\equiv C-H + H:^- \rightleftharpoons$

c. $CH_3NH_2 + HCl \rightleftharpoons$

d. $CH_3CH_2OH + H_2SO_4 \rightleftharpoons$

Problem 2.5 Draw the products formed from the acid–base reaction of HCl with each compound.

a. CH_3OH b. $(CH_3CH_2)_2O$ c. $(CH_3)_3N$ d. 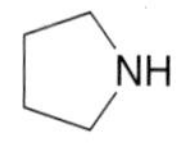
NH

2.3 Acid Strength and pK_a

Acid strength is the tendency of an acid to donate a proton.

- **The more readily a compound donates a proton, the stronger the acid.**

Acidity is measured by an equilibrium constant. When a Brønsted–Lowry acid H–A is dissolved in water, an acid–base reaction occurs, and an equilibrium constant K_{eq} can be written for the reaction.

Dissolving an acid in water

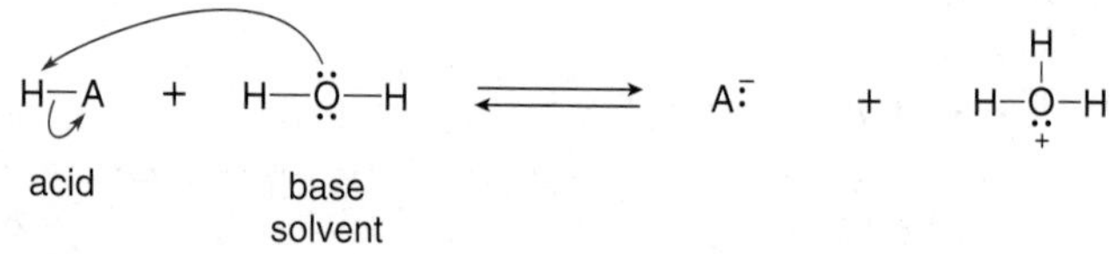
H–A
+
H–Ö–H
A:⁻
+
H
H–Ö–H
+
acid
base
solvent

Equilibrium constant

$$K_{eq} = \frac{[\text{products}]}{[\text{starting materials}]} = \frac{[H_3O^+][A:^-]}{[H{-}A][H_2O]}$$

Because the concentration of the solvent H_2O is essentially constant, the equation can be rearranged and a new equilibrium constant, called the **acidity constant, K_a,** can be defined.

$$\textbf{Acidity constant} = K_a = [H_2O]K_{eq} = \frac{[H_3O^+][A:^-]}{[H{-}A]}$$

How is the magnitude of K_a related to acid strength?

- The *stronger the acid,* the further the equilibrium lies to the right, and the *larger the* K_a.

For most organic compounds, K_a is small, typically 10^{-5} to 10^{-50}. This contrasts with the K_a values for many inorganic acids, which range from 10^{0} to 10^{10}. Because dealing with exponents can be cumbersome, it is often more convenient to use pK_a values instead of K_a values.

Definition: pK_a = −log K_a

How does pK_a relate to acid strength?

K_a		pK_a = −log K_a	
K_a values of typical organic acids		**pK_a values of typical organic acids**	
10^{-5}	**to 10^{-50}**	**+5**	**to +50**
larger number stronger acid	smaller number weaker acid	smaller number stronger acid	larger number weaker acid

Recall that a **log** is an **exponent;** for example, log 10^{-5} = −5.

- The *smaller* the pK_a, the *stronger* the acid.

Problem 2.6 Which compound in each pair is the stronger acid?

a. $CH_3CH_2CH_3$ (pK_a = 50) or CH_3CH_2OH (pK_a = 16)

b. 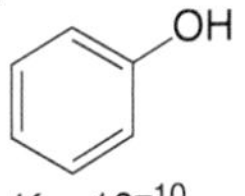

$K_a = 10^{-10}$ or 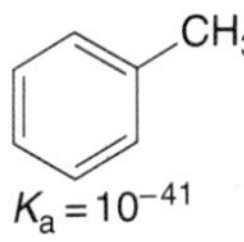

$K_a = 10^{-41}$

Problem 2.7 Use a calculator when necessary to answer the following questions.

a. What is the pK_a for each K_a: 10^{-10}, 10^{-21}, and 5.2×10^{-5}?

b. What is the K_a for each pK_a: 7, 11, and 3.2?

Understanding acid strength is the first step to understanding base strength (and vice versa), because **an inverse relationship exists between acidity and basicity.**

- A *strong acid* readily donates a proton, forming a *weak conjugate base.*
- A *strong base* readily accepts a proton, forming a *weak conjugate acid.*

Table 2.1 is a brief list of pK_a values for some common compounds, ranked in order of ***increasing*** **p*K*$_a$** and therefore ***decreasing*** **acidity.** Because strong acids form weak conjugate bases, this list

Table 2.1 Selected pK_a Values

	Acid	pK_a	Conjugate base	
Increasing acidity (↑)	H−Cl	−7	Cl^-	Increasing basicity (↓)
	$CH_3COO{-}H$	4.8	CH_3COO^-	
	HO−H	15.7	HO^-	
	$CH_3CH_2O{-}H$	16	$CH_3CH_2O^-$	
	HC≡CH	25	$HC{\equiv}C^-$	
	H−H	35	H^-	
	$H_2N{-}H$	38	H_2N^-	
	$CH_2{=}CH_2$	44	$CH_2{=}\bar{C}H$	
	$CH_3{-}H$	50	CH_3^-	

also ranks their conjugate bases, in order of ***increasing* basicity.** For example, CH_4 is the weakest acid in the list, because it has the highest pK_a (50). Its conjugate base, CH_3^-, is therefore the strongest conjugate base. An extensive pK_a table is located in Appendix A.

Comparing pK_a values thus provides two useful bits of information: the **relative acidity of two acids,** and the **relative basicity of their conjugate bases,** as shown in Sample Problem 2.3.

Sample Problem 2.3

Rank the following compounds in order of increasing acidity, and then rank their conjugate bases in order of increasing basicity.

$CH_2{=}CH_2$ HCl CH_3COOH

Solution

The pK_a values in Table 2.1 allow us to rank these compounds in order of increasing acidity: **the lower the pK_a,** the stronger the acid.

$CH_2{=}CH_2$	CH_3COOH	HCl
pK_a = 44	pK_a = 4.8	pK_a = –7

Increasing acidity →

Because strong acids form weak conjugate bases, the **basicity of conjugate bases increases with increasing pK_a** of their acids.

$CH_2{=}\bar{C}H$	CH_3COO^-	Cl^-

← **Increasing basicity**

Problem 2.8 Rank the conjugate bases of each group of acids in order of increasing basicity.

a. NH_3, H_2O, CH_4 b. $CH_2{=}CH_2$, $HC{\equiv}CH$, CH_4

Problem 2.9 Consider two acids: HCO_2H (formic acid, pK_a = 3.8) and pivalic acid [$(CH_3)_3CCO_2H$, pK_a = 5.0]. (a) Which acid has the larger K_a? (b) Which acid is the stronger acid? (c) Which acid forms the stronger conjugate base? (d) When each acid is dissolved in water, for which acid does the equilibrium lie further to the right?

The pK_a values in Table 2.1 span a large range (–7 to 50). The **pK_a scale is logarithmic,** so a small difference in pK_a translates into a large numerical difference. For example, the difference between the pK_a of NH_3 (38) and $CH_2{=}CH_2$ (44) is six pK_a units. This means that NH_3 is 10^6 or **one million times more acidic** than $CH_2{=}CH_2$.

Although Table 2.1 is abbreviated, it gives pK_a values of many common compounds seen in organic chemistry. It is also a useful tool for *estimating* the pK_a of a compound similar though not identical to one in the table.

Suppose you are asked to estimate the pK_a of the N–H bond of CH_3NH_2. Although CH_3NH_2 is not listed in the table, we have enough information to *approximate* its pK_a. Because the pK_a of the N–H bond of NH_3 is 38, we can estimate the pK_a of the N–H bond of CH_3NH_2 to be 38. Its actual pK_a is 40, so this is a good first approximation.

Problem 2.10 Estimate the pK_a of each of the indicated bonds.

a. 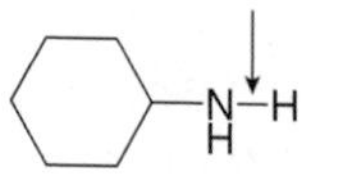

b. 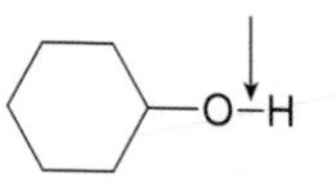

c. $BrCH_2COO{-}H$ (indicated bond: O–H)

2.4 Predicting the Outcome of Acid–Base Reactions

In a proton transfer reaction, the **stronger acid reacts with the stronger base** to form the weaker acid and the weaker base.

A proton transfer reaction represents an equilibrium. Because an acid donates a proton to a base, thus forming a conjugate acid and conjugate base, there are always two acids and two bases in the reaction mixture. Which pair of acids and bases is favored at equilibrium? **The position of the equilibrium depends on the relative strengths of the acids and bases.**

- **Equilibrium always favors formation of the weaker acid and base.**

Because a strong acid readily donates a proton and a strong base readily accepts one, these two species react to form a weaker conjugate acid and base that do not donate or accept a proton as readily. Comparing pK_a values allows us to determine the position of equilibrium, as illustrated in Sample Problem 2.4.

Sample Problem 2.4

Determine the direction of equilibrium when acetylene (HC≡CH) reacts with $^-NH_2$ in a proton transfer reaction.

Solution

Follow three steps to determine the position of equilibrium:

Step [1] Identify the acid and base in the starting materials.

- Assume $^-NH_2$ is the base because it bears a net negative charge. That makes HC≡CH the acid.

Step [2] Draw the products of proton transfer and identify the conjugate acid and base in the products.

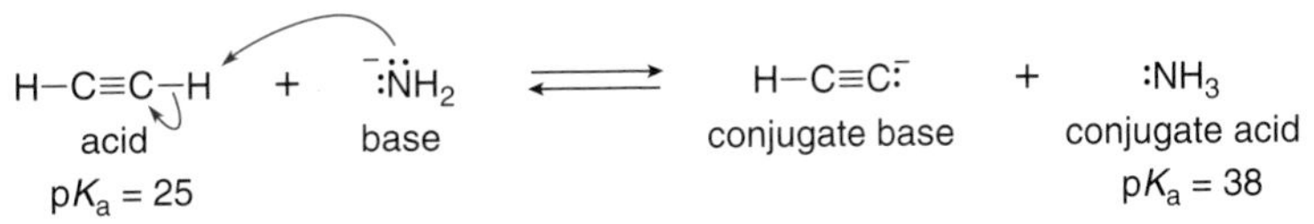

H–C≡C–H + $^-$:NH$_2$ ⇌ H–C≡C:$^-$ + :NH$_3$
acid
base
conjugate base
conjugate acid
pK$_a$ = 25
pK$_a$ = 38

Step [3] Compare the pK_a values of the acid and the conjugate acid. Equilibrium favors formation of the weaker acid with the higher pK_a.

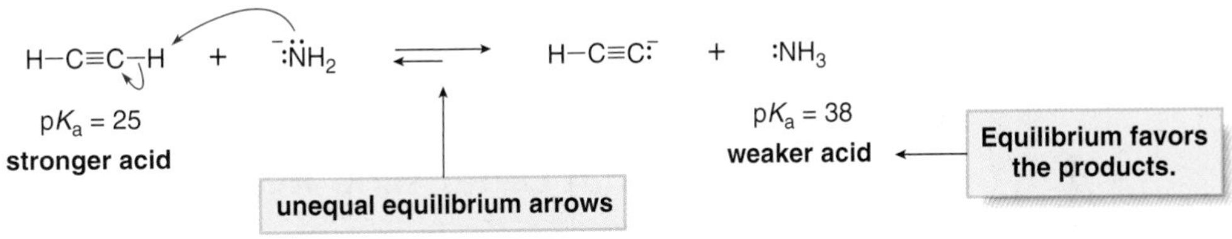

H–C≡C–H + $^-$:NH$_2$ ⇌ H–C≡C:$^-$ + :NH$_3$
pK$_a$ = 25
stronger acid
pK$_a$ = 38
weaker acid
Equilibrium favors the products.
unequal equilibrium arrows

- Because the pK_a of the starting acid (25) is ***lower*** than the pK_a of the conjugate acid (38), HC≡CH is a ***stronger*** acid and equilibrium favors the products.

Problem 2.11

Draw the products of each reaction and determine the direction of equilibrium.

a. $CH_2{=}CH_2$ + H^- ⇌

b. CH_4 + ^-OH ⇌

c. CH_3COOH + $CH_3CH_2O^-$ ⇌

d. Cl^- + CH_3CH_2OH ⇌

How can we know if a particular base is strong enough to deprotonate a given acid, so that the equilibrium lies to the right? The pK_a table readily gives us this information.

Compare any two entries in Table 2.1, such as ethanol (CH_3CH_2OH; pK_a = 16) and acetylene (HC≡CH; pK_a = 25), and their conjugate bases, ethoxide ($CH_3CH_2O^-$) and acetylide ($HC{\equiv}C^-$). Ethanol is a stronger acid than acetylene, so acetylide is a stronger base than ethoxide.

Because Table 2.1 is arranged from low to high pK_a, **an acid can be deprotonated by the conjugate base of any acid below it in the table.**

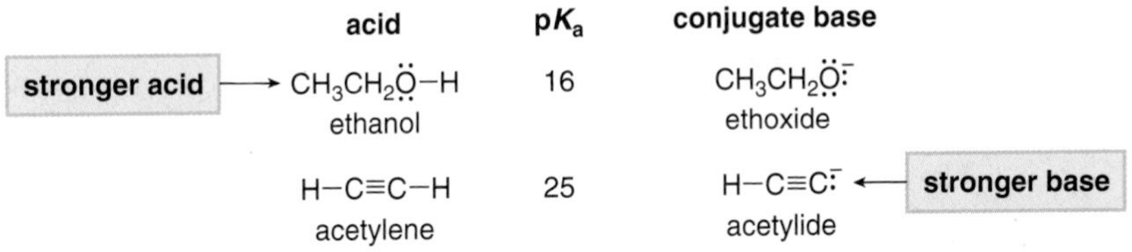

acid
pK$_a$
conjugate base
stronger acid
CH$_3$CH$_2$Ö–H
ethanol
16
CH$_3$CH$_2$Ö:$^-$
ethoxide
H–C≡C–H
acetylene
25
H–C≡C:$^-$
acetylide
stronger base

Two proton transfer reactions are possible.

[1] Reaction of acetylene with ethoxide forms acetylide and ethanol. Because the stronger acid is the product of the reaction, ***equilibrium favors the starting materials.*** **The base ethoxide is *not* strong enough to deprotonate acetylene.**

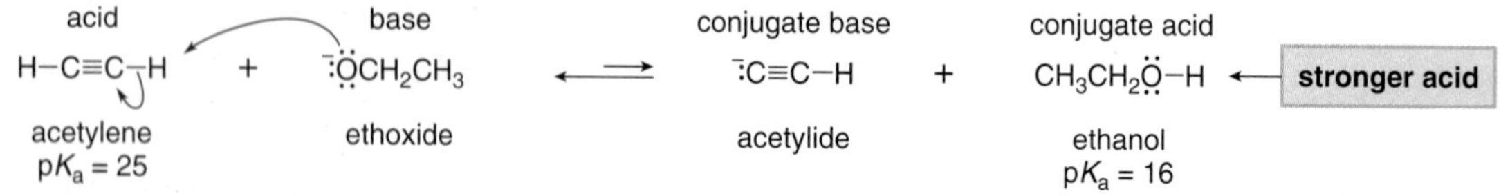
acid
base
conjugate base
conjugate acid
H−C≡C−H
+
:ÖCH₂CH₃
:C≡C−H
+
CH₃CH₂Ö−H
stronger acid
acetylene
pKa = 25
ethoxide
acetylide
ethanol
pKa = 16

Equilibrium favors the starting materials.

[2] Reaction of ethanol with acetylide forms ethoxide and acetylene. Because the weaker acid is the product of the reaction, ***equilibrium favors the products.*** Thus, **the base acetylide *is* strong enough to deprotonate ethanol.**

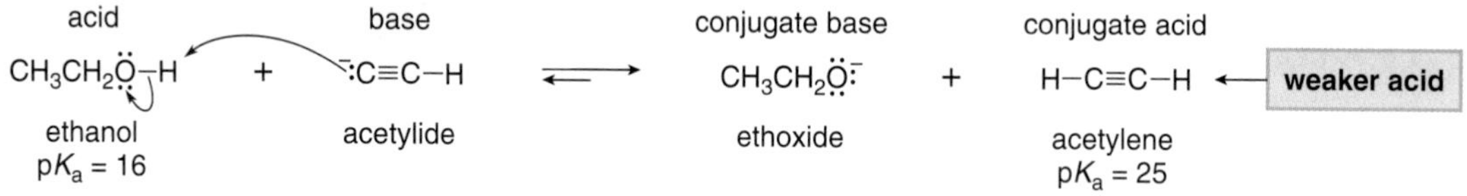
acid
base
conjugate base
conjugate acid
CH₃CH₂Ö−H
+
:C≡C−H
CH₃CH₂Ö:
+
H−C≡C−H
weaker acid
ethanol
pKa = 16
acetylide
ethoxide
acetylene
pKa = 25

Equilibrium favors the products.

In the second reaction, **ethanol is deprotonated by acetylide, the conjugate base of an acid *weaker* than itself.** This is a specific example of a general fact.

- **An acid can be deprotonated by the conjugate base of any acid having a *higher* pK_a.**

Problem 2.12 Using the data in Appendix A, determine which of the following bases is strong enough to deprotonate acetonitrile (CH_3CN) so that equilibrium favors the products: (a) NaH; (b) Na_2CO_3; (c) NaOH; (d) $NaNH_2$; (e) $NaHCO_3$.

2.5 Factors That Determine Acid Strength

We have already learned in Section 2.3 that a tremendous difference in acidity exists among compounds. HCl ($pK_a < 0$) is an extremely strong acid. Water ($pK_a = 15.7$) is moderate in acidity, and CH_4 ($pK_a = 50$) is an extremely weak acid. How are these differences explained? There is one general rule.

- **Anything that stabilizes a conjugate base A:$^-$ makes the starting acid H−A more acidic.**

For now we will concentrate on how structural differences between molecules can profoundly affect acidity. In Chapter 6, we will learn how to relate the stability of a species to its relative potential energy.

Four factors affect the acidity of H−A:

[1] Element effects

[2] Inductive effects

[3] Resonance effects

[4] Hybridization effects

No matter which factor is discussed, the same procedure is always followed. To compare the acidity of any two acids:

- **Always draw the conjugate bases.**
- **Determine which conjugate base is more stable.**
- **The *more stable* the conjugate base, the *more acidic* the acid.**

2.5A Element Effects—Trends in the Periodic Table

The most important factor determining the acidity of H–A is the location of A in the periodic table.

Comparing Elements in the Same Row of the Periodic Table

Examine acidity trends **across a row** of the periodic table by comparing CH_4 and H_2O, two compounds having H atoms bonded to a second-row element. We know from Table 2.1 that **H_2O has a much *lower* pK_a and therefore is much *more acidic* than CH_4,** but why is this the case?

To answer this question, first draw both conjugate bases and then determine which is more stable. Each conjugate base has a net negative charge, but the negative charge in ^-OH is on oxygen and in CH_3^- it is on carbon.

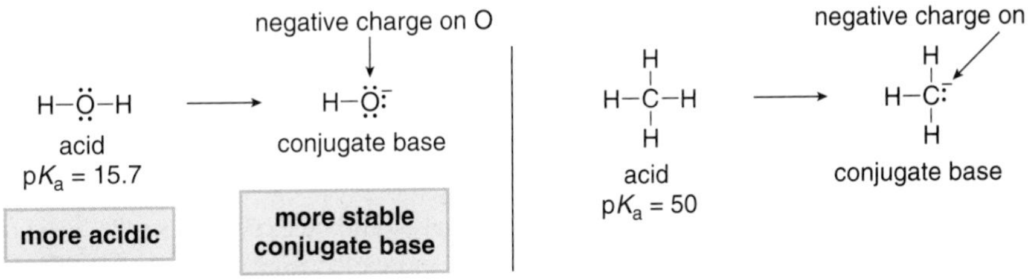

Because the oxygen atom is much **more electronegative** than carbon, oxygen more readily accepts a negative charge, making ^-OH much more stable than CH_3^-. **H_2O is a stronger acid than CH_4 because ^-OH is a more stable conjugate base than CH_3^-.** This is a specific example of a general trend.

- **Across a row of the periodic table, the acidity of H–A increases as the electronegativity of A increases.**

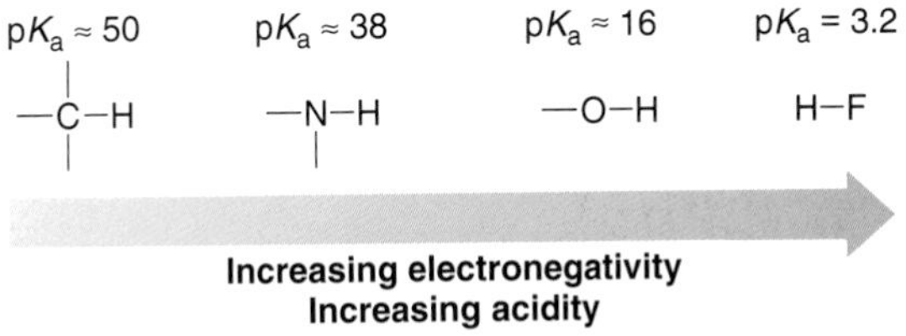

The enormity of this effect is evident by noting the approximate pK_a values for these bonds. **A C–H bond is approximately 10^{47} times *less acidic* than H–F.**

Comparing Elements Down a Column of the Periodic Table

Now examine acidity trends down a column of the periodic table by comparing H–F and H–Br. Once again, first draw both conjugate bases and then determine which is more stable. In this case, removal of a proton forms F^- and Br^-.

There are two important differences between F^- and Br^-—electronegativity and size. In this case, **size is more important than electronegativity.** The size of an atom or ion increases down a column of the periodic table, so Br^- is much larger than F^-, and this stabilizes the negative charge.

- **Positive or negative charge is stabilized when it is spread over a larger volume.**

Because Br^- is larger than F^-, Br^- is more stable than F^-, and H – Br is a stronger acid than H – F.

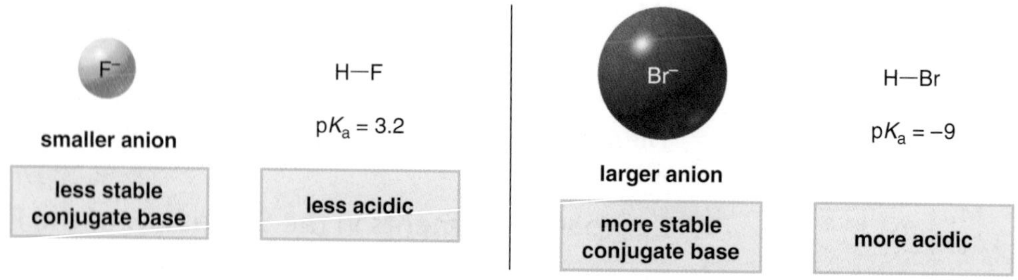

This again is a specific example of a general trend.

- **Down a column of the periodic table, the acidity of H – A increases as the size of A increases.**

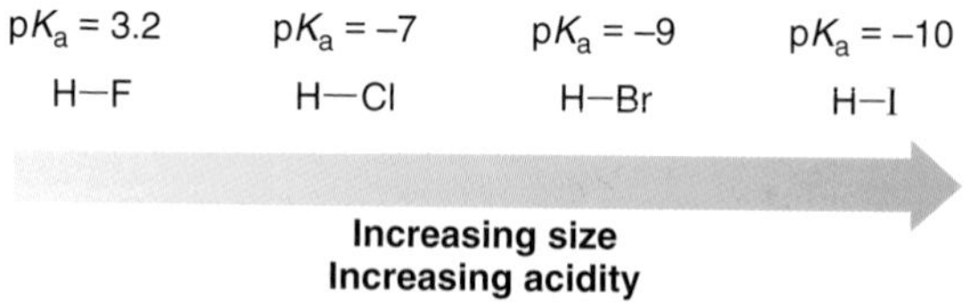

Because of carbon's position in the periodic table (in the second row and to the left of O, N, and the halogens), **C – H bonds are usually the *least acidic* bonds in a molecule.**

This is ***opposite*** to what would be expected on the basis of electronegativity differences between F and Br, because F is more electronegative than Br. **Size and *not* electronegativity determines acidity down a column.** Combining both trends together:

- **The acidity of H – A increases both left-to-right across a row and down a column of the periodic table.**

Sample Problem 2.5 Without reference to a pK_a table, decide which compound in each pair is the stronger acid:

a. H_2O or HF b. H_2S or H_2O

Solution

a. H_2O and H – F both have H atoms bonded to a second-row element. Because the acidity of H – A increases across a row of the periodic table, the H – F bond is more acidic than the H – O bond. **HF is a stronger acid than H_2O.**

b. H_2O and H_2S both have H atoms bonded to elements in the same column. Because the acidity of H – A increases down a column of the periodic table, the H – S bond is more acidic than the H – O bond. **H_2S is a stronger acid than H_2O.**

Problem 2.13 Without reference to a pK_a table, decide which compound in each pair is the stronger acid.

a. NH_3 or H_2O b. H_2S or HBr

Problem 2.14 Which compound in each pair of isomers is the stronger acid?

a. $CH_3CH_2CH_2NH_2$ or $(CH_3)_3N$ b. $CH_3CH_2OCH_3$ or $CH_3CH_2CH_2OH$

When discussing acidity, the most acidic proton in a compound is the one removed first by a base. Although four factors determine the overall acidity of a particular hydrogen atom, **element effects—the identity of A—is the single most important factor in determining the acidity of the H – A bond.**

To decide which hydrogen is most acidic, **first determine what element each hydrogen is bonded to and then decide its acidity based on periodic trends.** For example, $CH_3NHCH_2CH_2CH_2CH_3$ contains only C–H and N–H bonds. Since the acidity of H–A increases across a row of the periodic table, the single H on N is the most acidic H in this compound.

$CH_3-N(H)-CH_2CH_2CH_2CH_3$

most acidic hydrogen → H

Problem 2.15 Which hydrogen in each molecule is most acidic?

a. $CH_3CH_2CH_2CH_2OH$ b. $HOCH_2CH_2CH_2NH_2$ c. $(CH_3)_2NCH_2CH_2CH_2NH_2$

Problem 2.16 Which hydrogen in pseudoephedrine, the nasal decongestant in the commercial medication Sudafed, is most acidic?

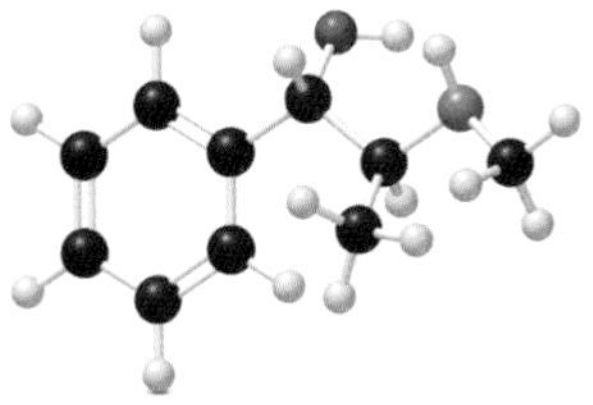

pseudoephedrine

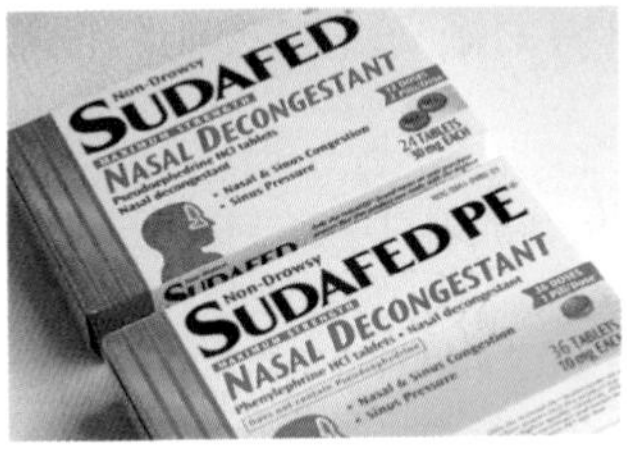

Because the pseudoephedrine (Problem 2.16) in Sudafed can be readily converted to the illegal, addictive drug methamphetamine, products that contain pseudoephedrine are now stocked behind the pharmacy counter so their sale can be more closely monitored. Sudafed PE is a related product that contains a decongestant less easily converted to methamphetamine.

2.5B Inductive Effects

A second factor affecting the acidity of H–A is the presence of electronegative atoms. To illustrate this phenomenon, compare ethanol (CH_3CH_2OH) and 2,2,2-trifluoroethanol (CF_3CH_2OH), two different compounds containing O–H bonds. The pK_a table in Appendix A indicates that CF_3CH_2OH is a stronger acid than CH_3CH_2OH. Because we are comparing the acidity of the O–H bond in both compounds, what causes the difference?

CH_3CH_2O-H	CF_3CH_2O-H
ethanol	2,2,2-trifluoroethanol
pK_a = 16	pK_a = 12.4 ← **stronger acid**

Once again first draw both conjugate bases and then determine which is more stable. Both bases have a negative charge on an electronegative oxygen, but the second anion has three additional electronegative fluorine atoms. These fluorine atoms withdraw electron density from the carbon to which they are bonded, making it electron deficient. Furthermore, this electron-deficient carbon pulls electron density through σ bonds from the negatively charged oxygen atom, stabilizing the negative charge. This is called an **inductive effect.**

$CH_3CH_2O^-$

No additional electronegative atoms stabilize the conjugate base.

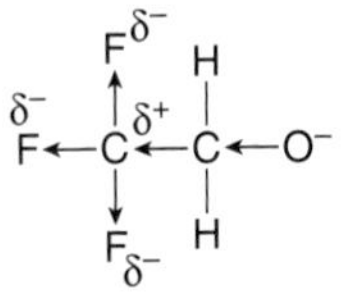

CF_3 withdraws electron density, stabilizing the conjugate base.

- **An *inductive effect* is the pull of electron density through σ bonds caused by electronegativity differences of atoms.**

In this case, the electron density is pulled away from the negative charge through σ bonds by the very electronegative fluorine atoms, and so it is called an **electron-*withdrawing* inductive effect.**

Figure 2.2
Electrostatic potential plots of $CH_3CH_2O^-$ and $CF_3CH_2O^-$

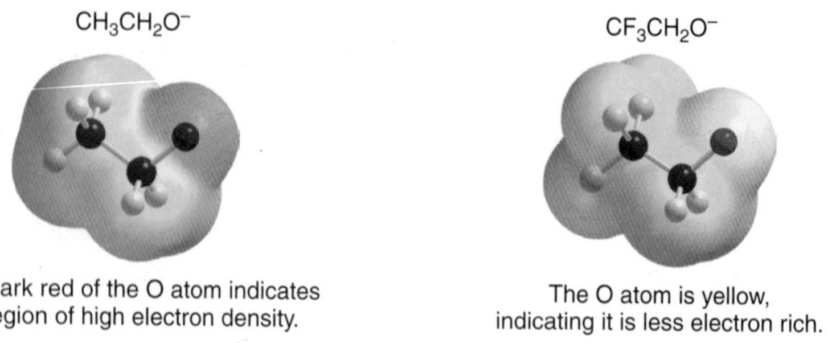

CH3CH2O−
CF3CH2O−
The dark red of the O atom indicates a region of high electron density.
The O atom is yellow, indicating it is less electron rich.

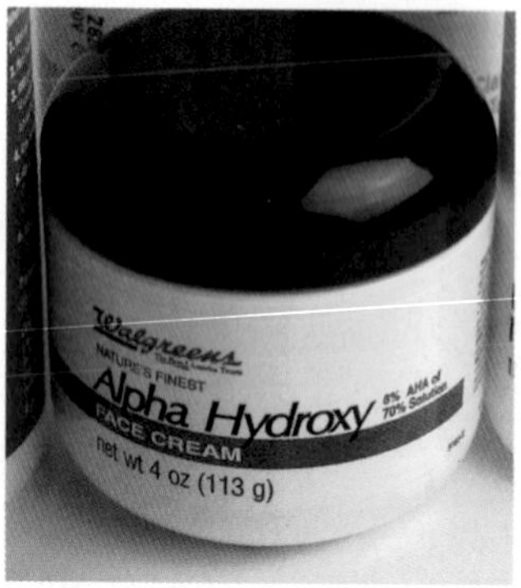

Walgreens
Alpha Hydroxy
FACE CREAM
net wt 4 oz (113 g)

α-Hydroxy acids (Problem 2.18) are used in skin care products that purportedly smooth fine lines and improve skin texture by reacting with the outer layer of skin cells, causing them to loosen and flake off.

Thus, the three electronegative fluorine atoms stabilize the negatively charged conjugate base $CF_3CH_2O^-$, making CF_3CH_2OH a stronger acid than CH_3CH_2OH. We have learned two important principles from this discussion:

- **More electronegative atoms stabilize regions of high electron density by an electron-withdrawing inductive effect.**
- **The acidity of H–A increases with the presence of electron-withdrawing groups in A.**

Inductive effects result because an electronegative atom stabilizes the negative charge of the conjugate base. **The *more electronegative* the atom and the *closer* it is to the site of the negative charge, the greater the effect.** This effect is discussed in greater detail in Chapter 19.

Electrostatic potential plots in Figure 2.2 compare the electron density around the oxygen atoms in these conjugate bases. The darker red around the O atom of $CH_3CH_2O^-$ indicates a higher concentration of electron density compared to the O atom of $CF_3CH_2O^-$.

Problem 2.17 Which compound in each pair is the stronger acid?

a. $ClCH_2COOH$ or FCH_2COOH
b. Cl_2CHCH_2OH or $Cl_2CHCH_2CH_2OH$
c. CH_3COOH or O_2NCH_2COOH

Problem 2.18 Glycolic acid, $HOCH_2CO_2H$, is the simplest member of a group of compounds called α-hydroxy acids, ingredients in skin care products that have an OH group on the carbon adjacent to a CO_2H group. Would you expect $HOCH_2CO_2H$ to be a stronger or weaker acid than acetic acid, CH_3CO_2H?

Problem 2.19 Explain the apparent paradox. HBr is a stronger acid than HCl, but HOCl is a stronger acid than HOBr.

2.5C Resonance Effects

Recall that resonance structures are two Lewis structures having the same placement of atoms but a different arrangement of electrons.

A third factor that determines acidity is resonance. Recall from Section 1.6 that resonance occurs whenever two or more different Lewis structures can be drawn for the same arrangement of atoms. To illustrate this phenomenon, compare ethanol (CH_3CH_2OH) and acetic acid (CH_3COOH), two different compounds containing O–H bonds. Based on Table 2.1, CH_3COOH is a stronger acid than CH_3CH_2OH:

$CH_3CH_2O{-}H$
ethanol
$pK_a = 16$

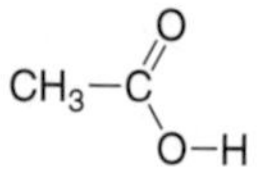

O
CH3–C
O–H

acetic acid
$pK_a = 4.8$ ← **stronger acid**

Draw the conjugate bases of these acids to illustrate the importance of resonance. For ethoxide ($CH_3CH_2O^-$), the conjugate base of ethanol, only one Lewis structure can be drawn. The negative charge of this conjugate base is *localized* on the O atom.

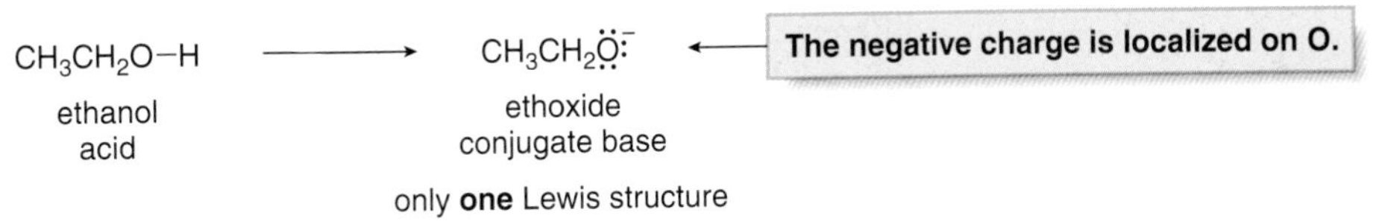

With acetate (CH_3COO^-), however, two resonance structures can be drawn.

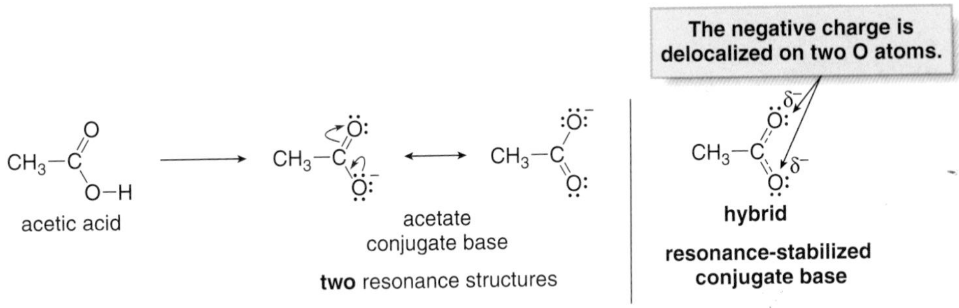

The difference in these two resonance structures is the **position of a π bond** and a **lone pair.** Although each resonance structure of acetate implies that the negative charge is localized on an O atom, in actuality, charge is ***delocalized*** over both O atoms. **Delocalization of electron density stabilizes acetate, making it a weaker base.**

Remember that neither resonance form adequately represents acetate. The true structure is a **hybrid** of both structures. In the hybrid, the electron pairs drawn in different locations in individual resonance structures are ***delocalized.*** With acetate, a dashed line is used to show that each C–O bond has partial double bond character. The symbol δ^- (partial negative) indicates that the charge is delocalized on both O atoms in the hybrid.

Resonance delocalization often produces a larger effect on pK_a than the inductive effects discussed in Section 2.5B. Resonance makes CH_3COOH ($pK_a = 4.8$) a much stronger acid than CH_3CH_2OH ($pK_a = 16$), while the inductive effects due to three electronegative F atoms make CF_3CH_2OH ($pK_a = 12.4$) a somewhat stronger acid than CH_3CH_2OH.

Thus, **resonance delocalization makes CH_3COO^- more stable than $CH_3CH_2O^-$, so CH_3COOH is a stronger acid than CH_3CH_2OH.** This is another example of a general rule.

- **The acidity of H–A increases when the conjugate base A:⁻ is resonance stabilized.**

Electrostatic potential plots of $CH_3CH_2O^-$ and CH_3COO^- in Figure 2.3 indicate that the negative charge is concentrated on a single O in $CH_3CH_2O^-$, but delocalized over the O atoms in CH_3COO^-.

Problem 2.20 The C–H bond in acetone, $(CH_3)_2C{=}O$, has a pK_a of 19.2. Draw two resonance structures for its conjugate base. Then, explain why acetone is much more acidic than propane, $CH_3CH_2CH_3$ ($pK_a = 50$).

Problem 2.21 Acetonitrile (CH_3CN) has a pK_a of 25, making it more acidic than many other compounds having only C–H bonds. Draw Lewis structures for acetonitrile and its conjugate base. Use resonance structures to account for the acidity of acetonitrile.

Figure 2.3
Electrostatic potential plots of $CH_3CH_2O^-$ and CH_3COO^-

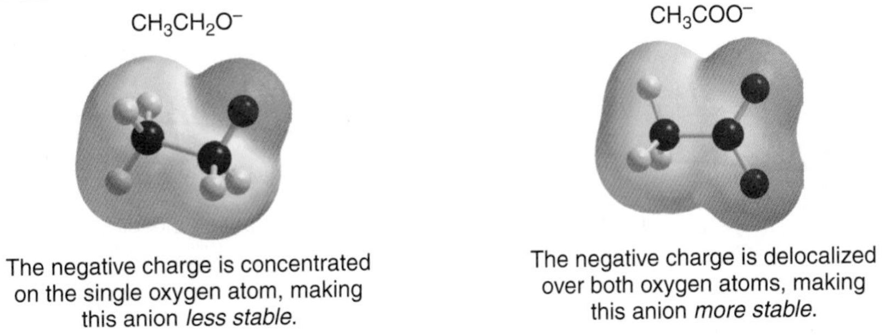

2.5D Hybridization Effects

The final factor affecting the acidity of H–A is the hybridization of A. To illustrate this phenomenon, compare ethane (CH_3CH_3), ethylene ($CH_2{=}CH_2$), and acetylene ($HC{\equiv}CH$), three different compounds containing C–H bonds. Appendix A indicates that there is a considerable difference in the pK_a values of these compounds.

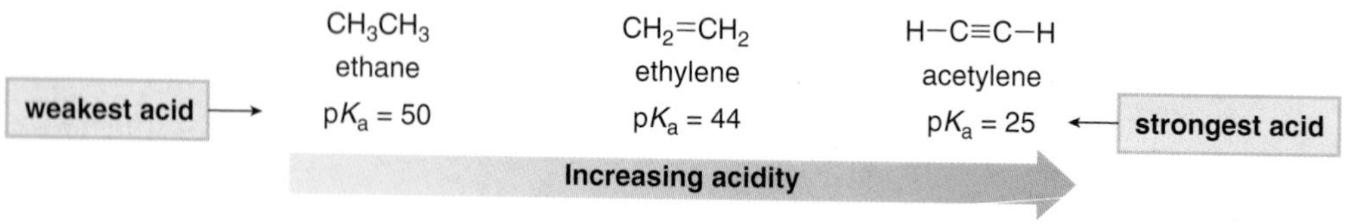

The conjugate bases formed by removing a proton from ethane, ethylene, and acetylene are each carbanions—**species with a negative charge on carbon.**

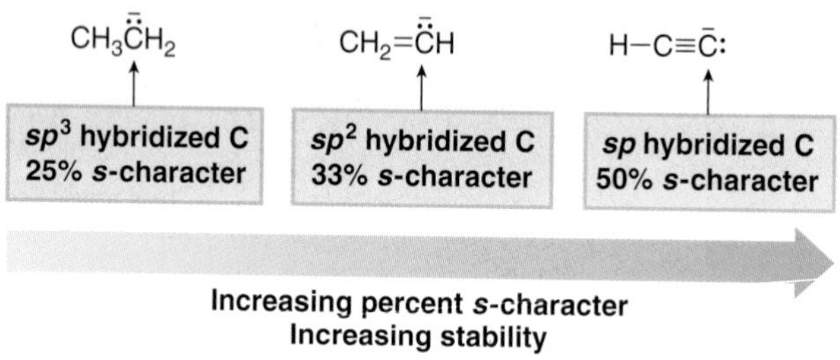

Note, however, that the hybridization of the carbon bearing the negative charge is different in each anion, so the lone pair of electrons occupies an orbital with a different percent *s*-character in each case. A higher percent *s*-character means a hybrid orbital has a larger fraction of the lower energy *s* orbital.

- The *higher* the percent s-character of the hybrid orbital, the **more stable** the conjugate base.

Thus, **acidity increases from CH_3CH_3 to $CH_2{=}CH_2$ to $HC{\equiv}CH$ as the negative charge of the conjugate base is stabilized by increasing percent *s*-character.** Once again this is a specific example of a general trend.

- The acidity of H–A increases as the percent s-character of the A:⁻ increases.

Electrostatic potential plots of these carbanions appear in Figure 2.4.

Figure 2.4
Electrostatic potential plots of three carbanions

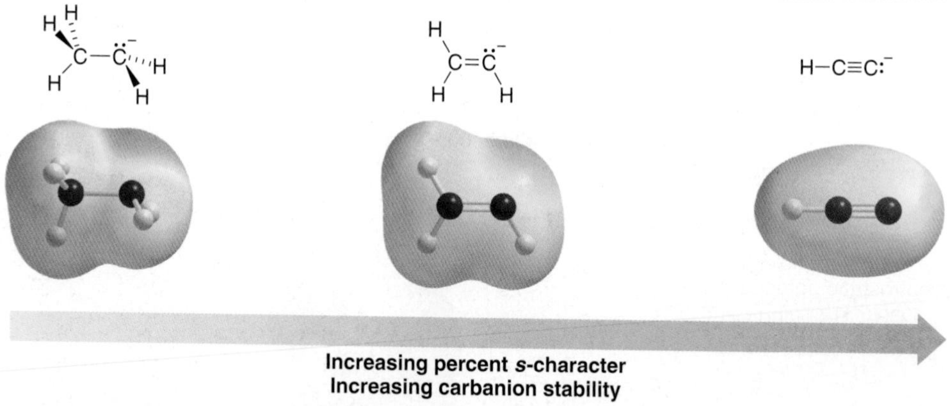

- As the lone pair of electrons is pulled closer to the nucleus, the negatively charged carbon appears less intensely red.

Problem 2.22 For each pair of compounds: [1] Which indicated H is more acidic? [2] Draw the conjugate base of each acid. [3] Which conjugate base is stronger?

a. $CH_3CH_2-C\equiv C-H$ or $CH_3CH_2CH_2CH_2-H$

b. 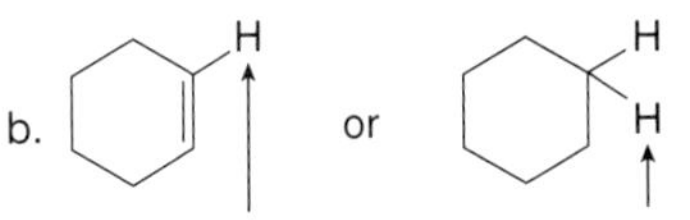

2.5E Summary of Factors Determining Acid Strength

The ability to recognize the most acidic site in a molecule will be important throughout the study of organic chemistry. All the factors that determine acidity are therefore summarized in Figure 2.5. The following two-step procedure shows how these four factors can be used to determine the relative acidity of protons.

Figure 2.5 Summary of the factors that determine acidity

Factor	Example
1. **Element effects:** The acidity of H–A increases both left-to-right across a row and down a column of the periodic table.	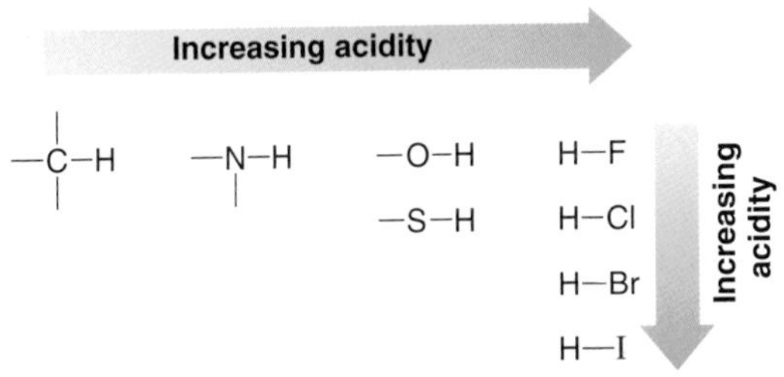 Increasing acidity —C—H —N—H —O—H H—F —S—H H—Cl H—Br H—I Increasing acidity
2. **Inductive effects:** The acidity of H–A increases with the presence of electron-withdrawing groups in A.	CH_3CH_2O-H ; CF_3CH_2O-H **more acidic**
3. **Resonance effects:** The acidity of H–A increases when the conjugate base A:⁻ is resonance stabilized.	CH_3CH_2O-H ; CH_3COO-H **more acidic**
4. **Hybridization effects:** The acidity of H–A increases as the percent *s*-character of A:⁻ increases.	CH_3CH_3 ; $CH_2=CH_2$; $H-C\equiv C-H$ → **Increasing acidity**

How To Determine the Relative Acidity of Protons

Step [1] **Identify the atoms bonded to hydrogen, and use periodic trends to assign relative acidity.**

- The most common H–A bonds in organic compounds are C–H, N–H, and O–H. Because acidity increases left-to-right across a row, the relative acidity of these bonds is C–H < N–H < O–H. Therefore, H atoms bonded to C atoms are usually *less acidic* than H atoms bonded to any heteroatom.

Step [2] **If the two H atoms in question are bonded to the same element, draw the conjugate bases and look for other points of difference. Ask three questions:**

- Do electron-withdrawing groups stabilize the conjugate base?
- Is the conjugate base resonance stabilized?
- How is the conjugate base hybridized?

Sample Problem 2.6 shows how to apply this procedure to actual compounds.

Sample Problem 2.6 Rank the following compounds in order of increasing acidity of their most acidic hydrogen atom.

$ClCH_2CH_2OH$	CH_3CH_2OH	$CH_3CH_2NH_2$
A	**B**	**C**

Solution

[1] Compounds **A, B,** and **C** contain C–H, N–H, and O–H bonds. Because acidity increases left-to-right across a row of the periodic table, the O–H bonds are most acidic. Compound **C** is thus the least acidic because it has *no* O–H bonds.

[2] The only difference between compounds **A** and **B** is the presence of an electronegative Cl in **A.** The Cl atom stabilizes the conjugate base of **A,** making it more acidic than **B.** Thus,

$CH_3CH_2NH_2$	CH_3CH_2OH	$ClCH_2CH_2OH$
C	**B**	**A**

Increasing acidity →

Problem 2.23 Rank the compounds in each group in order of increasing acidity.

a. $CH_3CH_2CH_3$, CH_3CH_2OH, $CH_3CH_2NH_2$
b. $BrCH_2COOH$, CH_3CH_2COOH, $CH_3CH_2CH_2OH$
c. $CH_3CH_2NH_2$, $(CH_3)_3N$, CH_3CH_2OH

Problem 2.24 Which proton in each of the following drugs is most acidic? THC is the active component in marijuana, and ketoprofen is an anti-inflammatory agent.

a. 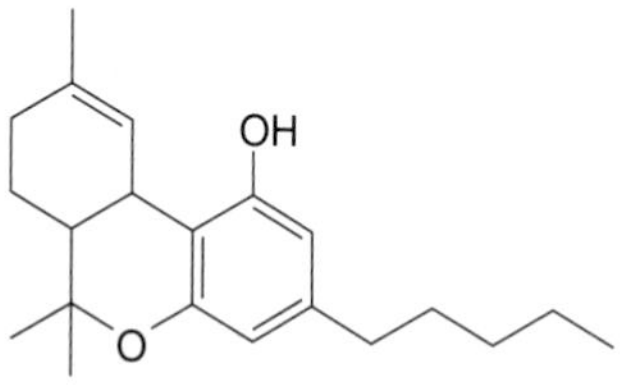

THC
tetrahydrocannabinol

b. 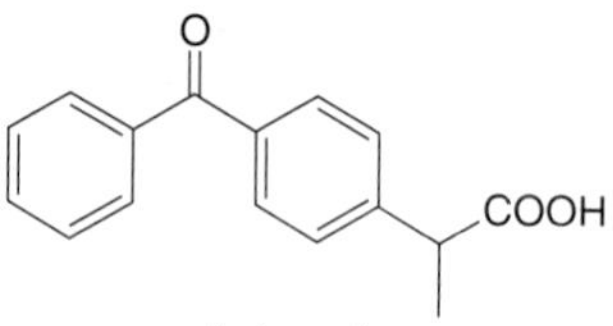

ketoprofen

2.6 Common Acids and Bases

Many strong or moderately strong acids and bases are used as reagents in organic reactions.

2.6A Common Acids

Sulfuric acid is the most widely produced industrial chemical. It is also formed when sulfur oxides, emitted into the atmosphere by burning fossil fuels high in sulfur content, dissolve in water. This makes rainwater acidic, forming acid rain.

Several organic reactions are carried out in the presence of strong inorganic acids, most commonly **HCl** and $\mathbf{H_2SO_4}$**.** These strong acids, with **pK_a values ≤ 0,** should be familiar from previous chemistry courses.

Two organic acids are also commonly used, namely **acetic acid** and ***p*-toluenesulfonic acid** (usually abbreviated as **TsOH**). Although acetic acid has a higher pK_a than the inorganic acids, making it a weaker acid, it is more acidic than most organic compounds. *p*-Toluenesulfonic acid is similar in acidity to the strong inorganic acids. Because it is a solid, small quantities can be easily weighed on a balance and then added to a reaction mixture.

CH_3COOH

acetic acid
pK_a = 4.8

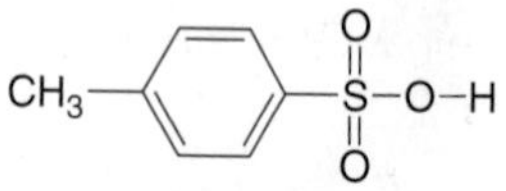

= TsOH

p-toluenesulfonic acid
pK_a = –7

2.6B Common Bases

Common strong bases used in organic reactions are more varied in structure. Three common kinds of negatively charged bases include:

[1] Negatively charged oxygen bases: **^{-}OH** (hydroxide) and its organic derivatives
[2] Negatively charged nitrogen bases: **$^{-}NH_2$** (amide) and its organic derivatives
[3] Hydride **(H^{-})**

Figure 2.6 gives examples of these strong bases. Each negatively charged base is used as a salt with a spectator ion (usually Li^{+}, Na^{+}, or K^{+}) that serves to balance charge.

- **Strong bases have weak conjugate acids with high pK_a values, usually > 12.**

Strong bases have a net negative charge, but not all negatively charged species are strong bases. For example, none of the halides, F^{-}, Cl^{-}, Br^{-}, or I^{-}, is a strong base. These anions have very strong conjugate acids and have little affinity for donating their electron pairs to a proton.

Carbanions, negatively charged carbon atoms discussed in Section 2.5D, are especially strong bases. Perhaps the most common example is **butyllithium.** Butyllithium and related compounds are discussed in greater detail in Chapter 20.

very strong base

$CH_3CH_2CH_2CH_2^{-}$ Li^{+}

butyllithium

Two other weaker organic bases are **triethylamine** and **pyridine.** These compounds have a lone pair on nitrogen, making them basic, but they are considerably weaker than the amide bases because they are neutral, not negatively charged.

$CH_3CH_2-\ddot{N}(CH_2CH_3)-CH_2CH_3$

triethylamine

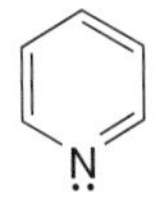
pyridine

Problem 2.25 Draw the products formed when 2-propanol [$(CH_3)_2CHOH$], the main ingredient in rubbing alcohol, is treated with each acid or base: (a) NaH; (b) H_2SO_4; (c) Li^{+} $^{-}N[CH(CH_3)_2]_2$; (d) CH_3CO_2H.

Figure 2.6 Some common negatively charged bases

oxygen bases		nitrogen bases	
Na^{+} **^{-}OH**	sodium hydroxide	Na^{+} **$^{-}NH_2$**	sodium amide
Na^{+} **$^{-}OCH_3$**	sodium methoxide	Li^{+} **$^{-}N[CH(CH_3)_2]_2$**	lithium diisopropylamide
Na^{+} **$^{-}OCH_2CH_3$**	sodium ethoxide	**hydride**	
K^{+} **$^{-}OC(CH_3)_3$**	potassium *tert*-butoxide	Na^{+} **H^{-}**	sodium hydride

2.7 Aspirin

Aspirin, or acetylsalicylic acid, is the most well known member of a group of compounds called **salicylates.** Although aspirin was first used in medicine for its analgesic (pain-relieving), antipyretic (fever-reducing), and anti-inflammatory properties, today it is commonly used as an antiplatelet agent in the treatment and prevention of heart attacks and strokes. **Aspirin is a synthetic compound;** it does not occur in nature, though some related salicylates are found in willow bark and meadowsweet blossoms (Figure 2.7).

Like many drugs, aspirin is capable of undergoing a proton transfer reaction. Its most acidic proton is the H bonded to O, and in the presence of base, this H is readily removed.

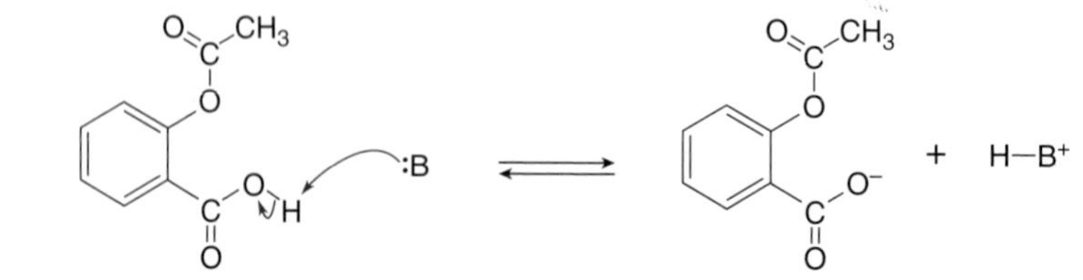

aspirin
acetylsalicylic acid
neutral form
This form exists in the **stomach.**

conjugate base
ionic form
This form exists in the **intestines.**

Why is this acid–base reaction important? After ingestion, aspirin first travels into the stomach and then the intestines. In the acidic environment of the stomach, aspirin remains in its neutral form, but in the basic environment of the small intestine, aspirin is deprotonated to form its conjugate base, an ion. Likewise, in the slightly basic environment of the blood, aspirin exists primarily as its ionic conjugate base.

We will learn more about solubility and the cell membrane in Section 3.7.

Whether aspirin is a neutral acid or an ionic conjugate base affects its transport throughout the body and its ability to pass through a cell membrane. In its ionic form, aspirin is readily soluble in the aqueous environment of the blood, and so it is transported in the bloodstream to tissues. Once aspirin has reached its target location, however, its conjugate base must be re-protonated to form the neutral acid that can pass through the nonpolar interior of a cell membrane where it inhibits prostaglandin synthesis, as we will learn in Chapter 19. Thus, in the body, aspirin undergoes acid–base reactions and these reactions are crucial in determining its properties and action.

Problem 2.26

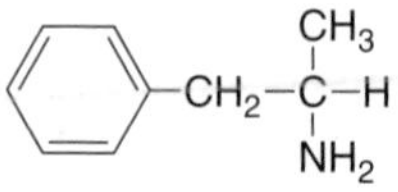

amphetamine

Compounds like amphetamine that contain nitrogen atoms are protonated by the HCl in the gastric juices of the stomach, and the resulting salt is then deprotonated in the basic environment of the intestines to regenerate the neutral form. Write proton transfer reactions for both of these processes. In which form will amphetamine pass through a cell membrane?

Figure 2.7
Salicin, an analgesic in willow bark

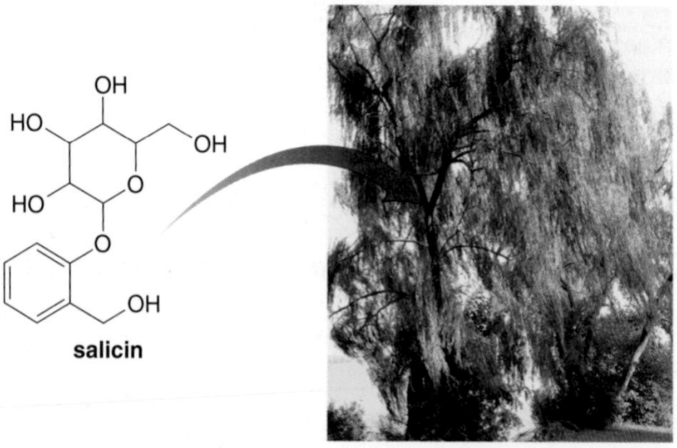

salicin

willow tree

- The modern history of aspirin dates back to 1763 when Reverend Edmund Stone reported on the analgesic effect of chewing on the bark of the willow tree. Willow bark is now known to contain *salicin,* which is structurally related to aspirin.

2.8 Lewis Acids and Bases

The Lewis definition of acids and bases is more general than the Brønsted–Lowry definition.

- A Lewis acid is an *electron pair acceptor.*
- A Lewis base is an *electron pair donor.*

Lewis bases are structurally the same as Brønsted–Lowry bases. Both have an **available electron pair**—a lone pair or an electron pair in a π bond. A Brønsted–Lowry base always donates this electron pair to a proton, but a Lewis base donates this electron pair to anything that is electron deficient.

All Brønsted–Lowry bases are Lewis bases.

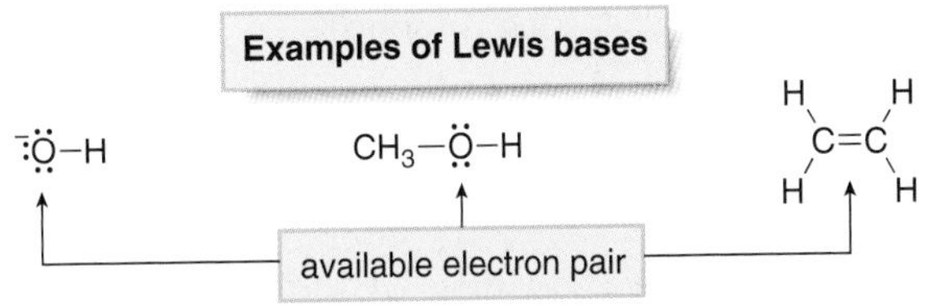

A Lewis acid must be able to accept an electron pair, but there are many ways for this to occur. **All Brønsted–Lowry acids are also Lewis acids, but the reverse is not necessarily true.** Any species that is electron deficient and capable of accepting an electron pair is also a Lewis acid.

Common examples of Lewis acids (which are not Brønsted–Lowry acids) include BF_3 and $AlCl_3$. These compounds contain elements in group 3A of the periodic table that can accept an electron pair because they do not have filled valence shells of electrons.

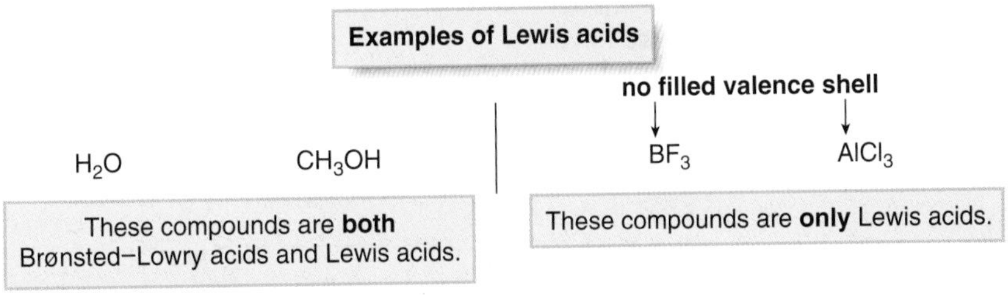

Problem 2.27 Which compounds are Lewis bases?

a. NH_3 b. $CH_3CH_2CH_3$ c. H^- d. H–C≡C–H

Problem 2.28 Which compounds are Lewis acids?

a. BBr_3 b. CH_3CH_2OH c. $(CH_3)_3C^+$ d. Br^-

Any reaction in which one species donates an electron pair to another species is a Lewis acid–base reaction.

In a Lewis acid–base reaction, a Lewis base donates an electron pair to a Lewis acid. Most of the reactions in organic chemistry involving movement of electron pairs can be classified as Lewis acid–base reactions. Lewis acid–base reactions illustrate a general pattern of reactivity in organic chemistry.

- **Electron-rich species react with electron-poor species.**

In the simplest Lewis acid–base reaction one bond is formed and no bonds are broken. This is illustrated with the reaction of BF_3 with H_2O. BF_3 has only six electrons around B, so it is the electron-deficient Lewis acid. H_2O has two lone pairs on O, so it is the electron-rich Lewis base.

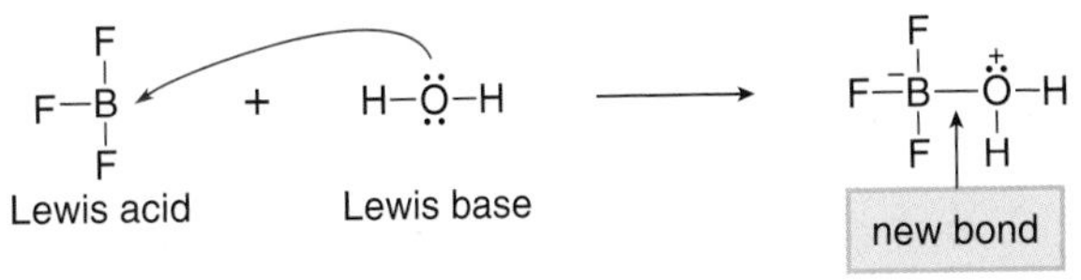

H_2O donates an electron pair to BF_3 to form one new bond. The electron pair in the new B–O bond comes from the oxygen atom, and a single product is formed. Both B and O bear formal charges in the product, but the overall product is neutral.

Nucleophile = nucleus loving.
Electrophile = electron loving.

- **A Lewis acid is also called an *electrophile.***
- **When a Lewis base reacts with an electrophile other than a proton, the Lewis base is also called a *nucleophile.***

In this Lewis acid–base reaction, **BF_3 is the electrophile** and **H_2O is the nucleophile.**

Two other examples are drawn. In each reaction the **electron pair is not removed from the Lewis base;** instead, the electron pair is donated to an atom of the Lewis acid, and one new covalent bond is formed.

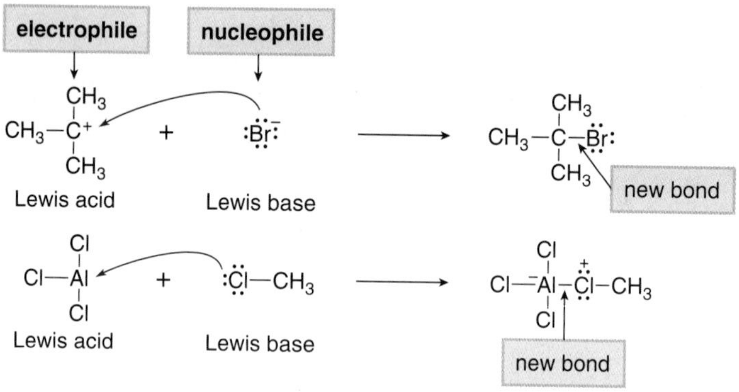

Problem 2.29 For each reaction, label the Lewis acid and base. Use curved arrow notation to show the movement of electron pairs.

a. BF_3 + $CH_3-\ddot{\underset{..}{O}}-CH_3$ ⟶ 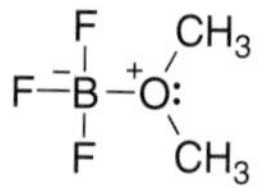

b. $(CH_3)_2\overset{+}{C}H$ + ^-OH ⟶ $(CH_3)_2CHOH$

Problem 2.30 Draw the products of each reaction, and label the nucleophile and electrophile.

a. $CH_3CH_2-\ddot{\underset{..}{O}}-CH_2CH_3$ + BBr_3 ⟶ b. 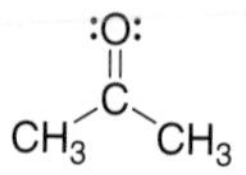 + $AlCl_3$ ⟶

Problem 2.31 Draw the product formed when $(CH_3CH_2)_3N$:, a Lewis base, reacts with each Lewis acid: (a) $B(CH_3)_3$; (b) $(CH_3)_3C^+$; (c) $AlCl_3$.

In some Lewis acid–base reactions, one bond is formed and one bond is broken. To draw the products of these reactions, keep the following steps in mind.

[1] Always identify the Lewis acid and base first.

[2] Draw a curved arrow from the electron pair of the base to the electron-deficient atom of the acid.

[3] Count electron pairs and break a bond when needed to keep the correct number of valence electrons.

Recall from Chapter 1 that a positively charged carbon atom is called a **carbocation.**

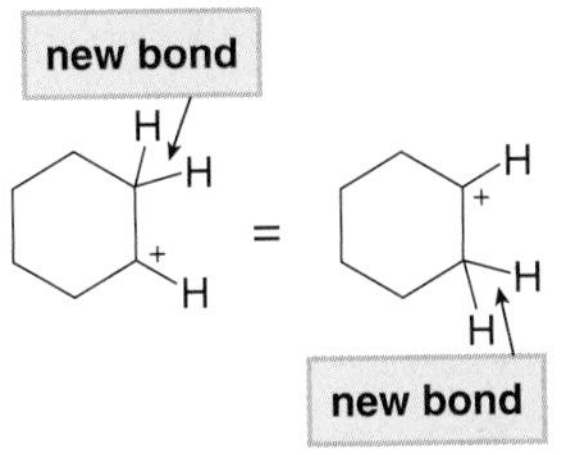
new bond
H
H
+
H
=
H
+
H
H
new bond

In the reaction of cyclohexene with HCl, the new bond to H could form at **either carbon of the double bond,** because the same carbocation results.

For example, draw the Lewis acid–base reaction between cyclohexene and H–Cl. The Brønsted–Lowry acid HCl is also a Lewis acid, and cyclohexene, having a π bond, is the Lewis base.

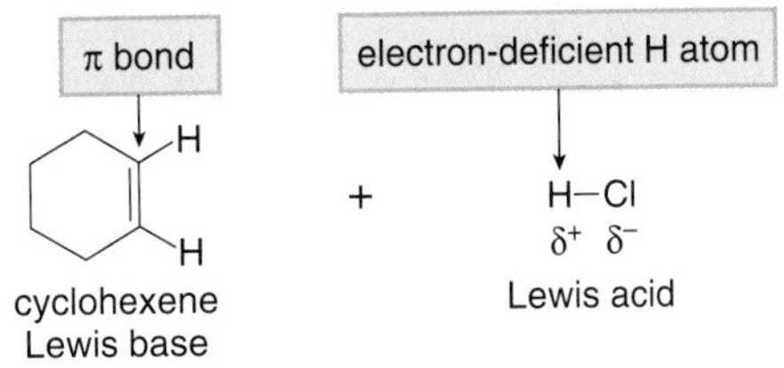
π bond
electron-deficient H atom
H
H
+
H–Cl
δ+ δ–
cyclohexene
Lewis base
Lewis acid

To draw the product of this reaction, the electron pair in the π bond of the Lewis base forms a new bond to the proton of the Lewis acid, forming a carbocation. The H–Cl bond must break, giving its two electrons to Cl, forming Cl^-. Because two electron pairs are involved, two curved arrows are needed.

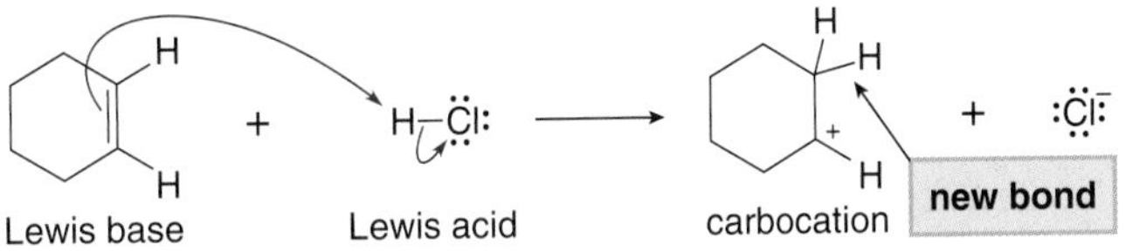
H
H
+
H–Cl:
H
H
H
+
:Cl:–
Lewis base
Lewis acid
carbocation
new bond

The Lewis acid–base reaction of cyclohexene with HCl is a specific example of a fundamental reaction of compounds containing C–C double bonds, as discussed in Chapter 10.

Problem 2.32 Label the Lewis acid and base. Use curved arrow notation to show the movement of electron pairs.

CH3
CH2=C
H
+
H3O+
CH3
CH3–C+
H
+
H2O:

KEY CONCEPTS

Acids and Bases

A Comparison of Brønsted–Lowry and Lewis Acids and Bases

Type	Definition	Structural feature	Examples
Brønsted–Lowry acid (2.1)	proton donor	a proton	HCl, H_2SO_4, H_2O, CH_3COOH, TsOH
Brønsted–Lowry base (2.1)	proton acceptor	a lone pair *or* a π bond	^-OH, $^-OCH_3$, H^-, $^-NH_2$, NH_3, $CH_2=CH_2$
Lewis acid (2.8)	electron pair acceptor	a proton, *or* an unfilled valence shell, *or* a partial (+) charge	BF_3, $AlCl_3$, HCl, CH_3COOH, H_2O
Lewis base (2.8)	electron pair donor	a lone pair *or* a π bond	^-OH, $^-OCH_3$, H^-, $^-NH_2$, NH_3, $CH_2=CH_2$

Acid–Base Reactions

[1] A Brønsted–Lowry acid donates a proton to a Brønsted–Lowry base (2.2).

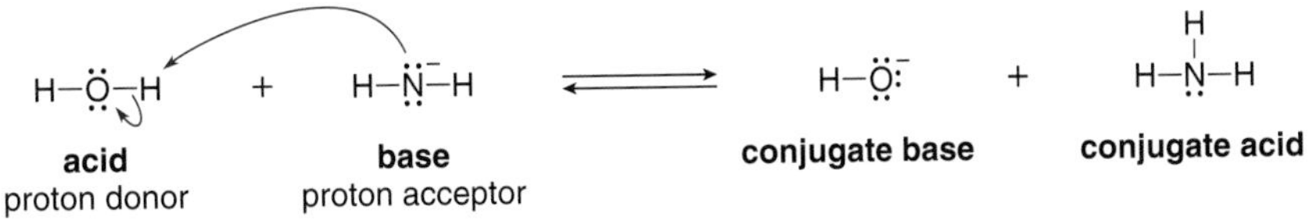
H–O–H
+
H–N–H
H–O:–
+
H
H–N–H
acid
proton donor
base
proton acceptor
conjugate base
conjugate acid

[2] A Lewis base donates an electron pair to a Lewis acid (2.8).

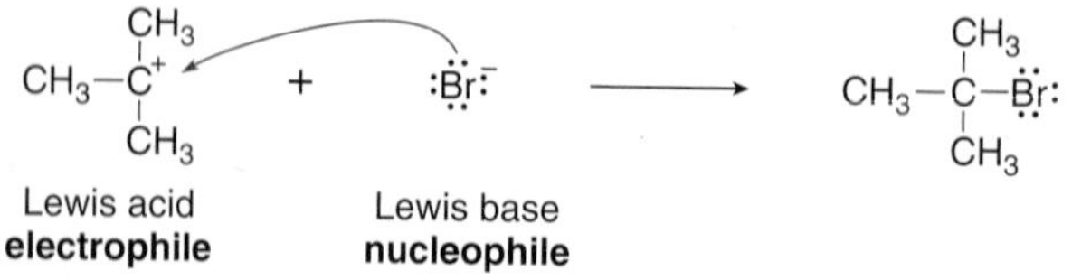
Lewis acid
electrophile
Lewis base
nucleophile

- Electron-rich species react with electron-poor ones.
- Nucleophiles react with electrophiles.

Important Facts

- Definition: **pK_a = –log K_a. The lower the pK_a, the stronger the acid** (2.3).
- The stronger the acid, the weaker the conjugate base (2.3).
- In proton transfer reactions, equilibrium favors the weaker acid and weaker base (2.4).
- An acid can be deprotonated by the conjugate base of any acid having a higher pK_a (2.4).

Periodic Trends in Acidity and Basicity (2.5A)

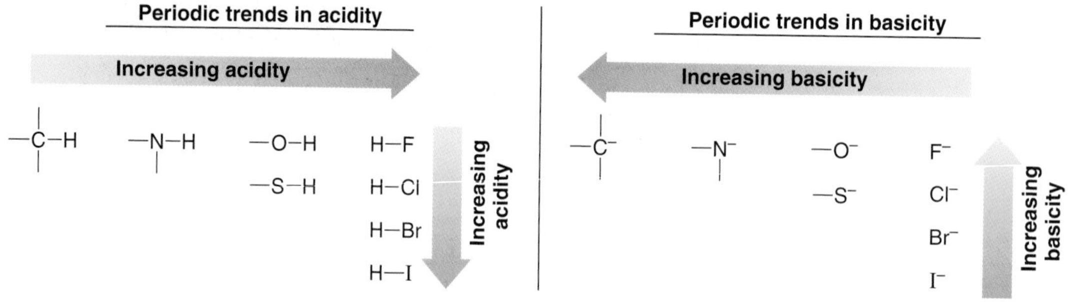
Periodic trends in acidity
Increasing acidity
Increasing acidity
Periodic trends in basicity
Increasing basicity
Increasing basicity

Factors That Determine Acidity (2.5)

[1] **Element effects** (2.5A)	The acidity of H–A increases both left-to-right across a row and down a column of the periodic table.
[2] **Inductive effects** (2.5B)	The acidity of H–A increases with the presence of electron-withdrawing groups in A.
[3] **Resonance effects** (2.5C)	The acidity of H–A increases when the conjugate base A:⁻ is resonance stabilized.
[4] **Hybridization effects** (2.5D)	The acidity of H–A increases as the percent *s*-character of A:⁻ increases.

PROBLEMS

Problems Using Three-Dimensional Models

2.33 Propranolol is an antihypertensive agent—that is, it lowers blood pressure. (a) Which proton in propranolol is most acidic? (b) What products are formed when propranolol is treated with NaH? (c) Which atom is most basic? (d) What products are formed when propranolol is treated with HCl?

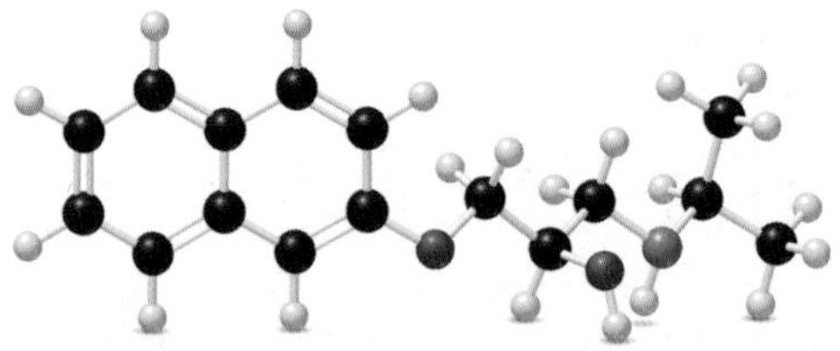

propranolol

2.34 Amphetamine is a powerful stimulant of the central nervous system. (a) Which proton in amphetamine is most acidic? (b) What products are formed when amphetamine is treated with NaH? (c) What products are formed when amphetamine is treated with HCl?

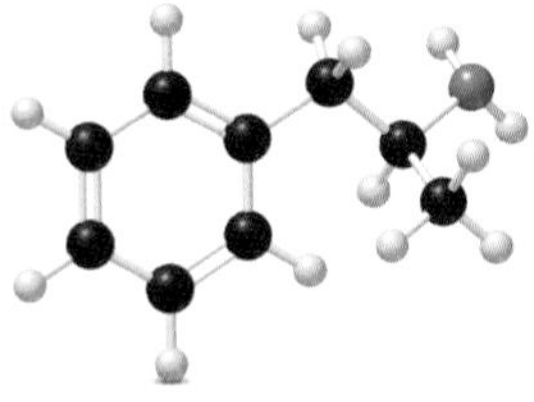

amphetamine

Brønsted–Lowry Acids and Bases

2.35 What is the conjugate acid of each base?

a. H_2O b. $^-NH_2$ c. HCO_3^- d. $CH_3CH_2NHCH_3$ e. CH_3OCH_3 f. CH_3COO^-

2.36 What is the conjugate base of each acid?

a. HCN b. HCO_3^- c. $(CH_3)_2\overset{+}{N}H_2$ d. $HC\equiv CH$ e. CH_3CH_2COOH f. CH_3SO_3H

2.37 (a) Draw the conjugate acid of ethylene, $CH_2=CH_2$. (b) Draw the conjugate base of ethylene.

Reactions of Brønsted–Lowry Acids and Bases

2.38 Draw the products formed from the acid–base reaction of H_2SO_4 with each compound.

a. 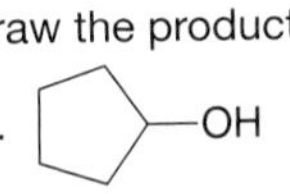
b. 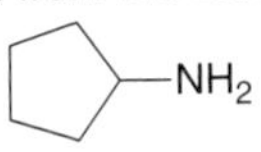
c. 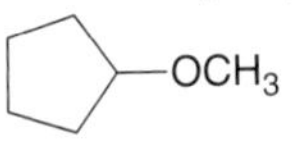
d. 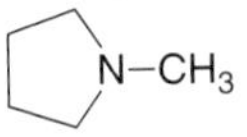

2.39 Draw the products formed from the acid–base reaction of KOH with each compound.

a. 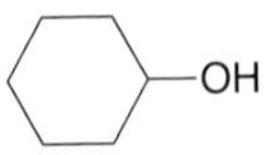
b. 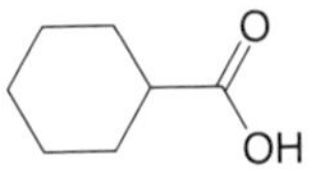
c. 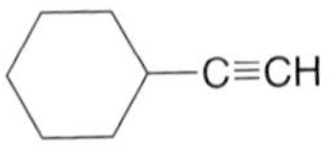
d. 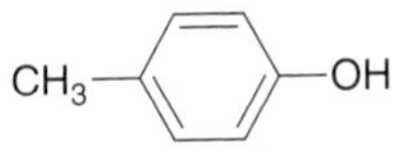

2.40 Draw the products of each proton transfer reaction. Label the acid and base in the starting materials, and the conjugate acid and base in the products.

a. $CH_3OH + {}^-NH_2 \rightleftharpoons$

b. 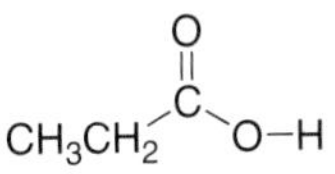 $+ CH_3O^- \rightleftharpoons$

c. $CH_3CH_2{-}O{-}H + H{-}Br \rightleftharpoons$

d. $CH_3C\equiv C^- + H_2O \rightleftharpoons$

2.41 Draw the products of each acid–base reaction.

a. 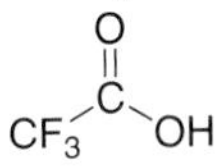 $+ NaHCO_3 \rightleftharpoons$

b. $CH_3{-}C\equiv C{-}H + NaNH_2 \rightleftharpoons$

c. $(CH_3)_2NH$ + 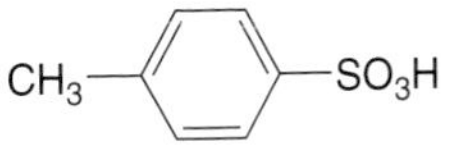 $\rightleftharpoons$

d. 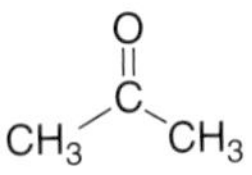 $+ H_2SO_4 \rightleftharpoons$

2.42 Draw the products of each acid–base reaction.

a. 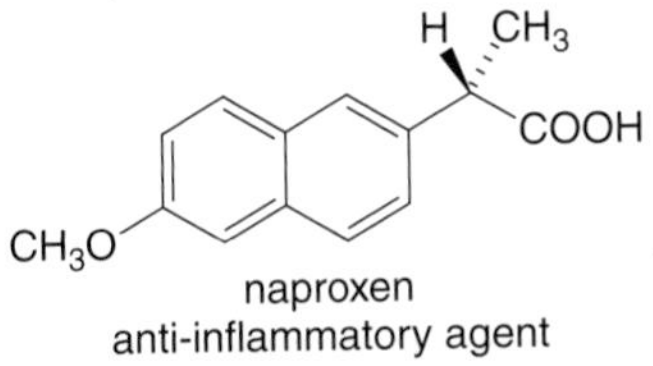 $+ NaOH \rightleftharpoons$

naproxen
anti-inflammatory agent

b. 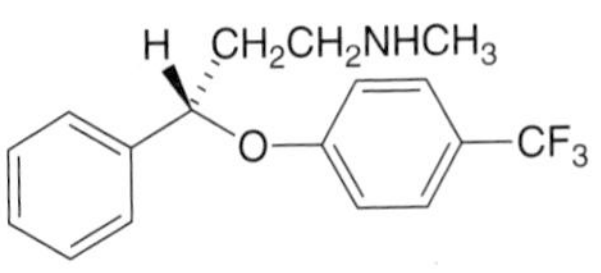 $+ HCl \rightleftharpoons$

fluoxetine
antidepressant

2.43 Fenfluramine and phentermine are two components of fen–phen, an appetite suppressant withdrawn from the market in 1997 after it was shown to damage the heart valves in some patients. What products are formed when fenfluramine and phentermine are each treated with acetic acid (CH_3CO_2H)?

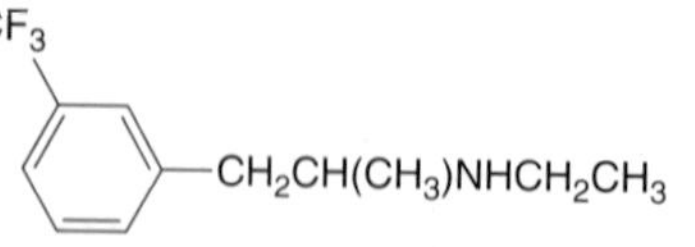

fenfluramine

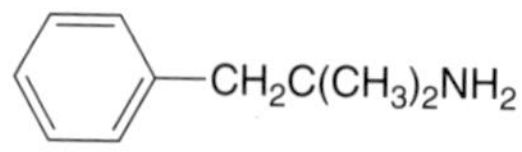

phentermine

pK_a, K_a, and the Direction of Equilibrium

2.44 What is K_a for each compound? Use a calculator when necessary.

a. H_2S pK_a = 7.0
b. $ClCH_2COOH$ pK_a = 2.8
c. HCN pK_a = 9.1

2.45 What is the pK_a for each compound? Use a calculator when necessary.

a. 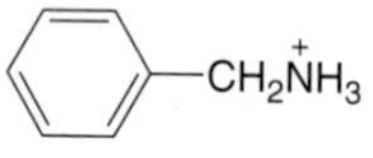 $K_a = 4.7 \times 10^{-10}$

b. 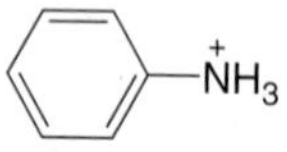 $K_a = 2.3 \times 10^{-5}$

c. CF_3COOH $K_a = 5.9 \times 10^{-1}$

2.46 Which of the following bases are strong enough to deprotonate $CH_3CH_2CH_2C{\equiv}CH$ (pK_a = 25), so that equilibrium favors the products: (a) H_2O; (b) NaOH; (c) $NaNH_2$; (d) NH_3; (e) NaH; (f) CH_3Li?

2.47 Which compounds can be deprotonated by ^-OH, so that equilibrium favors the products? Refer to the pK_a table in Appendix A.

a. HCOOH
b. H_2S
c. 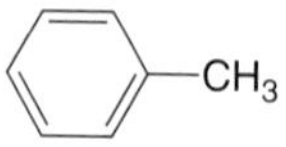
d. CH_3NH_2

2.48 Draw the products of each reaction. Use the pK_a table in Appendix A to decide if the equilibrium favors the starting materials or products.

a. 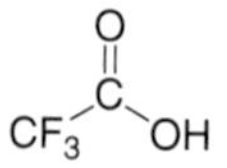 + $^-OCH_2CH_3$ ⇌

b. 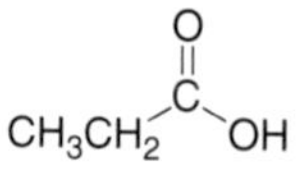 + NaCl ⇌

c. $(CH_3)_3COH$ + H_2SO_4 ⇌

d. 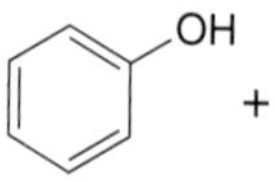 + $NaHCO_3$ ⇌

e. H−C≡C−H + $Li^{+\,-}CH_2CH_3$ ⇌

f. CH_3NH_2 + H_2SO_4 ⇌

Relative Acid Strength

2.49 Rank the following compounds in order of increasing acidity.

a. NH_3, H_2O, HF
b. HBr, HCl, HF
c. H_2O, H_3O^+, HO^-
d. NH_3, H_2O, H_2S
e. CH_3OH, CH_3NH_2, CH_3CH_3
f. HCl, H_2O, H_2S
g. $CH_3CH_2CH_3$, $ClCH_2CH_2OH$, CH_3CH_2OH
h. $HC{\equiv}CCH_2CH_3$, $CH_3CH_2CH_2CH_3$, $CH_3CH{=}CHCH_3$

2.50 Rank the following ions in order of increasing basicity.

a. $CH_3\bar{C}H_2$, $CH_3\bar{O}$, $CH_3\bar{N}H$
b. CH_3^-, HO^-, Br^-
c. CH_3COO^-, $CH_3CH_2O^-$, $ClCH_2COO^-$
d. 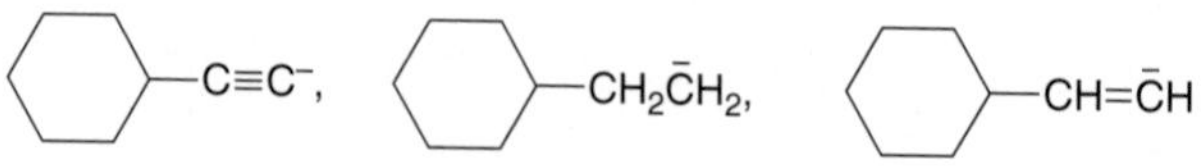

2.51 The pK_a's of the two ammonium cations drawn below are 8.33 and 11.1. Which pK_a corresponds to which cation? Explain your choice.

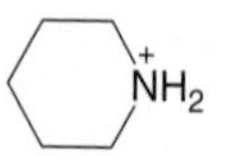

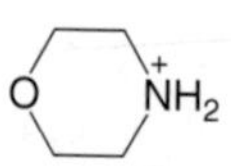

2.52 Explain why the pK_a of propiolic acid ($HC\equiv CCO_2H$, pK_a = 1.8) is significantly lower than the pK_a of propanoic acid ($CH_3CH_2CO_2H$, pK_a = 4.9).

2.53 The pK_a of three different C – H bonds is given below.

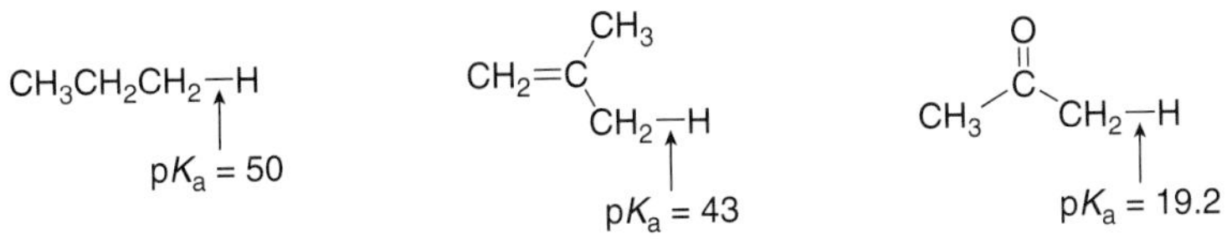

a. For each compound, draw the conjugate base, including all possible resonance structures.
b. Explain the observed trend in pK_a.

2.54 a. What is the conjugate acid of **A?**
b. What is the conjugate base of **A?**

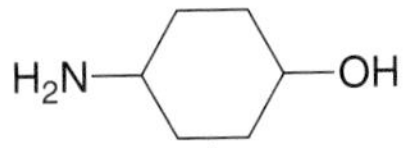

A

2.55 Draw the structure of a constitutional isomer of compound **B** that fits each description.
a. an isomer that is at least 10^5 times more acidic than **B**
b. an isomer that is at least 10^5 times less acidic than **B**
c. an isomer that is comparable in acidity to **B**

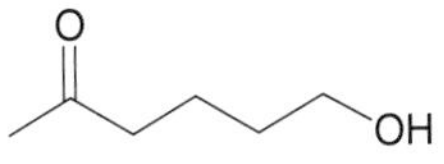

B

2.56 Many drugs are Brønsted–Lowry acids or bases.
a. What is the most acidic proton in the analgesic ibuprofen? Draw the conjugate base.
b. What is the most basic electron pair in cocaine? Draw the conjugate acid.

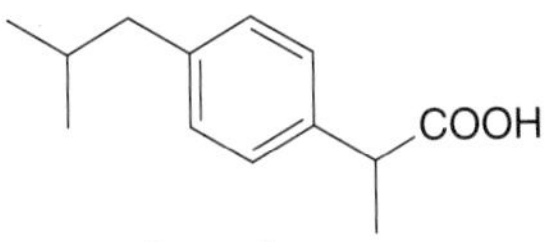

ibuprofen

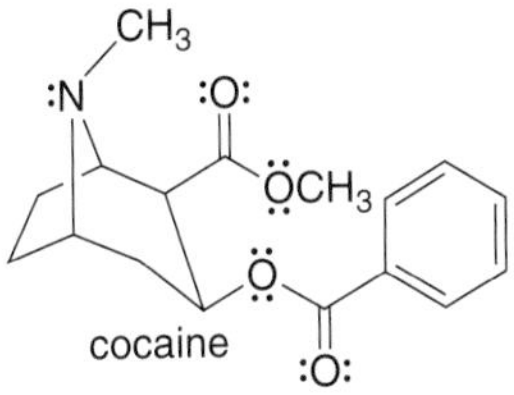

cocaine

2.57 Dimethyl ether (CH_3OCH_3) and ethanol (CH_3CH_2OH) are isomers, but CH_3OCH_3 has a pK_a of 40 and CH_3CH_2OH has a pK_a of 16. Why are these pK_a values so different?

2.58 Atenolol is a β (beta) blocker, a drug used to treat high blood pressure. Which of the indicated N – H bonds is more acidic? Explain your reasoning.

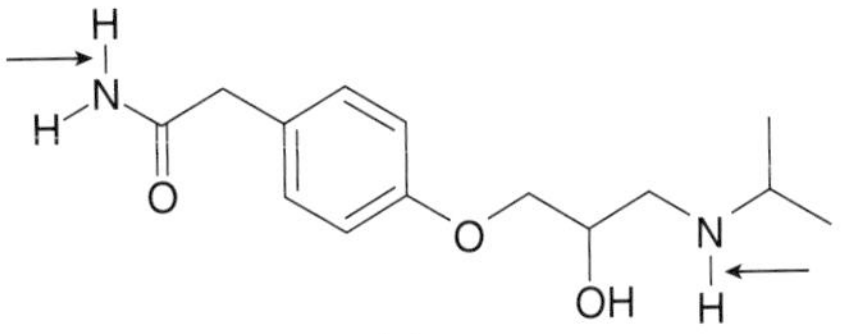

atenolol

2.59 Ethyl butanoate, $CH_3CH_2CH_2CO_2CH_2CH_3$, is one of the many organic compounds isolated from mangoes. Which hydrogen is most readily removed when ethyl butanoate is treated with base? Propose a reason for your choice, and using the data in Appendix A, estimate its pK_a.

2.60 Use the principles in Section 2.5 to label the most acidic hydrogen in each drug. Explain your choice.

a.

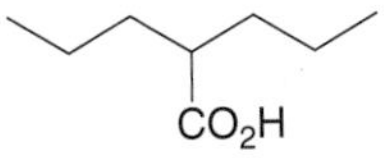

valproic acid
(used to treat epilepsy)

b.

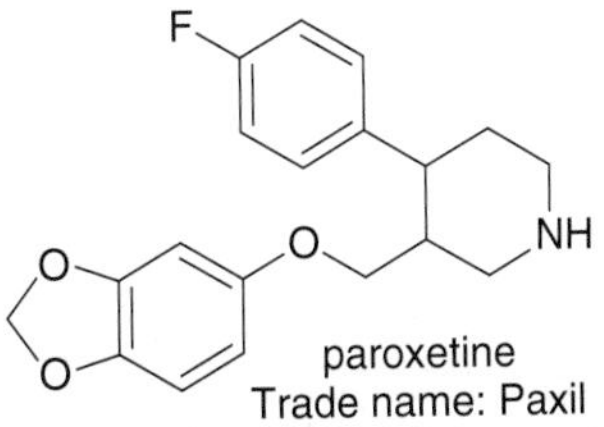

paroxetine
Trade name: Paxil
(used to treat depression)

c.

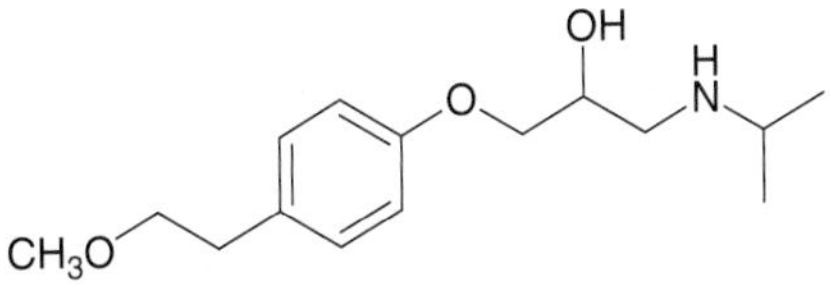

metoprolol
(used to treat high blood pressure)

2.61 Label the three most acidic hydrogen atoms in lactic acid, $CH_3CH(OH)CO_2H$, and rank them in order of decreasing acidity. Explain your reasoning.

Lewis Acids and Bases

2.62 Classify each compound as a Lewis base, a Brønsted–Lowry base, both, or neither.

a. 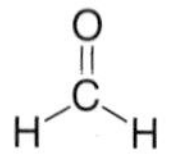 b. $CH_3{-}Cl$ c.  d. 

2.63 Classify each species as a Lewis acid, a Brønsted–Lowry acid, both, or neither.

a. H_3O^+ b. Cl_3C^+ c. BCl_3 d. BF_4^-

Lewis Acid–Base Reactions

2.64 Label the Lewis acid and Lewis base in each reaction. Use curved arrows to show the movement of electron pairs.

a. 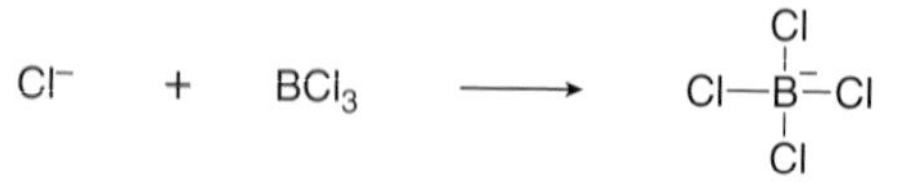

c. 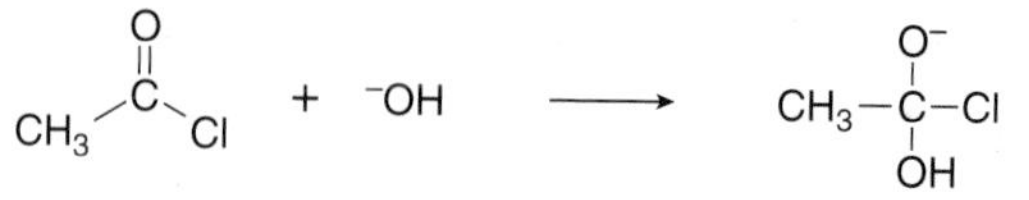

b. 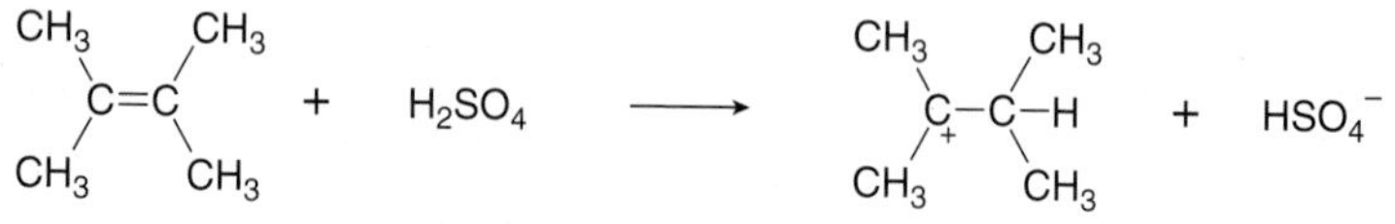

2.65 Draw the products of each Lewis acid–base reaction. Label the electrophile and nucleophile.

a. $CH_3CH_2OH + BF_3 \longrightarrow$

b. $CH_3SCH_3 + AlCl_3 \longrightarrow$

c. 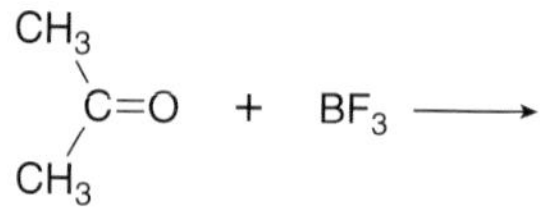

d. 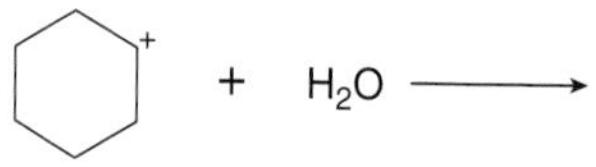

e. $Br_2 + FeBr_3 \longrightarrow$

2.66 Draw the product formed when the Lewis acid $(CH_3CH_2)_3C^+$ reacts with each Lewis base: (a) H_2O; (b) CH_3OH; (c) $(CH_3)_2O$; (d) NH_3; (e) $(CH_3)_2NH$.

General Problems

2.67 Classify each reaction as either a proton transfer reaction, or a reaction of a nucleophile with an electrophile. Use curved arrows to show how the electron pairs move.

a. 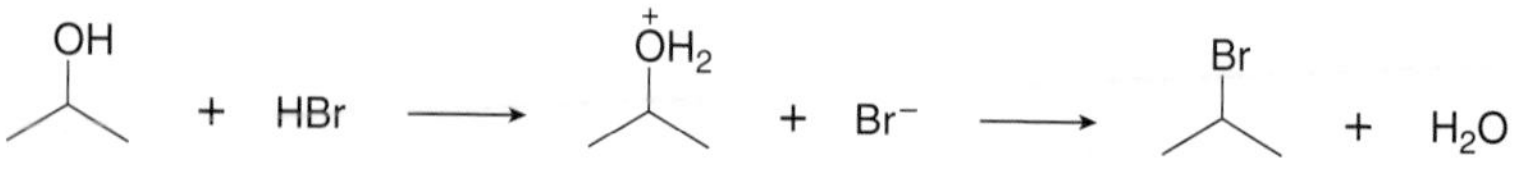

b. 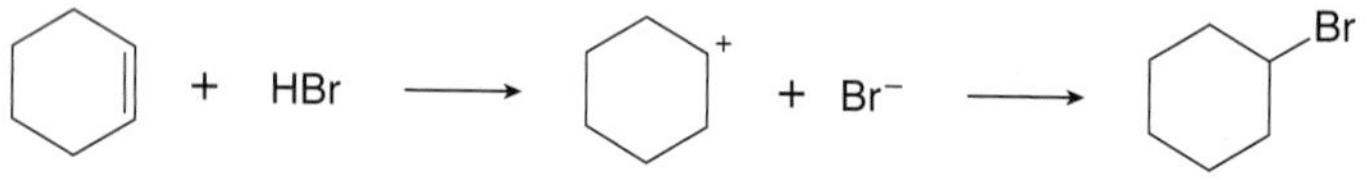

c. 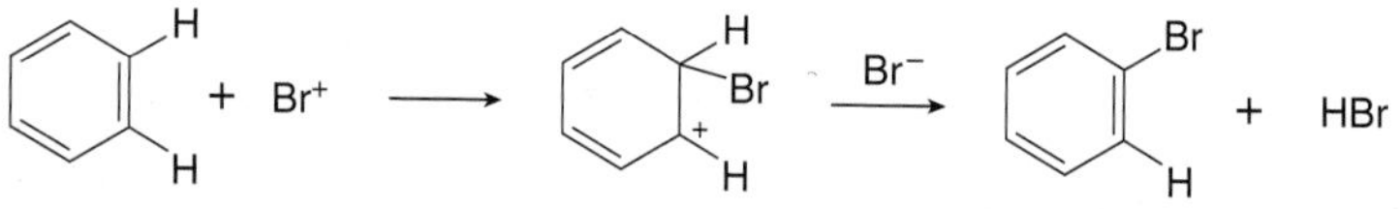

2.68 Hydroxide (^-OH) can react as a Brønsted–Lowry base (and remove a proton), or a Lewis base (and attack a carbon atom). (a) What organic product is formed when ^-OH reacts with the carbocation $(CH_3)_3C^+$ as a Brønsted–Lowry base? (b) What organic product is formed when ^-OH reacts with $(CH_3)_3C^+$ as a Lewis base?

2.69 Answer the following questions about esmolol, a drug used to treat high blood pressure sold under the trade name Brevibloc.

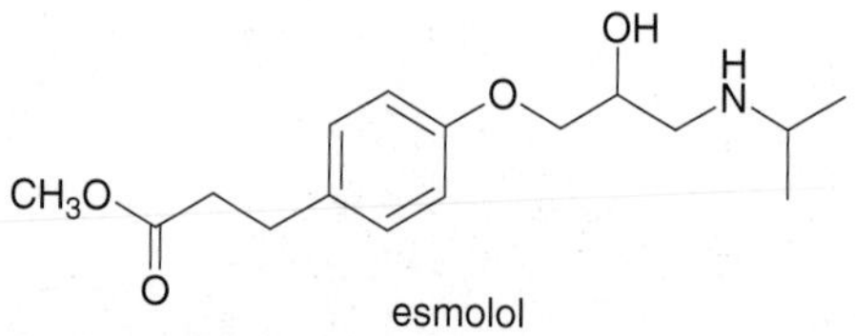

esmolol

a. Label the most acidic hydrogen atom in esmolol.

b. What products are formed when esmolol is treated with NaH?

c. What products are formed when esmolol is treated with HCl?

d. Label all sp^2 hybridized C atoms.

e. Label the only trigonal pyramidal atom.

f. Label all C's that bear a δ^+ charge.

Challenge Problems

2.70 Explain the large difference in the observed pK_a values for **P** and **Q.**

P pK_a = 11.1

Q pK_a = 1.2

2.71 DBU, 1,8-diazabicyclo[5.4.0]undec-7-ene, is a base we will encounter in elimination reactions in Chapter 8. Which N atom is more basic in DBU? Explain your choice.

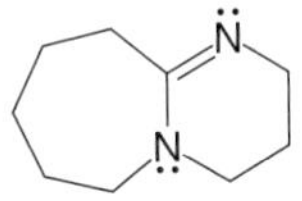

DBU

2.72 Molecules like acetamide (CH_3CONH_2) can be protonated on either their O or N atoms when treated with a strong acid like HCl. Which site is more readily protonated and why?

2.73 Two pK_a values are reported for malonic acid, a compound with two COOH groups. Explain why one pK_a is lower and one pK_a is higher than the pK_a of acetic acid (CH_3COOH, pK_a = 4.8).

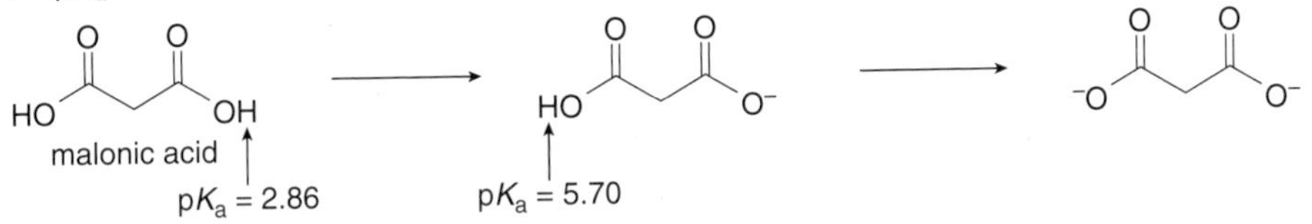

2.74 Amino acids such as glycine are the building blocks of large molecules called proteins that give structure to muscle, tendon, hair, and nails.

glycine zwitterion form

a. Explain why glycine does not actually exist in the form with all atoms uncharged, but actually exists as a salt called a zwitterion.
b. What product is formed when glycine is treated with concentrated HCl?
c. What product is formed when glycine is treated with NaOH?

2.75 Write a stepwise reaction sequence using proton transfer reactions to show how the following reaction occurs. (Hint: As a first step, use ^{-}OH to remove a proton from the CH_2 group between the C=O and C=C.)

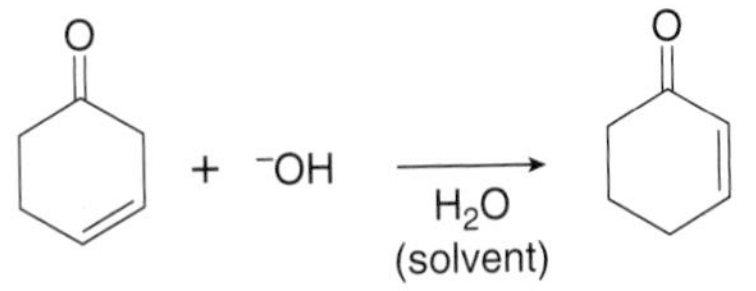

2.76 Which H atom in vitamin C (ascorbic acid) is most acidic?

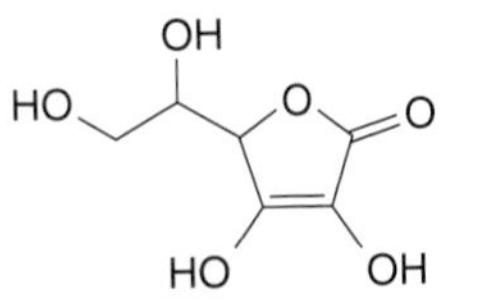

vitamin C
ascorbic acid

2.77 Which compound, **M** or **N,** is the stronger acid? Explain your choice.

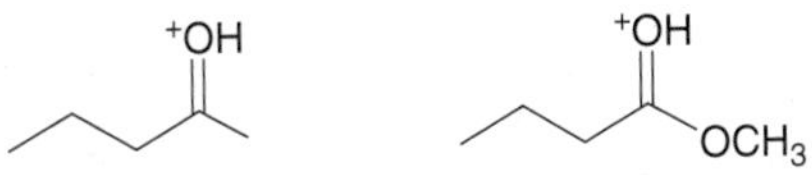

M **N**

3 Introduction to Organic Molecules and Functional Groups

- **3.1** Functional groups
- **3.2** An overview of functional groups
- **3.3** Intermolecular forces
- **3.4** Physical properties
- **3.5** Application: Vitamins
- **3.6** Application of solubility: Soap
- **3.7** Application: The cell membrane
- **3.8** Functional groups and reactivity
- **3.9** Biomolecules

Vitamin C, or **ascorbic acid,** is important in the formation of collagen, a protein that holds together the connective tissues of skin, muscle, and blood vessels. Citrus fruits—oranges, grapefruit, and lemons—are well known sources of vitamin C. A deficiency of vitamin C causes scurvy, a common disease of sailors in the 1600s when they had no access to fresh fruits on long voyages. Early Arctic explorers, however, were able to obtain vitamin C by eating scurvy grass, a low-growing plant found along the coasts of the Arctic region of the northern hemisphere. In Chapter 3, we learn why some vitamins like vitamin A can be stored in the fat cells in the body, whereas others like vitamin C are excreted in urine.

Having learned some basic concepts about structure, bonding, and acid–base chemistry in Chapters 1 and 2, we will now concentrate on organic molecules.

- What are the characteristic features of an organic compound?
- What determines the properties of an organic compound?

After these questions are answered, we can understand some important phenomena. For example, why do we store some vitamins in the body and readily excrete others? How does soap clean away dirt? We will also use the properties of organic molecules to explain some basic biological phenomena, such as the structure of cell membranes and the transport of species across these membranes.

3.1 Functional Groups

What are the characteristic features of an organic compound? Most organic molecules have C–C and C–H σ bonds. These bonds are strong, nonpolar, and not readily broken. Organic molecules may have the following structural features as well:

- ***Heteroatoms*—atoms other than carbon or hydrogen.** Common heteroatoms are nitrogen, oxygen, sulfur, phosphorus, and the halogens.
- ***π Bonds.*** The most common π bonds occur in C–C and C–O double bonds.

These structural features distinguish one organic molecule from another. They determine a molecule's geometry, physical properties, and reactivity, and comprise what is called a **functional group.**

- **A *functional group* is an atom or a group of atoms with characteristic chemical and physical properties. It is the *reactive part* of the molecule.**

Why do heteroatoms and π bonds confer reactivity on a particular molecule?

- **Heteroatoms have lone pairs and create electron-deficient sites on carbon.**
- **π Bonds are easily broken in chemical reactions. A π bond makes a molecule a base and a nucleophile.**

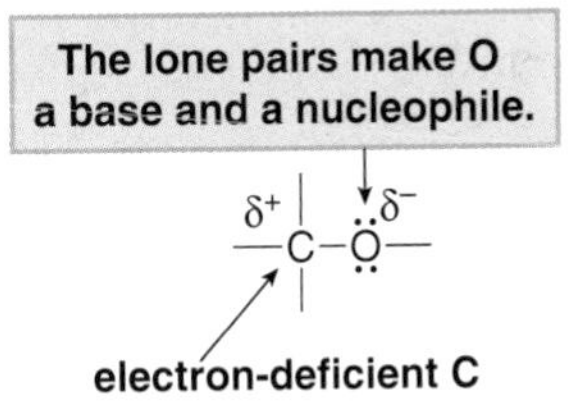

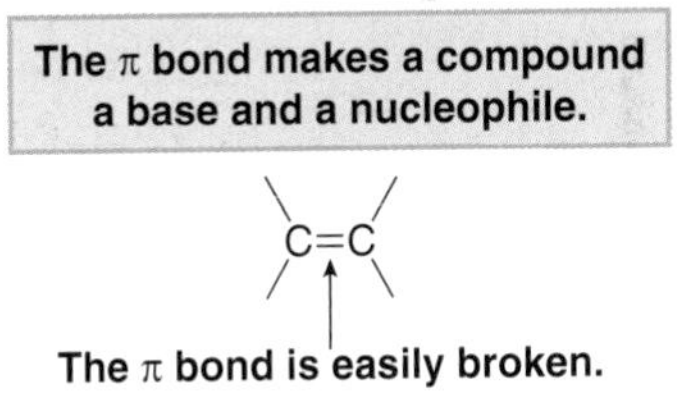

Don't think, though, that the C–C and C–H σ bonds are unimportant. They form the **carbon backbone** or **skeleton** to which the functional groups are bonded. A functional group usually behaves the same whether it is bonded to a carbon skeleton having as few as two or as many as 20 carbons. For this reason, we often abbreviate the carbon and hydrogen portion of the molecule by a capital letter **R,** and draw the **R** bonded to a particular functional group.

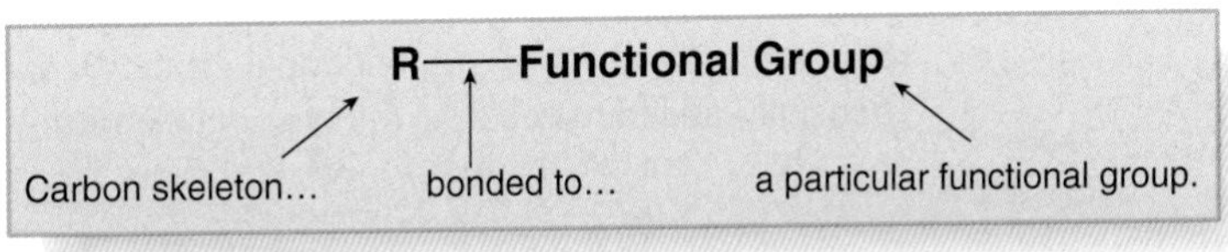

Ethane, for example, has only C–C and C–H σ bonds, so it has *no* functional group. Ethane has no polar bonds, no lone pairs, and no π bonds, so it has **no reactive sites.** Because of this, ethane and molecules like it are very unreactive.

Ethanol, on the other hand, has two carbons and five hydrogens in its carbon backbone, as well as an OH group, a functional group called a **hydroxy** group. Ethanol has lone pairs and polar bonds that make it reactive with a variety of reagents, including the acids and bases discussed in Chapter 2. The hydroxy group makes the properties of ethanol very different from the properties of ethane. Moreover, any organic molecule containing a hydroxy group has properties similar to ethanol.

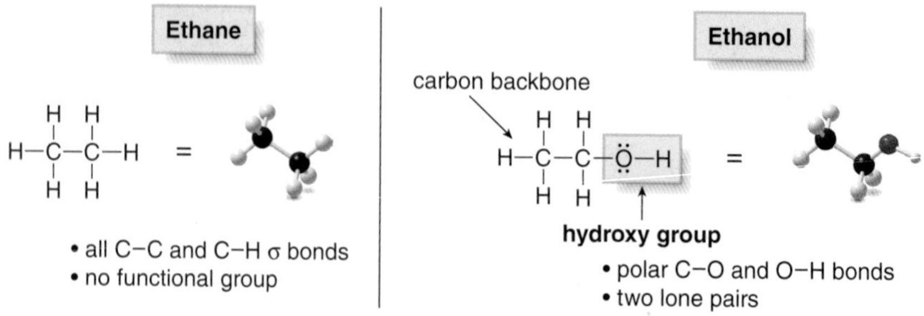

Most organic compounds can be grouped into a relatively small number of categories, based on the structure of their functional group. Ethane, for example, is an **alkane,** whereas ethanol is a simple **alcohol.**

Problem 3.1 What reaction occurs when CH_3CH_2OH is treated with (a) H_2SO_4? (b) NaH? What happens when CH_3CH_3 is treated with these same reagents?

3.2 An Overview of Functional Groups

We can subdivide the most common functional groups into three types. A more complete list of functional groups is presented on the inside front cover.

- **Hydrocarbons**
- **Compounds containing a C–Z σ bond** where Z = an electronegative element
- **Compounds containing a C=O group**

3.2A Hydrocarbons

To review the structure and bonding of the simple aliphatic hydrocarbons, return to Section 1.10.

The word *aliphatic* is derived from the Greek word *aleiphas* meaning *fat.* Aliphatic compounds have physical properties similar to fats.

Hydrocarbons **are compounds made up of only the elements carbon and hydrogen.** They may be **aliphatic** or **aromatic.**

[1] Aliphatic hydrocarbons. Aliphatic hydrocarbons can be divided into three subgroups.

- ***Alkanes*** have only C–C σ bonds and no functional group. Ethane, $\mathbf{CH_3CH_3}$, is a simple alkane.
- ***Alkenes*** have a C–C double bond as a functional group. Ethylene, $\mathbf{CH_2{=}CH_2}$, is a simple alkene.
- ***Alkynes*** have a C–C triple bond as a functional group. Acetylene, $\mathbf{HC{\equiv}CH}$, is a simple alkyne.

[2] Aromatic hydrocarbons. This class of hydrocarbons was so named because many of the earliest known aromatic compounds had strong, characteristic odors.

The simplest aromatic hydrocarbon is **benzene.** The six-membered ring and three π bonds of benzene comprise a *single* functional group. Benzene is a component of the **BTX** mixture (**B** for **b**enzene) added to gasoline to boost octane ratings.

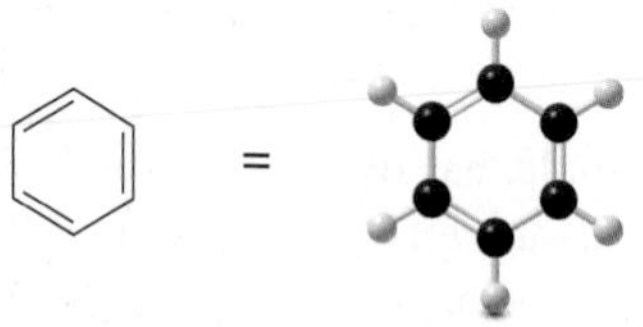

benzene
molecular formula C_6H_6

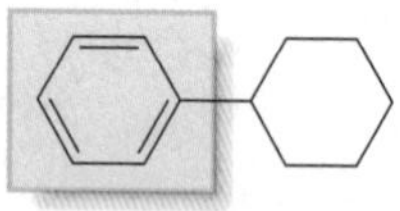

phenyl group
C_6H_5–
phenylcyclohexane

Table 3.1 Hydrocarbons

Type of compound	General structure	Example	Functional group
Alkane	R–H	CH_3CH_3	—
Alkene	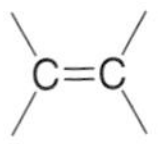	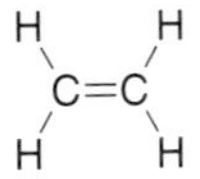	double bond
Alkyne	–C≡C–	H–C≡C–H	triple bond
Aromatic compound			phenyl group

Polyethylene is a synthetic plastic first produced in the 1930s, and initially used as insulating material for radar during World War II. It is now a plastic used in milk containers, sandwich bags, and plastic wrapping. Over 100 billion pounds of polyethylene are manufactured each year.

When a benzene ring is bonded to another group, it is called a **phenyl group.** In phenylcyclohexane, for example, a phenyl group is bonded to the six-membered cyclohexane ring. Table 3.1 summarizes the four different types of hydrocarbons.

Alkanes, which have no functional groups, are notoriously unreactive except under very drastic conditions. For example, **polyethylene** is a synthetic plastic and high molecular weight alkane, consisting of chains of $-CH_2-$ groups bonded together, hundreds or even thousands of atoms long. Because it is an alkane with no reactive sites, it is a very stable compound that does not readily degrade and thus persists for years in landfills.

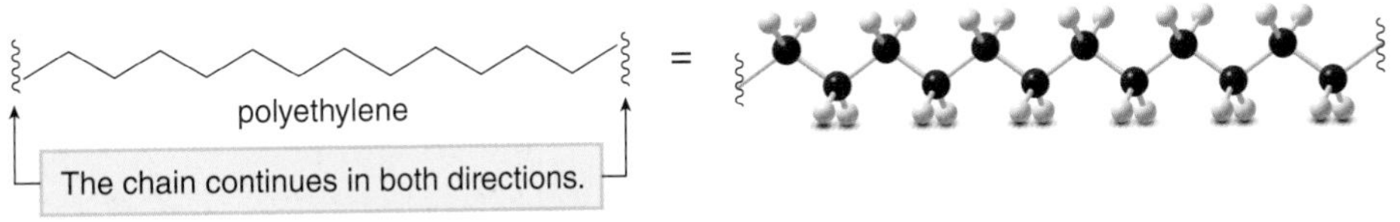

3.2B Compounds Containing C–Z σ Bonds

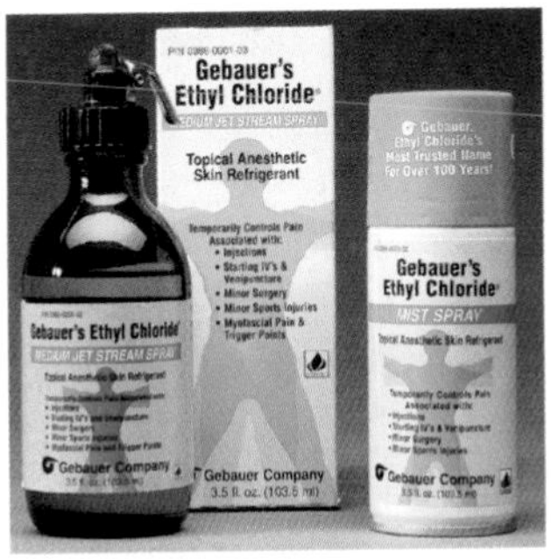

Chloroethane, CH_3CH_2Cl, is a local anesthetic.

Hemibrevetoxin B is a neurotoxin produced by algal blooms referred to as "red tides," because of the color often seen in shallow ocean waters when these algae proliferate.

Several types of functional groups that contain C–Z σ bonds are listed in Table 3.2. The electronegative heteroatom Z creates a polar bond, making carbon electron deficient. The lone pairs on Z are available for reaction with protons and other electrophiles, especially when Z = N or O.

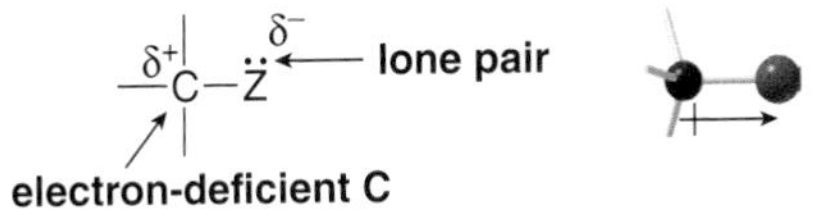

Several simple compounds in this category are widely used. As an example, chloroethane (CH_3CH_2Cl, commonly called ethyl chloride) is an alkyl halide used as a local anesthetic. Chloroethane quickly evaporates when sprayed on a wound, causing a cooling sensation that numbs the site of an injury.

Molecules containing these functional groups may be simple or very complex. Diethyl ether, the first common general anesthetic, is a simple ether because it contains a single O atom, depicted in red, bonded to two C atoms. Hemibrevetoxin B, on the other hand, contains four ether groups, in addition to other functional groups.

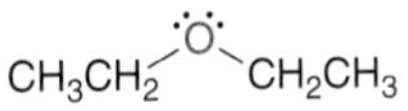

diethyl ether

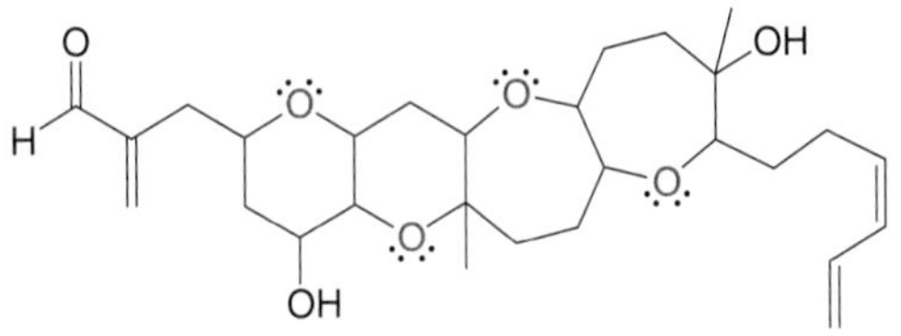

hemibrevetoxin B

Table 3.2 Compounds Containing C–Z σ Bonds

Type of compound	General structure	Example	3-D structure	Functional group
Alkyl halide	R–X: (X = F, Cl, Br, I)	CH_3–Br:	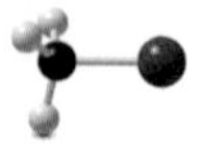	**–X** halo group
Alcohol	R–OH	CH_3–OH		**–OH** hydroxy group
Ether	R–O–R	CH_3–O–CH_3	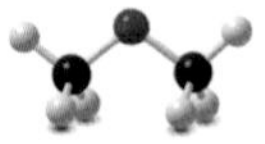	**–OR** alkoxy group
Amine	R–NH_2 or R_2NH or R_3N	CH_3–NH_2	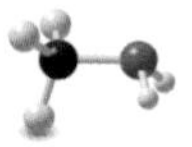	**–NH_2** amino group
Thiol	R–SH	CH_3–SH	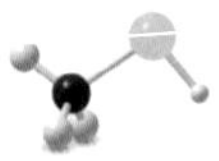	**–SH** mercapto group
Sulfide	R–S–R	CH_3–S–CH_3		**–SR** alkylthio group

3.2C Compounds Containing a C=O Group

Many different types of functional groups possess a C–O double bond (a **carbonyl group**), as shown in Table 3.3. The polar C–O bond makes the carbonyl carbon an electrophile, while the lone pairs on O allow it to react as a nucleophile and base. The carbonyl group also contains a π bond that is more easily broken than a C–O σ bond.

Reactive features of a carbonyl group

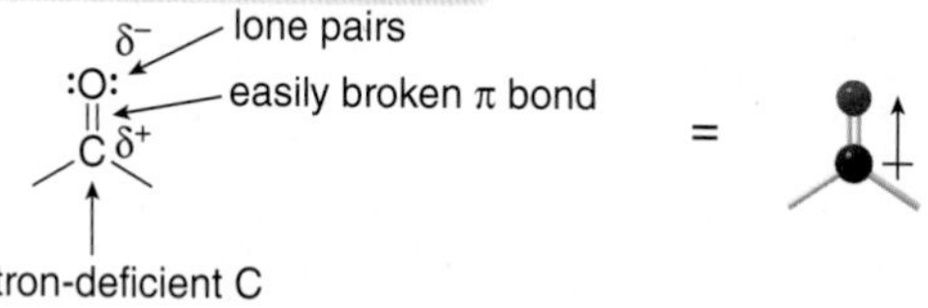

Atenolol and donepezil are examples of useful drugs that contain a variety of functional groups. **Atenolol is a β blocker,** a group of drugs used to treat hypertension. Donepezil, sold under the trade name Aricept, is used to treat mild to moderate dementia associated with Alzheimer's disease.

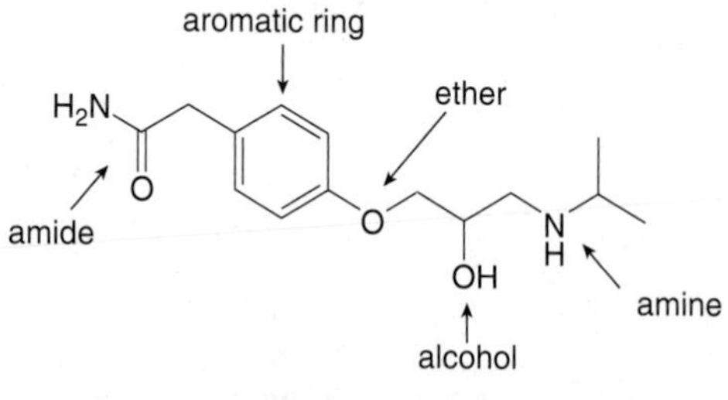

atenolol
(used to treat high blood pressure)

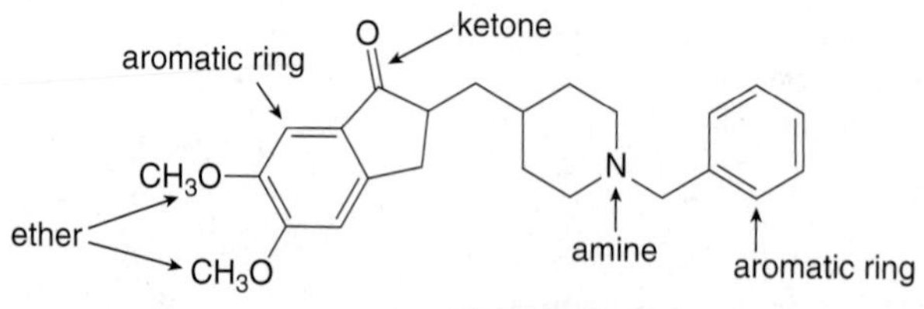

donepezil
(used to treat Alzheimer's disease)

Table 3.3 Compounds Containing a C=O Group

Type of compound	General structure	Example	3-D structure	Functional group
Aldehyde	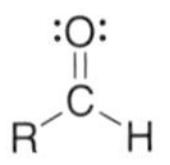	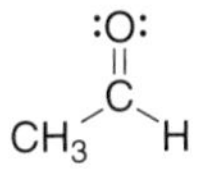	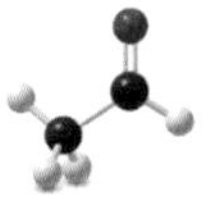	C=O carbonyl group
Ketone	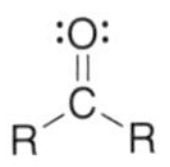	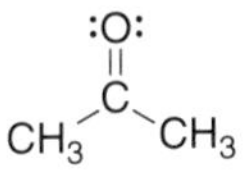	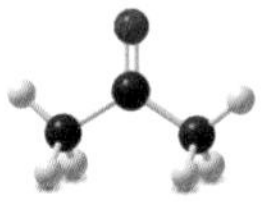	C=O carbonyl group
Carboxylic acid	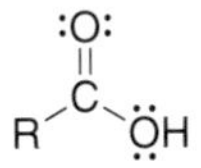	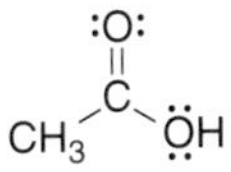	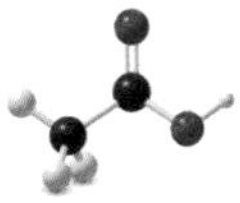	–COOH carboxy group
Ester	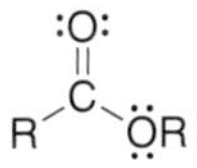	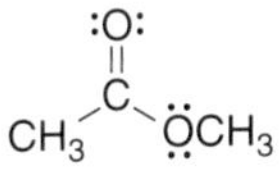	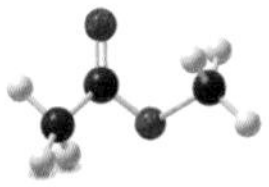	–COOR
Amide	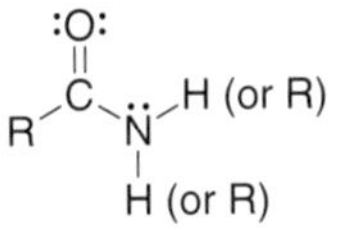	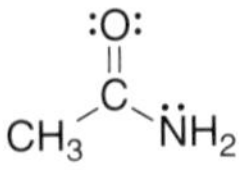	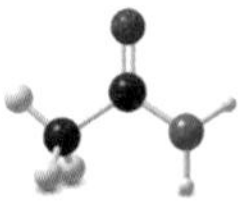	$-CONH_2$, –CONHR, or $-CONR_2$
Acid chloride	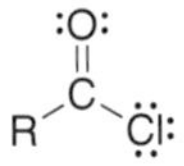	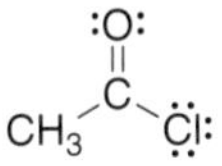	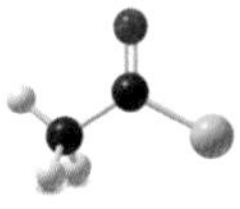	–COCl

The importance of a functional group cannot be overstated. A functional group determines all the following properties of a molecule:

- bonding and shape
- type and strength of intermolecular forces
- physical properties
- nomenclature
- chemical reactivity

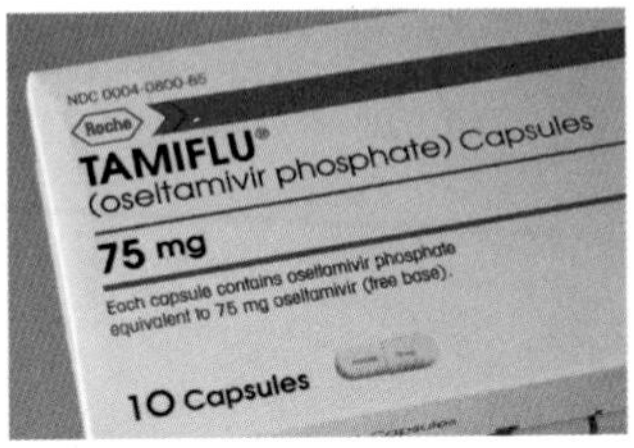

Tamiflu is the trade name for oseltamivir, an antiviral drug used to treat influenza.

Problem 3.2 Oseltamivir can be prepared in 10 steps from shikimic acid. Identify the functional groups in oseltamivir and shikimic acid.

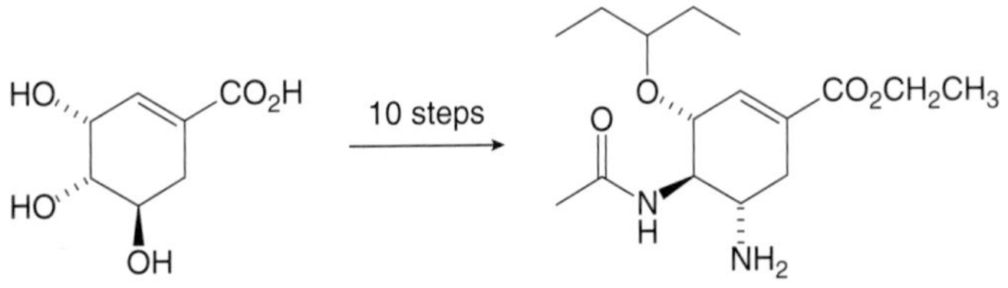

shikimic acid

oseltamivir

Problem 3.3 Draw the structure of a compound fitting each description:

a. an aldehyde with molecular formula C_4H_8O
b. a ketone with molecular formula C_4H_8O
c. a carboxylic acid with molecular formula $C_4H_8O_2$
d. an ester with molecular formula $C_4H_8O_2$

Problem 3.4 Draw structures that fit each description and name the functional group in each molecule: (a) two constitutional isomers with molecular formula $C_5H_{10}O$ that contain different functional groups; (b) two constitutional isomers with molecular formula $C_6H_{10}O$ that contain the same functional group.

3.3 Intermolecular Forces

Intermolecular forces are the interactions that exist *between* molecules. A functional group determines the type and strength of these interactions.

3.3A Ionic Compounds

Intermolecular forces are also referred to as **noncovalent interactions** or **nonbonded interactions.**

Ionic compounds contain oppositely charged particles held together by **extremely strong electrostatic interactions.** These ionic interactions are much stronger than the intermolecular forces present between covalent molecules, so it takes a great deal of energy to separate oppositely charged ions from each other.

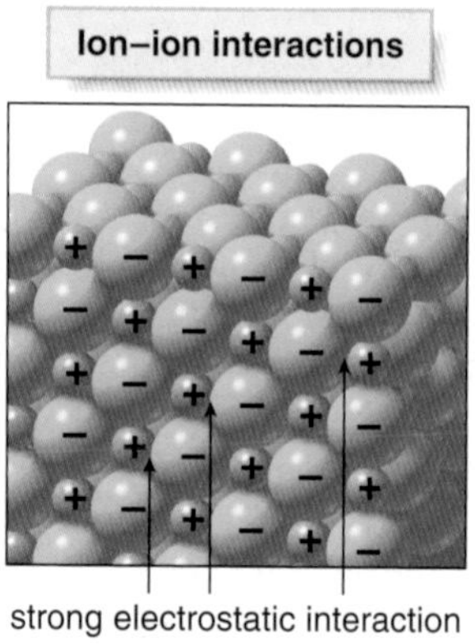

3.3B Covalent Compounds

Covalent compounds are composed of discrete molecules. The nature of the forces between the molecules depends on the functional group present. There are three different types of interactions, presented here in order of *increasing strength:*

- **van der Waals forces**
- **dipole–dipole interactions**
- **hydrogen bonding**

Van der Waals Forces

Van der Waals forces, also called **London forces,** are very weak interactions caused by the **momentary changes in electron density in a molecule.** Van der Waals forces are the only attractive forces present in nonpolar compounds.

Although any single van der Waals interaction is weak, a large number of van der Waals interactions creates a strong force. For example, geckos stick to walls and ceilings by van der Waals interactions of the surfaces with the 500,000 tiny hairs on each foot.

For example, although a nonpolar CH_4 molecule has no net dipole, at any one instant its electron density may not be completely symmetrical, creating a *temporary* dipole. This can induce a temporary dipole in another CH_4 molecule, with the partial positive and negative charges arranged close to each other. **The weak interaction of these temporary dipoles constitutes van der Waals forces.** All compounds exhibit van der Waals forces.

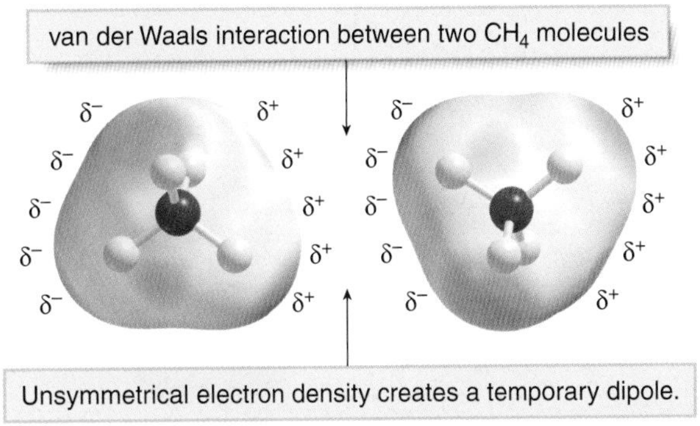
van der Waals interaction between two CH4 molecules
δ−
δ+
Unsymmetrical electron density creates a temporary dipole.

The surface area of a molecule determines the strength of the van der Waals interactions. **The larger the surface area, the larger the attractive force between two molecules, and the stronger the intermolecular forces.** Long, sausage-shaped molecules such as $CH_3CH_2CH_2CH_2CH_3$ (pentane) have stronger van der Waals interactions than compact spherical ones like $C(CH_3)_4$ (2,2-dimethylpropane), as shown in Figure 3.1.

Another factor affecting the strength of van der Waals forces is **polarizability.**

- ***Polarizability*** **is a measure of how the electron cloud around an atom responds to changes in its electronic environment.**

Larger atoms like iodine, which have more loosely held valence electrons, are more polarizable than smaller atoms like fluorine, which have more tightly held electrons. Because larger atoms have more easily induced dipoles, compounds containing them possess stronger intermolecular interactions.

Figure 3.1
Surface area and van der Waals forces

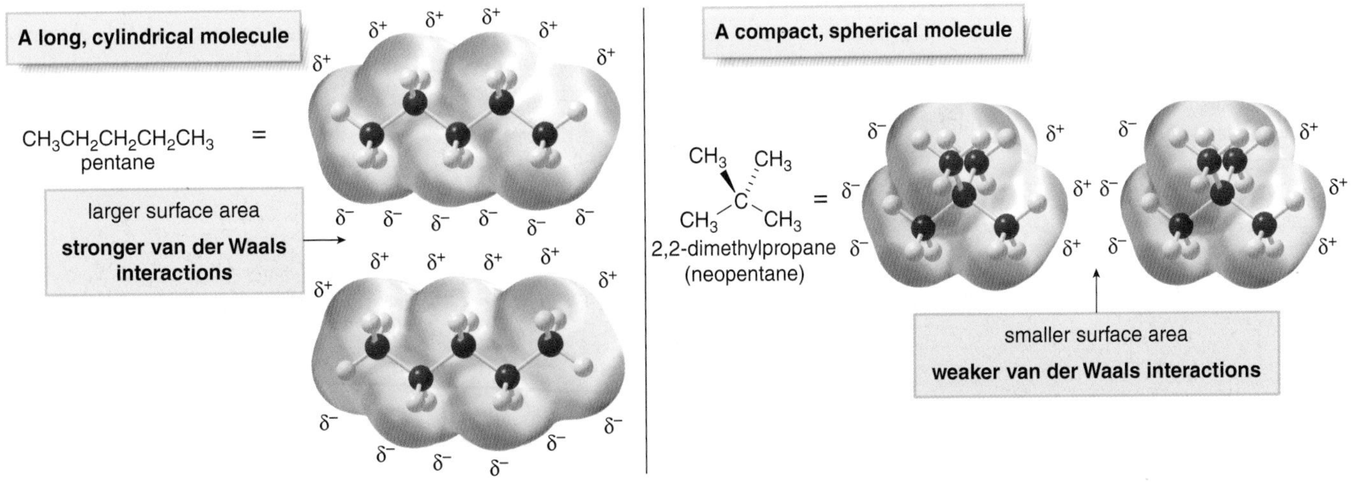
A long, cylindrical molecule
CH3CH2CH2CH2CH3 =
pentane
larger surface area
stronger van der Waals interactions
δ+
δ−
A compact, spherical molecule
CH3 CH3
C
CH3 CH3
=
2,2-dimethylpropane
(neopentane)
smaller surface area
weaker van der Waals interactions

Thus, two F_2 molecules have little force of attraction between them, because the electrons are held very tightly and temporary dipoles are difficult to induce. On the other hand, two I_2 molecules exhibit a much stronger force of attraction because the electrons are held much more loosely and temporary dipoles are easily induced.

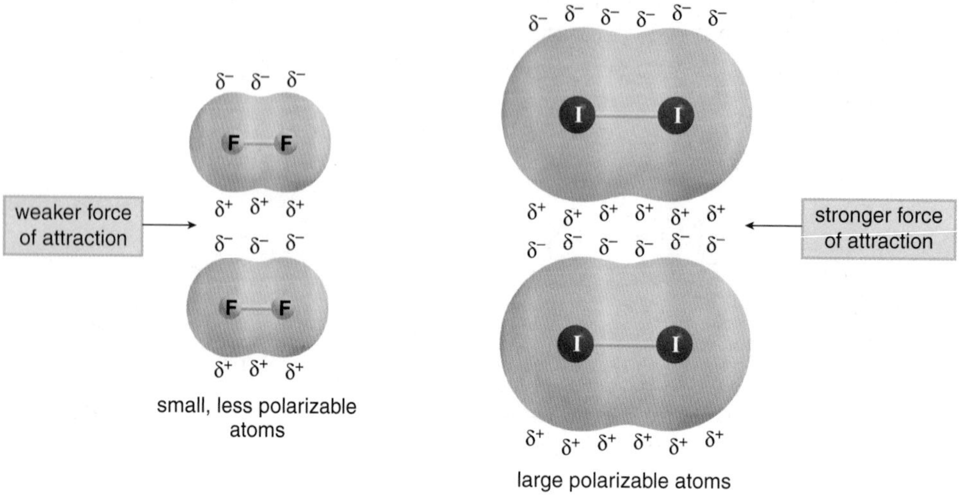

Dipole–Dipole Interactions

Dipole–dipole interactions **are the attractive forces between the permanent dipoles of two polar molecules.** In acetone, $(CH_3)_2C{=}O$, for example, the dipoles in adjacent molecules align so that the partial positive and partial negative charges are in close proximity. These attractive forces caused by permanent dipoles are much stronger than weak van der Waals forces.

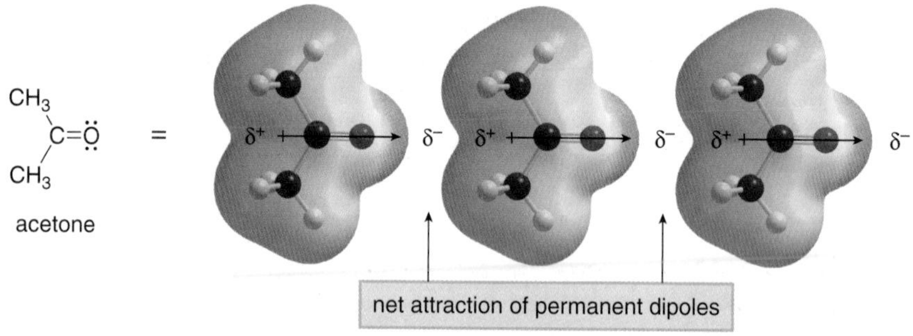

Hydrogen Bonding

Hydrogen bonding helps determine the three-dimensional shape of large biomolecules such as carbohydrates and proteins. See Chapters 28 and 29 for details.

Hydrogen bonding **typically occurs when a hydrogen atom bonded to O, N, or F is electrostatically attracted to a lone pair of electrons on an O, N, or F atom in another molecule.** Thus, H_2O molecules can hydrogen bond to each other. When they do, an H atom covalently bonded to O in one water molecule is attracted to a lone pair of electrons on the O in another water molecule. Hydrogen bonds are the strongest of the three types of intermolecular forces, though they are still much weaker than any covalent bond.

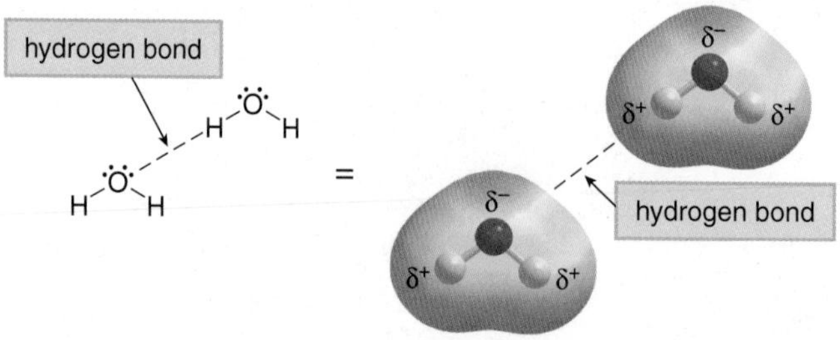

Sample Problem 3.1 illustrates how to determine the relative strength of intermolecular forces for a group of compounds. Table 3.4 summarizes the four types of interactions that affect the properties of all compounds.

Sample Problem 3.1

Rank the following compounds in order of increasing strength of intermolecular forces: $CH_3CH_2CH_2CH_2CH_3$ (pentane), $CH_3CH_2CH_2CH_2OH$ (1-butanol), and $CH_3CH_2CH_2CHO$ (butanal).

Solution

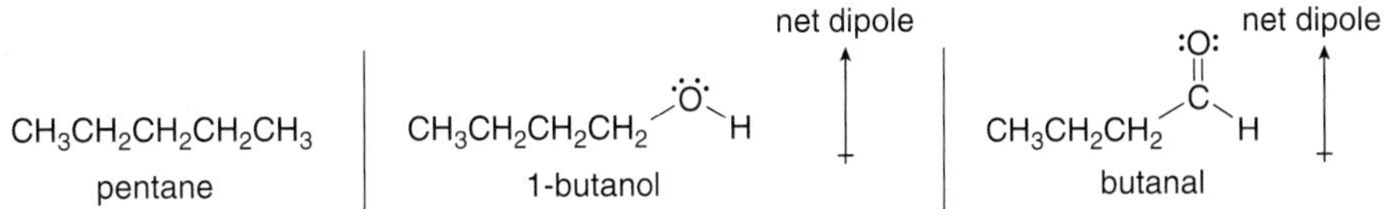

- nonpolar molecule

- bent molecule around O
- polar C–O and O–H bonds
- O–H bond for hydrogen bonding

- trigonal planar C
- polar C=O bond

- Pentane has only nonpolar C – C and C – H bonds, so its molecules are held together by only **van der Waals** forces.
- 1-Butanol is a polar bent molecule, so it can have **dipole–dipole** interactions in addition to **van der Waals** forces. Because it has an O – H bond, 1-butanol molecules are held together by intermolecular **hydrogen bonds** as well.
- Butanal has a trigonal planar carbon with a polar C = O bond, so it exhibits **dipole–dipole** interactions in addition to **van der Waals** forces. There is *no* H atom bonded to O, so two butanal molecules *cannot* hydrogen bond to each other.

$CH_3CH_2CH_2CH_2CH_3$ $CH_3CH_2CH_2CHO$ $CH_3CH_2CH_2CH_2OH$

Increasing strength of intermolecular forces →

Table 3.4 Summary of Types of Intermolecular Forces

Type of force	Relative strength	Exhibited by	Example
van der Waals	weak	all molecules	$CH_3CH_2CH_2CH_2CH_3$ $CH_3CH_2CH_2CHO$ $CH_3CH_2CH_2CH_2OH$
dipole–dipole	moderate	molecules with a net dipole	$CH_3CH_2CH_2CHO$ $CH_3CH_2CH_2CH_2OH$
hydrogen bonding	strong	molecules with an O – H, N – H, or H – F bond	$CH_3CH_2CH_2CH_2OH$
ion–ion	very strong	ionic compounds	NaCl, LiF

Problem 3.5

What types of intermolecular forces are present in each compound?

a. 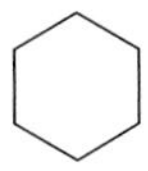

c. $(CH_3CH_2)_3N$

e. $CH_3CH_2CH_2COOH$

b. 

d. $CH_2=CHCl$

f. $CH_3-C\equiv C-CH_3$

3.4 Physical Properties

The strength of a compound's intermolecular forces determines many of its physical properties, including its boiling point, melting point, and solubility.

3.4A Boiling Point (bp)

The *boiling point* of a compound is the temperature at which a liquid is converted to a gas. In boiling, energy is needed to overcome the attractive forces in the more ordered liquid state.

- **The stronger the intermolecular forces, the higher the boiling point.**

Because **ionic compounds** are held together by extremely strong interactions, they have **very high boiling points.** The boiling point of NaCl, for example, is 1413 °C. **With covalent molecules, the boiling point depends on the identity of the functional group.** For compounds of approximately the same molecular weight:

compounds with van der Waals forces	compounds with dipole–dipole interactions	compounds with hydrogen bonding

Increasing strength of intermolecular forces
Increasing boiling point

Recall from Sample Problem 3.1, for example, that the relative strength of the intermolecular forces increases from pentane to butanal to 1-butanol. The boiling points of these compounds increase in the same order.

$CH_3CH_2CH_2CH_2CH_3$	$CH_3CH_2CH_2CHO$	$CH_3CH_2CH_2CH_2OH$
pentane	butanal	1-butanol
bp = 36 °C	bp = 76 °C	bp = 118 °C

Increasing strength of intermolecular forces
Increasing boiling point

Because surface area and polarizability affect the strength of intermolecular forces, they also affect the boiling point. For two compounds with similar functional groups:

- **The larger the surface area, the higher the boiling point.**
- **The more polarizable the atoms, the higher the boiling point.**

Examples of each phenomenon are illustrated in Figure 3.2. In comparing two ketones that differ in size, 3-pentanone has a higher boiling point than acetone because it has a greater molecular weight and larger surface area. In comparing two alkyl halides having the same number of carbon atoms, CH_3I has a higher boiling point than CH_3F because I is more polarizable than F.

Sample Problem 3.2 Which compound in each pair has the higher boiling point?

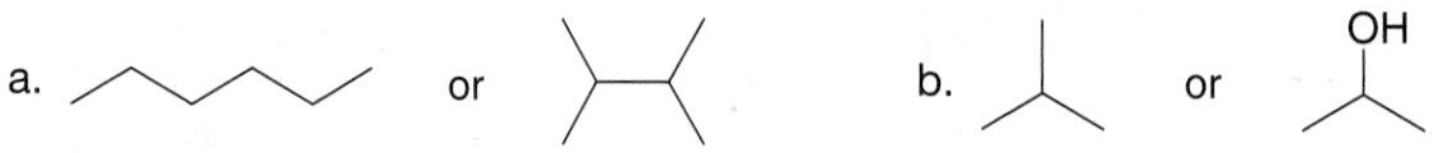

A B C D

Solution

a. Isomers **A** and **B** have only nonpolar C–C and C–H bonds, so they exhibit only van der Waals forces. Because **B** is more compact, it has less surface area and a lower boiling point.

b. Compounds **C** and **D** have approximately the same molecular weight but different functional groups. **C** is a nonpolar alkane, exhibiting only van der Waals forces. **D** is an alcohol with an O–H group available for hydrogen bonding, so it has stronger intermolecular forces and a higher boiling point.

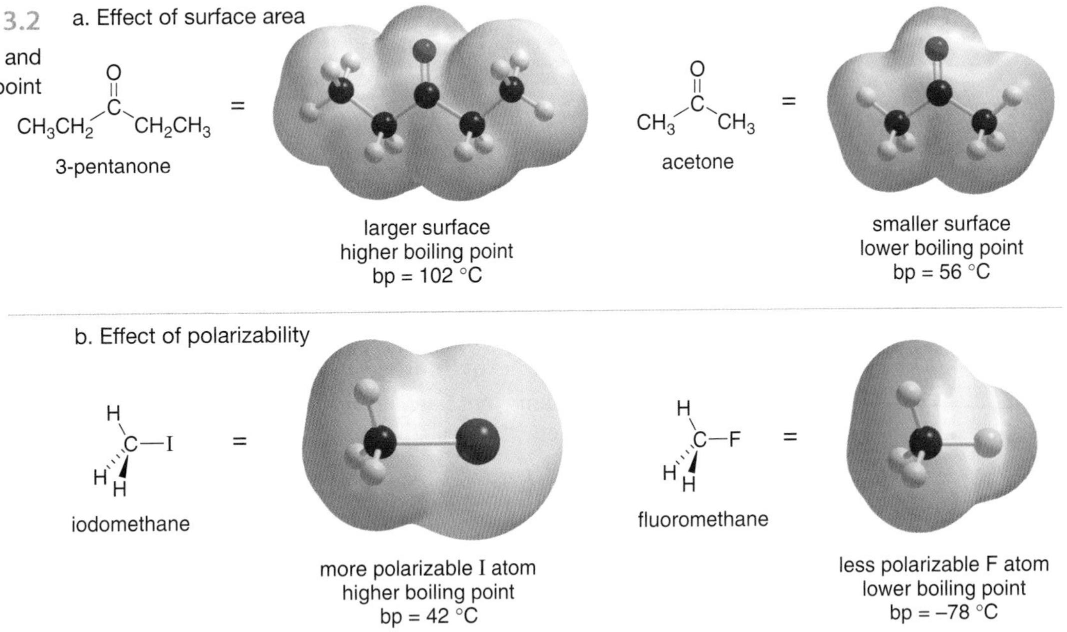
a. Effect of surface area
3-pentanone
larger surface
higher boiling point
bp = 102 °C
acetone
smaller surface
lower boiling point
bp = 56 °C
b. Effect of polarizability
iodomethane
more polarizable I atom
higher boiling point
bp = 42 °C
fluoromethane
less polarizable F atom
lower boiling point
bp = –78 °C

Figure 3.2 Effect of surface area and polarizability on boiling point

Problem 3.6 Which compound in each pair has the higher boiling point?

a. $(CH_3)_2C{=}CH_2$ or $(CH_3)_2C{=}O$
b. CH_3CH_2COOH or CH_3COOCH_3
c. $CH_3(CH_2)_4CH_3$ or $CH_3(CH_2)_5CH_3$
d. $CH_2{=}CHCl$ or $CH_2{=}CHI$

Problem 3.7 Explain why the boiling point of propanamide, $CH_3CH_2CONH_2$, is considerably higher than the boiling point of *N,N*-dimethylformamide, $HCON(CH_3)_2$ (213 °C vs. 153 °C), even though both compounds are isomeric amides.

Liquids having different boiling points can be separated in the laboratory using a *distillation* apparatus (Figure 3.3). When a mixture of two liquids is heated in the distilling flask,

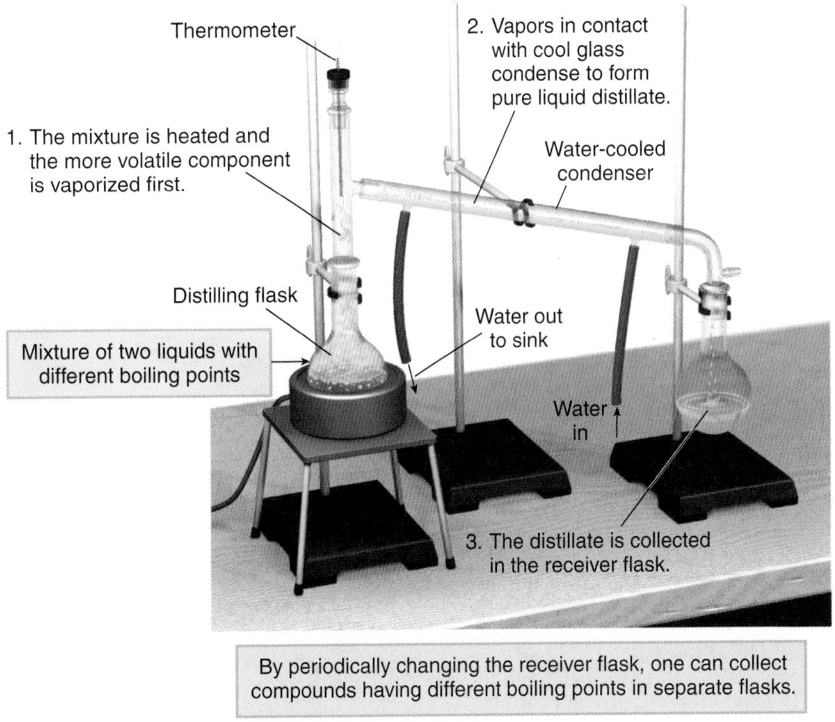
Thermometer
2. Vapors in contact with cool glass condense to form pure liquid distillate.
1. The mixture is heated and the more volatile component is vaporized first.
Water-cooled condenser
Distilling flask
Water out to sink
Mixture of two liquids with different boiling points
Water in
3. The distillate is collected in the receiver flask.
By periodically changing the receiver flask, one can collect compounds having different boiling points in separate flasks.

Figure 3.3 Schematic of a distillation apparatus

the lower boiling compound, the **more volatile component,** distills first, followed by the **less volatile, higher boiling component.** By collecting the distillate in a series of receiver flasks, the two liquids can usually be separated from each other. The best separations are generally achieved when the liquids in the mixture have widely different boiling points.

3.4B Melting Point (mp)

The *melting point* is the temperature at which a solid is converted to its liquid phase. In melting, energy is needed to overcome the attractive forces in the more ordered crystalline solid. Two factors determine the melting point of a compound.

- **The stronger the intermolecular forces, the higher the melting point.**
- **Given the same functional group, the more symmetrical the compound, the higher the melting point.**

Because **ionic compounds** are held together by extremely strong interactions, they have **very high melting points.** For example, the melting point of NaCl is 801 °C. With covalent molecules, the melting point once again depends on the identity of the functional group. For compounds of approximately the same molecular weight:

compounds with van der Waals forces	compounds with dipole–dipole interactions	compounds with hydrogen bonding

→

Increasing strength of intermolecular forces
Increasing melting point

The trend in the melting points of pentane, butanal, and 1-butanol parallels the trend observed in their boiling points.

$CH_3CH_2CH_2CH_2CH_3$	$CH_3CH_2CH_2CHO$	$CH_3CH_2CH_2CH_2OH$
pentane	butanal	1-butanol
mp = −130 °C	mp = −96 °C	mp = −90 °C

→

Increasing strength of intermolecular forces
Increasing melting point

Symmetry also plays a role in determining the melting points of compounds having the same functional group and similar molecular weights, but very different shapes. A compact symmetrical molecule like 2,2-dimethylpropane packs well into a crystalline lattice whereas 2-methylbutane, which has a CH_3 group dangling from a four-carbon chain, does not. Thus, 2,2-dimethylpropane has a much higher melting point.

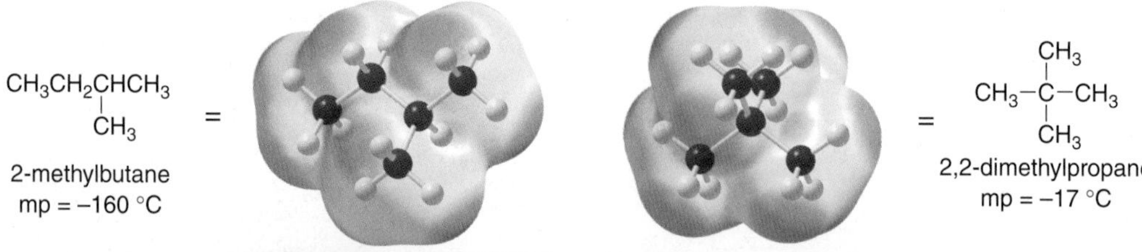

2-methylbutane
mp = −160 °C

2,2-dimethylpropane
mp = −17 °C

less symmetrical molecule
lower melting point

more symmetrical molecule
higher melting point

Problem 3.8 Predict which compound in each pair has the higher melting point.

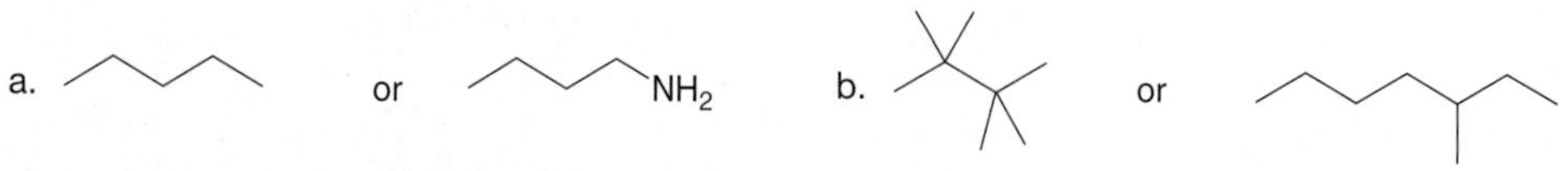

Problem 3.9 Consider acetic acid (CH_3CO_2H) and its conjugate base, sodium acetate (CH_3CO_2Na). (a) What intermolecular forces are present in each compound? (b) Explain why the melting point of sodium acetate (324 °C) is considerably higher than the melting point of acetic acid (17 °C).

3.4C Solubility

Quantitatively, a compound may be considered soluble when 3 g of solute dissolves in 100 mL of solvent.

Solubility* is the extent to which a compound, called the *solute,* dissolves in a liquid, called the *solvent. In dissolving a compound, the energy needed to break up the interactions between the molecules or ions of the solute comes from new interactions between the solute and the solvent.

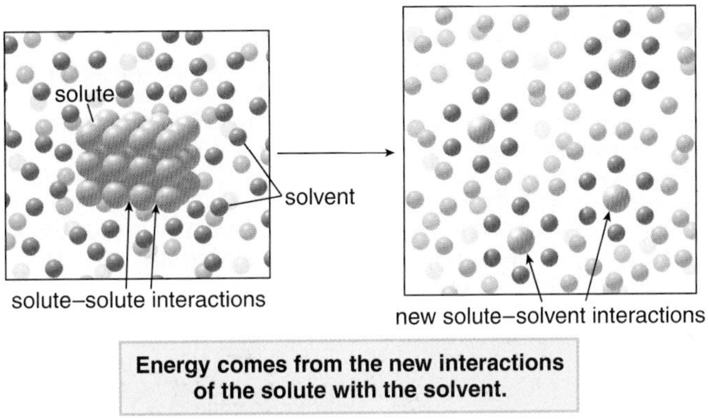

Compounds dissolve in solvents having similar kinds of intermolecular forces.

- "Like dissolves like."
- Polar compounds dissolve in polar solvents. Nonpolar or weakly polar compounds dissolve in nonpolar or weakly polar solvents.

Water and **organic liquids** are two different kinds of solvents. Water is very polar because it is capable of hydrogen bonding with a solute. Many organic solvents are either nonpolar, like carbon tetrachloride (CCl_4) and hexane [$CH_3(CH_2)_4CH_3$], or weakly polar like diethyl ether ($CH_3CH_2OCH_2CH_3$).

Ionic compounds are held together by strong electrostatic forces, so they need very polar solvents to dissolve. **Most ionic compounds are soluble in water, but are insoluble in organic solvents.** To dissolve an ionic compound, the strong ion–ion interactions must be replaced by many weaker **ion–dipole interactions,** as illustrated in Figure 3.4.

Figure 3.4 Dissolving an ionic compound in H_2O

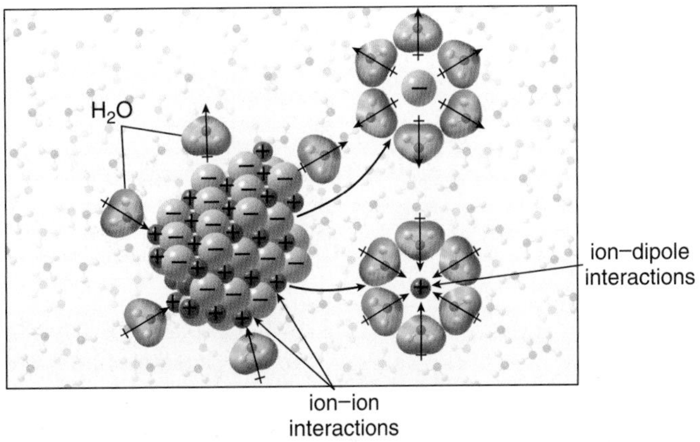

- When an ionic solid is dissolved in H_2O, the ion–ion interactions are replaced by ion–dipole interactions. Though these forces are weaker, there are so many of them that they compensate for the stronger ionic bonds.

Most organic compounds are soluble in organic solvents (remember, *like dissolves like*). **An organic compound is water soluble only if it contains one polar functional group capable of hydrogen bonding with the solvent for every five C atoms it contains.** In other words, a water-soluble organic compound has an O- or N-containing functional group that solubilizes its nonpolar carbon backbone.

Compare, for example, the solubility of butane and acetone in H_2O and CCl_4.

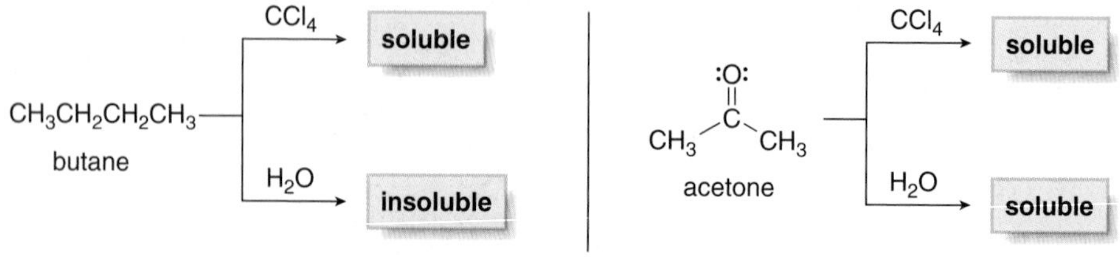

Because butane and acetone are both organic compounds having a C−C and C−H backbone, they are soluble in the organic solvent CCl_4. Butane, a nonpolar molecule, is insoluble in the polar solvent H_2O. Acetone, however, is H_2O soluble because it contains only three C atoms and its O atom can hydrogen bond with one H atom of H_2O. In fact, acetone is so soluble in water that acetone and water are **miscible**—they form solutions in all proportions with each other.

$(CH_3)_2C=O$ molecules cannot hydrogen bond to each other because they have no OH group. However, $(CH_3)_2C=O$ can hydrogen bond to H_2O because its O atom can hydrogen bond to one of the H atoms of H_2O.

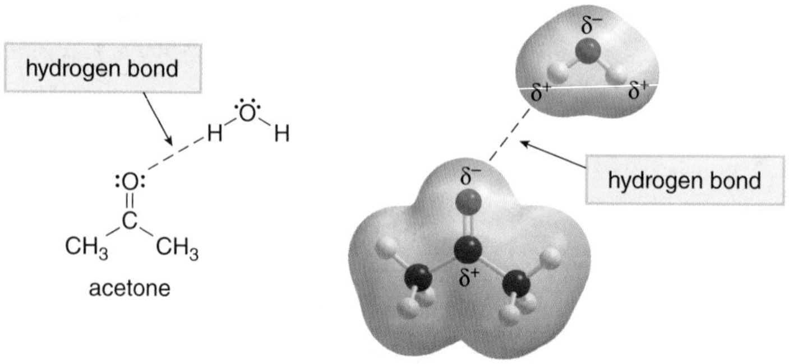

Hydrogen bonding makes the small polar molecule acetone H_2O soluble.

For an organic compound with one functional group, **a compound is water soluble only if it has ≤ five C atoms and contains an O or N atom.**

The size of an organic molecule with a polar functional group determines its water solubility. A low molecular weight alcohol like **ethanol is water soluble** because it has a small carbon skeleton (≤ five C atoms) compared to the size of its polar OH group. Cholesterol, on the other hand, has 27 carbon atoms and only one OH group. Its carbon skeleton is too large for the OH group to solubilize by hydrogen bonding, so **cholesterol is insoluble in water.**

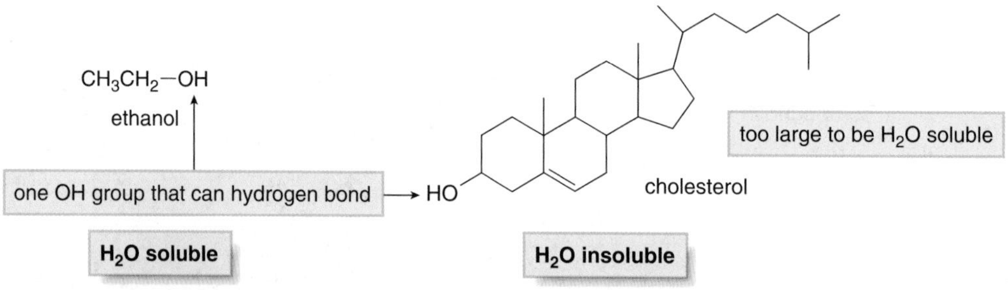

Hydrophobic = afraid of H_2O; hydrophilic = H_2O loving.

- **The nonpolar part of a molecule that is not attracted to H_2O is said to be *hydrophobic.***
- **The polar part of a molecule that can hydrogen bond to H_2O is said to be *hydrophilic.***

In cholesterol, for example, the **hydroxy group is hydrophilic,** whereas the **carbon skeleton is hydrophobic.**

MTBE (*tert*-butyl methyl ether) and 4,4'-dichlorobiphenyl (a polychlorinated biphenyl, abbreviated as PCB) demonstrate that solubility properties can help determine the fate of organic compounds in the environment.

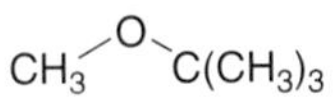

MTBE
tert-butyl methyl ether

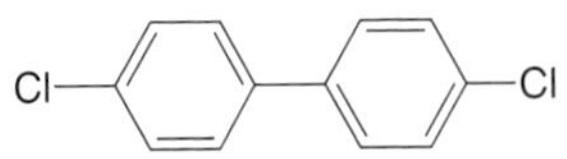

4,4'-dichlorobiphenyl
(a polychlorinated biphenyl, PCB)

Using **MTBE** as a high-octane additive in unleaded gasoline has had a negative environmental impact. Although MTBE is not toxic or carcinogenic, it has a distinctive, nauseating odor, and **it is water soluble.** Small amounts of MTBE have contaminated the drinking water in several communities, making it unfit for consumption. For this reason, the use of MTBE as a gasoline additive has steadily declined in the United States since 1999.

4,4'-Dichlorobiphenyl is a polychlorinated biphenyl **(PCB),** a compound that contains two benzene rings joined by a C–C bond, and substituted by one or more chlorine atoms on each ring. PCBs have been used as plasticizers in polystyrene coffee cups and coolants in transformers. They have been released into the environment during production, use, storage, and disposal, making them one of the most widespread organic pollutants. **PCBs are insoluble in H_2O, but very soluble in organic media,** so they are soluble in fatty tissue, including that found in all types of fish and birds around the world. Although PCBs are not acutely toxic, frequently ingesting large quantities of fish contaminated with PCBs has been shown to retard growth and memory retention in children.

Solubility properties of some representative compounds are summarized in Figure 3.5.

Figure 3.5 Solubility summary

Type of compound	Solubility in H_2O	Solubility in organic solvents (such as CCl_4)
• Ionic		
NaCl	**soluble**	**insoluble**
• Covalent		
$CH_3CH_2CH_2CH_3$	**insoluble** (no N or O atom to hydrogen bond to H_2O)	**soluble**
$CH_3CH_2CH_2OH$	**soluble** (≤ 5 C's and an O atom for hydrogen bonding to H_2O)	**soluble**
$CH_3(CH_2)_{10}OH$	**insoluble** (> 5 C's; too large to be soluble even though it has an O atom for hydrogen bonding to H_2O)	**soluble**

Sample Problem 3.3 Which compounds are water soluble?

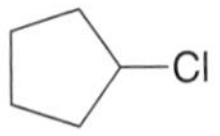

chlorocyclopentane
A

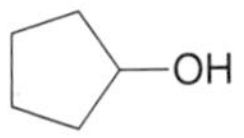

cyclopentanol
B

Solution

A has five C atoms and a polar C–Cl bond, but it is incapable of hydrogen bonding with H_2O, making it H_2O insoluble. **B** has five C atoms and a polar OH group able to hydrogen bond to H_2O, making it H_2O soluble.

Problem 3.10 Which compounds are water soluble?

a. $CH_3CH_2OCH_2CH_3$ b. $CH_3CH_2CH_2CH_2CH_3$ c. $(CH_3CH_2CH_2CH_2)_3N$

Sample Problem 3.4

a. Which of the following molecules can hydrogen bond to another molecule like itself?
b. Which of the following molecules can hydrogen bond with water?

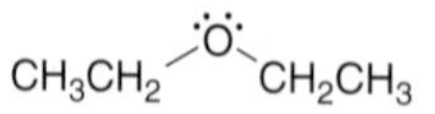

diethyl ether

A

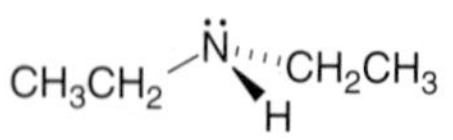

diethylamine

B

Solution

a. Compounds **A** and **B** have polar C – O and C – N bonds but **A** does not have an O – H bond, so it cannot hydrogen bond to another **A** molecule. **B,** on the other hand, has an N – H bond, so two **B** molecules can hydrogen bond with each other.
b. Because **A** has an electronegative O atom and **B** has an electronegative N atom, both **A** and **B** can hydrogen bond with a hydrogen atom in water.

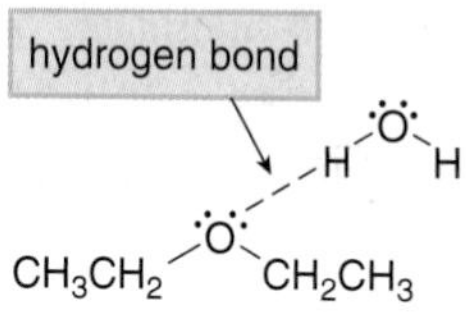

A

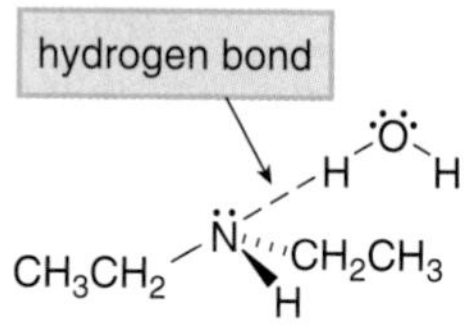

B

Problem 3.11 Label the hydrophobic and hydrophilic portions of each molecule:

a.

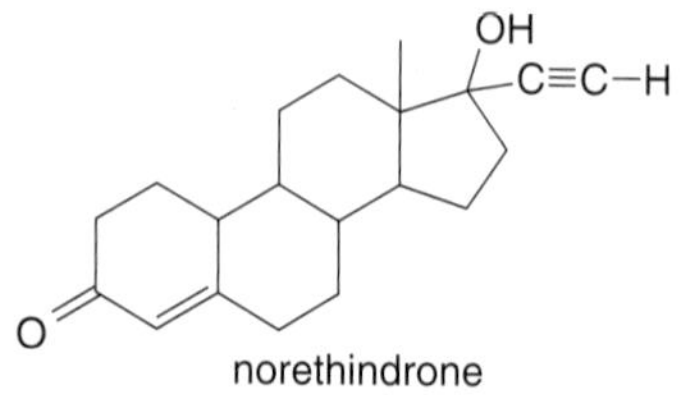

norethindrone
(oral contraceptive component)

b.

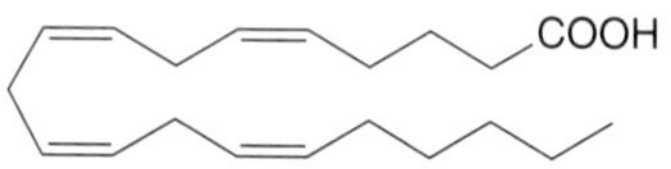

arachidonic acid
(fatty acid)

3.5 Application: Vitamins

Vitamins **are organic compounds needed in small amounts for normal cell function.** Our bodies cannot synthesize these compounds, so they must be obtained in the diet. Most vitamins are identified by a letter, such as A, C, D, E, and K. There are several different B vitamins, though, so a subscript is added to distinguish them: for example, B_1, B_2, and B_{12}.

Whether a vitamin is **fat soluble** (it dissolves in organic media) or **water soluble** can be determined by applying the solubility principles discussed in Section 3.4C. Vitamins A and C illustrate the differences between fat-soluble and water-soluble vitamins.

3.5A Vitamin A

The name **vitamin** was first used in 1912 by the Polish chemist Casimir Funk, who called them *vitamines,* because he thought that they all contained an *amine* functional group. Later the word was shortened to vitamin, because some are amines but others, like vitamins A and C, are not.

Vitamin A, or **retinol,** is an essential component of the vision receptors in the eyes. It also helps to maintain the health of mucous membranes and the skin, so many anti-aging creams contain vitamin A. A deficiency of this vitamin leads to a loss of night vision.

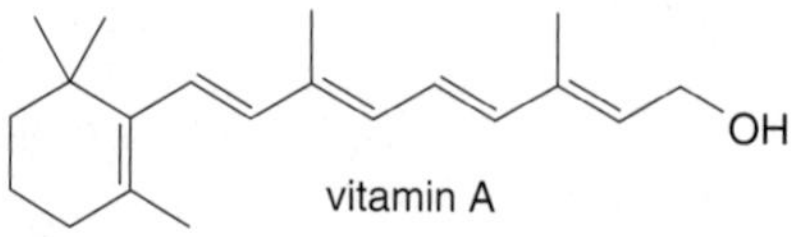

vitamin A

Vitamin A contains 20 carbons and a single OH group, making it **water insoluble.** Because it is organic, it is **soluble in any organic medium.** To understand the consequences of these solubility characteristics, we must learn about the chemical environment of the body.

About 70% of the body is composed of water. Fluids such as blood, gastric juices in the stomach, and urine are largely water with dissolved ions such as Na^+ and K^+. Vitamin A is insoluble in these fluids. There are also fat cells composed of organic compounds having C–C and C–H bonds. Vitamin A is soluble in this organic environment, and thus it is readily stored in these fat cells, particularly in the liver.

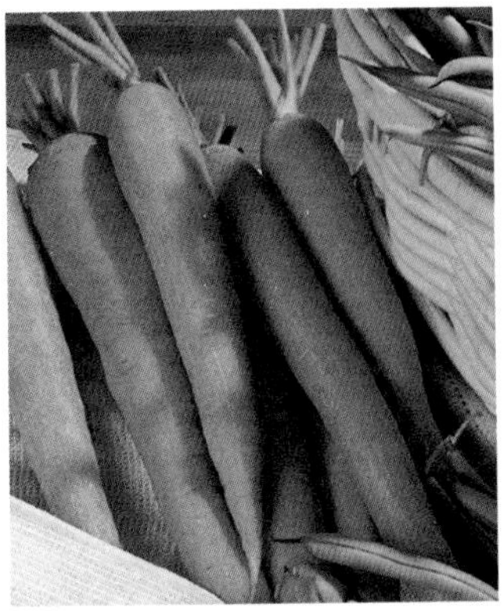

Vitamin A is synthesized from β-carotene, the orange pigment in carrots.

Vitamin A may be obtained directly from the diet. In addition, β-carotene, the orange pigment found in many plants including carrots, is readily converted to vitamin A in our bodies.

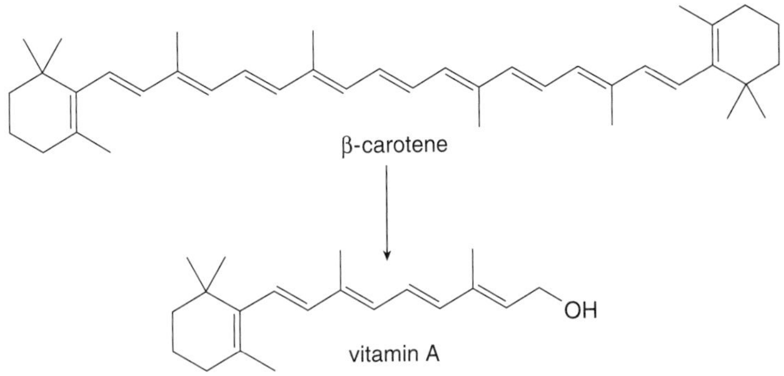

Eating too many carrots does not result in an excess of stored vitamin A. If you consume more β-carotene than you need, your body stores this precursor until it needs more vitamin A. Some β-carotene reaches the surface tissues of the skin and eyes, giving them an orange color. This phenomenon may look odd, but it is harmless and reversible. When stored β-carotene is converted to vitamin A and is no longer in excess, these tissues will return to their normal hue.

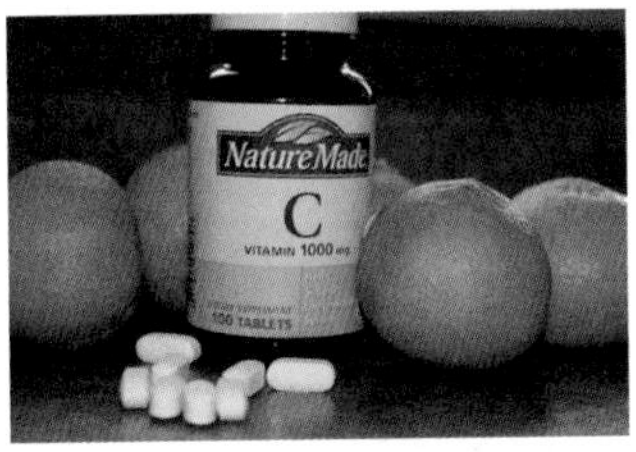

Vitamin C is obtained by eating citrus fruits and a wide variety of other fruits and vegetables. Individuals can also obtain the recommended daily dose of vitamin C by taking tablets that contain vitamin C prepared in the laboratory. Both the "natural" vitamin C in oranges and the "synthetic" vitamin C in vitamin supplements are identical.

3.5B Vitamin C

Although most animal species can synthesize vitamin C, humans, guinea pigs, the Indian fruit bat, and the bulbul bird must obtain this vitamin from dietary sources. Citrus fruits, strawberries, tomatoes, and sweet potatoes are all excellent sources of vitamin C.

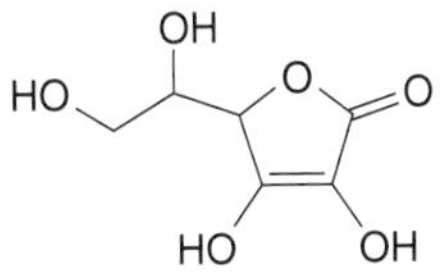

vitamin C
(ascorbic acid)

Vitamin C has six carbon atoms, each bonded to an oxygen atom that is capable of hydrogen bonding, making it **water soluble.** Vitamin C thus dissolves in urine. Although it has been acclaimed as a deterrent for all kinds of diseases, from the common cold to cancer, the consequences of taking large amounts of vitamin C are not really known, because any excess of the minimum daily requirement is excreted in the urine.

Problem 3.12 Predict the water solubility of each vitamin.

a. 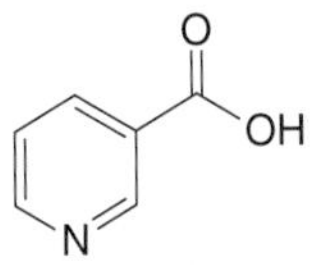

vitamin B_3
(niacin)

b. 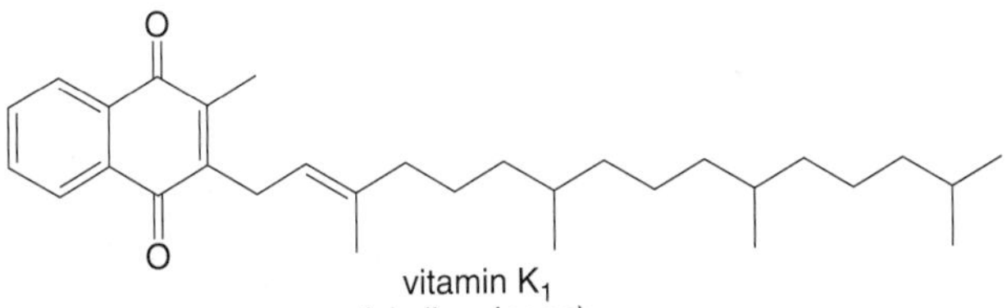

vitamin K_1
(phylloquinone)

Problem 3.13 (a) Identify the functional groups in the ball-and-stick model of pantothenic acid, vitamin B_5. (b) At which sites can pantothenic acid hydrogen bond to water? (c) Predict the water solubility of pantothenic acid.

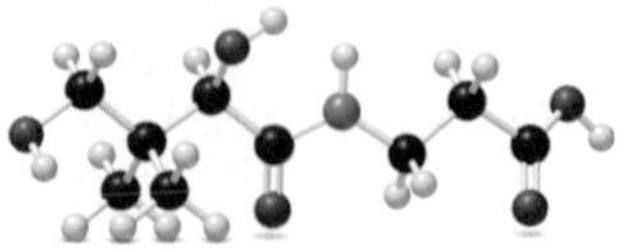

pantothenic acid
vitamin B_5

Avocados are an excellent dietary source of pantothenic acid, vitamin B_5.

3.6 Application of Solubility: Soap

Soap has been used by humankind for some 2000 years. Historical records describe its manufacture in the first century and document the presence of a soap factory in Pompeii. Before this time clothes were cleaned by rubbing them on rocks in water, or by forming soapy lathers from the roots, bark, and leaves of certain plants. These plants produced natural materials called *saponins,* which act in much the same way as modern soaps.

On a molecular level, soap has two distinct parts:

- **a hydrophilic portion composed of ions called the *polar head***
- **a hydrophobic carbon chain of nonpolar C–C and C–H bonds, called the *nonpolar tail***

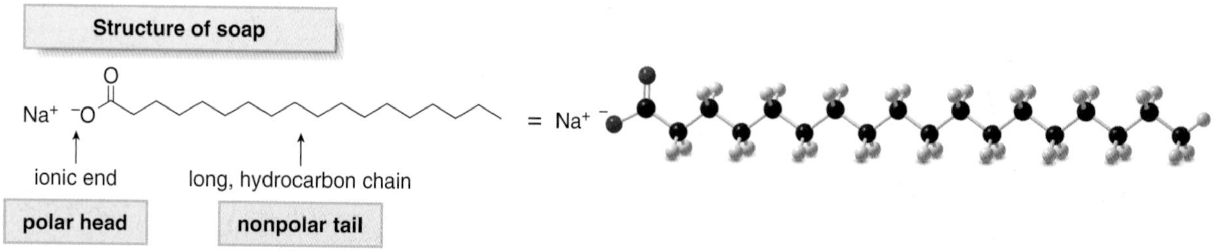
Structure of soap
O
Na⁺ ⁻O
= Na⁺ ⁻
ionic end
long, hydrocarbon chain
polar head
nonpolar tail

Dissolving soap in water forms ***micelles,* spherical droplets having the ionic heads on the surface and the nonpolar tails packed together in the interior,** as shown in Figure 3.6. In this arrangement, the ionic heads are solvated by the polar solvent water, thus solubilizing the nonpolar, "greasy" hydrocarbon portion of the soap.

How does soap dissolve grease and oil? Water alone cannot dissolve dirt, which is composed largely of nonpolar hydrocarbons. When soap is mixed with water, however, the nonpolar hydrocarbon tails dissolve the dirt in the interior of the micelle. The polar head of the soap remains on the surface of the micelle to interact with water. The nonpolar tails of the soap molecules are so well sealed off from the water by the polar head groups that the micelles are water soluble, allowing them to separate from the fibers of our clothes and be washed down the drain with water. In this way, soaps do a seemingly impossible task: they remove nonpolar hydrocarbon material from skin and clothes, by solubilizing it in the polar solvent water.

Cross-section of a soap micelle with a grease particle dissolved in the interior

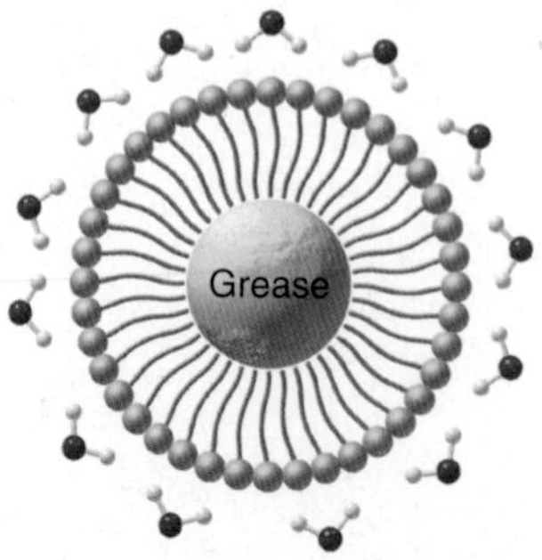
Grease

Figure 3.6
Dissolving soap in water

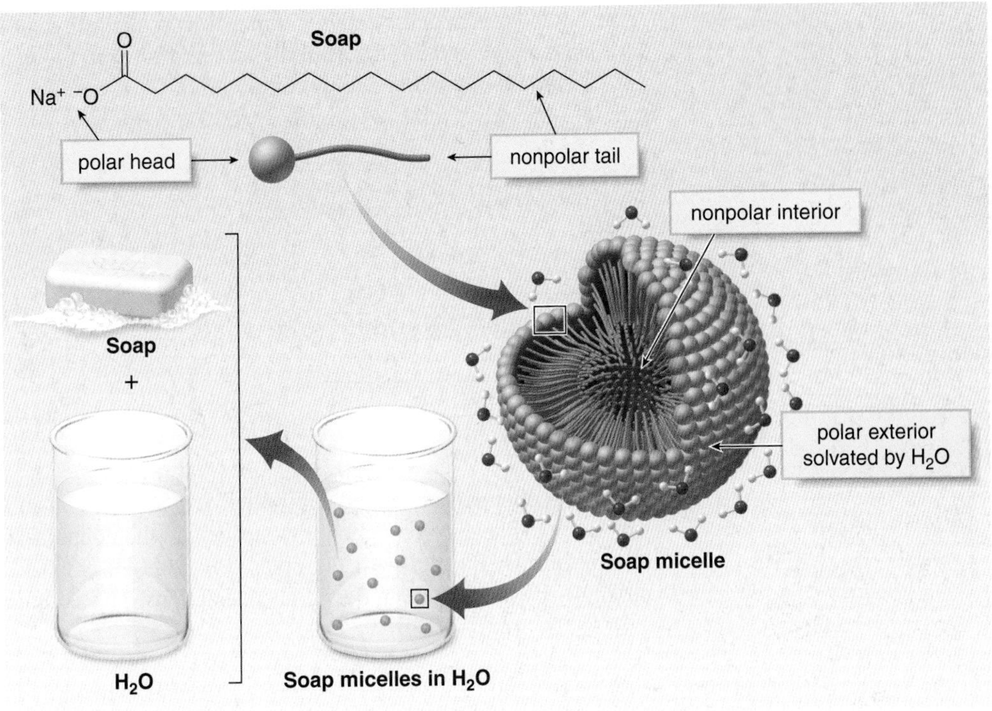

- When soap is dissolved in H_2O, it forms micelles with the nonpolar tails in the interior and the polar heads on the surface. The polar heads are solvated by ion–dipole interactions with H_2O molecules.

Problem 3.14 Which of the following structures represent soaps? Explain your answers.

a. $CH_3CO_2^-Na^+$ b. $CH_3(CH_2)_{14}CO_2^-Na^+$ c. $CH_3(CH_2)_{12}COOH$ d. $CH_3(CH_2)_9CO_2^-Na^+$

Problem 3.15 Today, synthetic detergents like the compound drawn here, not soaps, are used to clean clothes. Explain how this detergent cleans away dirt.

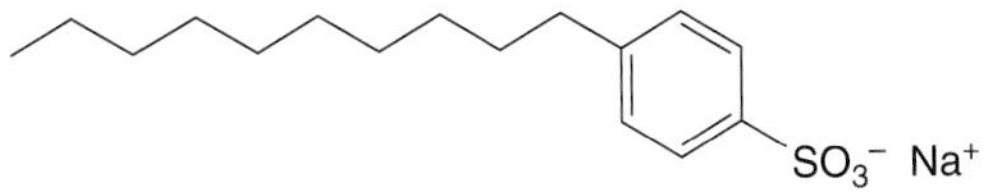

a detergent

3.7 Application: The Cell Membrane

The cell membrane is a beautifully complex example of how the principles of organic chemistry come into play in a biological system.

3.7A Structure of the Cell Membrane

The basic unit of living organisms is the **cell.** The cytoplasm is the aqueous medium inside the cell, separated from water outside the cell by the **cell membrane.** The cell membrane serves two apparently contradictory functions. It acts as a barrier to the passage of ions, water, and other molecules into and out of the cell, and it is also selectively permeable, letting nutrients in and waste out.

A major component of the cell membrane is a group of organic compounds called **phospholipids.** Like soap, they contain a hydrophilic ionic portion, and a hydrophobic hydrocarbon portion, in this case two long carbon chains composed of C–C and C–H bonds. **Phospholipids thus contain a polar head and *two* nonpolar tails.**

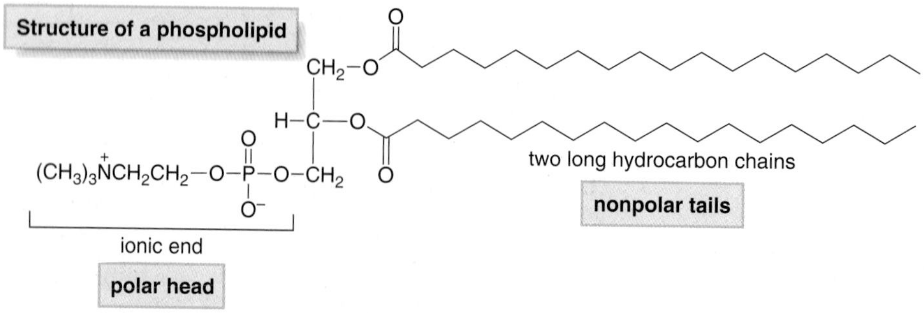

When phospholipids are mixed with water, they assemble in an arrangement called a **lipid bilayer,** with the ionic heads oriented on the outside and the nonpolar tails on the inside. The polar heads electrostatically interact with the polar solvent H_2O, while the nonpolar tails are held in close proximity by numerous van der Waals interactions. This is schematically illustrated in Figure 3.7.

Figure 3.7
The cell membrane

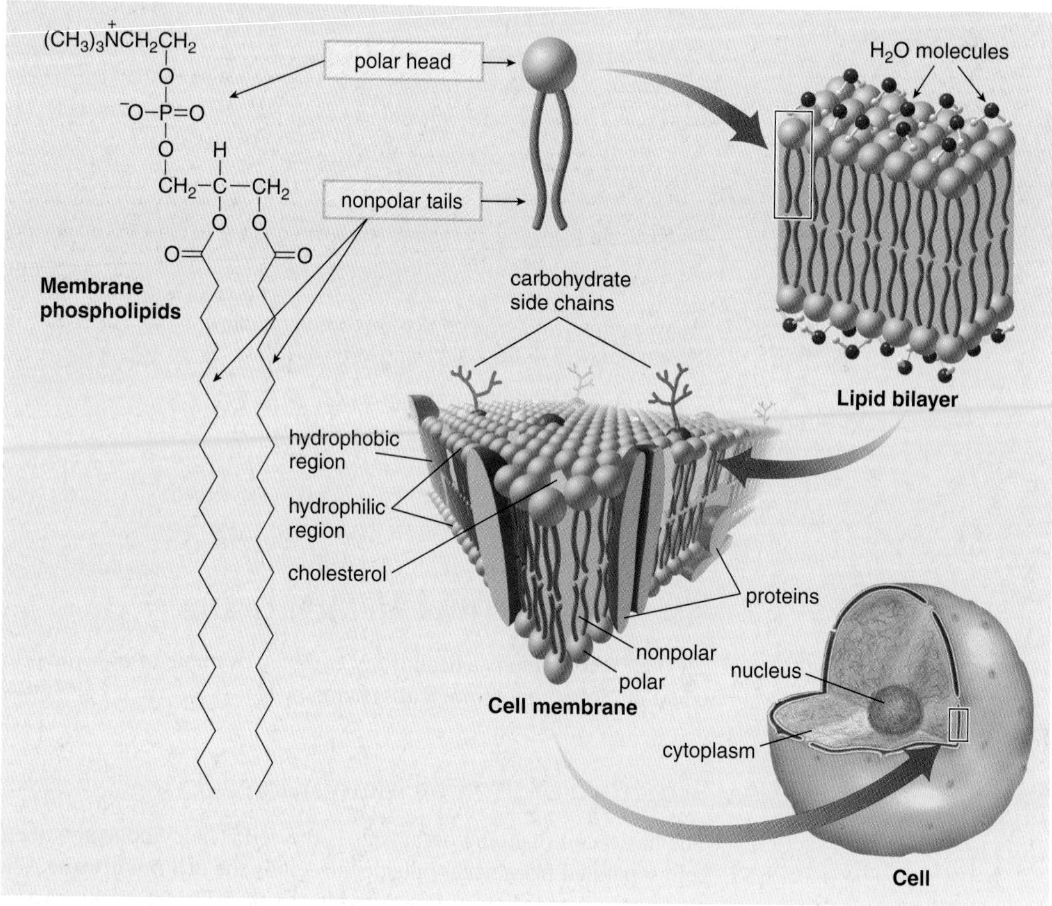

- Phospholipids contain an ionic or polar head, and two long nonpolar hydrocarbon tails. In an aqueous environment, phospholipids form a lipid bilayer, with the polar heads oriented toward the aqueous exterior and the nonpolar tails forming a hydrophobic interior. Cell membranes are composed largely of this lipid bilayer.

Cell membranes are composed of these lipid bilayers. The charged heads of the phospholipids are oriented toward the aqueous interior and exterior of the cell. The nonpolar tails form the hydrophobic interior of the membrane, thus serving as an insoluble barrier that protects the cell from the outside.

3.7B Transport Across a Cell Membrane

How does a polar molecule or ion in the water outside a cell pass through the nonpolar interior of the cell membrane and enter the cell? Some nonpolar molecules like O_2 are small enough to enter and exit the cell by diffusion. Polar molecules and ions, on the other hand, may be too large or too polar to diffuse efficiently. Some ions are transported across the membrane with the help of molecules called **ionophores.**

Ionophores **are organic molecules that complex cations.** They have a hydrophobic exterior that makes them soluble in the nonpolar interior of the cell membrane, and a central cavity with several oxygen atoms whose lone pairs complex with a given ion. The size of the cavity determines the identity of the cation with which the ionophore complexes. Two naturally occurring antibiotics that act as ionophores are **nonactin** and **valinomycin.**

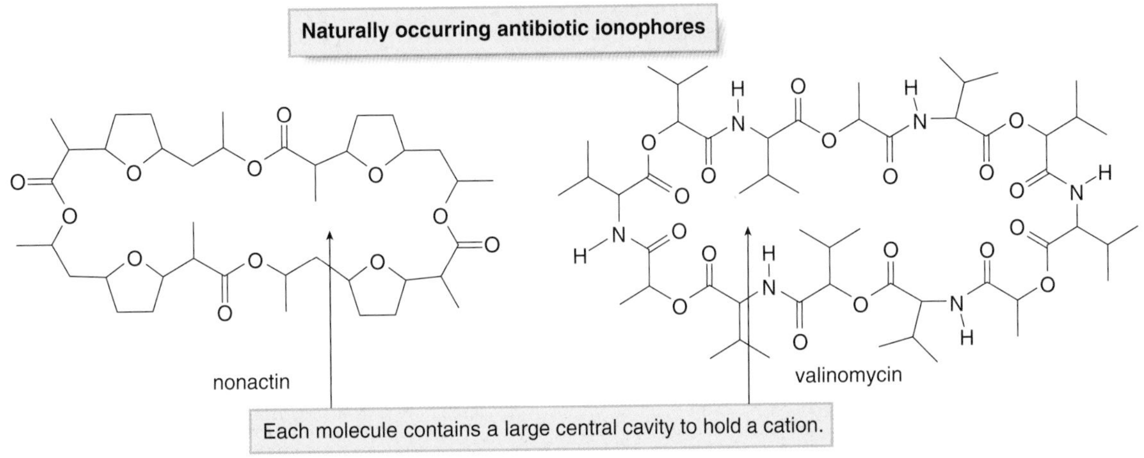
Naturally occurring antibiotic ionophores
nonactin
valinomycin
Each molecule contains a large central cavity to hold a cation.

Several synthetic ionophores have also been prepared, including one group called **crown ethers.** ***Crown ethers*** **are cyclic ethers containing several oxygen atoms that bind specific cations depending on the size of their cavity.** Crown ethers are named according to the general format ***x*-crown-*y*,** where ***x*** is the total number of atoms in the ring and ***y*** is the number of oxygen atoms. For example, 18-crown-6 contains 18 atoms in the ring, including 6 O atoms. This crown ether binds potassium ions. Sodium ions are too small to form a tight complex with the O atoms, and larger cations do not fit in the cavity.

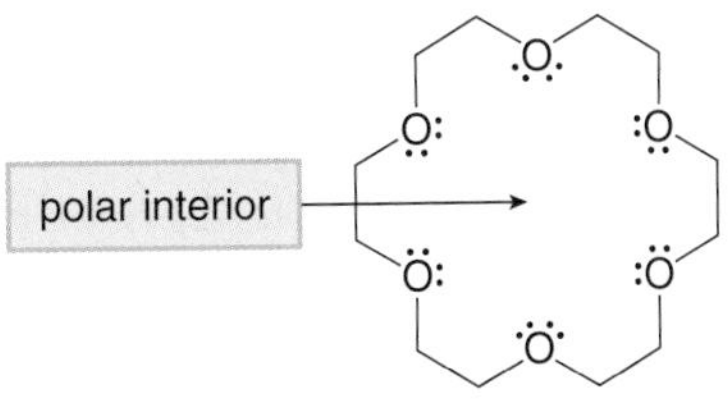
polar interior
K+

18-crown-6

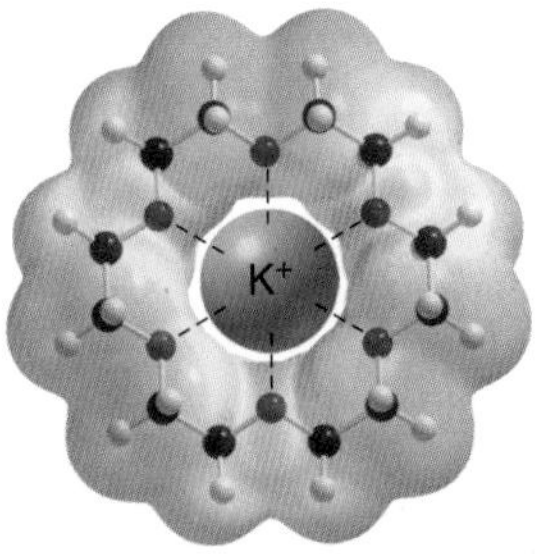
K+

complex with K+

Figure 3.8
Transport of ions across a cell membrane

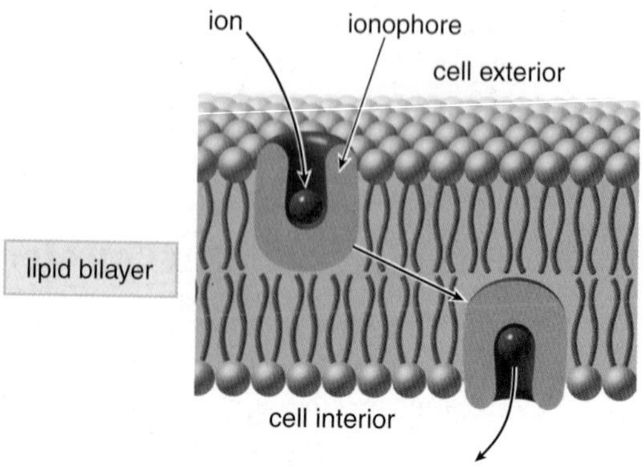

- By binding an ion on one side of a lipid bilayer (where the concentration of the ion is high) and releasing it on the other side of the bilayer (where the concentration of the ion is low), an ionophore transports an ion across a cell membrane.

How does an ionophore transfer an ion across a membrane? The ionophore binds the ion on one side of the membrane in its polar interior. It can then move across the membrane because its hydrophobic exterior interacts with the hydrophobic tails of the phospholipid. The ionophore then releases the ion on the other side of the membrane. This ion-transfer role is essential for normal cell function. This process is illustrated in Figure 3.8.

In this manner, antibiotic ionophores like nonactin transport ions across a cell membrane of bacteria. This disrupts the normal ionic balance in the cell, thus interfering with cell function and causing the bacteria to die.

Problem 3.16 Nonactin and valinomycin each contain only two different types of functional groups. What two functional groups are present in nonactin? In valinomycin?

Problem 3.17 Now that you have learned about solubility, explain why aspirin (Section 2.7) crosses a cell membrane as a neutral carboxylic acid rather than an ionic conjugate base.

3.8 Functional Groups and Reactivity

Much of Chapter 3 has been devoted to how a functional group determines the strength of intermolecular forces and, consequently, the physical properties of molecules. A functional group also determines reactivity. What type of reaction does a particular kind of organic compound undergo? Begin by recalling two fundamental concepts.

- **Functional groups create reactive sites in molecules.**
- **Electron-rich sites react with electron-poor sites.**

All functional groups contain a heteroatom, a π bond, or both, and these features make electron-deficient (or electrophilic) sites and electron-rich (or nucleophilic) sites in a molecule. Molecules react at these sites. To predict reactivity, first locate the functional group and then determine the resulting electron-rich or electron-deficient sites it creates. Keep three guidelines in mind.

- **An electronegative heteroatom like N, O, or X makes a carbon atom *electrophilic.***

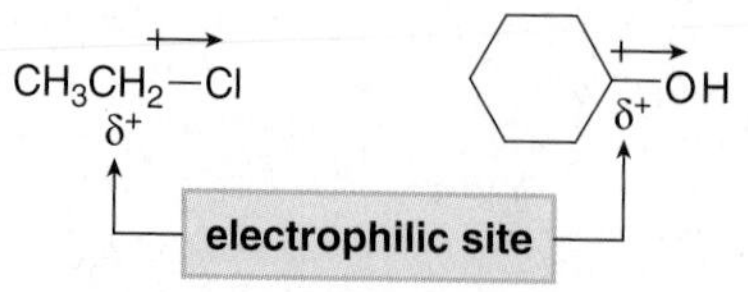

- **A lone pair on a heteroatom makes it basic and nucleophilic.**

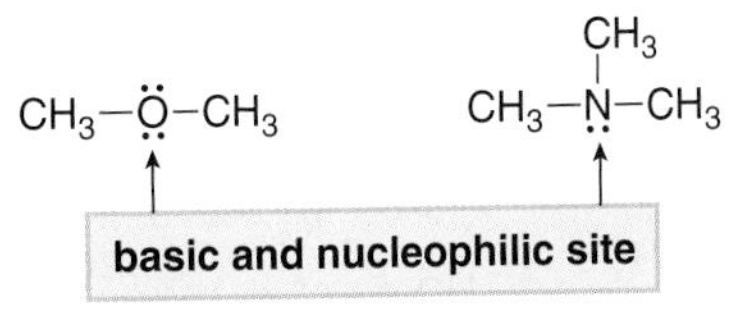

- **π Bonds create *nucleophilic* sites and are more easily broken than σ bonds.**

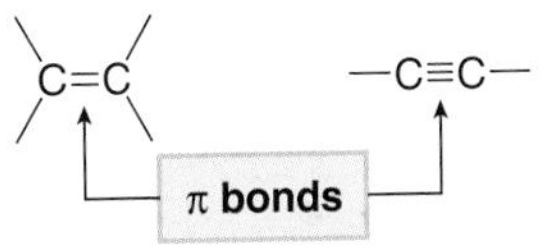

Problem 3.18 Label the electrophilic and nucleophilic sites in each molecule.

a. 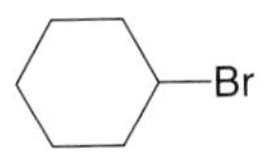 b. H_2O c. 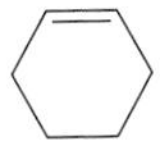 d. 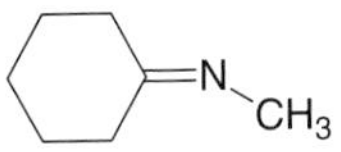

By identifying the nucleophilic and electrophilic sites in a compound you can begin to understand how it will react. In general, electron-rich sites react with electron-deficient sites:

:Nu⁻ = a nucleophile; E⁺ = an electrophile.

- **An electron-deficient carbon atom reacts with a nucleophile, symbolized as :Nu⁻.**
- **An electron-rich carbon reacts with an electrophile, symbolized as E⁺.**

At this point we don't know enough organic chemistry to draw the products of many reactions with confidence. We do know enough, however, to begin to predict if two compounds might react together based solely on electron density arguments, and at what atoms that reaction is most likely to occur.

For example, alkenes contain an electron-rich C–C double bond and so they react with electrophiles, E^+. On the other hand, alkyl halides possess an electrophilic carbon atom, so they react with electron-rich nucleophiles.

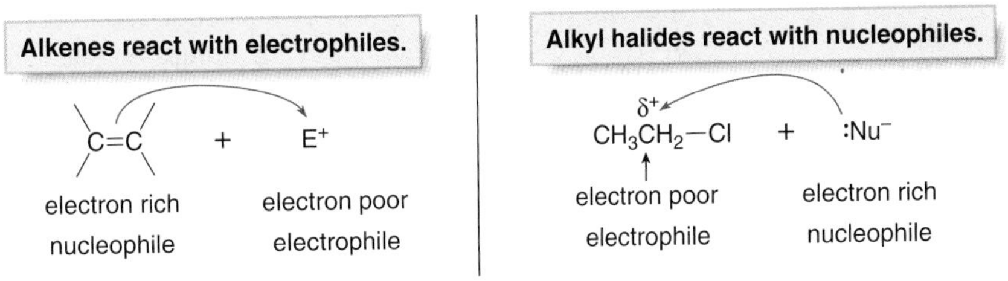

For now, you don't need to worry about the products of these reactions. At this point you should only be able to find reactive sites in molecules and begin to understand why a reaction might occur at these sites. After you learn more about the structure of organic molecules in Chapters 4 and 5, we will begin a detailed discussion of organic reactions in Chapter 6.

Problem 3.19 Considering only electron density, state whether the following reactions will occur:

a. $CH_3CH_2{-}Br \;+\; {}^{-}OH \;\longrightarrow$

b. $CH_3{-}C{\equiv}C{-}CH_3 \;+\; Br^- \;\longrightarrow$

c. 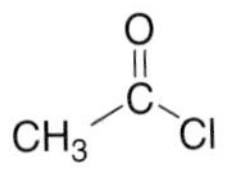 $+\; {}^{-}OCH_3 \;\longrightarrow$

d. $CH_3{-}C{\equiv}C{-}CH_3 \;+\; Br^+ \;\longrightarrow$

3.9 Biomolecules

***Biomolecules* are organic compounds found in biological systems.** Many are relatively small, with molecular weights of less than 1000 g/mol. There are four main families of these small molecules—simple sugars, amino acids, lipids, and nucleotides. Many simple biomolecules are used to synthesize larger compounds that have important cellular functions.

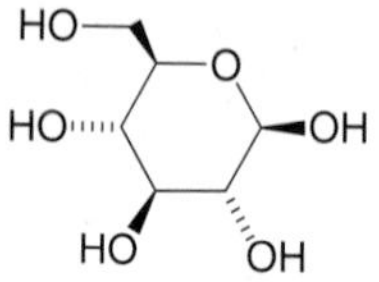

glucose
a simple sugar

oleic acid
a fatty acid

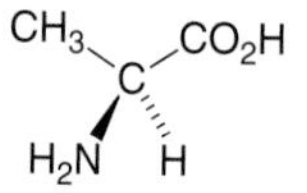

alanine
an amino acid

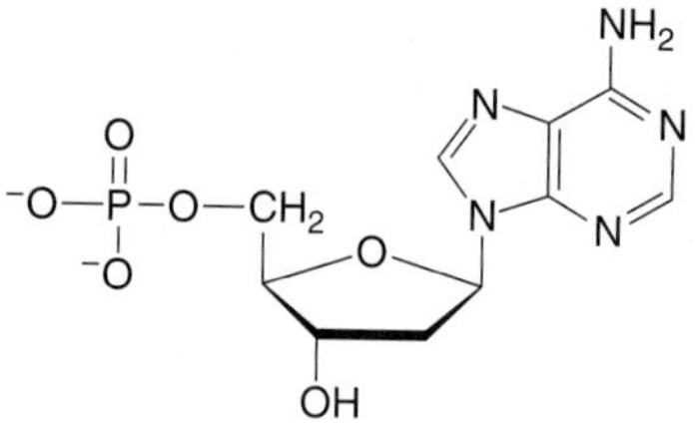

deoxyadenosine 5'-monophosphate
a nucleotide

Simple sugars such as glucose combine to form the complex carbohydrates starch and cellulose, as described in Chapter 28. Alanine is an amino acid used to synthesize proteins, the subject of Chapter 29. Fatty acids such as oleic acid react with alcohols to form triacylglycerols, the most prevalent lipids, first mentioned in Chapter 10, and discussed in more detail in Chapters 22 and 30. While these biomolecules all contain more than one functional group, their properties and reactions are explained by the principles of basic organic chemistry.

Finally, deoxyadenosine 5'-monophosphate is a nucleotide that combines with thousands of other nucleotides to form DNA, deoxyribonucleic acid, the high molecular weight polynucleotide that stores the genetic information of an organism. DNA consists of two polynucleotide chains that wind together in a double helix. Figure 3.9 illustrates the importance of hydrogen bonding in the structure of DNA. The two polynucleotide chains are held together by an extensive network of hydrogen bonds in which the N–H groups on one chain intermolecularly hydrogen bond to an oxygen or nitrogen atom on the adjacent chain.

Problem 3.20 The fact that sweet-tasting carbohydrates like table sugar are also high in calories has prompted the development of sweet, low-calorie alternatives. (a) Identify the functional groups in aspartame, the artificial sweetener in Equal. (b) Label all of the sites that can hydrogen bond to the oxygen atom of water. (c) Label all of the sites that can hydrogen bond with a hydrogen atom of water.

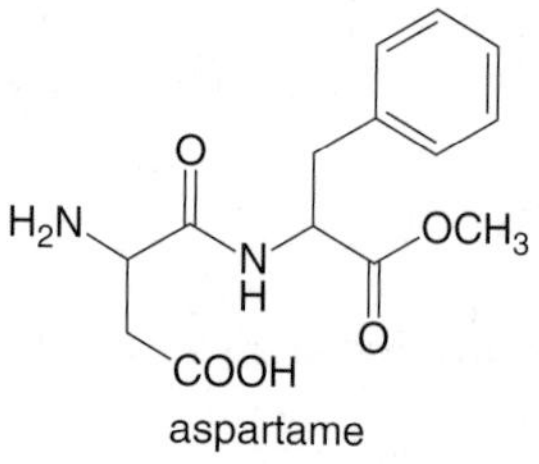

aspartame

Figure 3.9
The double helix of DNA

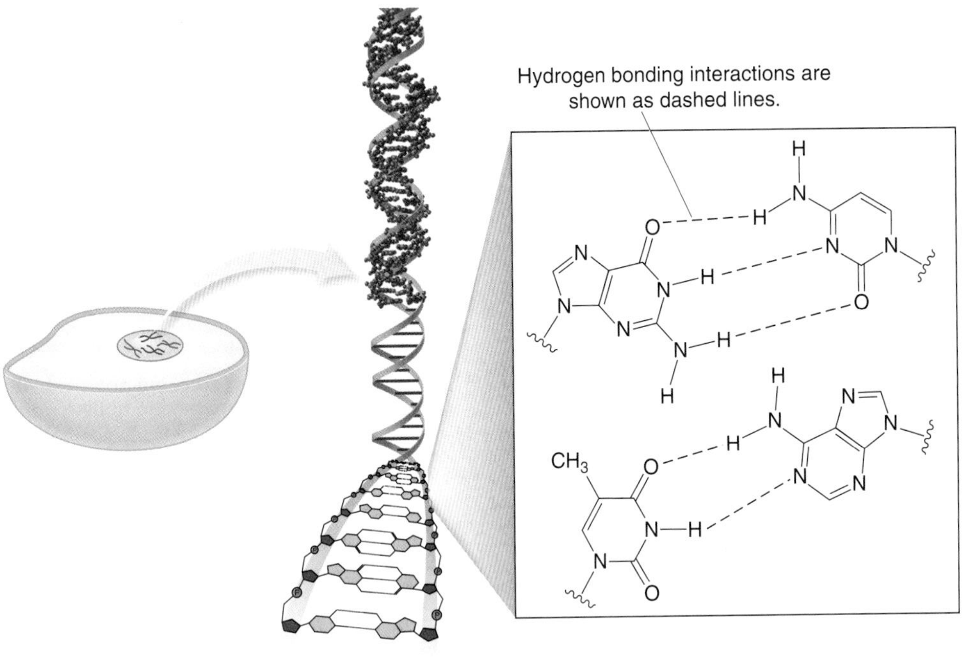
DNA double helix
Hydrogen bonding interactions are shown as dashed lines.
CH3

- DNA, which is contained in the chromosomes of the nucleus of a cell, stores all of the genetic information in an organism. DNA consists of two long strands of polynucleotides held together by hydrogen bonding.

KEY CONCEPTS

Introduction to Organic Molecules and Functional Groups

Types of Intermolecular Forces (3.3)

Increasing strength ↓

Type of force	Cause
van der Waals	Caused by the interaction of temporary dipoles • Larger surface area, stronger forces • Larger, more polarizable atoms, stronger forces
dipole–dipole	Caused by the interaction of permanent dipoles
hydrogen bonding	Caused by the electrostatic interaction of a H atom in an O–H, N–H, or H–F bond with the lone pair of another N, O, or F atom
ion–ion	Caused by the charge attraction of two ions

Physical Properties

Property	Observation
Boiling point (3.4A)	• For compounds of comparable molecular weight, the stronger the intermolecular forces the higher the bp.

$CH_3CH_2CH_2CH_2CH_3$	$CH_3CH_2CH_2CHO$	$CH_3CH_2CH_2CH_2OH$
VDW	VDW, DD	VDW, DD, HB
bp = 36 °C	bp = 76 °C	bp = 118 °C

→ **Increasing strength of intermolecular forces**
Increasing boiling point

	• For compounds with similar functional groups, the larger the surface area, the higher the bp. $CH_3CH_2CH_2CH_3$ bp = 0 °C → $CH_3CH_2CH_2CH_2CH_3$ bp = 36 °C **Increasing surface area** **Increasing boiling point** • For compounds with similar functional groups, the more polarizable the atoms, the higher the bp. CH_3F bp = −78 °C → CH_3I bp = 42 °C **Increasing polarizability** **Increasing boiling point**
Melting point (3.4B)	• For compounds of comparable molecular weight, the stronger the intermolecular forces the higher the mp. $CH_3CH_2CH_2CH_2CH_3$ VDW mp = −130 °C → $CH_3CH_2CH_2CHO$ VDW, DD mp = −96 °C → $CH_3CH_2CH_2CH_2OH$ VDW, DD, HB mp = −90 °C **Increasing strength of intermolecular forces** **Increasing melting point** • For compounds with similar functional groups, the more symmetrical the compound, the higher the mp. $CH_3CH_2CH(CH_3)_2$ mp = −160 °C → $(CH_3)_4C$ mp = −17 °C **Increasing symmetry** **Increasing melting point**
Solubility (3.4C)	Types of water-soluble compounds: • Ionic compounds • Organic compounds having ≤ 5 C's, and an O or N atom for hydrogen bonding (for a compound with one functional group). Types of compounds soluble in organic solvents: • Organic compounds regardless of size or functional group.

Key: VDW = van der Waals, DD = dipole–dipole, HB = hydrogen bonding

Reactivity (3.8)

- **Nucleophiles react with electrophiles.**
- Electronegative heteroatoms create electrophilic carbon atoms, which tend to react with nucleophiles.
- Lone pairs and π bonds are nucleophilic sites that tend to react with electrophiles.

PROBLEMS

Problems with Three-Dimensional Models

3.21 (a) Identify the functional groups in the ball-and-stick model of elemicin, a compound partly responsible for the flavor and fragrance of nutmeg. (b) Draw a skeletal structure of a constitutional isomer of elemicin that should have a higher boiling point and melting point. (c) Label all electrophilic carbon atoms.

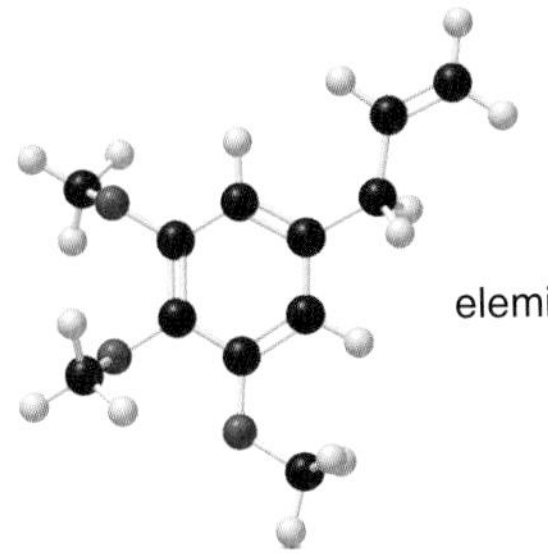

elemicin

3.22 (a) Identify the functional groups in the ball-and-stick model of neral, a compound with a lemony odor isolated from lemon grass. (b) Draw a skeletal structure of a constitutional isomer of neral that should be more water soluble. (c) Label the most electrophilic carbon atom.

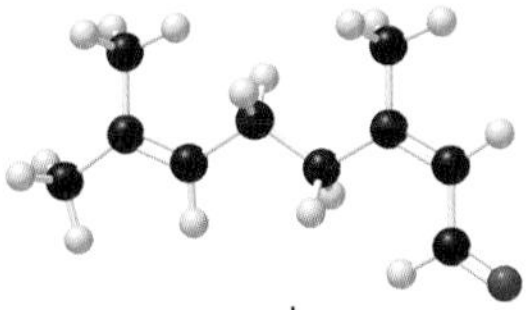

neral

Functional Groups

3.23 Identify the functional groups in each molecule.

a. 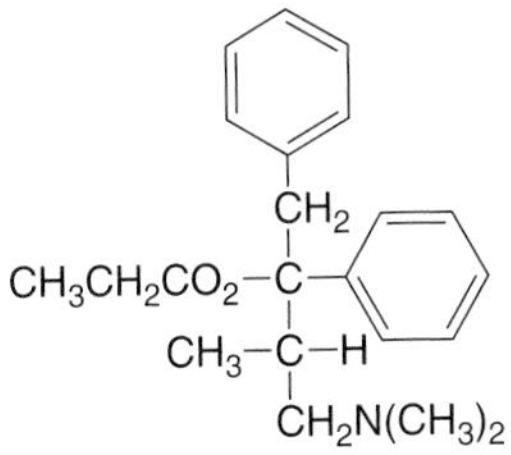

Darvon
(analgesic)

c. 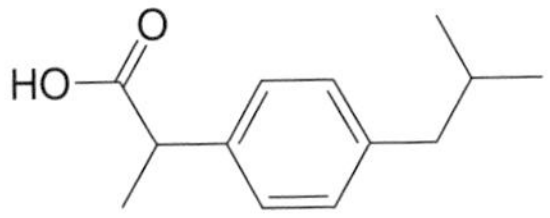

ibuprofen
(analgesic)

e. 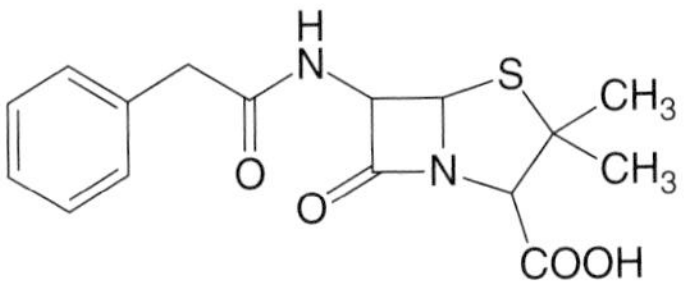

penicillin G
(an antibiotic)

b. 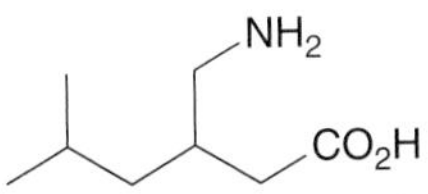

pregabalin
Trade name: Lyrica
(used in treating chronic pain)

d. 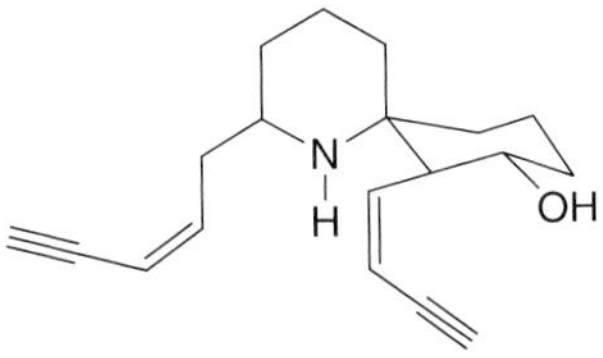

histrionicotoxin
(poison secreted by a South American frog)

f. 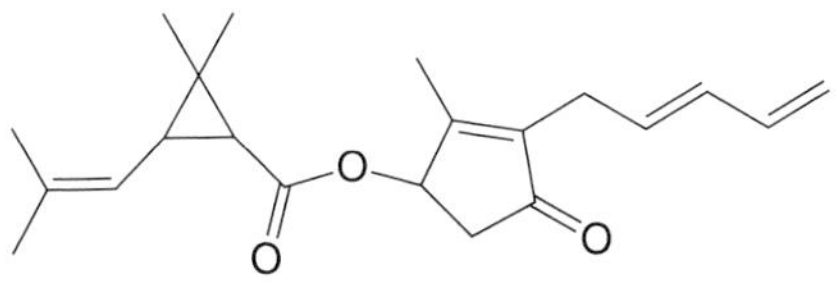

pyrethrin I
(potent insecticide from chrysanthemums)

3.24 Draw the seven constitutional isomers having molecular formula $C_4H_{10}O$. Identify the functional group in each isomer.

3.25 Identify each functional group located in the following rings. Which structure represents a lactone—a cyclic ester—and which represents a lactam—a cyclic amide?

a. 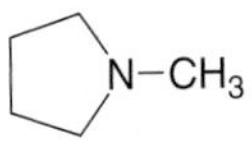
b. 
c. 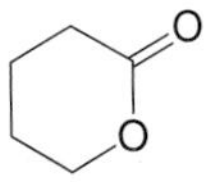
d. 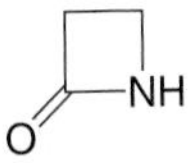

3.26 Draw seven constitutional isomers with molecular formula $C_3H_6O_2$ that contain a carbonyl group. Identify the functional group(s) in each isomer.

Intermolecular Forces

3.27 What types of intermolecular forces are exhibited by each compound?

a. 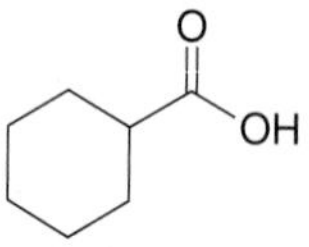
b. 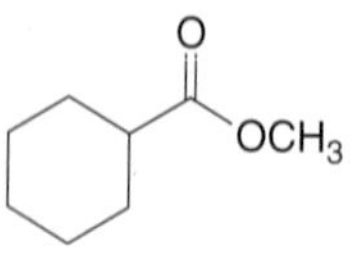
c. 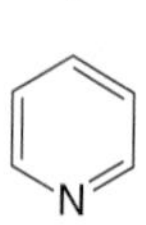
d. 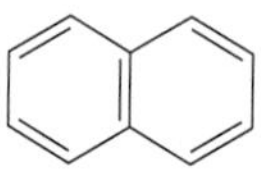

3.28 Rank the compounds in each group in order of increasing strength of intermolecular forces:

a. CH_3NH_2, CH_3CH_3, CH_3Cl
b. CH_3Br, CH_3I, CH_3Cl
c. $(CH_3)_2C{=}C(CH_3)_2$, $(CH_3)_2CHCOOH$, $(CH_3)_2CHCOCH_3$
d. NaCl, CH_3OH, CH_3Cl

3.29 Carboxylic acids (RCOOH) can exist as dimers in some situations, with two molecules held together by two intermolecular hydrogen bonds. Show how two molecules of acetic acid (CH_3CO_2H), the carboxylic acid present in vinegar, can hydrogen bond to each other.

3.30 Intramolecular forces of attraction are often important in holding large molecules together. For example, some proteins fold into compact shapes, held together by attractive forces between nearby functional groups. A schematic of a folded protein is drawn here, with the protein backbone indicated by a blue-green ribbon, and various appendages drawn dangling from the chain. What types of intramolecular forces occur at each labeled site (**A–F**)?

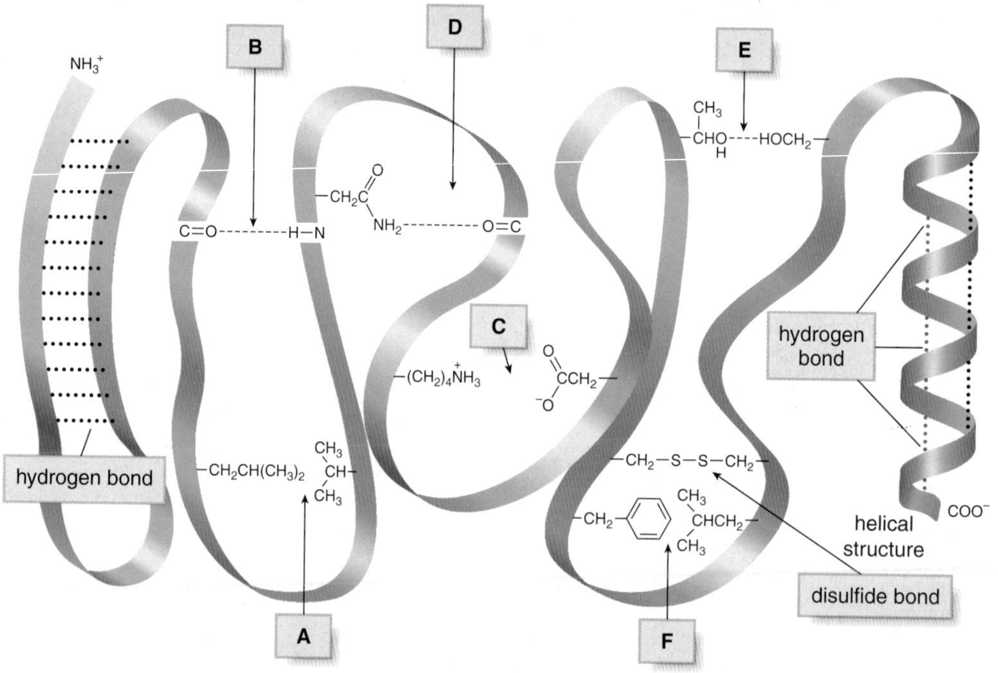

Physical Properties

3.31 (a) Draw four compounds with molecular formula $C_6H_{12}O$, each containing at least one different functional group. (b) Predict which compound has the highest boiling point, and explain your reasoning.

3.32 Rank the compounds in each group in order of increasing boiling point.

a. $CH_3(CH_2)_4I$, $CH_3(CH_2)_5I$, $CH_3(CH_2)_6I$
b. $CH_3CH_2CH_2NH_2$, $(CH_3)_3N$, $CH_3CH_2CH_2CH_3$
c. $(CH_3)_3COC(CH_3)_3$, $CH_3(CH_2)_3O(CH_2)_3CH_3$, $CH_3(CH_2)_7OH$
d. 
e. 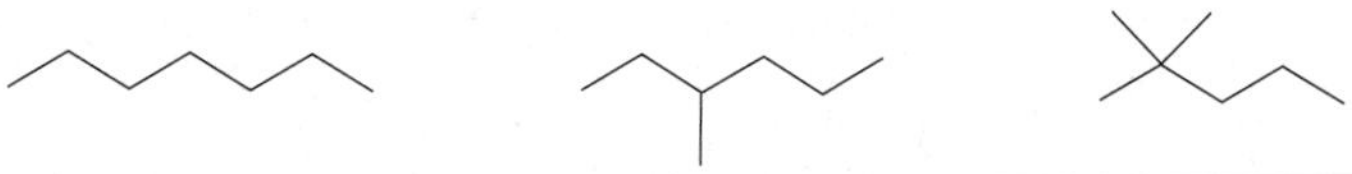
f. 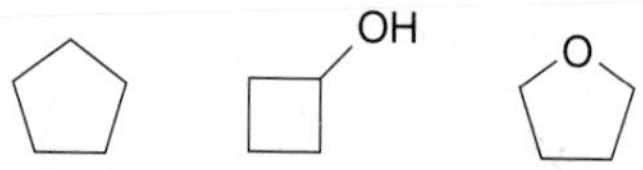

3.33 Explain why $CH_3CH_2NHCH_3$ has a higher boiling point than $(CH_3)_3N$, even though they have the same molecular weight.

3.34 Menthone and menthol are both isolated from mint. Explain why menthol is a solid at room temperature but menthone is a liquid.

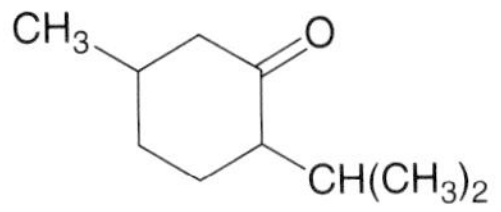

menthone

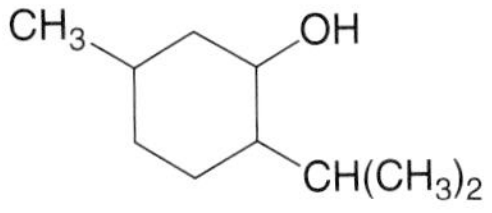

menthol

3.35 Rank the compounds in each group in order of increasing melting point.

a. $(CH_3)_2CHOH$, $(CH_3)_3CH$, $(CH_3)_2C{=}O$
b. CH_3F, CH_3Cl, CH_3I
c. 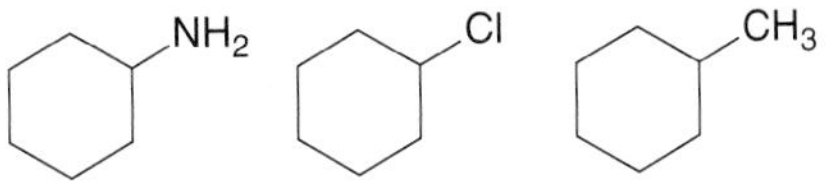

3.36 Explain the observed trend in the melting points for four isomers of molecular formula C_7H_{16}.

	mp (°C)
$CH_3CH_2CH_2CH(CH_3)CH_2CH_3$	−119
$CH_3CH_2CH_2CH_2CH(CH_3)_2$	−118
$CH_3CH_2CH_2CH_2CH_2CH_2CH_3$	−91
$(CH_3)_2CHC(CH_3)_3$	−25

3.37 Explain why benzene has a lower boiling point but much higher melting point than toluene.

benzene
bp = 80 °C
mp = 5 °C

and

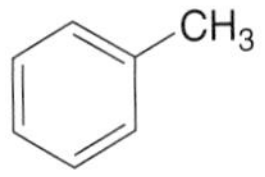

toluene
bp = 111 °C
mp = −93 °C

3.38 Rank the compounds in each group in order of increasing water solubility.

a. $(CH_3)_3CH$, $CH_3OCH_2CH_3$, $CH_3CH_2CH_2CH_3$, $CH_3CH_2CH_2OH$

b. 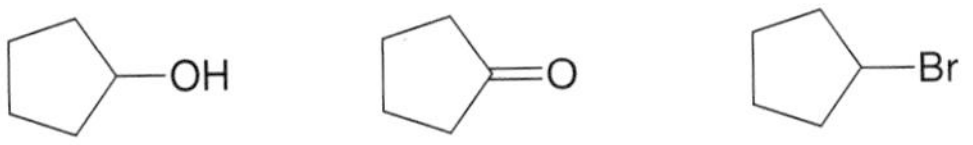

3.39 Which of the following molecules can hydrogen bond to another molecule of itself? Which can hydrogen bond with water?

a. CBr_3CH_3
b. CH_3NH_2
c. CH_3OCH_3
d. $(CH_3CH_2)_3N$
e. $CH_3CH_2CH_2CONH_2$
f. $CH_3CH_2CH_2Cl$
g. CH_3SOCH_3
h. $CH_3CH_2COOCH_3$

3.40 Explain why diethyl ether ($CH_3CH_2OCH_2CH_3$) and 1-butanol ($CH_3CH_2CH_2CH_2OH$) have similar solubility properties in water, but 1-butanol has a much higher boiling point.

3.41 Predict the water solubility of each of the following organic molecules:

a. 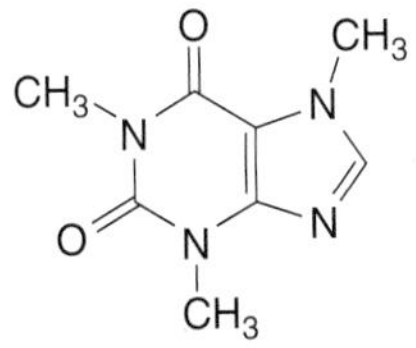

caffeine
(stimulant in coffee, tea, and many soft drinks)

c. 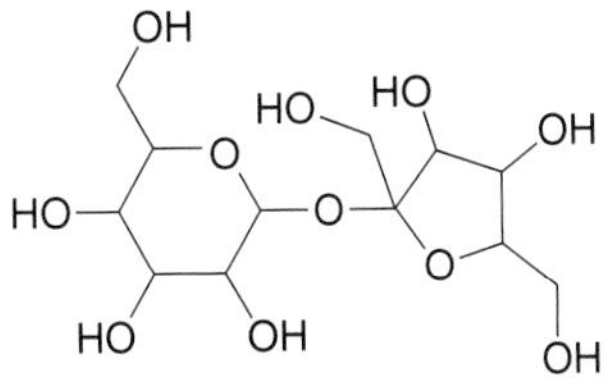

sucrose
(table sugar)

b. 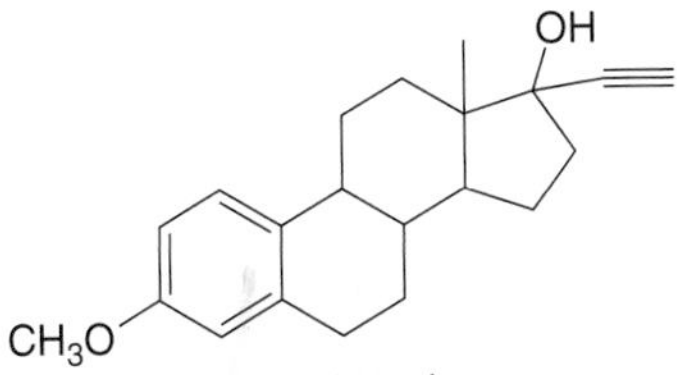

mestranol
(component in oral contraceptives)

d. 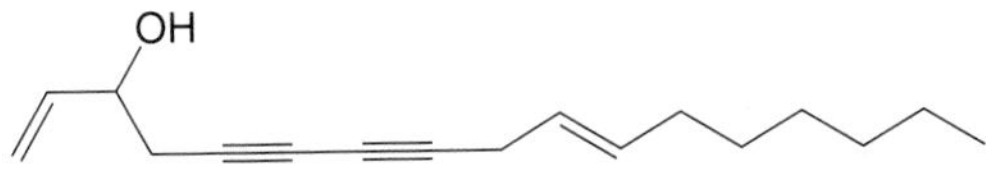

carotatoxin
(neurotoxin isolated from carrots)

Applications

3.42 Predict the solubility of each of the following vitamins in water and in organic solvents:

a. 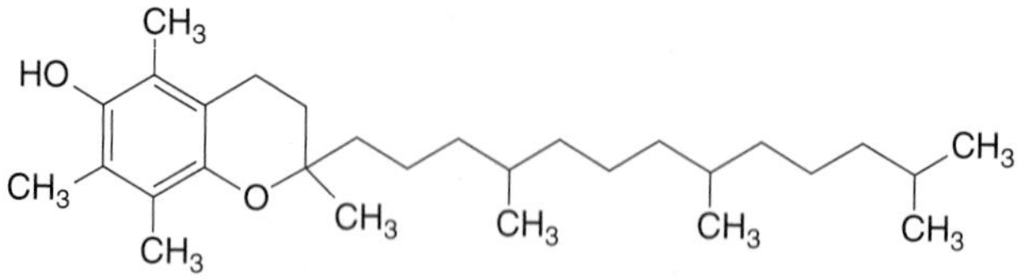

vitamin E

b. 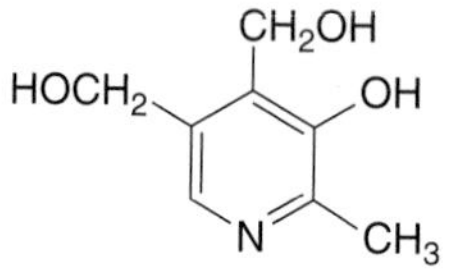

pyridoxine
vitamin B_6

3.43 Avobenzone and dioxybenzone are two commercial sunscreens. Using the principles of solubility, predict which sunscreen is more readily washed off when an individual goes swimming. Explain your choice.

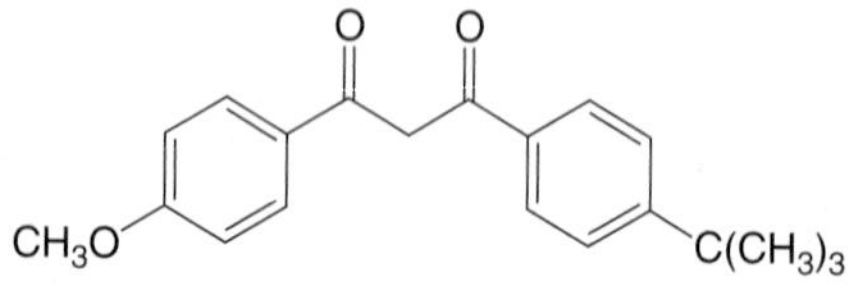

avobenzone

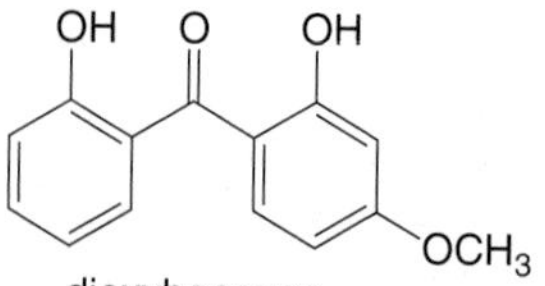

dioxybenzone

3.44 Poly(ethylene glycol) (PEG) and poly(vinyl chloride) (PVC) are examples of polymers, large organic molecules composed of repeating smaller units covalently bonded together. Polymers have very different properties depending (in part) on their functional groups. Discuss the water solubility of each polymer and suggest why PEG is used in shampoos while PVC is used to make garden hoses and pipes. Synthetic polymers are discussed in detail in Chapters 15 and 31.

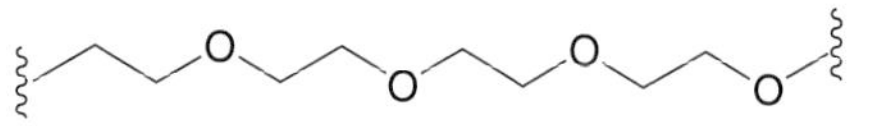

poly(ethylene glycol)
PEG

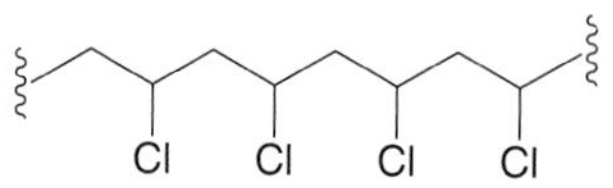

poly(vinyl chloride)
PVC

3.45 THC is the active component in marijuana, and ethanol is the alcohol in alcoholic beverages. Explain why drug screenings are able to detect the presence of THC but not ethanol weeks after these substances have been introduced into the body.

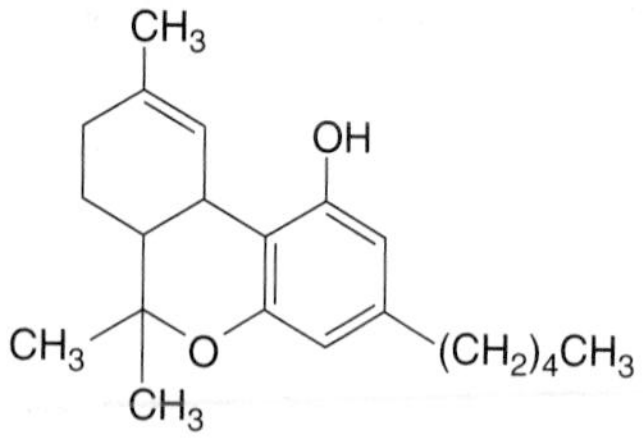

tetrahydrocannabinol
THC

$CH_3CH_2—OH$

ethanol

3.46 Cocaine is a widely abused, addicting drug. Cocaine is usually obtained as its hydrochloride salt (cocaine hydrochloride) but can be converted to crack (the neutral molecule) by treatment with base. Which of the two compounds here has a higher boiling point? Which is more soluble in water? How does the relative solubility explain why crack is usually smoked but cocaine hydrochloride is injected directly into the bloodstream?

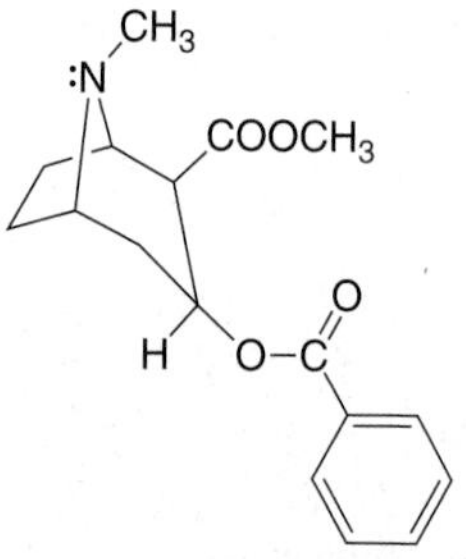

cocaine (crack)
neutral organic molecule

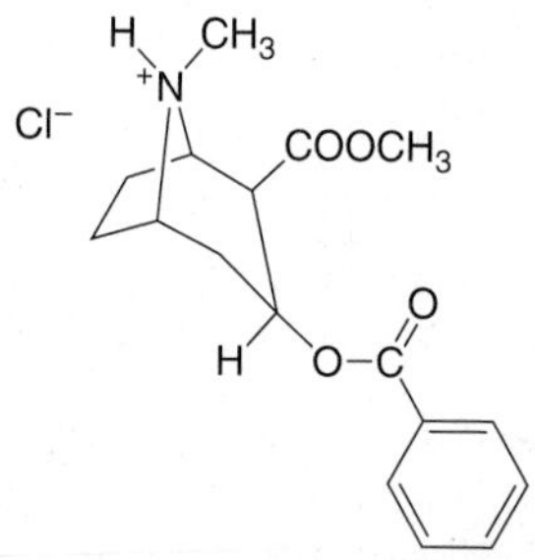

cocaine hydrochloride
a salt

3.47 Unlike soap, which is ionic, some liquid laundry detergents are neutral molecules. Explain how each of the following molecules behaves like soap and cleans away dirt.

a. 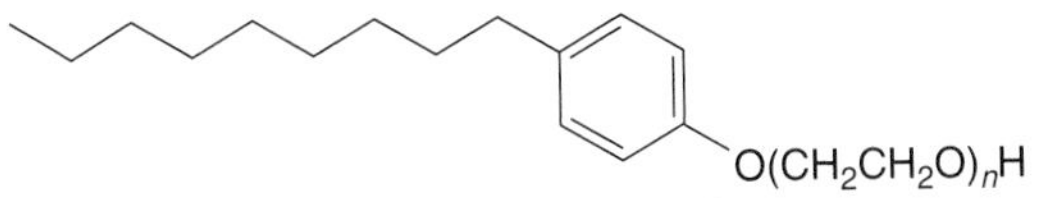
O(CH2CH2O)nH

$n = 7$ to 13

b. 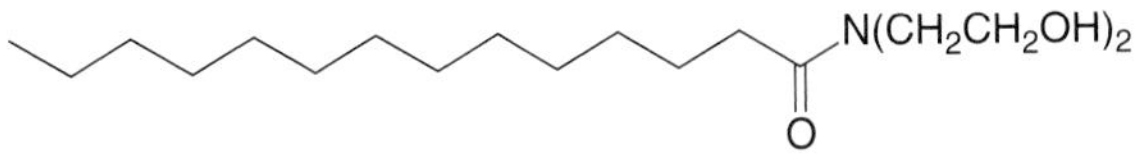
N(CH2CH2OH)2
O

3.48 Many drugs are sold as their hydrochloride salts ($R_2NH_2^+$ Cl^-), formed by reaction of an amine (R_2NH) with HCl.

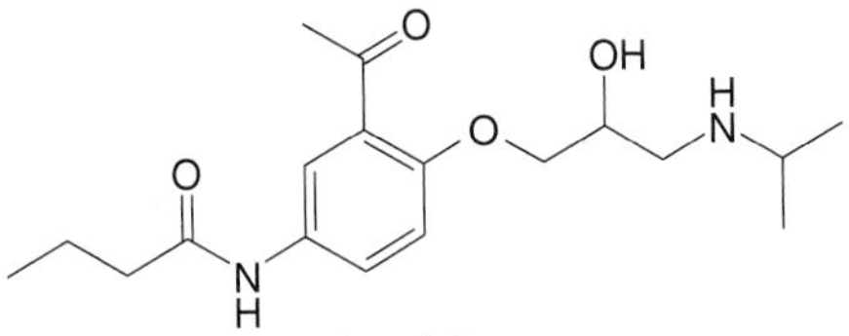
O
OH
H
N
O
O
N
H

acebutolol

a. Draw the product (a hydrochloride salt) formed by reaction of acebutolol with HCl. Acebutolol is a β blocker used to treat high blood pressure.
b. Discuss the solubility of acebutolol and its hydrochloride salt in water.
c. Offer a reason as to why the drug is marketed as a hydrochloride salt rather than a neutral amine.

Reactivity of Organic Molecules

3.49 Label the electrophilic and nucleophilic sites in each molecule.

a. 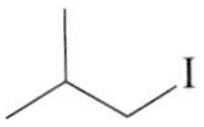
I

c. 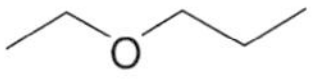
O

e. CH_3OH

b. 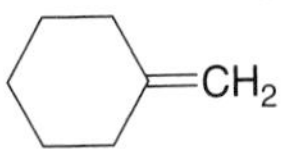
CH2

d. 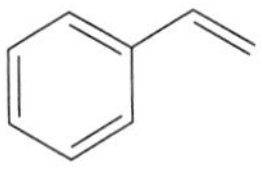

f. 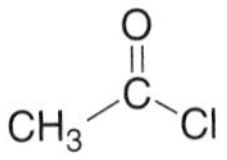
O
C
CH3
Cl

3.50 By using only electron density arguments, determine whether the following reactions will occur:

a. 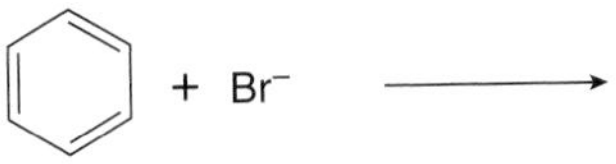
+ Br⁻

d. 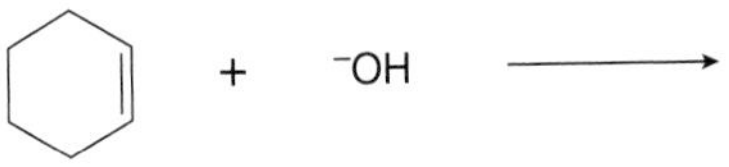
+ ⁻OH

b. 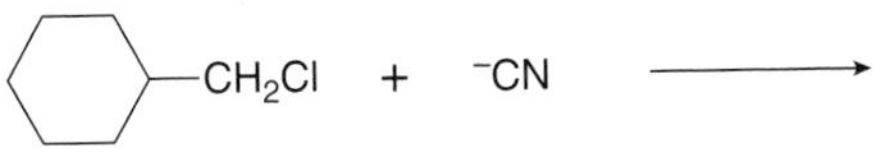
CH2Cl + ⁻CN

e. 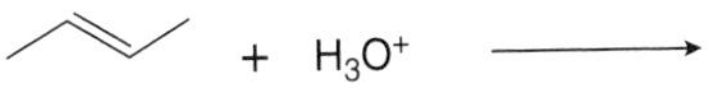
+ H3O+

c. 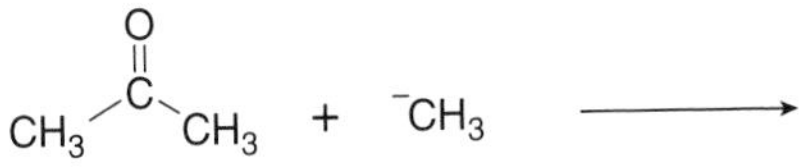
O
C
CH3
CH3
+ ⁻CH3

Cell Membrane

3.51 The composition of a cell membrane is not uniform for all types of cells. Some cell membranes are more rigid than others. Rigidity is determined by a variety of factors, one of which is the structure of the carbon chains in the phospholipids that comprise the membrane. One example of a phospholipid was drawn in Section 3.7A, and another, having C–C double bonds in its carbon chains, is drawn here. Which phospholipid would be present in the more rigid cell membrane and why?

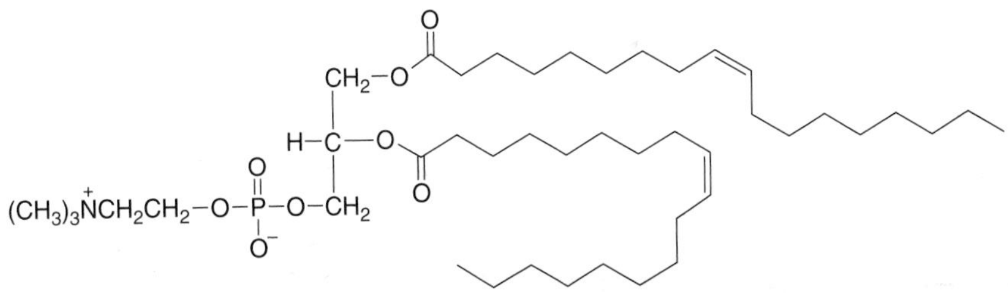
O
CH2–O
H–C–O
O
O
(CH3)3NCH2CH2–O–P–O–CH2
O⁻

a phospholipid with π bonds in the long hydrocarbon chains

General Question

3.52 Vancomycin is a useful antibiotic for treating infections in cancer patients on chemotherapy and renal patients on dialysis. Unlike mammalian cells, bacterial cells are surrounded by a fairly rigid cell wall, which is crucial to the bacterium's survival. Vancomycin kills bacteria by interfering with their cell wall synthesis.

a. How many amide functional groups are present in vancomycin?
b. Which OH groups are bonded to sp^3 hybridized carbon atoms and which are bonded to sp^2 hybridized carbons?
c. Would you expect vancomycin to be water soluble? Explain.
d. Which proton is the most acidic?
e. Label three *different* functional groups capable of hydrogen bonding.

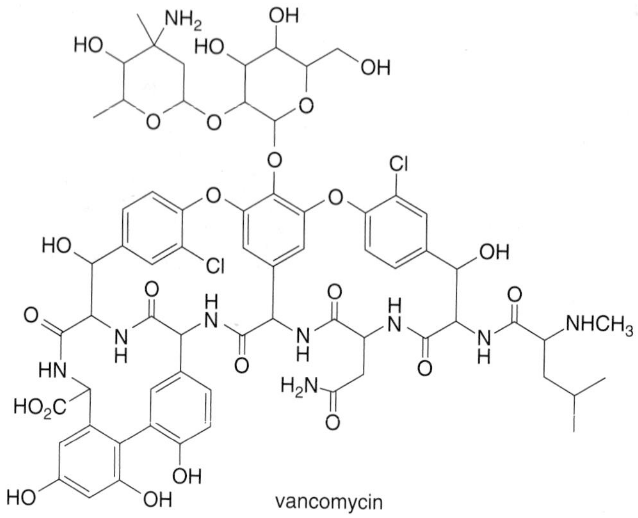

vancomycin

Challenge Problems

3.53 Although diethyl ether and tetrahydrofuran are both four-carbon ethers, one compound is much more water soluble than the other. Predict which compound has higher water solubility and offer an explanation.

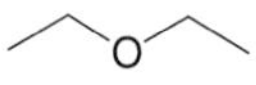

diethyl ether

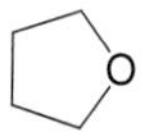

tetrahydrofuran

3.54 Answer the following questions by referring to the ball-and-stick model of fentanyl, a potent narcotic analgesic used in surgical procedures.

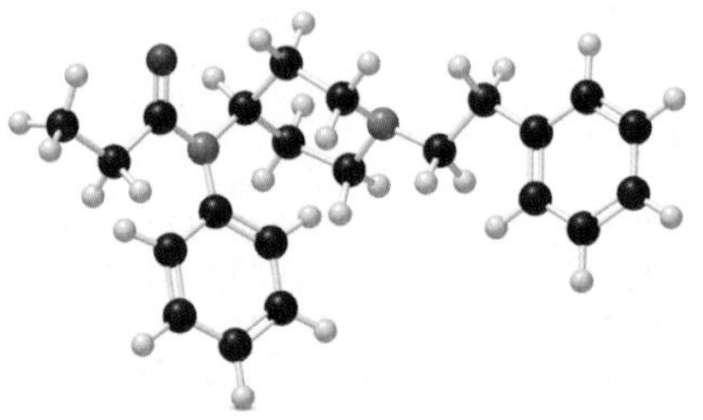

fentanyl

a. Identify the functional groups.
b. Label the most acidic proton.
c. Label the most basic atom.
d. What types of intermolecular forces are present between two molecules of fentanyl?
e. Draw an isomer predicted to have a higher boiling point.
f. Which sites in the molecule can hydrogen bond to water?
g. Label all electrophilic carbons.

3.55 Explain why **A** is less water soluble than **B,** even though both compounds have the same functional groups.

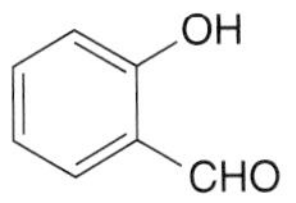

= **A**

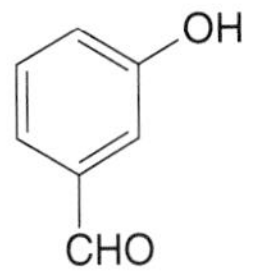

= **B**

3.56 Recall from Section 1.10B that there is restricted rotation around carbon–carbon double bonds. Maleic acid and fumaric acid are two isomers with vastly different physical properties and pK_a values for loss of both protons. Explain why each of these differences occurs.

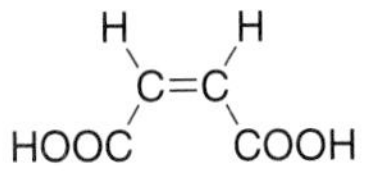

maleic acid

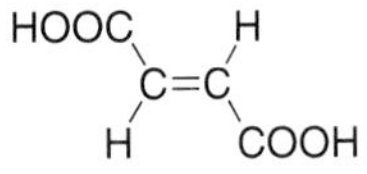

fumaric acid

	maleic acid	fumaric acid
mp (°C)	130	286
solubility (g/L) in H_2O at 25 °C	788	7
pK_{a1}	1.9	3.0
pK_{a2}	6.5	4.5

4 Alkanes

- **4.1** Alkanes—An introduction
- **4.2** Cycloalkanes
- **4.3** An introduction to nomenclature
- **4.4** Naming alkanes
- **4.5** Naming cycloalkanes
- **4.6** Common names
- **4.7** Fossil fuels
- **4.8** Physical properties of alkanes
- **4.9** Conformations of acyclic alkanes—Ethane
- **4.10** Conformations of butane
- **4.11** An introduction to cycloalkanes
- **4.12** Cyclohexane
- **4.13** Substituted cycloalkanes
- **4.14** Oxidation of alkanes
- **4.15** Lipids—Part 1

Alkanes, the simplest hydrocarbons, are found in all shapes and sizes and occur widely in nature. They are the major constituents of petroleum, a complex mixture of compounds that includes hydrocarbons such as **hexane** and **decane.** Crude petroleum spilled into the sea from a ruptured oil tanker creates an insoluble oil slick on the surface. Petroleum is refined to produce gasoline, diesel fuel, home heating oil, and a myriad of other useful compounds. In Chapter 4, we learn about the properties of alkanes, how to name them (nomenclature), and oxidation—one of their important reactions.

In Chapter 4, we apply the principles of bonding, shape, and reactivity discussed in Chapters 1–3 to our first family of organic compounds, the **alkanes.** Because alkanes have no functional group, they are much less reactive than other organic compounds, and for this reason, much of Chapter 4 is devoted to learning how to name and draw them, as well as to understanding what happens when rotation occurs about their carbon–carbon single bonds.

Studying alkanes also provides an opportunity to learn about **lipids,** a group of biomolecules similar to alkanes, in that they are composed mainly of nonpolar carbon–carbon and carbon–hydrogen σ bonds. Section 4.15 serves as a brief introduction only, so we will return to lipids in Chapters 10 and 30.

4.1 Alkanes—An Introduction

Secretion of **undecane** by a cockroach causes other members of the species to aggregate. Undecane is a ***pheromone,* a chemical substance used for communication** in an animal species, most commonly an insect population.

Cyclohexane is one component of the mango, the most widely consumed fruit in the world.

Recall from Section 3.2 that ***alkanes* are aliphatic hydrocarbons having only C–C and C–H σ bonds.** Because their carbon atoms can be joined together in chains or rings, they can be categorized as acyclic or cyclic.

- **Acyclic alkanes have the molecular formula C_nH_{2n+2} (where n = an integer) and contain only linear and branched chains of carbon atoms. They are also called saturated hydrocarbons because they have the maximum number of hydrogen atoms per carbon.**
- **Cycloalkanes contain carbons joined in one or more rings. Because their general formula is C_nH_{2n}, they have two fewer H atoms than an acyclic alkane with the same number of carbons.**

Undecane and cyclohexane are two naturally occurring alkanes.

An acyclic alkane

$CH_3(CH_2)_9CH_3$

undecane
$C_{11}H_{24}$

A cycloalkane

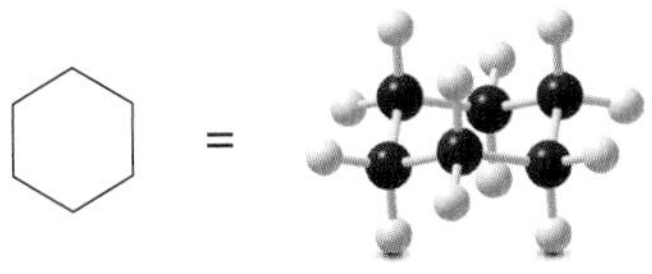

cyclohexane
C_6H_{12}

4.1A Acyclic Alkanes Having One to Five C Atoms

Structures for the two simplest acyclic alkanes were given in Chapter 1. **Methane, CH_4,** has a single carbon atom, and **ethane, CH_3CH_3,** has two. All C atoms in an alkane are surrounded by four groups, making them ***sp*³ hybridized** and **tetrahedral,** and all bond angles are 109.5°.

CH_4
methane =

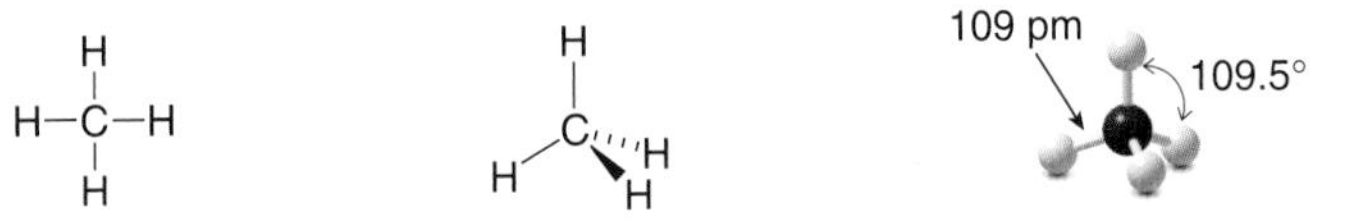

Lewis structure **3-D representation** **ball-and-stick model**

CH_3CH_3
ethane =

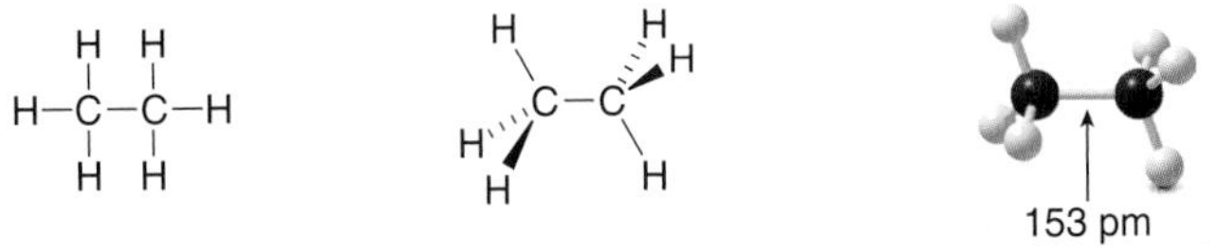

The three-carbon alkane $\mathbf{CH_3CH_2CH_3}$, called **propane,** has molecular formula C_3H_8. Each carbon in the three-dimensional drawing has two bonds in the plane (solid lines), one bond in front (on a wedge), and one bond behind the plane (on a dashed line).

To draw the structure of an alkane, join the carbon atoms together with single bonds, and add enough H atoms to make each C tetravalent.

$CH_3CH_2CH_3$ =
propane

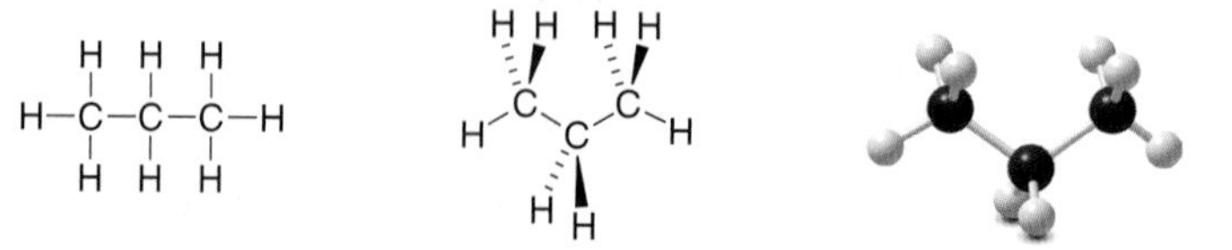

Lewis structure | 3-D representation | ball-and-stick model

Problem 4.1 Three components of the sex pheromone of the female sand bee (*Ophrys sphegodes*) are saturated hydrocarbons containing 23, 25, and 27 carbon atoms. How many H atoms does each of these alkanes contain? Interestingly, the early spider orchid emits a similar hydrocarbon mixture to attract male sand bees to pollinate its flowers.

The molecular formulas for methane, ethane, and propane fit into the general molecular formula for an alkane, $\mathbf{C_nH_{2n+2}}$:

- Methane = CH_4 = $C_1H_{2(1)+2}$
- Ethane = C_2H_6 = $C_2H_{2(2)+2}$
- Propane = C_3H_8 = $C_3H_{2(3)+2}$

The three-dimensional representations and the ball-and-stick models for these alkanes indicate the tetrahedral geometry around each carbon atom. In contrast, **the Lewis structures are not meant to imply any three-dimensional arrangement.** Moreover, in propane and higher molecular weight alkanes, the carbon skeleton can be drawn in a variety of different ways and still represent the same molecule.

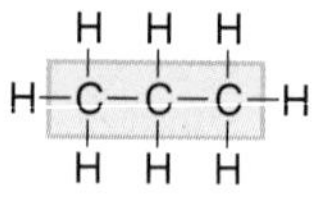

3 C's in a row

=

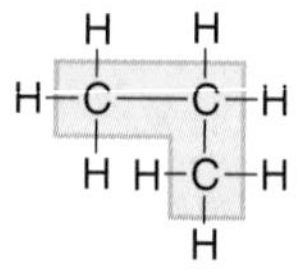

3 C's with a bend

For example, the three carbons of propane can be drawn in a horizontal row or with a bend. ***These representations are equivalent.*** If you follow the carbon chain from one end to the other, you move across the *same* three carbon atoms in both representations.

- **The bends in a carbon chain don't matter when it comes to identifying different compounds.**

There are two different ways to arrange four carbons, giving two compounds with molecular formula C_4H_{10}, named **butane** and **2-methylpropane** (or isobutane).

= $CH_3CH_2CH_2CH_3$

butane

4 C's in a row

straight-chain alkane

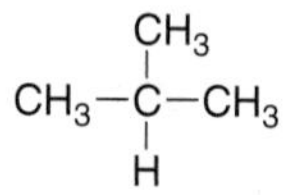

=

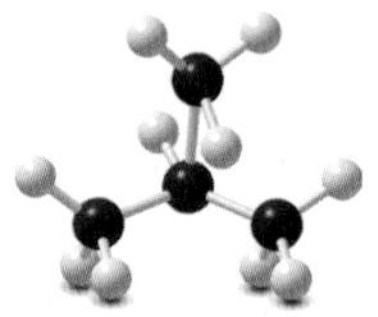

2-methylpropane
(or isobutane)
3 C's in a row with a one-carbon branch

branched-chain alkane

Butane and 2-methylpropane are ***isomers,*** **two different compounds with the same molecular formula** (Section 1.5). They belong to one of the two major classes of isomers called **constitutional** or **structural isomers.** The two isomers discussed in Section 1.5, CH_3OCH_3 and CH_3CH_2OH, are also constitutional isomers. We will learn about the second major class of isomers, called **stereoisomers,** in Section 4.13B.

- ***Constitutional isomers*** **differ in the way the atoms are connected to each other.**

Butane, which has four carbons in a row, is a **straight-chain** or **normal alkane** (an ***n*-alkane**). 2-Methylpropane, on the other hand, is a **branched-chain alkane.**

With alkanes having more than four carbons, the names of the straight-chain isomers are systematic and derive from Greek roots: ***pent*ane** for five C atoms, ***hex*ane** for six, and so on. There are three constitutional isomers for the five-carbon alkane, each having molecular formula C_5H_{12}: **pentane, 2-methylbutane** (or isopentane), and **2,2-dimethylpropane** (or neopentane).

$CH_3CH_2CH_2CH_2CH_3$

pentane

2-methylbutane (isopentane)

2,2-dimethylpropane (neopentane)

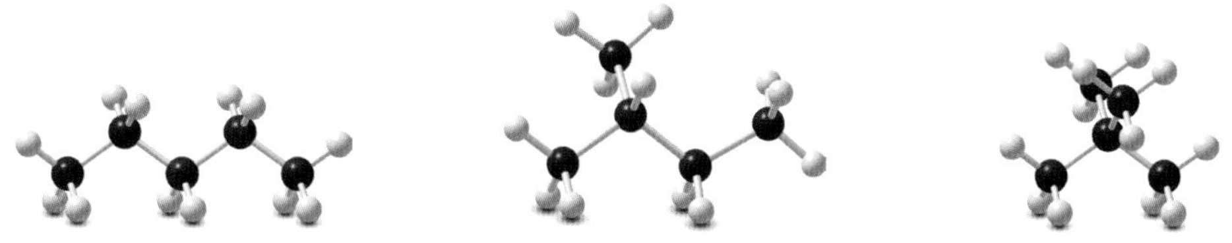

Problem 4.2 Which of the following is *not* another representation for 2-methylbutane?

a. 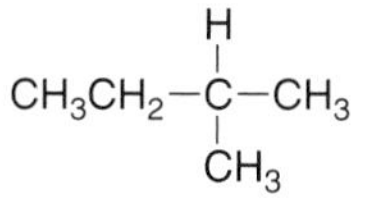

b. 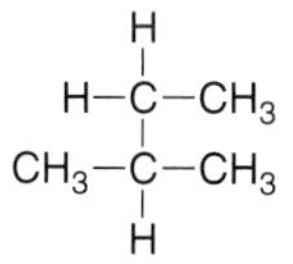

c. $CH_3CH_2CH(CH_3)_2$

d. 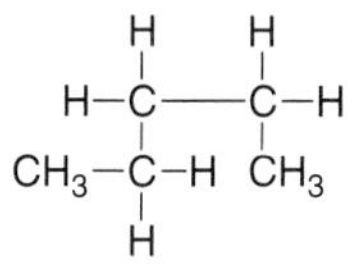

e. 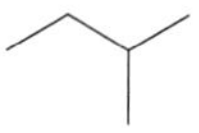

f. $CH_3CH(CH_3)CH_2CH_3$

Carbon atoms in alkanes and other organic compounds are classified by the number of other carbons directly bonded to them.

- A *primary carbon* (1° carbon) is bonded to *one* other C atom.
- A *secondary carbon* (2° carbon) is bonded to *two* other C atoms.
- A *tertiary carbon* (3° carbon) is bonded to *three* other C atoms.
- A *quaternary carbon* (4° carbon) is bonded to *four* other C atoms.

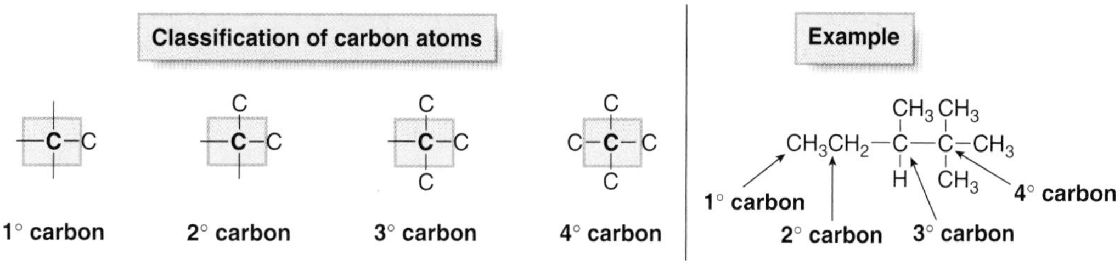

Hydrogen atoms are classified as **primary (1°), secondary (2°),** or **tertiary (3°)** depending on the **type of carbon atom** to which they are bonded.

- A *primary hydrogen* (1° H) is on a C bonded to one other C atom.
- A *secondary hydrogen* (2° H) is on a C bonded to two other C atoms.
- A *tertiary hydrogen* (3° H) is on a C bonded to three other C atoms.

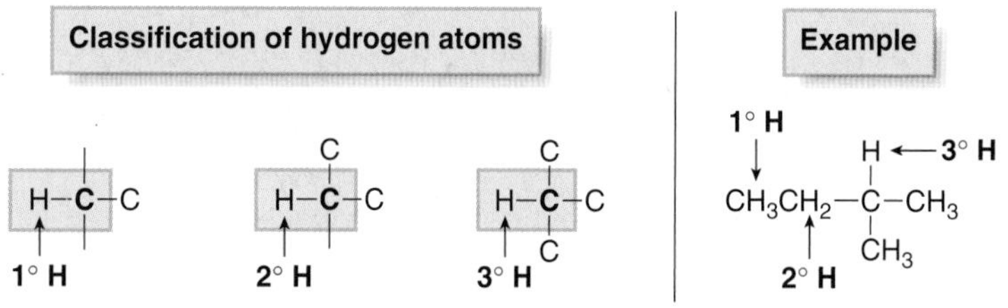

Sample Problem 4.1 (a) Classify the designated carbon atoms as 1°, 2°, 3°, or 4°. (b) Classify the designated hydrogen atoms as 1°, 2°, or 3°.

[1] 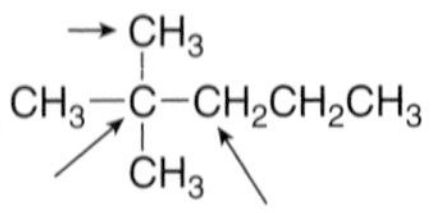

[2] 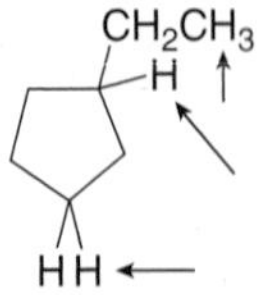

Solution

[1] 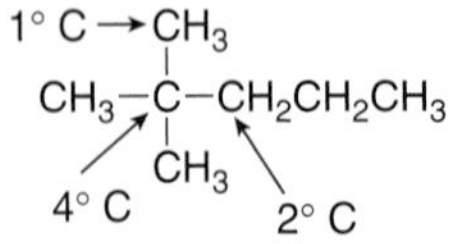

[2] 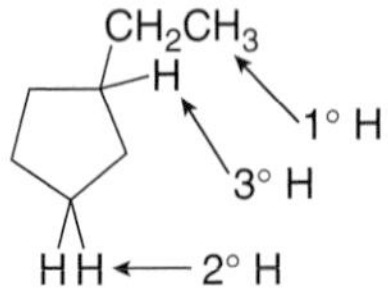

Problem 4.3 (a) Classify the carbon atoms in each compound as 1°, 2°, 3°, or 4°. (b) Classify the hydrogen atoms in each compound as 1°, 2°, or 3°.

[1] $CH_3CH_2CH_2CH_3$ [2] $(CH_3)_3CH$ [3] 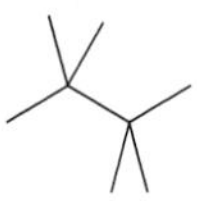 [4] 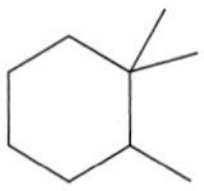

Problem 4.4 Classifying a carbon atom by the number of carbons to which it is bonded can also be done in more complex molecules that contain heteroatoms. Classify each sp^3 hybridized carbon atom in bilobalide, a compound isolated from *Ginkgo biloba* extracts, as 1°, 2°, 3°, or 4°.

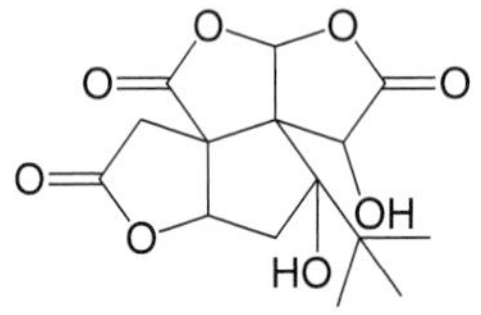

bilobalide

Bilobalide is obtained from *Ginkgo biloba,* the oldest seed-producing plant that currently lives on earth. Extracts from the leaves, roots, bark, and seeds of the ginkgo tree have been used in traditional Chinese medicine and currently comprise the most widely taken herbal supplements.

The suffix ***-ane*** identifies a molecule as an alk***ane.***

4.1B Acyclic Alkanes Having More Than Five C Atoms

The maximum number of possible constitutional isomers increases dramatically as the number of carbon atoms in the alkane increases, as shown in Table 4.1. For example, there are 75 possible isomers for an alkane having 10 carbon atoms, but 366,319 possible isomers for one having 20 carbons.

Each entry in Table 4.1 is formed from the preceding entry by adding a CH_2 group. **A CH_2 group is called a *methylene group.* A group of compounds that differ by only a CH_2 group is called a *homologous series.*** The names of all alkanes end in the suffix ***-ane,*** and the syllables preceding the suffix identify the number of carbon atoms in the chain.

Problem 4.5 Draw the five constitutional isomers having molecular formula C_6H_{14}.

Problem 4.6 Draw the structure of an alkane with molecular formula C_7H_{16} that contains (a) one 4° carbon; (b) only 1° and 2° carbons; (c) 1°, 2°, and 3° hydrogens.

Problem 4.7 Considering compounds **A–C,** which two structures represent the same compound?

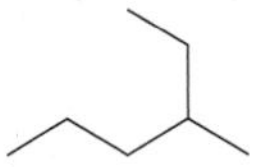

A

$CH_3(CH_2)_3CH(CH_3)_2$

B

$CH_3CH_2CH(CH_3)CH_2CH_2CH_3$

C

Table 4.1 Summary: Straight-Chain Alkanes

Number of C atoms	Molecular formula	Name (*n*-alkane)	Number of constitutional isomers	Number of C atoms	Molecular formula	Name (*n*-alkane)	Number of constitutional isomers
1	CH_4	methane	—	9	C_9H_{20}	nonane	35
2	C_2H_6	ethane	—	10	$C_{10}H_{22}$	decane	75
3	C_3H_8	propane	—	11	$C_{11}H_{24}$	undecane	159
4	C_4H_{10}	butane	2	12	$C_{12}H_{26}$	dodecane	355
5	C_5H_{12}	pentane	3	13	$C_{13}H_{28}$	tridecane	802
6	C_6H_{14}	hexane	5	14	$C_{14}H_{30}$	tetradecane	1858
7	C_7H_{16}	heptane	9	15	$C_{15}H_{32}$	pentadecane	4347
8	C_8H_{18}	octane	18	20	$C_{20}H_{42}$	eicosane	366,319

4.2 Cycloalkanes

Cycloalkanes have molecular formula C_nH_{2n} and contain carbon atoms arranged in a ring. Think of a cycloalkane as being formed by removing two H atoms from the end carbons of a chain, and then bonding the two carbons together. Simple cycloalkanes are named by adding the prefix **cyclo-** to the name of the acyclic alkane having the same number of carbons.

Cycloalkanes having three to six carbon atoms are shown in the accompanying figure. They are most often drawn in skeletal representations.

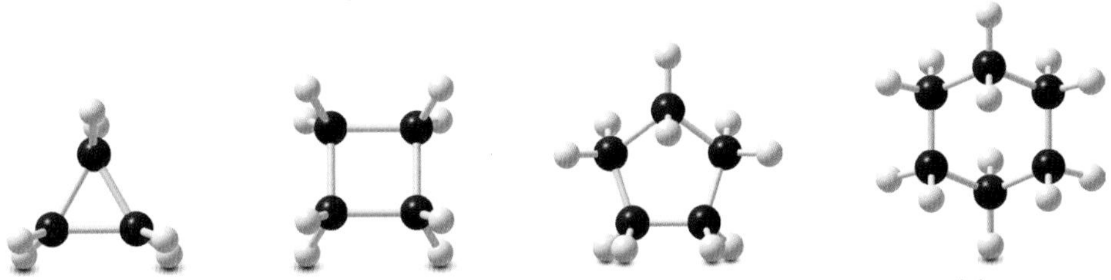

cyclopropane C_3H_6 — cyclobutane C_4H_8 — cyclopentane C_5H_{10} — cyclohexane C_6H_{12}

Problem 4.8 Draw the five constitutional isomers that have molecular formula C_5H_{10} and contain one ring.

Garlic has been a valued commodity throughout history. It has been used in Chinese herbal medicine for more than 4000 years, as a form of currency in Siberia, and as a repellent for witches by the Saxons. Today it is used as a dietary supplement because of its reported health benefits. **Allicin,** the molecule responsible for garlic's odor, is a rather unstable molecule that is not stored in the garlic bulb, but instead is produced by the action of enzymes when the bulb is crushed or bruised.

4.3 An Introduction to Nomenclature

How are organic compounds named? Long ago, the name of a compound was often based on the plant or animal source from which it was obtained. For example, the name for **formic acid,** a caustic compound isolated from certain ants, comes from the Latin word *formica,* meaning *ant;* and **allicin,** the pungent principle of garlic, is derived from the botanical name for garlic, *Allium sativum.* Other compounds were named by their discoverer for more personal reasons. Adolf von Baeyer supposedly named barbituric acid after a woman named Barbara, although speculation continues on Barbara's identity—a lover, a Munich waitress, or even St. Barbara.

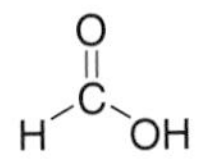

formic acid
(obtained from certain ants)

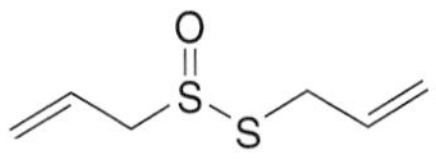

allicin
(odor of garlic)

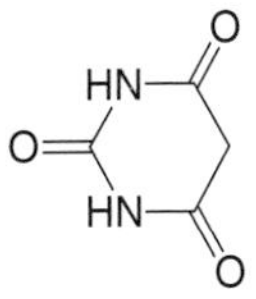

barbituric acid
(named for Barbara whom?)

With the isolation and preparation of thousands of new organic compounds it became clear that each organic compound must have an unambiguous name, derived from a set of easily remembered rules. A systematic method of naming compounds was developed by the ***I**nternational* ***U**nion of* ***P**ure and* ***A**pplied* ***C**hemistry.* It is referred to as the **IUPAC system of nomenclature;** how it can be used to name alkanes is explained in Sections 4.4 and 4.5.

The IUPAC system of nomenclature has been regularly revised since it was first adopted in 1892. Revisions in 1979 and 1993 and recent extensive recommendations in 2004 have given chemists a variety of acceptable names for compounds. Many changes are minor. For example, the 1979 nomenclature rules assign the name 1-butene to $CH_2{=}CHCH_2CH_3$, while the 1993 rules assign the name but-1-ene; that is, only the position of the number differs. In this text, the most generally used IUPAC conventions will be given, and often a margin note will be added to mention the differences between past and recent recommendations.

Naming organic compounds has become big business for drug companies. The IUPAC name of an organic compound can be long and complex, and may be comprehensible only to a chemist. As a result, most drugs have three names:

- **Systematic:** The systematic name follows the accepted rules of nomenclature and indicates the compound's chemical structure; this is the IUPAC name.
- **Generic:** The generic name is the official, internationally approved name for the drug.
- **Trade:** The trade name for a drug is assigned by the company that manufactures it. Trade names are often "catchy" and easy to remember. Companies hope that the public will continue to purchase a drug with an easily recalled trade name long after a cheaper generic version becomes available.

In the world of over-the-counter anti-inflammatory agents, the compound a chemist calls 2-[4-(2-methylpropyl)phenyl]propanoic acid has the generic name ibuprofen. It is marketed under a variety of trade names including Motrin and Advil.

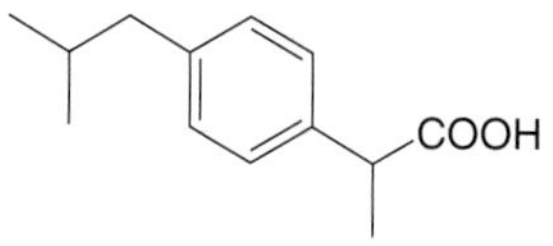
COOH

Systematic name:	2-[4-(2-methylpropyl)phenyl]propanoic acid
Generic name:	ibuprofen
Trade name:	Motrin or Advil

4.4 Naming Alkanes

The name of every organic molecule has three parts.

- The **parent name** indicates the number of carbons in the longest continuous carbon chain in the molecule.
- The **suffix** indicates what functional group is present.
- The **prefix** reveals the identity, location, and number of substituents attached to the carbon chain.

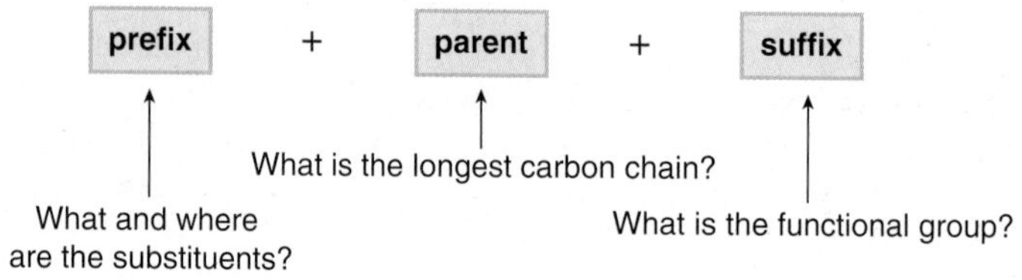
prefix
+
parent
+
suffix
What is the longest carbon chain?
What and where are the substituents?
What is the functional group?

The names listed in Table 4.1 of Section 4.1B for the simple *n*-alkanes consist of the parent name, which indicates the number of carbon atoms in the longest carbon chain, and the suffix

-ane, which indicates that the compounds are alkanes. The parent name for **one carbon is *meth-*,** for **two carbons is *eth-*,** and so on. Thus, we are already familiar with two parts of the name of an organic compound.

To determine the third part of a name, the prefix, we must learn how to name the carbon groups or ***substituents*** that are bonded to the longest carbon chain.

4.4A Naming Substituents

Carbon substituents bonded to a long carbon chain are called **alkyl groups.**

- **An *alkyl group* is formed by removing one hydrogen from an alkane.**

An alkyl group is a part of a molecule that is now able to bond to another atom or a functional group. **To name an alkyl group, change the *-ane* ending of the parent alkane to *-yl.*** Thus, methane (CH_4) becomes methyl (CH_3-) and ethane (CH_3CH_3) becomes ethyl (CH_3CH_2-). As we learned in Section 3.1, **R** denotes a general carbon group bonded to a functional group. **R** thus denotes any alkyl group.

Naming three- and four-carbon alkyl groups is more complicated because the parent hydrocarbons have more than one type of hydrogen atom. For example, propane has both 1° and 2° H atoms, and removal of each of these H atoms forms a different alkyl group with a different name, **propyl** or **isopropyl.**

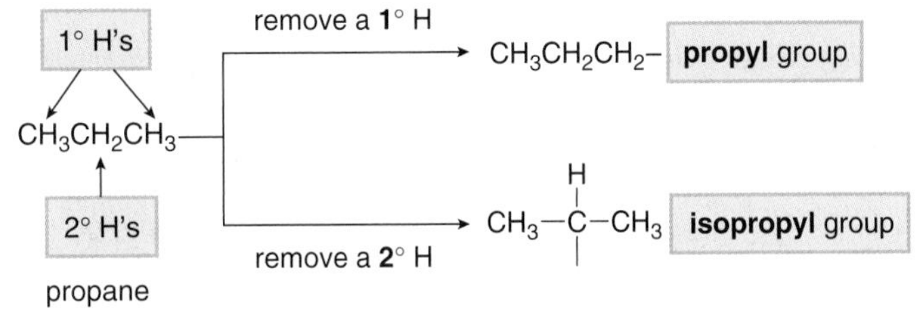

The prefix **iso-** is part of the words *propyl* and *butyl,* forming a single word: **isopropyl** and **isobutyl.** The prefixes ***sec-*** and ***tert-*** are separated from the word *butyl* by a hyphen: ***sec*-butyl** and ***tert*-butyl.**

Because there are two different butane isomers to begin with, each having two different kinds of H atoms, there are four possible alkyl groups containing four carbon atoms, each having a different name: **butyl, *sec*-butyl, isobutyl,** and ***tert*-butyl.**

From **butane:**

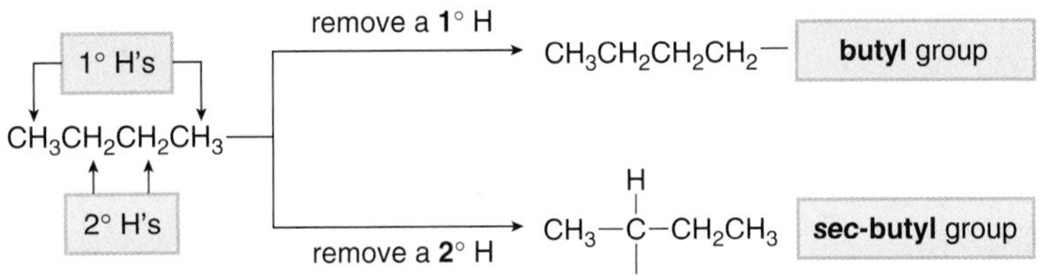

The prefix *sec-* is short for *secondary.* A *sec*-butyl group is formed by removal of a **2° H.** The prefix *tert-* is short for *tertiary.* A *tert*-butyl group is formed by removal of a **3° H.**

From **2-methylpropane:**

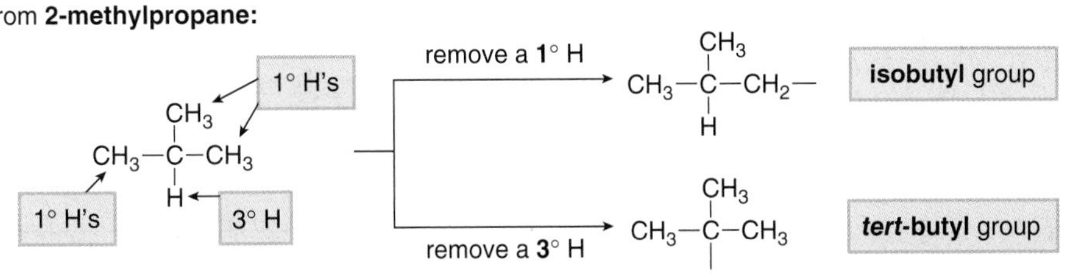

Abbreviations are sometimes used for certain common alkyl groups.

Alkyl group (abbreviation)

- methyl (Me)
- ethyl (Et)
- butyl (Bu)
- *tert*-butyl (*t*-Bu)

The names isopropyl, *sec*-butyl, isobutyl, and *tert*-butyl are recognized as acceptable substituent names in both the 1979 and 1993 revisions of IUPAC nomenclature. A general method to name these substituents, as well as alkyl groups that contain five or more carbon atoms, is described in Appendix B.

4.4B Naming an Acyclic Alkane

Four steps are needed to name an alkane. In the following examples, only the C atoms of the carbon skeleton are drawn. **Remember each C has enough H atoms to make it tetravalent.**

How To Name an Alkane Using the IUPAC System

Step [1] Find the parent carbon chain and add the suffix.

- Find the longest continuous carbon chain, and name the molecule by using the parent name for that number of carbons, given in Table 4.1. To the name of the parent, add the suffix ***-ane*** for an alkane. Each functional group has its own characteristic suffix.

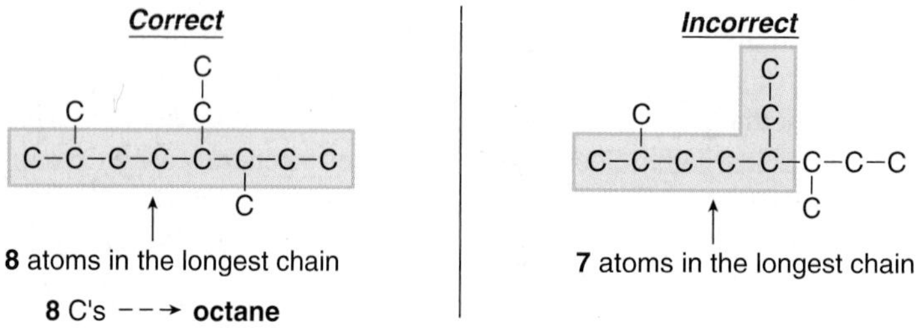

- Finding the longest chain is just a matter of trial and error. Place your pencil on one end of the chain, go to the other end without picking it up, and count carbons. Repeat this procedure until you have found the chain with the largest number of carbons.
- It does not matter if the chain is *straight* or has *bends.* All of the following representations are equivalent.

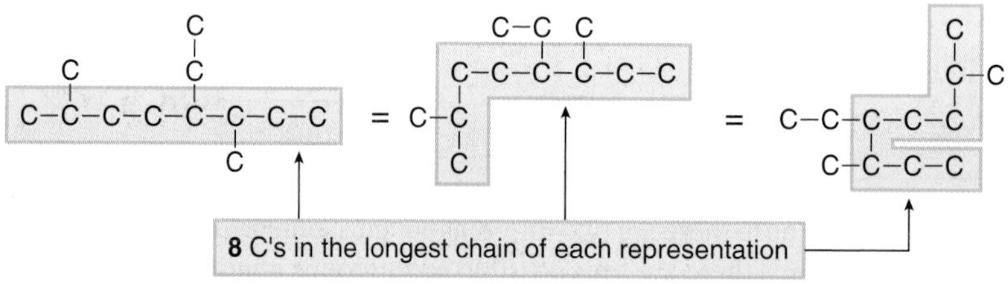

- If there are two chains of equal length, pick the chain with more substituents. In the following example, two different chains in the same alkane contain 7 C's, but the compound on the left has two alkyl groups attached to its long chain, whereas the compound to the right has only one.

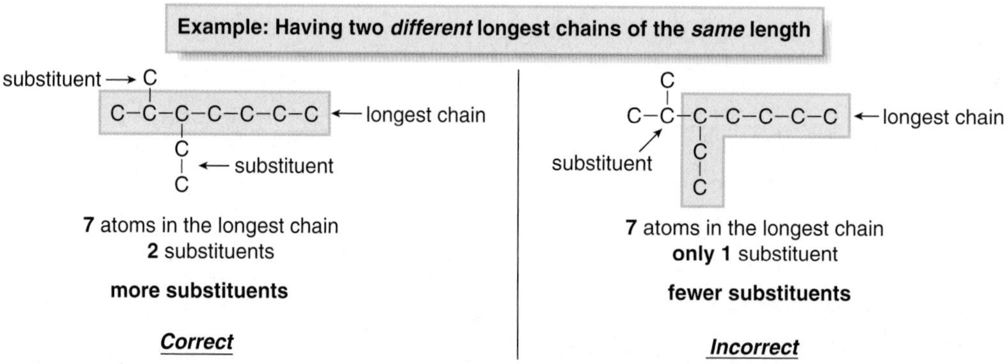

Step [2] Number the atoms in the carbon chain.

- Number the longest chain to give the *first* substituent the lower number.

Correct

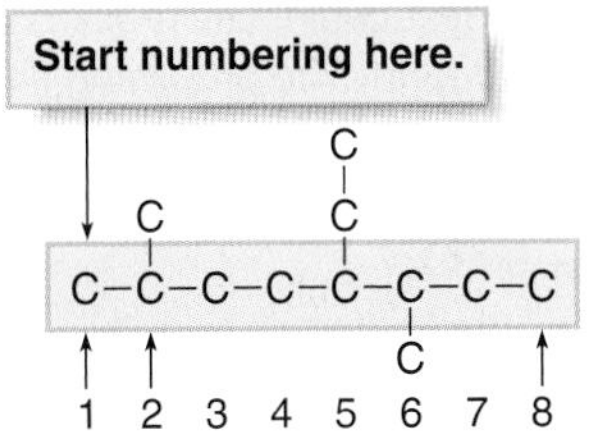

first substituent at C2

Incorrect

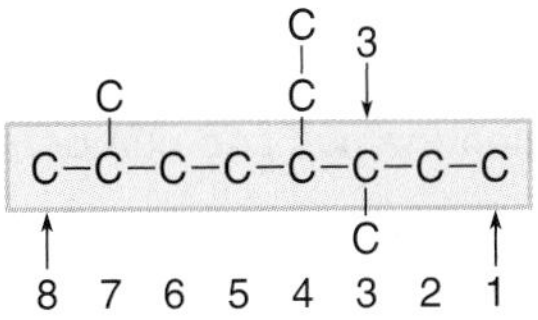

first substituent at C3

- If the first substituent is the same distance from both ends, number the chain to give the second substituent the lower number. Always look for the first point of difference in numbering from each end of the longest chain.

Example: Giving a lower number to the *second* substituent

Numbering from *left* to right

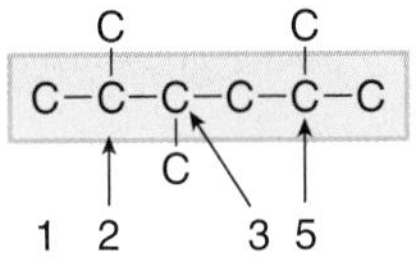

CH_3 groups at C2, **C3,** and C5.

The second substituent has a lower number.

Correct

Numbering from *right* to left

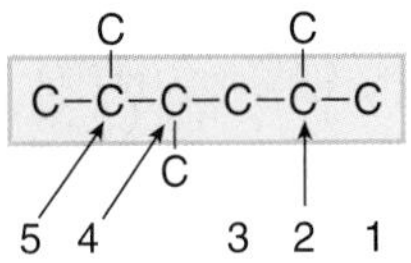

CH_3 groups at C2, **C4,** and C5.

higher number

Incorrect

- When numbering a carbon chain results in the same numbers from either end of the chain, assign the lower number *alphabetically* to the first substituent.

Example: Two *different* groups *equidistant* from the ends

Numbering from *left* to right

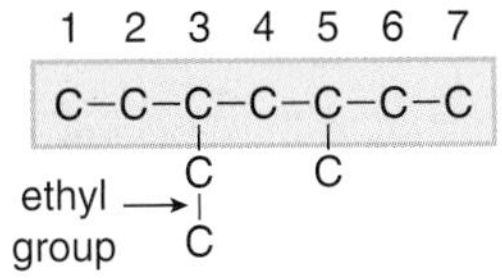

- **e**thyl at **C3**
- **m**ethyl at **C5**

Earlier letter ⟶ lower number

Correct

Numbering from *right* to left

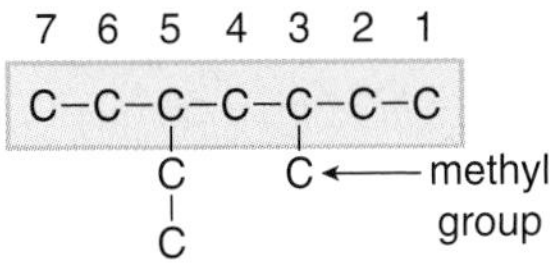

- **m**ethyl at **C3**
- **e**thyl at **C5**

Incorrect

Step [3] Name and number the substituents.

- Name the substituents as alkyl groups, and use the numbers from Step 2 to designate their location.

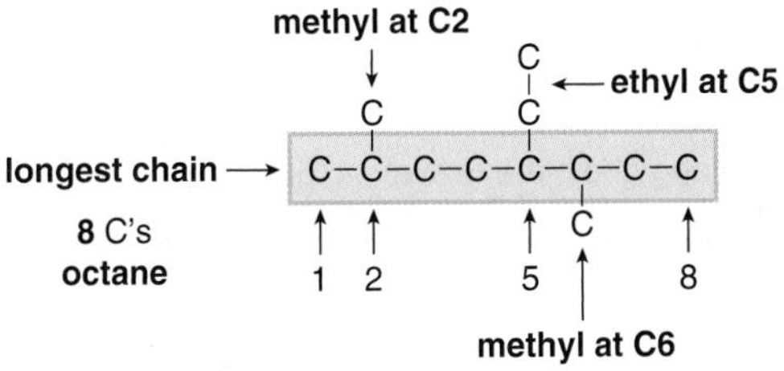

This molecule has three substituents bonded to the longest carbon chain.

—Continued

How To, continued . . .

- Every carbon belongs to *either* the longest chain or a substituent, but *not both.*
- Each substituent needs its *own* number.
- If two or more identical substituents are bonded to the longest chain, use prefixes to indicate how many: **di-** for two groups, **tri-** for three groups, **tetra-** for four groups, and so forth. The preceding molecule has two methyl substituents, and so its name contains the prefix di- before the word methyl → *di*methyl.

Step [4] **Combine substituent names and numbers + parent + suffix.**

- Precede the name of the parent by the names of the substituents.
- Alphabetize the names of the substituents, ignoring all prefixes except *iso,* as in isopropyl and isobutyl.
- Precede the name of each substituent by the number that indicates its location. There must be **one number for each substituent.**
- Separate numbers by commas and separate numbers from letters by hyphens. The name of an alkane is a single word, with no spaces after hyphens or commas.

[1] Identify all the pieces of a compound, using Steps 1–3.

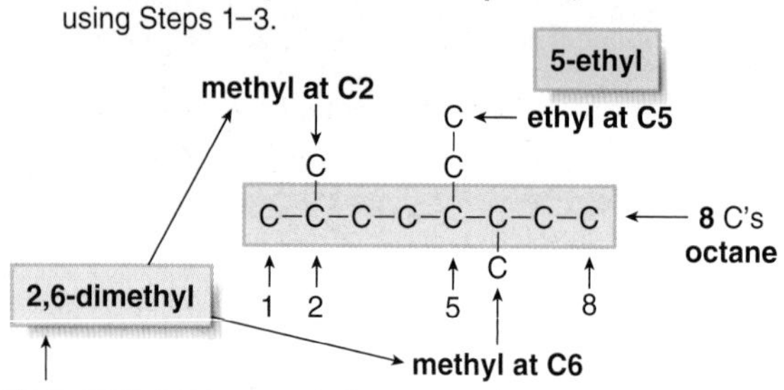

Each methyl group needs its own number.

[2] Then, put the pieces of the name together.

substituent names and numbers	+	parent	+	suffix
5-ethyl-2,6-dimethyl	+	**oct**	+	**ane**
Alphabetize: **e** for **ethyl,** then **m** for **methyl**		8 C's		an **alkane**

Answer: 5-ethyl-2,6-dimethyloctane

Several additional examples of alkane nomenclature are given in Figure 4.1.

Figure 4.1 Examples of alkane nomenclature

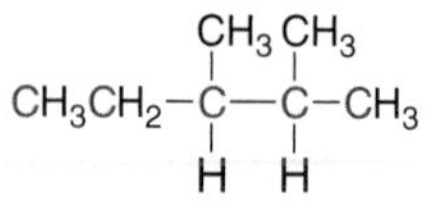

2,3-dimethylpentane

[Number to give the 1st methyl group the lower number.]

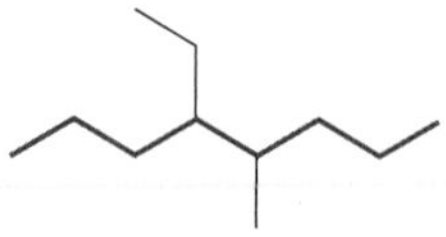

4-ethyl-5-methyloctane

[Assign the lower number to the 1st substituent alphabetically: the **e** of **e**thyl before the **m** of **m**ethyl.]

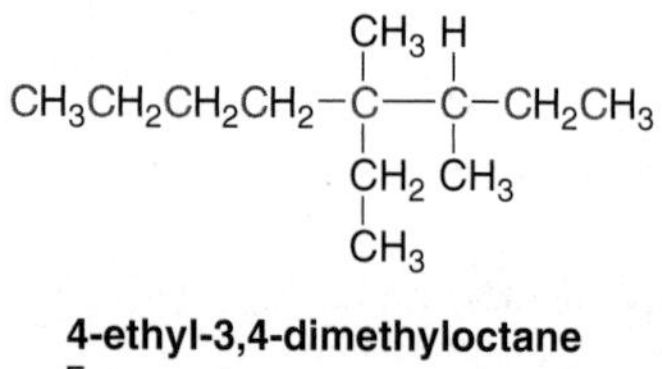

4-ethyl-3,4-dimethyloctane

[Alphabetize the **e** of **e**thyl before the **m** of **m**ethyl.]

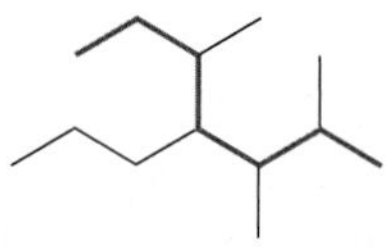

2,3,5-trimethyl-4-propylheptane

[Pick the long chain with more substituents.]

- The carbon atoms of each long chain are **drawn in red.**

Sample Problem 4.2 Give the IUPAC name for the following compound.

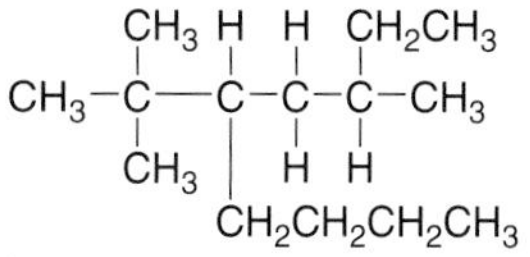

Solution

To help identify which carbons belong to the longest chain and which are substituents, always draw a box around the atoms of the long chain. Every other carbon atom then becomes a substituent that needs its own name as an alkyl group.

[H's on C's are omitted in the answer, for clarity.]

Step 1: Name the parent.

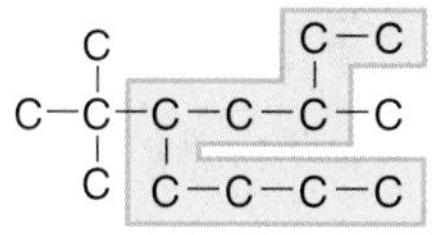

9 C's in the longest chain ----→ **nonane**

Step 2: Number the chain.

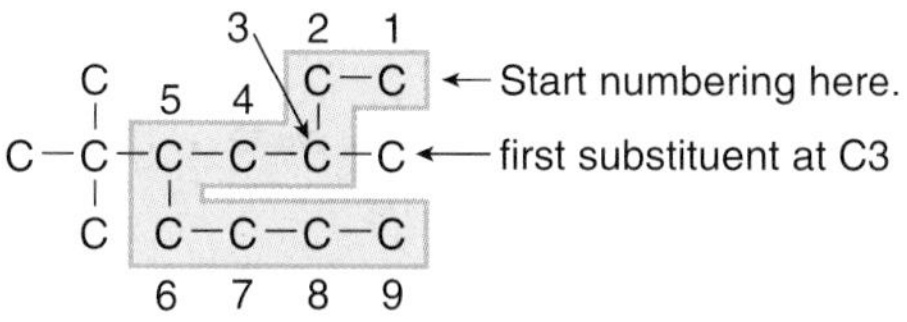
3
2
1
5
4
6 7 8 9
← Start numbering here.
← first substituent at C3

Step 3: Name and number the substituents.

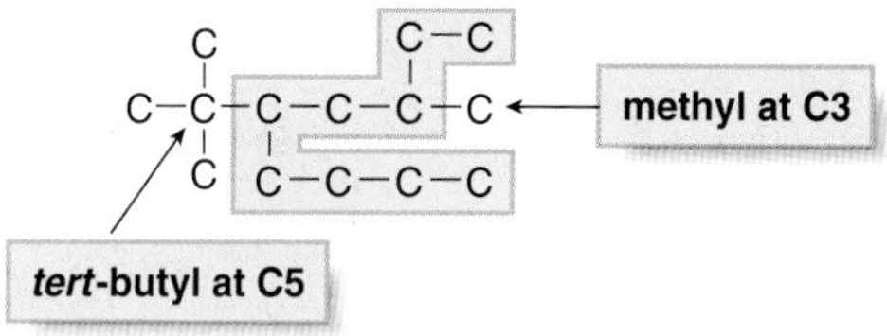
methyl at C3
tert-butyl at C5

Step 4: Combine the parts.

- Alphabetize: the **b** of **butyl** before the **m** of **methyl**

Answer: 5-*tert*-butyl-3-methylnonane

Problem 4.9 Give the IUPAC name for each compound.

a. 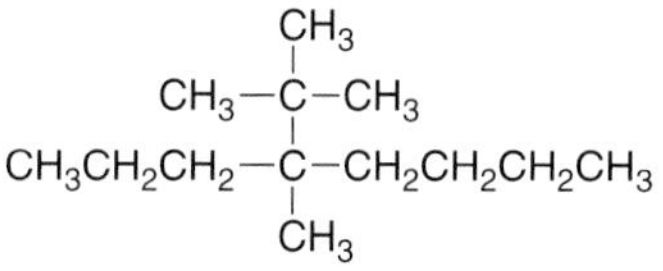

b. 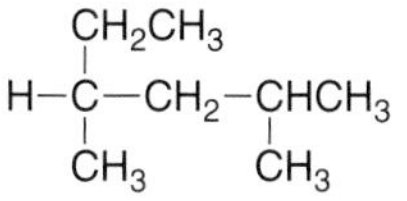

c. 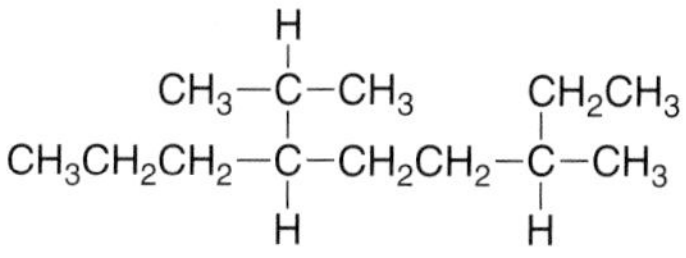

d. 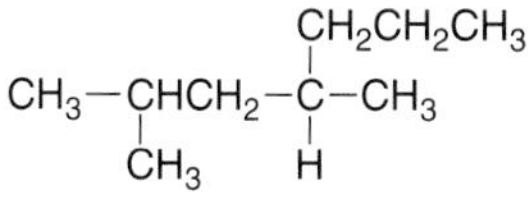

Problem 4.10 Give the IUPAC name for each compound.

a. $(CH_3)_3CCH_2CH(CH_2CH_3)_2$

b. $CH_3(CH_2)_3CH(CH_2CH_2CH_3)CH(CH_3)_2$

c. 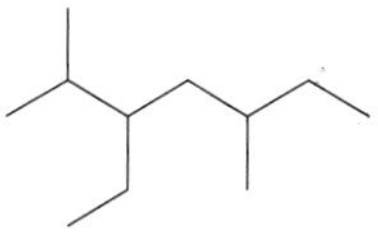

d. 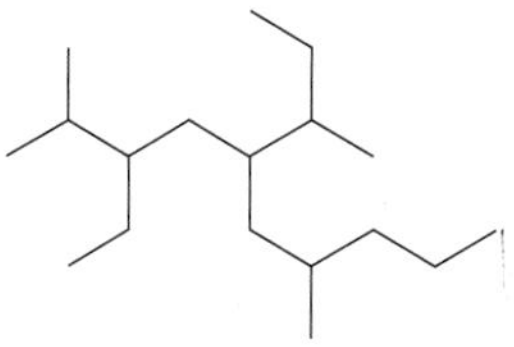

You must also know how to derive a structure from a given name. Sample Problem 4.3 illustrates a stepwise method.

Sample Problem 4.3 Give the structure corresponding to the following IUPAC name: 6-isopropyl-3,3,7-trimethyldecane.

Solution

Follow three steps to derive a structure from a name.

Step [1] Identify the parent name and functional group found at the *end* of the name.

decane ---→ **10** C's ---→ C–C–C–C–C–C–C–C–C–C

Step [2] Number the carbon skeleton in *either* direction.

1 2 3 4 5 6 7 8 9 10
C–C–C–C–C–C–C–C–C–C

Step [3] Add the substituents at the appropriate carbons.

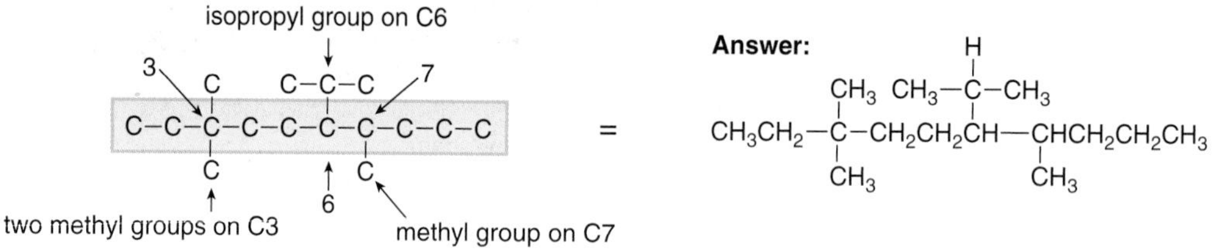
isopropyl group on C6
3
7
6
two methyl groups on C3
methyl group on C7
=
Answer:

Problem 4.11 Give the structure corresponding to each IUPAC name.

a. 3-methylhexane
b. 3,3-dimethylpentane
c. 3,5,5-trimethyloctane
d. 3-ethyl-4-methylhexane
e. 3-ethyl-5-isobutylnonane

Problem 4.12 Give the IUPAC name for each of the five constitutional isomers of molecular formula C_6H_{14} in Problem 4.5.

4.5 Naming Cycloalkanes

Cycloalkanes are named by using similar rules, but the prefix **cyclo-** immediately precedes the name of the parent.

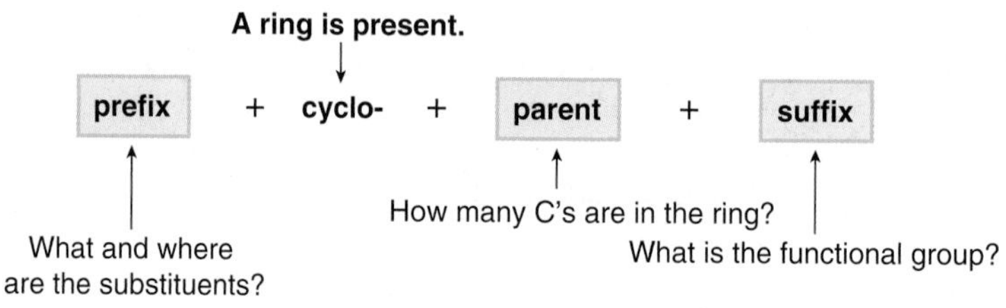
A ring is present.
prefix
+ cyclo- +
parent
+
suffix
What and where are the substituents?
How many C's are in the ring?
What is the functional group?

How To Name a Cycloalkane Using the IUPAC System

Step [1] **Find the parent cycloalkane.**

- Count the number of carbon atoms in the ring and use the parent name for that number of carbons. Add the prefix **cyclo-** and the suffix ***-ane*** to the parent name.

6 C's in the ring →
cyclohexane

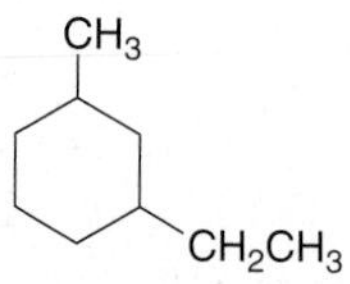
CH3
CH2CH3

Step [2] **Name and number the substituents.**

- No number is needed to indicate the location of a single substituent.

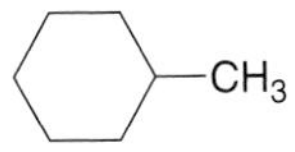

methylcyclohexane

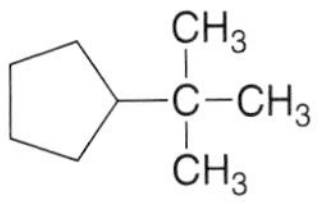

tert-butylcyclopentane

- For rings with more than one substituent, begin numbering at one substituent and proceed around the ring clockwise or counterclockwise to give the second substituent the lower number.

numbering clockwise

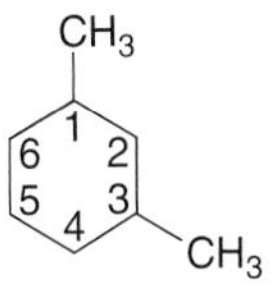

CH_3 groups at C1 and **C3**
The 2nd substituent has a lower number.

Correct: **1,3-dimethylcyclohexane**

numbering counterclockwise

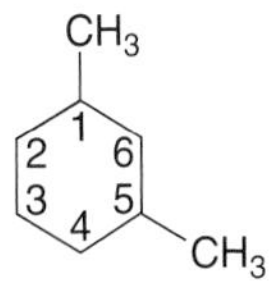

CH_3 groups at C1 and **C5**

Incorrect: 1,5-dimethylcyclohexane

- With two different substituents, number the ring to assign the lower number to the substituents *alphabetically.*

Begin numbering at the ethyl group.

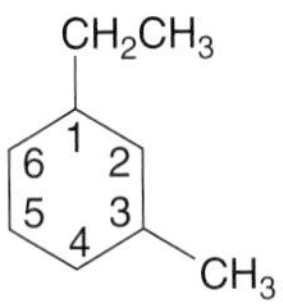

- **e**thyl group at **C1**
- **m**ethyl group at **C3**

earlier letter ⟶ lower number

Correct: **1-ethyl-3-methylcyclohexane**

Begin numbering at the methyl group.

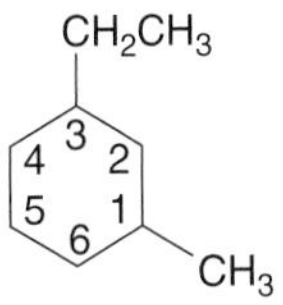

- **m**ethyl group at **C1**
- **e**thyl group at **C3**

Incorrect: 3-ethyl-1-methylcyclohexane

When an alkane is composed of both a ring and a long chain, what determines whether a compound is named as an acyclic alkane or a cycloalkane? If the number of carbons in the ring is greater than or equal to the number of carbons in the longest chain, the compound is named as a **cycloalkane,** as shown in Figure 4.2. Several examples of cycloalkane nomenclature are given in Figure 4.3.

Figure 4.2

Two contrasting examples—Naming compounds containing both a ring and a long chain of carbon atoms

More carbons in the ring

4 C's in the chain —
a **butyl** group

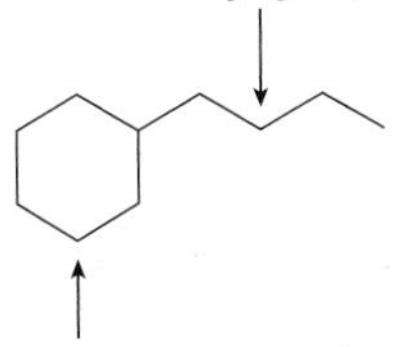

6 C's in the ring—**cyclohexane**

Name as a **cyclohexane** with a substituent.

Answer: butylcyclohexane

More carbons in the chain

6 C's in the chain —
a **hexane**

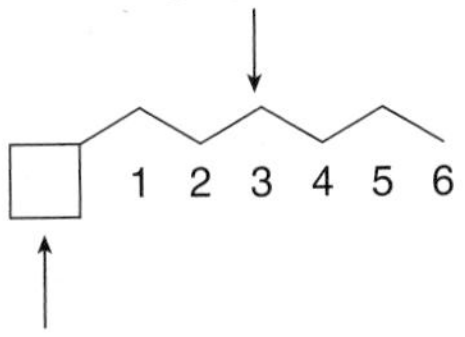

4 C's in the ring—a **cyclobutyl** group

Name as a *hexane* with a substituent.

Answer: 1-cyclobutylhexane

Figure 4.3
Examples of cycloalkane nomenclature

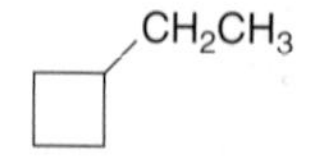

ethylcyclobutane

[No number is needed with only one substituent.]

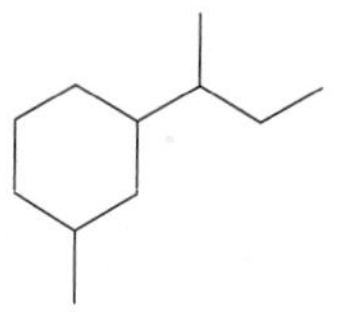

1-*sec*-butyl-3-methylcyclohexane

[Assign the lower number to the 1st substituent alphabetically: the **b** of **b**utyl before the **m** of **m**ethyl.]

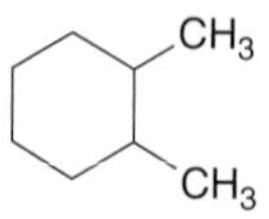

1,2-dimethylcyclohexane

[Number to give the 2nd CH_3 group the lower number: 1,2- not 1,6-.]

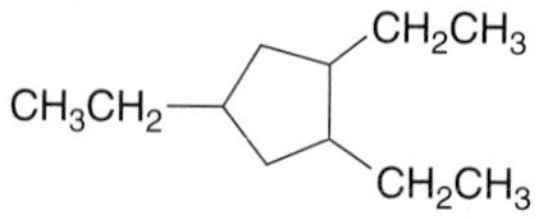

1,2,4-triethylcyclopentane

[Number to give the 2nd CH_3CH_2 group the lower number: 1,2,4- not 1,3,4- or 1,3,5-.]

Problem 4.13 Give the IUPAC name for each compound.

a. 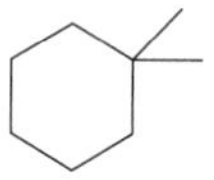

c. 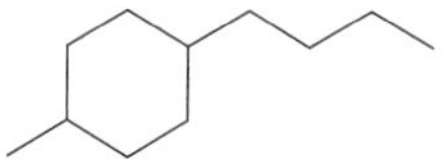

e. 

b. 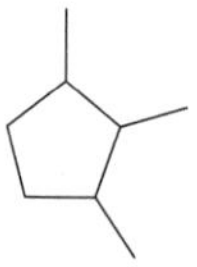

d. 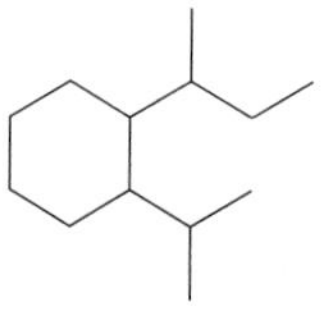

f. 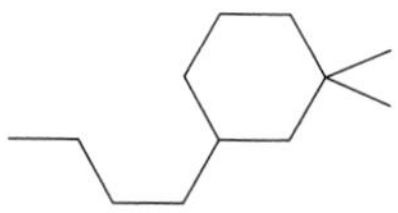

Problem 4.14 Give the structure corresponding to each IUPAC name.

a. 1,2-dimethylcyclobutane
b. 1,1,2-trimethylcyclopropane
c. 4-ethyl-1,2-dimethylcyclohexane
d. 1-*sec*-butyl-3-isopropylcyclopentane
e. 1,1,2,3,4-pentamethylcycloheptane

4.6 Common Names

Some organic compounds are identified using **common names** that do not follow the IUPAC system of nomenclature. Many of these names were given to molecules long ago, before the IUPAC system was adopted. These names are still widely used. For example, isopentane, an older name for one of the C_5H_{12} isomers, is still allowed by IUPAC rules, although it is also named 2-methylbutane. We will follow the IUPAC system except in cases in which a common name is widely accepted.

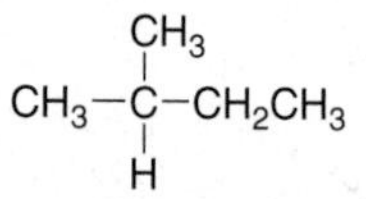

isopentane or 2-methylbutane

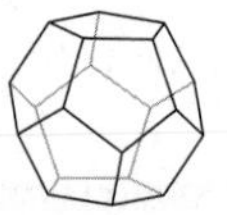

dodecahedrane

In the past several years organic chemists have attempted to synthesize some unusual cycloalkanes not found in nature. **Dodecahedrane,** a beautifully symmetrical compound composed of 12 five-membered rings, is one such molecule. It was first prepared at The Ohio State University in 1982. The IUPAC name for dodecahedrane is undecacyclo[9.9.0.$0^{2,9}$.$0^{3,7}$.$0^{4,20}$.$0^{5,18}$.$0^{6,16}$.$0^{8,15}$.$0^{10,14}$.$0^{12,19}$.$0^{13,17}$]-eicosane, a name so complex that few trained organic chemists would be able to identify its structure.

Figure 4.4
Common names for some polycyclic alkanes

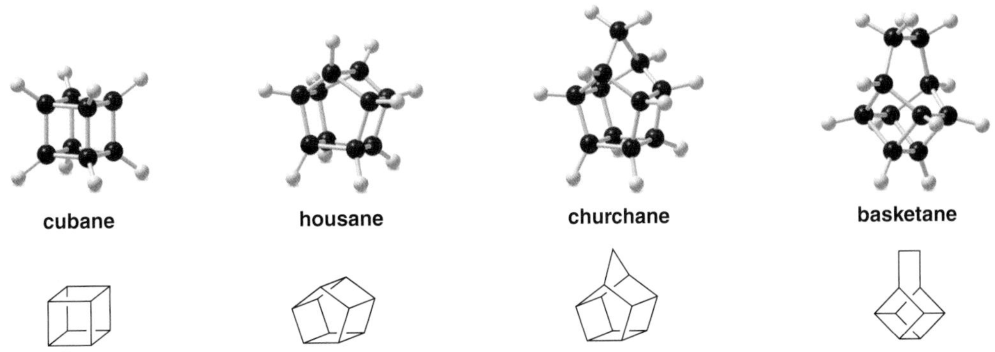

For a more comprehensive list of unusual polycyclic alkanes (including windowpane, davidane, catenane, propellane, and many others), see *Organic Chemistry: The Name Game* by Alex Nickon and Ernest Silversmith, Pergamon Press, 1987.

Because these systematic names are so unwieldy, organic chemists often assign a name to a polycyclic compound that is more descriptive of its shape and structure. Dodecahedrane is named because its 12 five-membered rings resemble a dodecahedron. Figure 4.4 shows the names and structures of several other cycloalkanes whose names were inspired by the shape of their carbon skeletons. All the names end in the suffix ***-ane,*** indicating that they refer to alkanes.

Natural gas is odorless. The smell observed in a gas leak is due to minute amounts of a sulfur additive such as methanethiol, CH_3SH, which provides an odor for easy detection.

Methane is formed and used in a variety of ways. The CH_4 released from decaying vegetable matter in New York City's main landfill is used for heating homes. CH_4 generators in China convert cow manure into energy in rural farming towns.

4.7 Fossil Fuels

Many alkanes occur in nature, primarily in natural gas and petroleum. Both of these fossil fuels serve as energy sources, formed from the degradation of organic material long ago.

Natural gas is composed largely of **methane** (60% to 80% depending on its source), with lesser amounts of ethane, propane, and butane. These organic compounds burn in the presence of oxygen, releasing energy for cooking and heating.

Petroleum is a complex mixture of compounds, most of which are hydrocarbons containing 1–40 carbon atoms. Distilling crude petroleum, a process called **refining,** separates it into usable fractions that differ in boiling point (Figure 4.5). Most products of petroleum refining provide

Figure 4.5
Refining crude petroleum into usable fuel and other petroleum products

a. **An oil refinery.** At an oil refinery, crude petroleum is separated into fractions of similar boiling point by the process of **distillation.**

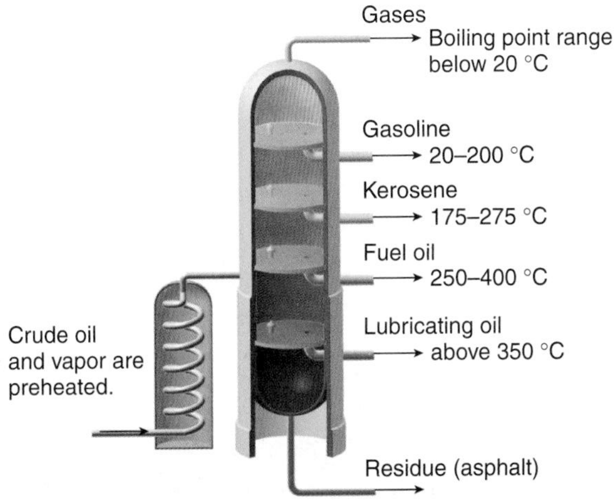

b. **Schematic of a refinery tower.** As crude petroleum is heated, the lower boiling, more volatile components distill first, followed by fractions of progressively higher boiling point.

fuel for home heating, automobiles, diesel engines, and airplanes. Each fuel type has a different composition of hydrocarbons:

- **gasoline:** $C_5H_{12}-C_{12}H_{26}$
- **kerosene:** $C_{12}H_{26}-C_{16}H_{34}$
- **diesel fuel:** $C_{15}H_{32}-C_{18}H_{38}$

Petroleum provides more than fuel. About 3% of crude oil is used to make plastics and other synthetic compounds including drugs, fabrics, dyes, and pesticides. These products are responsible for many of the comforts we now take for granted in industrialized countries. Imagine what life would be like without air conditioning, refrigeration, anesthetics, and pain relievers, all products of the petroleum industry.

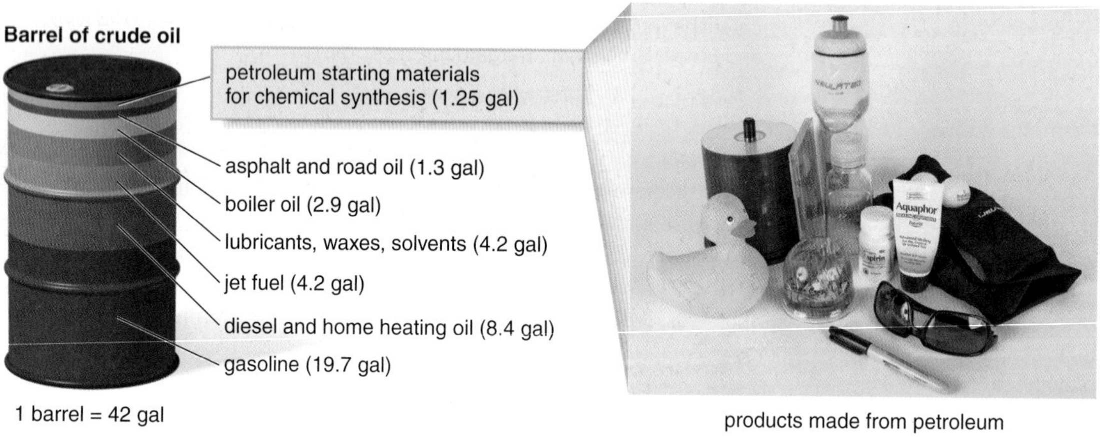
Barrel of crude oil
petroleum starting materials
for chemical synthesis (1.25 gal)
asphalt and road oil (1.3 gal)
boiler oil (2.9 gal)
lubricants, waxes, solvents (4.2 gal)
jet fuel (4.2 gal)
diesel and home heating oil (8.4 gal)
gasoline (19.7 gal)
1 barrel = 42 gal
Aquaphor
products made from petroleum

Energy from petroleum is ***nonrenewable,*** and the remaining known oil reserves are limited. Given our dependence on petroleum, not only for fuel, but also for the many necessities of modern society, it becomes clear that we must both conserve what we have and find alternate energy sources.

4.8 Physical Properties of Alkanes

Alkanes contain only nonpolar C–C and C–H bonds, and as a result they exhibit only **weak van der Waals forces.** Table 4.2 summarizes how these intermolecular forces affect the physical properties of alkanes.

The gasoline industry exploits the dependence of boiling point and melting point on alkane size by seasonally changing the composition of gasoline in locations where it gets very hot in the summer and very cold in the winter. Gasoline is refined to contain a larger fraction of higher boiling hydrocarbons in warmer weather, so it evaporates less readily. In colder weather, it is refined to contain more lower boiling hydrocarbons, so it freezes less readily.

The mutual insolubility of nonpolar oil and very polar water leads to the common expression, "Oil and water don't mix."

Because nonpolar alkanes are not water soluble, crude petroleum that leaks into the sea from an oil tanker creates an insoluble oil slick on the surface. The insoluble hydrocarbon oil poses a special threat to birds whose feathers are coated with natural nonpolar oils for insulation. Because these hydrophobic oils dissolve in the crude petroleum, birds lose their layer of natural protection and many die.

Problem 4.15 Arrange the following compounds in order of increasing boiling point.

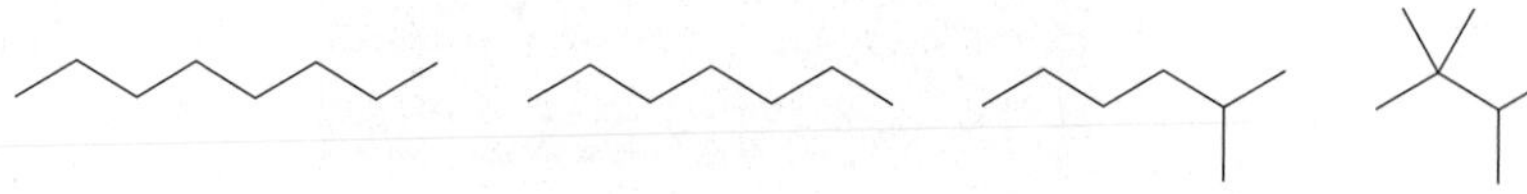

Table 4.2 Physical Properties of Alkanes

Property	Observation
Boiling point and melting point	• Alkanes have low bp's and mp's compared to more polar compounds of comparable size. $CH_3CH_2CH_3$ VDW bp = −42 °C mp = −190 °C → CH_3CHO VDW, DD bp = 21 °C mp = −121 °C **Increasing strength of intermolecular forces** **Increasing boiling point and melting point**
	• Bp and mp increase as the number of carbons increases because of increased surface area. $CH_3CH_2CH_2CH_3$ bp = 0 °C mp = −138 °C → $CH_3CH_2CH_2CH_2CH_2CH_3$ bp = 69 °C mp = −95 °C **Increasing surface area** **Increasing boiling point and melting point**
	• The bp of isomers decreases with branching because of decreased surface area. $(CH_3)_4C$ bp = 10 °C → $(CH_3)_2CHCH_2CH_3$ bp = 30 °C → $CH_3CH_2CH_2CH_2CH_3$ bp = 36 °C **Increasing surface area** **Increasing boiling point**
	• Mp increases with increased symmetry. $CH_3CH_2CH(CH_3)_2$ mp = −160 °C → $(CH_3)_4C$ mp = −17 °C **Increasing symmetry** **Increasing melting point**
Solubility	• Alkanes are soluble in organic solvents. • Alkanes are insoluble in water.

Key: bp = boiling point; mp = melting point; VDW = van der Waals; DD = dipole–dipole; HB = hydrogen bonding

4.9 Conformations of Acyclic Alkanes—Ethane

Let's now take a closer look at the three-dimensional structure of alkanes. The three-dimensional structure of molecules is called **stereochemistry.** In Chapter 4 we examine the effect of rotation around single bonds. In Chapter 5, we will learn about other aspects of stereochemistry.

Recall from Section 1.10A that **rotation occurs around carbon–carbon σ bonds.** Thus, the two CH_3 groups of ethane rotate, allowing the hydrogens on one carbon to adopt different orientations relative to the hydrogens on the other carbon. These arrangements are called **conformations.**

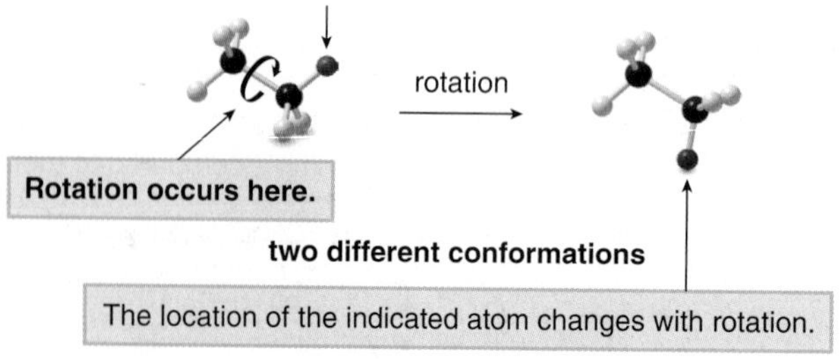
rotation
Rotation occurs here.
two different conformations
The location of the indicated atom changes with rotation.

- *Conformations* are different arrangements of atoms that are interconverted by rotation about single bonds.

Names are given to two different arrangements.

- In the *eclipsed conformation,* the C – H bonds on one carbon are directly aligned with the C – H bonds on the adjacent carbon.
- In the *staggered conformation,* the C – H bonds on one carbon bisect the H – C – H bond angle on the adjacent carbon.

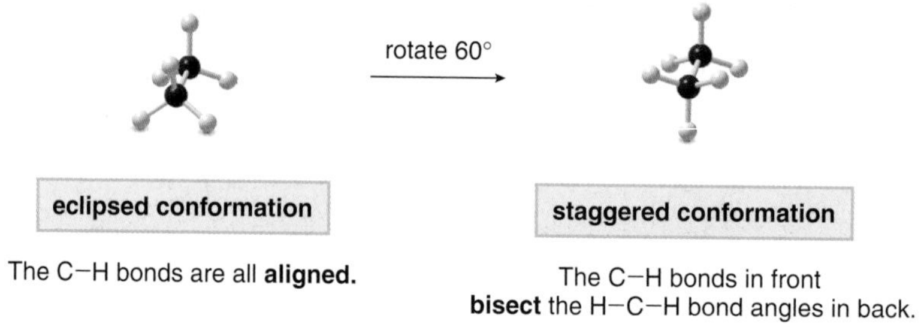
rotate 60°
eclipsed conformation
staggered conformation
The C–H bonds are all **aligned.**
The C–H bonds in front
bisect the H–C–H bond angles in back.

Rotating the atoms on one carbon by 60° converts an eclipsed conformation into a staggered conformation, and vice versa. These conformations are often viewed **end-on**—that is, looking directly down the carbon–carbon bond. The angle that separates a bond on one atom from a bond on an adjacent atom is called a **dihedral angle.** For ethane in the staggered conformation, the dihedral angle for the C – H bonds is **60°.** For eclipsed ethane, it is **0°.**

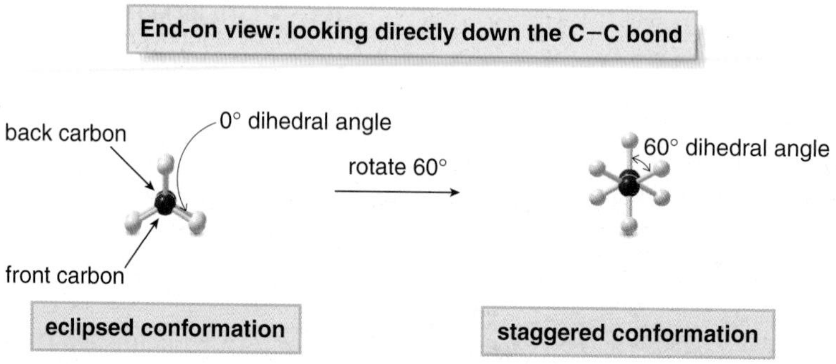
End-on view: looking directly down the C–C bond
back carbon
0° dihedral angle
rotate 60°
60° dihedral angle
front carbon
eclipsed conformation
staggered conformation

End-on representations for conformations are commonly drawn using a convention called a **Newman projection.** A Newman projection is a graphic that shows the three groups bonded to each carbon atom in a particular C – C bond, as well as the dihedral angle that separates them.

How To Draw a Newman Projection

Step [1] Look directly down the C–C bond (end-on), and draw a circle with a dot in the center to represent the carbons of the C–C bond.

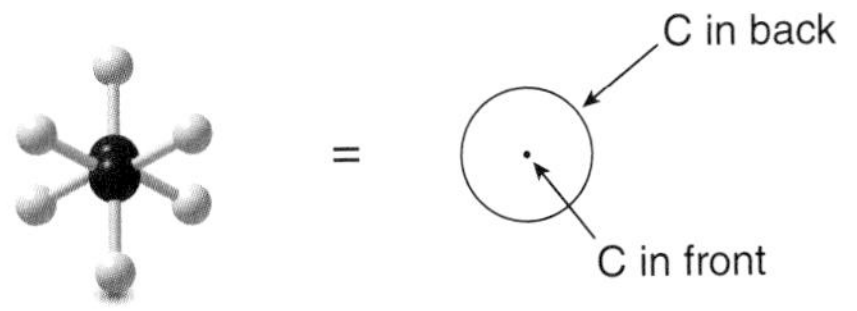
C in back
C in front

- The circle represents the back carbon and the dot represents the front carbon.

Step [2] Draw in the bonds.

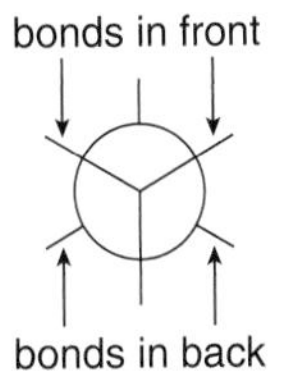
bonds in front
bonds in back

- Draw the bonds on the **front** C as three lines **meeting at the center** of the circle.
- Draw the bonds on the **back** C as three lines coming **out of the edge** of the circle.

Step [3] Add the atoms on each bond.

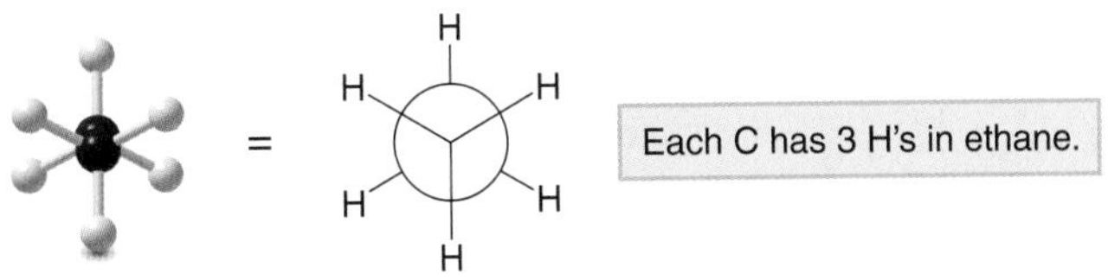
H
H
H
H
H
H
Each C has 3 H's in ethane.

Figure 4.6 illustrates the Newman projections for both the staggered and eclipsed **conformations** for ethane.

Follow this procedure for any C–C bond. With a Newman projection, **always consider *one* C–C bond only and draw the atoms bonded to the carbon atoms, *not* the carbon atoms in the bond itself.** Newman projections for the staggered and eclipsed conformations of propane are drawn in Figure 4.7.

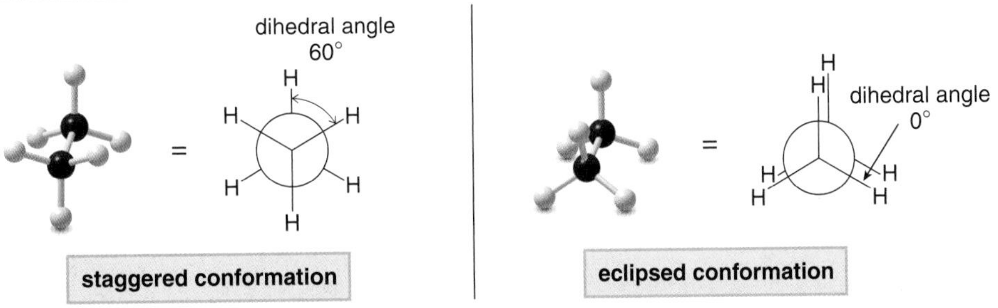
dihedral angle
60°
staggered conformation
dihedral angle
0°
eclipsed conformation

Figure 4.6 Newman projections for the staggered and eclipsed conformations of ethane

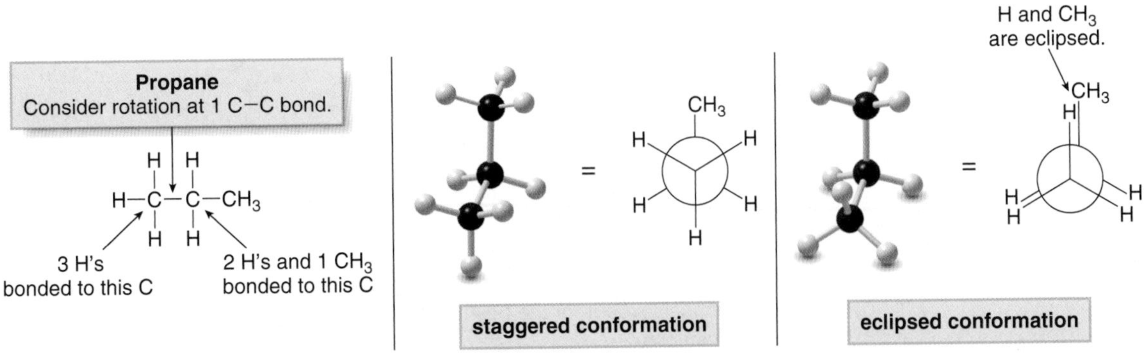
Propane
Consider rotation at 1 C–C bond.
3 H's
bonded to this C
2 H's and 1 CH3
bonded to this C
staggered conformation
H and CH3
are eclipsed.
eclipsed conformation

Figure 4.7 Newman projections for the staggered and eclipsed conformations of propane

Problem 4.16 Draw the staggered and eclipsed conformations that result from rotation around the C–C bond in CH_3-CH_2Br.

The staggered and eclipsed conformations of ethane interconvert at room temperature, but **each conformation is *not* equally stable.**

- **The staggered conformations are more stable (lower in energy) than the eclipsed conformations.**

The cause of this stability difference is the subject of some debate in the chemical literature. A contributing factor may be increased electron–electron repulsion between the bonds in the eclipsed conformation compared to the staggered conformation, where the bonding electrons are farther apart.

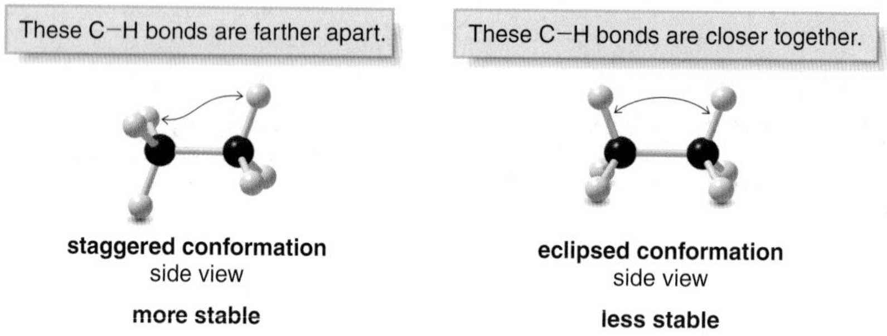
These C–H bonds are farther apart.
These C–H bonds are closer together.
staggered conformation
side view
more stable
eclipsed conformation
side view
less stable

The difference in energy between the staggered and eclipsed conformations is 12 kJ/mol (2.9 kcal/mol), a small enough difference that the rotation is still very rapid at room temperature, and the conformations cannot be separated. Because three eclipsed C–H bonds increase the energy of a conformation by 12 kJ/mol, **each eclipsed C–H bond results in an increase in energy of 4.0 kJ/mol (1.0 kcal/mol).** The energy difference between the staggered and eclipsed conformations is called **torsional energy.** Thus, eclipsing introduces **torsional strain** into a molecule.

- ***Torsional strain*** **is an increase in energy caused by eclipsing interactions.**

The graph in Figure 4.8 shows how the potential energy of ethane changes with dihedral angle as one CH_3 group rotates relative to the other. **The staggered conformation is the most stable**

Figure 4.8
Graph: Energy versus dihedral angle for ethane

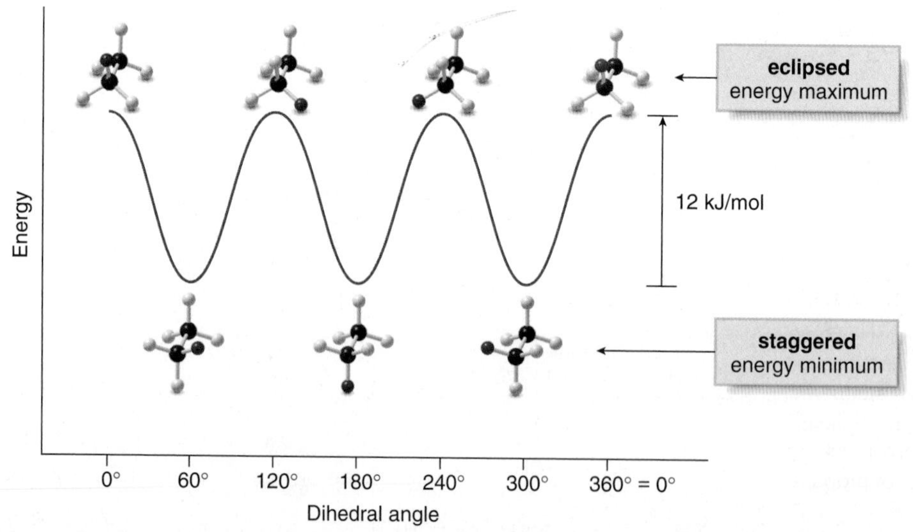
eclipsed
energy maximum
12 kJ/mol
Energy
staggered
energy minimum
0°
60°
120°
180°
240°
300°
360° = 0°
Dihedral angle

- Note the position of the labeled H atom after each 60° rotation. All three staggered conformations are identical (except for the position of the label), and the same is true for all three eclipsed conformations.

Each H,H eclipsing interaction contributes 4.0 kJ/mol of destabilization to the eclipsed conformation.

Strain results in an **increase in energy.** Torsional strain is the first of three types of strain discussed in this text. The other two are steric strain (Section 4.10) and angle strain (Section 4.11).

arrangement, so it is at an *energy minimum*. As the C–H bonds on one carbon are rotated relative to the C–H bonds on the other carbon, the energy increases as the C–H bonds get closer until a **maximum is reached after 60° rotation to the eclipsed conformation.** As rotation continues, the energy decreases until after 60° rotation, when the staggered conformation is reached once again. At any given moment, all ethane molecules do not exist in the more stable staggered conformation; rather, a higher percentage of molecules is present in the more stable staggered conformation than any other possible arrangement.

- **An energy minimum and maximum occur every 60° as the conformation changes from staggered to eclipsed. Conformations that are neither staggered nor eclipsed are intermediate in energy.**

Problem 4.17 The torsional energy in propane is 14 kJ/mol (3.4 kcal/mol). Because each H,H eclipsing interaction is worth 4.0 kJ/mol (1.0 kcal/mol) of destabilization, how much is one H,CH_3 eclipsing interaction worth in destabilization? (See Section 4.10 for an alternate way to arrive at this value.)

4.10 Conformations of Butane

Butane and higher molecular weight alkanes have several carbon–carbon bonds, all capable of rotation.

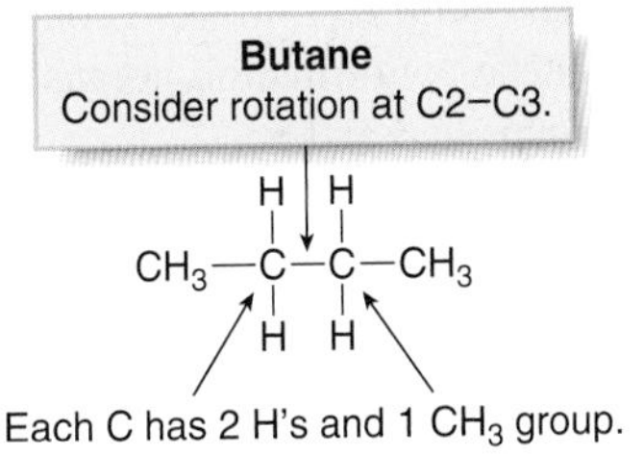

To analyze the different conformations that result from rotation about the C2–C3 bond, begin arbitrarily with one—for example, the staggered conformation that places two CH_3 groups 180° from each other—then,

It takes six 60° rotations to return to the original conformation.

- **Rotate one carbon atom in 60° increments either clockwise or counterclockwise, while keeping the other carbon fixed. Continue until you return to the original conformation.**

Figure 4.9 illustrates the six possible conformations that result from this process.

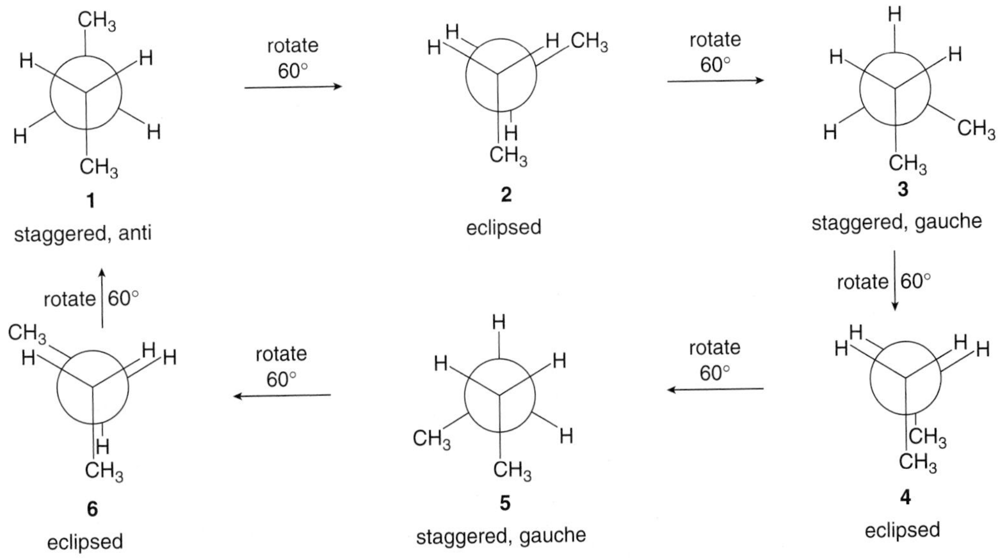

Figure 4.9 Six different conformations of butane

Although each 60° bond rotation converts a staggered conformation into an eclipsed conformation (or vice versa), neither all the staggered conformations nor all the eclipsed conformations are the same. For example, the dihedral angle between the methyl groups in staggered conformations **3** and **5** are both 60°, whereas it is 180° in staggered conformation **1.**

- **A staggered conformation with two larger groups 180° from each other is called *anti.***
- **A staggered conformation with two larger groups 60° from each other is called *gauche.***

Similarly, the methyl groups in conformations **2** and **6** both eclipse hydrogen atoms, whereas they eclipse each other in conformation **4.**

The staggered conformations (**1, 3,** and **5**) are lower in energy than the eclipsed conformations (**2, 4,** and **6**), but how do the energies of the individual staggered and eclipsed conformations compare to each other? The relative energies of the individual staggered conformations (or the individual eclipsed conformations) depend on their **steric strain.**

- ***Steric* strain is an increase in energy resulting when atoms are forced too close to one another.**

The methyl groups are farther apart in the anti conformation (**1**) than in the gauche conformations (**3** and **5**), so amongst the staggered conformations, **1** is lower in energy (more stable) than **3** and **5.** In fact, the anti conformation is 3.8 kJ/mol (0.9 kcal/mol) lower in energy than either gauche conformation because of the steric strain that results from the proximity of the methyl groups in **3** and **5.**

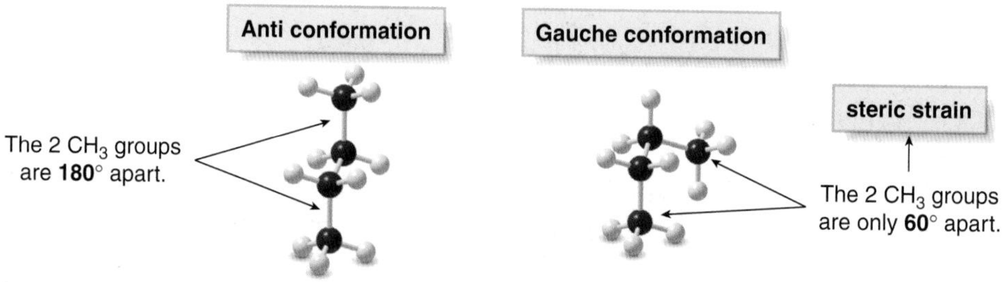

Anti conformation
Gauche conformation
steric strain
The 2 CH_3 groups are 180° apart.
The 2 CH_3 groups are only 60° apart.

lower in energy
1

higher in energy
3

- **Gauche conformations are generally higher in energy than anti conformations because of steric strain.**

Steric strain also affects the relative energies of eclipsed conformations. Conformation **4** is higher in energy than **2** or **6,** because the two larger CH_3 groups are forced close to each other, introducing considerable steric strain.

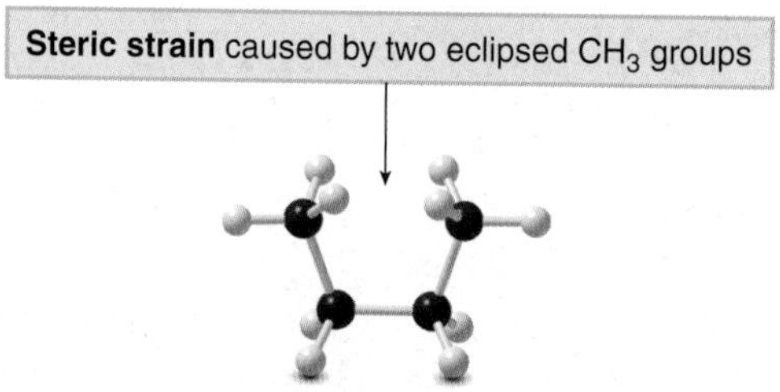

Steric strain caused by two eclipsed CH_3 groups

side view
4

To graph energy versus dihedral angle, keep in mind two considerations:

- **Staggered conformations are at energy minima and eclipsed conformations are at energy maxima.**
- **Unfavorable steric interactions increase energy.**

Figure 4.10
Graph: Energy versus dihedral angle for butane

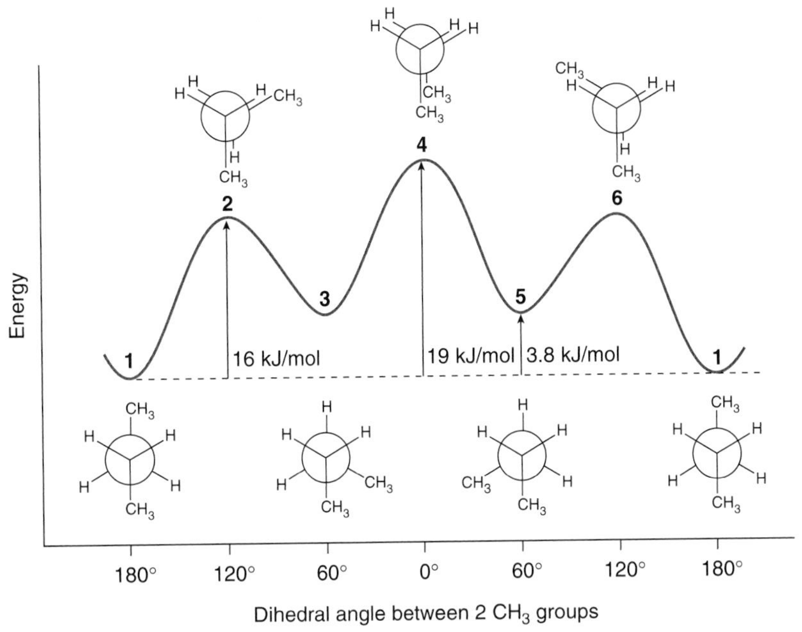

- Staggered conformations **1, 3,** and **5** are at energy minima.
- Anti conformation **1** is lower in energy than gauche conformations **3** and **5,** which possess steric strain.
- Eclipsed conformations **2, 4,** and **6** are at energy maxima.
- Eclipsed conformation **4,** which has additional steric strain due to two eclipsed CH_3 groups, is highest in energy.

For butane, this means that anti conformation **1** is lowest in energy, and conformation **4** with two eclipsed CH_3 groups is the highest in energy. The relative energy of other conformations is depicted in the energy versus rotation diagram for butane in Figure 4.10.

We can now use the values in Figure 4.10 to estimate the destabilization caused by other eclipsed groups. For example, conformation **4** is 19 kJ/mol less stable than the anti conformation **1.** Conformation **4** possesses two H,H eclipsing interactions, worth 4.0 kJ/mol each in destabilization (Section 4.9), and one CH_3,CH_3 eclipsing interaction. Thus, the **CH_3,CH_3 interaction** is worth 19 – 2(4.0) = **11 kJ/mol** of destabilization.

Similarly, conformation **2** is 16 kJ/mol less stable than the anti conformation **1,** and possesses one H,H eclipsing interaction (worth 4.0 kJ/mol of destabilization), and two H,CH_3 interactions. Thus **each H,CH_3 interaction** is worth 1/2(16 – 4.0) = **6.0 kJ/mol** of destabilization. These values are summarized in Table 4.3.

- **The energy difference between the lowest and highest energy conformations is called the *barrier to rotation.***

Table 4.3 Summary: Torsional and Steric Strain Energies in Acyclic Alkanes

	Energy increase	
Type of interaction	kJ/mol	kcal/mol
H,H eclipsing	4.0	1.0
H,CH_3 eclipsing	6.0	1.4
CH_3,CH_3 eclipsing	11	2.6
gauche CH_3 groups	3.8	0.9

We can use these same principles to determine conformations and relative energies for any acyclic alkane. Because the lowest energy conformation has all bonds staggered and all large groups anti, alkanes are often drawn in zigzag skeletal structures to indicate this.

A zigzag arrangement keeps all carbons **staggered** and **anti.**

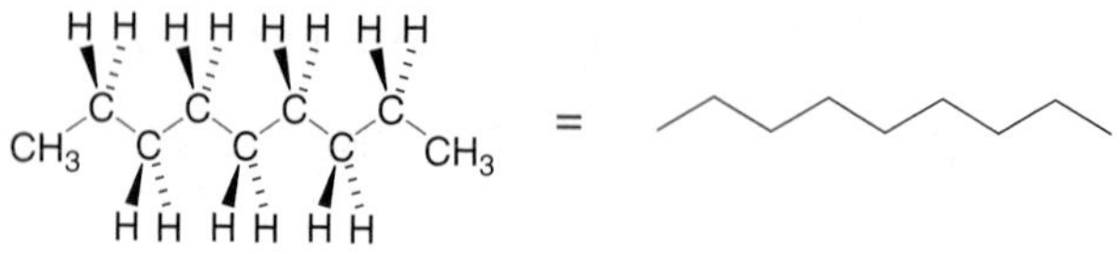

Problem 4.18

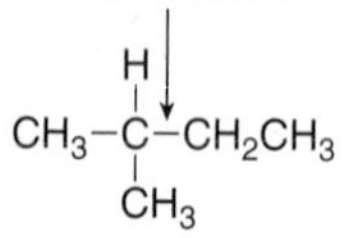
rotation here

a. Draw the three staggered and three eclipsed conformations that result from rotation around the designated bond using Newman projections.
b. Label the most stable and least stable conformation.

Problem 4.19 Consider rotation around the carbon–carbon bond in 1,2-dichloroethane ($ClCH_2CH_2Cl$).

a. Using Newman projections, draw all of the staggered and eclipsed conformations that result from rotation around this bond.
b. Graph energy versus dihedral angle for rotation around this bond.

Problem 4.20 Calculate the destabilization present in each eclipsed conformation.

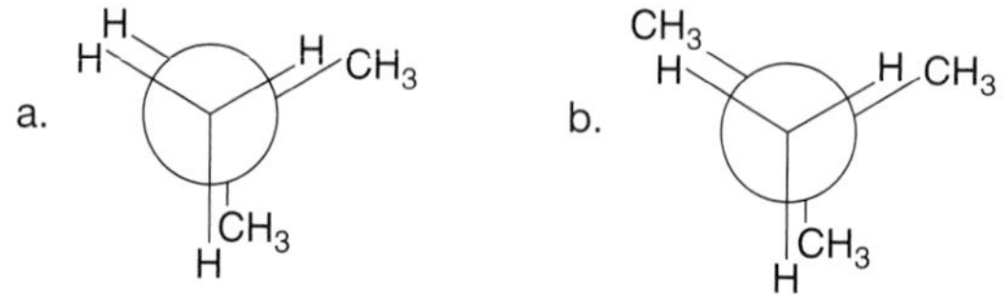

4.11 An Introduction to Cycloalkanes

Besides torsional strain and steric strain, the conformations of cycloalkanes are also affected by **angle strain.**

- ***Angle* strain is an increase in energy when tetrahedral bond angles deviate from the optimum angle of 109.5°.**

Originally cycloalkanes were thought to be flat rings, with the bond angles between carbon atoms determined by the size of the ring. For example, a flat cyclopropane ring would have 60° internal bond angles, a flat cyclobutane ring would have 90° angles, and large flat rings would have very large angles. It was assumed that rings with bond angles so different from the tetrahedral bond angle would be very strained and highly reactive. This is called the Baeyer strain theory.

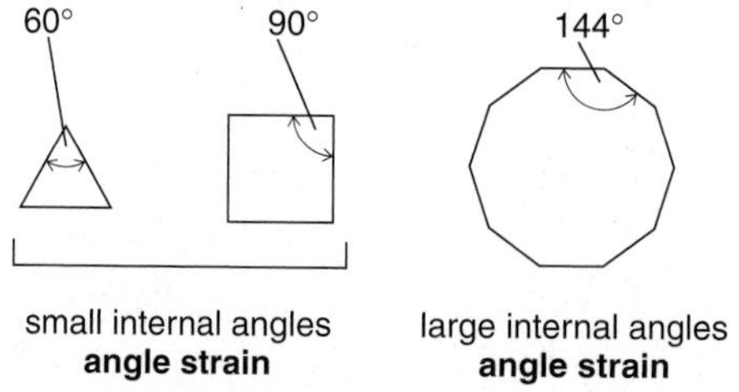
60°
90°
144°
small internal angles
angle strain
large internal angles
angle strain

It turns out, though, that **cycloalkanes with more than three C atoms in the ring are not flat molecules.** They are puckered to **reduce strain,** both angle strain and torsional strain. The three-dimensional structures of some simple cycloalkanes are shown in Figure 4.11. Three- and four-membered rings still possess considerable angle strain, but puckering reduces the internal bond angles in larger rings, thus reducing angle strain.

Figure 4.11
Three-dimensional structure of some cycloalkanes

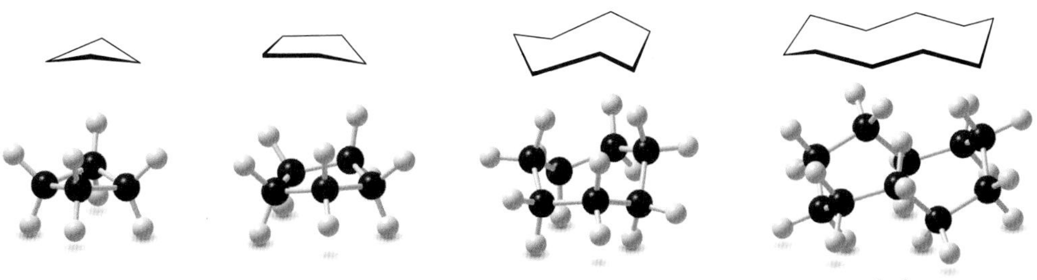
cyclobutane
cyclopentane
cycloheptane
cyclodecane

Many polycyclic hydrocarbons are of interest to chemists. For example, **dodecahedrane,** containing 12 five-membered rings bonded together, is one member of a family of three hydrocarbons that contain several rings of one size joined together. The two other members of this family are **tetrahedrane,** consisting of four three-membered rings, and **cubane,** consisting of six four-membered rings. These compounds are the simplest regular polyhedra whose structures resemble three of the highly symmetrical Platonic solids: the tetrahedron, the cube, and the dodecahedron.

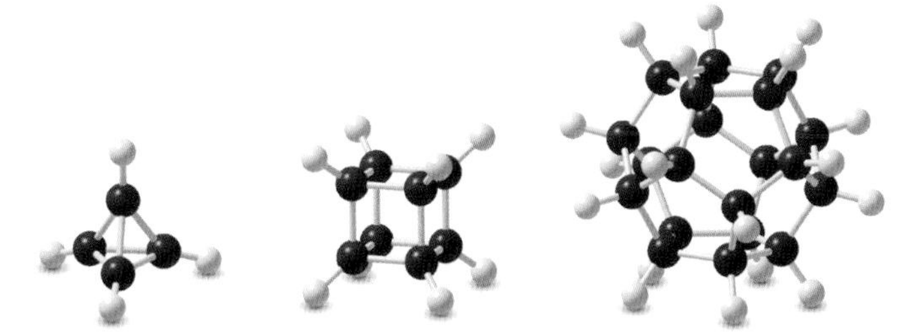
tetrahedrane
cubane
dodecahedrane

How stable are these compounds? Tetrahedrane (with internal 60° bond angles) is so strained that all attempts to prepare it have been thus far unsuccessful. Although cubane is also highly strained because of its 90° bond angles, it was first synthesized in 1964 and is a stable molecule at room temperature. Finally, dodecahedrane is very stable because it has bond angles very close to the tetrahedral bond angle (108° versus 109.5°). Its synthesis eluded chemists for years not because of its strain or inherent instability, but because of the enormous challenge of joining 12 five-membered rings together to form a sphere.

4.12 Cyclohexane

Let's now examine in detail the conformation of **cyclohexane,** the most common ring size in naturally occurring compounds.

4.12A The Chair Conformation

A planar cyclohexane ring would experience angle strain, because the internal bond angle between the carbon atoms would be 120°, and torsional strain, because all of the hydrogens on adjacent carbon atoms would be eclipsed.

If a cyclohexane ring were flat....

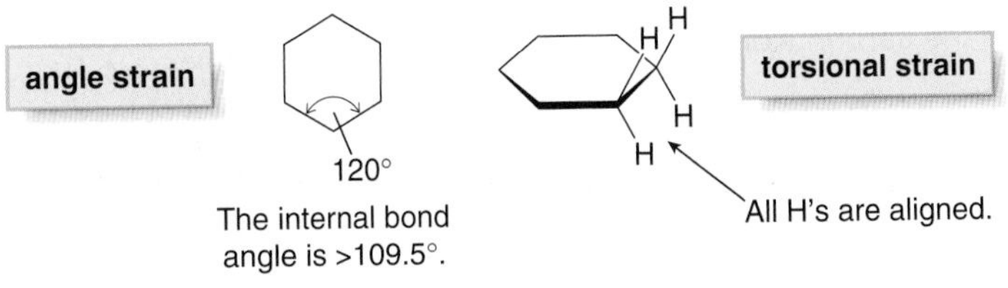
angle strain
120°
The internal bond angle is >109.5°.
H
H
H
H
torsional strain
All H's are aligned.

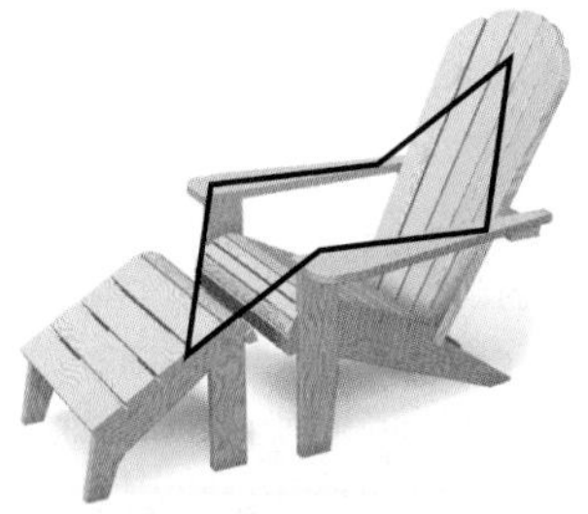

Visualizing the chair. If the cyclohexane chair conformation is tipped downward, we can more easily view it as a chair with a back, seat, and foot support.

In reality, cyclohexane adopts a puckered conformation, called the **chair** form, which is more stable than any other possible conformation.

The carbon skeleton of chair cyclohexane

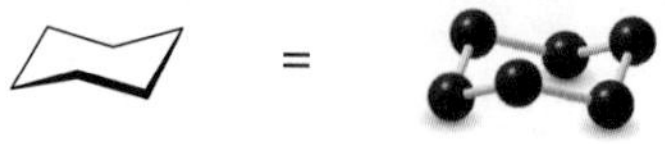

The chair conformation is so stable because it eliminates angle strain (**all C−C−C bond angles are 109.5°**) and torsional strain (all hydrogens on adjacent carbon atoms are **staggered,** not eclipsed).

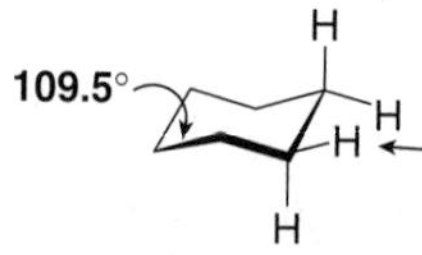
109.5°
H
H
H
H

All H's are **staggered.**

- **In cyclohexane, three C atoms pucker up and three C atoms pucker down, alternating around the ring. These C atoms are called *up* C's and *down* C's.**

Each carbon in cyclohexane has two different kinds of hydrogens.

- ***Axial* hydrogens are located above and below the ring (along a perpendicular axis).**
- ***Equatorial* hydrogens are located in the plane of the ring (around the equator).**

3 *up* C's and 3 *down* C's

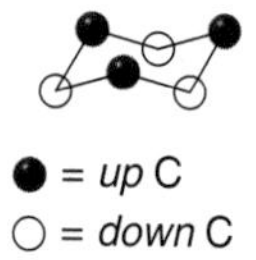
● = *up* C
○ = *down* C

Two kinds of H's

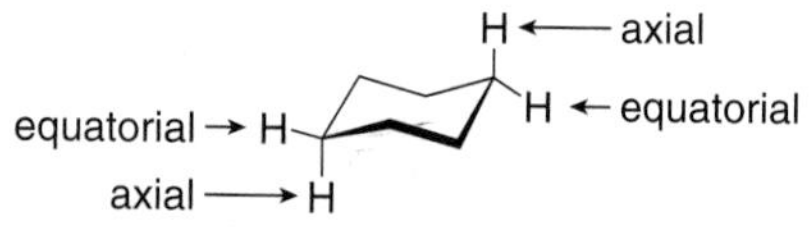
H ← axial
H ← equatorial
equatorial → H
axial → H

- **Axial** bonds are oriented **above** and **below.**
- **Equatorial** bonds are oriented around the **equator.**

Each cyclohexane carbon atom has one axial and one equatorial hydrogen.

A three-dimensional representation of the chair form is shown in Figure 4.12. Before continuing, we must first learn how to draw the chair form of cyclohexane.

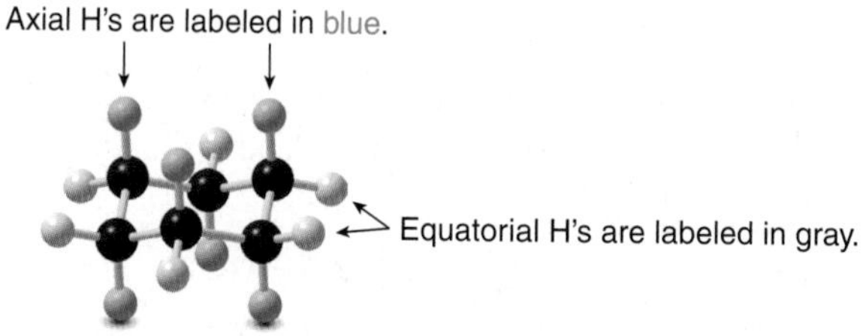
Axial H's are labeled in blue.
Equatorial H's are labeled in gray.

Figure 4.12 A three-dimensional model of the chair form of cyclohexane with all H atoms drawn

- Cyclohexane has **six axial H's** and **six equatorial H's.**

How To Draw the Chair Form of Cyclohexane

Step [1] Draw the carbon skeleton.

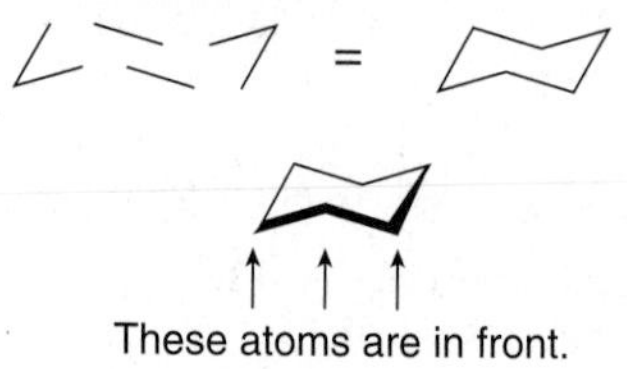
These atoms are in front.

- Draw three parts of the chair: **a wedge, a set of parallel lines,** and **another wedge.**
- Then, join them together.
- The bottom 3 C's come out of the page, and for this reason, bonds to them are often highlighted in bold.

Step [2] Label the *up* C's and *down* C's on the ring.

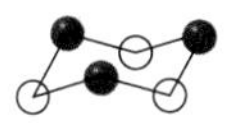

● = *up* C ○ = *down* C

- There are 3 *up* and 3 *down* C's, and they alternate around the ring.

Step [3] Draw in the axial H atoms.

3 axial H's **above** the ring →

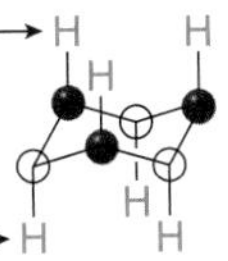

3 axial H's **below** the ring →

- On an *up* C the axial H is *up*.
- On a *down* C the axial H is *down*.

Step [4] Draw in the equatorial H atoms.

- The axial H is **down** on a down C, so the equatorial H must be up.
- The axial H is **up** on an up C, so the equatorial H must be down.

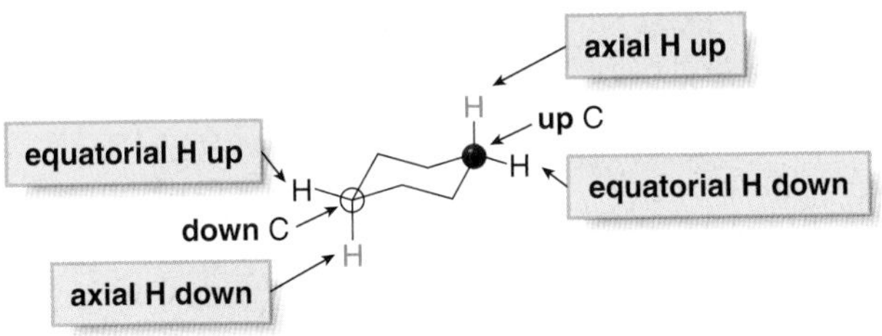
axial H up
up C
equatorial H up
equatorial H down
down C
axial H down

All equatorial H's drawn in.

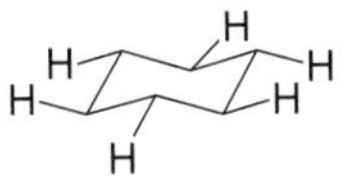

All H's drawn in.

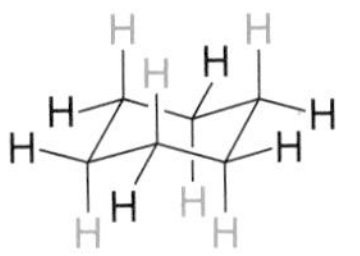

Axial H's are drawn in blue.

Problem 4.21 Classify the ring carbons as *up* C's or *down* C's. Identify the bonds highlighted in bold as axial or equatorial.

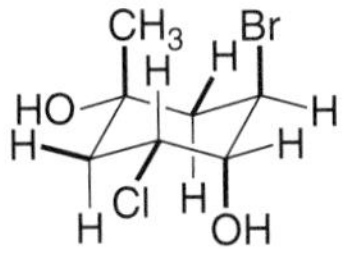

4.12B Ring-Flipping

Like acyclic alkanes, **cyclohexane does not remain in a single conformation.** The bonds twist and bend, resulting in new arrangements, but the movement is more restricted. One important conformational change involves **ring-flipping,** which can be viewed as a two-step process.

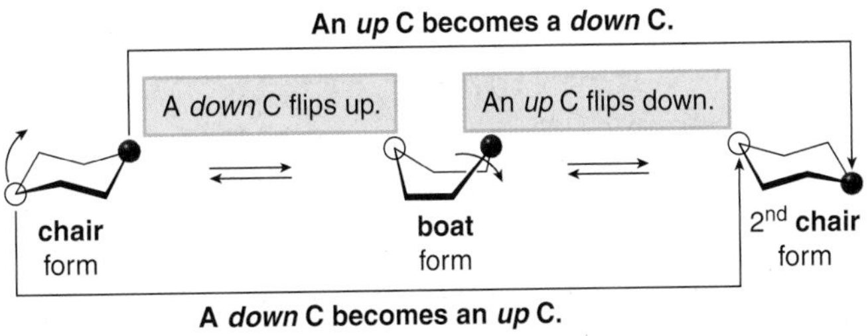
An up C becomes a down C.
A down C flips up.
An up C flips down.
chair form
boat form
2nd chair form
A down C becomes an up C.

- **A *down* carbon flips up.** This forms a new conformation of cyclohexane called a **boat.** The boat form has two carbons oriented above a plane containing the other four carbons.
- The boat form can flip in two possible ways. The original carbon (labeled with an open circle) can flip down, re-forming the initial conformation; or the **second *up* carbon** (labeled with a solid circle) **can flip down. This forms a second chair conformation.**

Because of ring-flipping, the ***up* carbons become *down* carbons and the *down* carbons become *up* carbons.** Thus, cyclohexane exists as two different chair conformations of equal stability, which rapidly interconvert at room temperature.

The process of ring-flipping also affects the orientation of cyclohexane's hydrogen atoms.

- **Axial and equatorial H atoms are interconverted during a ring flip. Axial H atoms become equatorial H atoms, and equatorial H atoms become axial H atoms (Figure 4.13).**

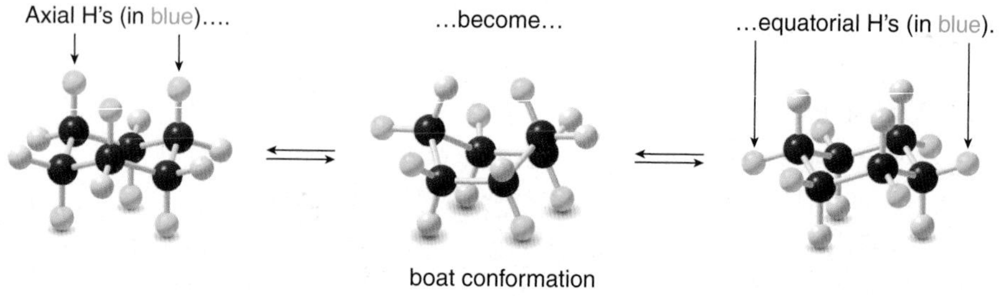

Axial H's (in blue)....
...become...
...equatorial H's (in blue).
boat conformation

Figure 4.13
Ring-flipping interconverts axial and equatorial hydrogens in cyclohexane.

The chair forms of cyclohexane are 30 kJ/mol more stable than the boat forms. The boat conformation is destabilized by torsional strain because the hydrogens on the four carbon atoms in the plane are eclipsed. Additionally, there is steric strain because two hydrogens at either end of the boat—the **flagpole hydrogens**—are forced close to each other, as shown in Figure 4.14.

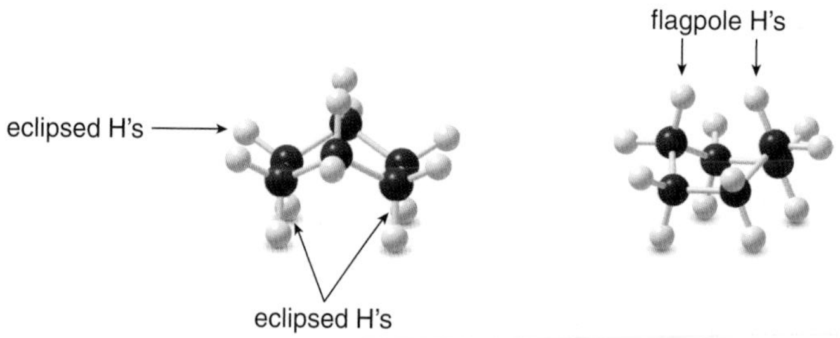

flagpole H's
eclipsed H's
eclipsed H's

Figure 4.14
Two views of the boat conformation of cyclohexane

The boat form of cyclohexane is less stable than the chair forms for two reasons.

- Eclipsing interactions between H's cause torsional strain.
- The proximity of the flagpole H's causes steric strain.

4.13 Substituted Cycloalkanes

What happens when one hydrogen on cyclohexane is replaced by a larger substituent? Is there a difference in the stability of the two cyclohexane conformations? To answer these questions, remember one rule.

- **The equatorial position has more room than the axial position, so larger substituents are more stable in the equatorial position.**

4.13A Cyclohexane with One Substituent

There are two possible chair conformations of a monosubstituted cyclohexane, such as methylcyclohexane, as shown in the following *How To*.

How To Draw the Two Conformations for a Substituted Cyclohexane

Step [1] Draw one chair form and add the substituents.

- Arbitrarily pick a ring carbon, classify it as an *up* or *down* carbon, and draw the bonds. Each C has one axial and one equatorial bond.
- Add the substituents, in this case H and CH_3, arbitrarily placing one axial and one equatorial. In this example, the CH_3 group is drawn equatorial.
- This forms one of the two possible chair conformations, labeled Conformation **1.**

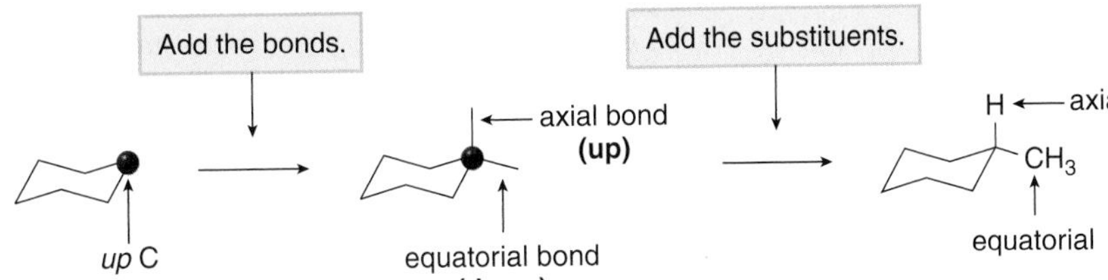

Conformation 1

Step [2] Ring-flip the cyclohexane ring.

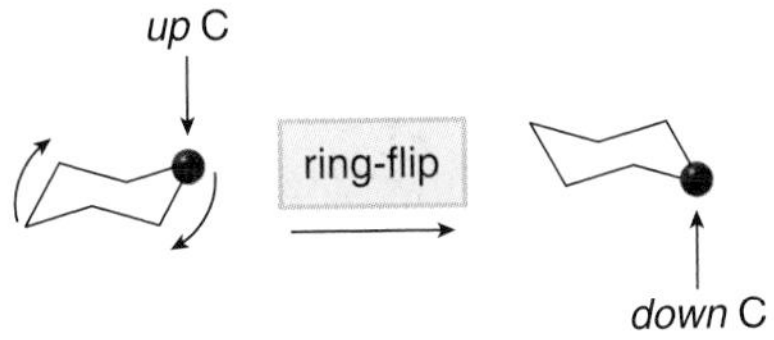

- Convert *up* C's to *down* C's and vice versa. The chosen *up* C now puckers down.

Step [3] Add the substituents to the second conformation.

- Draw axial and equatorial bonds. On a *down* C the axial bond is *down.*
- Ring-flipping converts axial bonds to equatorial bonds, and vice versa. The equatorial methyl becomes axial.
- This forms the other possible chair conformation, labeled Conformation **2.**

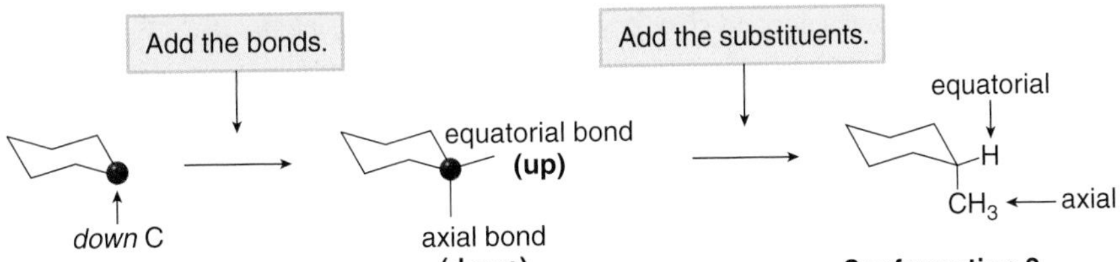

Conformation 2

Although the CH_3 group flips from equatorial to axial, it starts on a down bond, and stays on a down bond. It never flips from below the ring to above the ring.

- **A substituent always stays on the same side of the ring—either below or above—during the process of ring-flipping.**

Each carbon atom has one *up* and one *down* bond. An *up* bond can be either axial or equatorial, depending on the carbon to which it is attached. On an *up* C, the axial bond is *up,* but on a *down* C, the equatorial bond is *up.*

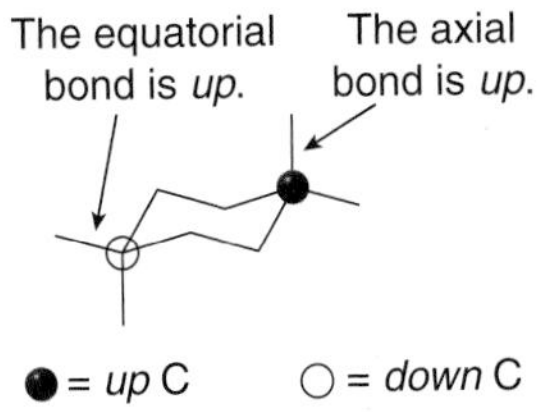

The two conformations of methylcyclohexane are different, so they are not equally stable. In fact, Conformation **1,** which places the larger methyl group in the roomier equatorial position, is considerably more stable than Conformation **2,** which places it axial.

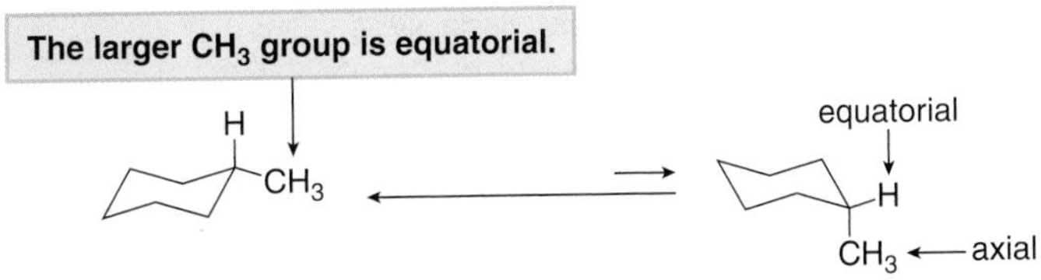

Conformation 1

more stable

95%

Conformation 2

5%

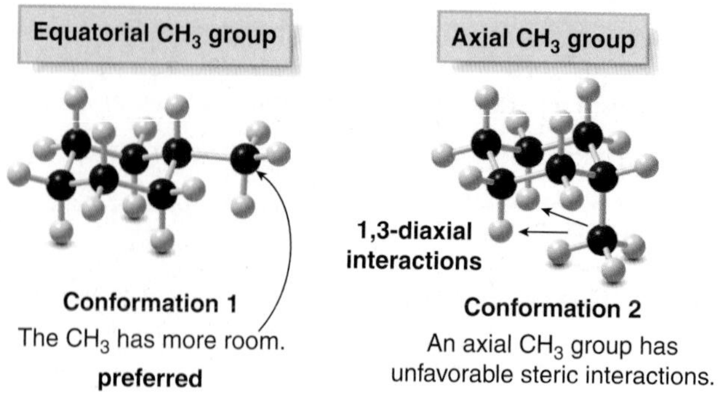

Equatorial CH_3 group
Axial CH_3 group
1,3-diaxial interactions
Conformation 1
The CH_3 has more room.
preferred
Conformation 2
An axial CH_3 group has unfavorable steric interactions.

Figure 4.15 Three-dimensional representations for the two conformations of methylcyclohexane

Why is a substituted cyclohexane ring more stable with a larger group in the equatorial position? Figure 4.15 shows that with an equatorial CH_3 group, steric interactions with nearby groups are minimized. An axial CH_3 group, however, is close to two other axial H atoms, creating two destabilizing steric interactions called **1,3-diaxial interactions.** Each unfavorable H,CH_3 interaction destabilizes the conformation by 3.8 kJ/mol, so Conformation **2** is 7.6 kJ/mol less stable than Conformation **1.**

- **Larger axial substituents create unfavorable 1,3-diaxial interactions, destabilizing a cyclohexane conformation.**

The larger the substituent on the six-membered ring, the higher the percentage of the conformation containing the equatorial substituent at equilibrium. In fact, with a very large substituent like *tert*-butyl [$(CH_3)_3C-$], essentially none of the conformation containing an axial *tert*-butyl group is present at room temperature, so **the ring is essentially anchored in a single conformation having an equatorial *tert*-butyl group.** This is illustrated in Figure 4.16.

Problem 4.22 Draw a second chair conformation for each cyclohexane. Then decide which conformation is present in higher concentration at equilibrium.

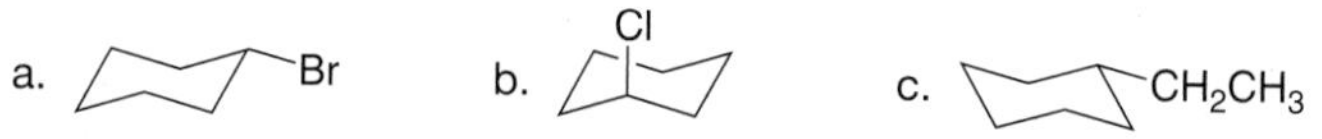

a.
Br
b.
Cl
c.
CH_2CH_3

Problem 4.23 When an ethyl group (CH_3CH_2-) is bonded to a cyclohexane ring, 96% of the molecules possess an equatorial CH_3CH_2- group at equilibrium. When an ethynyl group ($HC\equiv C-$) is bonded to a cyclohexane ring, only 67% of the molecules possess an equatorial $HC\equiv C-$ group at equilibrium. Suggest a reason for this difference.

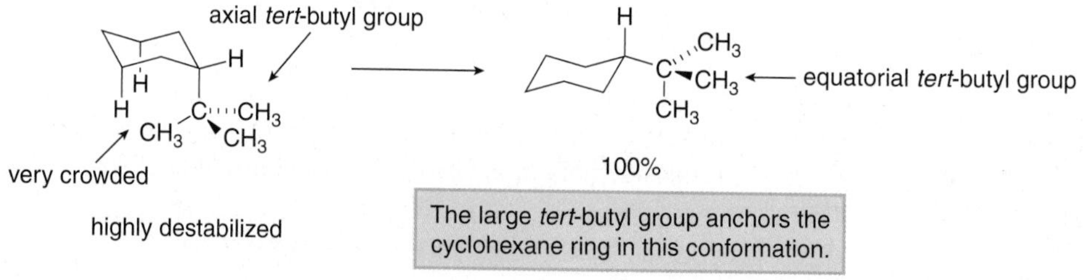

axial *tert*-butyl group
H
H
H
C
CH_3
CH_3
CH_3
very crowded
highly destabilized
H
CH_3
C
CH_3
CH_3
equatorial *tert*-butyl group
100%
The large *tert*-butyl group anchors the cyclohexane ring in this conformation.

Figure 4.16 The two conformations of *tert*-butylcyclohexane

4.13B A Disubstituted Cycloalkane

Rotation around the C–C bonds in the ring of a cycloalkane is restricted, so **a group on one side of the ring can *never* rotate to the other side of the ring.** As a result, there are two different 1,2-dimethylcyclopentanes—one having two CH_3 groups on the **same side** of the ring and one having them on **opposite sides** of the ring.

Wedges indicate bonds in front of the plane of the ring and dashes indicate bonds behind. For a review of this convention, see Section 1.7B. In this text, dashes are drawn equal in length, as recommended in the latest IUPAC guidelines. If a ring carbon is bonded to a CH_3 group in **front** of the ring (on a wedge), it is *assumed* that the other atom bonded to this carbon is hydrogen, located **behind** the ring (on a dash).

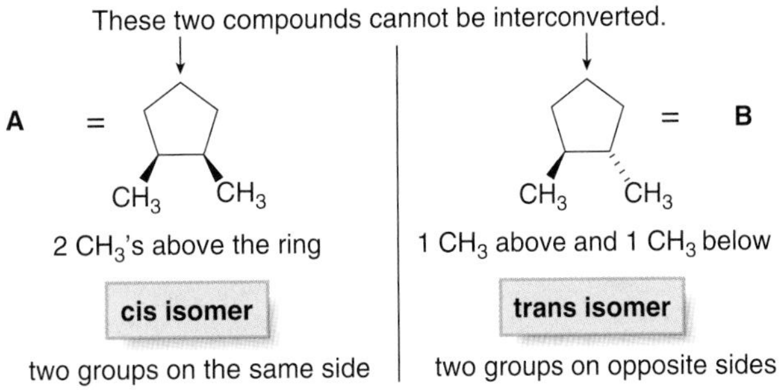
These two compounds cannot be interconverted.
A =
CH3 CH3
2 CH3's above the ring
cis isomer
two groups on the same side
= B
CH3 CH3
1 CH3 above and 1 CH3 below
trans isomer
two groups on opposite sides

A and **B** are **isomers,** because they are different compounds with the same molecular formula, but they represent the second major class of isomers called **stereoisomers.**

- ***Stereoisomers* are isomers that differ *only* in the way the atoms are oriented in space.**

The prefixes **cis** and **trans** are used to distinguish these stereoisomers.

Cis and **trans** isomers are named by adding the prefixes *cis* and *trans* to the name of the cycloalkane. Thus, **A** is *cis*-1,2-dimethylcyclopentane, and **B** is *trans*-1,2-dimethylcyclopentane.

- **The cis isomer has two groups on the *same side* of the ring.**
- **The trans isomer has two groups on *opposite sides* of the ring.**

Cis- and *trans*-1,2-dimethylcyclopentane can also be drawn as if the plane of the ring goes through the plane of the page. Each carbon in the ring then has one bond that points above the ring and one that points below.

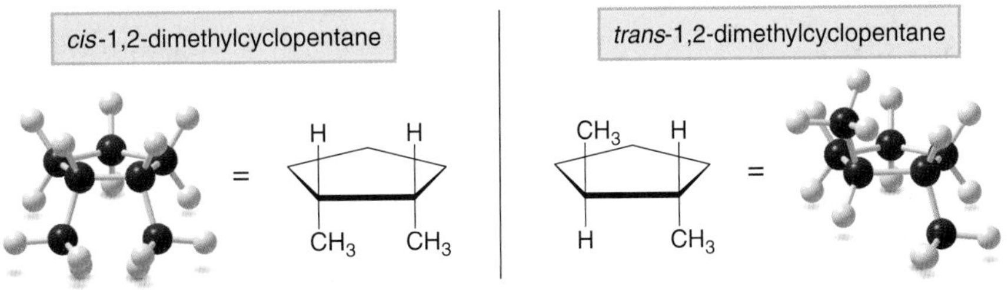
cis-1,2-dimethylcyclopentane
H H
=
CH3 CH3
trans-1,2-dimethylcyclopentane
CH3 H
=
H CH3

Problem 4.24 Draw the structure for each compound using wedges and dashes.

a. *cis*-1,2-dimethylcyclopropane b. *trans*-1-ethyl-2-methylcyclopentane

Problem 4.25 For *cis*-1,3-diethylcyclobutane, draw (a) a stereoisomer; (b) a constitutional isomer.

4.13C A Disubstituted Cyclohexane

A disubstituted cyclohexane like 1,4-dimethylcyclohexane also has cis and trans stereoisomers. In addition, each of these stereoisomers has two possible chair conformations.

CH3
CH3
H
H
CH3
CH3
H
H

***trans*-1,4-dimethylcyclohexane** ***cis*-1,4-dimethylcyclohexane**

All disubstituted cycloalkanes with two groups bonded to *different* atoms have cis and trans isomers.

To draw both conformations for each stereoisomer, follow the procedure in Section 4.13A for a monosubstituted cyclohexane, keeping in mind that two substituents must now be added to the ring.

How To Draw Two Conformations for a Disubstituted Cyclohexane

Step [1] Draw one chair form and add the substituents.

- For *trans*-1,4-dimethylcyclohexane, arbitrarily pick two C's located 1,4- to each other, classify them as *up* or *down* C's, and draw in the substituents.
- The trans isomer must have one group *above* the ring (on an *up* bond) and one group *below* the ring (on a *down* bond). The substituents can be either axial or equatorial, as long as one is up and one is down. The easiest trans isomer to visualize has two axial CH_3 groups. This arrangement is said to be **diaxial.**
- This forms one of the two possible chair conformations, labeled Conformation **1.**

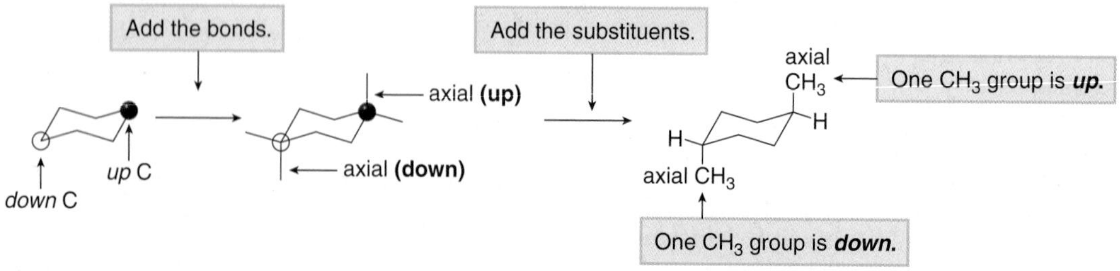

Conformation 1

Step [2] Ring-flip the cyclohexane ring.

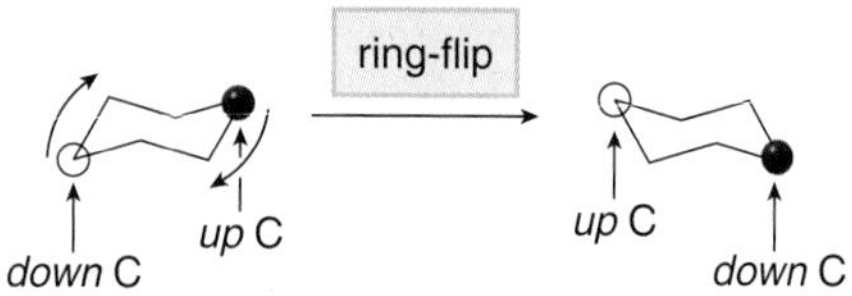

- The *up* C flips down, and the *down* C flips up.

Step [3] Add the substituents to the second conformation.

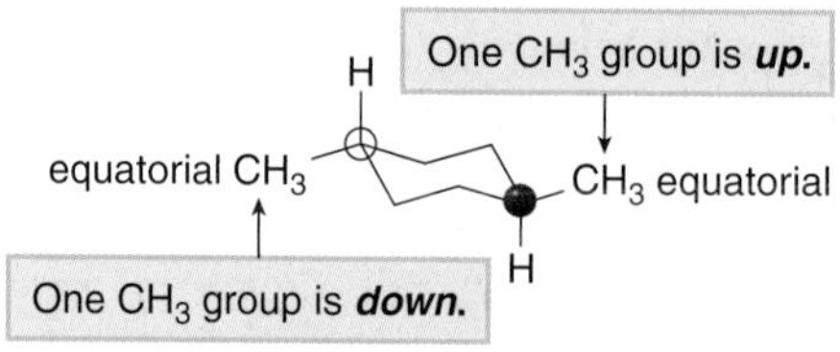

Conformation 2

- Ring-flipping converts axial bonds to equatorial bonds, and vice versa. The diaxial CH_3 groups become diequatorial. This trans conformation is less obvious to visualize. It is still trans, because one CH_3 group is above the ring (on an *up* bond), and one is below (on a *down* bond).

Conformations **1** and **2** are not equally stable. **Because Conformation 2 has both larger CH_3 groups in the roomier equatorial position, it is lower in energy.**

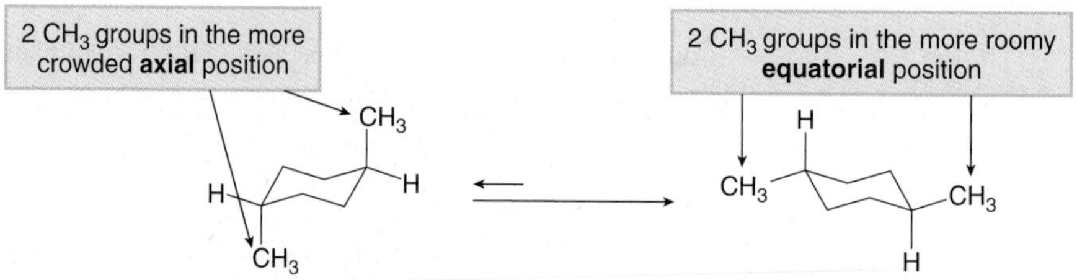

1
diaxial conformation

2
diequatorial conformation
more stable

Figure 4.17
The two conformations of *cis*-1,4-dimethylcyclohexane

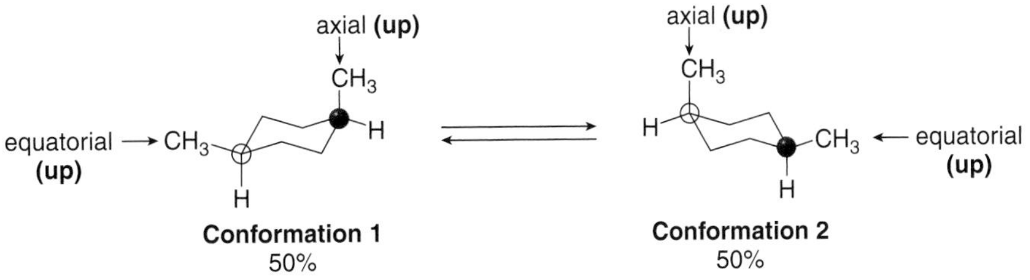
axial (up)
CH3
H
equatorial
(up)
CH3
H
Conformation 1
50%
axial (up)
CH3
H
CH3
equatorial
(up)
H
Conformation 2
50%

- A cis isomer has two groups on the same side of the ring, either both *up* or both *down*. In this example, Conformations **1** and **2** have two CH_3 groups drawn up.
- Both conformations have one CH_3 group axial and one equatorial, making them equally stable.

The cis isomer of 1,4-dimethylcyclohexane also has two conformations, as shown in Figure 4.17. Because each conformation has one CH_3 group axial and one equatorial, they are **identical in energy.** At room temperature, therefore, the two conformations exist in a 50:50 mixture at equilibrium.

The relative stability of the two conformations of any disubstituted cyclohexane can be analyzed using this procedure.

- **A cis isomer has two substituents on the same side, either both on *up* bonds or both on *down* bonds.**
- **A trans isomer has two substituents on opposite sides, one *up* and one *down*.**
- **Whether substituents are axial or equatorial depends on the relative location of the two substituents (on carbons 1,2-, 1,3-, or 1,4-).**

Sample Problem 4.4 Draw both chair conformations for *trans*-1,3-dimethylcyclohexane.

Solution

Step [1] Draw one chair form and add substituents.

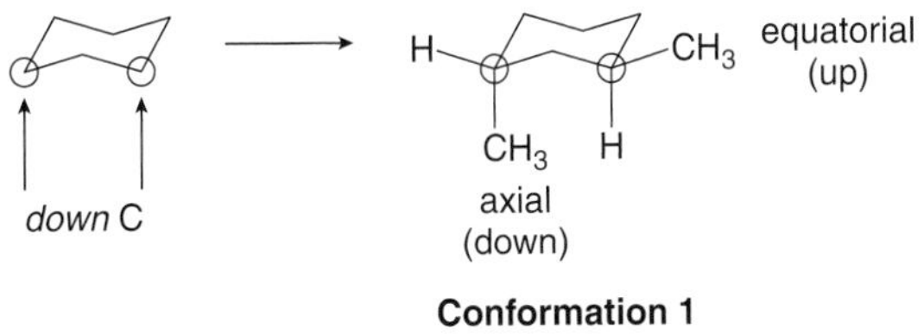
down C
H
CH3
equatorial
(up)
CH3
H
axial
(down)
Conformation 1

- Pick two C's 1,3- to each other.
- The trans isomer has two groups on **opposite sides.** In Conformation **1,** this means that one CH_3 is equatorial (on an *up* bond), and one group is axial (on a *down* bond).

Steps [2–3] Ring-flip and add substituents.

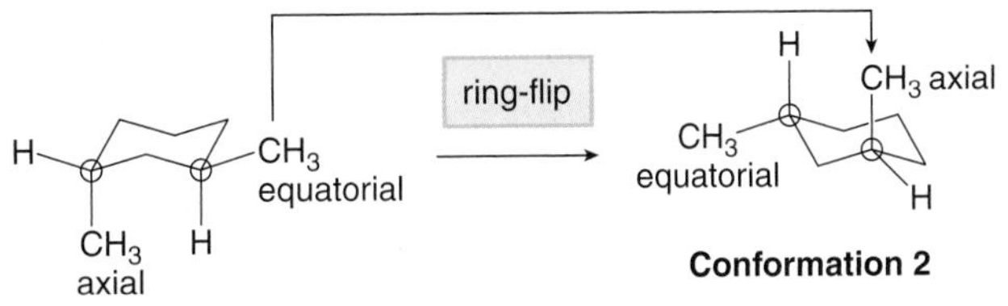
H
CH3
equatorial
CH3
axial
H
ring-flip
H
CH3 axial
CH3
equatorial
H
Conformation 2

- The two *down* C's flip up.
- The axial CH_3 flips equatorial (still a *down* bond) and the equatorial CH_3 flips axial (still an *up* bond). Conformation **2** is trans because the two CH_3's are still on opposite sides.
- **Conformations 1 and 2 are equally stable** because each has one CH_3 equatorial and one axial.

Problem 4.26 Label each compound as cis or trans. Then draw the second chair conformation.

a. 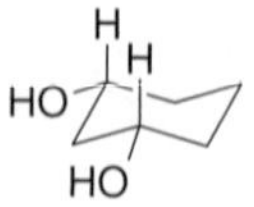
H
H
HO
HO

b. 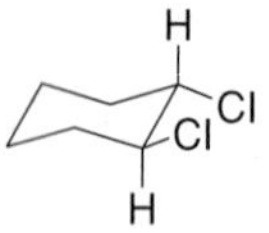
H
Cl
Cl
H

c. 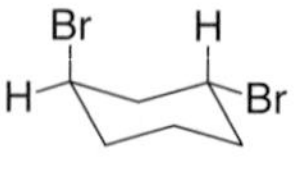
Br
H
H
Br

Problem 4.27 Consider 1,2-dimethylcyclohexane.

a. Draw structures for the cis and trans isomers using a hexagon for the six-membered ring.
b. Draw the two possible chair conformations for the cis isomer. Which conformation, if either, is more stable?
c. Draw the two possible chair conformations for the trans isomer. Which conformation, if either, is more stable?
d. Which isomer, cis or trans, is more stable and why?

Problem 4.28 Draw a chair conformation of cyclohexane with one CH_3CH_2 group and one CH_3 group that fits each description:

a. a 1,1-disubstituted cyclohexane with an axial CH_3CH_2 group
b. a cis-1,2-disubstituted cyclohexane with an axial CH_3 group
c. a trans-1,3-disubstituted cyclohexane with an equatorial CH_3 group
d. a trans-1,4-disubstituted cyclohexane with an equatorial CH_3CH_2 group

4.14 Oxidation of Alkanes

In Chapter 3 we learned that a functional group contains a heteroatom or π bond and constitutes **the reactive part of a molecule.** Alkanes are the only family of organic molecules that have no functional group, and therefore, **alkanes undergo few reactions.** In fact, alkanes are inert to reaction unless forcing conditions are used.

In Chapter 4, we consider only one reaction of alkanes—**combustion.** Combustion is an **oxidation–reduction** reaction.

4.14A Oxidation and Reduction Reactions

- *Oxidation* is the *loss* of electrons.
- *Reduction* is the *gain* of electrons.

Compounds that contain many C–H bonds and few C–Z bonds are said to be in a ***reduced state,*** whereas those that contain few C–H bonds and more C–Z bonds are in a ***more oxidized state.*** CH_4 is thus highly reduced, while CO_2 is highly oxidized.

Oxidation and reduction are opposite processes. As in acid–base reactions, there are always two components in these reactions. **One component is oxidized and one is reduced.**

To determine if an organic compound undergoes oxidation or reduction, we concentrate on the carbon atoms of the starting material and product, and **compare the relative number of C–H and C–Z bonds,** where Z = an element *more electronegative* than carbon (usually O, N, or X). Oxidation and reduction are then defined in two complementary ways.

- *Oxidation* results in an *increase* in the number of C–Z bonds; *or*
- *Oxidation* results in a *decrease* in the number of C–H bonds.

- *Reduction* results in a *decrease* in the number of C–Z bonds; *or*
- *Reduction* results in an *increase* in the number of C–H bonds.

Because Z is more electronegative than C, replacing C–H bonds with C–Z bonds decreases the electron density around C. Loss of electron density = oxidation.

Figure 4.18 illustrates the oxidation of CH_4 by replacing C–H bonds with C–O bonds (from left to right). The symbol **[O]** indicates oxidation. Because reduction is the reverse of oxidation, the molecules in Figure 4.18 are progressively reduced moving from right to left, from CO_2 to CH_4. The symbol **[H]** indicates reduction.

Figure 4.18
The oxidation and reduction of a carbon compound

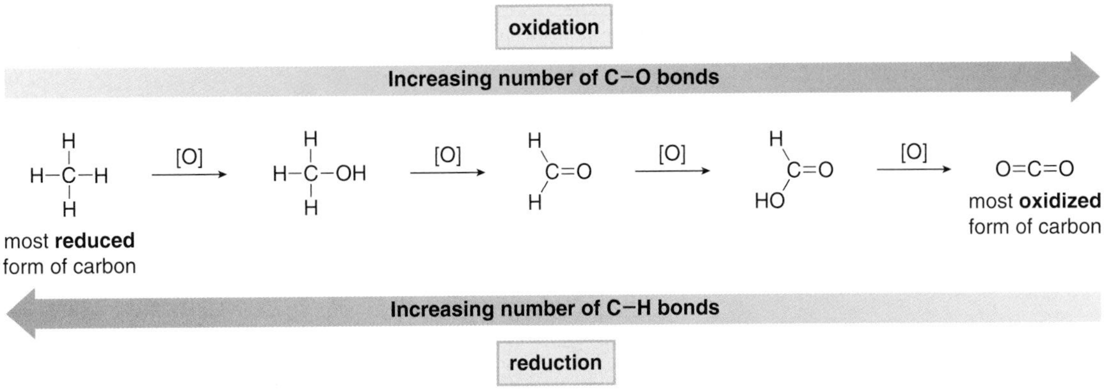

Sample Problem 4.5 Determine whether the organic compound is oxidized or reduced in each transformation.

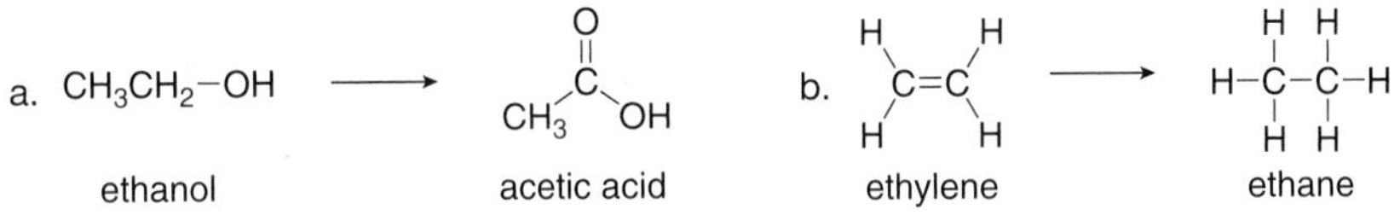

Solution

a. The conversion of ethanol to acetic acid is an **oxidation** because the number of C–O bonds increases: CH_3CH_2OH has one C–O bond and CH_3COOH has three C–O bonds.

b. The conversion of ethylene to ethane is a **reduction** because the number of C–H bonds increases: ethane has two more C–H bonds than ethylene.

Problem 4.29 Classify each transformation as an oxidation, reduction, or neither.

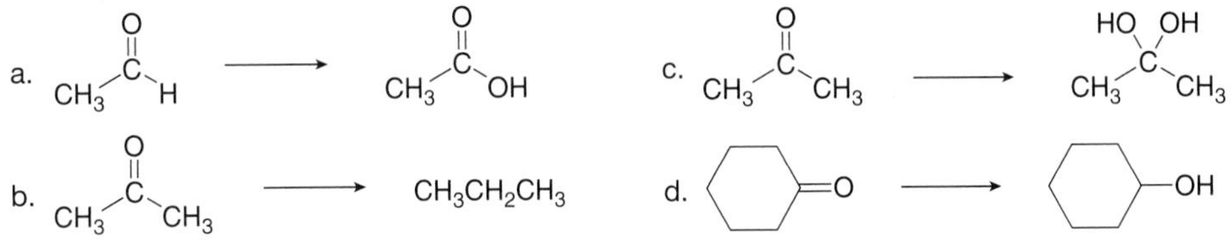

4.14B Combustion of Alkanes

When an organic compound is *oxidized* by a reagent, the reagent itself is *reduced.* Similarly, when an organic compound is *reduced* by a reagent, the reagent is *oxidized.* **Organic chemists identify a reaction as an oxidation or reduction by what happens to the *organic* component of the reaction.**

Alkanes undergo **combustion**—that is, **they burn in the presence of oxygen to form carbon dioxide and water.** This is a practical example of oxidation. Every C–H and C–C bond in the starting material is converted to a C–O bond in the product. The reactions drawn show the combustion of two different alkanes. Note that the products, $\mathbf{CO_2 + H_2O}$, are the same, regardless of the identity of the starting material. Combustion of alkanes in the form of natural gas, gasoline, or heating oil releases energy for heating homes, powering vehicles, and cooking food.

$$\underset{\text{methane}}{CH_4} + 2\,O_2 \xrightarrow[\text{flame}]{} CO_2 + 2\,H_2O + \text{(heat) energy}$$

$$\underset{\substack{\text{2,2,4-trimethylpentane}\\\text{(isooctane)}}}{2\,(CH_3)_3CCH_2CH(CH_3)_2} + 25\,O_2 \xrightarrow[\text{flame}]{} 16\,CO_2 + 18\,H_2O + \text{(heat) energy}$$

reduced starting material (isooctane) → **oxidized** product (CO_2)

Combustion requires a spark or a flame to initiate the reaction. Gasoline, therefore, which is composed largely of alkanes, can be safely handled and stored in the air, but the presence of a spark or match causes immediate and violent combustion.

Figure 4.19
The changing concentration of CO_2 in the atmosphere since 1958

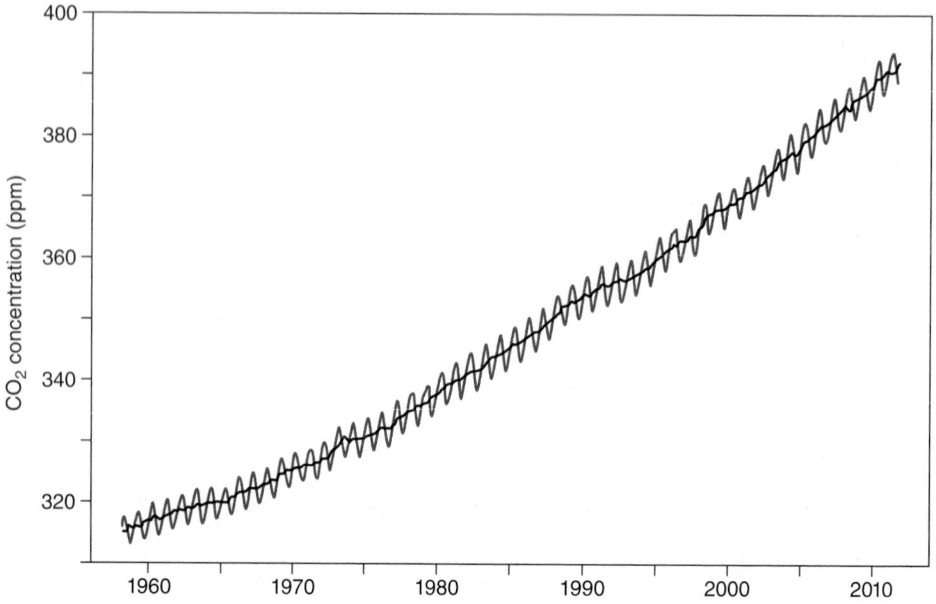

The increasing level of atmospheric CO_2 is clearly evident on the graph. Two data points are recorded each year. The sawtooth nature of the graph is due to seasonal variation of CO_2 level with the seasonal variation in photosynthesis. (Data recorded at Mauna Loa, Hawaii)

Driving an automobile 10,000 miles at 25 miles per gallon releases ~10,000 lb of CO_2 into the atmosphere.

The combustion of alkanes and other hydrocarbons obtained from fossil fuels adds a tremendous amount of CO_2 to the atmosphere each year. Quantitatively, data show over a 20% increase in the atmospheric concentration of CO_2 in the last 53 years (from 315 parts per million in 1958 to 389 parts per million in 2011; Figure 4.19). Although the composition of the atmosphere has changed over the lifetime of the earth, this may be the first time that the actions of humankind have altered that composition significantly and so quickly.

An increased CO_2 concentration in the atmosphere may have long-range and far-reaching effects. CO_2 absorbs thermal energy that normally radiates from the earth's surface, and redirects it back to the surface. Higher levels of CO_2 may therefore contribute to an increase in the average temperature of the earth's atmosphere. The global climate change resulting from these effects may lead to melting of the polar ice caps, a rise in sea level, and many more unforeseen consequences. How great a role CO_2 plays in this process is hotly debated.

Problem 4.30 Draw the products of each combustion reaction.

a. $CH_3CH_2CH_3 + O_2 \xrightarrow{\text{flame}}$

b. 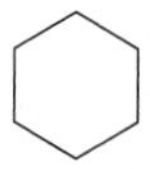 $+ O_2 \xrightarrow{\text{flame}}$

4.15 Lipids—Part 1

Lipids are biomolecules whose properties resemble those of alkanes and other hydrocarbons. They are unlike any other class of biomolecules, though, because they are defined by a **physical property,** not by the presence of a particular functional group.

- **Lipids are biomolecules that are soluble in organic solvents and insoluble in water.**

Lipids that contain carbon–carbon double bonds are discussed in Section 10.6.

Lipids have varied sizes and shapes, and a diverse number of functional groups. Fat-soluble vitamins like vitamin A and the phospholipids that comprise cell membranes are two examples of lipids that were presented in Sections 3.5 and 3.7. Other examples are shown in Figure 4.20. One unifying feature accounts for their solubility.

Figure 4.20
Three representative lipid molecules

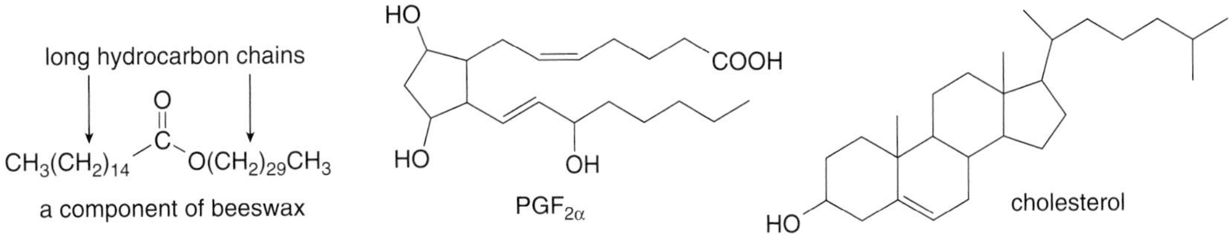

- **Lipids are composed of many nonpolar C–H and C–C bonds, and have few polar functional groups.**

Waxes are lipids having two long alkyl chains joined by a single oxygen-containing functional group. Because of their many C–C and C–H bonds, **waxes are hydrophobic.** They form a protective coating on the feathers of birds to make them water repellent, and on leaves to prevent water evaporation. Bees secrete $\mathbf{CH_3(CH_2)_{14}COO(CH_2)_{29}CH_3}$, a wax that forms the honeycomb in which they lay eggs.

$\mathbf{PGF_{2\alpha}}$ belongs to a class of lipids called **prostaglandins.** Prostaglandins contain many C–C and C–H bonds and a single COOH group (a **carboxy group**). Prostaglandins possess a wide range of biological activities. They control inflammation, affect blood-platelet aggregation, and stimulate uterine contractions. Nonsteroidal anti-inflammatory drugs such as ibuprofen operate by blocking the synthesis of prostaglandins, as discussed in Sections 19.6 and 30.6.

Cholesterol is a member of the steroid family, a group of lipids having four rings joined together. Because it has just one polar OH group, cholesterol is insoluble in the aqueous medium of the blood. It is synthesized in the liver and transported to other cells bound to water-soluble organic molecules. Elevated cholesterol levels can lead to coronary artery disease.

Cholesterol is a vital component of the cell membrane. Its hydrophobic carbon chain is embedded in the interior of the lipid bilayer, and its hydrophilic hydroxy group is oriented toward the aqueous exterior (Figure 4.21). Because its tetracyclic carbon skeleton is quite rigid compared to

Figure 4.21
Cholesterol embedded in a lipid bilayer of a cell membrane

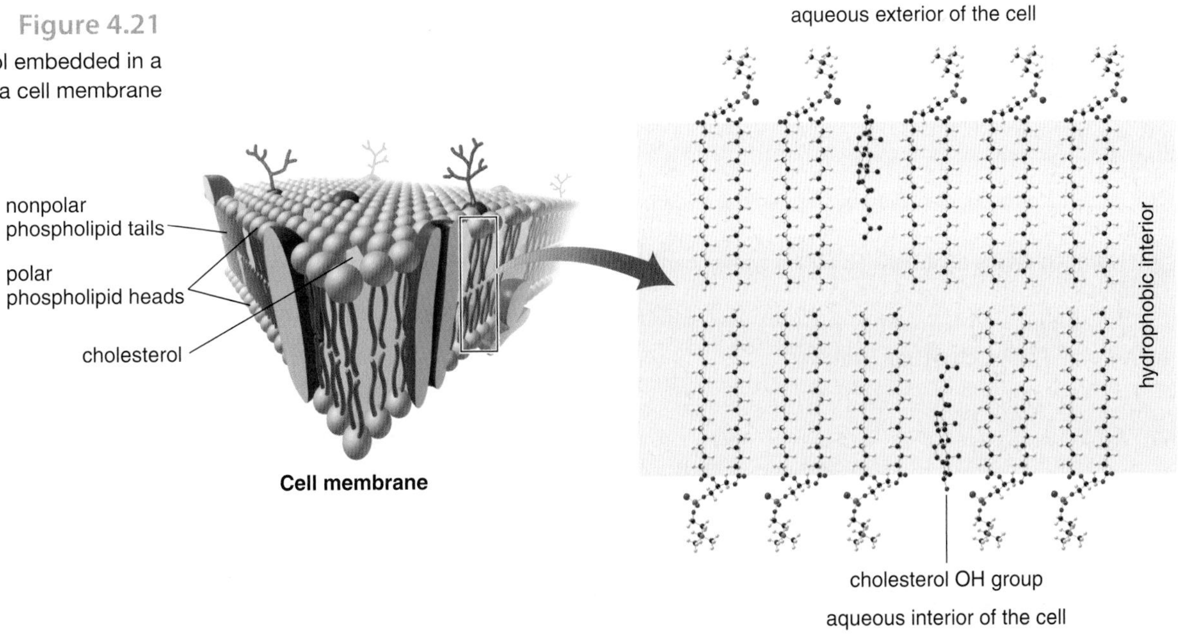

- The nonpolar hydrocarbon skeleton of cholesterol is embedded in the nonpolar interior of the cell membrane. Its rigid carbon skeleton stiffens the fluid lipid bilayer, giving it strength.
- Cholesterol's polar OH group is oriented toward the aqueous media inside and outside the cell.

the long floppy side chains of a phospholipid, cholesterol stiffens the cell membrane somewhat, giving it more strength.

Lipids have a high energy content, meaning that much energy is released on their metabolism. Because lipids are composed mainly of C–C and C–H bonds, they are oxidized with the release of energy, just like alkanes are. In fact, lipids are the most efficient biomolecules for the storage of energy. **The combustion of alkanes provides heat for our homes, and the metabolism of lipids provides energy for our bodies.**

Problem 4.31 Explain why beeswax is insoluble in H_2O, slightly soluble in ethanol (CH_3CH_2OH), and soluble in chloroform ($CHCl_3$).

Problem 4.32 Pristane is a high molecular weight alkane present in shark liver oil, a lipid used as a folk remedy and lubricant by coastal societies in northern Europe for centuries. What is the IUPAC name for pristane?

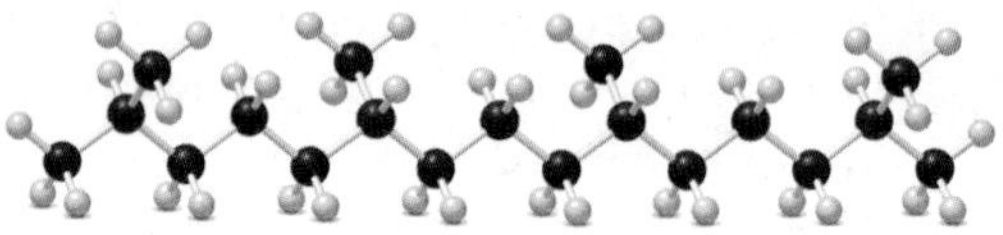

pristane

Shark liver oil, the source of pristane and other lipids, is obtained from sharks that inhabit the cold waters of the northern Atlantic and southern Pacific Oceans. (Photo © Eric Couture, courtesy Canadian Shark Research Laboratory.)

KEY CONCEPTS

Alkanes

General Facts About Alkanes (4.1–4.3)

- Alkanes are composed of **tetrahedral, *sp*³ hybridized** C atoms.
- There are two types of alkanes: acyclic alkanes having molecular formula C_nH_{2n+2}, and cycloalkanes having molecular formula C_nH_{2n}.
- Alkanes have only **nonpolar C–C and C–H bonds** and no functional group, so they undergo few reactions.
- Alkanes are named with the suffix ***-ane.***

Classifying C Atoms and H Atoms (4.1A)

- Carbon atoms are classified by the number of carbon atoms bonded to them; **a 1° carbon is bonded to one other carbon,** and so forth.
- Hydrogen atoms are classified by the type of carbon atom to which they are bonded; **a 1° H is bonded to a 1° carbon,** and so forth.

Names of Alkyl Groups (4.4A)

CH_3– methyl	=	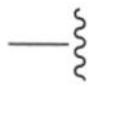	$CH_3CH_2CH_2CH_2$– butyl	=	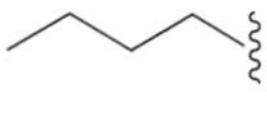
CH_3CH_2– ethyl	=	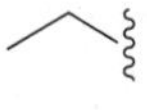	$CH_3CH_2CHCH_3$ (attached at CH) *sec*-butyl	=	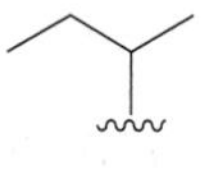
$CH_3CH_2CH_2$– propyl	=	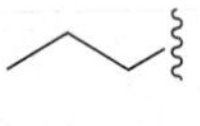	$(CH_3)_2CHCH_2$– isobutyl	=	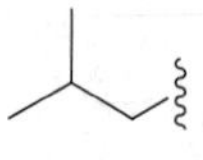
$(CH_3)_2CH$– isopropyl	=	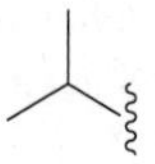	$(CH_3)_3C$– *tert*-butyl	=	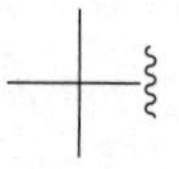

Conformations in Acyclic Alkanes (4.9, 4.10)

- Alkane conformations can be classified as **eclipsed, staggered, anti,** or **gauche** depending on the relative orientation of the groups on adjacent carbons.

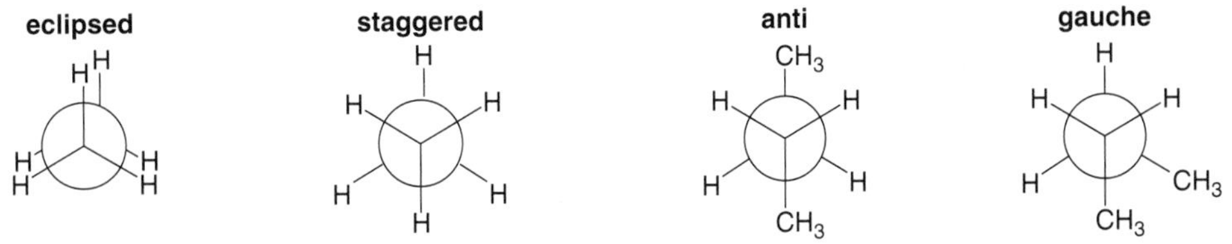

- dihedral angle = 0°
- dihedral angle = 60°
- dihedral angle of two CH_3 groups = 180°
- dihedral angle of two CH_3 groups = 60°

- A staggered conformation is **lower in energy** than an eclipsed conformation.
- An anti conformation is **lower in energy** than a gauche conformation.

Types of Strain

- **Torsional strain**—an increase in energy caused by eclipsing interactions (4.9).
- **Steric strain**—an increase in energy when atoms are forced too close to each other (4.10).
- **Angle strain**—an increase in energy when tetrahedral bond angles deviate from 109.5° (4.11).

Two Types of Isomers

[1] **Constitutional isomers**—isomers that differ in the way the atoms are connected to each other (4.1A).
[2] **Stereoisomers**—isomers that differ *only* in the way the atoms are oriented in space (4.13B).

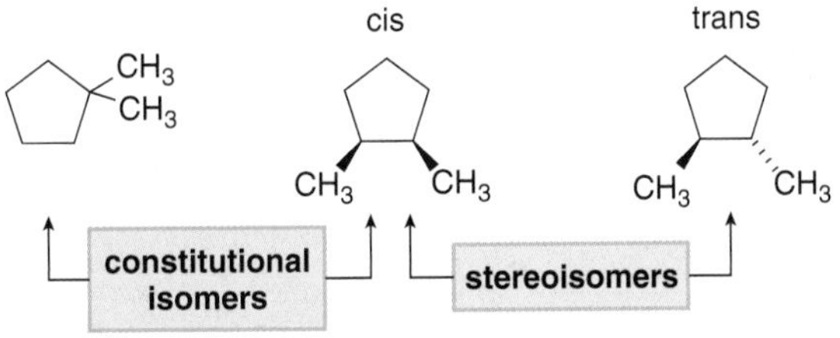

Conformations in Cyclohexane (4.12, 4.13)

- Cyclohexane exists as **two chair conformations** in rapid equilibrium at room temperature.
- Each carbon atom on a cyclohexane ring has **one axial** and **one equatorial hydrogen.** Ring-flipping converts axial H's to equatorial H's, and vice versa.

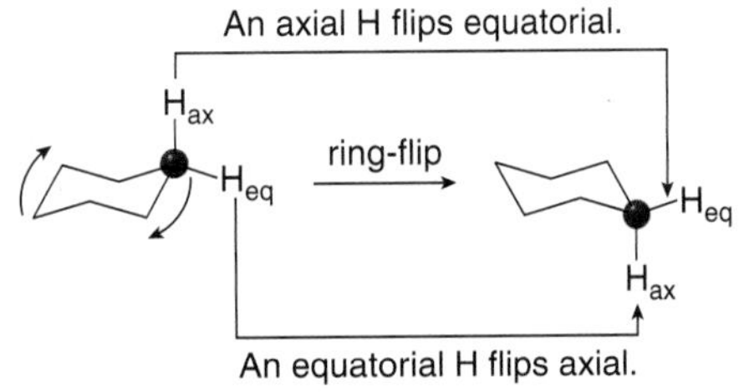

- In substituted cyclohexanes, groups larger than hydrogen are more stable in the **roomier equatorial position.**
- Disubstituted cyclohexanes with substituents on different atoms exist as two possible stereoisomers.
  - The **cis** isomer has two groups on the **same side** of the ring, either both up or both down.
  - The **trans** isomer has two groups on **opposite sides** of the ring, one up and one down.

Oxidation–Reduction Reactions (4.14)

- **Oxidation** results in an **increase in the number of C – Z bonds** or a **decrease in the number of C – H bonds.**
- **Reduction** results in a **decrease in the number of C – Z bonds** or an **increase in the number of C – H bonds.**

PROBLEMS

Problems Using Three-Dimensional Models

4.33 Name each alkane using the ball-and-stick model, and classify each carbon as 1°, 2°, 3°, or 4°.

a. 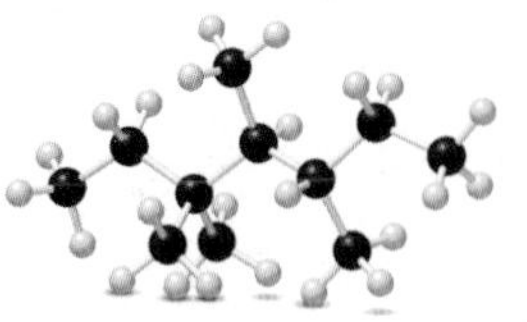

b. 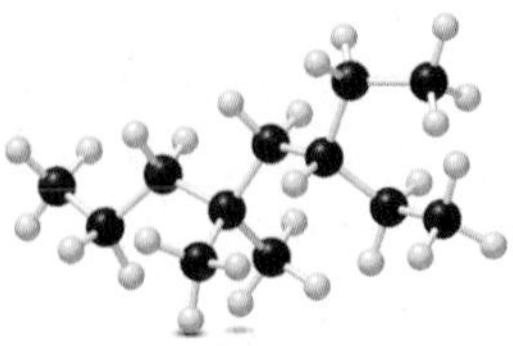

4.34 Consider the substituted cyclohexane shown in the ball-and-stick model.

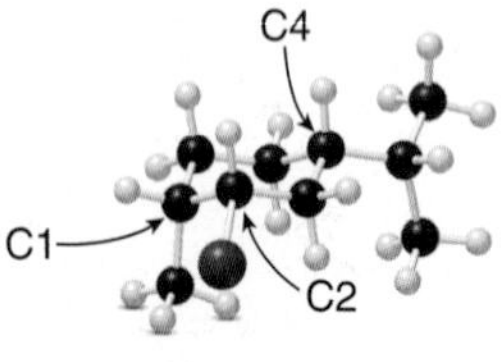

a. Label the substituents on C1, C2, and C4 as axial or equatorial.
b. Are the substituents on C1 and C2 cis or trans to each other?
c. Are the substituents on C2 and C4 cis or trans to each other?
d. Draw the second possible conformation in the chair form, and classify it as more stable or less stable than the conformation shown in the 3-D model.

4.35 Convert each three-dimensional model to a Newman projection around the indicated bond.

a. 

b. 

c. 

Classifying Carbons and Hydrogens

4.36 For each alkane: (a) classify each carbon atom as 1°, 2°, 3°, or 4°; (b) classify each hydrogen atom as 1°, 2°, or 3°.

[1] 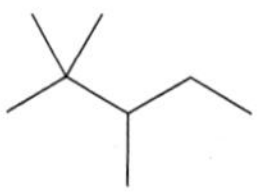

[2] 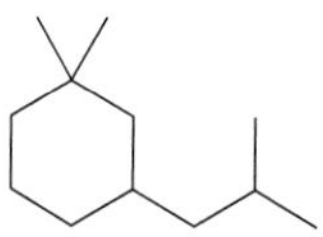

4.37 Draw the structure of an alkane that:

a. contains only 1° and 4° carbons
b. contains only 2° carbons
c. contains only 1° and 2° hydrogens
d. contains only 1° and 3° hydrogens

Constitutional Isomers

4.38 Draw the structure of all compounds that fit the following descriptions:

a. five constitutional isomers having the molecular formula C_4H_8
b. nine constitutional isomers having the molecular formula C_7H_{16}
c. twelve constitutional isomers having the molecular formula C_6H_{12} and containing one ring

IUPAC Nomenclature

4.39 Give the IUPAC name for each compound.

a. $CH_3CH_2CHCH_2CHCH_2CH_2CH_3$ (with CH_3 on C3 and CH_2CH_3 on C5)

$\quad\quad CH_3 \quad CH_2CH_3$

b. $\quad CH_2CH_3 \quad CH_3$

$CH_3CH_2CCH_2CH_2CHCHCH_2CH_2CH_3$

$\quad CH_2CH_3 \quad CH_2CH_3$

c. $CH_3CH_2CH_2C(CH_3)_2C(CH_3)_2CH_2CH_3$

d. $CH_3CH_2C(CH_2CH_3)_2CH(CH_3)CH(CH_2CH_2CH_3)_2$

e. $(CH_3CH_2)_3CCH(CH_3)CH_2CH_2CH_3$

f. $CH_3CH_2CH(CH_3)CH(CH_3)CH(CH_2CH_2CH_3)(CH_2)_3CH_3$

g. $(CH_3CH_2CH_2)_4C$

h. 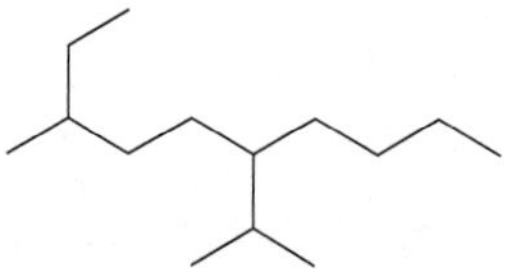

i. 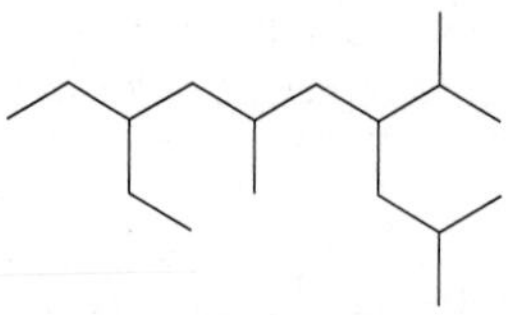

j. 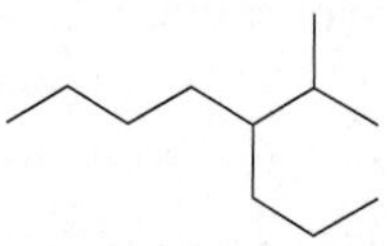

k. 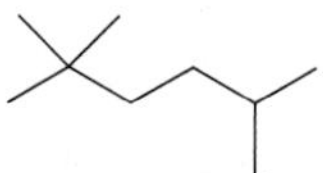

l. 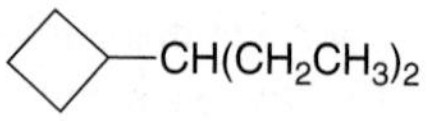

m. 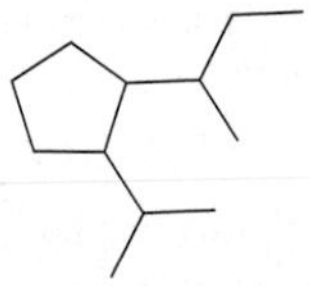

n. 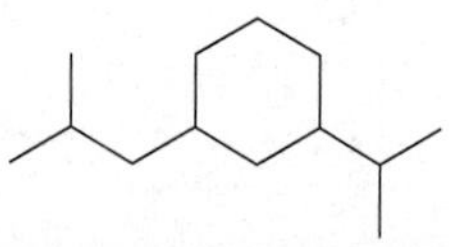

4.40 Give the structure and IUPAC name for each of the nine isomers having molecular formula C_9H_{20} that contains seven carbons in the longest chain and two methyl groups as substituents.

4.41 Draw the structure corresponding to each IUPAC name.

a. 3-ethyl-2-methylhexane
b. *sec*-butylcyclopentane
c. 4-isopropyl-2,4,5-trimethylheptane
d. cyclobutylcycloheptane
e. 3-ethyl-1,1-dimethylcyclohexane
f. 4-butyl-1,1-diethylcyclooctane
g. 6-isopropyl-2,3-dimethylnonane
h. 2,2,6,6,7-pentamethyloctane
i. *cis*-1-ethyl-3-methylcyclopentane
j. *trans*-1-*tert*-butyl-4-ethylcyclohexane

4.42 Which of the following compounds is not an isomer of undecane?

a. 2-methyldecane
b. 3,3-dimethylnonane
c. 3-ethyloctane
d. 3,4-diethylheptane
e. 2,2,3,3,4,4-hexamethylpentane

4.43 Each of the following IUPAC names is incorrect. Explain why it is incorrect and give the correct IUPAC name.

a. 2,2-dimethyl-4-ethylheptane
b. 5-ethyl-2-methylhexane
c. 2-methyl-2-isopropylheptane
d. 1,5-dimethylcyclohexane
e. 1-ethyl-2,6-dimethylcycloheptane
f. 5,5,6-trimethyloctane
g. 3-butyl-2,2-dimethylhexane
h. 1,3-dimethylbutane

4.44 Give the IUPAC name for each compound.

a. 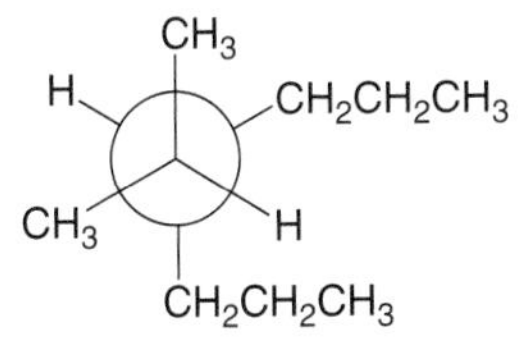
CH3
H
CH2CH2CH3
CH3
H
CH2CH2CH3

b. 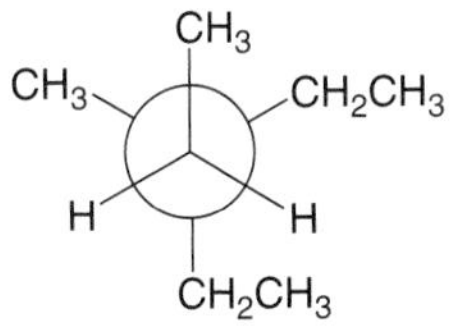
CH3
CH3
CH2CH3
H
H
CH2CH3

c. 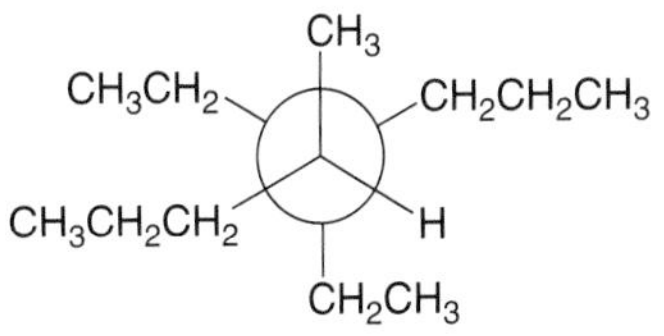
CH3
CH3CH2
CH2CH2CH3
CH3CH2CH2
H
CH2CH3

Physical Properties

4.45 Rank each group of alkanes in order of increasing boiling point. Explain your choice of order.

a. $CH_3CH_2CH_2CH_2CH_3$, $CH_3CH_2CH_2CH_3$, $CH_3CH_2CH_3$
b. $CH_3CH_2CH_2CH(CH_3)_2$, $CH_3(CH_2)_4CH_3$, $(CH_3)_2CHCH(CH_3)_2$

4.46 The melting points and boiling points of two isomeric alkanes are as follows: $CH_3(CH_2)_6CH_3$, mp = –57 °C and bp = 126 °C; $(CH_3)_3CC(CH_3)_3$, mp = 102 °C and bp = 106 °C. (a) Explain why one isomer has a lower melting point but higher boiling point. (b) Explain why there is a small difference in the boiling points of the two compounds, but a huge difference in their melting points.

Conformation of Acyclic Alkanes

4.47 Which conformation in each pair is *higher* in energy? Calculate the energy difference between the two conformations using the values given in Table 4.3.

a. 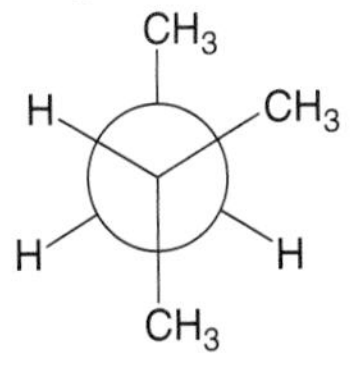
CH3
H
CH3
H
H
CH3
or
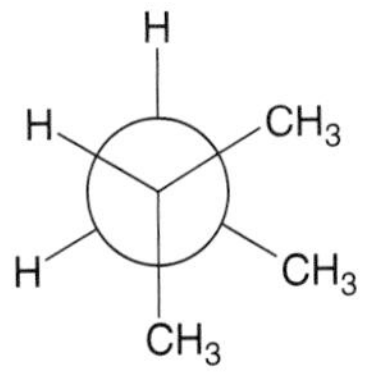
H
H
CH3
H
CH3
CH3

b. 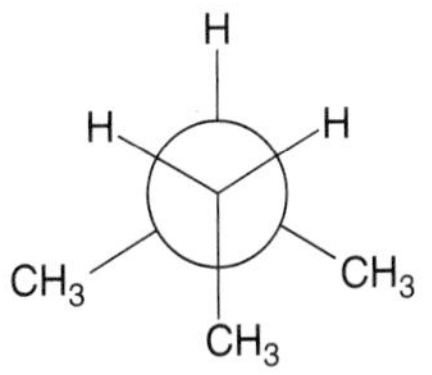
H
H
H
CH3
CH3
CH3
or
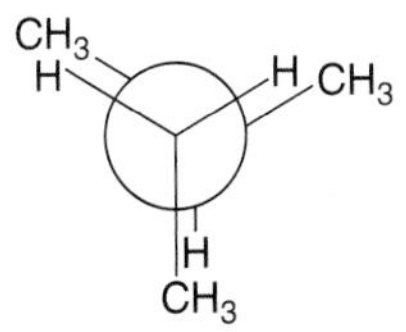
CH3
H
H
CH3
H
CH3

4.48 Considering rotation around the indicated bond in each compound, draw Newman projections for the most stable and least stable conformations.

a. CH_3–$CH_2CH_2CH_2CH_3$ (↑ indicated bond)

b. $CH_3CH_2CH_2$–$CH_2CH_2CH_3$ (↑ indicated bond)

4.49 Convert each structure to a Newman projection around the indicated bond.

a. 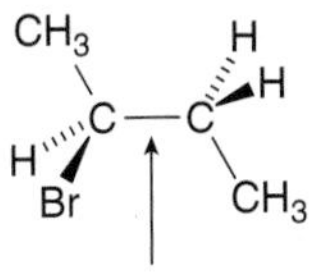
CH3
H
H
C
C
H
Br
CH3

b. 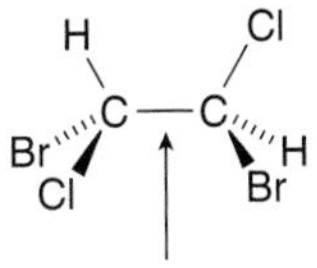
H
Cl
C
C
Br
H
Cl
Br

c. 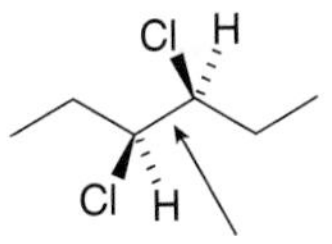
Cl
H
Cl
H

4.50 (a) Using Newman projections, draw all staggered and eclipsed conformations that result from rotation around the indicated bond in each molecule; (b) draw a graph of energy versus dihedral angle for rotation around this bond.

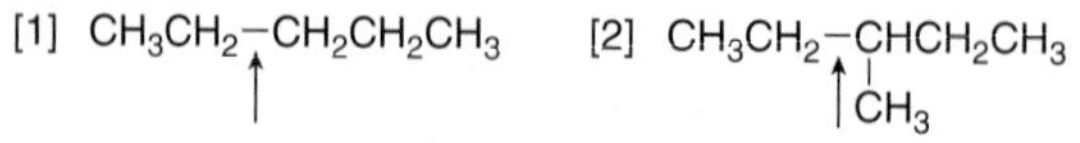
[1] CH3CH2–CH2CH2CH3
[2] CH3CH2–CHCH2CH3
CH3

4.51 Label the sites of torsional and steric strain in each conformation.

a. 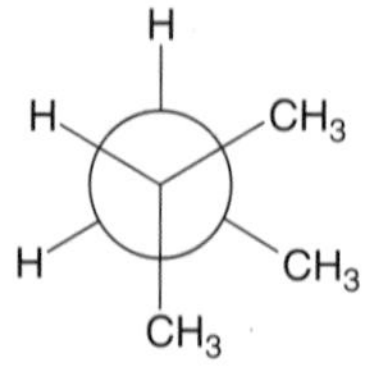
H
H
CH3
H
CH3
CH3

b. 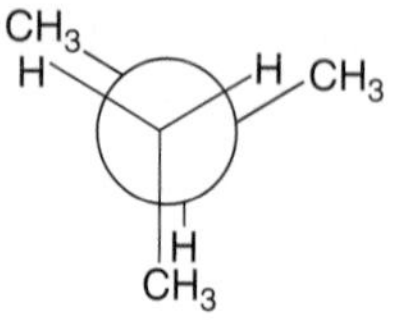
CH3
H
H
CH3
H
CH3

c. 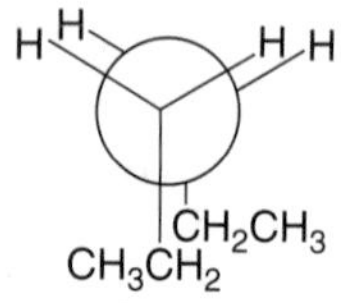
H
H
H
H
CH2CH3
CH3CH2

4.52 Calculate the barrier to rotation for each designated bond.

a. $CH_3{-}CH(CH_3)_2$ (arrow at the CH_3–CH bond)

b. $CH_3{-}C(CH_3)_3$ (arrow at the CH_3–C bond)

4.53 The eclipsed conformation of CH_3CH_2Cl is 15 kJ/mol less stable than the staggered conformation. How much is the H,Cl eclipsing interaction worth in destabilization?

4.54 (a) Draw the anti and gauche conformations for ethylene glycol ($HOCH_2CH_2OH$). (b) Ethylene glycol is unusual in that the gauche conformation is more stable than the anti conformation. Offer an explanation.

Conformations and Stereoisomers in Cycloalkanes

4.55 For each compound drawn below:

a. Label each OH, Br, and CH_3 group as axial or equatorial.

b. Classify each conformation as cis or trans.

c. Translate each structure into a representation with a hexagon for the six-membered ring, and wedges and dashes for groups above and below the ring.

d. Draw the second possible chair conformation for each compound.

[1] 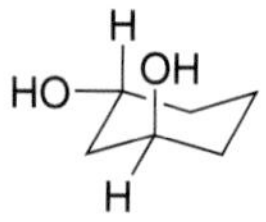
H
OH
HO
H

[2] 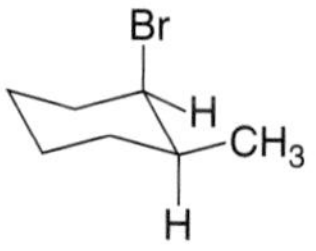
Br
H
CH3
H

[3] 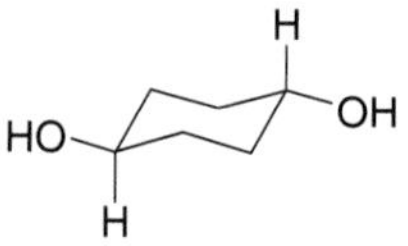
H
HO
OH
H

4.56 Draw the two possible chair conformations for *cis*-1,3-dimethylcyclohexane. Which conformation, if either, is more stable?

4.57 For each compound drawn below:

a. Draw representations for the cis and trans isomers using a hexagon for the six-membered ring, and wedges and dashes for substituents.

b. Draw the two possible chair conformations for the cis isomer. Which conformation, if either, is more stable?

c. Draw the two possible chair conformations for the trans isomer. Which conformation, if either, is more stable?

d. Which isomer, cis or trans, is more stable and why?

[1] 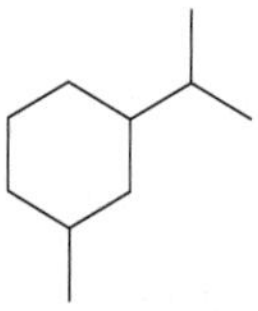

[2] 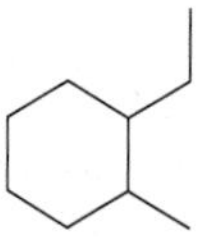

[3] 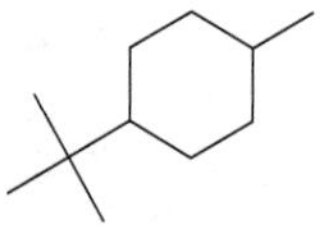

4.58 Convert each of the following structures into its more stable chair form. One structure represents menthol and one represents isomenthol. Menthol, the more stable isomer, is used in lip balms and mouthwash. Which structure corresponds to menthol?

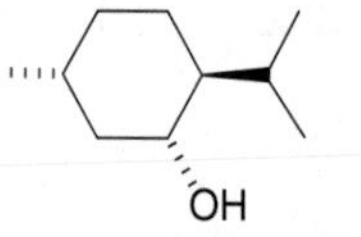
OH

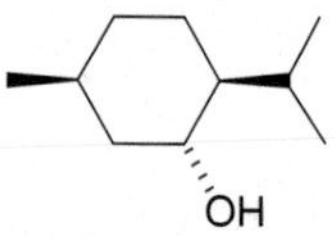
OH

4.59 Glucose is a simple sugar with five substituents bonded to a six-membered ring.

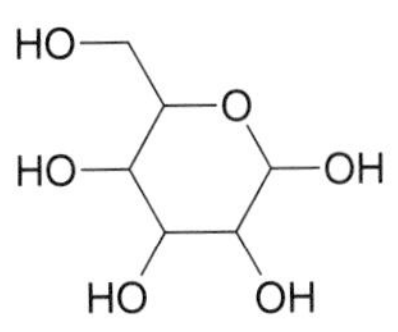

glucose

a. Using a chair representation, draw the most stable arrangement of these substituents on the six-membered ring.
b. Convert this representation into one that uses a hexagon with wedges and dashes.

4.60 Galactose is a simple sugar formed when lactose, a carbohydrate in milk, is hydrolyzed. Individuals with galactosemia, a rare inherited disorder, lack an enzyme needed to metabolize galactose, and must avoid cow's milk and all products derived from cow's milk. Galactose is a stereoisomer of glucose (Problem 4.59).

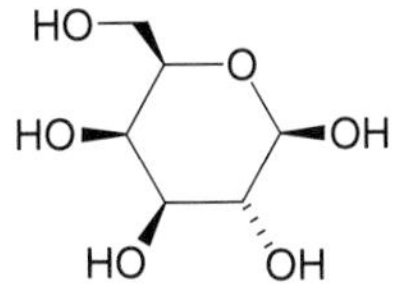

galactose

a. Draw both chair forms of galactose and label the more stable conformation.
b. Which simple sugar, galactose or glucose, is more stable? Explain.
c. Draw a constitutional isomer of galactose.
d. Draw a stereoisomer of galactose that is different from glucose.

Constitutional Isomers and Stereoisomers

4.61 Classify each pair of compounds as constitutional isomers, stereoisomers, identical molecules, or not isomers of each other.

a. 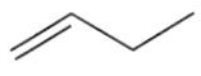 and 

b. 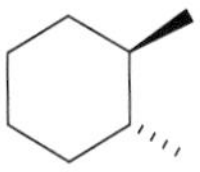 and 

c. 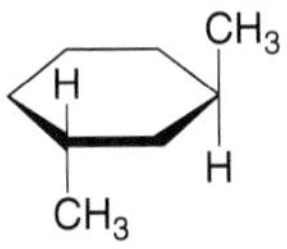 and 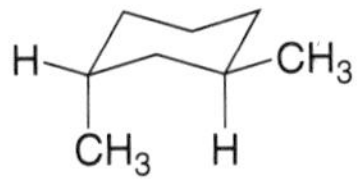

d. 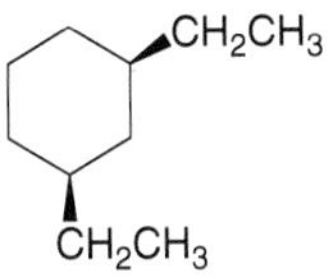 and 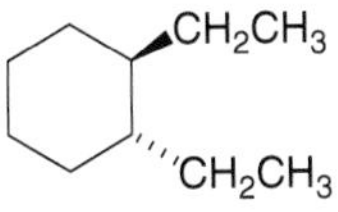

e. 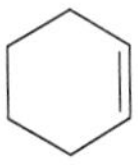 and 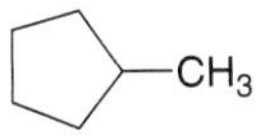

f. 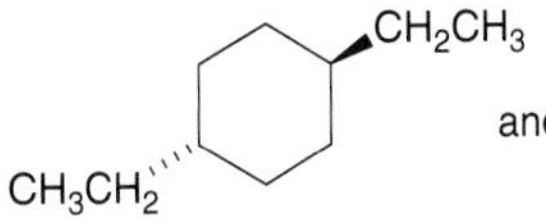 and 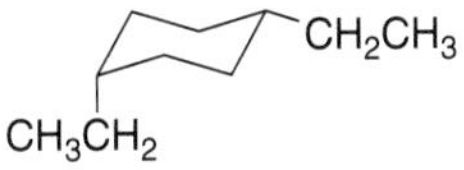

g. 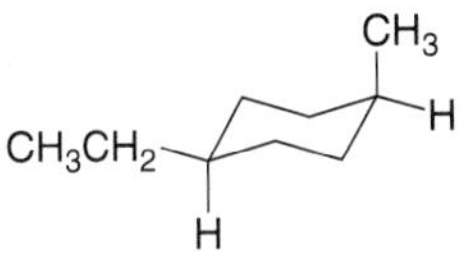 and 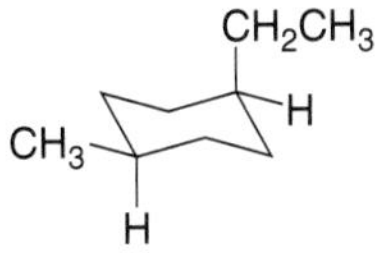

h. 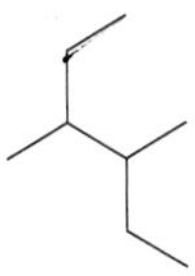 and 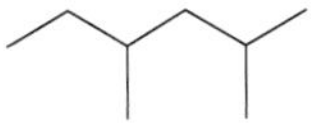

4.62 Classify each pair of compounds as constitutional isomers or identical molecules.

a. 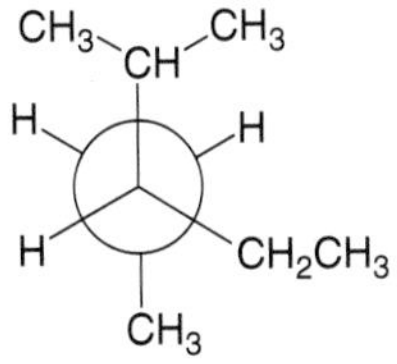 and 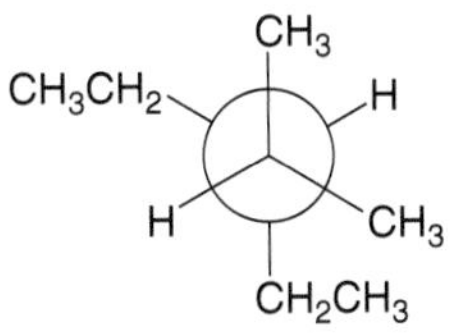

b. 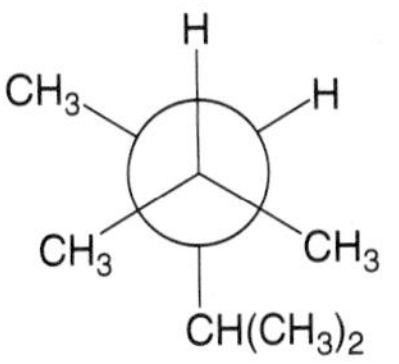 and 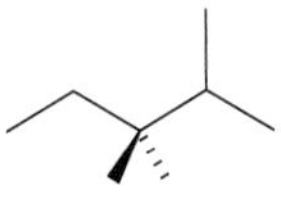

4.63 Draw a constitutional isomer and a stereoisomer for each compound.

a. 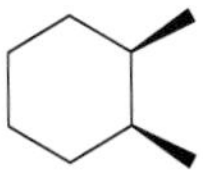

b. 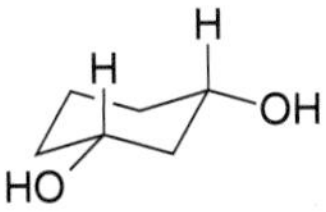

c. 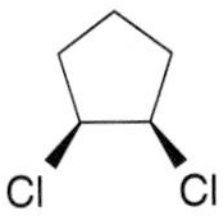

4.64 Draw the three constitutional isomers having molecular formula C_7H_{14} that contain a five-membered ring and two methyl groups as substituents. For each constitutional isomer that can have cis and trans isomers, draw the two stereoisomers.

Oxidation and Reduction

4.65 Classify each reaction as oxidation, reduction, or neither.

a. $CH_3CHO \longrightarrow CH_3CH_2OH$

b. $CH_2{=}CH_2 \longrightarrow H{-}C{\equiv}C{-}H$

c. 

d. $CH_3CH_2OH \longrightarrow CH_2{=}CH_2$

4.66 Draw the products of combustion of each alkane.

a. $CH_3CH_2CH_2CH_2CH(CH_3)_2$

b. 

4.67 Hydrocarbons like benzene are metabolized in the body to arene oxides, which rearrange to form phenols. This is an example of a general process in the body, in which an unwanted compound (benzene) is converted to a more water-soluble derivative called a *metabolite,* so that it can be excreted more readily from the body.

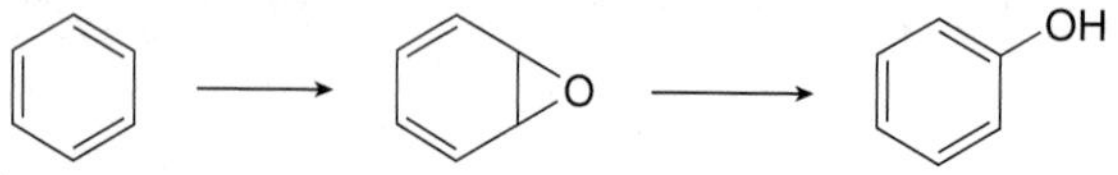

benzene arene oxide phenol

a. Classify each of these reactions as oxidation, reduction, or neither.
b. Explain why phenol is more water soluble than benzene. This means that phenol dissolves in urine, which is largely water, to a greater extent than benzene.

Lipids

4.68 Which of the following compounds are lipids?

a. 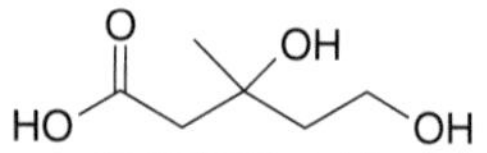

mevalonic acid

b. 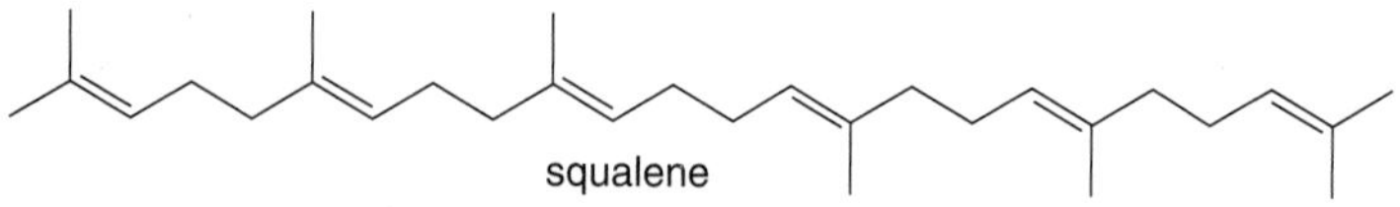

squalene

c. 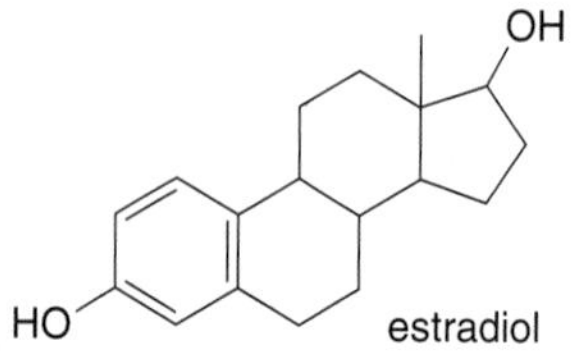

estradiol

d. 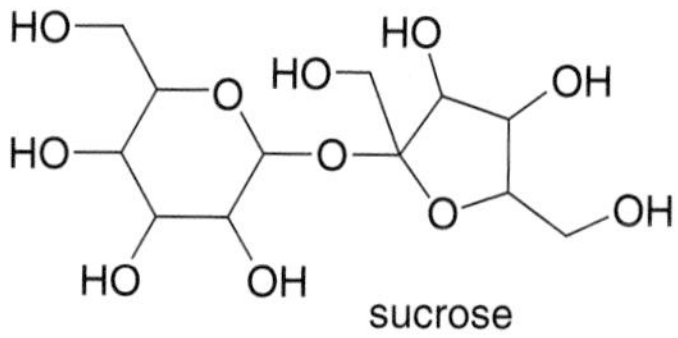

sucrose

4.69 Cholic acid, a compound called a **bile acid,** is converted to a **bile salt** in the body. Bile salts have properties similar to soaps, and they help transport lipids through aqueous solutions. Explain why this is so.

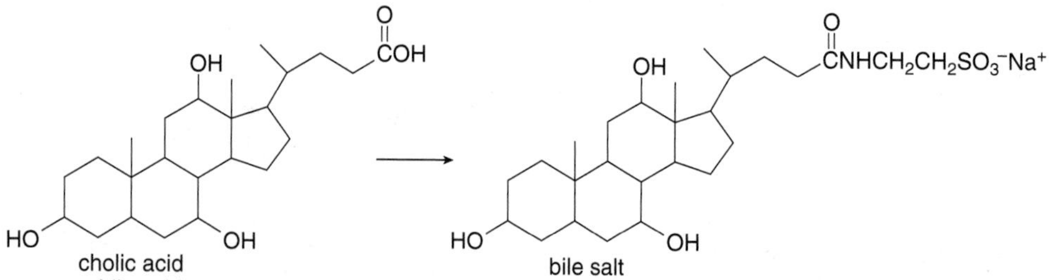

cholic acid
a bile acid

bile salt

4.70 Mineral oil, a mixture of high molecular weight alkanes, is sometimes used as a laxative. Why are individuals who use mineral oil for this purpose advised to avoid taking it at the same time they consume foods rich in fat-soluble vitamins such as vitamin A?

Challenge Problems

4.71 Cyclopropane and cyclobutane have similar strain energy despite the fact that the C–C–C bond angles of cyclopropane are much smaller than those of cyclobutane. Suggest an explanation for this observation, considering all sources of strain discussed in Chapter 4.

4.72 Although penicillin G has two amide functional groups, one is much more reactive than the other. Which amide is more reactive and why?

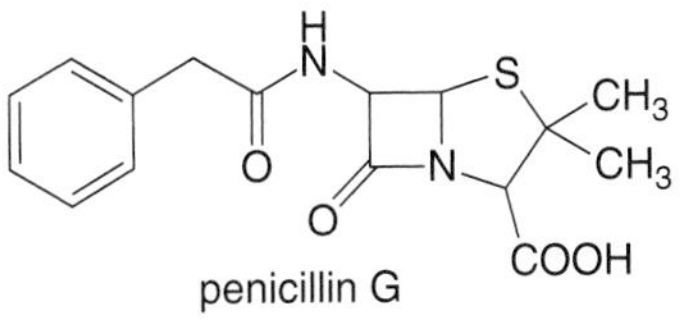

penicillin G

4.73 Haloethanes (CH_3CH_2X, X = Cl, Br, I) have similar barriers to rotation (13.4–15.5 kJ/mol) despite the fact that the size of the halogen increases, Cl → Br → I. Offer an explanation.

4.74 When two six-membered rings share a C–C bond, this bicyclic system is called a **decalin.** There are two possible arrangements: *trans*-decalin having two hydrogen atoms at the ring fusion on opposite sides of the rings, and *cis*-decalin having the two hydrogens at the ring fusion on the same side.

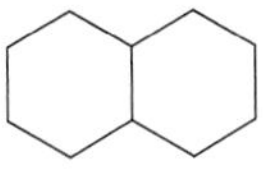

decalin

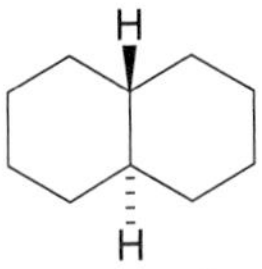

trans-decalin

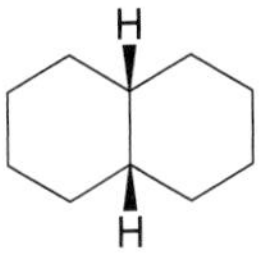

cis-decalin

a. Draw *trans*- and *cis*-decalin using the chair form for the cyclohexane rings.

b. The trans isomer is more stable. Explain why.

4.75 Consider the tricyclic structure **A.** (a) Label each substituent on the rings as axial or equatorial. (b) Draw a skeletal structure for **A,** using wedges and dashes to show whether the substituents are located above or below the rings.

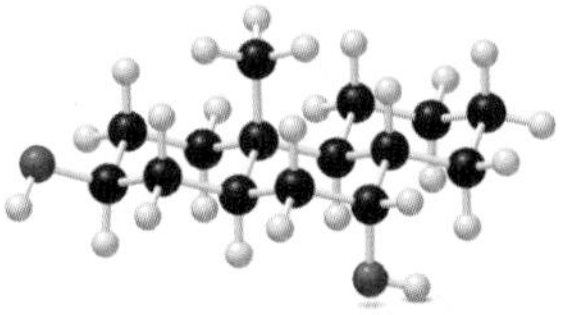

A

4.76 Consider the tricyclic structure **B.** (a) Label each substituent on the rings as axial or equatorial. (b) Draw **B** using chair conformations for each six-membered ring. (c) Label the atoms on the ring fusions (the carbons that join each set of two rings together) as cis or trans to each other.

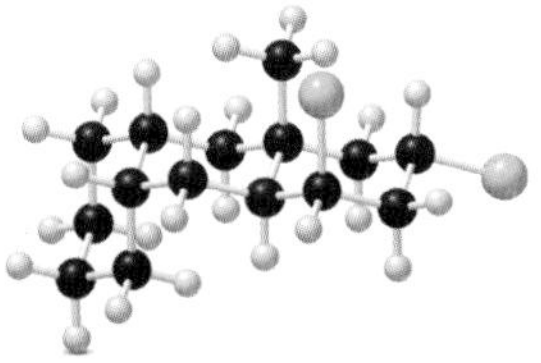

B

4.77 Read Appendix B on naming branched alkyl substituents, and draw all possible alkyl groups having the formula C_5H_{11}–. Give the IUPAC names for the eight compounds of molecular formula $C_{10}H_{20}$ that contain a cyclopentane ring with each of these alkyl groups as a substituent.

4.78 Read Appendix B on naming bicyclic compounds. Then give the IUPAC name for each of the following compounds.

a. 

b. 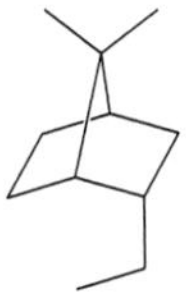

c. 

d. 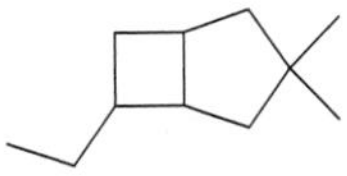

5 Stereochemistry

5.1 Starch and cellulose
5.2 The two major classes of isomers
5.3 Looking glass chemistry—Chiral and achiral molecules
5.4 Stereogenic centers
5.5 Stereogenic centers in cyclic compounds
5.6 Labeling stereogenic centers with *R* or *S*
5.7 Diastereomers
5.8 Meso compounds
5.9 *R* and *S* assignments in compounds with two or more stereogenic centers
5.10 Disubstituted cycloalkanes
5.11 Isomers—A summary
5.12 Physical properties of stereoisomers
5.13 Chemical properties of enantiomers

Thalidomide is a drug sold as a mixture of two stereoisomers that are mirror images of each other. Although thalidomide was once prescribed as a sedative and anti-nausea drug for pregnant women in Great Britain and Europe, this use was discontinued because one stereoisomer had beneficial effects, while the other stereoisomer produced fetal abnormalities. Today, thalidomide is prescribed under strict controls for the treatment of Hansen's disease (leprosy). Until 1969, individuals in Hawai'i with Hansen's disease were sent to Kalaupapa, a remote and inaccessible peninsula on the Hawaiian island of Moloka'i. Thus, the story of thalidomide is complex, but it begins with an understanding of how small structural differences can have a large effect on the properties of a molecule, the topic of Chapter 5.

Are you left-handed or right-handed? If you're right-handed, you've probably spent little time thinking about your hand preference. If you're left-handed, though, you probably learned at an early age that many objects—like scissors and baseball gloves—"fit" for righties, but are "backwards" for lefties. **Hands, like many objects in the world around us, are mirror images that are *not* identical.**

In Chapter 5 we examine the "handedness" of molecules, and ask, "How important is the three-dimensional shape of a molecule?"

5.1 Starch and Cellulose

Recall from Chapter 4 that ***stereochemistry* is the three-dimensional structure of a molecule.** How important is stereochemistry? Two biomolecules—starch and cellulose—illustrate how apparently minute differences in structure can result in vastly different properties.

Starch and **cellulose** are two polymers that belong to the family of biomolecules called **carbohydrates** (Figure 5.1). **A *polymer* is a large molecule composed of repeating smaller units—called monomers—that are covalently bonded together.**

Starch is the main carbohydrate in the seeds and roots of plants. When we humans ingest wheat, rice, or potatoes, for example, we consume starch, which is then hydrolyzed to the simple sugar **glucose,** one of the compounds our bodies use for energy. **Cellulose,** nature's most abundant organic material, gives rigidity to tree trunks and plant stems. Wood, cotton, and flax are composed largely of cellulose. Complete hydrolysis of cellulose also forms glucose, but unlike starch, humans cannot metabolize cellulose to glucose. In other words, we can digest starch but not cellulose.

Cellulose and starch are both composed of the same repeating unit—a six-membered ring containing an oxygen atom and three OH groups—joined by an oxygen atom. They differ in the position of the O atom joining the rings together.

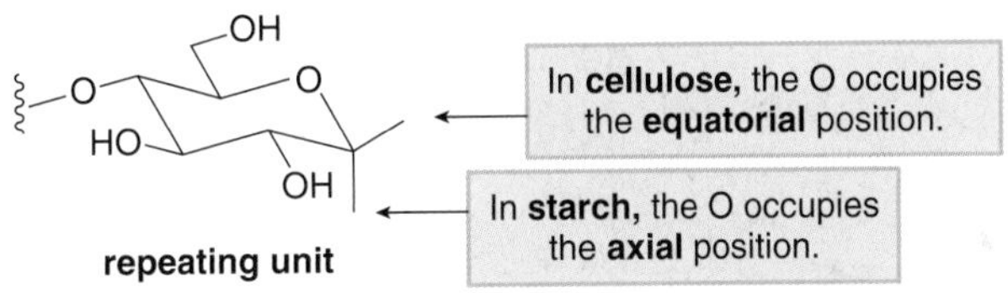

- **In cellulose, the O atom joins two rings using two equatorial bonds.**
- **In starch, the O atom joins two rings using one equatorial and one axial bond.**

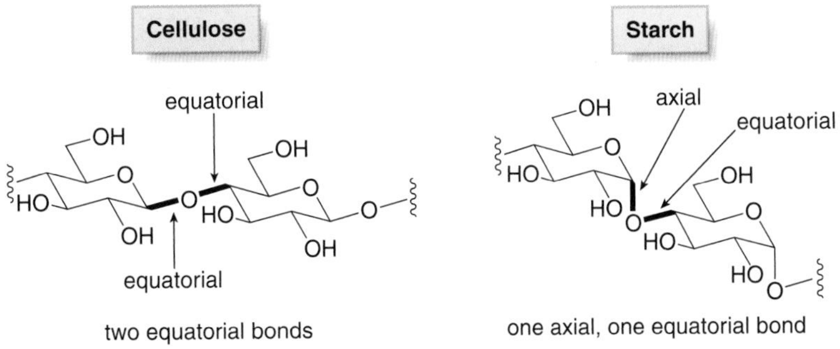

Starch and cellulose are **isomers** because they are different compounds with the same molecular formula $(C_6H_{10}O_5)_n$. They are **stereoisomers** because only the three-dimensional arrangement of atoms is different.

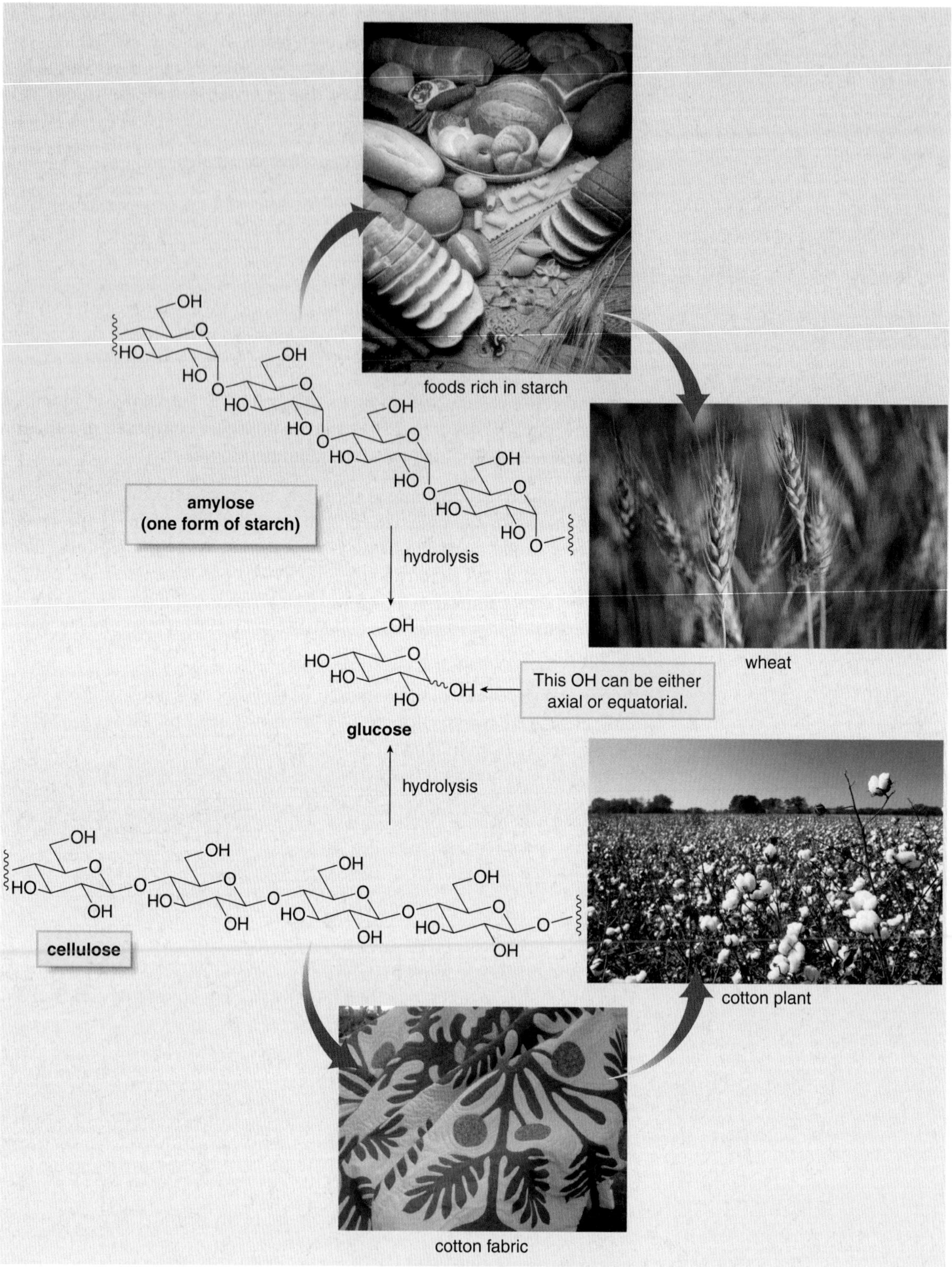
foods rich in starch
wheat
amylose
(one form of starch)
hydrolysis
glucose
This OH can be either
axial or equatorial.
hydrolysis
cellulose
cotton plant
cotton fabric

Figure 5.1 Starch and cellulose—Two common carbohydrates

Figure 5.2
Three-dimensional structure of cellulose and starch

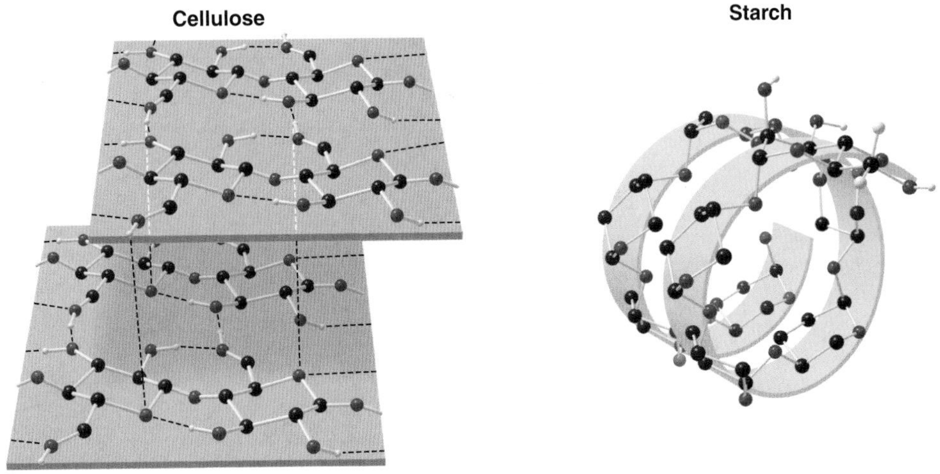

Cellulose consists of an extensive three-dimensional network held together by hydrogen bonds.

The starch polymer is composed of chains that wind into a helix.

How the six-membered rings are joined together has an enormous effect on the shape and properties of these carbohydrate molecules. Cellulose is composed of long chains held together by intermolecular hydrogen bonds, thus forming sheets that stack in an extensive three-dimensional network. The axial–equatorial ring junction in starch creates chains that fold into a helix (Figure 5.2). Moreover, the human digestive system contains the enzyme necessary to hydrolyze starch by cleaving its axial C–O bond, but not an enzyme to hydrolyze the equatorial C–O bond in cellulose.

Thus, an **apparently minor difference in the three-dimensional arrangement of atoms confers very different properties on starch and cellulose.**

Problem 5.1 Cellulose is water insoluble, despite its many OH groups. Considering its three-dimensional structure, why do you think this is so?

5.2 The Two Major Classes of Isomers

Because an understanding of isomers is integral to the discussion of stereochemistry, let's begin with an overview of isomers.

- **Isomers are different compounds with the same molecular formula.**

There are two major classes of isomers: **constitutional isomers** and **stereoisomers.** ***Constitutional (or structural) isomers*** **differ in the way the atoms are connected to each other.** Constitutional isomers have:

- different IUPAC names;
- the same or different functional groups;
- different physical properties, so they are separable by physical techniques such as distillation; and
- different chemical properties. They behave differently or give different products in chemical reactions.

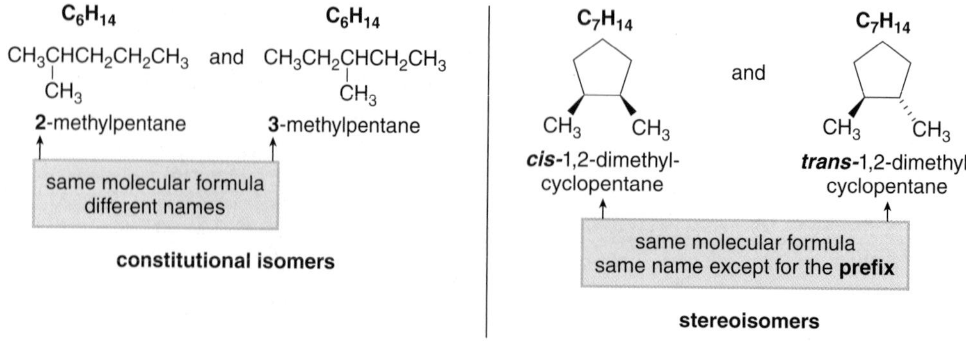

Figure 5.3 A comparison of constitutional isomers and stereoisomers

***Stereoisomers* differ *only* in the way atoms are oriented in space.** Stereoisomers have identical IUPAC names (except for a prefix like cis or trans). Because they differ only in the three-dimensional arrangement of atoms, stereoisomers always have the same functional group(s).

A particular three-dimensional arrangement is called a *configuration*. Thus, stereoisomers differ in configuration. The cis and trans isomers in Section 4.13B and the biomolecules starch and cellulose in Section 5.1 are two examples of stereoisomers.

Figure 5.3 illustrates examples of both types of isomers. Most of Chapter 5 relates to the types and properties of stereoisomers.

Problem 5.2 Classify each pair of compounds as constitutional isomers or stereoisomers.

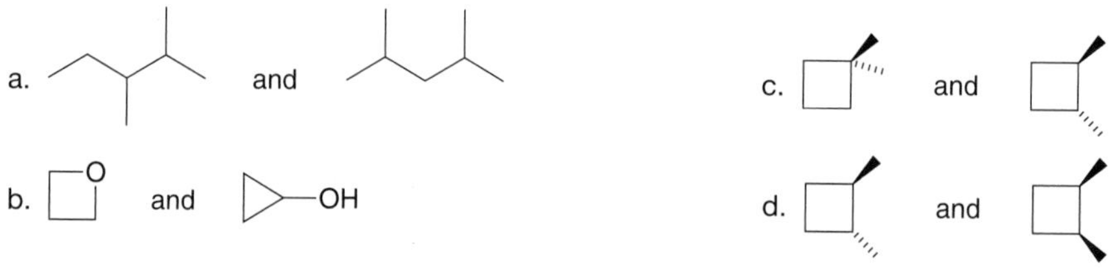

5.3 Looking Glass Chemistry—Chiral and Achiral Molecules

Despite the dominance of right-handedness over left-handedness, even identical twins can exhibit differences in hand preference. Pictured are Zachary (left-handed) and Matthew (right-handed), identical twin sons of the author.

Everything has a mirror image. What's important in chemistry is **whether a molecule is *identical* to or *different* from its mirror image.**

Some molecules are like hands. **Left and right hands are mirror images of each other, but they are *not* identical.** If you try to mentally place one hand inside the other hand, you can never superimpose either all the fingers, or the tops and palms. To *superimpose* an object on its mirror image means to align *all* parts of the object with its mirror image. With molecules, this means aligning all atoms and all bonds.

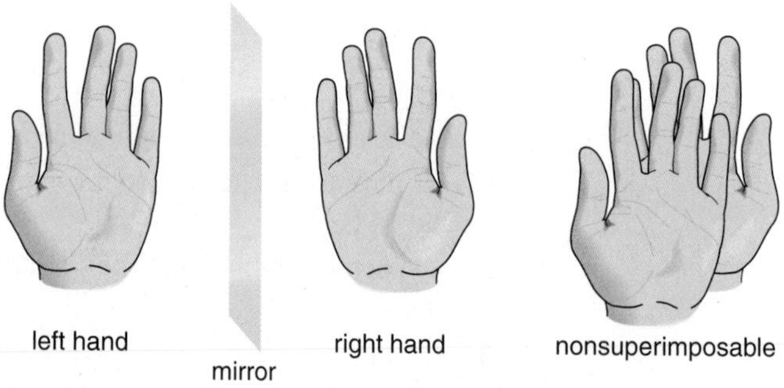

- A molecule (or object) that is *not* superimposable on its mirror image is said to be *chiral*.

Other molecules are like socks. **Two socks from a pair are mirror images that *are* superimposable.** One sock can fit inside another, aligning toes and heels, and tops and bottoms. A sock and its mirror image are *identical*.

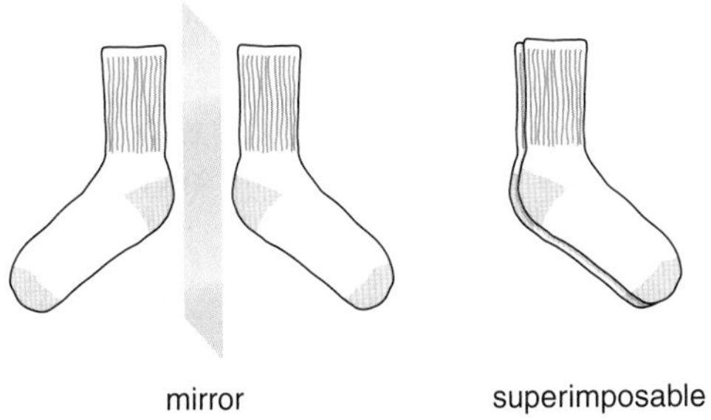

- A molecule (or object) that *is* superimposable on its mirror image is said to be *achiral.*

Let's determine whether three molecules—H_2O, CH_2BrCl, and CHBrClF—are superimposable on their mirror images; that is, **are H_2O, CH_2BrCl, and CHBrClF chiral or achiral?**

To test chirality:

- Draw the molecule in three dimensions.
- Draw its mirror image.
- Try to align all bonds and atoms. To superimpose a molecule and its mirror image you can perform any rotation but **you cannot break bonds.**

The adjective ***chiral*** comes from the Greek *cheir,* meaning "hand." Left and right hands are **chiral:** they are mirror images that do not superimpose on each other.

Few beginning students of organic chemistry can readily visualize whether a compound and its mirror image are superimposable by looking at drawings on a two-dimensional page. Molecular models can help a great deal in this process.

Following this procedure, H_2O and CH_2BrCl are both **achiral** molecules because each molecule is superimposable on its mirror image.

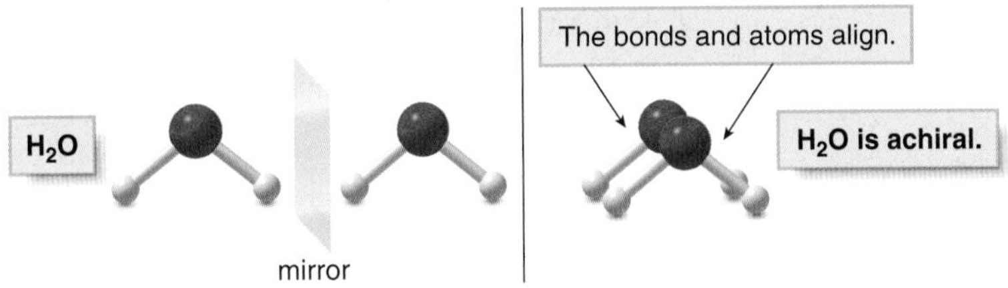

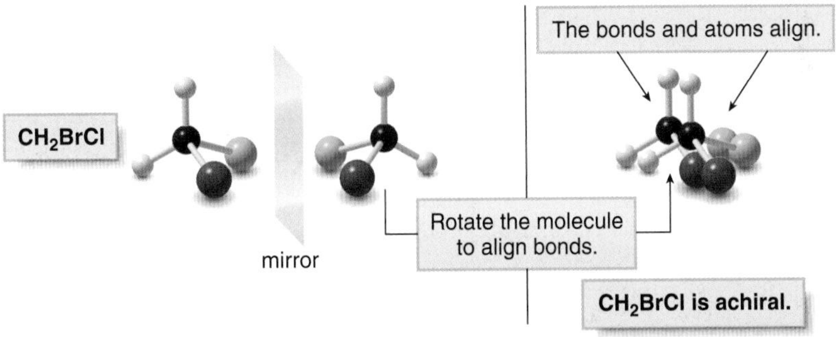

With CHBrClF, the result is different. The molecule (labeled **A**) and its mirror image (labeled **B**) are not superimposable. No matter how you rotate **A** and **B,** all the atoms never align. **CHBrClF is thus a chiral molecule,** and **A** and **B** are different compounds.

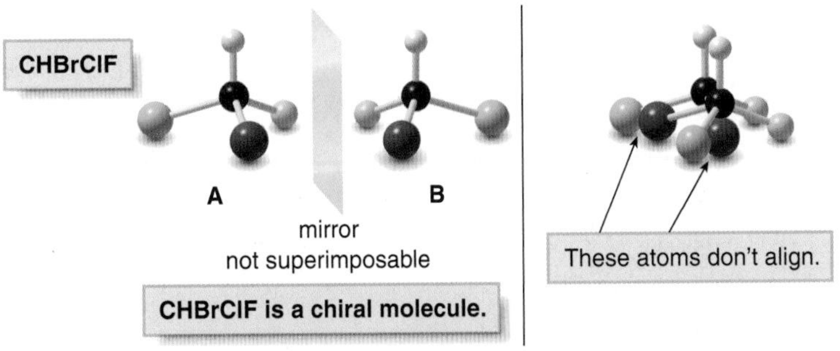

A and **B** are **stereoisomers** because they are isomers differing only in the three-dimensional arrangement of substituents. These stereoisomers are called **enantiomers.**

- ***Enantiomers* are mirror images that are not superimposable.**

CHBrClF contains a carbon atom bonded to four different groups. **A carbon atom bonded to four different groups is called a tetrahedral *stereogenic center.*** Most chiral molecules contain one or more stereogenic centers.

The general term *stereogenic center* refers to any site in a molecule at which the interchange of two groups forms a stereoisomer. A **carbon atom with four different groups is a *tetrahedral* stereogenic center,** because the interchange of two groups converts one enantiomer into another. We will learn about another type of stereogenic center in Section 8.2B.

Naming a carbon atom with four different groups is a topic that currently has no firm agreement among organic chemists. The IUPAC recommends the term *chirality center,* but the term has not gained wide acceptance among organic chemists since it was first suggested in 1996. Other terms in common use are chiral center, chiral carbon, asymmetric carbon, stereocenter, and stereogenic center, the term used in this text.

We have now learned two related but different concepts, and it is necessary to distinguish between them.

- **A molecule that is not superimposable on its mirror image is a *chiral molecule.***
- **A carbon atom bonded to four different groups is a *stereogenic center.***

Molecules can contain zero, one, or more stereogenic centers.

- **With no stereogenic centers, a molecule generally is not chiral.** H_2O and CH_2BrCl have *no* stereogenic centers and are *achiral* molecules. (There are a few exceptions to this generalization, as we will learn in Section 17.5.)
- **With one tetrahedral stereogenic center, a molecule is *always* chiral.** CHBrClF is a *chiral* molecule containing *one* stereogenic center.
- **With two or more stereogenic centers, a molecule *may* or *may not* be chiral,** as we will learn in Section 5.8.

Problem 5.3 Draw the mirror image of each compound. Label each molecule as chiral or achiral.

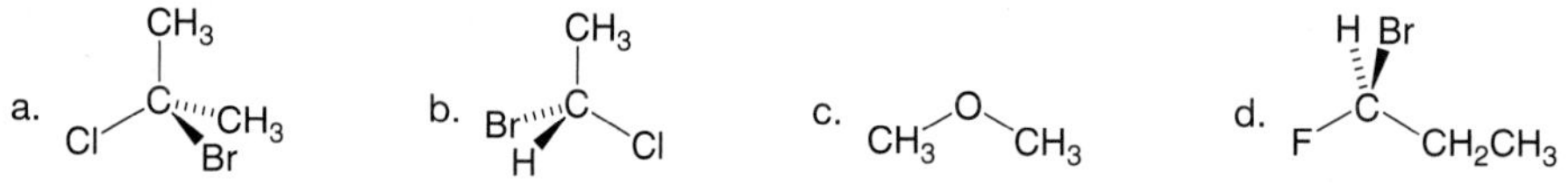
a.
b.
c.
d.

When trying to distinguish between chiral and achiral compounds, keep in mind the following:

- **A *plane of symmetry* is a mirror plane that cuts a molecule in half, so that one half of the molecule is a reflection of the other half.**

- **Achiral molecules usually contain a plane of symmetry but chiral molecules do not.**

The achiral molecule CH_2BrCl has a plane of symmetry, but the chiral molecule CHBrClF does not.

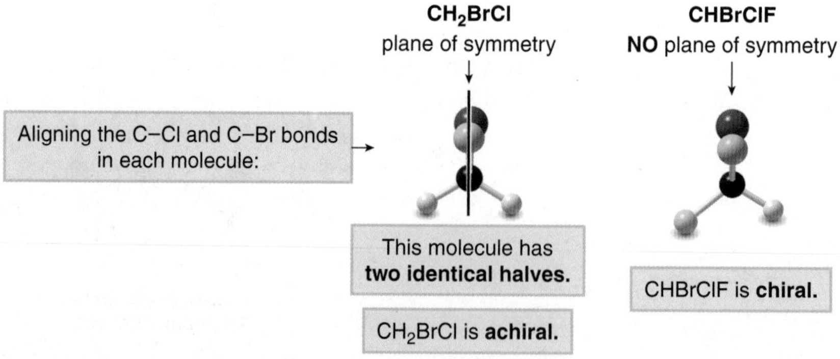
CH2BrCl
plane of symmetry
CHBrClF
NO plane of symmetry
Aligning the C–Cl and C–Br bonds in each molecule:
This molecule has two identical halves.
CH2BrCl is achiral.
CHBrClF is chiral.

Figure 5.4
Summary: The basic principles of chirality

- Everything has a mirror image. The fundamental question is whether a molecule and its mirror image are superimposable.
- If a molecule and its mirror image are *not* superimposable, the molecule and its mirror image are *chiral.*
- The terms *stereogenic center* and *chiral molecule* are related but distinct. In general, a chiral molecule must have one or more stereogenic centers.
- The presence of a *plane of symmetry* makes a molecule achiral.

Figure 5.4 summarizes the main facts about chirality we have learned thus far.

Problem 5.4 Draw in a plane of symmetry for each molecule.

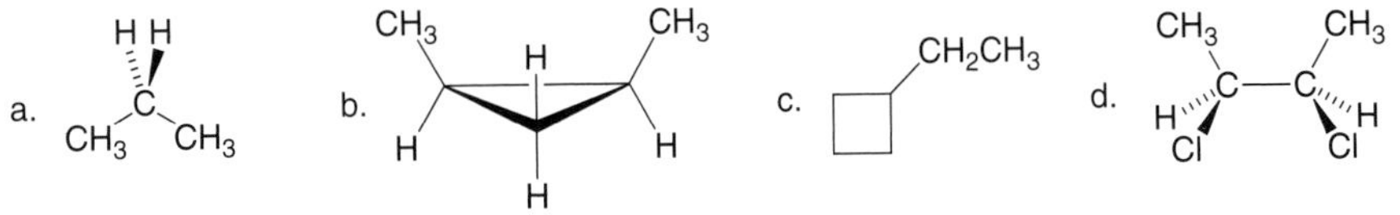

Problem 5.5 A molecule is achiral if it has a plane of symmetry in *any* conformation. The given conformation of 2,3-dibromobutane does not have a plane of symmetry, but rotation around the C2 – C3 bond forms a conformation that does have a plane of symmetry. Draw this conformation.

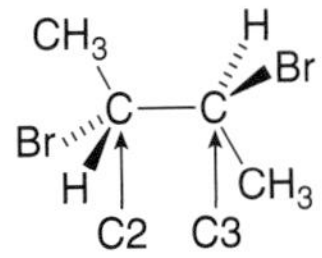

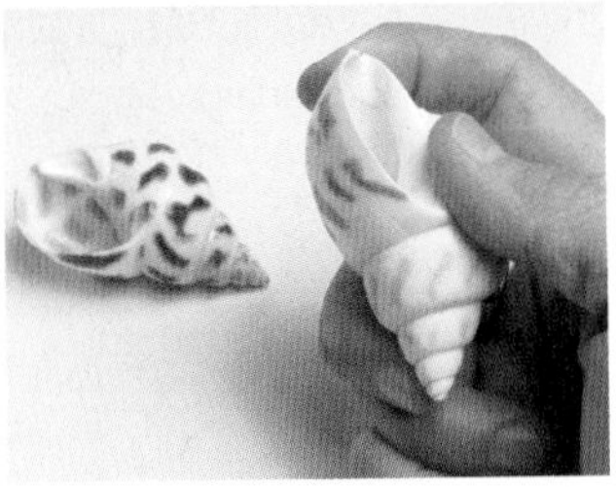

When a right-handed shell is held in the right hand with the thumb pointing towards the wider end, the opening is on the right side.

Stereochemistry may seem esoteric, but chirality pervades our very existence. On a molecular level, many biomolecules fundamental to life are chiral. On a macroscopic level, many naturally occurring objects possess handedness. Examples include chiral helical seashells shaped like right-handed screws, and plants such as honeysuckle that wind in a chiral left-handed helix. The human body is chiral, and hands, feet, and ears are not superimposable.

5.4 Stereogenic Centers

A necessary skill in the study of stereochemistry is the ability to locate and draw tetrahedral stereogenic centers.

5.4A Stereogenic Centers on Carbon Atoms That Are Not Part of a Ring

Recall from Section 5.3 that any carbon atom bonded to four different groups is a tetrahedral stereogenic center. To locate a stereogenic center, examine each *tetrahedral* carbon atom in a molecule, and look at the four ***groups***—not the four *atoms*—bonded to it. CBrClFI has one stereogenic center because its central carbon atom is bonded to four different elements. 3-Bromohexane also has one stereogenic center because one carbon is bonded to H, Br, CH_2CH_3, and $CH_2CH_2CH_3$. We consider all atoms in a group as a *whole unit,* not just the atom directly bonded to the carbon in question.

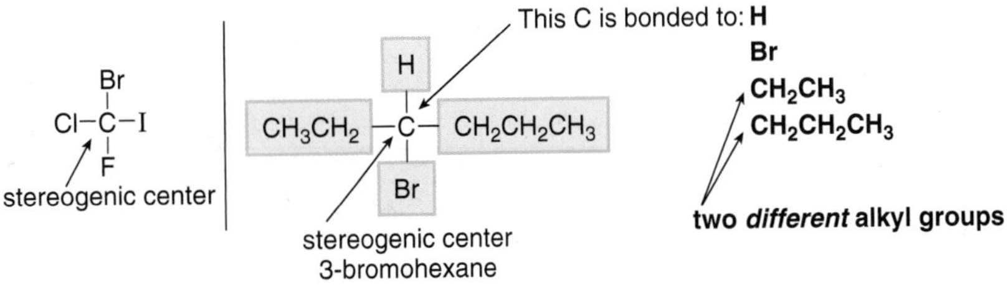

Ephedrine is isolated from ma huang, an herb used to treat respiratory ailments in traditional Chinese medicine. Once a popular drug to promote weight loss and enhance athletic performance, ephedrine has now been linked to episodes of sudden death, heart attack, and stroke.

Always omit from consideration all C atoms that can't be tetrahedral stereogenic centers. These include:

- CH_2 and CH_3 groups (more than one H bonded to C)
- any *sp* or sp^2 hybridized C (less than four groups around C)

Larger organic molecules can have two, three, or even hundreds of stereogenic centers. **Propoxyphene** and **ephedrine** each contain two stereogenic centers, and **fructose,** a simple carbohydrate, has three.

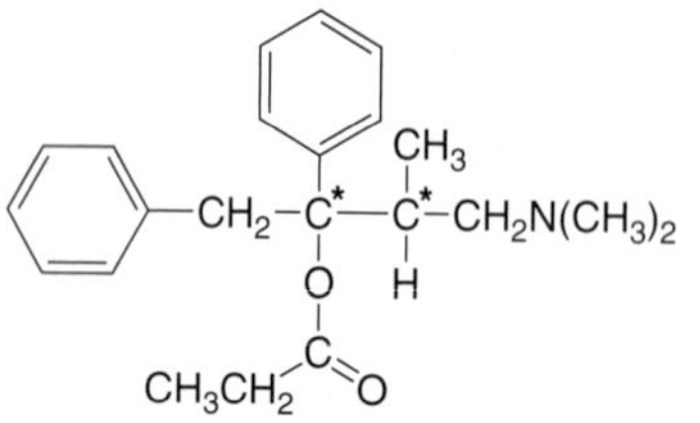

propoxyphene
Trade name: Darvon
(analgesic)

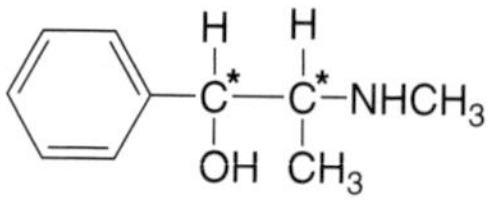

ephedrine
(bronchodilator, decongestant)

[* = stereogenic center]

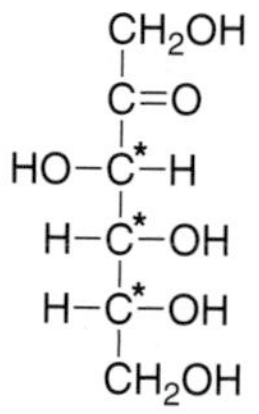

fructose
(a simple sugar)

Sample Problem 5.1 Locate the stereogenic center in each drug. Albuterol is a bronchodilator—that is, it widens airways—so it is used to treat asthma. Chloramphenicol is an antibiotic used extensively in developing countries because of its low cost.

a. 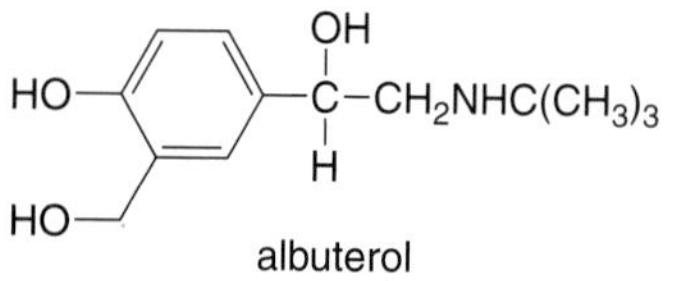

albuterol

b. 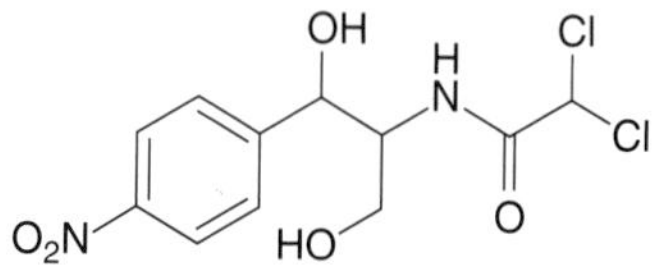

chloramphenicol

Solution

Omit all CH_2 and CH_3 groups and all doubly bonded (sp^2 hybridized) C's. In albuterol, one C has three CH_3 groups bonded to it, so it can be eliminated as well. When a molecule is drawn as a skeletal structure, draw in H atoms on tetrahedral C's to more clearly see the groups. This leaves one C in albuterol and two C's in chloramphenicol surrounded by four different groups, making them stereogenic centers.

Heteroatoms surrounded by four different groups are also stereogenic centers. Stereogenic N atoms are discussed in Chapter 25.

a. 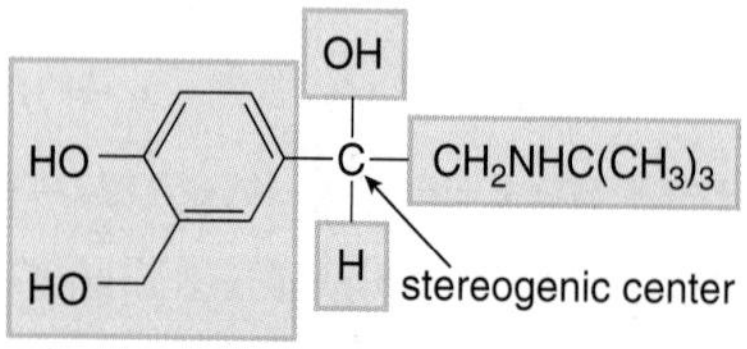

b. 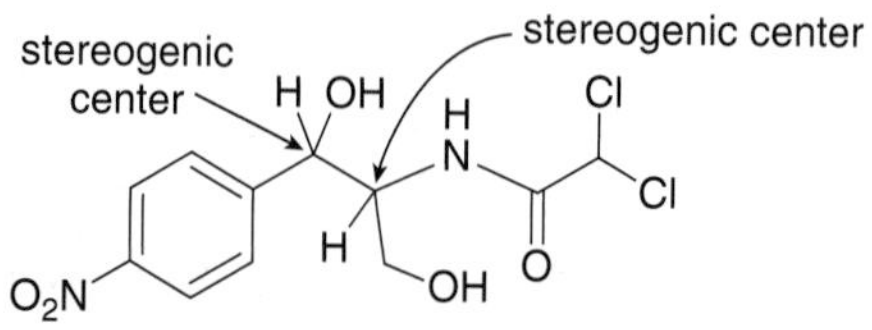

Problem 5.6 Locate the stereogenic centers in each molecule. Compounds may have zero, one, or more stereogenic centers.

a. $CH_3CH_2CH(Cl)CH_2CH_3$
b. $CH_3CH(OH)CH{=}CH_2$
c. $CH_3CH_2CH_2OH$
d. $(CH_3)_2CHCH_2CH_2CH(CH_3)CH_2CH_3$
e. $(CH_3)_2CHCH_2CH(NH_2)COOH$
f. 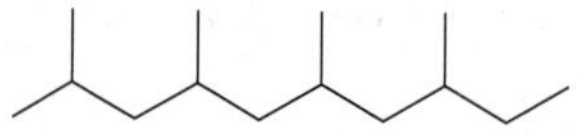

Problem 5.7 The facts in Section 5.4A can be used to locate stereogenic centers in any molecule, no matter how complicated. Always look for carbons surrounded by four different groups. With this in mind, locate the four stereogenic centers in aliskirin, a drug introduced in 2007 for the treatment of hypertension.

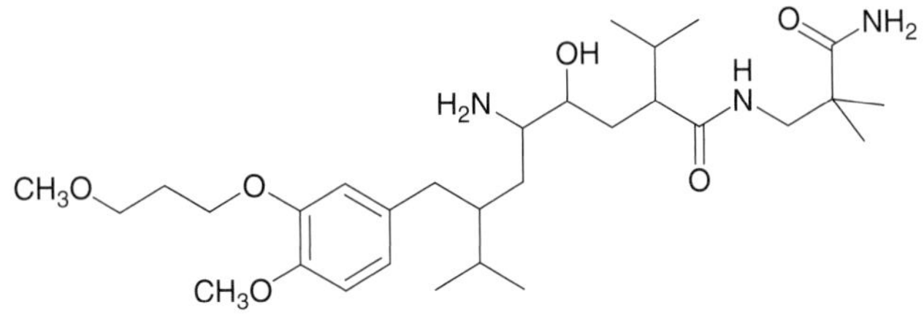

OH
O
NH2
H
N
H2N
O
CH3O
O
CH3O

aliskiren

5.4B Drawing a Pair of Enantiomers

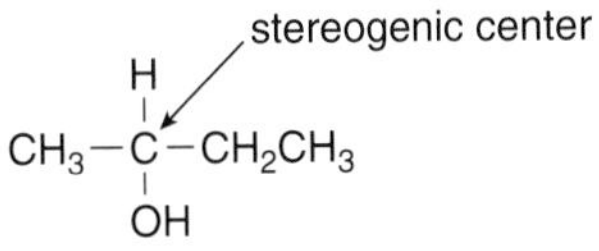

stereogenic center
H
CH3–C–CH2CH3
OH

2-butanol

- **Any molecule with one tetrahedral stereogenic center is a chiral compound and exists as a pair of enantiomers.**

2-Butanol, for example, has one stereogenic center. To draw both enantiomers, use the typical convention for depicting a tetrahedron: **place two bonds in the plane, one in front of the plane on a wedge, and one behind the plane on a dash.** Then, to form the first enantiomer **A,** arbitrarily place the four groups—H, OH, CH_3, and CH_2CH_3—on any bond to the stereogenic center.

In Section 28.2, we will learn about Fischer projection formulas, an older convention used for drawing stereogenic centers utilized mainly in carbohydrate chemistry.

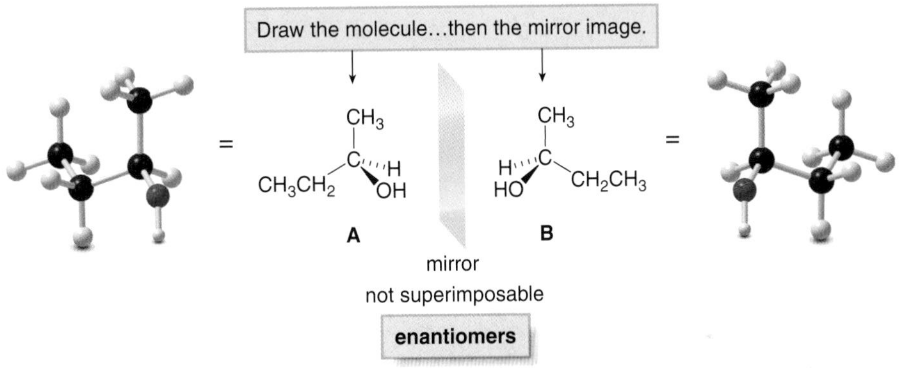

Draw the molecule…then the mirror image.
CH3
C
H
CH3CH2
OH
A
CH3
C
H
HO
CH2CH3
B
mirror
not superimposable
enantiomers

Then, draw a mirror plane and arrange the substituents in the mirror image so that they are a reflection of the groups in the first molecule, forming **B.** No matter how **A** and **B** are rotated, it is impossible to align all of their atoms. Because **A** and **B** are mirror images and not superimposable, **A** and **B** are a pair of **enantiomers.** Two other pairs of enantiomers are drawn in Figure 5.5.

Problem 5.8 Locate the stereogenic center in each compound and draw both enantiomers.

a. $CH_3CH(Cl)CH_2CH_3$ b. $CH_3CH_2CH(OH)CH_2OH$ c. $CH_3SCH_2CH_2CH(NH_2)COOH$

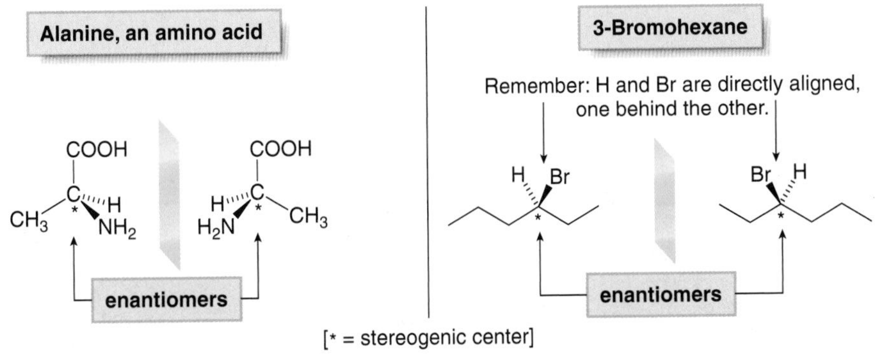

Alanine, an amino acid
COOH
C
H
CH3
NH2
COOH
C
H
CH3
H2N
enantiomers
3-Bromohexane
Remember: H and Br are directly aligned, one behind the other.
H Br
Br H
enantiomers
[* = stereogenic center]

Figure 5.5 Three-dimensional representations for pairs of enantiomers

5.5 Stereogenic Centers in Cyclic Compounds

In drawing a tetrahedron using solid lines, wedges, and dashes, always draw the two solid lines first; then draw the wedge and the dash on the *opposite side* of the solid lines.

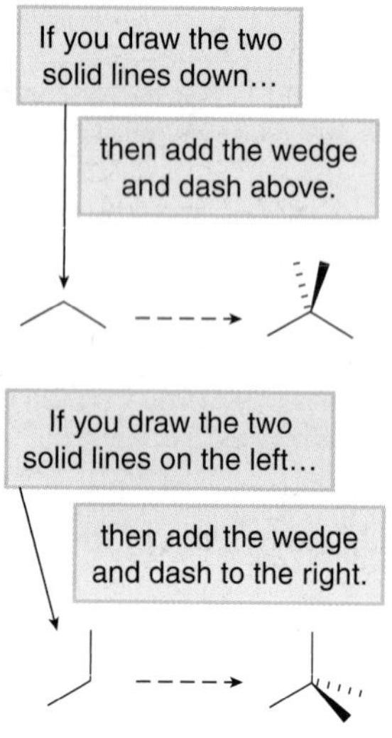
If you draw the two solid lines down...
then add the wedge and dash above.
If you draw the two solid lines on the left...
then add the wedge and dash to the right.

Stereogenic centers may also occur at carbon atoms that are part of a ring. To find stereogenic centers on ring carbons always draw the rings as flat polygons, and look for tetrahedral carbons that are bonded to four different groups, as usual. Each ring carbon is bonded to two other atoms in the ring, as well as two substituents attached to the ring. When the two substituents on the ring are *different,* we must compare the ring atoms equidistant from the atom in question.

Does methylcyclopentane have a stereogenic center? All of the carbon atoms are bonded to two or three hydrogen atoms except for C1, the ring carbon bonded to the methyl group. Next, compare the ring atoms and bonds on both sides equidistant from C1, and continue until a point of difference is reached, or until both sides meet, either at an atom or in the middle of a bond. In this case, there is no point of difference on either side, so C1 is bonded to identical alkyl groups that happen to be part of a ring. **C1, therefore, is *not* a stereogenic center.**

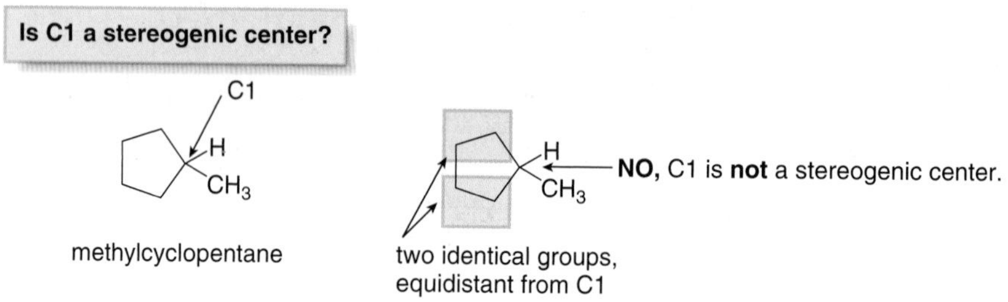
Is C1 a stereogenic center?
C1
H
CH3
methylcyclopentane
H
CH3
NO, C1 is not a stereogenic center.
two identical groups, equidistant from C1

With 3-methylcyclohexene, the result is different. All carbon atoms are bonded to two or three hydrogen atoms or are sp^2 hybridized except for C3, the ring carbon bonded to the methyl group. In this case, the atoms equidistant from C3 are different, so C3 is bonded to *different* alkyl groups in the ring. **C3 is therefore bonded to four different groups, making it a stereogenic center.**

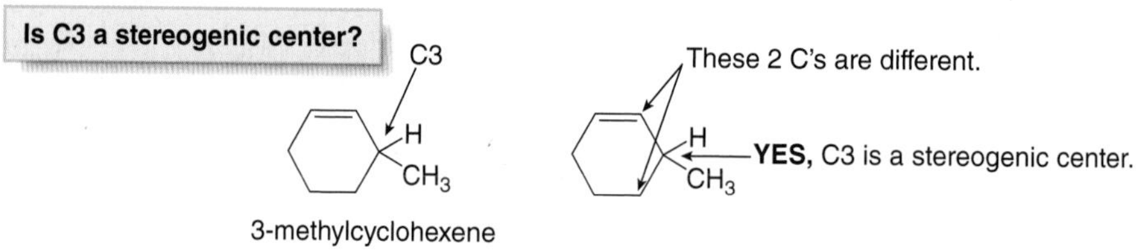
Is C3 a stereogenic center?
C3
H
CH3
3-methylcyclohexene
These 2 C's are different.
H
CH3
YES, C3 is a stereogenic center.

Two enantiomers are *different* compounds. To convert one enantiomer to another you must **switch the position of two atoms.** This amounts to breaking bonds.

Because 3-methylcyclohexene has one tetrahedral stereogenic center it is a chiral compound and exists as a pair of enantiomers.

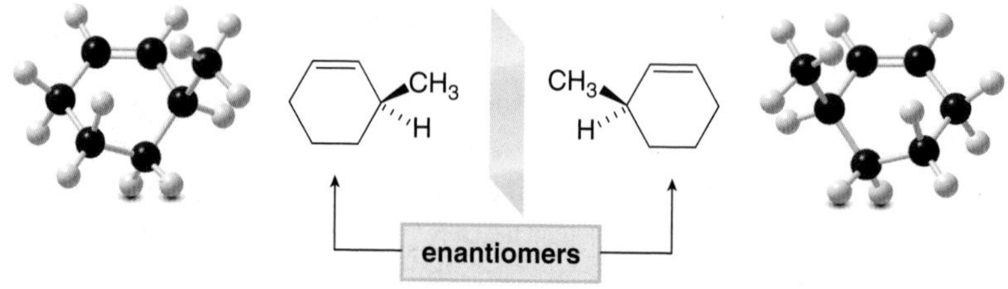
CH3
H
CH3
H
enantiomers

Many biologically active compounds contain one or more stereogenic centers on ring carbons. For example, **thalidomide,** the chapter-opening molecule, contains one such stereogenic center.

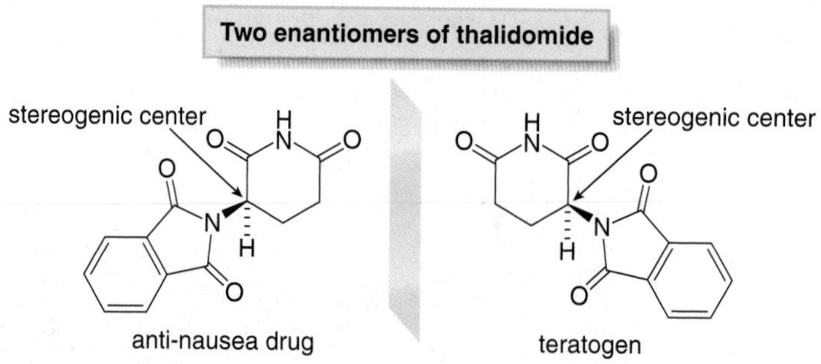
Two enantiomers of thalidomide
stereogenic center
stereogenic center
anti-nausea drug
teratogen

Initial studies with taxol were carried out with material isolated from the bark of the Pacific yew tree, but stripping the bark killed these magnificent trees. Taxol is now produced by a plant cell fermentation process.

Unfortunately thalidomide was sold as a mixture of its two enantiomers, and each of these stereoisomers has a different biological activity. This is a property not uncommon in chiral drugs, as we will see in Section 5.13. Although one enantiomer was an effective sedative and anti-nausea drug, the other enantiomer was responsible for thousands of catastrophic birth defects in children born to women who took the drug during pregnancy. Thalidomide was never approved for use in the United States due to the diligence of Frances Oldham Kelsey, a medical reviewing officer for the Food and Drug Administration, who insisted that the safety data on thalidomide were inadequate. Although it is a potent teratogen (a substance that causes fetal abnormalities), thalidomide exhibits several beneficial effects. It is now prescribed under strict control for the treatment of Hansen's disease (leprosy) and certain forms of cancer.

Sucrose and **taxol** are two useful molecules with several stereogenic centers at ring carbons. Identify the stereogenic centers in these more complicated compounds in exactly the same way, looking at one carbon at a time. **Sucrose,** with nine stereogenic centers on two rings, is the carbohydrate used as table sugar. **Taxol,** with 11 stereogenic centers, is an anticancer agent active against ovarian, breast, and some lung tumors.

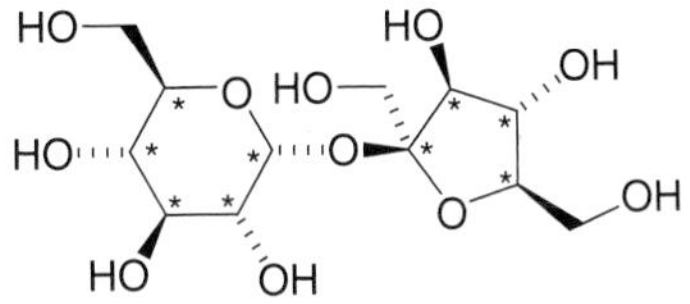

sucrose
(table sugar)

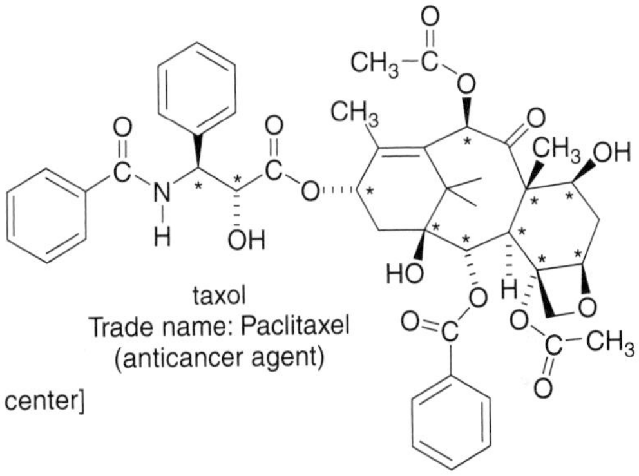

taxol
Trade name: Paclitaxel
(anticancer agent)

[* = stereogenic center]

Problem 5.9 Locate the stereogenic centers in each compound. A molecule may have zero, one, or more stereogenic centers. Gabapentin [part (d)] is used clinically to treat seizures and certain types of chronic pain. Gabapentin enacarbil [part (e)] is a related compound that is three times more potent.

a. 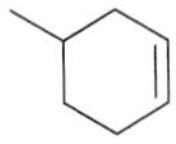

c. 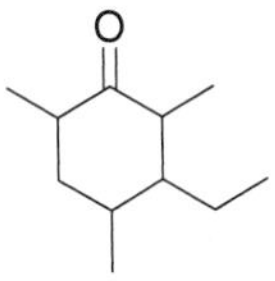

e. 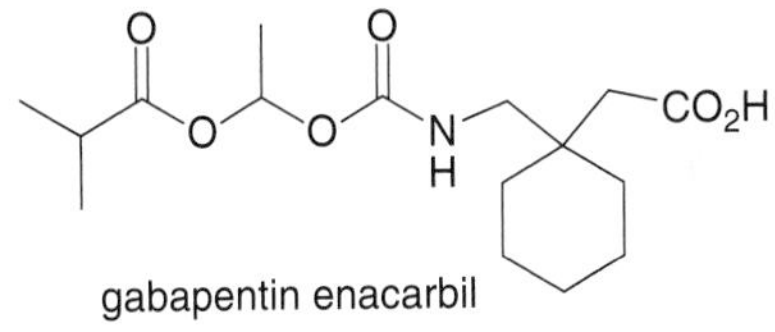

gabapentin enacarbil

b. 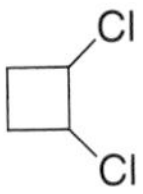

d. 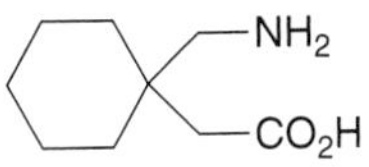

gabapentin

Problem 5.10 Locate the stereogenic centers in each compound.

a. 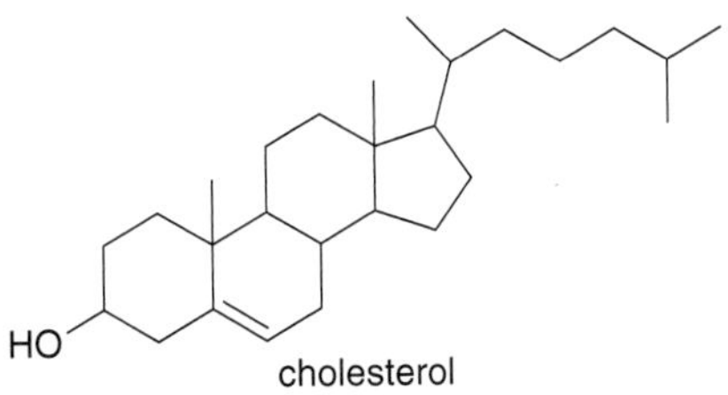

cholesterol

b. 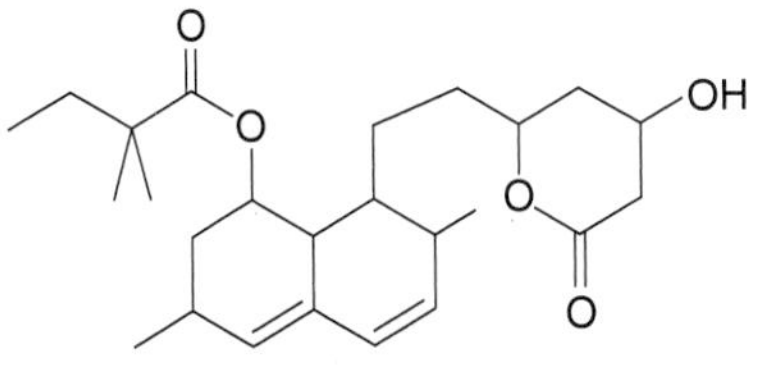

simvastatin
Trade name: Zocor
(cholesterol-lowering drug)

5.6 Labeling Stereogenic Centers with *R* or *S*

Naming enantiomers with the prefixes *R* or *S* is called the Cahn–Ingold–Prelog system after the three chemists who devised it.

Because enantiomers are two different compounds, we need to distinguish them by name. This is done by adding the prefix *R* or *S* to the IUPAC name of the enantiomer. To designate an enantiomer as *R* or *S*, first **assign a priority** (1, 2, 3, or 4) to each group bonded to the stereogenic center, and then use these priorities to label one enantiomer *R* and one *S*.

Rules Needed to Assign Priority

Rule 1 **Assign priorities (1, 2, 3, or 4) to the atoms directly bonded to the stereogenic center in order of decreasing atomic number. The atom of *highest* atomic number gets the *highest* priority (1).**

- In CHBrClF, priorities are assigned as follows: Br (1, highest) → Cl (2) → F (3) → H (4, lowest). In many molecules the lowest priority group will be H.

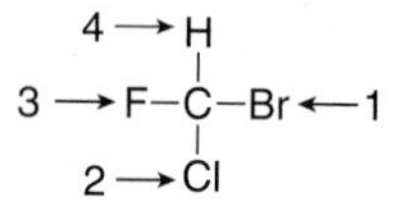

Rule 2 **If two atoms on a stereogenic center are the *same,* assign priority based on the atomic number of the atoms bonded to these atoms. *One* atom of higher atomic number determines a higher priority.**

- With 2-butanol, the O atom gets highest priority (1) and H gets lowest priority (4) using Rule 1. To assign priority (either 2 or 3) to the two C atoms, look at what atoms (other than the stereogenic center) are bonded to each C.

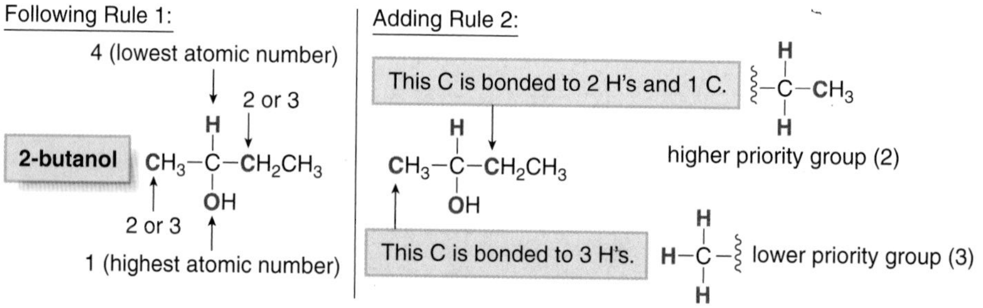

- The order of priority of groups in 2-butanol is: –OH **(1)**, $-CH_2CH_3$ **(2)**, $-CH_3$ **(3)**, and –H **(4)**.
- If priority still cannot be assigned, continue along a chain until a point of difference is reached.

Rule 3 **If two isotopes are bonded to the stereogenic center, assign priorities in order of decreasing *mass* number.**

- In comparing the three isotopes of hydrogen, the order of priorities is:

	Mass number	Priority
T (tritium)	3 (1 proton + 2 neutrons)	1
D (deuterium)	2 (1 proton + 1 neutron)	2
H (hydrogen)	1 (1 proton)	3

Rule 4 **To assign a priority to an atom that is part of a multiple bond, treat a multiply bonded atom as an equivalent number of singly bonded atoms.**

- For example, the C of a C=O is considered to be bonded to two O atoms.

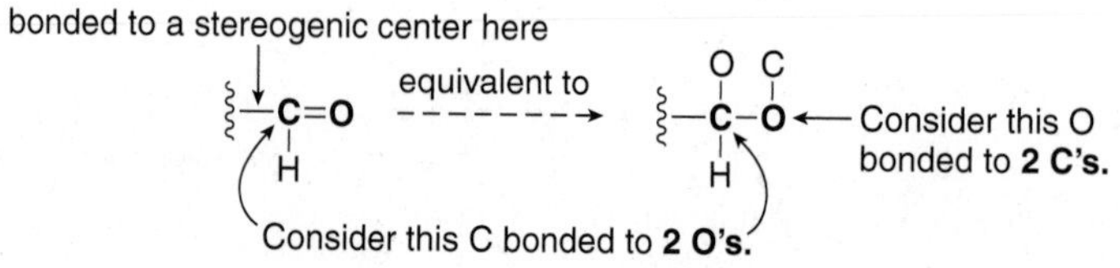

- Other common multiple bonds are drawn below.

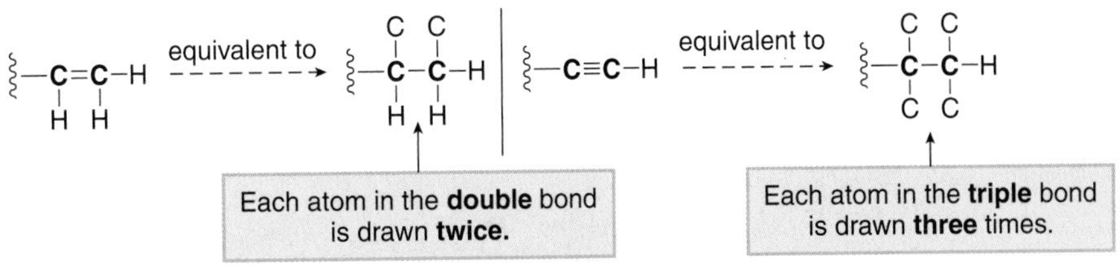

Figure 5.6 gives examples of priorities assigned to stereogenic centers.

Figure 5.6
Examples of assigning priorities to stereogenic centers

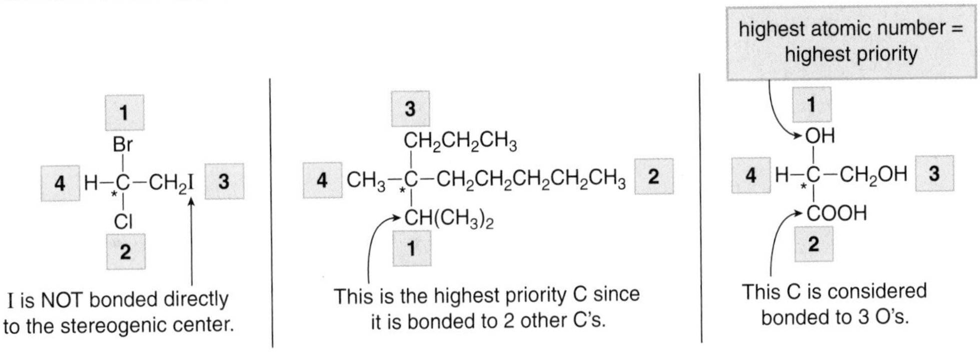

[* = stereogenic center]

Problem 5.11 Which group in each pair is assigned the *higher* priority?

a. $-CH_3$, $-CH_2CH_3$
b. $-I$, $-Br$
c. $-H$, $-D$
d. $-CH_2Br$, $-CH_2CH_2Br$
e. $-CH_2CH_2Cl$, $-CH_2CH(CH_3)_2$
f. $-CH_2OH$, $-CHO$

Problem 5.12 Rank the following groups in order of *decreasing* priority.

a. $-COOH$, $-H$, $-NH_2$, $-OH$
b. $-H$, $-CH_3$, $-Cl$, $-CH_2Cl$
c. $-CH_2CH_3$, $-CH_3$, $-H$, $-CH(CH_3)_2$
d. $-CH{=}CH_2$, $-CH_3$, $-C{\equiv}CH$, $-H$

R is derived from the Latin word *rectus* meaning "right" and *S* is from the Latin word *sinister* meaning "left."

Once priorities are assigned to the four groups around a stereogenic center, we can use three steps to designate the center as either *R* or *S*.

How To Assign *R* or *S* to a Stereogenic Center

Example Label each enantiomer as *R* or *S*.

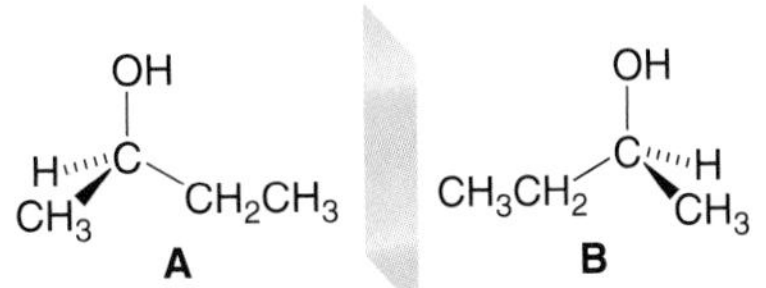

two enantiomers of 2-butanol

Step [1] **Assign priorities from 1 to 4 to each group bonded to the stereogenic center.**

- The priorities for the four groups around the stereogenic center in 2-butanol were given in Rule 2, on page 178.

$-OH$	$-CH_2CH_3$	$-CH_3$	$-H$
1	2	3	4
highest			lowest

Decreasing priority →

—Continued

How To, continued . . .

Step [2] Orient the molecule with the lowest priority group (4) *back* (on a *dash*), and visualize the relative positions of the remaining three groups (priorities 1, 2, and 3).

- For each enantiomer of 2-butanol, look toward the lowest priority group, drawn behind the plane, down the C–H bond.

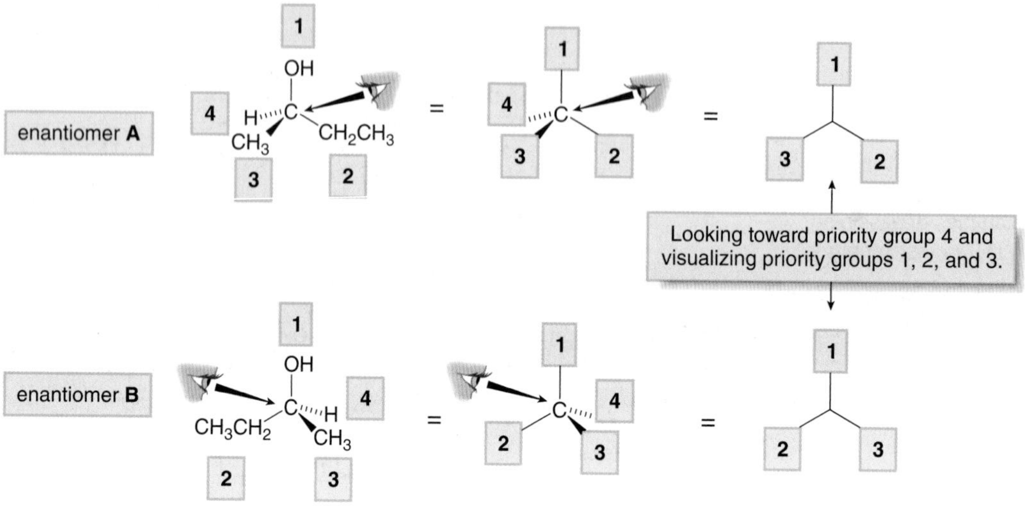

enantiomer A
1
OH
4
H
C
CH_3
CH_2CH_3
3
2
=
Looking toward priority group 4 and visualizing priority groups 1, 2, and 3.
enantiomer B
CH_3CH_2
H
CH_3

Step [3] Trace a circle from priority group 1 → 2 → 3.

- If tracing the circle goes in the **clockwise** direction—to the right from the noon position—the isomer is named ***R*.**
- If tracing the circle goes in the **counterclockwise** direction—to the left from the noon position—the isomer is named ***S*.**

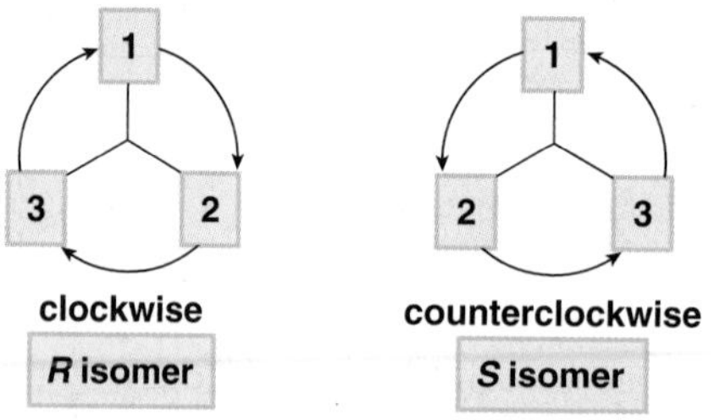

1
3
2
clockwise
R isomer
counterclockwise
S isomer

- The letters *R* or *S* precede the IUPAC name of the molecule. For the enantiomers of 2-butanol:

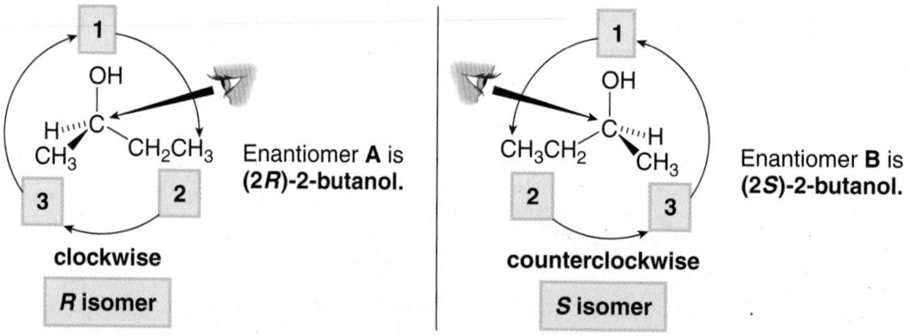

OH
H
C
CH_3
CH_2CH_3
Enantiomer **A** is **(2*R*)-2-butanol.**
clockwise
R isomer
CH_3CH_2
Enantiomer **B** is **(2*S*)-2-butanol.**
counterclockwise
S isomer

Sample Problem 5.2 Label the following compound as *R* or *S*.

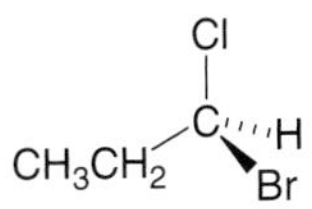
Cl
C
H
CH_3CH_2
Br

Solution

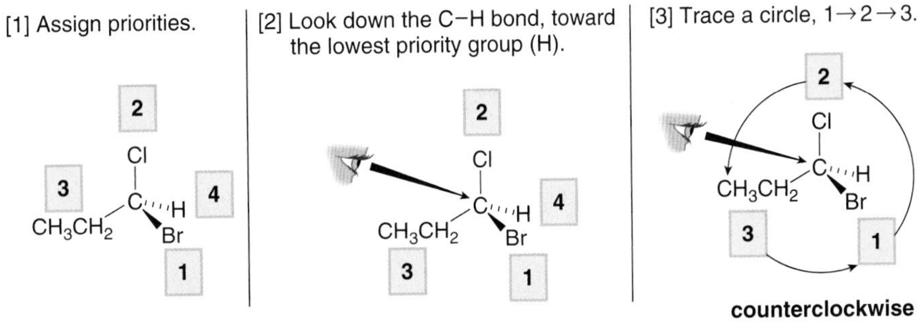
[1] Assign priorities.
[2] Look down the C–H bond, toward the lowest priority group (H).
[3] Trace a circle, 1→2→3.
2
Cl
3
C
H
4
CH_3CH_2
Br
1
counterclockwise

Answer: ***S*** isomer

How do you assign *R* or *S* to a molecule when the lowest priority group is not oriented toward the back, on a dashed line? You could rotate and flip the molecule until the lowest priority group is in the back, as shown in Figure 5.7; then follow the stepwise procedure for assigning the configuration. Or, if manipulating and visualizing molecules in three dimensions is difficult for you, try the procedure suggested in Sample Problem 5.3.

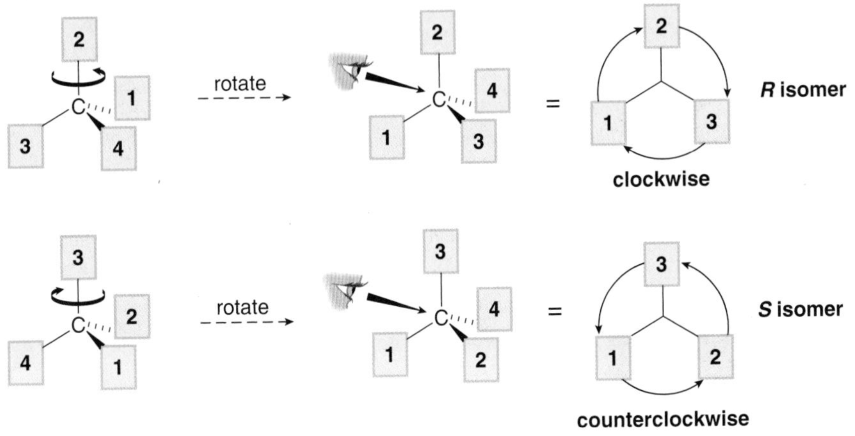
rotate
clockwise
R isomer
rotate
counterclockwise
S isomer

Figure 5.7 Examples: Orienting the lowest priority group in back

Sample Problem 5.3 Label the following compound as *R* or *S*.

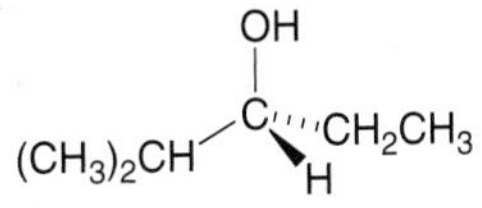
OH
C
CH_2CH_3
$(CH_3)_2CH$
H

Solution

In this problem, the lowest priority group (H) is oriented in **front** of, not behind, the page. To assign *R* or *S* in this case:

- **Switch** the position of the lowest priority group (H) with the group located behind the page ($-CH_2CH_3$).
- Determine *R* or *S* in the usual manner.

- **Reverse the answer.** Because we switched the position of two groups on the stereogenic center to begin with, and there are only two possibilities, the answer is **opposite** to the correct answer.

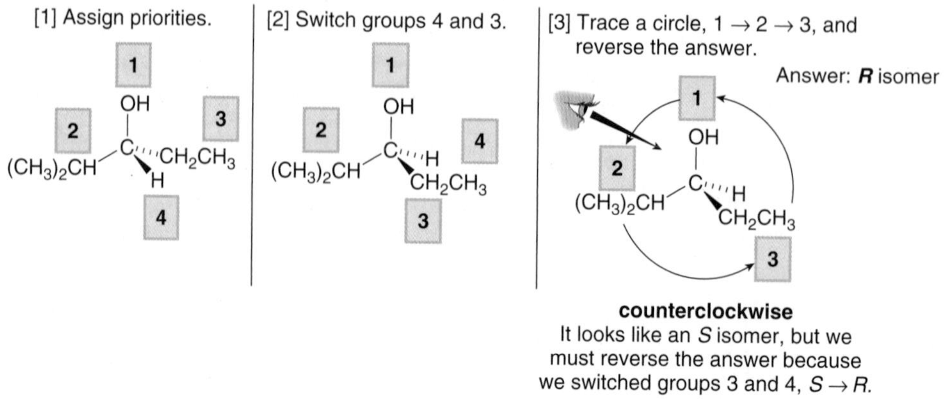

[1] Assign priorities.
[2] Switch groups 4 and 3.
[3] Trace a circle, 1 → 2 → 3, and reverse the answer.
Answer: ***R*** isomer
counterclockwise
It looks like an *S* isomer, but we must reverse the answer because we switched groups 3 and 4, *S* → *R*.

Problem 5.13 Label each compound as *R* or *S*.

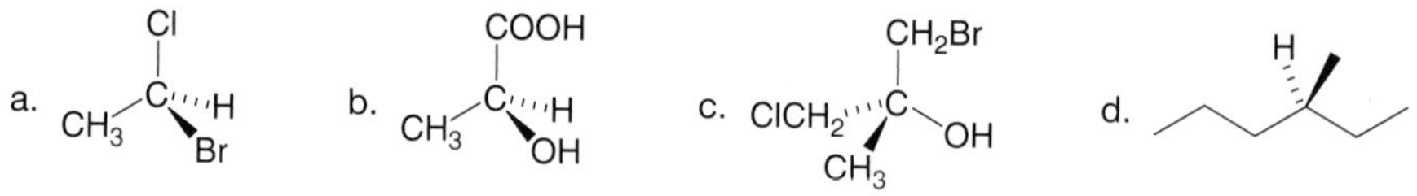

Problem 5.14 Draw both enantiomers of clopidogrel (trade name Plavix), a drug given to prevent the formation of blood clots in persons who have a history of stroke or coronary artery disease. Plavix is sold as a single enantiomer with the *S* configuration. Which enantiomer is Plavix?

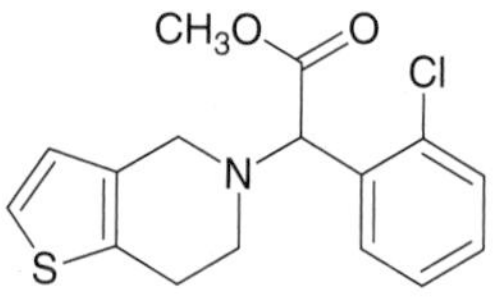

clopidogrel

Problem 5.15 (a) Locate the stereogenic centers in the ball-and-stick model of lisinopril, a drug used to treat high blood pressure. (b) Label each stereogenic center as *R* or *S*.

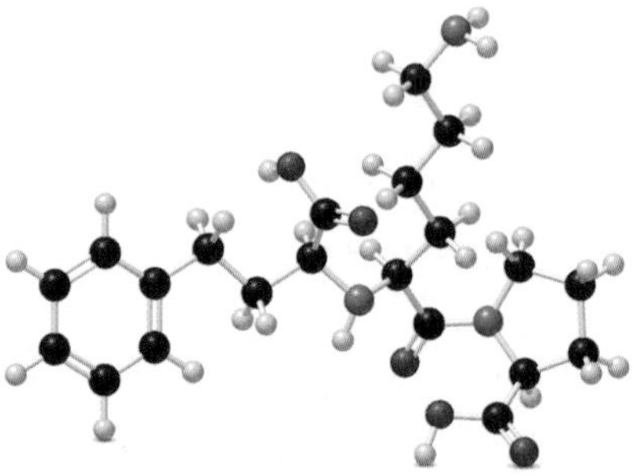

lisinopril

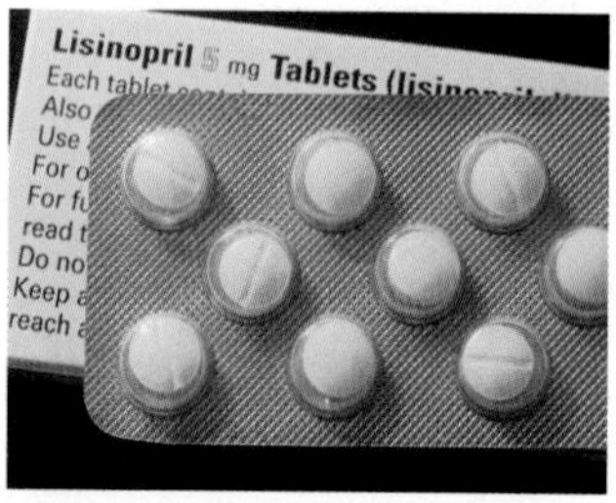

Lisinopril 5 mg Tablets

Lisinopril (trade name Zestril) is an ACE inhibitor, a drug that lowers blood pressure by decreasing the amount of angiotensin in the blood. Angiotensin is a polyamide that narrows blood vessels, thus increasing blood pressure.

5.7 Diastereomers

We have now seen many examples of compounds containing one tetrahedral stereogenic center. The situation is more complex for compounds with two stereogenic centers, because more stereoisomers are possible. Moreover, a molecule with two or more stereogenic centers ***may* or *may not* be chiral.**

- **For *n* stereogenic centers, the maximum number of stereoisomers is 2^n.**

- When ***n* = 1, 2^1 = 2.** With one stereogenic center there are always two stereoisomers and they are **enantiomers.**
- When ***n* = 2, 2^2 = 4.** With two stereogenic centers, the maximum number of stereoisomers is four, although sometimes there are *fewer* than four.

Problem 5.16 What is the maximum number of stereoisomers possible for a compound with: (a) three stereogenic centers; (b) eight stereogenic centers?

Let's illustrate a stepwise procedure for finding all possible stereoisomers using 2,3-dibromopentane.

In testing to see if one compound is superimposable on another, rotate atoms and flip the entire molecule, but **do not break any bonds.**

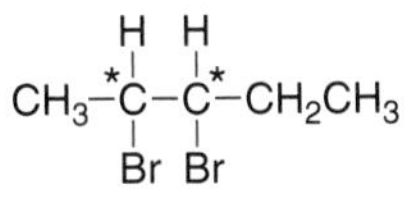

2,3-dibromopentane
[* = stereogenic center]
maximum number of stereoisomers = **4**

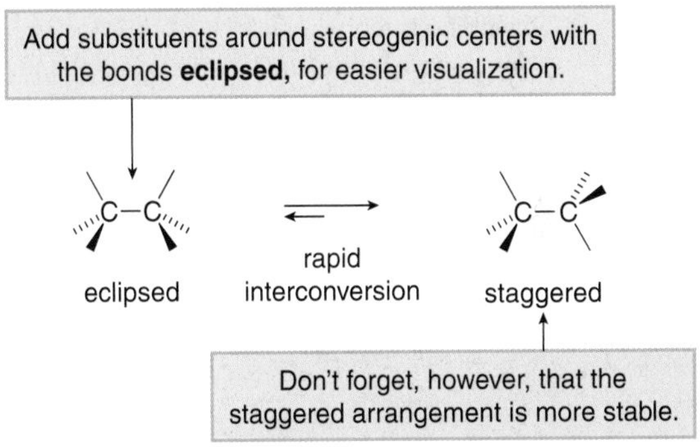
Add substituents around stereogenic centers with the bonds **eclipsed,** for easier visualization.
eclipsed
rapid interconversion
staggered
Don't forget, however, that the staggered arrangement is more stable.

How To Find and Draw All Possible Stereoisomers for a Compound with Two Stereogenic Centers

Step [1] **Draw one stereoisomer by arbitrarily arranging substituents around the stereogenic centers. Then draw its mirror image.**

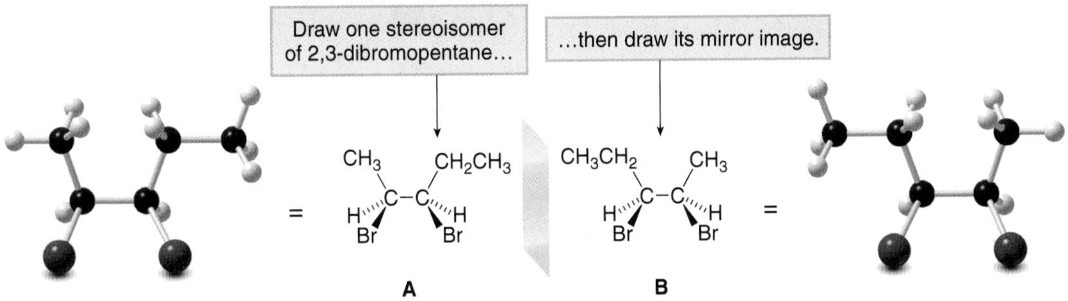
Draw one stereoisomer of 2,3-dibromopentane...
...then draw its mirror image.
A
B

- Arbitrarily add the H, Br, CH_3, and CH_2CH_3 groups to the stereogenic centers, forming **A.** Then draw the mirror image **B** so that substituents in **B** are a reflection of the substituents in **A.**
- Determine whether **A** and **B** are superimposable by flipping or rotating one molecule to see if all the atoms align.

—Continued

How To, continued . . .

- If you have drawn the compound and the mirror image in the described manner, you only have to do two operations to see if the atoms align. Place **B** directly on top of **A** (either in your mind or use models); and, rotate **B** 180° and place it on top of **A** to see if the atoms align.

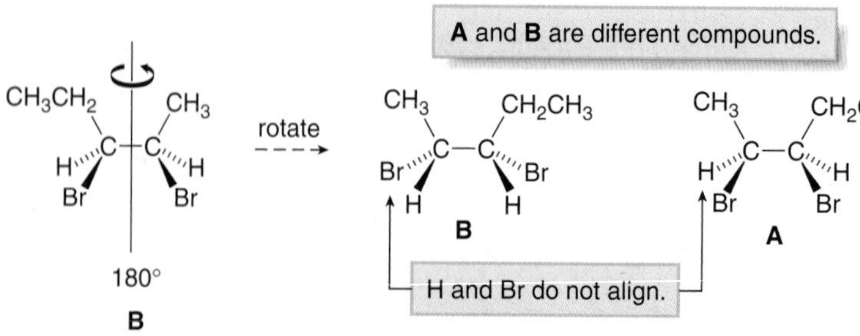
A and B are different compounds.
rotate
180°
B
B
A
H and Br do not align.

- In this case, the atoms of **A** and **B** do not align, making **A** and **B** nonsuperimposable mirror images—**enantiomers. A** and **B** are two of the four possible stereoisomers for 2,3-dibromopentane.

Step [2] **Draw a third possible stereoisomer by switching the positions of any two groups on *one* stereogenic center only. Then draw its mirror image.**

- Switching the positions of H and Br (or any two groups) on one stereogenic center of either **A** or **B** forms a new stereoisomer (labeled **C** in this example), which is different from both **A** and **B.** Then draw the mirror image of **C,** labeled **D. C** and **D** are nonsuperimposable mirror images—**enantiomers.** We have now drawn four stereoisomers for 2,3-dibromopentane, the maximum number possible.

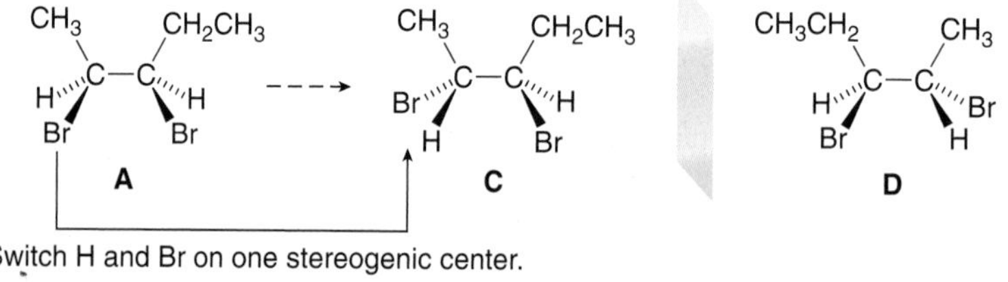
A
C
D
Switch H and Br on one stereogenic center.

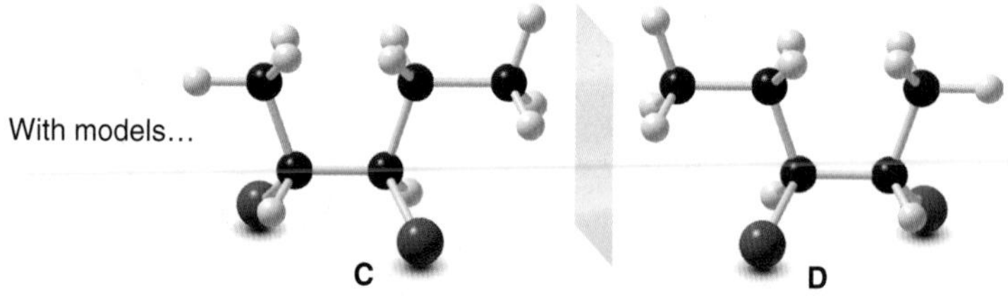
With models...
C
D

There are only two types of stereoisomers: ***Enantiomers* are stereoisomers that *are* mirror images. *Diastereomers* are stereoisomers that are *not* mirror images.**

There are four stereoisomers for 2,3-dibromopentane: enantiomers **A** and **B,** and enantiomers **C** and **D.** What is the relationship between two stereoisomers like **A** and **C? A** and **C** represent the second broad class of stereoisomers, called **diastereomers.** ***Diastereomers* are stereoisomers that are not mirror images of each other.** **A** and **B** are diastereomers of **C** and **D,** and vice versa. Figure 5.8 summarizes the relationships between the stereoisomers of 2,3-dibromopentane.

Problem 5.17 Label the two stereogenic centers in each compound and draw all possible stereoisomers: (a) $CH_3CH_2CH(Cl)CH(OH)CH_2CH_3$; (b) $CH_3CH(Br)CH_2CH(Cl)CH_3$.

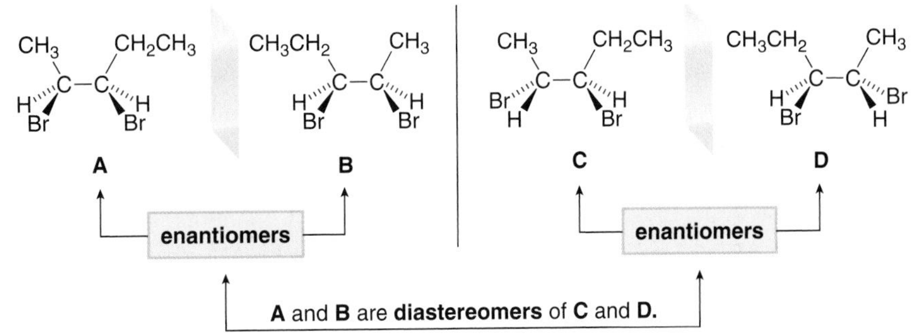

Figure 5.8
Summary: The four stereoisomers of 2,3-dibromopentane

- Pairs of enantiomers: **A** and **B; C** and **D.**
- Pairs of diastereomers: **A** and **C; A** and **D; B** and **C; B** and **D.**

5.8 Meso Compounds

Whereas 2,3-dibromopentane has two stereogenic centers and the maximum of four stereoisomers, **2,3-dibromobutane** has two stereogenic centers but fewer than the maximum number of stereoisomers.

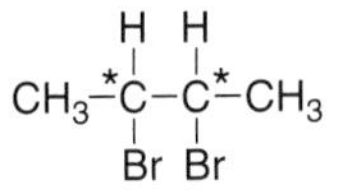

2,3-dibromobutane
[* = stereogenic center]

With two stereogenic centers, the **maximum** number of stereoisomers = **4.**

To find and draw all the stereoisomers of 2,3-dibromobutane, follow the same stepwise procedure outlined in Section 5.7. Arbitrarily add the H, Br, and CH_3 groups to the stereogenic centers, forming one stereoisomer **A,** and then draw its mirror image **B. A** and **B** are nonsuperimposable mirror images—**enantiomers.**

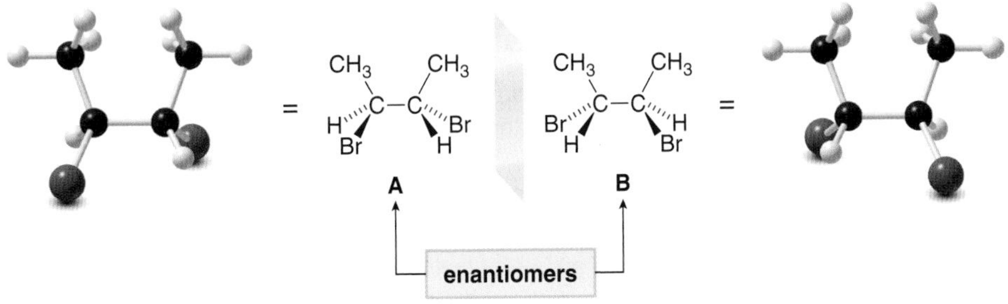

To find the other two stereoisomers (if they exist), switch the position of two groups on *one* stereogenic center of *one* enantiomer only. In this case, switching the positions of H and Br on one stereogenic center of **A** forms **C,** which is different from both **A** and **B** and is thus a new stereoisomer.

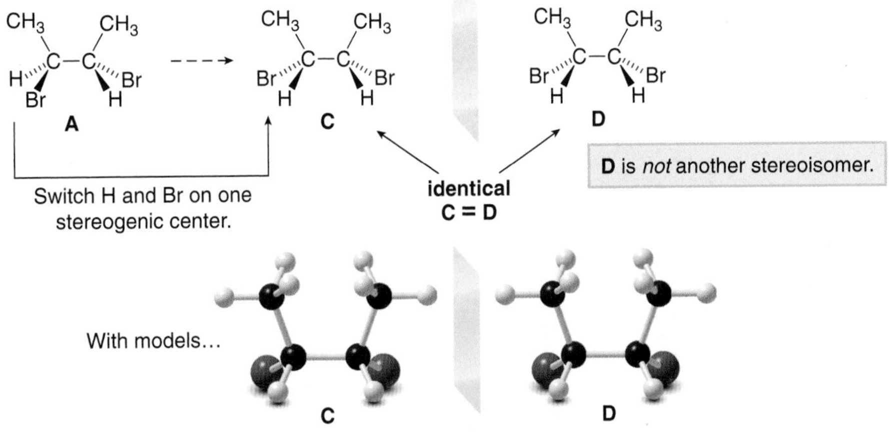

However, the mirror image of **C,** labeled **D,** is superimposable on **C,** so **C** and **D** are identical. Thus, **C** is achiral, even though it has two stereogenic centers. **C** is a **meso compound.**

- A *meso compound* is an achiral compound that contains tetrahedral stereogenic centers.

C contains a **plane of symmetry. Meso compounds generally have a plane of symmetry,** so they possess two identical halves.

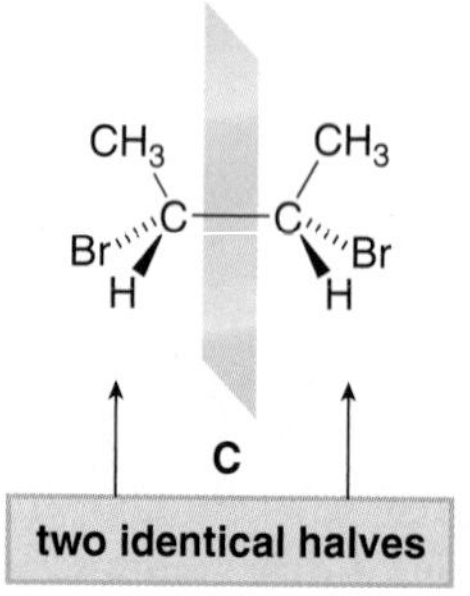
plane of symmetry
C
two identical halves

Because one stereoisomer of 2,3-dibromobutane is superimposable on its mirror image, there are only three stereoisomers and not four, as summarized in Figure 5.9.

Figure 5.9
Summary: The three stereoisomers of 2,3-dibromobutane

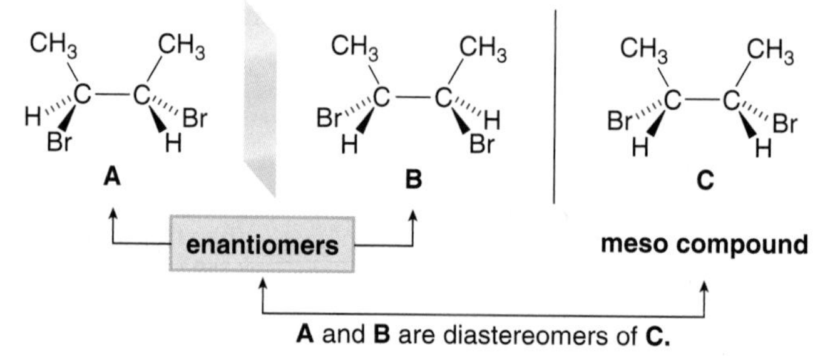
A
B
C
enantiomers
meso compound
A and B are diastereomers of C.

- Pair of enantiomers: **A** and **B.**
- Pairs of diastereomers: **A** and **C; B** and **C.**

Problem 5.18 Draw all the possible stereoisomers for each compound and label pairs of enantiomers and diastereomers: (a) $CH_3CH(OH)CH(OH)CH_3$; (b) $CH_3CH(OH)CH(Cl)CH_3$.

Problem 5.19 Which compounds are meso compounds?

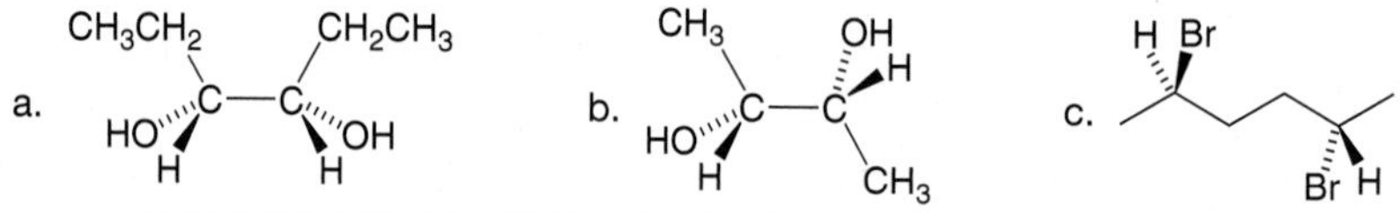

Problem 5.20 Draw a meso compound for each of the following molecules.

a. $BrCH_2CH_2CH(Cl)CH(Cl)CH_2CH_2Br$ b. 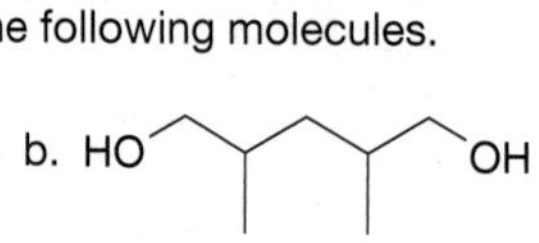 c. 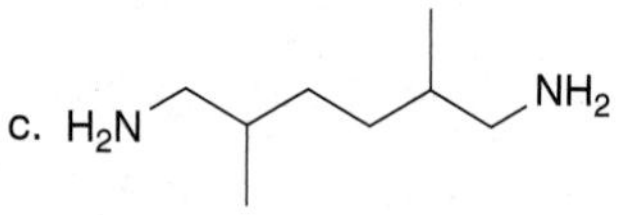

5.9 *R* and *S* Assignments in Compounds with Two or More Stereogenic Centers

When a compound has more than one stereogenic center, the *R* or *S* configuration must be assigned to each of them. In the stereoisomer of 2,3-dibromopentane drawn here, C2 has the *S* configuration and C3 has the *R*, so the complete name of the compound is (2*S*,3*R*)-2,3-dibromopentane.

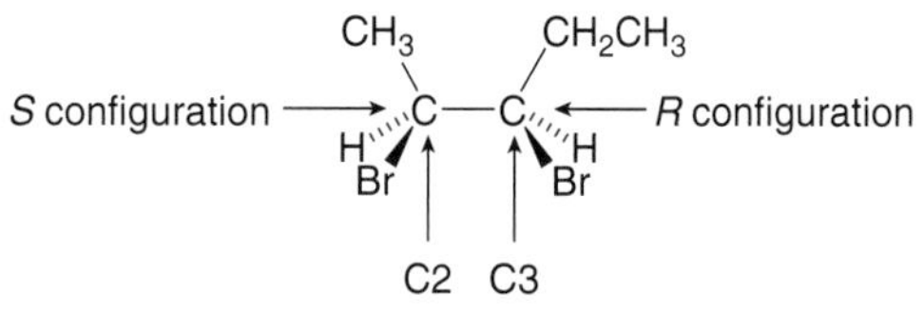

Complete name:
(2*S*,3*R*)-2,3-dibromopentane

one stereoisomer of 2,3-dibromopentane

R,S configurations can be used to determine whether two compounds are identical, enantiomers, or diastereomers.

- **Identical compounds have the *same R,S* designations at every tetrahedral stereogenic center.**
- **Enantiomers have exactly *opposite R,S* designations.**
- **Diastereomers have the *same R,S* designation for at least one stereogenic center and the *opposite* for at least one of the other stereogenic centers.**

For example, if a compound has two stereogenic centers, both with the *R* configuration, then its enantiomer is *S,S* and the diastereomers are either *R,S* or *S,R*.

Problem 5.21 If the two stereogenic centers of a compound are *R,S* in configuration, what are the *R,S* assignments for its enantiomer and two diastereomers?

Problem 5.22 Without drawing out the structures, label each pair of compounds as enantiomers or diastereomers.

a. (2*R*,3*S*)-2,3-hexanediol and (2*R*,3*R*)-2,3-hexanediol
b. (2*R*,3*R*)-2,3-hexanediol and (2*S*,3*S*)-2,3-hexanediol
c. (2*R*,3*S*,4*R*)-2,3,4-hexanetriol and (2*S*,3*R*,4*R*)-2,3,4-hexanetriol

Problem 5.23 (a) Label the four stereogenic centers in sorbitol as *R* or *S*. (b) How are sorbitol and **A** related? (c) How are sorbitol and **B** related?

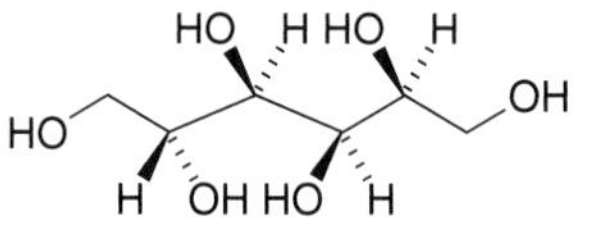
sorbitol

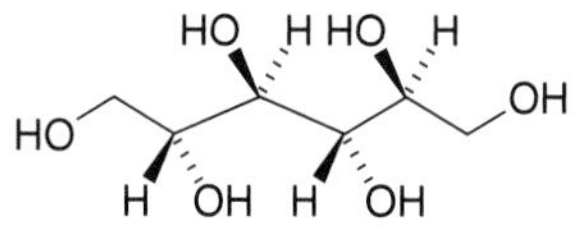
A

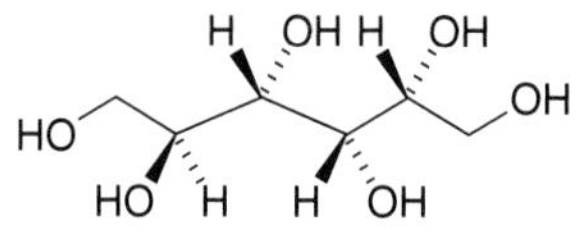
B

Sorbitol (Problem 5.23) occurs naturally in some berries and fruits. It is used as a substitute sweetener in sugar-free—that is, sucrose-free—candy and gum.

5.10 Disubstituted Cycloalkanes

Let us now turn our attention to disubstituted cycloalkanes, and draw all possible stereoisomers for **1,3-dibromocyclopentane.** Because 1,3-dibromocyclopentane has two stereogenic centers, it has a maximum of four stereoisomers.

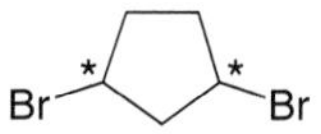

1,3-dibromocyclopentane
[* = stereogenic center]

With two stereogenic centers, the **maximum** number of stereoisomers = **4.**

Remember: In determining chirality in substituted cycloalkanes, always draw the rings as **flat polygons.** This is especially true for cyclohexane derivatives, where having two chair forms that interconvert can make analysis especially difficult.

To draw all possible stereoisomers, remember that a disubstituted cycloalkane can have two substituents on the same side of the ring (**cis isomer,** labeled **A**) or on opposite sides of the ring (**trans isomer,** labeled **B**). These compounds are **stereoisomers but not mirror images of each other,** making them **diastereomers. A** and **B** are two of the four possible stereoisomers.

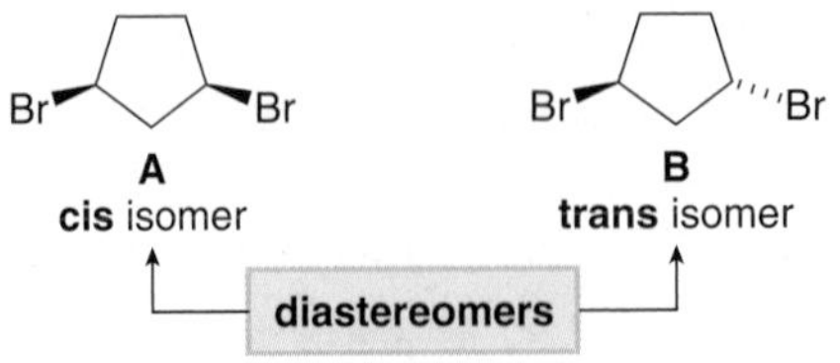

cis-1,3-Dibromocyclopentane contains a plane of symmetry.

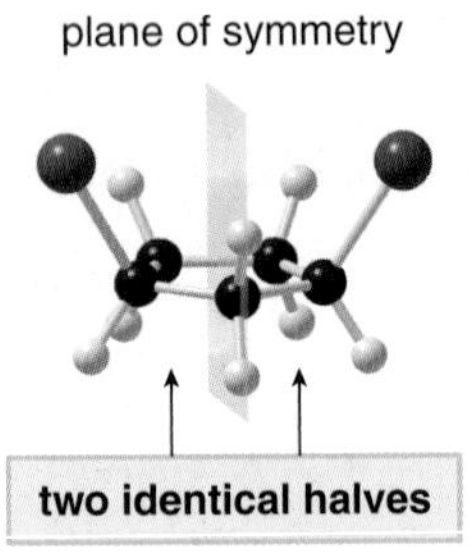

To find the other two stereoisomers (if they exist), draw the mirror image of each compound and determine whether the compound and its mirror image are superimposable.

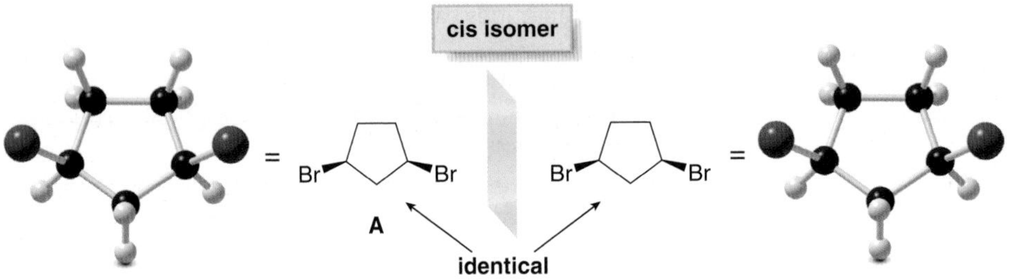

- The cis isomer is superimposable on its mirror image, making them *identical.* Thus, **A** is an **achiral meso compound.**

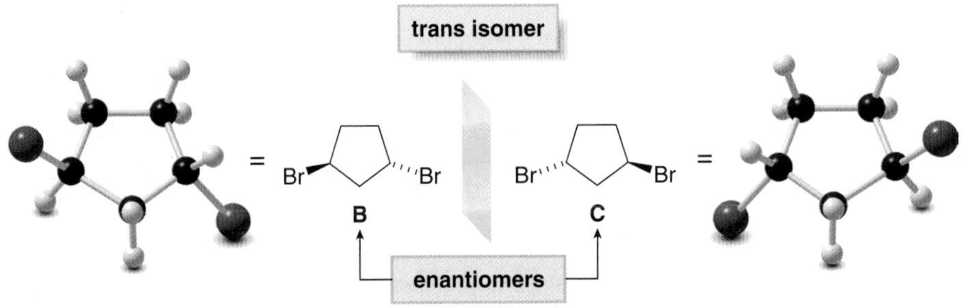

- The trans isomer **B** is *not* superimposable on its mirror image, labeled **C,** making **B** and **C** different compounds. Thus, **B** and **C** are **enantiomers.**

Because one stereoisomer of 1,3-dibromocyclopentane is superimposable on its mirror image, there are only three stereoisomers, not four. **A** is an achiral meso compound and **B** and **C** are a pair of chiral enantiomers. **A** and **B** are diastereomers, as are **A** and **C.**

Problem 5.24 Which of the following cyclic molecules are *meso* compounds?

a. 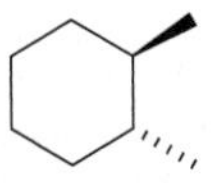

b. 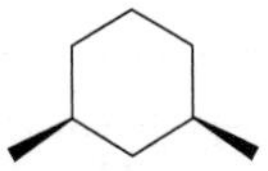

c. 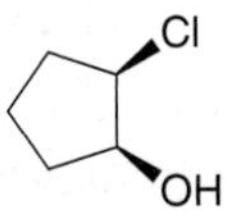

Problem 5.25 Draw all possible stereoisomers for each compound. Label pairs of enantiomers and diastereomers.

a. 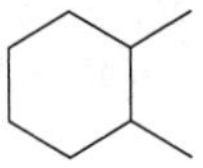

b. 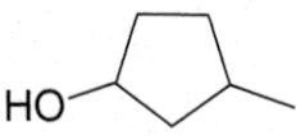

c. 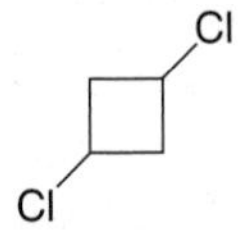

5.11 Isomers—A Summary

Before moving on to other aspects of stereochemistry, take the time to review Figures 5.10 and 5.11. Keep in mind the following facts, and use Figure 5.10 to summarize the types of isomers.

- **There are two major classes of isomers: constitutional isomers and stereoisomers.**
- **There are only two kinds of stereoisomers: enantiomers and diastereomers.**

Then, to determine the relationship between two nonidentical molecules, refer to the flowchart in Figure 5.11.

Problem 5.26 State how each pair of compounds is related. Are they enantiomers, diastereomers, constitutional isomers, or identical?

a. 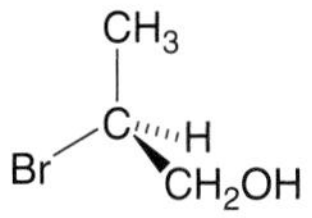

and 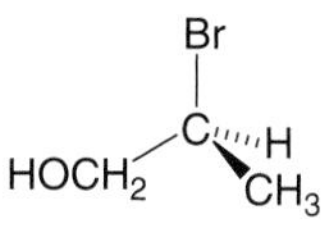

b. 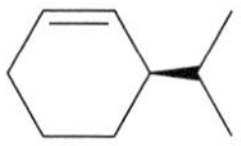 and 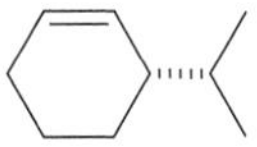

c. 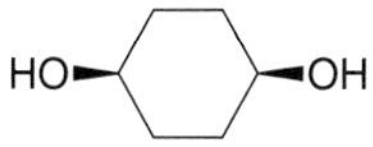

and 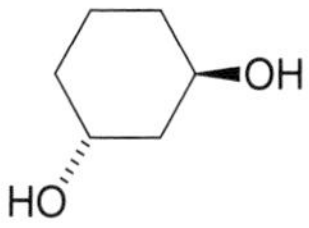

d. 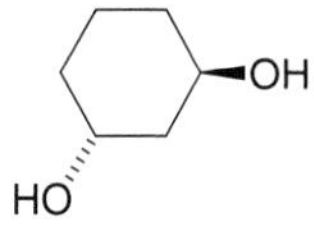

and 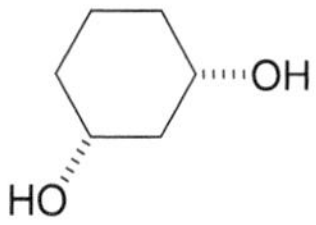

Figure 5.10
Summary—Types of isomers

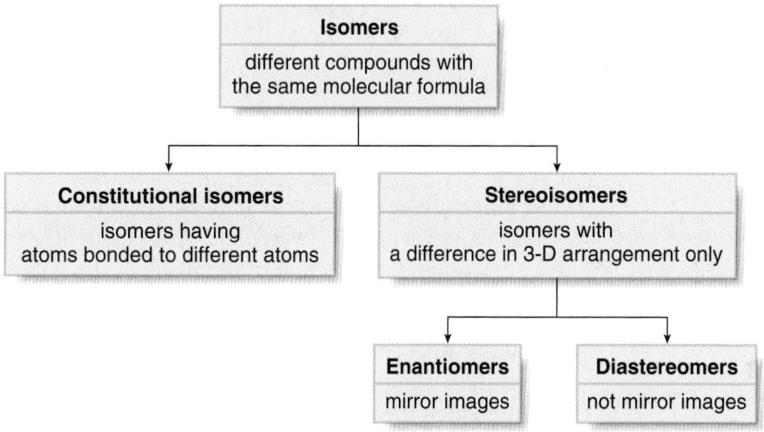

Figure 5.11
Determining the relationship between two nonidentical molecules

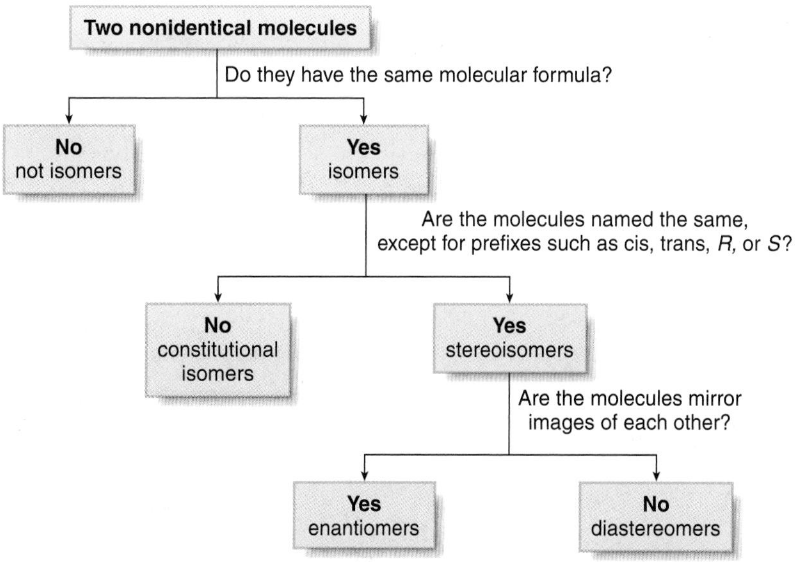

5.12 Physical Properties of Stereoisomers

Recall from Section 5.2 that constitutional isomers have different physical and chemical properties. How, then, do the physical and chemical properties of enantiomers compare?

- **The chemical and physical properties of two enantiomers are *identical* except in their interaction with *chiral* substances.**

5.12A Optical Activity

Two enantiomers have identical physical properties—melting point, boiling point, solubility—except for how they interact with plane-polarized light.

What is plane-polarized light? Ordinary light consists of electromagnetic waves that oscillate in all planes perpendicular to the direction in which the light travels. Passing light through a polarizer allows light in only one plane to come through. This is **plane-polarized light** (or simply **polarized light**), and it has an electric vector that oscillates in a single plane.

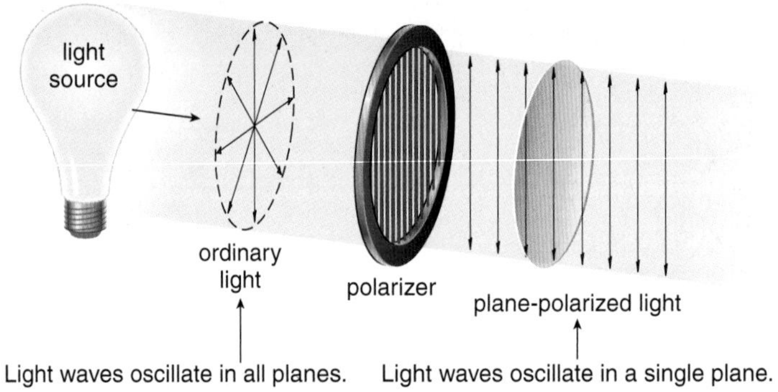

A **polarimeter** is an instrument that allows plane-polarized light to travel through a sample tube containing an organic compound. After the light exits the sample tube, an analyzer slit is rotated to determine the direction of the plane of the polarized light exiting the sample tube. There are two possible results.

With **achiral compounds,** the light exits the sample tube *unchanged,* and the plane of the polarized light is in the same position it was before entering the sample tube. **A compound that does not change the plane of polarized light is said to be *optically inactive.***

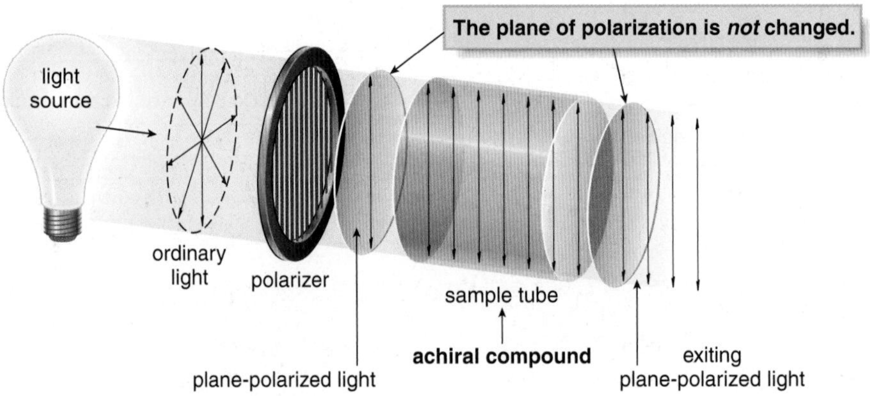

With **chiral compounds,** the plane of the polarized light is rotated through an angle α. The angle α, measured in degrees (°), is called the **observed rotation. A compound that rotates the plane of polarized light is said to be *optically active.***

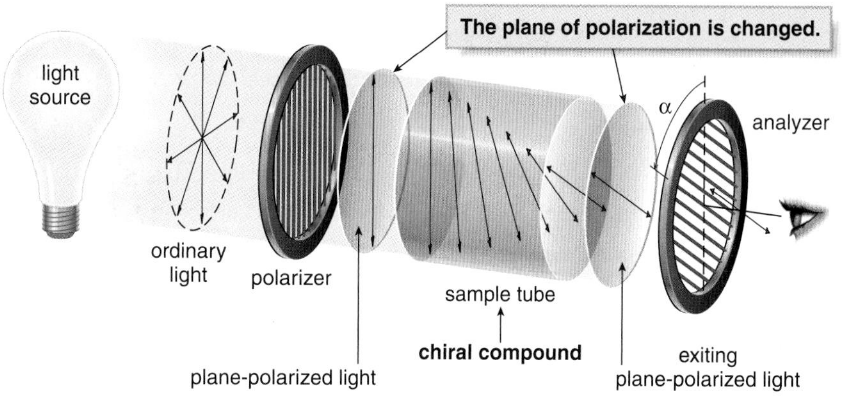

For example, the achiral compound CH_2BrCl is optically inactive, whereas a single enantiomer of CHBrClF, a chiral compound, is optically active.

The rotation of polarized light can be in the **clockwise** or **counterclockwise** direction.

- If the rotation is *clockwise* (to the right from the noon position), the compound is called *dextrorotatory.* The rotation is labeled *d* or (+).
- If the rotation is *counterclockwise* (to the left from noon), the compound is called *levorotatory.* The rotation is labeled *l* or (–).

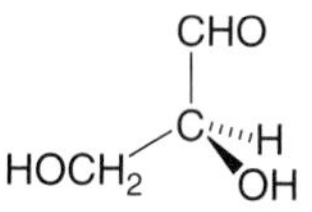

(*S*)-(–)-glyceraldehyde

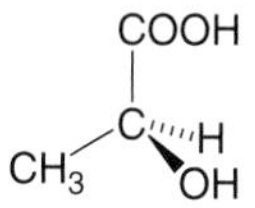

(*S*)-(+)-lactic acid

No relationship exists between the *R* and *S* prefixes that designate configuration and the (+) and (–) designations indicating optical rotation. For example, the *S* enantiomer of lactic acid is dextrorotatory (+), whereas the *S* enantiomer of glyceraldehyde is levorotatory (–).

How does the rotation of two enantiomers compare?

- Two enantiomers rotate plane-polarized light *to an equal extent* but in the *opposite* direction.

Thus, if enantiomer **A** rotates polarized light +5°, then the same concentration of enantiomer **B** rotates it –5°.

5.12B Racemic Mixtures

What is the observed rotation of an equal amount of two enantiomers? Because **two enantiomers rotate plane-polarized light to an equal extent but in opposite directions, the rotations cancel,** and no rotation is observed.

- An equal amount of two enantiomers is called a *racemic mixture* or a *racemate.* A racemic mixture is optically inactive.

Besides optical rotation, other physical properties of a racemate are not readily predicted. The melting point and boiling point of a racemic mixture are not necessarily the same as either pure enantiomer, and this fact is not easily explained. The physical properties of two enantiomers and their racemic mixture are summarized in Table 5.1.

Table 5.1 The Physical Properties of Enantiomers A and B Compared

Property	A alone	B alone	Racemic A + B
Melting point	identical to **B**	identical to **A**	may be different from **A** and **B**
Boiling point	identical to **B**	identical to **A**	may be different from **A** and **B**
Optical rotation	equal in magnitude but opposite in sign to **B**	equal in magnitude but opposite in sign to **A**	0°

5.12C Specific Rotation

The observed rotation depends on the number of chiral molecules that interact with polarized light. This in turn depends on the concentration of the sample and the length of the sample tube. To standardize optical rotation data, the quantity **specific rotation** ([α]) is defined using a specific sample tube length (usually 1 dm), concentration, temperature (25 °C), and wavelength (589 nm, the D line emitted by a sodium lamp).

$$\textbf{specific rotation} = [\alpha] = \frac{\alpha}{l \times c}$$

α = observed rotation (°)
l = length of sample tube (dm)
c = concentration (g/mL)

[dm = decimeter
1 dm = 10 cm]

Specific rotations are physical constants just like melting points or boiling points, and are reported in chemical reference books for a wide variety of compounds.

Problem 5.27 The amino acid (*S*)-alanine has the physical characteristics listed under the structure.

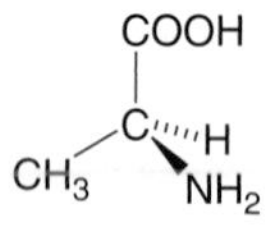

(*S*)-alanine
[α] = +8.5
mp = 297 °C

a. What is the melting point of (*R*)-alanine?
b. How does the melting point of a racemic mixture of (*R*)- and (*S*)-alanine compare to the melting point of (*S*)-alanine?
c. What is the specific rotation of (*R*)-alanine, recorded under the same conditions as the reported rotation of (*S*)-alanine?
d. What is the optical rotation of a racemic mixture of (*R*)- and (*S*)-alanine?
e. Label each of the following as optically active or inactive: a solution of pure (*S*)-alanine; an equal mixture of (*R*)- and (*S*)-alanine; a solution that contains 75% (*S*)- and 25% (*R*)-alanine.

Problem 5.28 A natural product was isolated in the laboratory, and its observed rotation was +10° when measured in a 1 dm sample tube containing 1.0 g of compound in 10 mL of water. What is the specific rotation of this compound?

5.12D Enantiomeric Excess

Sometimes in the laboratory we have neither a pure enantiomer nor a racemic mixture, but rather a mixture of two enantiomers in which one enantiomer is present in excess of the other. The **enantiomeric excess (*ee*),** also called the **optical purity,** tells how much more there is of one enantiomer.

- **Enantiomeric excess = *ee* = % of one enantiomer – % of the other enantiomer.**

Enantiomeric excess tells how much one enantiomer is present in excess of the racemic mixture. For example, if a mixture contains 75% of one enantiomer and 25% of the other, the enantiomeric excess is 75% – 25% = 50%. There is a 50% excess of one enantiomer over the racemic mixture.

Problem 5.29 What is the *ee* for each of the following mixtures of enantiomers **A** and **B?**

a. 95% **A** and 5% **B** b. 85% **A** and 15% **B**

Knowing the *ee* of a mixture makes it possible to calculate the amount of each enantiomer present, as shown in Sample Problem 5.4.

Sample Problem 5.4 If the enantiomeric excess is 95%, how much of each enantiomer is present?

Solution

Label the two enantiomers **A** and **B** and assume that **A** is in excess. A 95% *ee* means that the solution contains an excess of 95% of **A,** and 5% of the racemic mixture of **A** and **B.** Because a racemic mixture is an equal amount of both enantiomers, it has 2.5% of **A** and 2.5% of **B.**

- Total amount of **A** = 95% + 2.5% = 97.5%
- Total amount of **B** = 2.5% (or 100% – 97.5%)

Problem 5.30 For the given *ee* values, calculate the percentage of each enantiomer present.

a. 90% *ee* b. 99% *ee* c. 60% *ee*

The enantiomeric excess can also be calculated if two quantities are known—the specific rotation [α] of a mixture and the specific rotation [α] of a pure enantiomer.

$$ee = \frac{[\alpha]\text{ mixture}}{[\alpha]\text{ pure enantiomer}} \times 100\%$$

Sample Problem 5.5 Pure cholesterol has a specific rotation of –32. A sample of cholesterol prepared in the lab had a specific rotation of –16. What is the enantiomeric excess of this sample of cholesterol?

Solution

Calculate the *ee* of the mixture using the given formula.

$$ee = \frac{[\alpha]\text{ mixture}}{[\alpha]\text{ pure enantiomer}} \times 100\% = \frac{-16}{-32} \times 100\% = \boxed{50\%\ ee}$$

Problem 5.31 Pure MSG, a common flavor enhancer, exhibits a specific rotation of +24. (a) Calculate the *ee* of a solution whose [α] is +10. (b) If the *ee* of a solution of MSG is 80%, what is [α] for this solution?

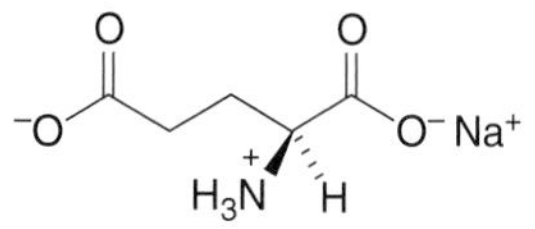

MSG
monosodium glutamate

Problem 5.32 (*S*)-Lactic acid has a specific rotation of +3.8. (a) If the *ee* of a solution of lactic acid is 60%, what is [α] for this solution? (b) How much of the dextrorotatory and levorotatory isomers does the solution contain?

5.12E The Physical Properties of Diastereomers

Diastereomers are not mirror images of each other, and as such, **their physical properties are different, including optical rotation.** Figure 5.12 compares the physical properties of the three stereoisomers of tartaric acid, consisting of a meso compound that is a diastereomer of a pair of enantiomers.

Figure 5.12
The physical properties of the three stereoisomers of tartaric acid

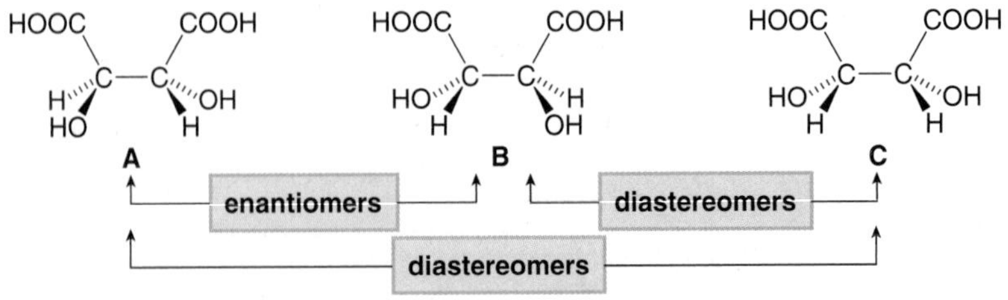

Property	A	B	C	A + B (1:1)
melting point (°C)	171	171	146	206
solubility (g/100 mL H_2O)	139	139	125	139
[α]	+13	–13	0	0
R,S designation	*R,R*	*S,S*	*R,S*	—
d,l designation	*d*	*l*	none	*d,l*

- The physical properties of **A** and **B** differ from their diastereomer **C.**
- The physical properties of a racemic mixture of **A** and **B** (last column) can also differ from either enantiomer and diastereomer **C.**
- **C** is an achiral meso compound, so it is optically inactive; [α] = 0.

Whether the physical properties of a set of compounds are the same or different has practical applications in the lab. Physical properties characterize a compound's physical state, and two compounds can usually be separated only if their physical properties are different.

Two enantiomers can be separated by the process of **resolution,** as described in Section 29.3.

- **Because two enantiomers have identical physical properties, they cannot be separated by common physical techniques like distillation.**
- **Diastereomers and constitutional isomers have different physical properties, and therefore they can be separated by common physical techniques.**

Problem 5.33 Compare the physical properties of the three stereoisomers of 1,3-dimethylcyclopentane.

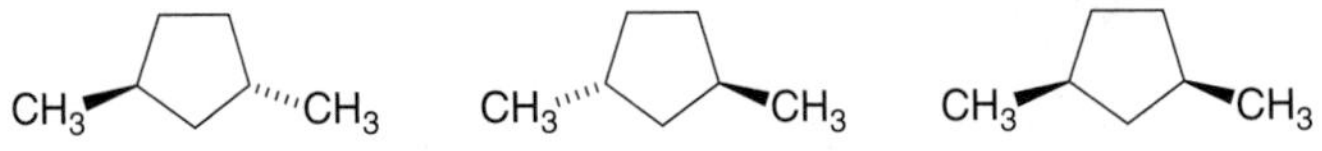

A B C

three stereoisomers of 1,3-dimethylcyclopentane

a. How do the boiling points of **A** and **B** compare? What about **A** and **C?**
b. Characterize a solution of each of the following as optically active or optically inactive: pure **A;** pure **B;** pure **C;** an equal mixture of **A** and **B;** an equal mixture of **A** and **C.**
c. A reaction forms a 1:1:1 mixture of **A, B,** and **C.** If this mixture is distilled, how many fractions would be obtained? Which fractions would be optically active and which would be optically inactive?

5.13 Chemical Properties of Enantiomers

When two enantiomers react with an achiral reagent, they react at the same rate, but when they react with a chiral, non-racemic reagent, they react at different rates.

- **Two enantiomers have exactly the same chemical properties except for their reaction with chiral, non-racemic reagents.**

For an everyday analogy, consider what happens when you are handed an achiral object like a pen and a chiral object like a right-handed glove. Your left and right hands are enantiomers, but they can both hold the achiral pen in the same way. With the glove, however, only your right hand can fit inside it, not your left.

We will examine specific reactions of chiral molecules with both chiral and achiral reagents later in this text. Here, we examine two more general applications.

5.13A Chiral Drugs

A living organism is a sea of chiral molecules. Many drugs are chiral, and often they must interact with a chiral receptor or a chiral enzyme to be effective. One enantiomer of a drug may treat a disease whereas its mirror image may be ineffective. Alternatively, one enantiomer may trigger one biochemical response and its mirror image may elicit a totally different response.

Although (*R*)-ibuprofen shows no anti-inflammatory activity itself, it is slowly converted to the *S* enantiomer in vivo.

For example, the drugs ibuprofen and fluoxetine each contain one stereogenic center, and thus exist as a pair of enantiomers, only one of which exhibits biological activity. **(*S*)-Ibuprofen** is the active component of the anti-inflammatory agents Motrin and Advil, and **(*R*)-fluoxetine** is the active component in the antidepressant Prozac.

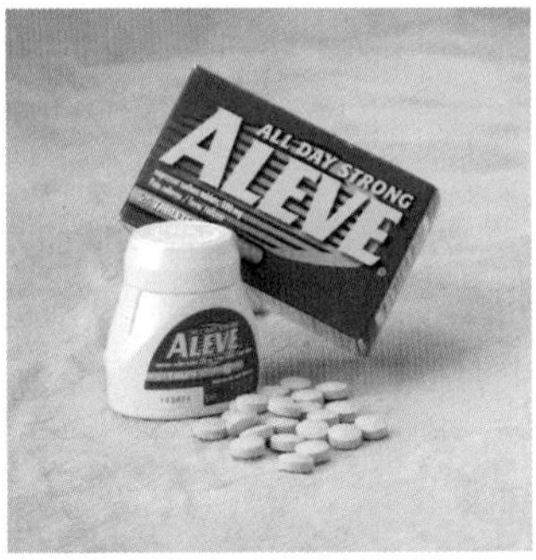

(*S*)-Naproxen is the active ingredient in the widely used pain relievers Naprosyn and Aleve.

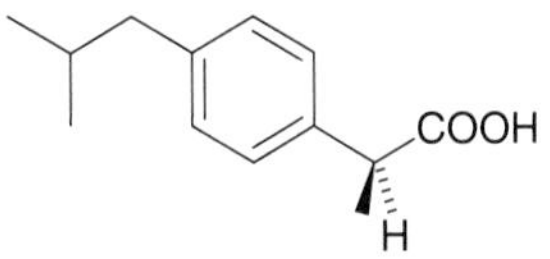

(*S*)-ibuprofen
anti-inflammatory agent

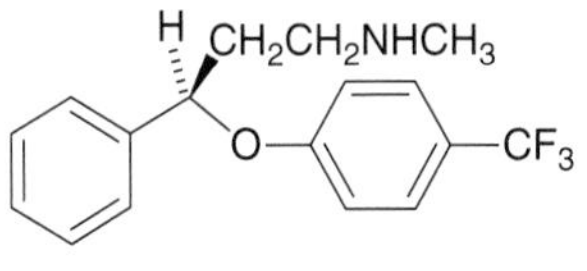

(*R*)-fluoxetine
antidepressant

Changing the orientation of two substituents to form a mirror image can also alter biological activity to produce an undesirable side effect in the other enantiomer. The *S* enantiomer of **naproxen** is an active anti-inflammatory agent, but the *R* enantiomer is a harmful liver toxin.

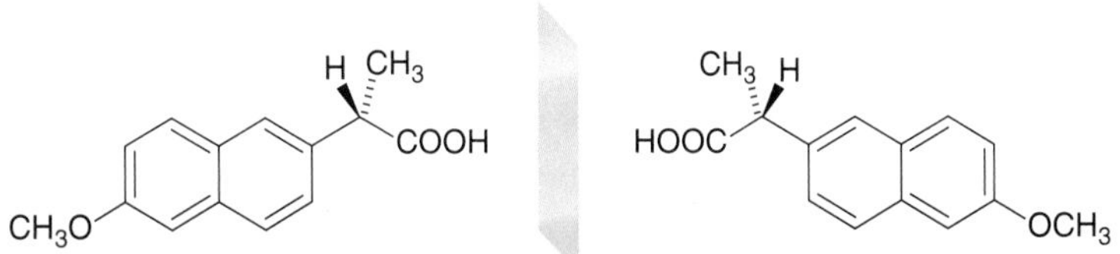

(*S*)-naproxen
anti-inflammatory agent

(*R*)-naproxen
liver toxin

For more examples of two enantiomers that exhibit very different biochemical properties, see *Journal of Chemical Education*, **1996,** *73,* 481–484.

If a chiral drug could be sold as a single active enantiomer, it should be possible to use smaller doses with fewer side effects. Many chiral drugs continue to be sold as racemic mixtures, however, because it is more difficult and therefore more costly to obtain a single enantiomer. An enantiomer is not easily separated from a racemic mixture because the two enantiomers have the same physical properties. In Chapter 12 we will study a reaction that can form a single active enantiomer, an important development in making chiral drugs more readily available.

5.13B Enantiomers and the Sense of Smell

Research suggests that the odor of a particular molecule is determined more by its shape than by the presence of a particular functional group. For example, hexachloroethane (Cl_3CCCl_3) and cyclooctane have no obvious structural similarities, but they both have a camphor-like odor, a fact attributed to their similar spherical shape. Each molecule binds to spherically shaped olfactory receptors present on the nerve endings in the nasal passage, resulting in similar odors (Figure 5.13).

Because enantiomers interact with chiral smell receptors, some enantiomers have different odors. There are a few well-characterized examples of this phenomenon in nature. For example, (*S*)-carvone is responsible for the odor of caraway, whereas (*R*)-carvone is responsible for the odor of spearmint.

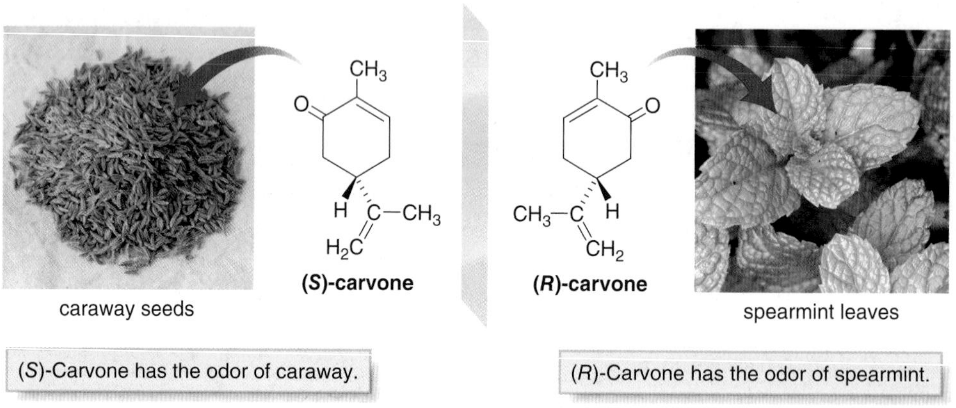
CH3
O
H C–CH3
H2C
(S)-carvone
caraway seeds
(S)-Carvone has the odor of caraway.
CH3
O
CH3–C H
CH2
(R)-carvone
spearmint leaves
(R)-Carvone has the odor of spearmint.

These examples demonstrate that understanding the three-dimensional structure of a molecule is very important in organic chemistry.

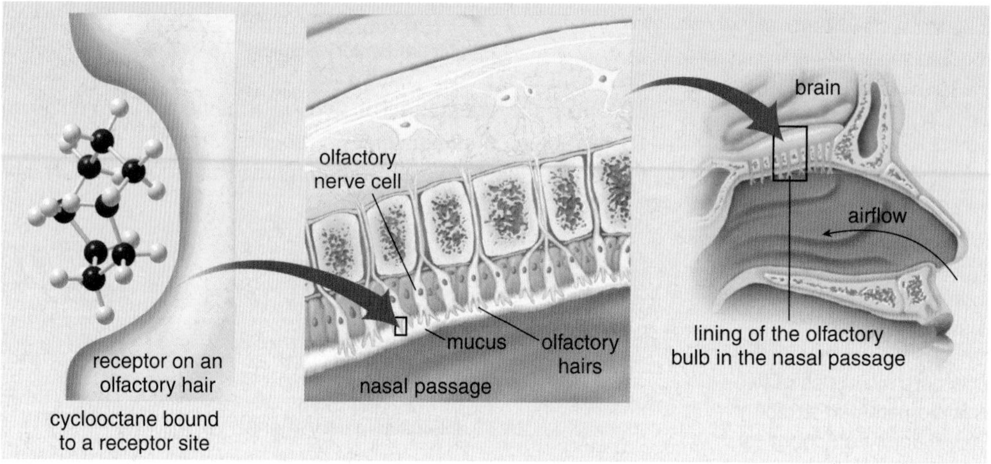
receptor on an olfactory hair
cyclooctane bound to a receptor site
olfactory nerve cell
mucus
olfactory hairs
nasal passage
brain
airflow
lining of the olfactory bulb in the nasal passage

Figure 5.13 The shape of molecules and the sense of smell

Cyclooctane and other molecules similar in shape bind to a particular olfactory receptor on the nerve cells that lie at the top of the nasal passage. Binding results in a nerve impulse that travels to the brain, which interprets impulses from particular receptors as specific odors.

KEY CONCEPTS

Stereochemistry

Isomers Are Different Compounds with the Same Molecular Formula (5.2, 5.11).

[1] **Constitutional isomers**—isomers that differ in the way the atoms are connected to each other. They have:
- different IUPAC names
- the same or different functional groups
- different physical and chemical properties

[2] **Stereoisomers**—isomers that differ only in the way atoms are oriented in space**.** They have the same functional group and the same IUPAC name except for prefixes such as cis, trans, *R,* and *S*.
- **Enantiomers**—stereoisomers that are nonsuperimposable mirror images of each other (5.4).
- **Diastereomers**—stereoisomers that are not mirror images of each other (5.7).

Some Basic Principles

- When a compound and its mirror image are **superimposable,** they are **identical achiral compounds.** When a compound has a plane of symmetry in one conformation, the compound is achiral (5.3).
- When a compound and its mirror image are **not superimposable,** they are **different chiral compounds** called **enantiomers.** A chiral compound has no plane of symmetry in any conformation (5.3).
- A **tetrahedral stereogenic center** is a carbon atom bonded to four different groups (5.4, 5.5).
- For ***n*** **stereogenic centers,** the maximum number of stereoisomers is $\mathbf{2^n}$ (5.7).

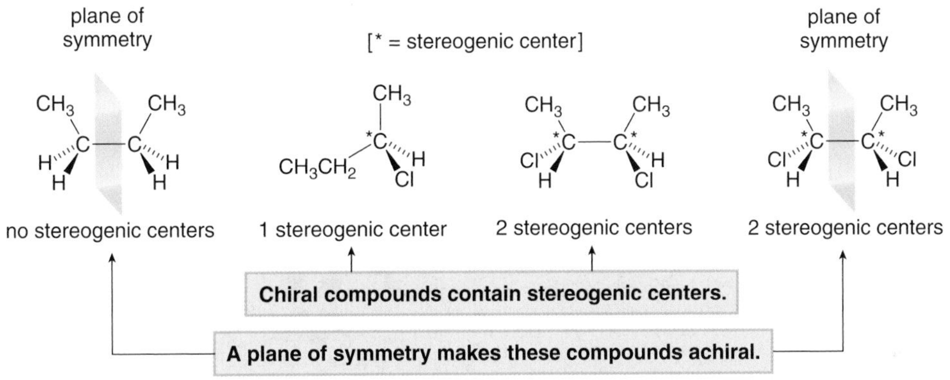

Optical Activity Is the Ability of a Compound to Rotate Plane-Polarized Light (5.12).

- An optically active solution contains a chiral compound.
- An optically inactive solution contains one of the following:
  - an achiral compound with no stereogenic centers
  - a meso compound—an achiral compound with two or more stereogenic centers
  - a racemic mixture—an equal amount of two enantiomers

The Prefixes *R* and *S* Compared with *d* and *l*

The prefixes *R* and *S* are labels used in nomenclature. Rules on assigning *R,S* are found in Section 5.6.

- An enantiomer has every stereogenic center opposite in configuration. If a compound with two stereogenic centers has the *R,R* configuration, its enantiomer has the *S,S* configuration.
- A diastereomer of this same compound has either the *R,S* or *S,R* configuration; one stereogenic center has the same configuration and one is opposite.

The prefixes *d* (or +) and *l* (or –) tell the direction a compound rotates plane-polarized light (5.12).

- Dextrorotatory (*d* or +) compounds rotate polarized light clockwise.
- Levorotatory (*l* or –) compounds rotate polarized light counterclockwise.
- There is no relation between whether a compound is *R* or *S* and whether it is *d* or *l*.

The Physical Properties of Isomers Compared (5.12)

Type of isomer	Physical properties
Constitutional isomers	Different
Enantiomers	Identical except for the direction polarized light is rotated
Diastereomers	Different
Racemic mixture	Possibly different from either enantiomer

Equations

- Specific rotation (5.12C):

$$\text{specific rotation} = [\alpha] = \frac{\alpha}{l \times c}$$

α = observed rotation (°)
l = length of sample tube (dm)
c = concentration (g/mL)

[dm = decimeter; 1 dm = 10 cm]

- Enantiomeric excess (5.12D):

$$ee = \text{\% of one enantiomer} - \text{\% of the other enantiomer}$$
$$= \frac{[\alpha]\ \text{mixture}}{[\alpha]\ \text{pure enantiomer}} \times 100\%$$

PROBLEMS

Problems Using Three-Dimensional Models

5.34 (a) Locate the stereogenic centers in the ball-and-stick model of ezetimibe (trade name Zetia), a cholesterol-lowering drug. (b) Label each stereogenic center as *R* or *S*.

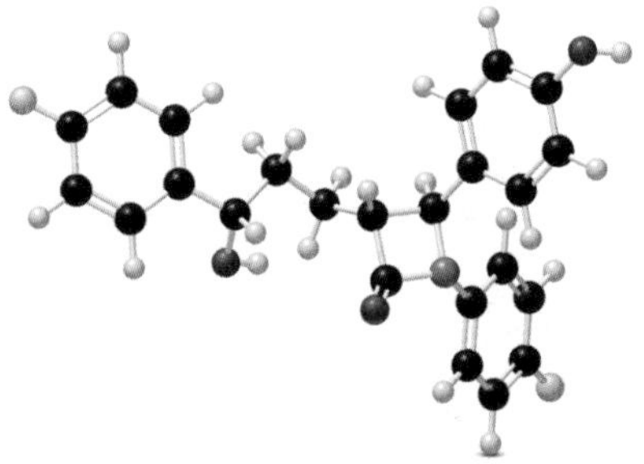

ezetimibe

5.35 Consider the ball-and-stick models **A–D**. How is each pair of compounds related: (a) **A** and **B;** (b) **A** and **C;** (c) **A** and **D;** (d) **C** and **D?** Choose from identical molecules, enantiomers, or diastereomers.

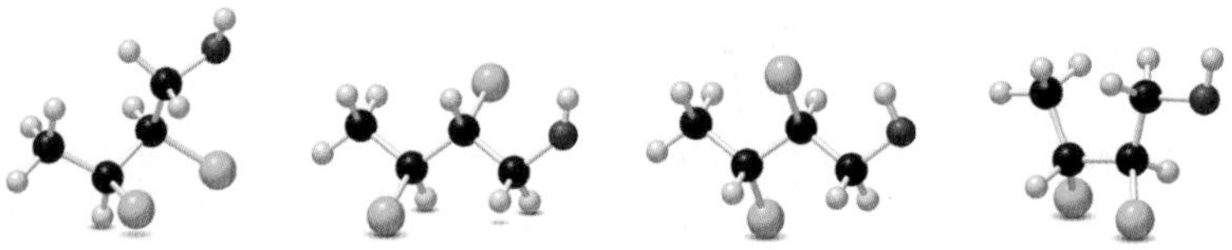

A **B** **C** **D**

Constitutional Isomers versus Stereoisomers

5.36 Label each pair of compounds as constitutional isomers, stereoisomers, or not isomers of each other.

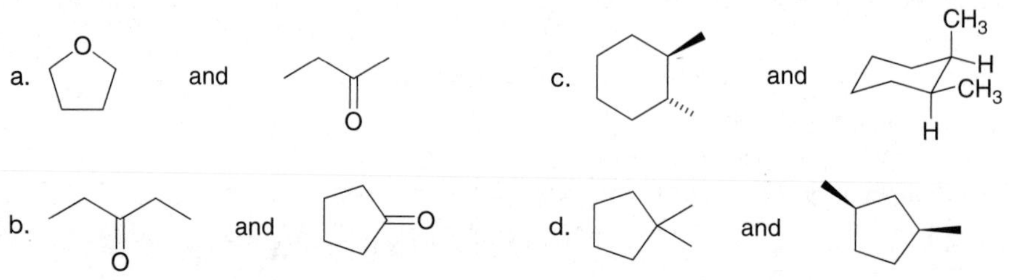

Mirror Images and Chirality

5.37 Draw the mirror image of each compound, and label the compound as chiral or achiral.

a. 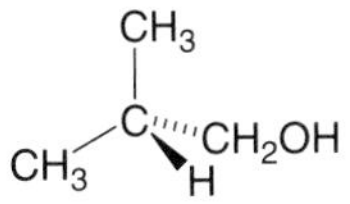

b. 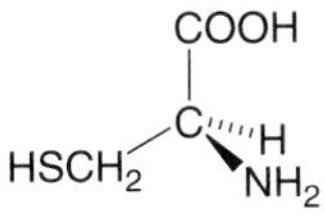

c. 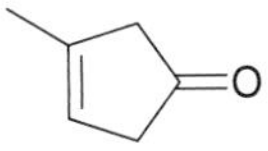

d. 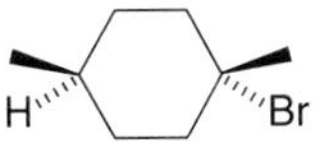

e. 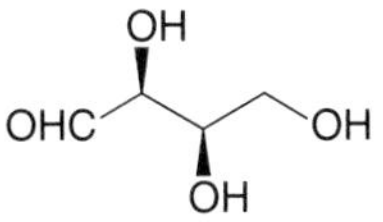

5.38 Determine if each compound is identical to or an enantiomer of **A**.

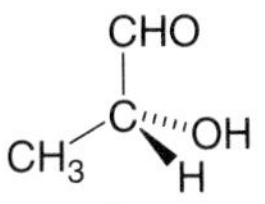

A

a. 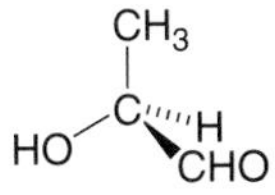

b. 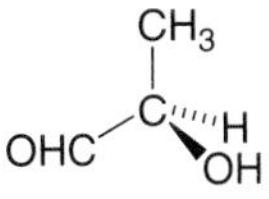

c. 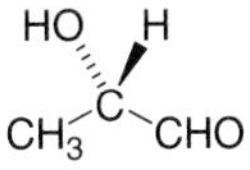

5.39 Indicate a plane of symmetry for each molecule that contains one. Some molecules require rotation around a carbon–carbon bond to see the plane of symmetry.

a. 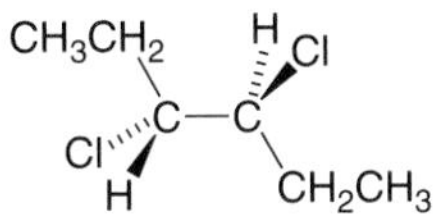

b. 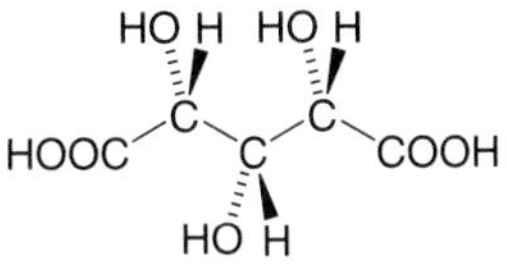

c. 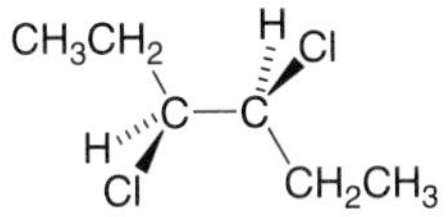

d. 

e. 

Finding and Drawing Stereogenic Centers

5.40 Locate the stereogenic center(s) in each compound. A molecule may have zero, one, or more stereogenic centers.

a. $CH_3CH_2CH_2CH_2CH_2CH_3$

b. $CH_3CH_2OCH(CH_3)CH_2CH_3$

c. $(CH_3)_2CHCH(OH)CH(CH_3)_2$

d. $(CH_3)_2CHCH_2CH(CH_3)CH_2CH(CH_3)CH(CH_3)CH_2CH_3$

e. 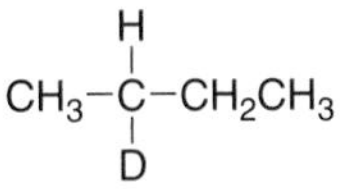

f. 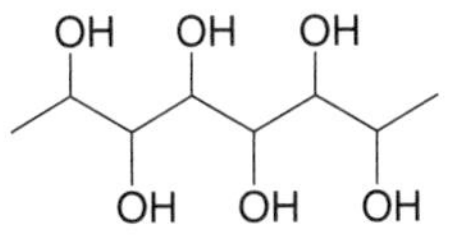

g. 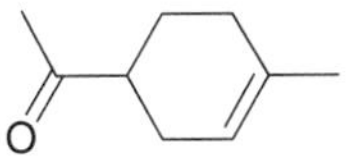

h. 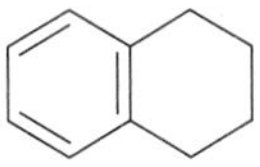

i. 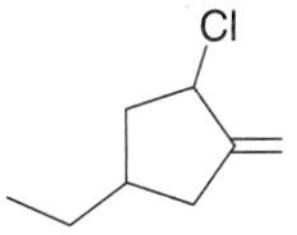

j. 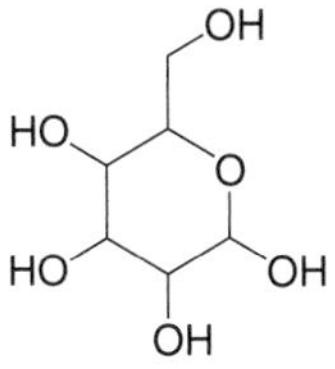

5.41 Draw the eight constitutional isomers having molecular formula $C_5H_{11}Cl$. Label any stereogenic centers.

5.42 Draw both enantiomers for each biologically active compound.

a. 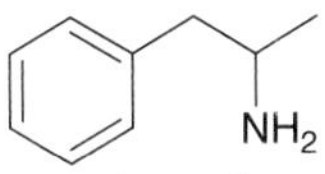

amphetamine
(a powerful central nervous stimulant)

b. 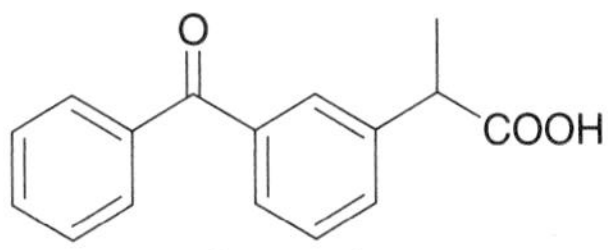

ketoprofen
(analgesic and anti-inflammatory agent)

5.43 Draw the lowest molecular weight chiral compound that contains only C, H, and O and fits each description: (a) an acyclic alcohol; (b) a ketone; (c) a cyclic ether.

Nomenclature

5.44 Which group in each pair is assigned the higher priority in *R,S* nomenclature?

a. $-CD_3$, $-CH_3$

b. $-CH(CH_3)_2$, $-CH_2OH$

c. $-CH_2Cl$, $-CH_2CH_2CH_2Br$

d. $-CH_2NH_2$, $-NHCH_3$

5.45 Rank the following groups in order of decreasing priority.

a. $-F$, $-NH_2$, $-CH_3$, $-OH$

b. $-CH_3$, $-CH_2CH_3$, $-CH_2CH_2CH_3$, $-(CH_2)_3CH_3$

c. $-NH_2$, $-CH_2NH_2$, $-CH_3$, $-CH_2NHCH_3$

d. $-COOH$, $-CH_2OH$, $-H$, $-CHO$

e. $-Cl$, $-CH_3$, $-SH$, $-OH$

f. $-C{\equiv}CH$, $-CH(CH_3)_2$, $-CH_2CH_3$, $-CH{=}CH_2$

5.46 Label each stereogenic center as *R* or *S*.

a. 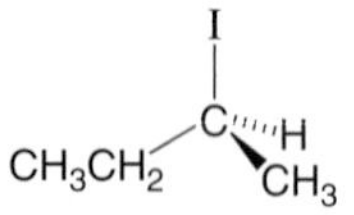

c. 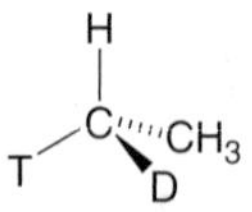

e. 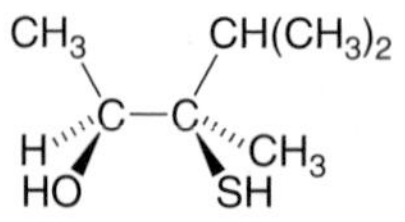

g. 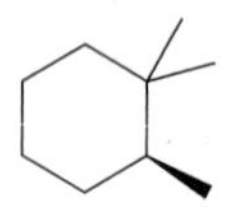

b. 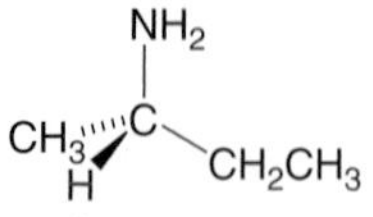

d. 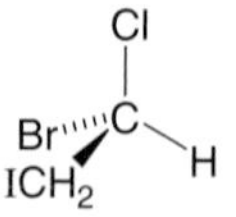

f. 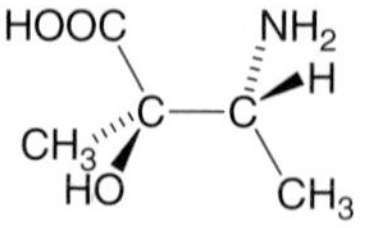

h. 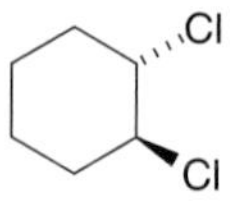

5.47 Draw the structure for each compound.

a. (3*R*)-3-methylhexane

b. (4*R*,5*S*)-4,5-diethyloctane

c. (3*R*,5*S*,6*R*)-5-ethyl-3,6-dimethylnonane

d. (3*S*,6*S*)-6-isopropyl-3-methyldecane

5.48 Give the IUPAC name for each compound, including the *R*,*S* designation for each stereogenic center.

a. 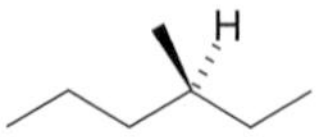

b. 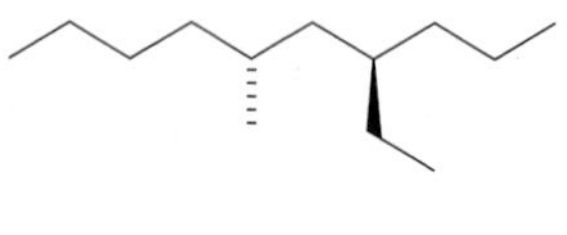

c. 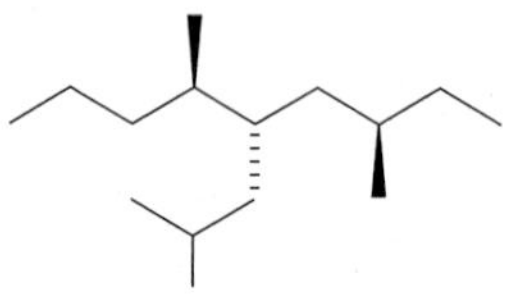

5.49 Draw the two enantiomers for the amino acid leucine, $HOOCCH(NH_2)CH_2CH(CH_3)_2$, and label each enantiomer as *R* or *S*. Only the *S* isomer exists in nature, and it has a bitter taste. Its enantiomer, however, is sweet.

5.50 Label the stereogenic center(s) in each drug as *R* or *S*. L-Dopa is used to treat Parkinson's disease (Chapter 1). Ketamine is an anesthetic. Enalapril belongs to a class of drugs called ACE inhibitors, which are used to lower blood pressure.

a. 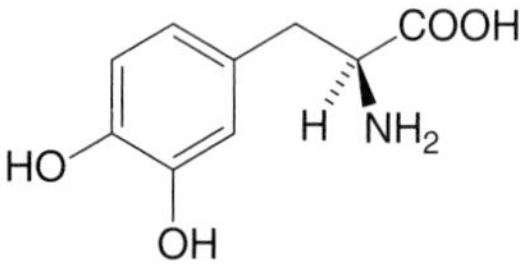

L-dopa

b. 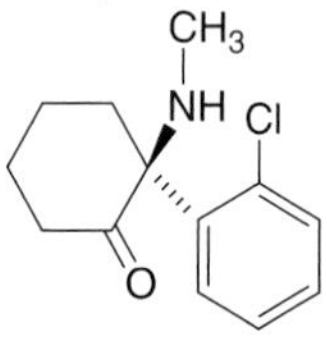

ketamine

c. 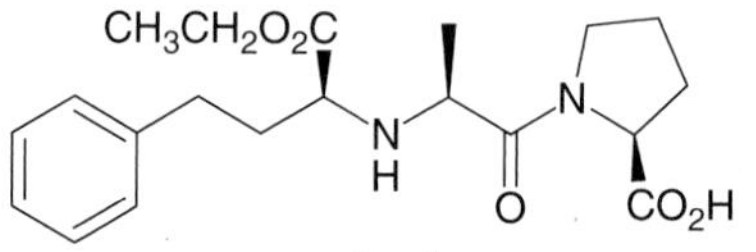

enalapril
Trade name: Vasotec

5.51 The shrub ma huang (Section 5.4A) contains two biologically active stereoisomers—ephedrine and pseudoephedrine—with two stereogenic centers as shown in the given structure. Ephedrine is one component of a once popular combination drug used by body builders to increase energy and alertness, while pseudoephedrine is a nasal decongestant.

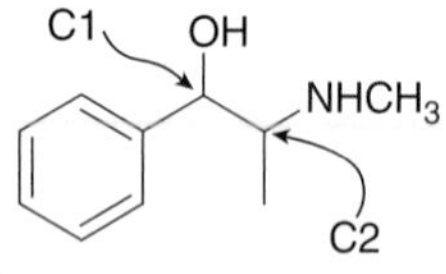

isolated from ma huang

a. Draw the structure of naturally occurring (–)-ephedrine, which has the 1*R*,2*S* configuration.

b. Draw the structure of naturally occurring (+)-pseudoephedrine, which has the 1*S*,2*S* configuration.

c. How are ephedrine and pseudoephedrine related?

d. Draw all other stereoisomers of (–)-ephedrine and (+)-pseudoephedrine and give the *R*,*S* designation for all stereogenic centers.

e. How is each compound drawn in part (d) related to (–)-ephedrine?

Compounds with More Than One Stereogenic Center

5.52 Locate the stereogenic centers in each drug.

a. 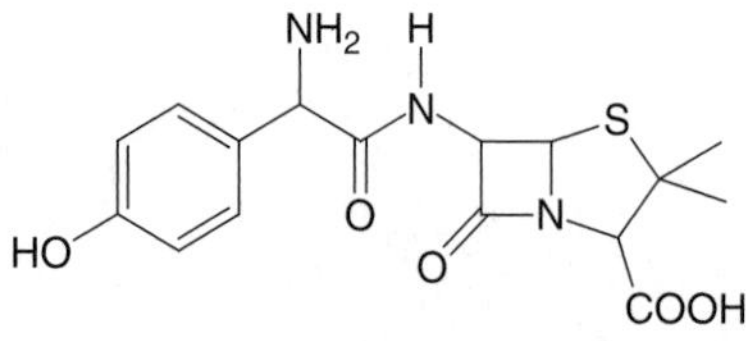

amoxicillin
(an antibiotic)

b. 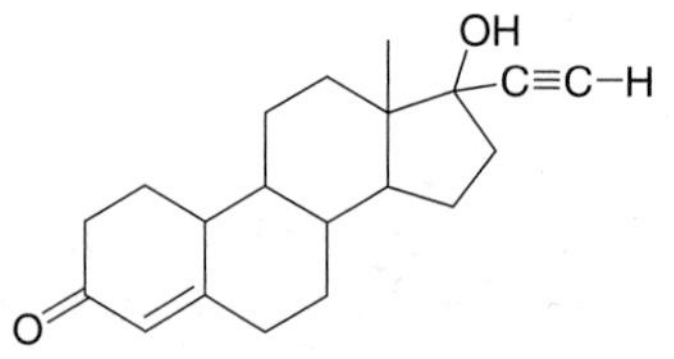

norethindrone
(oral contraceptive component)

c. 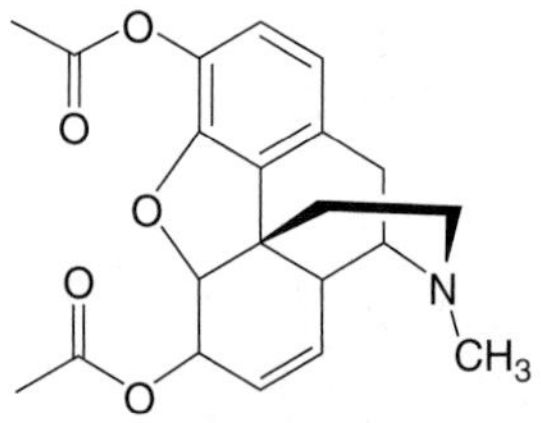

heroin
(an opiate)

5.53 What is the maximum number of stereoisomers possible for each compound?

a. $CH_3CH(OH)CH(OH)CH_2CH_3$

b. $CH_3CH_2CH_2CH(CH_3)_2$

c. 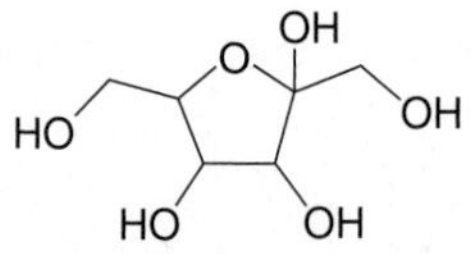

5.54 Draw all possible stereoisomers for each compound. Label pairs of enantiomers and diastereomers. Label any meso compound.

a. $CH_3CH(OH)CH(OH)CH_2CH_3$

b. $CH_3CH(OH)CH_2CH_2CH(OH)CH_3$

c. $CH_3CH(Cl)CH_2CH(Br)CH_3$

d. $CH_3CH(Br)CH(Br)CH(Br)CH_3$

5.55 Draw the enantiomer and a diastereomer for each compound.

a. 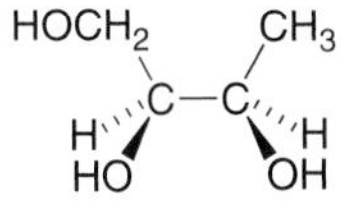
b. 
c. 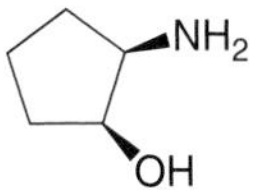
d. 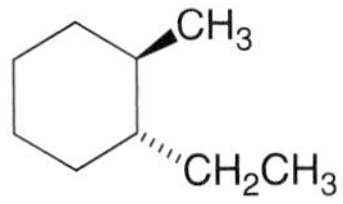

5.56 Draw all possible stereoisomers for each cycloalkane. Label pairs of enantiomers and diastereomers. Label any meso compound.

a. 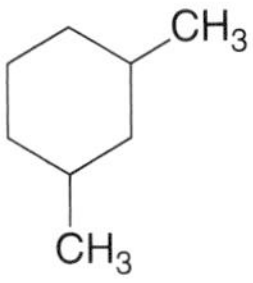
b. 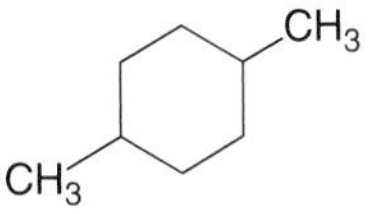
c. 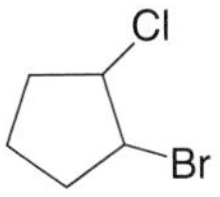

5.57 Draw all possible constitutional and stereoisomers for a compound of molecular formula C_6H_{12} having a cyclobutane ring and two methyl groups as substituents. Label each compound as chiral or achiral.

5.58 Explain each statement by referring to compounds **A–E**.

A

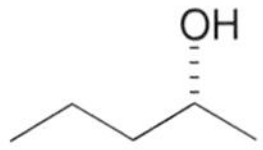
B

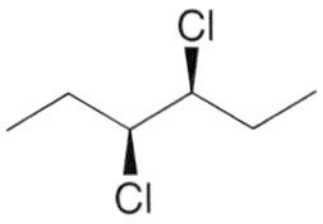
C

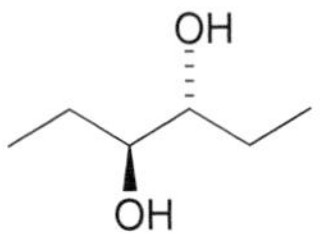
D

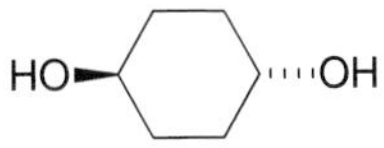
E

a. **A** has a mirror image but no enantiomer.

b. **B** has an enantiomer and no diastereomer.

c. **C** has both an enantiomer and a diastereomer.

d. **D** has a diastereomer but no enantiomer.

e. **E** has a diastereomer but no enantiomer.

Comparing Compounds: Enantiomers, Diastereomers, and Constitutional Isomers

5.59 How is each compound related to the simple sugar D-erythrose? Is it an enantiomer, diastereomer, or identical?

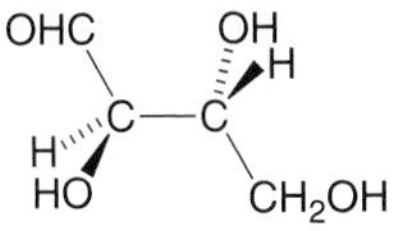
D-erythrose

a. 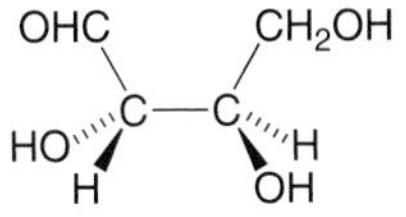
b. 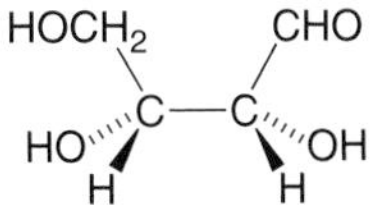
c. 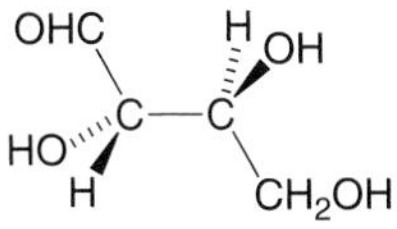
d. 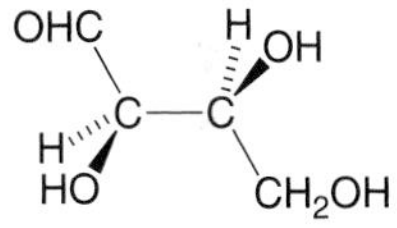

5.60 Consider Newman projections (**A–D**) for four-carbon carbohydrates. How is each pair of compounds related: (a) **A** and **B;** (b) **A** and **C;** (c) **A** and **D;** (d) **C** and **D?** Choose from identical molecules, enantiomers, or diastereomers.

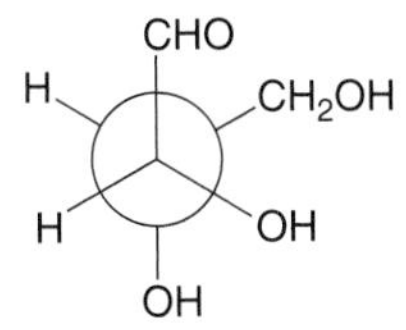
A

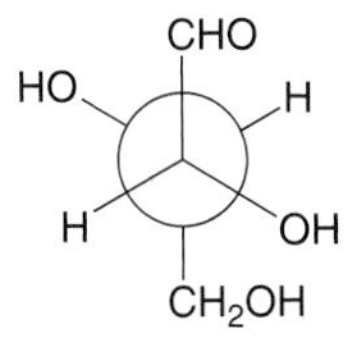
B

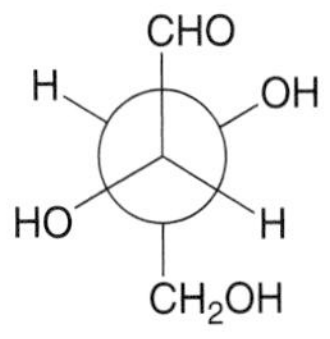
C

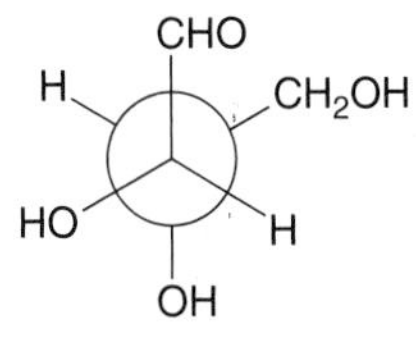
D

5.61 How is compound **A** related to compounds **B–E?** Choose from enantiomers, diastereomers, constitutional isomers, or identical molecules.

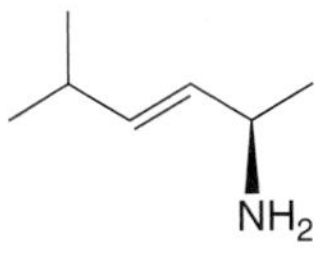
A

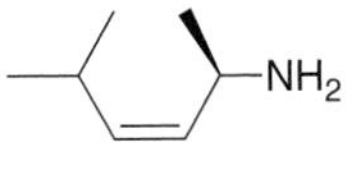
B

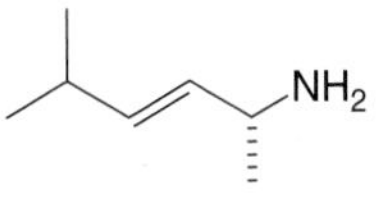
C

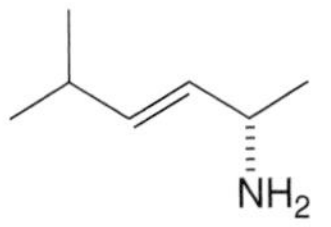
D

E

5.62 How are the compounds in each pair related to each other? Are they identical, enantiomers, diastereomers, constitutional isomers, or not isomers of each other?

a. 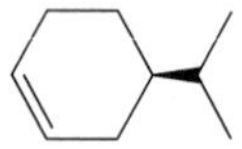 and 

b. 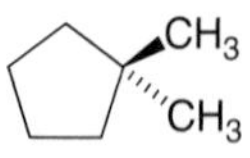

and 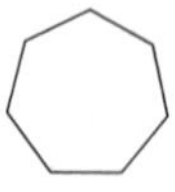

c. 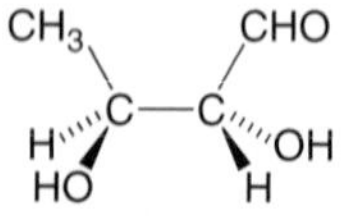

and 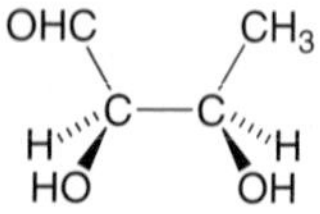

d. 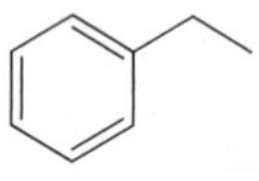 and 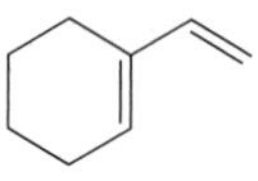

e. 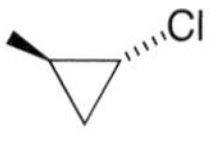

and 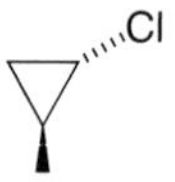

f. 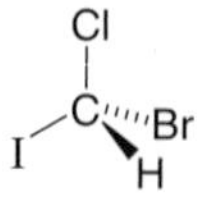

and 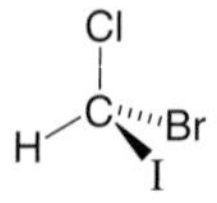

g. 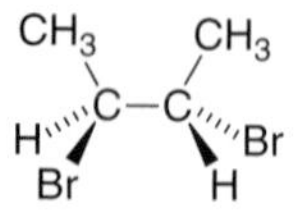

and 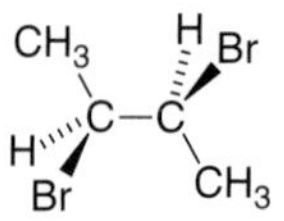

h. 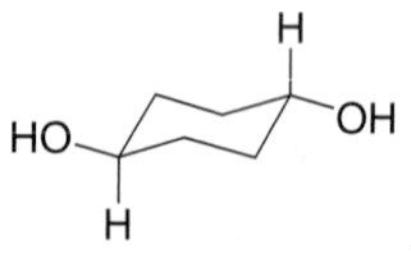

and 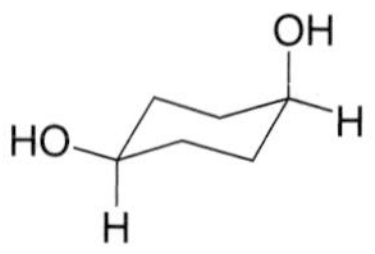

i.  and 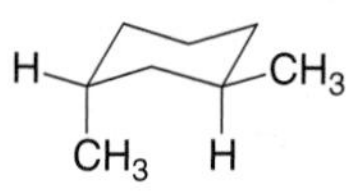

j. 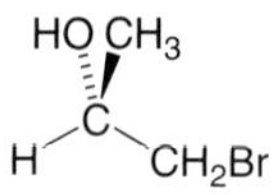

and 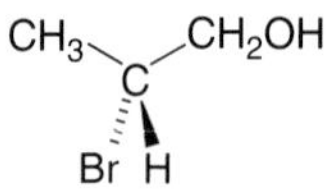

Physical Properties of Isomers

5.63 Drawn are four isomeric dimethylcyclopropanes.

A

B

C

D

a. How are the compounds in each pair related (enantiomers, diastereomers, constitutional isomers): **A** and **B; A** and **C; B** and **C; C** and **D?**
b. Label each compound as chiral or achiral.
c. Which compounds, alone, would be optically active?
d. Which compounds have a plane of symmetry?
e. How do the boiling points of the compounds in each pair compare: **A** and **B; B** and **C; C** and **D?**
f. Which of the compounds are meso compounds?
g. Would an equal mixture of compounds **C** and **D** be optically active? What about an equal mixture of **B** and **C?**

5.64 The [α] of pure quinine, an antimalarial drug, is –165.

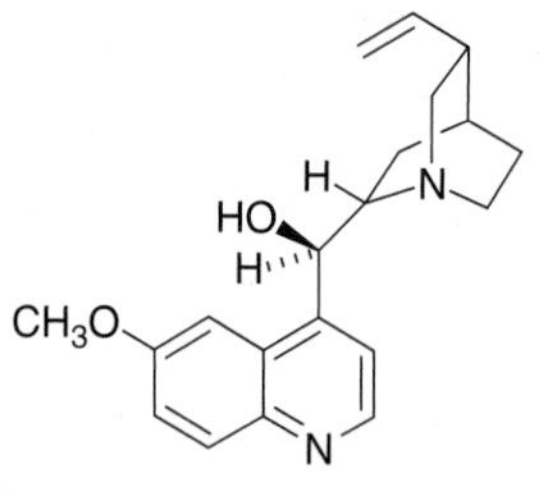

quinine
(antimalarial drug)

a. Calculate the *ee* of a solution with the following [α] values: –50, –83, and –120.
b. For each *ee,* calculate the percent of each enantiomer present.
c. What is [α] for the enantiomer of quinine?
d. If a solution contains 80% quinine and 20% of its enantiomer, what is the *ee* of the solution?
e. What is [α] for the solution described in part (d)?

5.65 Amygdalin, a compound isolated from the pits of apricots, peaches, and wild cherries, is sometimes called laetrile. Although it has no known therapeutic value, amygdalin has been used as an unsanctioned anticancer drug both within and outside of the United States. One hydrolysis product formed from amygdalin is mandelic acid, used in treating common skin problems caused by photo-aging and acne.

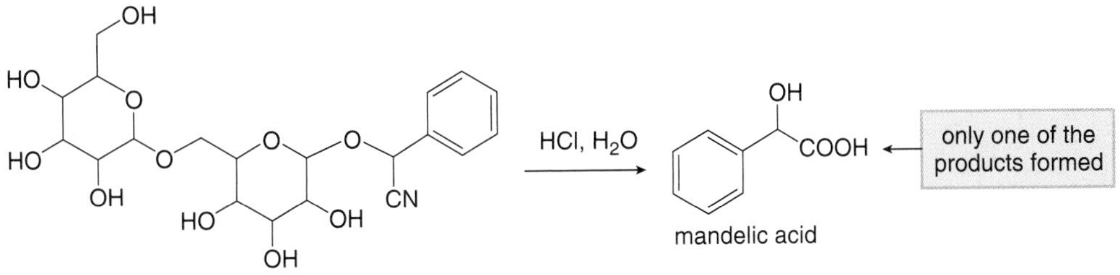
HCl, H_2O
only one of the products formed

mandelic acid

amygdalin

a. How many stereogenic centers are present in amygdalin? What is the maximum number of stereoisomers possible?
b. Draw both enantiomers of mandelic acid and label each stereogenic center as *R* or *S*.
c. Pure (*R*)-mandelic acid has a specific rotation of –154. If a sample contains 60% of the *R* isomer and 40% of its enantiomer, what is [α] of this solution?
d. Calculate the *ee* of a solution of mandelic acid having [α] = +50. What is the percentage of each enantiomer present?

General Problems

5.66 Artemisinin and mefloquine are widely used antimalarial drugs.

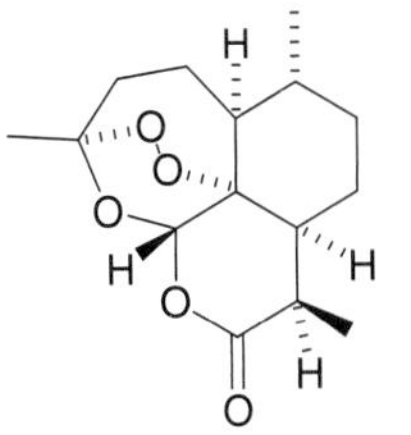

artemisinin

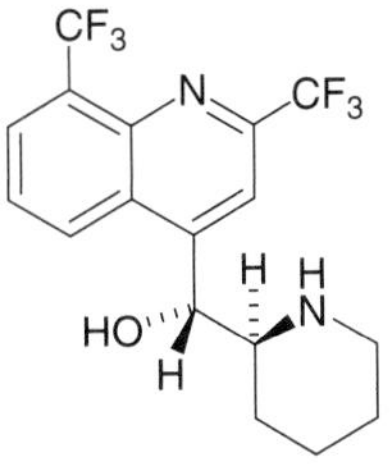

mefloquine

a. Locate the stereogenic centers in both drugs.
b. Label each stereogenic center in mefloquine as *R* or *S*.
c. What is the maximum number of stereoisomers possible for artemisinin?
d. How are the N atoms in mefloquine hybridized?
e. Can two molecules of artemisinin intermolecularly hydrogen bond to each other?
f. What product is formed when mefloquine is treated with HCl?

5.67 Saquinavir (trade name Invirase) belongs to a class of drugs called protease inhibitors, which are used to treat HIV (human immunodeficiency virus).

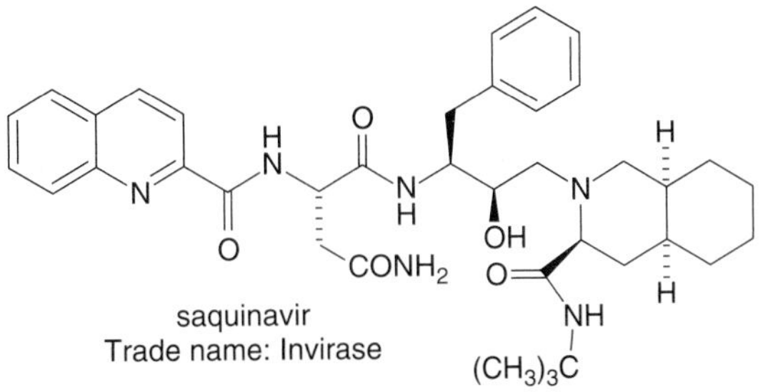

saquinavir
Trade name: Invirase

a. Locate all stereogenic centers in saquinavir, and label each stereogenic center as *R* or *S*.
b. Draw the enantiomer of saquinavir.
c. Draw a diastereomer of saquinavir.
d. Draw a constitutional isomer that contains at least one different functional group.

Challenge Problems

5.68 A limited number of chiral compounds having no stereogenic centers exist. For example, although **A** is achiral, constitutional isomer **B** is chiral. Make models and explain this observation. Compounds containing two double bonds that share a single carbon atom are called *allenes.* Locate the allene in the antibiotic mycomycin and decide whether mycomycin is chiral or achiral.

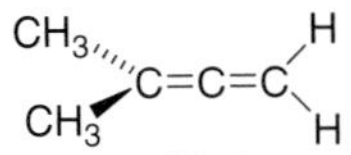

achiral
A

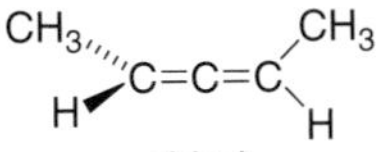

chiral
B

HC≡C–C≡C–CH=C=CH–CH=CH–CH=$CHCH_2CO_2H$
mycomycin

5.69 A trivalent, positively charged sulfur atom, called a sulfonium ion (R_3S^+), is a stereogenic center if three different alkyl groups are bonded to sulfur. In this case, sulfur is surrounded by four different groups, including its lone pair. In assigning an *R* or *S* designation to sulfur, the lone pair is always assigned the lowest priority (4). An example of a biologically active compound that contains a sulfonium ion is SAM, *S*-adenosylmethionine, which we will learn more about in Section 7.12. Locate all the stereogenic centers in SAM, and assign an *R,S* designation to each center.

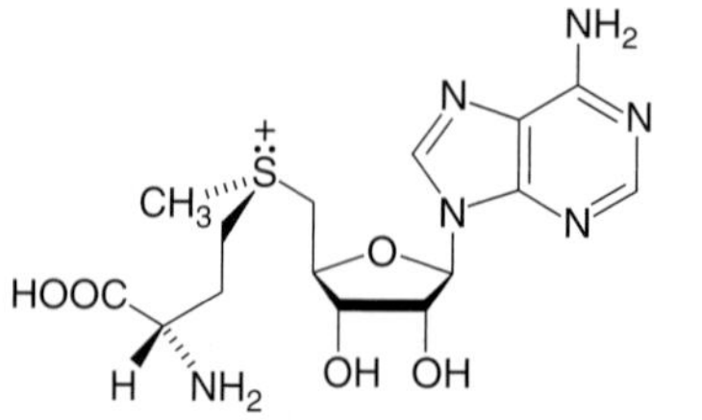

SAM

5.70 a. Locate all the tetrahedral stereogenic centers in discodermolide, a natural product isolated from the Caribbean marine sponge *Discodermia dissoluta.* Discodermolide is a potent tumor inhibitor, and shows promise as a drug for treating colon, ovarian, and breast cancers.

b. Certain carbon–carbon double bonds can also be stereogenic centers. With reference to the definition in Section 5.3, explain how this can occur, and then locate the three additional stereogenic centers in discodermolide.

c. Considering all stereogenic centers, what is the maximum number of stereoisomers possible for discodermolide?

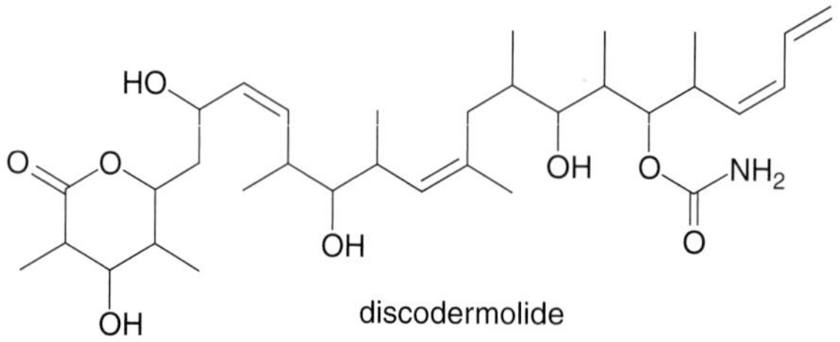

discodermolide

5.71 Label each compound as chiral or achiral. Compounds that contain a single carbon common to two rings are called spiro compounds. Because carbon is tetrahedral, the two rings are perpendicular to each other.

a. 

b. 

c. 

d. 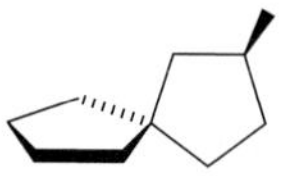

5.72 An acid–base reaction of (*R*)-*sec*-butylamine with a racemic mixture of 2-phenylpropanoic acid forms two products having different melting points and somewhat different solubilities. Draw the structure of these two products. Assign *R* and *S* to any stereogenic centers in the products. How are the two products related? Choose from enantiomers, diastereomers, constitutional isomers, or not isomers.

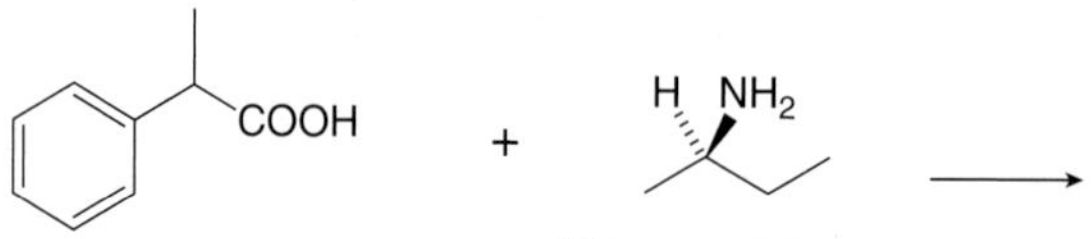

2-phenylpropanoic acid (racemic mixture)

(*R*)-*sec*-butylamine

Understanding Organic Reactions

6

6.1 Writing equations for organic reactions
6.2 Kinds of organic reactions
6.3 Bond breaking and bond making
6.4 Bond dissociation energy
6.5 Thermodynamics
6.6 Enthalpy and entropy
6.7 Energy diagrams
6.8 Energy diagram for a two-step reaction mechanism
6.9 Kinetics
6.10 Catalysts
6.11 Enzymes

Isooctane, a component of petroleum, and **glucose,** a simple sugar formed from starch during digestion, are very different organic molecules that share a common feature. On oxidation, both compounds release a great deal of energy. Isooctane is burned in gasoline to power automobiles, and glucose is metabolized in the body to provide energy for exercise. In Chapter 6, we learn about these energy changes that accompany chemical reactions.

Why do certain reactions occur when two compounds are mixed together whereas others do not? To answer this question we must learn how and why organic compounds react.

Reactions are at the heart of organic chemistry. An understanding of chemical processes has made possible the conversion of natural substances into new compounds with different, and sometimes superior, properties. Aspirin, ibuprofen, nylon, and polyethylene are all products of chemical reactions between substances derived from petroleum.

Reactions are difficult to learn when each reaction is considered a unique and isolated event. *Avoid this tendency.* Virtually all chemical reactions are woven together by a few basic themes. After we learn the general principles, specific reactions then fit neatly into a general pattern.

In our study of organic reactions we will begin with the functional groups, looking for electron-rich and electron-deficient sites, and bonds that might be broken easily. These reactive sites give us a clue as to the general type of reaction a particular class of compound undergoes. Finally, we will learn about how a reaction occurs. Does it occur in one step or in a series of steps? Understanding the details of an organic reaction allows us to determine when it might be used in preparing interesting and useful organic compounds.

6.1 Writing Equations for Organic Reactions

Often the solvent and temperature of a reaction are omitted from chemical equations, to further focus attention on the main substances involved in the reaction.

Solvent. Most organic reactions take place in a **liquid solvent.** Solvents solubilize key reaction components and serve as heat reservoirs to maintain a given temperature. Chapter 7 presents the two major types of reaction solvents and how they affect substitution reactions.

Like other reactions, equations for organic reactions are usually drawn with a single reaction arrow (→) between the starting material and product, but other conventions make these equations look different from those encountered in general chemistry.

The **reagent,** the chemical substance with which an organic compound reacts, is sometimes drawn on the left side of the equation with the other reactants. At other times, the reagent is drawn above the reaction arrow itself, to focus attention on the organic starting material by itself on the left side. The solvent and temperature of a reaction may be added above or below the arrow. **The symbols "*hν*" and "Δ" are used for reactions that require *light* or *heat,* respectively.** Figure 6.1 presents an organic reaction in different ways.

When two sequential reactions are carried out without drawing any intermediate compound, the steps are usually numbered above or below the reaction arrow. This convention signifies that the first step occurs *before* the second, and the reagents are added *in sequence,* not at the same time.

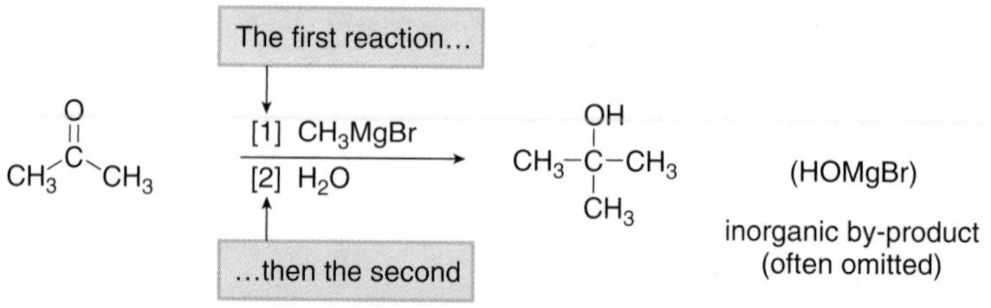

In this equation only the organic product is drawn on the right side of the arrow. Although the reagent CH_3MgBr contains both Mg and Br, these elements do not appear in the organic product, and they are often omitted on the product side of the equation. These elements have not disappeared. They are part of an inorganic by-product (HOMgBr in this case), and are often of little interest to an organic chemist.

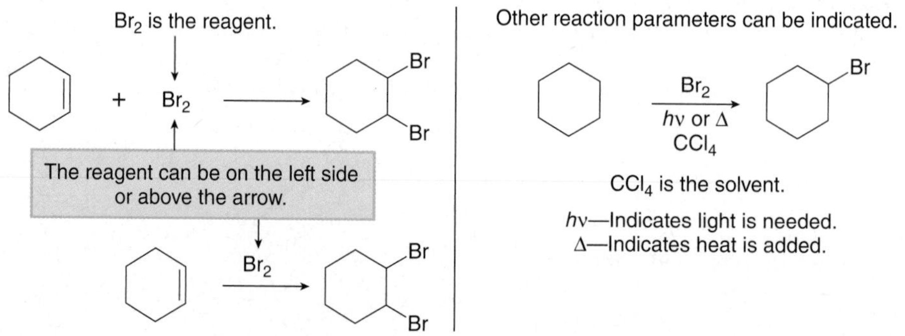

Figure 6.1
Different ways of writing organic reactions

6.2 Kinds of Organic Reactions

Like other compounds, organic molecules undergo acid–base and oxidation–reduction reactions, as discussed in Chapters 2 and 4. Organic molecules also undergo **substitution, elimination,** and **addition** reactions.

6.2A Substitution Reactions

- ***Substitution*** **is a reaction in which an atom or a group of atoms is *replaced* by another atom or group of atoms.**

Substitution

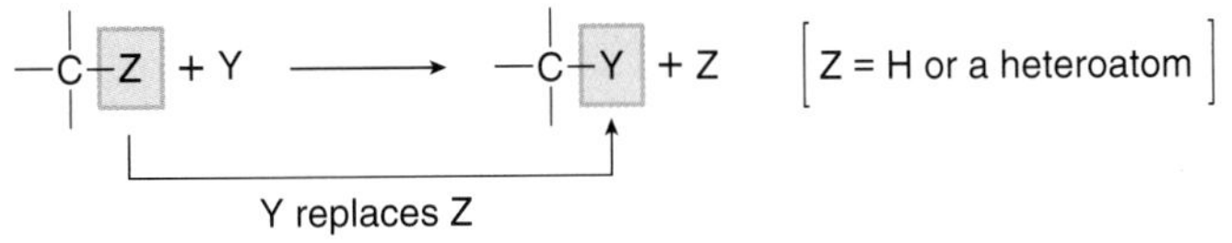

In a general substitution reaction, Y *replaces* Z on a carbon atom. **Substitution reactions involve σ bonds: one σ bond breaks and another forms at the same carbon atom.** The most common examples of substitution occur when Z is hydrogen or a heteroatom that is more electronegative than carbon.

Examples [1] [2]

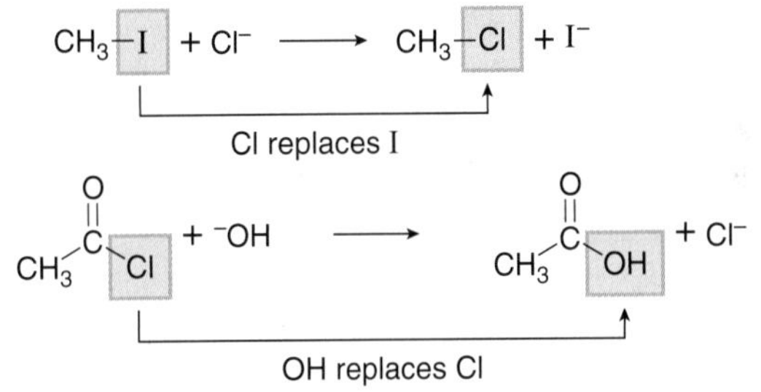

6.2B Elimination Reactions

- ***Elimination*** **is a reaction in which elements of the starting material are "lost" and a π bond is formed.**

Elimination

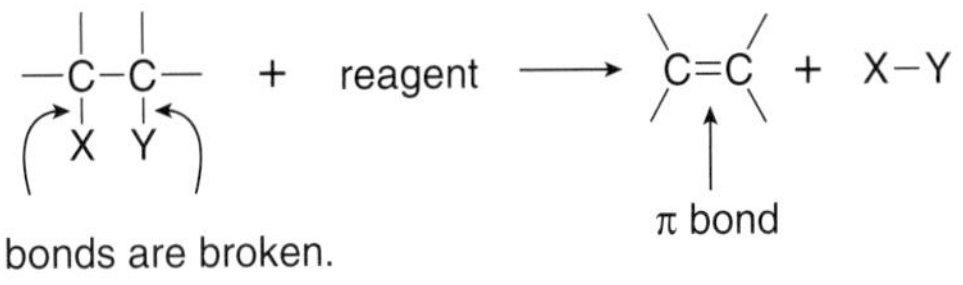

In an elimination reaction, two groups X and Y are removed from a starting material. **Two σ bonds are broken, and a π bond is formed between adjacent atoms.** The most common examples of elimination occur when X = H and Y is a heteroatom more electronegative than carbon.

Examples [1] [2]

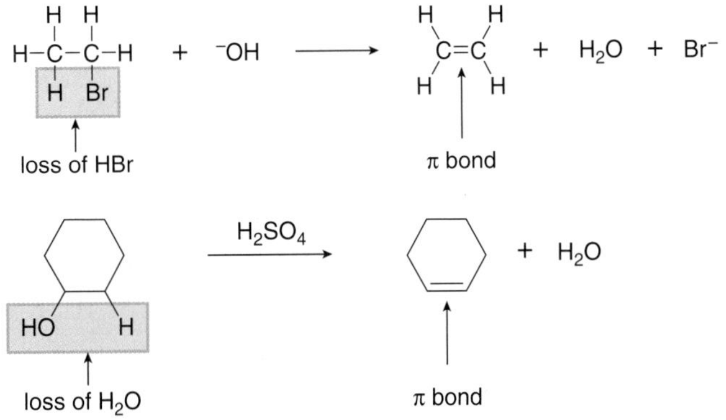

6.2C Addition Reactions

- *Addition* is a reaction in which elements are added to a starting material.

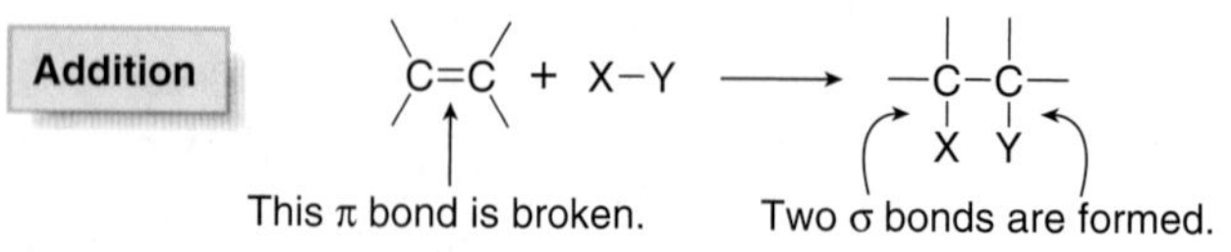
Addition
C=C + X–Y
C–C
X Y
This π bond is broken.
Two σ bonds are formed.

In an addition reaction, new groups X and Y are added to a starting material. **A π bond is broken and two σ bonds are formed.**

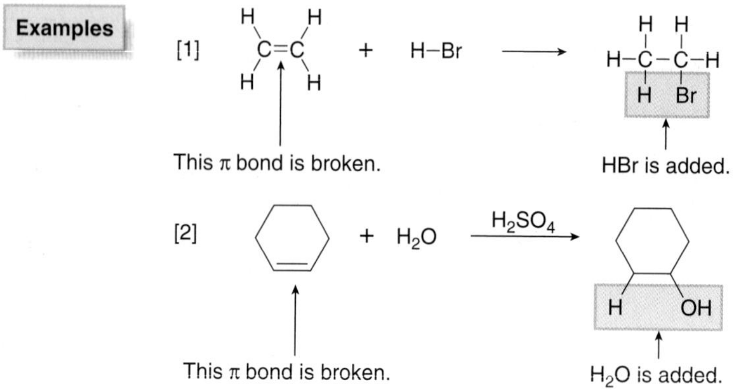
Examples
[1]
H–Br
HBr is added.
This π bond is broken.
[2]
+ H2O
H2SO4
H
OH
H2O is added.
This π bond is broken.

A summary of the general types of organic reactions is given in Appendix G.

Addition and elimination reactions are exactly opposite. A π bond is *formed* in elimination reactions, whereas a π bond is *broken* in addition reactions.

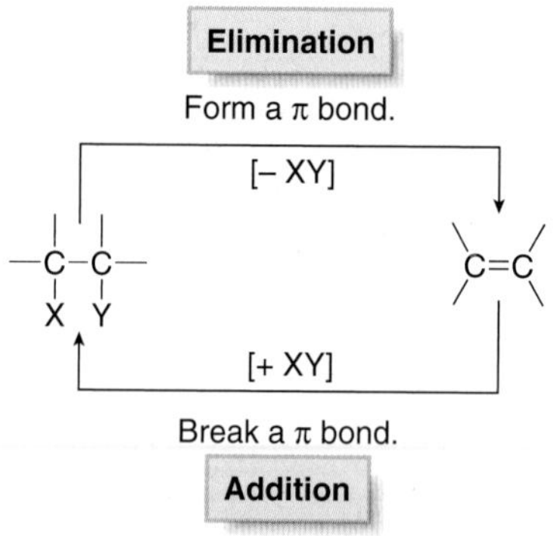
Elimination
Form a π bond.
[– XY]
[+ XY]
Break a π bond.
Addition

Problem 6.1 Classify each transformation as substitution, elimination, or addition.

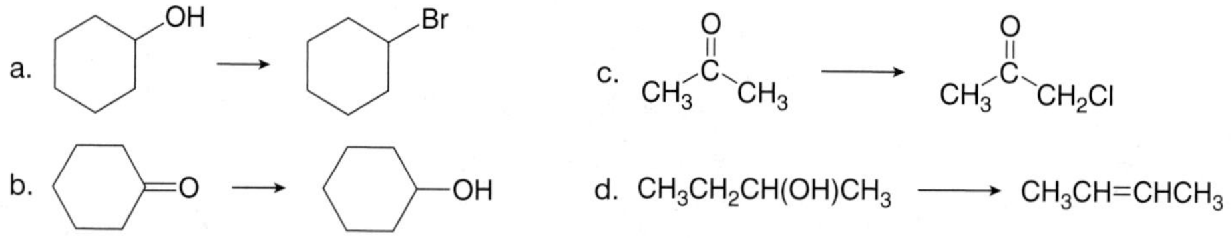
a.
OH
Br
b.
O
OH
c.
CH3
CH3
CH2Cl
d. CH3CH2CH(OH)CH3
CH3CH=CHCH3

6.3 Bond Breaking and Bond Making

Having now learned how to write and identify some common kinds of organic reactions, we can turn to a discussion of **reaction mechanism.**

- A *reaction mechanism* is a detailed description of how bonds are broken and formed as a starting material is converted to a product.

A reaction mechanism describes the relative order and rate of bond cleavage and formation. It explains all the known facts about a reaction and accounts for all products formed, and it is subject to modification or refinement as new details are discovered.

A reaction can occur either in one step or in a series of steps.

- **A one-step reaction is called a *concerted reaction.*** No matter how many bonds are broken or formed, a starting material is converted *directly* to a product.

$$\text{A} \longrightarrow \text{B}$$

- **A stepwise reaction** involves more than one step. A starting material is first converted to an unstable intermediate, called a **reactive intermediate,** which then goes on to form the product.

$$\text{A} \longrightarrow \text{reactive intermediate} \longrightarrow \text{B}$$

6.3A Bond Cleavage

Bonds are broken and formed in all chemical reactions. No matter how many steps there are in the reaction, however, there are only two ways to break (cleave) a bond: the electrons in the bond can be divided **equally** or **unequally** between the two atoms of the bond.

- Breaking a bond by **equally dividing the electrons** between the two atoms in the bond is called **homolysis** or **homolytic cleavage.**

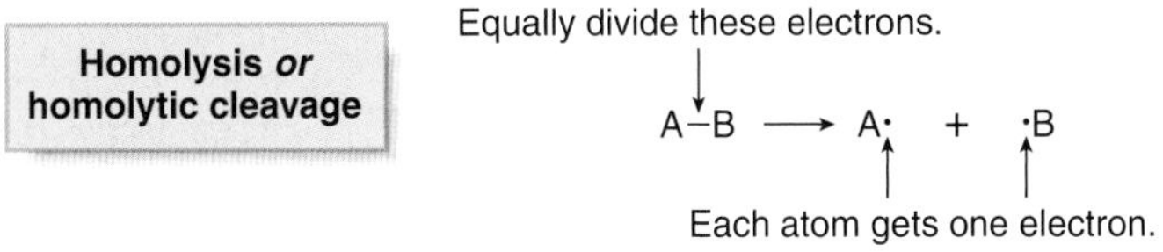

- Breaking a bond by **unequally dividing the electrons** between the two atoms in the bond is called **heterolysis** or **heterolytic cleavage.** Heterolysis of a bond between **A** and **B** can give either **A** or **B** the two electrons in the bond. When **A** and **B** have different electronegativities, the ***electrons normally end up on the more electronegative atom.***

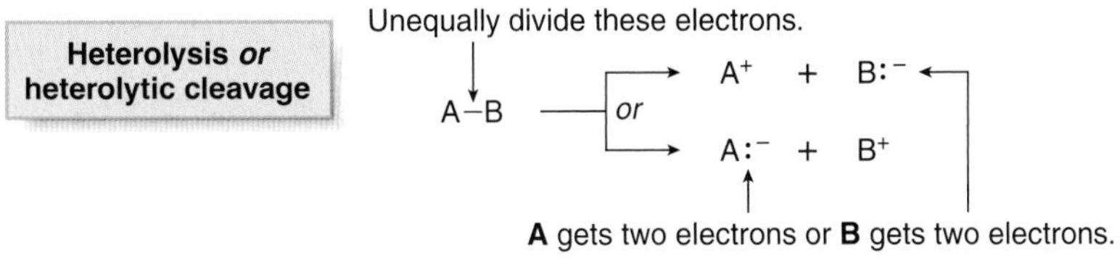

Homolysis and heterolysis require energy. Both processes generate reactive intermediates, but the products are different in each case.

- Homolysis generates uncharged reactive intermediates with *unpaired* electrons.
- Heterolysis generates *charged* intermediates.

Each of these reactive intermediates has a very short lifetime, and each reacts quickly to form a stable organic product.

6.3B Radicals, Carbocations, and Carbanions

The curved arrow notation first discussed in Section 1.6 works fine for heterolytic bond cleavage because it illustrates the movement of an **electron pair.** For homolytic cleavage, however, one electron moves to one atom in the bond and one electron moves to the other, so a different kind of curved arrow is needed.

- **To illustrate the movement of a single electron, use a half-headed curved arrow, sometimes called a *fishhook.***

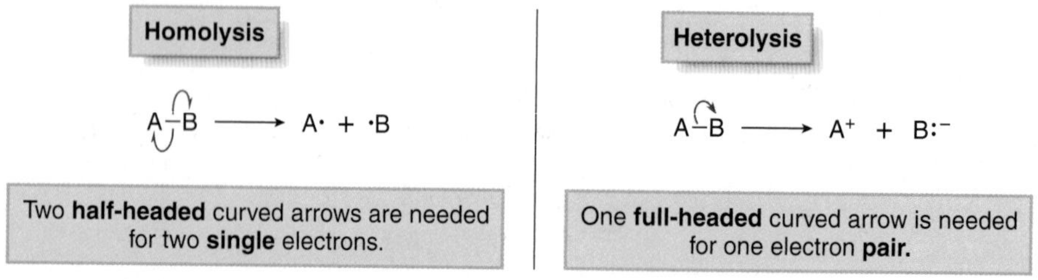

A full-headed curved arrow ( ) shows the movement of an electron *pair.* **A half-headed curved arrow** ( ) shows the movement of a *single* electron.

Figure 6.2 illustrates homolysis and two different heterolysis reactions for a carbon compound using curved arrows. Three different reactive intermediates are formed.

Homolysis of the C–Z bond generates two uncharged products with unpaired electrons.

- **A reactive intermediate with a single unpaired electron is called a *radical.***

Most radicals are highly unstable because they contain an atom that does not have an octet of electrons. Radicals typically have **no charge. They are intermediates in a group of reactions called *radical reactions,*** which are discussed in detail in Chapter 15.

Heterolysis of the C–Z bond can generate a **carbocation** or a **carbanion.**

- **Giving two electrons to Z and none to carbon generates a positively charged carbon intermediate called a *carbocation.***
- **Giving two electrons to C and none to Z generates a negatively charged carbon species called a *carbanion.***

Both carbocations and carbanions are unstable reactive intermediates: A carbocation contains a carbon atom surrounded by only six electrons. A carbanion has a negative charge on carbon, which is not a very electronegative atom. **Carbocations (electrophiles)** and **carbanions (nucleophiles)** can be intermediates in ***polar reactions*—reactions in which a nucleophile reacts with an electrophile.**

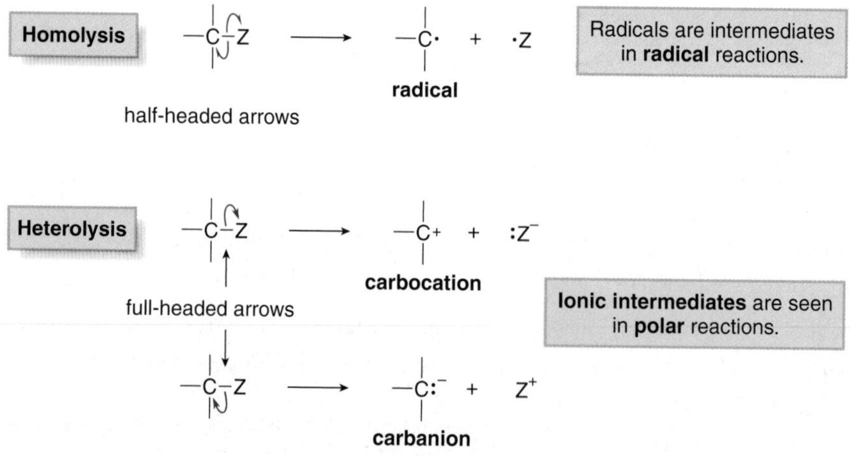

Figure 6.2 Three reactive intermediates resulting from homolysis and heterolysis of a C–Z bond

The chemistry of **carbenes,** another type of organic reactive intermediate, is discussed in Section 26.4.

Thus, homolysis and heterolysis generate radicals, carbocations, and carbanions, the three most common reactive intermediates in organic chemistry.

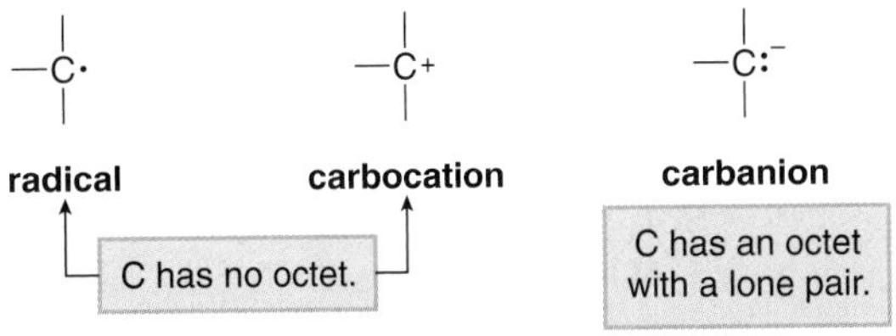

- **Radicals and carbocations are electrophiles because they contain an electron-deficient carbon.**
- **Carbanions are nucleophiles because they contain a carbon with a lone pair.**

Problem 6.2 By taking into account electronegativity differences, draw the products formed by heterolysis of the carbon–heteroatom bond in each molecule. Classify the organic reactive intermediate as a carbocation or a carbanion.

a. 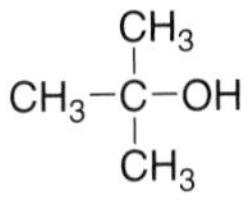

b. 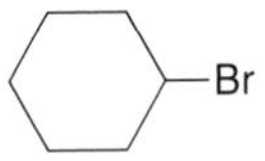

c. CH_3CH_2–Li

6.3C Bond Formation

Like bond cleavage, bond formation occurs in two different ways. Two radicals can each donate **one electron** to form a two-electron bond. Alternatively, two ions with unlike charges can come together, with the negatively charged ion donating **both electrons** to form the resulting two-electron bond. **Bond formation always releases energy.**

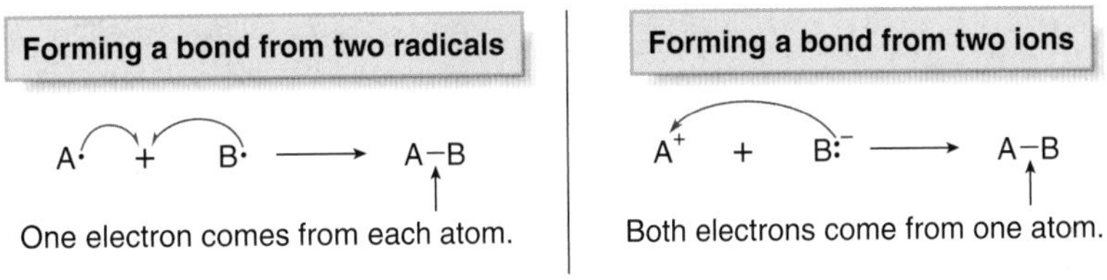

6.3D All Kinds of Arrows

Table 6.1 summarizes the many kinds of arrows used in describing organic reactions. Curved arrows are especially important because they explicitly show what electrons are involved in a reaction, how these electrons move in forming and breaking bonds, and if a reaction proceeds via a radical or polar pathway.

A more complete summary of the arrows used in organic chemistry is given in the table Common Abbreviations, Arrows, and Symbols, located on the inside back cover.

Table 6.1 A Summary of Arrow Types in Chemical Reactions

Arrow	Name	Use
→	Reaction arrow	Drawn between the starting materials and products in an equation (6.1)
⇌	Double reaction arrows (equilibrium arrows)	Drawn between the starting materials and products in an equilibrium equation (2.2)
↔	Double-headed arrow	Drawn between resonance structures (1.6)
	Full-headed curved arrow	Shows movement of an electron pair (1.6, 2.2)
	Half-headed curved arrow (fishhook)	Shows movement of a single electron (6.3)

Sample Problem 6.1 Use full-headed or half-headed curved arrows to show the movement of electrons in each equation.

a. 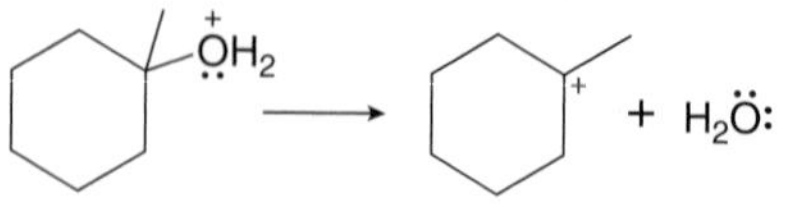

b. 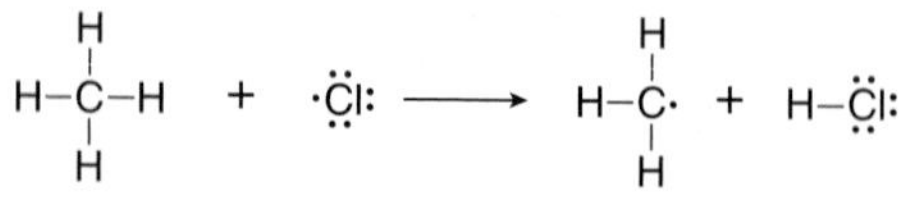

Solution

a. In this reaction, the C–O bond is broken heterolytically. Because only one electron pair is involved, **one full-headed curved arrow** is needed.

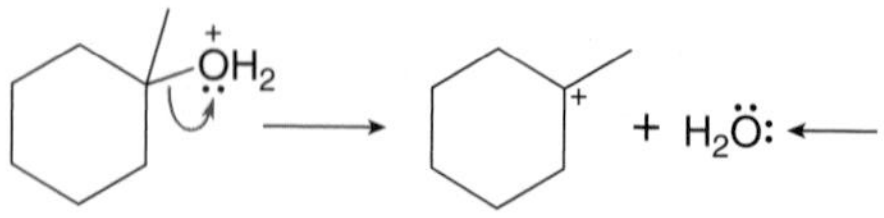
The electron pair in the C–O bond ends up on O.

b. This reaction involves radicals, so half-headed curved arrows are needed to show the movement of single electrons. One new two-electron bond is formed between H and Cl, and an unpaired electron is left on C. Because a total of three electrons are involved, **three half-headed curved arrows are needed.**

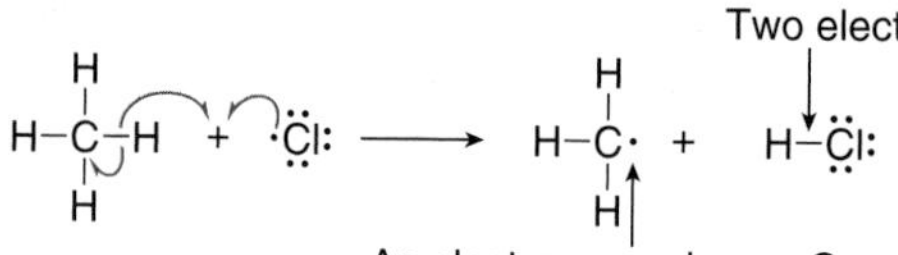
Two electrons form a bond.
An electron remains on C.

Problem 6.3 Use curved arrows to show the movement of electrons in each equation.

a. $(CH_3)_3C{-}\overset{+}{N}{\equiv}N{:}$ ⟶ $(CH_3)_3C^+$ + $:N{\equiv}N:$

b. $\cdot CH_3$ + $\cdot CH_3$ ⟶ $CH_3{-}CH_3$

c. 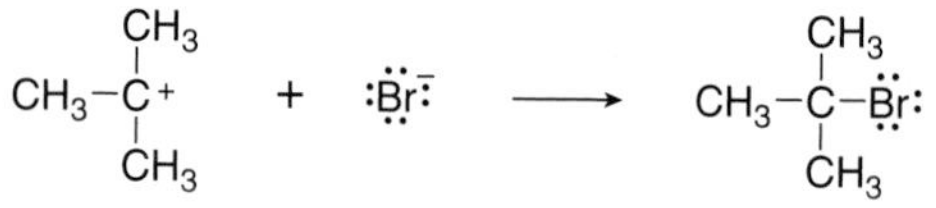

d. $H\ddot{O}{-}\ddot{O}H$ ⟶ $2\ H\ddot{O}\cdot$

6.4 Bond Dissociation Energy

Bond breaking can be quantified using the bond dissociation energy.

- **The *bond dissociation energy* is the energy needed to homolytically cleave a covalent bond.**

$$A{-}B \longrightarrow A\cdot + \cdot B \qquad \Delta H^\circ = \text{bond dissociation energy}$$

Homolysis requires energy.

The superscript (°) means that values are determined under standard conditions (pure compounds in their most stable state at 25 °C and 1 atm pressure).

The energy absorbed or released in any reaction, symbolized by ΔH°, is called the **enthalpy change** or **heat of reaction.**

- **When ΔH° is positive (+), energy is absorbed and the reaction is *endothermic*.**
- **When ΔH° is negative (–), energy is released and the reaction is *exothermic*.**

Additional bond dissociation energies for C–C multiple bonds are given in Table 1.5.

A bond dissociation energy is the $\Delta H°$ for a specific kind of reaction—the homolysis of a covalent bond to form two radicals. Because bond breaking requires energy, **bond dissociation energies are always *positive* numbers,** and homolysis is always **endothermic.** Conversely, **bond formation always *releases* energy,** so this reaction is always **exothermic.** The H–H bond requires +435 kJ/mol to cleave and releases –435 kJ/mol when formed. Table 6.2 contains a representative list of bond dissociation energies for many common bonds.

A table of bond dissociation energies also appears in Appendix C.

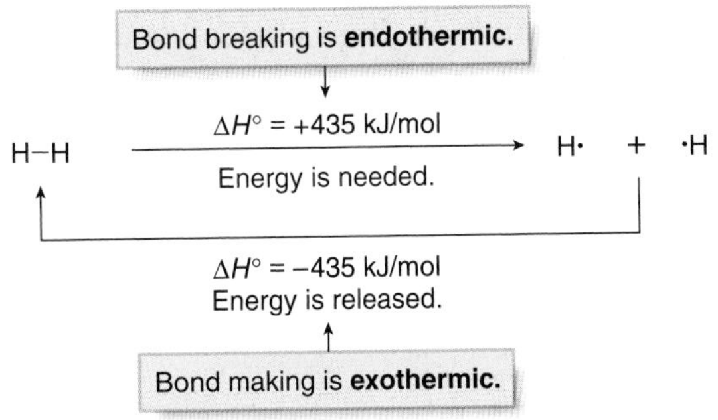

Table 6.2 Bond Dissociation Energies for Some Common Bonds [A–B → A· + ·B]

Bond	$\Delta H°$ kJ/mol	(kcal/mol)
H–Z bonds		
H–F	569	(136)
H–Cl	431	(103)
H–Br	368	(88)
H–I	297	(71)
H–OH	498	(119)
Z–Z bonds		
H–H	435	(104)
F–F	159	(38)
Cl–Cl	242	(58)
Br–Br	192	(46)
I–I	151	(36)
HO–OH	213	(51)
R–H bonds		
CH_3–H	435	(104)
CH_3CH_2–H	410	(98)
$CH_3CH_2CH_2$–H	410	(98)
$(CH_3)_2CH$–H	397	(95)
$(CH_3)_3C$–H	381	(91)
CH_2=CH–H	435	(104)
HC≡C–H	523	(125)
CH_2=$CHCH_2$–H	364	(87)
C_6H_5–H	460	(110)
$C_6H_5CH_2$–H	356	(85)
R–R bonds		
CH_3–CH_3	368	(88)
CH_3–CH_2CH_3	356	(85)
CH_3–CH=CH_2	385	(92)
CH_3–C≡CH	489	(117)
R–X bonds		
CH_3–F	456	(109)
CH_3–Cl	351	(84)
CH_3–Br	293	(70)
CH_3–I	234	(56)
CH_3CH_2–F	448	(107)
CH_3CH_2–Cl	339	(81)
CH_3CH_2–Br	285	(68)
CH_3CH_2–I	222	(53)
$(CH_3)_2CH$–F	444	(106)
$(CH_3)_2CH$–Cl	335	(80)
$(CH_3)_2CH$–Br	285	(68)
$(CH_3)_2CH$–I	222	(53)
$(CH_3)_3C$–F	444	(106)
$(CH_3)_3C$–Cl	331	(79)
$(CH_3)_3C$–Br	272	(65)
$(CH_3)_3C$–I	209	(50)
R–OH bonds		
CH_3–OH	389	(93)
CH_3CH_2–OH	393	(94)
$CH_3CH_2CH_2$–OH	385	(92)
$(CH_3)_2CH$–OH	401	(96)
$(CH_3)_3C$–OH	401	(96)

Comparing bond dissociation energies is equivalent to comparing **bond strength.**

- The *stronger* the bond, the *higher* its bond dissociation energy.

For example, the H–H bond is stronger than the Cl–Cl bond because its bond dissociation energy is higher [Table 6.2: 435 kJ/mol (H_2) versus 242 kJ/mol (Cl_2)]. The data in Table 6.2 demonstrate that **bond dissociation energies *decrease* down a column of the periodic table as the valence electrons used in bonding are farther from the nucleus.** Bond dissociation energies for a group of methyl–halogen bonds exemplify this trend.

Increasing size of the halogen →

CH_3–F	CH_3–Cl	CH_3–Br	CH_3–I
$\Delta H°$ = 456 kJ/mol	351 kJ/mol	293 kJ/mol	234 kJ/mol

← **Increasing bond strength**

Because bond length increases down a column of the periodic table, bond dissociation energies are a quantitative measure of the general phenomenon noted in Chapter 1—***shorter* bonds are *stronger* bonds.**

Problem 6.4 Without looking at a table of bond dissociation energies, determine which bond in each pair has the higher bond dissociation energy.

a. H–Cl or H–Br b. CH_3–OH or CH_3–SH c. $(CH_3)_2C{=}O$ or CH_3–OCH_3 (↑ σ + π bond) (↑)

Bond dissociation energies are also used to calculate the enthalpy change ($\Delta H°$) in a reaction in which several bonds are broken and formed. **$\Delta H°$ indicates the relative strength of bonds broken and formed in a reaction.**

- **When $\Delta H°$ is positive, more energy is needed to break bonds than is released in forming bonds. The bonds broken in the starting material are *stronger* than the bonds formed in the product.**

- **When $\Delta H°$ is negative, more energy is released in forming bonds than is needed to break bonds. The bonds formed in the product are *stronger* than the bonds broken in the starting material.**

To determine the overall $\Delta H°$ for a reaction:

[1] Beginning with a *balanced* equation, add the bond dissociation energies for all bonds broken in the starting materials. This (+) value represents the **energy needed** to break bonds.

[2] Add the bond dissociation energies for all bonds formed in the products. This (–) value represents the **energy released** in forming bonds.

[3] **The overall $\Delta H°$ is the sum in Step [1] *plus* the sum in Step [2].**

$\Delta H°$ **overall enthalpy change**	=	sum of $\Delta H°$ of bonds broken	+	(–) sum of $\Delta H°$ of bonds formed

Sample Problem 6.2 Use the values in Table 6.2 to determine $\Delta H°$ for the following reaction.

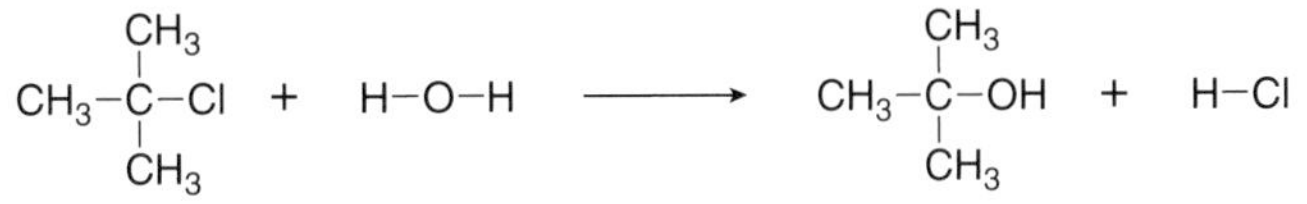

Solution

[1] Bonds broken

	$\Delta H°$ (kJ/mol)
$(CH_3)_3C{-}Cl$	+331
$H{-}OH$	+498
Total	+829 kJ/mol

Energy needed to break bonds.

[2] Bonds formed

	$\Delta H°$ (kJ/mol)
$(CH_3)_3C{-}OH$	−401
$H{-}Cl$	−431
Total	−832 kJ/mol

Energy released in forming bonds.

[3] Overall $\Delta H°$ =

sum in Step [1]
+
sum in Step [2]

+829 kJ/mol
−832 kJ/mol

Answer: −3 kJ/mol

Because $\Delta H°$ is a negative value, this reaction is **exothermic** and energy is released. **The bonds broken in the starting material are weaker than the bonds formed in the product.**

Problem 6.5 Use the values in Table 6.2 to calculate $\Delta H°$ for each reaction. Classify each reaction as endothermic or exothermic.

a. $CH_3CH_2{-}Br + H_2O \longrightarrow CH_3CH_2{-}OH + HBr$ b. $CH_4 + Cl_2 \longrightarrow CH_3Cl + HCl$

The oxidation of both isooctane and glucose, the two molecules that introduced Chapter 6, forms CO_2 and H_2O.

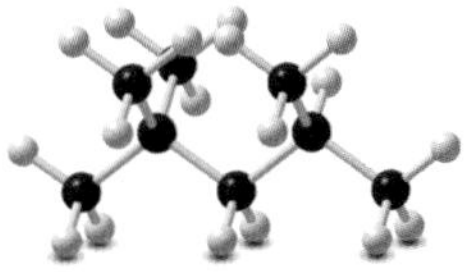

$(CH_3)_3CCH_2CH(CH_3)_2 + (25/2)\ O_2 \longrightarrow 8\ CO_2 + 9\ H_2O$ $\Delta H° = -5447$ kJ/mol

isooctane

Energy is released.

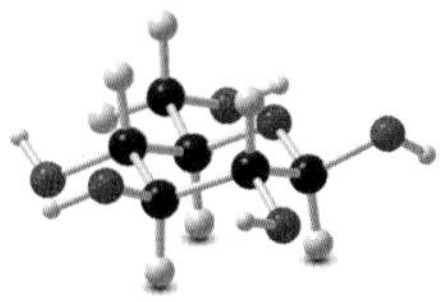

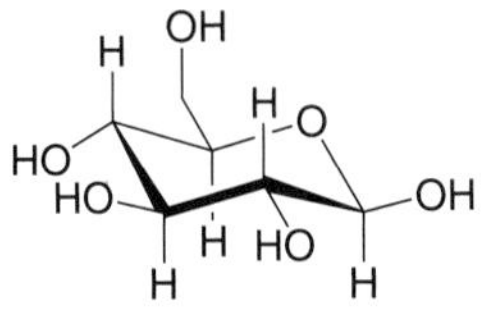

$+ 6\ O_2 \longrightarrow 6\ CO_2 + 6\ H_2O$ $\Delta H° = -2872$ kJ/mol

glucose

$\Delta H°$ is negative for both oxidations, so both reactions are exothermic. **Both isooctane and glucose release energy on oxidation because the bonds in the products are stronger than the bonds in the reactants.**

Bond dissociation energies have two important limitations. They present *overall* energy changes only. They reveal nothing about the reaction mechanism or how fast a reaction proceeds. Moreover, bond dissociation energies are determined for reactions in the gas phase, whereas most organic reactions are carried out in a liquid solvent where solvation energy contributes to the overall enthalpy of a reaction. As such, bond dissociation energies are imperfect indicators of energy changes in a reaction. Despite these limitations, using bond dissociation energies to calculate $\Delta H°$ gives a useful approximation of the energy changes that occur when bonds are broken and formed in a reaction.

Problem 6.6 Calculate $\Delta H°$ for each oxidation reaction. Each equation is balanced as written; remember to take into account the coefficients in determining the number of bonds broken or formed.
[$\Delta H°$ for O_2 = 497 kJ/mol; $\Delta H°$ for one C=O in CO_2 = 535 kJ/mol]

a. $CH_4 + 2\ O_2 \longrightarrow CO_2 + 2\ H_2O$ b. $2\ CH_3CH_3 + 7\ O_2 \longrightarrow 4\ CO_2 + 6\ H_2O$

6.5 Thermodynamics

For a reaction to be practical, the equilibrium must favor the products, *and* the reaction rate must be fast enough to form them in a reasonable time. These two conditions depend on the **thermodynamics** and the **kinetics** of a reaction, respectively.

- *Thermodynamics* describes energy and equilibrium. How do the *energies* of the reactants and the products compare? What are the relative *amounts* of reactants and products at equilibrium?

Reaction kinetics are discussed in Section 6.9.

- *Kinetics* describes reaction rates. How *fast* are reactants converted to products?

6.5A Equilibrium Constant and Free Energy Changes

K_{eq} was first defined in Section 2.3 for acid–base reactions.

The **equilibrium constant, K_{eq},** is a mathematical expression that relates the amount of starting material and product at equilibrium. For example, when starting materials **A** and **B** react to form products **C** and **D,** the equilibrium constant is given by the following expression.

Reaction

$$A + B \rightleftharpoons C + D$$

Equilibrium constant

$$K_{eq} = \frac{[\text{products}]}{[\text{starting materials}]} = \frac{[C][D]}{[A][B]}$$

The size of K_{eq} tells about the position of equilibrium; that is, it expresses whether the starting materials or products predominate once equilibrium has been reached.

- When $K_{eq} > 1$, equilibrium favors the products (**C** and **D**) and the equilibrium lies to the right as the equation is written.
- When $K_{eq} < 1$, equilibrium favors the starting materials (**A** and **B**) and the equilibrium lies to the left as the equation is written.

- **For a reaction to be useful, the equilibrium must favor the products, and $K_{eq} > 1$.**

What determines whether equilibrium favors the products in a given reaction? **The position of equilibrium is determined by the relative energies of the reactants and products.** The free energy of a molecule, also called its **Gibbs free energy,** is symbolized by ***G*°**. The **change in free energy** between reactants and products, symbolized by $\Delta G°$, determines whether the starting materials or products are favored at equilibrium.

- **$\Delta G°$ is the overall energy difference between reactants and products.**

Free energy change

$$\Delta G° = G°_{\text{products}} - G°_{\text{reactants}}$$

$G°_{\text{products}}$: free energy of the products

$G°_{\text{reactants}}$: free energy of the reactants

$\Delta G°$ is related to the equilibrium constant K_{eq} by the following equation:

$$\Delta G° = -2.303RT\log K_{eq}$$

[R = 8.314 J/(K•mol), the gas constant; T = Kelvin temperature (K)]

K_{eq} depends on the energy difference between reactants and products.

Using this expression we can determine the relationship between the equilibrium constant and the free energy change between reactants and products.

At 25 °C, $2.303RT = 5.9$ kJ/mol; thus, $\Delta G° = -5.9\log K_{eq}$.

$K_{eq} > 1$ when $\Delta G° < 0$, and equilibrium favors the products. $K_{eq} < 1$ when $\Delta G° > 0$, and equilibrium favors the starting materials.

- **When $K_{eq} > 1$, $\log K_{eq}$ is positive, making $\Delta G°$ negative, and energy is released. Thus, equilibrium favors the products when the energy of the products is *lower* than the energy of the reactants.**
- **When $K_{eq} < 1$, $\log K_{eq}$ is negative, making $\Delta G°$ positive, and energy is absorbed. Thus, equilibrium favors the reactants when the energy of the products is *higher* than the energy of the reactants.**

Compounds that are lower in energy have increased stability. Thus, **equilibrium favors the products when they are more stable (lower in energy) than the starting materials of a reaction.** This is summarized in Figure 6.3.

Figure 6.3

Summary of the relationship between $\Delta G°$ and K_{eq}

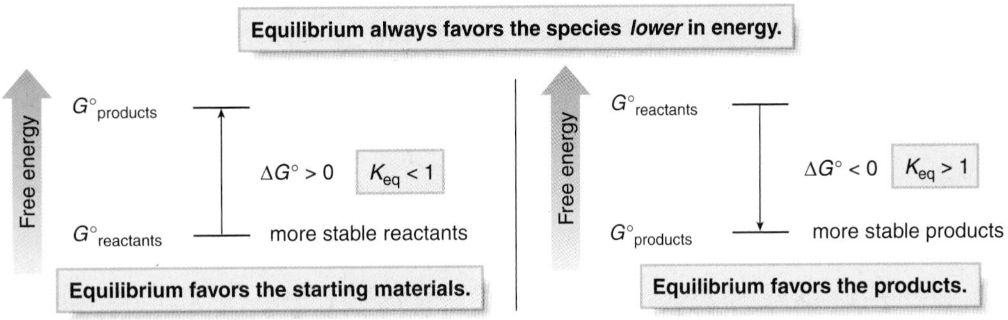

Because $\Delta G°$ depends on the logarithm of K_{eq}, a **small change in energy corresponds to a large difference in the relative amount of starting material and product at equilibrium.** Several values of $\Delta G°$ and K_{eq} are given in Table 6.3. For example, a difference in energy of only ~6 kJ/mol means that there is 10 times as much of the more stable species at equilibrium. A difference in energy of ~18 kJ/mol means that there is essentially only one compound, either starting material or product, at equilibrium.

The symbol ~ means *approximately.*

Table 6.3 Representative Values for $\Delta G°$ and K_{eq} at 25 °C, for a Reaction A → B

$\Delta G°$ (kJ/mol)	K_{eq}	Relative amount of A and B at equilibrium
+18	**10^{-3}**	**Essentially all A (99.9%)**
+12	10^{-2}	100 times as much **A** as **B**
+6	10^{-1}	10 times as much **A** as **B**
0	1	Equal amounts of **A** and **B**
−6	10^{1}	10 times as much **B** as **A**
−12	10^{2}	100 times as much **B** as **A**
−18	**10^{3}**	**Essentially all B (99.9%)**

Increasing [product]

A small difference in free energy means a large difference in the amount of **A** and **B** at equilibrium.

Problem 6.7 a. Which K_{eq} corresponds to a negative value of $\Delta G°$, $K_{eq} = 1000$ or $K_{eq} = .001$?
b. Which K_{eq} corresponds to a lower value of $\Delta G°$, $K_{eq} = 10^{-2}$ or $K_{eq} = 10^{-5}$?

Problem 6.8 Given each of the following values, is the starting material or product favored at equilibrium?
a. $K_{eq} = 5.5$ b. $\Delta G° = 40$ kJ/mol

Problem 6.9 Given each of the following values, is the starting material or product lower in energy?
a. $\Delta G° = 8.0$ kJ/mol b. $K_{eq} = 10$ c. $\Delta G° = -12$ kJ/mol d. $K_{eq} = 10^{-3}$

6.5B Energy Changes and Conformational Analysis

These equations can be used for any process with two states in equilibrium. As an example, monosubstituted cyclohexanes exist as two different chair conformations that rapidly interconvert at room temperature, with the conformation having the substituent in the roomier equatorial position favored (Section 4.13). Knowing the energy difference between the two conformations allows us to calculate the amount of each at equilibrium.

For example, the energy difference between the two chair conformations of phenylcyclohexane is –12.1 kJ/mol, as shown in the accompanying equation. Using the values in Table 6.3, this corresponds to an equilibrium constant of ~100, meaning that there is approximately 100 times more **B** (equatorial phenyl group) than **A** (axial phenyl group) at equilibrium.

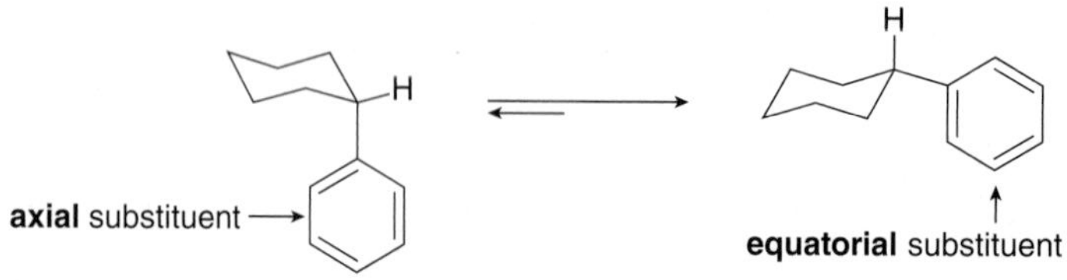
H
H
axial substituent
equatorial substituent

$\Delta G° = -12.1$ kJ/mol

A **B**

$\Delta G° = -2.303RT \log K_{eq}$

–12.1 kJ/mol → $K_{eq} = \sim 100$ → ~100 times more **B** than **A** at equilibrium

Problem 6.10 The equilibrium constant for the conversion of the axial to the equatorial conformation of methoxycyclohexane is 2.7.

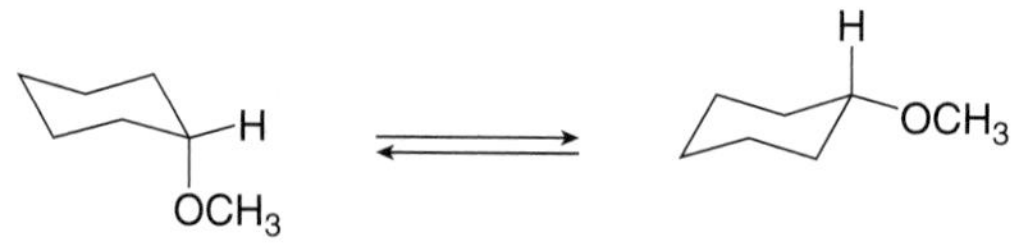
H
OCH3
H
OCH3

$K_{eq} = 2.7$

a. Given these data, which conformation is present in the larger amount at equilibrium?
b. Is $\Delta G°$ for this process positive or negative?
c. From the values in Table 6.3, approximate the size of $\Delta G°$.

6.6 Enthalpy and Entropy

The **free energy change ($\Delta G°$)** depends on the **enthalpy change ($\Delta H°$)** and the **entropy change ($\Delta S°$).** $\Delta H°$ indicates relative bond strength, but what does $\Delta S°$ measure?

Entropy is a rather intangible concept that comes up again and again in chemistry courses. One way to remember the relation between entropy and disorder is to consider a handful of chopsticks. Dropped on the floor, they are arranged randomly (a state of high entropy). Placed end-to-end in a straight line, they are arranged intentionally (a state of low entropy). The more disordered, random arrangement is favored and easier to achieve energetically.

***Entropy* ($S°$) is a measure of the randomness in a system.** The more freedom of motion or the more disorder present, the higher the entropy. Gas molecules move more freely than liquid molecules and are higher in entropy. Cyclic molecules have more restricted bond rotation than similar acyclic molecules and are lower in entropy.

The *entropy change* ($\Delta S°$) is the change in the amount of disorder between reactants and products. $\Delta S°$ is positive (+) when the products are more disordered than the reactants. $\Delta S°$ is negative (–) when the products are less disordered (more ordered) than the reactants.

- **Reactions resulting in an increase in entropy are favored.**

$\Delta G°$ is related to $\Delta H°$ and $\Delta S°$ by the following equation:

Total energy change → $\Delta G° = \Delta H° - T\Delta S°$ [T = Kelvin temperature]

$\Delta H°$: change in bonding energy

$T\Delta S°$: change in disorder

This equation tells us that the total energy change in a reaction is due to two factors: the change in the **bonding energy** and the change in **disorder.** The change in bonding energy can be calculated from bond dissociation energies (Section 6.4). Entropy changes, on the other hand, are more difficult to assess, but they are important when:

- The number of molecules of starting material *differs* from the number of molecules of product in the balanced chemical equation.
- An acyclic molecule is *cyclized* to a cyclic one, or a cyclic molecule is converted to an acyclic one.

For example, **when a single starting material forms two products,** as in the homolytic cleavage of a bond to form two radicals, **entropy increases** and favors formation of the products. In contrast, **entropy decreases when an acyclic compound forms a ring,** because a ring has fewer degrees of freedom. In this case, therefore, entropy does *not* favor formation of the product.

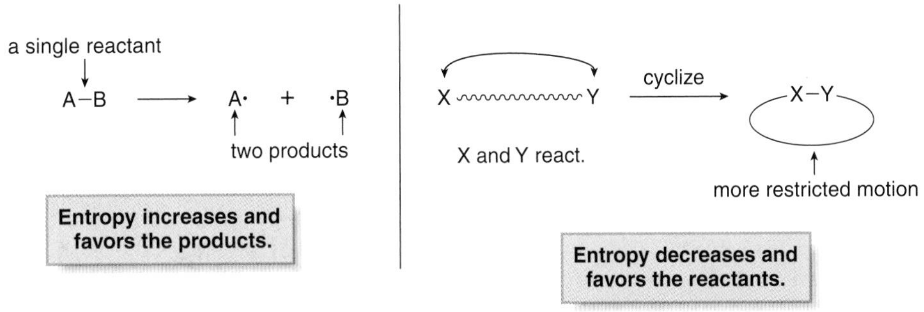

The metabolism of glucose (Section 6.4) is favored by entropy because the number of molecules of products formed (6 CO_2 and 6 H_2O) is greater than the number of molecules of reactants ($C_6H_{12}O_6$ and 6 O_2). Moreover, a cyclic reactant is cleaved to form 12 acyclic product molecules.

In most other reactions that are not carried out at high temperature, the entropy term ($T\Delta S°$) is small compared to the enthalpy term ($\Delta H°$) and it can be neglected. Thus, **we will often approximate the overall free energy change of a reaction by the change in the bonding energy only.** Keep in mind that this is an approximation, but it gives us a starting point from which to decide if the reaction is energetically favorable.

Recall from Section 6.4 that a reaction is endothermic when $\Delta H°$ is positive and exothermic when $\Delta H°$ is negative. A reaction is **endergonic when $\Delta G°$ is positive** and **exergonic when $\Delta G°$ is negative.** $\Delta G°$ is usually approximated by $\Delta H°$ in this text, so the terms endergonic and exergonic are rarely used.

$\Delta G° \approx \Delta H°$

- The total energy change is approximated by the change in bonding energy only.

According to this approximation:

- **The product is favored in reactions in which $\Delta H°$ is a *negative* value; that is, the bonds in the product are *stronger* than the bonds in the starting material.**

- **The starting material is favored in a reaction in which $\Delta H°$ is a *positive* value; that is, the bonds in the starting material are *stronger* than the bonds in the product.**

Problem 6.11 Considering each of the following values and neglecting entropy, tell whether the starting material or product is favored at equilibrium: (a) $\Delta H°$ = 80 kJ/mol; (b) $\Delta H°$ = –40 kJ/mol.

Problem 6.12 For a reaction with $\Delta H°$ = 40 kJ/mol, decide which of the following statements is (are) true. Correct any false statement to make it true. (a) The reaction is exothermic; (b) $\Delta G°$ for the reaction is positive; (c) K_{eq} is greater than 1; (d) the bonds in the starting materials are stronger than the bonds in the product; and (e) the product is favored at equilibrium.

Problem 6.13 Answer Problem 6.12 for a reaction with $\Delta H°$ = –20 kJ/mol.

6.7 Energy Diagrams

An **energy diagram** is a schematic representation of the energy changes that take place as reactants are converted to products. An energy diagram indicates how readily a reaction proceeds, how many steps are involved, and how the energies of the reactants, products, and intermediates compare.

Consider, for example, a concerted reaction between molecule **A–B** with anion **C:⁻** to form products **A:⁻** and **B–C.** If the reaction occurs in a single step, the bond between **A** and **B** is broken *as* the bond between **B** and **C** is formed. Let's assume that the products are lower in energy than the reactants in this hypothetical reaction.

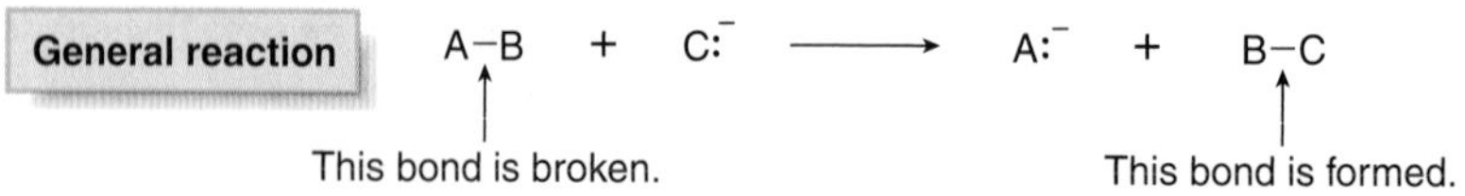

An energy diagram plots **energy on the *y* axis** versus the progress of reaction, often labeled the **reaction coordinate,** on the ***x* axis.** As the starting materials **A–B** and **C:⁻** approach one another, their electron clouds feel some repulsion, causing an increase in energy, until a maximum value is reached. This unstable energy maximum is called the **transition state.** In the transition state the bond between **A** and **B** is partially broken, and the bond between **B** and **C** is partially formed. Because it is at the top of an energy "hill," **a transition state can never be isolated.**

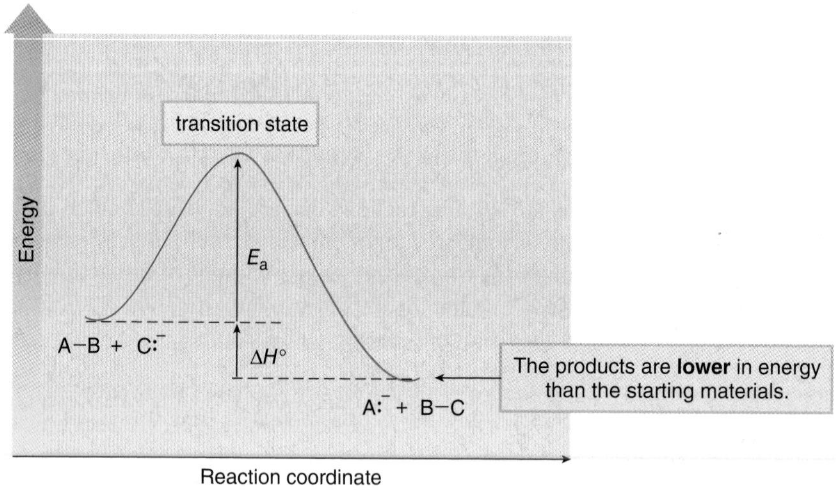

At the transition state, the bond between **A** and **B** can re-form to regenerate starting material, *or* the bond between **B** and **C** can form to generate product. As the bond forms between **B** and **C** the energy decreases until some stable energy minimum of the products is reached.

- **The energy difference between the reactants and products is $\Delta H°$. Because the products are at lower energy than the reactants, this reaction is exothermic and energy is released.**

- **The energy difference between the transition state and the starting material is called the *energy of activation,* symbolized by E_a.**

The *energy of activation* is the minimum amount of energy needed to break bonds in the reactants. It represents an **energy barrier** that must be overcome for a reaction to occur. The size of E_a tells us about the reaction rate.

A slow reaction has a large E_a. A fast reaction has a low E_a.

- **The larger the E_a, the greater the amount of energy that is needed to break bonds, and the slower the reaction rate.**

How can we draw the structure of the unstable transition state? The structure of the transition state is somewhere in between the structures of the starting material and product. Any bond that is partially broken or formed is drawn with a dashed line. Any atom that gains or loses a charge contains a partial charge in the transition state. Transition states are drawn in brackets, with a superscript double dagger (‡).

In the hypothetical reaction between **A – B** and **C:**$^-$ to form **A:**$^-$ and **B – C,** the bond between **A** and **B** is partially broken, and the bond between **B** and **C** is partially formed. Because **A** gains a negative charge and **C** loses a charge in the course of the reaction, each atom bears a partial negative charge in the transition state.

Drawing the structure of a transition state

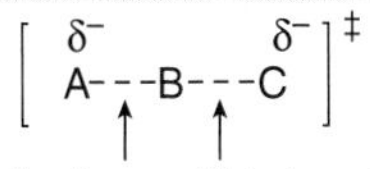

This bond is partially broken. This bond is partially formed.

Several energy diagrams are drawn in Figure 6.4. For any energy diagram:

- **E_a determines the height of the energy barrier.**
- **$\Delta H°$ determines the relative position of the reactants and products.**

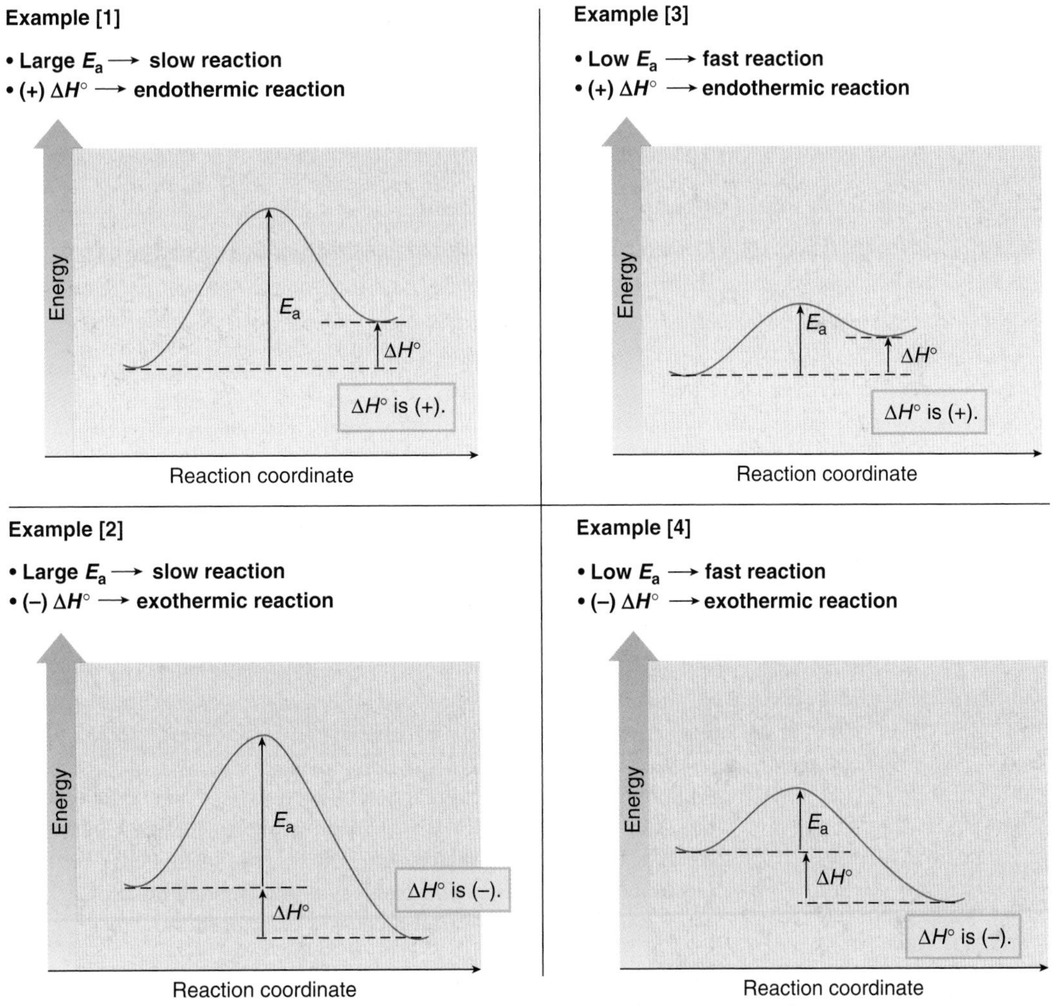

Figure 6.4 Some representative energy diagrams

Figure 6.5
Comparing $\Delta H°$ and E_a in two energy diagrams

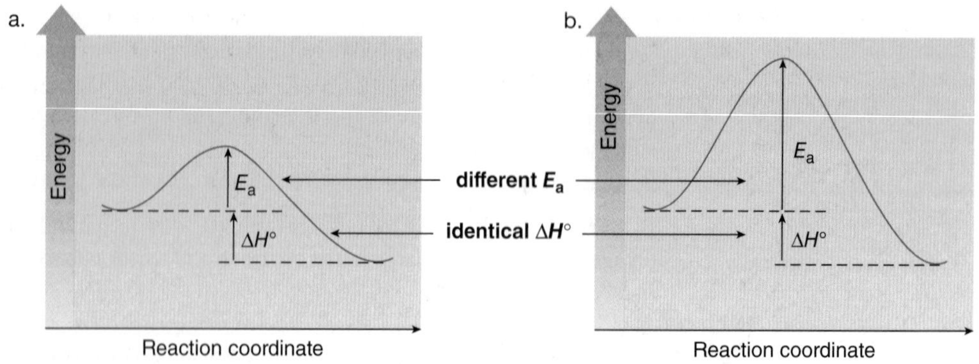

- Energy diagrams in (a) and (b) both depict exothermic reactions with the same negative value of $\Delta H°$.
- E_a in (a) is lower than E_a in (b), so reaction (a) is faster than reaction (b).

The two variables, **E_a and $\Delta H°$, are independent** of each other. Two reactions can have identical values for $\Delta H°$ but very different E_a values. In Figure 6.5, both reactions have the same negative $\Delta H°$ favoring the products, but the second reaction has a much higher E_a, so it proceeds more slowly.

Problem 6.14 Draw an energy diagram for a reaction in which the products are higher in energy than the starting materials and E_a is large. Clearly label all of the following on the diagram: the axes, the starting materials, the products, the transition state, $\Delta H°$, and E_a.

Problem 6.15 Draw the structure for the transition state in each reaction.

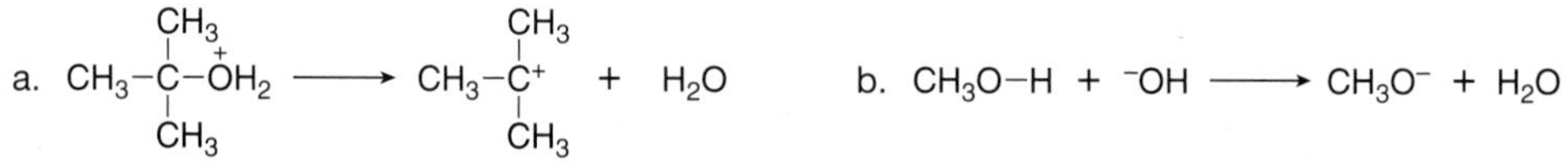

Problem 6.16 Compound **A** can be converted to either **B** or **C.** The energy diagrams for both processes are drawn on the graph below.

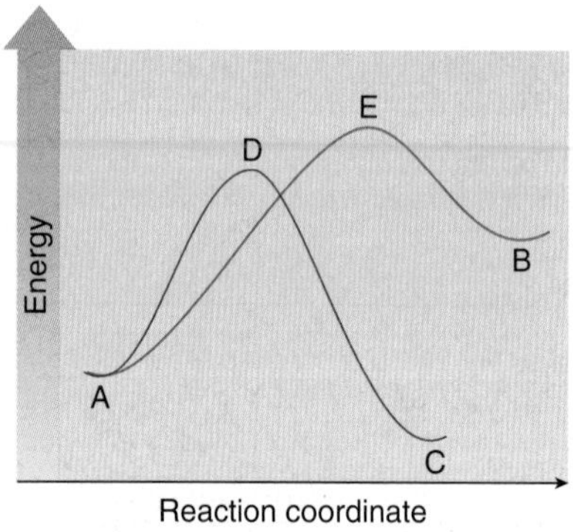

a. Label each reaction as endothermic or exothermic.
b. Which reaction is faster?
c. Which reaction generates the product lower in energy?
d. Which points on the graphs correspond to transition states?
e. Label the energy of activation for each reaction.
f. Label the $\Delta H°$ for each reaction.

6.8 Energy Diagram for a Two-Step Reaction Mechanism

Although the hypothetical reaction in Section 6.7 is concerted, many reactions involve more than one step with formation of a reactive intermediate. Consider the same overall reaction, **A–B + C:$^-$** to form products **A:$^-$ + B–C,** but in this case begin with the assumption that the reaction occurs by a *stepwise* pathway—that is, bond breaking occurs *before* bond making. Once again, assume that the overall process is exothermic.

Same overall reaction A–B + C:$^-$ ⟶ A:$^-$ + B–C

This bond is broken... ***before*** ...this bond is formed.

One possible stepwise mechanism involves heterolysis of the **A – B** bond to form two ions **A:⁻** and **B⁺**, followed by reaction of **B⁺** with anion **C:⁻** to form product **B – C,** as outlined in the accompanying equations. Species **B⁺** is a **reactive intermediate.** It is formed as a product in Step [1], and then goes on to react with **C:⁻** in Step [2].

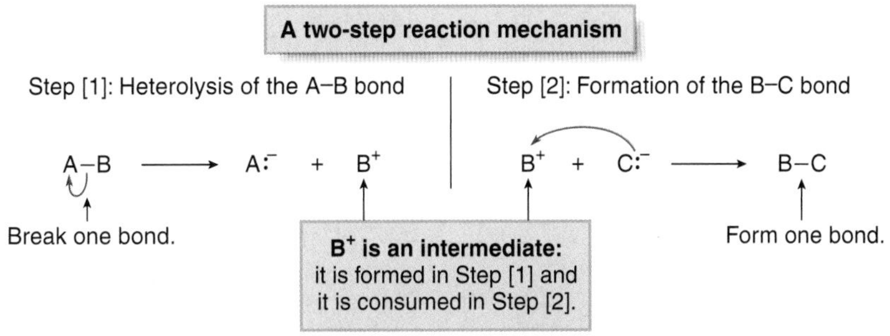

We must draw an energy diagram for each step, and then combine them in an energy diagram for the overall two-step mechanism. Each step has its own energy barrier, with a transition state at the energy maximum.

Step [1] is endothermic because energy is needed to cleave the **A – B** bond, making $\Delta H°$ a positive value and placing the products of Step [1] at higher energy than the starting materials. In the transition state, the **A – B** bond is partially broken.

Energy diagram for Step [1]

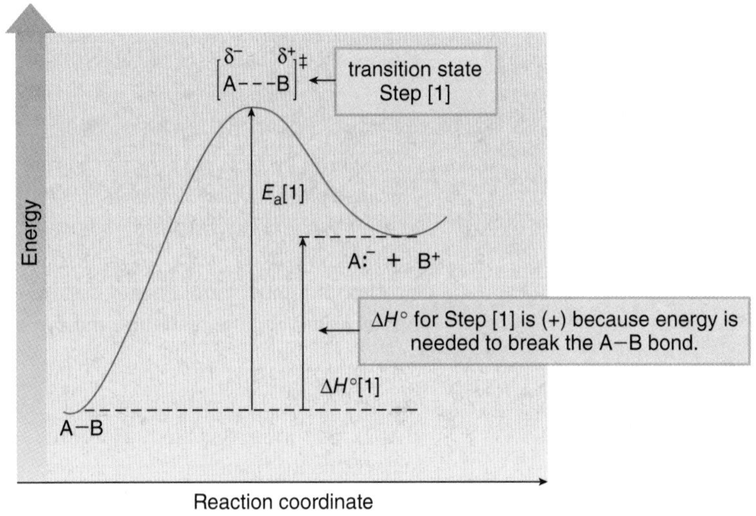

Step [2] is exothermic because energy is released in forming the **B – C** bond, making $\Delta H°$ a negative value and placing the products of Step [2] at lower energy than the starting materials of Step [2]. In the transition state, the **B – C** bond is partially formed.

Energy diagram for Step [2]

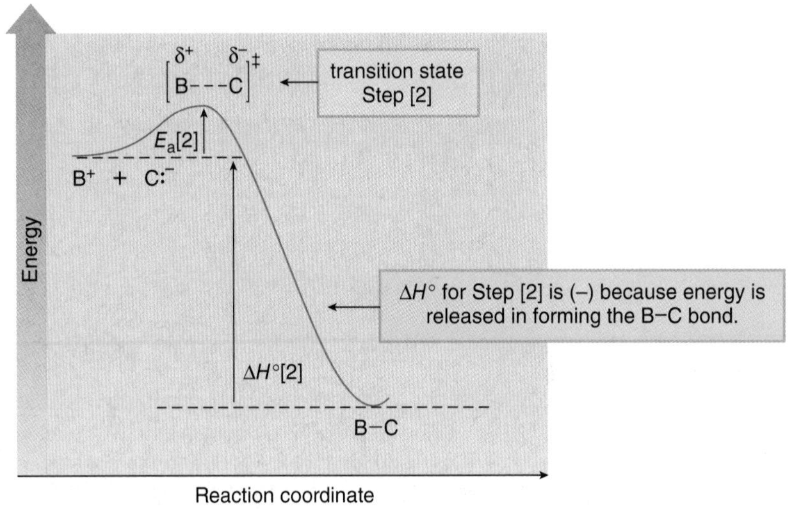

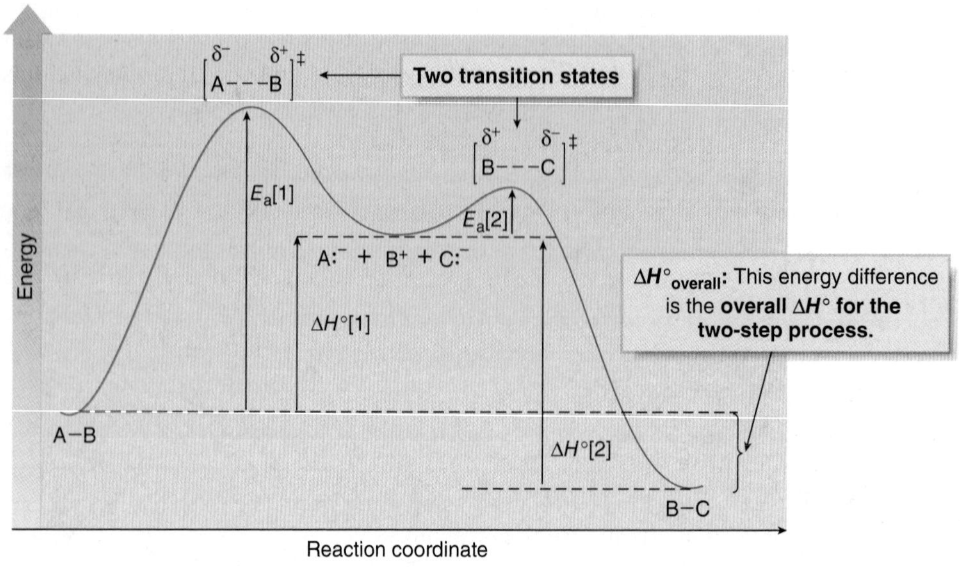

Figure 6.6
Complete energy diagram for the two-step conversion of $A-B + C:^- \rightarrow A:^- + B-C$

- **The transition states are located at energy maxima, while the reactive intermediate B^+ is located at an energy minimum.**
- Each step is characterized by its own value of $\Delta H°$ and E_a.
- The overall energy difference between starting material and products is called $\Delta H°_{overall}$. In this example, the products of the two-step sequence are at lower energy than the starting materials.
- Since Step [1] has the higher energy transition state, it is the **rate-determining step.**

The overall process is shown in Figure 6.6 as a single energy diagram that combines both steps. Because the reaction has two steps, there are two transition states, each corresponding to an energy barrier. The transition states are separated by an energy minimum, at which the reactive intermediate $\mathbf{B^+}$ is located. Because we made the assumption that the overall two-step process is exothermic, the overall energy difference between the reactants and products, labeled $\Delta H°_{overall}$, has a negative value, and the final products are at a lower energy than the starting materials.

The energy barrier for Step [1], labeled $E_a[1]$, is higher than the energy barrier for Step [2], labeled $E_a[2]$. This is because bond cleavage (Step [1]) is more difficult (requires more energy) than bond formation (Step [2]). A higher energy transition state for Step [1] makes it the slower step of the mechanism.

- **In a multistep mechanism, the step with the highest energy transition state is called the rate-determining step.**

In this reaction, the rate-determining step is Step [1].

Problem 6.17 Consider the following energy diagram.

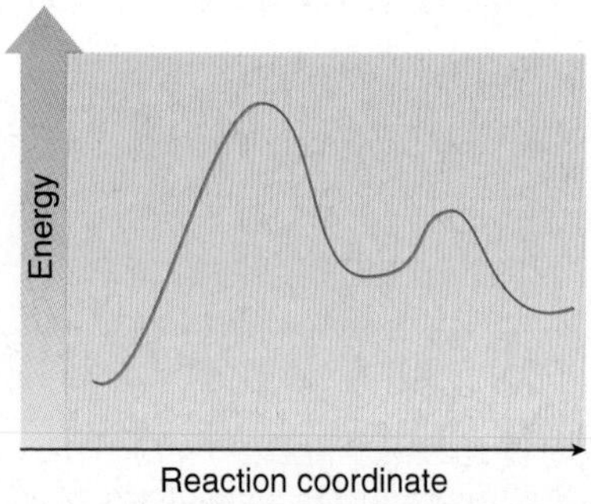

a. How many steps are involved in this reaction?
b. Label $\Delta H°$ and E_a for each step, and label $\Delta H°_{overall}$.
c. Label each transition state.
d. Which point on the graph corresponds to a reactive intermediate?
e. Which step is rate-determining?
f. Is the overall reaction endothermic or exothermic?

Problem 6.18 Draw an energy diagram for a two-step reaction, $A \rightarrow B \rightarrow C$, where the relative energy of these compounds is $C < A < B$, and the conversion of $B \rightarrow C$ is rate-determining.

6.9 Kinetics

We now turn to a more detailed discussion of **reaction rate**—that is, how fast a particular reaction proceeds. **The study of reaction rates is called *kinetics*.**

The rate of chemical processes affects many facets of our lives. Aspirin is an effective anti-inflammatory agent because it rapidly inhibits the synthesis of prostaglandins (Section 19.6). Butter turns rancid with time because its lipids are only slowly oxidized by oxygen in the air to undesirable by-products (Section 15.11). DDT (Section 7.4) is a persistent environmental pollutant because it does not react appreciably with water, oxygen, or any other chemical with which it comes into contact. All of these processes occur at different rates, resulting in beneficial or harmful effects.

6.9A Energy of Activation

Some reactions have a very favorable equilibrium constant (K_{eq} >> 1), but the rate is very slow. Gasoline can be safely handled in the air because its reaction with O_2 is slow unless there is a spark to provide energy to initiate the reaction.

As we learned in Section 6.7, the energy of activation, E_a, is the energy difference between the reactants and the transition state. It is the **energy barrier** that must be exceeded for reactants to be converted to products.

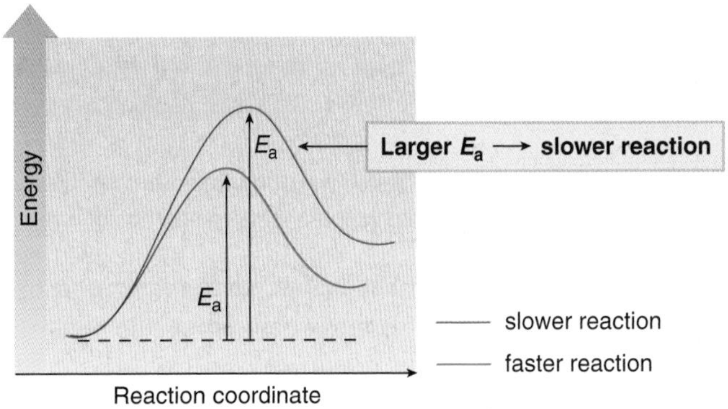

- The *larger* the E_a, the *slower* the reaction.

Concentration and temperature also affect reaction rate.

- The *higher* the concentration, the *faster* the rate. Increasing concentration increases the number of collisions between reacting molecules, which in turn increases the rate.

- The *higher* the temperature, the *faster* the rate. Increasing temperature increases the average kinetic energy of the reacting molecules. Because the kinetic energy of colliding molecules is used for bond cleavage, increasing the average kinetic energy increases the rate.

Practically, the effect of temperature on reaction rate is used to an advantage in the kitchen. Food is stored in a cold refrigerator to slow the reactions that cause spoilage.

The E_a values of most organic reactions are 40–150 kJ/mol. When E_a < 80 kJ/mol, the reaction occurs readily at or below room temperature. When E_a > 80 kJ/mol, higher temperatures are needed. As a rule of thumb, increasing the temperature by 10 °C doubles the reaction rate. Thus, reactions in the lab are often heated to increase their rates so they occur in a reasonable amount of time.

Keep in mind that certain **reaction quantities have *no effect* on reaction rate.**

- $\Delta G°$, $\Delta H°$, and K_{eq} do not determine the rate of a reaction. These quantities indicate the direction of equilibrium and the relative energy of reactants and products.

Problem 6.19 Which value (if any) corresponds to a faster reaction: (a) E_a = 40 kJ/mol or E_a = 4 kJ/mol; (b) a reaction temperature of 0 °C or a reaction temperature of 25 °C; (c) K_{eq} = 10 or K_{eq} = 100; (d) $\Delta H°$ = –10 kJ/mol or $\Delta H°$ = 10 kJ/mol?

Problem 6.20 For a reaction with K_{eq} = 0.8 and E_a = 80 kJ/mol, decide which of the following statements is (are) true. Correct any false statement to make it true. Ignore entropy considerations. (a) The reaction is faster than a reaction with K_{eq} = 8 and E_a = 80 kJ/mol. (b) The reaction is faster than a reaction with K_{eq} = 0.8 and E_a = 40 kJ/mol. (c) $\Delta G°$ for the reaction is a positive value. (d) The starting materials are lower in energy than the products of the reaction. (e) The reaction is exothermic.

6.9B Rate Equations

The rate of a chemical reaction is determined by measuring the decrease in the concentration of the reactants over time, or the increase in the concentration of the products over time. A **rate law** (or **rate equation**) is an equation that shows the relationship between the rate of a reaction and the concentration of the reactants. A rate law is determined *experimentally,* and it depends on the mechanism of the reaction.

A rate law has two important terms: the **rate constant symbolized by *k*,** and the **concentration of the reactants.** Not all reactant concentrations may appear in the rate equation, as we shall soon see.

Rate law or **Rate equation**

rate = ***k* [reactants]**

(**rate constant** ↓ *k*; ↑ **concentration** of reactants)

A rate constant k and the energy of activation E_a are inversely related. **A high E_a corresponds to a small *k*.**

A rate constant k is a fundamental characteristic of a reaction. It is a complex mathematical term that takes into account the dependence of a reaction rate on temperature and the energy of activation.

- **Fast reactions have large rate constants.**
- **Slow reactions have small rate constants.**

What concentration terms appear in the rate equation? That depends on the mechanism. For the organic reactions we will encounter:

- **A rate equation contains concentration terms for *all* reactants involved in a *one-step* mechanism.**
- **A rate equation contains concentration terms for *only* the reactants involved in the *rate-determining step* in a multistep reaction.**

For example, in the one-step reaction of **A–B** + **C:⁻** to form **A:⁻** + **B–C,** *both* reactants appear in the transition state of the only step of the mechanism. The **concentration of *both* reactants affects the reaction rate** and *both* terms appear in the rate equation. This type of reaction involving two reactants is said to be **bimolecular.**

A one-step reaction

A–B + C:⁻ ⟶ A:⁻ + B–C

Both reactants are involved in the only step.
Both reactants determine the rate.

rate = *k* [AB][C:⁻]

sum of the exponents = **2**

Second-order rate equation

The ***order* of a rate equation equals the sum of the exponents of the concentration terms** in the rate equation. In the rate equation for the concerted reaction of **A–B** + **C:⁻**, there are two concentration terms, each with an exponent of one. Thus, the sum of the exponents is two and the **rate equation is *second order*** (the reaction follows second-order kinetics).

Because the rate of the reaction depends on the concentration of both reactants, doubling the concentration of *either* **A–B** or **C:⁻** doubles the rate of the reaction. Doubling the concentration of *both* **A–B** and **C:⁻** increases the reaction rate by a factor of *four.*

The situation is different in the stepwise conversion of **A−B** + **C:⁻** to form **A:⁻** + **B−C.** The mechanism shown in Section 6.8 has two steps: a slow step (the **rate-determining** step) in which the **A−B** bond is broken, and a fast step in which the **B−C** bond is formed.

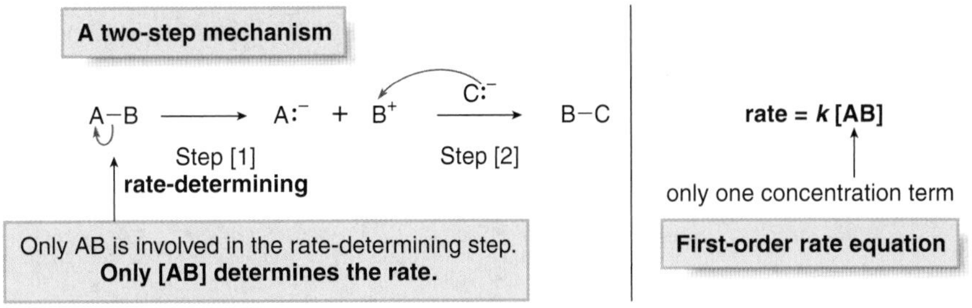

In a multistep mechanism, a reaction can occur no faster than its rate-determining step. **Only the concentrations of the reactants affecting the rate-determining step appear in the rate equation.** In this example, the rate depends on the concentration of **A−B** *only,* because only **A−B** appears in the rate-determining step. A reaction involving only one reactant is said to be **unimolecular.** Because there is only one concentration term (raised to the first power), the **rate equation is *first order*** (the reaction follows first-order kinetics).

Because the rate of the reaction depends on the concentration of only *one* reactant, doubling the concentration of **A−B** doubles the rate of the reaction, but **doubling the concentration of C:⁻ has *no effect* on the reaction rate.**

This might seem like a puzzling result. If **C:⁻** is involved in the reaction, why doesn't it affect the overall rate of the reaction? Not only can you change the concentration of **C:⁻** and not affect the rate, but you also can replace it by a different anion without affecting the rate. How can this be? **C:⁻ is not involved in the slow step of the reaction, so neither its concentration nor its identity affects the reaction rate.**

The following analogy is useful. Let's say three students must make 20 peanut butter and jelly sandwiches for a class field trip. Student (**1**) spreads the peanut butter on the bread. Student (**2**) spreads on the jelly, and student (**3**) cuts the sandwiches in half. Suppose student (**2**) is very slow in spreading the jelly. It doesn't matter how fast students (**1**) and (**3**) are; they can't finish making sandwiches any faster than student (**2**) can add the jelly. Five more students can spread on the peanut butter, or an entirely different individual can replace student (**3**), and this doesn't speed up the process. How fast the sandwiches are made is determined entirely by the rate-determining step—that is, spreading the jelly.

Rate equations provide very important information about the mechanism of a reaction. Rate laws for new reactions with unknown mechanisms are determined by a set of experiments that measure how a reaction's rate changes with concentration. Then, a mechanism is suggested based on which reactants affect the rate.

Problem 6.21 For each rate equation, what effect does the indicated concentration change have on the overall rate of the reaction?

[1] rate = $k[CH_3CH_2Br][^{-}OH]$

a. tripling the concentration of CH_3CH_2Br only

b. tripling the concentration of ^{-}OH only

c. tripling the concentration of both CH_3CH_2Br and ^{-}OH

[2] rate = $k[(CH_3)_3COH]$

a. doubling the concentration of $(CH_3)_3COH$

b. increasing the concentration of $(CH_3)_3COH$ by a factor of 10

Problem 6.22 Write a rate equation for each reaction, given the indicated mechanism.

a. $CH_3CH_2{-}Br + {}^{-}OH \longrightarrow CH_2{=}CH_2 + H_2O + Br^-$

b. $(CH_3)_3C{-}Br \xrightarrow[\text{slow}]{} (CH_3)_3C^+ + Br^- \xrightarrow[\text{fast}]{^{-}OH} (CH_3)_2C{=}CH_2 + H_2O$

6.10 Catalysts

Some reactions do not occur in a reasonable time unless a **catalyst** is added.

- **A *catalyst* is a substance that speeds up the rate of a reaction. A catalyst is recovered unchanged in a reaction, and it does not appear in the product.**

Common catalysts in organic reactions are **acids** and **metals.** Two examples are shown in the accompanying equations.

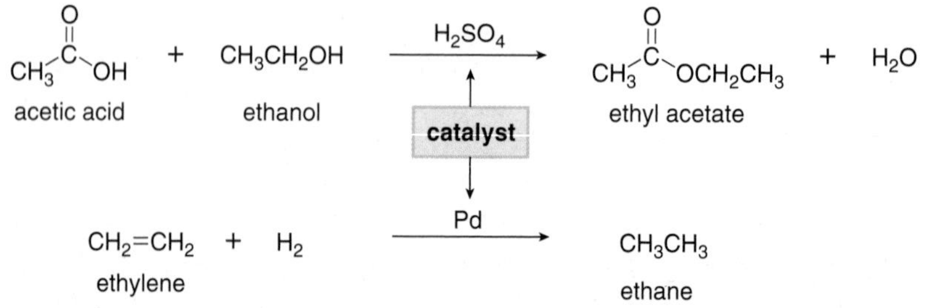

The reaction of acetic acid with ethanol to yield ethyl acetate and water occurs in the presence of an acid catalyst. The acid catalyst is written over or under the arrow to emphasize that it is not part of the starting materials or the products. The details of this reaction are discussed in Chapter 22.

The reaction of ethylene with hydrogen to form ethane occurs only in the presence of a metal catalyst such as palladium, platinum, or nickel. The metal provides a surface that binds both the ethylene and the hydrogen, and in doing so, facilitates the reaction. We return to this mechanism in Chapter 12.

Catalysts accelerate a reaction by lowering the energy of activation (Figure 6.7). They have no effect on the equilibrium constant, so they do not change the amount of reactant and product at equilibrium. Thus, catalysts affect how *quickly* equilibrium is achieved, but not the relative amounts of reactants and products at equilibrium. If a catalyst is somehow used up in one step of a reaction sequence, it must be regenerated in another step. Because only a small amount of a catalyst is needed relative to starting material, it is said to be present in a **catalytic amount.**

Problem 6.23 Identify the catalyst in each equation.

a. $CH_2{=}CH_2 \xrightarrow[H_2SO_4]{H_2O} CH_3CH_2OH$

b. $CH_3Cl \xrightarrow[^-OH]{I^-} CH_3OH + Cl^-$

c. 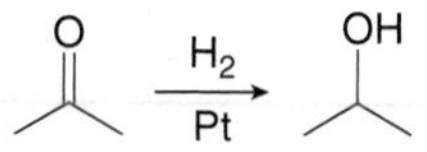

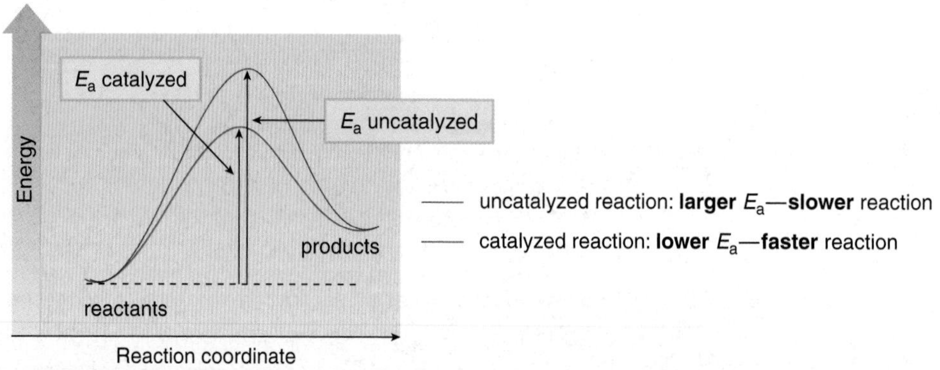

Figure 6.7
The effect of a catalyst on a reaction

- The catalyst lowers the energy of activation, thus **increasing the rate of the catalyzed reaction.**
- The energy of the reactants and products is the same in both the uncatalyzed and catalyzed reactions, so the **position of equilibrium is unaffected.**

6.11 Enzymes

The catalysts that synthesize and break down biomolecules in living organisms are governed by the same principles as the acids and metals in organic reactions. The catalysts in living organisms, however, are usually protein molecules called **enzymes.**

- ***Enzymes* are biochemical catalysts composed of amino acids held together in a very specific three-dimensional shape.**

An enzyme contains a region called its **active site,** which binds an organic reactant, called a **substrate.** When bound, this unit is called the **enzyme–substrate complex,** as shown schematically in Figure 6.8 for the enzyme lactase, the enzyme that binds lactose, the principal carbohydrate in milk. Once bound, the organic substrate undergoes a very specific reaction at an enhanced rate. In this example, lactose is converted into two simpler sugars, glucose and galactose. When individuals lack adequate amounts of lactase, they are unable to digest lactose, causing abdominal cramping and diarrhea.

An enzyme speeds up a biological reaction in a variety of ways. It may hold reactants in the proper conformation to facilitate reaction, or it may provide an acidic site needed for a particular transformation. Once the reaction is completed, the enzyme releases the substrate and it is then able to catalyze another reaction.

Figure 6.8
Lactase, an example of a biological catalyst

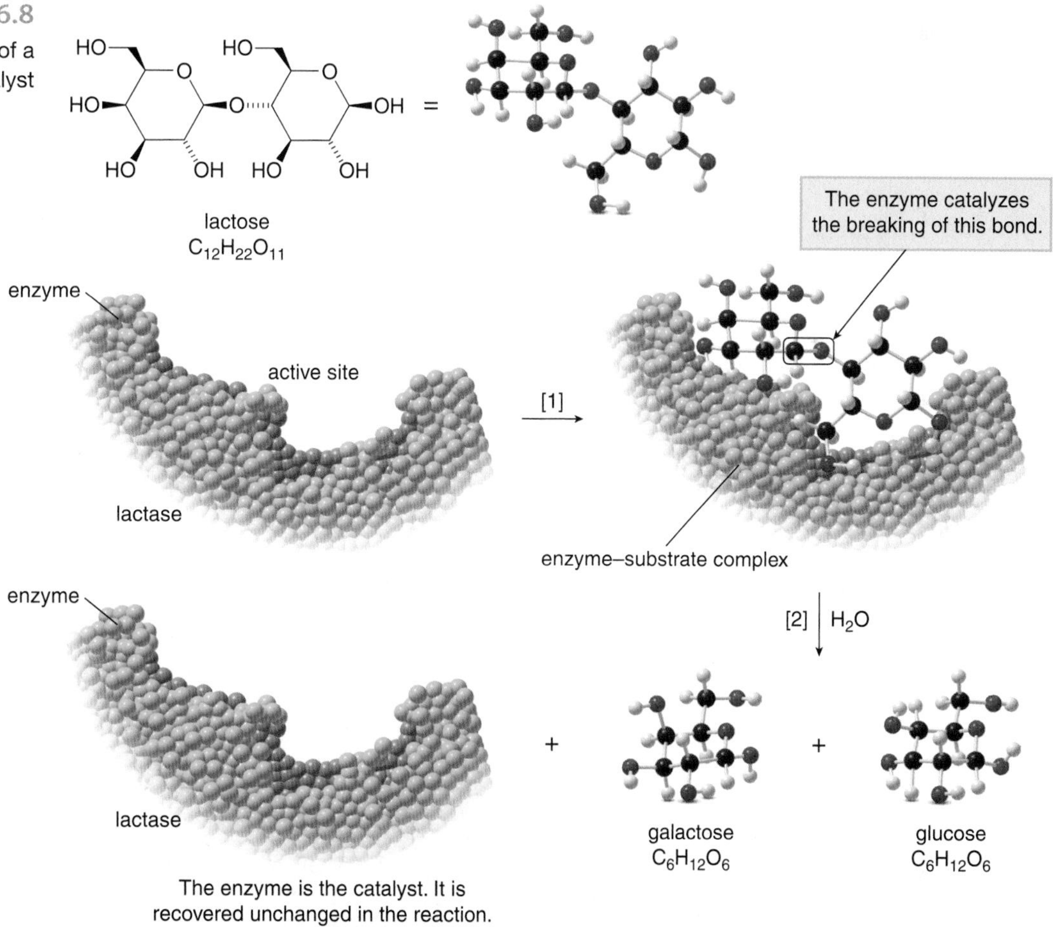
HO
HO
O
HO
O
O
OH
=
HO
OH
HO
OH
lactose
$C_{12}H_{22}O_{11}$
The enzyme catalyzes the breaking of this bond.
enzyme
active site
[1]
lactase
enzyme–substrate complex
enzyme
[2]
H_2O
+
+
lactase
galactose
$C_6H_{12}O_6$
glucose
$C_6H_{12}O_6$
The enzyme is the catalyst. It is recovered unchanged in the reaction.

The enzyme lactase binds the carbohydrate lactose ($C_{12}H_{22}O_{11}$) in its active site in Step [1]. Lactose then reacts with water to break a bond and form two simpler sugars, galactose and glucose, in Step [2]. This process is the first step in digesting lactose, the principal carbohydrate in milk.

KEY CONCEPTS

Understanding Organic Reactions

Writing Equations for Organic Reactions (6.1)

- Use curved arrows to show the movement of electrons. Full-headed arrows are used for electron pairs and half-headed arrows are used for single electrons.
- Reagents can be drawn either on the left side of an equation or over the reaction arrow. Catalysts are drawn over or under the reaction arrow.

Types of Reactions (6.2)

[1] Substitution	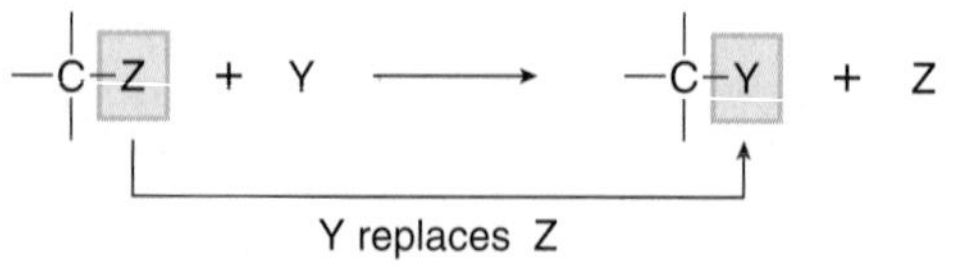+ Y + Z Y replaces Z [Z = H or a heteroatom]
[2] Elimination	+ reagent + X–Y Two σ bonds are broken. π bond
[3] Addition	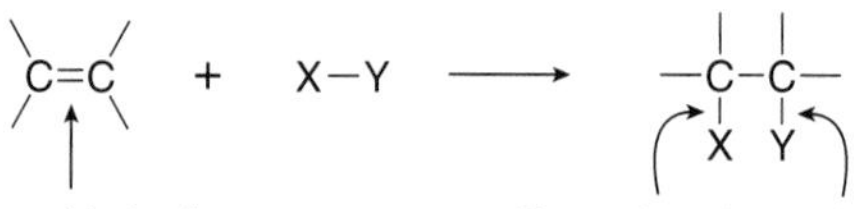+ X–Y This π bond is broken. Two σ bonds are formed.

Important Trends

Values compared	Trend
Bond dissociation energy and **bond strength**	The ***higher*** the bond dissociation energy, the ***stronger*** the bond (6.4).
Energy and **stability**	The ***higher*** the energy, the ***less stable*** the species (6.5A).
E_a and **reaction rate**	The ***larger*** the energy of activation, the ***slower*** the reaction (6.9A).
E_a and **rate constant**	The ***larger*** the energy of activation, the ***smaller*** the rate constant (6.9B).

Reactive Intermediates (6.3)

- Breaking bonds generates reactive intermediates.
- Homolysis generates radicals with unpaired electrons.
- Heterolysis generates ions.

Reactive intermediate	General structure	Reactive feature	Reactivity
Radical	$-\dot{\mathrm{C}}$	Unpaired electron	Electrophilic
Carbocation	$-\mathrm{C}^{+}$	Positive charge; only six electrons around C	Electrophilic
Carbanion	$-\mathrm{C}{:}^{-}$	Net negative charge; lone electron pair on C	Nucleophilic

Energy Diagrams (6.7, 6.8)

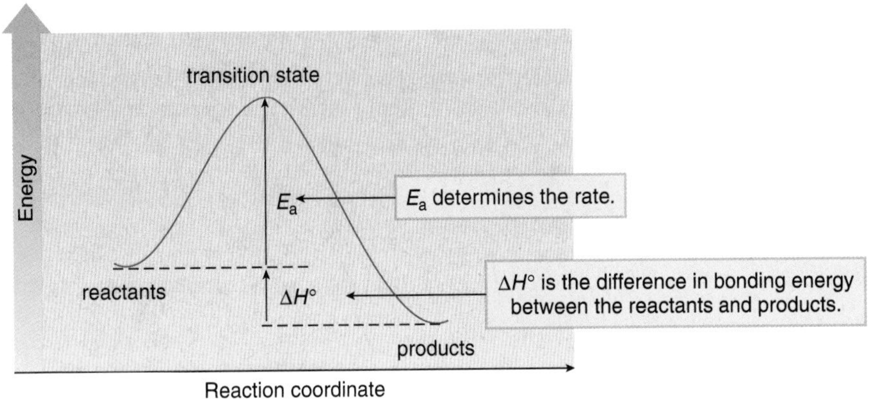

Conditions Favoring Product Formation (6.5, 6.6)

Variable	Value	Meaning
K_{eq}	$K_{eq} > 1$	More products than reactants are present at equilibrium.
$\Delta G°$	$\Delta G° < 0$	The free energy of the products is **lower** than the energy of the reactants.
$\Delta H°$	$\Delta H° < 0$	Bonds in the products are **stronger** than bonds in the reactants.
$\Delta S°$	$\Delta S° > 0$	The products are **more disordered** than the reactants.

Equations (6.5, 6.6)

$$\Delta \mathbf{G}° = -2.303RT \log \mathbf{K_{eq}}$$

K_{eq} depends on the energy difference between reactants and products.

R = 8.314 J/(K•mol), the gas constant
T = Kelvin temperature (K)

$$\Delta \mathbf{G}° = \Delta \mathbf{H}° - \mathbf{T}\Delta \mathbf{S}°$$

- $\Delta G°$: free energy change
- $\Delta H°$: change in bonding energy
- $T\Delta S°$: change in disorder

T = Kelvin temperature (K)

Factors Affecting Reaction Rate (6.9)

Factor	Effect
Energy of activation	Larger E_a ---→ slower reaction
Concentration	Higher concentration ---→ faster reaction
Temperature	Higher temperature ---→ faster reaction

PROBLEMS

Problems Using Three-Dimensional Models

6.24 Draw the products of homolysis or heterolysis of each indicated bond. Use electronegativity differences to decide on the location of charges in the heterolysis reaction. Classify each carbon reactive intermediate as a radical, carbocation, or carbanion.

a. 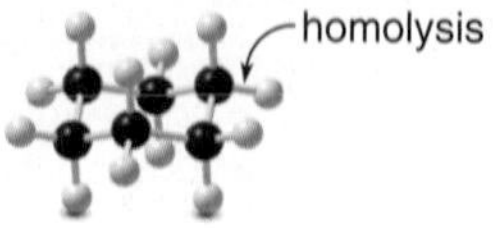

b. 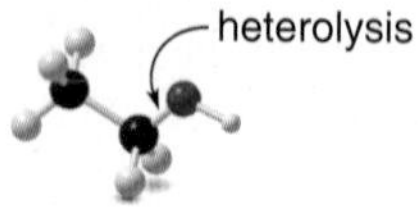

6.25 Explain why the bond dissociation energy for bond (a) is lower than the bond dissociation energy for bond (b).

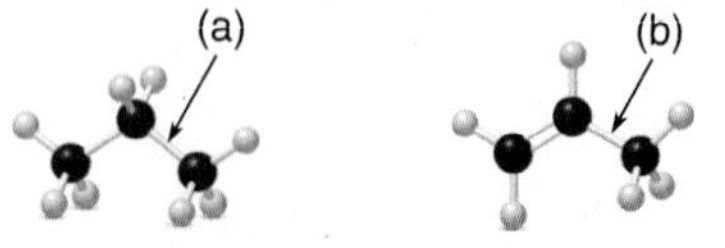

$\Delta H° = 356$ kJ/mol $\Delta H° = 385$ kJ/mol

Types of Reactions

6.26 Classify each transformation as substitution, elimination, or addition.

a. 

b. 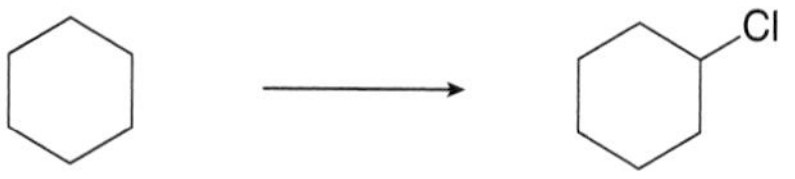

c. 

d. 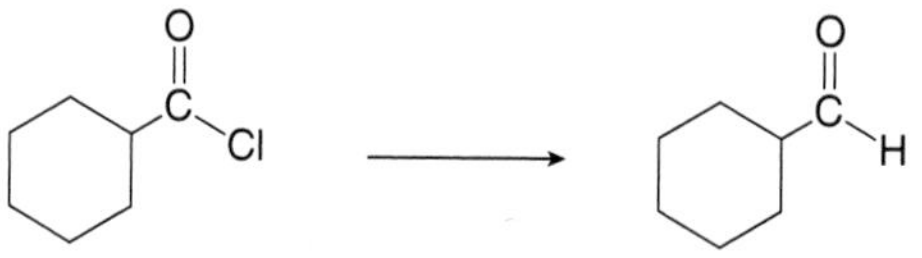

Curved Arrows

6.27 Use full-headed or half-headed curved arrows to show the movement of electrons in each reaction.

a. 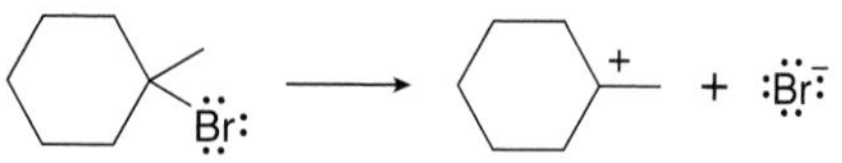

b. 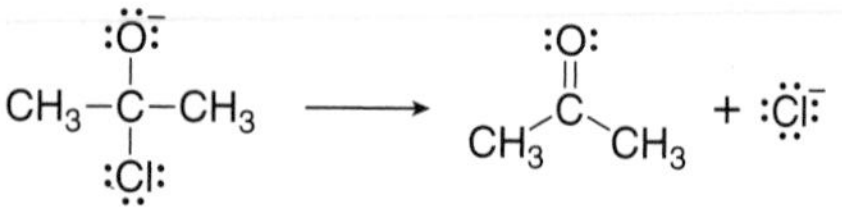

c. $\cdot CH_3$ + $\cdot$Cl: ⟶ CH_3–Cl:

d. 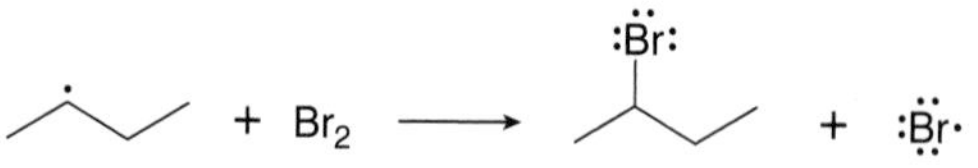

e. CH_3CH_2Br: + $^{-}$:OH ⟶ CH_3CH_2OH + :Br:$^{-}$

f. 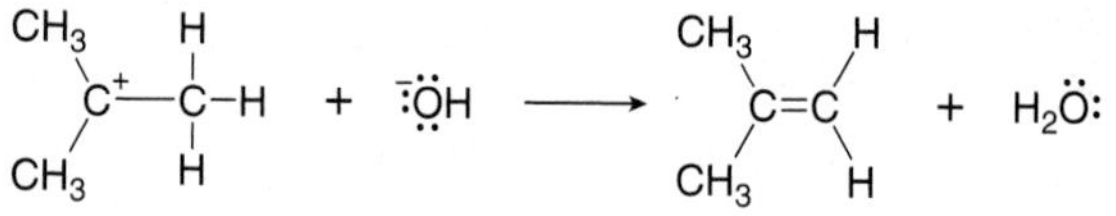

6.28 Draw the products of each reaction by following the curved arrows.

a. 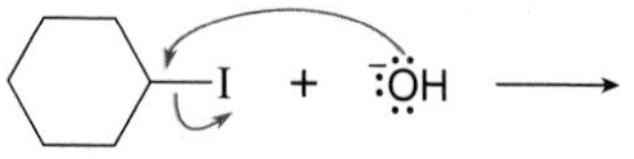

b. 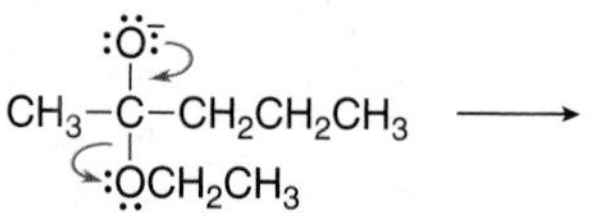

c. 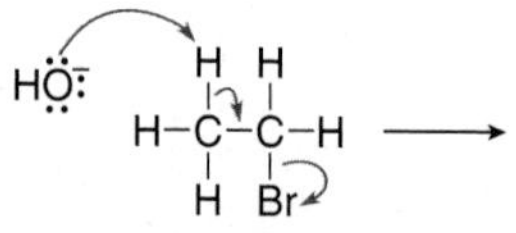

d. 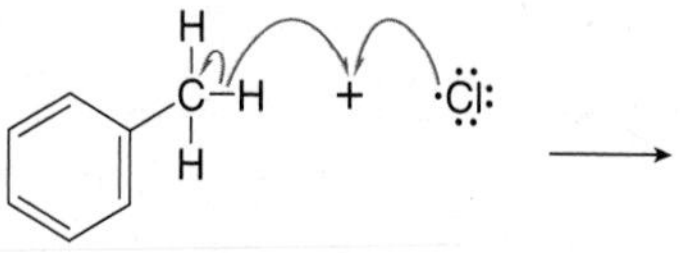

6.29 (a) Draw in the curved arrows to show how **A** is converted to **B** in Step [1]. (b) Identify **X,** using the curved arrows drawn for Step [2].

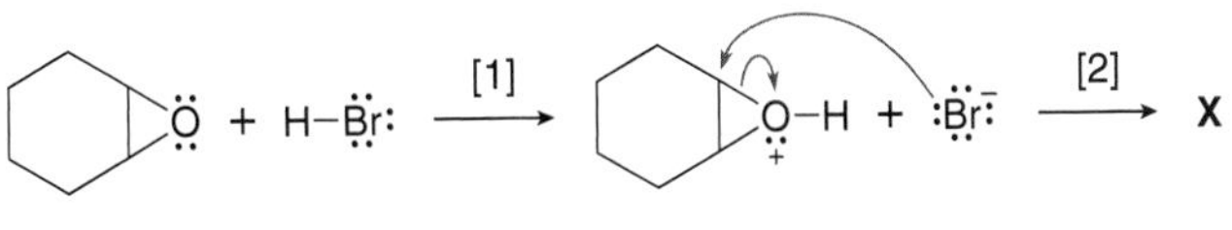

A **B**

6.30 $PGF_{2\alpha}$ (Section 4.15) is synthesized in cells using a cyclooxygenase enzyme that catalyzes a multistep radical pathway. Two steps in the pathway are depicted in the accompanying equations. (a) Draw in curved arrows to illustrate how **C** is converted to **D** in Step [1]. (b) Identify **Y,** the product of Step [2], using the curved arrows that are drawn on compound **D.** We will learn more about this process in Section 30.6.

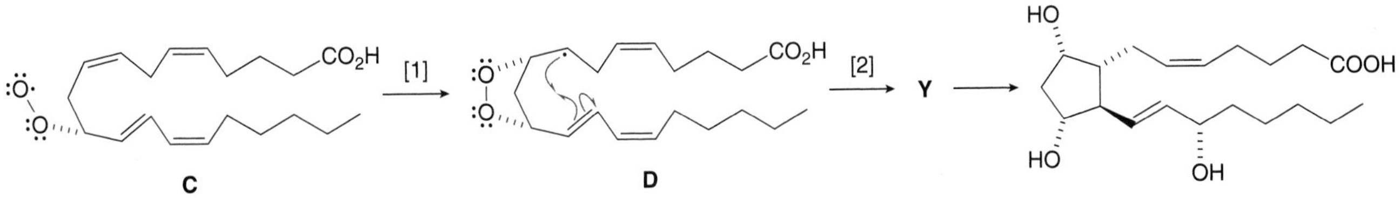

C **D** $PGF_{2\alpha}$

Bond Dissociation Energy and Calculating $\Delta H°$

6.31 Rank each of the indicated bonds in order of increasing bond dissociation energy.

a. $Cl{-}CCl_3$, $I{-}CCl_3$, $Br{-}CCl_3$ b. $N{\equiv}N$, $HN{=}NH$, $H_2N{-}NH_2$

6.32 Calculate $\Delta H°$ for each reaction.

a. $CH_3CH_3 + Br_2 \longrightarrow CH_3CH_2Br + HBr$
b. $HO\cdot + CH_4 \longrightarrow \cdot CH_3 + H_2O$
c. $CH_3OH + HBr \longrightarrow CH_3Br + H_2O$
d. $Br\cdot + CH_4 \longrightarrow H\cdot + CH_3Br$

6.33 Homolysis of the indicated C–H bond in propene forms a resonance-stabilized radical.

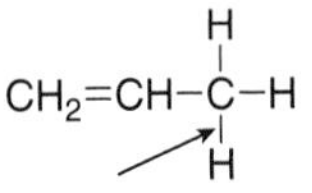

a. Draw the two possible resonance structures for this radical.
b. Use half-headed curved arrows to illustrate how one resonance structure can be converted to the other.
c. Draw a structure for the resonance hybrid.

6.34 Because propane ($CH_3CH_2CH_3$) has both 1° and 2° carbon atoms, it has two different types of C–H bonds.
a. Draw the carbon radical formed by homolysis of each of these C–H bonds.
b. Use the values in Table 6.2 to determine which C–H bond is stronger.
c. Explain how this information can also be used to determine the relative stability of the two radicals formed. Which radical formed from propane is more stable?

Thermodynamics, $\Delta G°$, $\Delta H°$, $\Delta S°$, and K_{eq}

6.35 Given each value, determine whether the starting material or product is favored at equilibrium.

a. $K_{eq} = 0.5$
b. $\Delta G° = -100$ kJ/mol
c. $\Delta H° = 8.0$ kJ/mol
d. $K_{eq} = 16$
e. $\Delta G° = 2.0$ kJ/mol
f. $\Delta H° = 200$ kJ/mol
g. $\Delta S° = 8$ J/(K•mol)
h. $\Delta S° = -8$ J/(K•mol)

6.36 a. Which value corresponds to a negative value of $\Delta G°$: $K_{eq} = 10^{-2}$ or $K_{eq} = 10^{2}$?
b. In a unimolecular reaction with five times as much starting material as product at equilibrium, what is the value of K_{eq}? Is $\Delta G°$ positive or negative?
c. Which value corresponds to a larger K_{eq}: $\Delta G° = -8$ kJ/mol or $\Delta G° = 20$ kJ/mol?

6.37 As we learned in Chapter 4, monosubstituted cyclohexanes exist as an equilibrium mixture of two conformations having either an axial or equatorial substituent.

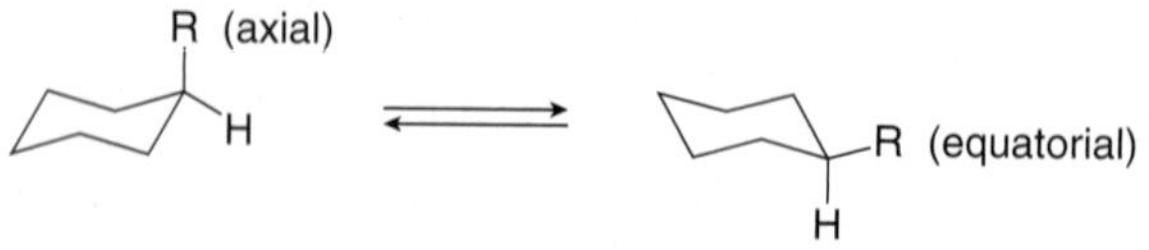

R	K_{eq}
$-CH_3$	18
$-CH_2CH_3$	23
$-CH(CH_3)_2$	38
$-C(CH_3)_3$	4000

a. When R = CH_3, which conformation is present in higher concentration?
b. Which R shows the highest percentage of equatorial conformation at equilibrium?
c. Which R shows the highest percentage of axial conformation at equilibrium?
d. For which R is $\Delta G°$ most negative?
e. How is the size of R related to the amount of axial and equatorial conformations at equilibrium?
f. Challenge question: Explain why three monosubstituted cycloalkanes [R = $-CH_3$, $-CH_2CH_3$, $-CH(CH_3)_2$] have similar values of K_{eq}, but K_{eq} for *tert*-butylcyclohexane [R = $-C(CH_3)_3$] is much higher.

6.38 At 25 °C, the energy difference ($\Delta G°$) for the conversion of axial fluorocyclohexane to its equatorial conformation is –1.0 kJ/mol. (a) Calculate K_{eq} for this equilibrium. (b) Calculate the percentage of axial and equatorial conformations present at equilibrium.

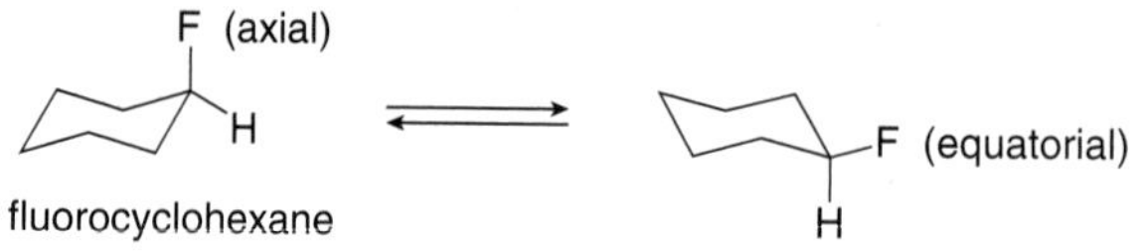

6.39 For which of the following reactions is $\Delta S°$ a positive value?

a. 

b. $CH_3\cdot$ + $CH_3\cdot$ ⟶ CH_3CH_3

c. $(CH_3)_2C(OH)_2$ ⟶ $(CH_3)_2C{=}O$ + H_2O

d. CH_3COOCH_3 + H_2O ⟶ CH_3COOH + CH_3OH

Energy Diagrams and Transition States

6.40 Draw the transition state for each reaction.

a. 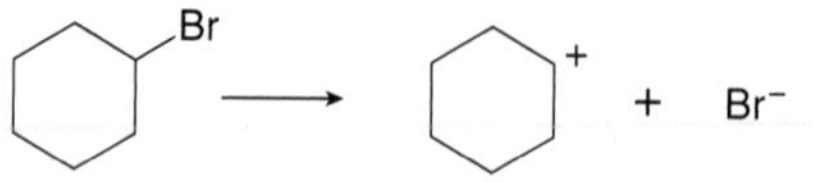

b. BF_3 + Cl^- ⟶ 

c. 

d. 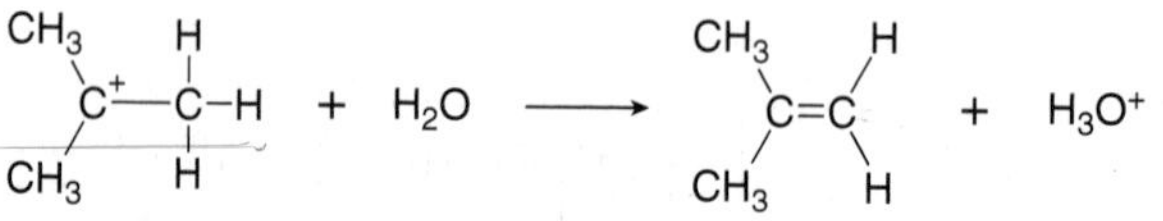

6.41 Draw an energy diagram for each reaction. Label the axes, the starting material, product, transition state, $\Delta H°$, and E_a.
a. a concerted, exothermic reaction with a low energy of activation
b. a one-step endothermic reaction with a high energy of activation
c. a two-step reaction, **A → B → C,** in which the relative energy of the compounds is **A < C < B,** and the step **A → B** is rate-determining
d. a concerted reaction with $\Delta H°$ = –80 kJ/mol and E_a = 16 kJ/mol

6.42 Consider the following reaction: $CH_4 + Cl\cdot \rightarrow \cdot CH_3 + HCl$.
a. Use curved arrows to show the movement of electrons.
b. Calculate $\Delta H°$ using the bond dissociation energies in Table 6.2.
c. Draw an energy diagram assuming that E_a = 16 kJ/mol.
d. What is E_a for the reverse reaction ($\cdot CH_3 + HCl \rightarrow CH_4 + Cl\cdot$)?

6.43 Consider the following energy diagram for the conversion of **A** → **G**.

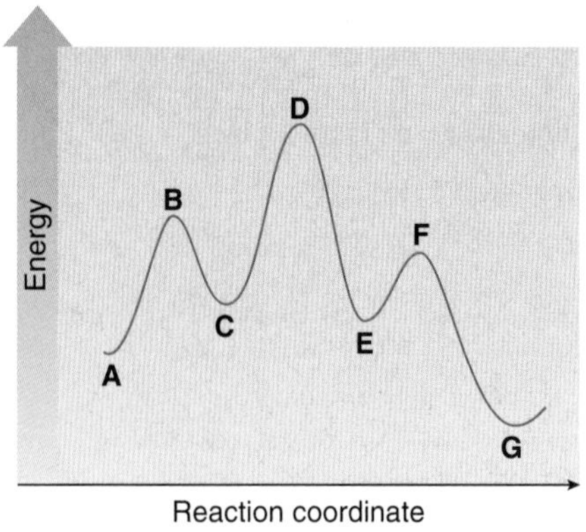

Energy
A
B
C
D
E
F
G
Reaction coordinate

a. Which points on the graph correspond to transition states?
b. Which points on the graph correspond to reactive intermediates?
c. How many steps are present in the reaction mechanism?
d. Label each step of the mechanism as endothermic or exothermic.
e. Label the overall reaction as endothermic or exothermic.

6.44 Draw an energy diagram for the Brønsted–Lowry acid–base reaction of CH_3CO_2H with $^{-}OC(CH_3)_3$ to form $CH_3CO_2^{-}$ and $(CH_3)_3COH$. Label the axes, starting materials, products, $\Delta H°$, and E_a. Draw the structure of the transition state.

6.45 Consider the following two-step reaction:

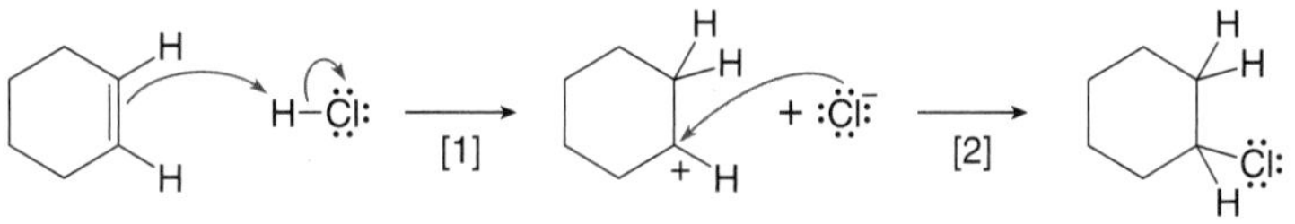

[1]
[2]

a. How many bonds are broken and formed in Step [1]? Would you predict $\Delta H°$ of Step [1] to be positive or negative?
b. How many bonds are broken and formed in Step [2]? Would you predict the $\Delta H°$ of Step [2] to be positive or negative?
c. Which step is rate-determining?
d. Draw the structure for the transition state in both steps of the mechanism.
e. If $\Delta H°_{overall}$ is negative for this two-step reaction, draw an energy diagram illustrating all of the information in parts (a)–(d).

6.46 Consider the following energy diagram for the overall reaction: $(CH_3)_3COH + HI \rightarrow (CH_3)_3CI + H_2O$.

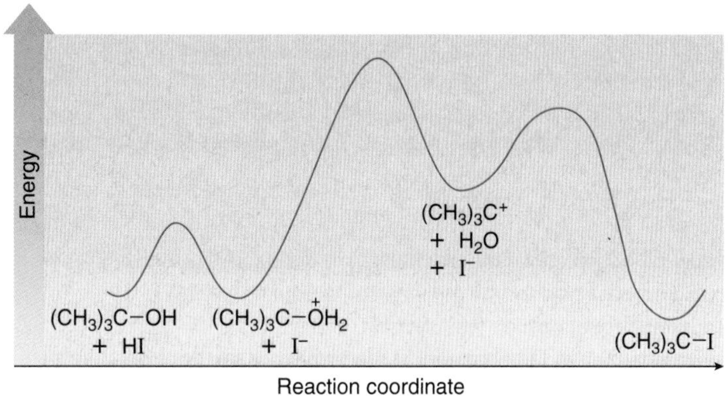

Energy
(CH3)3C–OH + HI
(CH3)3C–OH2 + I⁻
(CH3)3C+ + H2O + I⁻
(CH3)3C–I
Reaction coordinate

a. How many steps are in the reaction mechanism?
b. Label the E_a and $\Delta H°$ for each step, and the $\Delta H°_{overall}$ for the reaction.
c. Draw the structure of the transition state for each step and indicate its location on the energy diagram.
d. Which step is rate-determining? Why?

Kinetics and Rate Laws

6.47 Indicate which factors affect the rate of a reaction.

a. $\Delta G°$
b. $\Delta H°$
c. E_a
d. temperature
e. concentration
f. K_{eq}
g. k
h. catalysts
i. $\Delta S°$

6.48 The following is a concerted, bimolecular reaction: $CH_3Br + NaCN \rightarrow CH_3CN + NaBr$.

a. What is the rate equation for this reaction?

b. What happens to the rate of the reaction if $[CH_3Br]$ is doubled?

c. What happens to the rate of the reaction if [NaCN] is halved?

d. What happens to the rate of the reaction if $[CH_3Br]$ and [NaCN] are both increased by a factor of five?

6.49 The conversion of acetyl chloride to methyl acetate occurs via the following two-step mechanism:

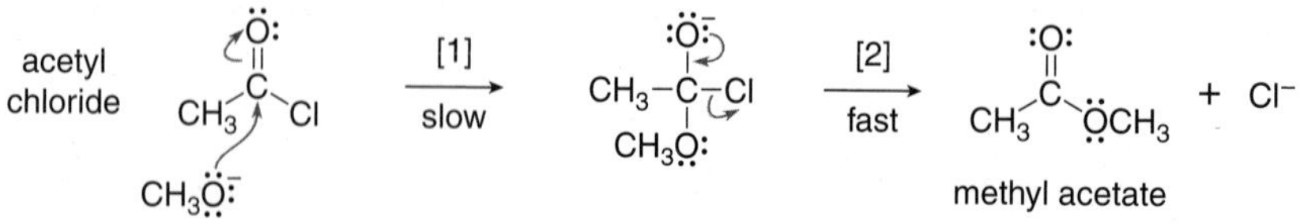

a. Write the rate equation for this reaction, assuming the first step is rate-determining.

b. If the concentration of $^-OCH_3$ were increased 10 times, what would happen to the rate of the reaction?

c. If the concentrations of both CH_3COCl and $^-OCH_3$ were increased 10 times, what would happen to the rate of the reaction?

d. Classify the conversion of acetyl chloride to methyl acetate as an addition, elimination, or substitution.

6.50 Label each statement as true or false. Correct any false statement to make it true.

a. Increasing temperature increases reaction rate.

b. If a reaction is fast, it has a large rate constant.

c. A fast reaction has a large negative $\Delta G°$ value.

d. When E_a is large, the rate constant k is also large.

e. Fast reactions have equilibrium constants > 1.

f. Increasing the concentration of a reactant always increases the rate of a reaction.

General Problem

6.51 The conversion of $(CH_3)_3CI$ to $(CH_3)_2C{=}CH_2$ can occur by either a one-step or a two-step mechanism, as shown in Equations [1] and [2].

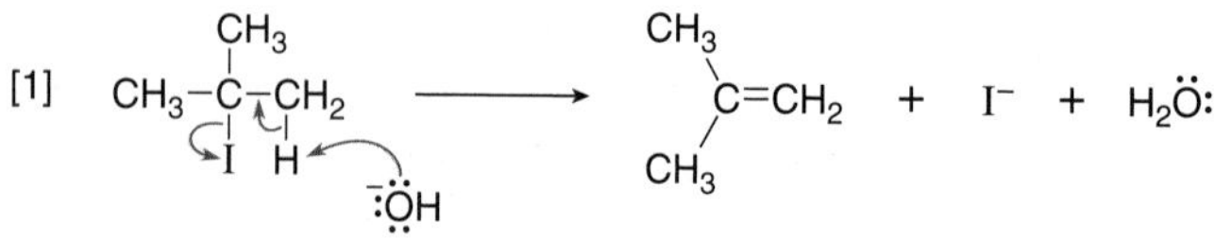

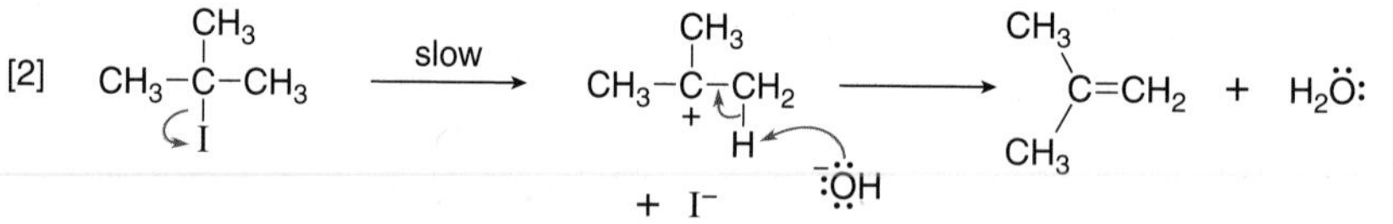

a. What rate equation would be observed for the mechanism in Equation [1]?

b. What rate equation would be observed for the mechanism in Equation [2]?

c. What is the order of each rate equation (i.e., first, second, and so forth)?

d. How can these rate equations be used to show which mechanism is the right one for this reaction?

e. Assume Equation [1] represents an endothermic reaction and draw an energy diagram for the reaction. Label the axes, reactants, products, E_a, and $\Delta H°$. Draw the structure for the transition state.

f. Assume Equation [2] represents an endothermic reaction and that the product of the rate-determining step is higher in energy than the reactants or products. Draw an energy diagram for this two-step reaction. Label the axes, reactants and products for each step, and the E_a and $\Delta H°$ for each step. Label $\Delta H°_{overall}$. Draw the structure for both transition states.

Challenge Problems

6.52 Explain why HC≡CH is more acidic than CH_3CH_3, even though the C–H bond in HC≡CH has a higher bond dissociation energy than the C–H bond in CH_3CH_3.

6.53 The use of curved arrows is a powerful tool that illustrates even complex reactions.

a. Add curved arrows to show how carbocation **A** is converted to carbocation **B.** Label each new σ bond formed. Similar reactions have been used in elegant syntheses of steroids (Section 30.8, Problem 30.40).

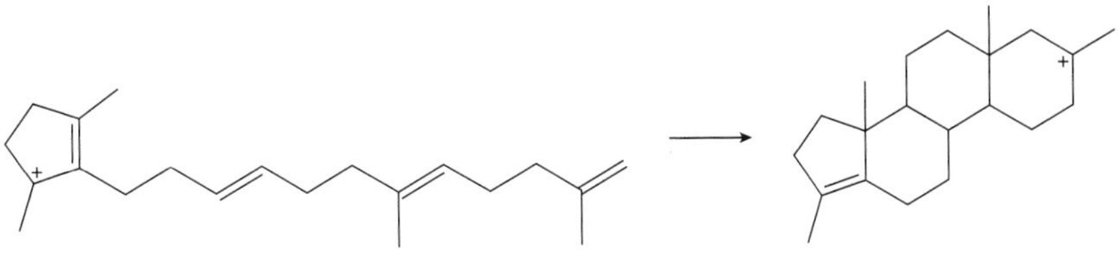

A **B**

b. Draw the product by following the curved arrows. This reaction is an example of a [3,3] sigmatropic rearrangement, as we will learn in Chapter 27.

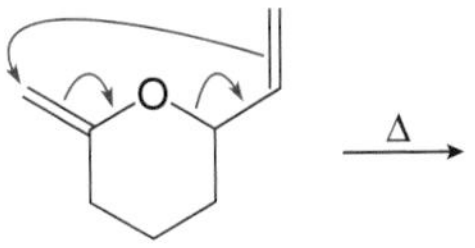

6.54

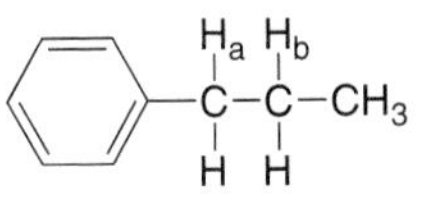

propylbenzene

a. What carbon radical is formed by homolysis of the C–H_a bond in propylbenzene? Draw all reasonable resonance structures for this radical.

b. What carbon radical is formed by homolysis of the C–H_b bond in propylbenzene? Draw all reasonable resonance structures for this radical.

c. The bond dissociation energy of one of the C–H bonds is considerably less than the bond dissociation energy of the other. Which C–H bond is weaker? Offer an explanation.

6.55 Esterification is the reaction of a carboxylic acid (RCOOH) with an alcohol (R'OH) to form an ester (RCOOR') with loss of water. Equation [1] is an example of an *intermolecular* esterification reaction. Equation [2] is an example of an *intramolecular* esterification reaction; that is, the carboxylic acid and alcohol are contained in the same starting material, forming a cyclic ester as product. The equilibrium constants for both reactions are given. Explain why K_{eq} is different for these two apparently similar reactions.

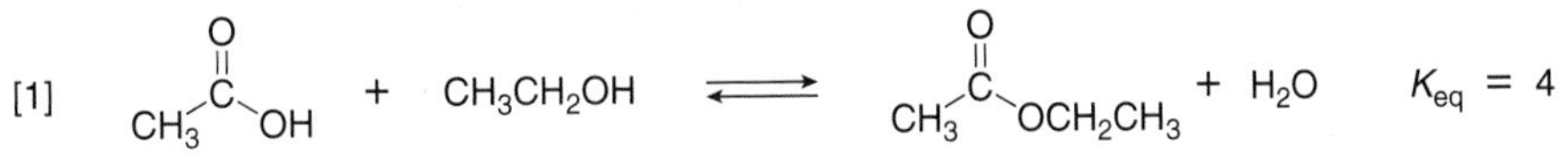

ethyl acetate

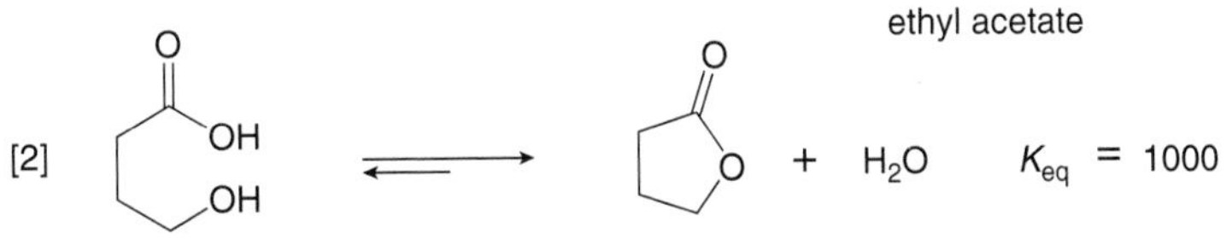

6.56 Although K_{eq} of Equation [1] in Problem 6.55 does not greatly favor formation of the product, it is sometimes possible to use Le Châtelier's principle to increase the yield of ethyl acetate. Le Châtelier's principle states that if an equilibrium is disturbed, a system will react to counteract this disturbance. How can Le Châtelier's principle be used to drive the equilibrium to increase the yield of ethyl acetate? Another example of Le Châtelier's principle is given in Section 9.8.

6.57 As we will learn in Section 15.12, many antioxidants—compounds that prevent unwanted radical oxidation reactions from occurring—are phenols, compounds that contain an OH group bonded directly to a benzene ring.

a. Explain why homolysis of the O–H bond in phenol requires considerably less energy than homolysis of the O–H bond in ethanol (362 kJ/mol vs. 438 kJ/mol).

b. Why is the C–O bond in phenol shorter than the C–O bond in ethanol?

phenol ethanol

7 Alkyl Halides and Nucleophilic Substitution

7.1 Introduction to alkyl halides
7.2 Nomenclature
7.3 Physical properties
7.4 Interesting alkyl halides
7.5 The polar carbon–halogen bond
7.6 General features of nucleophilic substitution
7.7 The leaving group
7.8 The nucleophile
7.9 Possible mechanisms for nucleophilic substitution
7.10 Two mechanisms for nucleophilic substitution
7.11 The S_N2 mechanism
7.12 Application: Useful S_N2 reactions
7.13 The S_N1 mechanism
7.14 Carbocation stability
7.15 The Hammond postulate
7.16 Application: S_N1 reactions, nitrosamines, and cancer
7.17 When is the mechanism S_N1 or S_N2?
7.18 Vinyl halides and aryl halides
7.19 Organic synthesis

Organic halides constitute a growing list of useful naturally occurring molecules, many produced by marine organisms. Some have irritating odors or an unpleasant taste and are synthesized by organisms for self-defense or feeding deterrents. Examples include $Br_2C{=}CHCHCl_2$ (1,1-dibromo-3,3-dichloropropene) and $Br_2C{=}CHCHBr_2$ (1,1,3,3-tetrabromopropene), isolated from the red seaweed *Asparagopsis taxiformis,* known as *limu kohu* (supreme seaweed) in Hawai'i. This seaweed has a strong and characteristic odor and flavor, in part probably because of these organic halides. In Chapter 7, we learn about alkyl halides, and one of their characteristic reactions—nucleophilic substitution.

This is the first of three chapters dealing with an in-depth study of the organic reactions of compounds containing C−Z σ bonds, where Z is an element more electronegative than carbon. In Chapter 7 we learn about **alkyl halides** and one of their characteristic reactions, **nucleophilic substitution.** In Chapter 8, we look at **elimination,** a second general reaction of alkyl halides. We conclude this discussion in Chapter 9 by examining other molecules that also undergo nucleophilic substitution and elimination reactions.

7.1 Introduction to Alkyl Halides

Alkyl halides are organic molecules containing a halogen atom X bonded to an sp^3 hybridized carbon atom. Alkyl halides are classified as **primary (1°), secondary (2°),** or **tertiary (3°)** depending on the number of carbons bonded to the carbon with the halogen.

Alkyl halides have the general molecular formula $C_nH_{2n+1}X$, and are formally derived from an alkane by replacing a hydrogen atom with a halogen.

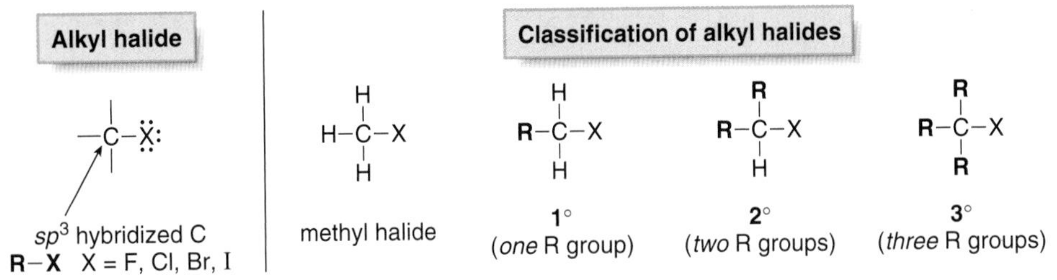

Whether an alkyl halide is 1°, 2°, or 3° is the *most important factor* in determining the course of its chemical reactions. Figure 7.1 illustrates three examples.

Figure 7.1 Examples of 1°, 2°, and 3° alkyl halides

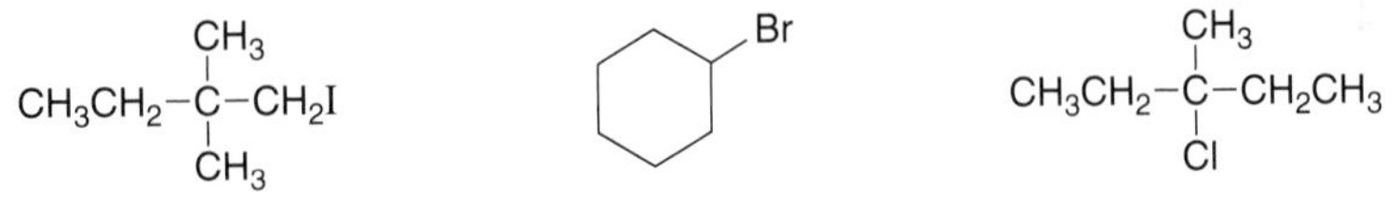

Four types of organic halides having the halogen atom in close proximity to a π bond are illustrated in Figure 7.2. **Vinyl halides** have a halogen atom bonded to a carbon–carbon double bond, and **aryl halides** have a halogen atom bonded to a benzene ring. These two types of organic halides with X bonded directly to an sp^2 hybridized carbon atom do *not* undergo the reactions presented in Chapter 7, as discussed in Section 7.18.

Figure 7.2 Four types of organic halides (RX) having X near a π bond

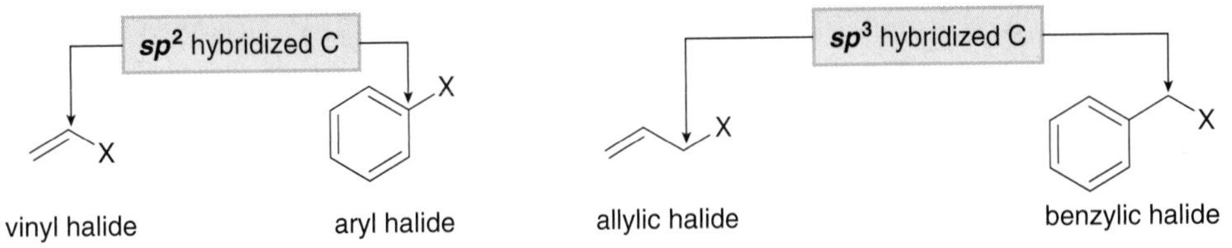

Allylic halides and benzylic halides have halogen atoms bonded to sp^3 hybridized carbon atoms and *do* undergo the reactions described in Chapter 7. **Allylic halides** have X bonded to the carbon atom *adjacent* to a carbon–carbon double bond, and **benzylic halides** have X bonded to the carbon atom *adjacent* to a benzene ring. The synthesis of allylic and benzylic halides is discussed in Sections 15.10 and 18.14, respectively.

Problem 7.1 Classify each alkyl halide as 1°, 2°, or 3°.

a. $CH_3CH_2CH_2CH_2CH_2-Br$

b. 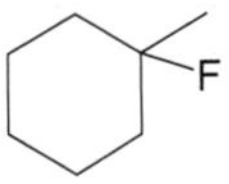

c. 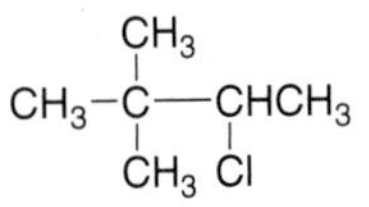

d. 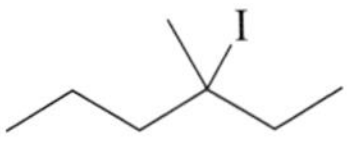

Problem 7.2 Telfairine, a naturally occurring insecticide, and halomon, an antitumor agent, are two polyhalogenated compounds isolated from red algae. (a) Classify each halide bonded to an sp^3 hybridized carbon as 1°, 2°, or 3°. (b) Label each halide as vinyl, allylic, or neither.

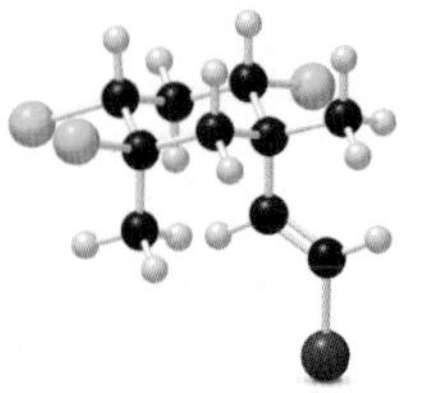

telfairine

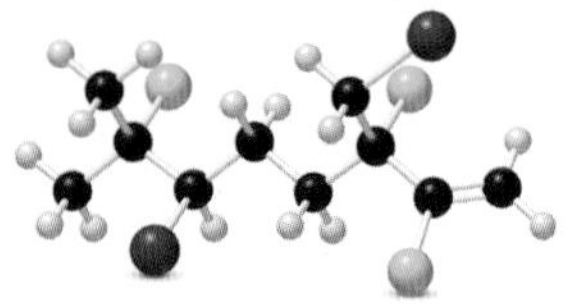

halomon

Problem 7.3 Draw the structure of an alkyl bromide with molecular formula $C_6H_{13}Br$ that fits each description: (a) a 1° alkyl bromide with one stereogenic center; (b) a 2° alkyl bromide with two stereogenic centers; (c) an achiral 3° alkyl bromide.

7.2 Nomenclature

The systematic (IUPAC) method for naming alkyl halides follows from the basic rules described in Chapter 4. Common names are also discussed in Section 7.2B, because many low molecular weight alkyl halides are often referred to by their common names.

7.2A IUPAC System

An alkyl halide is named as an alkane with a halogen substituent—that is, as a ***halo alkane.*** To name a halogen substituent, change the ***-ine*** ending of the name of the halogen to the suffix ***-o*** (chlor*ine* → chlor*o*).

How To Name an Alkyl Halide Using the IUPAC System

Example Give the IUPAC name of the following alkyl halide:

$$CH_3CH_2\overset{\overset{CH_3}{|}}{C}HCH_2CH_2\overset{\overset{Cl}{|}}{C}HCH_3$$

Step [1] Find the parent carbon chain and name it as an alkane.

$$CH_3CH_2\overset{\overset{CH_3}{|}}{C}HCH_2CH_2\overset{\overset{Cl}{|}}{C}HCH_3$$

7 C's in the longest chain

7 C's ---→ **heptane**

- Name the parent chain as an ***alkane,*** with the halogen as a substituent bonded to the longest chain.

Step [2] Apply all other rules of nomenclature.

a. **Number** the chain.

$$CH_3CH_2\overset{\overset{CH_3}{|}}{C}HCH_2CH_2\overset{\overset{Cl}{|}}{C}HCH_3$$

7 6 5 4 3 2 1

- Begin at the end nearest the first substituent, either alkyl or halogen.

b. **Name** and **number** the substituents.

methyl at **C5** **chloro** at **C2**

$$CH_3CH_2\overset{\overset{CH_3}{|}}{C}HCH_2CH_2\overset{\overset{Cl}{|}}{C}HCH_3$$

7 6 5 4 3 2 1

c. **Alphabetize: c** for **c**hloro, then **m** for **m**ethyl.

ANSWER: 2-chloro-5-methylheptane

7.2B Common Names

Common names for alkyl halides are used only for simple alkyl halides. To assign a common name:

- Name all the carbon atoms of the molecule as a single **alkyl group.**
- Name the halogen bonded to the alkyl group. To name the halogen, change the ***-ine*** ending of the halogen name to the suffix ***-ide;*** for example, **brom*ine* → brom*ide*.**
- Combine the names of the alkyl group and halide, separating the words with a space.

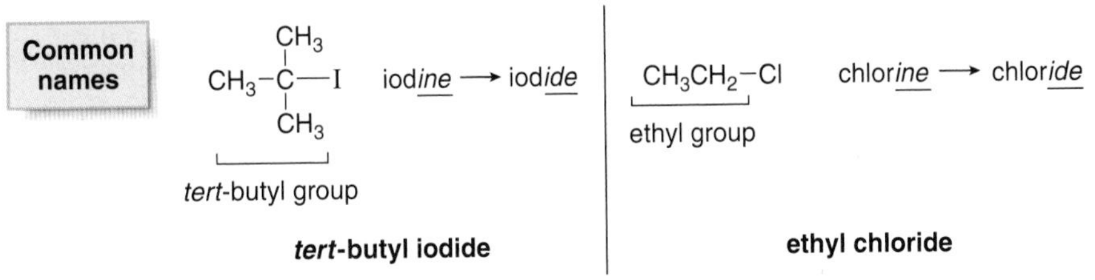

Common names
CH_3
CH_3-C-I
CH_3
iodine ⟶ iodide
tert-butyl group
tert-butyl iodide
CH_3CH_2-Cl
ethyl group
chlorine ⟶ chloride
ethyl chloride

Other examples of alkyl halide nomenclature are given in Figure 7.3.

Figure 7.3
Examples: Nomenclature of alkyl halides

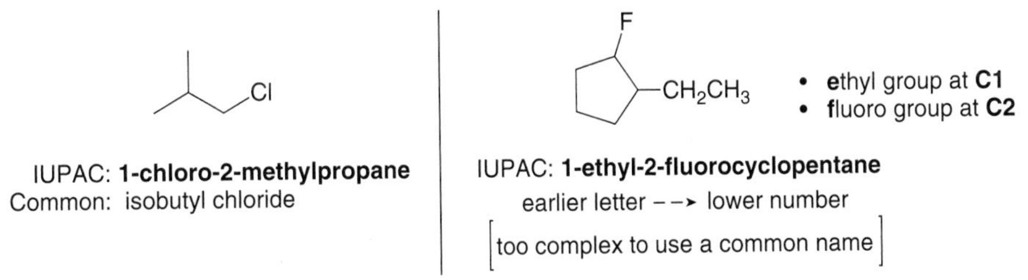

Cl
IUPAC: 1-chloro-2-methylpropane
Common: isobutyl chloride
F
$-CH_2CH_3$
• ethyl group at C1
• fluoro group at C2
IUPAC: 1-ethyl-2-fluorocyclopentane
earlier letter - - → lower number
too complex to use a common name

Problem 7.4 Give the IUPAC name for each compound.

a. $(CH_3)_2CHCH(Cl)CH_2CH_3$

b. 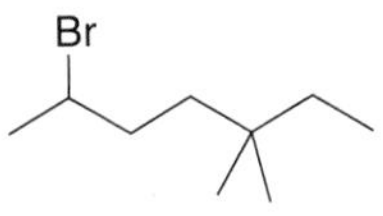

Br

c. 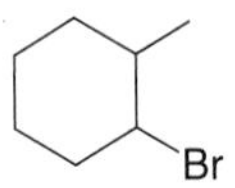

Br

d. 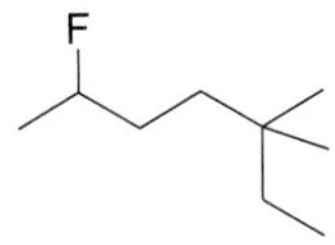

F

Problem 7.5 Give the structure corresponding to each name.

a. 3-chloro-2-methylhexane
b. 4-ethyl-5-iodo-2,2-dimethyloctane
c. *cis*-1,3-dichlorocyclopentane
d. 1,1,3-tribromocyclohexane
e. propyl chloride
f. *sec*-butyl bromide

7.3 Physical Properties

Alkyl halides are weakly polar molecules. They exhibit **dipole–dipole** interactions because of their polar C–X bond, but because the rest of the molecule contains only C–C and C–H bonds they are incapable of intermolecular hydrogen bonding. How this affects their physical properties is summarized in Table 7.1.

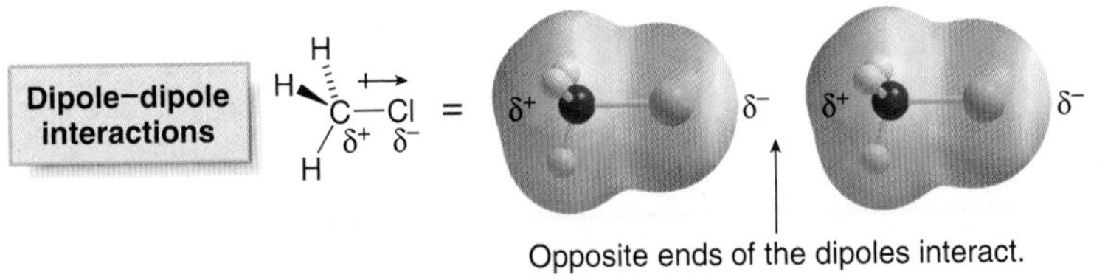

Dipole–dipole interactions
H
H
C—Cl
δ+ δ−
H
=
δ+
δ−
δ+
δ−
Opposite ends of the dipoles interact.

Table 7.1 Physical Properties of Alkyl Halides

Property	Observation
Boiling point and melting point	• Alkyl halides have higher bp's and mp's than alkanes having the same number of carbons. CH_3CH_3 (bp = −89 °C) and CH_3CH_2Br (bp = 39 °C)
	• Bp's and mp's increase as the size of R increases. CH_3CH_2Cl (mp = −136 °C, bp = 12 °C) and $CH_3CH_2CH_2Cl$ (mp = −123 °C, bp = 47 °C) ← **larger surface area higher mp and bp**
	• Bp's and mp's increase as the size of X increases. CH_3CH_2Cl (mp = −136 °C, bp = 12 °C) and CH_3CH_2Br (mp = −119 °C, bp = 39 °C) ← **more polarizable halogen higher mp and bp**
Solubility	• RX is soluble in organic solvents. • RX is insoluble in water.

Problem 7.6 An sp^3 hybridized C–Cl bond is more polar than an sp^2 hybridized C–Cl bond. (a) Explain why this phenomenon arises. (b) Rank the following compounds in order of increasing boiling point.

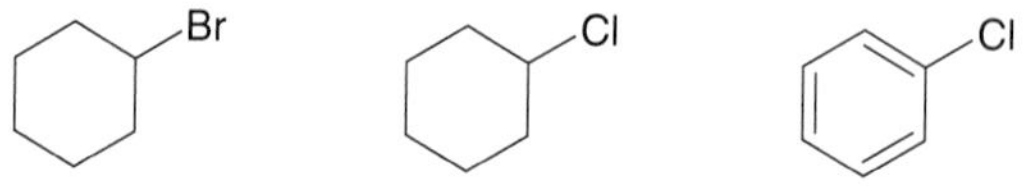

7.4 Interesting Alkyl Halides

Many simple alkyl halides make excellent solvents because they are not flammable and dissolve a wide variety of organic compounds. Compounds in this category include $\mathbf{CHCl_3}$ (chloroform or trichloromethane) and $\mathbf{CCl_4}$ (carbon tetrachloride or tetrachloromethane). Large quantities of these solvents are produced industrially each year, but like many chlorinated organic compounds, both chloroform and carbon tetrachloride are toxic if inhaled or ingested. Other simple alkyl halides are shown in Figure 7.4.

Figure 7.4 Some simple alkyl halides

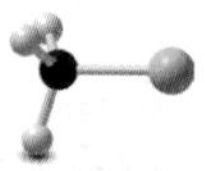

CH_3Cl

• **Chloromethane (CH_3Cl)** is produced by giant kelp and algae and also found in emissions from volcanoes such as Hawai'i's Kilauea. Almost all of the atmospheric chloromethane results from these natural sources.

CH_2Cl_2

• **Dichloromethane (or methylene chloride, CH_2Cl_2)** is an important solvent, once used to decaffeinate coffee. Coffee is now decaffeinated by using supercritical CO_2 due to concerns over the possible ill effects of trace amounts of residual CH_2Cl_2 in the coffee. Subsequent studies on rats have shown, however, that no cancers occurred when animals ingested the equivalent of over 100,000 cups of decaffeinated coffee per day.

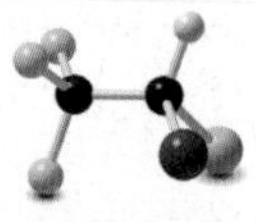

$CF_3CHClBr$

• **Halothane ($CF_3CHClBr$)** is a safe general anesthetic that has now replaced other organic anesthetics such as $CHCl_3$, which causes liver and kidney damage, and $CH_3CH_2OCH_2CH_3$ (diethyl ether), which is very flammable.

Synthetic organic halides are also used in insulating materials, plastic wrap, and coatings. Two such compounds are **Teflon** and **poly(vinyl chloride) (PVC).**

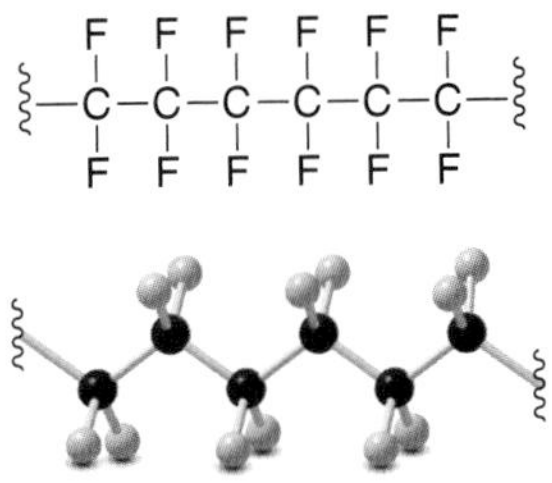

Teflon
(nonstick coating)

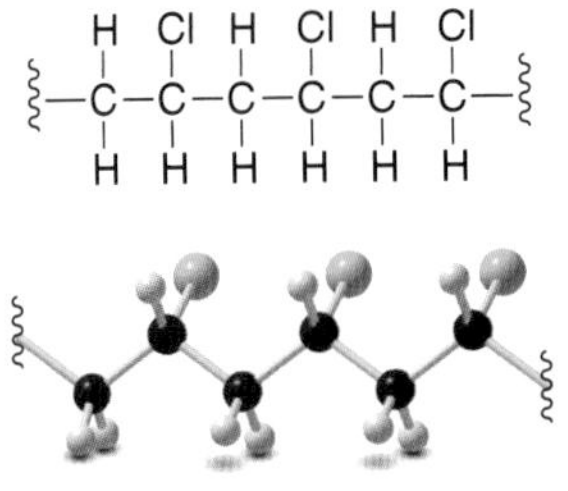

poly(vinyl chloride) (PVC)
(plastic used in films, pipes, and insulation)

Hundreds of organic halides with diverse structures and biological activities have been isolated from red algae of the genus *Laurencia,* seaweed that grows in shallow water at the edges of reefs.

Thousands of organic halides have now been isolated from a variety of marine organisms. The characteristic smell of the ocean is due in part to simple alkyl halides found in seaweed. While many sponges and corals use these compounds as a chemical defense against predators and parasites, recent research has shown that some may have novel medicinal properties that offer treatment for cancer and other diseases. Two polyhalogenated compounds are ma'ilione, isolated from the Hawaiian red algae *Laurencia cartilaginea,* and plocoralide B, which kills esophageal cancer cells.

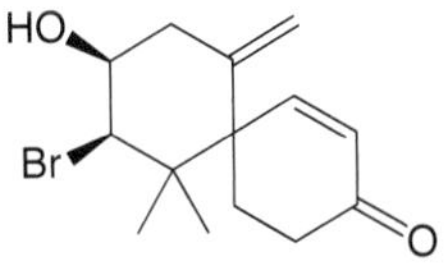

ma'ilione

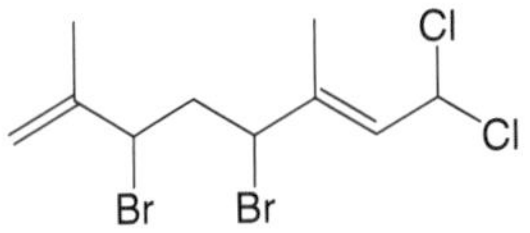

plocoralide B

Although the beneficial effects of many organic halides are undisputed, certain synthetic chlorinated organics such as the **chlorofluorocarbons** and the pesticide **DDT** have caused lasting harm to the environment.

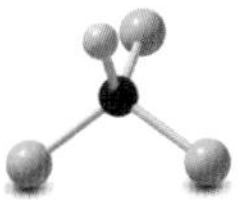

$CFCl_3$
CFC 11
Freon 11

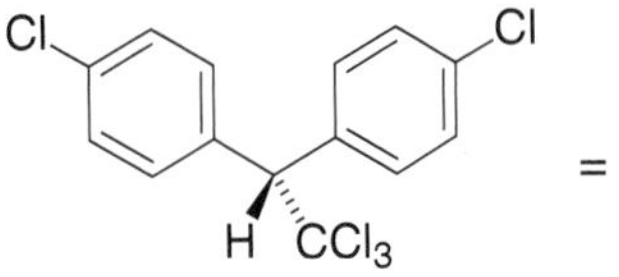

DDT

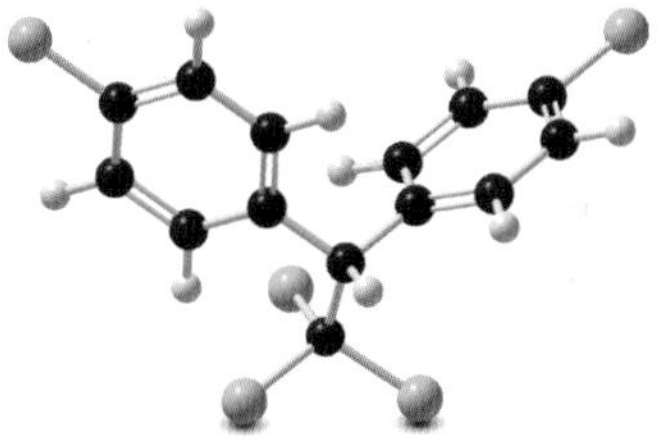

DDT, a nonbiodegradable pesticide, has been labeled both a "miraculous" discovery by Winston Churchill in 1945 and the "elixir of death" by Rachel Carson in her 1962 book *Silent Spring.* DDT use was banned in the United States in 1973, but because of its effectiveness and low cost, it is still widely used to control insect populations in developing countries.

Chlorofluorocarbons (CFCs) have the general molecular structure **CF_xCl_{4-x}**. Trichlorofluoromethane [$CFCl_3$, CFC 11, or Freon 11 (trade name)] is an example of these easily vaporized compounds, having been extensively used as a refrigerant and an aerosol propellant. CFCs slowly rise to the stratosphere, where sunlight catalyzes their decomposition, a process that contributes to the destruction of the ozone layer, the thin layer of atmosphere that shields the earth's surface from harmful ultraviolet radiation (Section 15.9). Although it is now easy to second-guess the extensive use of CFCs, it is also easy to see why they were used so widely. **CFCs made refrigeration available to the general public.** Would you call your refrigerator a comfort or a necessity?

Time Magazine, June 30, 1947.

The story of the insecticide **DDT** (***d***ichloro***d***iphenyl***t***richloroethane) follows the same theme: DDT is an organic molecule with valuable short-term effects that has caused long-term problems. DDT kills insects that spread diseases such as malaria and typhus, and in controlling insect populations, DDT has saved millions of lives worldwide. DDT is a weakly polar organic compound that persists in the environment for years. Because DDT is soluble in organic media, it accumulates in fatty tissues. Most adults in the United States have low concentrations of DDT (or a degradation product of DDT) in their bodies. DDT is acutely toxic to many types of marine life (crayfish, sea shrimp, and some fish), but the long-term effect on humans is not known.

Problem 7.7 Chondrocole A is a marine natural product isolated from red seaweed that grows in regions of heavy surf in the Pacific Ocean. (a) Predict the solubility of chondrocole A in water and CH_2Cl_2. (b) Locate the stereogenic centers and label each as *R* or *S*. (c) Draw a stereoisomer and a constitutional isomer of chondrocole A.

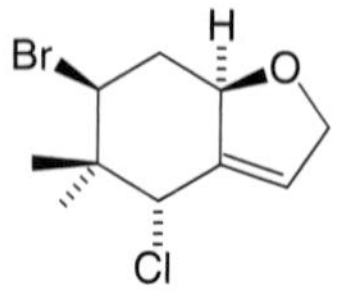
Br
H
O
Cl

chondrocole A

7.5 The Polar Carbon–Halogen Bond

The properties of alkyl halides dictate their reactivity. The electrostatic potential maps of four simple alkyl halides in Figure 7.5 illustrate that the electronegative halogen X creates a polar C–X bond, making the carbon atom electron deficient. **The chemistry of alkyl halides is determined by this polar C–X bond.**

What kind of reactions do alkyl halides undergo? **The characteristic reactions of alkyl halides are substitution and elimination.** Because alkyl halides contain an electrophilic carbon, they react with electron-rich reagents—Lewis bases (nucleophiles) and Brønsted–Lowry bases.

- **Alkyl halides undergo substitution reactions with nucleophiles.**

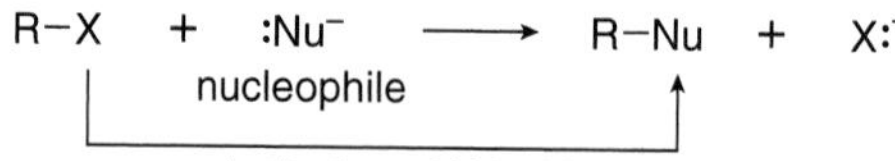
R–X + :Nu⁻ → R–Nu + X:⁻
nucleophile
substitution of X by Nu

In a substitution reaction of RX, **the halogen X is replaced by an electron-rich nucleophile :Nu⁻.** The C–X σ bond is broken and the C–Nu σ bond is formed.

- **Alkyl halides undergo elimination reactions with Brønsted–Lowry bases.**

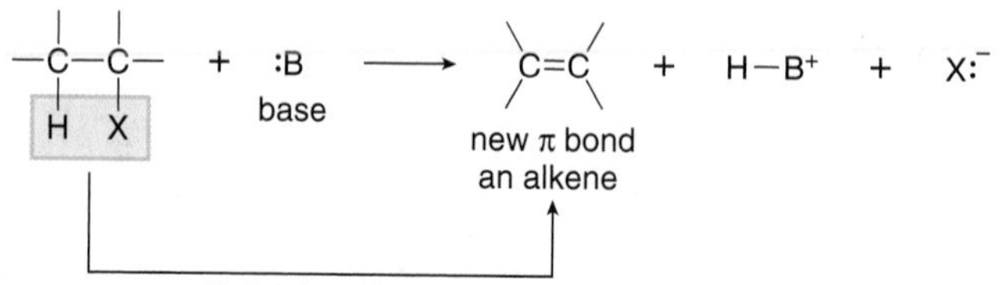
H X
+ :B
base
C=C
new π bond
an alkene
+ H–B⁺ + X:⁻
elimination of HX

In an elimination reaction of RX, the **elements of HX are removed by a Brønsted–Lowry base :B.**

The remainder of Chapter 7 is devoted to a discussion of the substitution reactions of alkyl halides. Elimination reactions are discussed in Chapter 8.

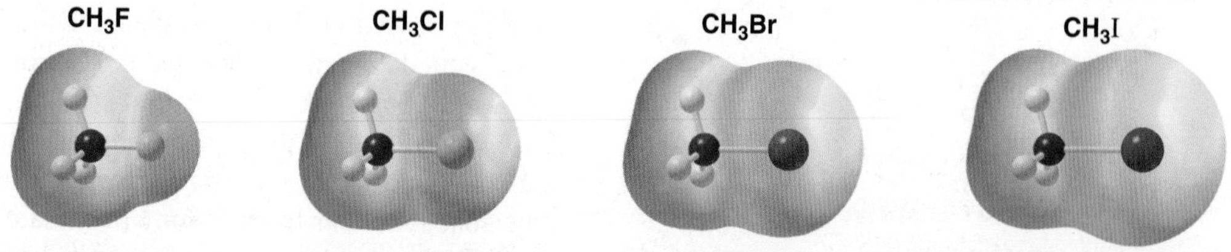
CH_3F
CH_3Cl
CH_3Br
CH_3I

Figure 7.5 Electrostatic potential maps of four halomethanes (CH_3X)

- The polar C–X bond makes the carbon atom *electron deficient* in each CH_3X molecule.

7.6 General Features of Nucleophilic Substitution

Three components are necessary in any substitution reaction.

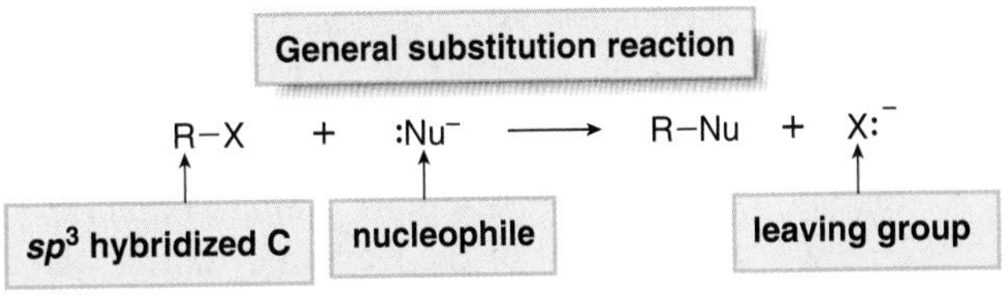
General substitution reaction
R–X + :Nu⁻ ⟶ R–Nu + X:⁻
sp³ hybridized C
nucleophile
leaving group

[1] **R**—An alkyl group R containing an *sp*^{3} hybridized carbon bonded to X.

[2] **X**—An atom X (or a group of atoms) called **a leaving group,** which is able to accept the electron density in the C–X bond. The most common leaving groups are halide anions (X^-), but H_2O (from ROH_2^+) and N_2 (from RN_2^+) are also encountered.

[3] **:Nu$^-$**—A **nucleophile.** Nucleophiles contain a lone pair or a π bond but not necessarily a negative charge.

Because these substitution reactions involve electron-rich nucleophiles, they are called ***nucleophilic* substitution reactions.** Examples are shown in Equations [1]–[3]. **Nucleophilic substitutions are Lewis acid–base reactions.** The nucleophile donates its electron pair, the alkyl halide (Lewis acid) accepts it, and the C–X bond is heterolytically cleaved. Curved arrow notation can be used to show the movement of electron pairs, as shown in Equation [3].

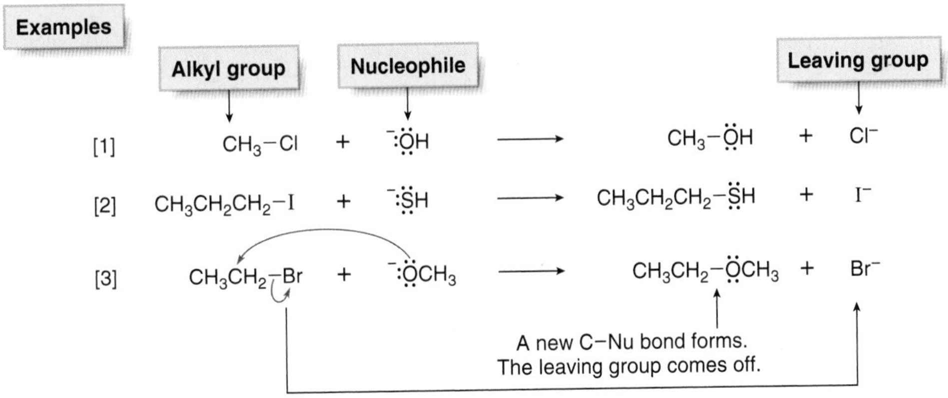
Examples
Alkyl group
Nucleophile
Leaving group
[1] CH₃–Cl + ⁻:ÖH ⟶ CH₃–ÖH + Cl⁻
[2] CH₃CH₂CH₂–I + ⁻:SH ⟶ CH₃CH₂CH₂–SH + I⁻
[3] CH₃CH₂–Br + ⁻:ÖCH₃ ⟶ CH₃CH₂–ÖCH₃ + Br⁻
A new C–Nu bond forms.
The leaving group comes off.

Negatively charged nucleophiles like ^-OH and ^-SH are used as **salts** with Li^+, Na^+, or K^+ counterions to balance charge. The identity of the cation is usually inconsequential, and therefore it is often omitted from the chemical equation.

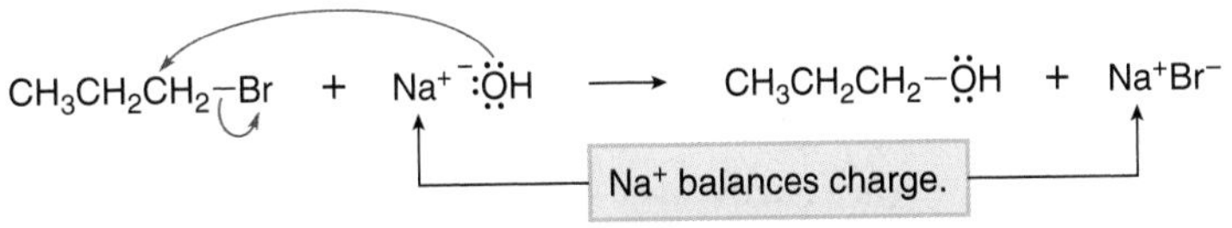
CH₃CH₂CH₂–Br + Na⁺ ⁻:ÖH ⟶ CH₃CH₂CH₂–ÖH + Na⁺Br⁻
Na⁺ balances charge.

When a neutral nucleophile is used, the substitution product bears a positive charge. **Note that all atoms originally bonded to the nucleophile stay bonded to it after substitution occurs.** All three CH_3 groups stay bonded to the N atom in the given example.

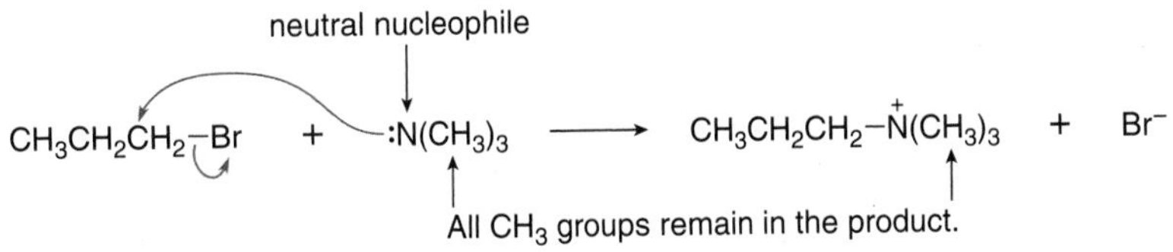
neutral nucleophile
CH₃CH₂CH₂–Br + :N(CH₃)₃ ⟶ CH₃CH₂CH₂–N⁺(CH₃)₃ + Br⁻
All CH₃ groups remain in the product.

The reaction of alkyl halides with NH_3 to form amines (RNH_2) is discussed in Chapter 25.

Furthermore, when the substitution product bears a positive charge and also contains a proton bonded to O or N, the initial substitution product readily loses a proton in a Brønsted–Lowry acid–base reaction, forming a neutral product.

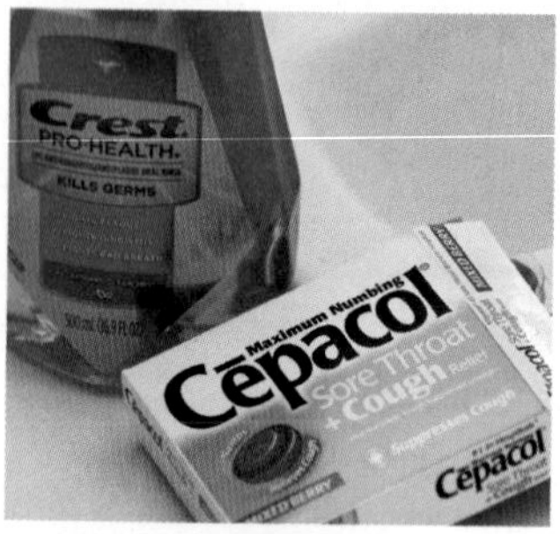

Cepacol throat lozenges and Crest Pro-Health Mouth Rinse contain the antiseptic CPC, which is prepared by nucleophilic substitution (Problem 7.10).

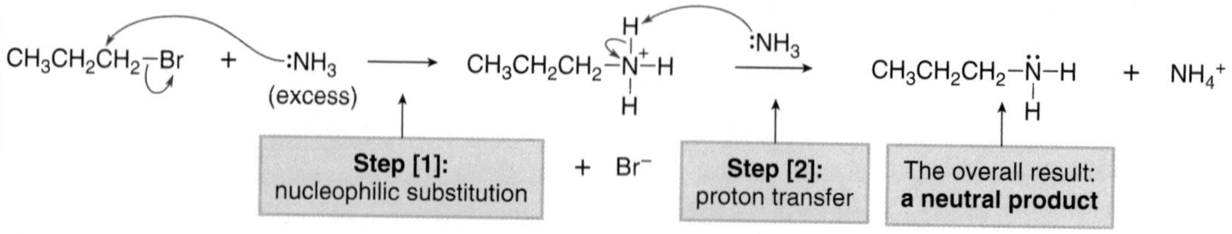

All of these reactions are nucleophilic substitutions and have the same overall result—**replacement of the leaving group by the nucleophile,** regardless of the identity or charge of the nucleophile. To draw any nucleophilic substitution product:

- **Find the *sp*^{3} hybridized carbon with the leaving group.**
- **Identify the nucleophile, the species with a lone pair or π bond.**
- **Substitute the nucleophile for the leaving group and assign charges (if necessary) to any atom that is involved in bond breaking or bond formation.**

Problem 7.8 Identify the nucleophile and leaving group and draw the products of each substitution reaction.

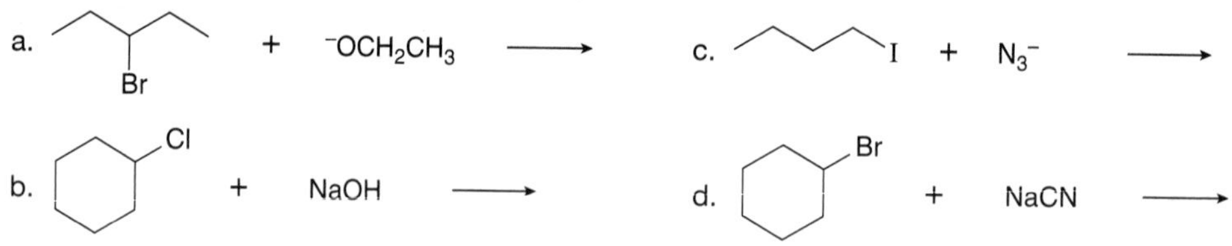

Problem 7.9 Draw the product of nucleophilic substitution with each neutral nucleophile. When the initial substitution product can lose a proton to form a neutral product, draw the product after proton transfer.

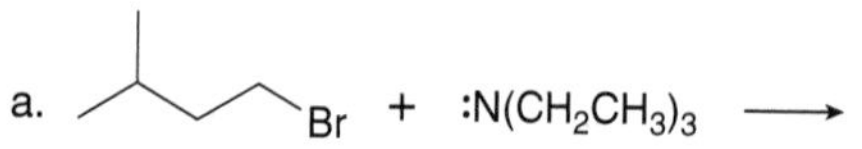

b. $(CH_3)_3C{-}Cl + H_2\ddot{O}: \longrightarrow$

Problem 7.10 CPC (cetylpyridinium chloride), an antiseptic found in throat lozenges and mouthwash, is synthesized by the following reaction. Draw the structure of CPC.

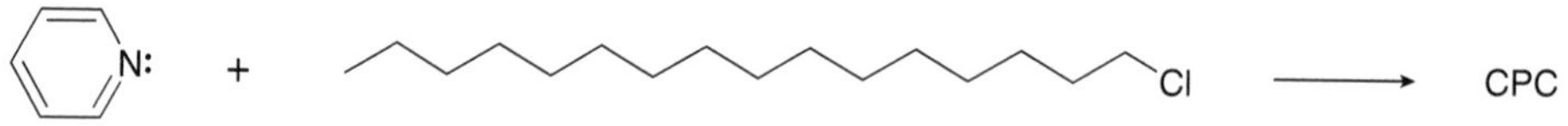

7.7 The Leaving Group

Nucleophilic substitution is a general reaction of organic compounds. Why, then, are alkyl halides the most common substrates, and halide anions the most common leaving groups? To answer this question, we must understand leaving group ability. **What makes a good leaving group?**

In a nucleophilic substitution reaction of R–X, the C–X bond is heterolytically cleaved, and the leaving group departs with the electron pair in that bond, forming X:$^-$. **The more stable the leaving group X:$^-$, the better able it is to accept an electron pair,** giving rise to the following generalization:

- **In comparing two leaving groups, the better leaving group is the weaker base.**

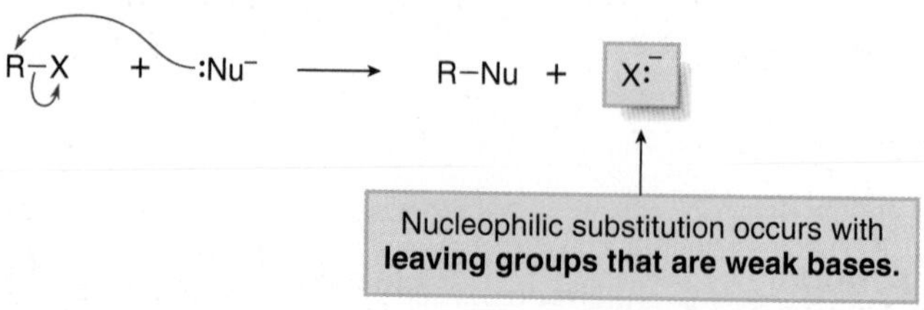

For example, H_2O is a better leaving group than ^-OH because H_2O is a weaker base. Moreover, the periodic trends in basicity can now be used to identify **periodic trends in leaving group ability:**

- **Left-to-right across a row of the periodic table, basicity *decreases* so leaving group ability *increases.***

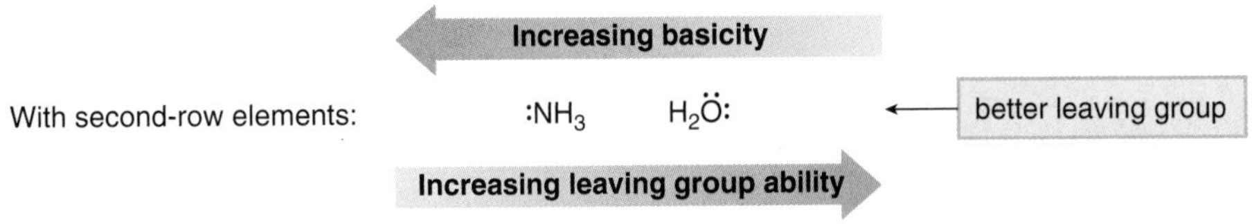

- **Down a column of the periodic table, basicity *decreases* so leaving group ability *increases.***

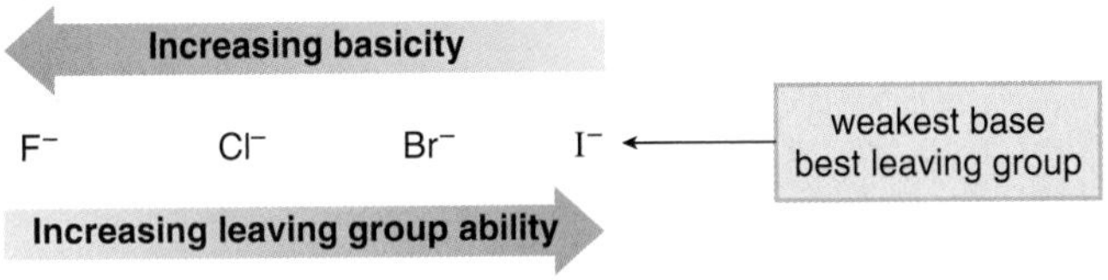

All good leaving groups are weak bases with strong conjugate acids having low pK_a values. Thus, all halide anions except F^- are good leaving groups because their conjugate acids (HCl, HBr, and HI) have low pK_a values. Tables 7.2 and 7.3 list good and poor leaving groups for nucleophilic substitution reactions, respectively. Nucleophilic substitution does not occur with any of the leaving groups in Table 7.3 because these leaving groups are strong bases.

Table 7.2 Good Leaving Groups for Nucleophilic Substitution

Starting material	Leaving group	Conjugate acid	pK_a
R–Cl	Cl^-	HCl	−7
R–Br	Br^-	HBr	−9
R–I	I^-	HI	−10
R–OH_2^+	H_2O	H_3O^+	−1.7

These molecules undergo nucleophilic substitution. (starting materials)

good leaving groups (leaving groups)

Table 7.3 Poor Leaving Groups for Nucleophilic Substitution

Starting material	Leaving group	Conjugate acid	pK_a
R–F	F^-	HF	3.2
R–OH	^-OH	H_2O	15.7
R–NH_2	$^-NH_2$	NH_3	38
R–H	H^-	H_2	35
R–R	R^-	RH	50

These molecules do *not* undergo nucleophilic substitution. (starting materials)

poor leaving groups (leaving groups)

Problem 7.11 Which is the better leaving group in each pair?

a. Cl^-, I^- b. NH_3, $^-NH_2$ c. H_2O, H_2S

Problem 7.12 Which molecules contain good leaving groups?

a. $CH_3CH_2CH_2Br$ b. $CH_3CH_2CH_2OH$ c. $CH_3CH_2\overset{+}{O}H_2$ d. CH_3CH_3

Given a particular nucleophile and leaving group, how can we determine whether the equilibrium will favor products in a nucleophilic substitution? We can often correctly predict the direction of equilibrium by comparing the basicity of the nucleophile and the leaving group.

- **Equilibrium favors the products of nucleophilic substitution when the leaving group is a weaker base than the nucleophile.**

Sample Problem 7.1 illustrates how to apply this general rule.

Sample Problem 7.1 Will the following substitution reaction favor formation of the products?

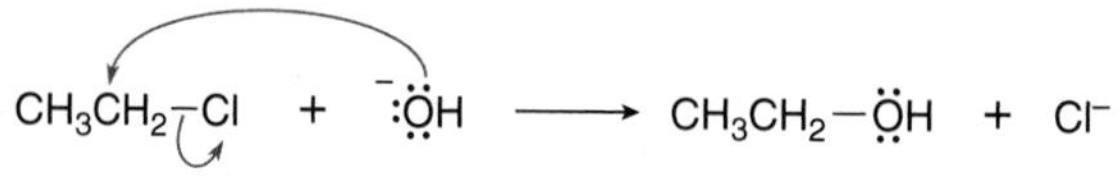

Solution

Compare the basicity of the nucleophile (^-OH) and the leaving group (Cl^-) by comparing the pK_a values of their conjugate acids. **The stronger the conjugate acid, the weaker the base, and the better the leaving group.**

			conjugate acids	
nucleophile	^-OH	→	H_2O	$pK_a = 15.7$
leaving group	Cl^-	→	HCl	$pK_a = -7$
	↑ **weaker base**		↑ **stronger acid**	

Because Cl^-, the leaving group, is a weaker base than ^-OH, the nucleophile, the reaction favors the products.

Problem 7.13 Does the equilibrium favor the reactants or products in each substitution reaction?

a. $CH_3CH_2{-}NH_2 + Br^- \longrightarrow CH_3CH_2{-}Br + {}^-NH_2$

b. 

Problem 7.14 Should it be possible to convert $CH_3CH_2CH_2OH$ to $CH_3CH_2CH_2Cl$ by a nucleophilic substitution reaction with NaCl? Explain why or why not.

7.8 The Nucleophile

We use the word *base* to mean *Brønsted–Lowry* base and the word *nucleophile* to mean a *Lewis base* that reacts with electrophiles *other than* protons.

Nucleophiles and bases are structurally similar: both have a lone pair or a π bond. They differ in what they attack.

- Bases attack protons. Nucleophiles attack other electron-deficient atoms (usually carbons).

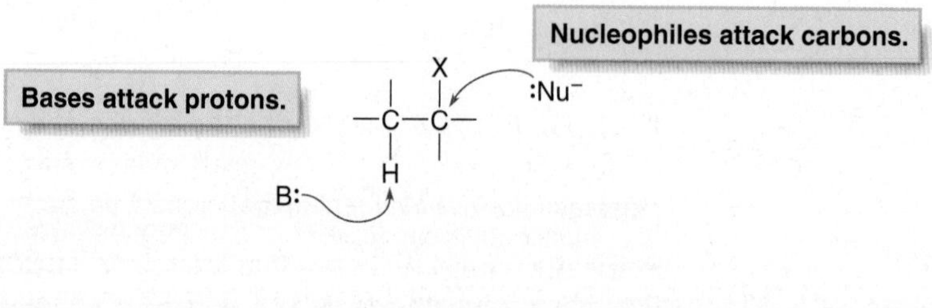

7.8A Nucleophilicity Versus Basicity

How is **nucleophilicity** (nucleophile strength) related to basicity? Although it is generally true that **a strong base is a strong nucleophile,** nucleophile size and steric factors can sometimes change this relationship.

Nucleophilicity parallels basicity in three instances:

[1] For two nucleophiles with the same nucleophilic atom, the stronger base is the stronger nucleophile.

- The relative nucleophilicity of ^-OH and CH_3COO^-, two oxygen nucleophiles, is determined by comparing the pK_a values of their conjugate acids (H_2O and CH_3COOH). CH_3COOH (pK_a = 4.8) is a stronger acid than H_2O (pK_a = 15.7), so ^-OH is a stronger base and stronger nucleophile than CH_3COO^-.

[2] A negatively charged nucleophile is always stronger than its conjugate acid.

- ^-OH is a stronger base and stronger nucleophile than H_2O, its conjugate acid.

[3] Right-to-left across a row of the periodic table, nucleophilicity increases as basicity increases.

For second-row elements with the same charge:

CH_3^- $^-NH_2$ ^-OH F^-

← **Increasing basicity**
Increasing nucleophilicity

Problem 7.15 Identify the stronger nucleophile in each pair.

a. NH_3, $^-NH_2$ b. CH_3NH_2, CH_3OH c. CH_3COO^-, $CH_3CH_2O^-$

7.8B Steric Effects and Nucleophilicity

All steric effects arise because two atoms cannot occupy the same space. In Chapter 4, for example, we learned that **steric strain** is an increase in energy when big groups (occupying a large volume) are forced close to each other.

Nucleophilicity does not parallel basicity when **steric hindrance** becomes important. ***Steric hindrance*** **is a decrease in reactivity resulting from the presence of bulky groups at the site of a reaction.**

For example, although pK_a tables indicate that *tert*-butoxide [$(CH_3)_3CO^-$] is a stronger base than ethoxide ($CH_3CH_2O^-$), **ethoxide is the *stronger* nucleophile.** The three CH_3 groups around the O atom of *tert*-butoxide create steric hindrance, making it more difficult for this big, bulky base to attack a tetravalent carbon atom.

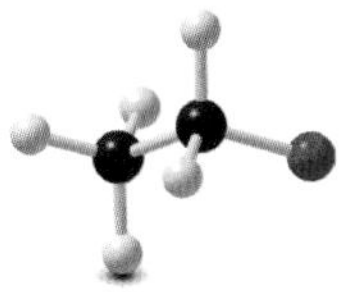
= $CH_3CH_2-\ddot{O}:^-$

ethoxide

stronger nucleophile

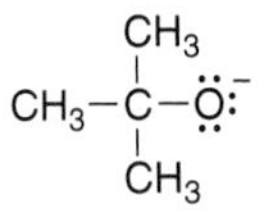

=
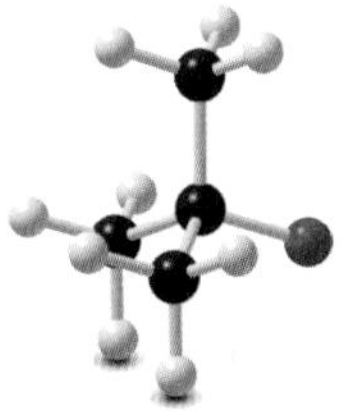

tert-butoxide

stronger base

Three CH_3 groups sterically hinder the O atom, making it a **weaker nucleophile.**

Steric hindrance decreases nucleophilicity but *not* basicity. Because bases pull off small, easily accessible protons, they are unaffected by steric hindrance. Nucleophiles, on the other hand, must attack a crowded tetrahedral carbon, so bulky groups decrease reactivity.

Sterically hindered bases that are poor nucleophiles are called *nonnucleophilic bases.* Potassium *tert*-butoxide [$K^+ \, ^-OC(CH_3)_3$] is a strong, nonnucleophilic base.

7.8C Comparing Nucleophiles of Different Size—Solvent Effects

Atoms vary greatly in size down a column of the periodic table, and in this case, **nucleophilicity depends on the solvent used in a substitution reaction.** Although solvent has thus far been ignored, most organic reactions take place in a liquid solvent that dissolves all reactants to some extent. Because substitution reactions involve polar starting materials, polar solvents are used to dissolve them. There are two main kinds of polar solvents—**polar *protic* solvents and polar *aprotic* solvents.**

Polar Protic Solvents

In addition to dipole–dipole interactions, **polar *protic* solvents are capable of intermolecular hydrogen bonding,** because they contain an O–H or N–H bond. The most common polar protic solvents are water and alcohols (ROH), as seen in the examples in Figure 7.6. **Polar protic solvents solvate *both* cations and anions well.**

- **Cations are solvated by ion–dipole interactions.**
- **Anions are solvated by hydrogen bonding.**

Figure 7.6 Examples of polar protic solvents

H_2O	CH_3OH	CH_3CH_2OH	$(CH_3)_3COH$	CH_3COOH
	methanol	ethanol	*tert*-butanol	acetic acid

For example, if the salt NaBr is used as a source of the nucleophile Br^- in H_2O, the Na^+ cations are solvated by ion–dipole interactions with H_2O molecules, and the Br^- anions are solvated by strong hydrogen bonding interactions.

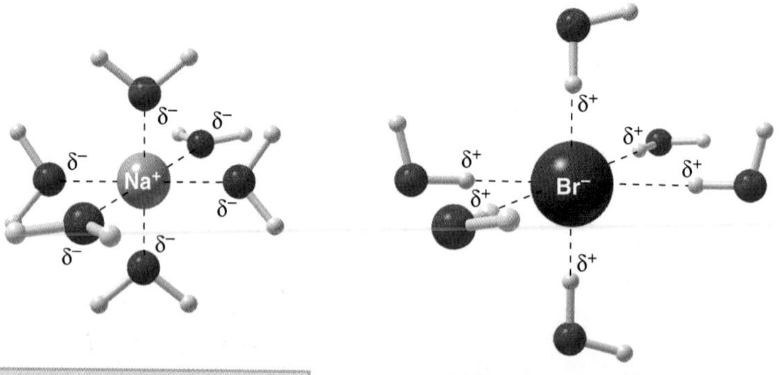

Na^+ is solvated by ion–dipole interactions with H_2O.

Br^- is solvated by hydrogen bonding with H_2O.

How do polar protic solvents affect nucleophilicity? **In polar protic solvents, nucleophilicity *increases* down a column of the periodic table as the size of the anion increases. This is *opposite* to basicity.** A small electronegative anion like F^- is very well solvated by hydrogen bonding, effectively shielding it from reaction. On the other hand, a large, less electronegative anion like I^- does not hold onto solvent molecules as tightly. The solvent does not "hide" a large nucleophile as well, and the nucleophile is much more able to donate its electron pairs in a reaction. Thus, **nucleophilicity increases down a column** even though basicity decreases, giving rise to the following trend in polar protic solvents:

I^- is a weak base but a strong nucleophile in polar protic solvents.

Down a column of the periodic table

F^- Cl^- Br^- I^- →

Increasing nucleophilicity in polar protic solvents

Polar Aprotic Solvents

Polar *aprotic* solvents also exhibit dipole–dipole interactions, but they have no O–H or N–H bond so they are **incapable of hydrogen bonding.** Examples of polar aprotic solvents are shown in Figure 7.7. **Polar aprotic solvents solvate only cations well.**

- **Cations are solvated by ion–dipole interactions.**
- **Anions are not well solvated because the solvent cannot hydrogen bond to them.**

Figure 7.7 Examples of polar aprotic solvents

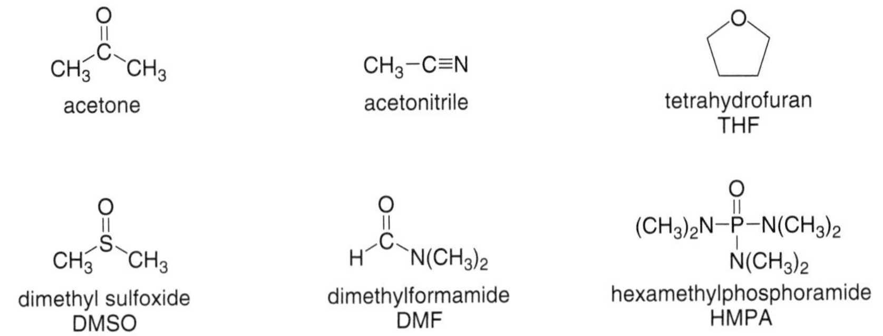
acetone
CH$_3$–C≡N
acetonitrile
tetrahydrofuran
THF
dimethyl sulfoxide
DMSO
dimethylformamide
DMF
(CH$_3$)$_2$N–P–N(CH$_3$)$_2$
N(CH$_3$)$_2$
hexamethylphosphoramide
HMPA

Abbreviations are often used in organic chemistry, instead of a compound's complete name. A list of common abbreviations is given on the inside back cover.

When the salt NaBr is dissolved in acetone, $(CH_3)_2C{=}O$, the Na^+ cations are solvated by ion–dipole interactions with the acetone molecules, but, with no possibility for hydrogen bonding, the Br^- anions are not well solvated. Often these anions are called **naked anions** because they are not bound by tight interactions with solvent.

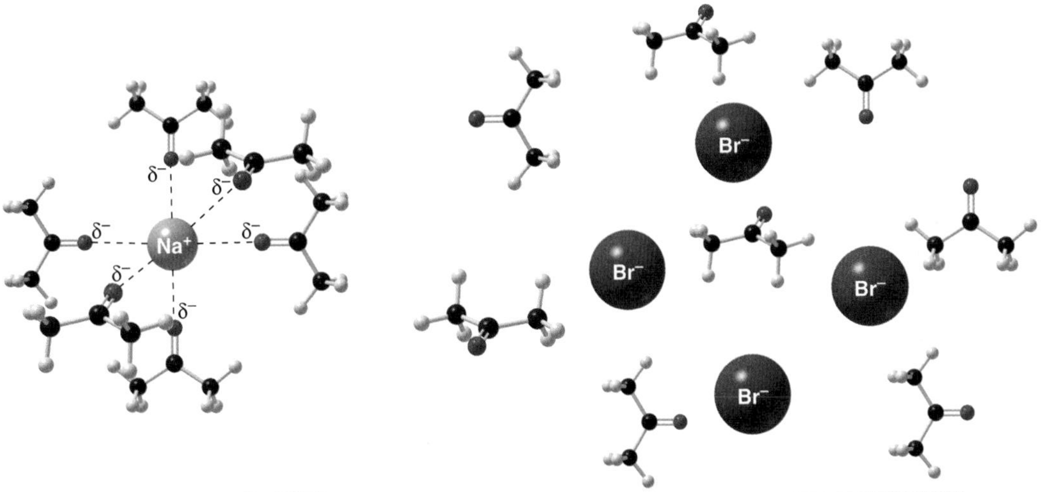
Na+
δ–
Br–

$(CH_3)_2C{=}O$ solvates Na^+ well by ion–dipole interactions.

Br^- anions are surrounded by solvent but not well solvated by the $(CH_3)_2C{=}O$ molecules.

How do polar aprotic solvents affect nucleophilicity? Because anions are not well solvated in polar aprotic solvents, there is no need to consider whether solvent molecules more effectively hide one anion than another. Nucleophilicity once again parallels basicity and **the stronger base is the stronger nucleophile.** Because basicity decreases with size down a column, nucleophilicity decreases as well:

Down a column of the periodic table

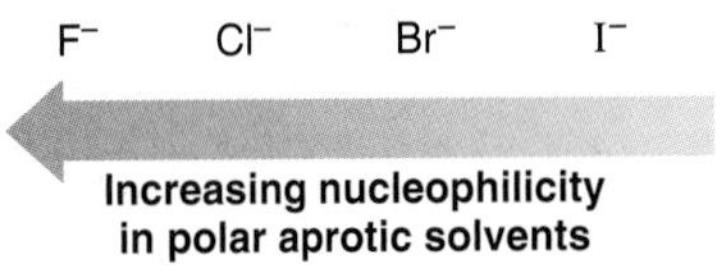
F–
Cl–
Br–
I–
Increasing nucleophilicity
in polar aprotic solvents

Problem 7.16 Classify each solvent as protic or aprotic.

a. $HOCH_2CH_2OH$ b. $CH_3CH_2OCH_2CH_3$ c. $CH_3COOCH_2CH_3$

Problem 7.17 Identify the stronger nucleophile in each pair of anions.

a. Br^- or Cl^- in a polar protic solvent
b. HO^- or Cl^- in a polar aprotic solvent
c. HS^- or F^- in a polar protic solvent

7.8D Summary

This long discussion of nucleophilicity has brought together many new concepts, such as steric hindrance and solvent effects, both of which we will meet again in our study of organic chemistry. Keep in mind, however, the central relationship between nucleophilicity and basicity in comparing two nucleophiles.

- **It is generally true that the *stronger* base is the *stronger* nucleophile.**
- **In polar protic solvents, however, nucleophilicity increases with increasing size of an anion (opposite to basicity).**
- **Steric hindrance decreases nucleophilicity without decreasing basicity, making $(CH_3)_3CO^-$ a stronger base but a weaker nucleophile than $CH_3CH_2O^-$.**

Table 7.4 lists some common nucleophiles used in nucleophilic substitution reactions.

Problem 7.18 Rank the nucleophiles in each group in order of increasing nucleophilicity.

a. ^-OH, $^-NH_2$, H_2O b. ^-OH, Br^-, F^- (polar aprotic solvent) c. H_2O, ^-OH, CH_3COO^-

Problem 7.19 What nucleophile is needed to convert $(CH_3)_2CHCH_2CH_2-Br$ to each product?

a. $(CH_3)_2CHCH_2CH_2-SH$
b. $(CH_3)_2CHCH_2CH_2-OCH_2CH_3$
c. $(CH_3)_2CHCH_2CH_2-OCOCH_3$
d. $(CH_3)_2CHCH_2CH_2-C\equiv CH$

Table 7.4 Common Nucleophiles in Organic Chemistry

	Negatively charged nucleophiles			Neutral nucleophiles	
Oxygen	^-OH	^-OR	CH_3COO^-	H_2O	ROH
Nitrogen	N_3^-			NH_3	RNH_2
Carbon	^-CN	$HC\equiv C^-$			
Halogen	Cl^-	Br^-	I^-		
Sulfur	HS^-	RS^-		H_2S	RSH

7.9 Possible Mechanisms for Nucleophilic Substitution

Now that you know something about the general features of nucleophilic substitution, you can begin to understand the mechanism.

Overall reaction

$$R-X \quad + \quad :Nu^- \longrightarrow R-Nu \quad + \quad X:^-$$

This σ bond is broken. This σ bond is formed.

Nucleophilic substitution at an sp^3 hybridized carbon involves two σ bonds: the bond to the leaving group, which is broken, and the bond to the nucleophile, which is formed. To understand the mechanism of this reaction, though, we must know the timing of these two events; that is, **what is the order of bond breaking and bond making?** Do they happen at the same time, or does one event precede the other? There are three possibilities.

[1] **Bond breaking and bond making occur at the *same* time.**

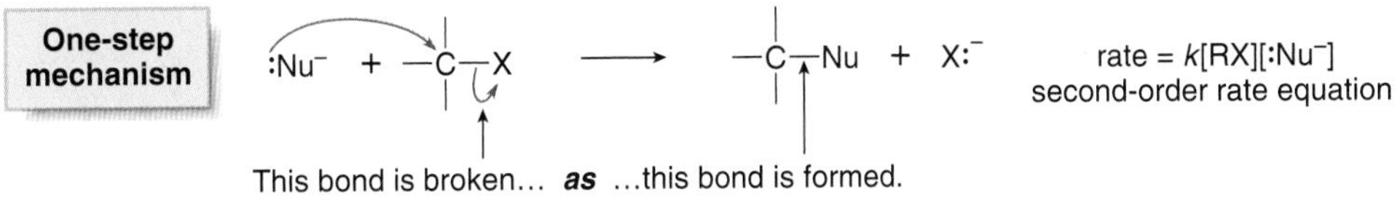

- If the C – X bond is broken ***as*** the C – Nu bond is formed, the mechanism has **one step.** As we learned in Section 6.9, the rate of such a bimolecular reaction depends on the concentration of both reactants; that is, the rate equation is **second order.**

[2] **Bond breaking occurs *before* bond making.**

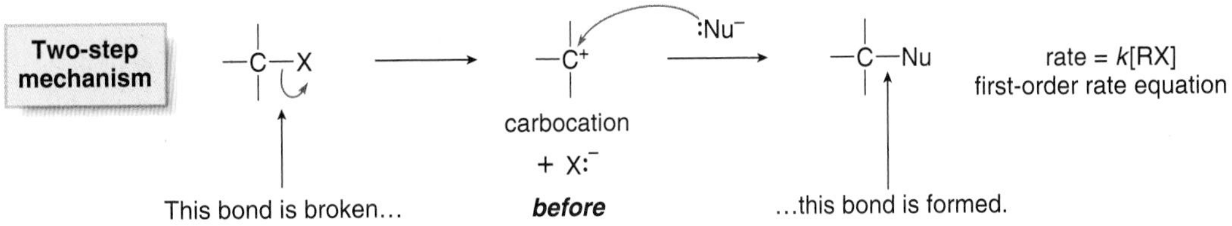

- If the C – X bond is broken ***first*** and then the C – Nu bond is formed, the mechanism has **two steps** and a **carbocation** is formed as an intermediate. Because the first step is rate-determining, the rate depends on the concentration of RX only; that is, the rate equation is **first order.**

[3] **Bond making occurs *before* bond breaking.**

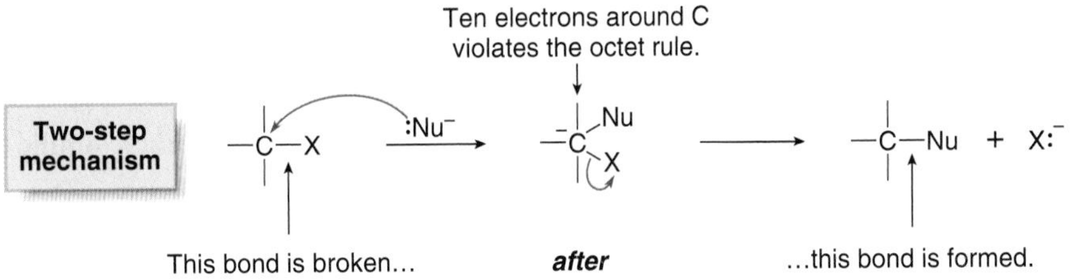

- If the C – Nu bond is formed ***first*** and then the C – X bond is broken, the mechanism has **two steps,** but this mechanism has an inherent problem. The intermediate generated in the first step has 10 electrons around carbon, violating the octet rule. Because two other mechanistic possibilities do not violate a fundamental rule, this last possibility can be disregarded.

The preceding discussion has generated two possible mechanisms for nucleophilic substitution: **a one-step mechanism in which bond breaking and bond making are simultaneous, and a two-step mechanism in which bond breaking comes before bond making.** In Section 7.10 we look at data for two specific nucleophilic substitution reactions and see if those data fit either of these proposed mechanisms.

7.10 Two Mechanisms for Nucleophilic Substitution

Rate equations for two different reactions give us insight into the possible mechanism for nucleophilic substitution.

Reaction of bromomethane (CH_3Br) with the nucleophile acetate (CH_3COO^-) affords the substitution product methyl acetate with loss of Br^- as the leaving group (Equation [1]). Kinetic data show that the reaction rate depends on the concentration of *both* reactants; that is, the rate equation is **second order.** This suggests a **bimolecular reaction with a one-step mechanism** in which the C–X bond is broken *as* the C–Nu bond is formed.

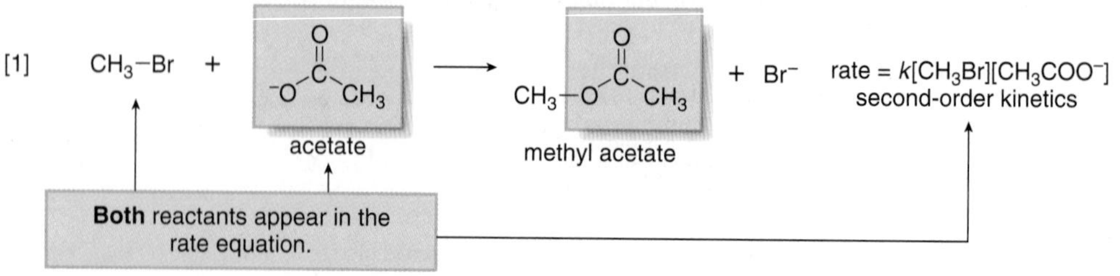
[1]
CH3–Br +
acetate
CH3–O–C(=O)–CH3
methyl acetate
+ Br–
rate = k[CH3Br][CH3COO–]
second-order kinetics
Both reactants appear in the rate equation.

Equation [2] illustrates a similar nucleophilic substitution reaction with a different alkyl halide, $(CH_3)_3CBr$, which also leads to substitution of Br^- by CH_3COO^-. Kinetic data show that this reaction rate depends on the concentration of only *one* reactant, the alkyl halide; that is, the rate equation is **first order.** This suggests a **two-step mechanism in which the rate-determining step involves the alkyl halide only.**

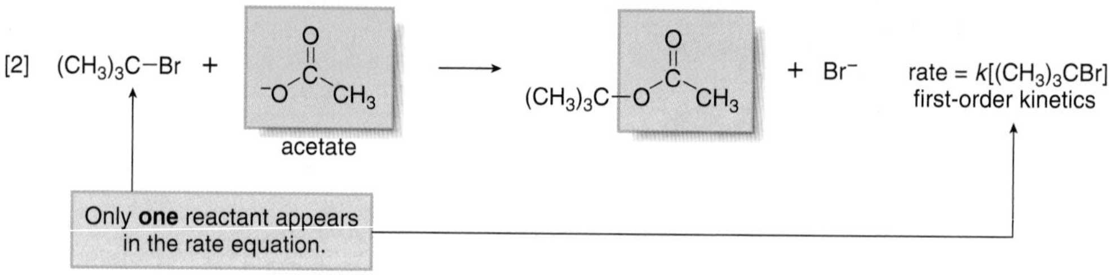
[2] (CH3)3C–Br +
acetate
(CH3)3C–O–C(=O)–CH3
+ Br–
rate = k[(CH3)3CBr]
first-order kinetics
Only one reactant appears in the rate equation.

The numbers **1** and **2** in the names S_N1 and S_N2 refer to the kinetic order of the reactions. For example, S_N**2** means that the kinetics are **second** order. The number *2* does *not* refer to the number of steps in the mechanism.

How can these two different results be explained? Although these two reactions have the same nucleophile and leaving group, **there must be two different mechanisms** because there are two different rate equations. These equations are specific examples of two well known mechanisms for nucleophilic substitution at an sp^3 hybridized carbon:

- The **S_N2 mechanism (substitution nucleophilic bimolecular),** illustrated by the reaction in Equation [1].
- The **S_N1 mechanism (substitution nucleophilic unimolecular),** illustrated by the reaction in Equation [2].

We will now examine the characteristics of the S_N2 and S_N1 mechanisms.

7.11 The S_N2 Mechanism

The reaction of CH_3Br with CH_3COO^- is an example of an **S_N2 reaction.** What are the general features of this mechanism?

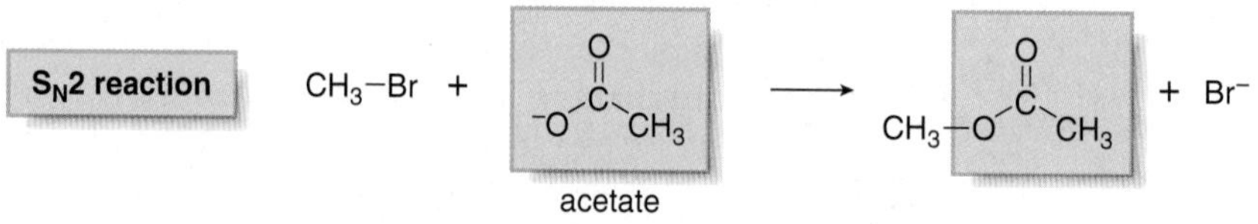
SN2 reaction
CH3–Br +
acetate
CH3–O–C(=O)–CH3
+ Br–

7.11A Kinetics

An S_N2 reaction exhibits **second-order kinetics;** that is, the reaction is **bimolecular** and both the alkyl halide and the nucleophile appear in the rate equation.

- rate = $k[CH_3Br][CH_3COO^-]$

Changing the concentration of *either* reactant affects the rate. For example, doubling the concentration of *either* the nucleophile or the alkyl halide doubles the rate. Doubling the concentration of *both* reactants increases the rate by a factor of four.

Problem 7.20 What happens to the rate of an S_N2 reaction under each of the following conditions?

a. [RX] is tripled, and [:Nu⁻] stays the same.
b. Both [RX] and [:Nu⁻] are tripled.
c. [RX] is halved, and [:Nu⁻] stays the same.
d. [RX] is halved, and [:Nu⁻] is doubled.

7.11B A One-Step Mechanism

The most straightforward explanation for the observed second-order kinetics is a **concerted reaction—bond breaking and bond making occur at the *same* time,** as shown in Mechanism 7.1.

Mechanism 7.1 The S_N2 Mechanism

One step The C – Br bond breaks as the C – O bond forms.

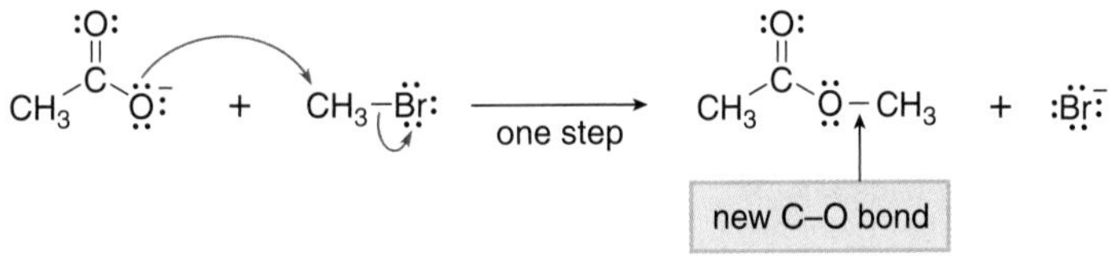

An energy diagram for the reaction of $CH_3Br + CH_3COO^-$ is shown in Figure 7.8. The reaction has one step, so there is one energy barrier between reactants and products. Because the equilibrium for this S_N2 reaction favors the products, they are drawn at lower energy than the starting materials.

Problem 7.21 Draw the structure of the transition state in each of the following S_N2 reactions.

a. $CH_3CH_2CH_2{-}Cl + {}^-OCH_3 \longrightarrow CH_3CH_2CH_2{-}OCH_3 + Cl^-$

b. 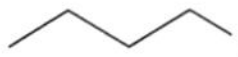 Br + ⁻SH ⟶  SH + Br⁻

Problem 7.22 Draw an energy diagram for the reaction in Problem 7.21a. Label the axes, the starting material, the product, and the transition state. Assume the reaction is exothermic. Label $\Delta H°$ and E_a.

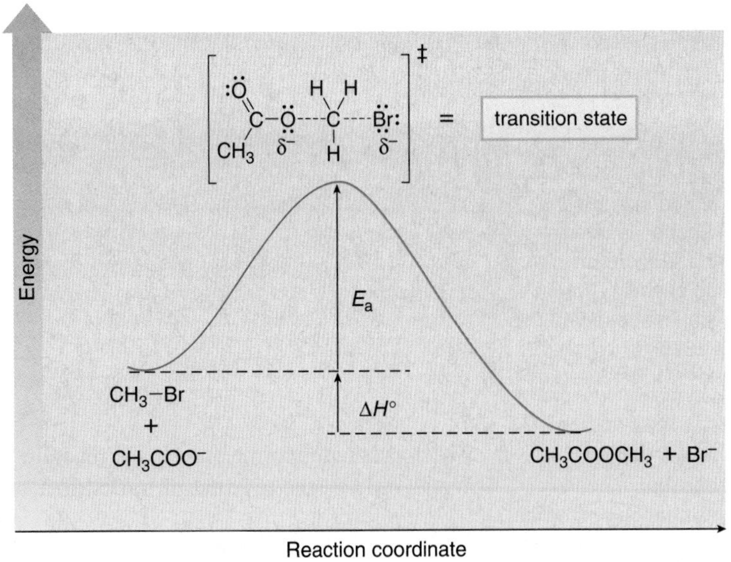

Figure 7.8
An energy diagram for the S_N2 reaction:
$CH_3Br + CH_3COO^- \rightarrow CH_3COOCH_3 + Br^-$

- In the transition state, the C—Br bond is partially broken, the C—O bond is partially formed, and both the attacking nucleophile and the departing leaving group bear a partial negative charge.

7.11C Stereochemistry of the S_N2 Reaction

From what direction does the nucleophile approach the substrate in an S_N2 reaction? There are two possibilities.

- **Frontside attack:** The nucleophile approaches from the ***same*** side as the leaving group.
- **Backside attack:** The nucleophile approaches from the side ***opposite*** the leaving group.

The results of frontside and backside attack of a nucleophile are illustrated with $CH_3CH(D)Br$ as substrate and the general nucleophile :Nu⁻. This substrate has the leaving group bonded to a stereogenic center, thus allowing us to see the structural difference that results when the nucleophile attacks from two different directions.

In **frontside attack,** the nucleophile approaches from the **same** side as the leaving group, forming **A.** In this example, the leaving group was drawn on the right, so the nucleophile attacks from the right, and all other groups remain in their original positions. Because the nucleophile and leaving group are in the same position relative to the other three groups on carbon, frontside attack results in **retention of configuration** around the stereogenic center.

Recall from Section 1.1 that D stands for the isotope deuterium (^2H).

Frontside attack

A

Nu replaces Br on the **same** side.

In **backside attack,** the nucleophile approaches from the **opposite** side to the leaving group, forming **B.** In this example, the leaving group was drawn on the right, so the nucleophile attacks from the left. Because the nucleophile and leaving group are in the opposite position relative to the other three groups on carbon, backside attack results in **inversion of configuration** around the stereogenic center.

Backside attack

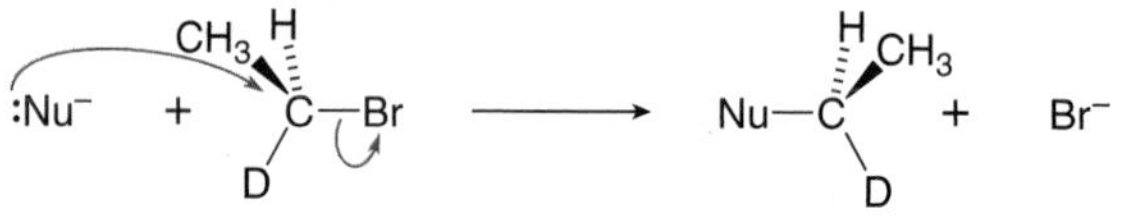

B

Nu replaces Br on the **opposite** side.

The products of frontside and backside attack are *different* compounds. **A** and **B** are stereoisomers that are nonsuperimposable—they are **enantiomers.**

Inversion of configuration in an S_N2 reaction is often called **Walden inversion,** after Latvian chemist Dr. Paul Walden, who first observed this process in 1896.

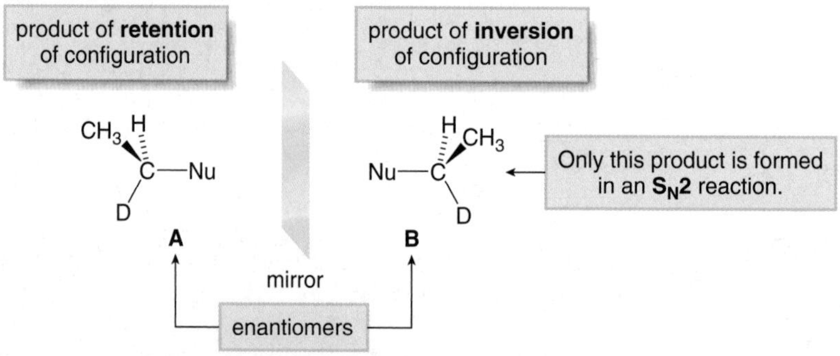

Backside attack occurs in all S_N2 reactions, but we can observe this change only when the leaving group is bonded to a stereogenic center.

Which product is formed in an S_N2 reaction? When the stereochemistry of the product is determined, **only B, the product of backside attack, is formed.**

- **All S_N2 reactions proceed with backside attack of the nucleophile, resulting in *inversion* of configuration at a stereogenic center.**

One explanation for backside attack is based on an electronic argument. Both the nucleophile and leaving group are electron rich and these like charges repel each other. Backside attack keeps these two groups as far away from each other as possible. In the transition state, the nucleophile and leaving group are 180° away from each other, and the other three groups around carbon occupy a plane, as illustrated in Figure 7.9.

Figure 7.9 Stereochemistry of the S_N2 reaction

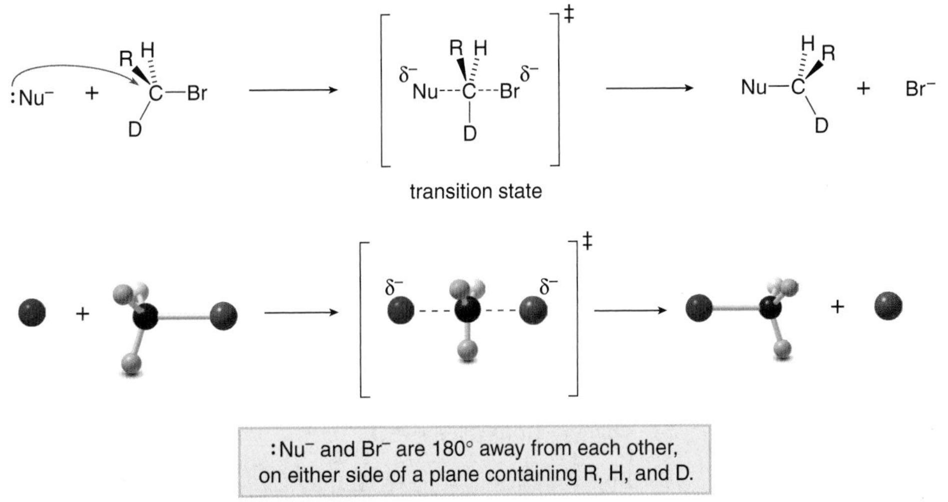

Two additional examples of inversion of configuration in S_N2 reactions are given in Figure 7.10.

Figure 7.10 Two examples of inversion of configuration in the S_N2 reaction

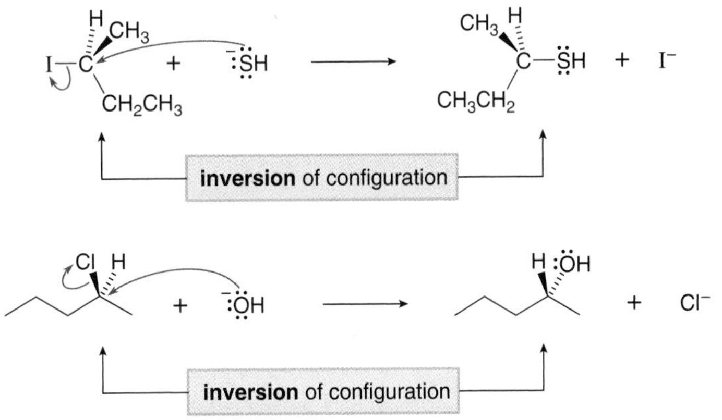

- The bond to the nucleophile in the product is always on the **opposite side** relative to the bond to the leaving group in the starting material.

Sample Problem 7.2 Label the nucleophile and leaving group, and draw the product (including stereochemistry) of the following S_N2 reaction.

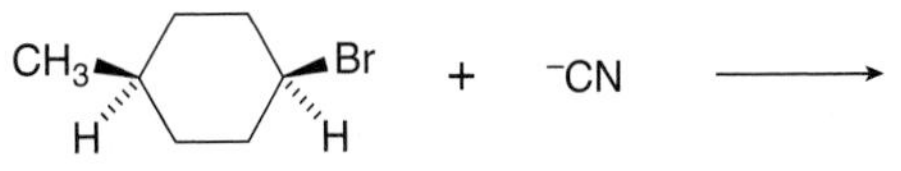

Solution

Br^- is the leaving group and ^-CN is the nucleophile. Because S_N2 reactions proceed with **inversion** of configuration and the leaving group is drawn above the ring (on a wedge), the nucleophile must come in from below (ending up on a dashed bond).

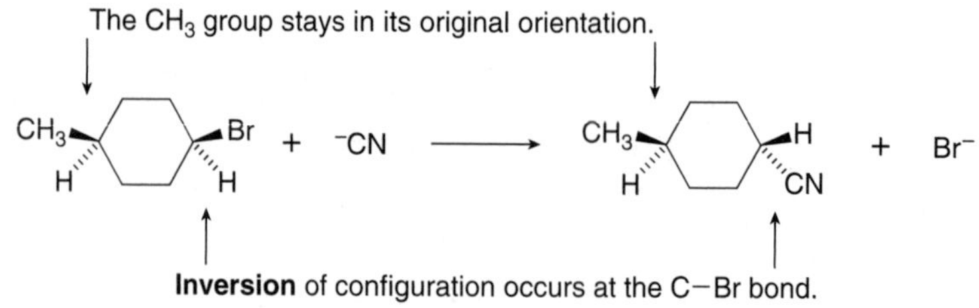
The CH_3 group stays in its original orientation.
CH_3
H
Br
H
+ ^{-}CN
CH_3
H
H
CN
+ Br^{-}
Inversion of configuration occurs at the C–Br bond.

Backside attack converts the starting material, which has two groups **cis** to each other, to a product with two groups **trans** to each other because the nucleophile (^{-}CN) attacks from below the plane of the ring.

Problem 7.23 Draw the product of each S_N2 reaction and indicate stereochemistry.

a. 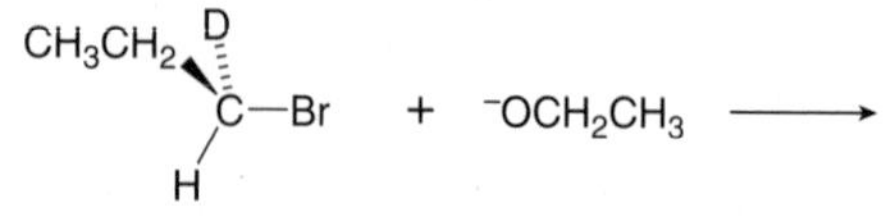
CH_3CH_2
D
C–Br
H
+ $^{-}OCH_2CH_3$

b. 
I
+ ^{-}CN

7.11D The Identity of the R Group

How does the rate of an S_N2 reaction change as the alkyl group in the substrate alkyl halide changes from CH_3 --→ 1° --→ 2° --→ 3°?

- As the number of R groups on the carbon with the leaving group *increases,* the rate of an S_N2 reaction *decreases.*

CH_3–X	RCH_2–X	R_2CH–X	R_3C–X
methyl	**1°**	**2°**	**3°**

← **Increasing rate of an S_N2 reaction**

- Methyl and 1° alkyl halides undergo S_N2 reactions with ease.
- 2° Alkyl halides react more slowly.
- 3° Alkyl halides *do not* undergo S_N2 reactions.

This order of reactivity can be explained by steric effects. As small H atoms are replaced by larger alkyl groups, **steric hindrance caused by bulky R groups makes nucleophilic attack from the back side more difficult,** slowing the reaction rate. Figure 7.11 illustrates the effect of increasing steric hindrance in a series of alkyl halides.

Figure 7.11
Steric effects in the S_N2 reaction

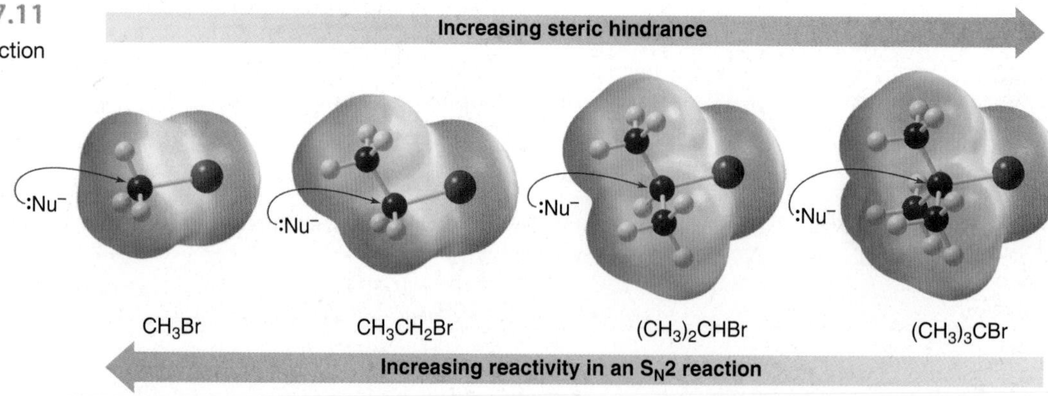
Increasing steric hindrance
:Nu⁻
:Nu⁻
:Nu⁻
:Nu⁻
CH_3Br
CH_3CH_2Br
$(CH_3)_2CHBr$
$(CH_3)_3CBr$
Increasing reactivity in an S_N2 reaction

The effect of steric hindrance on the rate of an S_N2 reaction is reflected in the energy of the transition state, too. Let's compare the reaction of ^{-}OH with two different alkyl halides, CH_3Br and $(CH_3)_2CHBr$, as shown in Figure 7.12. The transition state of each S_N2 reaction consists of

Figure 7.12

Two energy diagrams depicting the effect of steric hindrance in S_N2 reactions

a. $CH_3Br + {}^-OH \rightarrow CH_3OH + Br^-$

b. $(CH_3)_2CHBr + {}^-OH \rightarrow (CH_3)_2CHOH + Br^-$

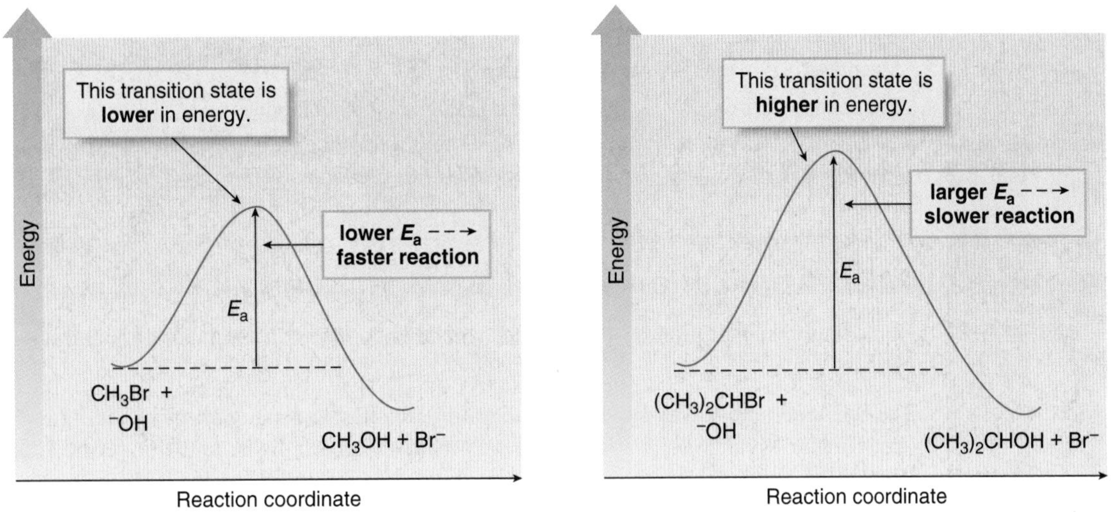

- CH_3Br is an unhindered alkyl halide. The transition state in the S_N2 reaction is lower in energy, making E_a lower and increasing the reaction rate.
- $(CH_3)_2CHBr$ is a sterically hindered alkyl halide. The transition state in the S_N2 reaction is higher in energy, making E_a higher and decreasing the reaction rate.

five groups around the central carbon atom—three bonds to either H or R groups and two partial bonds to the leaving group and the nucleophile. **Crowding around the central carbon atom increases as H atoms are successively replaced by R groups,** so the central carbon is much more sterically hindered in the transition state for $(CH_3)_2CHBr$ than for CH_3Br. This increased crowding in the transition state makes it higher in energy (increases E_a), so the rate of the S_N2 reaction decreases.

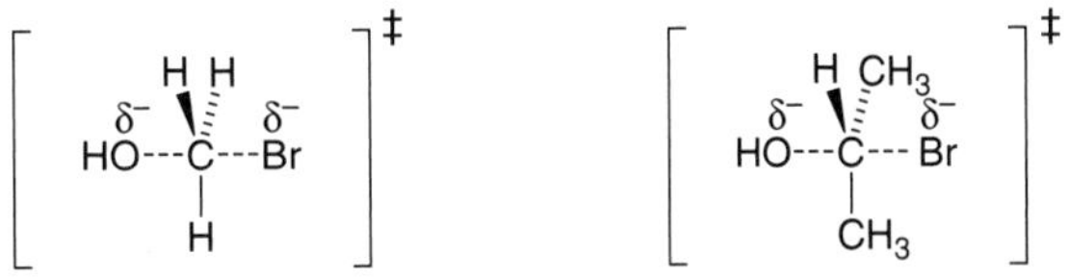

less crowded transition state
lower in energy

faster S_N2 reaction

more crowded transition state
higher in energy

slower S_N2 reaction

- **Increasing the number of R groups on the carbon with the leaving group *increases crowding* in the transition state, *decreasing* the rate of an S_N2 reaction.**

- **The S_N2 reaction is fastest with unhindered halides.**

Problem 7.24 Which compound in each pair undergoes a faster S_N2 reaction?

a. 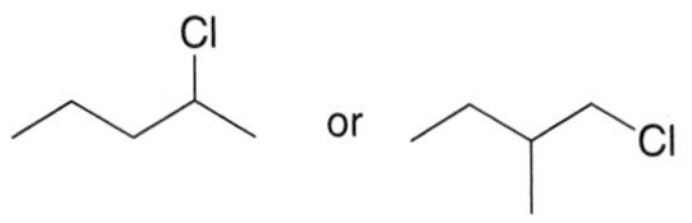

b. 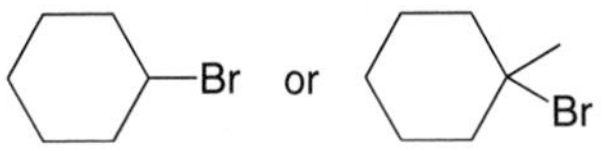

Table 7.5 summarizes what we have learned thus far about an S_N2 mechanism.

Table 7.5 Characteristics of the S_N2 Mechanism

Characteristic	Result
Kinetics	• Second-order kinetics; rate = k[RX][:Nu$^-$]
Mechanism	• One step
Stereochemistry	• Backside attack of the nucleophile • Inversion of configuration at a stereogenic center
Identity of R	• Unhindered halides react fastest. • Rate: $CH_3X > RCH_2X > R_2CHX > R_3CX$

SAM, a nutritional supplement sold under the name SAMe (pronounced sammy), has been used in Europe to treat depression and arthritis for over 20 years. In cells, SAM is used in nucleophilic substitutions that synthesize key amino acids, hormones, and neurotransmitters.

7.12 Application: Useful S_N2 Reactions

Nucleophilic substitution by an S_N2 mechanism is common in the laboratory and in biological systems.

The S_N2 reaction is a key step in the laboratory synthesis of many drugs including **ethambutol** (trade name Myambutol), used in the treatment of tuberculosis, and **fluoxetine** (trade name Prozac), an antidepressant, as illustrated in Figure 7.13.

Nucleophilic substitution reactions are important in biological systems as well. The most common reaction involves nucleophilic substitution at the CH_3 group in *S*-adenosylmethionine, or **SAM.** SAM is the cell's equivalent of CH_3I. The many polar functional groups in SAM make it soluble in the aqueous environment in the cell.

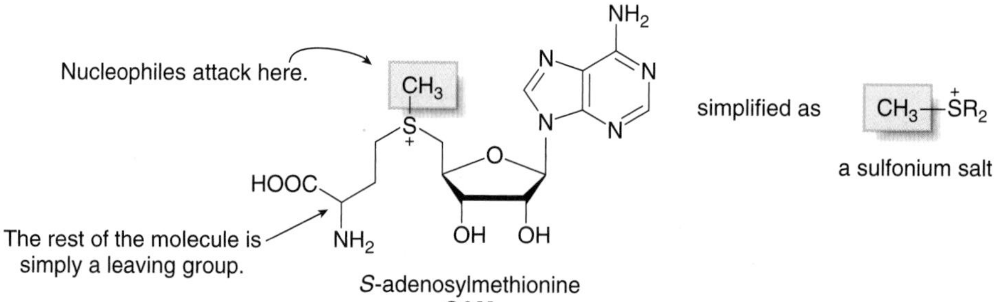

S-adenosylmethionine
SAM

Figure 7.13
Nucleophilic substitution in the synthesis of two useful drugs

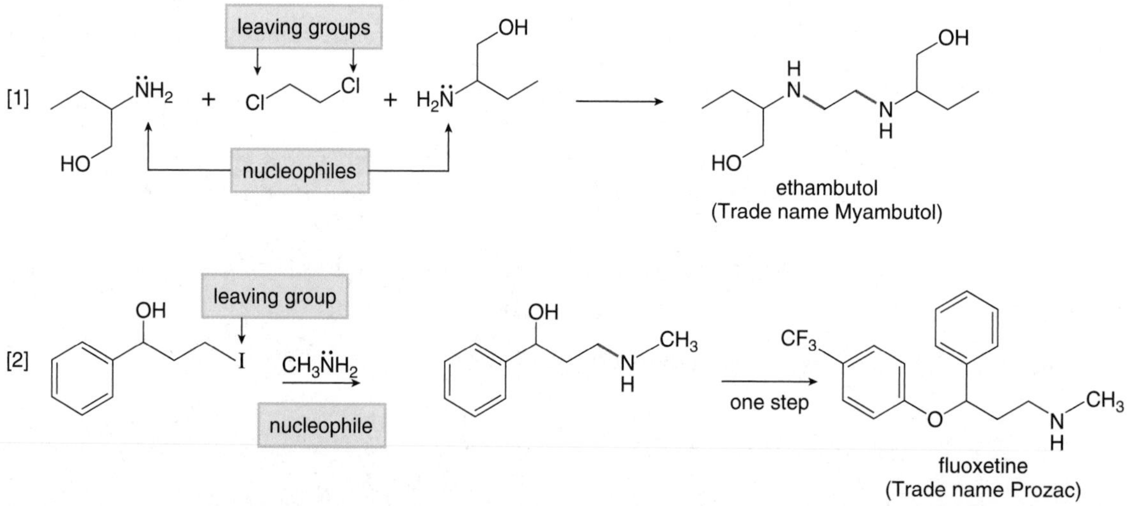

- In both examples, the initial substitution product bears a positive charge and goes on to lose a proton to form the product drawn.
- The NH_2 group serves as a neutral nucleophile to displace halogen in each synthesis. The new bonds formed by nucleophilic substitution are drawn in red in the products.

The CH_3 group in SAM [abbreviated as $(CH_3SR_2)^+$] is part of a sulfonium salt, a positively charged sulfur species that contains a good leaving group. Nucleophilic attack at the CH_3 group of SAM displaces R_2S, a good neutral leaving group. This reaction is called **methylation,** because a CH_3 group is transferred from one compound (SAM) to another ($:Nu^-$).

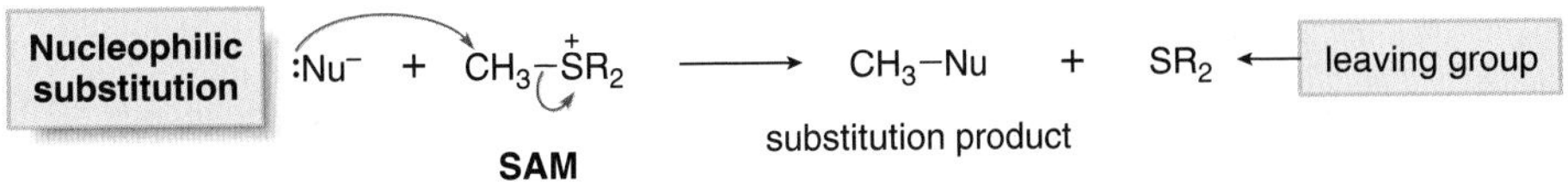

For example, **adrenaline** (epinephrine) is a hormone synthesized in the adrenal glands from noradrenaline (norepinephrine) by nucleophilic substitution using SAM (Figure 7.14). When an individual senses danger or is confronted by stress, the hypothalamus region of the brain signals

Figure 7.14 Adrenaline synthesis from noradrenaline in response to stress

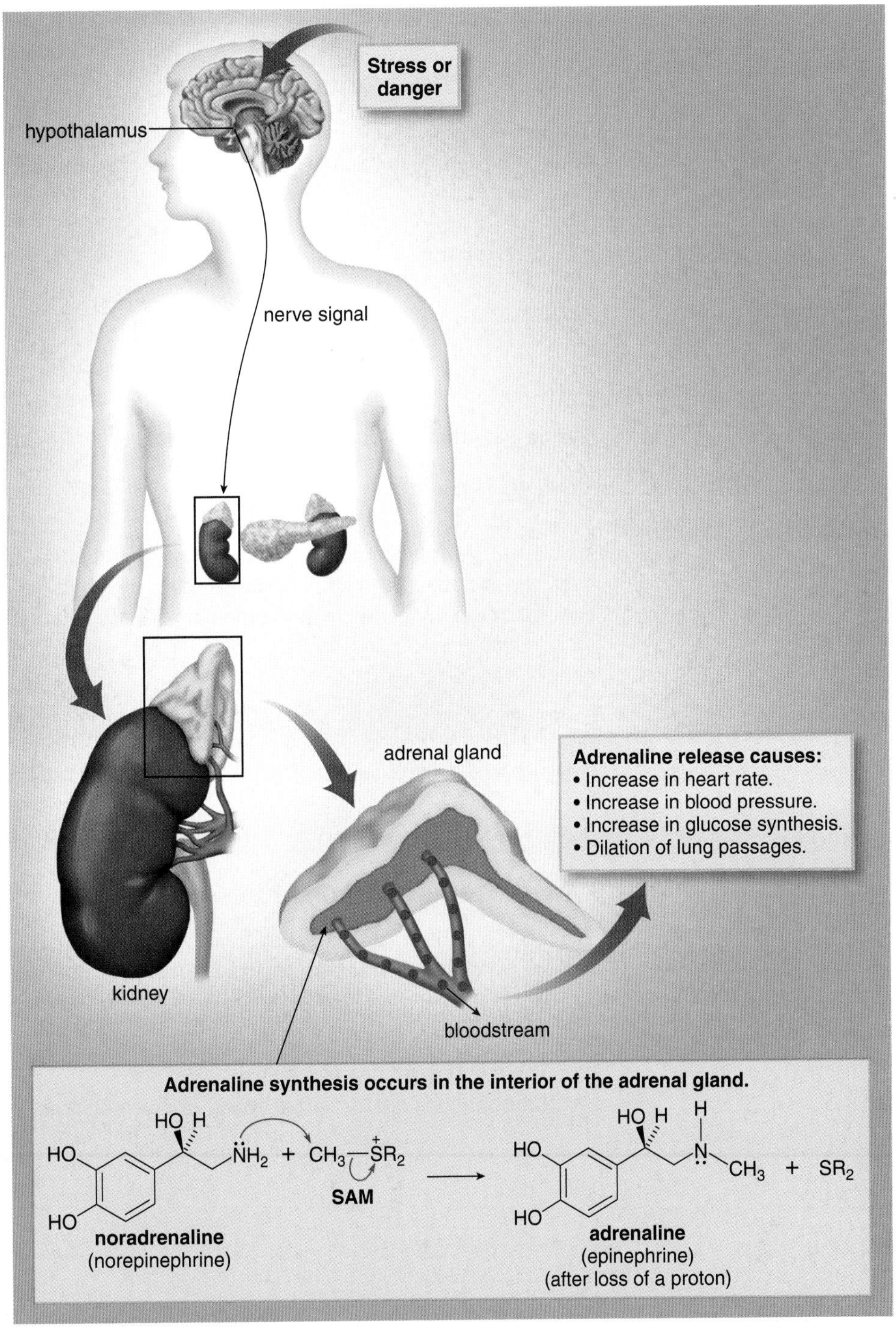

the adrenal glands to synthesize and release adrenaline, which enters the bloodstream and then stimulates a response in many organs. Stored carbohydrates are metabolized in the liver to form glucose, which is further metabolized to provide an energy boost. Heart rate and blood pressure increase, and lung passages are dilated. These physiological changes result from the "rush of adrenaline," and prepare an individual for "fight or flight."

Problem 7.25 Nicotine, a toxic and addictive component of tobacco, is synthesized from **A** using SAM. Write out the reaction that converts **A** into nicotine.

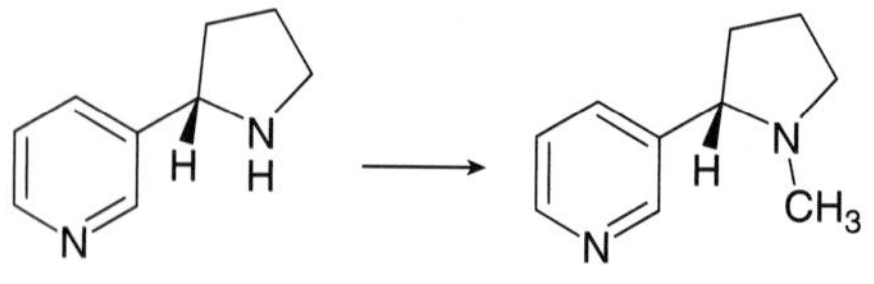

A nicotine

7.13 The S_N1 Mechanism

The reaction of $(CH_3)_3CBr$ with CH_3COO^- is an example of the second mechanism for nucleophilic substitution, the **S_N1 mechanism.** What are the general features of this mechanism?

S_N1 reaction

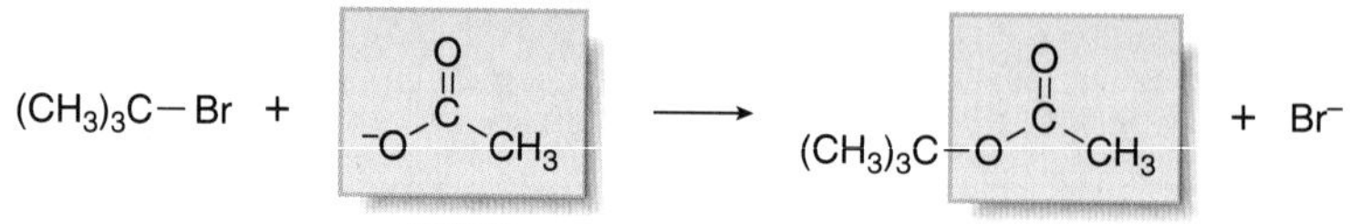

acetate

7.13A Kinetics

The S_N1 reaction exhibits **first-order kinetics.**

- rate = $k[(CH_3)_3CBr]$

As we learned in Section 7.10, this suggests that the S_N1 mechanism involves **more than one step,** and that the slow step is **unimolecular,** involving *only* the alkyl halide. **The identity and concentration of the nucleophile have no effect on the reaction rate.** For example, doubling the concentration of $(CH_3)_3CBr$ doubles the rate, but doubling the concentration of the nucleophile has no effect.

Problem 7.26 What happens to the rate of an S_N1 reaction under each of the following conditions?

a. [RX] is tripled, and [:Nu⁻] stays the same.
b. Both [RX] and [:Nu⁻] are tripled.
c. [RX] is halved, and [:Nu⁻] stays the same.
d. [RX] is halved, and [:Nu⁻] is doubled.

7.13B A Two-Step Mechanism

The most straightforward explanation for the observed first-order kinetics is a **two-step mechanism** in which **bond breaking occurs *before* bond making,** as shown in Mechanism 7.2.

The key features of the S_N1 mechanism are:

- The mechanism has two steps.
- Carbocations are formed as reactive intermediates.

Mechanism 7.2 The S_N1 Mechanism

Step [1] The C – Br bond is broken.

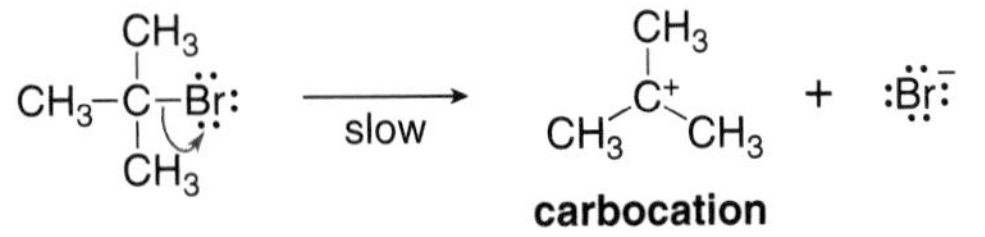

- **Heterolysis of the C – Br bond** forms an intermediate **carbocation.** This step is rate-determining because it involves only bond cleavage.

Step [2] The C – O bond is formed.

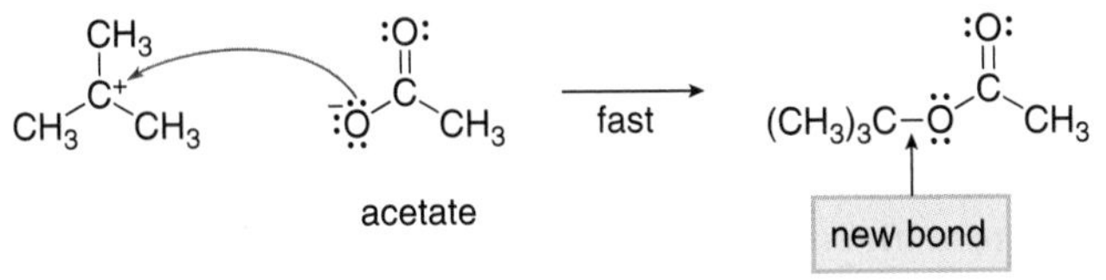

- **Nucleophilic attack of acetate** on the carbocation forms the new C – O bond in the product. This is a **Lewis acid–base reaction;** the nucleophile is the Lewis base and the carbocation is the Lewis acid. Step [2] is *faster* than Step [1] because no bonds are broken and one bond is formed.

An energy diagram for the reaction of $(CH_3)_3CBr + CH_3COO^-$ is shown in Figure 7.15. Each step has its own energy barrier, with a transition state at each energy maximum. Because the transition state for Step [1] is at higher energy, Step [1] is rate-determining. $\Delta H°$ for Step [1] has a positive value because only bond breaking occurs, whereas $\Delta H°$ of Step [2] has a negative value because only bond making occurs. The overall reaction is assumed to be exothermic, so the final product is drawn at lower energy than the initial starting material.

Figure 7.15
An energy diagram for the S_N1 reaction: $(CH_3)_3CBr + CH_3COO^- \rightarrow (CH_3)_3COCOCH_3 + Br^-$

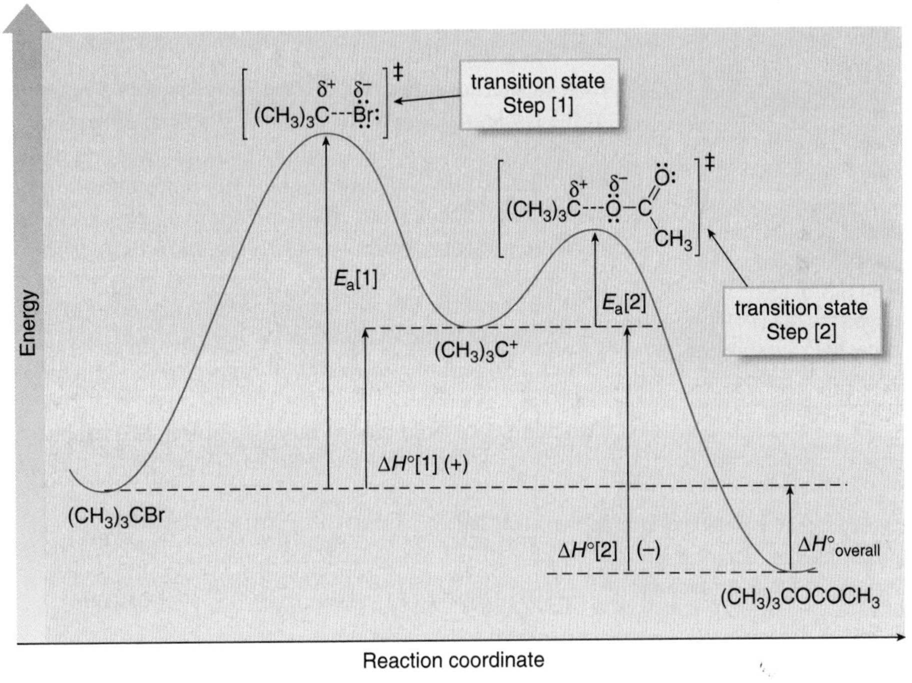

- Since the S_N1 mechanism has two steps, there are two energy barriers.
- $E_a[1] > E_a[2]$ since Step [1] involves bond breaking and Step [2] involves bond formation.
- In each step only one bond is broken or formed, so the transition state for each step has one partial bond.

7.13C Stereochemistry of the S_N1 Reaction

To understand the stereochemistry of the S_N1 reaction, we must examine the geometry of the carbocation intermediate.

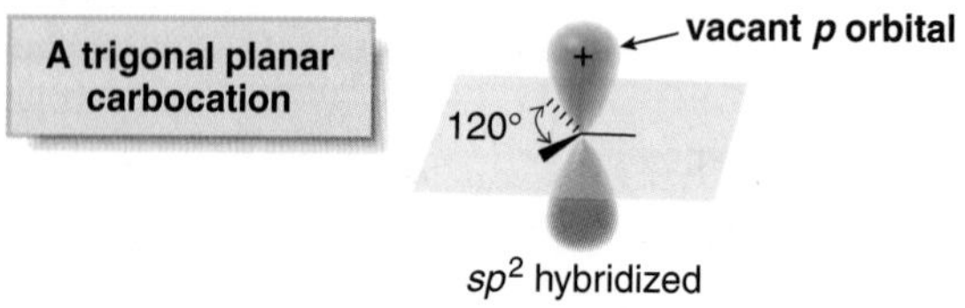

- **A carbocation (with three groups around C) is *sp*² hybridized and trigonal planar, and contains a vacant *p* orbital extending above and below the plane.**

To illustrate the consequences of having a trigonal planar carbocation formed as a reactive intermediate, we examine the S_N1 reaction of a 3° alkyl halide **A** having the leaving group bonded to a stereogenic carbon.

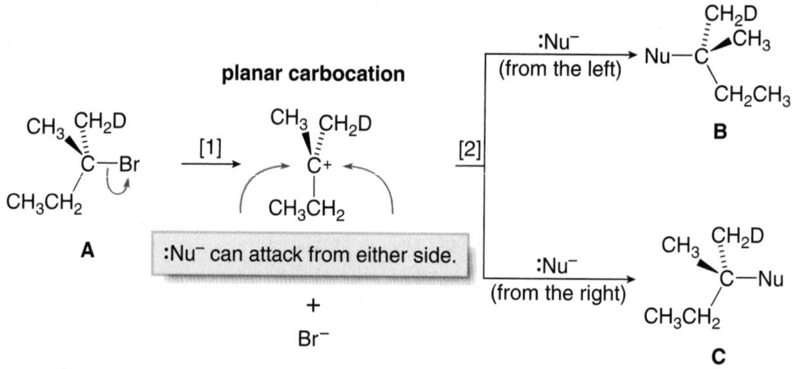

Loss of the leaving group in Step [1] generates a planar carbocation that is now achiral. Attack of the nucleophile in Step [2] can occur from either side to afford two products, **B** and **C.** These two products are *different* compounds containing one stereogenic center. **B** and **C** are stereoisomers that are not superimposable—they are **enantiomers.** Because there is no preference for nucleophilic attack from either direction, an equal amount of the two enantiomers is formed—a **racemic mixture.** We say that ***racemization*** has occurred.

Nucleophilic attack from both sides of a planar carbocation occurs in S_N1 reactions, but we see the result of this phenomenon only when the leaving group is bonded to a stereogenic center.

- ***Racemization* is the formation of equal amounts of two enantiomeric products from a single starting material.**
- **S_N1 reactions proceed with *racemization* at a single stereogenic center.**

Two additional examples of racemization in S_N1 reactions are given in Figure 7.16.

Figure 7.16
Two examples of racemization in the S_N1 reaction

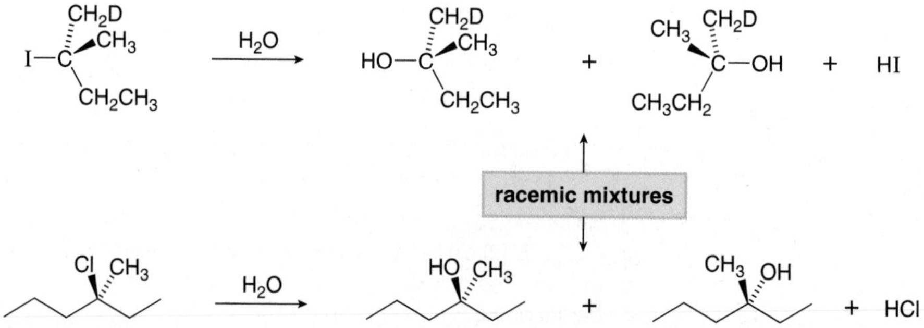

- Nucleophilic substitution of each starting material by an S_N1 mechanism forms a **racemic mixture** of two products.
- With H_2O, a neutral nucleophile, the initial product of nucleophilic substitution (ROH_2^+) loses a proton to form the final neutral product, ROH (Section 7.6).

Sample Problem 7.3 Label the nucleophile and leaving group, and draw the products (including stereochemistry) of the following S_N1 reaction.

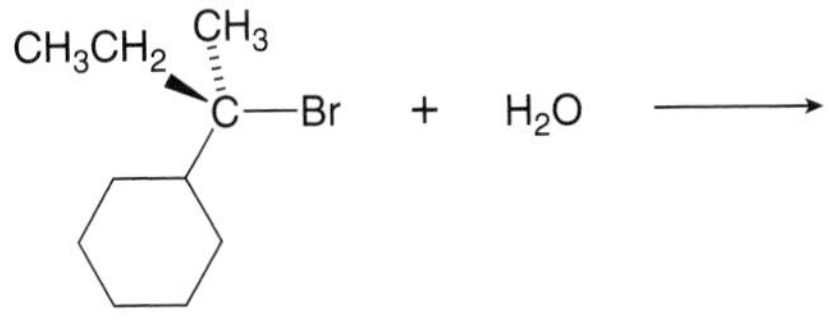

Solution

Br^- is the leaving group and H_2O is the nucleophile. Loss of the leaving group generates a trigonal planar carbocation, which can react with the nucleophile from either direction to form two products.

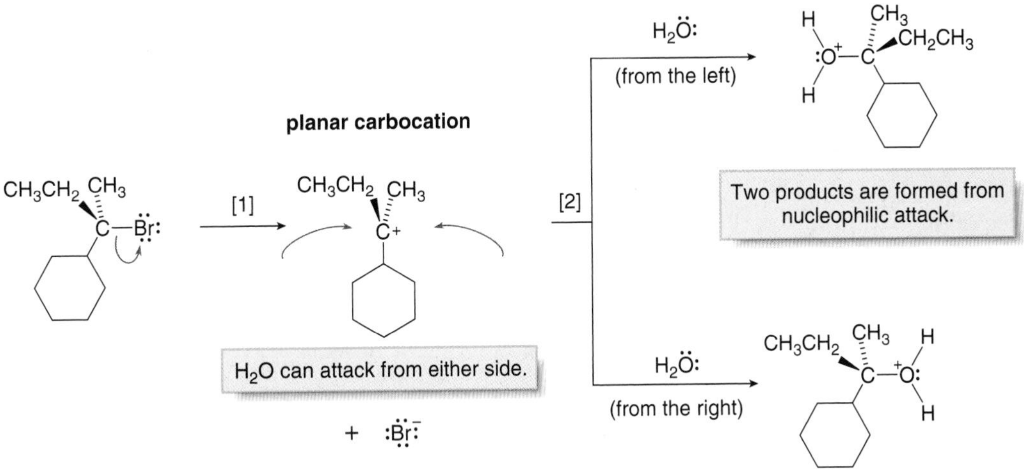

In this example, the initial products of nucleophilic substitution bear a positive charge. They readily lose a proton to form neutral products. The overall process with a neutral nucleophile thus has **three steps:** the first two constitute the **two-step S_N1 mechanism** (loss of the leaving group and attack of the nucleophile), and the third is a **Brønsted–Lowry acid–base reaction** leading to a neutral organic product.

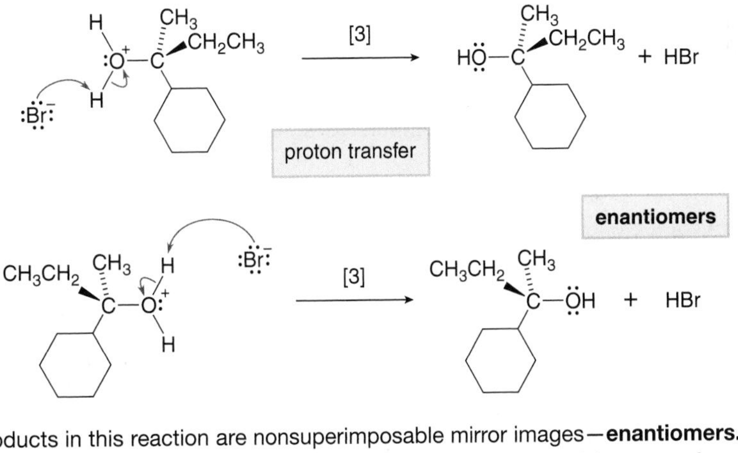

The two products in this reaction are nonsuperimposable mirror images—**enantiomers.** Because nucleophilic attack on the trigonal planar carbocation occurs with equal frequency from both directions, a **racemic mixture is formed.**

Problem 7.27 Draw the products of each S_N1 reaction and indicate the stereochemistry of any stereogenic centers.

a. 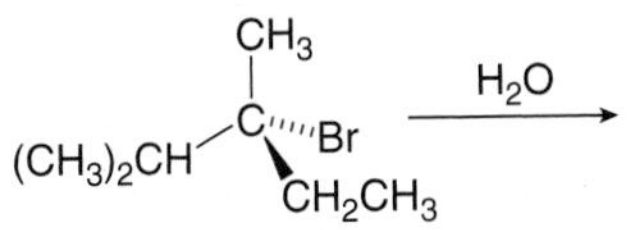

b. 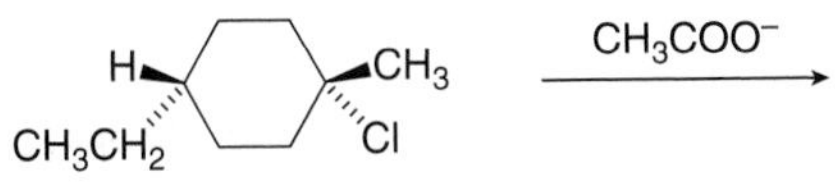

7.13D The Identity of the R Group

How does the rate of an S_N1 reaction change as the alkyl group in the substrate alkyl halide changes from CH_3 --→ 1° --→ 2° --→ 3°?

- As the number of R groups on the carbon with the leaving group *increases*, the rate of an S_N1 reaction *increases*.

CH_3-X	RCH_2-X	R_2CH-X	R_3C-X
methyl	**1°**	**2°**	**3°**

Increasing rate of an S_N1 reaction →

- **3° Alkyl halides undergo S_N1 reactions rapidly.**
- **2° Alkyl halides react more slowly.**
- **Methyl and 1° alkyl halides do *not* undergo S_N1 reactions.**

Table 7.6 summarizes the characteristics of the S_N1 mechanism.

This trend is exactly opposite to that observed for the S_N2 mechanism. To explain this result, we must examine the rate-determining step, the formation of the carbocation, and learn about the effect of alkyl groups on **carbocation stability.**

Table 7.6 Characteristics of the S_N1 Mechanism

Characteristic	Result
Kinetics	• First-order kinetics; rate = k[RX]
Mechanism	• Two steps
Stereochemistry	• Trigonal planar carbocation intermediate • Racemization at a single stereogenic center
Identity of R	• More substituted halides react fastest. • Rate: $R_3CX > R_2CHX > RCH_2X > CH_3X$

7.14 Carbocation Stability

Carbocations are classified as **primary (1°), secondary (2°), or tertiary (3°)** by the number of R groups bonded to the charged carbon atom. As the number of R groups on the positively charged carbon atom increases, the stability of the carbocation **increases.**

$\overset{+}{C}H_3$	$R\overset{+}{C}H_2$	$R_2\overset{+}{C}H$	$R_3\overset{+}{C}$
methyl	**1°**	**2°**	**3°**

Increasing carbocation stability →

When we speak of carbocation stability, we really mean *relative* stability. Tertiary carbocations are too unstable to isolate, but they are more stable than secondary carbocations. We will examine the reason for this order of stability by invoking two different principles: **inductive effects** and **hyperconjugation.**

Problem 7.28 Classify each carbocation as 1°, 2°, or 3°.

a.  b. $(CH_3)_3C\overset{+}{C}H_2$ c. 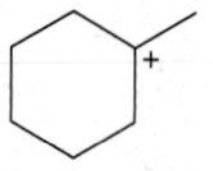 d. 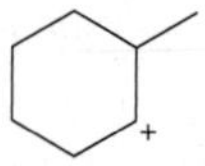

Problem 7.29 Draw the structure of a 1°, 2°, and 3° carbocation, each having molecular formula $C_4H_9^+$. Rank the three carbocations in order of increasing stability.

7.14A Inductive Effects

Inductive effects are electronic effects that occur through σ bonds. In Section 2.5B, for example, we learned that more electronegative atoms stabilize a negative charge by an **electron-withdrawing inductive effect.**

Electron donor groups (Z) stabilize a (+) charge; Z→Y^+. Electron-withdrawing groups (W) stabilize a (–) charge; W←Y^-.

To stabilize a positive charge, **electron-donating groups** are needed. **Alkyl groups are electron donor groups that stabilize a positive charge.** An alkyl group with several σ bonds is more polarizable than a hydrogen atom, and more able to donate electron density. Thus, as R groups successively replace the H atoms in CH_3^+, **the positive charge is more dispersed on the electron donor R groups, and the carbocation is more stabilized.**

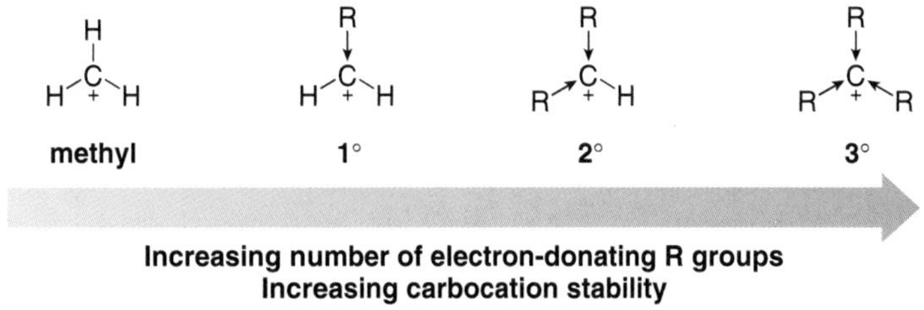
methyl
1°
2°
3°
Increasing number of electron-donating R groups
Increasing carbocation stability

Electrostatic potential maps for four carbocations in Figure 7.17 illustrate the effect of increasing alkyl substitution on the positive charge of the carbocation.

Problem 7.30 Rank the following carbocations in order of increasing stability.

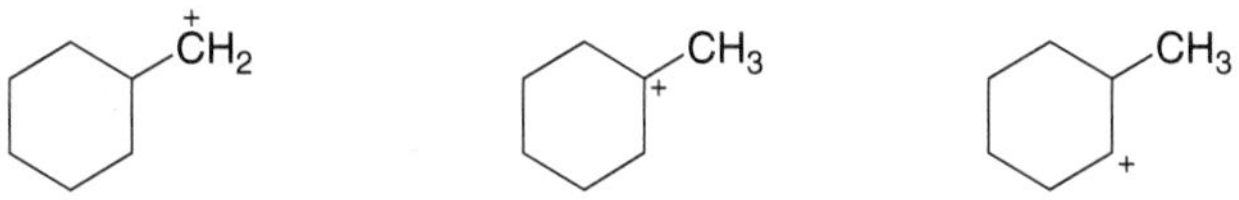

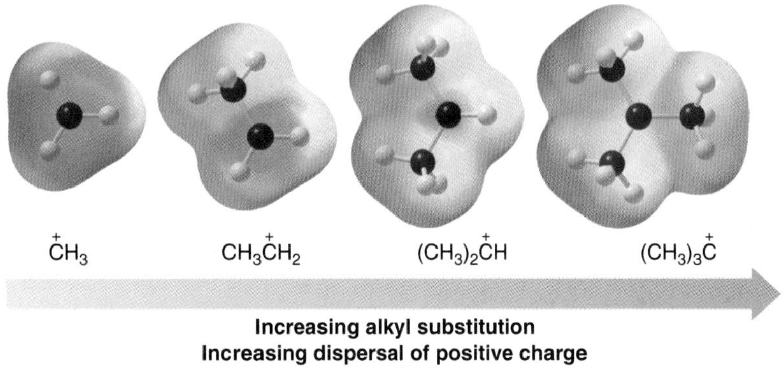
$\overset{+}{C}H_3$
$CH_3\overset{+}{C}H_2$
$(CH_3)_2\overset{+}{C}H$
$(CH_3)_3\overset{+}{C}$
Increasing alkyl substitution
Increasing dispersal of positive charge

Figure 7.17 Electrostatic potential maps for different carbocations

- Dark blue areas in electrostatic potential plots indicate regions low in electron density. As alkyl substitution increases, the region of positive charge is less concentrated on carbon.

7.14B Hyperconjugation

A second explanation for the observed trend in carbocation stability is based on orbital overlap. A 3° carbocation is more stable than a 2°, 1°, or methyl carbocation because the positive charge is delocalized over more than one atom.

- **Spreading out charge by the overlap of an empty *p* orbital with an adjacent σ bond is called *hyperconjugation.***

For example, CH_3^+ cannot be stabilized by hyperconjugation, but $(CH_3)_2CH^+$ can:

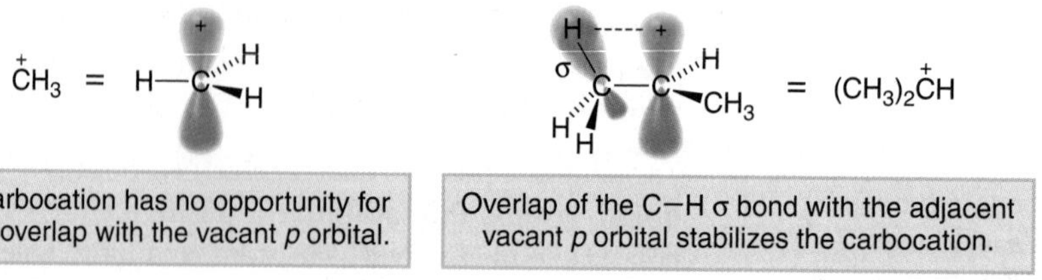
This carbocation has no opportunity for orbital overlap with the vacant p orbital.
Overlap of the C–H σ bond with the adjacent vacant p orbital stabilizes the carbocation.

Both carbocations contain an sp^2 hybridized carbon, so both are trigonal planar with a vacant *p* orbital extending above and below the plane. There are no adjacent C–H σ bonds with which the *p* orbital can overlap in CH_3^+, but there *are* adjacent C–H σ bonds in $(CH_3)_2CH^+$. This overlap (the **hyperconjugation**) delocalizes the positive charge on the carbocation, spreading it over a larger volume, and this stabilizes the carbocation.

The larger the number of alkyl groups on the adjacent carbons, the greater the possibility for hyperconjugation, and the larger the stabilization. Hyperconjugation thus provides an alternate way of explaining why **carbocations with a larger number of R groups are more stabilized.**

7.15 The Hammond Postulate

The rate of an S_N1 reaction depends on the rate of formation of the carbocation (the product of the rate-determining step) via heterolysis of the C–X bond.

- **The rate of an S_N1 reaction *increases* as the number of R groups on the carbon with the leaving group *increases.***
- **The stability of a carbocation *increases* as the number of R groups on the positively charged carbon *increases.***

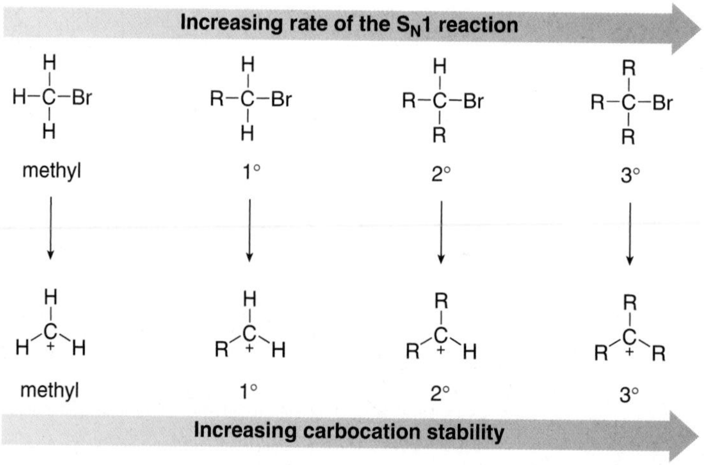
Increasing rate of the SN1 reaction
methyl
1°
2°
3°
methyl
1°
2°
3°
Increasing carbocation stability

- **Thus, the rate of an S_N1 reaction *increases* as the stability of the carbocation *increases.***

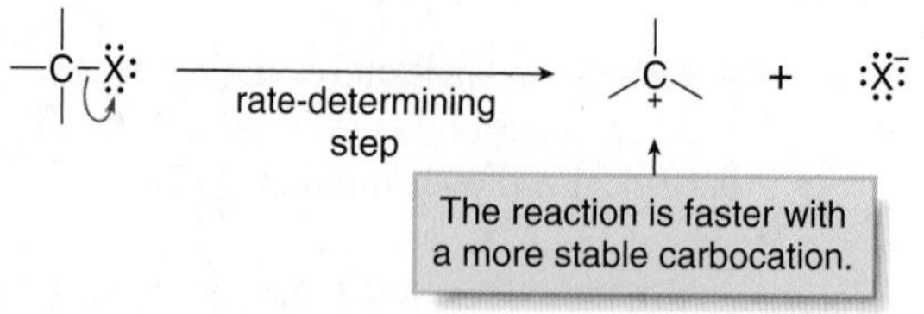
rate-determining step
The reaction is faster with a more stable carbocation.

The rate of a reaction depends on the magnitude of E_a, and the stability of a product depends on $\Delta G°$. The **Hammond postulate,** first proposed in 1955, **relates rate to stability.**

7.15A The General Features of the Hammond Postulate

The Hammond postulate provides a qualitative estimate of the energy of a transition state. Because the energy of the transition state determines the energy of activation and therefore the reaction rate, predicting the relative energy of two transition states allows us to determine the relative rates of two reactions.

According to the Hammond postulate, the transition state of a reaction resembles the structure of the species (reactant or product) to which it is closer in energy. In **endothermic reactions,** the transition state is closer in energy to the **products.** In **exothermic reactions,** the transition state is closer in energy to the **reactants.**

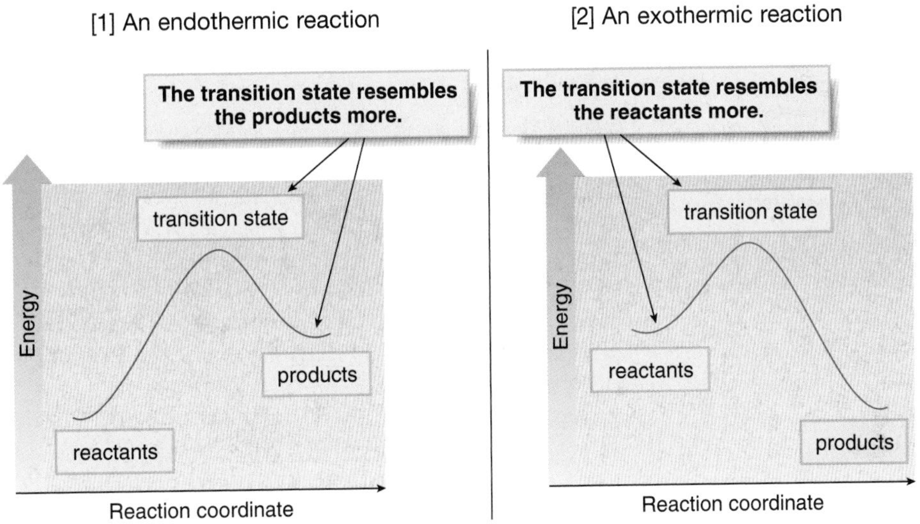

- **Transition states in endothermic reactions resemble the products.**
- **Transition states in exothermic reactions resemble the reactants.**

What happens to the reaction rate if the energy of the product is lowered? In an **endothermic reaction,** the transition state resembles the products, so anything that stabilizes the product stabilizes the transition state, too. **Lowering the energy of the transition state *decreases* the energy of activation (E_a), which *increases* the reaction rate.**

Suppose there are two possible products of an endothermic reaction, but one is more stable (lower in energy) than the other (Figure 7.18). According to the Hammond postulate, **the transition state to form the more stable product is lower in energy, so this reaction should occur faster.**

Figure 7.18
An endothermic reaction—How the energies of the transition state and products are related

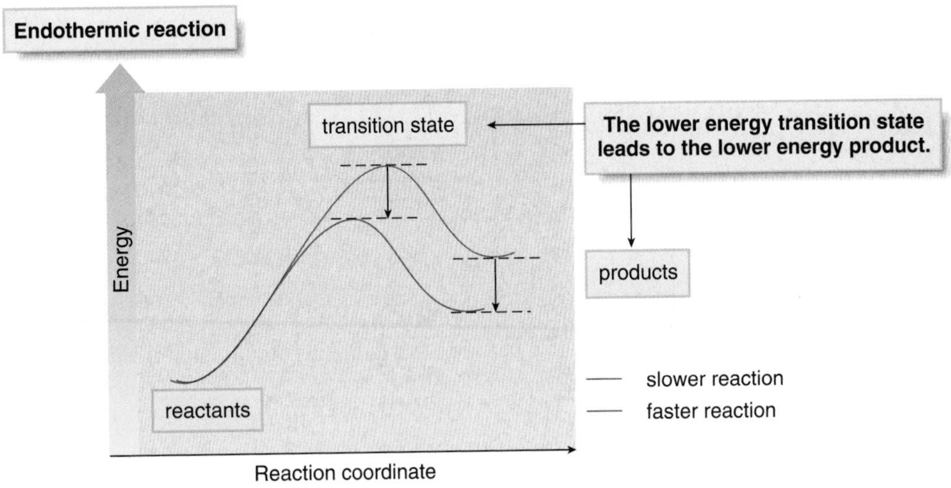

- **Conclusion: In an endothermic reaction, the more stable product forms faster.**

What happens to the reaction rate of an **exothermic reaction** if the energy of the product is lowered? The transition state resembles the reactants, so **lowering the energy of the products has little or no effect on the energy of the transition state.** If E_a is unaffected, then the reaction rate is unaffected, too, as shown in Figure 7.19.

- **Conclusion: In an exothermic reaction, the more stable product may or may not form faster because E_a is similar for both products.**

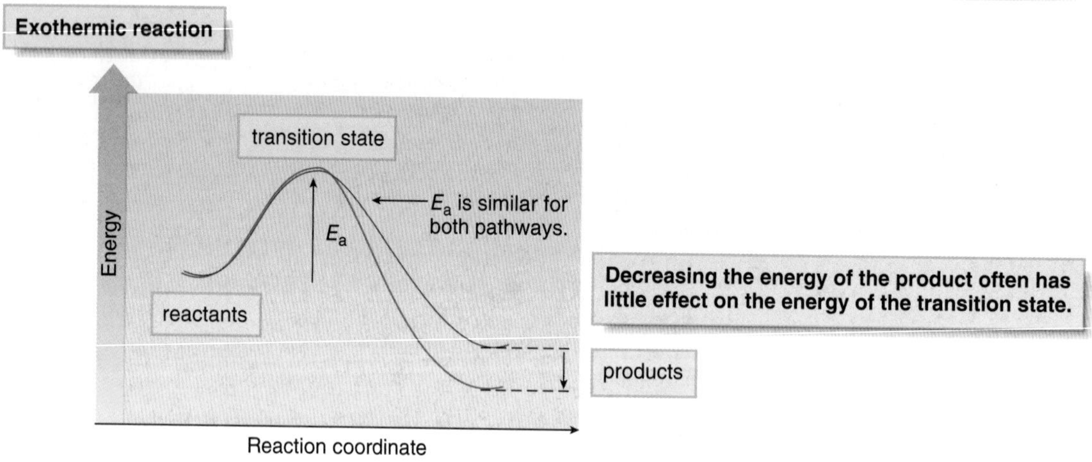

Figure 7.19 An exothermic reaction—How the energies of the transition state and products are related

7.15B The Hammond Postulate and the S_N1 Reaction

In the S_N1 reaction, the rate-determining step is the formation of the carbocation, an *endothermic* reaction. According to the Hammond postulate, the **stability of the carbocation determines the rate of its formation.**

For example, heterolysis of the C–Cl bond in $(CH_3)_2CHCl$ affords a less stable 2° carbocation, $(CH_3)_2CH^+$ (Equation [1]), whereas heterolysis of the C–Cl bond in $(CH_3)_3CCl$ affords a more stable 3° carbocation, $(CH_3)_3C^+$ (Equation [2]). The Hammond postulate states that Reaction [2] is faster than Reaction [1], because the transition state to form the more stable 3° carbocation is lower in energy. Figure 7.20 depicts an energy diagram comparing these two endothermic reactions.

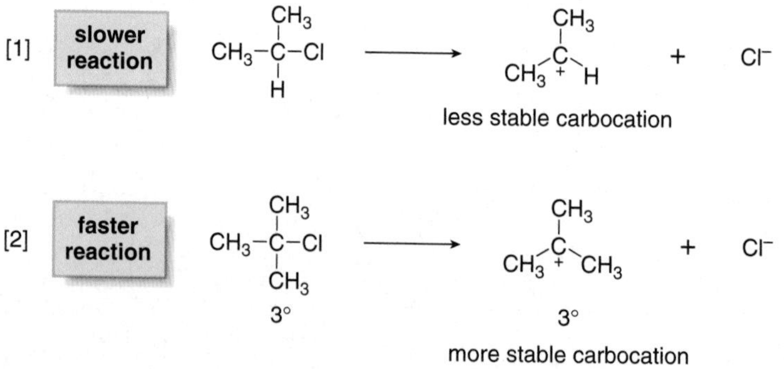

In conclusion, the Hammond postulate can be used to predict the relative rates of two reactions. In the S_N1 reaction the rate-determining step is endothermic, so the more stable carbocation is formed faster.

Figure 7.20
Energy diagram for carbocation formation in two different S_N1 reactions

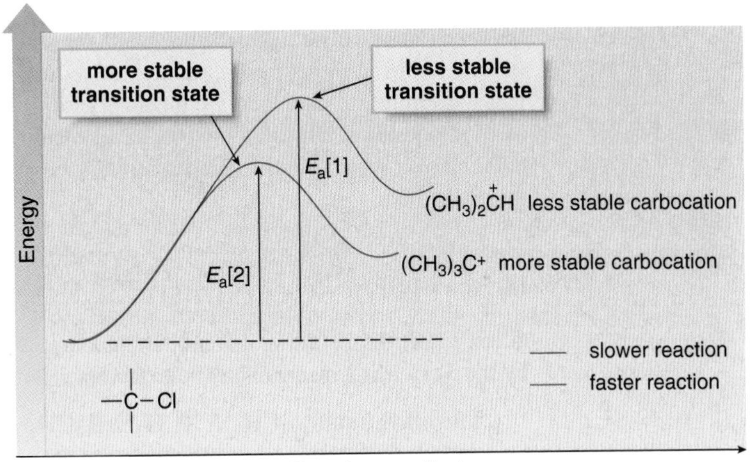

- Since $(CH_3)_2CH^+$ is less stable than $(CH_3)_3C^+$, $E_a[1] > E_a[2]$, and Reaction [1] is slower.

Problem 7.31 Which alkyl halide in each pair reacts faster in an S_N1 reaction?

a. $(CH_3)_3CBr$ or $(CH_3)_3CCH_2Br$

b. 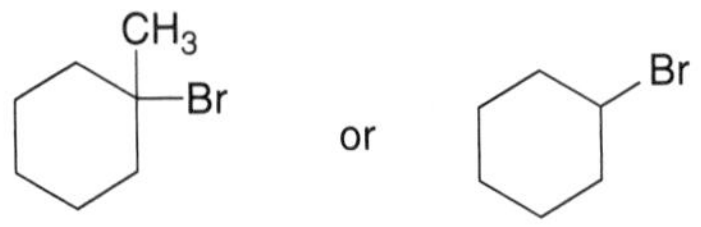

7.16 Application: S_N1 Reactions, Nitrosamines, and Cancer

Spam, a widely consumed canned meat in Alaska, Hawai'i, and other parts of the United States, contains sodium nitrite.

Two common nitrosamines:

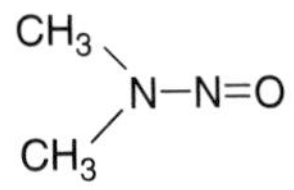

N-nitrosodimethylamine

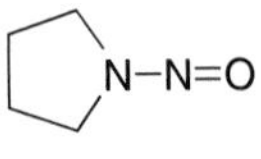

N-nitrosopyrrolidine

S_N1 reactions are thought to play a role in how **nitrosamines,** compounds having the general structure $\mathbf{R_2NN{=}O}$, act as toxins and carcinogens. Nitrosamines are present in many foods, especially cured meats and smoked fish, and they are also found in tobacco smoke, alcoholic beverages, and cosmetics. Nitrosamines cause many forms of cancer.

Nitrosamines can be formed when amines that occur naturally in food react with sodium nitrite, $NaNO_2$, a preservative added to meats such as ham, bacon, and hot dogs to inhibit the growth of *Clostridium botulinum,* a bacterium responsible for a lethal form of food poisoning. Nitrosamines are also formed in vivo in the gastrointestinal tract when bacteria in the body convert nitrates (NO_3^-) into nitrites (NO_2^-), which then react with amines.

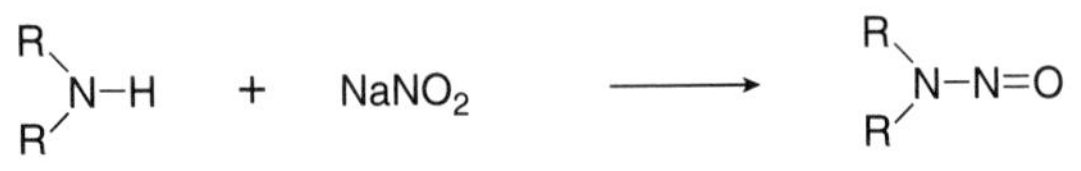

In the presence of acid or heat, nitrosamines are converted to **diazonium ions,** which contain a very good leaving group, N_2. With certain R groups, these diazonium compounds form carbocations, which then react with biological nucleophiles (such as DNA or an enzyme) in the cell. If this nucleophilic substitution reaction occurs at a crucial site in a biomolecule, it can disrupt normal cell function leading to cancer or cell death. This two-step process—loss of N_2 as a leaving group and reaction with a nucleophile—is an **S_N1 reaction.**

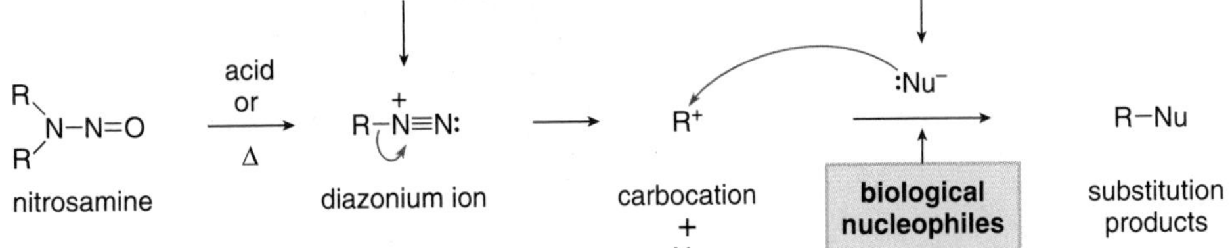

The use of sodium nitrite as a preservative is a classic example of the often delicate balance between risk and benefit. On the one hand, there is an enormous benefit in reducing the prevalence of fatal toxins in meats by the addition of sodium nitrite. On the other, there is the potential risk that sodium nitrite may increase the level of nitrosamines in certain foods. Nitrites are still used as food additives, but the allowable level of nitrites in cured meats has been reduced. Debate continues on whether nitrite preservatives used at their current low levels actually pose a risk to the consumer.

7.17 When Is the Mechanism S_N1 or S_N2?

Given a particular starting material and nucleophile, how do we know whether a reaction occurs by the S_N1 or S_N2 mechanism? Four factors are examined:

- **The alkyl halide—CH_3X, RCH_2X, R_2CHX, or R_3CX**
- **The nucleophile—strong or weak**
- **The leaving group—good or poor**
- **The solvent—protic or aprotic**

7.17A The Alkyl Halide—The Most Important Factor

The most important factor in determining whether a reaction follows the S_N1 or S_N2 mechanism is the *identity of the alkyl halide.*

- Increasing alkyl substitution favors S_N1.
- Decreasing alkyl substitution favors S_N2.

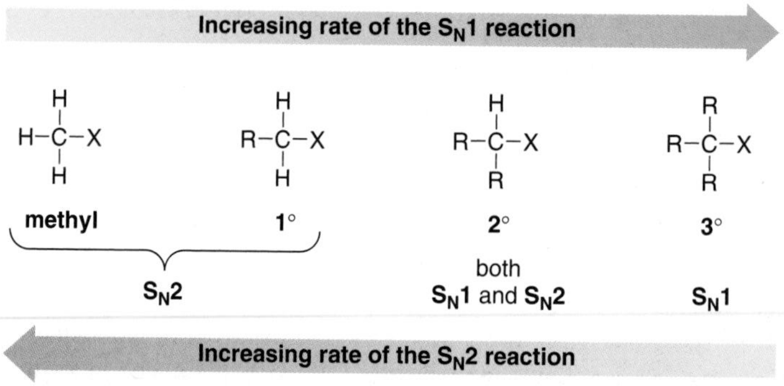

- Methyl and 1° halides (CH_3X and RCH_2X) undergo S_N2 reactions only.
- 3° Alkyl halides (R_3CX) undergo S_N1 reactions only.
- 2° Alkyl halides (R_2CHX) undergo both S_N1 and S_N2 reactions. Other factors determine the mechanism.

Examples are given in Figure 7.21.

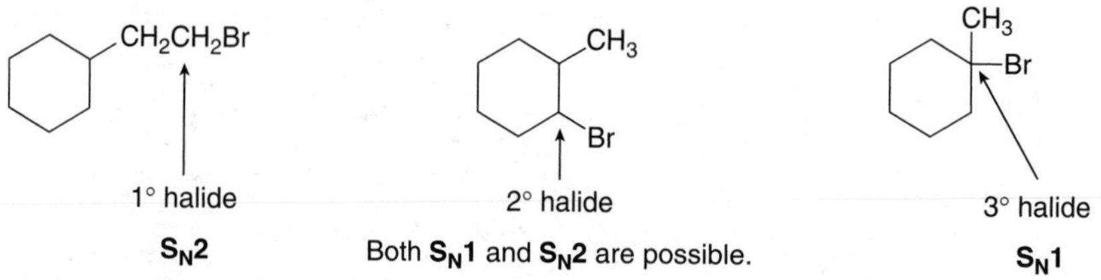

Figure 7.21
Examples: The identity of RX and the mechanism of nucleophilic substitution

Problem 7.32 What is the likely mechanism of nucleophilic substitution for each alkyl halide?

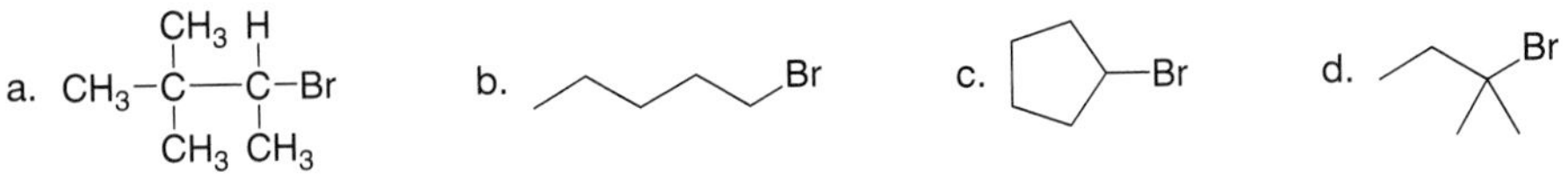

7.17B The Nucleophile

How does the strength of the nucleophile affect an S_N1 or S_N2 mechanism? The rate of the S_N1 reaction is unaffected by the identity of the nucleophile because the nucleophile does not appear in the rate equation (rate = k[RX]). The identity of the nucleophile *is* important for the S_N2 reaction, however, because the nucleophile does appear in the rate equation for this mechanism (rate = $k[RX][:Nu^-]$).

- **Strong nucleophiles present in high concentration favor S_N2 reactions.**
- **Weak nucleophiles favor S_N1 reactions by decreasing the rate of any competing S_N2 reaction.**

The most common nucleophiles in S_N2 reactions bear a net negative charge. The most common nucleophiles in S_N1 reactions are weak nucleophiles such as H_2O and ROH. The identity of the nucleophile is especially important in determining the mechanism and therefore the stereochemistry of nucleophilic substitution when 2° alkyl halides are starting materials.

Let's compare the substitution products formed when the 2° alkyl halide **A** (*cis*-1-bromo-4-methylcyclohexane) is treated with either the strong nucleophile ^-OH or the weak nucleophile H_2O. Because a 2° alkyl halide can react by either mechanism, the strength of the nucleophile determines which mechanism takes place.

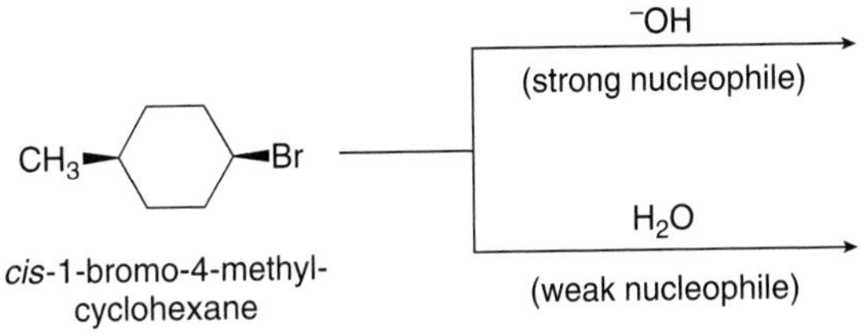

cis-1-bromo-4-methyl-cyclohexane

A

The **strong nucleophile ^-OH favors an S_N2 reaction,** which occurs with **backside** attack of the nucleophile, resulting in **inversion of configuration.** Because the leaving group Br^- is above the plane of the ring, the nucleophile attacks from below, and a single product **B** is formed.

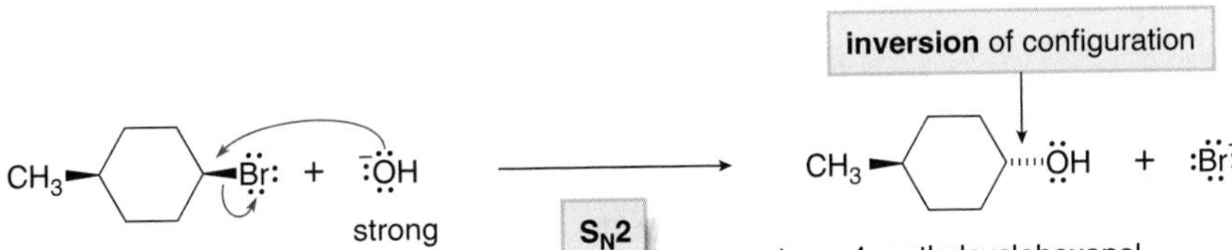

A

trans-4-methylcyclohexanol

B

The **weak nucleophile H_2O favors an S_N1 reaction,** which occurs by way of an intermediate carbocation. Loss of the leaving group in **A** forms the carbocation, which undergoes nucleophilic attack from both above and below the plane of the ring to afford two products, **C** and **D.** Loss of a proton by proton transfer forms the final products, **B** and **E. B** and **E** are diastereomers of each other (**B** is a trans isomer and **E** is a cis isomer).

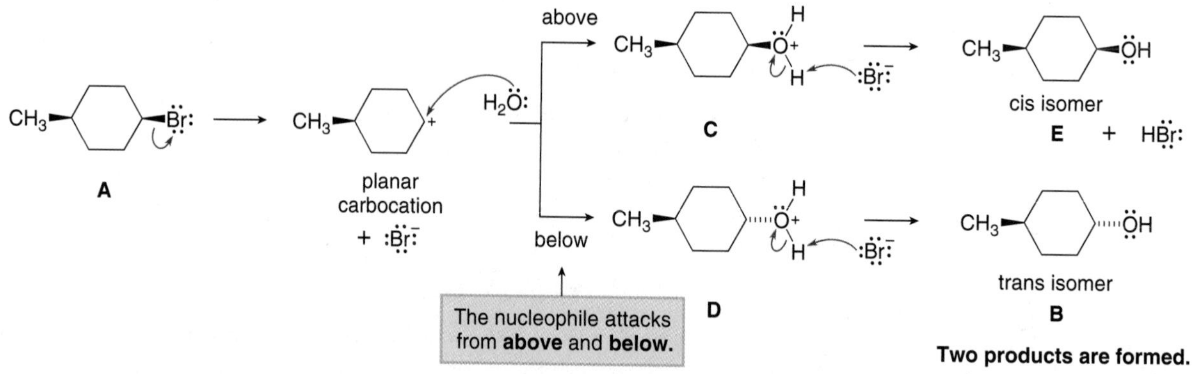

Thus, the mechanism of nucleophilic substitution determines the stereochemistry of the products formed.

Problem 7.33 For each alkyl halide and nucleophile: [1] Draw the product of nucleophilic substitution; [2] determine the likely mechanism (S_N1 or S_N2) for each reaction.

Problem 7.34 Draw the products (including stereochemistry) for each reaction.

7.17C The Leaving Group

How does the identity of the leaving group affect an S_N1 or S_N2 reaction?

- **A better leaving group increases the rate of *both* S_N1 and S_N2 reactions.**

Because the bond to the leaving group is partially broken in the transition state of the only step of the S_N2 mechanism and the slow step of the S_N1 mechanism, **a better leaving group increases the rate of both reactions.** The better the leaving group, the more willing it is to accept the electron pair in the C–X bond, and the faster the reaction.

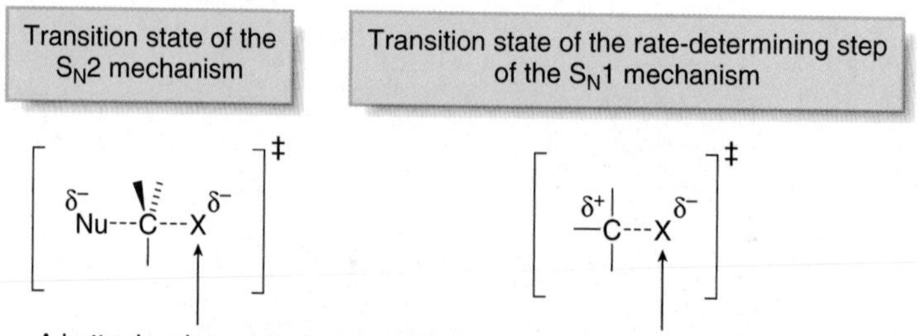

A better leaving group is more able to accept the negative charge.

For alkyl halides, the following order of reactivity is observed for the S_N1 and the S_N2 mechanisms:

R–F R–Cl R–Br R–I

Increasing leaving group ability
Increasing rate of S_N1 and S_N2 reactions

Problem 7.35 Which compound in each pair reacts faster in nucleophilic substitution?

a. $CH_3CH_2CH_2Cl$ or $CH_3CH_2CH_2I$
b. $(CH_3)_3CBr$ or $(CH_3)_3CI$
c. $(CH_3)_3COH$ or $(CH_3)_3COH_2^+$
d. $CH_3CH_2CH_2OH$ or $CH_3CH_2CH_2OCOCH_3$

7.17D The Solvent

Polar protic solvents and polar aprotic solvents affect the rates of S_N1 and S_N2 reactions differently.

- **Polar *protic* solvents are especially good for S_N1 reactions.**
- **Polar *aprotic* solvents are especially good for S_N2 reactions.**

See Section 7.8C to review the differences between polar protic solvents and polar aprotic solvents.

Polar protic solvents like H_2O and ROH solvate both cations and anions well, and this characteristic is important for the S_N1 mechanism, in which two ions (a carbocation and a leaving group) are formed by heterolysis of the C–X bond. The carbocation is solvated by ion–dipole interactions with the polar solvent, and the leaving group is solvated by hydrogen bonding, in much the same way that Na^+ and Br^- are solvated in Section 7.8C. These interactions stabilize the reactive intermediate. In fact, a polar protic solvent is generally needed for an S_N1 reaction.

Summary of solvent effects:

- Polar protic solvents favor S_N1 reactions because the ionic intermediates are stabilized by solvation.
- Polar aprotic solvents favor S_N2 reactions because nucleophiles are not well solvated, and therefore are more nucleophilic.

Polar aprotic solvents exhibit dipole–dipole interactions but not hydrogen bonding, and as a result, they do not solvate anions well. This has a pronounced effect on the nucleophilicity of anionic nucleophiles. Because these nucleophiles are not "hidden" by strong interactions with the solvent, they are **more nucleophilic.** Because stronger nucleophiles favor S_N2 reactions, **polar aprotic solvents are especially good for S_N2 reactions.**

Problem 7.36 Which solvents favor S_N1 reactions and which favor S_N2 reactions?

a. CH_3CH_2OH b. CH_3CN c. CH_3COOH d. $CH_3CH_2OCH_2CH_3$

Problem 7.37 For each reaction, use the identity of the alkyl halide and nucleophile to determine which substitution mechanism occurs. Then determine which solvent affords the faster reaction.

a.
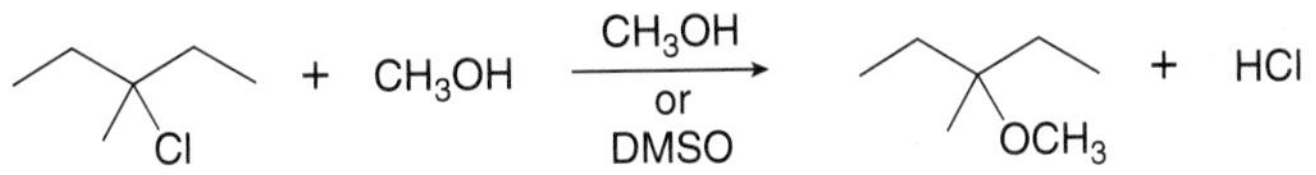

b.
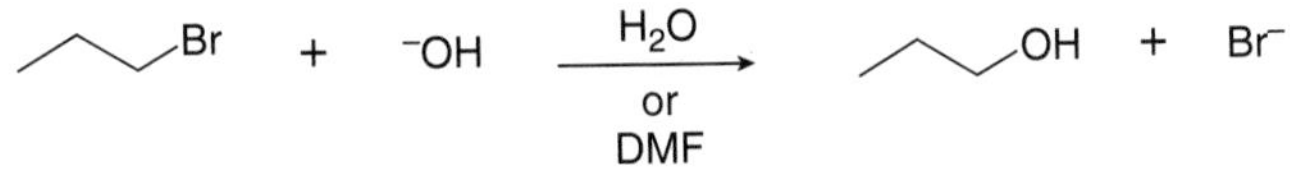

c.
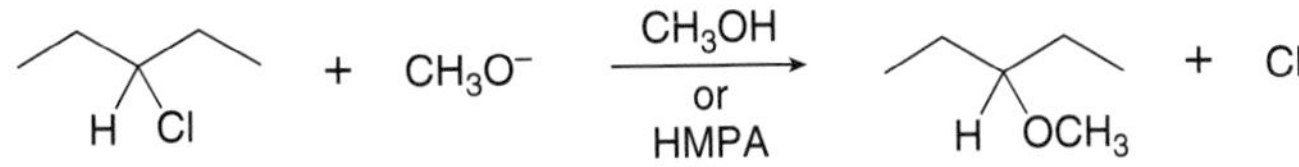

7.17E Summary of Factors That Determine Whether the S_N1 or S_N2 Mechanism Occurs

Table 7.7 summarizes the factors that determine whether a reaction occurs by the S_N1 or S_N2 mechanism. Sample Problems 7.4 and 7.5 illustrate how these factors are used to determine the mechanism of a given reaction.

Table 7.7 Summary of Factors That Determine the S_N1 or S_N2 Mechanism

Alkyl halide	Mechanism	Other factors
CH_3X RCH_2X (1°)	$\mathbf{S_N2}$	Favored by • **strong nucleophiles** (usually a net negative charge) • polar **aprotic** solvents
R_3CX (3°)	$\mathbf{S_N1}$	Favored by • **weak nucleophiles** (usually neutral) • polar **protic** solvents
R_2CHX (2°)	$\mathbf{S_N1}$ **or** $\mathbf{S_N2}$	The mechanism depends on the conditions. • **Strong nucleophiles favor the S_N2 mechanism over the S_N1 mechanism.** For example, RO^- is a stronger nucleophile than ROH, so RO^- favors the S_N2 reaction and ROH favors the S_N1 reaction. • **Protic solvents favor the S_N1 mechanism and aprotic solvents favor the S_N2 mechanism.** For example, H_2O and CH_3OH are polar protic solvents that favor the S_N1 mechanism, whereas acetone [$(CH_3)_2C=O$] and DMSO [$(CH_3)_2S=O$] are polar aprotic solvents that favor the S_N2 mechanism.

Sample Problem 7.4 Determine the mechanism of nucleophilic substitution for each reaction and draw the products.

a. $CH_3CH_2CH_2{-}Br \quad + \quad {}^-{:}C{\equiv}CH \longrightarrow$

b. 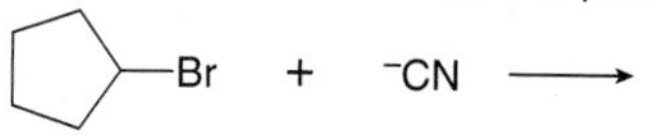
Br
+
⁻CN

Solution

a. The alkyl halide is 1°, so it must react by an S_N2 mechanism with the nucleophile ${}^-{:}C{\equiv}CH$.

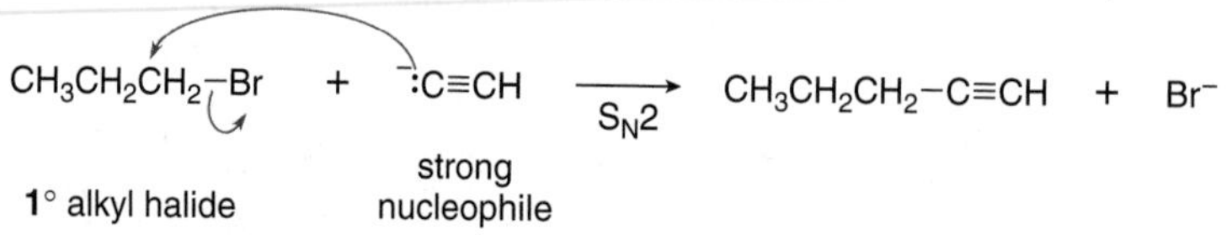
CH3CH2CH2–Br
+
:C≡CH
SN2
CH3CH2CH2–C≡CH
+
Br⁻
1° alkyl halide
strong
nucleophile

b. The alkyl halide is 2°, so it can react by either the S_N1 or S_N2 mechanism. The strong nucleophile (^-CN) favors the S_N2 mechanism.

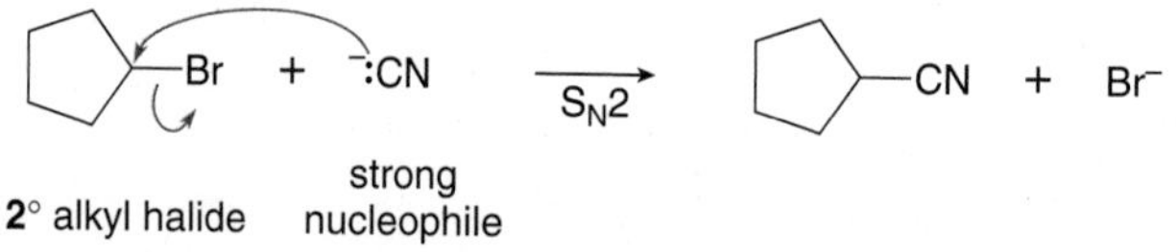
Br
+
:CN
SN2
CN
+
Br⁻
2° alkyl halide
strong
nucleophile

Sample Problem 7.5 Determine the mechanism of nucleophilic substitution for each reaction and draw the products, including stereochemistry.

a. 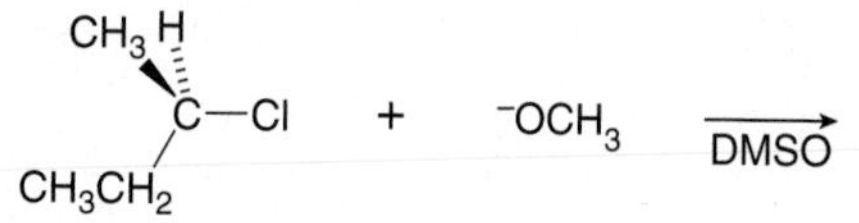
CH3
H
C–Cl
CH3CH2
+
⁻OCH3
DMSO

b. 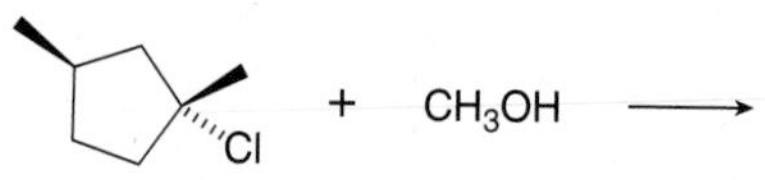
Cl
+
CH3OH

Solution

a. The 2° alkyl halide can react by either the S_N1 or S_N2 mechanism. The strong nucleophile ($^-OCH_3$) favors the S_N2 mechanism, as does the polar aprotic solvent (DMSO). S_N2 reactions proceed with inversion of configuration.

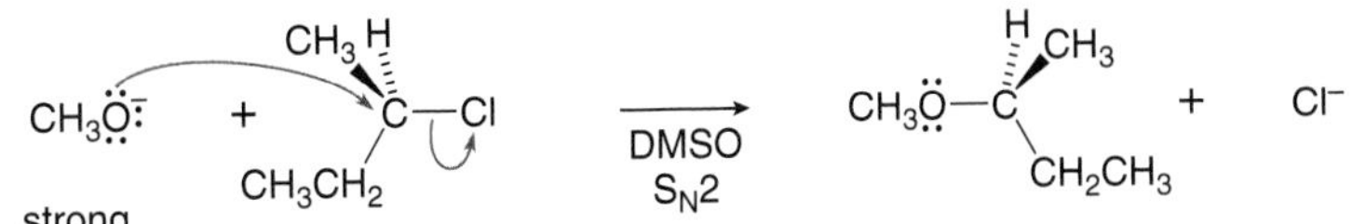

strong nucleophile — 2° alkyl halide — **inversion** of configuration

b. The alkyl halide is 3°, so it reacts by an S_N1 mechanism with the weak nucleophile CH_3OH. S_N1 reactions proceed with racemization at a single stereogenic center, so two products are formed.

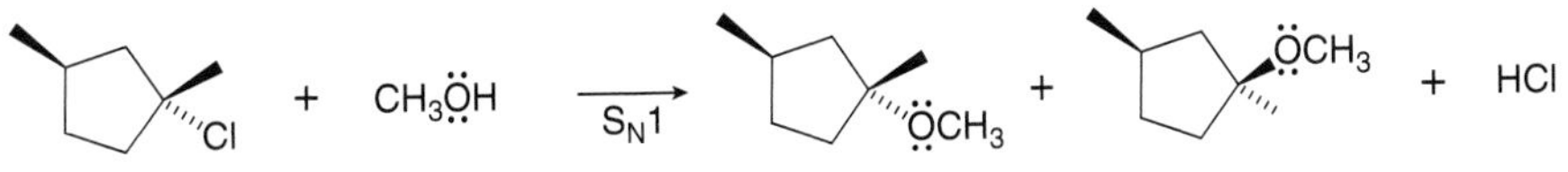

3° alkyl halide — weak nucleophile — two products of nucleophilic substitution

Problem 7.38 Determine the mechanism and draw the products of each reaction. Include the stereochemistry at all stereogenic centers.

a. 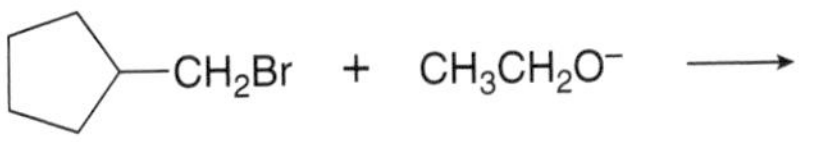

b. 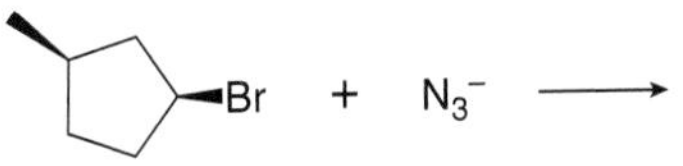

c. 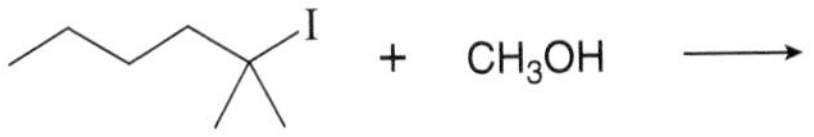

d. 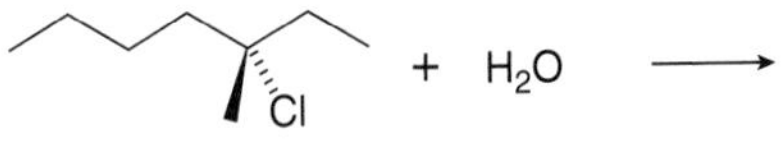

7.18 Vinyl Halides and Aryl Halides

S_N1 and S_N2 reactions occur only at *sp^3* hybridized carbon atoms. Now that we have learned about the mechanisms for nucleophilic substitution we can understand why **vinyl halides** and **aryl halides,** which have a halogen atom bonded to an sp^2 hybridized C, do not undergo nucleophilic substitution by either the S_N1 or S_N2 mechanism. The discussion here centers on vinyl halides, but similar arguments hold for aryl halides as well.

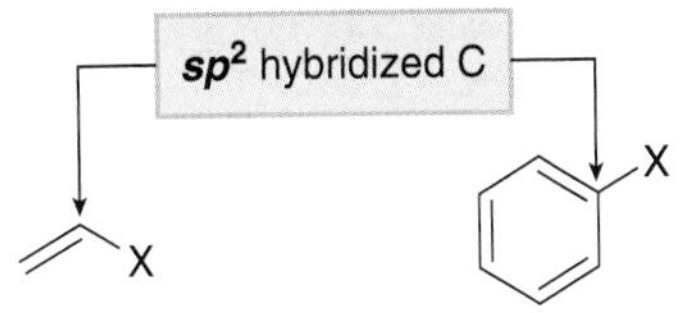

vinyl halide — aryl halide

Vinyl halides do not undergo S_N2 reactions in part because of the percent *s*-character in the hybrid orbital of the carbon atom in the C–X bond. The higher percent *s*-character in the sp^2 hybrid orbital of the vinyl halide compared to the sp^3 hybrid orbital of the alkyl halide (33% vs. 25%) makes the bond shorter and stronger.

Vinyl halides do not undergo S_N1 reactions because heterolysis of the C–X bond would form a **highly unstable vinyl carbocation.** Because this carbocation has only two groups around the positively charged carbon, it is ***sp*** hybridized. These carbocations are even less stable than 1° carbocations, so the S_N1 reaction does not take place.

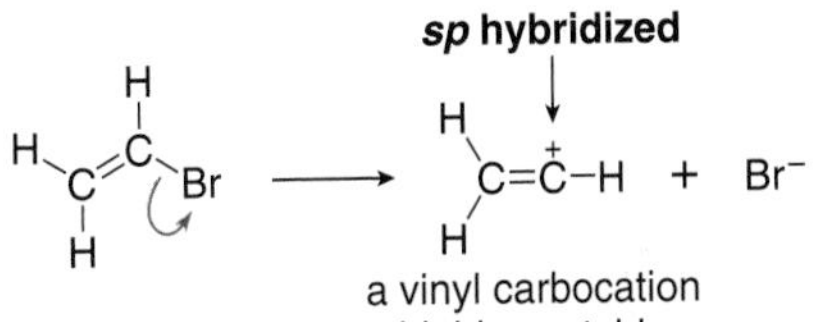

a vinyl carbocation
highly unstable

Problem 7.39 Rank the following carbocations in order of increasing stability.

a. $CH_3CH_2CH_2CH_2CH=\overset{+}{C}H$ b. $CH_3CH_2CH_2CH_2\overset{+}{C}HCH_3$ c. $CH_3CH_2CH_2CH_2CH_2\overset{+}{C}H_2$

7.19 Organic Synthesis

Thus far we have concentrated on the starting material in nucleophilic substitution—the alkyl halide—and have not paid much attention to the product formed. Nucleophilic substitution reactions, and in particular S_N2 reactions, introduce a wide variety of different functional groups in molecules, depending on the nucleophile. For example, when ^-OH, ^-OR, and ^-CN are used as nucleophiles, the products are alcohols (ROH), ethers (ROR), and nitriles (RCN), respectively. Table 7.8 lists some functional groups readily introduced using nucleophilic substitution.

$$R-X \quad + \quad :Nu^- \longrightarrow \quad \boxed{R-Nu} \quad + \quad X:^-$$

One starting material forms many different products.

By thinking of **nucleophilic substitution as a reaction that *makes* a particular kind of organic compound,** we begin to think about ***synthesis.***

- **Organic synthesis is the systematic preparation of a compound from a readily available starting material by one or many steps.**

Table 7.8 Molecules Synthesized from R–X by the S_N2 Reaction

	Nucleophile (:Nu⁻)	Product	Name
Oxygen compounds	^-OH	R–OH	alcohol
	$^-OR'$	R–OR'	ether
	$^-O-C(=O)-R'$	$R-O-C(=O)-R'$	ester
Carbon compounds	^-CN	R–CN	nitrile
	$^-:C\equiv C-H$	$R-C\equiv C-H$	alkyne
Nitrogen compounds	N_3^-	$R-N_3$	azide
	$:NH_3$	$R-NH_2$	amine
Sulfur compounds	^-SH	R–SH	thiol
	$^-SR'$	R–SR'	sulfide
		↑ products of nucleophilic substitution	

7.19A Background on Organic Synthesis

Phenol, the starting material for the aspirin synthesis, is a petroleum product, like most of the starting materials used in large quantities in industrial syntheses. A shortage of petroleum reserves thus affects the availability not only of fuels for transportation, but also of raw materials needed for most chemical synthesis.

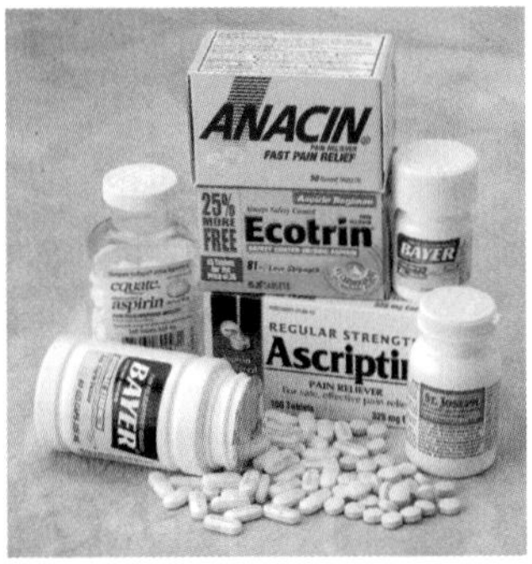
ANACIN
Ecotrin
BAYER
Ascripti
REGULAR STRENGTH
BAYER

Aspirin is synthesized by a two-step procedure from simple, cheap starting materials.

Chemists synthesize molecules for many reasons. Sometimes a **natural product,** a compound isolated from natural sources, has useful medicinal properties, but is produced by an organism in only minute quantities. Synthetic chemists then prepare this molecule from simpler starting materials so that it can be made available to a large number of people.

Sometimes, chemists prepare molecules that do not occur in nature (although they may be similar to those in nature), because these molecules have superior properties to their naturally occurring relatives. **Aspirin, or acetylsalicylic acid** (Section 2.7), is a well known example. Acetylsalicylic acid is prepared from phenol, a product of the petroleum industry, by a two-step procedure (Figure 7.22). Aspirin has become one of the most popular and widely used drugs in the world because it has excellent analgesic and anti-inflammatory properties, *and* it is cheap and readily available.

Figure 7.22 Synthesis of aspirin

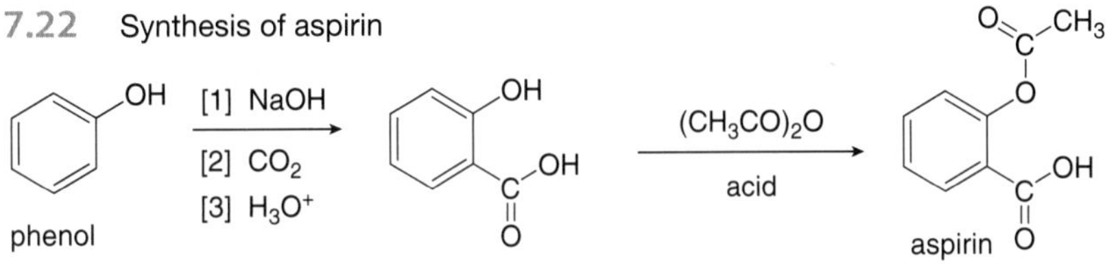
OH
[1] NaOH
[2] CO_2
[3] H_3O^+
phenol
OH
C
OH
O
$(CH_3CO)_2O$
acid
O
C
CH_3
O
C
OH
O
aspirin

7.19B Nucleophilic Substitution and Organic Synthesis

To carry out synthesis we must think backwards. We examine a compound and ask: **What starting material and reagent are needed to make it?** If we are using nucleophilic substitution, we must determine what alkyl halide and what nucleophile can be used to form a specific product. This is the simplest type of synthesis because it involves only one step. In Chapter 11 we will learn about multistep syntheses.

Suppose, for example, that we are asked to prepare $(CH_3)_2CHCH_2OH$ (2-methyl-1-propanol) from an alkyl halide and any required reagents. To accomplish this synthesis, we must "fill in the boxes" for the starting material and reagent in the accompanying equation.

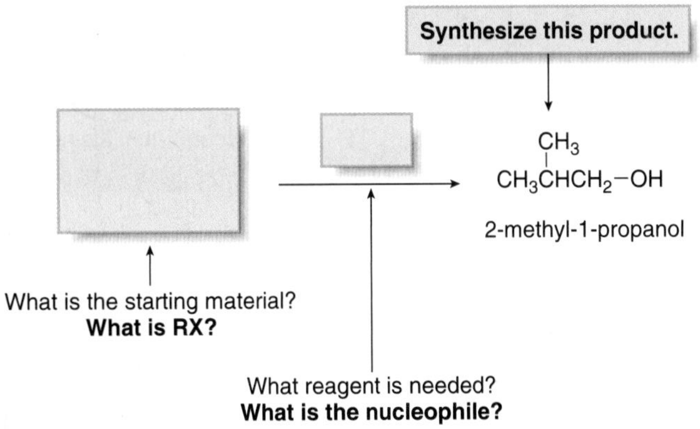
Synthesize this product.
CH_3
CH_3CHCH_2-OH
2-methyl-1-propanol
What is the starting material?
What is RX?
What reagent is needed?
What is the nucleophile?

To determine the two components needed for the synthesis, remember that the carbon atoms come from the organic starting material, in this case a 1° alkyl halide $[(CH_3)_2CHCH_2Br]$. The functional group comes from the nucleophile, ^-OH in this case. With these two components, we can "fill in the boxes" to complete the synthesis.

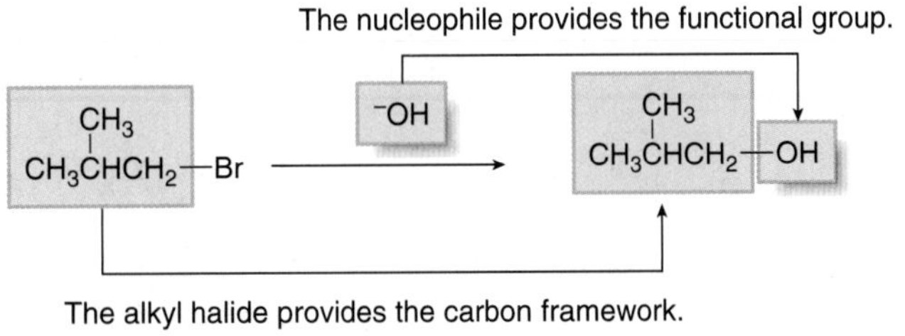
The nucleophile provides the functional group.
CH_3
CH_3CHCH_2-Br
^-OH
CH_3
CH_3CHCH_2-OH
The alkyl halide provides the carbon framework.

After any synthesis is proposed, check to see if it is reasonable, given what we know about reactions. Will the reaction written give a high yield of product? The synthesis of $(CH_3)_2CHCH_2OH$ is reasonable, because the starting material is a 1° alkyl halide and the nucleophile (^-OH) is strong, and both facts contribute to a successful S_N2 reaction.

Problem 7.40 What alkyl halide and nucleophile are needed to prepare each compound?

a. 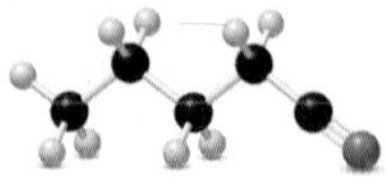
b. 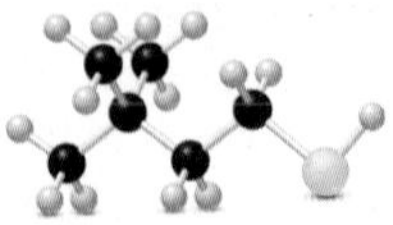
c. 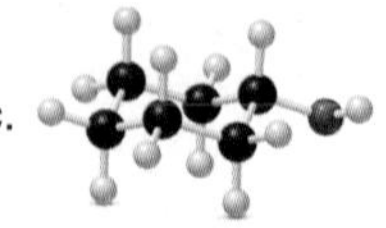
d. 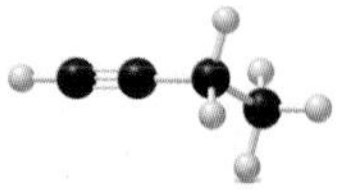

Problem 7.41 The ether, $CH_3OCH_2CH_3$, can be prepared by two different nucleophilic substitution reactions, one using CH_3O^- as nucleophile and the other using $CH_3CH_2O^-$ as nucleophile. Draw both routes.

KEY CONCEPTS

Alkyl Halides and Nucleophilic Substitution

General Facts about Alkyl Halides

- Alkyl halides contain a halogen atom X bonded to an sp^3 hybridized carbon (7.1).
- Alkyl halides are named as halo alkanes, with the halogen as a substituent (7.2).
- Alkyl halides have a polar C – X bond, so they exhibit dipole–dipole interactions but are incapable of intermolecular hydrogen bonding (7.3).
- The polar C – X bond containing an electrophilic carbon makes alkyl halides reactive towards nucleophiles and bases (7.5).

The Central Theme (7.6)

- Nucleophilic substitution is one of the two main reactions of alkyl halides. A nucleophile replaces a leaving group on an sp^3 hybridized carbon.

$$R{-}X \;+\; :Nu^- \longrightarrow R{-}Nu \;+\; X:^-$$

:Nu⁻ = nucleophile; X:⁻ = leaving group

The electron pair in the C—Nu bond comes from the nucleophile.

- One σ bond is broken and one σ bond is formed.
- There are two possible mechanisms: S_N1 and S_N2.

S_N1 and S_N2 Mechanisms Compared

	S_N2 mechanism	S_N1 mechanism
[1] Mechanism	• One step (7.11B)	• Two steps (7.13B)
[2] Alkyl halide	• Order of reactivity: $CH_3X > RCH_2X > R_2CHX > R_3CX$ (7.11D)	• Order of reactivity: $R_3CX > R_2CHX > RCH_2X > CH_3X$ (7.13D)
[3] Rate equation	• Rate = k[RX][:Nu⁻]	• Rate = k[RX]
	• Second-order kinetics (7.11A)	• First-order kinetics (7.13A)
[4] Stereochemistry	• Backside attack of the nucleophile (7.11C)	• Trigonal planar carbocation intermediate (7.13C)
	• Inversion of configuration at a stereogenic center	• Racemization at a single stereogenic center
[5] Nucleophile	• Favored by stronger nucleophiles (7.17B)	• Favored by weaker nucleophiles (7.17B)
[6] Leaving group	• Better leaving group ⇢ faster reaction (7.17C)	• Better leaving group ⇢ faster reaction (7.17C)
[7] Solvent	• Favored by polar aprotic solvents (7.17D)	• Favored by polar protic solvents (7.17D)

Important Trends

- The best leaving group is the weakest base. Leaving group ability increases left-to-right across a row and down a column of the periodic table (7.7).
- Nucleophilicity decreases left-to-right across a row of the periodic table (7.8A).
- Nucleophilicity decreases down a column of the periodic table in polar aprotic solvents (7.8C).
- Nucleophilicity increases down a column of the periodic table in polar protic solvents (7.8C).
- The stability of a carbocation increases as the number of R groups bonded to the positively charged carbon increases (7.14).

Important Principles

Principle	Example
• Electron-donating groups (such as R groups) stabilize a positive charge (7.14A).	• 3° Carbocations (R_3C^+) are more stable than 2° carbocations (R_2CH^+), which are more stable than 1° carbocations (RCH_2^+).
• Steric hindrance decreases nucleophilicity but not basicity (7.8B).	• $(CH_3)_3CO^-$ is a stronger base but a weaker nucleophile than $CH_3CH_2O^-$.
• Hammond postulate: In an endothermic reaction, the more stable product is formed faster. In an exothermic reaction, this is not necessarily true (7.15).	• S_N1 reactions are faster when more stable (more substituted) carbocations are formed, because the rate-determining step is endothermic.
• Planar, *sp*^{2} hybridized atoms react with reagents from both sides of the plane (7.13C).	• A trigonal planar carbocation reacts with nucleophiles from both sides of the plane.

PROBLEMS

Problems Using Three-Dimensional Models

7.42 Give the IUPAC name for each compound, including any *R,S* designation.

a. 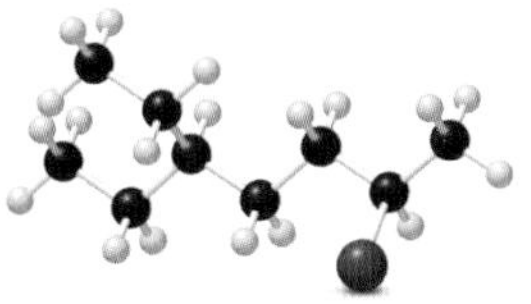

b. 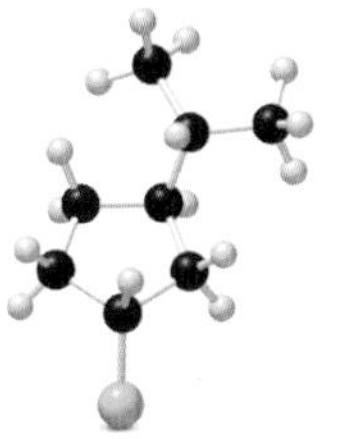

7.43 Draw the products formed when each alkyl halide is treated with NaCN.

a. 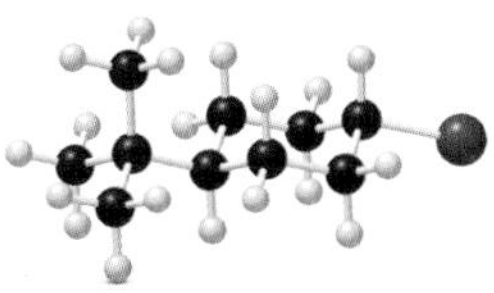

b. 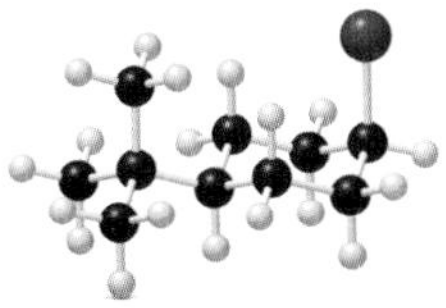

Nomenclature

7.44 Give the IUPAC name for each compound.

a. $CH_3-\underset{CH_3}{\overset{CH_3}{C}}-CH_2CH_2F$

b. 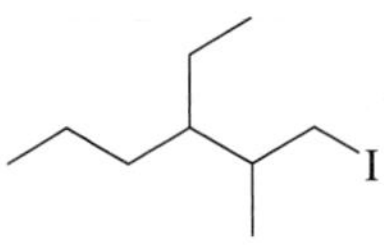

c. $(CH_3)_3CCH_2Br$

d. 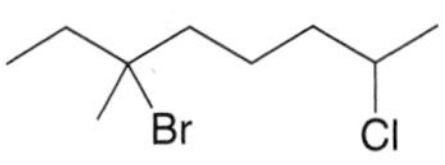

e. 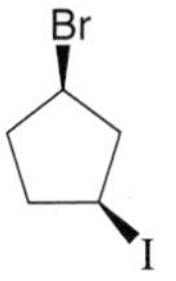

f. 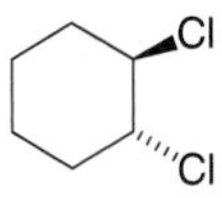

g. $(CH_3)_3CCH_2CH(Cl)CH_2Cl$

h. 

(Also, label this compound as *R* or *S*.)

7.45 Give the structure corresponding to each name.

a. isopropyl bromide
b. 3-bromo-4-ethylheptane
c. 1,1-dichloro-2-methylcyclohexane
d. *trans*-1-chloro-3-iodocyclobutane
e. 1-bromo-4-ethyl-3-fluorooctane
f. (3*S*)-3-iodo-2-methylnonane
g. (1*R*,2*R*)-*trans*-1-bromo-2-chlorocyclohexane
h. (5*R*)-4,4,5-trichloro-3,3-dimethyldecane

7.46 Classify each alkyl halide in Problem 7.44 as 1°, 2°, or 3°. When a compound has more than one halogen, assign each separately.

7.47 Draw the eight constitutional isomers having the molecular formula $C_5H_{11}Cl$.

a. Give the IUPAC name for each compound (ignoring *R* and *S* designations).
b. Label any stereogenic centers.
c. For each constitutional isomer that contains a stereogenic center, draw all possible stereoisomers, and label each stereogenic center as *R* or *S*.

Physical Properties

7.48 Which compound in each pair has the higher boiling point?

a. $(CH_3)_3CBr$ or $CH_3CH_2CH_2CH_2Br$

b. 

or 

c. 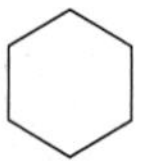 or 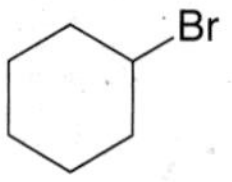

General Nucleophilic Substitution, Leaving Groups, and Nucleophiles

7.49 Draw the substitution product that results when $CH_3CH_2CH_2CH_2Br$ reacts with each nucleophile.

a. ^-OH
b. ^-SH
c. ^-CN
d. $^-OCH(CH_3)_2$
e. $^-C{\equiv}CH$
f. H_2O
g. NH_3
h. NaI
i. NaN_3

7.50 Draw the products of each nucleophilic substitution reaction.

a. 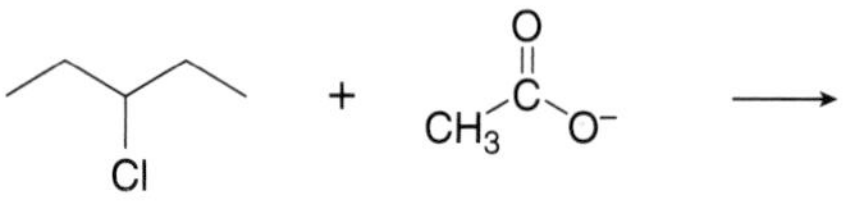

b. 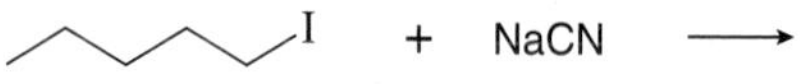

c. 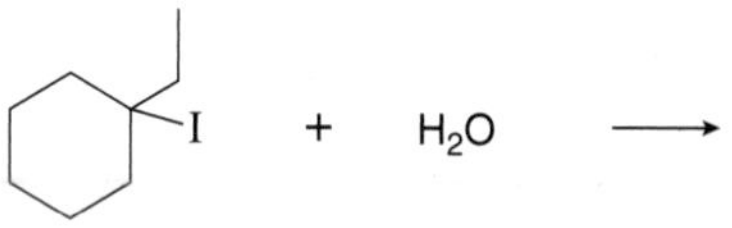

d. 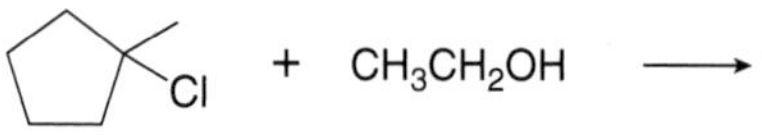

e. 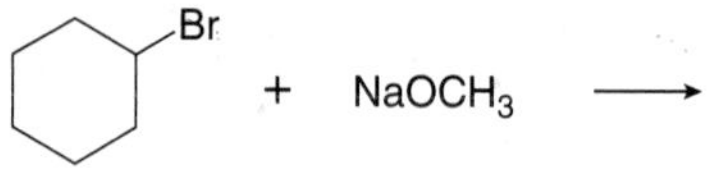

f. 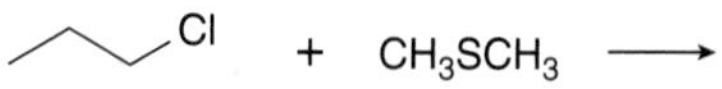

7.51 Which of the following molecules contain a good leaving group?

a. 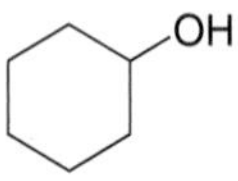

b. $CH_3CH_2CH_2CH_2Cl$

c. 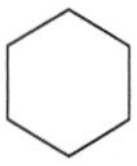

d. 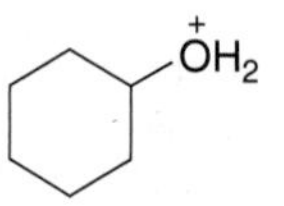

e. $CH_3CH_2NH_2$

f. $CH_3CH_2CH_2I$

7.52 Rank the species in each group in order of increasing leaving group ability.

a. ^-OH, F^-, $^-NH_2$
b. H_2O, $^-NH_2$, ^-OH
c. Br^-, Cl^-, I^-
d. NH_3, H_2S, H_2O

7.53 Which of the following nucleophilic substitution reactions will take place?

a. 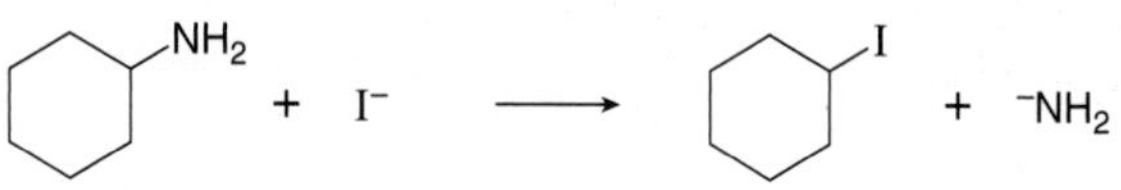

b. $CH_3CH_2I + CH_3O^- \longrightarrow CH_3CH_2OCH_3 + I^-$

c. 

7.54 Rank the species in each group in order of increasing nucleophilicity.

a. CH_3^-, ^-OH, $^-NH_2$
b. H_2O, ^-OH, ^-SH in CH_3OH
c. $CH_3CH_2S^-$, $CH_3CH_2O^-$, CH_3COO^- in CH_3OH
d. CH_3NH_2, CH_3SH, CH_3OH in acetone
e. ^-OH, F^-, Cl^- in acetone
f. HS^-, F^-, Cl^- in CH_3OH

7.55 Classify each solvent as protic or aprotic.

a. $(CH_3)_2CHOH$
b. CH_3NO_2
c. CH_2Cl_2
d. NH_3
e. $N(CH_3)_3$
f. $HCONH_2$

7.56 Why is the amine N atom more nucleophilic than the amide N atom in $CH_3CONHCH_2CH_2CH_2NHCH_3$?

The S_N2 Reaction

7.57 Consider the following S_N2 reaction:

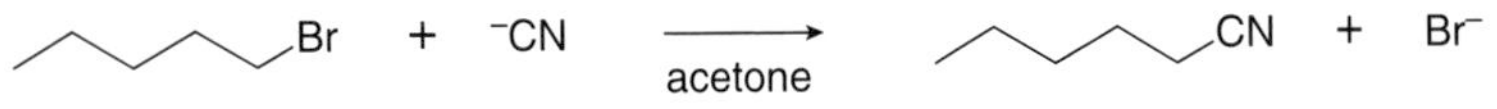

a. Draw a mechanism using curved arrows.
b. Draw an energy diagram. Label the axes, the reactants, products, E_a, and $\Delta H°$. Assume that the reaction is exothermic.
c. Draw the structure of the transition state.
d. What is the rate equation?
e. What happens to the reaction rate in each of the following instances? [1] The leaving group is changed from Br^- to I^-; [2] The solvent is changed from acetone to CH_3CH_2OH; [3] The alkyl halide is changed from $CH_3(CH_2)_4Br$ to $CH_3CH_2CH_2CH(Br)CH_3$; [4] The concentration of ^-CN is increased by a factor of five; and [5] The concentrations of both the alkyl halide and ^-CN are increased by a factor of five.

7.58 Rank the organic halides in each group in order of increasing S_N2 reactivity.

a. 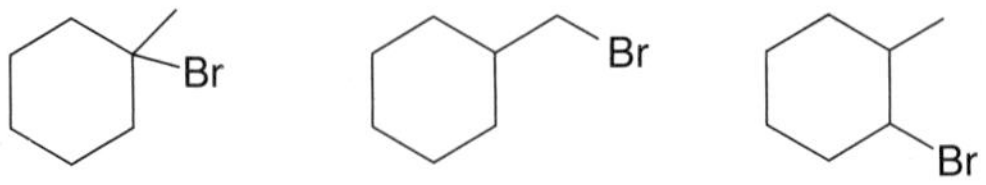

b. 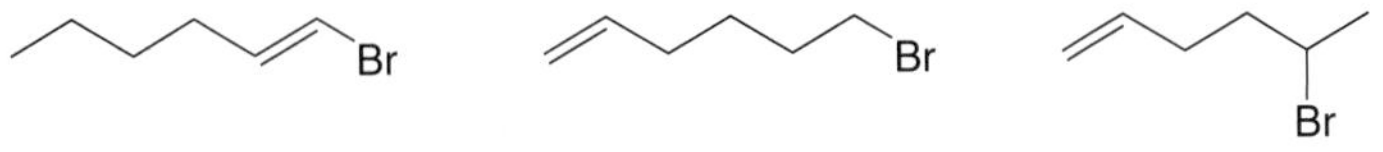

7.59 Which S_N2 reaction in each pair is faster?

a. CH_3CH_2Br + ^-OH ⟶

CH_3CH_2Cl + ^-OH ⟶

b. 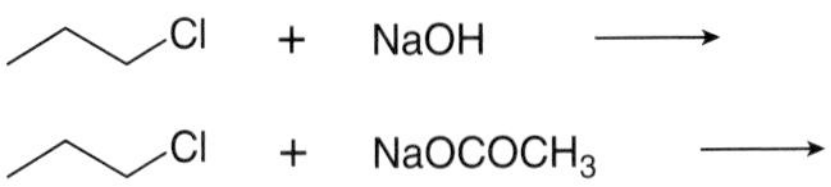

c. 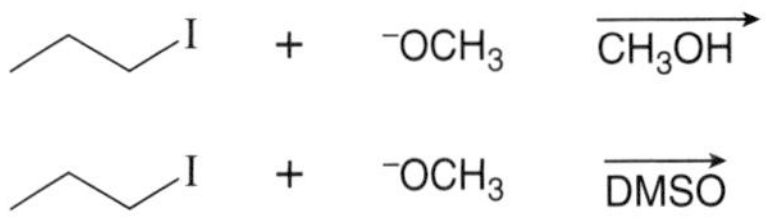

d. 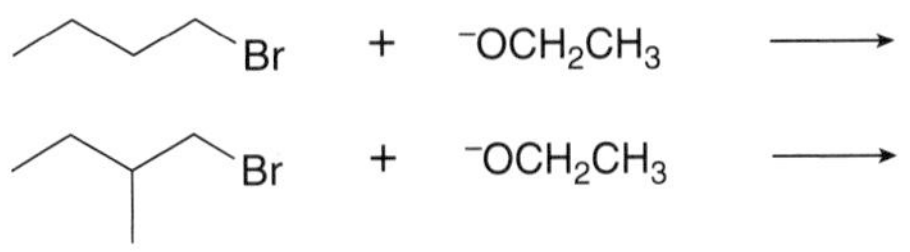

7.60 Draw the products of each S_N2 reaction and indicate the stereochemistry where appropriate.

a. 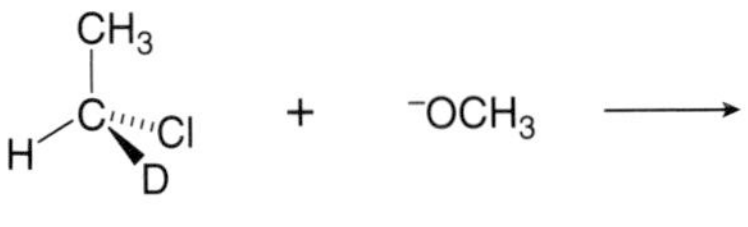

b. 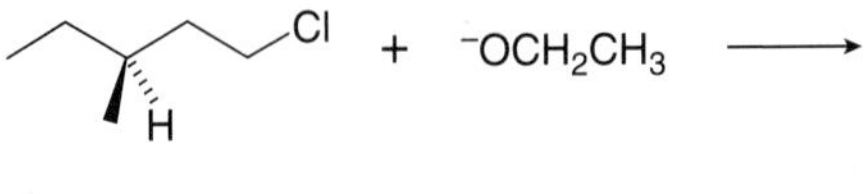

c. 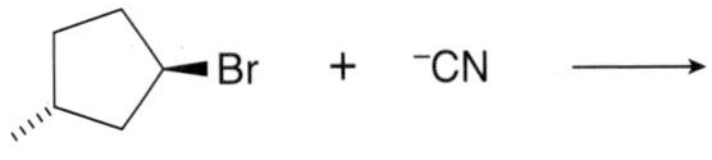

Carbocations

7.61 Classify each carbocation as 1°, 2°, or 3°.

a. $CH_3CH_2\overset{+}{C}HCH_2CH_3$

b. 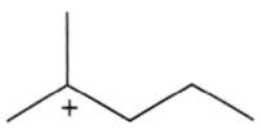

c. 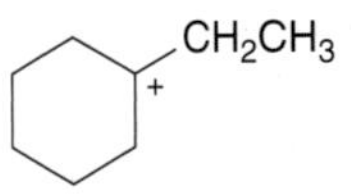

d. 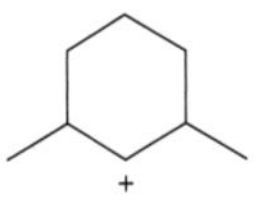

e. 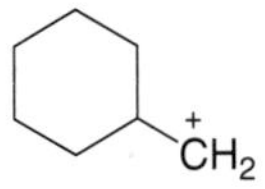

7.62 Rank the carbocations in each group in order of increasing stability.

a. 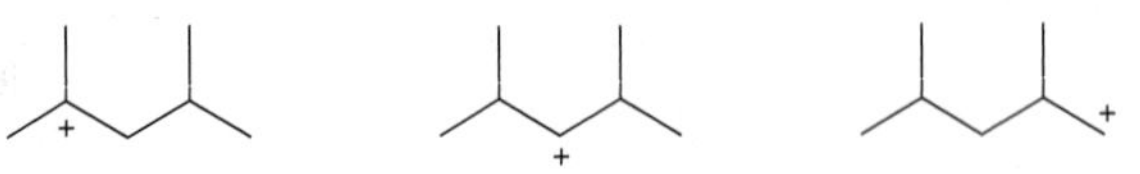

b. 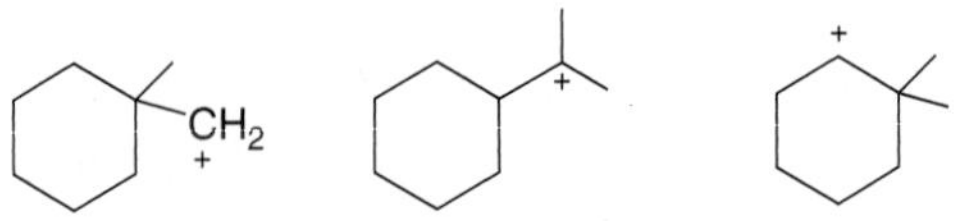

7.63 Which of the following carbocations (**A** or **B**) is more stable? Explain your choice.

A **B**

The S_N1 Reaction

7.64 Consider the following S_N1 reaction.

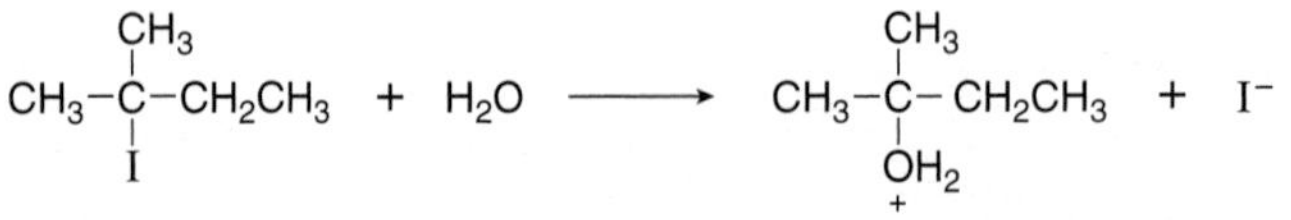

a. Draw a mechanism for this reaction using curved arrows.
b. Draw an energy diagram. Label the axes, starting material, product, E_a, and $\Delta H°$. Assume that the starting material and product are equal in energy.
c. Draw the structure of any transition states.
d. What is the rate equation for this reaction?
e. What happens to the reaction rate in each of the following instances? [1] The leaving group is changed from I^- to Cl^-; [2] The solvent is changed from H_2O to DMF; [3] The alkyl halide is changed from $(CH_3)_2C(I)CH_2CH_3$ to $(CH_3)_2CHCH(I)CH_3$; [4] The concentration of H_2O is increased by a factor of five; and [5] The concentrations of both the alkyl halide and H_2O are increased by a factor of five.

7.65 Rank the organic halides in each group in order of increasing S_N1 reactivity.

a. 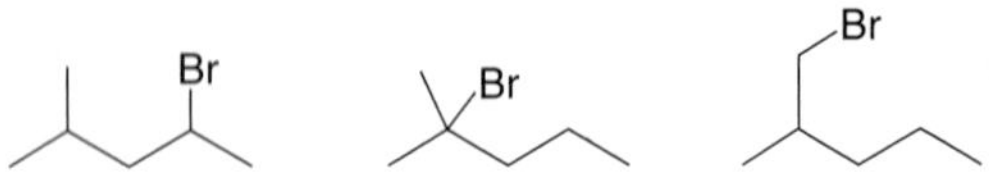

b. 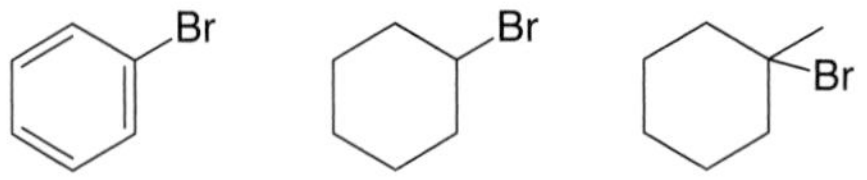

7.66 Which S_N1 reaction in each pair is faster?

a. $(CH_3)_3CCl + H_2O \longrightarrow$

$(CH_3)_3CI + H_2O \longrightarrow$

c. 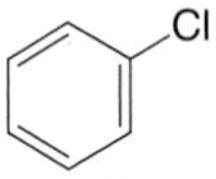 $+ H_2O \longrightarrow$

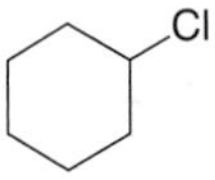 $+ H_2O \longrightarrow$

b. 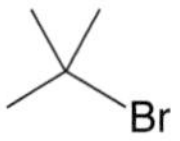 $+ CH_3OH \longrightarrow$

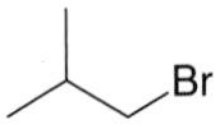 $+ CH_3OH \longrightarrow$

d. 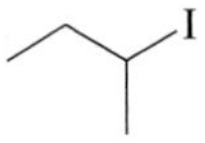 $+ CH_3CH_2OH \xrightarrow{CH_3CH_2OH}$

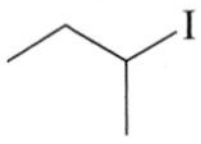 $+ CH_3CH_2OH \xrightarrow{DMSO}$

7.67 Draw the products of each S_N1 reaction and indicate the stereochemistry when necessary.

a. 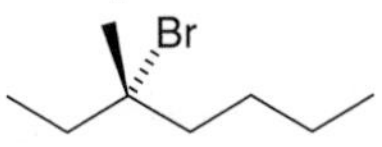 $+ CH_3CH_2OH \longrightarrow$

b. 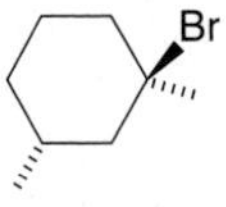 $+ H_2O \longrightarrow$

7.68 Draw a stepwise mechanism for the following reaction that illustrates why two substitution products are formed. Explain why 1-bromo-2-hexene reacts rapidly with a weak nucleophile (CH_3OH) under S_N1 reaction conditions, even though it is a 1° alkyl halide.

$$CH_3CH_2CH_2CH{=}CHCH_2Br \xrightarrow{CH_3OH} CH_3CH_2CH_2CH{=}CHCH_2OCH_3 + CH_3CH_2CH_2\underset{\large OCH_3}{CH}CH{=}CH_2 + HBr$$

1-bromo-2-hexene

S_N1 and S_N2 Reactions

7.69 Determine the mechanism of nucleophilic substitution of each reaction and draw the products, including stereochemistry.

a. 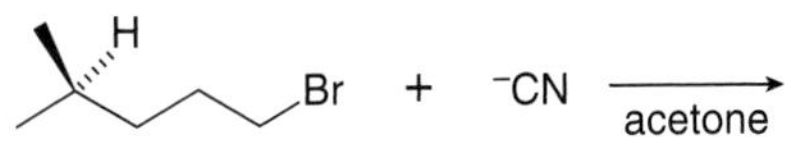

b. 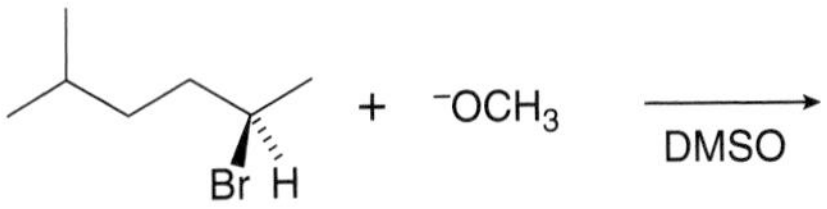

c. 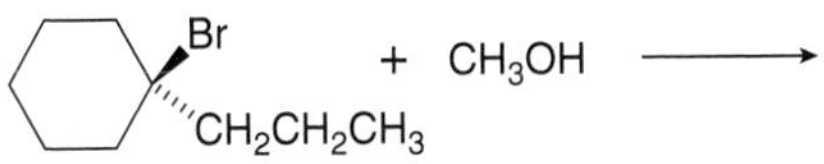

d. 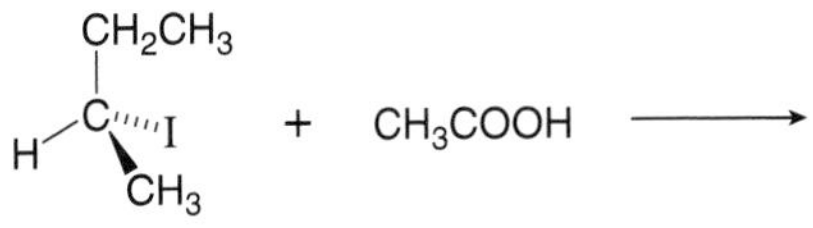

e. 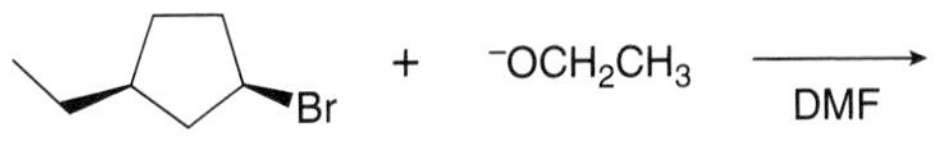

f. 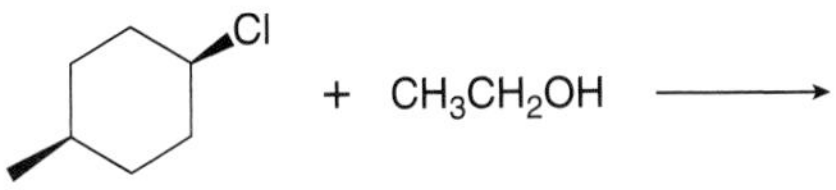

7.70 Diphenhydramine, the antihistamine in Benadryl, can be prepared by the following two-step sequence. What is the structure of diphenhydramine?

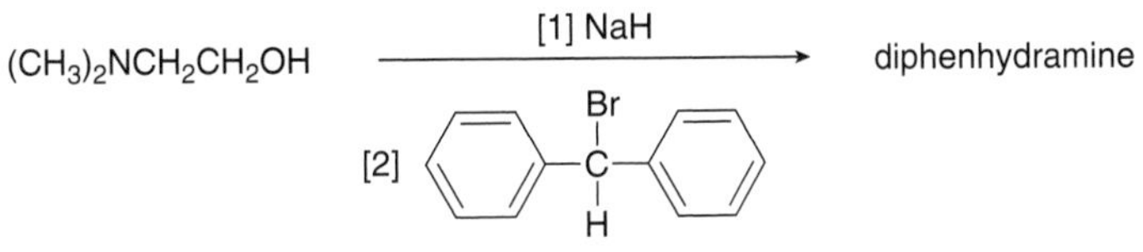

7.71 Draw a stepwise, detailed mechanism for the following reaction. Use curved arrows to show the movement of electrons.

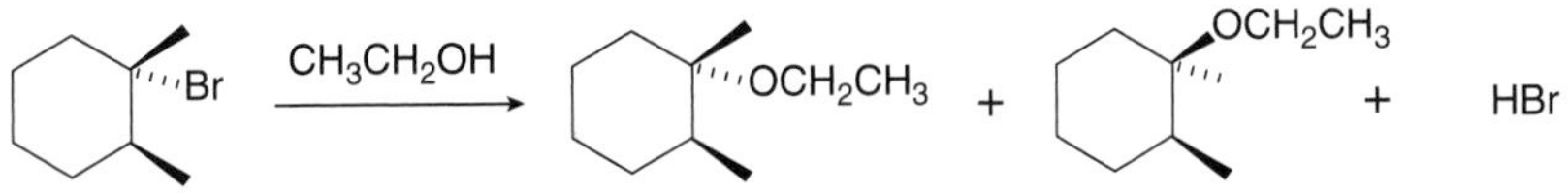

7.72 When a single compound contains both a nucleophile and a leaving group, an **intramolecular** reaction may occur. With this in mind, draw the product of the following reaction.

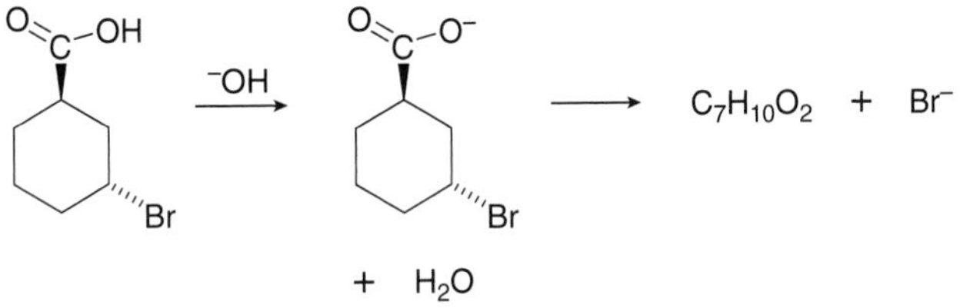

7.73 Nicotine can be made when the following ammonium salt is treated with Na_2CO_3. Draw a stepwise mechanism for this reaction.

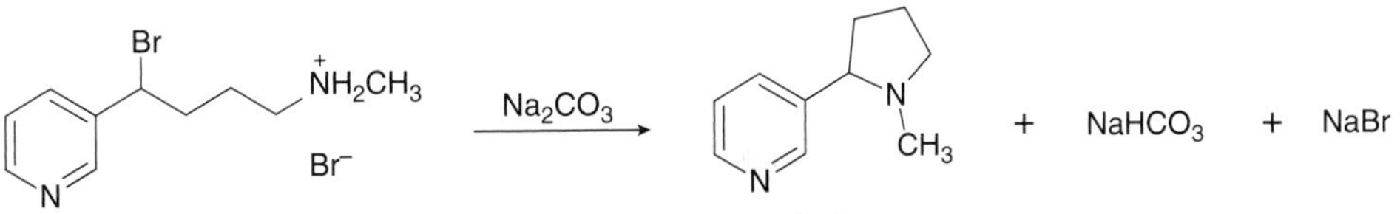

nicotine

7.74 Quinapril (trade name Accupril) is a drug used to treat high blood pressure and congestive heart failure. One step in the synthesis of quinapril involves reaction of the racemic alkyl bromide **A** with a single enantiomer of the amino ester **B.** (a) What two products are formed in this reaction? (b) Given the structure of quinapril, which one of these two products is needed to synthesize the drug?

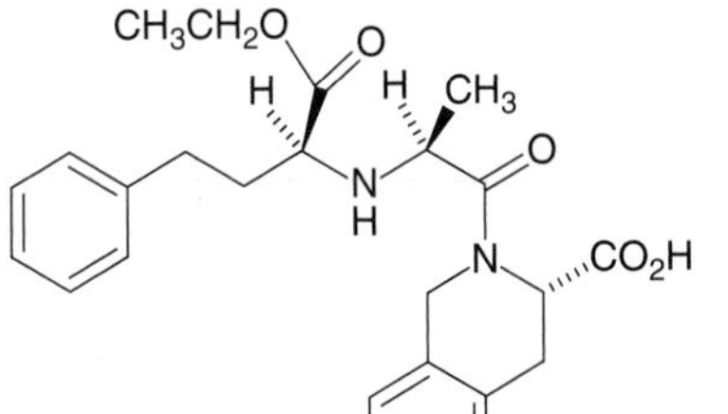

quinapril

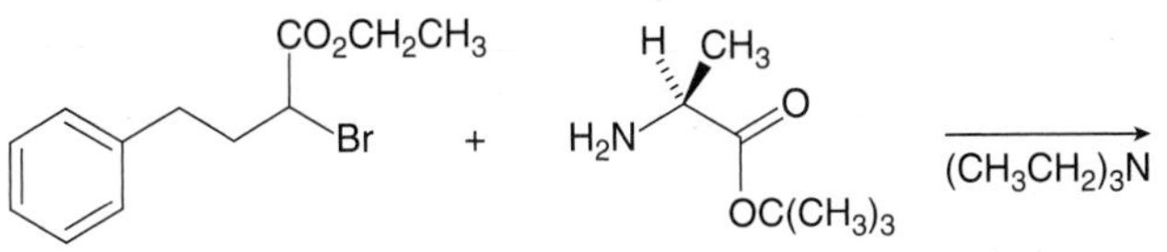

racemic **A** **B**

7.75 Draw a stepwise, detailed mechanism for the following reaction.

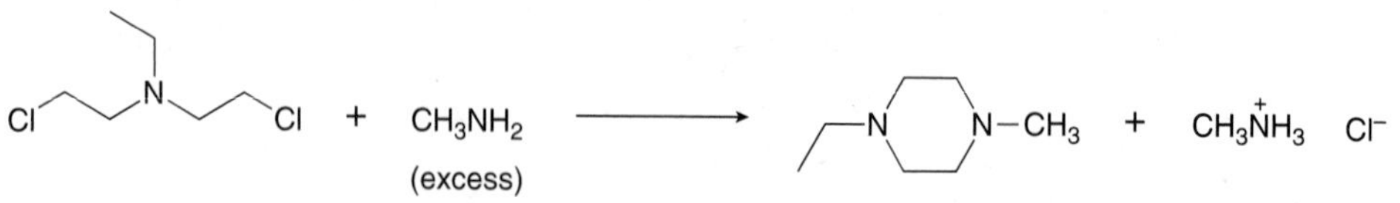

7.76 When (6*R*)-6-bromo-2,6-dimethylnonane is dissolved in CH_3OH, nucleophilic substitution yields an optically inactive solution. When the isomeric halide (5*R*)-2-bromo-2,5-dimethylnonane is dissolved in CH_3OH under the same conditions, nucleophilic substitution forms an optically active solution. Draw the products formed in each reaction, and explain why the difference in optical activity is observed.

Synthesis

7.77 Fill in the appropriate reagent or starting material in each of the following reactions.

a. 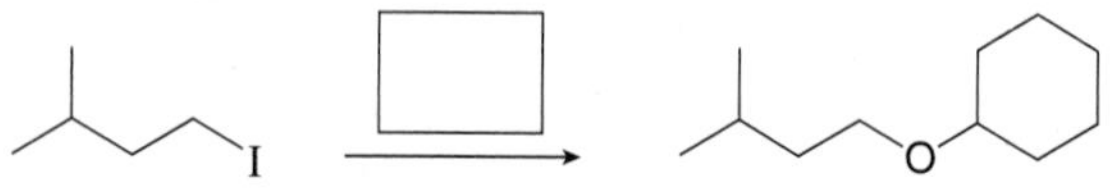

c. 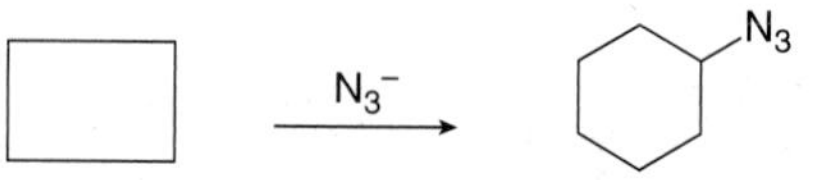

b. 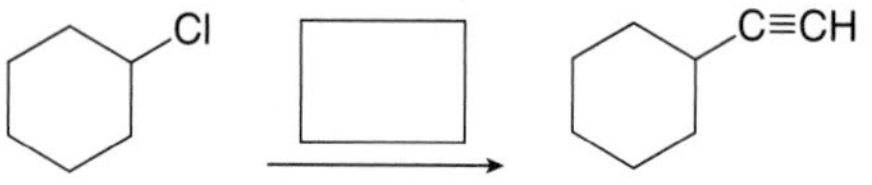

d. 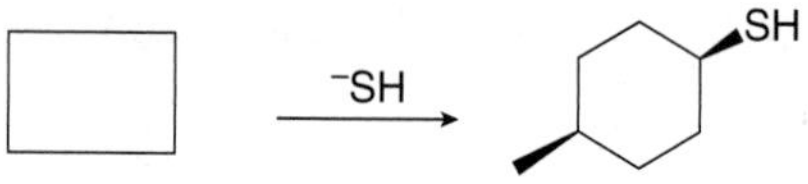

7.78 Devise a synthesis of each compound from an alkyl halide using any other organic or inorganic reagents.

a. 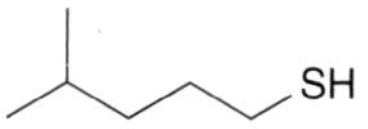

b. 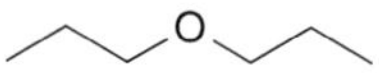

c. CH_3CH_2CN

d. 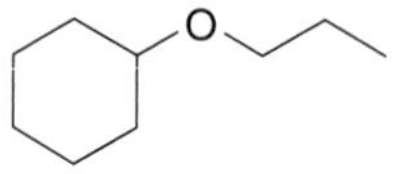

e. $CH_3CH_2OCOCH_3$

7.79 Benzalkonium chloride (**A**) is a weak germicide used in topical antiseptics and mouthwash. **A** can be prepared from amines **B** or **C** by S_N2 reaction with an alkyl chloride. (a) What alkyl chloride is needed to prepare **A** from **B?** (b) What alkyl chloride is needed to prepare **A** from **C?**

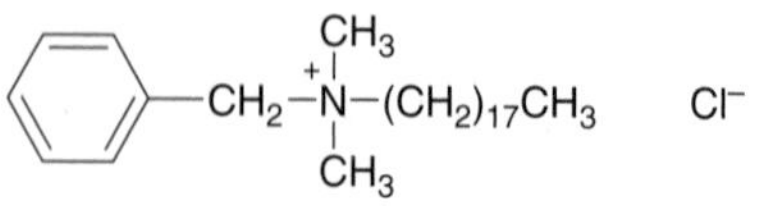

benzalkonium chloride

A

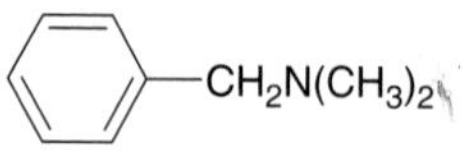

B

$CH_3(CH_2)_{17}N(CH_3)_2$

C

7.80 Suppose you have compounds **A–D** at your disposal. Using these compounds, devise two different ways to make **E.** Which one of these methods is preferred, and why?

CH_3I

A

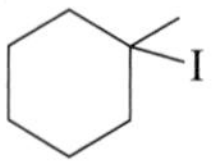

B

$NaOCH_3$

C

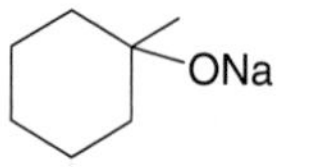

D

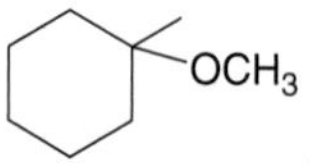

E

7.81 Muscalure, the sex pheromone of the common housefly, can be prepared by a reaction sequence that uses two nucleophilic substitutions. Identify compounds **A–D** in the following synthesis of muscalure.

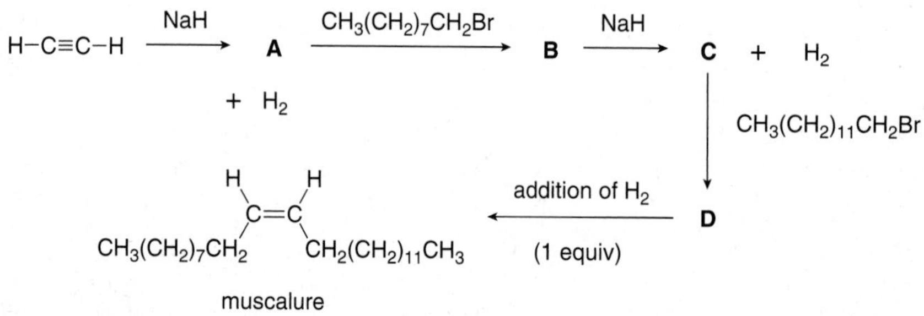

Challenge Problems

7.82 We will return often to nucleophilic substitution, in particular the S_N2 reaction, in subsequent chapters. In each instance we will concentrate on the *nucleophile,* rather than the alkyl halide, as we have done in this chapter. By using different nucleophiles, nucleophilic substitution allows the synthesis of a wide variety of organic compounds with many different functional groups.

With this in mind, draw the products of each two-step sequence. (Hint: Step [1] in each part involves an acid–base reaction that removes the most acidic hydrogen from the starting material.)

a. 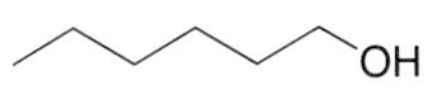 $\xrightarrow[\text{[2] } CH_3Br]{\text{[1] NaH}}$
(Chapter 9)

c. $CH_2(CO_2CH_2CH_3)_2$ $\xrightarrow[\text{[2] } C_6H_5CH_2Br]{\text{[1] } NaOCH_2CH_3}$
(Chapter 23)

b. $CH_3CH_2CH_2{-}C{\equiv}C{-}H$ $\xrightarrow[\text{[2] } CH_3CH_2Br]{\text{[1] } NaNH_2}$
(Chapter 11)

7.83 Explain why quinuclidine is a much more reactive nucleophile than triethylamine, even though both compounds have N atoms surrounded by three R groups.

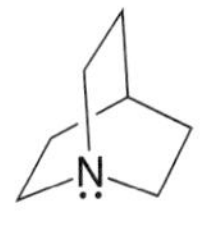
quinuclidine

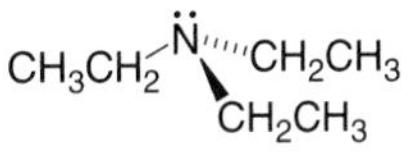

triethylamine

7.84 Draw a stepwise mechanism for the following reaction sequence.

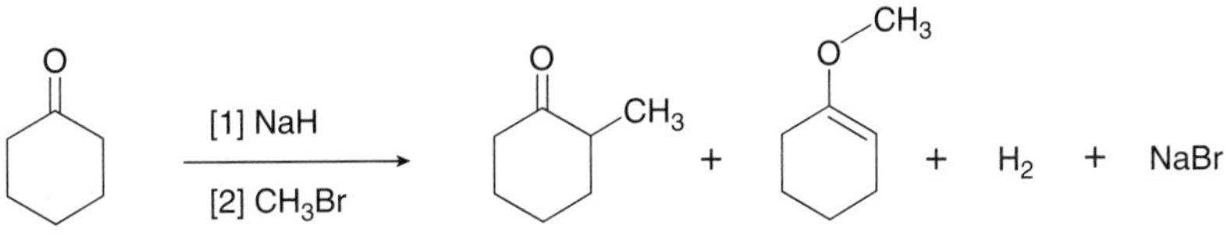

major product minor product

7.85 As we will learn in Chapter 9, an epoxide is an ether with an oxygen atom in a three-membered ring. Epoxides can be made by intramolecular S_N2 reactions of intermediates that contain a nucleophile and a leaving group on adjacent carbons, as shown.

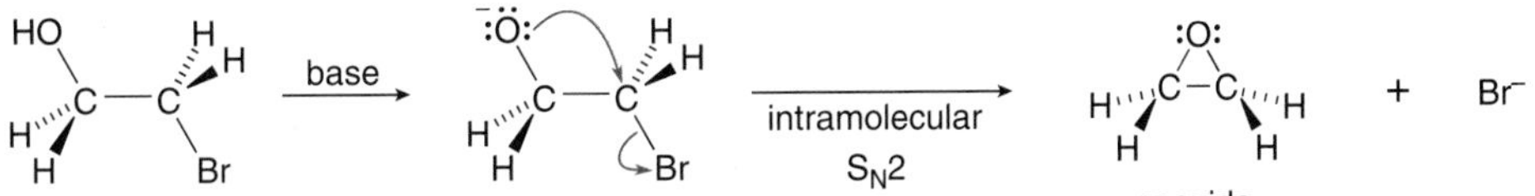

epoxide

Assume that each of the following starting materials can be converted to an epoxide by this reaction. Draw the product formed (including stereochemistry) from each starting material. Why might some of these reactions be more difficult than others in yielding nucleophilic substitution products?

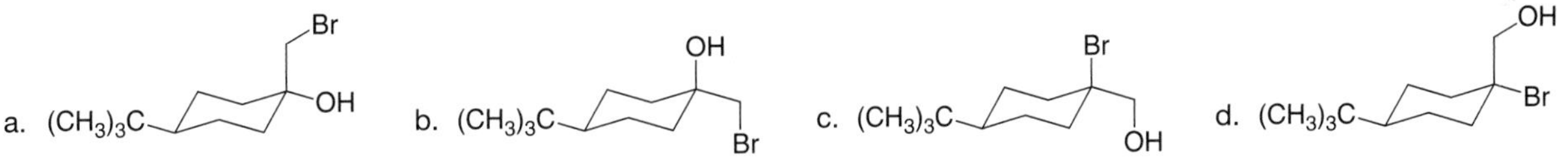

7.86 When trichloride **J** is treated with CH_3OH, nucleophilic substitution forms the dihalide **K.** Draw a mechanism for this reaction and explain why one Cl is much more reactive than the other two Cl's so that a single substitution product is formed.

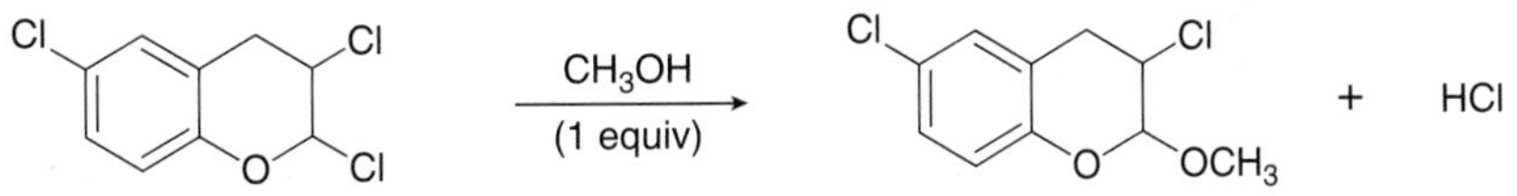

J **K**

7.87 In some nucleophilic substitutions under S_N1 conditions, complete racemization does not occur and a small excess of one enantiomer is present. For example, treatment of optically pure 1-bromo-1-phenylpropane with water forms 1-phenyl-1-propanol. (a) Calculate how much of each enantiomer is present using the given optical rotation data. (b) Which product predominates—the product of inversion or the product of retention of configuration? (c) Suggest an explanation for this phenomenon.

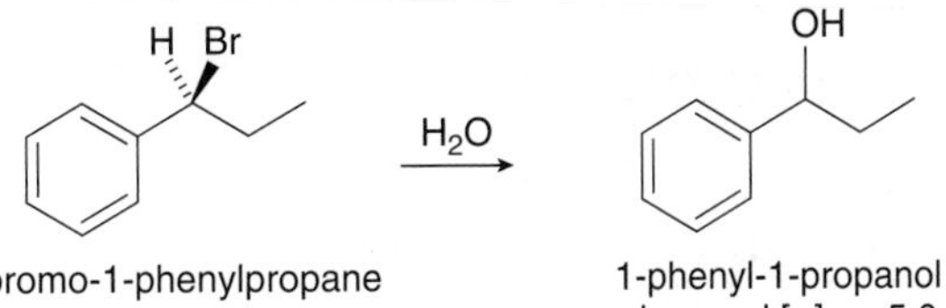

1-bromo-1-phenylpropane

1-phenyl-1-propanol
observed [α] = +5.0
optically pure *S* isomer, [α] = −48

8 Alkyl Halides and Elimination Reactions

8.1 General features of elimination

8.2 Alkenes—The products of elimination reactions

8.3 The mechanisms of elimination

8.4 The E2 mechanism

8.5 The Zaitsev rule

8.6 The E1 mechanism

8.7 S_N1 and E1 reactions

8.8 Stereochemistry of the E2 reaction

8.9 When is the mechanism E1 or E2?

8.10 E2 reactions and alkyne synthesis

8.11 When is the reaction S_N1, S_N2, E1, or E2?

DDE, *d*ichlorodiphenyl*d*ichloro*e*thylene, is formed by the elimination of HCl from the pesticide DDT. DDE and DDT accumulate in the fatty tissues of predator birds such as osprey that feed on fish contaminated with DDT. When DDE and DDT concentration is high, mother osprey produce eggs with very thin shells that are easily crushed, so fewer osprey chicks hatch. In Chapter 8, we learn about **elimination reactions,** the second general reaction of alkyl halides, which form alkenes like DDE.

Elimination reactions introduce π bonds into organic compounds, so they can be used to synthesize **alkenes** and **alkynes**—hydrocarbons that contain one and two π bonds, respectively. Like nucleophilic substitution, elimination reactions can occur by two different pathways, depending on the conditions. By the end of Chapter 8, therefore, you will have learned four different reaction mechanisms, two for nucleophilic substitution (S_N1 and S_N2) and two for elimination (E1 and E2).

The biggest challenge with this material is learning how to sort out two different reactions that follow four different mechanisms. **Will a particular alkyl halide undergo substitution or elimination with a given reagent, and by which of the four possible mechanisms?** To answer this question, we conclude Chapter 8 with a summary that allows you to predict which reaction and mechanism are likely for a given substrate.

8.1 General Features of Elimination

All **elimination reactions** involve loss of elements from the starting material to form a new π bond in the product.

- **Alkyl halides undergo elimination reactions with Brønsted–Lowry bases. The elements of HX are lost and an alkene is formed.**

General elimination reaction

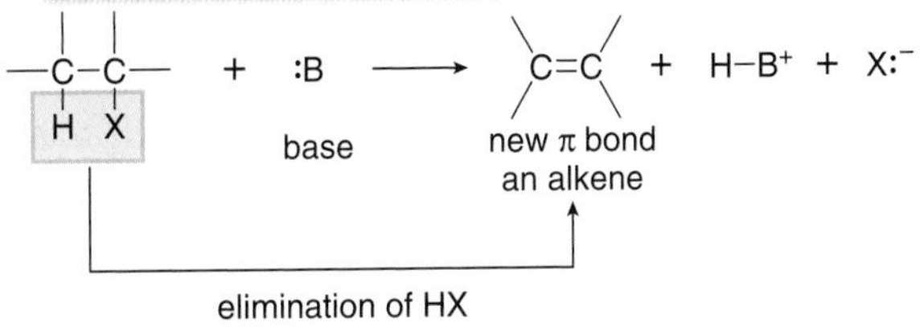

Equations [1] and [2] illustrate examples of elimination reactions. In both reactions a base removes the elements of an acid, HBr or HCl, from the organic starting material.

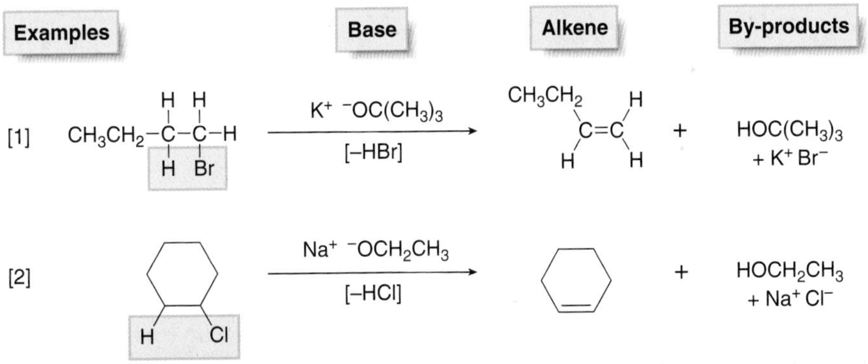

Removal of the elements of HX, called **dehydrohalogenation,** is one of the most common methods to introduce a π bond and prepare an alkene. Dehydrohalogenation is an example of **β elimination,** because it involves loss of elements from two adjacent atoms: the **α carbon** bonded to the leaving group X, and the **β carbon** adjacent to it. Three curved arrows illustrate how four bonds are broken or formed in the process.

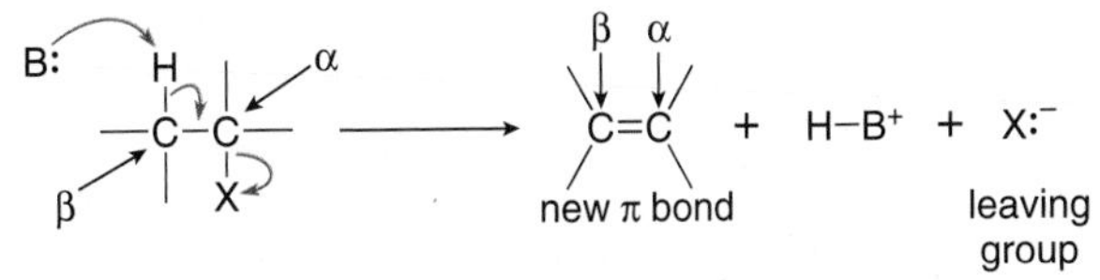

- The base (B:) removes a proton on the β carbon, thus forming $H-B^+$.
- The electron pair in the β C–H bond forms the new π bond between the α and β carbons.
- The electron pair in the C–X bond ends up on halogen, forming the leaving group $:X^-$.

The most common bases used in elimination reactions are negatively charged oxygen compounds such as ^-OH and its alkyl derivatives, ^-OR, called **alkoxides,** listed in Table 8.1. Potassium *tert*-butoxide, K^+ $^-OC(CH_3)_3$, a bulky nonnucleophilic base, is especially useful (Section 7.8B).

Table 8.1 Common Bases Used in Dehydrohalogenation

Structure	Name
Na^+ ^-OH	sodium hydroxide
K^+ ^-OH	potassium hydroxide
Na^+ $^-OCH_3$	sodium methoxide
Na^+ $^-OCH_2CH_3$	sodium ethoxide
K^+ $^-OC(CH_3)_3$	potassium *tert*-butoxide

To draw any product of dehydrohalogenation:

- **Find the α carbon—the *sp*³ hybridized carbon bonded to the leaving group.**
- **Identify all β carbons with H atoms.**
- **Remove the elements of H and X from the α and β carbons and form a π bond.**

For example, 2-bromo-2-methylpropane has three β carbons (three CH_3 groups), but because all three are *identical,* only *one* alkene is formed upon elimination of HBr. In contrast, 2-bromobutane has two *different* β carbons (labeled β_1 and β_2), so elimination affords *two* constitutional isomers by loss of HBr across either the α and β_1 carbons, or the α and β_2 carbons. We learn about which product predominates and why in Section 8.5.

Three identical β C's:

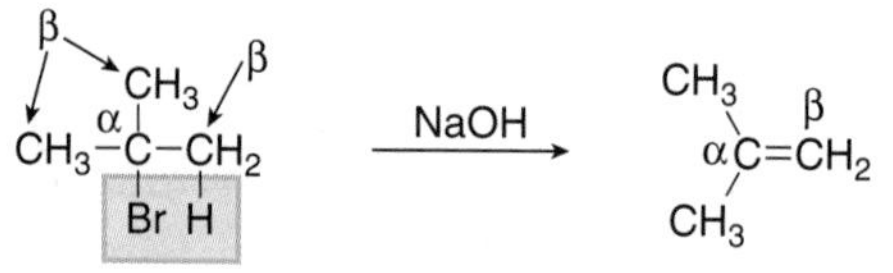

2-bromo-2-methylpropane

One alkene is formed.

Two different β C's:

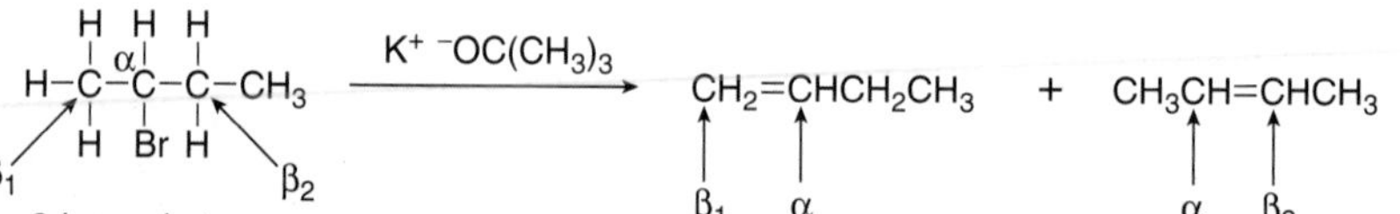

2-bromobutane

Two constitutional isomers are formed.

An elimination reaction is the first step in the slow degradation of the **pesticide DDT** (Chapter 8 opening paragraph and Section 7.4). Elimination of HCl from DDT forms the degradation product **DDE** (dichlorodiphenyldichloroethylene). This stable alkene is found in minute concentration in the fatty tissues of most adults in the United States.

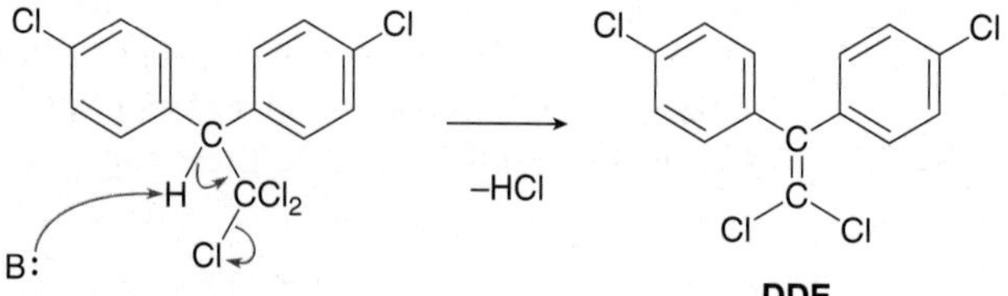

DDT **DDE**

Problem 8.1 Label the α and β carbons in each alkyl halide. Draw all possible elimination products formed when each alkyl halide is treated with K^+ $^-OC(CH_3)_3$.

a. $CH_3CH_2CH_2CH_2CH_2$–Cl

b. 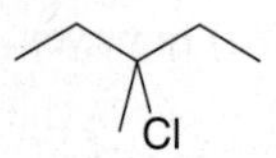

c. 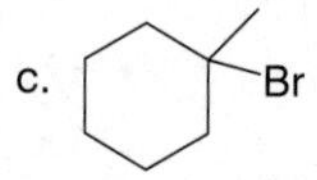

8.2 Alkenes—The Products of Elimination Reactions

Because elimination reactions of alkyl halides form alkenes, let's review earlier material on alkene structure and learn some additional facts as well.

8.2A Bonding in a Carbon–Carbon Double Bond

Ethylene, the simplest alkene, is a hormone that regulates plant growth and fruit ripening. A ripe banana speeds up the ripening of green tomatoes because the banana gives off ethylene.

Recall from Section 1.10B that alkenes are hydrocarbons containing a carbon–carbon double bond. Each carbon of the double bond is sp^2 hybridized and trigonal planar, and all bond angles are 120°.

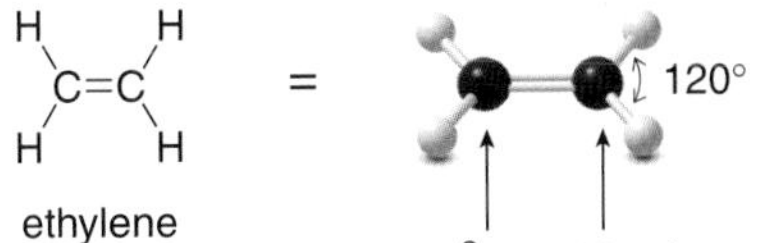
120°
ethylene
sp^2 hybridized

The double bond of an alkene consists of a σ bond and a π bond.

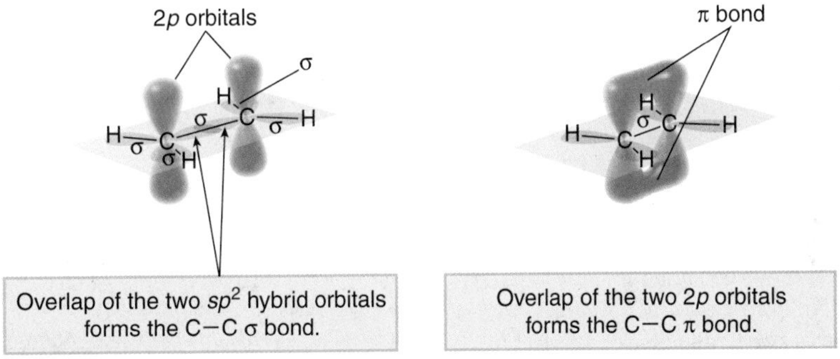
2p orbitals
π bond
Overlap of the two sp^2 hybrid orbitals forms the C–C σ bond.
Overlap of the two 2p orbitals forms the C–C π bond.

- **The σ bond, formed by end-on overlap of the two sp^2 hybrid orbitals, lies in the plane of the molecule.**
- **The π bond, formed by side-by-side overlap of two 2*p* orbitals, lies perpendicular to the plane of the molecule. The π bond is formed during elimination.**

Alkenes are classified according to the number of carbon atoms bonded to the carbons of the double bond. A **monosubstituted alkene** has one carbon atom bonded to the carbons of the double bond. A **disubstituted alkene** has two carbon atoms bonded to the carbons of the double bond, and so forth.

monosubstituted (*one* R group) | disubstituted (*two* R groups) | trisubstituted (*three* R groups) | tetrasubstituted (*four* R groups)

Figure 8.1 shows several alkenes and how they are classified. You must be able to classify alkenes in this way to determine the major and minor products of elimination reactions, when a mixture of alkenes is formed.

Figure 8.1 Classifying alkenes by the number of R groups bonded to the double bond

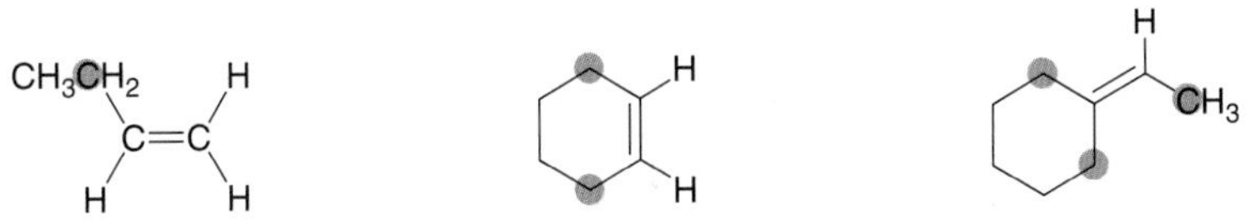

monosubstituted | disubstituted | trisubstituted

- Carbon atoms bonded to the double bond are screened in red.

Problem 8.2 Classify each alkene in the following vitamins by the number of carbon substituents bonded to the double bond.

a. 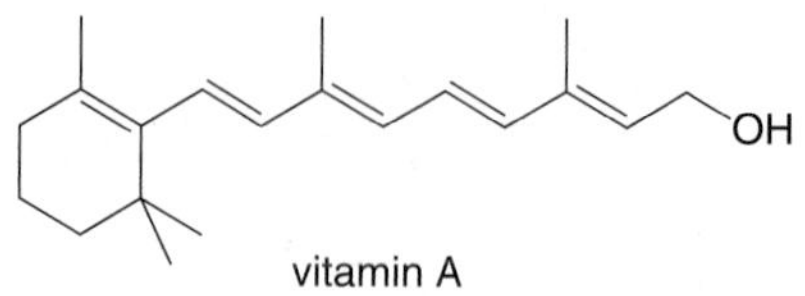
OH

vitamin A

b. 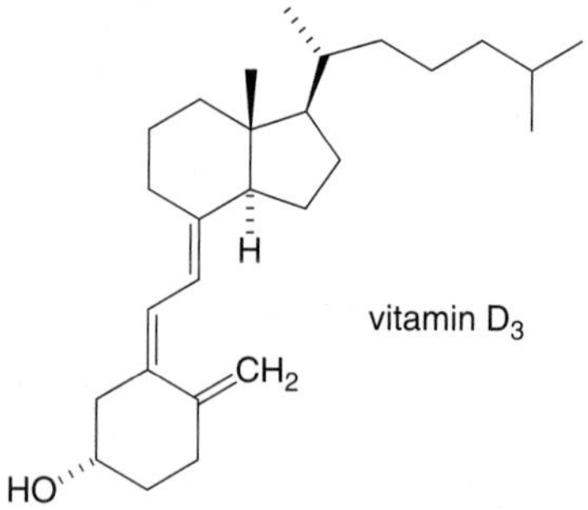
H
CH2
HO

vitamin D_3

8.2B Restricted Rotation

Figure 8.2 shows that there is free rotation about the carbon–carbon single bonds of butane, but *not* around the carbon–carbon double bond of 2-butene. Because of restricted rotation, two stereoisomers of 2-butene are possible.

- **The cis isomer has two groups on the *same side* of the double bond.**
- **The trans isomer has two groups on *opposite sides* of the double bond.**

The concept of cis and trans isomers was first introduced for disubstituted cycloalkanes in Chapter 4. In both cases, a ring or a double bond restricts motion, preventing the rotation of a group from one side of the ring or double bond to the other.

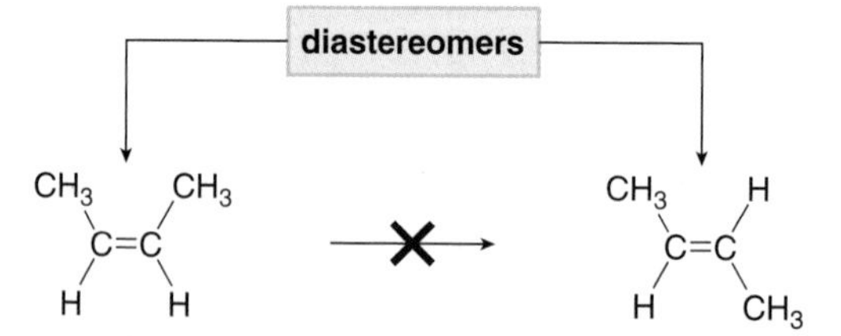
diastereomers
CH3 CH3
C=C
H H
CH3 H
C=C
H CH3

cis-2-butene — two R groups on the **same** side

trans-2-butene — two R groups on **opposite** sides

cis-2-Butene and *trans*-2-butene are stereoisomers, but not mirror images of each other, so they are **diastereomers.**

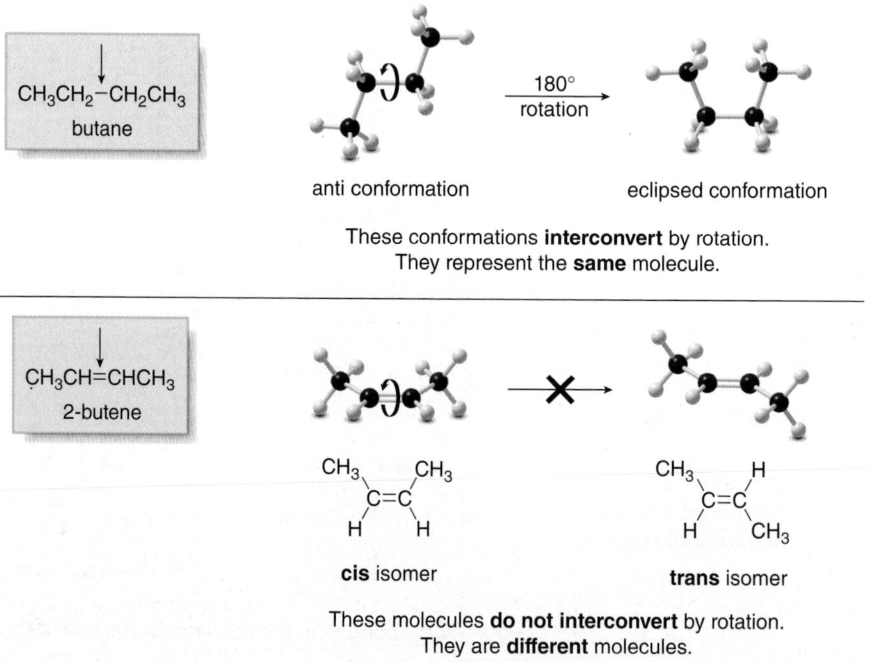
CH3CH2–CH2CH3
butane
180°
rotation
anti conformation
eclipsed conformation
These conformations **interconvert** by rotation.
They represent the **same** molecule.
CH3CH=CHCH3
2-butene
CH3 CH3
C=C
H H
CH3 H
C=C
H CH3
cis isomer
trans isomer
These molecules **do not interconvert** by rotation.
They are **different** molecules.

Figure 8.2
Rotation around C–C and C=C compared

The cis and trans isomers of 2-butene are a specific example of a general type of stereoisomer occurring at carbon–carbon double bonds. **Whenever the two groups on *each* end of a carbon–carbon double bond are *different from each other,* two diastereomers are possible.**

Stereoisomers on a C=C are possible when:

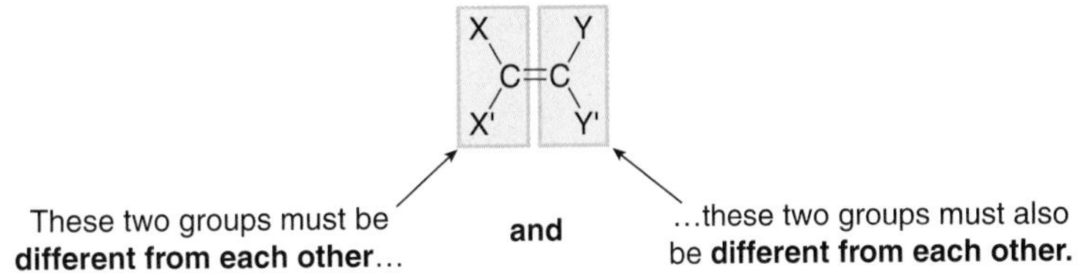
X
Y
C=C
X'
Y'
These two groups must be **different from each other**...
and
...these two groups must also be **different from each other.**

Problem 8.3 For which alkenes are stereoisomers possible?

a. 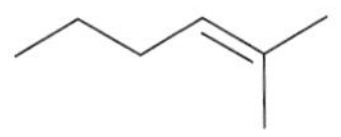 b. $CH_3CH_2CH{=}CHCH_3$ c. 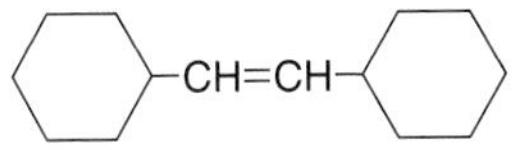
–CH=CH–

Problem 8.4 (a) Which double bonds in (*E*)-ocimene, a major component of the odor of lilac flowers, can exhibit stereoisomerism? (b) Draw a diastereomer of (*E*)-ocimene.

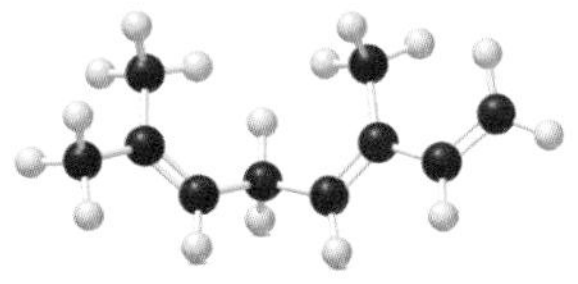

(*E*)-ocimene

The characteristic fragrance of lilac is a mixture of (*E*)-ocimene and other volatile ethers, aldehydes, and alcohols.

Problem 8.5 Label each pair of alkenes as constitutional isomers, stereoisomers, or identical.

a. 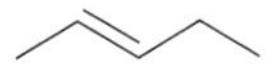 and 

b. 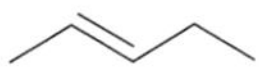 and 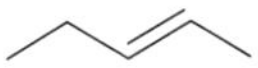

c.  and 

d. 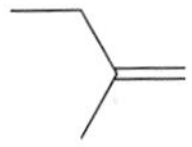 and 

8.2C Stability of Alkenes

Some alkenes are more stable than others. For example, **trans alkenes are generally more stable than cis alkenes** because the groups bonded to the double bond carbons are farther apart, reducing steric interactions.

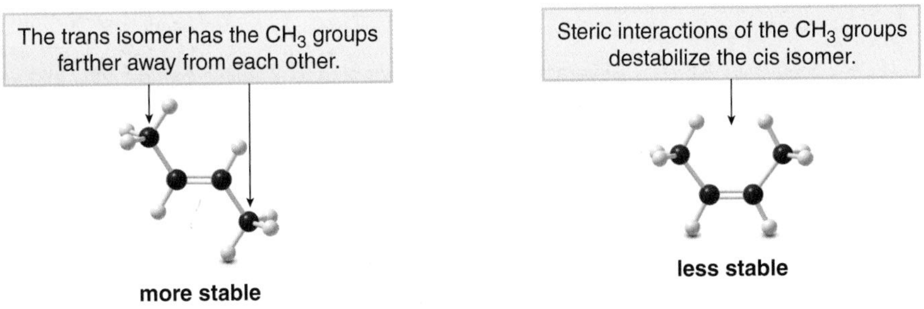
The trans isomer has the CH_3 groups farther away from each other.
more stable
Steric interactions of the CH_3 groups destabilize the cis isomer.
less stable

The stability of an alkene increases, moreover, as the **number of R groups bonded to the double bond carbons increases.**

least stable — most stable

$CH_2{=}CH_2$ < $RCH{=}CH_2$ < $R_2C{=}CH_2$ ~ $RCH{=}CHR$ < $R_2C{=}CHR$ < $R_2C{=}CR_2$

Increasing number of R groups
Increasing stability

R groups increase the stability of an alkene because R groups are sp^3 hybridized, whereas the carbon atoms of the double bond are sp^2 hybridized. Recall from Sections 1.11B and 2.5D that the percent *s*-character of a hybrid orbital increases from 25% to 33% in going from sp^3 to sp^2. The higher the percent *s*-character, the more readily an atom accepts electron density. Thus, **sp^2 hybridized carbon atoms are more able to *accept* electron density** and **sp^3 hybridized carbon atoms are more able to *donate* electron density.**

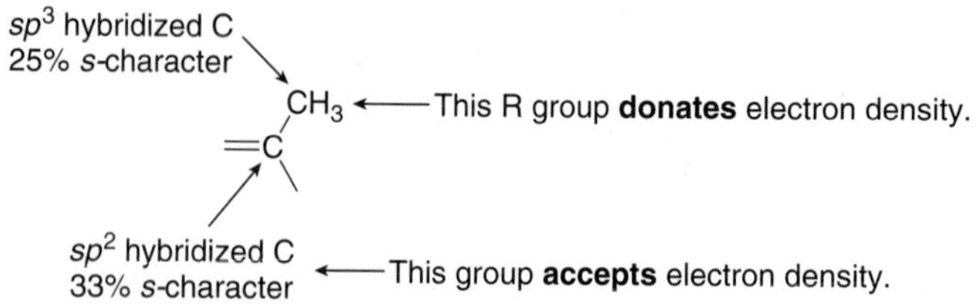
*sp*3 hybridized C
25% *s*-character
CH3
This R group **donates** electron density.
*sp*2 hybridized C
33% *s*-character
This group **accepts** electron density.

- **As a result, increasing the number of electron-donating R groups on a carbon atom able to accept electron density makes the alkene more stable.**

Thus, *trans*-2-butene (a disubstituted alkene) is more stable than *cis*-2-butene (another disubstituted alkene), but both are more stable than 1-butene (a monosubstituted alkene).

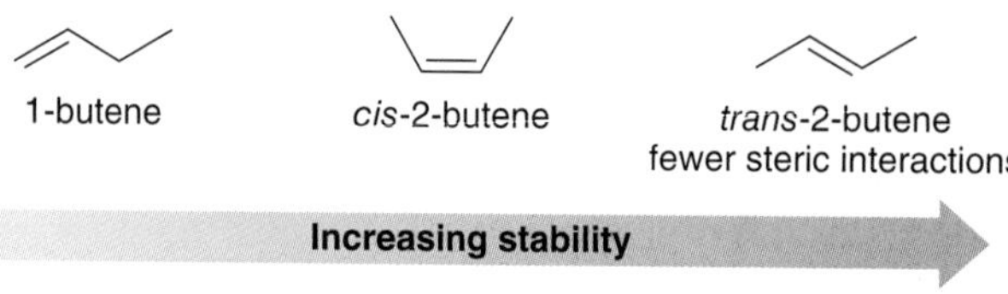
1-butene
cis-2-butene
trans-2-butene
fewer steric interactions
Increasing stability

In summary:

- **Trans alkenes are more stable than cis alkenes because they have fewer steric interactions.**
- **Increasing alkyl substitution stabilizes an alkene by an electron-donating inductive effect.**

Problem 8.6 Which alkene in each pair is more stable?

a. 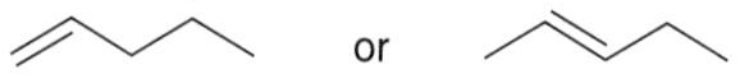

c. 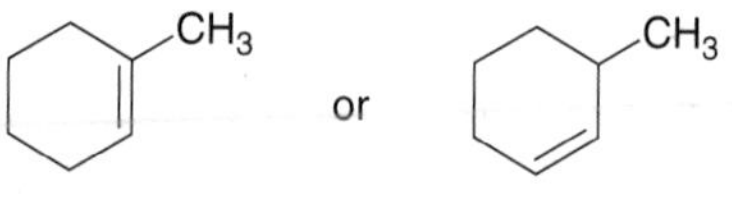
CH3
or
CH3

b. 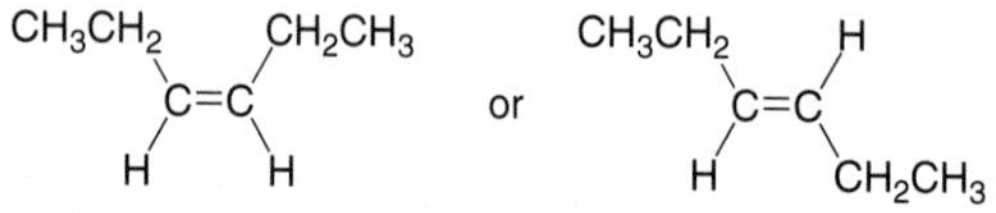
CH3CH2
CH2CH3
C=C
H
H
or
CH3CH2
H
C=C
H
CH2CH3

Problem 8.7 Several factors can affect alkene stability. Explain why alkene **A** is more stable than alkene **B** even though both contain disubstituted carbon–carbon double bonds.

A
B

8.3 The Mechanisms of Elimination

What is the mechanism for elimination? What is the order of bond breaking and bond making? Is the reaction a one-step process or does it occur in many steps?

There are two mechanisms for elimination—E2 and E1—just as there are two mechanisms for nucleophilic substitution—S_N2 and S_N1.

- The **E2 mechanism (bimolecular elimination)**
- The **E1 mechanism (unimolecular elimination)**

The E2 and E1 mechanisms differ in the timing of bond cleavage and bond formation, analogous to the S_N2 and S_N1 mechanisms. In fact, E2 and S_N2 reactions have some features in common, as do E1 and S_N1 reactions.

8.4 The E2 Mechanism

The most common mechanism for dehydrohalogenation is the E2 mechanism. For example, $(CH_3)_3CBr$ reacts with ^-OH to form $(CH_3)_2C{=}CH_2$ via an E2 mechanism.

E2 reaction

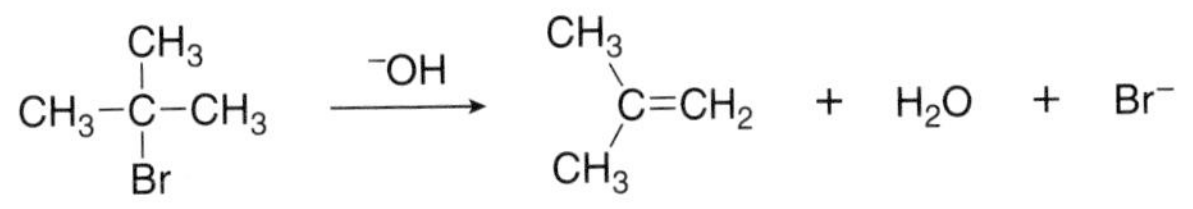

8.4A Kinetics

An E2 reaction exhibits **second-order kinetics;** that is, the reaction is **bimolecular** and both the alkyl halide and the base appear in the rate equation.

- rate = $k[(CH_3)_3CBr][^-OH]$

8.4B A One-Step Mechanism

The most straightforward explanation for the second-order kinetics is a **concerted reaction: all bonds are broken and formed in a single step,** as shown in Mechanism 8.1.

Mechanism 8.1 The E2 Mechanism

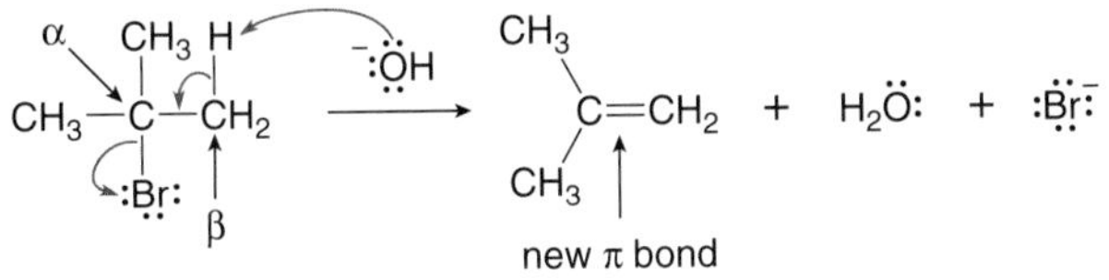

- The base ^-OH removes a proton from the β carbon, forming H_2O (a by-product).
- The electron pair in the β C–H bond forms the new π bond.
- The leaving group Br^- comes off with the electron pair in the C–Br bond.

An energy diagram for the reaction of $(CH_3)_3CBr$ with ^-OH is shown in Figure 8.3. The reaction has one step, so there is one energy barrier between reactants and products. Two bonds are broken

Figure 8.3
An energy diagram for an E2 reaction: $(CH_3)_3CBr + {^-OH} \rightarrow (CH_3)_2C{=}CH_2 + H_2O + Br^-$

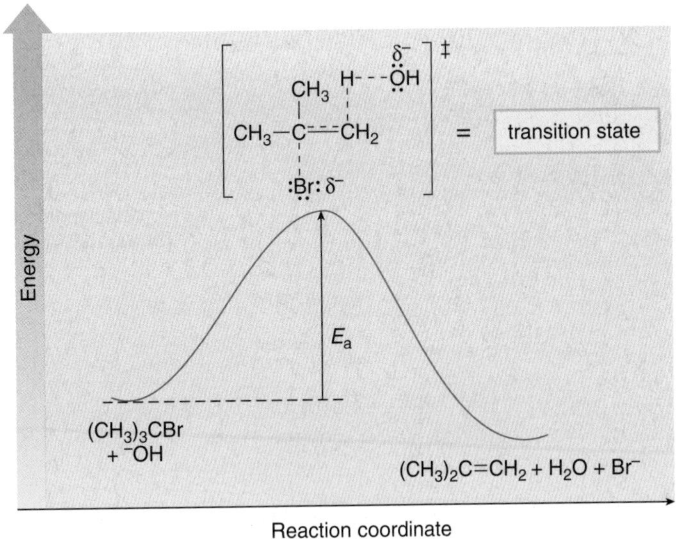

- In the transition state, the C–H and C–Br bonds are partially broken, the O–H and π bonds are partially formed, and both the base and the departing leaving group bear a partial negative charge.

(C–H and C–Br) and two bonds are formed (H–OH and the π bond) in a single step, so the transition state contains four partial bonds, with the negative charge distributed over the base and the leaving group. Entropy favors the products of an E2 reaction because two molecules of starting material form three molecules of product.

Problem 8.8 Use curved arrows to show the movement of electrons in the following E2 mechanism. Draw the structure of the transition state.

$$(CH_3CH_2)_3CBr \xrightarrow{^{-}OCH_2CH_3} (CH_3CH_2)_2C{=}CHCH_3 + HOCH_2CH_3 + Br^-$$

There are close parallels between the E2 and S_N2 mechanisms in how the identity of the base, the leaving group, and the solvent affect the rate.

The Base

- **The base appears in the rate equation, so the rate of the E2 reaction increases as the strength of the base increases.**

The IUPAC names for **DBN** and **DBU** are rarely used because the names are complex. **DBN** stands for 1,5-**d**iaza**b**icyclo[4.3.0]-**n**on-5-ene, and **DBU** stands for 1,8-**d**iaza**b**icyclo[5.4.0]-**u**ndec-7-ene.

E2 reactions are generally run with strong, negatively charged bases like ^{-}OH and ^{-}OR. Two strong, sterically hindered nitrogen bases, called **DBN** and **DBU,** are also sometimes used. An example of an E2 reaction with DBN is shown in Figure 8.4.

Two useful bases for E2 reactions

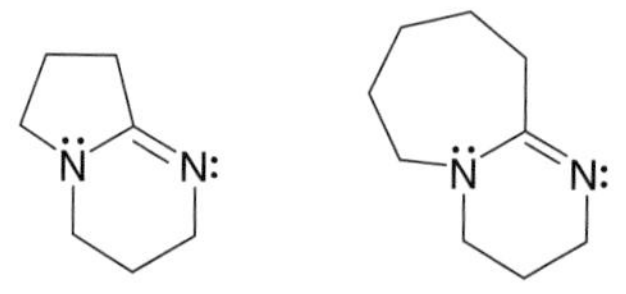

DBN DBU

Figure 8.4 An E2 elimination with DBN used as the base

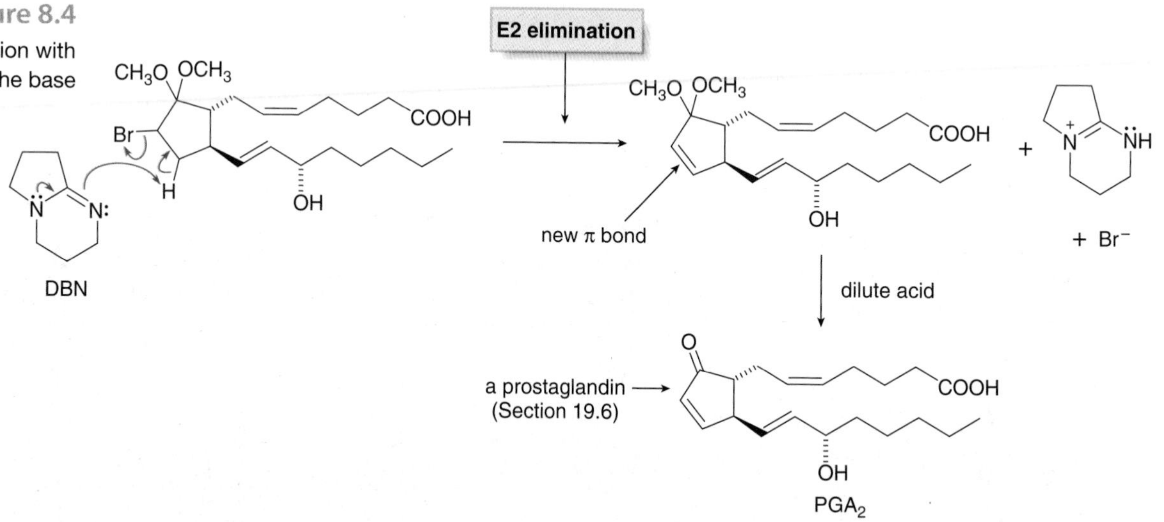
E2 elimination
CH3O OCH3
Br
COOH
H
OH
DBN
CH3O OCH3
COOH
OH
new π bond
+
+ Br−
dilute acid
O
a prostaglandin
(Section 19.6)
COOH
OH
PGA2

The Leaving Group

- **Because the bond to the leaving group is partially broken in the transition state, the better the leaving group the faster the E2 reaction.**

Order of reactivity of RX: R–F R–Cl R–Br R–I

→ **Increasing leaving group ability**
Increasing rate of the E2 reaction

The Solvent

- **Polar aprotic solvents increase the rate of E2 reactions.**

Because **polar aprotic solvents** like $(CH_3)_2C{=}O$ do not solvate anions well, a negatively charged base is not "hidden" by strong interactions with the solvent (Section 7.17D), and the base is stronger. **A stronger base increases the reaction rate.**

Problem 8.9 Consider an E2 reaction between CH_3CH_2Br and $KOC(CH_3)_3$. What effect does each of the following changes have on the rate of elimination? (a) The base is changed to KOH. (b) The alkyl halide is changed to CH_3CH_2Cl.

8.4C The Identity of the Alkyl Halide

The S_N2 and E2 mechanisms differ in how the R group affects the reaction rate.

- **As the number of R groups on the carbon with the leaving group increases, the rate of the E2 reaction increases.**

← **Increasing rate of an S_N2 reaction**

$RCH_2{-}X$	$R_2CH{-}X$	$R_3C{-}X$
1°	2°	3°

→ **Increasing rate of an E2 reaction**

This trend is exactly *opposite* to the reactivity of alkyl halides in S_N2 reactions, where increasing alkyl substitution decreases the rate of reaction (Section 7.11D).

Why does increasing alkyl substitution increase the rate of an E2 reaction? In the transition state, the double bond is partially formed, so increasing the stability of the double bond with alkyl substituents stabilizes the transition state (i.e., it lowers E_a), which increases the rate of the reaction.

Transition state for an E2 reaction with an alkoxide (^-OR) as base

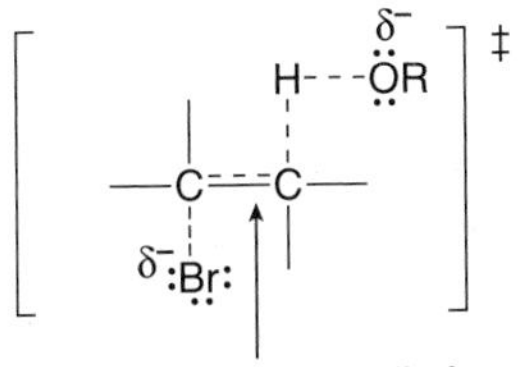

The double bond is partially formed.

- **Increasing the number of R groups on the carbon with the leaving group forms more highly substituted, more stable alkenes in E2 reactions.**

For example, the E2 reaction of a 1° alkyl halide (1-bromobutane) forms a monosubstituted alkene, whereas the E2 reaction of a 3° alkyl halide (2-bromo-2-methylpropane) forms a disubstituted alkene. The disubstituted alkene is more stable, so the 3° alkyl halide reacts faster than the 1° alkyl halide.

1° RX

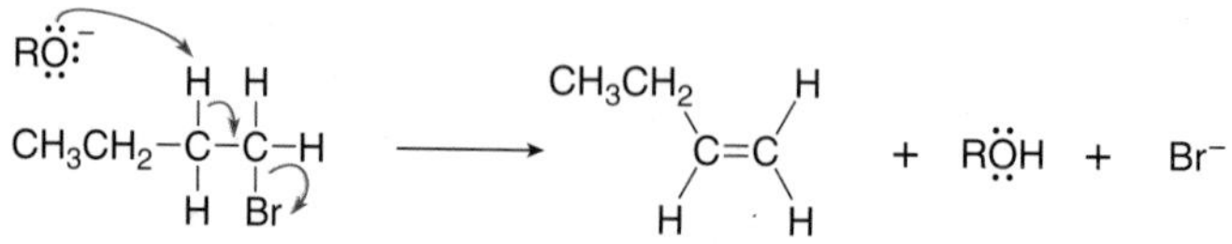

1-bromobutane → monosubstituted alkene **less stable**

3° RX

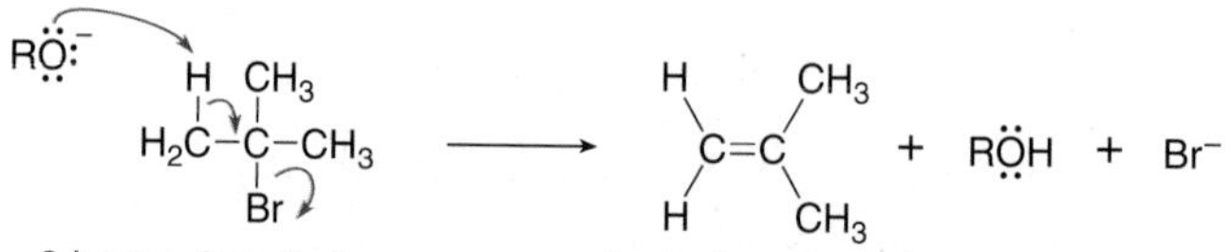

2-bromo-2-methylpropane → disubstituted alkene **more stable**

Problem 8.10 Rank the alkyl halides in each group in order of increasing reactivity in an E2 reaction.

a. $(CH_3)_2C(Br)CH_2CH_2CH_3$ $(CH_3)_2CHCH_2CH_2CH_2Br$ $(CH_3)_2CHCH_2CH(Br)CH_3$

b.

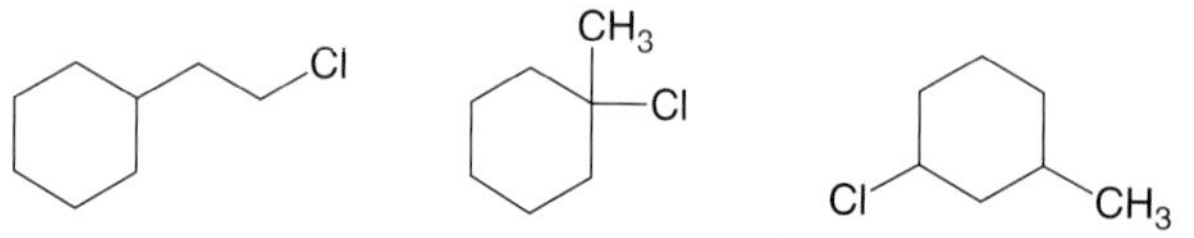

Table 8.2 summarizes the characteristics of the E2 mechanism, and Figure 8.5 illustrates two examples of E2 reactions used in the synthesis of **quinine** and **estradiol,** two naturally occurring compounds.

Problem 8.11 How does each of the following changes affect the rate of an E2 reaction?

a. tripling [RX]
b. halving [B:]
c. changing the solvent from CH_3OH to DMSO
d. changing the leaving group from I^- to Br^-
e. changing the base from ^-OH to H_2O
f. changing the alkyl halide from CH_3CH_2Br to $(CH_3)_2CHBr$

Table 8.2 Characteristics of the E2 Mechanism

Characteristic	Result
Kinetics	• Second order
Mechanism	• One step
Identity of R	• More substituted halides react faster. • Rate: $R_3CX > R_2CHX > RCH_2X$
Base	• Favored by strong bases
Leaving group	• Better leaving group ---→ faster reaction
Solvent	• Favored by polar aprotic solvents

Figure 8.5
Two examples of the E2 reaction used in organic synthesis

Quinine, a natural product isolated from the bark of the cinchona tree native to the Andes Mountains, is a powerful antipyretic—that is, it reduces fever—and for centuries, it was the only effective treatment for malaria.

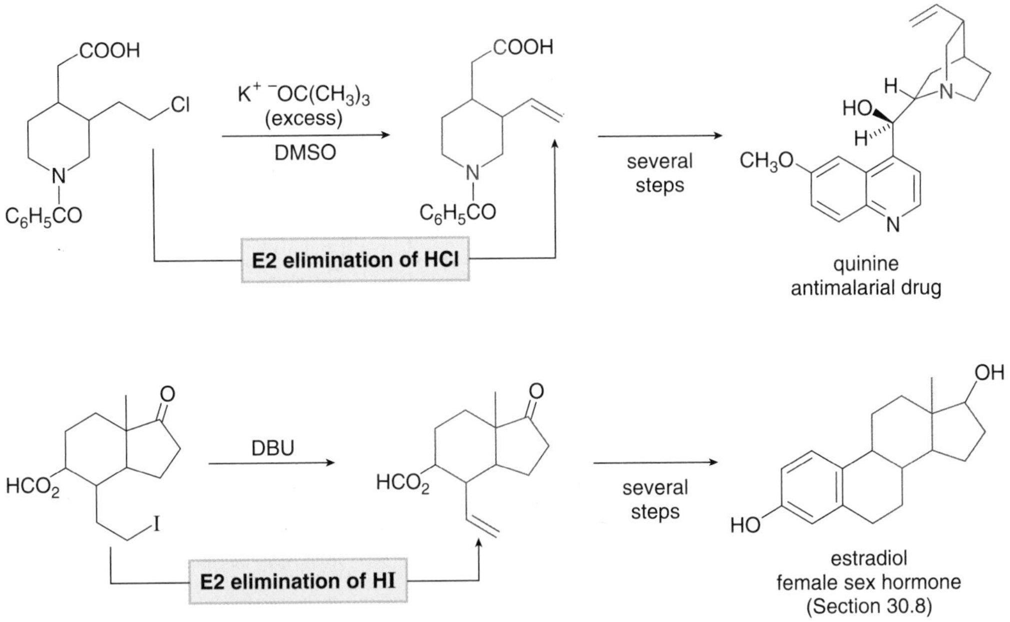

- Bonds and atoms in quinine and estradiol that originate in the alkene intermediate are shown in red.

8.5 The Zaitsev Rule

Recall from Section 8.1 that a mixture of alkenes can form from the dehydrohalogenation of alkyl halides having two or more different β carbon atoms. When this occurs, one of the products usually predominates. The **major product is the more stable product—the one with the more substituted double bond.** For example, elimination of the elements of H and I from 1-iodo-1-methylcyclohexane yields two constitutional isomers: the trisubstituted alkene **A** (the major product) and the disubstituted alkene **B** (the minor product).

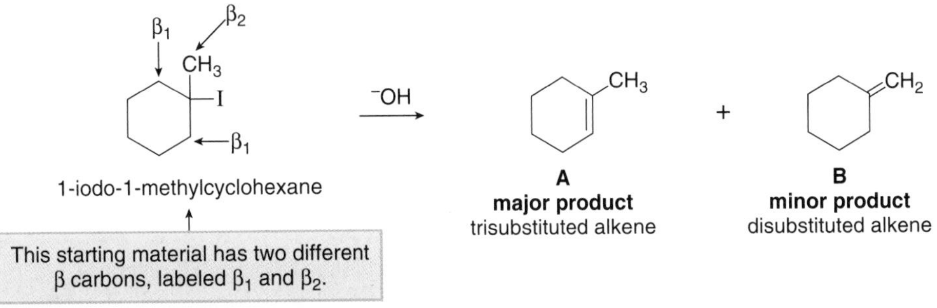

This phenomenon is called the **Zaitsev rule** (also called the **Saytzeff rule,** depending on the translation) for the Russian chemist who first noted this trend.

- **The Zaitsev rule: The major product in β elimination has the more substituted double bond.**

A reaction is *regioselective* when it yields predominantly or exclusively one constitutional isomer when more than one is possible. The E2 reaction is **regioselective** because the more substituted alkene predominates.

The Zaitsev rule results because the double bond is partially formed in the transition state for the E2 reaction. Thus, increasing the stability of the double bond by adding R groups lowers the energy of the transition state, which increases the reaction rate. For example, E2 elimination of HBr from 2-bromo-2-methylbutane yields alkenes **C** and **D. D,** having the more substituted double bond, is the major product, because the transition state leading to its formation is lower in energy.

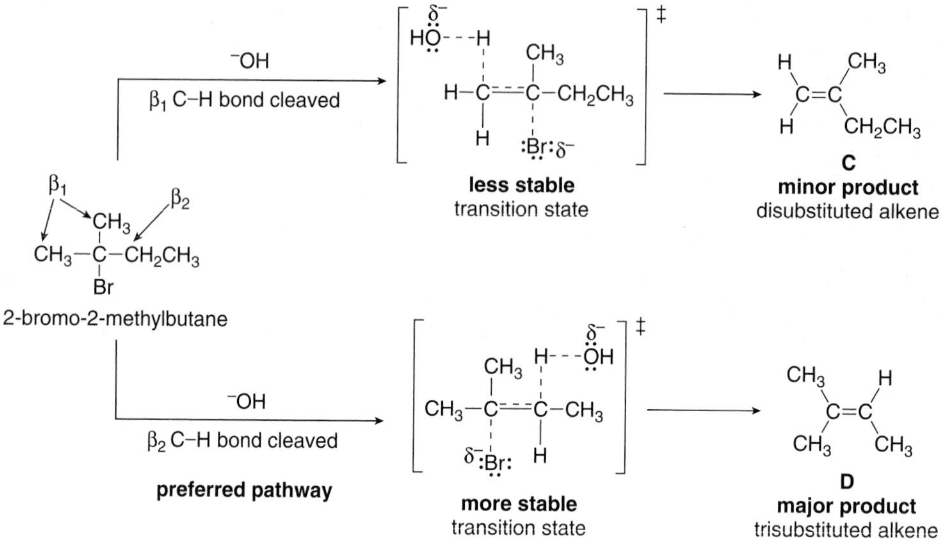

When a mixture of stereoisomers is possible from dehydrohalogenation, the **major product is the more stable stereoisomer.** For example, dehydrohalogenation of alkyl halide **X** forms a mixture of trans and cis alkenes, **Y** and **Z.** The trans alkene **Y** is the major product because it is more stable.

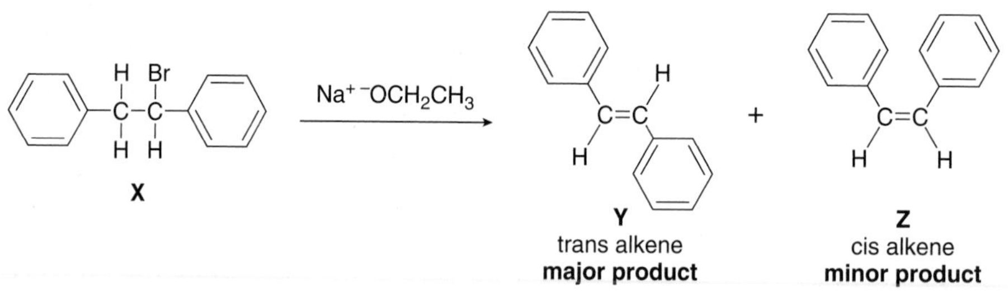

A reaction is *stereoselective* when it forms predominantly or exclusively one stereoisomer when two or more are possible. The **E2 reaction is stereoselective** because one stereoisomer is formed preferentially.

Sample Problem 8.1 Predict the major product in the following E2 reaction.

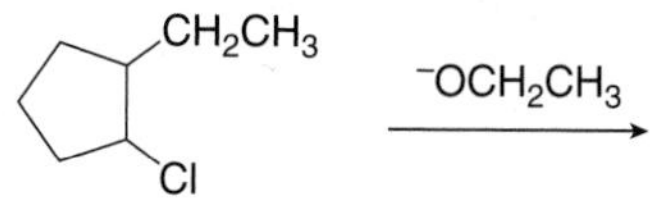

Solution

The alkyl halide has two different β C atoms (labeled β_1 and β_2), so two different alkenes are possible: one formed by removal of HCl across the α and β_1 carbons, and one formed by removal of HCl across the α and β_2 carbons. Using the Zaitsev rule, the major product should be **A,** because it has the more substituted double bond.

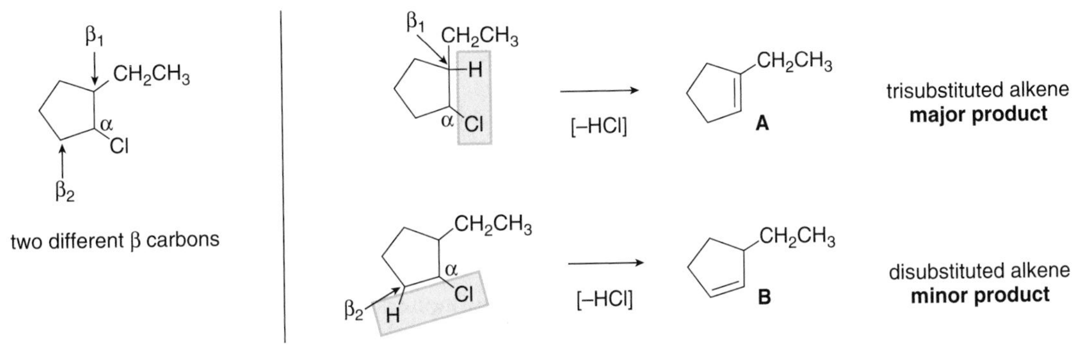

Problem 8.12 What alkenes are formed from each alkyl halide by an E2 reaction? Use the Zaitsev rule to predict the major product.

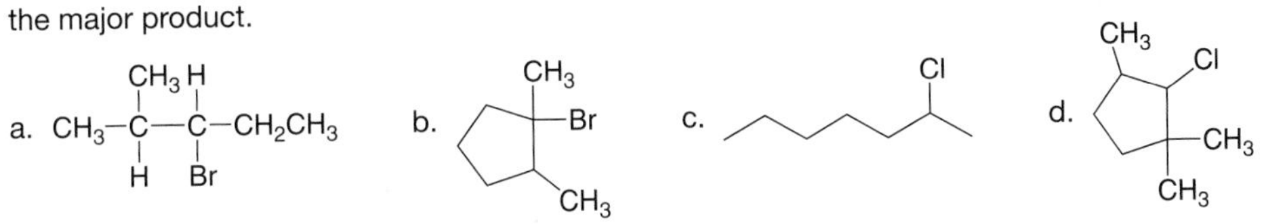

8.6 The E1 Mechanism

The dehydrohalogenation of $(CH_3)_3CI$ with H_2O to form $(CH_3)_2C{=}CH_2$ can be used to illustrate the second general mechanism of elimination, the **E1 mechanism.**

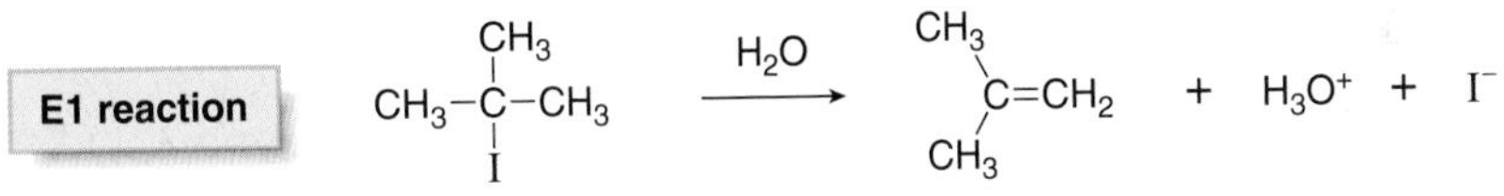

8.6A Kinetics

An E1 reaction exhibits first-order kinetics.

- **rate = k[$(CH_3)_3CI$]**

Like the S_N1 mechanism, the kinetics suggest that the reaction mechanism involves more than one step, and that the slow step is **unimolecular,** involving *only* the alkyl halide.

8.6B A Two-Step Mechanism

The most straightforward explanation for the observed first-order kinetics is a **two-step reaction: the bond to the leaving group breaks first *before* the π bond is formed,** as shown in Mechanism 8.2.

Mechanism 8.2 The E1 Mechanism

Step [1] The C–I bond is broken.

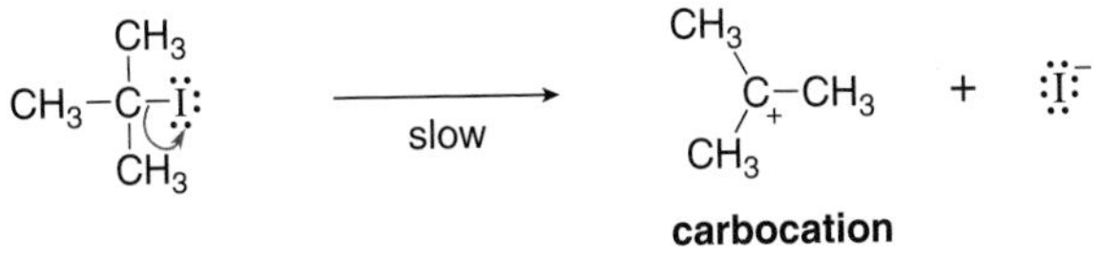

- **Heterolysis of the C–I bond** forms an intermediate **carbocation.** This is the same first step as the S_N1 mechanism. It is responsible for the first-order kinetics because it is rate-determining.

Step [2] A C–H bond is cleaved and the π bond is formed.

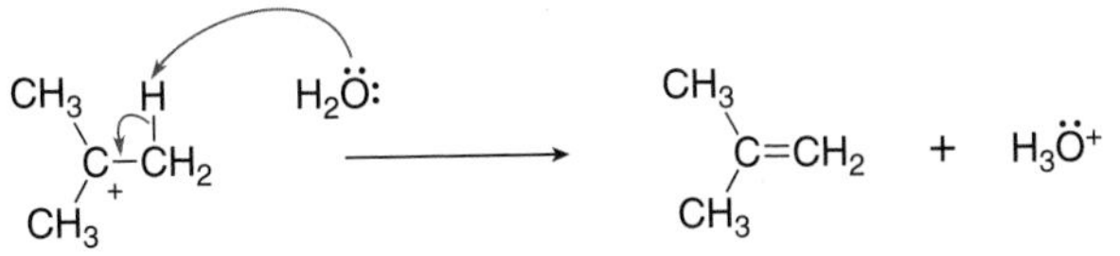

- **A base** (such as H_2O or I^-) **removes a proton from a carbon adjacent to the carbocation** (a β carbon). The electron pair in the C–H bond is used to form the new π bond.

The E1 and E2 mechanisms both involve the same number of bonds broken and formed. **The only difference is the timing.**

- **In an E1 reaction, the leaving group comes off *before* the β proton is removed, and the reaction occurs in two steps.**
- **In an E2 reaction, the leaving group comes off *as* the β proton is removed, and the reaction occurs in one step.**

An energy diagram for the reaction of $(CH_3)_3CI + H_2O$ is shown in Figure 8.6. Each step has its own energy barrier, with a transition state at each energy maximum. Because its transition state is higher in energy, Step [1] is rate-determining. $\Delta H°$ for Step [1] is positive because only bond breaking occurs, whereas $\Delta H°$ of Step [2] is negative because two bonds are formed and only one is broken.

Problem 8.13 Draw an E1 mechanism for the following reaction. Draw the structure of the transition state for each step.

$$(CH_3)_2C(Cl)CH_2CH_3 + CH_3OH \longrightarrow (CH_3)_2C{=}CHCH_3 + CH_3\overset{+}{O}H_2 + Cl^-$$

Figure 8.6 Energy diagram for an E1 reaction: $(CH_3)_3CI + H_2O \rightarrow (CH_3)_2C{=}CH_2 + H_3O^+ + I^-$

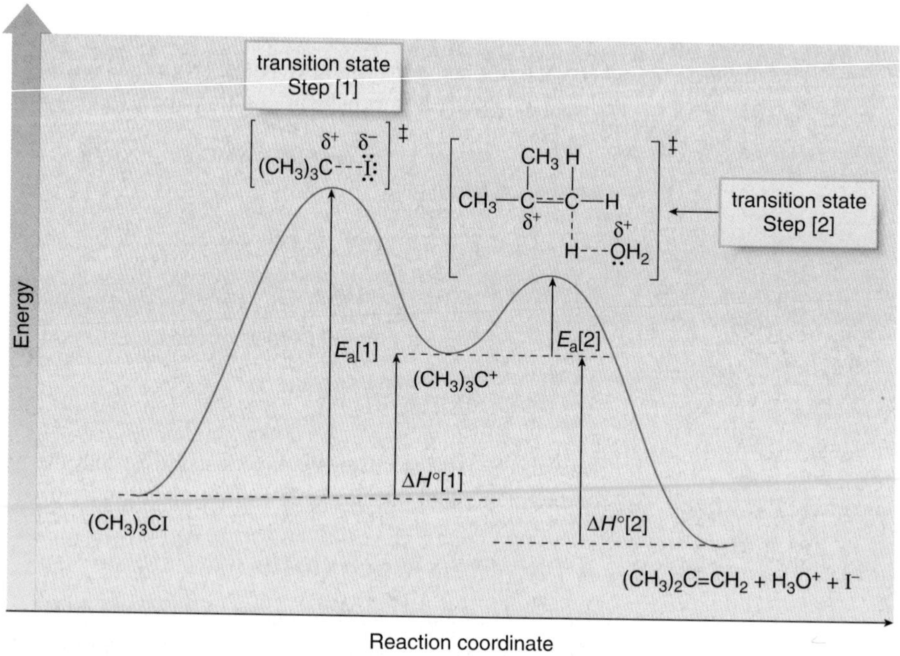

- Since the E1 mechanism has two steps, there are two energy barriers.
- Step [1] is rate-determining.

8.6C Other Characteristics of E1 Reactions

Three other features of E1 reactions are worthy of note.

[1] The rate of an E1 reaction increases as the number of R groups on the carbon with the leaving group increases.

Increasing alkyl substitution has the same effect on the rate of *both* an E1 and E2 reaction; increasing rate of the E1 and E2 reactions: RCH_2X (1°) < R_2CHX (2°) < R_3CX (3°).

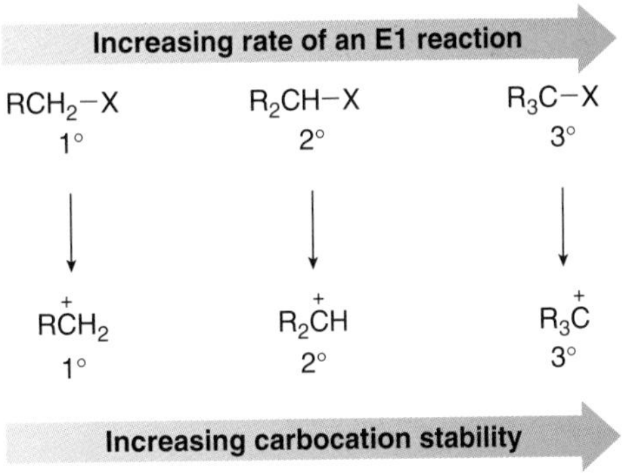

Like an S_N1 reaction, more substituted alkyl halides yield more substituted (and more stable) carbocations in the rate-determining step. Increasing the stability of a carbocation, in turn, decreases E_a for the slow step, which increases the rate of the E1 reaction according to the Hammond postulate.

[2] Because the base does not appear in the rate equation, weak bases favor E1 reactions.

The strength of the base usually determines whether a reaction follows the E1 or E2 mechanism.

- **Strong bases like ^-OH and ^-OR favor E2 reactions, whereas weaker bases like H_2O and ROH favor E1 reactions.**

[3] E1 reactions are regioselective, favoring formation of the more substituted, more stable alkene.

The Zaitsev rule applies to E1 reactions, too. For example, E1 elimination of HBr from 1-bromo-1-methylcyclopentane yields alkenes **A** and **B. A,** having the more substituted double bond, is the major product.

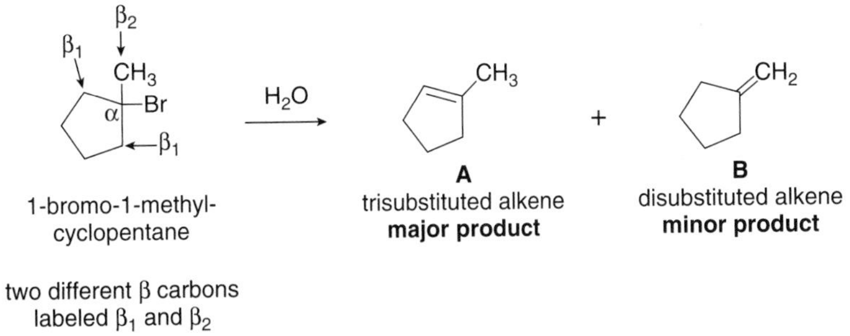

Table 8.3 summarizes the characteristics of E1 reactions.

Table 8.3 Characteristics of the E1 Mechanism

Characteristic	Result
Kinetics	• First order
Mechanism	• Two steps
Identity of R	• More substituted halides react faster. • Rate: $R_3CX > R_2CHX > RCH_2X$
Base	• Favored by weaker bases such as H_2O and ROH
Leaving group	• A better leaving group makes the reaction faster because the bond to the leaving group is partially broken in the rate-determining step.
Solvent	• Polar protic solvents that solvate the ionic intermediates are needed.

Problem 8.14 What alkenes are formed from each alkyl halide by an E1 reaction? Use the Zaitsev rule to predict the major product.

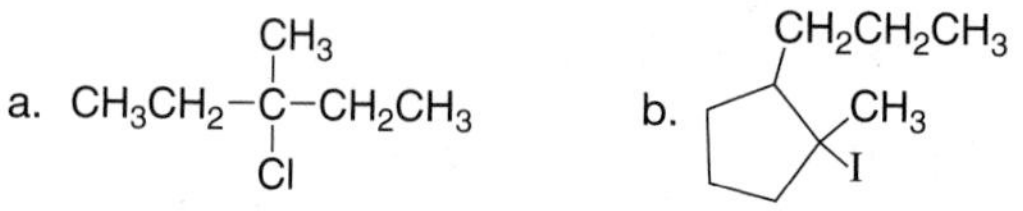
a.
b.

Problem 8.15 How does each of the following changes affect the rate of an E1 reaction?

a. doubling [RX]
b. doubling [B:]
c. changing the halide from $(CH_3)_3CBr$ to $CH_3CH_2CH_2Br$
d. changing the leaving group from Cl^- to Br^-
e. changing the solvent from DMSO to CH_3OH

8.7 S_N1 and E1 Reactions

S_N1 and E1 reactions have exactly the same first step—formation of a carbocation. They differ in what happens to the carbocation.

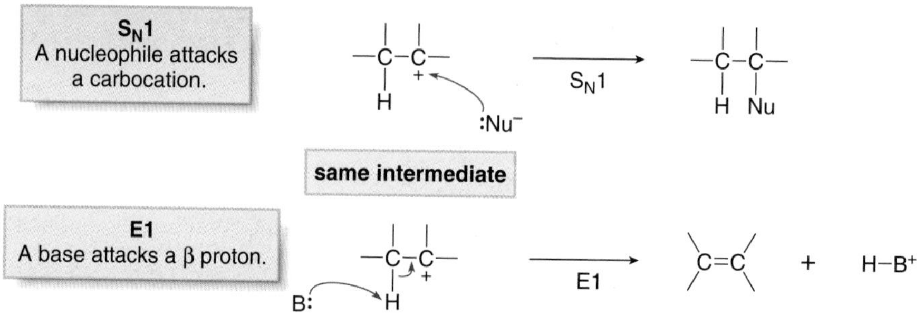
SN1
A nucleophile attacks a carbocation.
same intermediate
E1
A base attacks a β proton.
SN1
E1
H Nu
:Nu⁻
B:
H–B⁺

- **In an S_N1 reaction, a nucleophile attacks the carbocation, forming a substitution product.**
- **In an E1 reaction, a base removes a proton, forming a new π bond.**

The same conditions that favor substitution by an S_N1 mechanism also favor elimination by an E1 mechanism: a 3° alkyl halide as substrate, a weak nucleophile or base as reagent, and a polar protic solvent. As a result, both reactions usually occur in the same reaction mixture to afford a mixture of products, as illustrated in Sample Problem 8.2.

Sample Problem 8.2 Draw the S_N1 and E1 products formed in the reaction of $(CH_3)_3CBr$ with H_2O.

Solution

The first step in both reactions is heterolysis of the C–Br bond to form a **carbocation.**

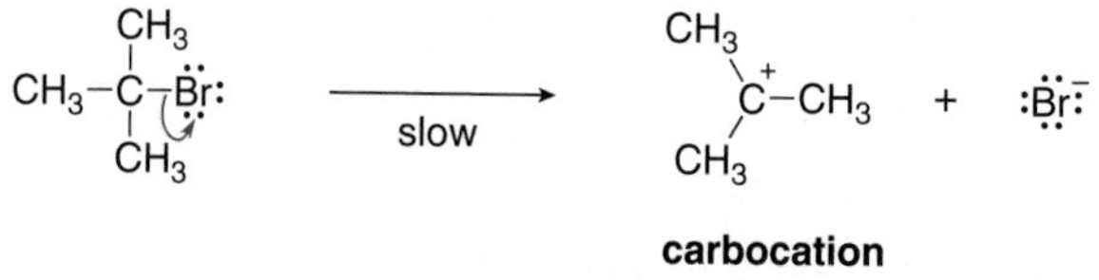
slow
carbocation

Reaction of the carbocation with H_2O as a nucleophile affords the substitution product (Reaction [1]). Alternatively, H_2O acts as a base to remove a proton, affording the elimination product (Reaction [2]). **Two products are formed.**

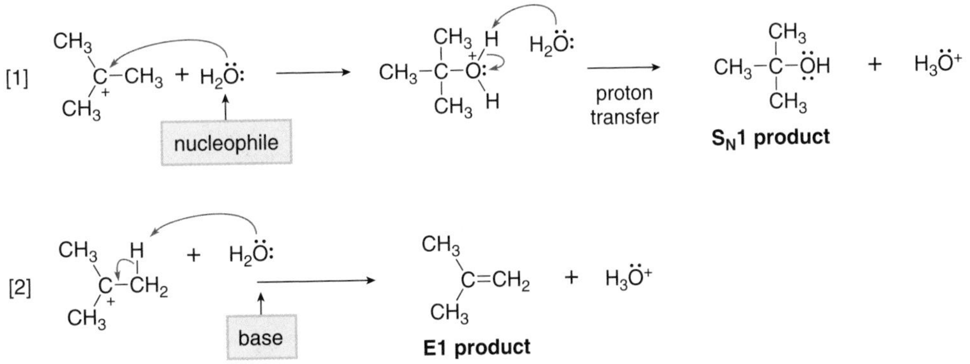

Because E1 reactions often occur with a competing S_N1 reaction, **E1 reactions of alkyl halides are *much less useful* than E2 reactions.**

Problem 8.16 Draw both the S_N1 and E1 products of each reaction.

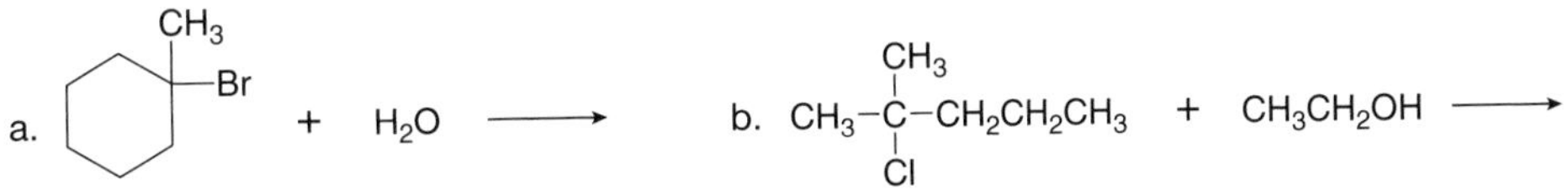

8.8 Stereochemistry of the E2 Reaction

Although the E2 reaction does not produce products with tetrahedral stereogenic centers, its transition state consists of four atoms that react at the same time, and they react only if they possess a particular stereochemical arrangement.

8.8A General Stereochemical Features

The transition state of an E2 reaction consists of **four atoms** from the alkyl halide—one hydrogen atom, two carbon atoms, and the leaving group (X)—**all aligned in a plane.** There are two ways for the C–H and C–X bonds to be coplanar.

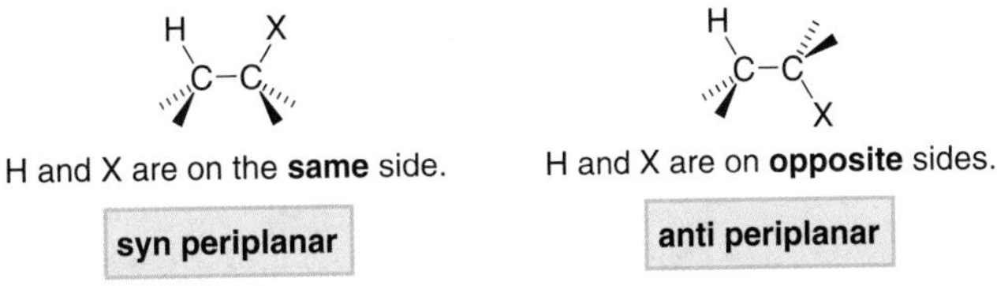

The dihedral angle for the C–H and C–X bonds equals 0° for the syn periplanar arrangement and 180° for the anti periplanar arrangement.

- **The H and X atoms can be oriented on the same side of the molecule. This geometry is called *syn periplanar.***
- **The H and X atoms can be oriented on opposite sides of the molecule. This geometry is called *anti periplanar.***

All evidence suggests that **E2 elimination occurs most often in the anti periplanar geometry.** This arrangement allows the molecule to react in the lower energy *staggered* conformation. It also allows two electron-rich species, the incoming base and the departing leaving group, to be farther away from each other, as illustrated in Figure 8.7.

Figure 8.7
Two possible geometries for the E2 reaction

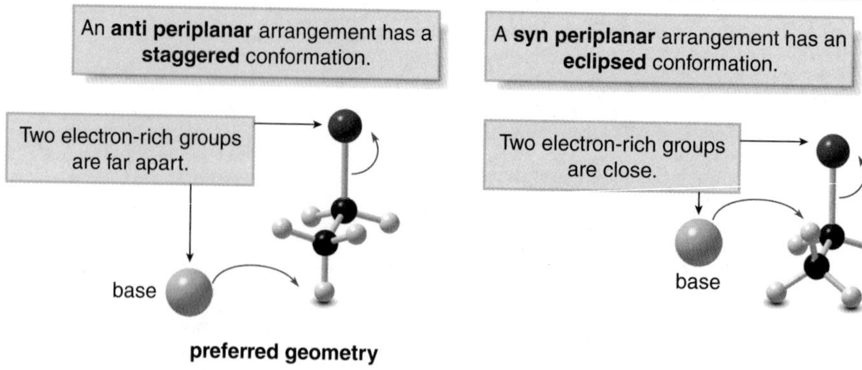
An **anti periplanar** arrangement has a **staggered** conformation.
A **syn periplanar** arrangement has an **eclipsed** conformation.
Two electron-rich groups are far apart.
Two electron-rich groups are close.
base
base
preferred geometry

Anti periplanar geometry is the preferred arrangement for any alkyl halide undergoing E2 elimination, regardless of whether it is cyclic or acyclic. This stereochemical requirement has important consequences for compounds containing six-membered rings.

Problem 8.17 Draw the anti periplanar geometry for the E2 reaction of $(CH_3)_2CHCH_2Br$ with base. Then draw the product that results after elimination of HBr.

Problem 8.18 Given that an E2 reaction proceeds with anti periplanar stereochemistry, draw the products of each elimination. The alkyl halides in (a) and (b) are diastereomers of each other. How are the products of these two reactions related? Recall from Section 3.2A that C_6H_5- is a phenyl group, a benzene ring bonded to another group.

a. 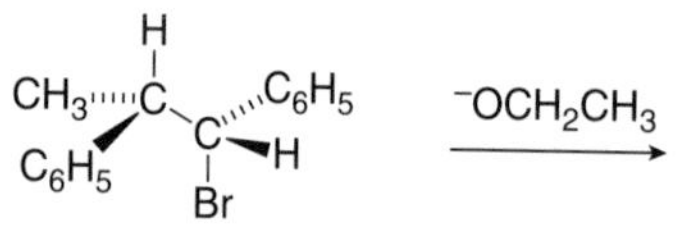
H
CH_3
C
C
C_6H_5
C_6H_5
H
Br
$^-OCH_2CH_3$

b. 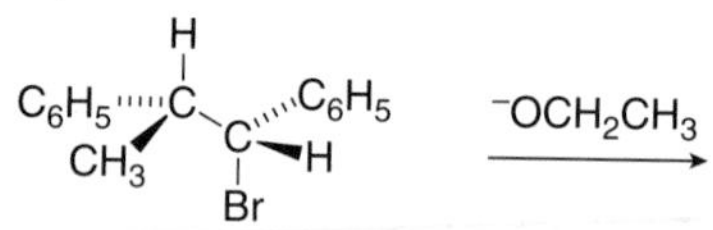
H
C_6H_5
C
C
C_6H_5
CH_3
H
Br
$^-OCH_2CH_3$

8.8B Anti Periplanar Geometry and Halocyclohexanes

Recall from Section 4.13 that cyclohexane exists as two chair conformations that rapidly interconvert, and that substituted cyclohexanes are more stable with substituents in the roomier equatorial position. Thus, chlorocyclohexane exists as two chair conformations, but **X** is preferred because the Cl group is equatorial.

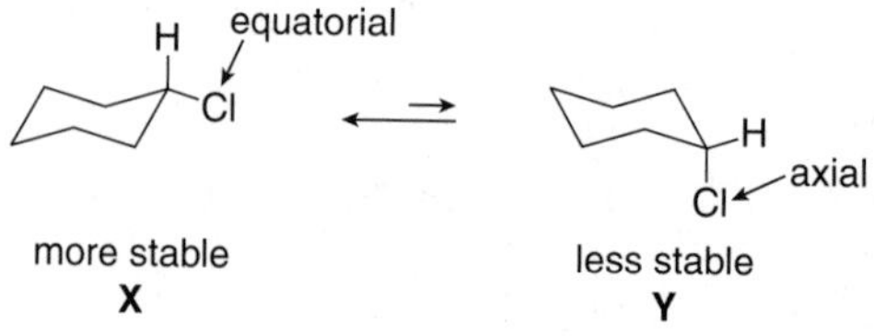
H
equatorial
Cl
H
axial
Cl
more stable
X
less stable
Y
chlorocyclohexane

For E2 elimination, **the C–Cl bond must be anti periplanar to a C–H bond on a β carbon,** and this occurs only when the H and Cl atoms are both in the **axial** position. This requirement for **trans diaxial geometry** means that E2 elimination must occur from the less stable conformation **Y,** as shown in Figure 8.8.

Figure 8.8
The trans diaxial geometry for the E2 elimination in chlorocyclohexane

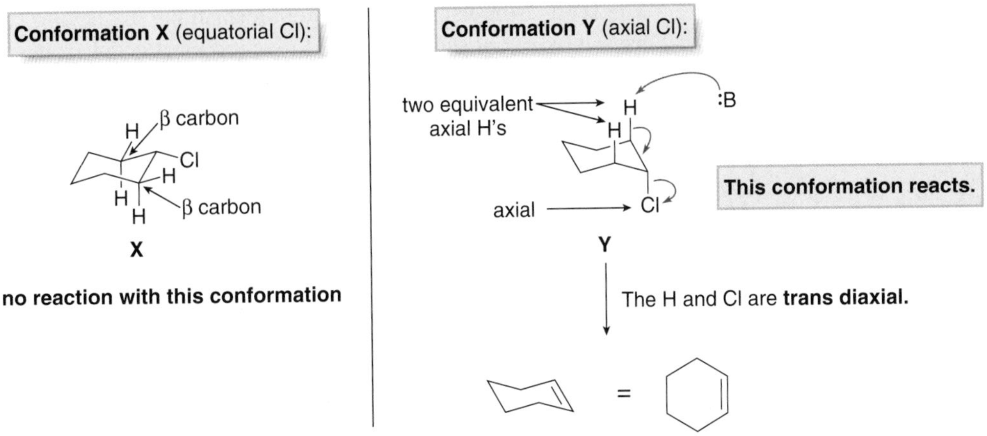

- In conformation **X** (**equatorial** Cl group), a β C–H bond and a C–Cl bond are never anti periplanar; therefore, no E2 elimination can occur.
- In conformation **Y** (**axial** Cl group), a β C–H bond and a C–Cl bond are **trans diaxial;** therefore, E2 elimination occurs.

Sometimes this rigid stereochemical requirement affects the regioselectivity of the E2 reaction of substituted cyclohexanes. Dehydrohalogenation of *cis*- and *trans*-1-chloro-2-methylcyclohexane via an E2 mechanism illustrates this phenomenon.

cis-1-chloro-2-methyl-cyclohexane   *trans*-1-chloro-2-methyl-cyclohexane

The **cis isomer** exists as two conformations (**A** and **B**), each of which has one group axial and one group equatorial. E2 reaction must occur from conformation **B,** which contains an axial Cl atom.

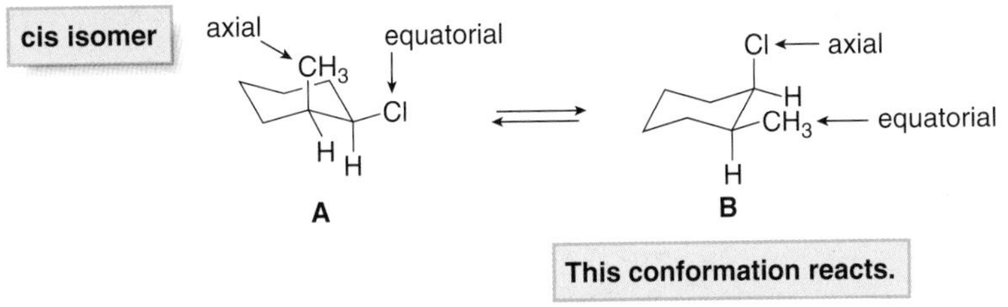

Because conformation **B** has two different axial β H atoms, labeled H_a and H_b, E2 reaction occurs in two different directions to afford two alkenes. **The major product contains the more stable trisubstituted double bond, as predicted by the Zaitsev rule.**

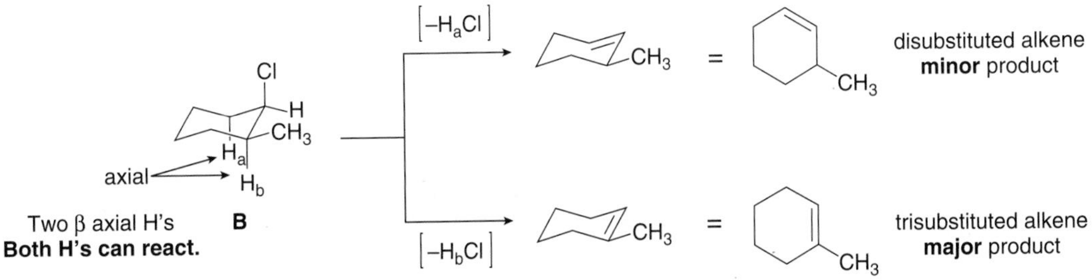

The **trans isomer** exists as two conformations, **C,** having two equatorial substituents, and **D,** having two axial substituents. E2 reaction must occur from conformation **D,** which contains an axial Cl atom.

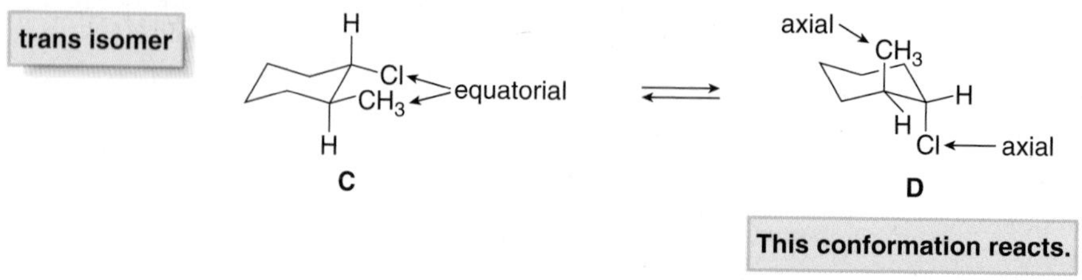

Because conformation **D** has **only one axial β H,** E2 reaction occurs in only one direction to afford a **single product,** having the disubstituted double bond. This is *not* predicted by the Zaitsev rule. E2 reaction requires H and Cl to be trans and diaxial, and with the trans isomer, this is possible only when the less stable alkene is formed as product.

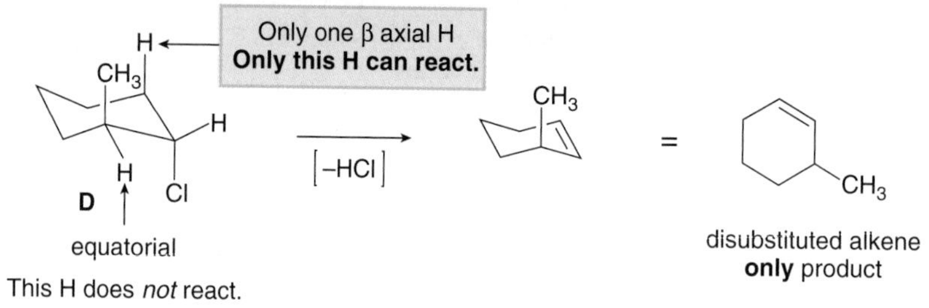

- **In conclusion, with substituted cyclohexanes, E2 elimination must occur with a trans diaxial arrangement of H and X, and as a result of this requirement, the more substituted alkene is not necessarily the major product.**

Sample Problem 8.3

Draw the major E2 elimination product formed from the following alkyl halide.

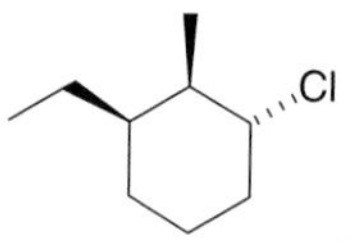

Solution

To draw the elimination products, locate the β carbons and look for H atoms that are trans to the leaving group. The given alkyl chloride has two different β carbons, labeled β_1 and β_2. Elimination can occur only when the leaving group (Cl) and a H atom on the β carbon are trans.

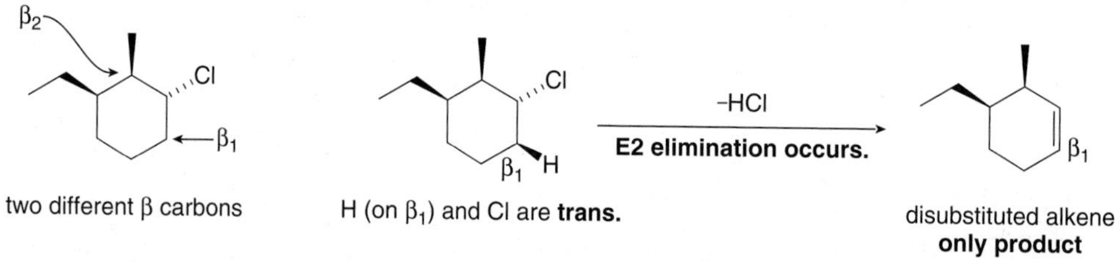

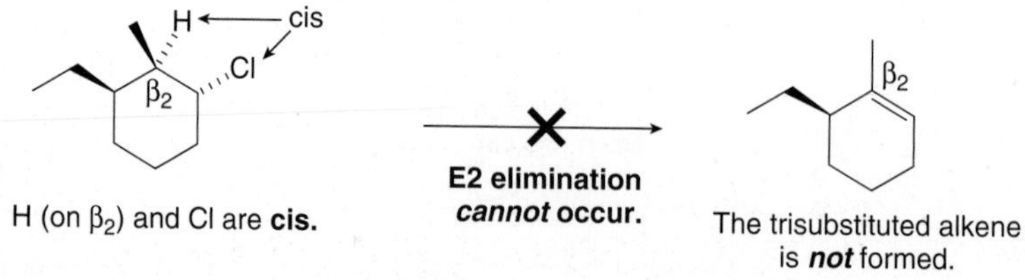

Since the β_1 C has a H atom trans to Cl, E2 elimination occurs to form a disubstituted alkene. Since there is no trans H on the β_2 C, E2 elimination cannot occur in this direction, and the more stable trisubstituted alkene is *not* formed. Although this result is not predicted by the Zaitsev rule, it is consistent with the requirement that the H and X atoms in an E2 elimination must be located trans to each other.

Problem 8.19 Draw the major E2 elimination products from each of the following alkyl halides.

a. 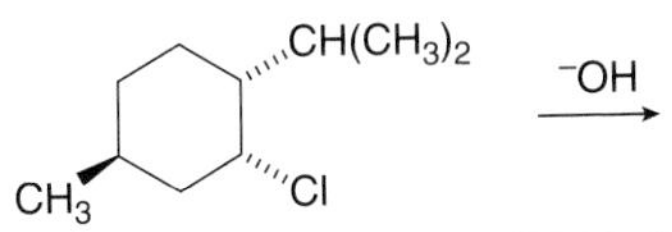

b. 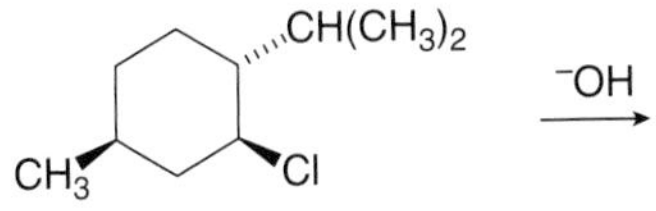

Problem 8.20 Explain why *cis*-1-chloro-2-methylcyclohexane undergoes E2 elimination much faster than its trans isomer.

8.9 When Is the Mechanism E1 or E2?

Given a particular starting material and base, how do we know whether a reaction occurs by the E1 or E2 mechanism?

Because the rate of *both* the E1 and E2 reactions increases as the number of R groups on the carbon with the leaving group increases, you cannot use the identity of the alkyl halide to decide which elimination mechanism occurs. This makes determining the mechanisms for substitution and elimination very different processes.

- **The strength of the base is the most important factor in determining the mechanism for elimination. Strong bases favor the E2 mechanism. Weak bases favor the E1 mechanism.**

Table 8.4 compares the E1 and E2 mechanisms.

Problem 8.21 Which mechanism, E1 or E2, will occur in each reaction?

a. $CH_3-C(CH_3)(Cl)-CH_3 + {}^{-}OCH_3 \longrightarrow$

b. 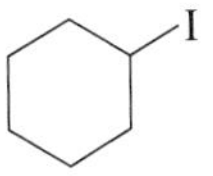 $+ H_2O \longrightarrow$

c. 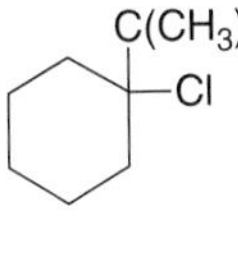 $+ CH_3OH \longrightarrow$

d. $CH_3CH_2Br + {}^{-}OC(CH_3)_3 \longrightarrow$

Table 8.4 A Comparison of the E1 and E2 Mechanisms

Mechanism	Comment
E2 mechanism	• Much more common and useful • Favored by strong, negatively charged bases, especially ^{-}OH and ^{-}OR • The reaction occurs with 1°, 2°, and 3° alkyl halides. Order of reactivity: $R_3CX > R_2CHX > RCH_2X$.
E1 mechanism	• Much less useful because a mixture of S_N1 and E1 products usually results • Favored by weaker, neutral bases, such as H_2O and ROH • This mechanism does not occur with 1° RX because they form highly unstable 1° carbocations.

8.10 E2 Reactions and Alkyne Synthesis

Recall from Section 1.10C that the carbon–carbon triple bond of alkynes consists of one σ and two π bonds.

A single elimination reaction produces the π bond of an alkene. Two consecutive elimination reactions produce the two π bonds of an alkyne.

One elimination reaction is needed. **Two** elimination reactions are needed.

- **Alkynes are prepared by two successive dehydrohalogenation reactions.**

Two elimination reactions are needed to remove two moles of HX from a **dihalide** as substrate. Two different starting materials can be used.

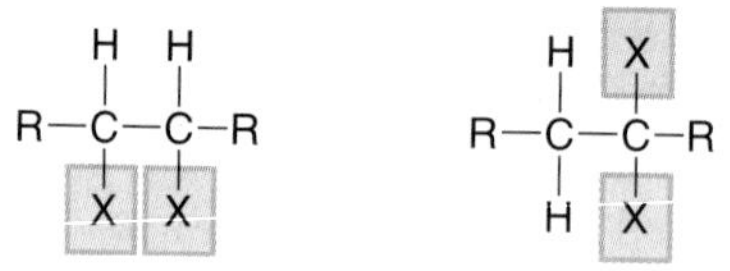

vicinal dihalide geminal dihalide

- A **vicinal dihalide** has two X atoms on *adjacent* carbon atoms.
- A **geminal dihalide** has two X atoms on the *same* carbon atom.

The word *geminal* comes from the Latin *geminus,* meaning *twin.*

Equations [1] and [2] illustrate how two moles of HX can be removed from these dihalides with base. Two equivalents of strong base are used and each step follows an E2 mechanism.

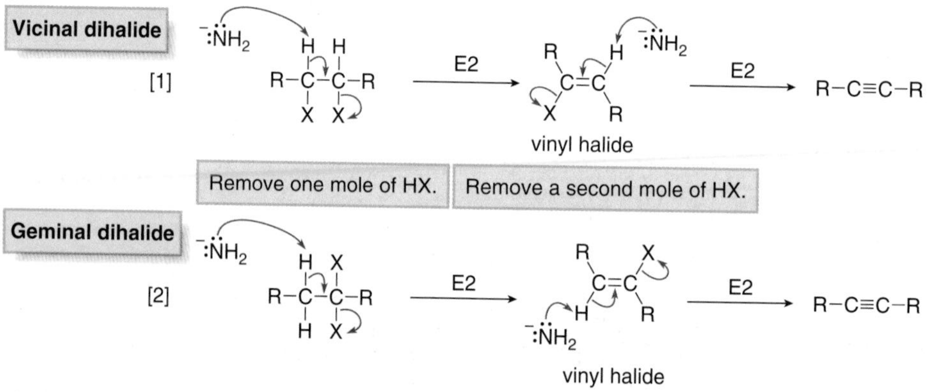

The relative strength of C–H bonds depends on the hybridization of the carbon atom: $sp > sp^2 > sp^3$. For more information, review Section 1.11B.

Stronger bases are needed to synthesize alkynes by dehydrohalogenation than are needed to synthesize alkenes. The typical base is **amide ($^-NH_2$),** used as the sodium salt $NaNH_2$ (sodium amide). $KOC(CH_3)_3$ can also be used with DMSO as solvent. Because DMSO is a polar aprotic solvent, the anionic base is not well solvated, thus **increasing its basicity** and making it strong enough to remove two equivalents of HX. Examples are given in Figure 8.9.

The strongly basic conditions needed for alkyne synthesis result from the difficulty of removing the second equivalent of HX from the intermediate vinyl halide, RCH=C(R)X. Since H and X are both bonded to sp^2 hybridized carbons, these bonds are shorter and stronger than the sp^3 hybridized C–H and C–X bonds of an alkyl halide, necessitating the use of a stronger base.

Figure 8.9 Examples of dehydrohalogenation of dihalides to afford alkynes

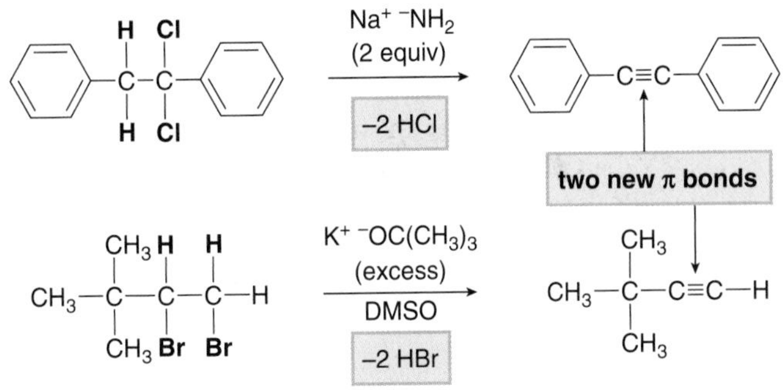

Problem 8.22 Draw the alkynes formed in each reaction. Two equivalents of each base are used.

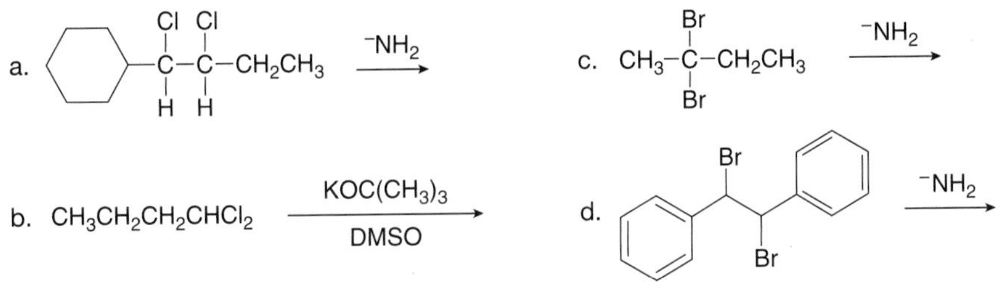

8.11 When Is the Reaction S_N1, S_N2, E1, or E2?

We have now considered two different kinds of reactions (substitution and elimination) and four different mechanisms (S_N1, S_N2, E1, and E2) that begin with one class of compounds (alkyl halides). How do we know if a given alkyl halide will undergo substitution or elimination with a given base or nucleophile, and by what mechanism?

Unfortunately, there is no easy answer, and often mixtures of products result. Two generalizations help to determine whether substitution or elimination occurs.

[1] Good nucleophiles that are weak bases favor substitution over elimination.

Certain anions generally give products of substitution because they are good nucleophiles but weak bases. These include: **I^-, Br^-, HS^-, ^-CN,** and **CH_3COO^-.**

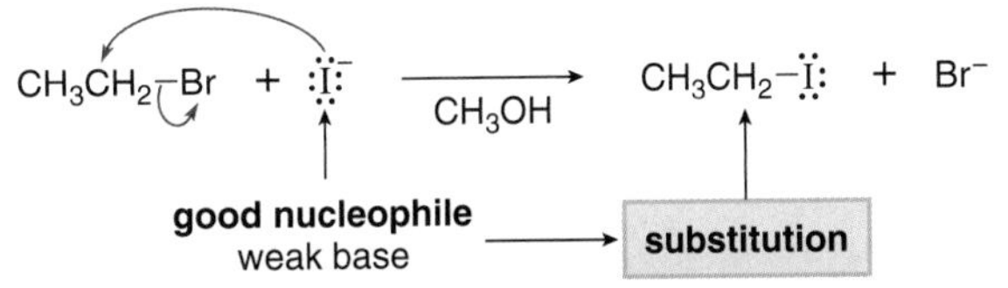

[2] Bulky, nonnucleophilic bases favor elimination over substitution.

$KOC(CH_3)_3$, DBU, and DBN are too sterically hindered to attack a tetravalent carbon, but are able to remove a small proton, favoring elimination over substitution.

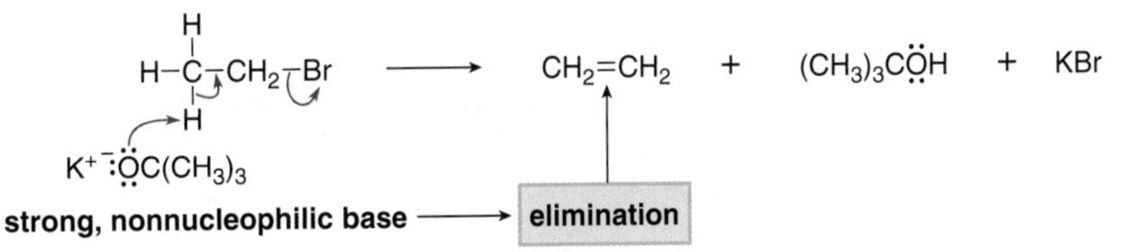

Most often, however, we will have to rely on other criteria to predict the outcome of these reactions. To determine the product of a reaction with an alkyl halide:

[1] Classify the alkyl halide as 1°, 2°, or 3°.

[2] Classify the base or nucleophile as strong, weak, or bulky.

Predicting the substitution and elimination products of a reaction can then be organized by the type of alkyl halide, as shown in Figure 8.10.

Figure 8.10 **Determining whether an alkyl halide reacts by an S_N1, S_N2, E1, or E2 mechanism**

[1] 3° Alkyl halides (R_3CX react by all mechanisms except S_N2.)

- With strong bases
  - **Elimination occurs by an E2 mechanism.**
  - Rationale: A strong base or nucleophile favors an S_N2 or E2 mechanism, but 3° halides are too sterically hindered to undergo an S_N2 reaction, so only E2 elimination occurs.
  - Example:

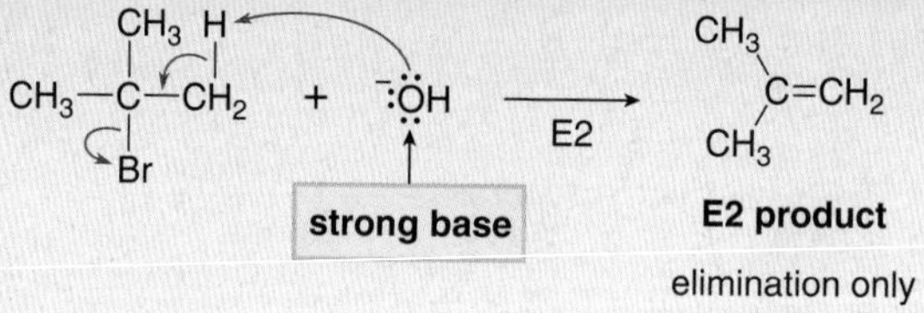

- With weak nucleophiles or bases
  - **A mixture of S_N1 and E1 products results.**
  - Rationale: A weak base or nucleophile favors S_N1 and E1 mechanisms, and both occur.
  - Example:

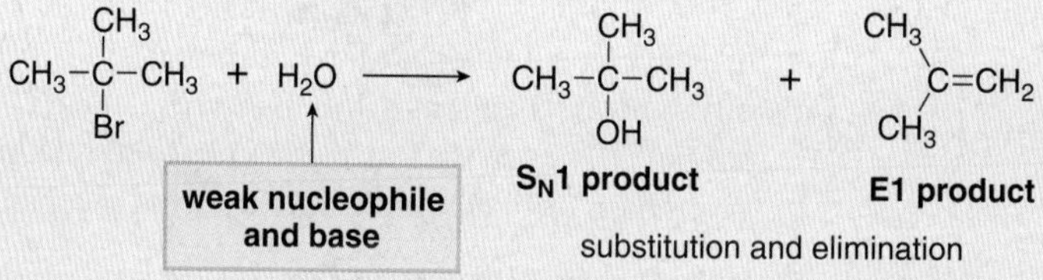

[2] 1° Alkyl halides (RCH_2X react by S_N2 and E2 mechanisms.)

- With strong nucleophiles
  - **Substitution occurs by an S_N2 mechanism.**
  - Rationale: A strong base or nucleophile favors S_N2 or E2, but 1° halides are the least reactive halide type in elimination; therefore, only an S_N2 reaction occurs.
  - Example:

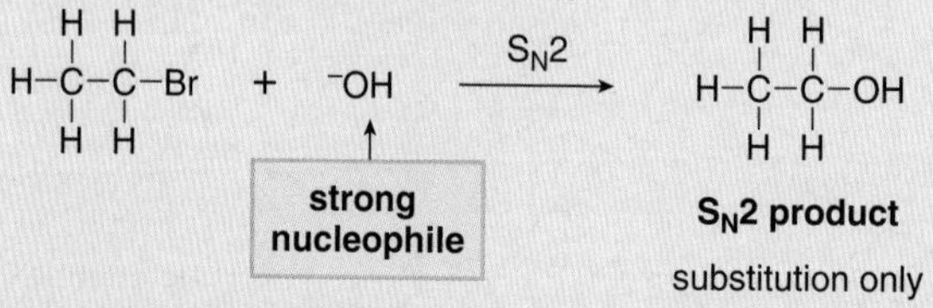

- With strong, sterically hindered bases
  - **Elimination occurs by an E2 mechanism.**
  - Rationale: A strong, sterically hindered base cannot act as a nucleophile, so elimination occurs and the mechanism is E2.
  - Example:

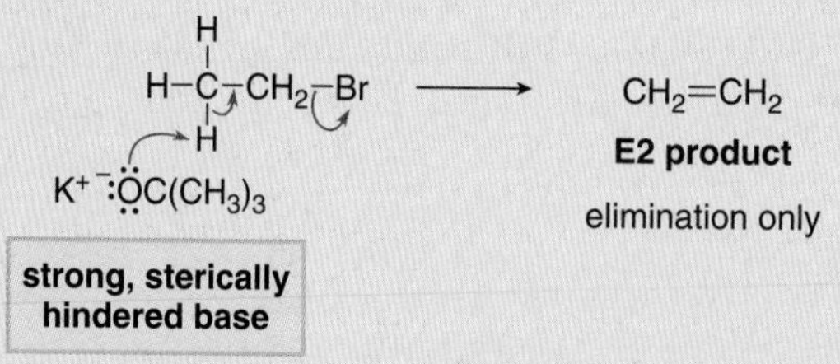

[3] 2° Alkyl halides (R_2CHX react by all mechanisms.)

- With strong bases and nucleophiles
  - **A mixture of S_N2 and E2 products results.**
  - Rationale: A strong base that is also a strong nucleophile gives a mixture of S_N2 and E2 products.
  - Example:

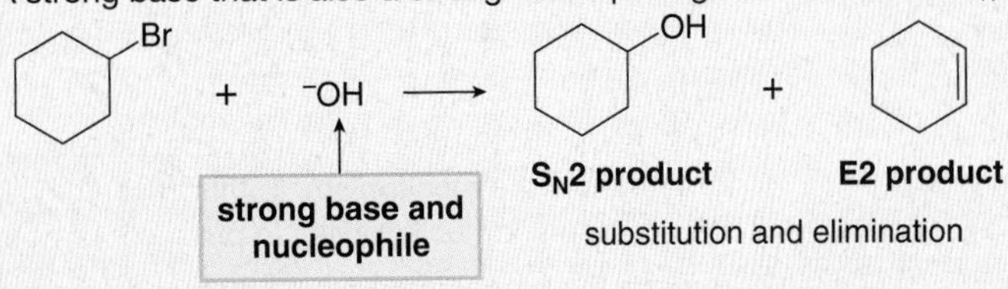

- With strong, sterically hindered bases
  - **Elimination occurs by an E2 mechanism.**
  - Rationale: A strong, sterically hindered base cannot act as a nucleophile, so elimination occurs and the mechanism is E2.
  - Example:

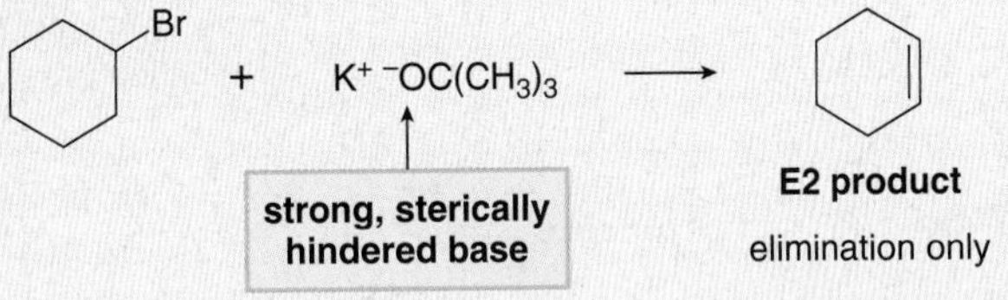

- With weak nucleophiles or bases
  - **A mixture of S_N1 and E1 products results.**
  - Rationale: A weak base or nucleophile favors S_N1 and E1 mechanisms, and both occur.
  - Example:

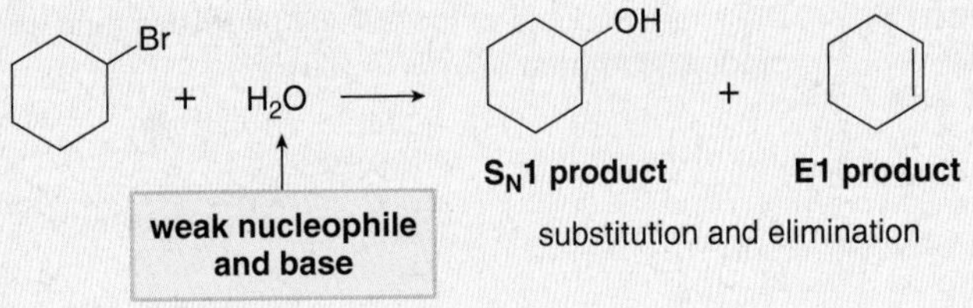

Sample Problems 8.4–8.6 illustrate how to apply the information in Figure 8.10 to specific alkyl halides.

Sample Problem 8.4

Draw the products of the following reaction.

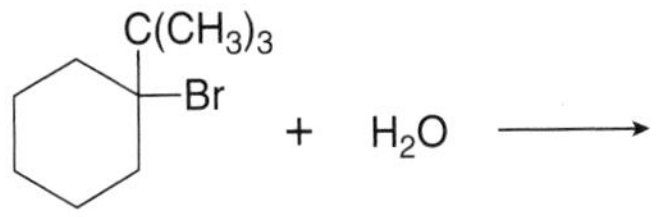

Solution

[1] Classify the halide as 1°, 2°, or 3° and the reagent as a strong or weak base (and nucleophile) to determine the mechanism. In this case, the alkyl halide is 3° and the reagent (H_2O) is a weak base and nucleophile, so products of both S_N1 and E1 mechanisms are formed.

[2] To draw the products of substitution and elimination:

S_N1 product

Substitute the nucleophile (H_2O) for the leaving group (Br^-), and draw the neutral product after loss of a proton.

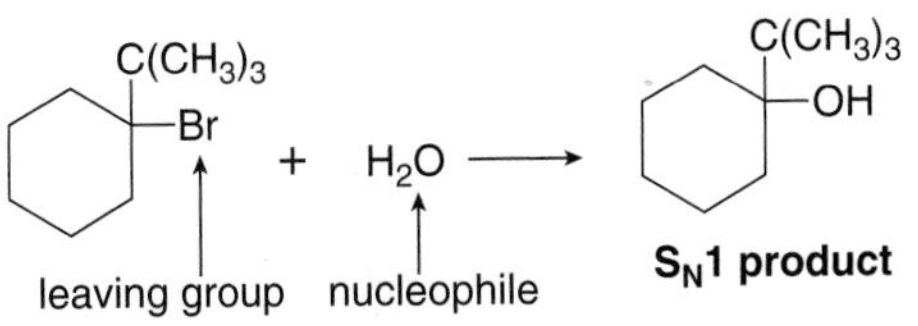

E1 product

Remove the elements of H and Br from the α and β carbons. There are two identical β C atoms with H atoms, so only one elimination product is possible.

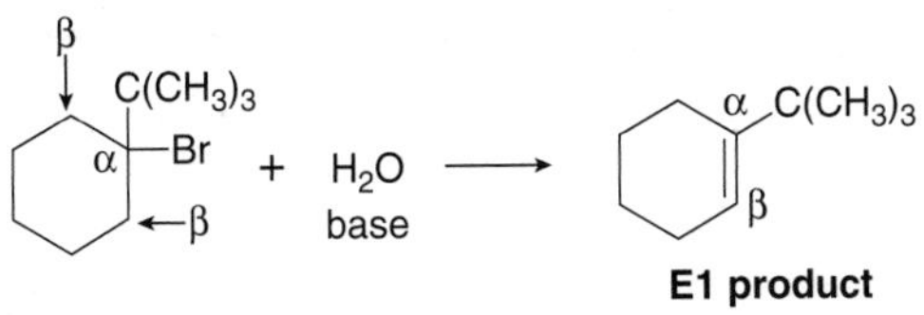

Sample Problem 8.5 Draw the products of the following reaction.

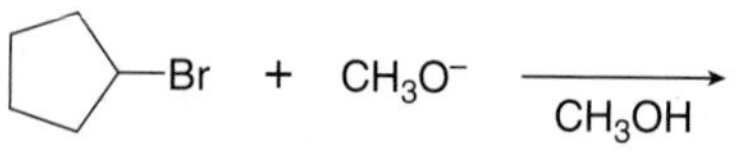

Br
+ CH3O−
CH3OH

Solution

[1] Classify the halide as 1°, 2°, or 3° and the reagent as a strong or weak base (and nucleophile) to determine the mechanism. In this case, the alkyl halide is 2° and the reagent (CH_3O^-) is a strong base and nucleophile, so products of both **S_N2** and **E2** mechanisms are formed.

[2] To draw the products of substitution and elimination:

S_N2 product	**E2 product**
Substitute the nucleophile (CH_3O^-) for the leaving group (Br^-).	Remove the elements of H and Br from the α and β carbons. There are two identical β C atoms with H atoms, so only one elimination product is possible.

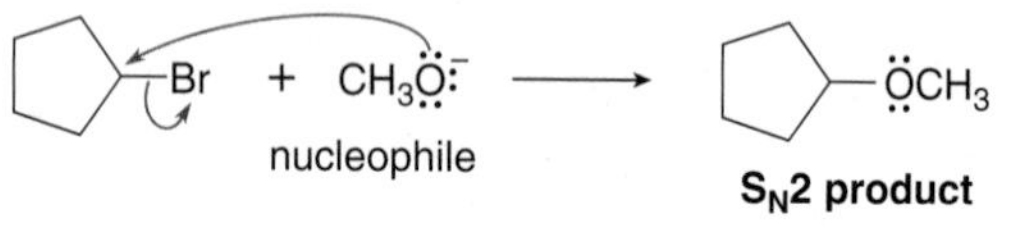

Br
+ CH3O:
nucleophile
OCH3
SN2 product

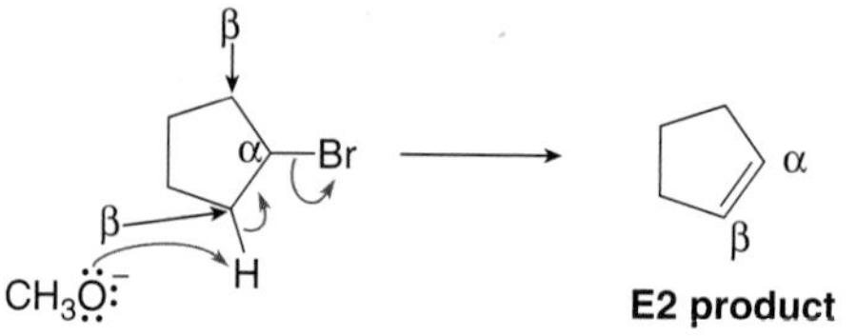

β
α
Br
β
H
CH3O:
α
β
E2 product

Sample Problem 8.6 Draw the products of the following reaction, and include the mechanism showing how each product is formed.

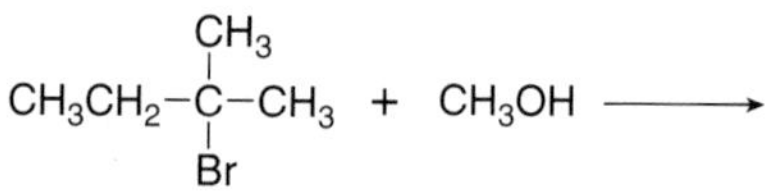

CH3
CH3CH2–C–CH3 + CH3OH
Br

Solution

[1] Classify the halide as 1°, 2°, or 3° and the reagent as a strong or weak base (and nucleophile) to determine the mechanism. In this case, the alkyl halide is 3° and the reagent (CH_3OH) is a weak base and nucleophile, so products of both **S_N1** and **E1** mechanisms are formed.

[2] Draw the steps of the mechanisms to give the products. Both mechanisms begin with the same first step: loss of the leaving group to form a carbocation.

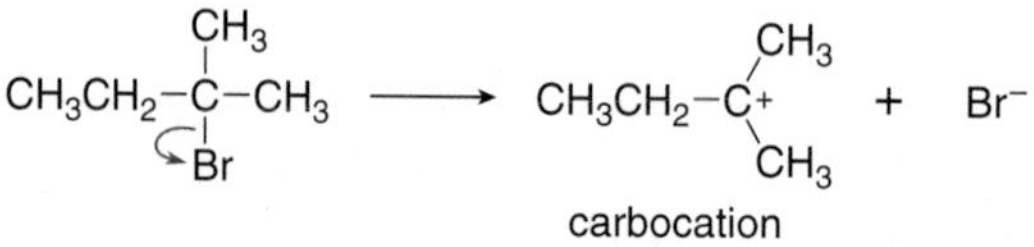

CH3
CH3CH2–C–CH3
Br
CH3
CH3CH2–C+
CH3
+ Br−
carbocation

- **For S_N1:** The carbocation reacts with a nucleophile. Nucleophilic attack of CH_3OH on the carbocation generates a positively charged intermediate that loses a proton to afford the neutral S_N1 product.

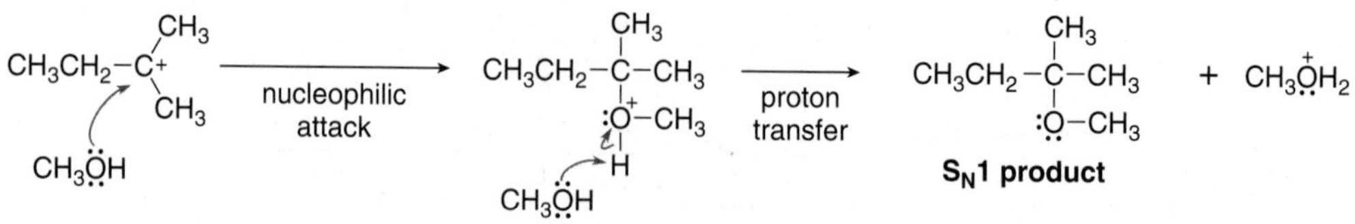

CH3
CH3CH2–C+
CH3
CH3OH
nucleophilic
attack
CH3
CH3CH2–C–CH3
:O–CH3
H
CH3OH
proton
transfer
CH3
CH3CH2–C–CH3
:O–CH3
SN1 product
+ CH3OH2

- **For E1:** The carbocation reacts with a base (CH_3OH or Br^-). Two different products of elimination can form because the carbocation has two different β carbons.

Proton removal from the β_1 C

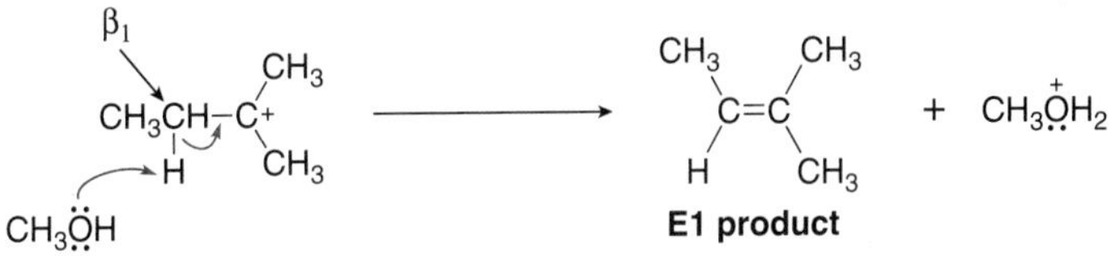

Proton removal from the β_2 C

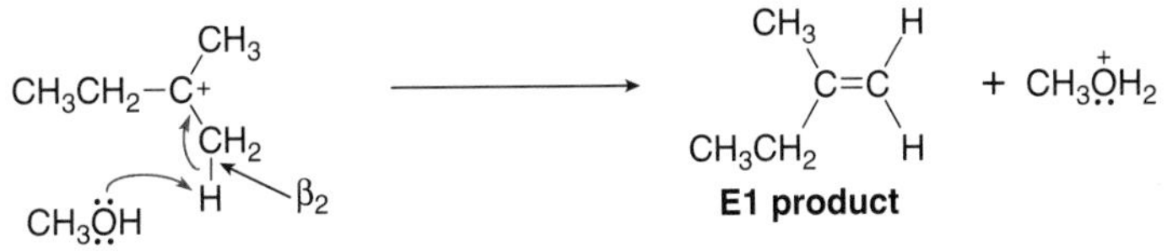

In this problem, three products are formed: one from an S_N1 reaction and two from E1 reactions.

Problem 8.23 Draw the products in each reaction.

a. 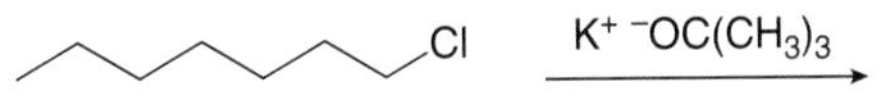

b. 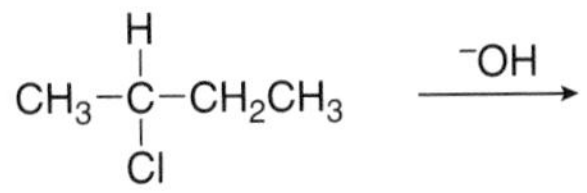

c. 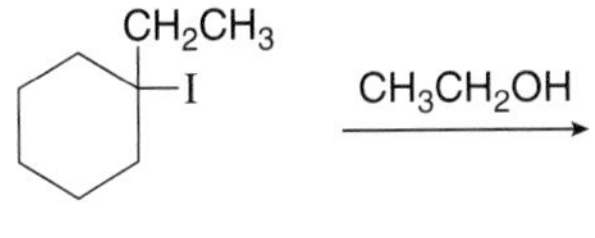

d. 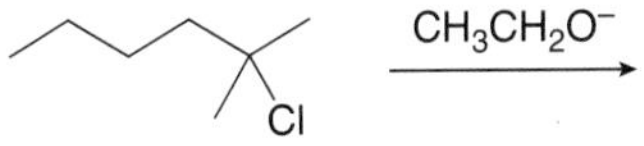

Problem 8.24 Draw a stepwise mechanism for the following reaction.

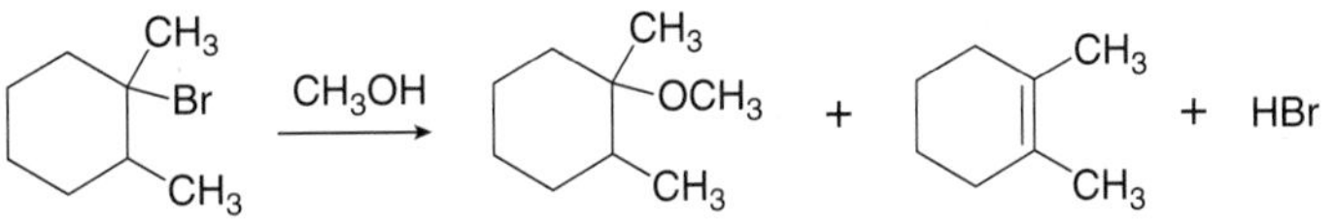

KEY CONCEPTS

Alkyl Halides and Elimination Reactions

A Comparison Between Nucleophilic Substitution and β Elimination

Nucleophilic substitution—A nucleophile attacks a carbon atom (7.6).

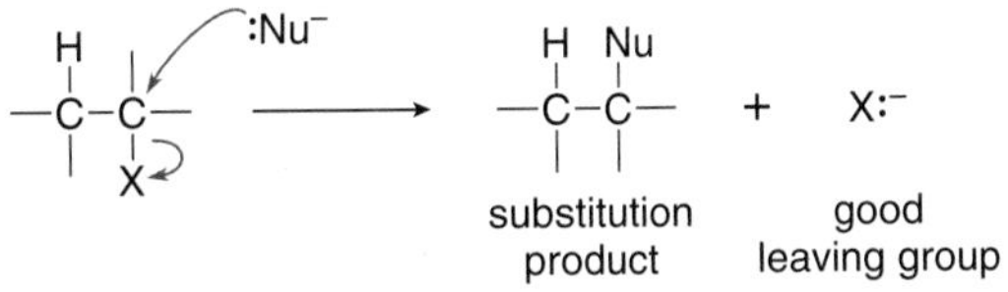

β Elimination—A base attacks a proton (8.1).

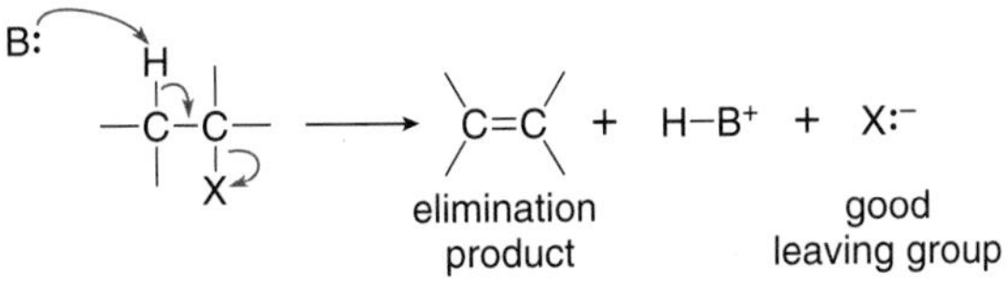

Similarities	Differences
• In both reactions RX acts as an electrophile, reacting with an electron-rich reagent.	• In substitution, a nucleophile attacks a single carbon atom.
• Both reactions require a **good leaving group X:⁻** that can accept the electron density in the C–X bond.	• In elimination, a Brønsted–Lowry base removes a proton to form a π bond, and two carbons are involved in the reaction.

The Importance of the Base in E2 and E1 Reactions (8.9)

The strength of the base determines the mechanism of elimination.

- Strong bases favor E2 reactions.
- Weak bases favor E1 reactions.

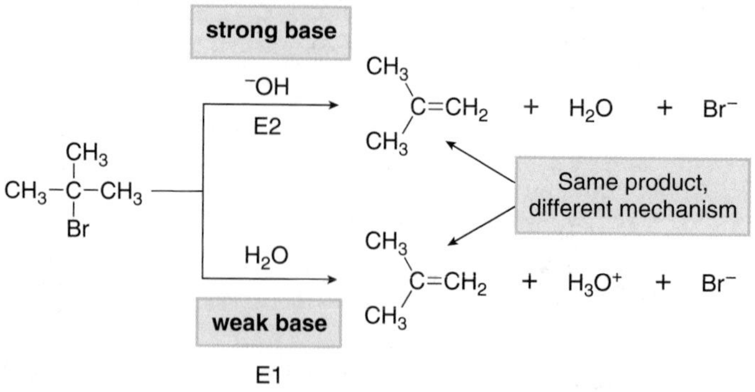

E1 and E2 Mechanisms Compared

	E2 mechanism	E1 mechanism
Mechanism	• One step (8.4B)	• Two steps (8.6B)
Alkyl halide	• Rate: $R_3CX > R_2CHX > RCH_2X$ (8.4C)	• Rate: $R_3CX > R_2CHX > RCH_2X$ (8.6C)
Rate equation	• Rate = k[RX][B:]	• Rate = k[RX]
	• Second-order kinetics (8.4A)	• First-order kinetics (8.6A)
Stereochemistry	• Anti periplanar arrangement of H and X (8.8)	• Trigonal planar carbocation intermediate (8.6B)
Base	• Favored by strong bases (8.4B)	• Favored by weak bases (8.6C)
Leaving group	• Better leaving group ⇢ faster reaction (8.4B)	• Better leaving group ⇢ faster reaction (Table 8.3)
Solvent	• Favored by polar aprotic solvents (8.4B)	• Favored by polar protic solvents (Table 8.3)
Product	• More substituted alkene favored (Zaitsev rule, 8.5)	• More substituted alkene favored (Zaitsev rule, 8.6C)

Summary Chart on the Four Mechanisms: S_N1, S_N2, E1, or E2

Alkyl halide type	Conditions		Mechanism
1° RCH_2X	strong nucleophile	⇢	**S_N2**
	strong bulky base	⇢	**E2**
2° R_2CHX	strong base and nucleophile	⇢	**S_N2 + E2**
	strong bulky base	⇢	**E2**
	weak base and nucleophile	⇢	**S_N1 + E1**
3° R_3CX	weak base and nucleophile	⇢	**S_N1 + E1**
	strong base	⇢	**E2**

PROBLEMS

Problems Using Three-Dimensional Models

8.25 Rank the alkenes shown in the ball-and-stick models (**A–C**) in order of increasing stability.

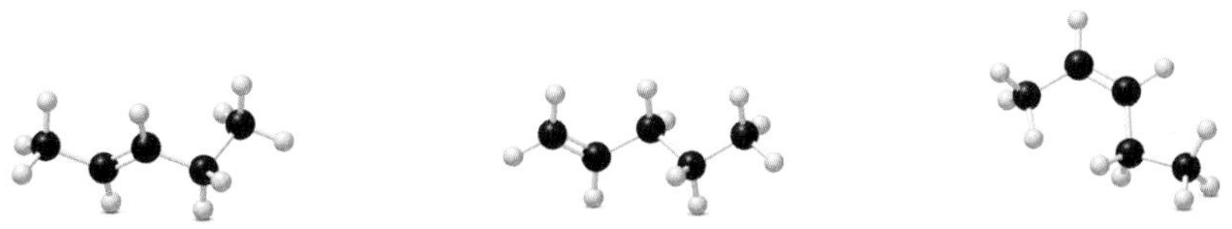

A **B** **C**

8.26 Name each compound and decide which stereoisomer will react faster in an E2 elimination reaction. Explain your choice.

D **E**

8.27 What is the major E2 elimination product formed from each alkyl halide?

a. 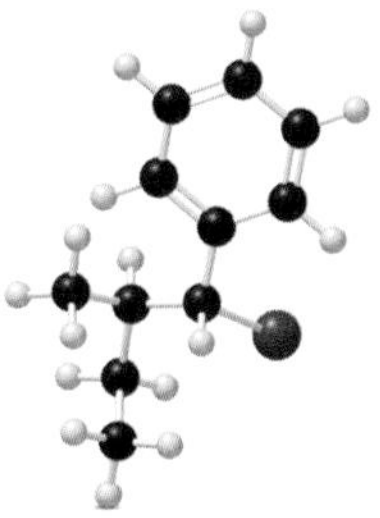

b. 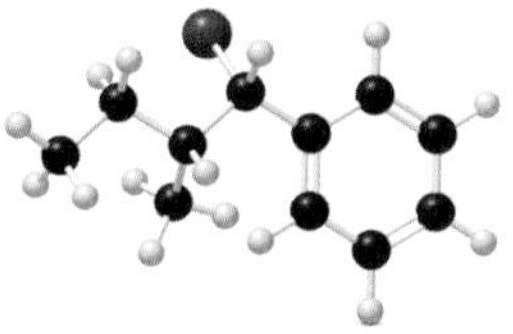

General Elimination

8.28 Draw all possible constitutional isomers formed by dehydrohalogenation of each alkyl halide.

a. $CH_3CH_2CH_2CH_2CH_2CH_2Br$

b. 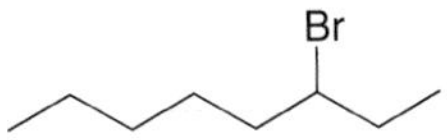

c. $CH_3CH_2CH(CH_3)CH(Cl)CH_3$

d. 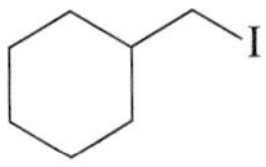

8.29 What alkyl halide forms each of the following alkenes as the *only* product in an elimination reaction?

a. $CH_2{=}CHCH_2CH_2CH_3$

b. $(CH_3)_2CHCH{=}CH_2$

c. 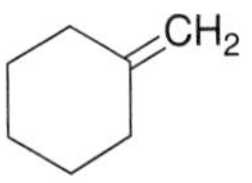

d. 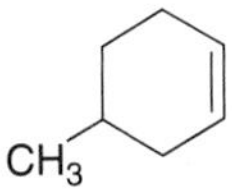

e. 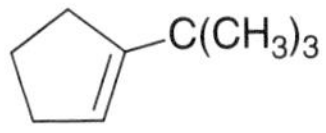

Alkenes

8.30 Which double bonds in the following natural products can exhibit stereoisomerism? Nerolidol is isolated from the Angel's trumpet plant, and caryophyllene is present in hemp.

a. 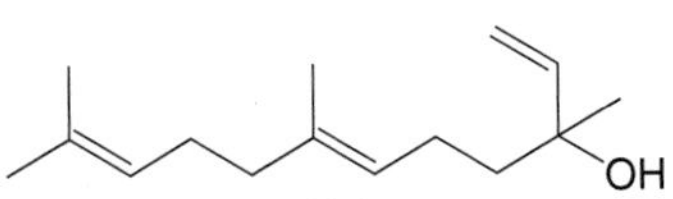

nerolidol

b. 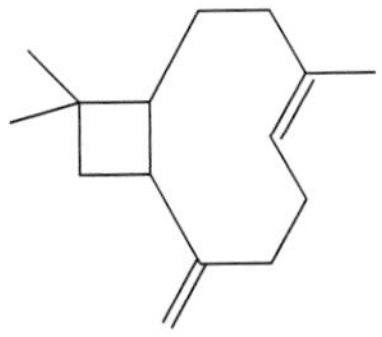

caryophyllene

8.31 Label each pair of alkenes as constitutional isomers, stereoisomers, or identical.

a. 

b. 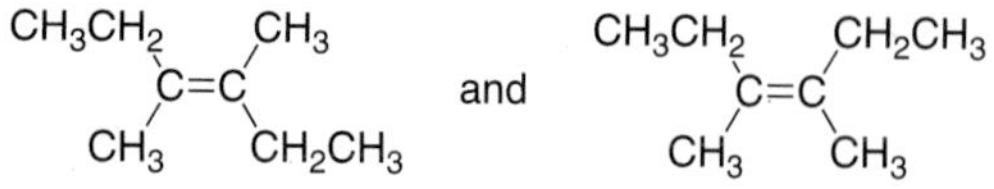

c. 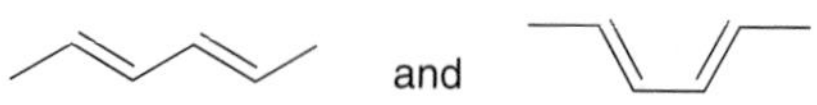

d. 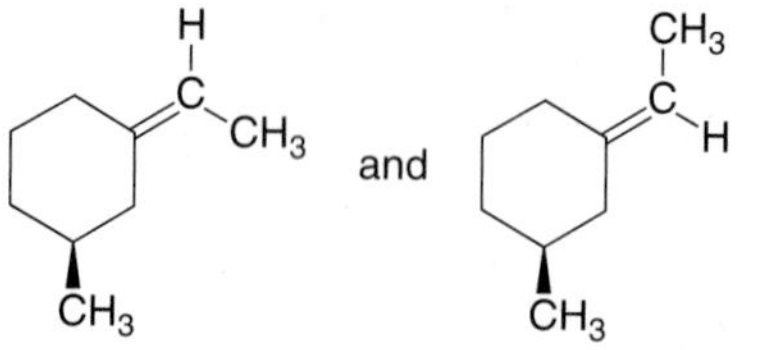

8.32 $PGF_{2\alpha}$ is a prostaglandin, a group of compounds that are responsible for inflammation (Section 19.6). (a) How many tetrahedral stereogenic centers does $PGF_{2\alpha}$ contain? (b) How many double bonds can exist as cis and trans isomers? (c) Considering both double bonds and tetrahedral stereogenic centers, what is the maximum number of stereoisomers that can exist for $PGF_{2\alpha}$?

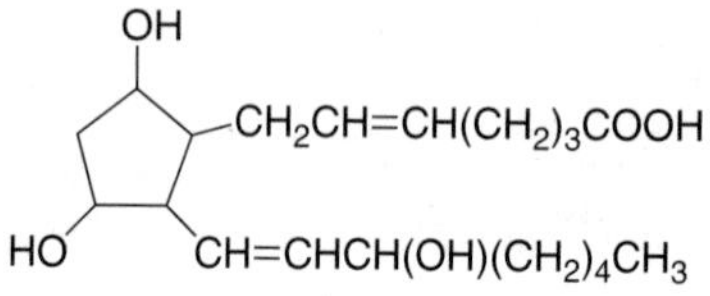

$PGF_{2\alpha}$

8.33 Rank the following alkenes in order of increasing stability: $CH_2{=}C(CH_3)CH_2CH_3$, $CH_2{=}CHCH(CH_3)_2$, and $(CH_3)_2C{=}CHCH_3$.

8.34 $\Delta H°$ values obtained for a series of similar reactions are one set of experimental data used to determine the relative stability of alkenes. Explain how the following data suggest that *cis*-2-butene is more stable than 1-butene (Section 12.3A).

$$\underset{\text{1-butene}}{CH_2{=}CHCH_2CH_3} + H_2 \longrightarrow CH_3CH_2CH_2CH_3 \quad \Delta H° = -127 \text{ kJ/mol}$$

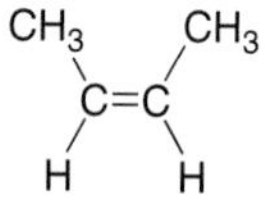 $+ H_2 \longrightarrow CH_3CH_2CH_2CH_3 \quad \Delta H° = -120$ kJ/mol

cis-2-butene

E2 Reaction

8.35 Draw all constitutional isomers formed in each E2 reaction and predict the major product using the Zaitsev rule.

a. 

b. 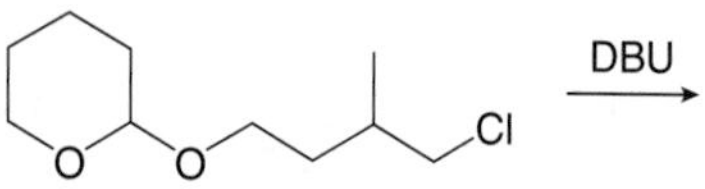

c. 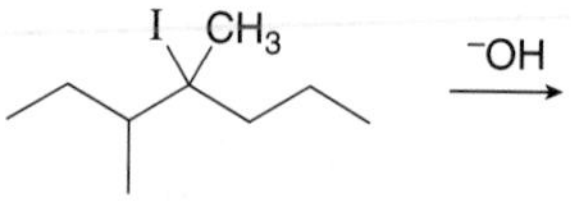

d. 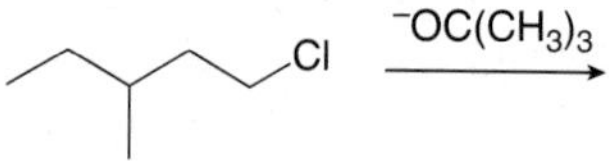

e. 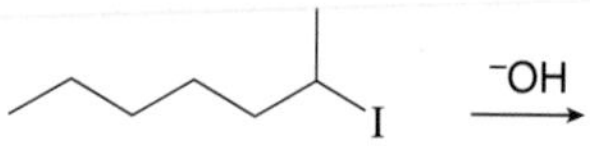

f. 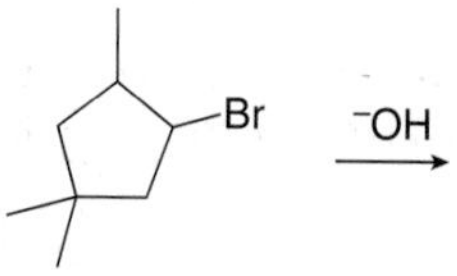

8.36 For each of the following alkenes, draw the structure of two different alkyl halides that yield the given alkene as the only product of dehydrohalogenation.

a. $(CH_3)_2C{=}CH_2$ b. 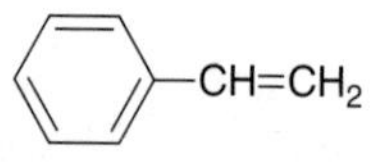 c. 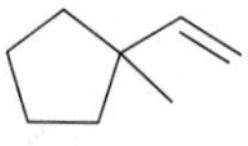

8.37 Explain why $(CH_3)_2CHCH(Br)CH_2CH_3$ reacts faster than $(CH_3)_2CHCH_2CH(Br)CH_3$ in an E2 reaction, even though both alkyl halides are 2°.

8.38 Consider the following E2 reaction.

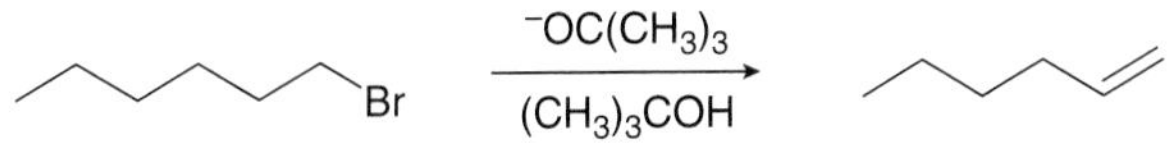

a. Draw the by-products of the reaction and use curved arrows to show the movement of electrons.

b. What happens to the reaction rate with each of the following changes? [1] The solvent is changed to DMF. [2] The concentration of $^{-}OC(CH_3)_3$ is decreased. [3] The base is changed to ^{-}OH. [4] The halide is changed to $CH_3CH_2CH_2CH_2CH(Br)CH_3$. [5] The leaving group is changed to I^-.

8.39 Dehydrohalogenation of 1-chloro-1-methylcyclopropane affords two alkenes (**A** and **B**) as products. Explain why **A** is the major product despite the fact that it contains the less substituted double bond.

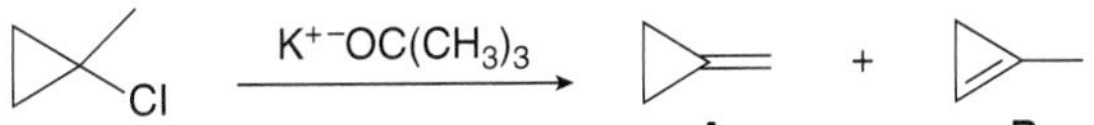

A **B**

1-chloro-1-methyl-cyclopropane

8.40 What is the major stereoisomer formed in each reaction?

a. 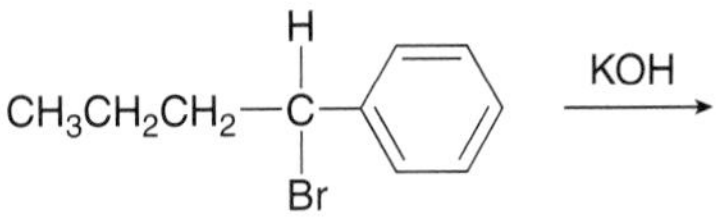

b. 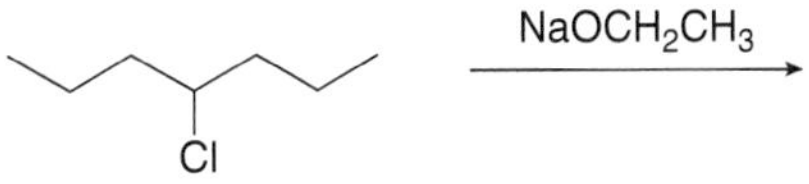

E1 Reaction

8.41 What alkene is the major product formed from each alkyl halide in an E1 reaction?

a. 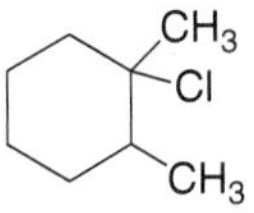

b. 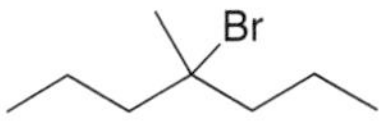

c. 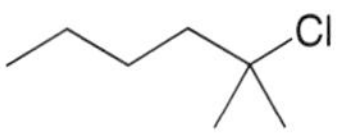

E1 and E2

8.42 Draw all constitutional isomers formed in each elimination reaction. Label the mechanism as E2 or E1.

a. 

c. 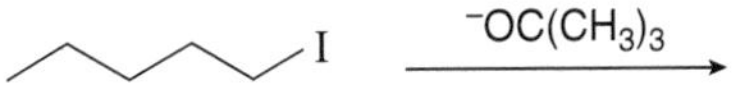

e. 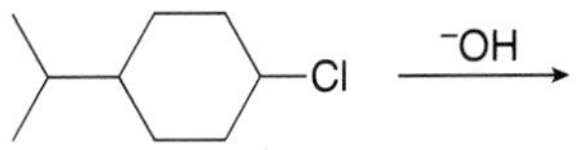

b. 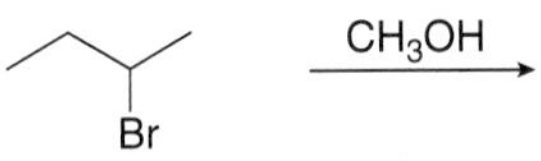

d. 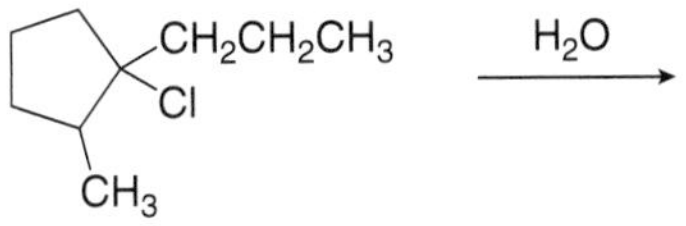

f. 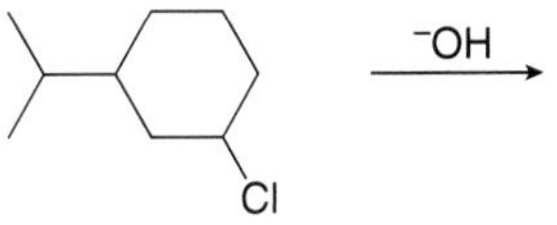

8.43 Rank the alkyl halides in order of increasing E2 reactivity. Then do the same for E1 reactivity.

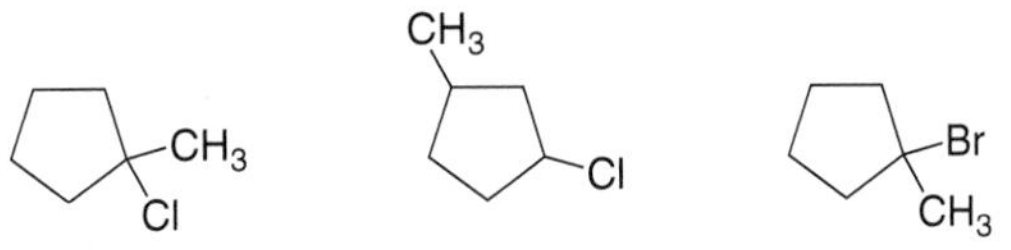

8.44 Which elimination reaction in each pair is faster?

a. 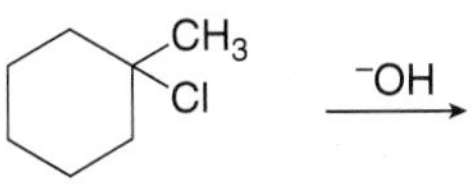

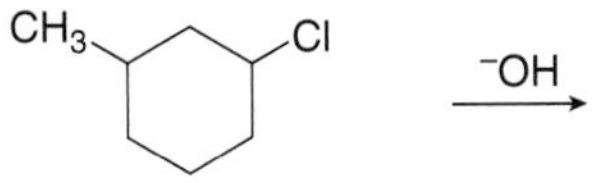

b. 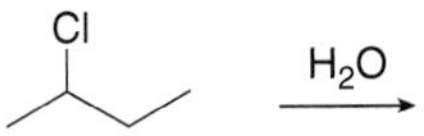

c. $(CH_3)_3CCl \xrightarrow[H_2O]{^{-}OH}$

$(CH_3)_3CCl \xrightarrow[DMSO]{^{-}OH}$

8.45 In the dehydrohalogenation of bromocyclodecane, the major product is *cis*-cyclodecene rather than *trans*-cyclodecene. Offer an explanation.

8.46 Explain the following observation. Treatment of alkyl chloride **A** with $NaOCH_2CH_3$ yields only one product **B,** whereas treatment of **A** with very dilute base in CH_3CH_2OH yields a mixture of alkenes **B** and **C,** with **C** predominating.

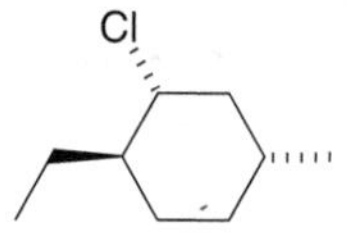

A

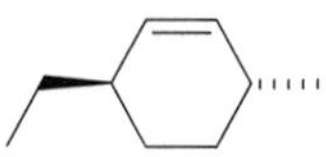

B

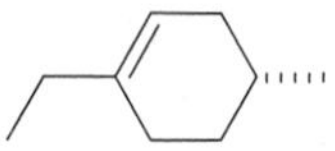

C

8.47 Elimination of HBr from 2-bromobutane affords a mixture of 1-butene and 2-butene. With sodium ethoxide as base, 2-butene constitutes 81% of the alkene products, but with potassium *tert*-butoxide, 2-butene constitutes only 67% of the alkene products. Offer an explanation for this difference.

Stereochemistry and the E2 Reaction

8.48 What is the major E2 elimination product formed from each halide?

a. 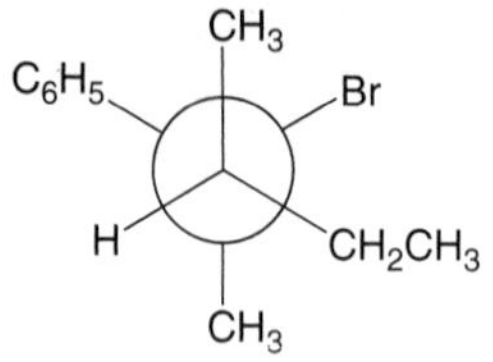

b. 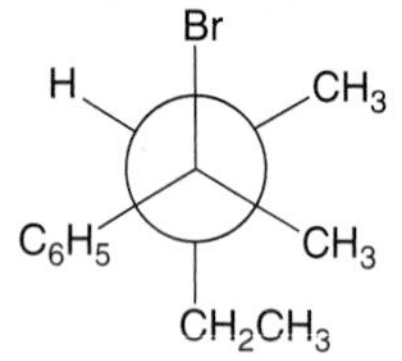

c. 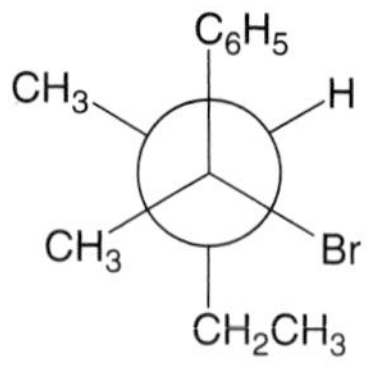

8.49 Taking into account anti periplanar geometry, predict the major E2 product formed from each starting material.

a. 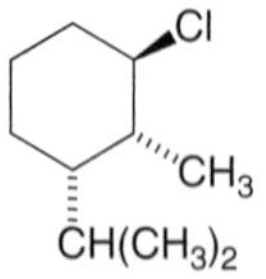

b. 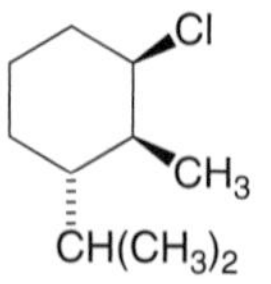

c. 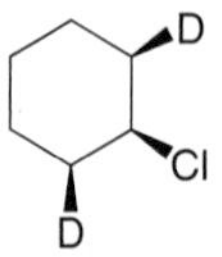

d. 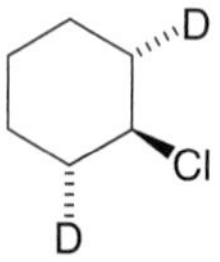

8.50 a. Draw three-dimensional representations for all stereoisomers of 2-chloro-3-methylpentane, and label pairs of enantiomers.

b. Considering dehydrohalogenation across C2 and C3 only, draw the E2 product that results from each of these alkyl halides. How many different products have you drawn?

c. How are these products related to each other?

Alkynes

8.51 Draw the products of each reaction.

a. 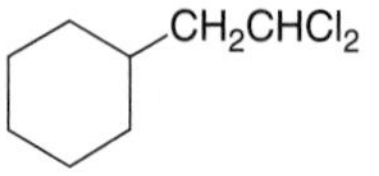 $\xrightarrow[\text{(2 equiv)}]{NaNH_2}$

b. $CH_3CH_2-C(CH_3)_2-CH(Br)CH_2Br \xrightarrow[\text{(2 equiv)}]{NaNH_2}$

c. $CH_3-CCl_2-CH_2CH_3 \xrightarrow[\text{(excess)}]{NaNH_2}$

d. 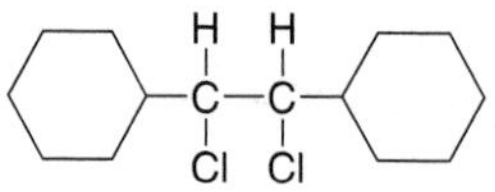 $\xrightarrow[\text{(2 equiv)}]{NaNH_2}$

8.52 Draw the structure of a dihalide that could be used to prepare each alkyne. There may be more than one possible dihalide.

a. $CH_3C{\equiv}CCH_3$

b. $CH_3-C(CH_3)_2-C{\equiv}CH$

c. 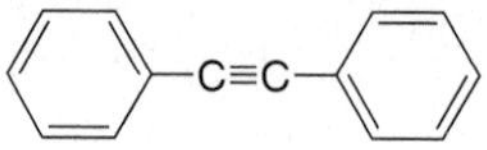

8.53 Under certain reaction conditions, 2,3-dibromobutane reacts with two equivalents of base to give three products, each of which contains two new π bonds. Product **A** has two *sp* hybridized carbon atoms, product **B** has one *sp* hybridized carbon atom, and product **C** has none. What are the structures of **A, B,** and **C?**

S_N1, S_N2, E1, and E2 Mechanisms

8.54 For which reaction mechanisms—S_N1, S_N2, E1, or E2—are each of the following statements true? A statement may be true for one or more mechanisms.

a. The mechanism involves carbocation intermediates.
b. The mechanism has two steps.
c. The reaction rate increases with better leaving groups.
d. The reaction rate increases when the solvent is changed from CH_3OH to $(CH_3)_2SO$.
e. The reaction rate depends on the concentration of the alkyl halide only.
f. The mechanism is concerted.
g. The reaction of CH_3CH_2Br with NaOH occurs by this mechanism.
h. Racemization at a stereogenic center occurs.
i. Tertiary (3°) alkyl halides react faster than 2° or 1° alkyl halides.
j. The reaction follows a second-order rate equation.

8.55 Draw the organic products formed in each reaction.

a. 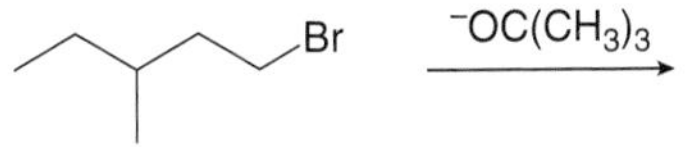

b. 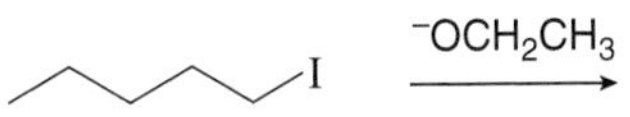

c. 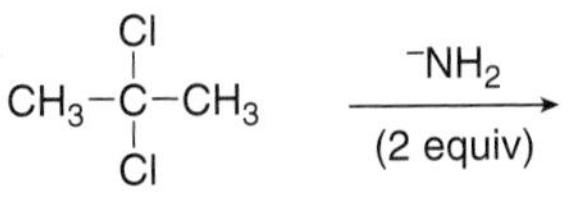

d. 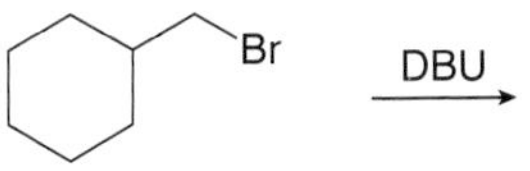

e. 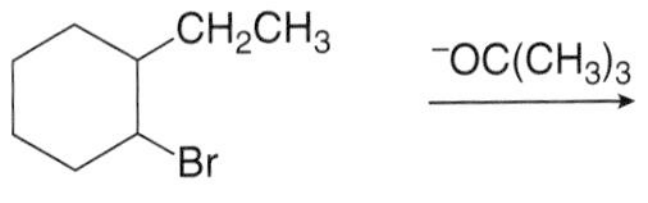

f. 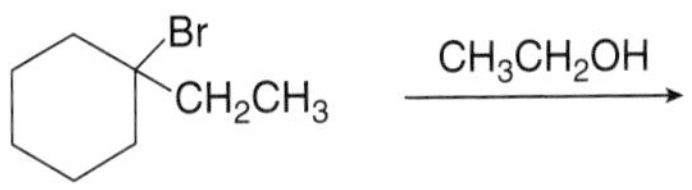

g. 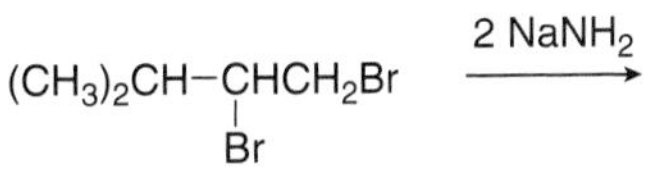

h. 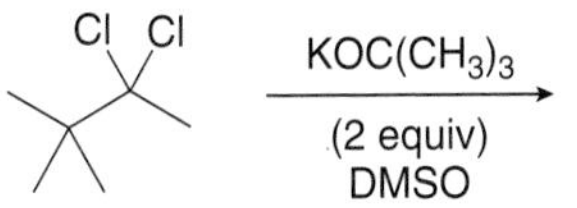

i. 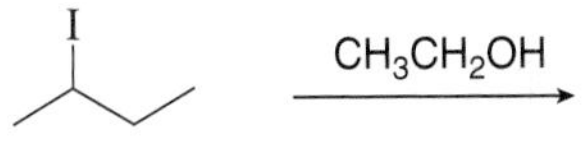

j. 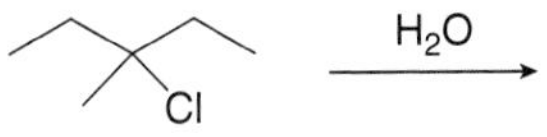

8.56 What is the major product formed when each alkyl halide is treated with each of the following reagents: [1] $NaOCOCH_3$; [2] $NaOCH_3$; [3] $KOC(CH_3)_3$? If it is not possible to predict the major product, identify the products in the mixture and the mechanism by which each is formed.

a. CH_3Cl

b. 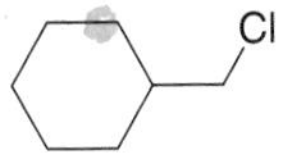

c. 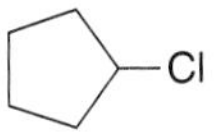

d. 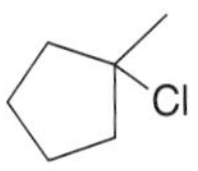

8.57

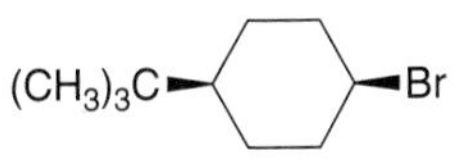

cis-1-bromo-4-*tert*-butylcyclohexane

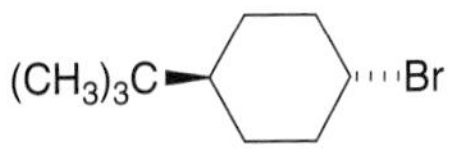

trans-1-bromo-4-*tert*-butylcyclohexane

a. The cis and trans isomers of 1-bromo-4-*tert*-butylcyclohexane react at different rates with $KOC(CH_3)_3$ to afford the same mixture of enantiomers **A** and **B.** Draw the structures of **A** and **B.**
b. Which isomer reacts faster with $KOC(CH_3)_3$? Offer an explanation for this difference in reactivity.
c. Reaction of *cis*-1-bromo-4-*tert*-butylcyclohexane with $NaOCH_3$ affords **C** as the major product, whereas reaction of *trans*-1-bromo-4-*tert*-butylcyclohexane affords **D** as the major product. Draw the structures for **C** and **D.**
d. The cis and trans isomers react at different rates with $NaOCH_3$. Which isomer reacts faster? Offer an explanation for the difference in reactivity.
e. Why are different products formed from these alkyl halides when two different alkoxides are used as reagents?

8.58 Draw all products, including stereoisomers, in each reaction.

a. 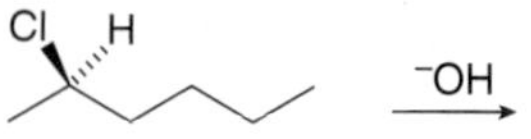

b. 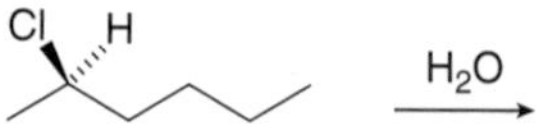

c. 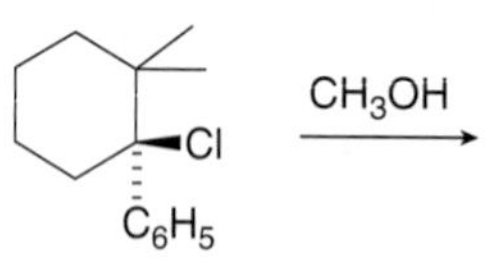

d. 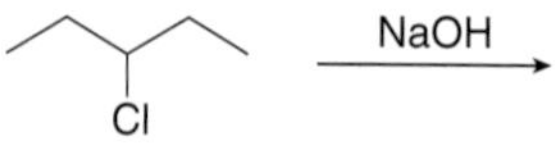

e. 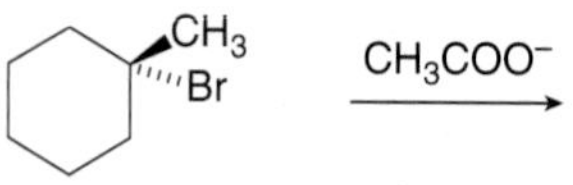

f. 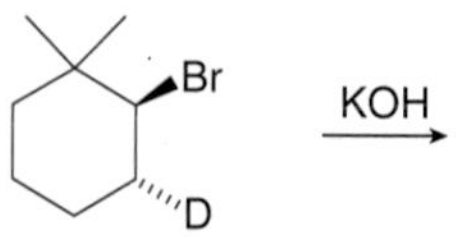

8.59 Draw all of the substitution and elimination products formed from the following alkyl halide with each reagent. Indicate the stereochemistry around the stereogenic centers present in the products, as well as the mechanism by which each product is formed.

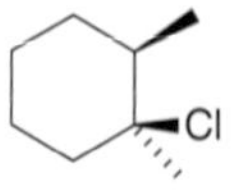

a. CH_3OH b. KOH

8.60 The following reactions do not afford the major product that is given. Explain why this is so, and draw the structure of the major product actually formed.

a. 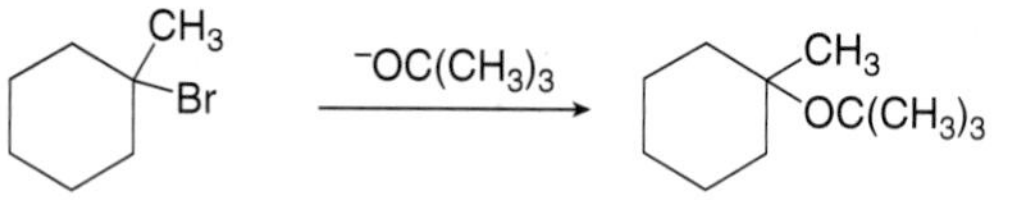

c. 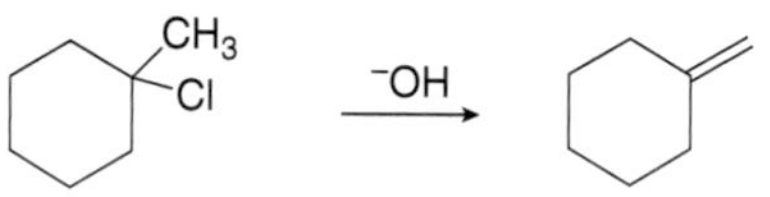

b. 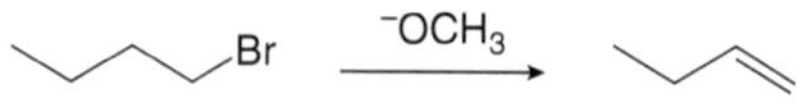

d. 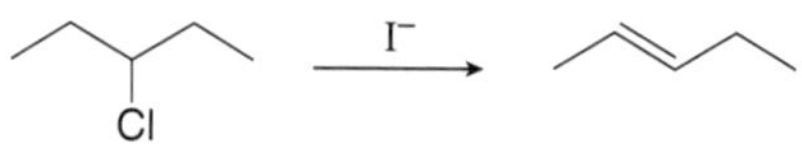

8.61 Draw a stepwise, detailed mechanism for each reaction.

a. 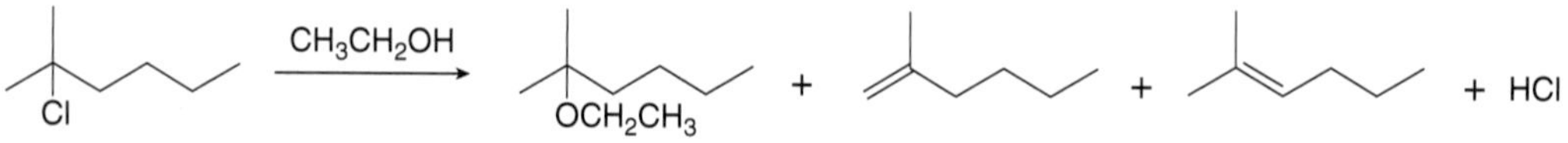

b. 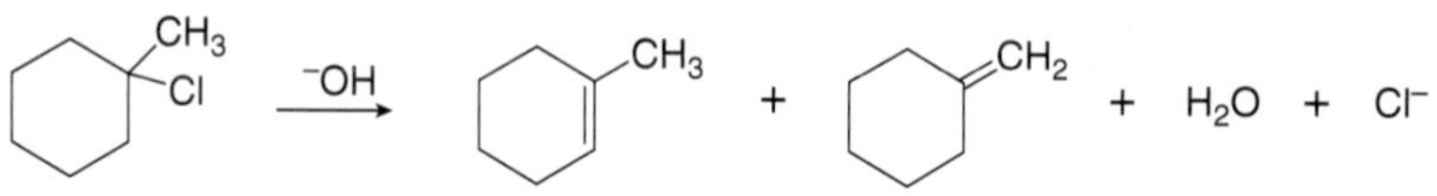

8.62 Draw the major product formed when (3*R*)-1-chloro-3-methylpentane is treated with each reagent: (a) $NaOCH_2CH_3$; (b) KCN; (c) DBU.

8.63 Draw a stepwise, detailed mechanism for the following reaction.

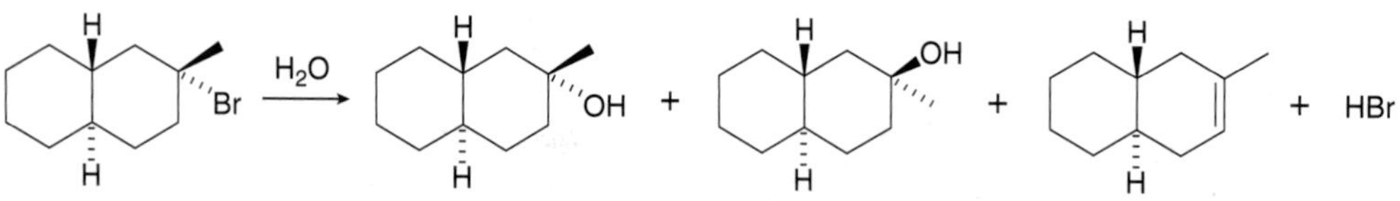

8.64 Explain why the reaction of 2-bromopropane with $NaOCOCH_3$ gives $(CH_3)_2CHOCOCH_3$ exclusively as product, but the reaction of 2-bromopropane with $NaOCH_2CH_3$ gives a mixture of $(CH_3)_2CHOCH_2CH_3$ (20%) and $CH_3CH{=}CH_2$ (80%).

Challenge Problems

8.65 Draw a stepwise detailed mechanism that illustrates how four organic products are formed in the following reaction.

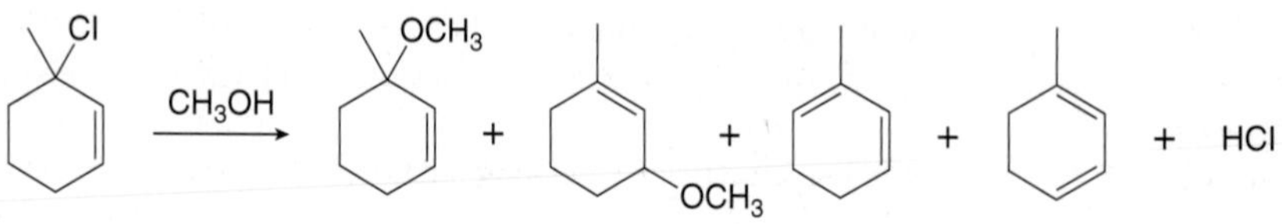

8.66 Although there are nine stereoisomers of 1,2,3,4,5,6-hexachlorocyclohexane, one stereoisomer reacts 7000 times more slowly than any of the others in an E2 elimination. Draw the structure of this isomer and explain why this is so.

8.67 Explain the selectivity observed in the following reactions.

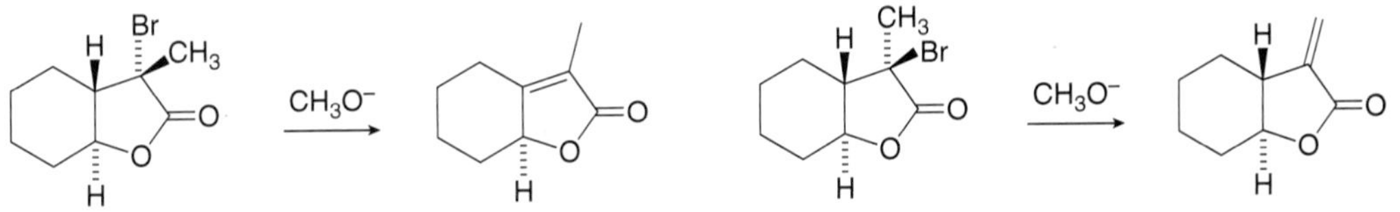

8.68 Draw a stepwise mechanism for the following reaction. The four-membered ring in the starting material and product is called a β-lactam. This functional group confers biological activity on penicillin and many related antibiotics, as is discussed in Chapter 22. (Hint: The mechanism begins with β elimination and involves only two steps.)

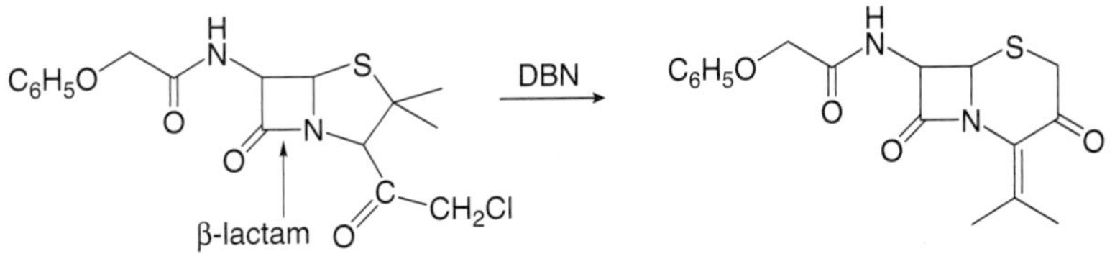

8.69 Although dehydrohalogenation occurs with anti periplanar geometry, some eliminations have syn periplanar geometry. Examine the starting material and product of each elimination, and state whether the elimination occurs with syn or anti periplanar geometry.

a.

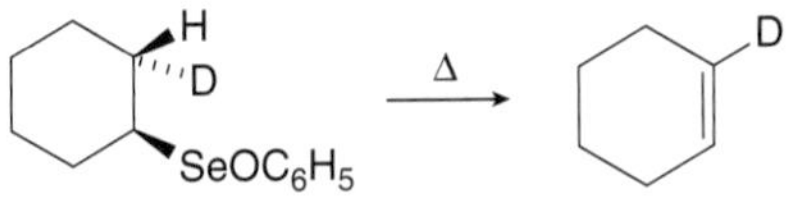

b.

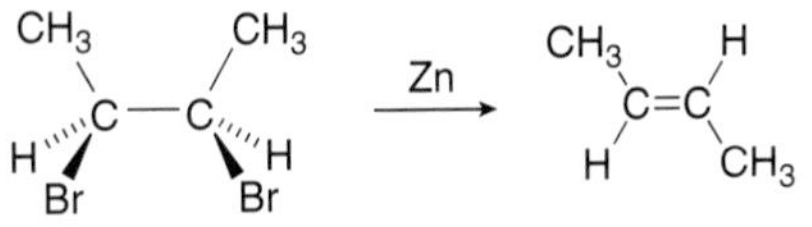

8.70 (a) Draw all products formed by treatment of each dibromide (**A** and **B**) with one equivalent of $NaNH_2$. (b) Label pairs of diastereomers and constitutional isomers.

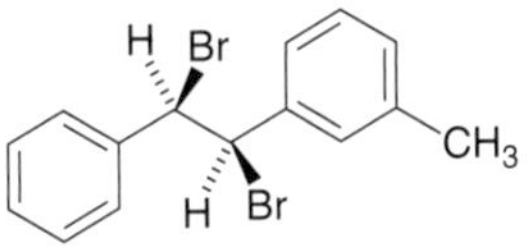

A

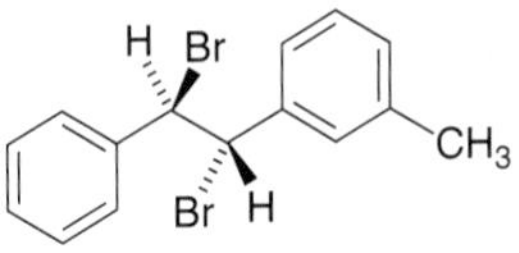

B

9 Alcohols, Ethers, and Epoxides

9.1 Introduction
9.2 Structure and bonding
9.3 Nomenclature
9.4 Physical properties
9.5 Interesting alcohols, ethers, and epoxides
9.6 Preparation of alcohols, ethers, and epoxides
9.7 General features—Reactions of alcohols, ethers, and epoxides
9.8 Dehydration of alcohols to alkenes
9.9 Carbocation rearrangements
9.10 Dehydration using $POCl_3$ and pyridine
9.11 Conversion of alcohols to alkyl halides with HX
9.12 Conversion of alcohols to alkyl halides with $SOCl_2$ and PBr_3
9.13 Tosylate—Another good leaving group
9.14 Reaction of ethers with strong acid
9.15 Reactions of epoxides
9.16 Application: Epoxides, leukotrienes, and asthma
9.17 Application: Benzo[*a*]-pyrene, epoxides, and cancer

Palytoxin ($C_{129}H_{223}N_3O_{54}$), first isolated from marine soft corals of the genus *Palythoa,* is a potent poison that contains several hydroxy (OH) groups. Historically used by ancient Hawaiians to poison their spears, palytoxin was isolated in 1971 at the University of Hawai'i at Mānoa, and its structure determined simultaneously by two different research groups in 1981. Its many functional groups and stereogenic centers made it a formidable synthetic target, but in 1994, Harvard chemists synthesized palytoxin in the laboratory. In Chapter 9 we learn about the properties of alcohols like palytoxin, as well as related oxygen-containing functional groups.

In Chapter 9, we take the principles learned in Chapters 7 and 8 about leaving groups, nucleophiles, and bases, and apply them to **alcohols, ethers,** and **epoxides,** three new functional groups that contain polar C–O bonds. In the process, you will discover that all of the reactions in Chapter 9 follow one of the four mechanisms introduced in Chapters 7 and 8—S_N1, S_N2, E1, or E2—so there are **no new general mechanisms to learn.**

Although alcohols, ethers, and epoxides share many characteristics, each functional group has its own distinct reactivity, making each unique and different from the alkyl halides studied in Chapters 7 and 8. Appreciate the similarities but pay attention to the differences.

9.1 Introduction

Alcohols, ethers, and **epoxides** are three functional groups that contain carbon–oxygen σ bonds.

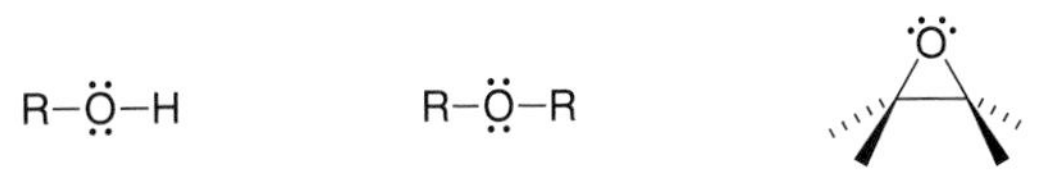

alcohol **ether** **epoxide**

Alcohols **contain a hydroxy group (OH** group) bonded to an sp^3 hybridized carbon atom. Alcohols are classified as **primary (1°), secondary (2°),** or **tertiary (3°)** based on the number of carbon atoms bonded to the carbon with the OH group.

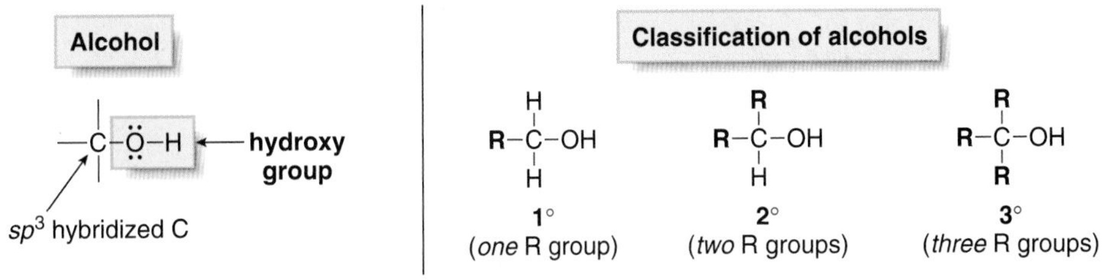

Compounds having a hydroxy group on an sp^2 hybridized carbon atom—**enols** and **phenols**—undergo different reactions than alcohols and are discussed in Chapters 11 and 19, respectively. **Enols** have an OH group on a carbon of a C–C double bond. **Phenols** have an OH group on a benzene ring.

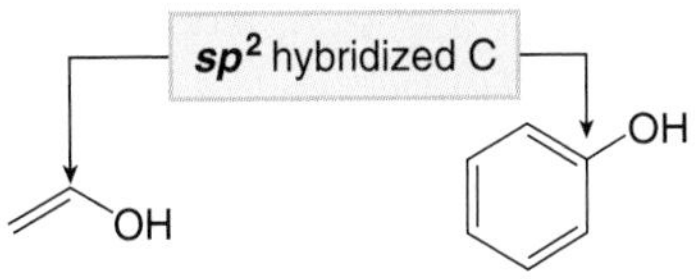

enol phenol

Ethers **have two alkyl groups bonded to an oxygen atom.** An ether is **symmetrical** if the two alkyl groups are the same, and **unsymmetrical** if they are different. Both alcohols and ethers are organic derivatives of H_2O, formed by replacing one or both of the hydrogens on the oxygen atom by R groups, respectively.

R–Ö–R	CH_3CH_2–Ö–CH_2CH_3	CH_3–Ö–CH_2CH_3
Ether	**symmetrical ether**	**unsymmetrical ether**
	R groups are the **same.**	R groups are **different.**

Epoxides **are ethers having the oxygen atom in a three-membered ring.** Epoxides are also called **oxiranes.**

epoxide or **oxirane**

Problem 9.1 Draw all constitutional isomers having molecular formula $C_4H_{10}O$. Classify each compound as a 1°, 2°, or 3° alcohol, or a symmetrical or unsymmetrical ether.

Problem 9.2 Classify each OH group in dexamethasone, a halogen-containing, synthetic steroid, as 1°, 2°, or 3°.

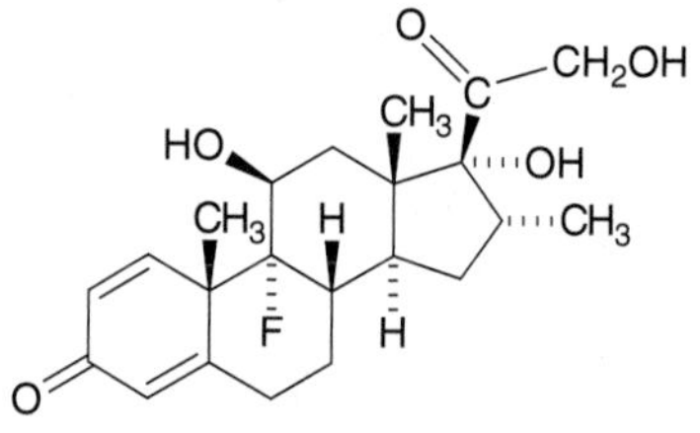

dexamethasone

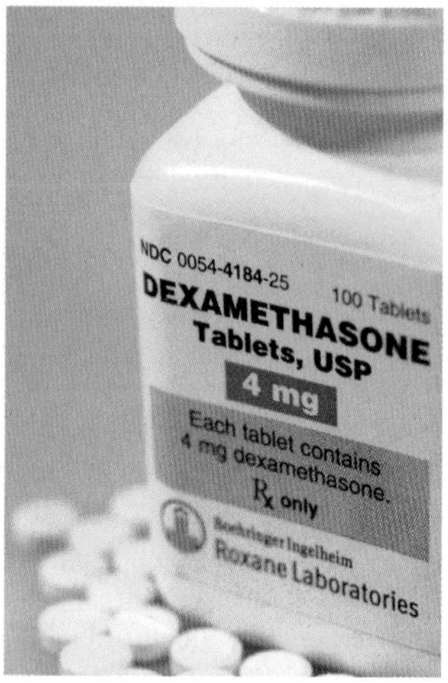

Dexamethasone relieves inflammation and is used to treat some forms of arthritis, skin conditions, and asthma.

9.2 Structure and Bonding

Alcohols, ethers, and epoxides each contain an oxygen atom surrounded by two atoms and two nonbonded electron pairs, making the O atom **tetrahedral** and ***sp*^{3}** hybridized. Because only two of the four groups around O are atoms, alcohols and ethers have a **bent** shape like H_2O.

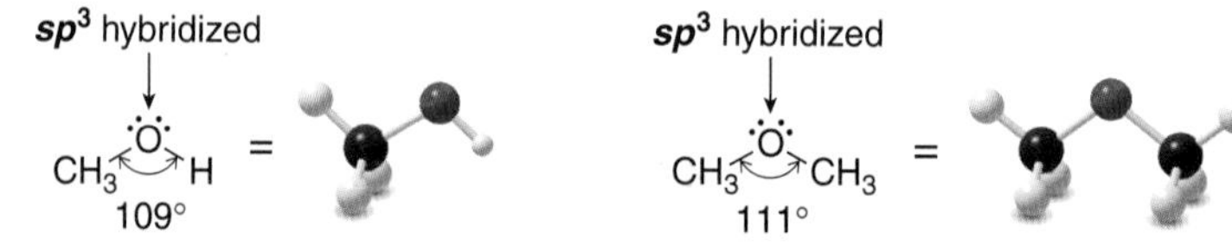

The bond angle around the O atom in an alcohol or ether is similar to the tetrahedral bond angle of **109.5°.** In contrast, the C–O–C bond angle of an epoxide must be **60°,** a considerable deviation from the tetrahedral bond angle. For this reason, **epoxides have angle strain,** making them much more reactive than other ethers.

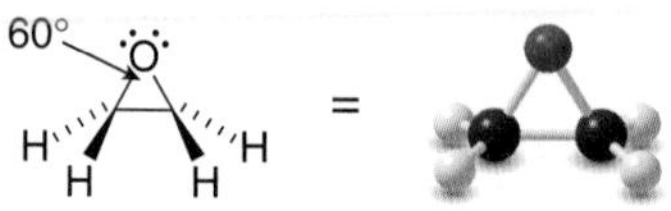

a strained, three-membered ring

Because oxygen is much more electronegative than carbon or hydrogen, the C–O and O–H bonds are all polar, with the O atom electron rich and the C and H atoms electron poor. The electrostatic potential maps in Figure 9.1 show these polar bonds for all three functional groups.

Figure 9.1 Electrostatic potential maps for a simple alcohol, ether, and epoxide

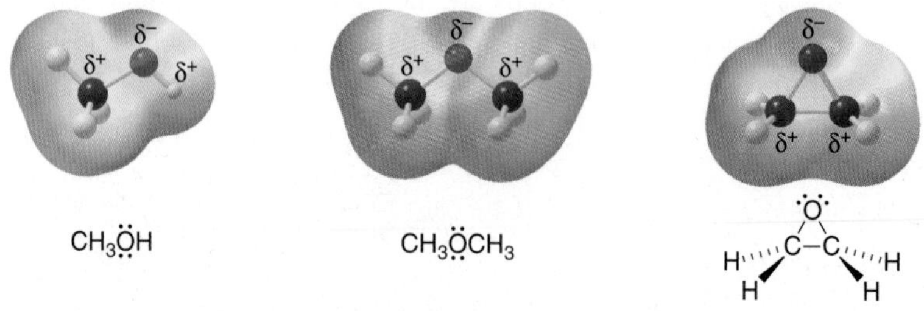

- Electron-rich regions are shown by the red around the O atoms.

9.3 Nomenclature

To name an alcohol, ether, or epoxide using the IUPAC system, we must learn how to name the functional group either as a substituent or by using a suffix added to the parent name.

9.3A Naming Alcohols

- **In the IUPAC system, alcohols are identified by the suffix *-ol.***

How To Name an Alcohol Using the IUPAC System

Example Give the IUPAC name of the following alcohol:

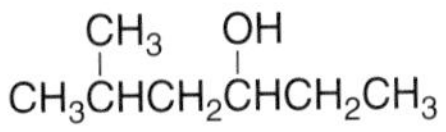

Step [1] Find the longest carbon chain containing the carbon bonded to the OH group.

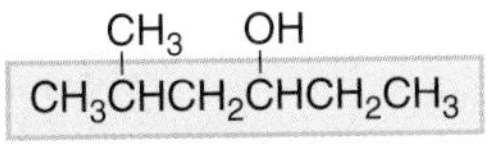

6 C's in the longest chain

6 C's ⟶ **hexan*e*** ⟶ **hexan*ol***

- Change the **-*e*** ending of the parent alkane to the suffix ***-ol.***

Step [2] Number the carbon chain to give the OH group the lower number, and apply all other rules of nomenclature.

a. **Number** the chain.

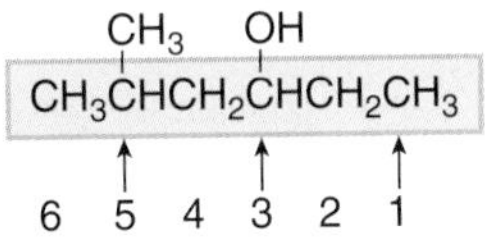
6 5 4 3 2 1

- Number the chain to put the OH group at C3, not C4.

3-hexanol

b. **Name** and **number** the substituents.

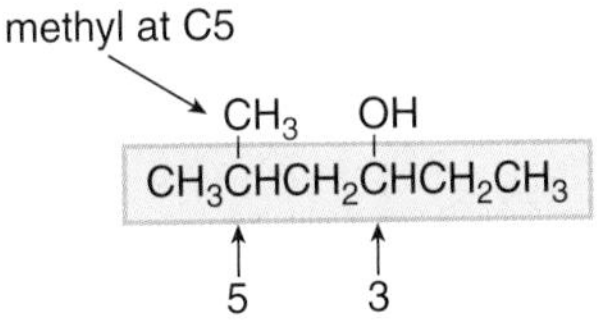
methyl at C5
5
3

Answer: 5-methyl-3-hexanol

$CH_3CH_2CH_2CH_2OH$ is named as 1-butanol using the 1979 IUPAC recommendations and butan-1-ol using the 1993 IUPAC recommendations. The first convention is more widely used, so we follow it in this text.

When an OH group is bonded to a ring, the **ring is numbered beginning with the OH group.** Because the functional group is always at C1, the "1" is usually omitted from the name. The ring is then numbered in a clockwise or counterclockwise fashion to give the next substituent the lower number. Representative examples are given in Figure 9.2.

Figure 9.2
Examples: Naming cyclic alcohols

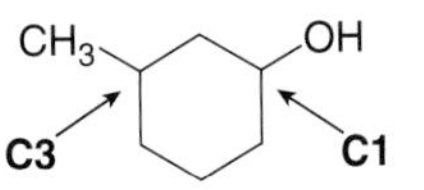
C3
C1

3-methylcyclohexanol

[The OH group is at C1; the second substituent (CH_3) gets the lower number.]

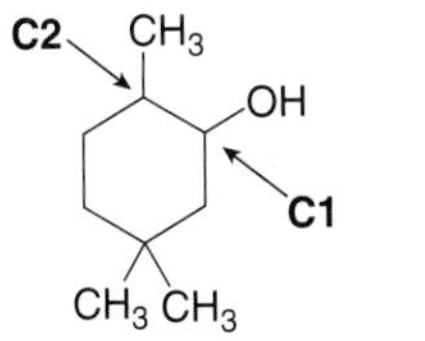
C2
C1

2,5,5-trimethylcyclohexanol

[The OH group is at C1; the second substituent (CH_3) gets the lower number.]

Common names are often used for simple alcohols. To assign a common name:

- Name all the carbon atoms of the molecule as a single **alkyl group.**
- Add the word **alcohol,** separating the words with a space.

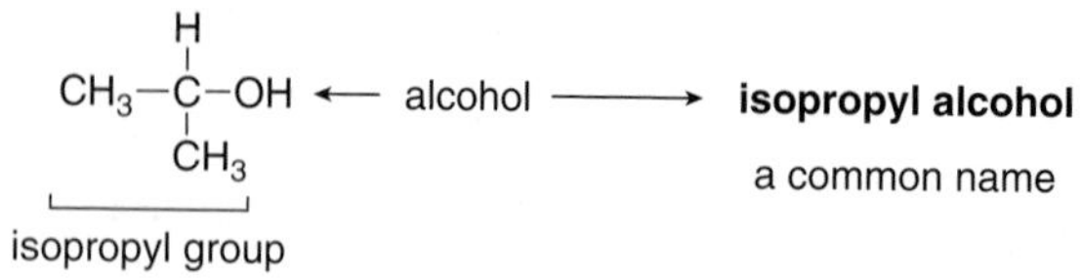
H
CH_3–C–OH
CH_3
alcohol
isopropyl alcohol
a common name
isopropyl group

Compounds with two hydroxy groups are called **diols** (using the IUPAC system) or **glycols.** Compounds with three hydroxy groups are called **triols,** and so forth. To name a diol, for example, the suffix ***-diol*** is added to the name of the parent alkane, and numbers are used in the prefix to indicate the location of the two OH groups.

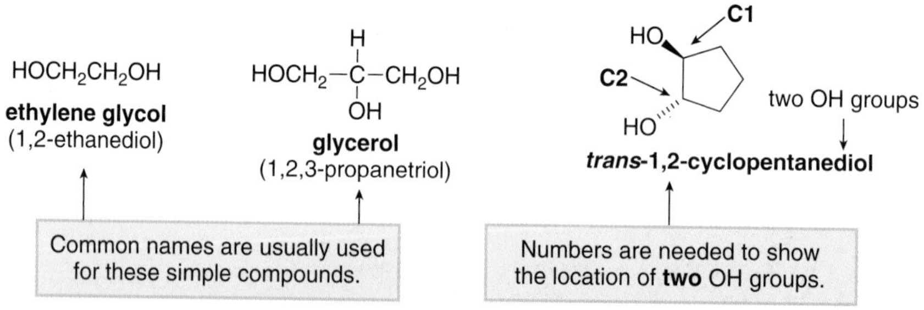
$HOCH_2CH_2OH$
ethylene glycol
(1,2-ethanediol)
H
$HOCH_2$–C–CH_2OH
OH
glycerol
(1,2,3-propanetriol)
HO
C1
C2
HO
two OH groups
trans-1,2-cyclopentanediol
Common names are usually used for these simple compounds.
Numbers are needed to show the location of two OH groups.

Problem 9.3 Give the IUPAC name for each compound.

a. 
OH

b. 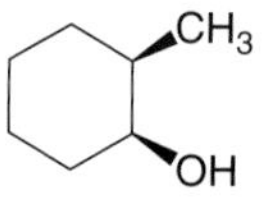
CH_3
OH

c. 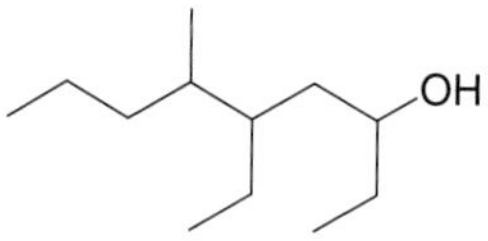
OH

Problem 9.4 Give the structure corresponding to each name.

a. 7,7-dimethyl-4-octanol
b. 5-methyl-4-propyl-3-heptanol
c. 2-*tert*-butyl-3-methylcyclohexanol
d. *trans*-1,2-cyclohexanediol

9.3B Naming Ethers

Simple ethers are usually assigned common names. To do so, **name both alkyl groups** bonded to the oxygen, arrange these names alphabetically, and add the word **ether.** For symmetrical ethers, name the alkyl group and add the prefix **di-.**

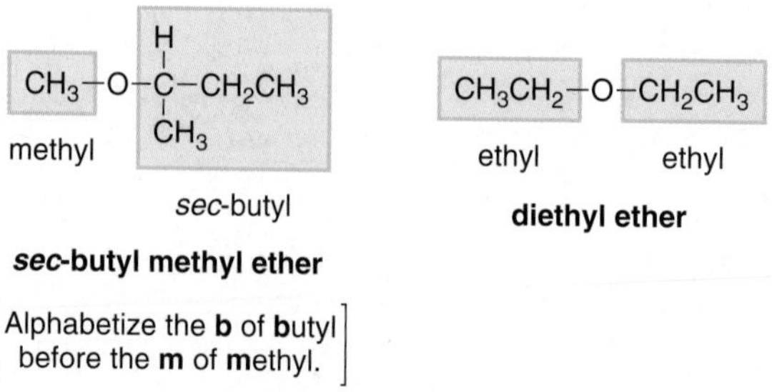
H
CH_3–O–C–CH_2CH_3
CH_3
methyl
sec-butyl
sec-butyl methyl ether
Alphabetize the b of butyl before the m of methyl.
CH_3CH_2–O–CH_2CH_3
ethyl
ethyl
diethyl ether

More complex ethers are named using the IUPAC system. One alkyl group is named as a hydrocarbon chain, and the other is named as part of a substituent bonded to that chain.

- Name the simpler alkyl group + O atom as an **alkoxy** substituent by changing the ***-yl*** ending of the alkyl group to ***-oxy.***

Common alkoxy groups

CH_3O- methoxy

CH_3CH_2O- ethoxy

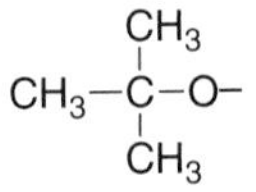
CH3
CH3–C–O–
CH3

tert-butoxy

- Name the remaining alkyl group as an alkane, with the alkoxy group as a substituent bonded to this chain.

Sample Problem 9.1 Give the IUPAC name for the following ether.

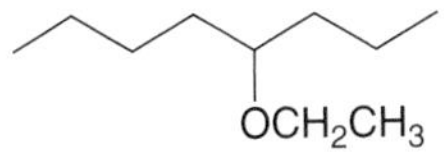
OCH2CH3

Solution

[1] Name the longer chain as an alkane and the shorter chain as an alkoxy group.

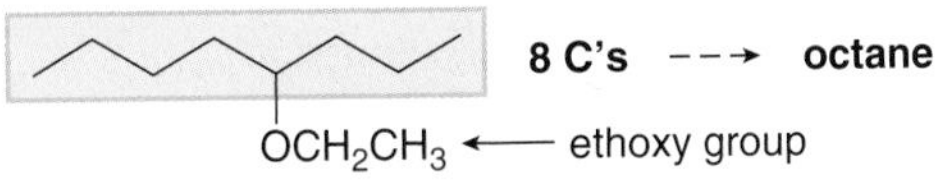
8 C's → octane
OCH2CH3 ← ethoxy group

[2] Apply the other nomenclature rules to complete the name.

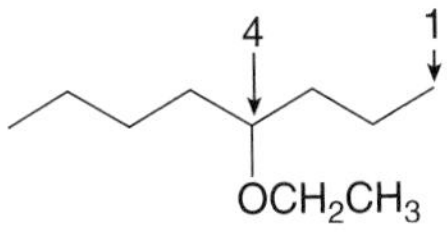
4
1
OCH2CH3

Answer: 4-ethoxyoctane

Problem 9.5 Name each of the following ethers.

a. $CH_3-O-CH_2CH_2CH_2CH_3$

b. 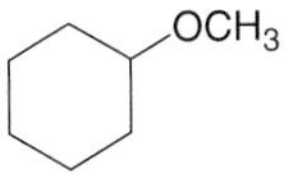
OCH3

c. $CH_3CH_2CH_2-O-CH_2CH_2CH_3$

Problem 9.6 Name $(CH_3)_3COCH_3$, a gasoline additive commonly referred to as MTBE, as an alkoxy alkane.

O

tetrahydrofuran
THF

Cyclic ethers have an O atom in a ring. A common cyclic ether is **tetrahydrofuran (THF),** a polar aprotic solvent used in nucleophilic substitution (Section 7.8C) and many other organic reactions.

9.3C Naming Epoxides

Any cyclic compound containing a heteroatom is called a *heterocycle.*

Epoxides are named in three different ways—**epoxyalkanes, oxiranes,** or **alkene oxides.**

To name an epoxide as an **epoxyalkane,** first name the alkane chain or ring to which the oxygen is attached, and use the prefix ***epoxy*** to name the epoxide as a substituent. Use two numbers to designate the location of the atoms to which the O's are bonded.

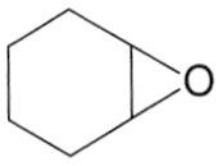
O

1,2-epoxycyclohexane

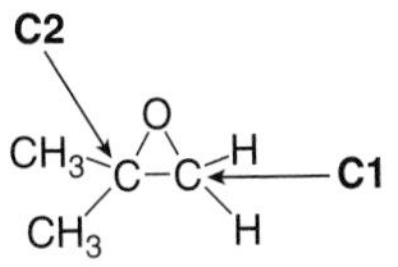
C2
O
CH3
C
C
H
C1
CH3
H

1,2-epoxy-2-methylpropane

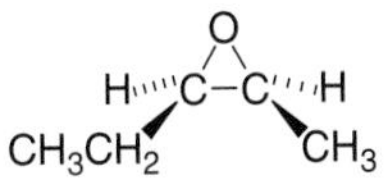
O
H
C
C
H
CH3CH2
CH3

***cis*-2,3-epoxypentane**

Epoxides bonded to a chain of carbon atoms can also be named as derivatives of **oxirane,** the simplest epoxide having two carbons and one oxygen atom in a ring. The oxirane ring is numbered to put the O atom at position "1," and the first substituent at position "2." No number is used for a substituent in a monosubstituted oxirane.

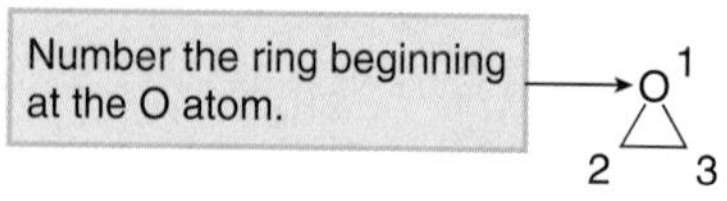
Number the ring beginning at the O atom.
1
2
3

oxirane

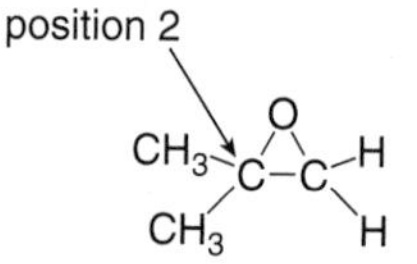
position 2

2,2-dimethyloxirane

Epoxides are also named as **alkene oxides,** since they are often prepared by adding an O atom to an alkene (Chapter 12). To name an epoxide this way, mentally replace the epoxide oxygen by a double bond, name the alkene (Section 10.3), and then add the word ***oxide.*** For example, the common name for oxirane is ethylene oxide, since it is an epoxide derived from the alkene ethylene. We will use this method of naming epoxides after the details of alkene nomenclature are presented in Chapter 10.

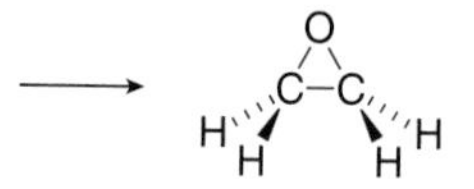
$CH_2{=}CH_2$
ethylene

ethylene oxide
oxirane

Problem 9.7 Name each epoxide.

a. 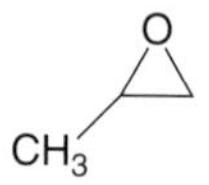 (two ways)

b. 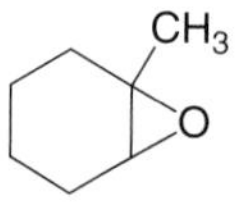

c. 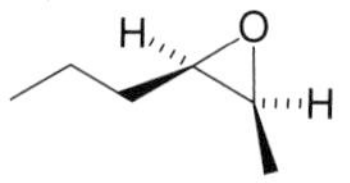 (two ways)

9.4 Physical Properties

Alcohols, ethers, and epoxides exhibit dipole–dipole interactions because they have a bent structure with two polar bonds. **Alcohols are also capable of intermolecular hydrogen bonding,** because they possess a hydrogen atom on an oxygen, making alcohols much more polar than ethers and epoxides.

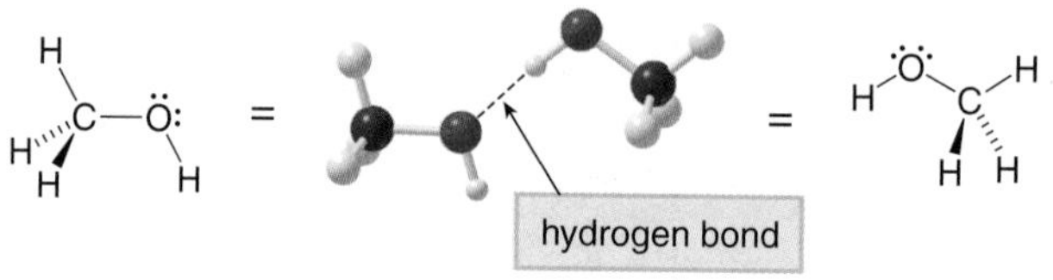
hydrogen bond

Steric factors affect the extent of hydrogen bonding. Although all alcohols can hydrogen bond, increasing the number of R groups around the carbon atom bearing the OH group decreases the extent of hydrogen bonding. Thus, 3° alcohols are least able to hydrogen bond, whereas 1° alcohols are most able to.

← Increasing ability to hydrogen bond

RCH_2–OH	R_2CH–OH	R_3C–OH
1°	**2°**	**3°**

Increasing steric hindrance →

How these factors affect the physical properties of alcohols, ethers, and epoxides is summarized in Table 9.1.

Table 9.1 Physical Properties of Alcohols, Ethers, and Epoxides

Property	Observation
Boiling point and melting point	• For compounds of comparable molecular weight, the **stronger** the intermolecular forces, the **higher** the bp or mp. $CH_3CH_2CH_2CH_3$ VDW bp 0 °C — $CH_3OCH_2CH_3$ VDW, DD bp 11 °C — $CH_3CH_2CH_2OH$ VDW, DD, HB bp 97 °C **Increasing boiling point** → • Bp's **increase** as the extent of hydrogen bonding **increases.** $(CH_3)_3C{-}OH$ 3° bp 83 °C — OH over $CH_3CH_2CHCH_3$ 2° bp 98 °C — $CH_3CH_2CH_2CH_2{-}OH$ 1° bp 118 °C → **Increasing ability to hydrogen bond** **Increasing boiling point**
Solubility	• Alcohols, ethers, and epoxides having ≤ 5 C's are H_2O soluble because they each have an oxygen atom capable of hydrogen bonding to H_2O (Section 3.4C). • Alcohols, ethers, and epoxides having > 5 C's are H_2O insoluble because the nonpolar alkyl portion is too large to dissolve in H_2O. • Alcohols, ethers, and epoxides of any size are soluble in organic solvents.

Key: VDW = van der Waals forces; DD = dipole–dipole; HB = hydrogen bonding

Problem 9.8 Rank the following compounds in order of increasing boiling point.

a.

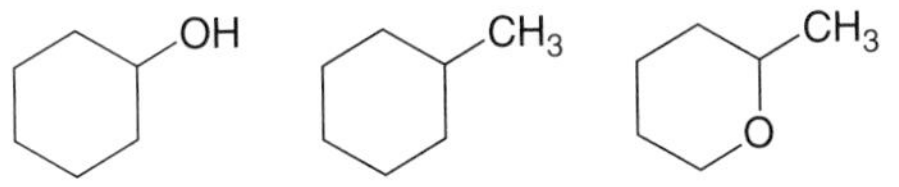

b.

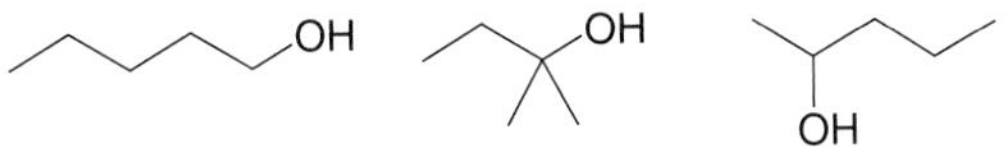

9.5 Interesting Alcohols, Ethers, and Epoxides

A large number of alcohols, ethers, and epoxides have interesting and useful properties.

9.5A Interesting Alcohols

The structure and properties of three simple alcohols—methanol, 2-propanol, and ethylene glycol—are given in Figure 9.3. **Ethanol** (CH_3CH_2OH), formed by the fermentation of the carbohydrates in grains, grapes, and potatoes, is the alcohol present in alcoholic beverages. It is perhaps the first organic compound synthesized by humans, because alcohol production has been known for at least 4000 years. Ethanol depresses the central nervous system, increases the production of stomach acid, and dilates blood vessels, producing a flushed appearance. Ethanol is also a common laboratory solvent, which is sometimes made unfit to ingest by adding small amounts of benzene or methanol (both of which are toxic).

Figure 9.3
Some simple alcohols

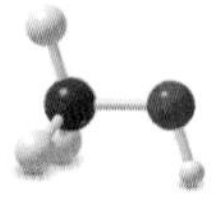

CH_3OH

- **Methanol (CH_3OH)** is also called wood alcohol, because it can be obtained by heating wood at high temperatures in the absence of air. Methanol is extremely toxic because of the oxidation products formed when it is metabolized in the liver (Section 12.14). Ingestion of as little as 15 mL causes blindness, and 100 mL causes death.

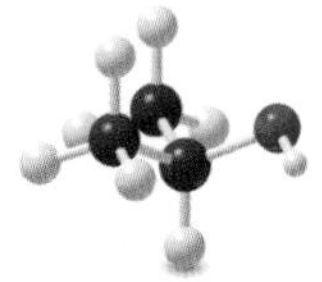

$(CH_3)_2CHOH$

- **2-Propanol [$(CH_3)_2CHOH$]** is the major component of rubbing alcohol. When rubbed on the skin it evaporates readily, producing a pleasant cooling sensation. Because it has weak antibacterial properties, 2-propanol is used to clean skin before minor surgery and to sterilize medical instruments.

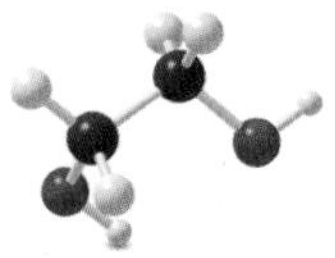

$HOCH_2CH_2OH$

- **Ethylene glycol ($HOCH_2CH_2OH$)** is the major component of antifreeze. It is readily prepared from ethylene oxide by reactions discussed in Section 9.15. It is sweet tasting but toxic.

Ethanol is a common gasoline additive, widely touted as an environmentally friendly fuel source. Two common gasoline–ethanol fuels are gasohol, which contains 10% ethanol, and E-85, which contains 85% ethanol. Ethanol is now routinely prepared from the carbohydrates in corn (Figure 9.4). Starch, a complex carbohydrate polymer, can be hydrolyzed to the simple sugar glucose, which forms ethanol by the process of fermentation. Combining ethanol with gasoline forms a usable fuel, which combusts to form CO_2, H_2O, and a great deal of energy.

Since green plants use sunlight to convert CO_2 and H_2O to carbohydrates during photosynthesis, next year's corn crop removes CO_2 from the atmosphere to make new molecules of starch as the corn grows. While in this way ethanol is a renewable fuel source, the need for large-scale farm equipment and the heavy reliance on fertilizers and herbicides make ethanol expensive to produce. Moreover, many criticize the use of valuable farmland for an energy-producing crop rather than for food production. As a result, discussion continues on ethanol as an alternative to fossil fuels.

Figure 9.4 Ethanol from corn, a renewable fuel source

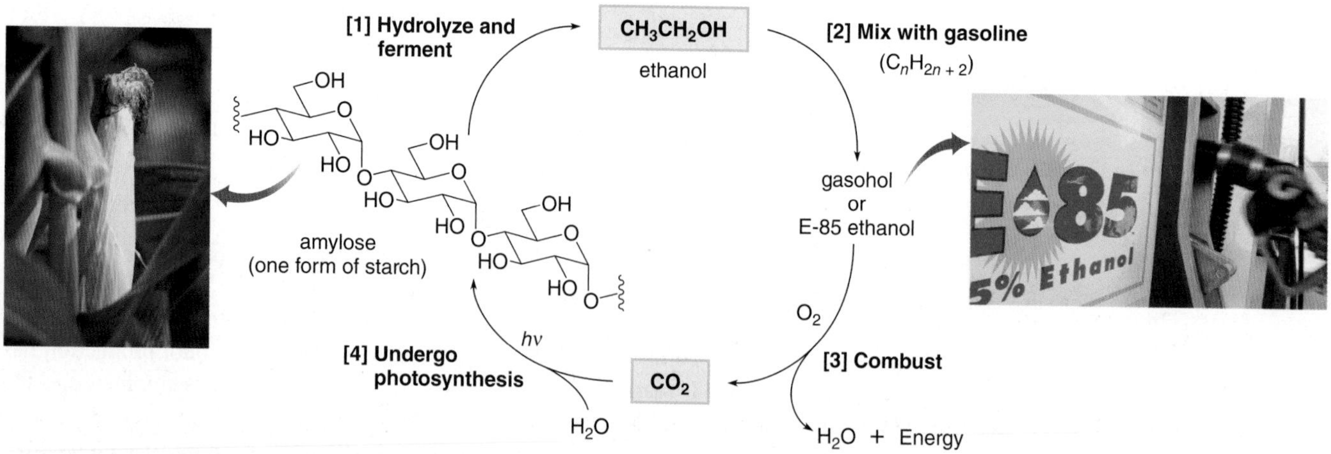

- Hydrolysis of starch and fermentation of the resulting simple sugars (Step [1]) yield ethanol, which is mixed with hydrocarbons from petroleum refining (Step [2]) to form usable fuels.
- Combustion of this ethanol–hydrocarbon fuel forms CO_2 and releases a great deal of energy (Step [3]).
- Photosynthesis converts atmospheric CO_2 back to plant carbohydrates in Step [4], and the cycle continues.

9.5B Interesting Ethers

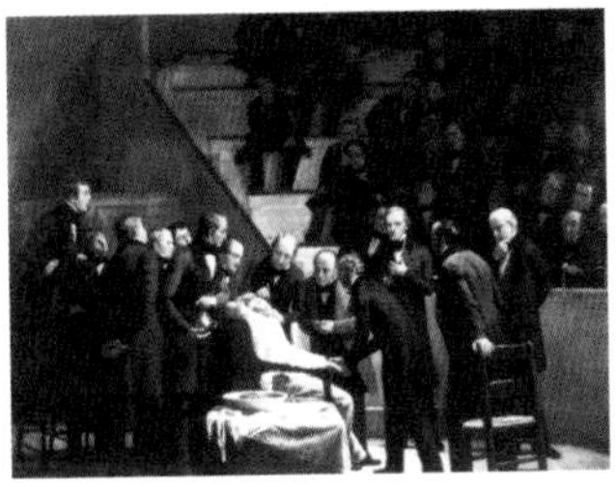

This painting by Robert Hinckley depicts a public demonstration of the use of diethyl ether as an anesthetic at the Massachusetts General Hospital in Boston in the 1840s.

The discovery that **diethyl ether** ($CH_3CH_2OCH_2CH_3$) is a general anesthetic revolutionized surgery in the nineteenth century. For years, a heated controversy existed over who first discovered diethyl ether's anesthetic properties and recognized the enormous benefit in its use. Early experiments were performed by a dentist, Dr. William Morton, resulting in a public demonstration of diethyl ether as an anesthetic in Boston in 1846. In fact, Dr. Crawford Long, a Georgia physician, had been using diethyl ether in surgery and obstetrics for several years, but had not presented his findings to a broader audience.

Diethyl ether is an imperfect anesthetic, but considering the alternatives in the nineteenth century, it was a miracle drug. It is safe, easy to administer, and causes little patient mortality, but it is highly flammable and causes nausea in many patients. For these reasons, it has largely been replaced by halothane (Figure 7.4), which is non-flammable and causes little patient discomfort.

Recall from Section 3.7B that some cyclic **polyethers**—compounds with two or more ether linkages—contain cavities that can complex specific-sized cations. For example, 18-crown-6 binds K^+, whereas 12-crown-4 binds Li^+.

Recall from Section 3.7B that crown ethers are named as ***x*-crown-*y*,** where ***x*** is the total number of atoms in the ring and ***y*** is the number of O atoms.

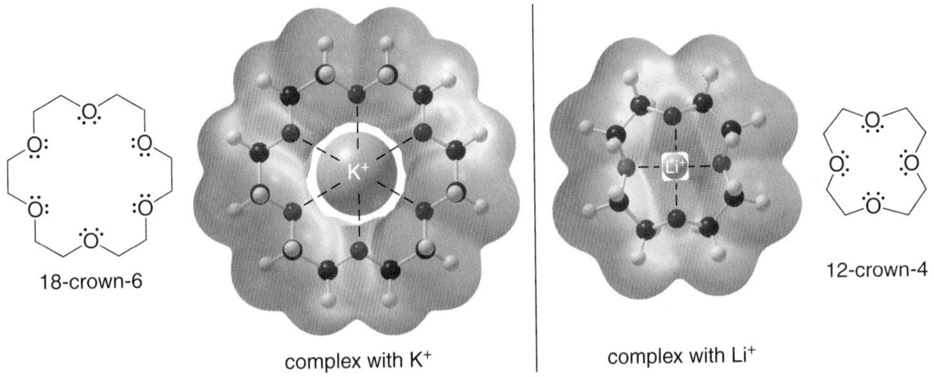

- A crown ether–cation complex is called a *host–guest* complex. The crown ether is the *host* and the cation is the *guest.*
- The ability of a host molecule to bind specific guests is called *molecular recognition.*

The ability of crown ethers to complex cations can be exploited in nucleophilic substitution reactions, as shown in Figure 9.5. Nucleophilic substitution reactions are usually run in polar solvents to dissolve both the polar organic substrate and the ionic nucleophile. With a crown ether, though, the reaction can be run in a nonpolar solvent under conditions that enhance nucleophilicity.

Figure 9.5 The use of crown ethers in nucleophilic substitution reactions

KCN is insoluble in nonpolar solvents alone, but with 18-crown-6:

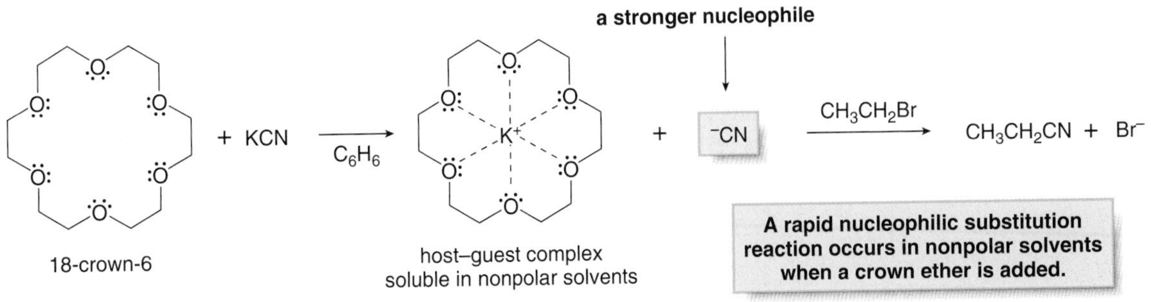

When 18-crown-6 is added to the reaction of CH_3CH_2Br with KCN, for example, the crown ether forms a tight complex with K^+ that has nonpolar C–H bonds on the outside, making the complex soluble in nonpolar solvents like benzene (C_6H_6) or hexane. When the crown ether/K^+ complex dissolves in the nonpolar solvent, it carries the ^-CN along with it to maintain electrical neutrality. The result is a solution of tightly complexed cation and relatively unsolvated anion (nucleophile). The anion, therefore, is extremely nucleophilic because it is not hidden from the substrate by solvent molecules.

Problem 9.9 Which mechanism is favored by the use of crown ethers in nonpolar solvents, S_N1 or S_N2?

9.5C Interesting Epoxides

Although epoxides occur less widely in natural products than alcohols or ethers, interesting and useful epoxides are also known. As an example, two recently introduced drugs that contain an epoxide are eplerenone and tiotropium bromide. Eplerenone (trade name Inspra) is prescribed to reduce cardiovascular risk in patients who have already had a heart attack. Tiotropium bromide (trade name Spiriva) is a long-acting bronchodilator used to treat the chronic obstructive pulmonary disease of smokers and those routinely exposed to secondhand smoke.

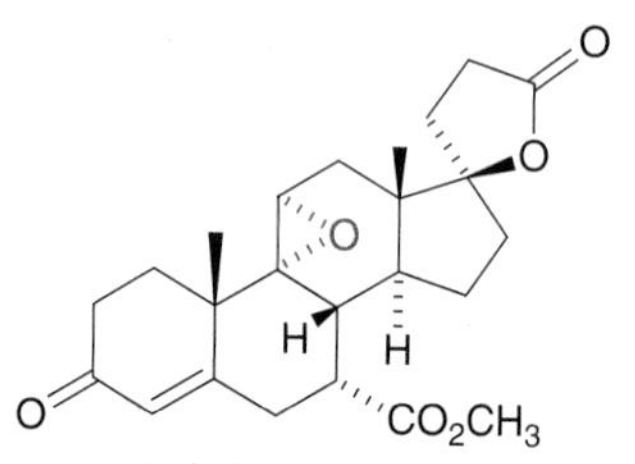

eplerenone

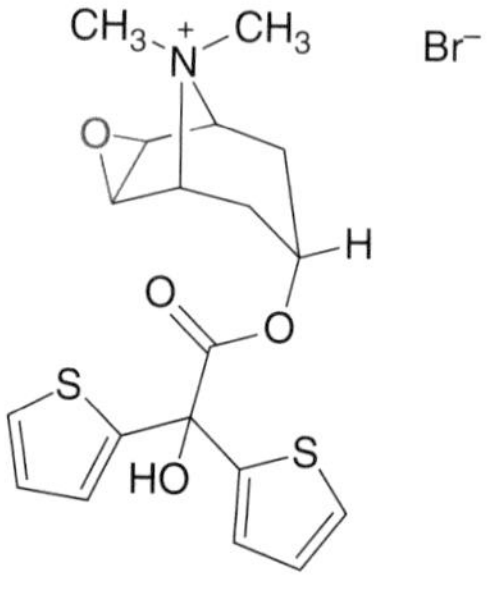

tiotropium bromide

9.6 Preparation of Alcohols, Ethers, and Epoxides

Alcohols and ethers are both common products of nucleophilic substitution. They are synthesized from alkyl halides by S_N2 reactions using strong nucleophiles. As in all S_N2 reactions, highest yields of products are obtained with unhindered methyl and 1° alkyl halides.

		nucleophile		product	
$CH_3CH_2{-}Br$	+	^-OH	$\xrightarrow{S_N2}$	$CH_3CH_2{-}OH$	alcohol
$CH_3CH_2CH_2{-}Cl$	+	$^-OCH_3$	$\xrightarrow{S_N2}$	$CH_3CH_2CH_2{-}OCH_3$	unsymmetrical ether
$CH_3CH_2{-}Br$	+	$^-OCH_2CH_3$	$\xrightarrow{S_N2}$	$CH_3CH_2{-}OCH_2CH_3$	symmetrical ether

The preparation of ethers by this method is called the **Williamson ether synthesis,** and, although it was first reported in the 1800s, it is still the most general method to prepare an ether. Unsymmetrical ethers can be synthesized in two different ways, but often one path is preferred.

For example, isopropyl methyl ether can be prepared from CH_3O^- and 2-bromopropane (Path [a]), or from $(CH_3)_2CHO^-$ and bromomethane (Path [b]). Because the mechanism is S_N2, **the preferred path uses the less sterically hindered halide,** CH_3Br—Path [b].

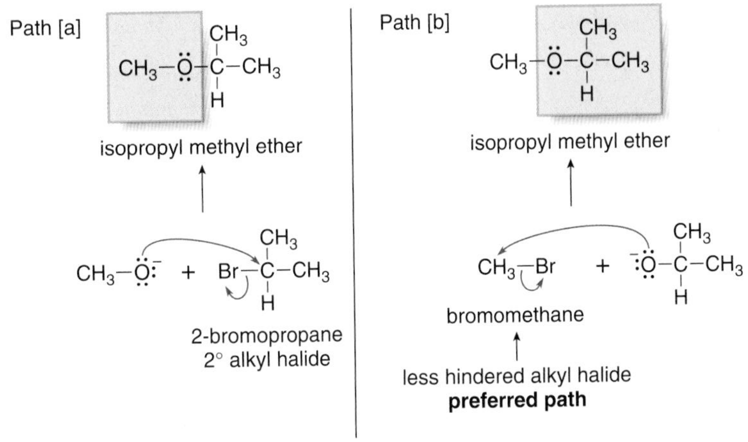
Path [a]
isopropyl methyl ether
2-bromopropane
2° alkyl halide
Path [b]
isopropyl methyl ether
bromomethane
less hindered alkyl halide
preferred path

Problem 9.10 Draw the organic product of each reaction and classify the product as an alcohol, symmetrical ether, or unsymmetrical ether.

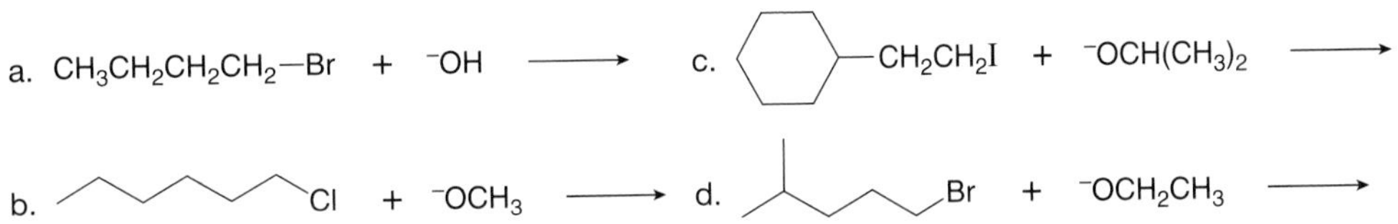
a. CH3CH2CH2CH2—Br + ⁻OH
b. Cl + ⁻OCH3
c. CH2CH2I + ⁻OCH(CH3)2
d. Br + ⁻OCH2CH3

Problem 9.11 A key step in the synthesis of the antidepressant paroxetine (trade name Paxil) involves a Williamson ether synthesis of the acyclic ether in **X.** Draw two different routes to this ether and state which is preferred.

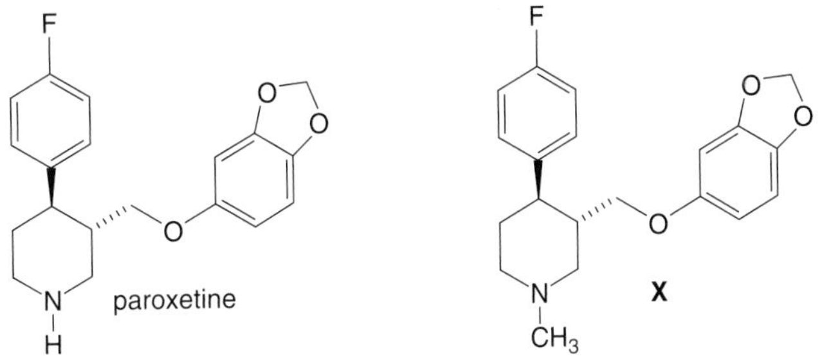
paroxetine
X

A **hydroxide** nucleophile is needed to synthesize an alcohol, and salts such as **NaOH** and **KOH** are inexpensive and commercially available. An **alkoxide** salt is needed to make an ether. Simple alkoxides such as sodium methoxide ($NaOCH_3$) can be purchased, but others are prepared from alcohols by a Brønsted–Lowry acid–base reaction. For example, **sodium ethoxide ($NaOCH_2CH_3$)** is prepared by treating ethanol with NaH.

NaH is an especially good base for forming an alkoxide, because the by-product of the reaction, H_2, is a gas that just bubbles out of the reaction mixture.

An acid–base reaction

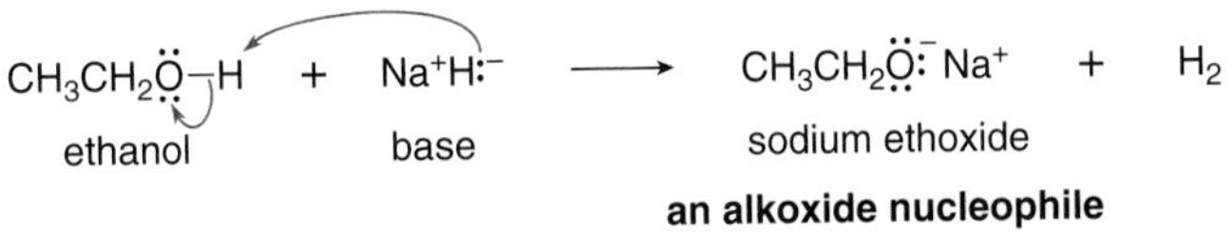
ethanol
base
sodium ethoxide
an alkoxide nucleophile

Sample Problem 9.2 Draw the product of the following two-step reaction sequence.

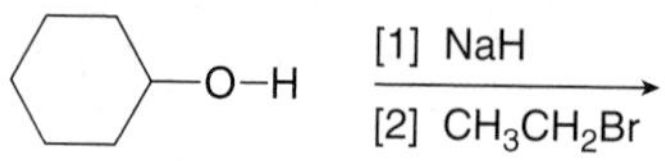
O–H
[1] NaH
[2] CH_3CH_2Br

Solution

[1] The base removes a proton from the OH group, forming an alkoxide.

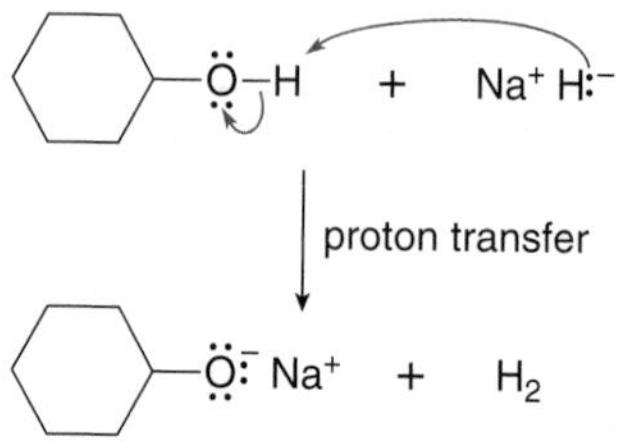
+ Na⁺ H:⁻
proton transfer
Na⁺ + H_2

alkoxide nucleophile

[2] The alkoxide acts as a nucleophile in an S_N2 reaction, forming an ether.

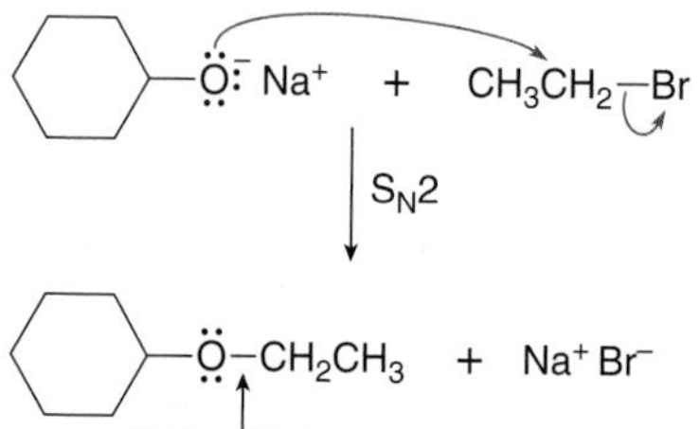
Na⁺ + CH_3CH_2–Br
S_N2
CH_2CH_3 + Na⁺ Br⁻

new bond

- This two-step sequence converts an alcohol to an ether.

When an organic compound contains both a hydroxy group and a halogen atom on adjacent carbon atoms, an *intramolecular* version of this reaction forms an epoxide. The starting material for this two-step sequence, a **halohydrin,** is prepared from an alkene, as we will learn in Chapter 10.

Epoxide synthesis—A two-step procedure

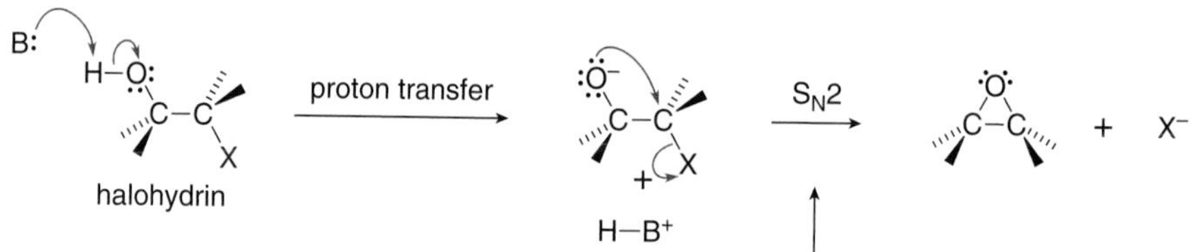
B:
proton transfer
H–B⁺
S_N2
+ X⁻

halohydrin

intramolecular S_N2 reaction

Problem 9.12 Draw the products of each reaction.

a. $CH_3CH_2CH_2$–OH + NaH ⟶

b. 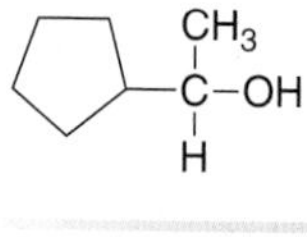 + $NaNH_2$ ⟶

c. 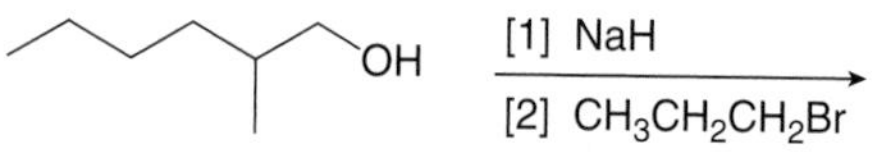
OH
[1] NaH
[2] $CH_3CH_2CH_2Br$

d. 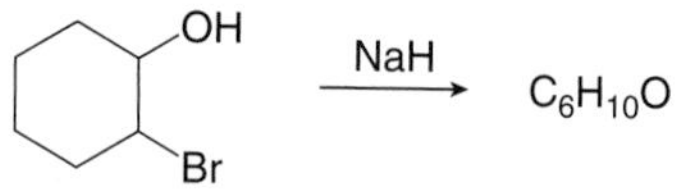
OH
Br
NaH
$C_6H_{10}O$

9.7 General Features—Reactions of Alcohols, Ethers, and Epoxides

We begin our discussion of the chemical reactions of alcohols, ethers, and epoxides with a look at the general reactive features of each functional group.

9.7A Alcohols

Unlike many families of molecules, the reactions of alcohols do *not* fit neatly into a single reaction class. In Chapter 9, we discuss only the substitution and β elimination reactions of alcohols. Alcohols are also key starting materials in oxidation reactions (Chapter 12), and their polar O–H bond makes them more acidic than many other organic compounds, a feature we will explore in Chapter 19.

Alcohols are similar to alkyl halides in that both contain an electronegative element bonded to an sp^3 hybridized carbon atom. Alkyl halides contain a good leaving group (X^-), however, whereas alcohols do not. Nucleophilic substitution with ROH as starting material would displace $^-$**OH, a strong base and therefore a poor leaving group.**

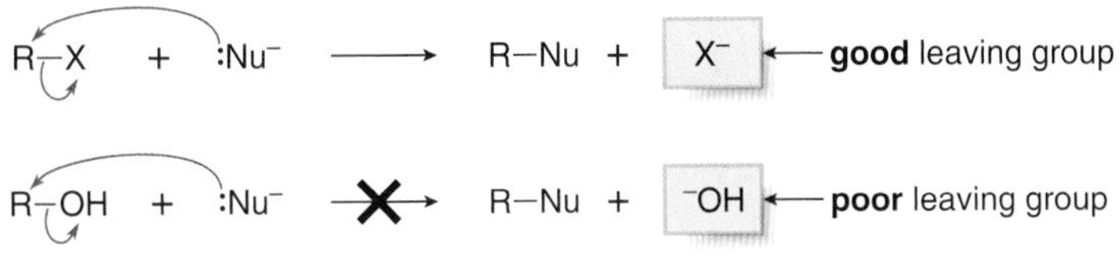

For an alcohol to undergo a nucleophilic substitution or elimination reaction, the **OH group must be converted into a better leaving group.** This can be done by reaction with acid. Treatment of an alcohol with a strong acid like HCl or H_2SO_4 protonates the O atom via an acid–base reaction. This transforms the $^-$OH leaving group into **H_2O, a weak base and therefore a good leaving group.**

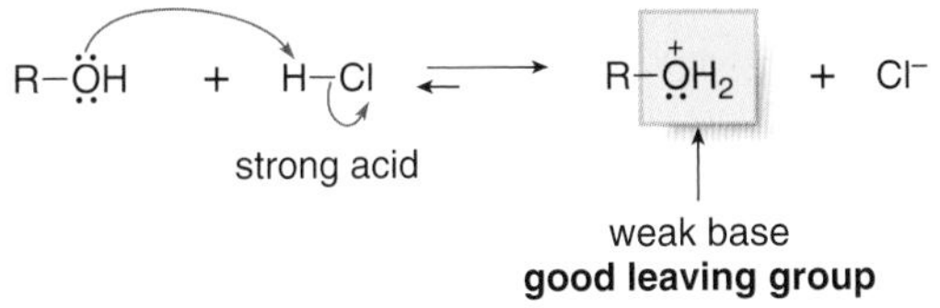

If the OH group of an alcohol is made into a good leaving group, alcohols *can* undergo β elimination and nucleophilic substitution, as described in Sections 9.8–9.12.

Because the pK_a of $(ROH_2)^+$ is ~−2, protonation of an alcohol occurs only with very strong acids—namely, those having a pK_a ≤ −2.

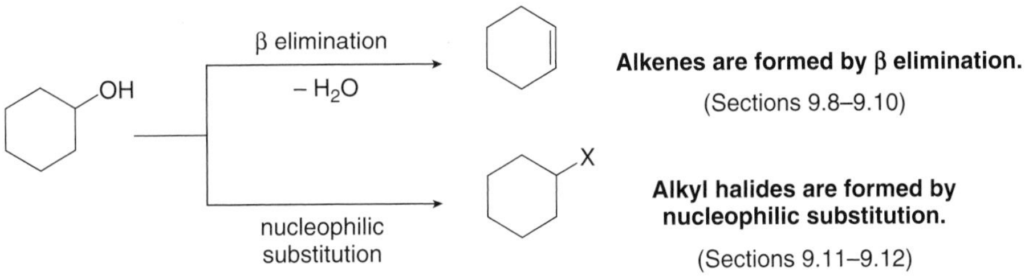

9.7B Ethers and Epoxides

Like alcohols, **ethers do not contain a good leaving group,** which means that nucleophilic substitution and β elimination do not occur directly. Ethers undergo fewer useful reactions than alcohols.

Epoxides don't have a good leaving group either, but they have one characteristic that neither alcohols nor ethers have: **the "leaving group" is contained in a strained three-membered ring.** Nucleophilic attack opens the three-membered ring and relieves angle strain, making nucleophilic attack a favorable process that occurs even with the poor leaving group. Specific examples are presented in Section 9.15.

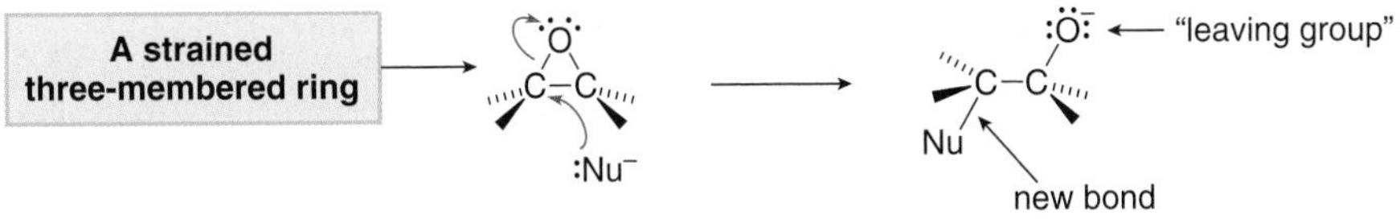

9.8 Dehydration of Alcohols to Alkenes

The dehydrohalogenation of alkyl halides, discussed in Chapter 8, is one way to introduce a π bond into a molecule. Another way is to eliminate water from an alcohol in a **dehydration** reaction.

- **Dehydration, like dehydrohalogenation, is a β elimination reaction in which the elements of OH and H are removed from the α and β carbon atoms, respectively.**

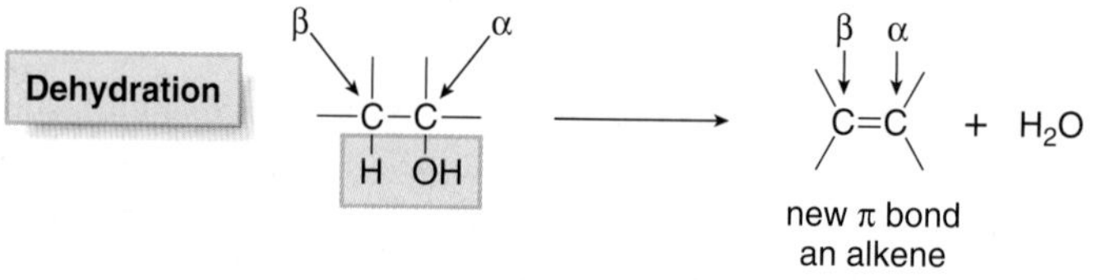
Dehydration
β
α
H OH
β α
+ H_2O
new π bond
an alkene

Dehydration is typically carried out using H_2SO_4 and other strong acids, or phosphorus oxychloride ($POCl_3$) in the presence of an amine base. We consider dehydration in acid first, followed by dehydration with $POCl_3$ in Section 9.10.

9.8A General Features of Dehydration in Acid

Alcohols undergo dehydration in the presence of strong acid to afford alkenes, as illustrated in Equations [1] and [2]. Typical acids used for this conversion are H_2SO_4 or *p*-toluenesulfonic acid (abbreviated as TsOH).

Recall from Section 2.6 that *p*-toluenesulfonic acid is a strong organic acid ($pK_a = -7$).

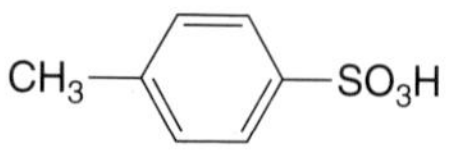
CH_3
SO_3H

p-toluenesulfonic acid
TsOH

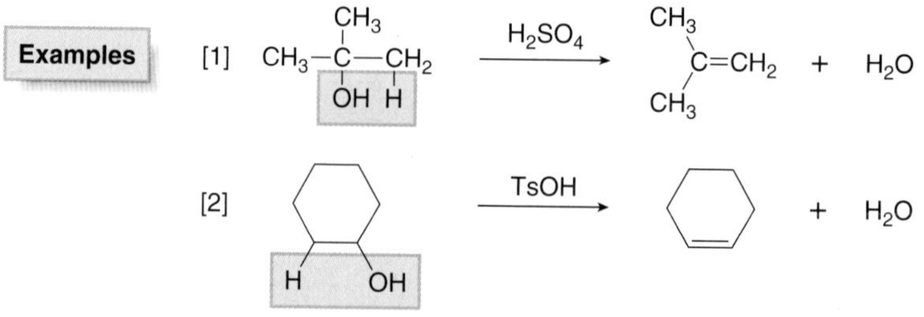
Examples
[1]
CH_3
CH_3-C-CH_2
OH H
H_2SO_4
$C=CH_2$
+ H_2O
[2]
H OH
TsOH
+ H_2O

More substituted alcohols dehydrate more readily, giving rise to the following order of reactivity:

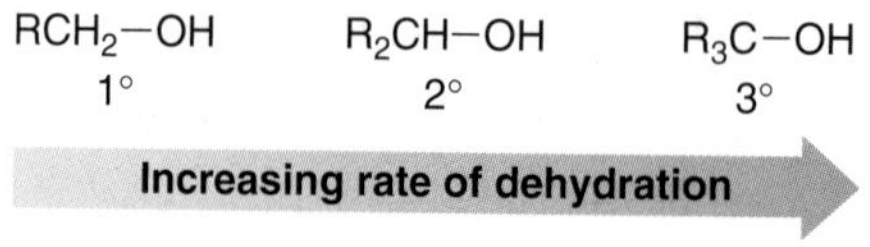
RCH_2-OH
1°
R_2CH-OH
2°
R_3C-OH
3°
Increasing rate of dehydration

When an alcohol has two or three different β carbons, dehydration is regioselective and follows the Zaitsev rule. **The more substituted alkene is the major product when a mixture of constitutional isomers is possible.** For example, elimination of H and OH from 2-methyl-2-butanol yields two constitutional isomers: the trisubstituted alkene **A** as major product and the disubstituted alkene **B** as minor product.

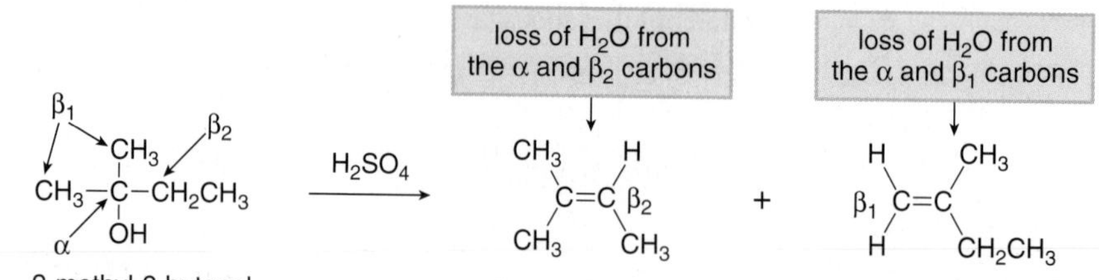
loss of H_2O from the α and $β_2$ carbons
loss of H_2O from the α and $β_1$ carbons
$β_1$
$β_2$
CH_3
$CH_3-C-CH_2CH_3$
OH
α
H_2SO_4
CH_3 H
C=C $β_2$
CH_3 CH_3
+
H CH_3
$β_1$ C=C
H CH_2CH_3

2-methyl-2-butanol

two different β carbons, labeled $β_1$ and $β_2$

A
major product
trisubstituted alkene

B
minor product
disubstituted alkene

Problem 9.13 Draw the products formed when each alcohol undergoes dehydration with TsOH, and label the major product when a mixture results.

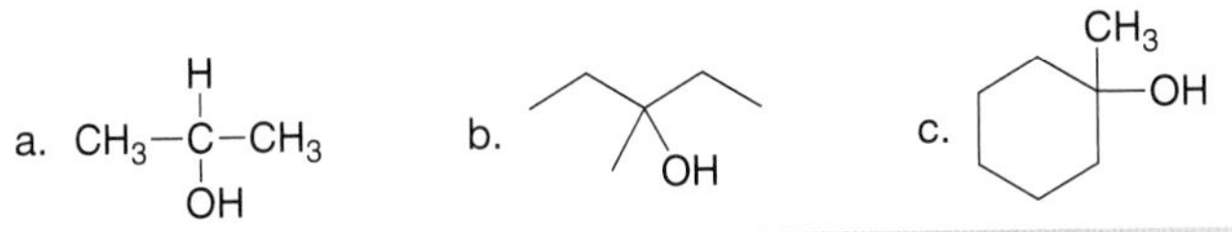

Problem 9.14 Rank the alcohols in order of increasing reactivity when dehydrated with H_2SO_4.

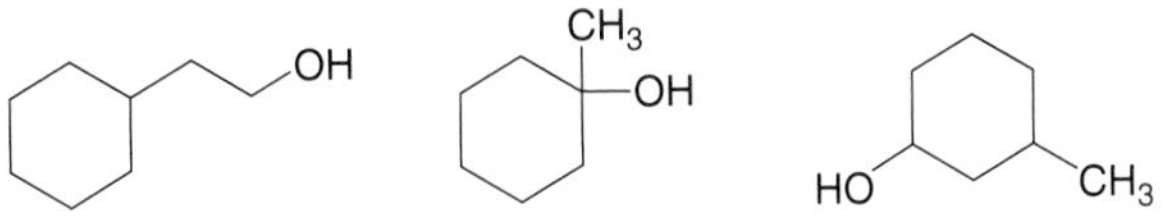

9.8B The E1 Mechanism for the Dehydration of 2° and 3° Alcohols

The mechanism of dehydration depends on the structure of the alcohol: **2° and 3° alcohols react by an E1 mechanism, whereas 1° alcohols react by an E2 mechanism.** Regardless of the type of alcohol, however, strong acid is *always* needed to protonate the O atom to form a good leaving group.

The E1 dehydration of 2° and 3° alcohols is illustrated with $(CH_3)_3COH$ (a 3° alcohol) as starting material to form $(CH_3)_2C{=}CH_2$ as product (Mechanism 9.1). The mechanism consists of **three steps.**

Mechanism 9.1 Dehydration of 2° and 3° ROH—An E1 Mechanism

Step [1] The O atom is protonated.

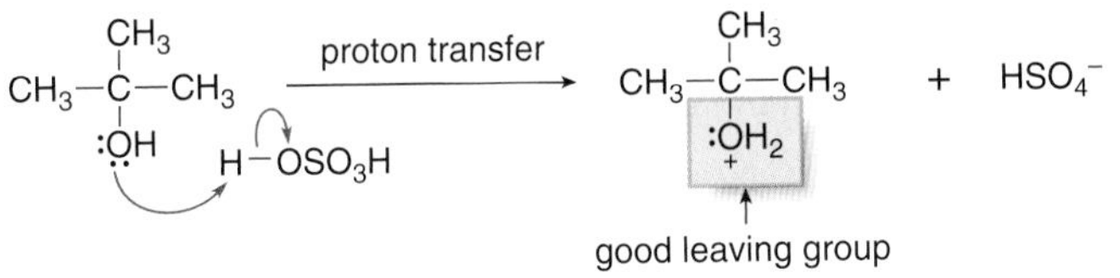

- **Protonation of the oxygen atom** of the alcohol converts a poor leaving group (^-OH) into a good leaving group (H_2O).

Step [2] The C–O bond is broken.

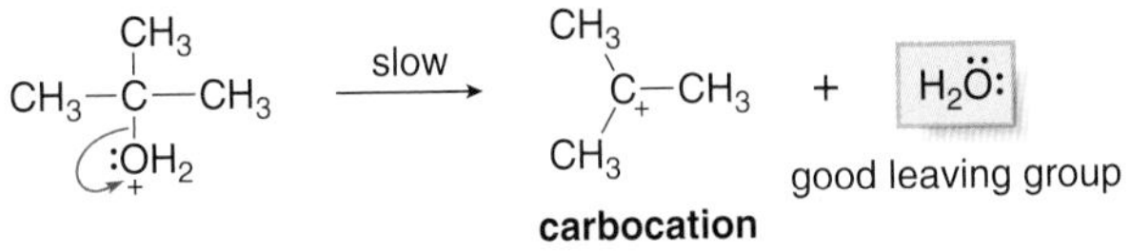

- **Heterolysis of the C–O bond forms a carbocation.** This step is rate-determining because it involves only bond cleavage.

Step [3] A C–H bond is cleaved and the π bond is formed.

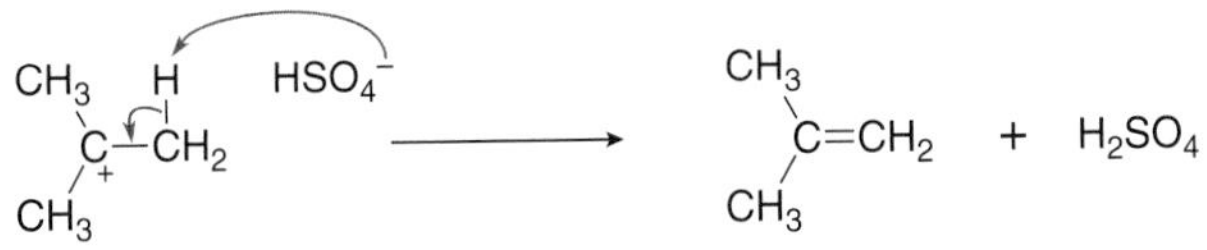

- **A base (such as HSO_4^- or H_2O) removes a proton** from a carbon adjacent to the carbocation (a β carbon). The electron pair in the C–H bond is used to form the new π bond.

Thus, **dehydration of 2° and 3° alcohols occurs via an E1 mechanism with an added first step.**

- Step [1] protonates the OH group to make a good leaving group.
- Steps [2] and [3] are the two steps of an E1 mechanism: loss of a leaving group (H_2O in this case) to form a carbocation, followed by removal of a β proton to form a π bond.
- The acid used to protonate the alcohol in Step [1] is regenerated upon removal of the proton in Step [3], so dehydration is **acid-catalyzed.**

The E1 dehydration of 2° and 3° alcohols with acid gives clean elimination products without by-products formed from an S_N1 reaction. This makes the E1 dehydration of alcohols much more synthetically useful than the E1 dehydrohalogenation of alkyl halides (Section 8.7). Clean elimination takes place because the reaction mixture contains no good nucleophile to react with the intermediate carbocation, so no competing S_N1 reaction occurs.

9.8C The E2 Mechanism for the Dehydration of 1° Alcohols

Because 1° carbocations are highly unstable, the dehydration of 1° alcohols cannot occur by an E1 mechanism involving a carbocation intermediate. With 1° alcohols, therefore, **dehydration follows an E2 mechanism.** The two-step process for the conversion of $CH_3CH_2CH_2OH$ (a 1° alcohol) to $CH_3CH{=}CH_2$ with H_2SO_4 as acid catalyst is shown in Mechanism 9.2.

Mechanism 9.2 Dehydration of a 1° ROH—An E2 Mechanism

Step [1] The O atom is protonated.

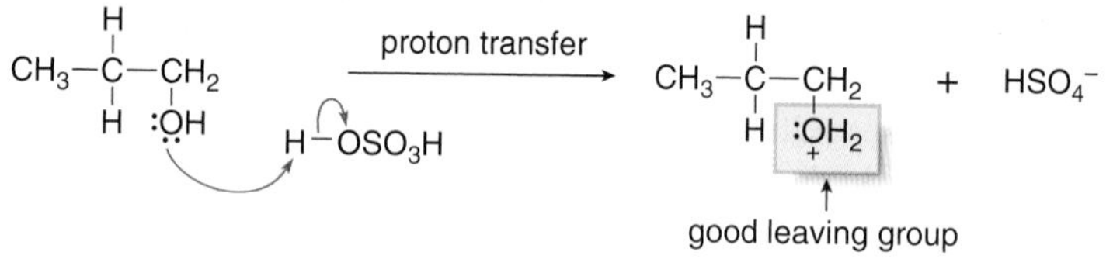

- **Protonation of the oxygen atom** of the alcohol converts a poor leaving group (^-OH) into a good leaving group (H_2O).

Step [2] The C–H and C–O bonds are broken and the π bond is formed.

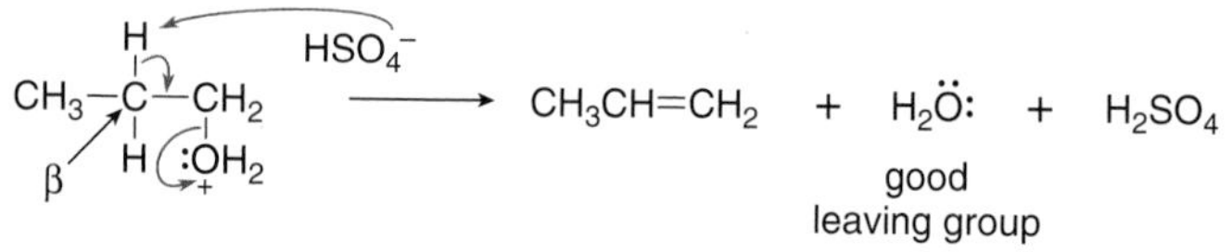

- **Two bonds are broken and two bonds are formed in a single step:** the base (HSO_4^- or H_2O) removes a proton from the β carbon; the electron pair in the β C–H bond forms the new π bond; the leaving group (H_2O) comes off with the electron pair in the C–O bond.

The dehydration of a 1° alcohol begins with the protonation of the OH group to form a good leaving group, just as in the dehydration of a 2° or 3° alcohol. With 1° alcohols, however, loss of the leaving group and removal of a β proton occur at the *same* time, so that no highly unstable 1° carbocation is generated.

Problem 9.15 Draw the structure of each transition state in the two-step mechanism for the reaction, $CH_3CH_2CH_2OH + H_2SO_4 \rightarrow CH_3CH{=}CH_2 + H_2O$.

9.8D Le Châtelier's Principle

Although entropy favors product formation in dehydration (one molecule of reactant forms two molecules of products), enthalpy does not, because the two σ bonds broken in the reactant are stronger than the σ and π bonds formed in the products. For example, $\Delta H°$ for the dehydration of CH_3CH_2OH to $CH_2{=}CH_2$ is +38 kJ/mol (Figure 9.6).

According to **Le Châtelier's principle, a system at equilibrium will react to counteract any disturbance to the equilibrium.** Thus, removing a product from a reaction mixture as it is formed drives the equilibrium to the right, forming more product.

Le Châtelier's principle can be used to favor products in dehydration reactions because the alkene product has a lower boiling point than the alcohol reactant. Thus, the alkene can be distilled from the reaction mixture as it is formed, leaving the alcohol and acid to react further, forming more product.

Figure 9.6
The dehydration of CH_3CH_2OH to $CH_2{=}CH_2$—An endothermic reaction

Overall reaction:

$$CH_3CH_2OH \xrightarrow{H_2SO_4} CH_2{=}CH_2 + H_2O$$

$\Delta H°$ calculation:

[1] Bonds broken

	$\Delta H°$ (kJ/mol)
CH_3CH_2–OH	+393
$HOCH_2CH_2$–H	+410
Total	+803 kJ/mol

Energy needed to break bonds.

[2] Bonds formed

	$\Delta H°$ (kJ/mol)
$CH_2{=}CH_2$ π bond	–267
H–OH	–498
Total	–765 kJ/mol

Energy released in forming bonds.

[3] Overall $\Delta H°$ =

sum in Step [1] + sum in Step [2]

+803 kJ/mol
–765 kJ/mol

$\Delta H°$ = +38 kJ/mol

The reaction is endothermic.

[Values taken from Appendix C.]

9.9 Carbocation Rearrangements

Sometimes "unexpected" products are formed in dehydration; that is, the carbon skeletons of the starting material and product might be different, or the double bond might be in an unexpected location. For example, the dehydration of 3,3-dimethyl-2-butanol yields two alkenes, whose carbon skeletons do not match the carbon framework of the starting material.

The carbon skeletons of the reactant and products are different.

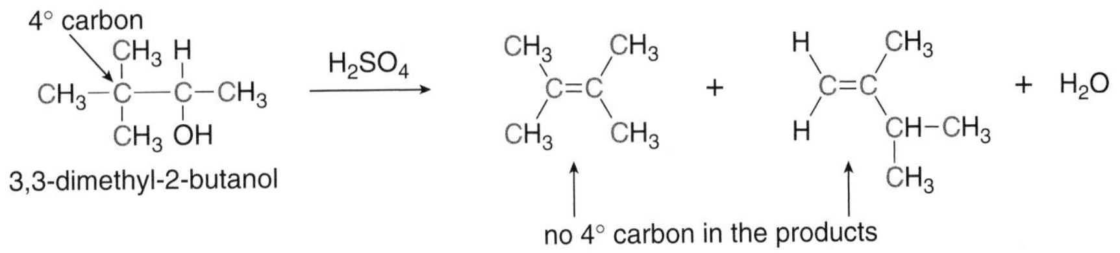

This phenomenon sometimes occurs when carbocations are reactive intermediates. **A less stable carbocation can rearrange to a more stable carbocation by shift of a hydrogen atom or an alkyl group.** These rearrangements are called **1,2-shifts,** because they involve migration of an alkyl group or hydrogen atom from one carbon to an adjacent carbon atom. The migrating group moves with the two electrons that bonded it to the carbon skeleton.

Because the migrating group in a 1,2-shift moves with two bonding electrons, the carbon it leaves behind now has only three bonds (six electrons), giving it a net positive (+) charge.

Carbocation rearrangement

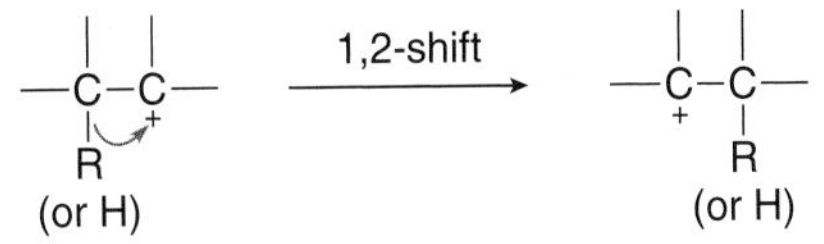

- **Movement of a hydrogen atom is called a 1,2-hydride shift.**
- **Movement of an alkyl group is called a 1,2-alkyl shift.**

The dehydration of 3,3-dimethyl-2-butanol illustrates the rearrangement of a 2° to a 3° carbocation by a **1,2-methyl shift,** as shown in Mechanism 9.3. The carbocation rearrangement occurs in Step [3] of the four-step mechanism.

Mechanism 9.3 A 1,2-Methyl Shift—Carbocation Rearrangement During Dehydration

Steps [1] and [2] Formation of a 2° carbocation

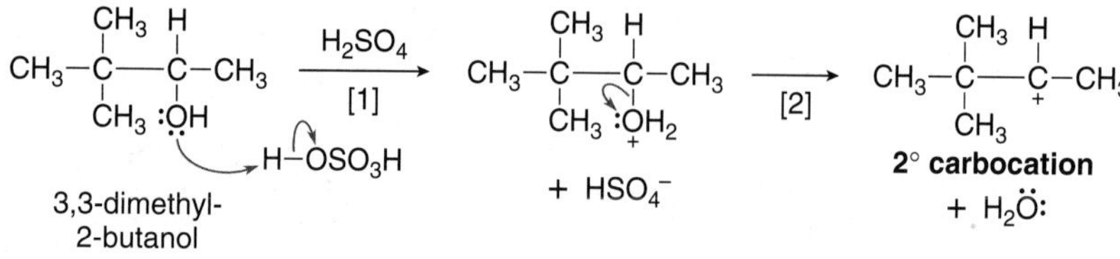

- **Protonation of the oxygen atom** on the alcohol in Step [1] forms a good leaving group (H_2O), and loss of H_2O in Step [2] forms a **2° carbocation.**

Step [3] Rearrangement of the carbocation by a 1,2-CH_3 shift

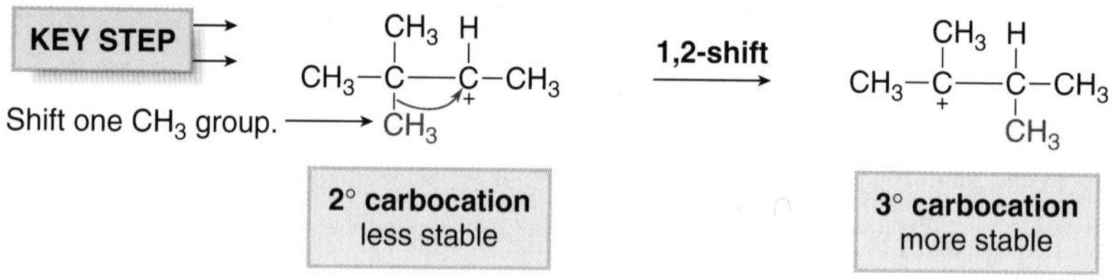

- **1,2-Shift** of a CH_3 group from one carbon to the adjacent carbon converts the 2° carbocation to a more stable 3° carbocation.

Step [4] Loss of a proton to form the π bond

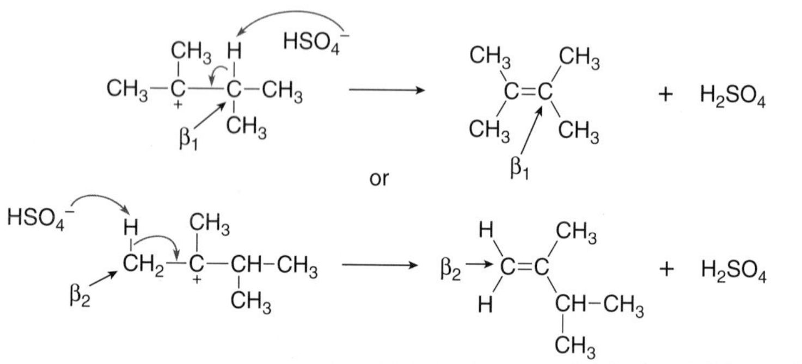

- **Loss of a proton** from a β carbon (labeled β_1 and β_2) forms two different alkenes.

Steps [1], [2], and [4] in the mechanism for the dehydration of 3,3-dimethyl-2-butanol are exactly the same steps previously seen in dehydration: protonation, loss of H_2O, and loss of a proton. Only Step [3], rearrangement of the less stable 2° carbocation to the more stable 3° carbocation, is new.

- **1,2-Shifts convert a less stable carbocation to a more stable carbocation.**

For example, 2° carbocation **A** rearranges to the more stable 3° carbocation by a 1,2-hydride shift, whereas carbocation **B** does not rearrange because it is 3° to begin with.

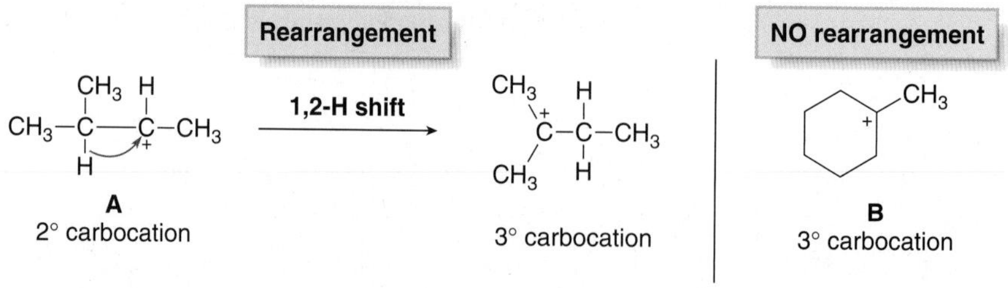

Sample Problem 9.3 illustrates a dehydration reaction that occurs with a **1,2-hydride** shift.

Sample Problem 9.3 Show how the dehydration of alcohol **X** forms alkene **Y** using a 1,2-hydride shift.

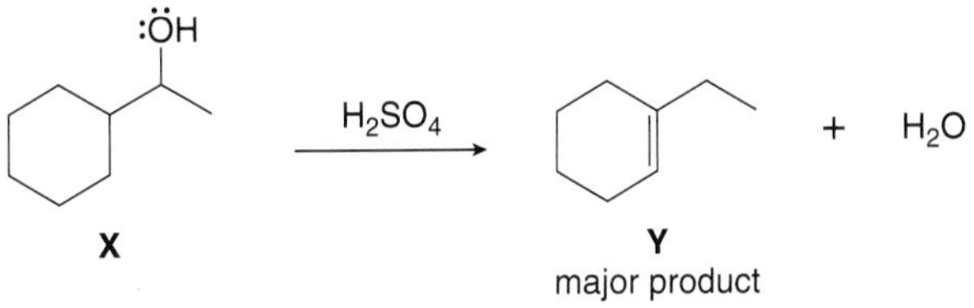

Solution

Steps [1] and [2] Protonation of **X** and loss of H_2O form a 2° carbocation.

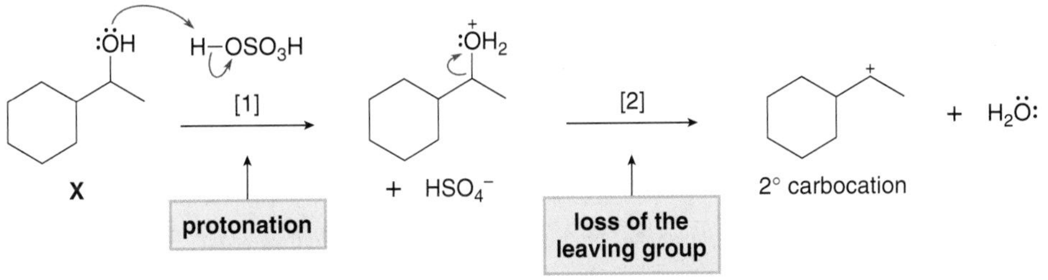

Steps [3] and [4] Rearrangement of the 2° carbocation by a 1,2-hydride shift forms a more stable 3° carbocation. Loss of a proton from a β carbon forms alkene **Y.**

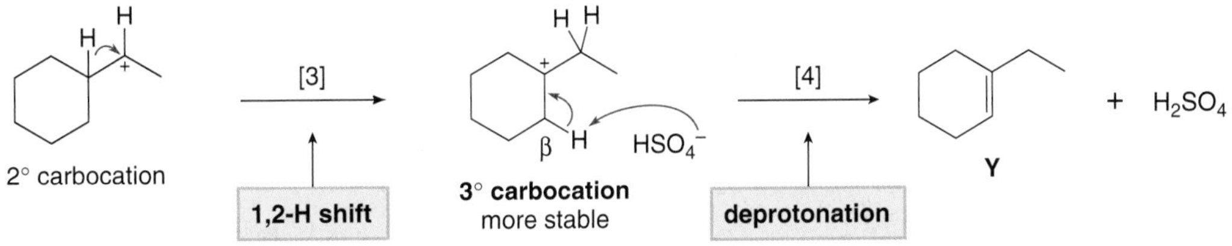

Problem 9.16 What other alkene is also formed along with **Y** in Sample Problem 9.3? What alkenes would form from **X** if no carbocation rearrangement occurred?

Rearrangements are not unique to dehydration reactions. **Rearrangements can occur whenever a carbocation is formed as reactive intermediate,** meaning any S_N1 or E1 reaction. In fact, the formation of rearranged products often indicates the presence of a carbocation intermediate.

Problem 9.17 Show how a 1,2-shift forms a more stable carbocation from each intermediate.

a. $(CH_3)_2CH\overset{+}{C}HCH_2CH_3$

b. 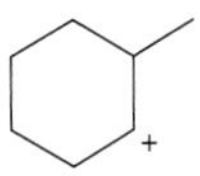

c. 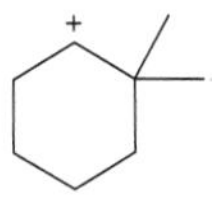

Problem 9.18 Explain how the reaction of $(CH_3)_2CHCH(Cl)CH_3$ with H_2O yields two substitution products, $(CH_3)_2CHCH(OH)CH_3$ and $(CH_3)_2C(OH)CH_2CH_3$.

9.10 Dehydration Using $POCl_3$ and Pyridine

Because some organic compounds decompose in the presence of strong acid, other methods that avoid strong acid have been developed to convert alcohols to alkenes. A common method uses phosphorus oxychloride ($POCl_3$) and pyridine (an amine base) in place of H_2SO_4 or TsOH. For example, the treatment of cyclohexanol with $POCl_3$ and pyridine forms cyclohexene in good yield.

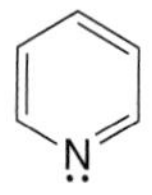
pyridine

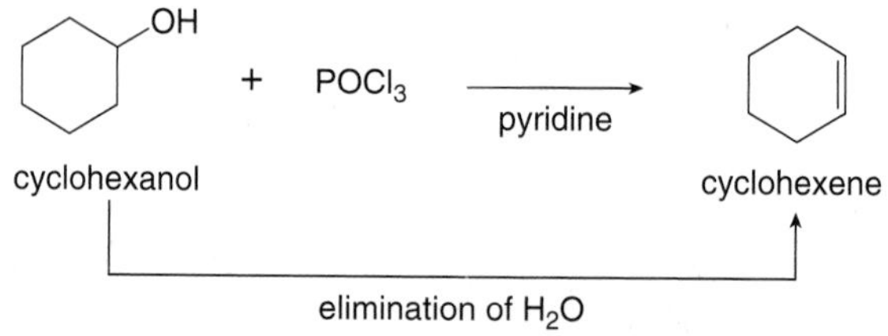

$POCl_3$ serves much the same role as strong acid does in acid-catalyzed dehydration. **It converts a poor leaving group (^-OH) into a good leaving group.** Dehydration then proceeds by an **E2 mechanism,** as shown in Mechanism 9.4. Pyridine is the base that removes a β proton during elimination.

Mechanism 9.4 Dehydration Using $POCl_3$ + Pyridine—An E2 Mechanism

Steps [1] and [2] Conversion of OH to a good leaving group

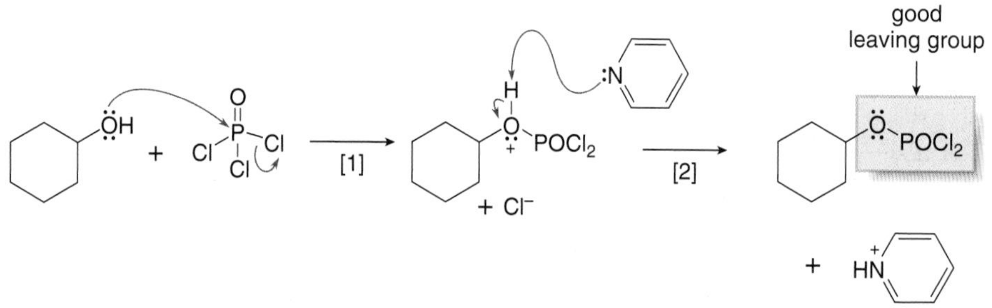

- A two-step process converts an OH group into $OPOCl_2$, **a good leaving group:** reaction of the OH group with $POCl_3$ followed by removal of a proton.

Step [3] The C–H and C–O bonds are broken and the π bond is formed.

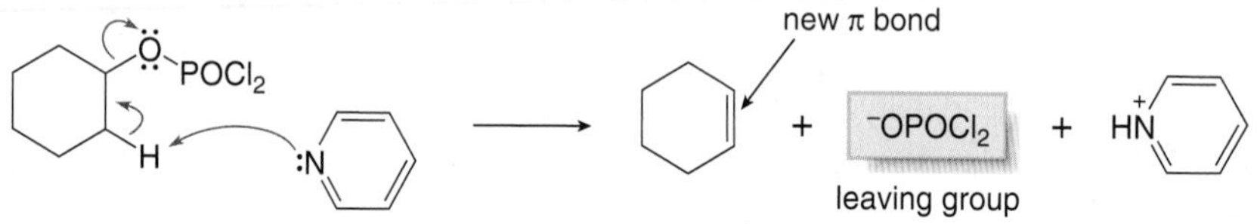

- **Two bonds are broken and two bonds are formed in a single step:** the base (pyridine) removes a proton from the β carbon; the electron pair in the β C–H bond forms the new π bond; the leaving group ($^-OPOCl_2$) comes off with the electron pair from the C–O bond.

- Steps [1] and [2] of the mechanism convert the OH group to a good leaving group.
- In Step [3], the C–H and C–O bonds are broken and the π bond is formed.
- No rearrangements occur during dehydration with $POCl_3$, suggesting that carbocations are not formed as intermediates in this reaction.

We have now learned about two different reagents for alcohol dehydration—strong acid (H_2SO_4 or TsOH) and $POCl_3$ + pyridine. The best dehydration method for a given alcohol is often hard to know ahead of time, and this is why organic chemists develop more than one method for a given type of transformation. Two examples of dehydration reactions used in the synthesis of natural products are given in Figure 9.7.

Figure 9.7

Dehydration reactions in the synthesis of two natural products

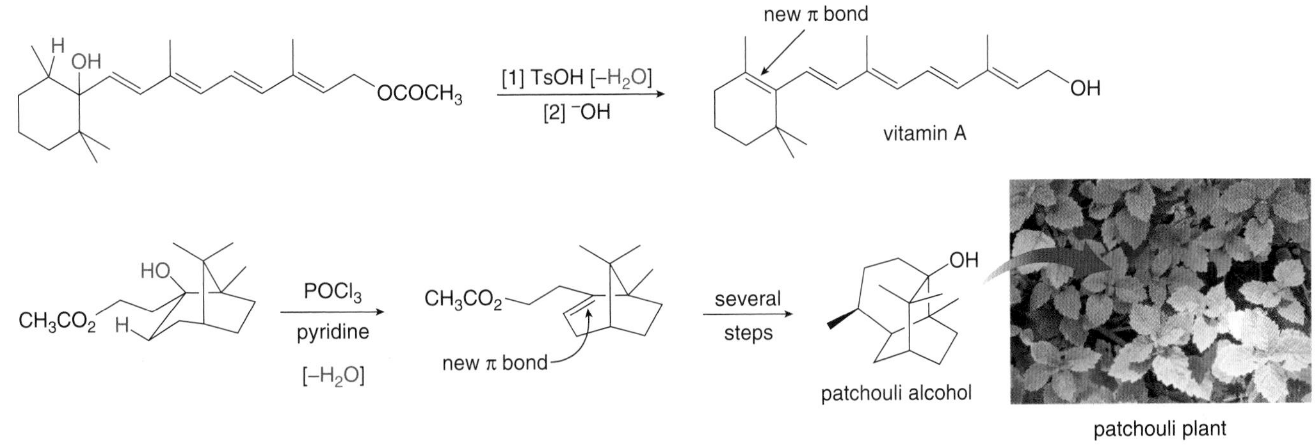

- **Patchouli alcohol,** obtained from the patchouli plant native to Malaysia, has been used in perfumery because of its exotic fragrance. In the 1800s, shawls imported from India were often packed with patchouli leaves to ward off insects, thus permeating the clothing with the distinctive odor.

9.11 Conversion of Alcohols to Alkyl Halides with HX

Alcohols undergo nucleophilic substitution reactions only if the OH group is converted into a better leaving group before nucleophilic attack. Thus, substitution does *not* occur when an alcohol is treated with X^- because ^-OH is a poor leaving group (Reaction [1]), but substitution *does* occur on treatment of an alcohol with HX because H_2O is now the leaving group (Reaction [2]).

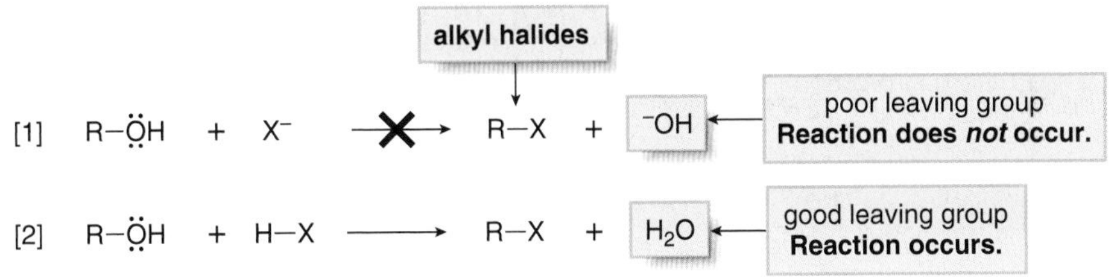

- **The reaction of alcohols with HX (X = Cl, Br, I) is a general method to prepare 1°, 2°, and 3° alkyl halides.**

$$CH_3CH_2CH_2{-}OH \xrightarrow{HBr} CH_3CH_2CH_2{-}Br + H_2O$$

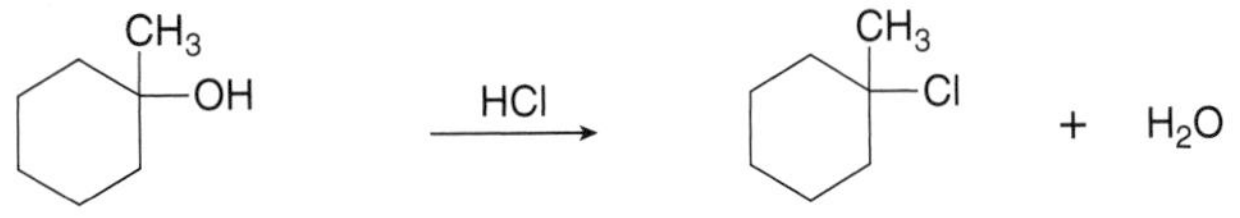

More substituted alcohols usually react more rapidly with HX:

$RCH_2{-}OH$	$R_2CH{-}OH$	$R_3C{-}OH$
1°	2°	3°

Increasing rate of reaction with HX →

Problem 9.19 Draw the products of each reaction.

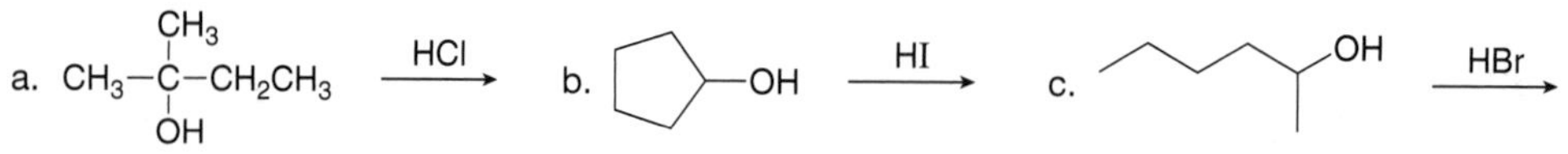

9.11A Two Mechanisms for the Reaction of ROH with HX

How does the reaction of ROH with HX occur? Acid–base reactions are very fast, so the strong acid HX protonates the OH group of the alcohol, forming a **good leaving group** (H_2O) and a **good nucleophile** (the conjugate base, X^-). Both components are needed for nucleophilic substitution. The mechanism of substitution of X^- for H_2O then depends on the structure of the R group.

When there is an oxygen-containing reactant and a strong acid, generally the first step in the mechanism is protonation of the oxygen atom.

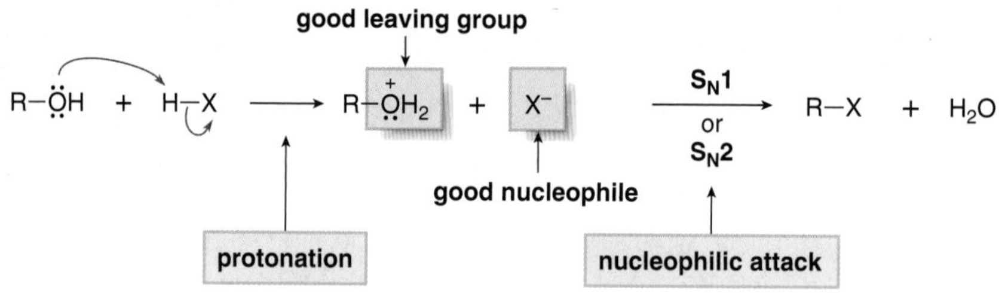

- **Methyl and 1° ROH form RX by an S_N2 mechanism.**
- **Secondary (2°) and 3° ROH form RX by an S_N1 mechanism.**

The reaction of CH_3CH_2OH with HBr illustrates the S_N2 mechanism of a 1° alcohol (Mechanism 9.5). Nucleophilic attack on the protonated alcohol occurs in one step: **the bond to the nucleophile X^- is formed *as* the bond to the leaving group (H_2O) is broken.**

Mechanism 9.5 Reaction of a 1° ROH with HX—An S_N2 Mechanism

Step [1] The O atom is protonated.

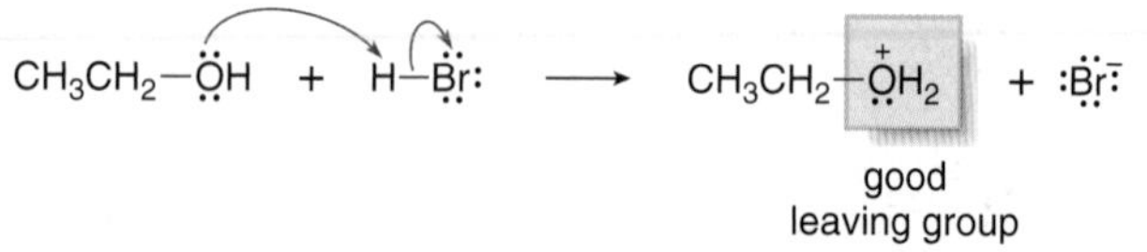

- **Protonation of the OH group** forms a good leaving group (H_2O).

Step [2] The C–O bond is broken as the C–Br bond is formed.

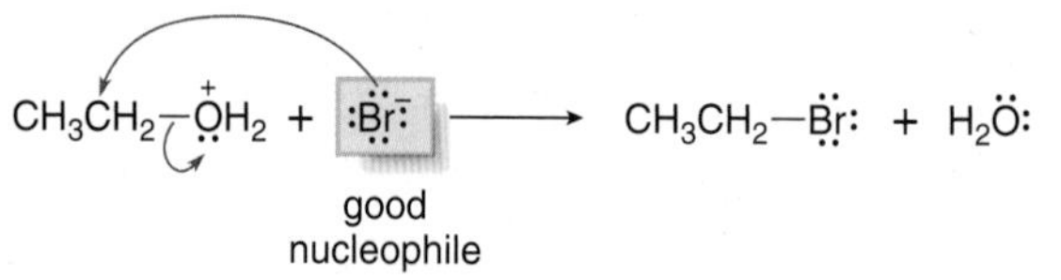

- **Nucleophilic attack of Br^- and loss of the leaving group** occur in a single step.

The reaction of $(CH_3)_3COH$ with HBr illustrates the S_N1 mechanism of a 3° alcohol (Mechanism 9.6). Nucleophilic attack on the protonated alcohol occurs in two steps: **the bond to the leaving group (H_2O) is broken *before* the bond to the nucleophile X^- is formed.**

Mechanism 9.6 Reaction of 2° and 3° ROH with HX—An S_N1 Mechanism

Step [1] The O atom is protonated.

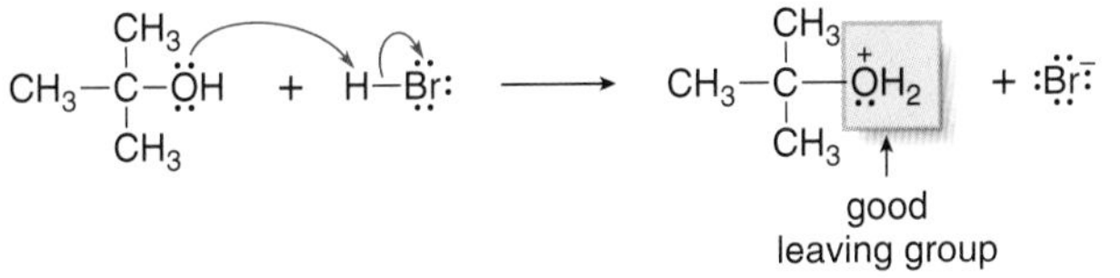

- **Protonation of the OH group** forms a good leaving group (H_2O).

Steps [2] and [3] The C–O bond is broken, and then the C–Br bond is formed.

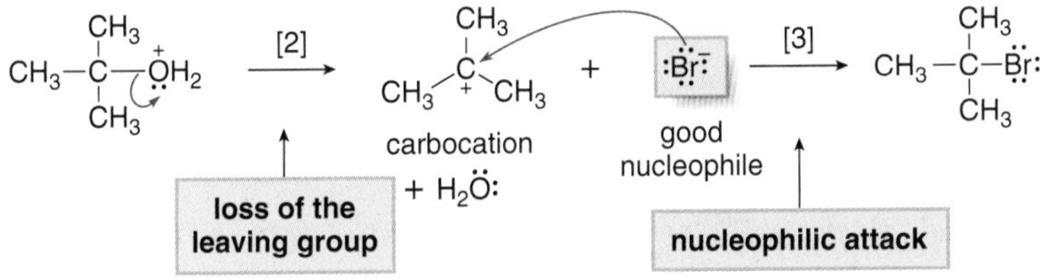

- Loss of the leaving group in Step [2] forms a **carbocation,** which reacts with the nucleophile (Br^-) in Step [3] to form the substitution product.

Both mechanisms begin with the same first step—protonation of the O atom to form a good leaving group—and both mechanisms give an alkyl halide (RX) as product. The mechanisms differ only in the timing of bond breaking and bond making.

The reactivity of hydrogen halides increases with increasing acidity:

H–Cl H–Br H–I

Increasing reactivity toward ROH →

Because Cl^- is a poorer nucleophile than Br^- or I^-, the reaction of 1° alcohols with HCl occurs only when an additional Lewis acid catalyst, usually $\mathbf{ZnCl_2}$, is added. $ZnCl_2$ complexes with the O atom of the alcohol in a Lewis acid–base reaction, making a leaving group and facilitating the S_N2 reaction.

1° Alcohols

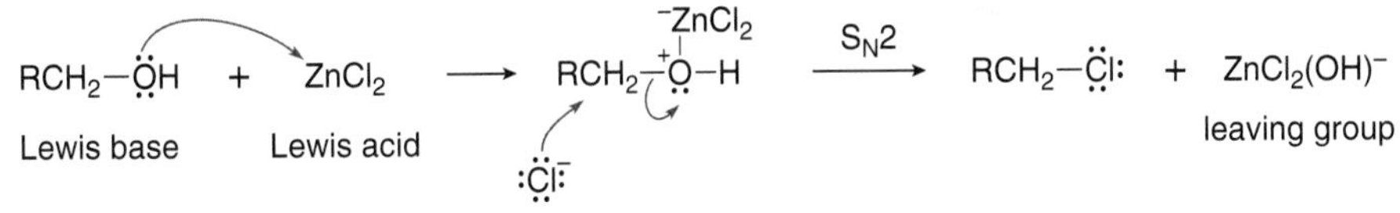

Knowing the mechanism allows us to predict the stereochemistry of the products when reaction occurs at a stereogenic center.

S_N2

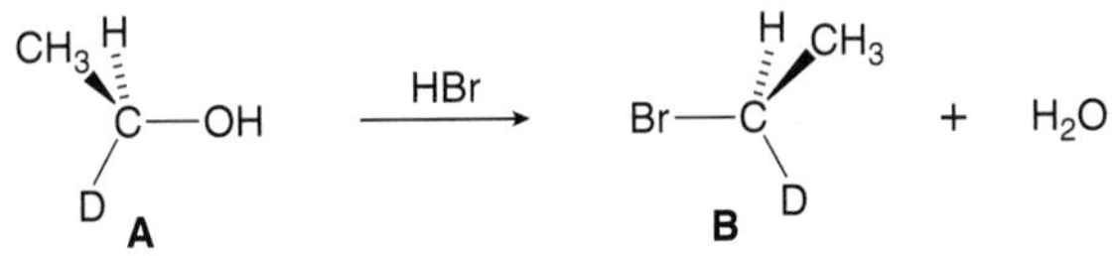

1° alcohol

product of inversion

S_N1

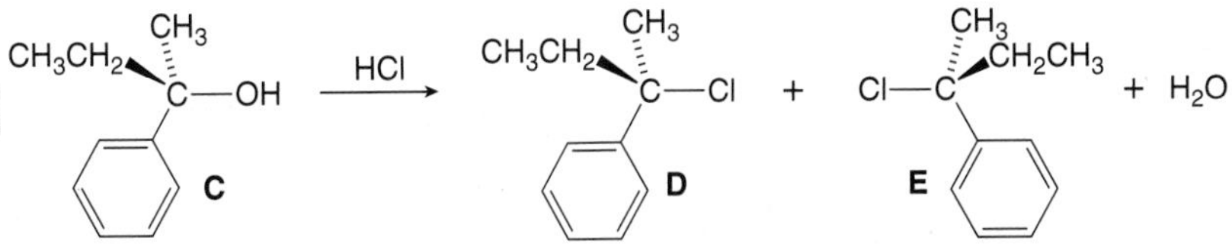

3° alcohol

racemic mixture

- The 1° alcohol **A** reacts with HBr via an S_N2 mechanism to yield the alkyl bromide **B** with **inversion** of stereochemistry at the stereogenic center.
- The 3° alcohol **C** reacts with HCl via an S_N1 mechanism to yield a **racemic mixture** of alkyl chlorides **D** and **E,** because a trigonal planar carbocation intermediate is formed.

Problem 9.20 Draw the products of each reaction, indicating the stereochemistry around any stereogenic centers.

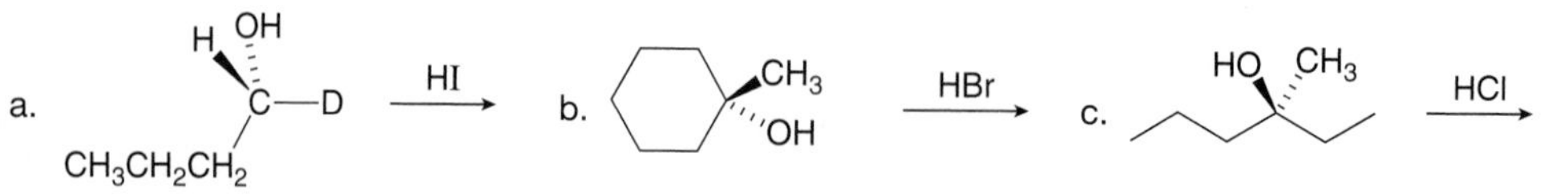

9.11B Carbocation Rearrangement in the S_N1 Reaction

Because carbocations are formed in the S_N1 reaction of 2° and 3° alcohols with HX, **carbocation rearrangements are possible,** as illustrated in Sample Problem 9.4.

Sample Problem 9.4 Draw a stepwise mechanism for the following reaction.

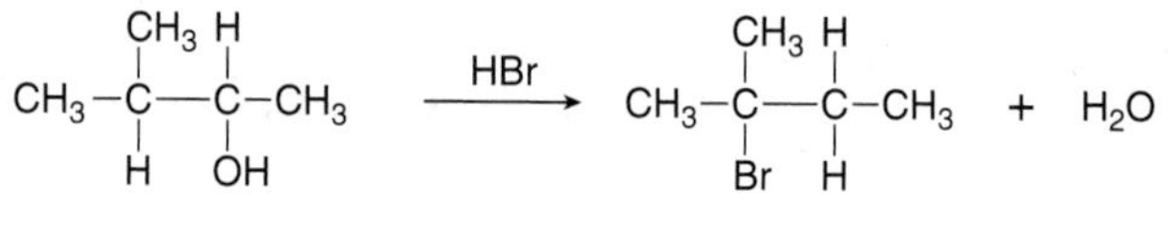

Solution

A 2° alcohol reacts with HBr by an S_N1 mechanism. Because substitution converts a 2° alcohol to a 3° alkyl halide in this example, a carbocation rearrangement must occur.

Steps [1] and [2] Protonation of the O atom and then loss of H_2O form a 2° carbocation.

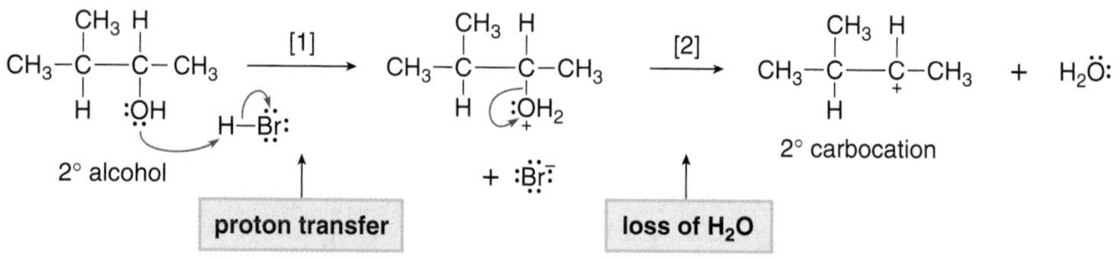

Steps [3] and [4] **Rearrangement of the 2° carbocation by a 1,2-hydride shift forms a more stable 3° carbocation.** Nucleophilic attack forms the substitution product.

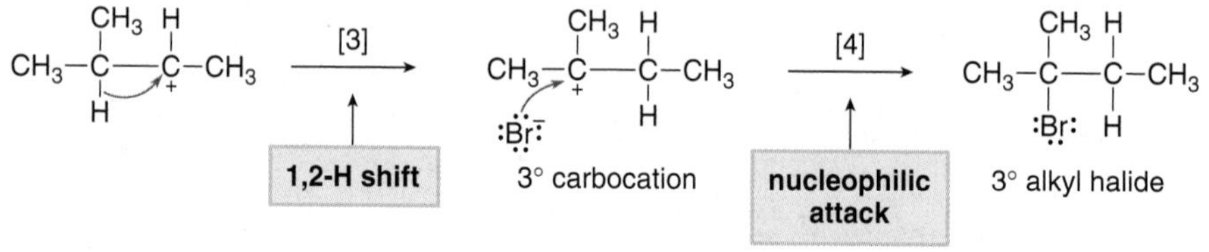

Problem 9.21 What is the major product formed when each alcohol is treated with HCl?

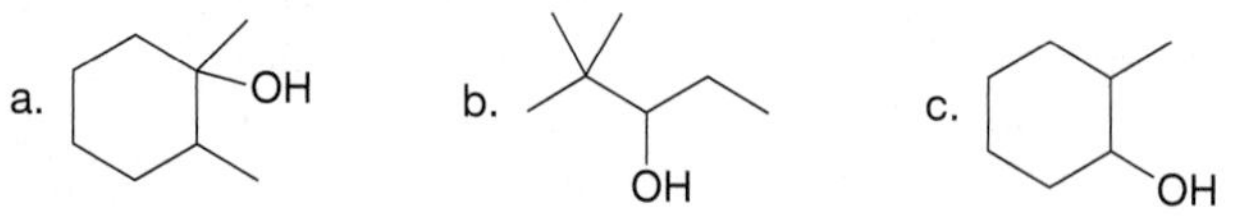

9.12 Conversion of Alcohols to Alkyl Halides with $SOCl_2$ and PBr_3

Primary (1°) and 2° alcohols can be converted to alkyl halides using $SOCl_2$ and PBr_3.

- **$SOCl_2$ (thionyl chloride) converts alcohols into alkyl chlorides.**
- **PBr_3 (phosphorus tribromide) converts alcohols into alkyl bromides.**

Both reagents convert ^-OH into a good leaving group *in situ*—that is, directly in the reaction mixture—as well as provide the **nucleophile,** either Cl^- or Br^-, to displace the leaving group.

9.12A Reaction of ROH with $SOCl_2$

The treatment of a 1° or 2° alcohol with thionyl chloride, $SOCl_2$, and pyridine forms an alkyl chloride, with SO_2 and HCl as by-products.

General reaction

$$R{-}OH + SOCl_2 \xrightarrow{\text{pyridine}} R{-}Cl + SO_2 + HCl$$

Examples

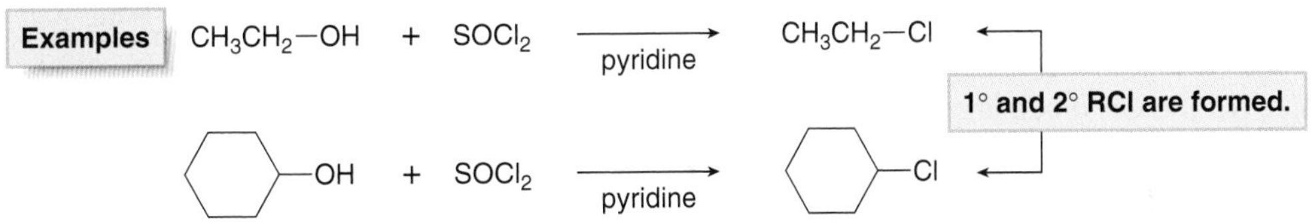

The mechanism for this reaction consists of two parts: **conversion of the OH group into a better leaving group, and nucleophilic attack by Cl^- via an S_N2 reaction,** as shown in Mechanism 9.7.

Mechanism 9.7 Reaction of ROH with $SOCl_2$ + Pyridine—An S_N2 Mechanism

Steps [1] and [2] The OH group is converted into a good leaving group.

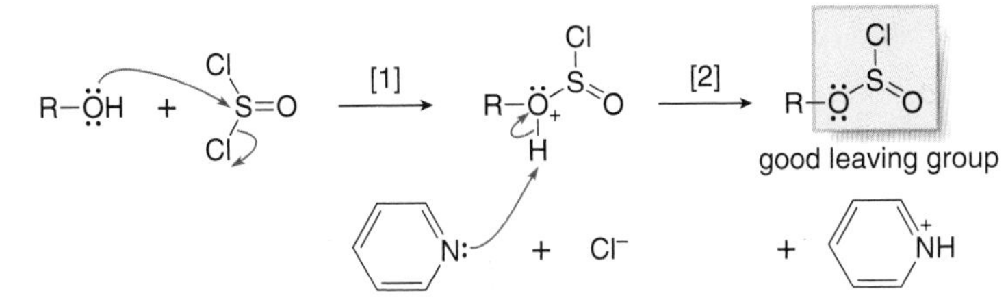

- Reaction of the alcohol with $SOCl_2$ forms an intermediate that loses a proton by reaction with pyridine in Step [2]. This two-step process converts the OH group into OSOCl, a **good leaving group,** and also generates the **nucleophile (Cl^-)** needed for Step [3].

Step [3] The C–O bond is broken *as* the C–Cl bond is formed.

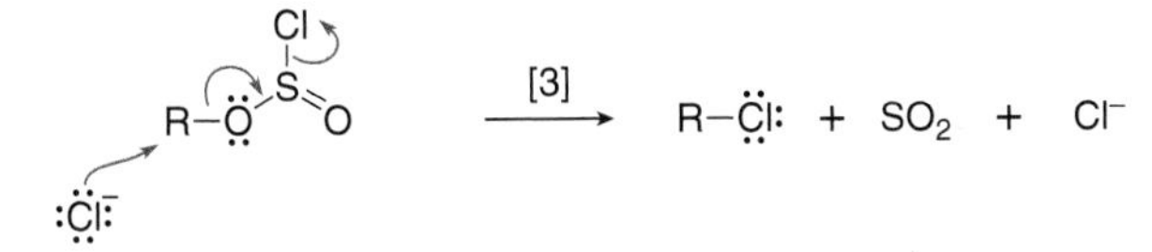

- **Nucleophilic attack of Cl^- and loss of the leaving group (SO_2 + Cl^-)** occur in a single step.

Problem 9.22 If the reaction of an alcohol with $SOCl_2$ and pyridine follows an S_N2 mechanism, what is the stereochemistry of the alkyl chloride formed from (2*R*)-2-butanol?

9.12B Reaction of ROH with PBr_3

In a similar fashion, the treatment of a 1° or 2° alcohol with phosphorus tribromide, PBr_3, forms an alkyl bromide.

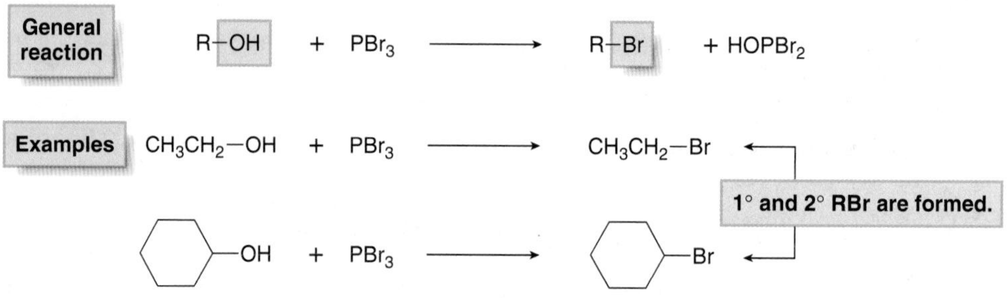

General reaction
R—OH + PBr3 → R—Br + HOPBr2
Examples
CH3CH2—OH + PBr3 → CH3CH2—Br
OH + PBr3 → Br
1° and 2° RBr are formed.

The mechanism for this reaction also consists of two parts: **conversion of the OH group into a better leaving group, and nucleophilic attack by Br^- via an S_N2 reaction,** as shown in Mechanism 9.8.

Mechanism 9.8 Reaction of ROH with PBr_3—An S_N2 Mechanism

Step [1] The OH group is converted into a good leaving group.

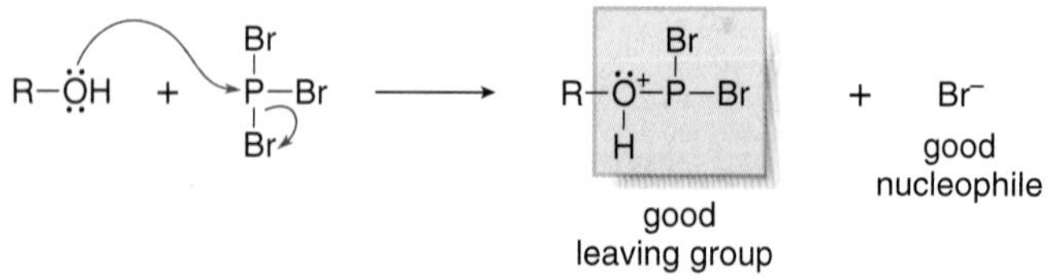

R—ÖH + P—Br
Br
Br
R—Ö+—P—Br
H
good leaving group
+ Br−
good nucleophile

- Reaction of the alcohol with PBr_3 converts the OH group into a **better leaving group,** and also generates the **nucleophile (Br^-)** needed for Step [2].

Step [2] The C–O bond is broken *as* the C–Br bond is formed.

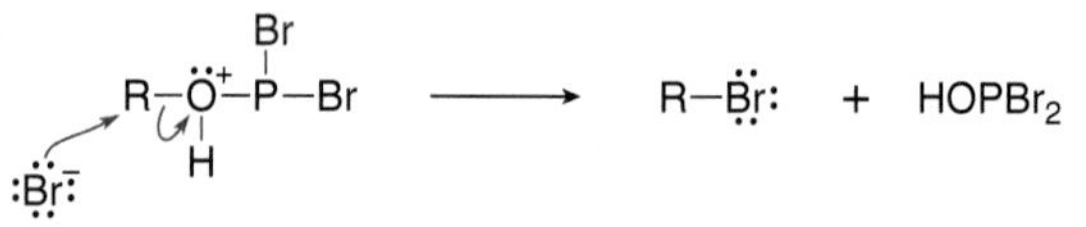

R—Ö+—P—Br
Br
H
:Br:−
R—Br: + HOPBr2

- **Nucleophilic attack of Br^- and loss of the leaving group ($HOPBr_2$)** occur in a single step.

Table 9.2 summarizes the methods for converting an alcohol to an alkyl halide presented in Sections 9.11 and 9.12.

Table 9.2 Summary of Methods for ROH → RX

Overall reaction	Reagent	Comment
ROH → RCl	HCl	• Useful for all ROH • An S_N1 mechanism for 2° and 3° ROH; an S_N2 mechanism for CH_3OH and 1° ROH
	$SOCl_2$	• Best for CH_3OH, and 1° and 2° ROH • An S_N2 mechanism
ROH → RBr	HBr	• Useful for all ROH • An S_N1 mechanism for 2° and 3° ROH; an S_N2 mechanism for CH_3OH and 1° ROH
	PBr_3	• Best for CH_3OH, and 1° and 2° ROH • An S_N2 mechanism
ROH → RI	HI	• Useful for all ROH • An S_N1 mechanism for 2° and 3° ROH; an S_N2 mechanism for CH_3OH and 1° ROH

Problem 9.23 If the reaction of an alcohol with PBr_3 follows an S_N2 mechanism, what is the stereochemistry of the alkyl bromide formed from (2*R*)-2-butanol?

Problem 9.24 Draw the organic products formed in each reaction, and indicate the stereochemistry of products that contain stereogenic centers.

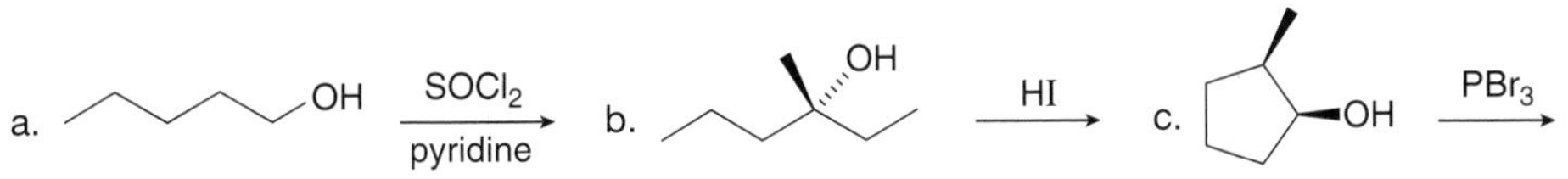
a.
OH
$SOCl_2$
pyridine
b.
OH
HI
c.
OH
PBr_3

9.12C The Importance of Making RX from ROH

We have now learned two methods to prepare an alkyl chloride and two methods to prepare an alkyl bromide from an alcohol. If there is one good way to carry out a reaction, why search for more? A particular reagent might work well for one starting material, but not so well for another. Thus, organic chemists try to devise several different ways to perform the same overall reaction. For now, though, concentrate on one or two of the most general methods, so you can better understand the underlying concepts.

Why are there so many ways to convert an alcohol to an alkyl halide? Alkyl halides are versatile starting materials in organic synthesis, as shown in Sample Problem 9.5.

Sample Problem 9.5 Convert 1-propanol to butanenitrile (**A**).

$$\underset{\text{1-propanol}}{CH_3CH_2CH_2{-}OH} \xrightarrow{?} \underset{\substack{\text{butanenitrile}\\ \textbf{A}}}{CH_3CH_2CH_2{-}CN}$$

Solution

Direct conversion of 1-propanol to **A** using ^-CN as a nucleophile is not possible because ^-OH is a poor leaving group. However, conversion of the OH group to a Br atom forms a good leaving group, which can then readily undergo an S_N2 reaction with ^-CN to yield **A**. **This two-step sequence is our first example of a multistep synthesis.**

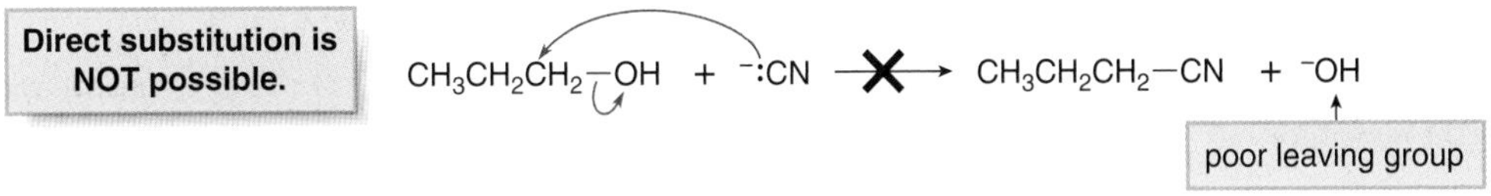
Direct substitution is NOT possible.
$CH_3CH_2CH_2{-}OH$ + $^-$:CN
$CH_3CH_2CH_2{-}CN$ + ^-OH
poor leaving group

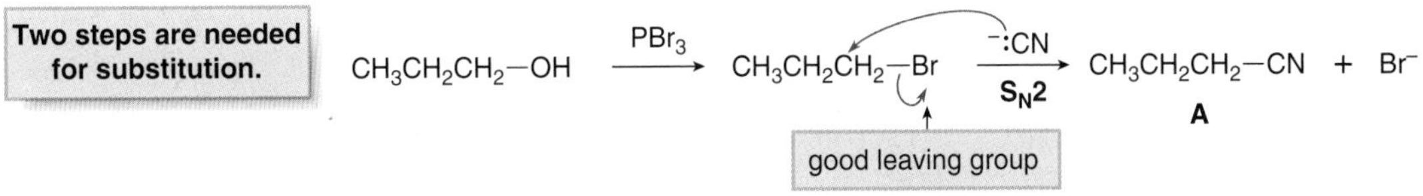
Two steps are needed for substitution.
$CH_3CH_2CH_2{-}OH$
PBr_3
$CH_3CH_2CH_2{-}Br$
$^-$:CN
S_N2
$CH_3CH_2CH_2{-}CN$ + Br^-
A
good leaving group

The overall result: $^-$CN replaces $^-$OH.

Problem 9.25 Draw two steps to convert $(CH_3)_2CHOH$ into each of the following compounds: $(CH_3)_2CHN_3$ and $(CH_3)_2CHOCH_2CH_3$.

9.13 Tosylate—Another Good Leaving Group

We have now learned two methods to convert the OH group of an alcohol to a better leaving group: treatment with strong acids (Section 9.8), and conversion to an alkyl halide (Sections 9.11–9.12). Alcohols can also be converted to **alkyl tosylates.**

Recall from Section 1.5 that a third-row element like sulfur can have 10 or 12 electrons around it in a valid Lewis structure.

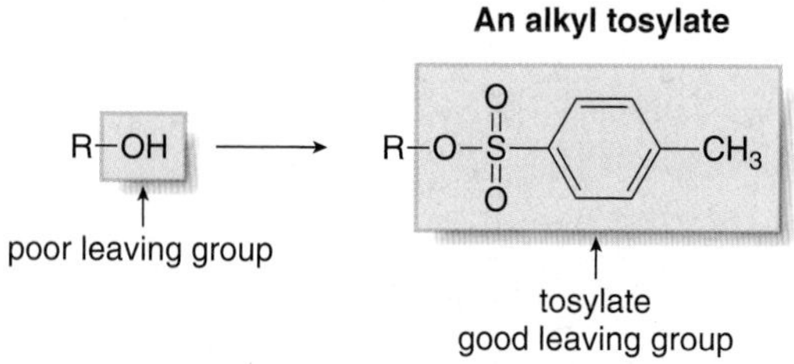

An alkyl tosylate is often called simply a **tosylate.**

An **alkyl tosylate** is composed of two parts: the **alkyl group R,** derived from an alcohol; and the **tosylate** (short for ***p*-toluenesulfonate**), which is a good leaving group. A tosyl group, $CH_3C_6H_4SO_2-$, is abbreviated as **Ts,** so an alkyl tosylate becomes **ROTs.**

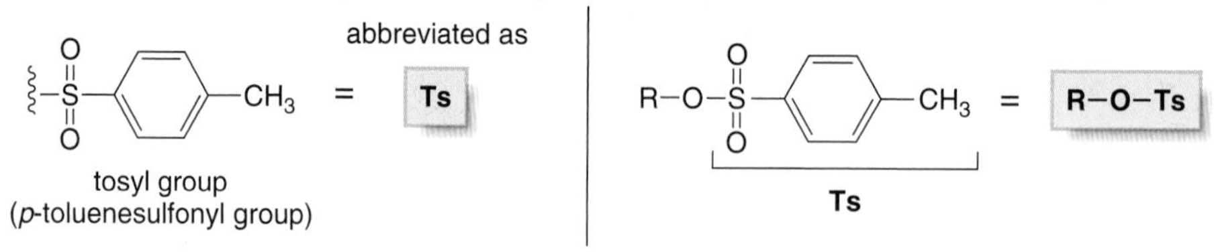

9.13A Conversion of Alcohols to Alkyl Tosylates

A tosylate (TsO^-) is similar to I^- in leaving group ability.

Alcohols are converted to alkyl tosylates by treatment with *p*-toluenesulfonyl chloride (TsCl) in the presence of pyridine. This overall process converts a poor leaving group (^-OH) into a good one (^-OTs). A tosylate is a good leaving group because its conjugate acid, *p*-toluenesulfonic acid ($CH_3C_6H_4SO_3H$, TsOH), is a strong acid ($pK_a = -7$, Section 2.6).

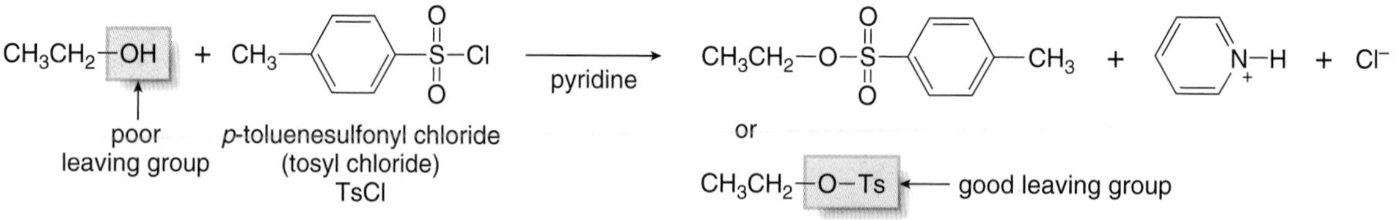

(2*S*)-2-Butanol is converted to its tosylate with **retention of configuration** at the stereogenic center. Thus, the C–O bond of the alcohol must *not* be broken when the tosylate is formed.

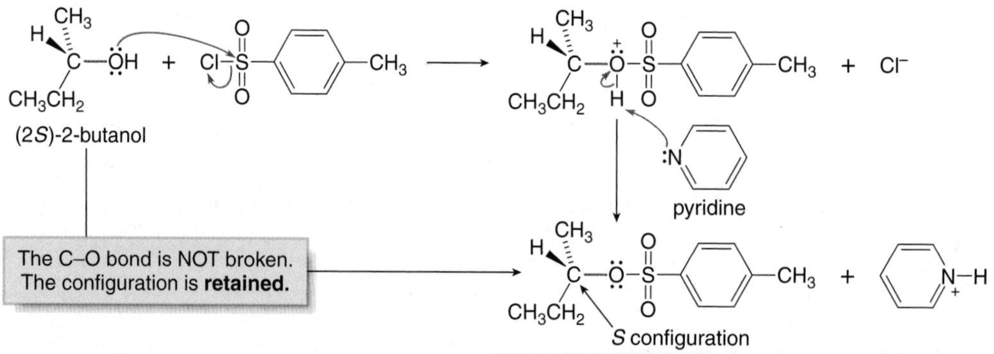

Problem 9.26 Draw the products of each reaction, and indicate the stereochemistry at any stereogenic centers.

a. 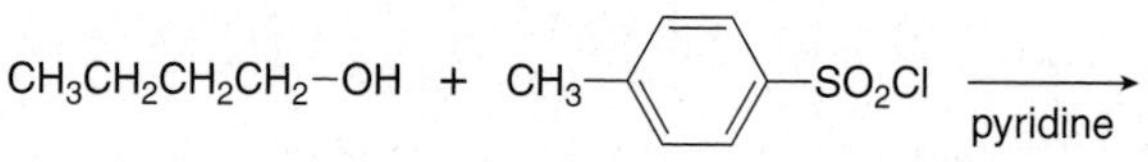

b. 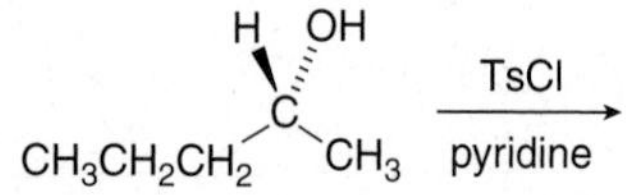

9.13B Reactions of Alkyl Tosylates

Because alkyl tosylates have good leaving groups, **they undergo both nucleophilic substitution and β elimination,** exactly as alkyl halides do. Generally, alkyl tosylates are treated with strong nucleophiles and bases, so that the mechanism of substitution is $\mathbf{S_N2}$ and the mechanism of elimination is **E2.**

For example, ethyl tosylate, which has the leaving group on a 1° carbon, reacts with $NaOCH_3$ to yield ethyl methyl ether, the product of nucleophilic substitution by an S_N2 mechanism. It reacts with $KOC(CH_3)_3$, a strong bulky base, to yield ethylene by an E2 mechanism.

Two reactions of ethyl tosylate

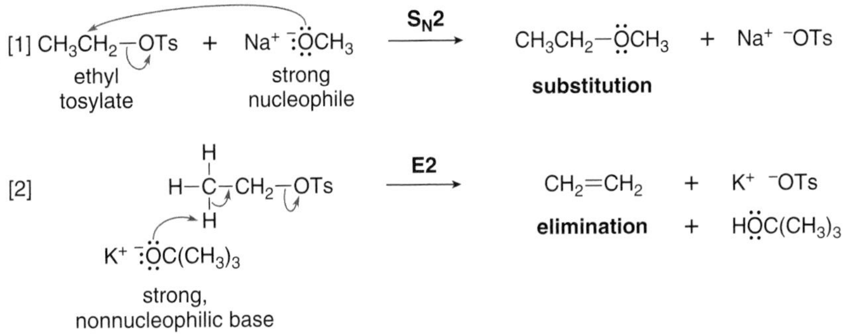

Because substitution occurs via an $\mathbf{S_N2}$ mechanism, **inversion of configuration** results when the leaving group is bonded to a stereogenic center.

Backside attack

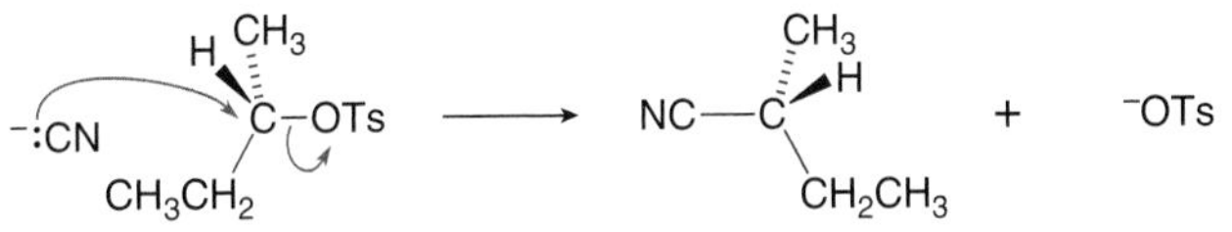

inversion of configuration

Sample Problem 9.6 Draw the product of the following reaction, including stereochemistry.

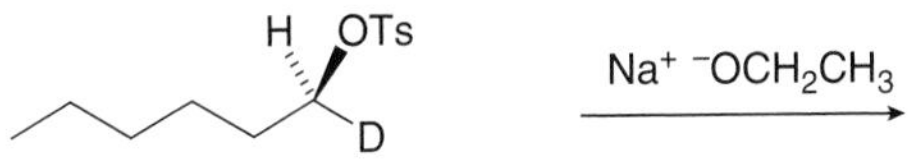

Solution

The 1° alkyl tosylate and the strong nucleophile both favor substitution by an $\mathbf{S_N2}$ mechanism, which proceeds by backside attack, resulting in **inversion** of configuration at the stereogenic center.

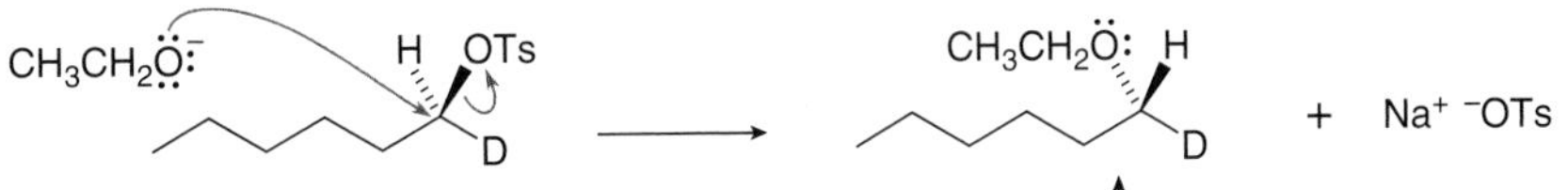

1° tosylate

The nucleophile attacks from the back.

Problem 9.27 Draw the products of each reaction, and include the stereochemistry at any stereogenic centers in the products.

a. 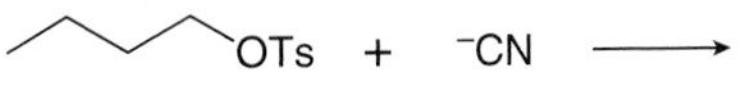

b. $CH_3CH_2CH_2{-}OTs \; + \; K^+ \; {}^-OC(CH_3)_3 \longrightarrow$

c. 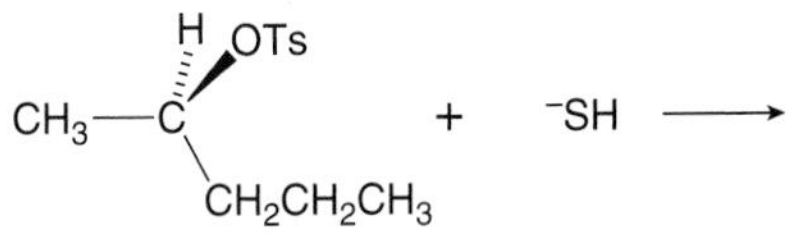

9.13C The Two-Step Conversion of an Alcohol to a Substitution Product

We now have another **two-step method to convert an alcohol to a substitution product:** reaction of an alcohol with TsCl and pyridine to form an alkyl tosylate (Step [1]), followed by nucleophilic attack on the tosylate (Step [2]).

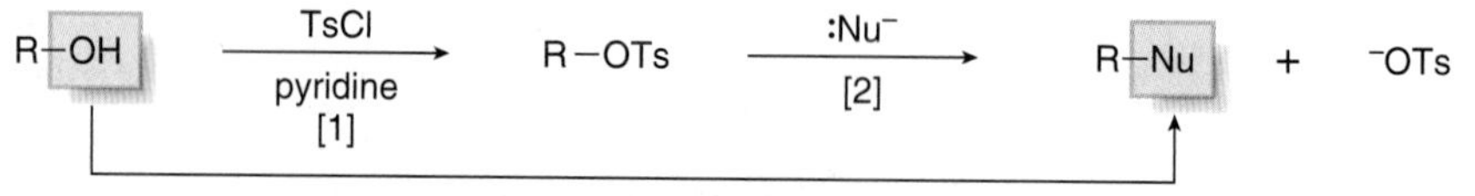

Overall process—Nucleophilic substitution

Let's look at the stereochemistry of this two-step process.

- Step [1], formation of the tosylate, proceeds with **retention** of configuration at a stereogenic center because the C–O bond remains intact.
- Step [2] is an S_N2 reaction, so it proceeds with **inversion of configuration** because the nucleophile attacks from the back side.
- Overall there is a **net inversion of configuration** at a stereogenic center.

For example, the treatment of *cis*-3-methylcyclohexanol with *p*-toluenesulfonyl chloride and pyridine forms a cis tosylate **A,** which undergoes backside attack by the nucleophile $^{-}OCH_3$ to yield the trans ether **B.**

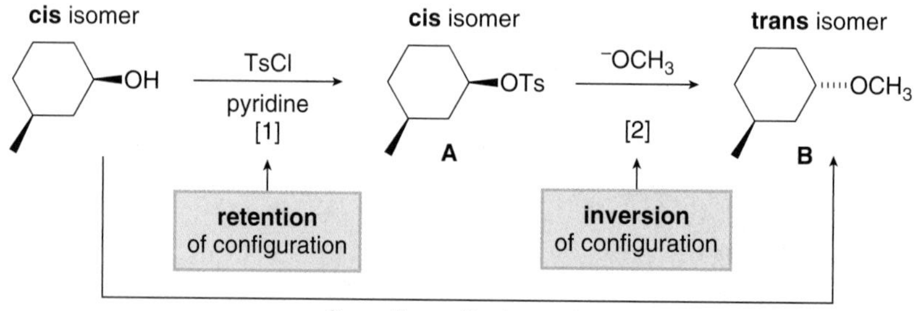

Overall result—Inversion

Problem 9.28 Draw the products formed when (2*S*)-2-butanol is treated with TsCl and pyridine, followed by NaOH. Label the stereogenic center in each compound as *R* or *S*. What is the stereochemical relationship between the starting alcohol and the final product?

9.13D A Summary of Substitution and Elimination Reactions of Alcohols

The reactions of alcohols in Sections 9.8–9.13C share two similarities:

- **The OH group is converted into a better leaving group by treatment with acid or another reagent.**
- **The resulting product undergoes either elimination or substitution, depending on the reaction conditions.**

Figure 9.8 summarizes these reactions with cyclohexanol as starting material.

Problem 9.29 Draw the product formed when $(CH_3)_2CHOH$ is treated with each reagent.

a. $SOCl_2$, pyridine
b. TsCl, pyridine
c. H_2SO_4
d. HBr
e. PBr_3, then NaCN
f. $POCl_3$, pyridine

Figure 9.8 Summary: Nucleophilic substitution and β elimination reactions of alcohols

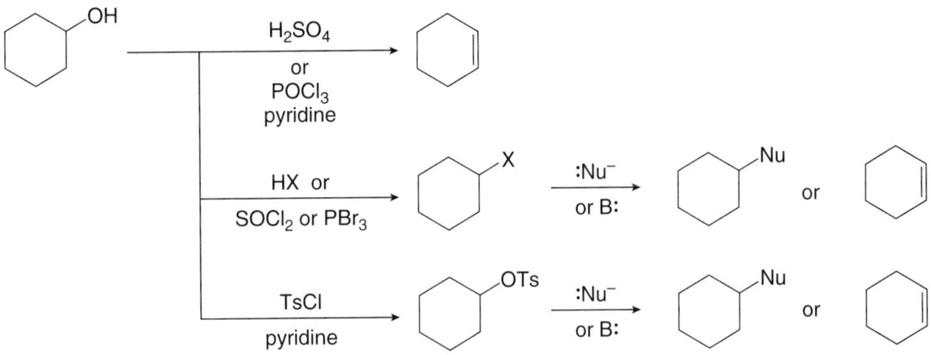

9.14 Reaction of Ethers with Strong Acid

Because ethers are so unreactive, diethyl ether and tetrahydrofuran (THF) are often used as solvents for organic reactions.

Recall from Section 9.7B that ethers have a poor leaving group, so they cannot undergo nucleophilic substitution or β elimination reactions directly. Instead, they must first be converted to a good leaving group by reaction with strong acids. Only **HBr** and **HI** can be used, though, because they are strong acids that are also sources of good nucleophiles (Br^- and I^-, respectively). **When ethers react with HBr or HI, both C–O bonds are cleaved and two alkyl halides are formed as products.**

General reaction

$$R{-}O{-}R' \; + \; H{-}X \; \xrightarrow{} \; R{-}X \; + \; R'{-}X \; + \; H_2O$$

(2 equiv) (X = Br or I)

Two C–O bonds are broken. Two new C–X bonds are formed.

Examples

$$CH_3{-}O{-}CH_2CH_3 \; + \; \underset{\text{(2 equiv)}}{HBr} \; \longrightarrow \; CH_3{-}Br \; + \; CH_3CH_2{-}Br \; + \; H_2O$$

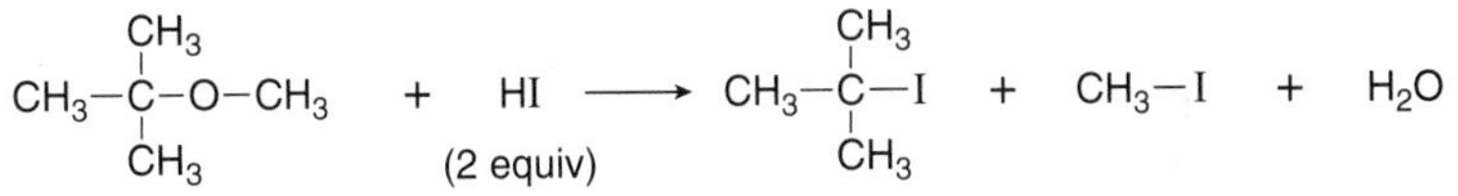

HBr or HI serves as a strong acid that both protonates the O atom of the ether and is the source of a good nucleophile (Br^- or I^-). Because both C–O bonds in the ether are broken, **two successive nucleophilic substitution reactions occur.**

- **The mechanism of ether cleavage is S_N1 or S_N2, depending on the identity of R.**
- **With 2° or 3° alkyl groups bonded to the ether oxygen, the C–O bond is cleaved by an S_N1 mechanism involving a carbocation; with methyl or 1° R groups, the C–O bond is cleaved by an S_N2 mechanism.**

For example, cleavage of $(CH_3)_3COCH_3$ with HI occurs at two bonds, as shown in Mechanism 9.9. The 3° alkyl group undergoes nucleophilic substitution by an $\mathbf{S_N1}$ mechanism, resulting in the cleavage of one C–O bond. The methyl group undergoes nucleophilic substitution by an $\mathbf{S_N2}$ mechanism, resulting in the cleavage of the second C–O bond.

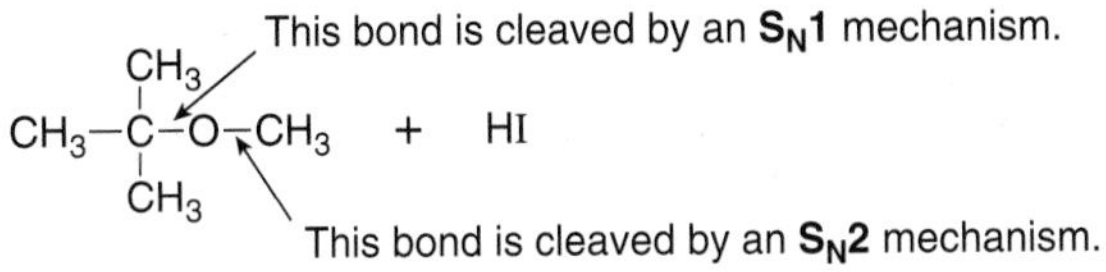

Mechanism 9.9 Mechanism of Ether Cleavage in Strong Acid—$(CH_3)_3COCH_3 + HI \rightarrow (CH_3)_3CI + CH_3I + H_2O$

Part [1] Cleavage of the 3° C–O bond by an S_N1 mechanism

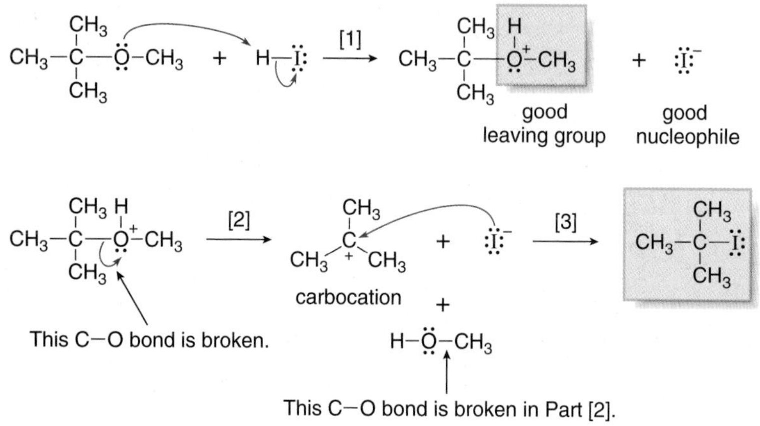
[1]
good
leaving group
good
nucleophile
[2]
[3]
carbocation
This C–O bond is broken.
This C–O bond is broken in Part [2].

- **Protonation** of the O atom forms a good leaving group in Step [1]. Cleavage of the C–O bond then occurs in two steps: the bond to the leaving group is broken to form a **carbocation,** and then the bond to the nucleophile (I^-) is formed. This generates one of the alkyl iodides, $\mathbf{(CH_3)_3CI}$.

Part [2] Cleavage of the CH_3–O bond by an S_N2 mechanism

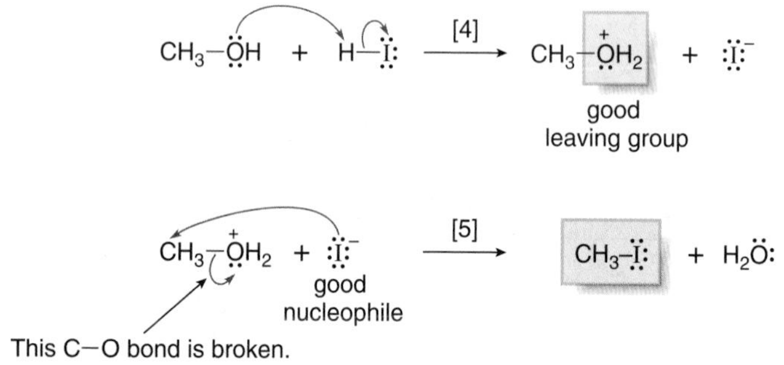
[4]
good
leaving group
[5]
good
nucleophile
This C–O bond is broken.

- **Protonation of the OH group** forms a good leaving group (H_2O), and then nucleophilic attack by I^- forms the second alkyl iodide, $\mathbf{CH_3I}$, and $\mathbf{H_2O}$.

The mechanism illustrates the central role of HX in the reaction:

- **HX protonates the ether oxygen, thus making a good leaving group.**
- **HX provides a source of X^- for nucleophilic attack.**

Problem 9.30 What alkyl halides are formed when each ether is treated with HBr?

a. $CH_3CH_2–O–CH_2CH_3$ b. $(CH_3)_2CH–O–CH_2CH_3$ c.

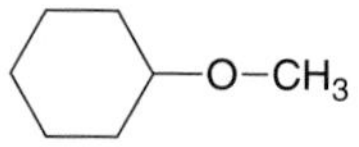
O–CH3

Problem 9.31 Explain why the treatment of anisole with HBr yields phenol and CH_3Br, but not bromobenzene.

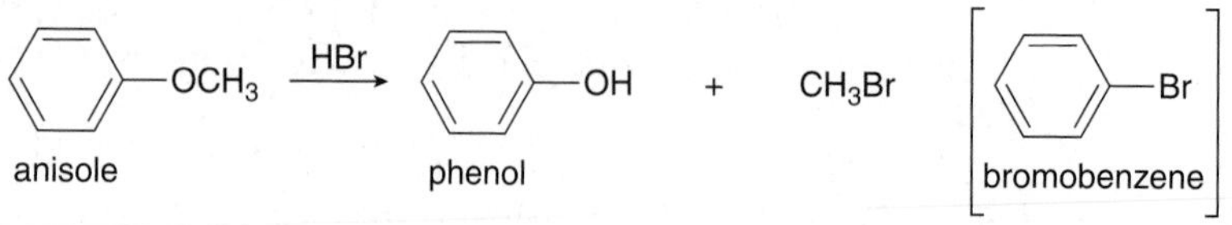
OCH3
HBr
OH
CH3Br
Br
anisole
phenol
bromobenzene

9.15 Reactions of Epoxides

Although epoxides do not contain a good leaving group, they contain a strained three-membered ring with two polar bonds. **Nucleophilic attack opens the strained three-membered ring,** making it a favorable process even with the poor leaving group.

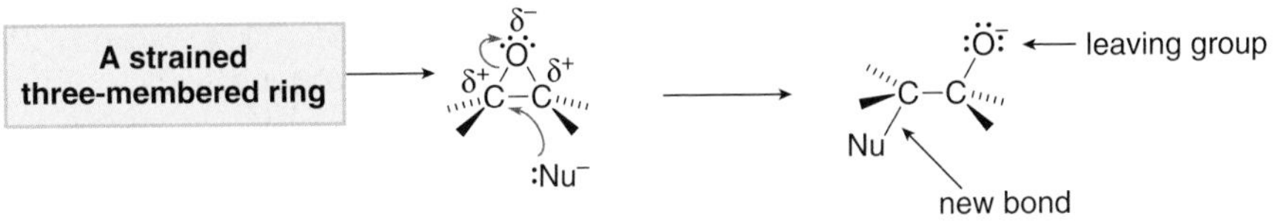

This reaction occurs readily with strong nucleophiles, and with acids like HZ, where Z is a nucleophilic atom.

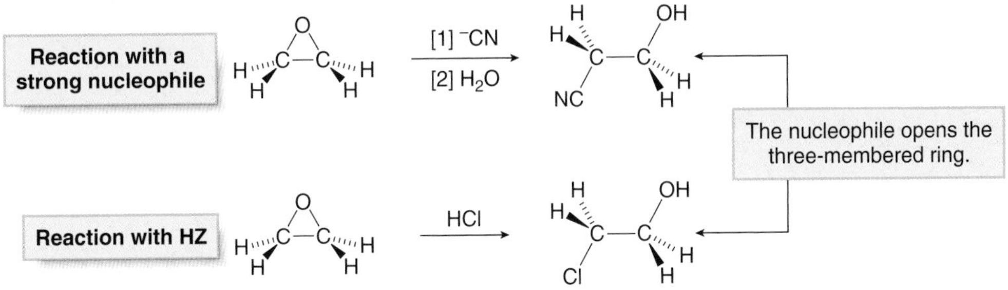

9.15A Opening of Epoxide Rings with Strong Nucleophiles

Virtually all strong nucleophiles open an epoxide ring by a two-step reaction sequence:

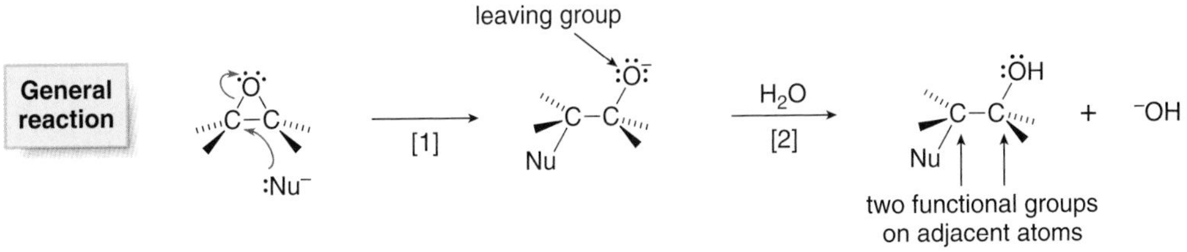

- **Step [1]:** The nucleophile attacks an electron-deficient carbon of the epoxide, thus cleaving a C–O bond and relieving the strain of the three-membered ring.
- **Step [2]:** Protonation of the alkoxide with water generates a neutral product with two functional groups on adjacent atoms.

Common nucleophiles that open epoxide rings include ^-OH, ^-OR, ^-CN, ^-SR, and NH_3. With these strong nucleophiles, the reaction occurs via an S_N2 **mechanism,** resulting in two consequences:

- **The nucleophile opens the epoxide ring from the back side.**

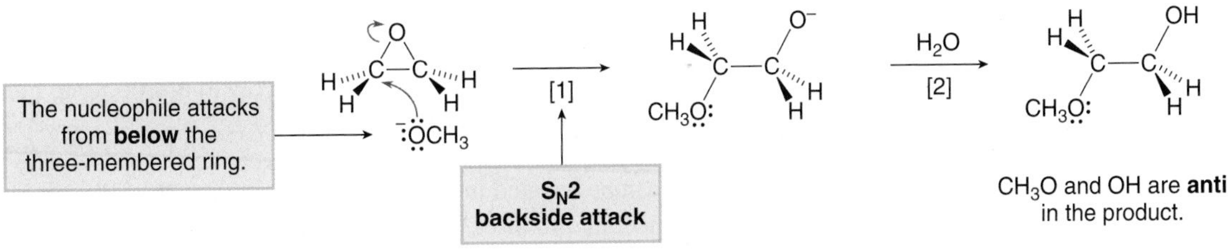

Other examples of the nucleophilic opening of epoxide rings are presented in Sections 12.6 and 20.14.

- **In an unsymmetrical epoxide, the nucleophile attacks at the less substituted carbon atom.**

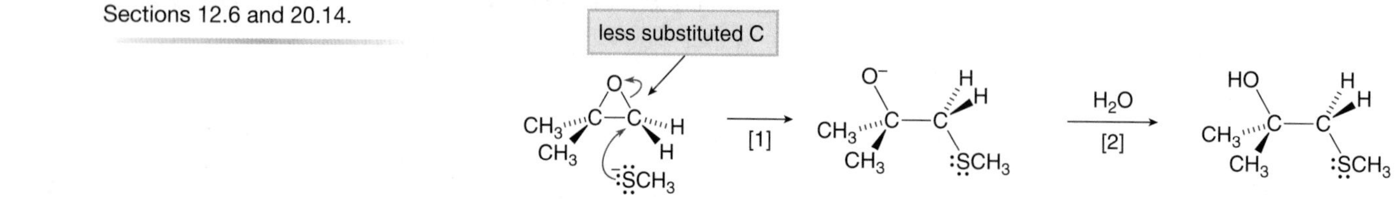

Problem 9.32 Draw the product of each reaction, indicating the stereochemistry at any stereogenic centers.

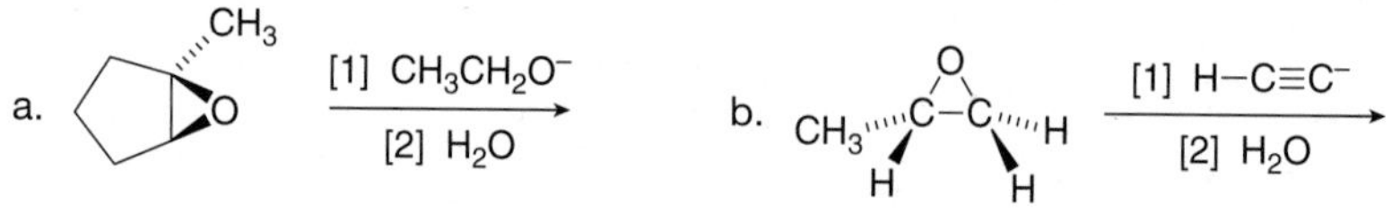

1,2-Epoxycyclohexane is a symmetrical epoxide that is achiral because it possesses a plane of symmetry. It reacts with $^-OCH_3$, however, to yield two *trans*-1,2-disubstituted cyclohexanes, **A** and **B,** which are **enantiomers;** each has two stereogenic centers.

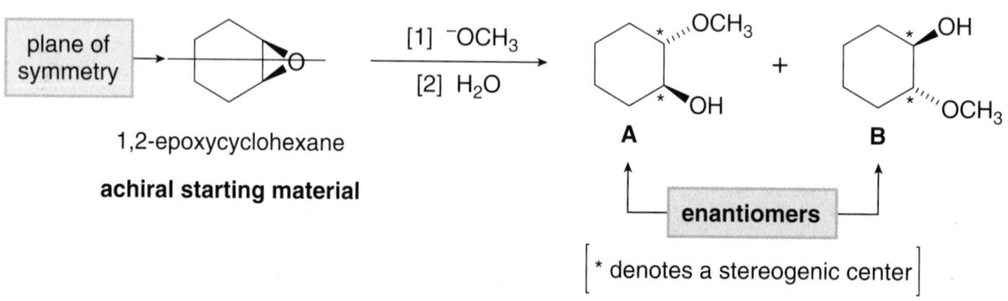

In this case, **nucleophilic attack of $^-OCH_3$ occurs from the back side at *either* C–O bond, because both ends are equally substituted.** Because attack at either side occurs with equal probability, an equal amount of the two enantiomers is formed—**a racemic mixture.** This is a specific example of a general rule concerning the stereochemistry of products obtained from an achiral reactant.

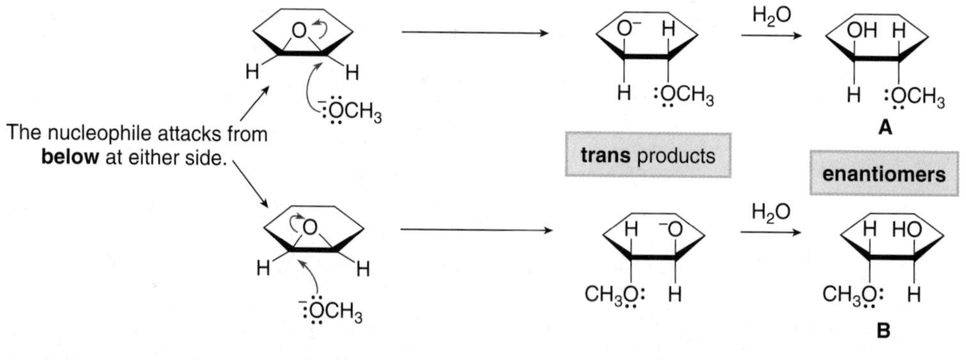

- **Whenever an achiral reactant yields a product with stereogenic centers, the product must be achiral (meso) or racemic.**

This general rule can be restated in terms of optical activity. Recall from Section 5.12 that achiral compounds and racemic mixtures are optically inactive.

- **Optically inactive starting materials give optically inactive products.**

Problem 9.33 The cis and trans isomers of 2,3-dimethyloxirane both react with ^{-}OH to give 2,3-butanediol. One stereoisomer gives a single achiral product, and one gives two chiral enantiomers. Which epoxide gives one product and which gives two?

cis-2,3-dimethyloxirane

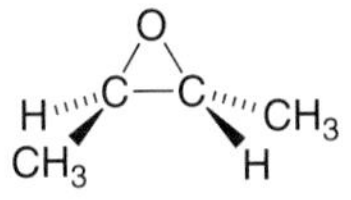

one enantiomer of *trans*-2,3-dimethyloxirane

9.15B Reaction with Acids HZ

Acids **HZ** that contain a nucleophile **Z** also open epoxide rings by a two-step reaction sequence:

General reaction

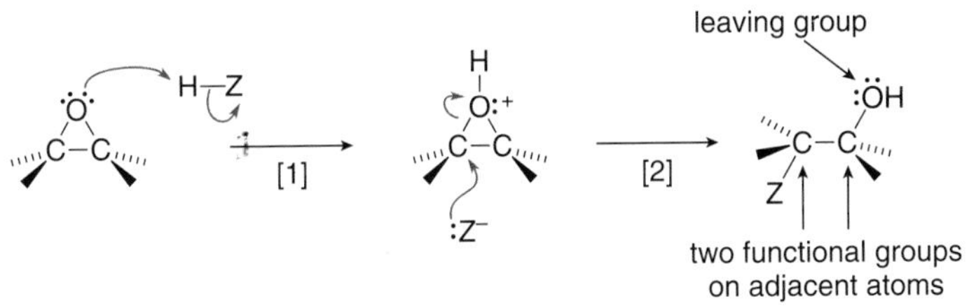

- **Step [1]:** Protonation of the epoxide oxygen with HZ makes the epoxide oxygen into a good leaving group (OH). It also provides a source of a good nucleophile (Z^{-}) to open the epoxide ring.
- **Step [2]:** The nucleophile Z^{-} then opens the protonated epoxide ring by **backside** attack.

These two steps—**protonation followed by nucleophilic attack**—are the exact reverse of the opening of epoxide rings with strong nucleophiles, where nucleophilic attack precedes protonation.

HCl, HBr, and **HI** all open an epoxide ring in this manner. $\mathbf{H_2O}$ and **ROH** can, too, but acid must also be added. Regardless of the reaction, the product has an OH group from the epoxide on one carbon and a new functional group Z from the nucleophile on the adjacent carbon. With epoxides fused to rings, ***trans*-1,2-disubstituted cycloalkanes** are formed.

Examples

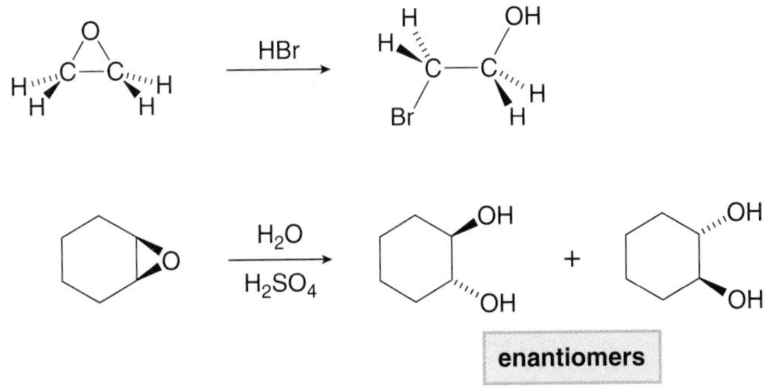

Although backside attack of the nucleophile suggests that this reaction follows an S_N2 mechanism, the regioselectivity of the reaction with unsymmetrical epoxides does not.

- **With unsymmetrical epoxides, nucleophilic attack occurs at the *more* substituted carbon atom.**

For example, the treatment of 2,2-dimethyloxirane with HCl results in nucleophilic attack at the carbon with two methyl groups.

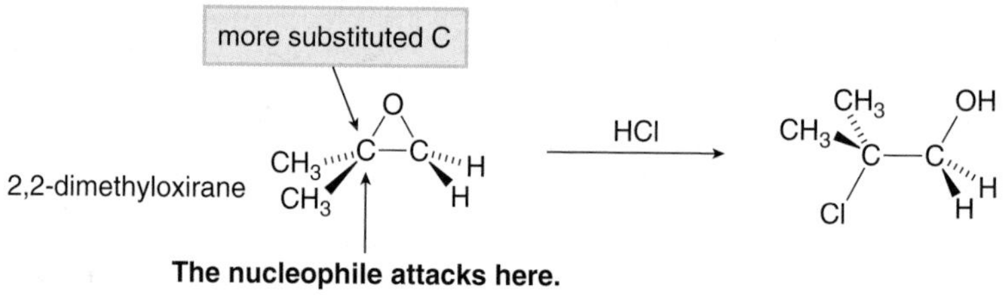

Backside attack of the nucleophile suggests an S_N2 mechanism, but attack at the more substituted carbon suggests an S_N1 mechanism. To explain these results, the **mechanism of nucleophilic attack is thought to be somewhere in between S_N1 and S_N2.**

Figure 9.9 illustrates two possible pathways for the reaction of 2,2-dimethyloxirane with HCl. Backside attack of Cl^- at the more substituted carbon proceeds via transition state **A,** whereas backside attack of Cl^- at the less substituted carbon proceeds via transition state **B. Transition state A has a partial positive charge on a more substituted carbon, making it more stable.** Thus, the preferred reaction path takes place by way of the lower energy transition state **A.**

Opening of an epoxide ring with either a strong nucleophile $:Nu^-$ or an acid HZ is **regioselective,** because one constitutional isomer is the major or exclusive product. The **site selectivity of these two reactions, however, is *exactly the opposite.***

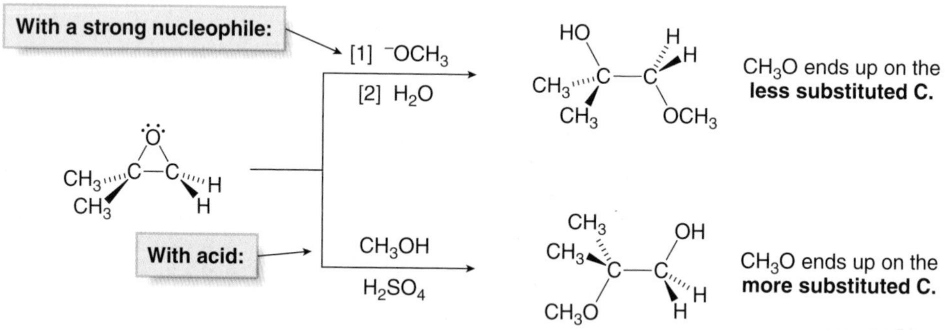

Figure 9.9

Opening of an unsymmetrical epoxide ring with HCl

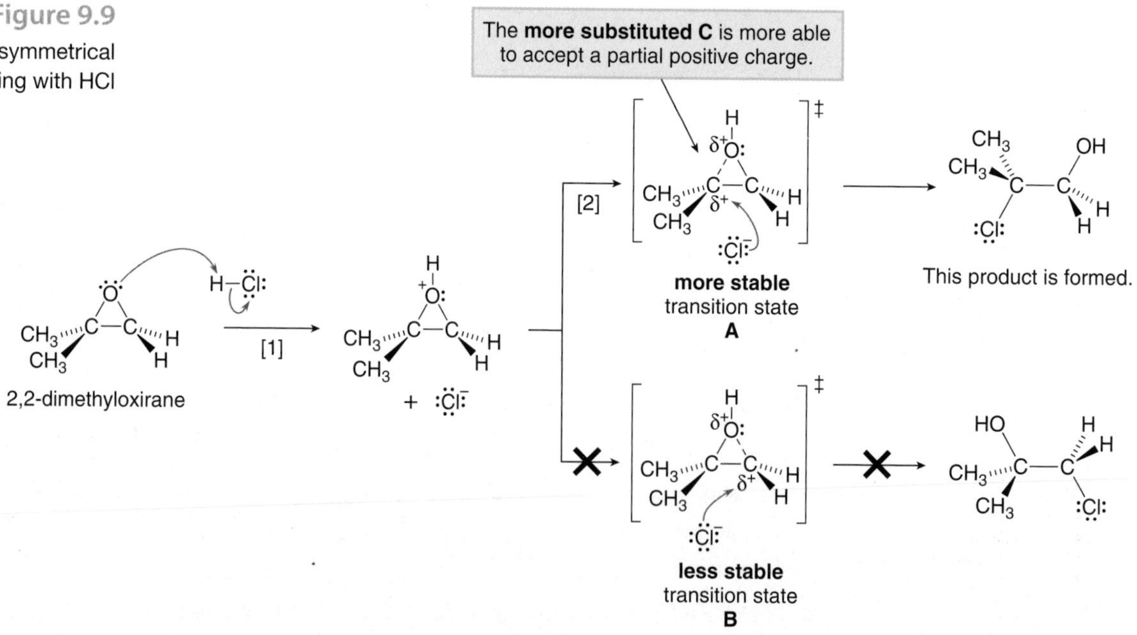

- Transition state **A** is lower in energy because the partial positive charge (δ^+) is located on the more substituted carbon. In this case, therefore, nucleophilic attack occurs from the back side (an S_N2 characteristic) at the more substituted carbon (an S_N1 characteristic).

Figure 9.10 The synthesis of two bronchodilators uses the opening of an epoxide ring.

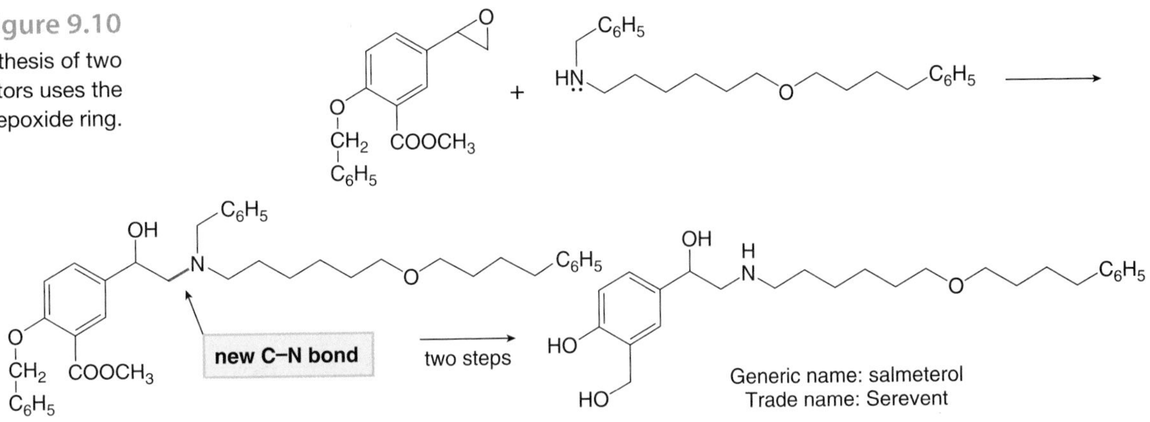

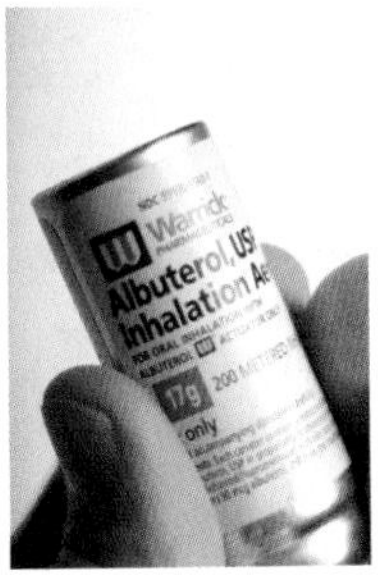

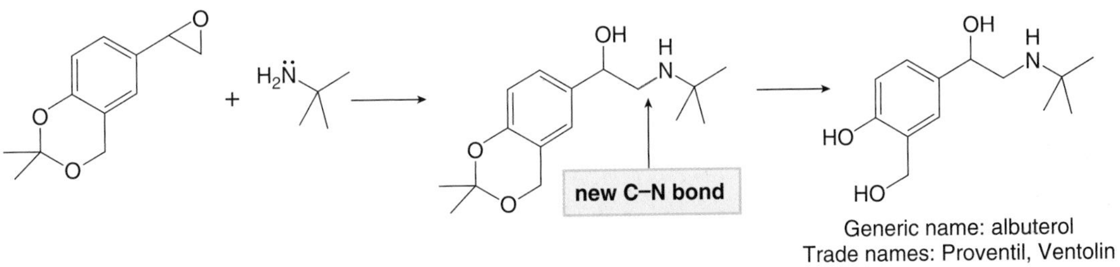

- A key step in each synthesis is the opening of an epoxide ring with a nitrogen nucleophile to form a new C – N bond.

- **With a strong nucleophile, :Nu⁻ attacks at the less substituted carbon.**
- **With an acid HZ, the nucleophile attacks at the more substituted carbon.**

The reaction of epoxide rings with nucleophiles is important for the synthesis of many biologically active compounds, including **salmeterol** and **albuterol,** two bronchodilators used in the treatment of asthma (Figure 9.10).

Problem 9.34 Draw the product of each reaction.

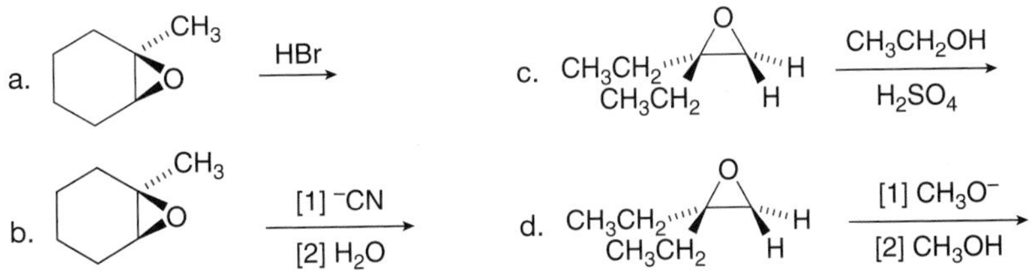

9.16 Application: Epoxides, Leukotrienes, and Asthma

The opening of epoxide rings with nucleophiles is a key step in some important biological processes.

9.16A Asthma and Leukotrienes

Asthma is an obstructive lung disease that affects millions of Americans. Because it involves episodic constriction of small airways, bronchodilators such as albuterol (Figure 9.10) are used to treat symptoms by widening airways. Because asthma is also characterized by chronic inflammation, inhaled steroids that reduce inflammation are also commonly used.

The **leukotrienes** are molecules that contribute to the asthmatic response. A typical example, **leukotriene C_4,** is shown. Although its biological activity was first observed in the 1930s, the chemical structure of leukotriene C_4 was not determined until 1979. Structure determination and chemical synthesis were difficult because leukotrienes are highly unstable and extremely potent, and are therefore present in tissues in exceedingly small amounts.

Leukotrienes were first synthesized in 1980 in the laboratory of Professor E. J. Corey, the 1990 recipient of the Nobel Prize in Chemistry.

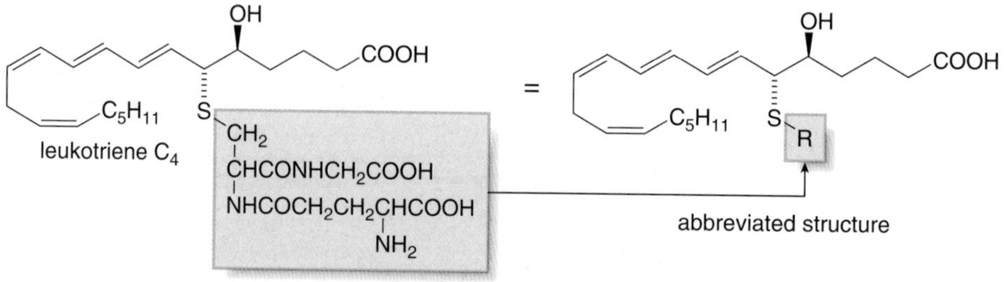

9.16B Leukotriene Synthesis and Asthma Drugs

Leukotrienes are synthesized in cells by the oxidation of **arachidonic acid** to 5-HPETE, which is then converted to an epoxide, **leukotriene A_4.** Opening of the epoxide ring with a sulfur nucleophile **RSH** yields leukotriene C_4.

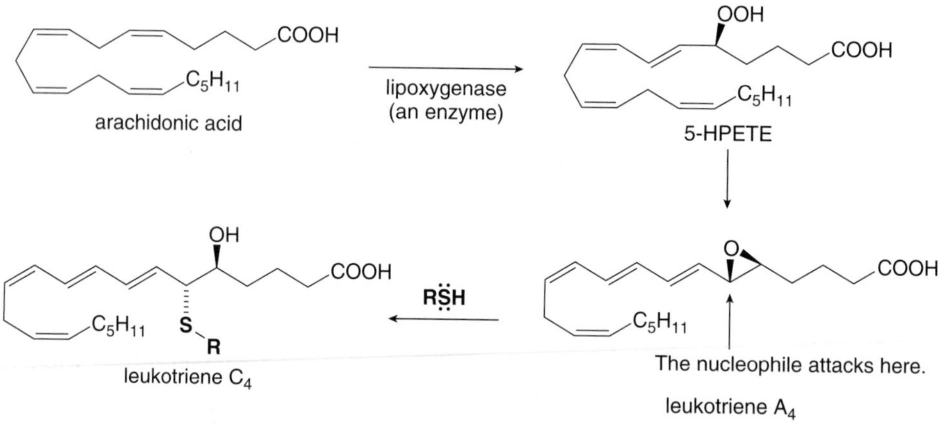

New asthma drugs act by blocking the synthesis of leukotriene C_4 from arachidonic acid. For example, **zileuton** (trade name Zyflo) inhibits the enzyme (called a lipoxygenase) needed for the first step of this process. By blocking the synthesis of leukotriene C_4, a compound responsible for the disease, zileuton treats the **cause of asthma,** not just its symptoms.

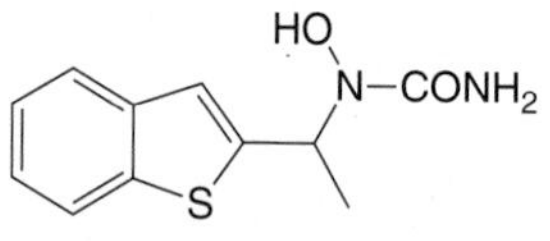

Generic name: zileuton
Trade name: Zyflo
anti-asthma drug

9.17 Application: Benzo[*a*]pyrene, Epoxides, and Cancer

The sooty exhaust from trucks and buses contains PAHs such as benzo[*a*]pyrene.

Benzo[*a*]pyrene is a widespread environmental pollutant, produced during the combustion of all types of organic material—gasoline, fuel oil, wood, garbage, and cigarettes. It is a **polycyclic aromatic hydrocarbon (PAH),** a class of compounds that are discussed further in Chapter 17.

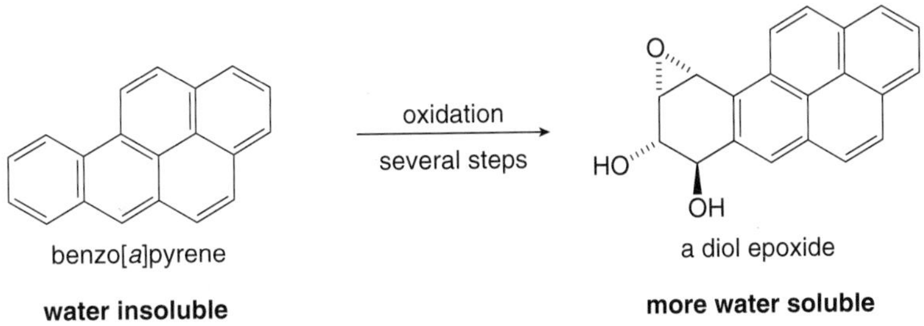

After this nonpolar and water-insoluble hydrocarbon is inhaled or ingested, it is oxidized in the liver to a diol epoxide. Oxidation is a common fate of foreign substances that are not useful nutrients for the body. The oxidation product has three oxygen-containing functional groups, making it much more water soluble, and more readily excreted in urine. It is also a potent carcinogen. The strained three-membered ring of the epoxide reacts readily with biological nucleophiles (such as DNA or an enzyme), leading to ring-opened products that often disrupt normal cell function, causing cancer or cell death.

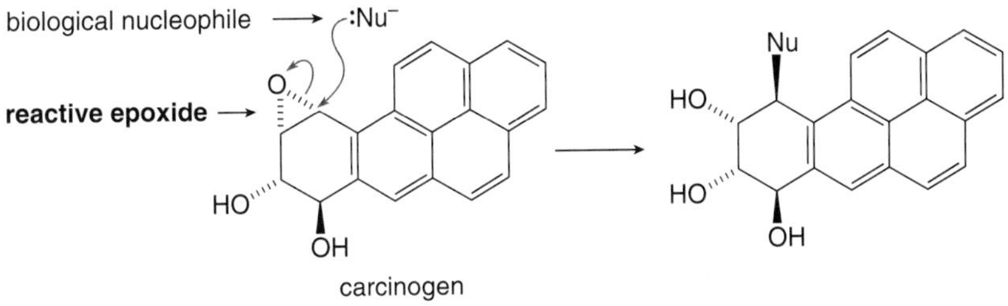

These examples illustrate the central role of the nucleophilic opening of epoxide rings in two well-defined cellular processes.

KEY CONCEPTS

Alcohols, Ethers, and Epoxides

General Facts about ROH, ROR, and Epoxides

- All three compounds contain an O atom that is sp^3 hybridized and tetrahedral (9.2).
- All three compounds have polar C–O bonds, but only alcohols have an O–H bond for intermolecular hydrogen bonding (9.4).
- Alcohols and ethers do not contain a good leaving group. Nucleophilic substitution can occur only after the OH (or OR) group is converted to a better leaving group (9.7A).
- Epoxides have a leaving group located in a strained three-membered ring, making them reactive to strong nucleophiles and acids HZ that contain a nucleophilic atom Z (9.15).

A New Reaction of Carbocations (9.9)

- Less stable carbocations rearrange to more stable carbocations by the shift of a hydrogen atom or an alkyl group.

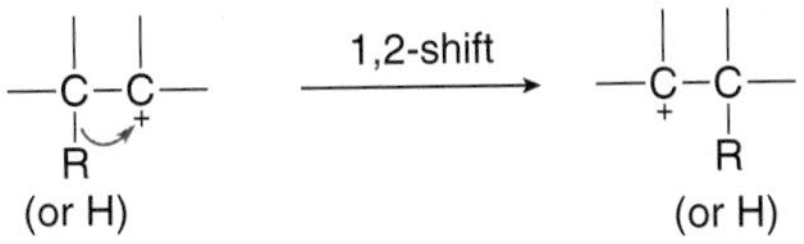

- Besides rearranging, a carbocation can also react with a nucleophile (7.13) and a base (8.6).

Preparation of Alcohols, Ethers, and Epoxides (9.6)

[1] Preparation of alcohols

$$R{-}X \quad + \quad {}^{-}OH \longrightarrow R{-}OH \quad + \quad X^{-}$$

- The mechanism is S_N2.
- The reaction works best for CH_3X and 1° RX.

[2] Preparation of alkoxides—A Brønsted–Lowry acid–base reaction

$$R{-}O{-}H \quad + \ Na^{+}H^{-} \longrightarrow R{-}O^{-} \ Na^{+} \quad + \ H_2$$

alkoxide

[3] Preparation of ethers (Williamson ether synthesis)

$$R{-}X \quad + \quad {}^{-}OR' \longrightarrow R{-}OR \quad + \quad X^{-}$$

- The mechanism is S_N2.
- The reaction works best for CH_3X and 1° RX.

[4] Preparation of epoxides—Intramolecular S_N2 reaction

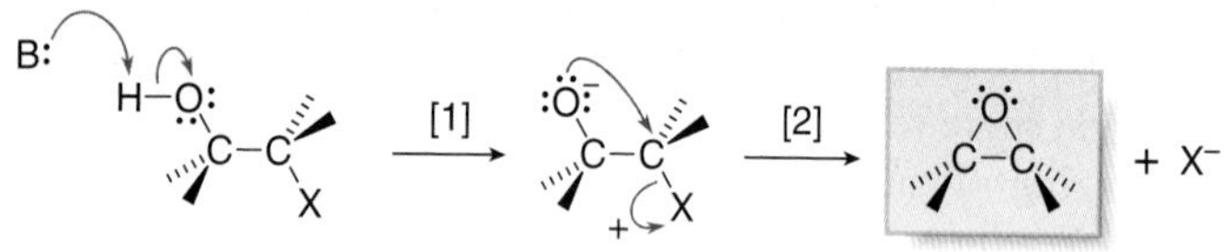

halohydrin H–B⁺

- A two-step reaction sequence:
  - [1] The removal of a proton with base forms an alkoxide.
  - [2] An intramolecular $\mathbf{S_N2}$ reaction forms the epoxide.

Reactions of Alcohols

[1] Dehydration to form alkenes

a. Using strong acid (9.8, 9.9)

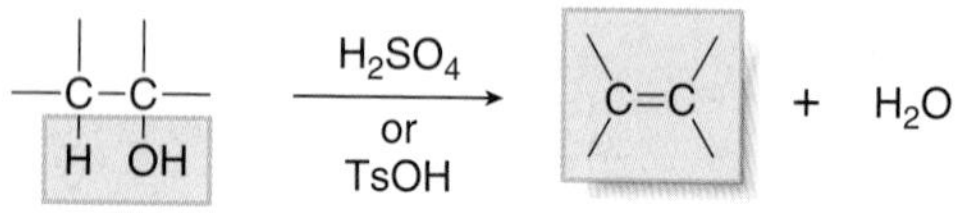

- Order of reactivity: $R_3COH > R_2CHOH > RCH_2OH$.
- The mechanism for 2° and 3° ROH is E1—carbocations are intermediates and rearrangements occur.
- The mechanism for 1° ROH is E2.
- The Zaitsev rule is followed.

b. Using $POCl_3$ and pyridine (9.10)

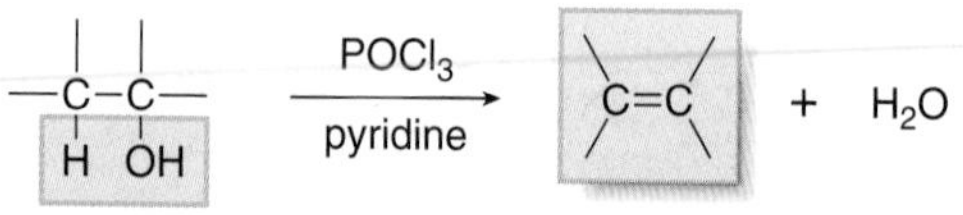

- The mechanism is E2.
- No carbocation rearrangements occur.

[2] Reaction with HX to form RX (9.11)

$$R{-}OH \ + \ H{-}X \longrightarrow R{-}X \ + \ H_2O$$

- Order of reactivity: $R_3COH > R_2CHOH > RCH_2OH$.
- The mechanism for 2° and 3° ROH is S_N1—carbocations are intermediates and rearrangements occur.
- The mechanism for CH_3OH and 1° ROH is S_N2.

[3] Reaction with other reagents to form RX (9.12)

$$R{-}OH \quad + \ SOCl_2 \xrightarrow[\text{pyridine}]{} R{-}Cl$$

$$R{-}OH \quad + \ PBr_3 \longrightarrow R{-}Br$$

- Reactions occur with CH_3OH and 1° and 2° ROH.
- The reactions follow an S_N2 mechanism.

[4] Reaction with tosyl chloride to form alkyl tosylates (9.13A)

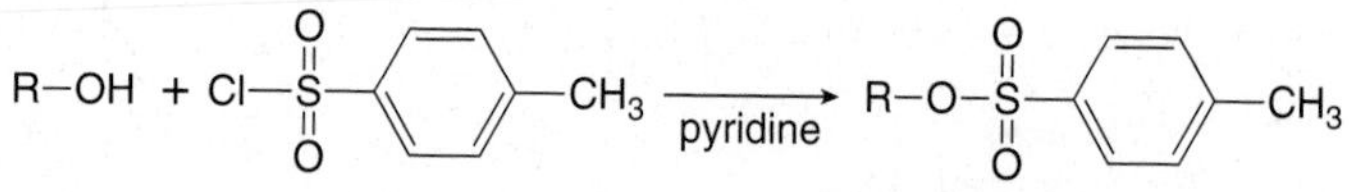

R–OTs

- The C–O bond is not broken, so the configuration at a stereogenic center is retained.

Reactions of Alkyl Tosylates

Alkyl tosylates undergo either substitution or elimination, depending on the reagent (9.13B).

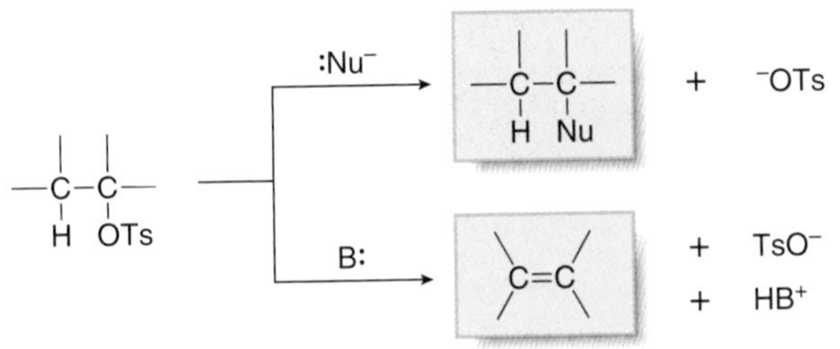

- Substitution is carried out with a strong :Nu‾, so the mechanism is S_N2.
- Elimination is carried out with a strong base, so the mechanism is E2.

Reactions of Ethers

Only one reaction is useful: cleavage with strong acids (9.14).

$$R{-}O{-}R' \; + \; H{-}X \longrightarrow \boxed{R{-}X} + \boxed{R'{-}X} + H_2O$$
(2 equiv)
[X = Br or I]

- With 2° and 3° R groups, the mechanism is S_N1.
- With CH_3 and 1° R groups, the mechanism is S_N2.

Reactions of Epoxides

Epoxide rings are opened with nucleophiles :Nu‾ and acids HZ (9.15).

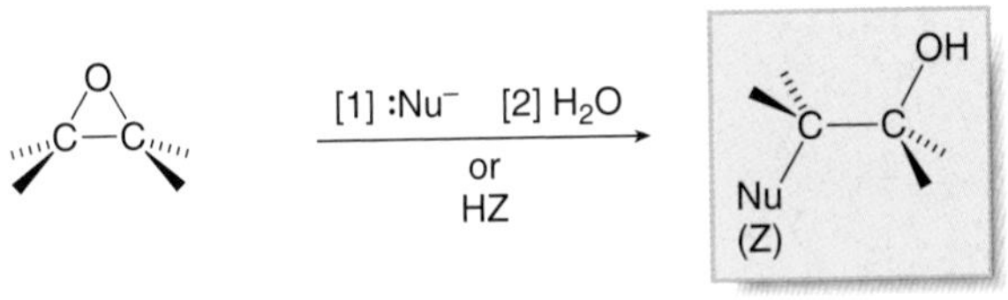

- The reaction occurs with backside attack, resulting in trans or anti products.
- With :Nu‾, the mechanism is S_N2, and nucleophilic attack occurs at the less substituted C.
- With HZ, the mechanism is between S_N1 and S_N2, and attack of Z‾ occurs at the more substituted C.

PROBLEMS

Problems Using Three-Dimensional Models

9.35 Name each compound depicted in the ball-and-stick models.

a. 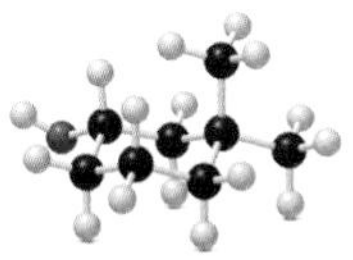

b. 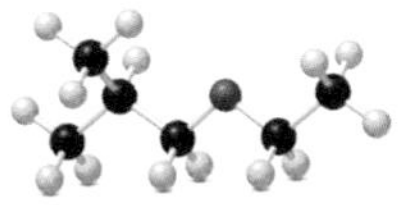

c. 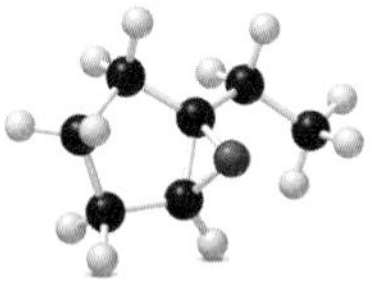

9.36 Answer each question using the ball-and-stick model of compound **A**.

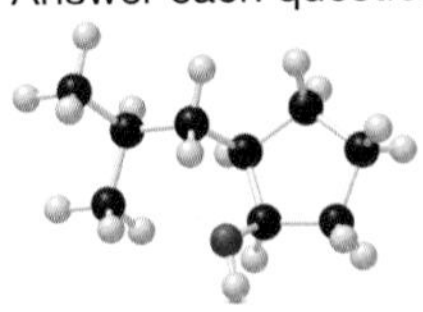

A

a. Give the IUPAC name for **A,** including *R,S* designations for stereogenic centers.
b. Classify **A** as a 1°, 2°, or 3° alcohol.
c. Draw a stereoisomer for **A** and give its IUPAC name.
d. Draw a constitutional isomer that contains an OH group and give its IUPAC name.
e. Draw a constitutional isomer that contains an ether and give its IUPAC name.
f. Draw the products formed (including stereochemistry) when **A** is treated with each reagent: [1] NaH; [2] H_2SO_4; [3] $POCl_3$, pyridine; [4] HCl; [5] $SOCl_2$, pyridine; [6] TsCl, pyridine.

9.37 Draw the product and indicate the stereochemistry when the given alcohol is treated with each reagent: (a) HBr; (b) PBr_3; (c) HCl; (d) $SOCl_2$ and pyridine.

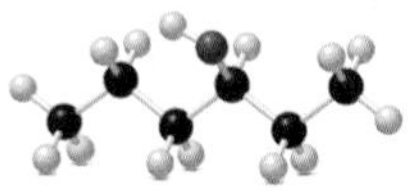

Structure and Nomenclature

9.38 a. Draw the structure of a 1°, 2°, and 3° alcohol with molecular formula C_4H_8O.
b. Draw the structure of an enol with molecular formula C_4H_8O.

9.39 Give the IUPAC name for each alcohol.

a. $(CH_3)_2CHCH_2CH_2CH_2OH$

b. $(CH_3)_2CHCH_2CH(CH_2CH_3)CH(OH)CH_2CH_3$

c.
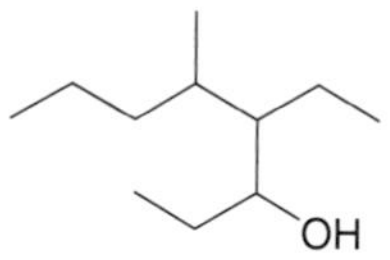

d.

e.
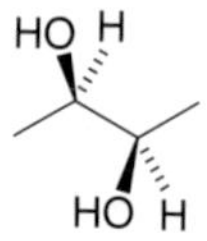

[Also label the stereogenic centers as *R* or *S*.]

f.
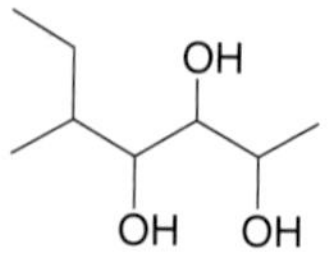

g.
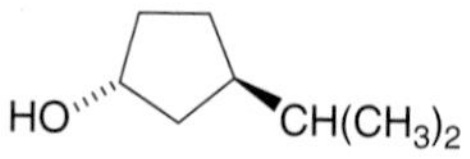

9.40 Name each ether and epoxide.

a.
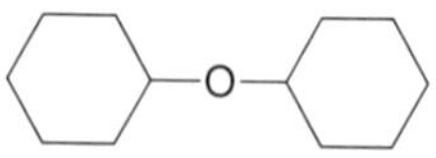

b.
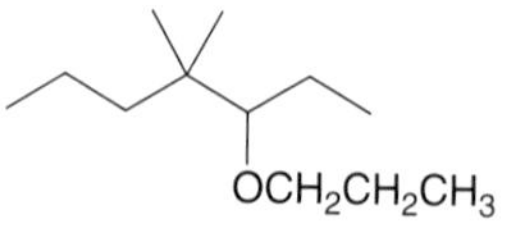

c.
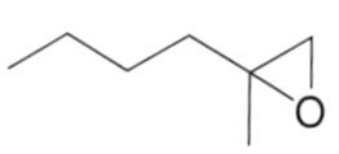

d.
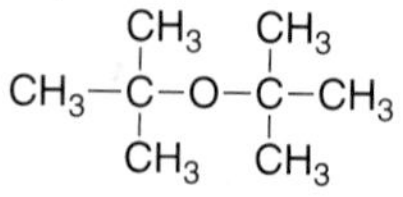

9.41 Give the structure corresponding to each name.
a. 4-ethyl-3-heptanol
b. *trans*-2-methylcyclohexanol
c. 2,3,3-trimethyl-2-butanol
d. 6-*sec*-butyl-7,7-diethyl-4-decanol
e. 3-chloro-1,2-propanediol
f. diisobutyl ether
g. 1,2-epoxy-1,3,3-trimethylcyclohexane
h. 1-ethoxy-3-ethylheptane
i. (2*R*,3*S*)-3-isopropyl-2-hexanol
j. (2*S*)-2-ethoxy-1,1-dimethylcyclopentane

9.42 Draw the eight constitutional isomers with molecular formula $C_5H_{12}O$ that contain an OH group. Give the IUPAC name for each compound. Classify each alcohol as 1°, 2°, or 3°.

Physical Properties

9.43 Rank each group of compounds in order of:
a. increasing boiling point: $CH_3CH_2CH_2OH$, $(CH_3)_2CHOH$, $CH_3CH_2OCH_3$
b. increasing water solubility: $CH_3(CH_2)_5OH$, $HO(CH_2)_6OH$, $CH_3(CH_2)_4CH_3$

9.44 Explain the observed trend in the melting points of the following three isomeric alcohols: $(CH_3)_2CHCH_2OH$ (–108 °C), $CH_3CH_2CH_2CH_2OH$ (–90 °C), $(CH_3)_3COH$ (26 °C).

9.45 Why is the boiling point of 1,3-propanediol ($HOCH_2CH_2CH_2OH$) higher than the boiling point of 1,2-propanediol [$HOCH_2CH(OH)CH_3$] (215 °C vs. 187 °C)? Why do both diols have a higher boiling point than 1-butanol ($CH_3CH_2CH_2CH_2OH$, 118 °C)?

Alcohols

9.46 Draw the organic product(s) formed when $CH_3CH_2CH_2OH$ is treated with each reagent.
a. H_2SO_4
b. NaH
c. HCl + $ZnCl_2$
d. HBr
e. $SOCl_2$, pyridine
f. PBr_3
g. TsCl, pyridine
h. [1] NaH; [2] CH_3CH_2Br
i. [1] TsCl, pyridine; [2] NaSH

9.47 Draw the organic product(s) formed when 1-methylcyclohexanol is treated with each reagent. In some cases no reaction occurs.
a. NaH
b. NaCl
c. HBr
d. HCl
e. H_2SO_4
f. $NaHCO_3$
g. [1] NaH; [2] CH_3CH_2Br
h. $POCl_3$, pyridine

9.48 What alkenes are formed when each alcohol is dehydrated with TsOH? Label the major product when a mixture results.

a. 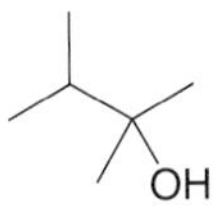 b. 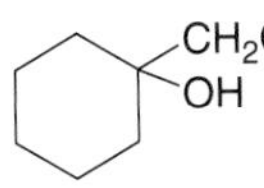 c. 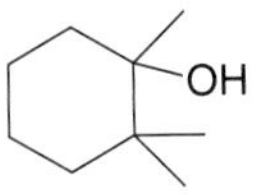 d. $CH_3CH_2CH_2CH_2OH$ e. 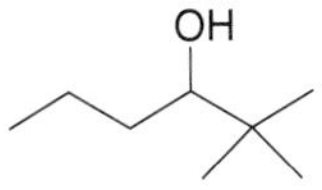

9.49 What three alkenes are formed when $CH_3CH_2CH_2CH(OH)CH_3$ is treated with H_2SO_4? Label the major product.

9.50 Draw the products formed when $CH_3CH_2CH_2CH_2OTs$ is treated with each reagent.

a. CH_3SH b. $NaOCH_2CH_3$ c. NaOH d. $KOC(CH_3)_3$

9.51 Draw the products of each reaction and indicate stereochemistry around stereogenic centers.

a. 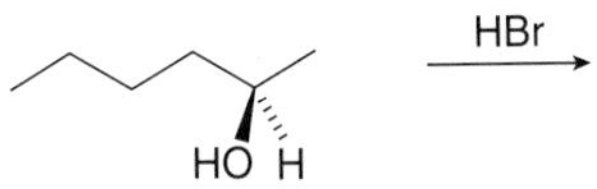

c. 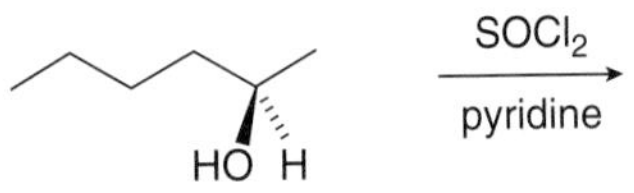

b. 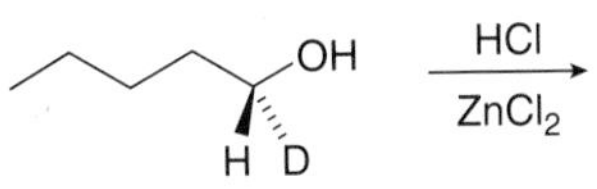

d. 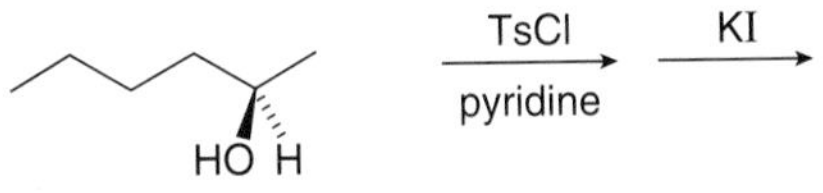

9.52 Draw the substitution product formed (including stereochemistry) when (2*R*)-2-hexanol is treated with each series of reagents: (a) NaH, followed by CH_3I; (b) TsCl and pyridine, followed by $NaOCH_3$; (c) PBr_3, followed by $NaOCH_3$. Which two routes produce identical products?

9.53 Draw a stepwise mechanism for the following reaction.

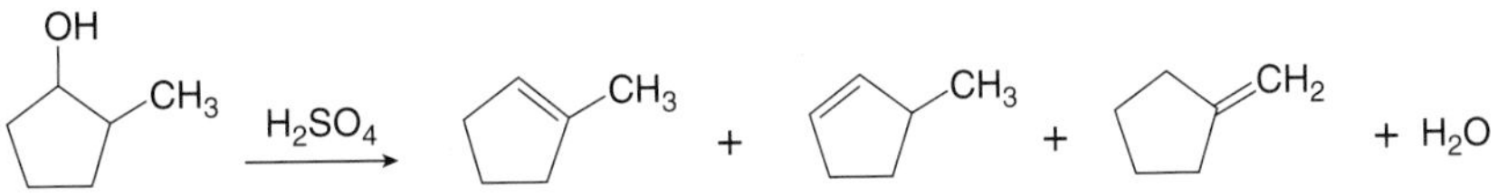

9.54 Although alcohol **V** gives a single alkene **W** when treated with $POCl_3$ and pyridine, three isomeric alkenes (**X–Z**) are formed on dehydration with H_2SO_4. Draw a stepwise mechanism for each reaction and explain why the difference occurs.

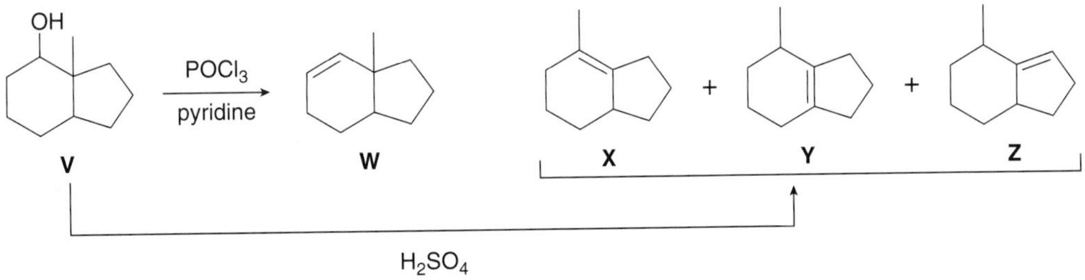

9.55 Sometimes carbocation rearrangements can change the size of a ring. Draw a stepwise, detailed mechanism for the following reaction.

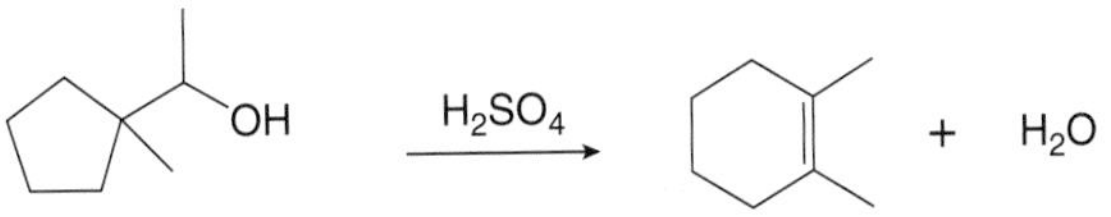

9.56 Explain the following observation. When 3-methyl-2-butanol is treated with HBr, a single alkyl bromide is isolated, resulting from a 1,2-shift. When 2-methyl-1-propanol is treated with HBr, no rearrangement occurs to form an alkyl bromide.

9.57 An allylic alcohol contains an OH group on a carbon atom adjacent to a C–C double bond. Treatment of allylic alcohol **A** with HCl forms a mixture of two allylic chlorides, **B** and **C.** Draw a stepwise mechanism that illustrates how both products are formed.

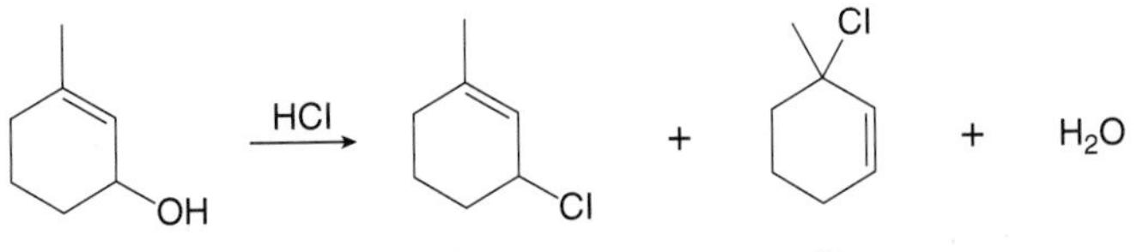

A **B** **C**

9.58 When $CH_3CH_2CH_2CH_2OH$ is treated with H_2SO_4 + NaBr, $CH_3CH_2CH_2CH_2Br$ is the major product, and $CH_3CH_2CH{=}CH_2$ and $CH_3CH_2CH_2CH_2OCH_2CH_2CH_2CH_3$ are isolated as minor products. Draw a mechanism that accounts for the formation of each of these products.

9.59 Draw a stepwise, detailed mechanism for the following reaction.

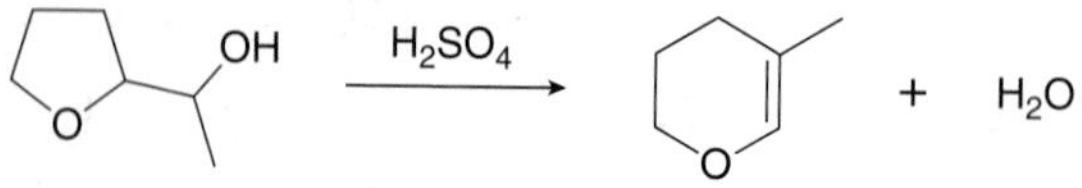

9.60 Draw a stepwise, detailed mechanism for the following intramolecular reaction that forms a cyclic ether.

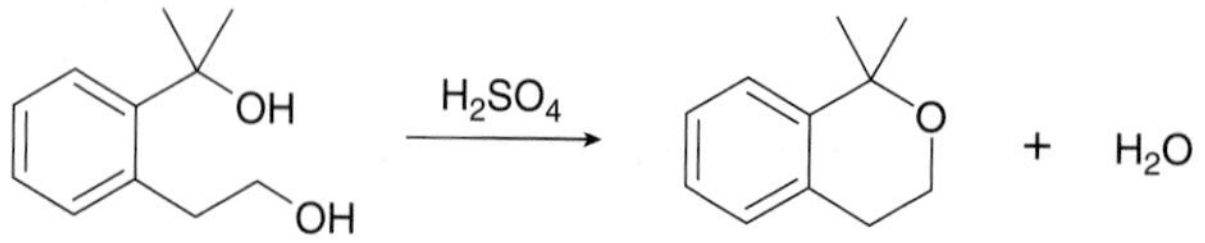

Ethers

9.61 Draw two different routes to each of the following ethers using a Williamson ether synthesis. Indicate the preferred route (if there is one).

a. 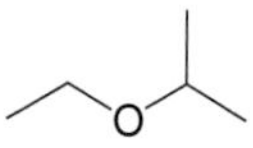

b. 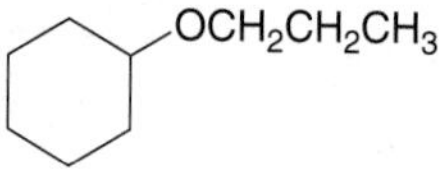

c. $CH_3CH_2OCH_2CH_2CH_3$

9.62 Explain why it is not possible to prepare the following ether using a Williamson ether synthesis.

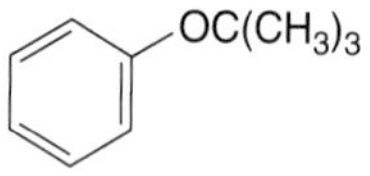

9.63 Draw the products formed when each ether is treated with two equivalents of HBr.

a. $(CH_3)_3COCH_2CH_2CH_3$

b. 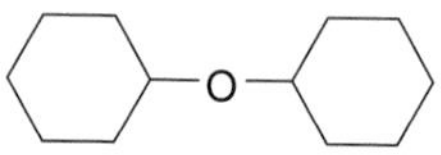

c. 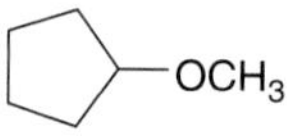

9.64 Draw a stepwise mechanism for each reaction.

a. 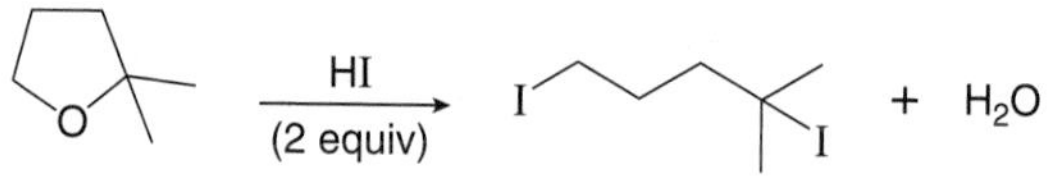

b. 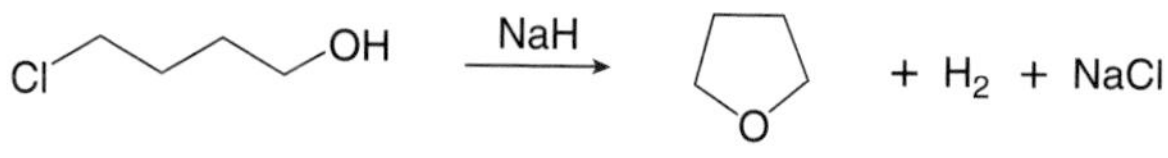

9.65 Draw a stepwise, detailed mechanism for the following reaction.

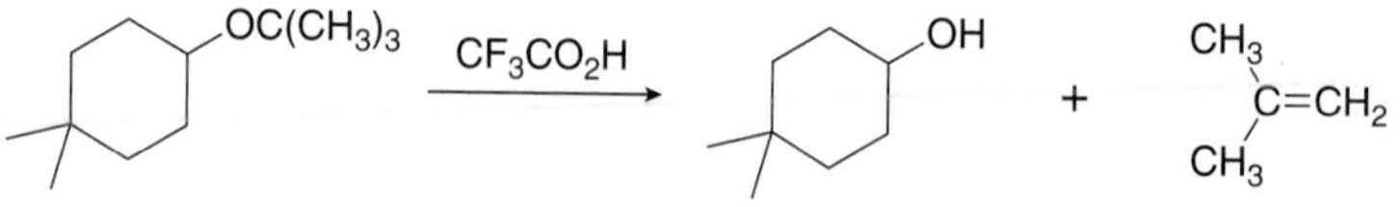

Epoxides

9.66 Draw the products formed when ethylene oxide is treated with each reagent.

a. HBr

b. H_2O (H_2SO_4)

c. [1] $CH_3CH_2O^-$; [2] H_2O

d. [1] $HC{\equiv}C^-$; [2] H_2O

e. [1] ^-OH; [2] H_2O

f. [1] CH_3S^-; [2] H_2O

9.67 Draw the products of each reaction.

a. 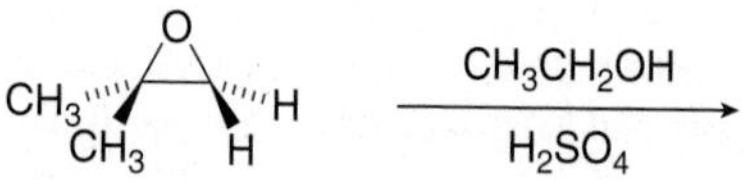

b. 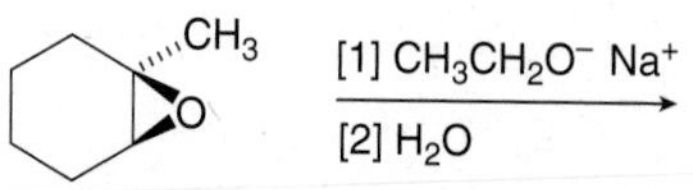

c. 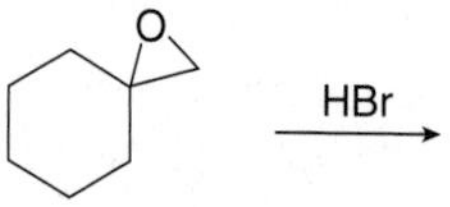

d. 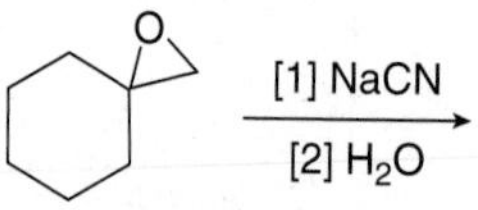

9.68 When each halohydrin is treated with NaH, a product of molecular formula C_4H_8O is formed. Draw the structure of the product and indicate its stereochemistry.

a. 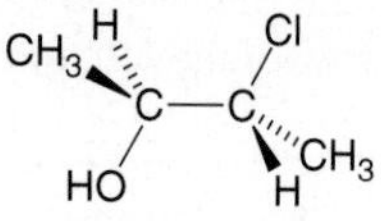

b. 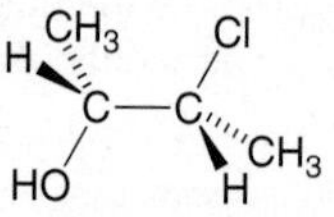

c. 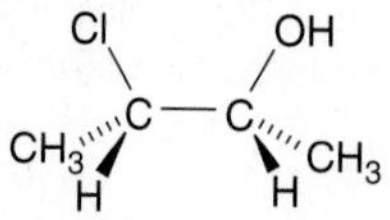

9.69 (a) What reaction conditions are needed to convert (2*R*)-2-ethyl-2-methyloxirane to (2*R*)-2-methyl-1,2-butanediol? (b) What reaction conditions are needed to convert (2*R*)-2-ethyl-2-methyloxirane to (2*S*)-2-methyl-1,2-butanediol?

9.70 Devise a stepwise mechanism for the following reaction.

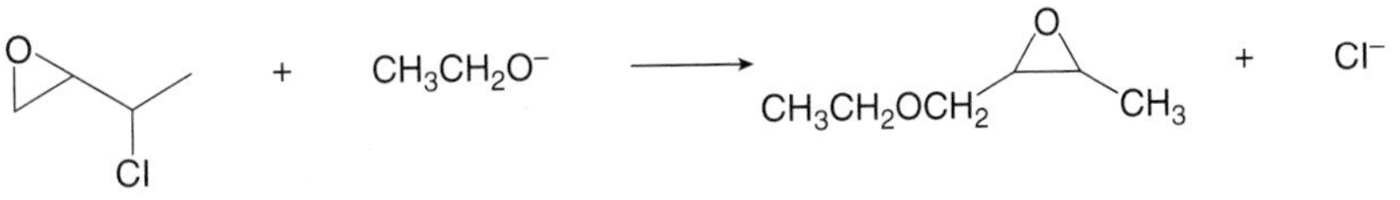

General Problems

9.71 Draw the products of each reaction, and indicate the stereochemistry where appropriate.

a. 

b. 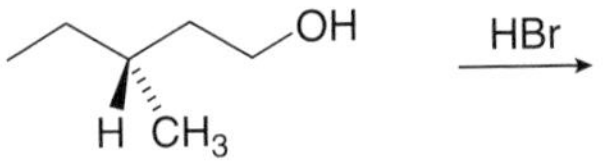

c. 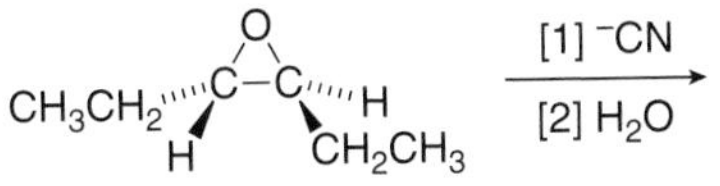

d. 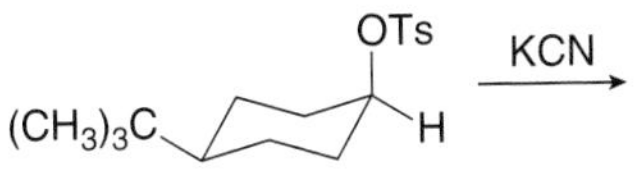

e. 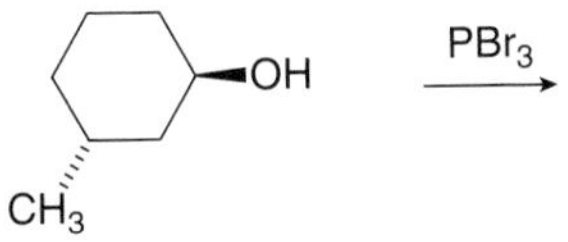

f. 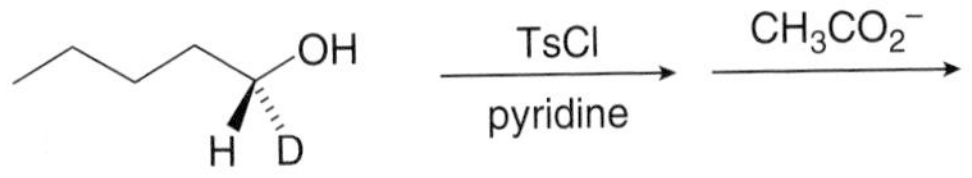

g. 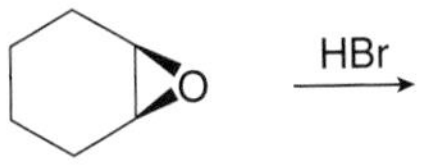

h. 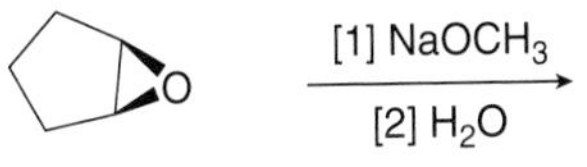

i. 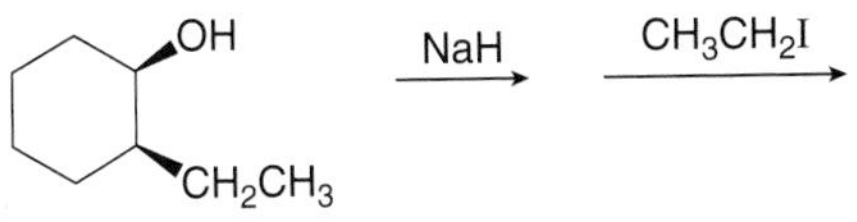

j. 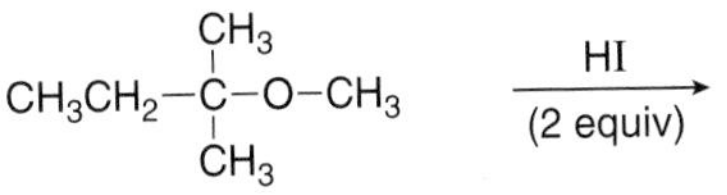

9.72 Prepare each compound from $CH_3CH_2CH_2CH_2OH$. More than one step may be needed.

a. $CH_3CH_2CH_2CH_2Br$ b. $CH_3CH_2CH_2CH_2Cl$ c. $CH_3CH_2CH_2CH_2OCH_2CH_3$ d. $CH_3CH_2CH_2CH_2N_3$

9.73 Prepare each compound from cyclopentanol. More than one step may be needed.

a. 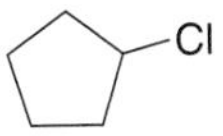

b. 

c. 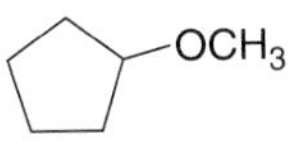

d. 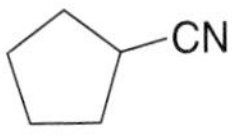

9.74 Identify the reagents (a–h) needed to carry out each reaction.

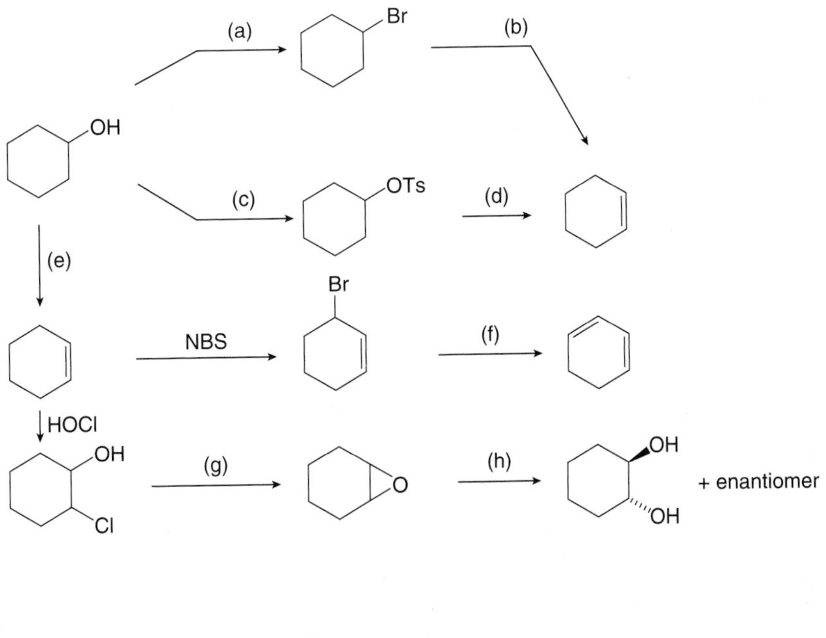

9.75 **Propranolol,** an antihypertensive agent used in the treatment of high blood pressure, can be prepared from 1-naphthol, epichlorohydrin, and isopropylamine using two successive nucleophilic substitution reactions. Devise a stepwise synthesis of propranolol from these starting materials.

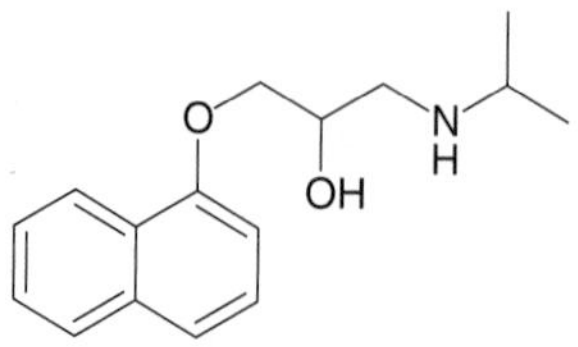

propranolol

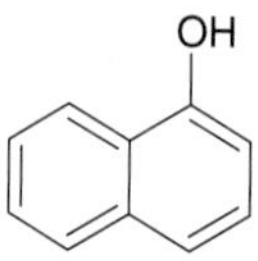

1-naphthol

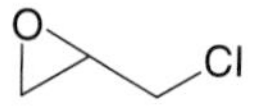

epichlorohydrin

$(CH_3)_2CHNH_2$

isopropylamine

Challenge Problems

9.76 Treatment of *cis*-4-bromocyclohexanol with HO^- affords compound **A** and 3-cyclohexen-1-ol. Treatment of *trans*-4-bromocyclohexanol under the same conditions forms compound **B** and 3-cyclohexen-1-ol. **A** and **B** contain different functional groups and are not isomers of each other. Propose structures for **A** and **B** and offer an explanation for their formation.

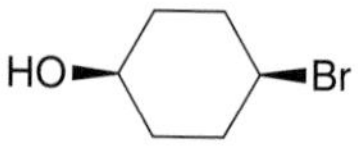

cis-4-bromocyclohexanol

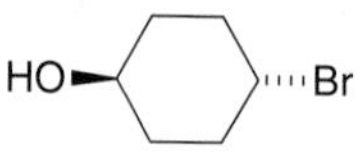

trans-4-bromocyclohexanol

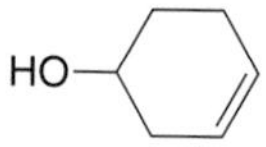

3-cyclohexen-1-ol

9.77 Epoxides are converted to allylic alcohols with nonnucleophilic bases such as lithium diethylamide [$LiN(CH_2CH_3)_2$]. Draw a stepwise mechanism for the conversion of 1,2-epoxycyclohexane to 2-cyclohexen-1-ol with this base. Explain why a strong bulky base must be used in this reaction.

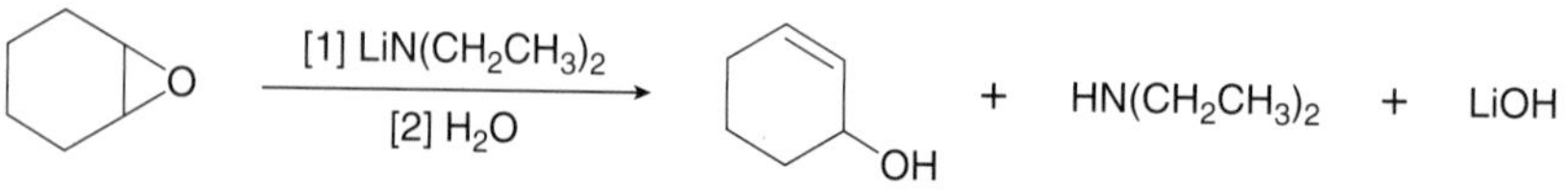

2-cyclohexen-1-ol

9.78 Rearrangements can occur during the dehydration of 1° alcohols even though no 1° carbocation is formed—that is, a 1,2-shift occurs as the $C-OH_2^+$ bond is broken, forming a more stable 2° or 3° carbocation, as shown. Using this information, draw a stepwise mechanism that shows how $CH_3CH_2CH_2CH_2OH$ is dehydrated with H_2SO_4 to form a mixture of $CH_3CH_2CH{=}CH_2$ and the cis and trans isomers of $CH_3CH{=}CHCH_3$. We will see another example of this type of rearrangement in Section 18.5C.

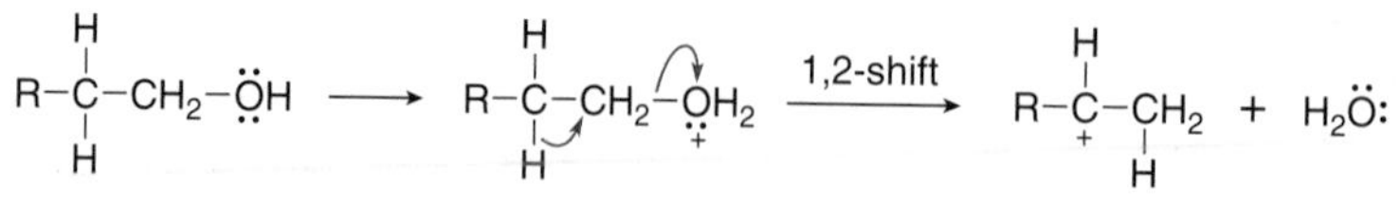

1° alcohol

no 1° carbocation at this step

2° carbocation

9.79 Draw a stepwise, detailed mechanism for the following reaction.

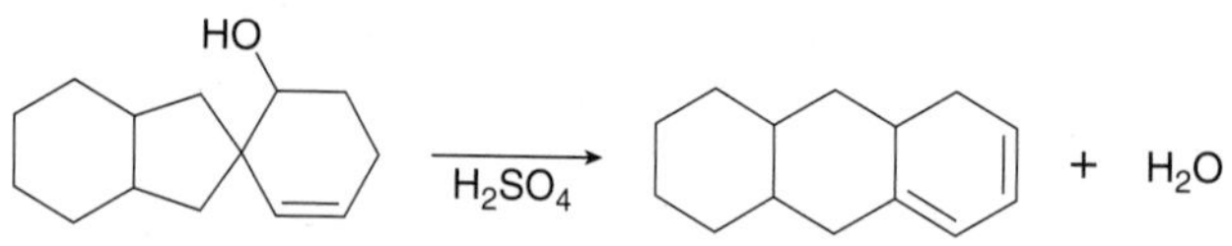

9.80 Dehydration of 1,2,2-trimethylcyclohexanol with H_2SO_4 affords 1-*tert*-butylcyclopentene as a minor product. (a) Draw a stepwise mechanism that shows how this alkene is formed. (b) Draw other alkenes formed in this dehydration. At least one must contain a five-membered ring.

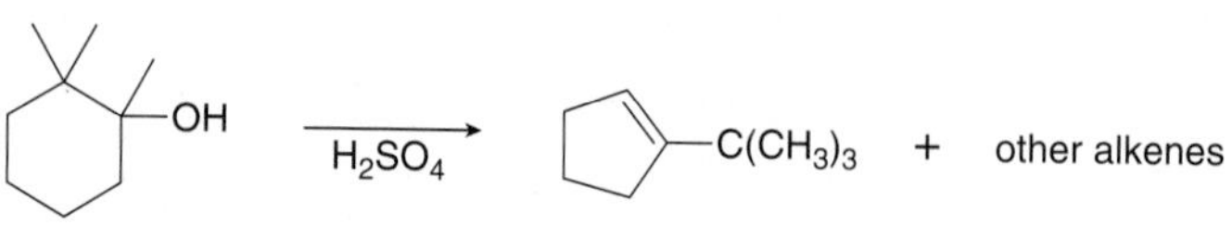

1,2,2-trimethylcyclohexanol

1-*tert*-butylcyclopentene

9.81 1,2-Diols are converted to carbonyl compounds when treated with strong acids, in a reaction called the *pinacol rearrangement.*
(a) Draw a stepwise mechanism for this reaction. (Hint: The reaction proceeds by way of carbocation intermediates.)
(b) Assuming that the pinacol rearrangement occurs via the more stable carbocation, draw the rearrangement product formed from diol **D.**

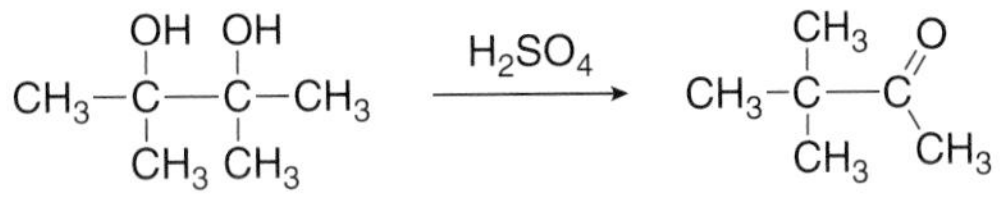

pinacol pinacolone

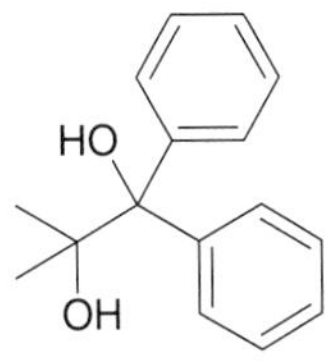

D

9.82 Draw a stepwise mechanism for the following reaction.

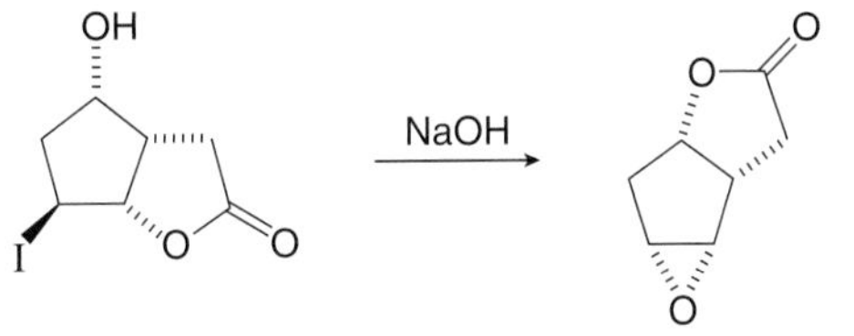

9.83 Aziridines are heterocycles that contain an N atom in a three-membered ring. Like epoxides, aziridines are strained and reactive because the 60° bond angles of the three-membered ring deviate greatly from the theoretical tetrahedral bond angle. One step in the synthesis of the drug oseltamivir (trade name Tamiflu, Section 3.2) involves the conversion of amine **X** to diamine **Y,** a reaction that occurs by way of an intermediate aziridine. Draw a stepwise mechanism for the conversion of **X** to **Y.** Indicate the structure of the aziridine intermediate, and explain the trans stereochemistry of the two amines in **Y.**

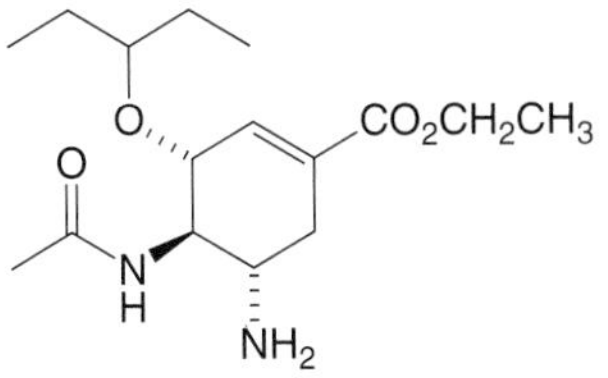

oseltamivir

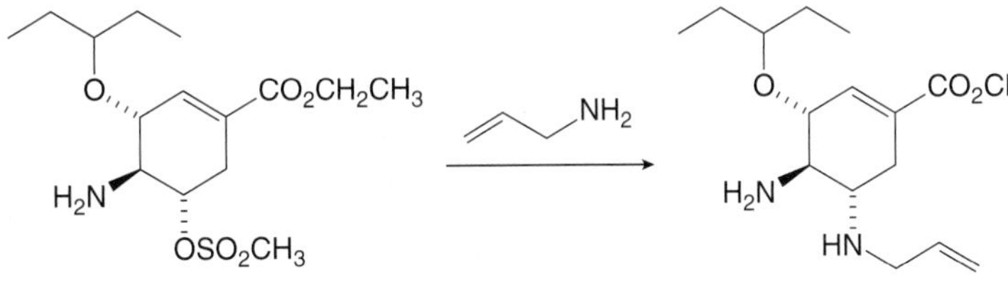

X **Y**

10 Alkenes

10.1 Introduction
10.2 Calculating degrees of unsaturation
10.3 Nomenclature
10.4 Physical properties
10.5 Interesting alkenes
10.6 Lipids—Part 2
10.7 Preparation of alkenes
10.8 Introduction to addition reactions
10.9 Hydrohalogenation—Electrophilic addition of HX
10.10 Markovnikov's rule
10.11 Stereochemistry of electrophilic addition of HX
10.12 Hydration—Electrophilic addition of water
10.13 Halogenation—Addition of halogen
10.14 Stereochemistry of halogenation
10.15 Halohydrin formation
10.16 Hydroboration–oxidation
10.17 Keeping track of reactions
10.18 Alkenes in organic synthesis

Stearic acid and **oleic acid** are fatty acids, compounds that contain a carboxy group (COOH) attached to the end of a long carbon chain. Stearic acid is a **saturated fatty acid** because each carbon atom in its long chain has the maximum number of bonds to hydrogen. Oleic acid is an **unsaturated fatty acid** because its carbon chain contains one (cis) double bond. The presence of a double bond greatly affects the chemical and physical properties of these fatty acids. In Chapter 10 we learn about alkenes, organic compounds that contain carbon–carbon double bonds.

In Chapters 10 and 11 we turn our attention to **alkenes** and **alkynes,** compounds that contain one and two π bonds, respectively. Because π bonds are easily broken, alkenes and alkynes undergo **addition,** the third general type of organic reaction. These multiple bonds also make carbon atoms electron rich, so alkenes and alkynes react with a wide variety of electrophilic reagents in addition reactions.

In Chapter 10 we review the properties and synthesis of alkenes first, and then concentrate on reactions. **Every new reaction in Chapter 10 is an *addition reaction.*** The most challenging part is learning the reagents, mechanism, and stereochemistry that characterize each individual reaction.

10.1 Introduction

Alkenes are also called **olefins.**

Alkenes are compounds that contain a carbon–carbon double bond. **Terminal alkenes** have the double bond at the end of the carbon chain, whereas **internal alkenes** have at least one carbon atom bonded to each end of the double bond. **Cycloalkenes** contain a double bond in a ring.

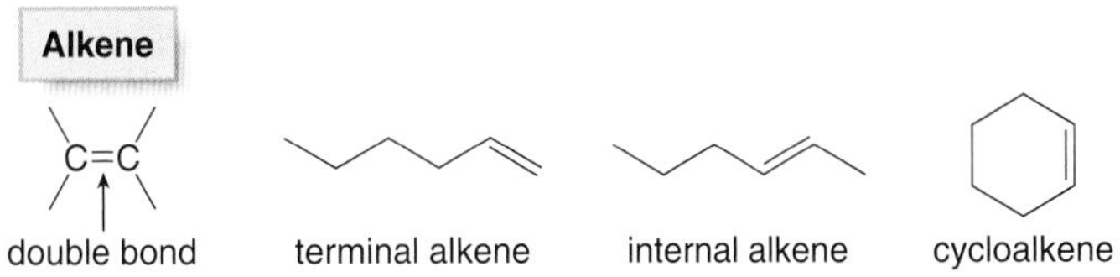

The double bond of an alkene consists of one σ bond and one π bond. Each carbon is sp^2 hybridized and trigonal planar, and all bond angles are approximately 120° (Section 8.2A).

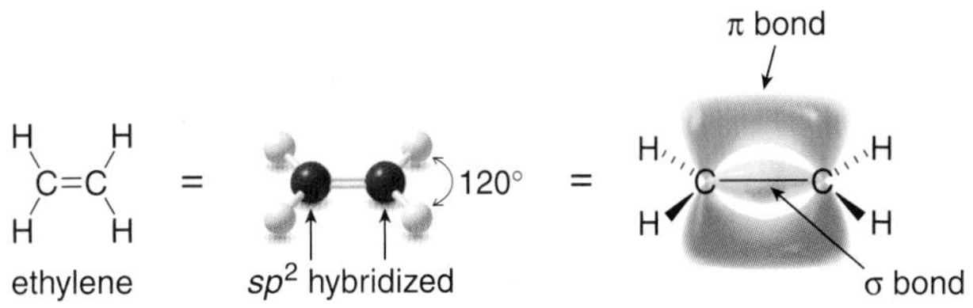

Bond dissociation energies of the C–C bonds in ethane (a σ bond only) and ethylene (one σ and one π bond) can be used to estimate the strength of the π component of the double bond. If we assume that the σ bond in ethylene is similar in strength to the σ bond in ethane (368 kJ/mol), then the π bond is worth 267 kJ/mol.

$$\underset{(\sigma + \pi \text{ bond})}{\underset{635 \text{ kJ/mol}}{CH_2{=}CH_2}} \quad - \quad \underset{(\sigma \text{ bond})}{\underset{368 \text{ kJ/mol}}{CH_3{-}CH_3}} \quad = \quad \underset{\pi \textbf{ bond only}}{267 \text{ kJ/mol}}$$

- **The π bond is much weaker than the σ bond of a C–C double bond, making it much more easily broken. As a result, alkenes undergo many reactions that alkanes do not.**

Other features of the carbon–carbon double bond, which were presented in Chapter 8, are summarized in Table 10.1.

Table 10.1 Properties of the Carbon–Carbon Double Bond

Property	Result
Restricted rotation	• **The rotation around the C – C double bond is restricted.** Rotation can occur only if the π bond breaks and then re-forms, a process that is unfavorable (Section 8.2B).
Stereoisomerism	• Whenever the two groups on each end of a C=C are different from each other, two diastereomers are possible. *Cis-* and *trans-*2-butene (drawn at the bottom of Table 10.1) are diastereomers (Section 8.2B).
Stability	• **Trans** alkenes are generally more stable than **cis** alkenes. • **The stability of an alkene increases as the number of R groups on the C=C increases** (Section 8.2C).

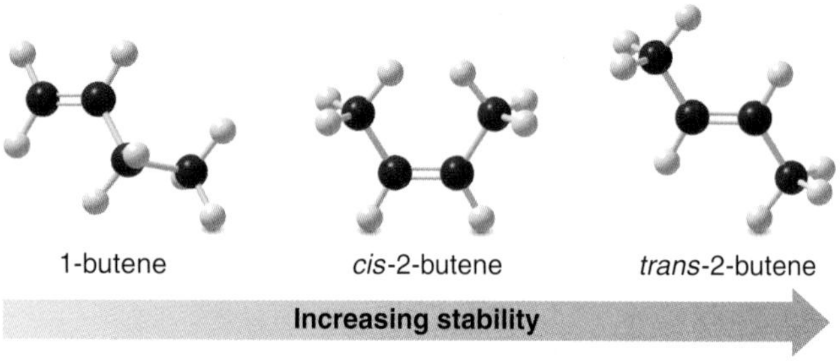
1-butene
cis-2-butene
trans-2-butene
Increasing stability

Cycloalkenes having fewer than eight carbon atoms have a cis geometry. A trans cycloalkene must have a carbon chain long enough to connect the ends of the double bond without introducing too much strain. *trans*-Cyclooctene is the smallest, isolable trans cycloalkene, but it is considerably less stable than *cis*-cyclooctene, making it one of the few alkenes having a higher energy trans isomer.

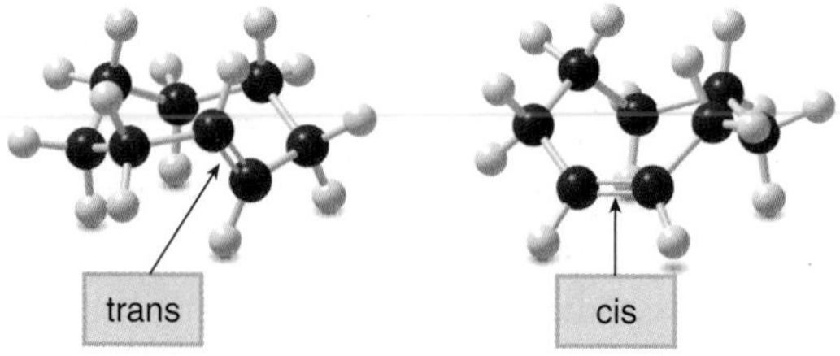
trans
trans-cyclooctene
cis
cis-cyclooctene

Problem 10.1 Draw the six alkenes of molecular formula C_5H_{10}. Label one pair of diastereomers.

10.2 Calculating Degrees of Unsaturation

An acyclic alkene has the general molecular formula C_nH_{2n}, giving it two fewer hydrogens than an acyclic alkane with the same number of carbons.

- **Alkenes are *unsaturated hydrocarbons* because they have fewer than the maximum number of hydrogen atoms per carbon.**

In Chapter 12 we will learn how to use the hydrogenation of π bonds to determine how many degrees of unsaturation result from π bonds and how many result from rings.

Cycloalkanes also have the general molecular formula C_nH_{2n}. Thus, **each π bond or ring removes two hydrogen atoms from a molecule, and this introduces one *degree of unsaturation.*** The number of degrees of unsaturation for a given molecular formula can be calculated by comparing the actual number of H atoms in a compound and the maximum number of H atoms possible. Remember that for *n* carbons, the maximum number of H atoms is $2n + 2$ (Section 4.1). This procedure gives the total number of rings and π bonds in a molecule.

Sample Problem 10.1 Calculate the number of degrees of unsaturation in a compound of molecular formula C_4H_6, and propose possible structures.

Solution

[1] Calculate the maximum number of H's possible.

- For n carbons, the maximum number of H's is $2n + 2$; in this example, $2n + 2 = 2(4) + 2 = 10$.

[2] Subtract the actual number of H's from the maximum number and divide by two.

- 10 H's (maximum) – 6 H's (actual) = 4 H's fewer than the maximum number.

$$\frac{\text{4 H's fewer than the maximum}}{\text{2 H's removed for each degree of unsaturation}} =$$

two degrees of unsaturation

A compound with two degrees of unsaturation has:

two rings	*or*	**two π bonds**	*or*	**one ring and one π bond**

Possible structures for C_4H_6:

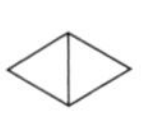

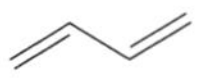

H–C≡C–CH_2CH_3

This procedure can be extended to compounds that contain heteroatoms such as oxygen, nitrogen, and halogen, as illustrated in Sample Problem 10.2.

Sample Problem 10.2 Calculate the number of degrees of unsaturation for each molecular formula: (a) C_5H_8O; (b) $C_6H_{11}Cl$; (c) C_8H_9N. Propose one possible structure for each compound.

Solution

a. **You can ignore the presence of an O atom** when calculating degrees of unsaturation; that is, use only the given number of C's and H's for the calculation (C_5H_8).

[1] For 5 C's, the maximum number of H's = $2n + 2 = 2(5) + 2 = 12$.

[2] Because the compound contains only 8 H's, it has 12 – 8 = 4 H's fewer than the maximum number.

[3] Each degree of unsaturation removes 2 H's, so the answer in Step [2] must be divided by 2.
Answer: two degrees of unsaturation

b. **A compound with a halogen atom is equivalent to a hydrocarbon having one more H;** that is, $C_6H_{11}Cl$ is equivalent to C_6H_{12} when calculating degrees of unsaturation.

[1] For 6 C's, the maximum number of H's = $2n + 2 = 2(6) + 2 = 14$.

[2] Because the compound contains only 12 H's, it has 14 – 12 = 2 H's fewer than the maximum number.

[3] Each degree of unsaturation removes 2 H's, so the answer in Step [2] must be divided by 2.
Answer: one degree of unsaturation

c. **A compound with a nitrogen atom is equivalent to a hydrocarbon having one fewer H;** that is, C_8H_9N is equivalent to C_8H_8 when calculating degrees of unsaturation.

[1] For 8 C's, the maximum number of H's = $2n + 2 = 2(8) + 2 = 18$.

[2] Since the compound contains only 8 H's, it has 18 – 8 = 10 H's fewer than the maximum number.

[3] Each degree of unsaturation removes 2 H's, so the answer in Step [2] must be divided by 2.
Answer: five degrees of unsaturation

Possible structures:

a.
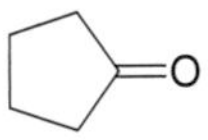

b.
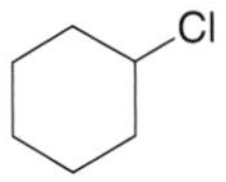

c.
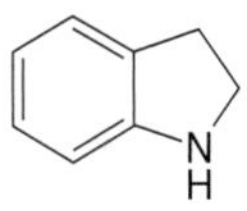

Problem 10.2 How many degrees of unsaturation are present in each compound?

a. C_2H_2 b. C_6H_6 c. C_8H_{18} d. C_7H_8O e. $C_7H_{11}Br$ f. C_5H_9N

Problem 10.3 Give an example of a compound with molecular formula C_6H_{10} that satisfies each criterion.

a. a compound with two π bonds
b. a compound with one ring and one π bond
c. a compound with two rings
d. a compound with one triple bond

10.3 Nomenclature

- **In the IUPAC system, an alkene is identified by the suffix *-ene*.**

10.3A General IUPAC Rules

How To Name an Alkene

Example Give the IUPAC name of the following alkene:

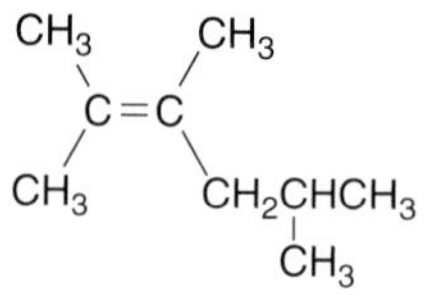

Step [1] Find the longest chain that contains *both* carbon atoms of the double bond.

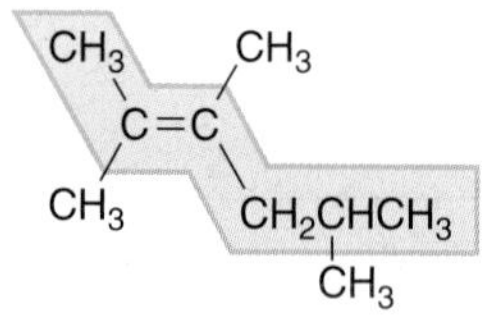

6 C's in the longest chain

hex*ane* ---→ hex*ene*

- Change the ***-ane*** ending of the parent alkane to ***-ene.***

Step [2] Number the carbon chain to give the double bond the lower number, and apply all other rules of nomenclature.

a. **Number** the chain, and name using the ***first* number** assigned to the C=C.

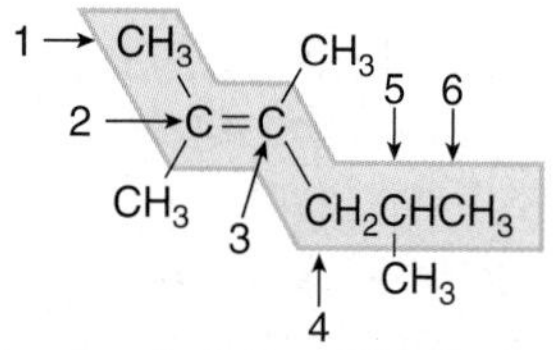

- Number the chain to put the C=C at C2, not C4.

2-hexene

b. **Name** and **number** the substituents.

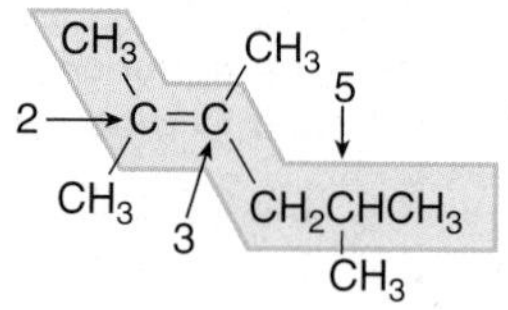

three methyl groups at C2, C3, and C5

Answer: 2,3,5-trimethyl-2-hexene

Compounds with two double bonds are named as **dienes** by changing the ***-ane*** ending of the parent alkane to the suffix ***-adiene.*** Compounds with three double bonds are named as **trienes,** and so forth. Always choose the longest chain that contains *both* atoms of the double bond. In Figure 10.1, the alkene is named as a derivative of heptene because the seven-carbon chain contains both atoms of the double bond, but the eight-carbon chain does not.

Figure 10.1 Naming an alkene in which the longest carbon chain does not contain both atoms of the double bond

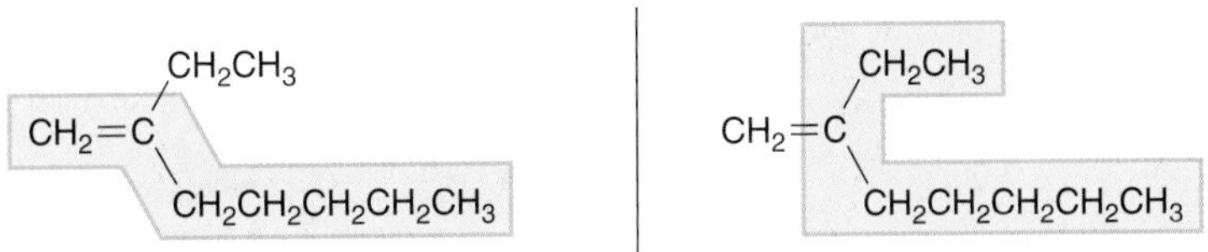

7 C's ---→ heptene

Both C's of the C=C are contained in this long chain.

***Correct:* 2-ethyl-1-heptene**

8 C's

Both C's of the C=C are NOT contained in this long chain.

Incorrect

In naming cycloalkenes, the double bond is located between C1 and C2, and the "1" is usually omitted in the name. The ring is numbered clockwise or counterclockwise to give the first substituent the lower number. Representative examples are given in Figure 10.2.

Figure 10.2 Examples of cycloalkene nomenclature

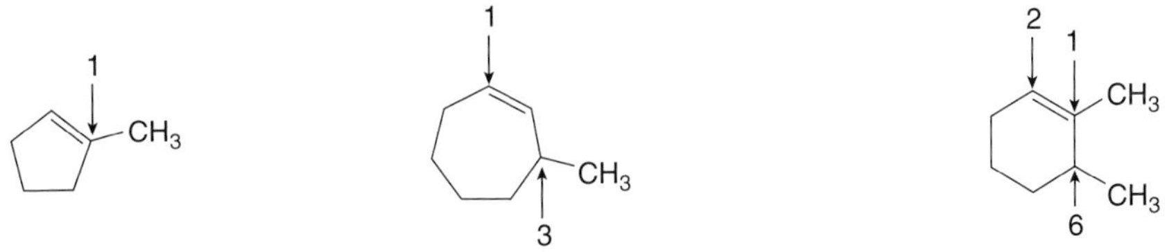

1-methylcyclopentene **3-methylcycloheptene** **1,6-dimethylcyclohexene**

[Number clockwise beginning at the C=C and place the CH_3 at C3.]

[Number counterclockwise beginning at the C=C and place the first CH_3 at C1.]

$CH_3CH_2CH{=}CH_2$ is named as 1-butene using the 1979 IUPAC recommendations and but-1-ene using the 1993 IUPAC recommendations. The first convention is more widely used, so we follow it in this text.

Compounds that contain both a double bond and a hydroxy group are named as **alkenols,** and the chain (or ring) is numbered to give the OH group the lower number.

2-propen-1-ol **6-methyl-6-hepten-2-ol**

Problem 10.4 Give the IUPAC name for each alkene.

a. $CH_2{=}CHCH(CH_3)CH_2CH_3$
b. $(CH_3CH_2)_2C{=}CHCH_2CH_2CH_3$

c. d. e.

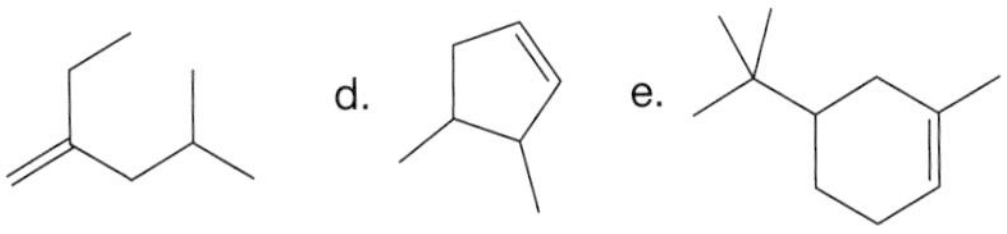

Problem 10.5 Give the IUPAC name for each polyfunctional compound.

a. b. c.

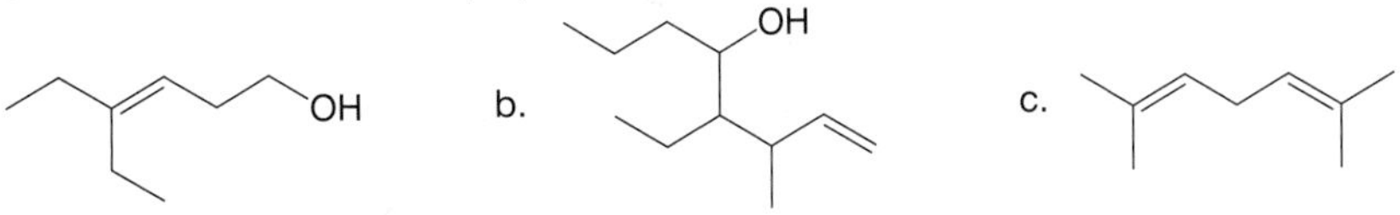

10.3B Naming Stereoisomers

A prefix is needed to distinguish two alkenes when diastereomers are possible.

Using Cis and Trans as Prefixes

An alkene having one alkyl group bonded to each carbon atom can be named using the prefixes **cis** and **trans** to designate the relative location of the two alkyl groups. For example, *cis*-3-hexene has two ethyl groups on the **same side** of the double bond, whereas *trans*-3-hexene has two ethyl groups on **opposite sides** of the double bond.

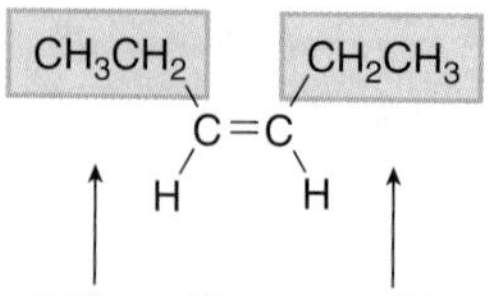

2 R's on the **same** side

***cis*-3-hexene**

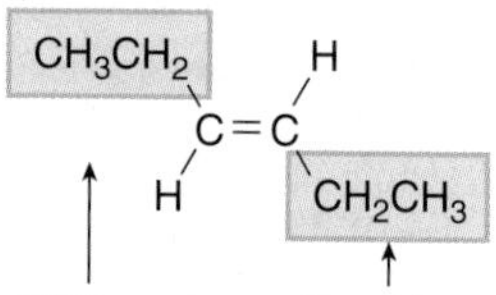

2 R's on **opposite** sides

***trans*-3-hexene**

Using the Prefixes *E* and *Z*

E stands for the German word ***entgegen*** meaning "opposite." *Z* stands for the German word ***zusammen***, meaning "together." Using *E,Z* nomenclature, a cis isomer has the *Z* configuration and a trans isomer has the *E* configuration.

Although the prefixes cis and trans can be used to distinguish diastereomers when two alkyl groups are bonded to the C=C, they cannot be used when there are three or four alkyl groups bonded to the C=C.

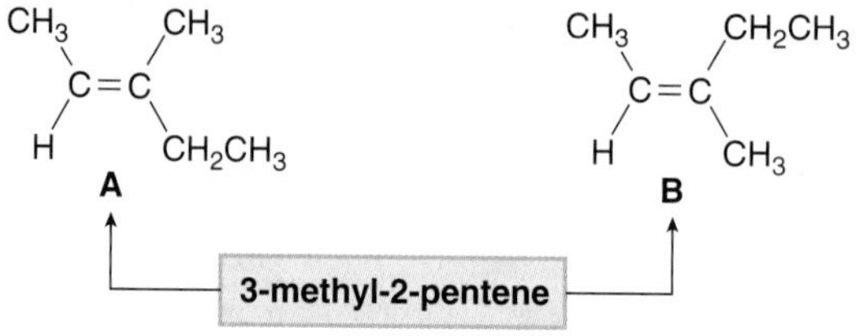

For example, alkenes **A** and **B** are two *different* compounds that are both called 3-methyl-2-pentene. In **A** the two CH_3 groups are cis, whereas in **B** the CH_3 and CH_2CH_3 groups are cis. The ***E,Z* system of nomenclature** has been devised to unambiguously name these kinds of alkenes.

How To Assign the Prefixes *E* and *Z* to an Alkene

Step [1] Assign priorities to the two substituents on each end of the C=C by using the priority rules for *R,S* nomenclature (Section 5.6).

- Divide the double bond in half, and assign the numbers **1** and **2** to indicate the relative priority of the two groups on each end—the higher priority group is labeled **1,** and the lower priority group is labeled **2.**

Divide the double bond in half.

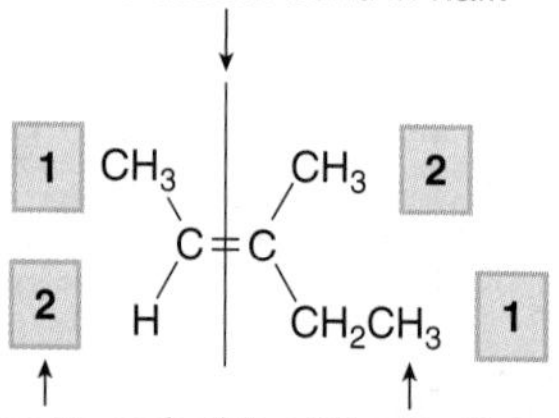

Assign priorities to each side of the C=C separately.

Step [2] Assign *E* or *Z* based on the location of the two higher priority groups (1).

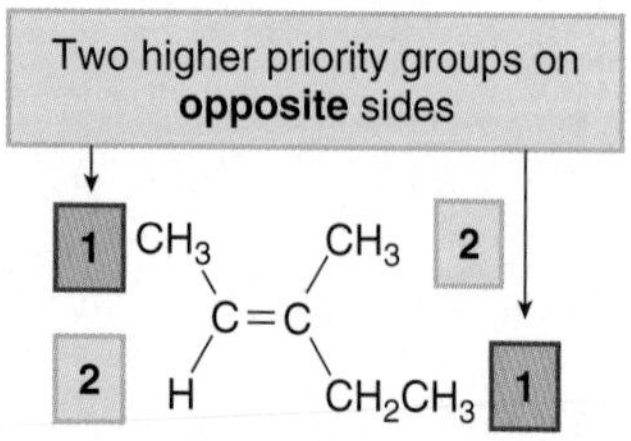

***E* isomer**

(2*E*)-3-methyl-2-pentene

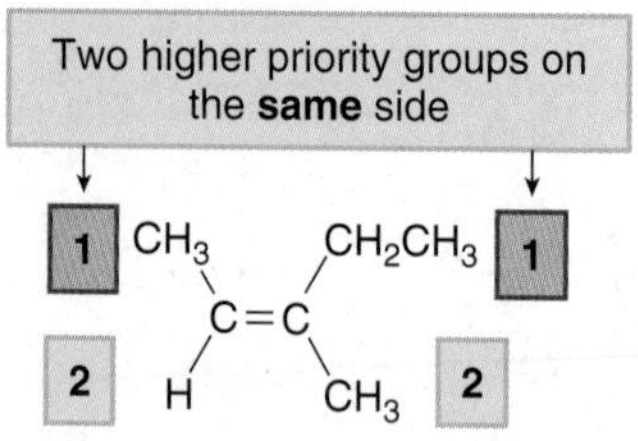

***Z* isomer**

(2*Z*)-3-methyl-2-pentene

- The ***E*** isomer has the two higher priority groups on the **opposite sides.**
- The ***Z*** isomer has the two higher priority groups on the **same side.**

Problem 10.6 Label each C – C double bond as *E* or *Z*. Kavain is a naturally occurring relaxant isolated from kava root.

a. 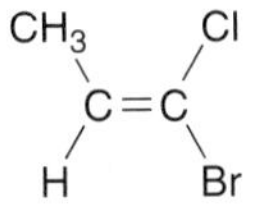

b. 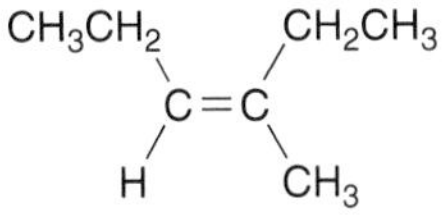

c. 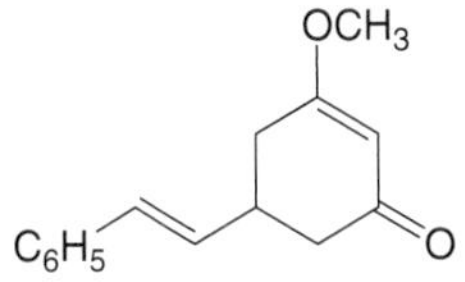

kavain

Problem 10.7 Label each carbon–carbon double bond in 11-*cis*-retinal as *E* or *Z*. As we will learn in Section 21.11, the isomerization of one double bond in this compound to a less crowded stereoisomer takes place when light strikes the retina of the eye.

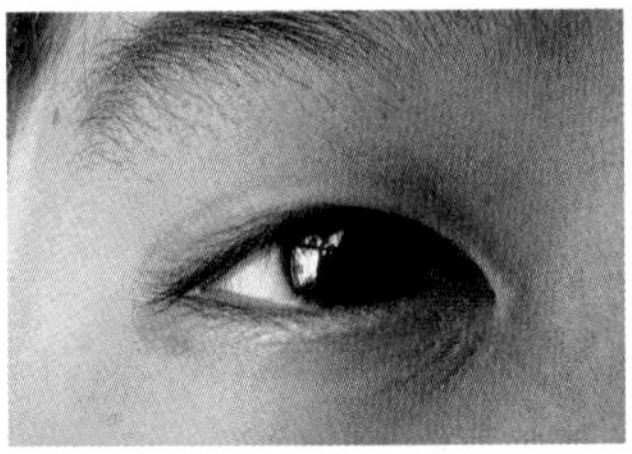

11-*cis*-Retinal is the light-sensitive aldehyde that plays a key role in the chemistry of vision for all vertebrates, arthropods, and mollusks.

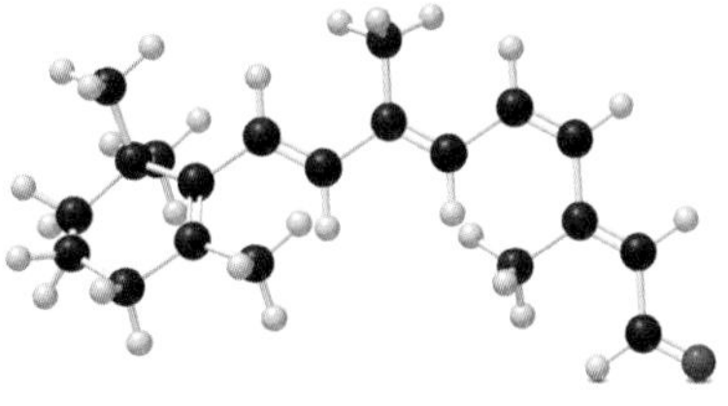

11-*cis*-retinal

Problem 10.8 Draw the structure corresponding to each IUPAC name.

a. (3*Z*)-4-ethyl-3-heptene b. (2*E*)-3,5,6-trimethyl-2-octene c. (1*Z*)-2-bromo-1-iodo-1-hexene

Problem 10.9 Draw and name all the stereoisomers of $CH_3CH=CH-CH=CHCH_3$.

10.3C Common Names

The simplest alkene, $\mathbf{CH_2{=}CH_2}$, named in the IUPAC system as **ethene,** is often called **ethylene,** its common name. The common names for three **alkyl groups** derived from alkenes are also used. Two examples of naming organic molecules using these common names are shown in Figure 10.3.

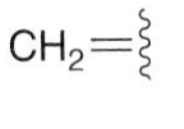

methylene group

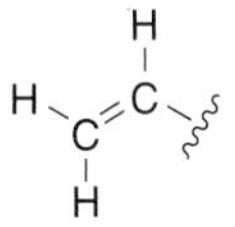

vinyl group

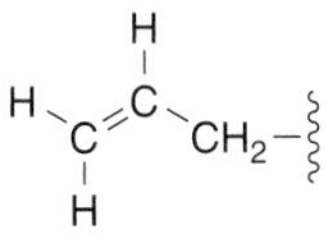

allyl group

Figure 10.3 Naming alkenes with common substituent names

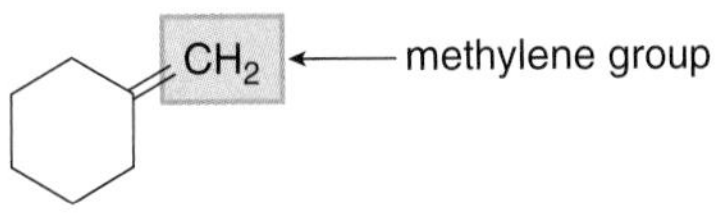

methylenecyclohexane

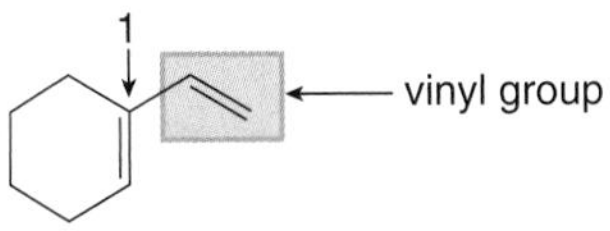

1-vinylcyclohexene

10.4 Physical Properties

Most alkenes exhibit only weak van der Waals interactions, so their physical properties are similar to alkanes of comparable molecular weight.

- **Alkenes have low melting points and boiling points.**
- **Melting points and boiling points increase as the number of carbons increases because of increased surface area.**
- **Alkenes are soluble in organic solvents and insoluble in water.**

Cis and trans alkenes often have somewhat different physical properties. For example, *cis*-2-butene has a higher boiling point (4 °C) than *trans*-2-butene (1 °C). This difference arises because the C–C single bond between an alkyl group and one of the double-bond carbons of an alkene is slightly polar. **The sp^3 hybridized alkyl carbon donates electron density to the sp^2 hybridized alkenyl carbon.**

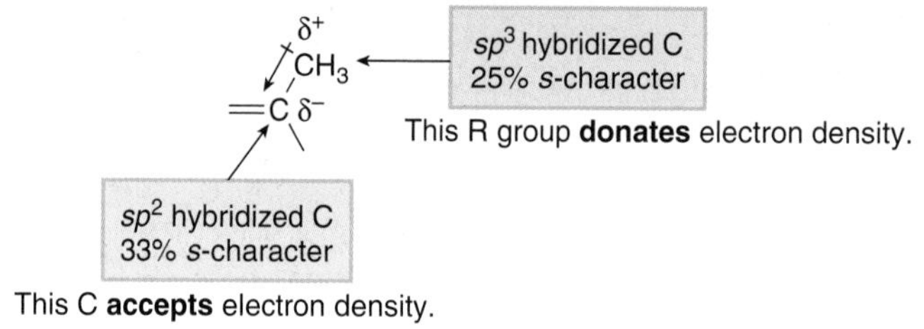
δ+
CH3
C δ−
sp3 hybridized C
25% s-character
This R group donates electron density.
sp2 hybridized C
33% s-character
This C accepts electron density.

Related arguments involving $C_{sp^3}-C_{sp^2}$ bonds were used in Section 8.2C to explain why the stability of an alkene increases with increasing alkyl substitution.

The bond dipole places a partial negative charge on the alkenyl carbon (sp^2) relative to the alkyl carbon (sp^3) because an sp^2 hybridized orbital has greater percent *s*-character (33%) than an sp^3 hybridized orbital (25%). **In a cis isomer, the two $C_{sp^3}-C_{sp^2}$ bond dipoles reinforce each other, yielding a small net molecular dipole. In a trans isomer, the two bond dipoles cancel.**

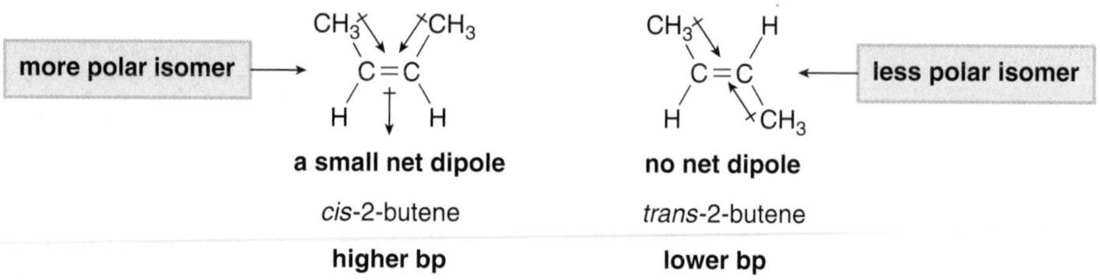
more polar isomer
CH3
CH3
C=C
H
H
a small net dipole
cis-2-butene
higher bp
CH3
H
C=C
H
CH3
less polar isomer
no net dipole
trans-2-butene
lower bp

- **A cis alkene is more polar than a trans alkene, giving it a slightly higher boiling point and making it more soluble in polar solvents.**

Problem 10.10 Rank the following isomers in order of increasing boiling point.

10.5 Interesting Alkenes

Ethylene is prepared from petroleum by a process called **cracking.** Ethylene is the most widely produced organic chemical, serving as the starting material not only for the polymer **polyethylene,** a widely used plastic, but also for many other useful organic compounds, as shown in Figure 10.4.

Figure 10.4
Ethylene, an industrial starting material for many useful products

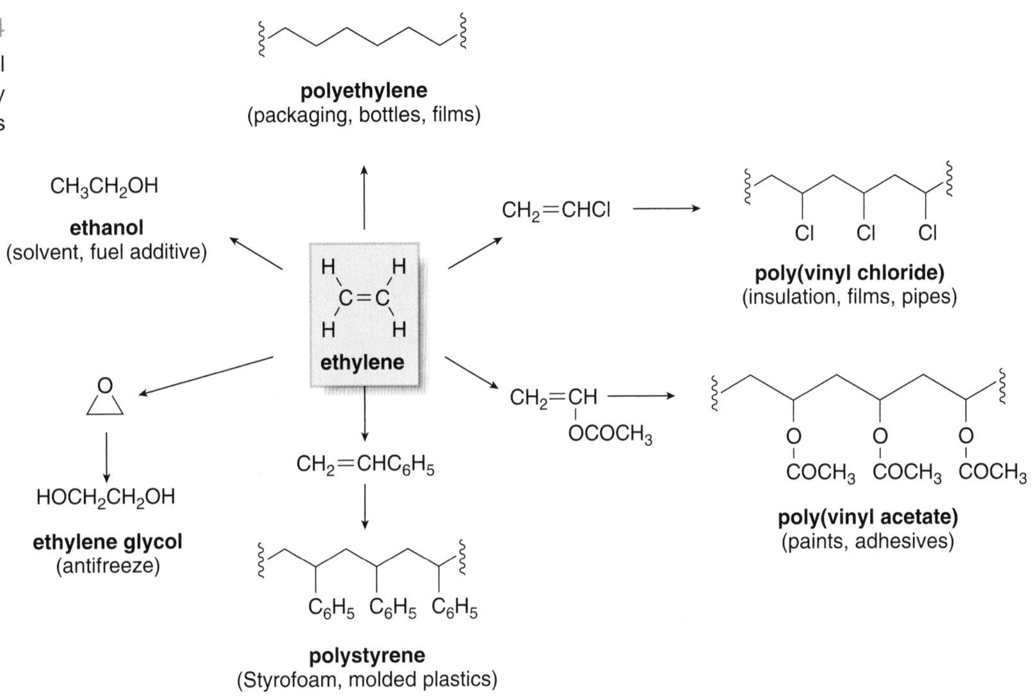
polyethylene
(packaging, bottles, films)
CH3CH2OH
ethanol
(solvent, fuel additive)
H H C=C H H
ethylene
CH2=CHCl
Cl Cl Cl
poly(vinyl chloride)
(insulation, films, pipes)
CH2=CH OCOCH3
O O O
COCH3 COCH3 COCH3
poly(vinyl acetate)
(paints, adhesives)
O
HOCH2CH2OH
ethylene glycol
(antifreeze)
CH2=CHC6H5
C6H5 C6H5 C6H5
polystyrene
(Styrofoam, molded plastics)

Numerous organic compounds containing carbon–carbon double bonds have been isolated from natural sources (Figure 10.5).

Figure 10.5
Four naturally occurring alkenes

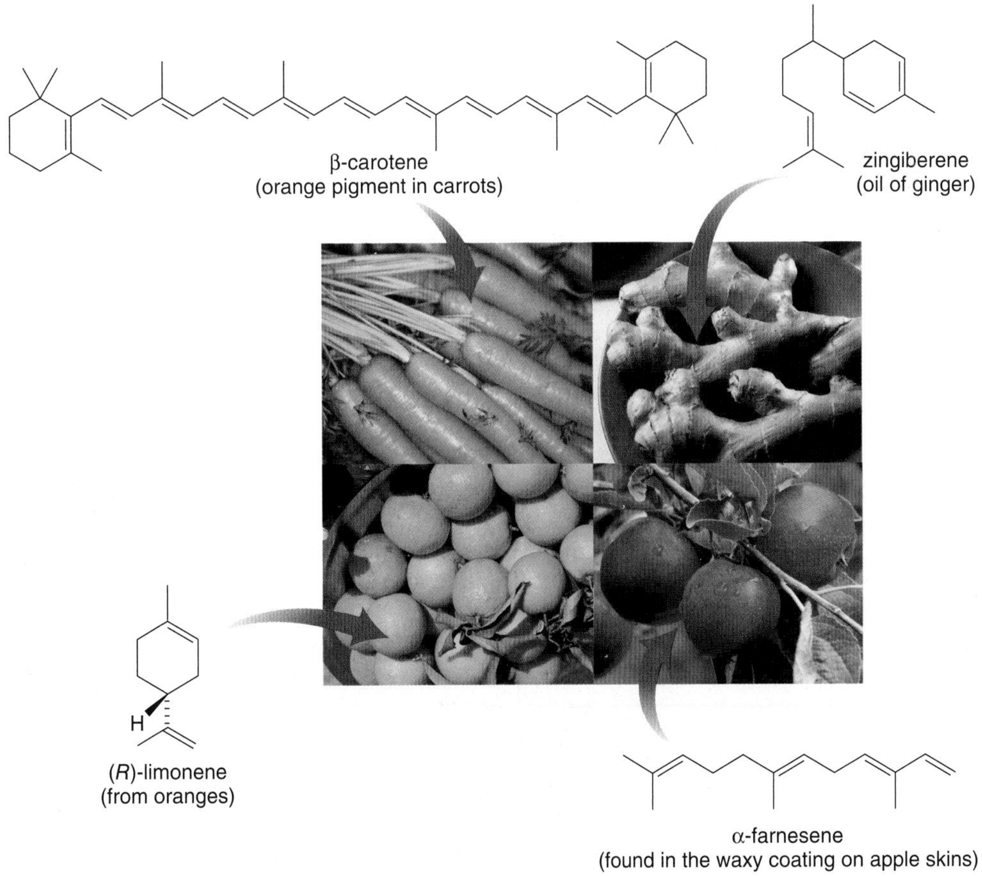
β-carotene
(orange pigment in carrots)
zingiberene
(oil of ginger)
H
(R)-limonene
(from oranges)
α-farnesene
(found in the waxy coating on apple skins)

The alkenes in Figure 10.5 all originate from the same five-carbon starting material in nature, as we will learn in Chapter 30.

10.6 Lipids—Part 2

Lipids are water-insoluble biomolecules composed largely of nonpolar C – C and C – H bonds (Section 4.15).

General structure of an ester:

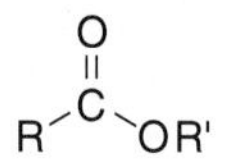

Understanding the geometry of C–C double bonds provides an insight into the properties of **triacylglycerols,** the most abundant lipids. Triacylglycerols contain three ester groups, each having a long carbon chain (abbreviated as R, R', and R") bonded to a carbonyl group (C=O).

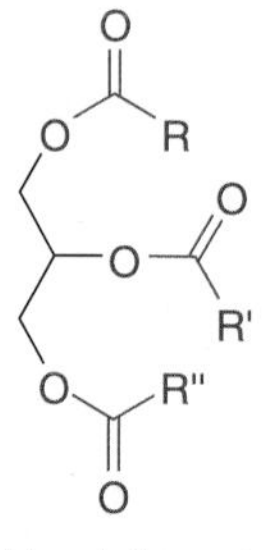

triacylglycerol

R groups have 11–19 C's.

[Three ester groups are labeled in red.]

10.6A Fatty Acids

Triacylglycerols are hydrolyzed to glycerol (a triol), and three **fatty acids** of general structure RCOOH. Naturally occurring fatty acids contain 12–20 carbon atoms, with a carboxy group (COOH) at one end.

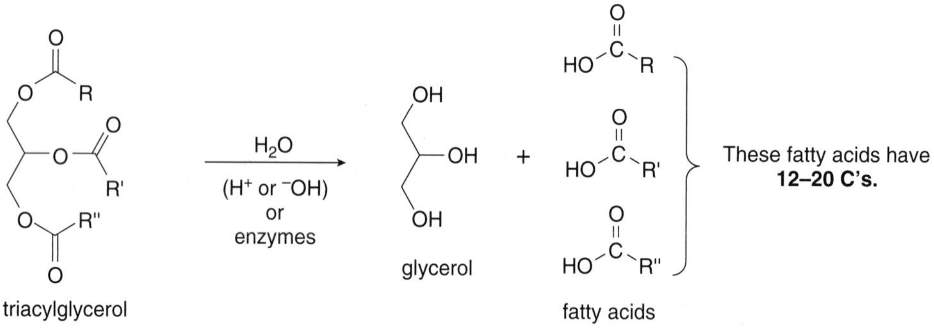

Linoleic and linolenic acids are essential fatty acids, meaning they cannot be synthesized in the body and must therefore be obtained in the diet. A common source of these essential fatty acids is whole milk. Babies fed a diet of nonfat milk in their early months do not thrive because they do not obtain enough of these essential fatty acids.

- **Saturated fatty acids have no double bonds in their long hydrocarbon chains, and unsaturated fatty acids have one or more double bonds in their hydrocarbon chains.**
- **Double bonds in naturally occurring fatty acids have the *Z* configuration.**

Table 10.2 lists the structure and melting point of four fatty acids containing 18 carbon atoms. Stearic acid is one of the two most common saturated fatty acids, and oleic and linoleic acids are the most common unsaturated ones. The data show the effect of *Z* double bonds on the melting point of fatty acids.

- **As the number of double bonds in the fatty acid *increases,* the melting point *decreases.***

The three-dimensional structures of the fatty acids in Figure 10.6 illustrate how *Z* double bonds introduce kinks in the long hydrocarbon chain, decreasing the ability of the fatty acid to pack well in a crystalline lattice. **The larger the number of *Z* double bonds, the more kinks in the hydrocarbon chain, and the lower the melting point.**

Table 10.2 The Effect of Double Bonds on the Melting Point of Fatty Acids

Name	Structure	Mp (°C)
Stearic acid (0 C=C)	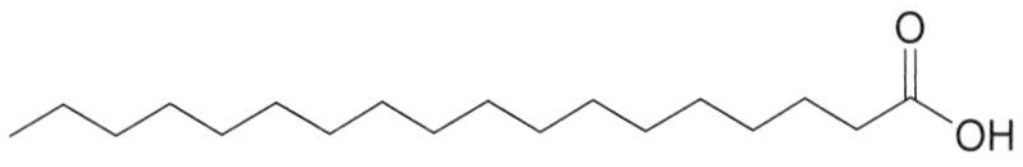	69
Oleic acid (1 C=C)	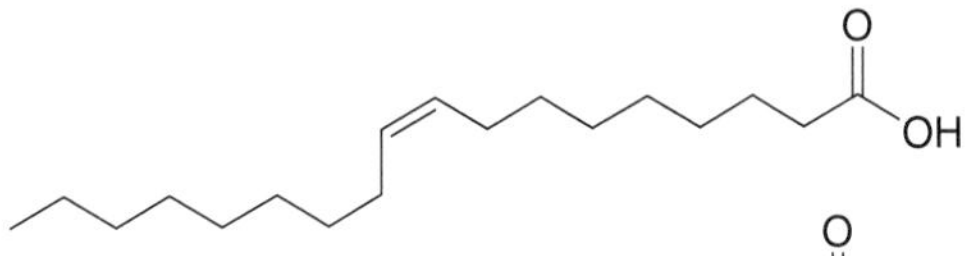	4
Linoleic acid (2 C=C)	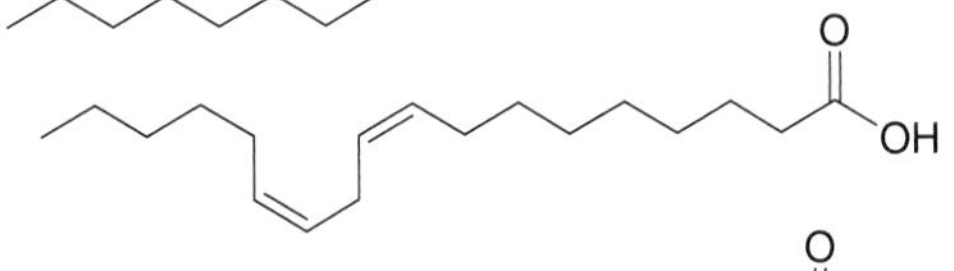	–5
Linolenic acid (3 C=C)	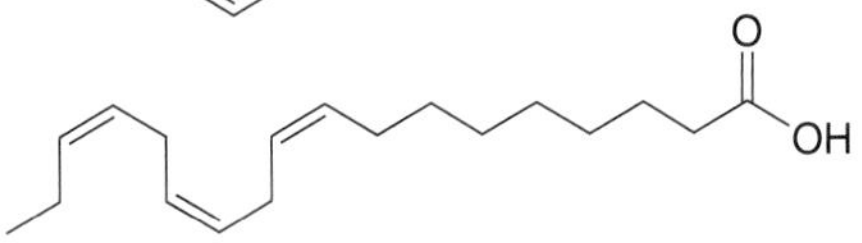	–11

Increasing number of double bonds

Problem 10.11 Linolenic acid (Table 10.2) and stearidonic acid are omega-3 fatty acids, unsaturated fatty acids that contain the first double bond located at C3, when numbering begins at the methyl end of the chain. Predict how the melting point of stearidonic acid compares with the melting points of linolenic and stearic acids. A current avenue of research is examining the use of soybean oil enriched in stearidonic acid as a healthier alternative to vegetable oils that contain fewer degrees of unsaturation.

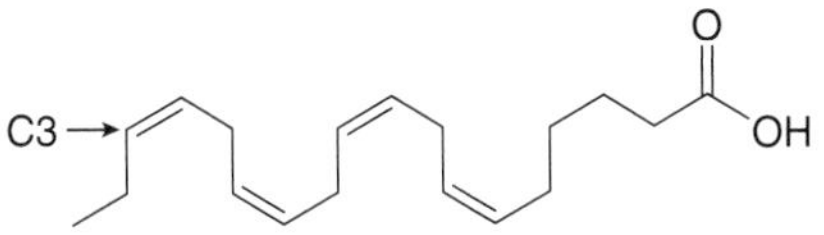
C3
OH

stearidonic acid

Figure 10.6 Three-dimensional structure of four C_{18} fatty acids

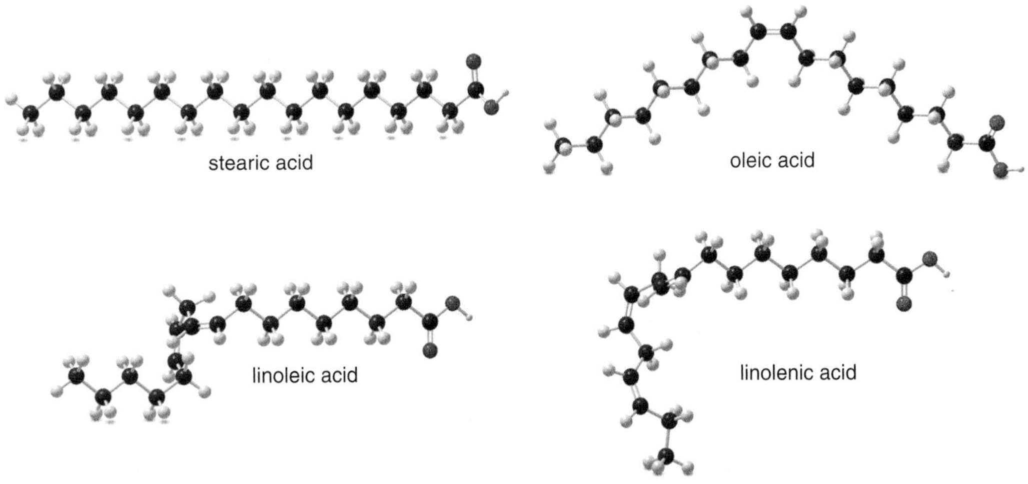
stearic acid
oleic acid
linoleic acid
linolenic acid

10.6B Fats and Oils

Canola Oil

Canola, soybeans, and flaxseed are excellent dietary sources of linolenic acid, an essential fatty acid. Oils derived from omega-3 fatty acids (Problem 10.11) are currently thought to be especially beneficial for individuals at risk of developing coronary artery disease.

Fats and **oils** are triacylglycerols with different physical properties.

- Fats have higher melting points—they are *solids* at room temperature.
- Oils have lower melting points—they are *liquids* at room temperature.

The identity of the three fatty acids in the triacylglycerol determines whether it is a fat or an oil. **Increasing the number of double bonds in the fatty acid side chains decreases the melting point of the triacylglycerol.**

- Fats are derived from fatty acids having few double bonds.
- Oils are derived from fatty acids having a larger number of double bonds.

Saturated fats are typically obtained from animal sources, whereas unsaturated oils are common in vegetable sources. Thus, butter and lard are high in saturated triacylglycerols, and olive oil and safflower oil are high in unsaturated triacylglycerols. An exception to this generalization is coconut oil, which is composed largely of saturated alkyl side chains.

Considerable evidence suggests that an elevated cholesterol level is linked to an increased risk of heart disease. Saturated fats stimulate cholesterol synthesis in the liver, thus increasing the cholesterol concentration in the blood.

10.7 Preparation of Alkenes

Recall from Chapters 8 and 9 that alkenes can be prepared from alkyl halides and alcohols via elimination reactions. For example, **dehydrohalogenation of alkyl halides with strong base yields alkenes via an E2 mechanism** (Sections 8.4 and 8.5).

- Typical bases include ^{-}OH and ^{-}OR [especially $^{-}OC(CH_3)_3$], and nonnucleophilic bases such as DBU and DBN.
- Alkyl tosylates can also be used as starting materials under similar reaction conditions (Section 9.13).

Examples

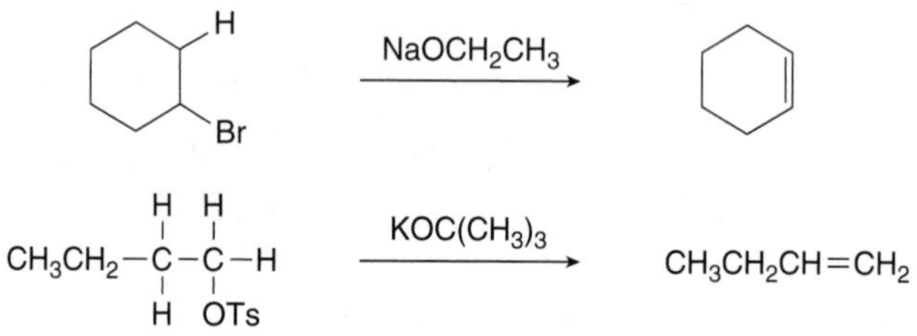
H
Br
NaOCH2CH3
H H
CH3CH2—C—C—H
H OTs
KOC(CH3)3
CH3CH2CH=CH2

The acid-catalyzed dehydration of alcohols with H_2SO_4 or TsOH yields alkenes, too (Sections 9.8 and 9.9). The reaction occurs via an E1 mechanism for 2° and 3° alcohols, and an E2 mechanism for 1° alcohols. E1 reactions involve carbocation intermediates, so rearrangements are possible. **Dehydration can also be carried out with $POCl_3$ and pyridine** by an E2 mechanism (Section 9.10).

Examples

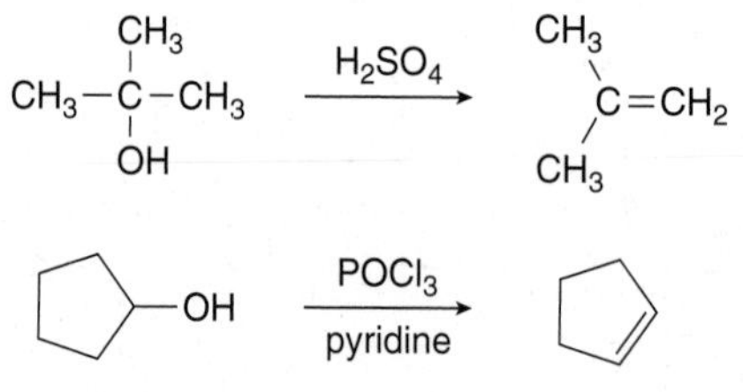
CH3
CH3—C—CH3
OH
H2SO4
CH3
C=CH2
CH3
OH
POCl3
pyridine

These elimination reactions are stereoselective and regioselective, so the most stable alkene is usually formed as the major product.

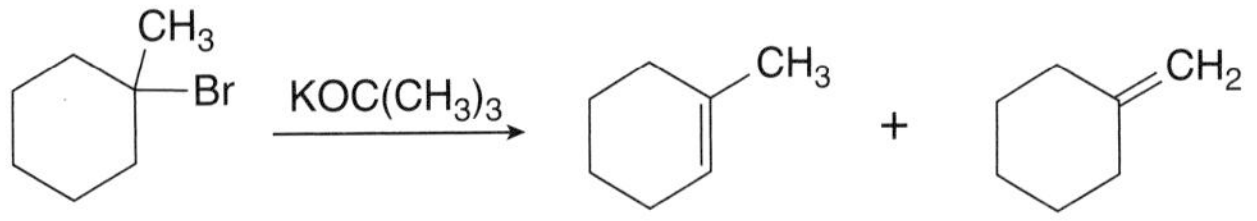

major product

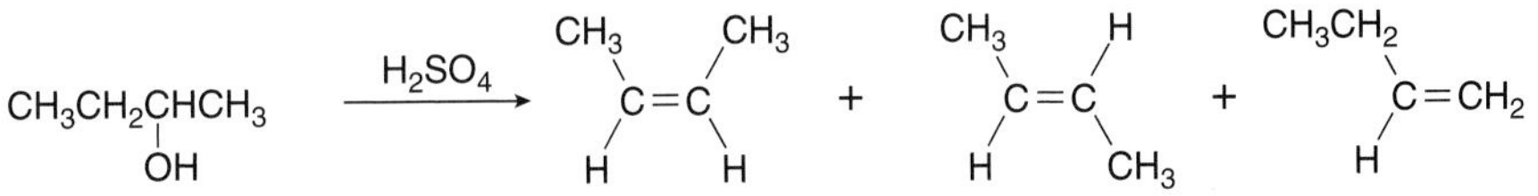

major product
trans disubstituted alkene

Problem 10.12 Draw the products of each elimination reaction.

a. 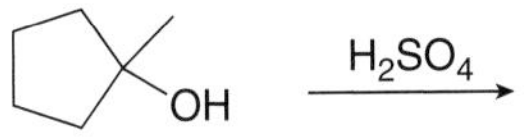

b. 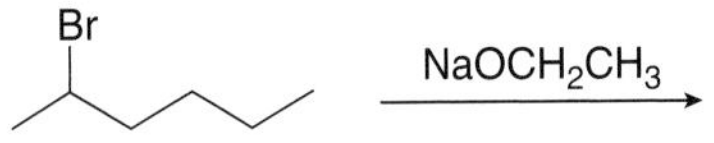

10.8 Introduction to Addition Reactions

Because the C–C π bond of an alkene is much weaker than a C–C σ bond, the characteristic reaction of alkenes is **addition: the π bond is broken and two new σ bonds are formed.**

Addition reaction

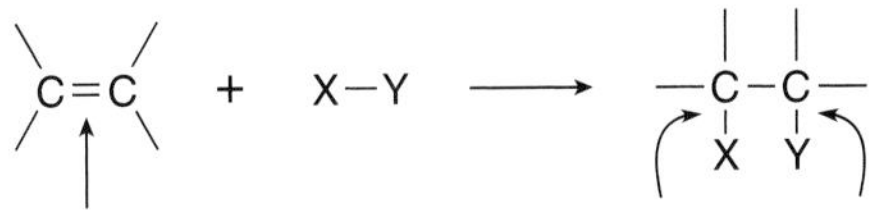

This π bond is broken. Two σ bonds are formed.

Alkenes are electron rich, as seen in the electrostatic potential plot in Figure 10.7. The electron density of the π bond is concentrated above and below the plane of the molecule, making the π bond more exposed than the σ bond.

What kinds of reagents add to the weak, electron-rich π bond of alkenes? There are many of them, and that can make alkene chemistry challenging. To help you organize this information, keep in mind the following:

The addition reactions of alkenes are discussed in Sections 10.9–10.16 and in Chapter 12 (Oxidation and Reduction).

- **Every reaction of alkenes involves addition: the π bond is always broken.**
- **Because alkenes are electron rich, simple alkenes do *not* react with nucleophiles or bases, reagents that are themselves electron rich. Alkenes react with *electrophiles.***

Figure 10.7
Electrostatic potential plot of ethylene

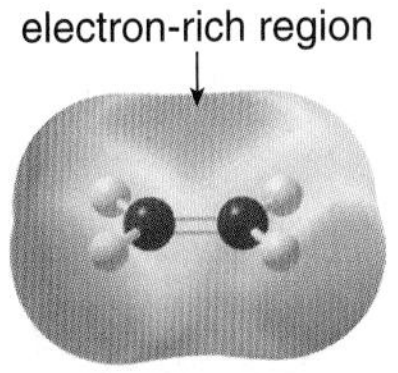

- The red electron-rich region of the π bond is located above and below the plane of the molecule. Because the plane of the alkene depicted in this electrostatic potential plot is tipped, only the red region above the molecule is visible.

The stereochemistry of addition is often important in delineating a reaction's mechanism. Because the carbon atoms of a double bond are both trigonal planar, the elements of X and Y can be added to them from the **same side** or from **opposite sides.**

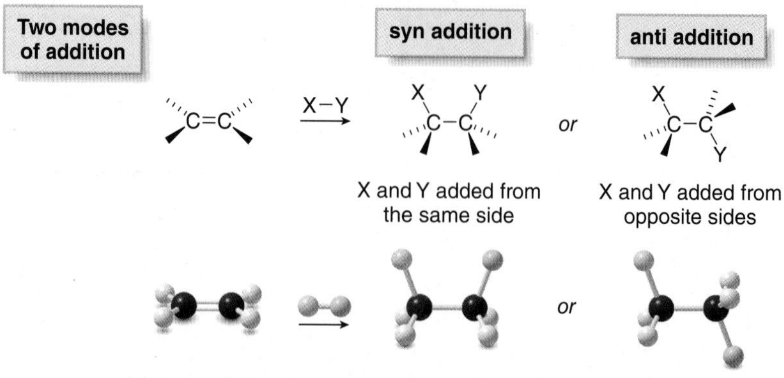

- *Syn addition* takes place when both X and Y are added from the *same* side.
- *Anti addition* takes place when X and Y are added from *opposite* sides.

Five reactions of alkenes are discussed in Chapter 10 and each is illustrated in Figure 10.8, using cyclohexene as the starting material.

Figure 10.8
Five addition reactions of cyclohexene

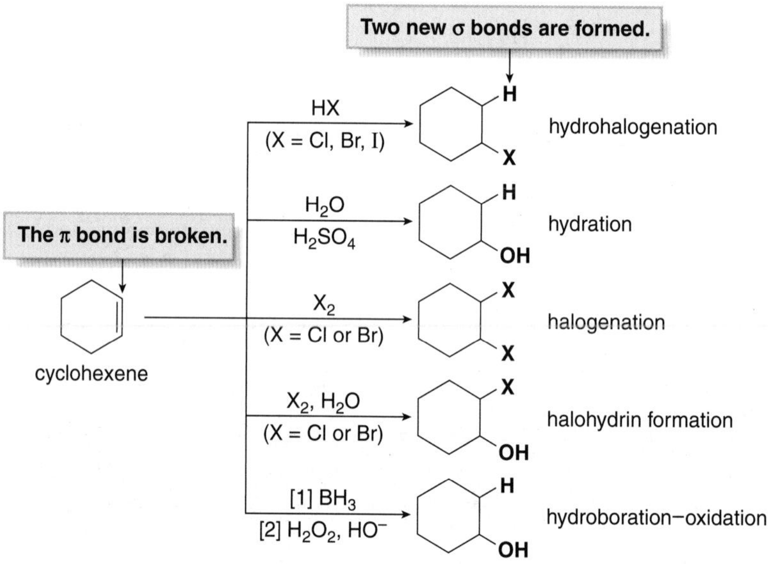

10.9 Hydrohalogenation—Electrophilic Addition of HX

Hydrohalogenation of an alkene to form an alkyl halide is the reverse of the dehydrohalogenation of an alkyl halide to form an alkene, a reaction discussed in detail in Sections 8.4 and 8.5.

Hydrohalogenation is the addition of hydrogen halides HX (X = Cl, Br, and I) to alkenes to form alkyl halides.

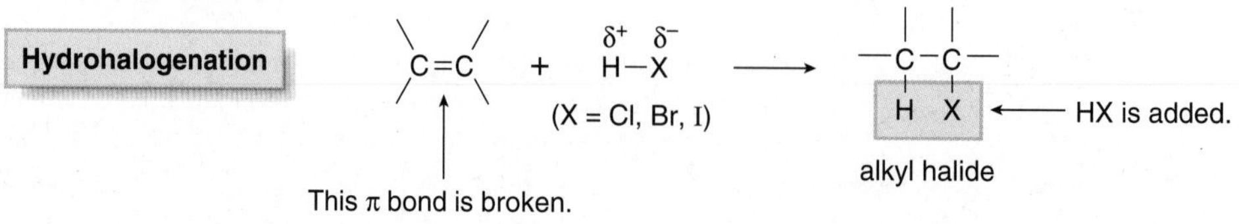

Two bonds are broken in this reaction—the weak π bond of the alkene and the HX bond—and two new σ bonds are formed—one to H and one to X. Because X is more electronegative than H, the H–X bond is polarized, with a partial positive charge on H. Because the electrophilic (H) end of HX is attracted to the electron-rich double bond, these reactions are called **electrophilic additions.**

To draw the products of an addition reaction:

- **Locate the C–C double bond.**
- **Identify the σ bond of the reagent that breaks—namely, the H–X bond in hydrohalogenation.**
- **Break the π bond of the alkene and the σ bond of the reagent, and form two new σ bonds to the C atoms of the double bond.**

Examples

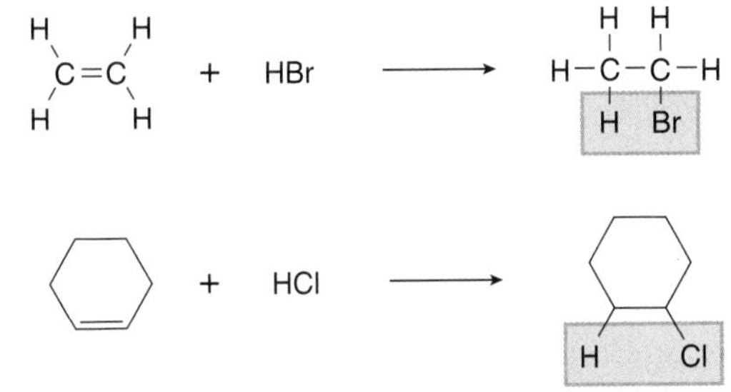

Addition reactions are exothermic because the two σ bonds formed in the product are stronger than the σ and π bonds broken in the reactants. For example, $\Delta H°$ for the addition of HBr to ethylene is –60 kJ/mol, as illustrated in Figure 10.9.

Figure 10.9
The addition of HBr to $CH_2=CH_2$, an exothermic reaction

Overall reaction:

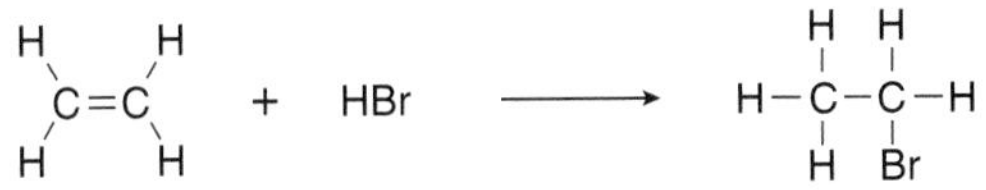

$\Delta H°$ calculation:

[1] Bonds broken

	$\Delta H°$ (kJ/mol)
$CH_2=CH_2$ π bond	+267
H–Br	+368
total	+635 kJ/mol

↑ **Energy needed to break bonds.**

[2] Bonds formed

	$\Delta H°$ (kJ/mol)
$BrCH_2CH_2$–H	–410
CH_3CH_2–Br	–285
total	–695 kJ/mol

↑ **Energy released in forming bonds.**

[3] Overall $\Delta H°$ =

sum in Step [1]
+
sum in Step [2]

+635 kJ/mol
–695 kJ/mol

$\Delta H°$ = –60 kJ/mol

↑ **The reaction is exothermic.**

[Values taken from Appendix C.]

The mechanism of electrophilic addition of HX consists of **two steps:** addition of H^+ to form a carbocation, followed by nucleophilic attack of X^-. The mechanism is illustrated for the reaction of *cis*-2-butene with HBr in Mechanism 10.1.

Mechanism 10.1 Electrophilic Addition of HX to an Alkene

Step [1] Addition of the electrophile (H^+) to the π bond

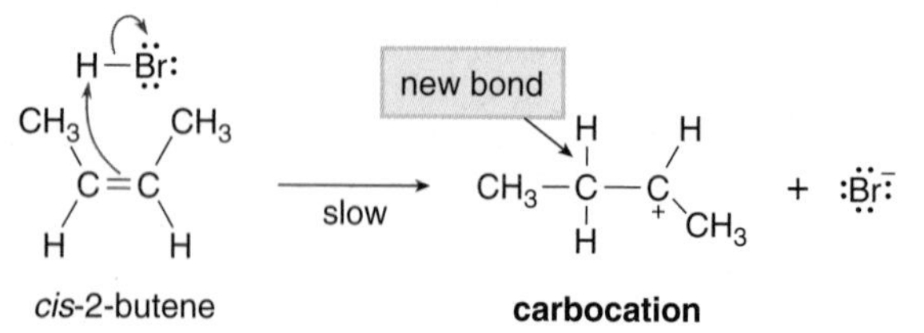

- The π bond attacks the H atom of HBr, thus forming a new C–H bond while breaking the H–Br bond. Because the remaining carbon atom of the original double bond is left with only six electrons, a **carbocation** intermediate is formed. This step is **rate-determining** because two bonds are broken but only one bond is formed.

Step [2] Nucleophilic attack of Br^-

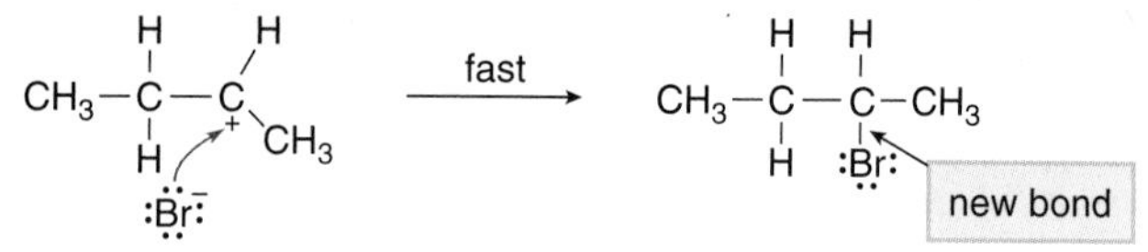

- **Nucleophilic attack of Br^-** on the carbocation forms the new C–Br bond.

The mechanism of electrophilic addition consists of two successive Lewis acid–base reactions. In Step [1], the **alkene is the Lewis base** that donates an electron pair to **H–Br, the Lewis acid,** while in Step [2], **Br^- is the Lewis base** that donates an electron pair to the **carbocation, the Lewis acid.**

An energy diagram for the reaction of $CH_3CH{=}CHCH_3$ with HBr is given in Figure 10.10. Each step has its own energy barrier with a transition state at each energy maximum. Because Step [1] has a higher energy transition state, it is rate-determining. $\Delta H°$ for Step [1] is positive because more bonds are broken than formed, whereas $\Delta H°$ for Step [2] is negative because only bond making occurs.

Figure 10.10

Energy diagram for electrophilic addition: $CH_3CH{=}CHCH_3 + HBr \rightarrow CH_3CH_2CH(Br)CH_3$

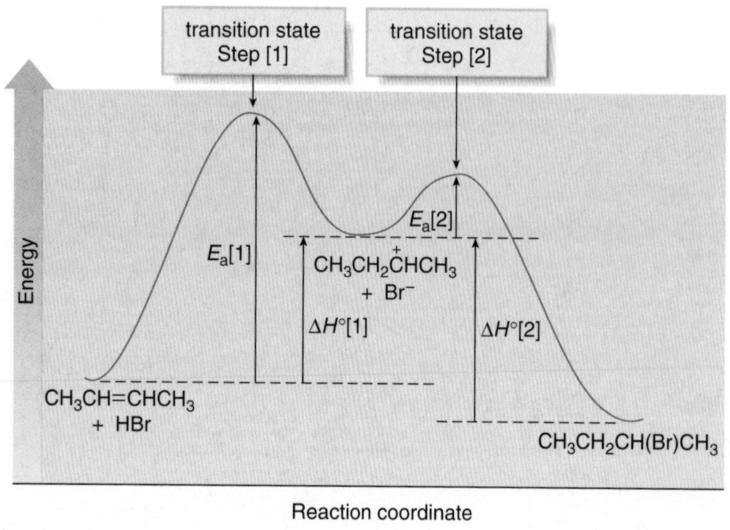

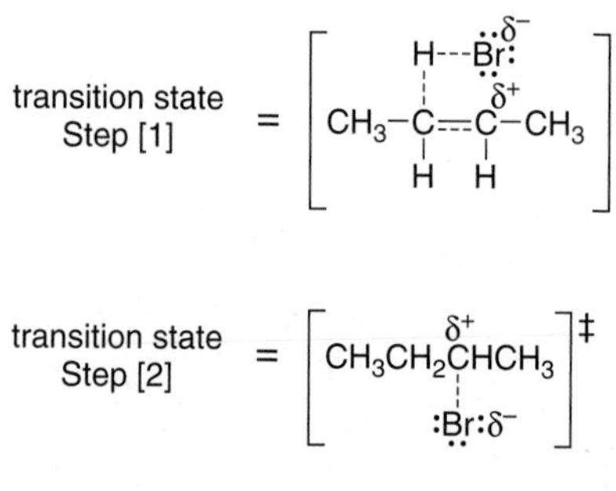

- The mechanism has two steps, so there are two energy barriers.
- Step [1] is rate-determining.

Problem 10.13 What product is formed when each alkene is treated with HCl?

a. 

b. $CH_3CH_2CH_2CH{=}CHCH_2CH_2CH_3$

c. 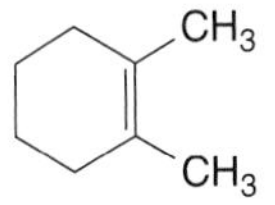

Problem 10.14 Draw a stepwise mechanism for the following reaction. Draw the transition state for each step.

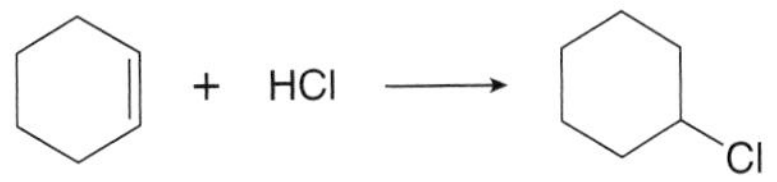

10.10 Markovnikov's Rule

With an unsymmetrical alkene, HX can add to the double bond to give two constitutional isomers.

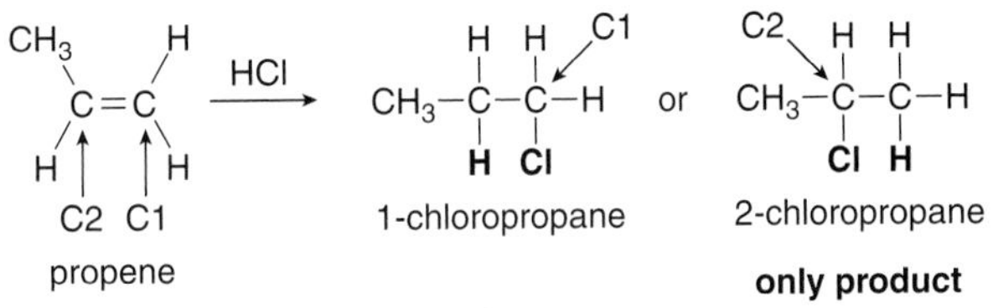
HCl
C1
C2
C2 C1
propene
or
1-chloropropane
2-chloropropane
only product

For example, HCl addition to propene could in theory form 1-chloropropane by addition of H and Cl to C2 and C1, respectively, and 2-chloropropane by addition of H and Cl to C1 and C2, respectively. In fact, **electrophilic addition forms *only* 2-chloropropane.** This is a specific example of a general trend called **Markovnikov's rule,** named for the Russian chemist who first determined the regioselectivity of electrophilic addition of HX.

- **Markovnikov's rule: In the addition of HX to an unsymmetrical alkene, the H atom bonds to the less substituted carbon atom—that is, the carbon that has more H atoms to begin with.**

The basis of Markovnikov's rule is the formation of a carbocation in the rate-determining step of the mechanism. With propene, there are two possible paths for this first step, depending on which carbon atom of the double bond forms the new bond to hydrogen.

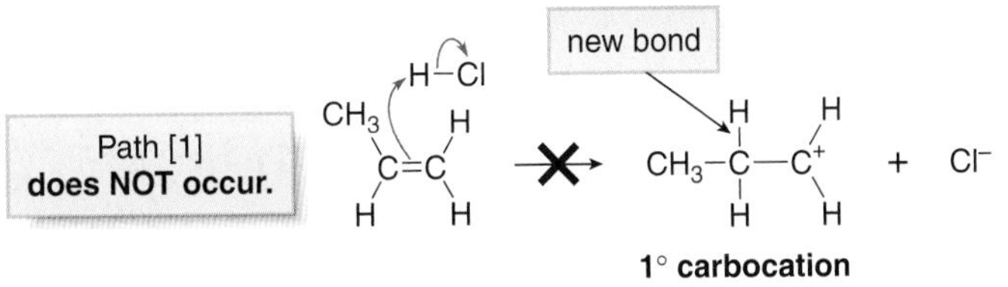
Path [1]
does NOT occur.
new bond
1° carbocation

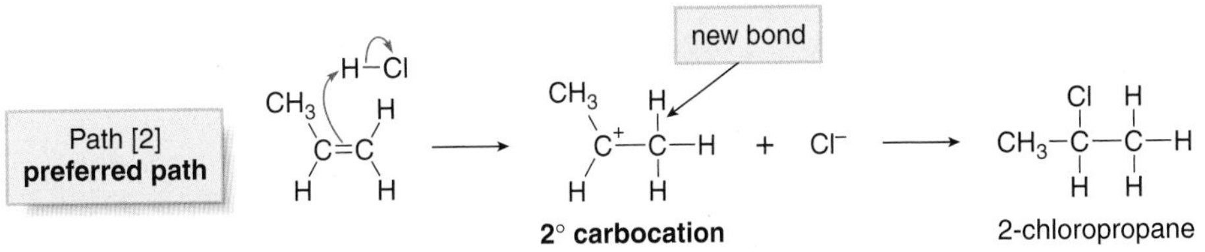
Path [2]
preferred path
new bond
2° carbocation
2-chloropropane

Figure 10.11
Electrophilic addition and the Hammond postulate

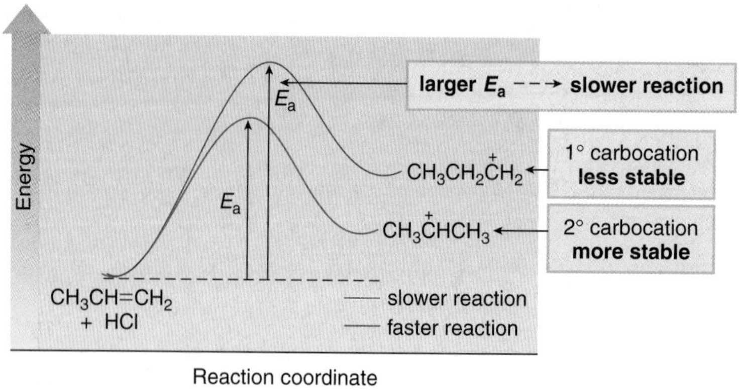

- The E_a for formation of the more stable 2° carbocation is lower than the E_a for formation of the 1° carbocation. The 2° carbocation is formed faster.

The Hammond postulate was first introduced in Section 7.15 to explain the relative rate of S_N1 reactions with 1°, 2°, and 3° RX.

Path [1] forms a highly unstable 1° carbocation, whereas Path [2] forms a **more stable 2° carbocation.** According to the Hammond postulate, Path [2] is faster because formation of the carbocation is an endothermic process, so **the transition state to form the more stable 2° carbocation is lower in energy** (Figure 10.11).

- **In the addition of HX to an unsymmetrical alkene, the H atom is added to the less substituted carbon to form the more stable, more substituted carbocation.**

Similar results are seen in any electrophilic addition involving an intermediate carbocation: **the more stable, more substituted carbocation is formed by addition of the electrophile to the less substituted carbon.**

Problem 10.15 Draw the products formed when each alkene is treated with HCl.

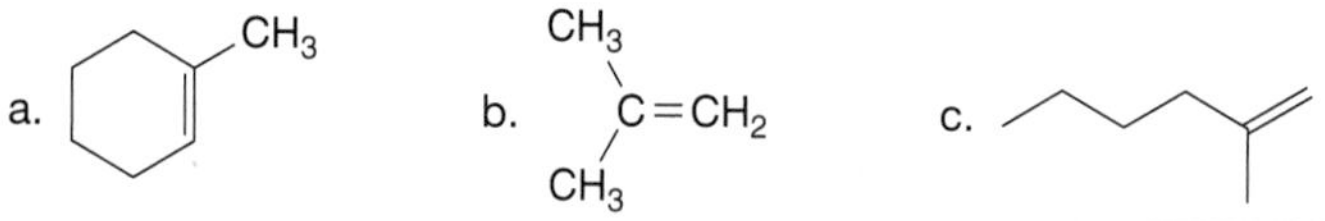

Problem 10.16 Use the Hammond postulate to explain why $(CH_3)_2C{=}CH_2$ reacts faster than $CH_3CH{=}CH_2$ in electrophilic addition of HX.

Because carbocations are formed as intermediates in hydrohalogenation, carbocation rearrangements can occur, as illustrated in Sample Problem 10.3.

Sample Problem 10.3 Draw a stepwise mechanism for the following reaction.

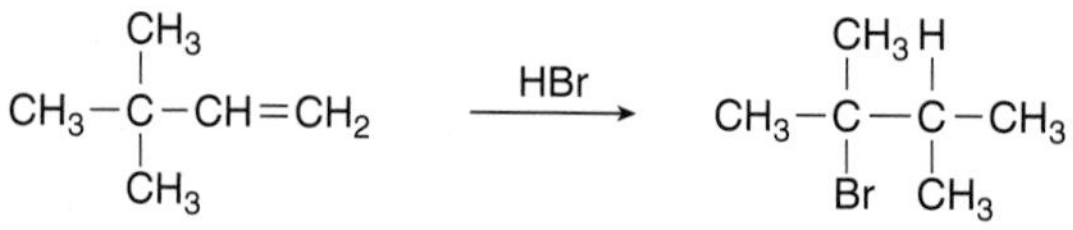

Solution

Because the carbon skeletons of the starting material and product are different—the alkene reactant has a 4° carbon and the product alkyl halide does not—a carbocation rearrangement must have occurred.

Step [1] **Markovnikov addition of HBr** adds H^+ to the less substituted end of the double bond, forming a 2° carbocation.

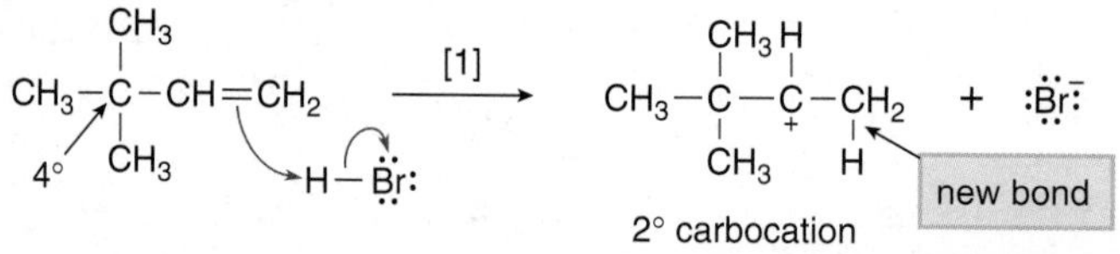

Steps [2] and [3] **Rearrangement of the 2° carbocation by a 1,2-methyl shift forms a more stable 3° carbocation.** Nucleophilic attack of Br^- forms the product, a 3° alkyl halide.

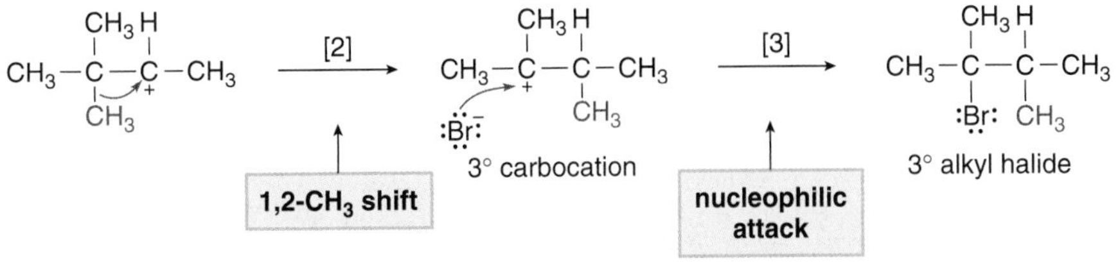

Problem 10.17 Treatment of 3-methylcyclohexene with HCl yields two products, 1-chloro-3-methylcyclohexane and 1-chloro-1-methylcyclohexane. Draw a mechanism to explain this result.

Problem 10.18 Addition of HBr to which of the following alkenes will lead to a rearrangement?
a. $CH_2=C(CH_3)CH_2CH_3$ b. $CH_3CH=CHCH_2CH_3$ c. $CH_3CH=CHCH(CH_3)_2$

10.11 Stereochemistry of Electrophilic Addition of HX

To understand the stereochemistry of electrophilic addition, recall two stereochemical principles learned in Chapters 7 and 9.

- **Trigonal planar atoms react with reagents from two directions with equal probability (Section 7.13C).**
- **Achiral starting materials yield achiral or racemic products (Section 9.15).**

Many hydrohalogenation reactions begin with an **achiral reactant** and form an **achiral product.** For example, the addition of HBr to cyclohexene, an achiral alkene, forms bromocyclohexane, an achiral alkyl halide.

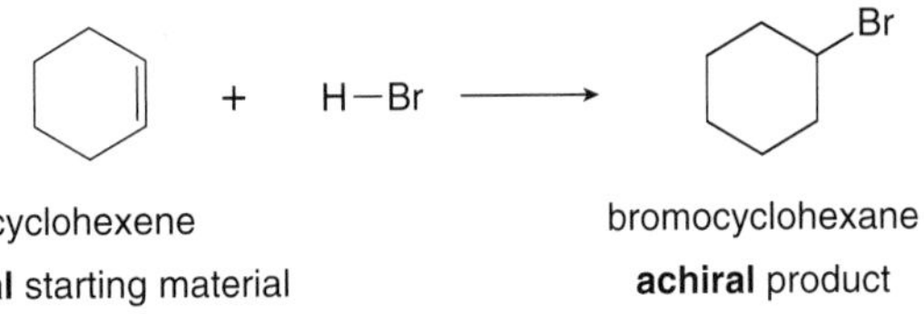

Because addition converts sp^2 hybridized carbons to sp^3 hybridized carbons, however, sometimes new stereogenic centers are formed from hydrohalogenation. For example, Markovnikov addition of HCl to 2-ethyl-1-pentene, an achiral alkene, forms one constitutional isomer, 3-chloro-3-methylhexane. Because this product now has a stereogenic center at one of the newly formed sp^3 hybridized carbons, **an equal amount of two enantiomers—a racemic mixture—**must form.

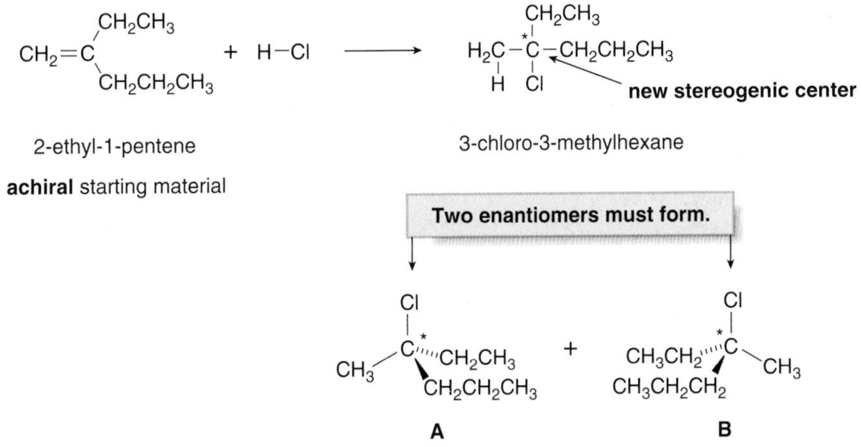

The mechanism of hydrohalogenation illustrates why two enantiomers are formed. Initial addition of the electrophile H^+ (from HCl) occurs from **either side of the planar double bond** to form a carbocation. Both modes of addition (from above and below) generate the same **achiral carbocation.** Either representation of this carbocation can then be used to draw the second step of the mechanism.

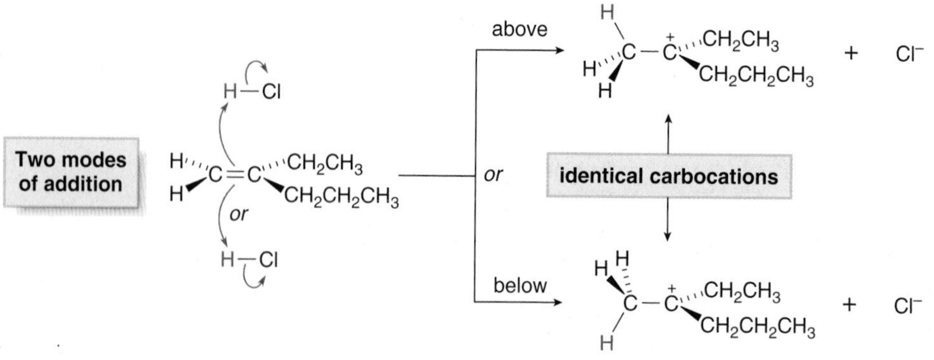

Nucleophilic attack of Cl^- on the trigonal planar carbocation also occurs from two different directions, forming two products, **A** and **B,** having a new stereogenic center. **A** and **B** are not superimposable, so they are **enantiomers.** Because attack from either direction occurs with equal probability, a **racemic mixture** of **A** and **B** is formed.

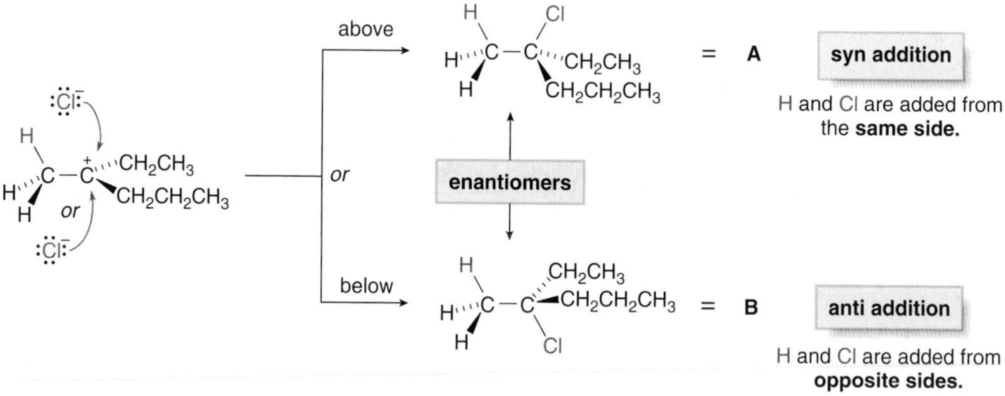

Because hydrohalogenation begins with a **planar** double bond and forms a **planar** carbocation, addition of H and Cl occurs in two different ways. The elements of H and Cl can both be added from the same side of the double bond—that is, **syn addition**—or they can be added from opposite sides—that is, **anti addition.** *Both* modes of addition occur in this two-step reaction mechanism.

- **Hydrohalogenation occurs with syn and anti addition of HX.**

The terms **cis** and **trans** refer to the arrangement of groups in a particular compound, usually an alkene or a disubstituted cycloalkane. The terms **syn** and **anti** describe the stereochemistry of a process—for example, how two groups are added to a double bond.

Finally, addition of HCl to 1,2-dimethylcyclohexene forms **two** new stereogenic centers. Initial addition of H^+ (from HCl) forms two enantiomeric carbocations that react with the Cl^- nucleophile from two different directions, forming **four stereoisomers, A – D—two pairs of enantiomers** (Figure 10.12).

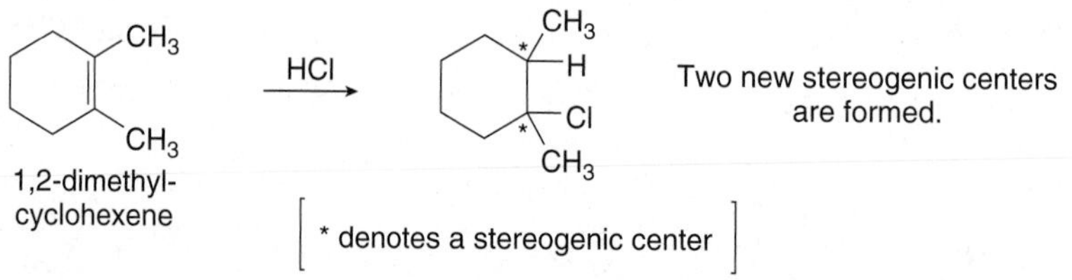

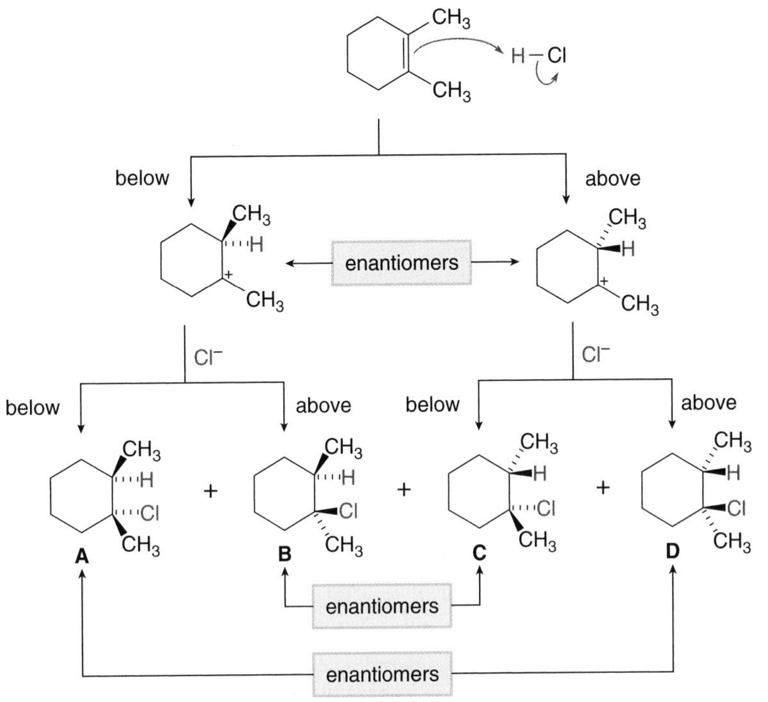

Figure 10.12 Reaction of 1,2-dimethylcyclohexene with HCl

Four stereoisomers are formed:
- Compounds **A** and **D** are enantiomers formed in equal amounts.
- Compounds **B** and **C** are enantiomers formed in equal amounts.

Table 10.3 summarizes the characteristics of electrophilic addition of HX to alkenes.

Problem 10.19 Draw the products, including stereochemistry, of each reaction.

a. 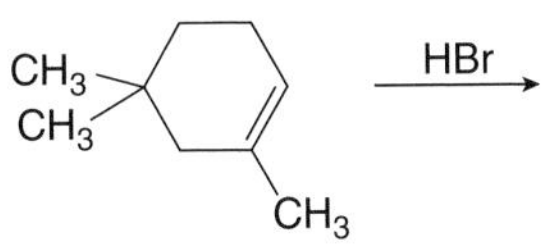

b. 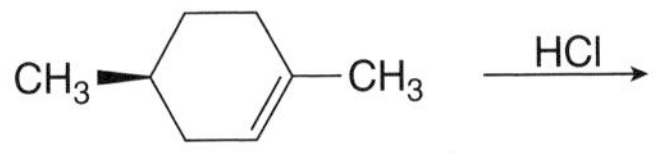

Problem 10.20 Which compounds (**A**–**D**) in Figure 10.12 are formed by syn addition of HCl and which are formed by anti addition?

Table 10.3 Summary: Electrophilic Addition of HX to Alkenes

	Observation
Mechanism	• The mechanism involves two steps. • The rate-determining step forms a carbocation. • Rearrangements can occur.
Regioselectivity	• Markovnikov's rule is followed. In unsymmetrical alkenes, H bonds to the less substituted C to form the more stable carbocation.
Stereochemistry	• Syn and anti addition occur.

10.12 Hydration—Electrophilic Addition of Water

Hydration is the addition of water to an alkene to form an alcohol. H_2O itself is too weak an acid to protonate an alkene, but with added H_2SO_4, H_3O^+ is formed and addition readily occurs.

Hydration

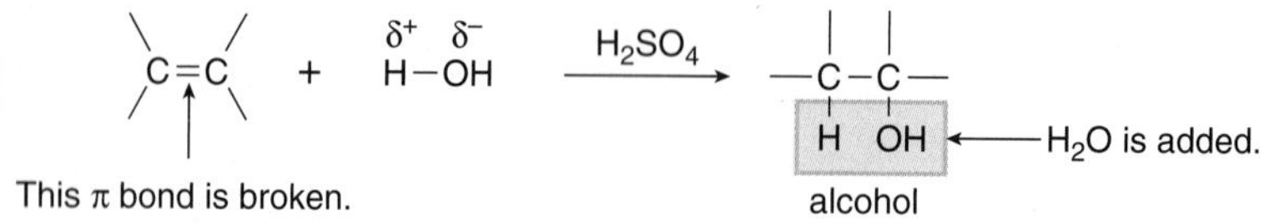

δ+ δ−
H−OH
H2SO4
H OH
H2O is added.
This π bond is broken.
alcohol

Examples

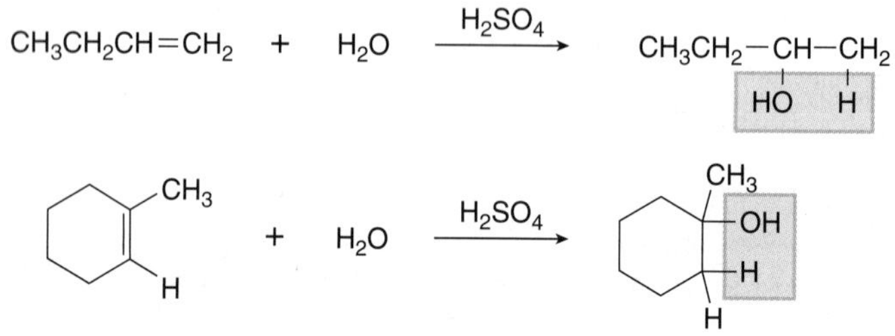

CH3CH2CH=CH2 + H2O
H2SO4
CH3CH2−CH−CH2
HO H
CH3
H
+ H2O
H2SO4
CH3
OH
H
H

Hydration is simply another example of **electrophilic addition.** The first two steps of the mechanism are similar to those of electrophilic addition of HX—that is, addition of H^+ (from H_3O^+) to generate a carbocation, followed by nucleophilic attack of H_2O. Mechanism 10.2 illustrates the addition of H_2O to cyclohexene to form cyclohexanol.

Mechanism 10.2 Electrophilic Addition of H_2O to an Alkene—Hydration

Step [1] Addition of the electrophile (H^+) to the π bond

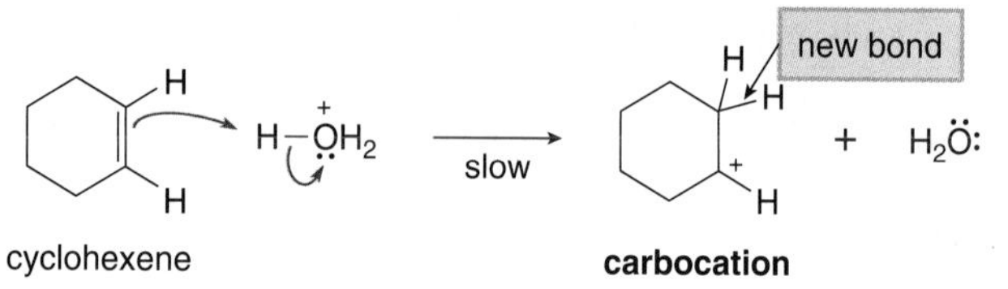

H
H
H−OH2
slow
cyclohexene
new bond
H
H
H
+ H2Ö:
carbocation

- The π bond attacks H_3O^+, thus forming a new C−H bond while breaking the H−O bond. Because the remaining carbon atom of the original double bond is left with only six electrons, a **carbocation** intermediate is formed. This step is **rate-determining** because two bonds are broken but only one bond is formed.

Step [2] Nucleophilic attack of H_2O

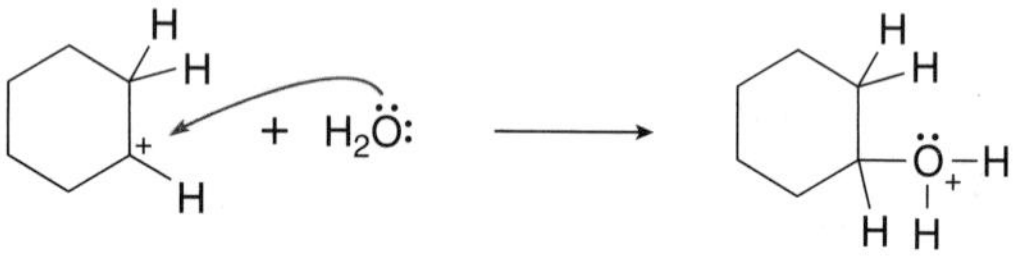

H
H
+ H2Ö:
H
H
H
Ö−H
H H

- **Nucleophilic attack of H_2O** on the carbocation forms the new C−O bond.

Step [3] Loss of a proton

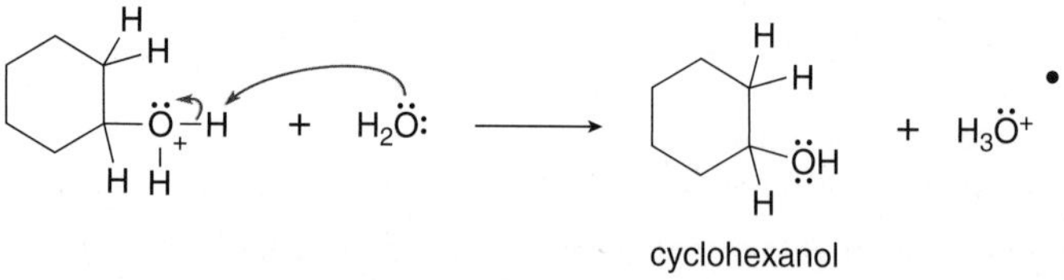

H
H
Ö−H
H H
+ H2Ö:
H
H
ÖH
H
+ H3Ö+
cyclohexanol

- Removal of a proton with a base (H_2O) forms a neutral alcohol. Because the acid used in Step [1] is regenerated in Step [3], hydration is **acid-catalyzed.**

Hydration of an alkene to form an alcohol is the reverse of the dehydration of an alcohol to form an alkene, a reaction discussed in detail in Section 9.8.

There are three consequences to the formation of carbocation intermediates:

- **In unsymmetrical alkenes, H adds to the less substituted carbon to form the more stable carbocation; that is, Markovnikov's rule holds.**
- **Addition of H and OH occurs in both a syn and anti fashion.**
- **Carbocation rearrangements can occur.**

Alcohols add to alkenes, forming ethers, using the same mechanism. Addition of CH_3OH to 2-methylpropene, for example, forms *tert*-butyl methyl ether (**MTBE**), a high octane fuel additive described in Section 3.4C.

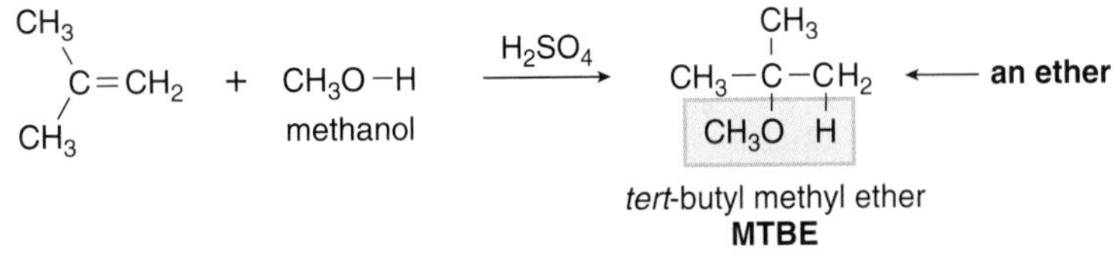

Problem 10.21 What two alkenes give rise to each alcohol as the major product of acid-catalyzed hydration?

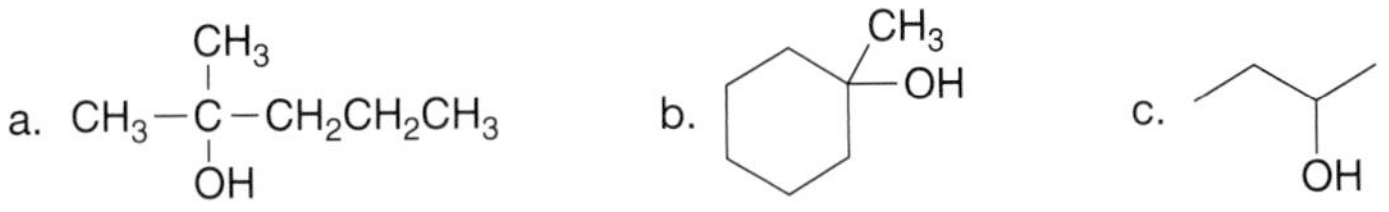

Problem 10.22 What stereoisomers are formed when 1-pentene is treated with H_2O and H_2SO_4?

10.13 Halogenation—Addition of Halogen

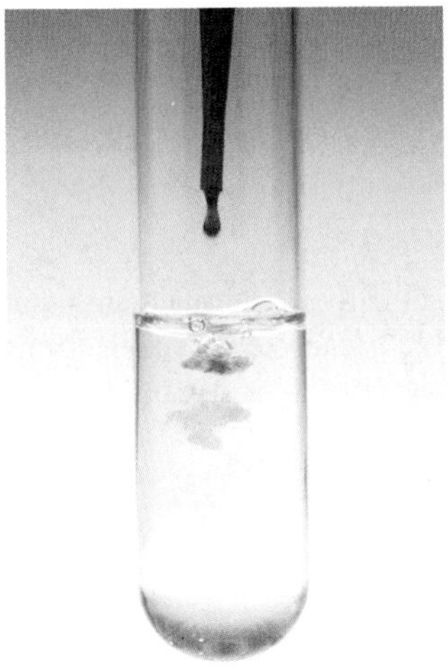

Bromination is a simple chemical test for the presence of π bonds in unknown compounds. When bromine, a fuming red liquid, is added to an alkene dissolved in the solvent CCl_4, the bromine adds to the double bond and the red color disappears. The disappearance of the red color is therefore a positive test for π bonds.

Halogenation is the addition of halogen X_2 (X = Cl or Br) to an alkene, forming a **vicinal dihalide.**

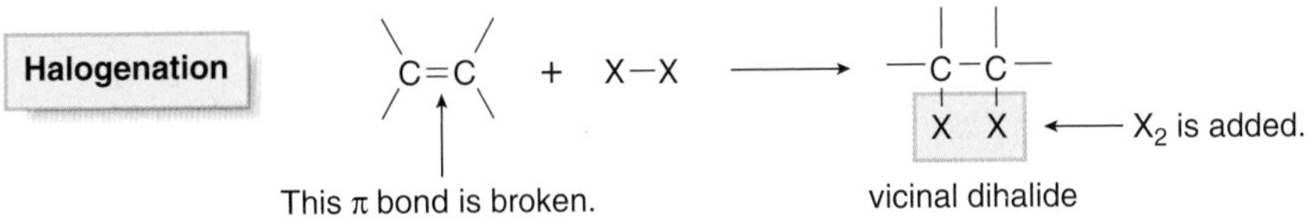

Halogenation is synthetically useful only with Cl_2 and Br_2. The dichlorides and dibromides formed in this reaction serve as starting materials for the synthesis of alkynes, as we learned in Section 8.10.

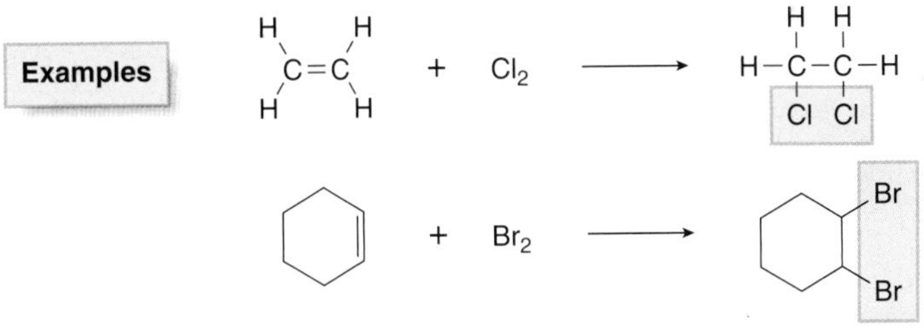

Halogens add to π bonds because halogens are **polarizable.** The electron-rich double bond induces a dipole in an approaching halogen molecule, making one halogen atom electron deficient and the other electron rich ($X^{\delta+}-X^{\delta-}$). **The electrophilic halogen atom is then attracted to the nucleophilic double bond,** making addition possible.

Two facts demonstrate that halogenation follows a different mechanism from that of hydrohalogenation or hydration. First, no rearrangements occur, and second, only anti addition of X_2 is observed. For example, treatment of cyclohexene with Br_2 yields two **trans** enantiomers formed by **anti addition.**

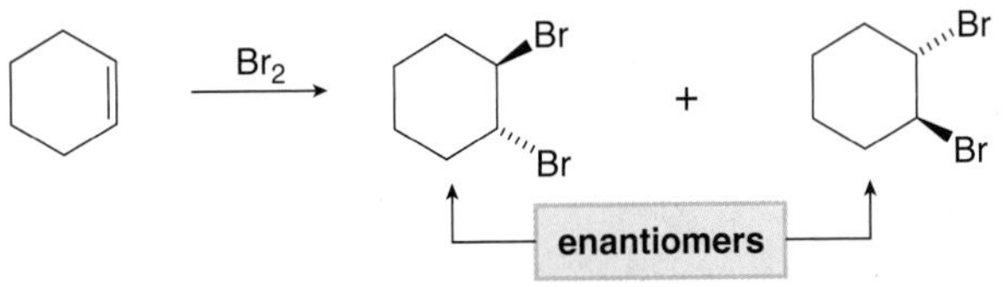

These facts suggest that **carbocations are *not* intermediates in halogenation.** Unstable carbocations rearrange, and both syn and anti addition is possible with carbocation intermediates. The accepted mechanism for halogenation comprises **two steps,** but it does *not* proceed with formation of a carbocation, as shown in Mechanism 10.3.

Mechanism 10.3 Addition of X_2 to an Alkene—Halogenation

Step [1] Addition of the electrophile (X^+) to the π bond

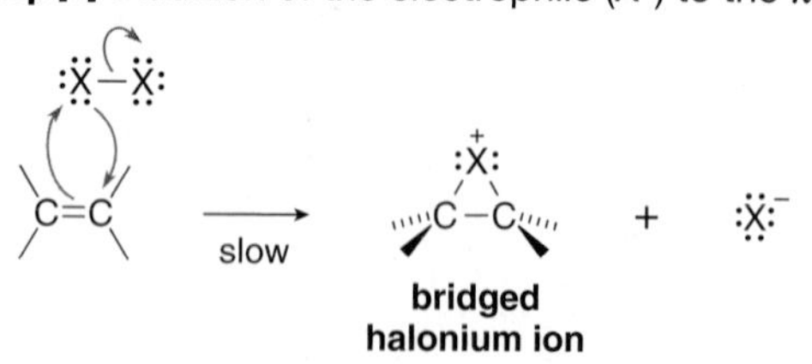

- Four bonds are broken or formed in this step: the electron pair in the π bond and a lone pair on a halogen atom are used to form two new C–X bonds. The X–X bond is also cleaved heterolytically, forming X^-. This step is rate-determining.
- The three-membered ring containing a positively charged halogen atom is called a **bridged halonium ion.** This strained three-membered ring is highly unstable, making it amenable to opening of the ring in the second step.

Step [2] Nucleophilic attack of X^-

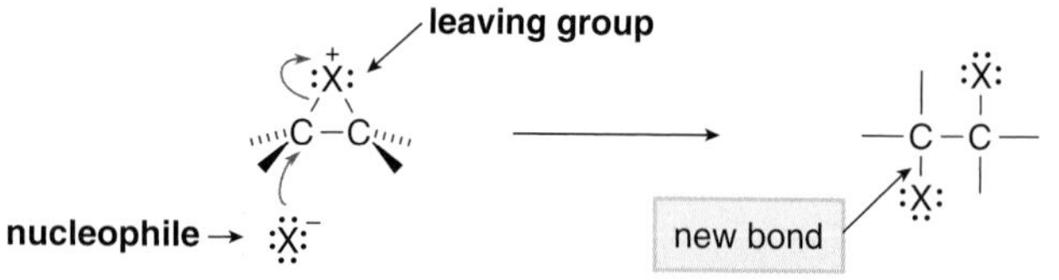

- **Nucleophilic attack of X^-** opens the ring of the halonium ion, forming a new C–X bond and relieving the strain in the three-membered ring.

Bridged halonium ions resemble carbocations in that they are short-lived intermediates that react readily with nucleophiles. Carbocations are inherently unstable because only six electrons surround carbon, whereas **halonium ions are unstable because they contain a strained three-membered ring** with a positively charged halogen atom.

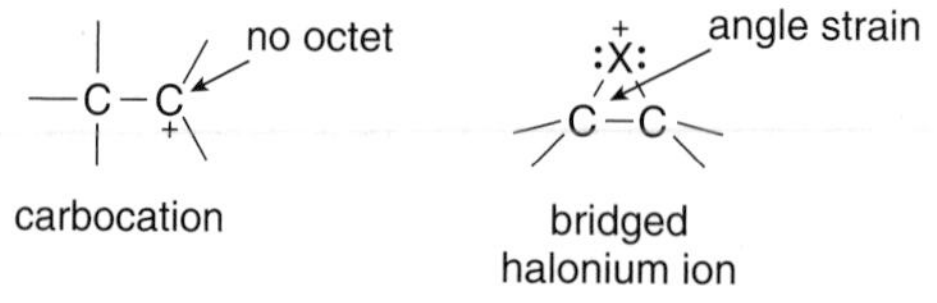

Problem 10.23 Draw the products of each reaction, including stereochemistry.

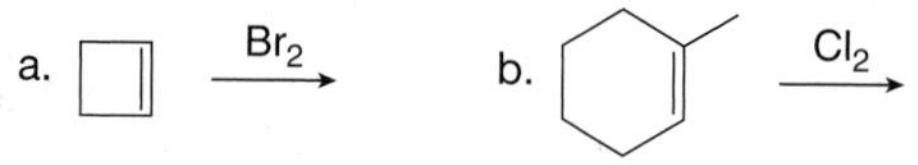

10.14 Stereochemistry of Halogenation

How does the proposed mechanism invoking a bridged halonium ion intermediate explain the observed **trans products of halogenation?** For example, chlorination of cyclopentene affords both enantiomers of *trans*-1,2-dichlorocyclopentane, with *no* cis products.

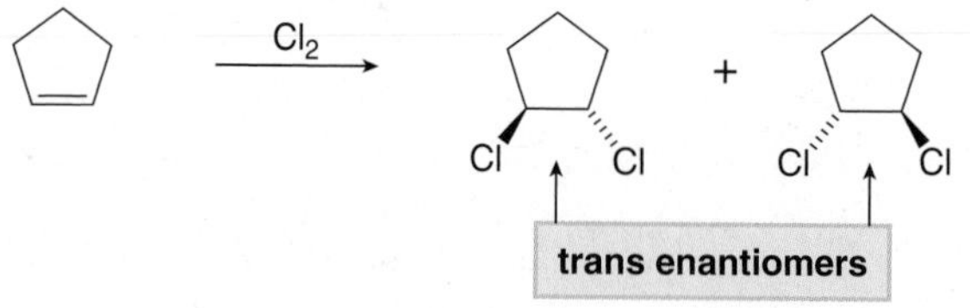

Initial addition of the electrophile Cl^+ (from Cl_2) occurs from either side of the planar double bond to form the bridged chloronium ion. In this example, both modes of addition (from above and below) generate the same **achiral** intermediate, so either representation can be used to draw the second step.

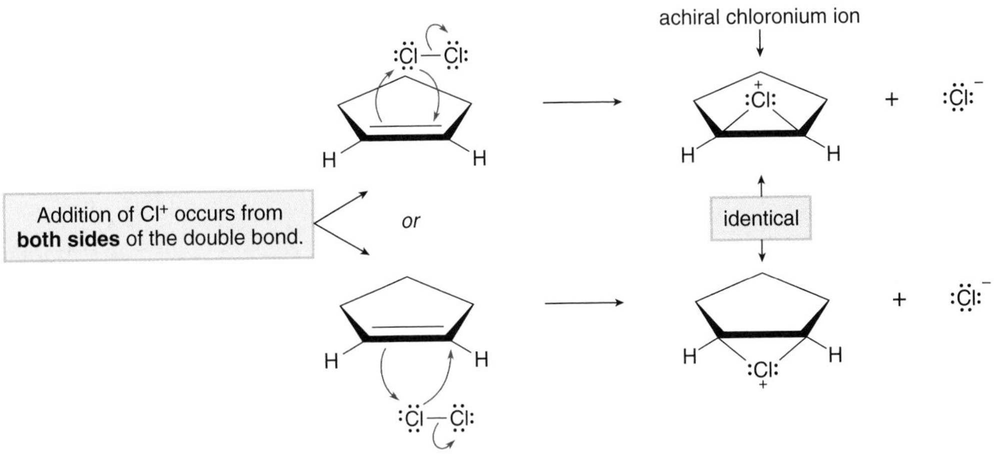

The opening of bridged halonium ion intermediates resembles the opening of epoxide rings with nucleophiles discussed in Section 9.15.

In the second step, **nucleophilic attack of Cl^- must occur from the back side**—that is, from the side of the five-membered ring opposite to the side having the bridged chloronium ion. Because the nucleophile attacks from below in this example and the leaving group departs from above, the two Cl atoms in the product are oriented **trans** to each other. Backside attack occurs with equal probability at either carbon of the three-membered ring to yield an equal amount of two enantiomers—**a racemic mixture.**

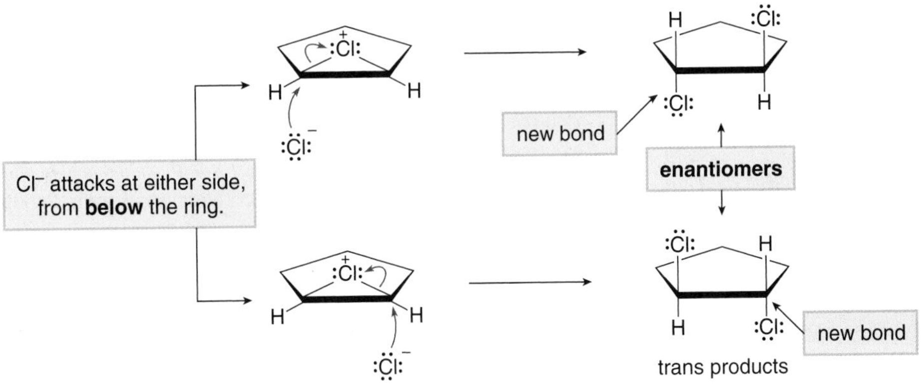

In summary, the mechanism for halogenation of alkenes occurs in two steps:

- **Addition of X^+ forms an unstable bridged halonium ion in the rate-determining step.**
- **Nucleophilic attack of X^- occurs from the back side to form trans products. The overall result is anti addition of X_2 across the double bond.**

Because halogenation occurs exclusively in an anti fashion, cis and trans alkenes yield different stereoisomers. Halogenation of alkenes is a **stereospecific reaction.**

- **A reaction is stereospecific when each of two specific stereoisomers of a starting material yields a particular stereoisomer of a product.**

Figure 10.13
Halogenation of *cis*- and *trans*-2-butene

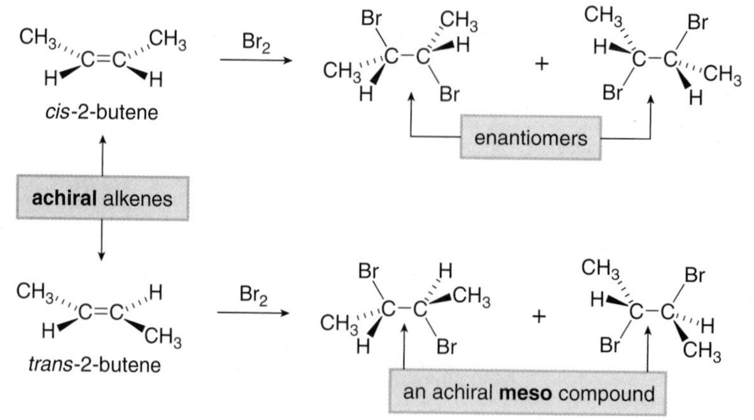
cis-2-butene
Br2
enantiomers
achiral alkenes
trans-2-butene
Br2
an achiral meso compound

To draw the products of halogenation:

- Add Br_2 in an **anti** fashion across the double bond, leaving all other groups in their original orientations. Draw the products such that a given Br atom is above the plane in one product and below the plane in the other product.
- Sometimes this reaction produces two stereoisomers, as in the case of *cis*-2-butene, which forms an equal amount of two enantiomers. Sometimes it produces a single compound, as in the case of *trans*-2-butene, where a meso compound is formed.

cis-2-Butene yields two enantiomers, whereas *trans*-2-butene yields a single achiral meso compound, as shown in Figure 10.13.

Problem 10.24 Draw all stereoisomers formed in each reaction.

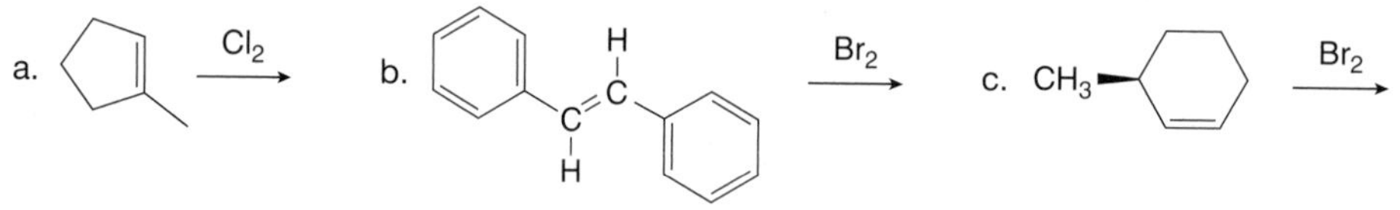
a.
Cl2
b.
Br2
c. CH3
Br2

Problem 10.25 Draw a stepwise mechanism for the conversion of *trans*-2-butene to the meso dibromide in Figure 10.13.

10.15 Halohydrin Formation

Treatment of an alkene with a halogen $\mathbf{X_2}$ and $\mathbf{H_2O}$ forms a **halohydrin** by addition of the elements of **X** and **OH** to the double bond.

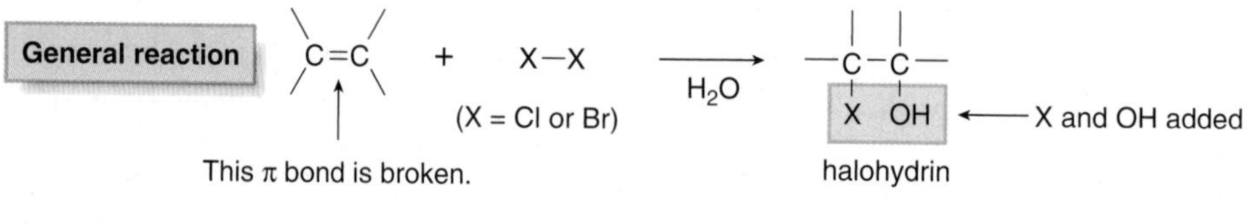
General reaction
(X = Cl or Br)
H2O
X and OH added
This π bond is broken.
halohydrin

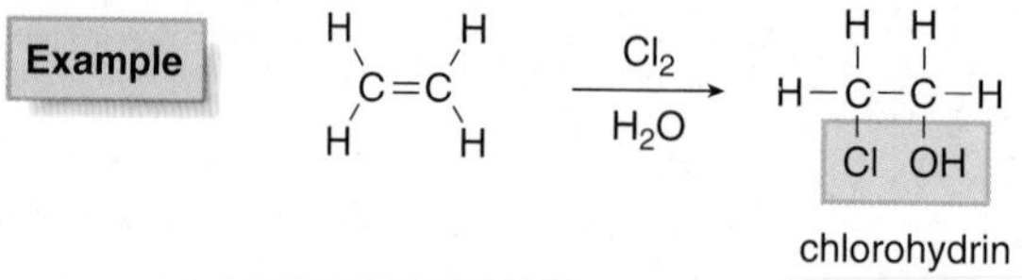
Example
Cl2
H2O
chlorohydrin

The mechanism for halohydrin formation is similar to the mechanism for halogenation: addition of the electrophile X^+ (from X_2) to form a **bridged halonium ion,** followed by nucleophilic attack by H_2O from the back side on the three-membered ring (Mechanism 10.4). Even though X^- is formed in Step [1] of the mechanism, its concentration is small compared to H_2O (often the solvent), so H_2O and *not* X^- is the nucleophile.

Mechanism 10.4 Addition of X and OH—Halohydrin Formation

Step [1] Addition of the electrophile (X^+) to the π bond

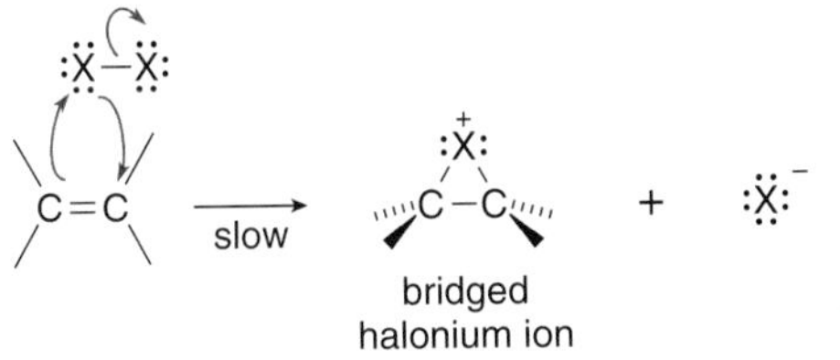

- Four bonds are broken or formed in this step: the electron pair in the π bond and a lone pair on a halogen atom are used to form two new C–X bonds in the bridged halonium ion. The X–X bond is also cleaved heterolytically, forming X^-. This step is rate-determining.

Steps [2] and [3] Nucleophilic attack of H_2O and loss of a proton

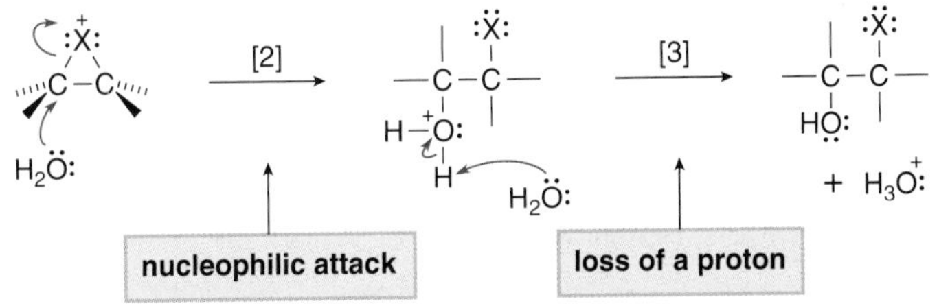

- **Nucleophilic attack of H_2O** opens the halonium ion ring, forming a new C–O bond. Subsequent loss of a proton forms the neutral halohydrin.

Recall from Section 7.8C that DMSO (dimethyl sulfoxide) is a polar aprotic solvent.

Although the combination of Br_2 and H_2O effectively forms **bromohydrins** from alkenes, other reagents can also be used. Bromohydrins are also formed with ***N*-bromosuccinimide** (abbreviated as **NBS**) in **aqueous DMSO** [$(CH_3)_2S{=}O$]. NBS serves as a source of Br_2, which then goes on to form a bromohydrin by the same reaction mechanism.

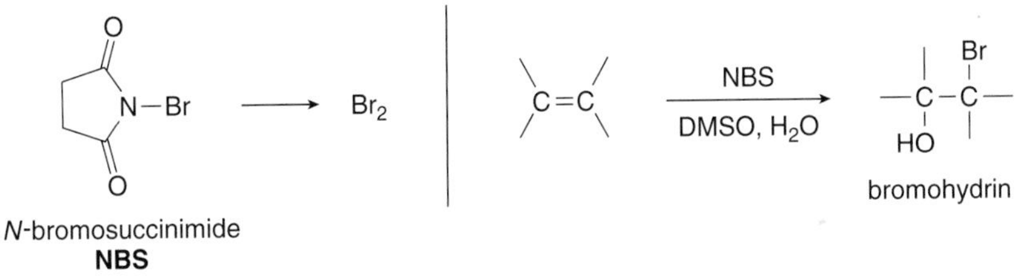

10.15A Stereochemistry and Regioselectivity of Halohydrin Formation

Because the bridged halonium ion ring is opened by backside attack of H_2O, addition of X and OH occurs in an **anti** fashion and **trans** products are formed.

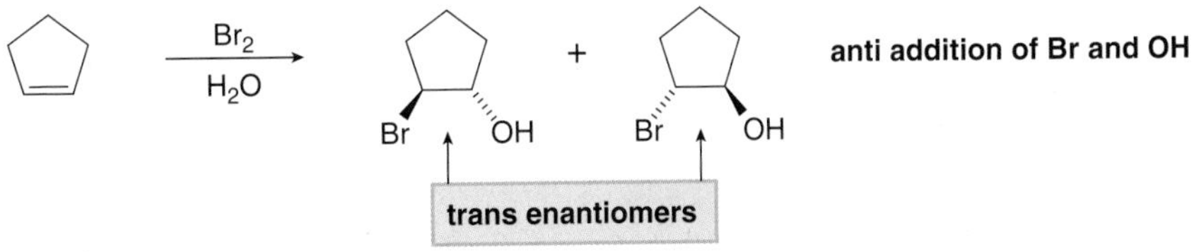

Sample Problem 10.4 Draw the products of the following reaction, including stereochemistry.

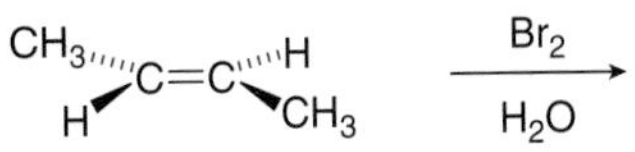

trans-2-butene

Solution

The reagent (Br_2 + H_2O) adds the elements of Br and OH to a double bond in an **anti** fashion—that is, from **opposite** sides. To draw two products of anti addition: add Br from above and OH from below in one product; then add Br from below and OH from above in the other product. In this example, the two products are nonsuperimposable mirror images—**enantiomers.**

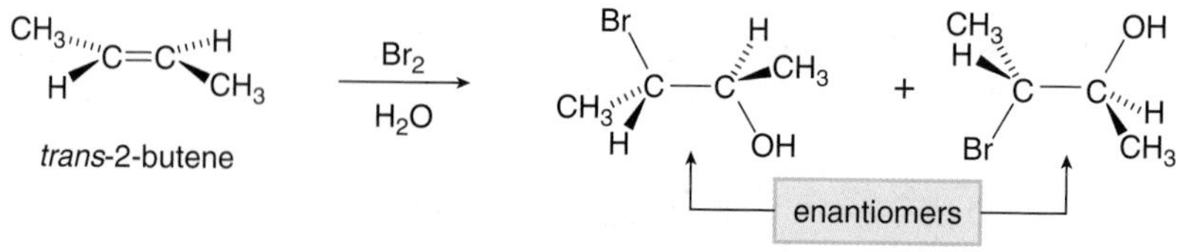

trans-2-butene
Br2
H2O
enantiomers

With unsymmetrical alkenes, two constitutional isomers are possible from addition of X and OH, but only one is formed. **The preferred product has the electrophile X^+ bonded to the less substituted carbon atom**—that is, the carbon that has more H atoms to begin with in the reacting alkene. Thus, the **nucleophile (H_2O) bonds to the more substituted carbon.**

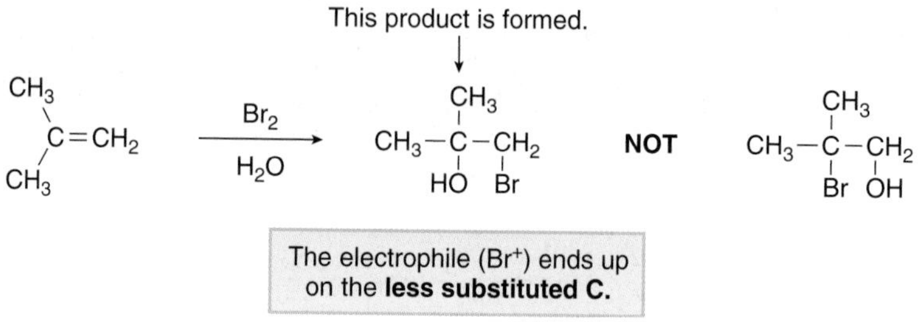

This product is formed.
Br2
H2O
NOT
The electrophile (Br+) ends up on the less substituted C.

This result is reminiscent of the opening of epoxide rings with acids HZ (Z = a nucleophile), which we encountered in Section 9.15B. As in the opening of an epoxide ring, **nucleophilic attack occurs at the more substituted carbon end of the bridged halonium ion** because that carbon is better able to accommodate a partial positive charge in the transition state.

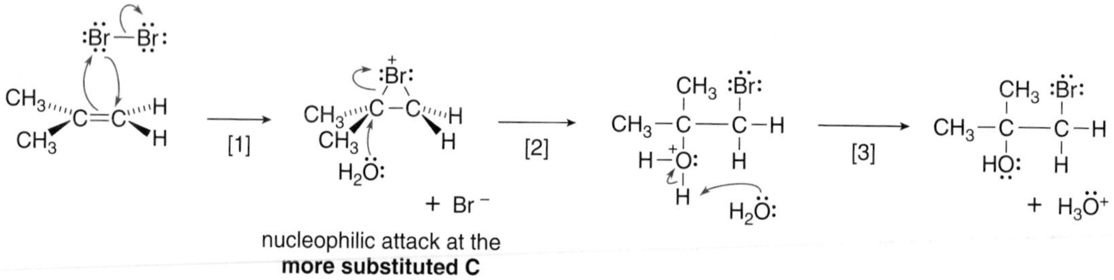

[1]
[2]
[3]
+ Br−
+ H3O+
nucleophilic attack at the more substituted C

Table 10.4 summarizes the characteristics of halohydrin formation.

Problem 10.26 Draw the products of each reaction and indicate their stereochemistry.

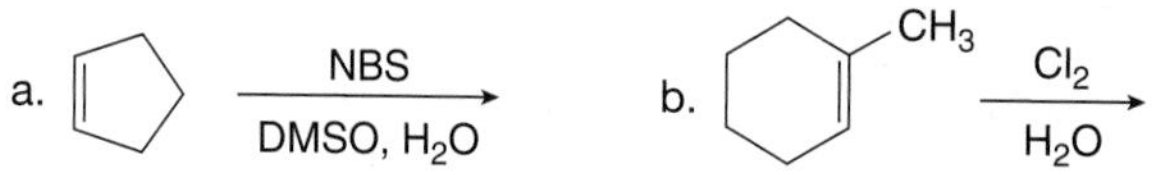

a.
NBS
DMSO, H2O
b.
Cl2
H2O

Table 10.4 Summary: Conversion of Alkenes to Halohydrins

	Observation
Mechanism	• The mechanism involves three steps. • The rate-determining step forms a bridged halonium ion. • No rearrangements can occur.
Regioselectivity	• The electrophile X^+ bonds to the less substituted carbon.
Stereochemistry	• Anti addition occurs.

10.15B Halohydrins: Useful Compounds in Organic Synthesis

Because halohydrins are easily converted to epoxides by intramolecular S_N2 reaction (Section 9.6), they have been used in the synthesis of many naturally occurring compounds. Key steps in the synthesis of estrone, a female sex hormone, are illustrated in Figure 10.14.

Figure 10.14
The synthesis of estrone from a chlorohydrin

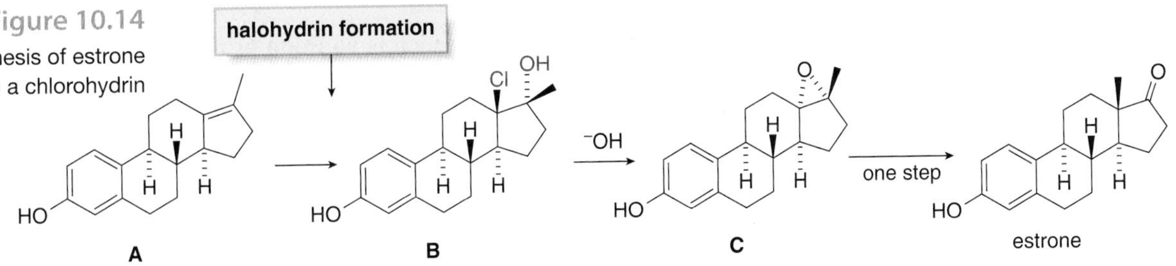

- Chlorohydrin **B,** prepared from alkene **A** by addition of Cl and OH, is converted to epoxide **C** with base. **C** is converted to estrone in one step.

10.16 Hydroboration–Oxidation

Hydroboration–oxidation is a two-step reaction sequence that converts an alkene to an alcohol.

Hydroboration–oxidation

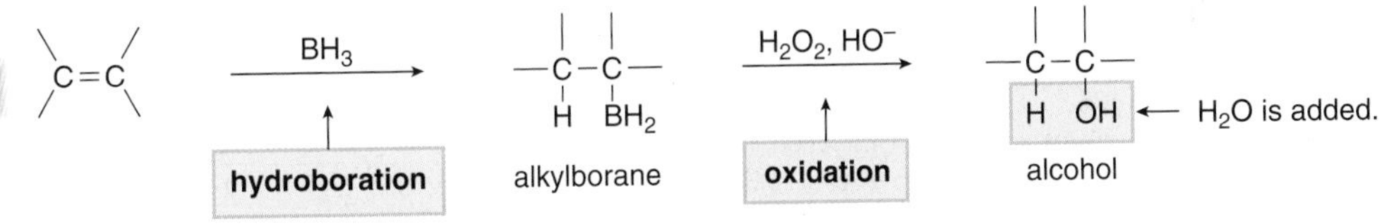

- *Hydroboration* is the addition of borane (BH_3) to an alkene, forming an alkylborane.
- *Oxidation* converts the C–B bond of the alkylborane to a C–O bond.

Hydroboration–oxidation results in **addition of H_2O** to an alkene.

Examples

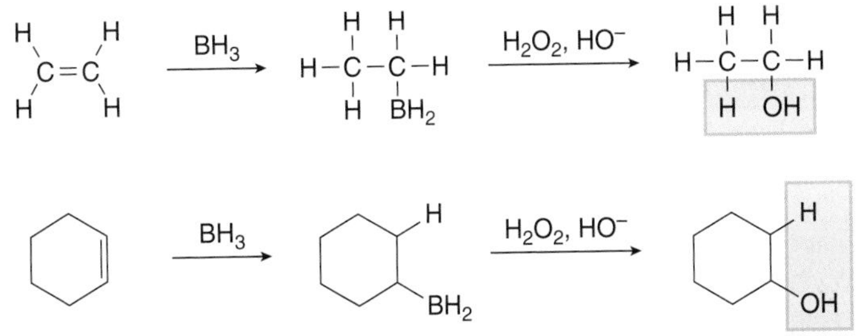

Borane (BH_3) is a reactive gas that exists mostly as the dimer, diborane (B_2H_6). Borane is a strong **Lewis acid** that reacts readily with Lewis bases. For ease in handling in the laboratory, it is commonly used as a complex with tetrahydrofuran (THF).

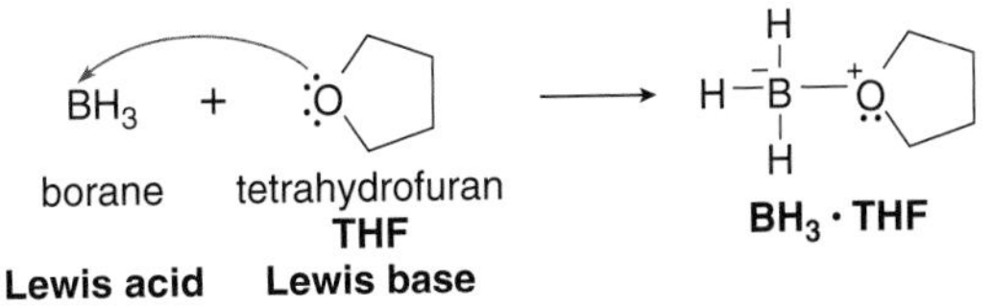

Problem 10.27 Borane is sold for laboratory use as a complex with many other Lewis bases. Draw the Lewis acid–base complex that forms between BH_3 and each compound.

a. $(CH_3)_2S$ b. $(CH_3CH_2)_3N$ c. $(CH_3CH_2CH_2CH_2)_3P$

10.16A Hydroboration

The first step in hydroboration–oxidation is **addition of the elements of H and BH_2** to the π bond of the alkene, forming an intermediate alkylborane.

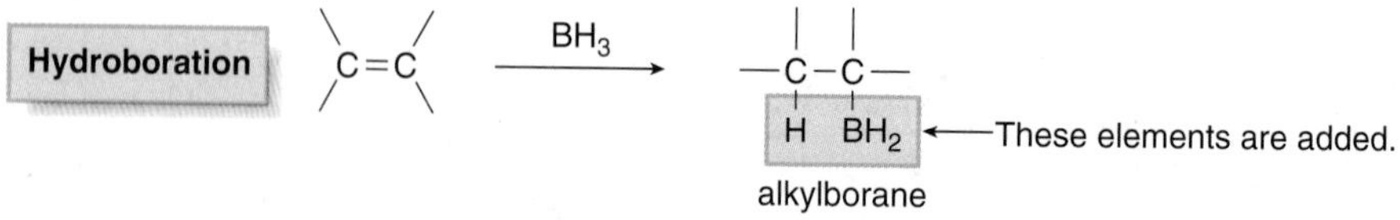

Because syn addition to the double bond occurs and no carbocation rearrangements are observed, carbocations are *not* formed during hydroboration, as shown in Mechanism 10.5. The proposed mechanism involves a **concerted addition of H and BH_2 from the same side of the planar double bond:** the π bond and $H-BH_2$ bond are broken as two new σ bonds are formed. Because four atoms are involved, the transition state is said to be **four-centered.**

Mechanism 10.5 Addition of H and BH_2—Hydroboration

One step The π bond and $H-BH_2$ bonds break *as* the C–H and C–B bonds form.

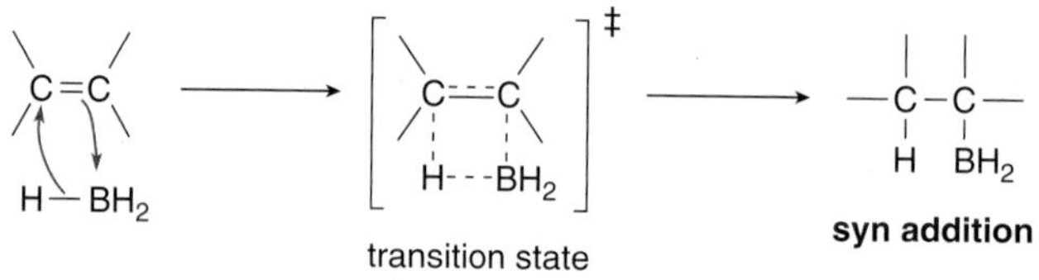

Because the alkylborane formed by reaction with one equivalent of alkene still has two B–H bonds, it can react with two more equivalents of alkene to form a trialkylborane. This is illustrated in Figure 10.15 for the reaction of $CH_2{=}CH_2$ with BH_3.

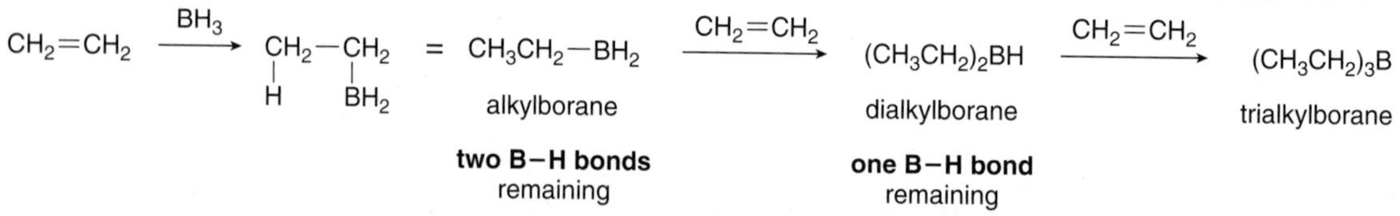

Figure 10.15 Conversion of BH_3 to a trialkylborane with three equivalents of $CH_2{=}CH_2$

- We often draw hydroboration as if addition stopped after one equivalent of alkene reacts with BH_3. Instead, all three B–H bonds actually react with three equivalents of an alkene to form a trialkylborane. The term **organoborane** is used for any compound with a carbon–boron bond.

Because only one B–H bond is needed for hydroboration, commercially available dialkylboranes having the general structure $\mathbf{R_2BH}$ are sometimes used instead of BH_3. A common example is 9-borabicyclo[3.3.1]nonane **(9-BBN).** 9-BBN undergoes hydroboration in the same manner as BH_3.

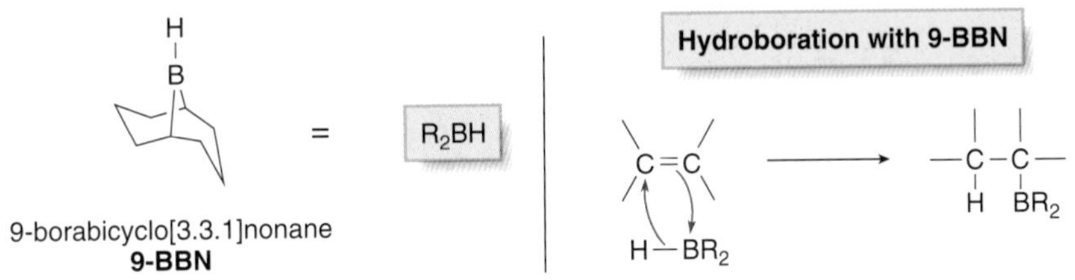
9-borabicyclo[3.3.1]nonane
9-BBN
R2BH
Hydroboration with 9-BBN

Hydroboration is regioselective. **With unsymmetrical alkenes, the boron atom bonds to the less substituted carbon atom.** For example, addition of BH_3 to propene forms an alkylborane with the B bonded to the terminal carbon atom.

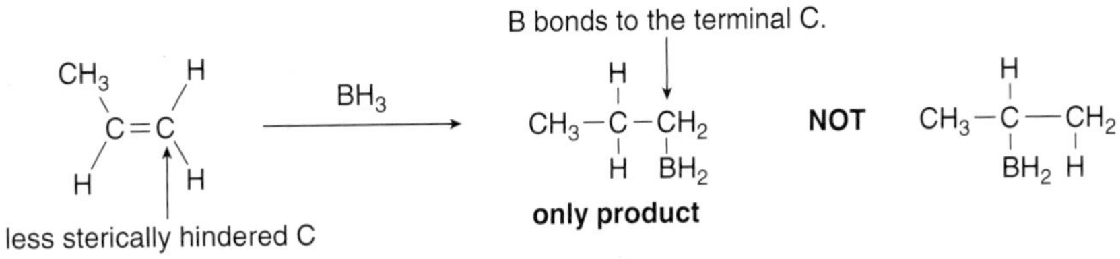
B bonds to the terminal C.
BH3
less sterically hindered C
only product
NOT

Because H is more electronegative than B, the B–H bond is polarized to give boron a partial positive charge ($H^{\delta-}-B^{\delta+}$), making BH_2 the electrophile in hydroboration.

Steric factors explain this regioselectivity. The larger boron atom bonds to the less sterically hindered, more accessible carbon atom.

Electronic factors are also used to explain this regioselectivity. If bond breaking and bond making are not completely symmetrical, boron bears a partial negative charge in the transition state and carbon bears a partial positive charge. Because alkyl groups stabilize a positive charge, the more stable transition state has the partial positive charge on the more substituted carbon, as illustrated in Figure 10.16.

- **In hydroboration, the boron atom bonds to the less substituted carbon.**

Figure 10.16
Hydroboration of an unsymmetrical alkene

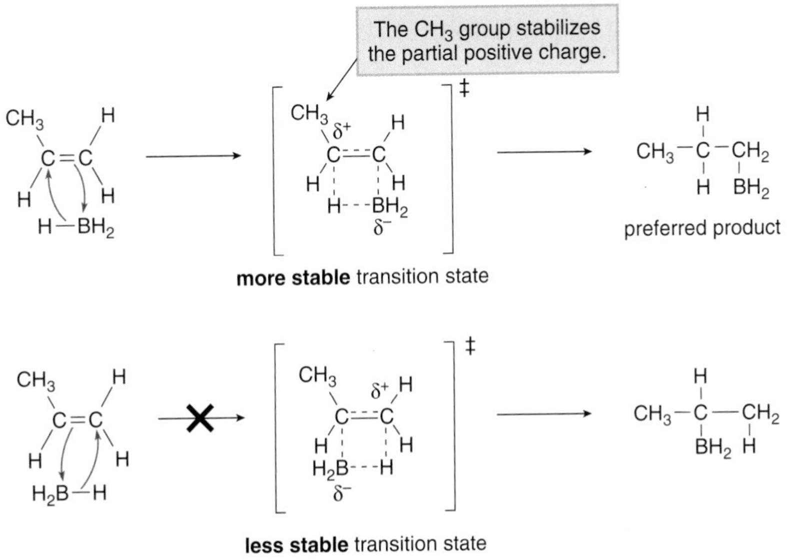
The CH3 group stabilizes the partial positive charge.
more stable transition state
preferred product
less stable transition state

Problem 10.28 What alkylborane is formed from hydroboration of each alkene?

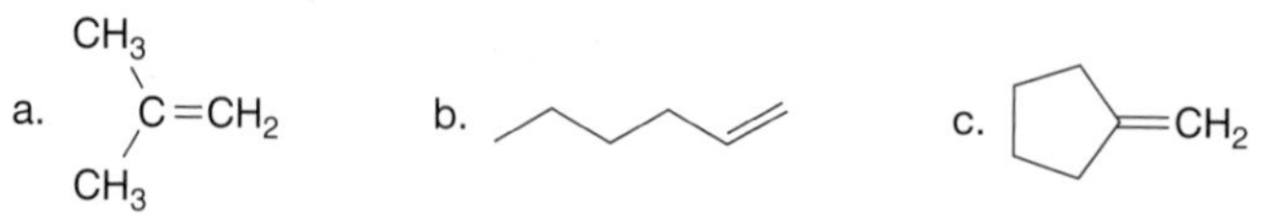

10.16B Oxidation of the Alkylborane

Because alkylboranes react rapidly with water and spontaneously burn when exposed to the air, they are oxidized, without isolation, with basic hydrogen peroxide (H_2O_2, HO^-). **Oxidation replaces the C–B bond with a C–O bond, forming a new OH group with retention of configuration;** that is, the **OH group replaces the BH_2 group in the same position** relative to the other three groups on carbon.

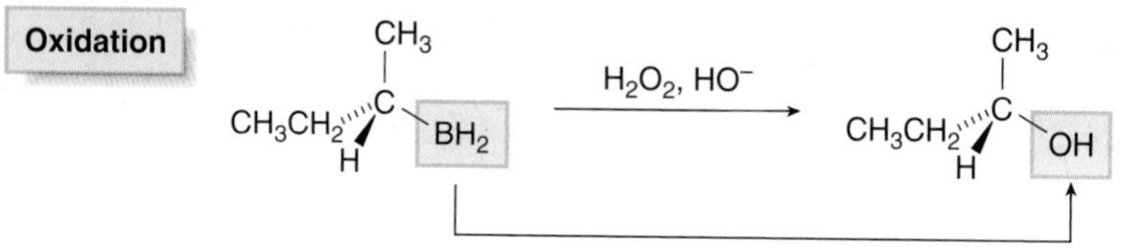

Thus, to draw the product of a hydroboration–oxidation reaction, keep in mind two stereochemical facts:

- **Hydroboration occurs with syn addition.**
- **Oxidation occurs with retention of configuration.**

The overall result of this two-step sequence is **syn addition of the elements of H and OH** to a double bond, as illustrated in Sample Problem 10.5. The OH group bonds to the less substituted carbon.

Sample Problem 10.5 Draw the product of the following reaction sequence, including stereochemistry.

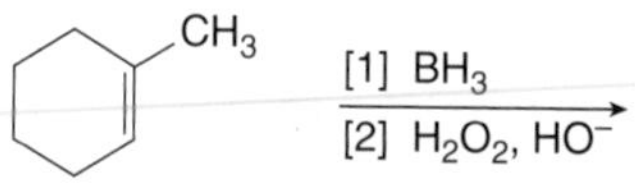

Solution

In Step [1], **syn addition of BH_3 to the unsymmetrical alkene adds the BH_2 group to the less substituted carbon from above and below the planar double bond.** Two enantiomeric alkylboranes are formed. In Step [2], oxidation replaces the BH_2 group with OH in each enantiomer with **retention of configuration** to yield two alcohols that are also enantiomers.

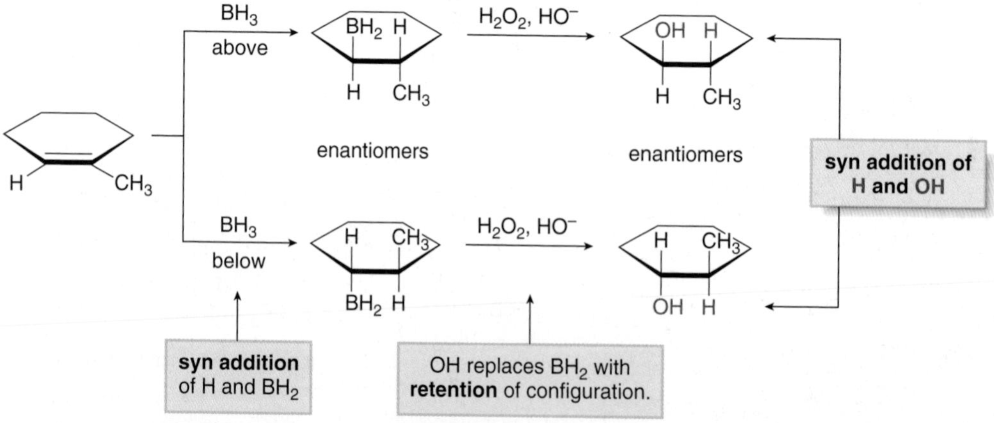

Hydroboration–oxidation results in the **addition of H and OH in a syn fashion** across the double bond. The achiral alkene is converted to an equal mixture of two enantiomers—that is, a **racemic mixture of alcohols.**

Problem 10.29 Draw the products formed when each alkene is treated with BH_3 followed by H_2O_2, HO^-. Include the stereochemistry at all stereogenic centers.

a. $CH_3CH_2CH{=}CH_2$

b. 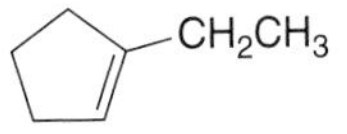
CH2CH3

c. 
CH3
CH3

Problem 10.30 What alkene can be used to prepare each alcohol as the exclusive product of a two-step hydroboration–oxidation sequence?

a. 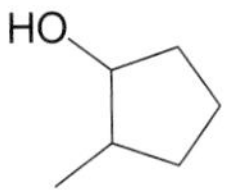
HO

b. 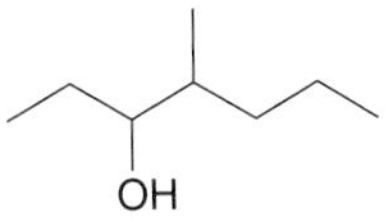
OH

c. 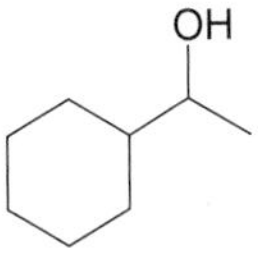
OH

Table 10.5 summarizes the features of hydroboration–oxidation.

Hydroboration–oxidation is a very common method for adding H_2O across a double bond. One example is shown in the synthesis of **artemisinin** (or **qinghaosu**), the active component of **qinghao,** a Chinese herbal remedy used for the treatment of malaria (Figure 10.17).

Table 10.5 Summary: Hydroboration–Oxidation of Alkenes

	Observation
Mechanism	• The addition of H and BH_2 occurs in one step. • No rearrangements can occur.
Regioselectivity	• The OH group bonds to the less substituted carbon atom.
Stereochemistry	• Syn addition occurs. • OH replaces BH_2 with retention of configuration.

Figure 10.17 An example of hydroboration–oxidation in synthesis

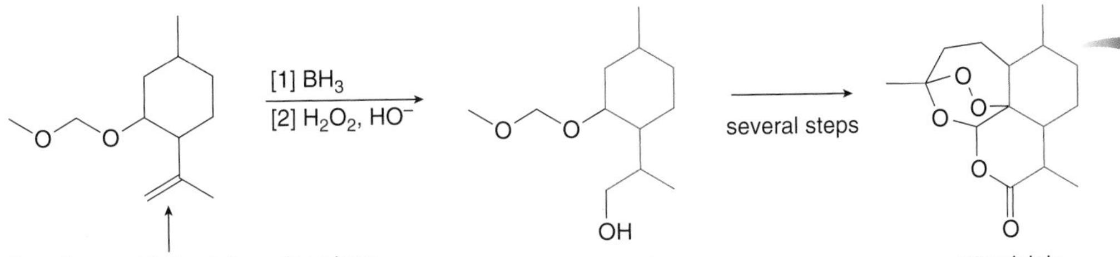
[1] BH3
[2] H2O2, HO−
O
O
OH
several steps
O
O
O
O
O

Hydroboration–oxidation takes place here.

A

artemisinin (antimalarial drug)

Artemisia annua, source of the antimalarial agent artemisinin

• The carbon atoms of artemisinin that come from alcohol **A** are indicated in red.

10.16C A Comparison of Hydration Methods

Hydration (H_2O, H^+) and hydroboration–oxidation (BH_3 followed by H_2O_2, HO^-) both add the elements of H_2O across a double bond. Despite their similarities, these reactions often form different constitutional isomers, as shown in Sample Problem 10.6.

Sample Problem 10.6 Draw the product formed when $CH_3CH_2CH_2CH_2CH{=}CH_2$ is treated with (a) H_2O, H_2SO_4; and (b) BH_3 followed by H_2O_2, HO^-.

Solution

With H_2O + H_2SO_4, electrophilic addition of H and OH places the **H atom on the less substituted carbon** of the alkene to yield a **2° alcohol.** In contrast, addition of BH_3 gives an alkylborane with the **BH_2 group on the less substituted terminal carbon** of the alkene. Oxidation replaces BH_2 by OH to yield a **1° alcohol.**

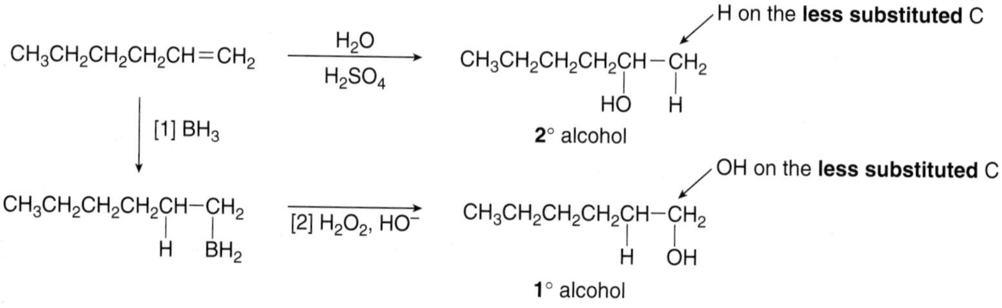
H on the **less substituted** C
CH3CH2CH2CH2CH=CH2
H2O
H2SO4
CH3CH2CH2CH2CH–CH2
HO H
2° alcohol
[1] BH3
OH on the **less substituted** C
CH3CH2CH2CH2CH–CH2
H BH2
[2] H2O2, HO–
CH3CH2CH2CH2CH–CH2
H OH
1° alcohol

Problem 10.31 Draw the constitutional isomer formed when the following alkenes are treated with each set of reagents: [1] H_2O, H_2SO_4; or [2] BH_3 followed by H_2O_2, ^-OH.

a. 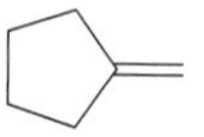 b. 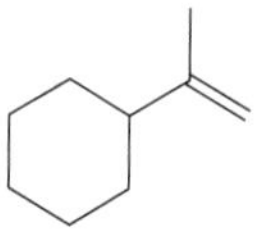 c. 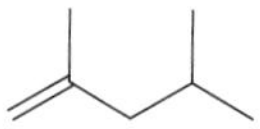

10.17 Keeping Track of Reactions

Chapters 7–10 have introduced three basic kinds of organic reactions: **nucleophilic substitution, β elimination,** and **addition.** In the process, many specific reagents have been discussed and the stereochemistry that results from many different mechanisms has been examined. **How can we keep track of all the reactions?**

To make the process easier, **remember that most organic molecules undergo only one or two different kinds of reactions.** For example:

- **Alkyl halides undergo substitution and elimination because they have good leaving groups.**
- **Alcohols also undergo substitution and elimination, but can do so only when OH is made into a good leaving group.**
- **Alkenes undergo addition because they have easily broken π bonds.**

You must still learn many reaction details, and in truth, there is no one method to learn them. ***You must practice these reactions over and over again, not by merely looking at them, but by writing them.*** Some students do this by making a list of specific reactions for each functional group, and then rewriting them with different starting materials. Others make flash cards: index cards that have the starting material and reagent on one side and the product on the other. Whatever method you choose, **the details must become second nature,** much like the answers to simple addition problems, such as, what is the sum of 2 + 2?

Learning reactions is really a two-step process.

- **First, learn the basic type of reaction for a functional group. This provides an overall organization to the reactions.**
- **Then, learn the specific reagents for each reaction. It helps to classify the reagent according to its properties. Is it an acid or a base? Is it a nucleophile or an electrophile? Is it an oxidizing agent or a reducing agent?**

Sample Problem 10.7 illustrates this process.

Sample Problem 10.7 Draw the product of each reaction.

a. $(CH_3CH_2)_2CHCH_2{-}Br \xrightarrow{KOC(CH_3)_3}$ b. $(CH_3CH_2)_2CHCH{=}CH_2 \xrightarrow[H_2O]{Br_2}$

Solution

In each problem, identify the functional group to determine the general reaction type—substitution, elimination, or addition. Then, determine if the reagent is an electrophile, nucleophile, acid, base, and so forth.

a. The reactant is a **1° alkyl halide,** which can undergo substitution and elimination. The reagent [$KOC(CH_3)_3$] is a **strong nonnucleophilic base,** favoring elimination by an E2 mechanism (Figure 8.10).

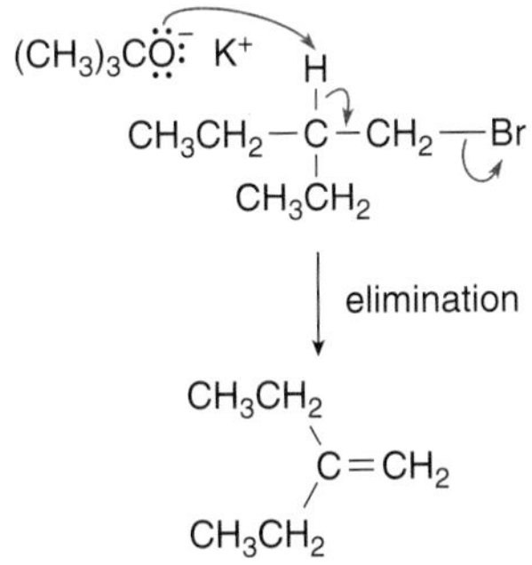
$(CH_3)_3CO^-$ K^+
H
$CH_3CH_2-C-CH_2-Br$
CH_3CH_2
elimination
CH_3CH_2
$C{=}CH_2$
CH_3CH_2

E2 product

b. The reactant is an **alkene,** which undergoes addition reactions to its π bond. The reagent (Br_2 + H_2O) serves as the source of the **electrophile Br^+,** resulting in **addition** of Br and OH to the double bond (Section 10.15).

This π bond is broken.

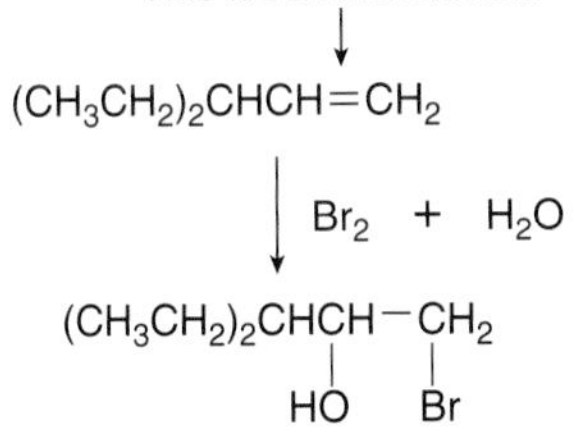
$(CH_3CH_2)_2CHCH{=}CH_2$
Br_2 + H_2O
$(CH_3CH_2)_2CHCH-CH_2$
HO Br

addition product

Problem 10.32 Draw the products of each reaction using the two-part strategy from Sample Problem 10.7.

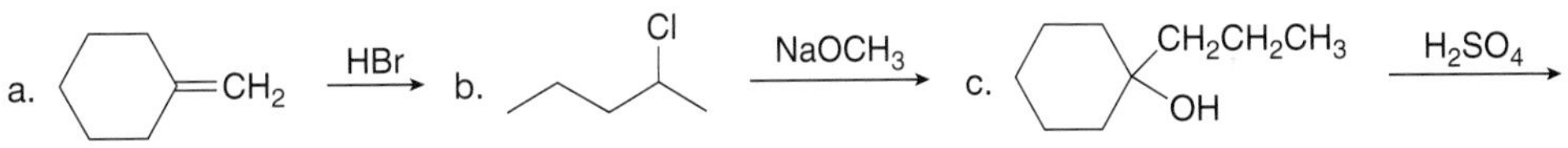
a.
$=CH_2$
HBr
b.
Cl
$NaOCH_3$
c.
$CH_2CH_2CH_3$
OH
H_2SO_4

10.18 Alkenes in Organic Synthesis

Alkenes are a central functional group in organic chemistry. **Alkenes are easily prepared by elimination reactions** such as dehydrohalogenation and dehydration. **Because their π bond is easily broken, they undergo many addition reactions** to prepare a variety of useful compounds.

Suppose, for example, that we must synthesize 1,2-dibromocyclohexane from cyclohexanol, a cheap and readily available starting material. Because there is no way to accomplish this transformation in one step, this synthesis must have at least two steps.

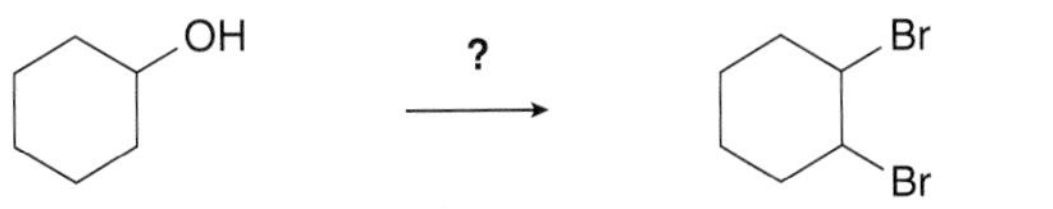
OH
?
Br
Br

cyclohexanol — **starting material**

1,2-dibromocyclohexane — **product**

To solve this problem we must:

- **Work backwards from the product by asking: What type of reactions introduce the functional groups in the product?**
- **Work forwards from the starting material by asking: What type of reactions does the starting material undergo?**

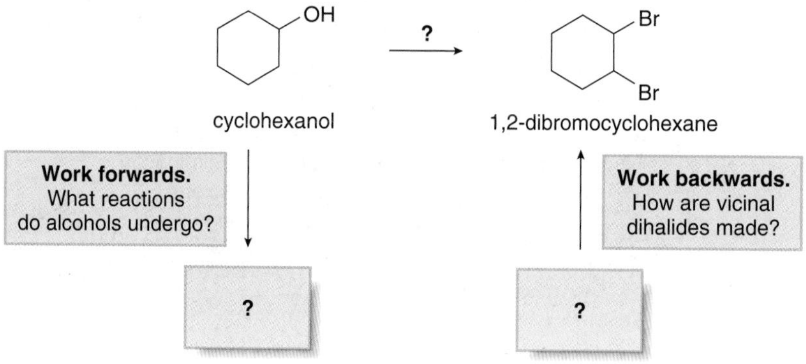

In Chapter 11 we will learn about retrosynthetic analysis in more detail.

Working backwards from the product to determine the starting material from which it is made is called *retrosynthetic analysis*.

We know reactions that answer each of these questions.

Working backwards:

[1] 1,2-Dibromocyclohexane, a vicinal dibromide, can be prepared by the addition of Br_2 to **cyclohexene.**

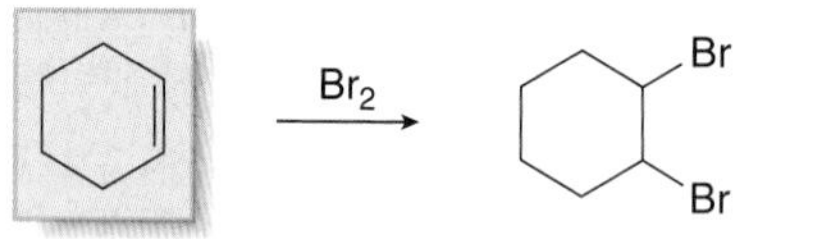

cyclohexene 1,2-dibromocyclohexane

Working forwards:

[2] Cyclohexanol can undergo acid-catalyzed dehydration to form **cyclohexene.**

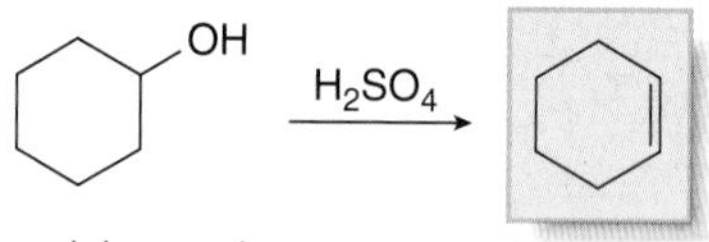

cyclohexanol cyclohexene

A **reactive intermediate** is an unstable intermediate like a carbocation, which is formed during the conversion of a stable starting material to a stable product. A **synthetic intermediate** is a stable compound that is the product of one step and the starting material of another in a multistep synthesis.

Cyclohexene is called a **synthetic intermediate,** or simply an **intermediate,** because it is the **product of one step and the starting material of another.** We now have a two-step sequence to convert cyclohexanol to 1,2-dibromocyclohexane, and the synthesis is complete. Take note of the central role of the alkene in this synthesis.

A two-step synthesis

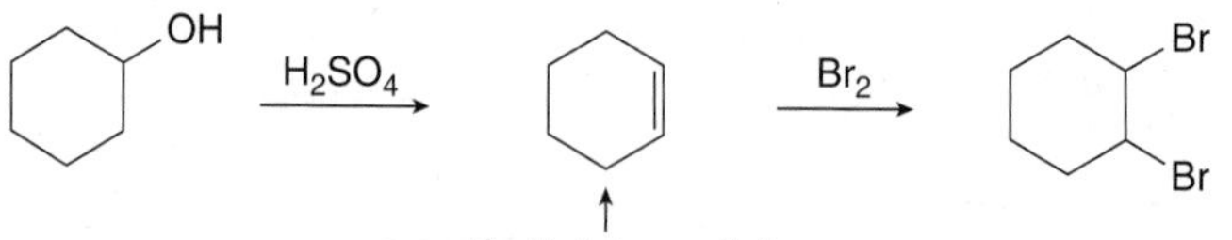

a synthetic intermediate

Problem 10.33 Devise a synthesis of each compound from the indicated starting material.

a. 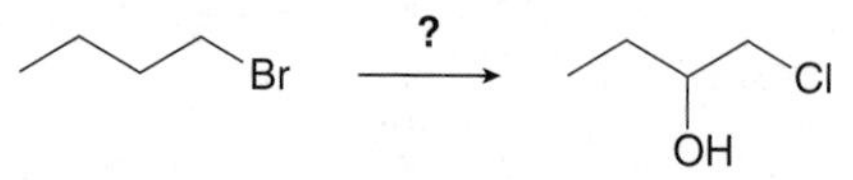

b. 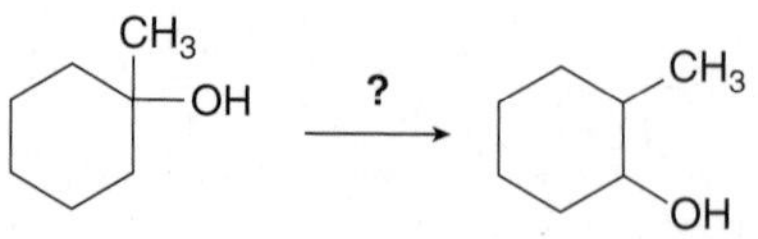

KEY CONCEPTS

Alkenes

General Facts About Alkenes

- Alkenes contain a carbon–carbon double bond consisting of a stronger σ bond and a weaker π bond. Each carbon is sp^2 hybridized and trigonal planar (10.1).
- Alkenes are named using the suffix ***-ene*** (10.3).
- Alkenes with different groups on each end of the double bond exist as a pair of diastereomers, identified by the prefixes *E* and *Z* (10.3B).
- Alkenes have weak intermolecular forces, giving them low mp's and bp's, and making them water insoluble. A cis alkene is more polar than a trans alkene, giving it a slightly higher boiling point (10.4).
- Because a π bond is electron rich and much weaker than a σ bond, alkenes undergo addition reactions with electrophiles (10.8).

Stereochemistry of Alkene Addition Reactions (10.8)

A reagent XY adds to a double bond in one of three different ways:

- **Syn addition**—X and Y add from the same side.

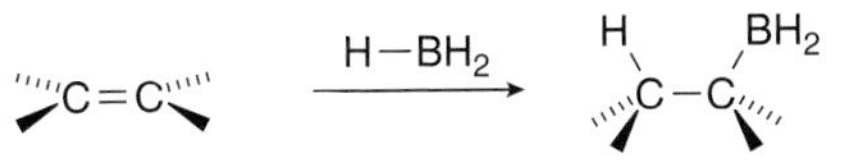
H−BH2
H
BH2

- Syn addition occurs in **hydroboration.**

- **Anti addition**—X and Y add from opposite sides.

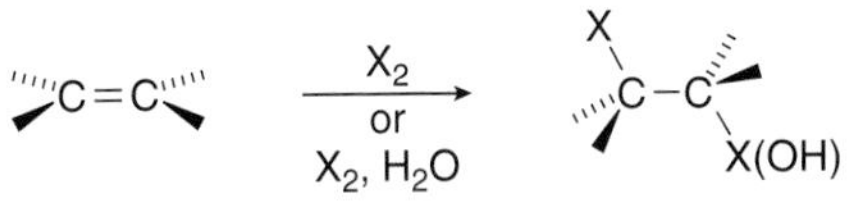
X2
or
X2, H2O
X
X(OH)

- Anti addition occurs in **halogenation** and **halohydrin formation.**

- **Both syn and anti addition** occur when carbocations are intermediates.

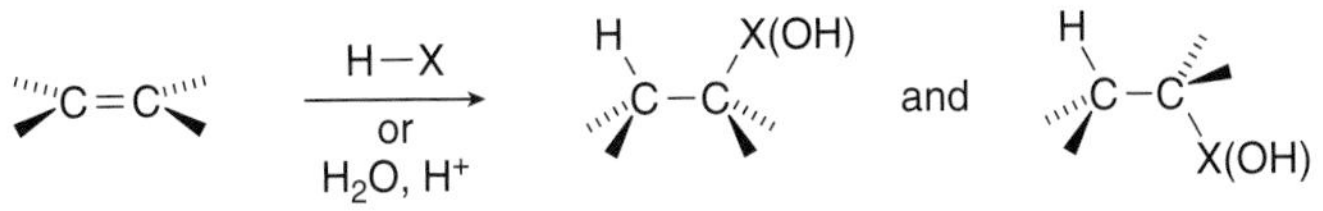
H−X
or
H2O, H+
H
X(OH)
and
H
X(OH)

- Syn and anti addition occur in **hydrohalogenation** and **hydration.**

Addition Reactions of Alkenes

[1] Hydrohalogenation—Addition of HX (X = Cl, Br, I) (10.9–10.11)

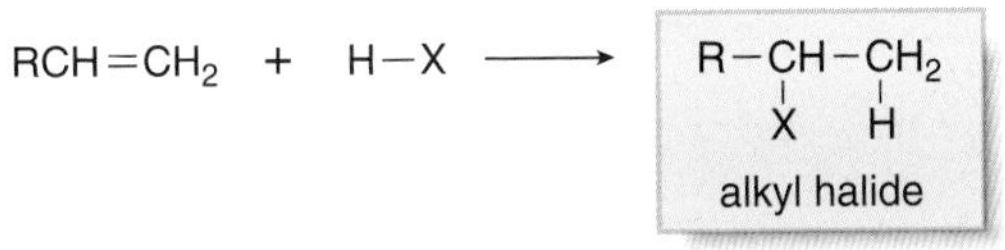
RCH=CH2 + H−X
R−CH−CH2
X H
alkyl halide

- The mechanism has two steps.
- Carbocations are formed as intermediates.
- Carbocation rearrangements are possible.
- Markovnikov's rule is followed. H bonds to the less substituted C to form the more stable carbocation.
- Syn and anti addition occur.

[2] Hydration and related reactions (Addition of H_2O or ROH) (10.12)

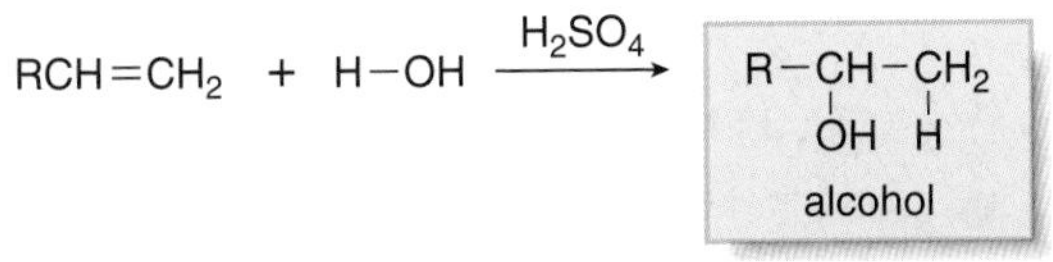
RCH=CH2 + H−OH
H2SO4
R−CH−CH2
OH H
alcohol

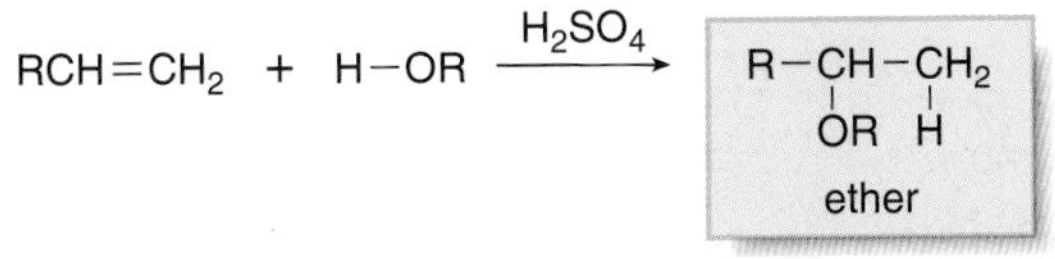
RCH=CH2 + H−OR
H2SO4
R−CH−CH2
OR H
ether

For both reactions:

- The mechanism has three steps.
- Carbocations are formed as intermediates.
- Carbocation rearrangements are possible.
- Markovnikov's rule is followed. H bonds to the less substituted C to form the more stable carbocation.
- Syn and anti addition occur.

[3] Halogenation (Addition of X_2; X = Cl or Br) (10.13–10.14)

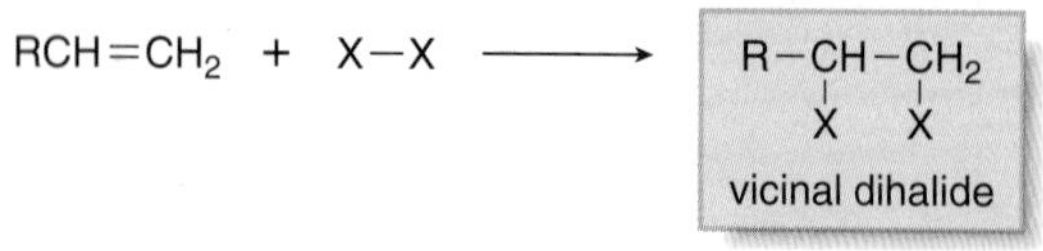
RCH=CH2 + X−X
R−CH−CH2
X X
vicinal dihalide

- The mechanism has two steps.
- Bridged halonium ions are formed as intermediates.
- No rearrangements can occur.
- Anti addition occurs.

[4] Halohydrin formation (Addition of OH and X; X = Cl, Br) (10.15)

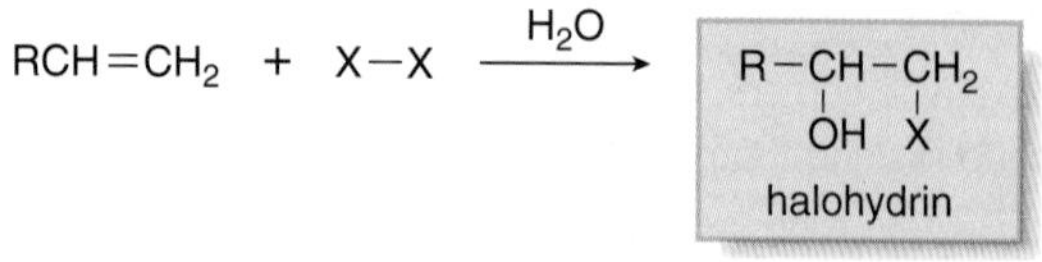
RCH=CH2 + X−X
H2O
R−CH−CH2
OH X
halohydrin

- The mechanism has three steps.
- Bridged halonium ions are formed as intermediates.
- No rearrangements can occur.
- X bonds to the less substituted C.
- Anti addition occurs.
- NBS in DMSO and H_2O adds Br and OH in the same fashion.

[5] Hydroboration–oxidation (Addition of H_2O) (10.16)

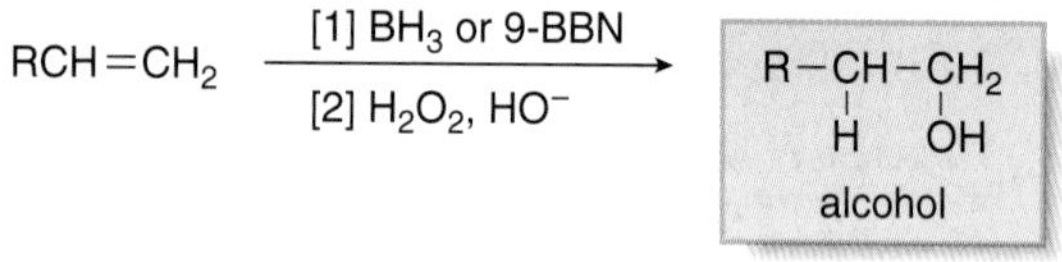
RCH=CH2
[1] BH3 or 9-BBN
[2] H2O2, HO−
R−CH−CH2
H OH
alcohol

- Hydroboration has a one-step mechanism.
- No rearrangements can occur.
- OH bonds to the less substituted C.
- Syn addition of H_2O results.

PROBLEMS

Problems Using Three-Dimensional Models

10.34 Give the IUPAC name for each compound.

a. 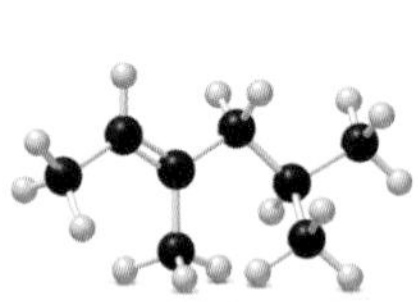

b. 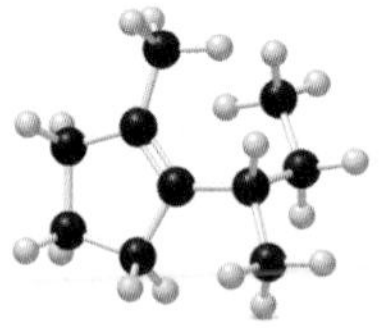

10.35 (a) Label the carbon–carbon double bond in **A** as *E* or *Z*. (b) Draw the products (including stereoisomers) formed when **A** is treated with H_2O in the presence of H_2SO_4.

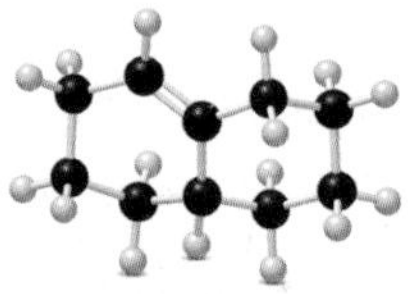

A

10.36 Name the alkene depicted in the ball-and-stick model and draw the constitutional isomers formed when the alkene is treated with each reagent: (a) Br_2; (b) Br_2 in H_2O; (c) Br_2 in CH_3OH.

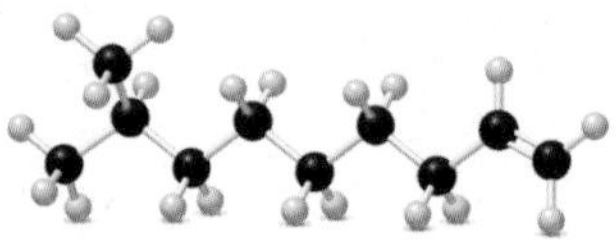

Degrees of Unsaturation

10.37 Calculate the number of degrees of unsaturation for each molecular formula.

a. C_3H_4 c. $C_{40}H_{56}$ e. $C_{10}H_{16}O_2$ g. C_8H_9ClO i. $C_7H_{11}N$

b. C_6H_8 d. C_8H_8O f. C_8H_9Br h. C_7H_9Br j. C_4H_8BrN

10.38 How many rings and π bonds does a compound with molecular formula $C_{10}H_{14}$ possess? List all possibilities.

Nomenclature and Stereochemistry

10.39 The fertility drug clomiphene (trade name Clomid) is sold as a mixture of diastereomers, enclomiphene and zuclomiphene. Designate each alkene as an *E* or *Z* isomer. What is wrong with the statement, "Clomid is a mixture of two isomers, 30% cis and the remainder trans"?

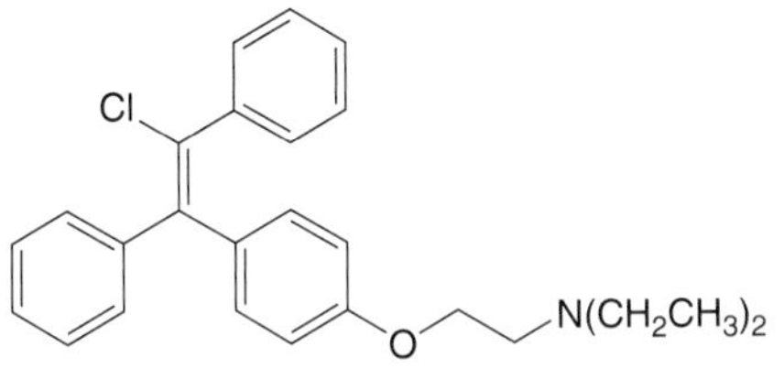

enclomiphene

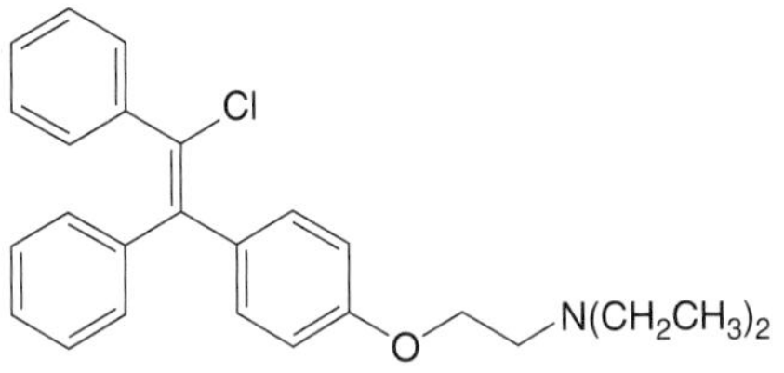

zuclomiphene

10.40 Give the IUPAC name for each compound.

a. $CH_2{=}CHCH_2CH(CH_3)CH_2CH_3$

b. 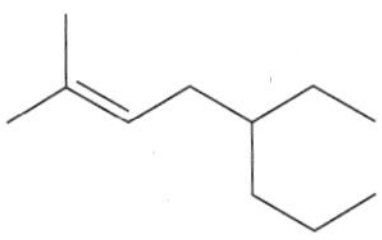

c. 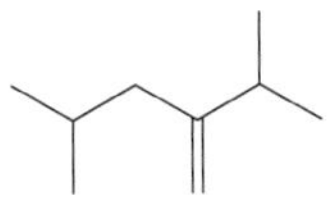

d. 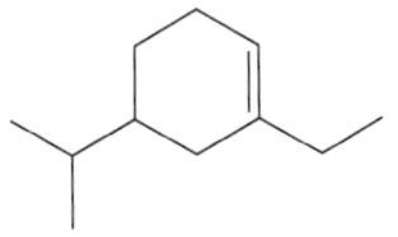

e. 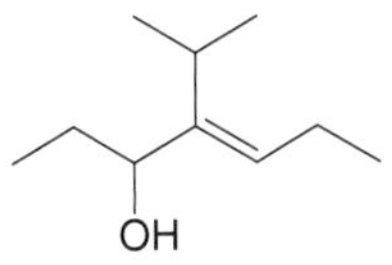

f. 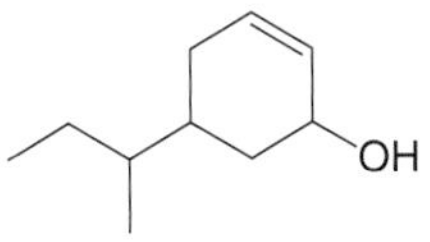

10.41 Give the structure corresponding to each name.

a. (3*E*)-4-ethyl-3-heptene
b. 3,3-dimethylcyclopentene
c. *cis*-4-octene
d. 4-vinylcyclopentene
e. (2*Z*)-3-isopropyl-2-heptene
f. *cis*-3,4-dimethylcyclopentene
g. *trans*-2-heptene
h. 1-isopropyl-4-propylcyclohexene

10.42 (a) Draw all possible stereoisomers of 4-methyl-2-nonene, and name each isomer, including its *E,Z* and *R,S* prefixes. (b) Label two pairs of enantiomers. (c) Label four pairs of diastereomers.

10.43 (a) Draw the structure of (1*E*,4*R*)-1,4-dimethylcyclodecene. (b) Draw the enantiomer and name it, including its *E,Z* and *R,S* prefixes. (c) Draw two diastereomers and name them, including the *E,Z* and *R,S* prefixes.

10.44 Now that you have learned how to name alkenes in Section 10.3, name each of the following epoxides as an alkene oxide, as described in Section 9.3.

a. 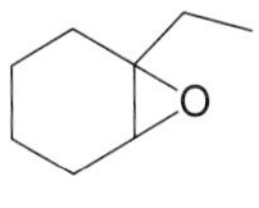

b. 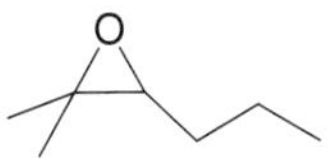

c. 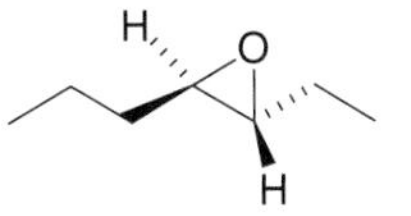

d. 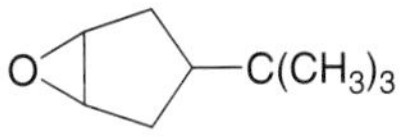

10.45 Each of the following names is incorrect. Explain why it is incorrect and give the correct IUPAC name.

a. 2-butyl-3-methyl-1-pentene
b. (*Z*)-2-methyl-2-hexene
c. (*E*)-1-isopropyl-1-butene
d. 5-methylcyclohexene
e. 4-isobutyl-2-methylcyclohexene
f. 1-*sec*-butyl-2-cyclopentene
g. 1-cyclohexen-4-ol
h. 3-ethyl-3-octen-5-ol

10.46 Iejimalide B, an anticancer agent with a 24-membered ring, is isolated from a tunicate found off Ie Island in Okinawa. (a) Label each double bond in iejimalide B as *E* or *Z*. (b) Label each tetrahedral stereogenic center as *R* or *S*. (c) How many stereoisomers are possible for iejimalide B?

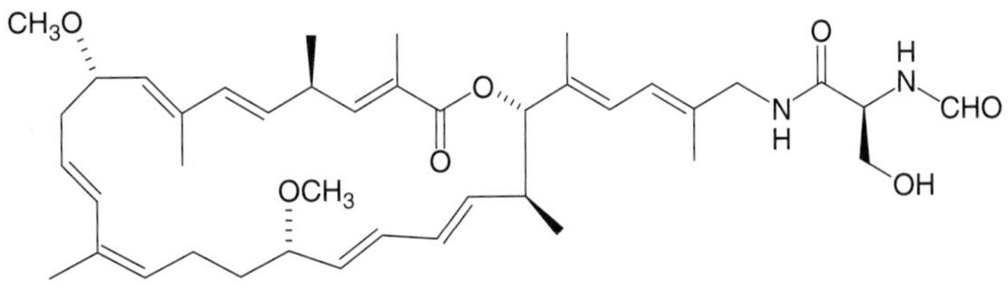

iejimalide B

Lipids

10.47 Although naturally occurring unsaturated fatty acids generally have the *Z* configuration, elaidic acid, a C_{18} fatty acid having an *E* double bond, is present in processed foods such as margarine and cooking oils. Predict how the melting point of elaidic acid compares with the melting points of stearic and oleic acids (Table 10.2).

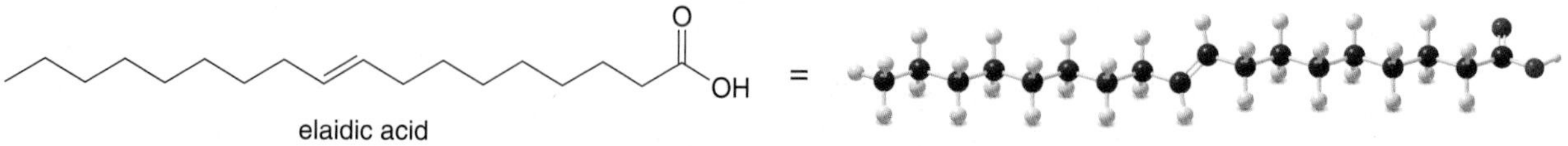

elaidic acid

10.48 Eleostearic acid is an unsaturated fatty acid obtained from the seeds of the tung oil tree (*Aleurites fordii*), a deciduous tree native to China. (a) Draw the structure of a stereoisomer that has a higher melting point than eleostearic acid. (b) Draw the structure of a stereoisomer that has a lower melting point.

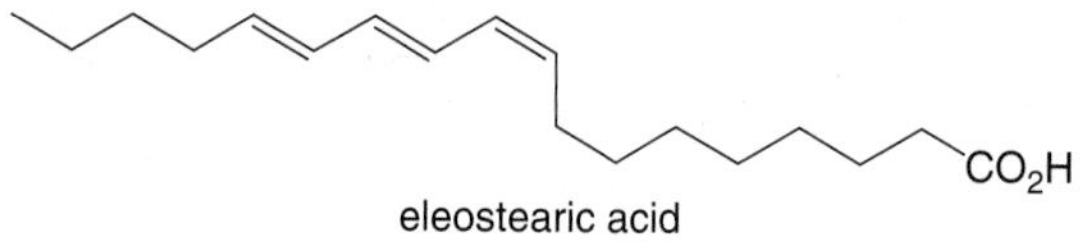

eleostearic acid

$\Delta H°$ Calculations

10.49 By using the bond dissociation energies in Appendix C, calculate $\Delta H°$ for the addition of HCl and HI to ethylene to form chloroethane and iodoethane, respectively. Assuming entropy changes for both reactions are similar, which reaction has the larger K_{eq}?

Reactions of Alkenes

10.50 Draw the products formed when cyclohexene is treated with each reagent.

a. HBr
b. HI
c. H_2O, H_2SO_4
d. CH_3CH_2OH, H_2SO_4
e. Cl_2
f. Br_2, H_2O
g. NBS (aqueous DMSO)
h. [1] BH_3; [2] H_2O_2, HO^-
i. [1] 9-BBN; [2] H_2O_2, HO^-

10.51 Repeat Problem 10.50 with $(CH_3)_2C{=}CH_2$ as the starting material.

10.52 What alkene can be used to prepare each alkyl halide or dihalide as the exclusive or major product of an addition reaction?

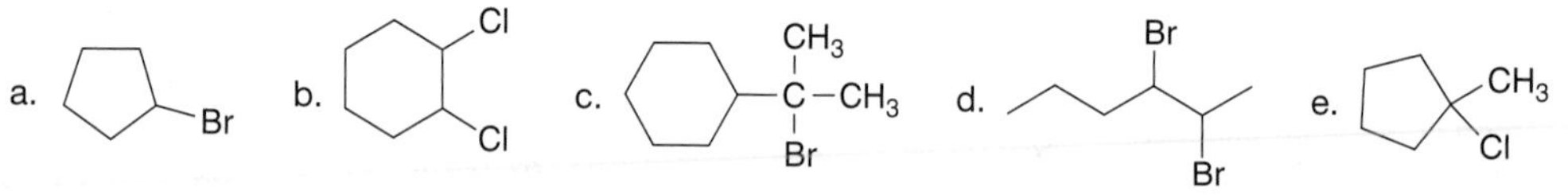

f. $(CH_3CH_2)_3CBr$

10.53 Which alcohols can be prepared as a single product by hydroboration–oxidation of an alkene? Which alcohols can be prepared as a single product by the acid-catalyzed addition of H_2O to an alkene?

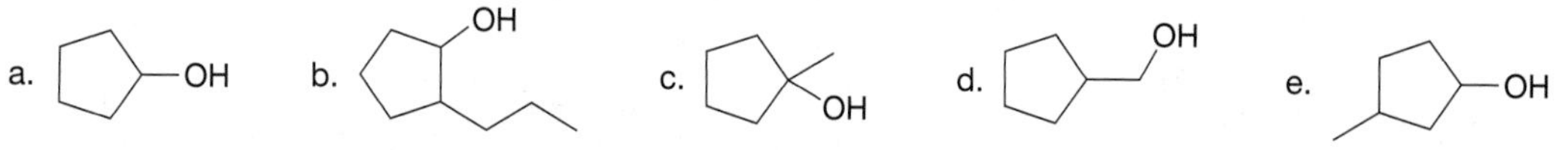

10.54 Draw the constitutional isomer formed in each reaction.

a. $(CH_3CH_2)_2C{=}CHCH_2CH_3 \xrightarrow{HCl}$

b. $(CH_3CH_2)_2C{=}CH_2 \xrightarrow[H_2SO_4]{H_2O}$

c. $(CH_3)_2C{=}CHCH_3 \xrightarrow[\text{[2] } H_2O_2,\ HO^-]{\text{[1] } BH_3}$

d. 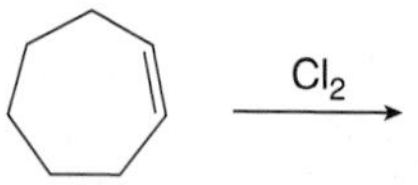

e. 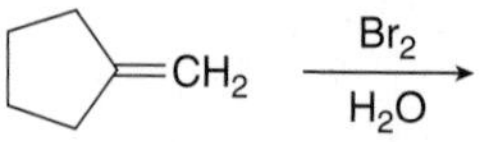

f. 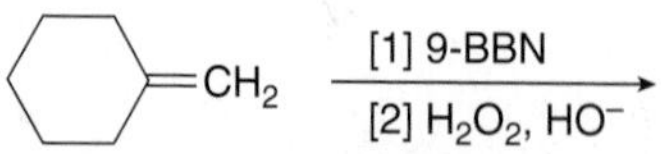

g. 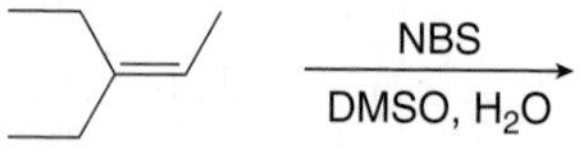

h. 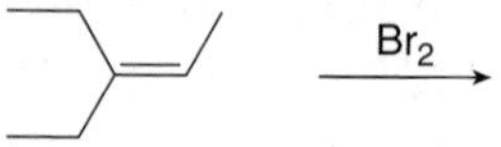

10.55 What three alkenes (excluding stereoisomers) can be used to prepare 3-chloro-3-methylhexane by addition of HCl?

10.56 Draw all stereoisomers formed in each reaction.

a. 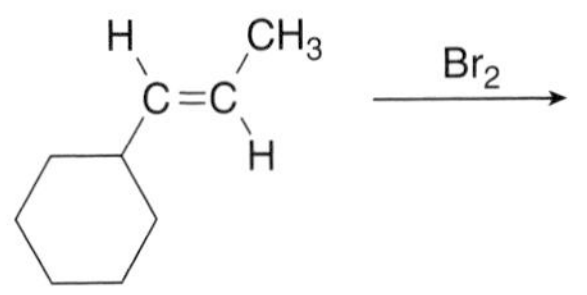

b. 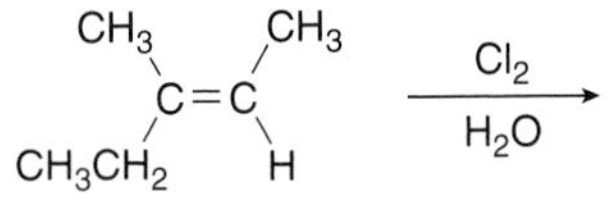

c. 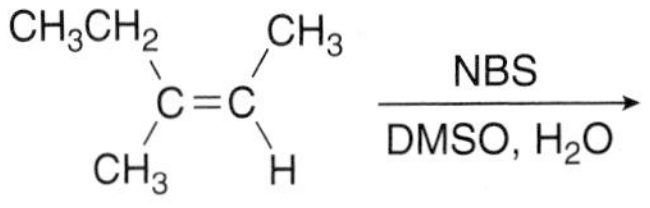

10.57 Draw the products of each reaction, including stereoisomers.

a. 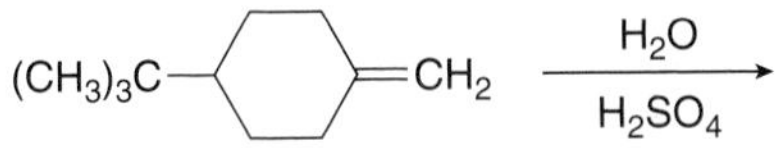

b. 

c. 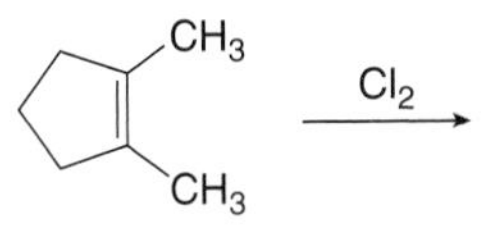

d. 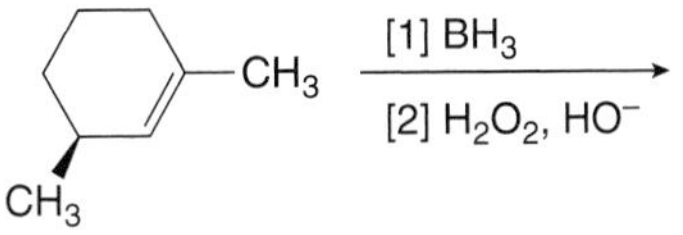

e. 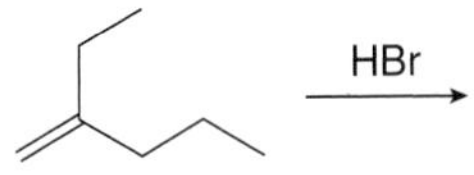

f. 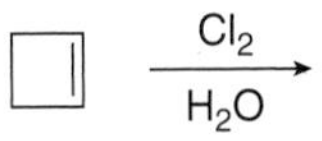

g. 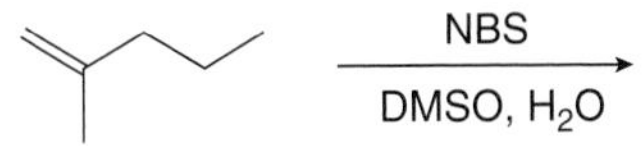

h. $CH_3CH{=}CHCH_2CH_3 \xrightarrow[H_2SO_4]{H_2O}$

10.58 (a) Which diastereomer of 4-octene yields a mixture of two enantiomers, (4*R*,5*R*)- and (4*S*,5*S*)-4,5-dibromooctane on reaction with Br_2? (b) Which diastereomer of 4-octene yields a single meso compound, (4*R*,5*S*)-4,5-dibromooctane?

10.59 Using *cis*- and *trans*-3-hexene, demonstrate that the addition of HCl is not a stereospecific reaction. Draw the structure of the stereoisomers formed from each alkene.

Mechanisms

10.60 Draw a stepwise mechanism for each reaction.

a. 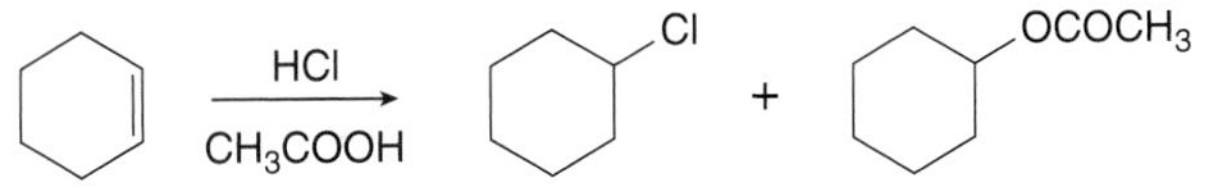

b. 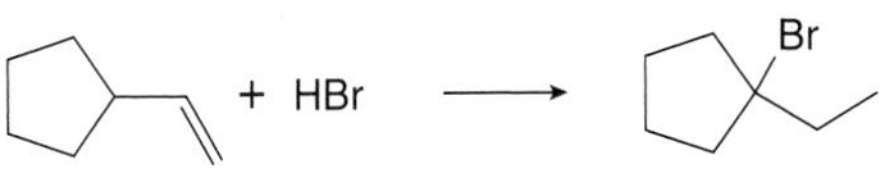

10.61 Draw a stepwise mechanism for each reaction.

a. 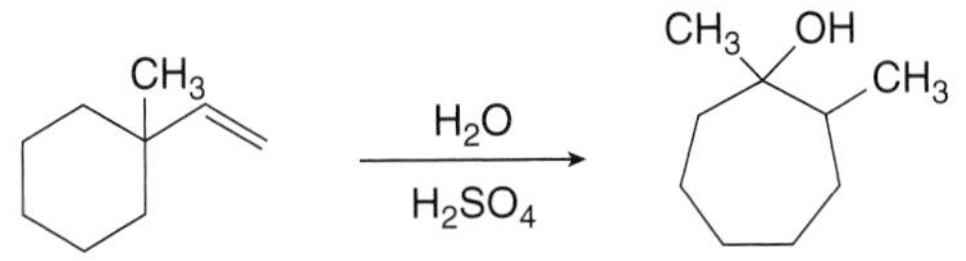

b. 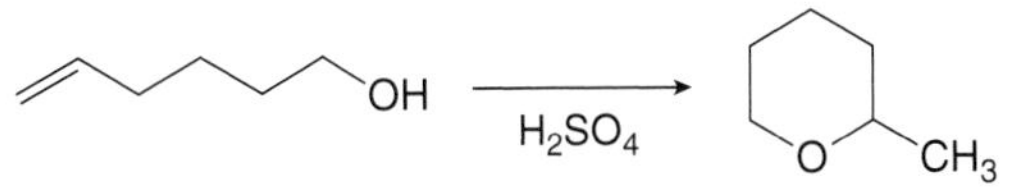

10.62 Draw a stepwise mechanism that shows how all three alcohols are formed from the bicyclic alkene.

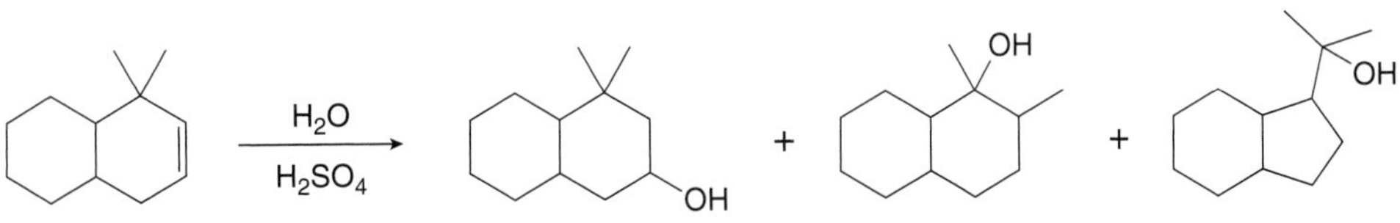

10.63 Less stable alkenes can be isomerized to more stable alkenes by treatment with strong acid. For example, 2,3-dimethyl-1-butene is converted to 2,3-dimethyl-2-butene when treated with H_2SO_4. Draw a stepwise mechanism for this isomerization process.

10.64 When 1,3-butadiene ($CH_2{=}CH{-}CH{=}CH_2$) is treated with HBr, two constitutional isomers are formed, $CH_3CHBrCH{=}CH_2$ and $BrCH_2CH{=}CHCH_3$. Draw a stepwise mechanism that accounts for the formation of both products.

10.65 Explain why the addition of HBr to alkenes **A** and **C** is regioselective, forming addition products **B** and **D,** respectively.

A **B** **C** **D**

10.66 Bromoetherification, the addition of the elements of Br and OR to a double bond, is a common method for constructing rings containing oxygen atoms. This reaction has been used in the synthesis of the polyether antibiotic monensin (Problem 21.36). Draw a stepwise mechanism for the following intramolecular bromoetherification reaction.

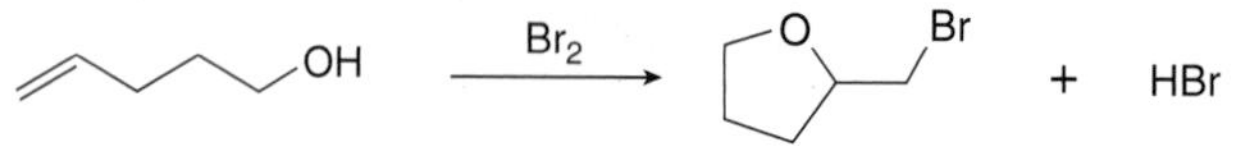

Synthesis

10.67 Devise a synthesis of each product from the given starting material. More than one step is required.

a. 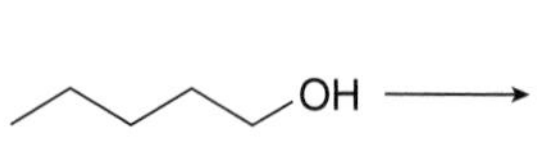

c. 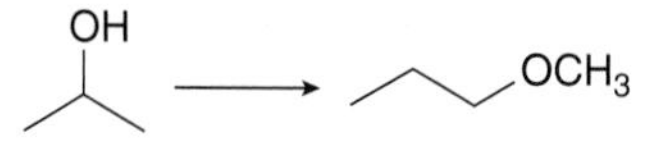

e. 

b. $CH_3-CHBr-CH_3 \longrightarrow CH_3-CHBr-CH_2Br$

d. $(CH_3)_2CHCH_2I \longrightarrow (CH_3)_3CCl$

f. $CH_3CH{=}CH_2 \longrightarrow CH_3C{\equiv}CH$

10.68 Devise a synthesis of each compound from cyclohexene as the starting material. More than one step is needed.

a. 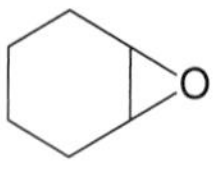

b. 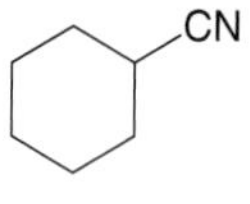

c. 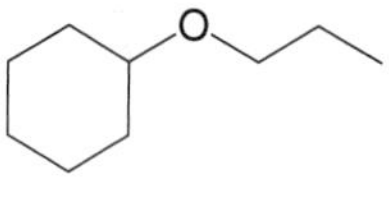

d. 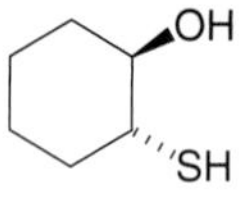

+ enantiomer

e. 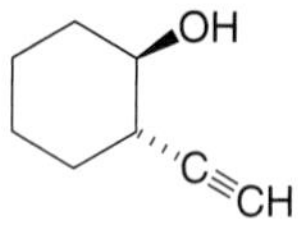

+ enantiomer

10.69 Devise a synthesis of each compound from $(CH_3)_2CHCH_2CH_2Br$. You may use any needed organic or inorganic reagents. More than one step may be required.

a. 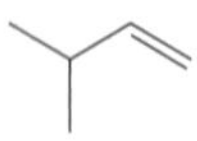

b. 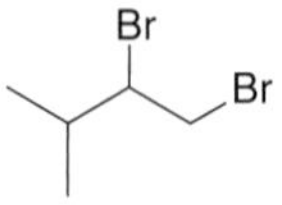

c. 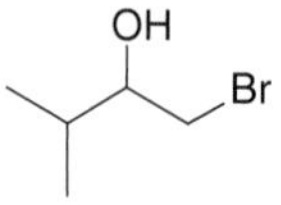

d. 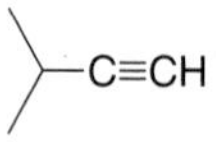

e. 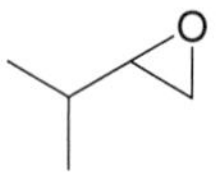

10.70 Devise a synthesis of each epoxide (**B** and **C**) from alcohol **A.** (Hint: Determine what alkene is needed to make each epoxide, and begin each synthesis with a reaction that yields the needed alkene from an elimination reaction.)

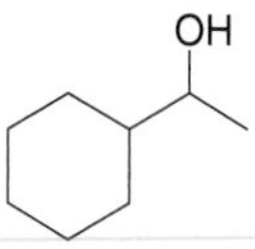

A

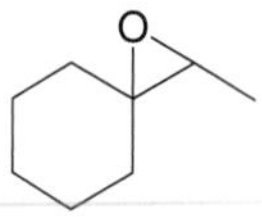

B

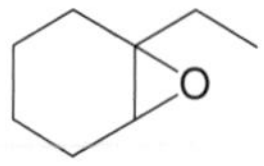

C

Challenge Problems

10.71 Explain why **A** is a stable compound but **B** is not.

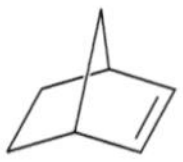

A

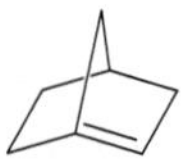

B

10.72 (a) What product(s) are formed when the *E* isomer of $C_6H_5CH{=}CHC_6H_5$ is treated with Br_2, followed by one equivalent of KOH? Label the resulting alkene(s) as *E* or *Z*. (b) What product(s) are formed when the *Z* isomer of $C_6H_5CH{=}CHC_6H_5$ is subjected to the same reaction sequence? (c) How are the compounds in parts (a) and (b) related to each other?

10.73 Alkene **A** can be isomerized to isocomene, a natural product isolated from goldenrod, by treatment with TsOH. Draw a stepwise mechanism for this conversion. (Hint: Look for a carbocation rearrangement.)

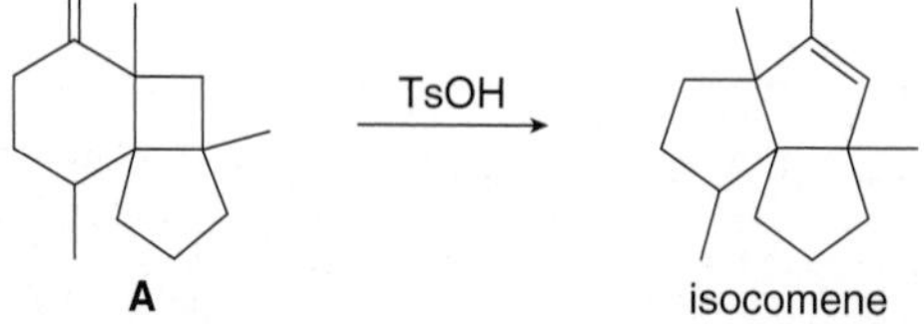

A isocomene

10.74 Lactones, cyclic esters such as compound **A,** are prepared by halolactonization, an addition reaction to an alkene. For example, iodolactonization of **B** forms lactone **C,** a key intermediate in the synthesis of prostaglandin $PGF_{2\alpha}$ (Section 4.15). Draw a stepwise mechanism for this addition reaction.

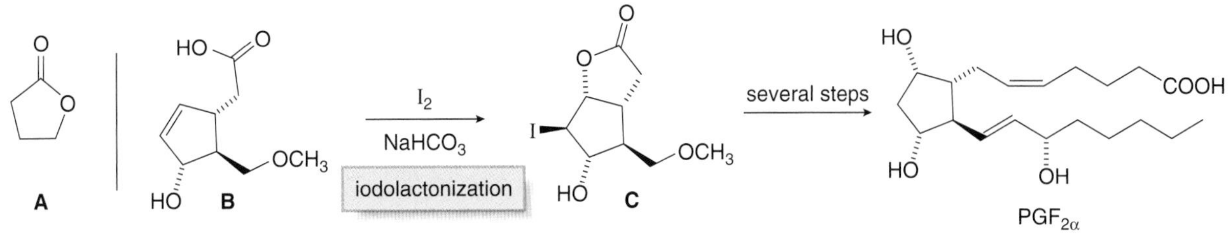

10.75 Draw a stepwise mechanism for the following reaction.

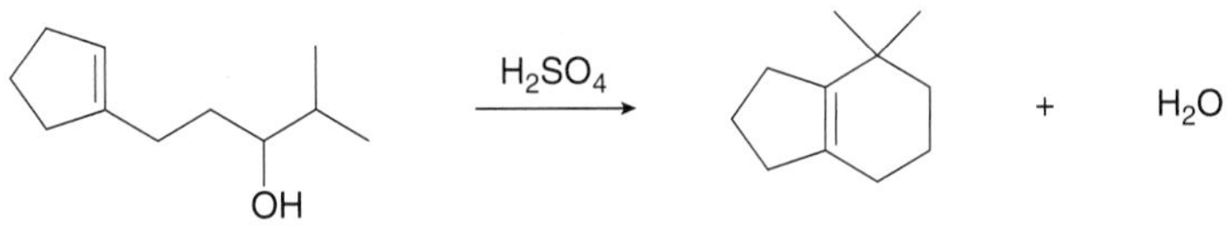

10.76 Like other electrophiles, carbocations add to alkenes to form new carbocations, which can then undergo substitution or elimination reactions depending on the reaction conditions. With this in mind, consider the following reactions of nerol, a natural product isolated from lemon grass and other plant sources. Treatment of nerol with TsOH forms α-terpineol as the major product, whereas treatment of nerol with chlorosulfonic acid, HSO_3Cl, forms a constitutional isomer, α-cyclogeraniol. Write stepwise mechanisms for both processes. Each mechanism involves the addition of an electrophile—a carbocation—to a double bond.

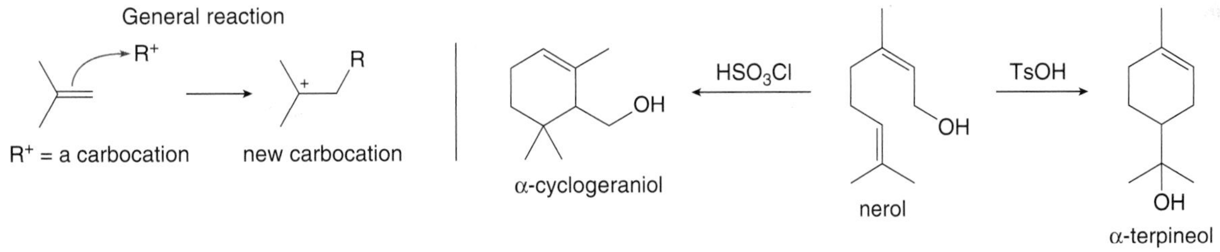

10.77 Draw a stepwise mechanism for the following reaction. This reaction combines two processes together: the opening of an epoxide ring with a nucleophile and the addition of an electrophile to a carbon–carbon double bond. (Hint: Begin the mechanism by protonating the epoxide ring.)

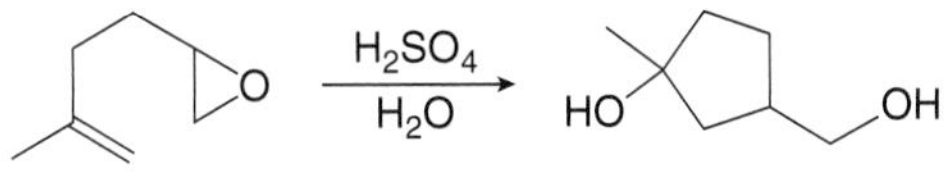

11 Alkynes

11.1 Introduction
11.2 Nomenclature
11.3 Physical properties
11.4 Interesting alkynes
11.5 Preparation of alkynes
11.6 Introduction to alkyne reactions
11.7 Addition of hydrogen halides
11.8 Addition of halogen
11.9 Addition of water
11.10 Hydroboration–oxidation
11.11 Reaction of acetylide anions
11.12 Synthesis

Ethynylestradiol is a synthetic compound whose structure closely resembles the carbon skeleton of female estrogen hormones. Because it is more potent than its naturally occurring analogues, it is a component of several widely used oral contraceptives. Ethynylestradiol and related compounds with similar biological activity contain a carbon–carbon triple bond. In Chapter 11 we learn about alkynes, hydrocarbons that contain triple bonds.

In Chapter 11 we continue our focus on organic molecules with electron-rich functional groups by examining ***alkynes,*** **compounds that contain a carbon–carbon triple bond.** Like alkenes, **alkynes are nucleophiles with easily broken π bonds,** and as such, they undergo **addition** reactions with electrophilic reagents.

Alkynes also undergo a reaction that has no analogy in alkene chemistry. Because a C–H bond of an alkyne is more acidic than a C–H bond in an alkene or an alkane, alkynes are readily deprotonated with strong base. The resulting nucleophiles react with electrophiles to form new carbon–carbon σ bonds, so that complex molecules can be prepared from simple starting materials. The study of alkynes thus affords an opportunity to learn more about organic synthesis.

11.1 Introduction

Alkynes contain a carbon–carbon triple bond. A **terminal alkyne** has the triple bond at the end of the carbon chain, so that a hydrogen atom is directly bonded to a carbon atom of the triple bond. An **internal alkyne** has a carbon atom bonded to each carbon atom of the triple bond.

Alkyne

—C≡C— (triple bond)

$CH_3CH_2CH_2$—C≡C—H
terminal alkyne

$CH_3CH_2CH_2$—C≡C—CH_2CH_3
internal alkyne

An alkyne has the general molecular formula $\mathbf{C_nH_{2n-2}}$, giving it four fewer hydrogens than the maximum number possible. Because every degree of unsaturation removes two hydrogens, a **triple bond introduces two degrees of unsaturation.**

Problem 11.1 Draw structures for the three alkynes having molecular formula C_5H_8 and classify each as an internal or terminal alkyne.

Each carbon of a triple bond is ***sp*** hybridized and **linear,** and all bond angles are **180°** (Section 1.10C).

H–C≡C–H
acetylene
=

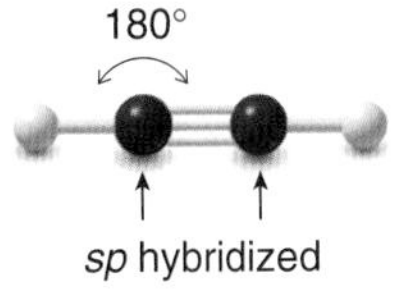
180°
sp hybridized

The triple bond of an alkyne consists of one σ bond and two π bonds.

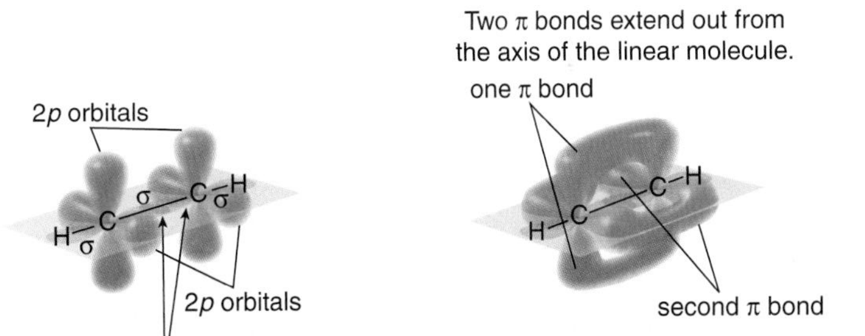
2p orbitals
H
C
σ
σ
C
H
σ
2p orbitals
Two π bonds extend out from the axis of the linear molecule.
one π bond
H
C
C–H
second π bond

Overlap of the two *sp* hybrid orbitals forms the C–C σ bond.

Overlap of two sets of two 2*p* orbitals forms two C–C π bonds.

- **The σ bond is formed by end-on overlap of the two *sp* hybrid orbitals.**
- **Each π bond is formed by side-by-side overlap of two 2*p* orbitals.**

Bond dissociation energies of the C−C bonds in ethylene (one σ and one π bond) and acetylene (one σ and two π bonds) can be used to estimate the strength of the second π bond of the triple bond. If we assume that the σ bond and first π bond in acetylene are similar in strength to the σ and π bonds in ethylene (368 and 267 kJ/mol, respectively), then the second π bond is worth 202 kJ/mol.

HC≡CH		CH_2=CH_2		
837 kJ/mol (σ + two π bonds)	−	635 kJ/mol (σ + π bond)	=	202 kJ/mol ↑ **second π bond**

- **Both π bonds of a C−C triple bond are weaker than a C−C σ bond, making them much more easily broken. As a result, alkynes undergo many addition reactions.**
- **Alkynes are more polarizable than alkenes because the electrons in their π bonds are more loosely held.**

Like trans cycloalkenes, cycloalkynes with small rings are unstable. The carbon chain must be long enough to connect the two ends of the triple bond without introducing too much strain. Cyclooctyne is the smallest isolated cycloalkyne, though it decomposes upon standing at room temperature after a short time.

Skeletal structures for alkynes may look somewhat unusual, but they follow the customary convention: a carbon atom is located at the intersection of any two lines and at the end of any line; thus,

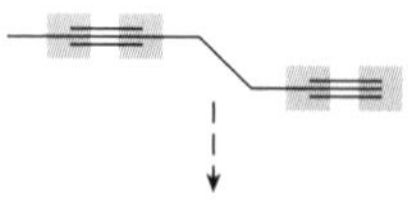

$CH_3C{\equiv}CCH_2CH_2C{\equiv}CH$

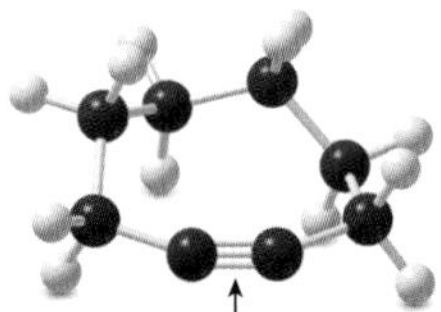

cyclooctyne

To accommodate the triple bond in a ring, bending occurs around the *sp* hybridized C's, destabilizing the molecule.

Problem 11.2 Santalbic acid, a fatty acid isolated from the seeds of the sandalwood tree, is an unusual fatty acid that contains a carbon–carbon triple bond. What orbitals are used to form each of the three indicated single bonds in santalbic acid? Rank these σ bonds in order of increasing bond strength.

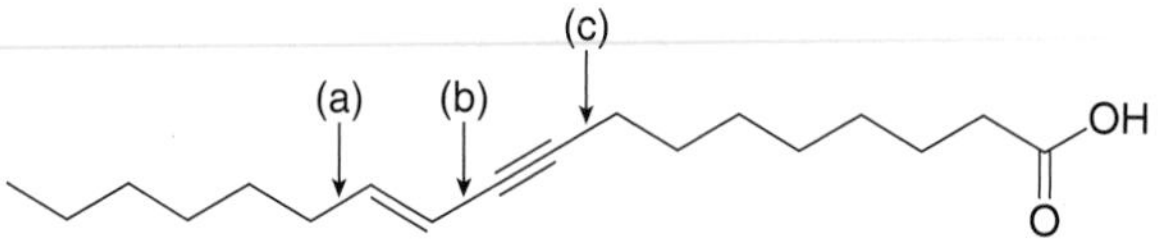

santalbic acid

11.2 Nomenclature

Alkynes are named in the same way that alkenes were named in Section 10.3.

- **In the IUPAC system, change the *-ane* ending of the parent alkane to the suffix *-yne.***
- **Choose the longest carbon chain that contains both atoms of the triple bond and number the chain to give the triple bond the lower number.**
- **Compounds with two triple bonds are named as *diynes,* those with three are named as *triynes,* and so forth.**
- **Compounds with both a double and a triple bond are named as *enynes.* The chain is numbered to give the first site of unsaturation (either C=C or C≡C) the lower number.**

Sample Problem 11.1 Give the IUPAC name for the following alkyne.

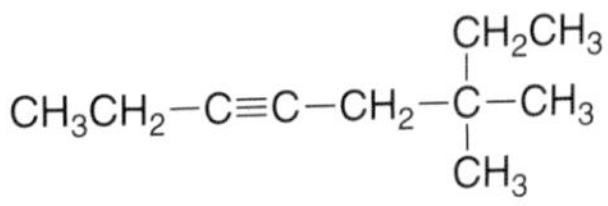

Solution

[1] Find the longest chain that contains both carbons of the triple bond.

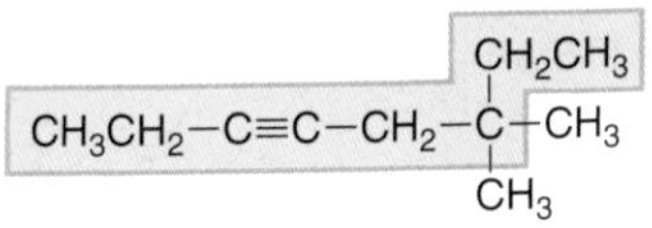

8 C's in the longest chain

octane ---→ octyne

[2] Number the long chain; then name and number the substituents.

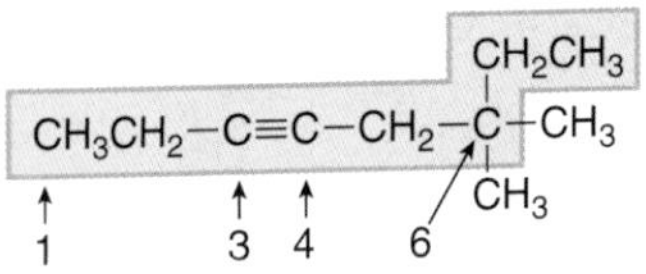

two methyl groups at C6

Answer: 6,6-dimethyl-3-octyne

The simplest alkyne, HC≡CH, named in the IUPAC system as **ethyne,** is more often called **acetylene,** its common name. The two-carbon alkyl group derived from acetylene is called an **ethynyl group** (HC≡C–). Examples of alkyne nomenclature are shown in Figure 11.1.

Problem 11.3 Give the IUPAC name for each compound.

a. $H-C\equiv C-CH_2C(CH_2CH_2CH_3)_3$

b. $CH_3C\equiv CC(CH_3)ClCH_2CH_3$

c. $CH_2=CHCH_2CH(CH_2CH_3)C\equiv CC(CH_3)_2CH_2CH_2CH_3$

d. 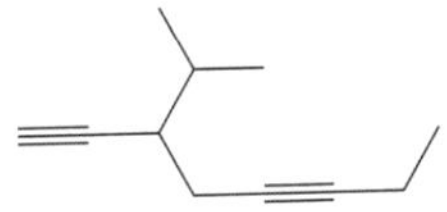

Problem 11.4 Give the structure corresponding to each of the following names.

a. *trans*-2-ethynylcyclopentanol b. 4-*tert*-butyl-5-decyne c. 3-methylcyclononyne

Figure 11.1 Examples of alkyne nomenclature

2,5-dimethyl-3-heptyne

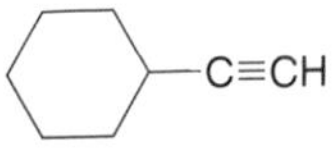

ethynylcyclohexane

$CH_3CH_2-C\equiv C-C\equiv CH$

1,3-hexadiyne

$HC\equiv C-CH_2CH=C(CH_3)_2$

5-methyl-4-hexen-1-yne

11.3 Physical Properties

The physical properties of alkynes resemble those of hydrocarbons having a similar shape and molecular weight.

- **Alkynes have low melting points and boiling points.**
- **Melting points and boiling points increase as the number of carbons increases.**
- **Alkynes are soluble in organic solvents and insoluble in water.**

Problem 11.5 Explain why an alkyne often has a slightly higher boiling point than an alkene of similar molecular weight. For example, the bp of 1-pentyne is 39 °C, and the bp of 1-pentene is 30 °C.

11.4 Interesting Alkynes

Acetylene, HC≡CH, is a colorless gas with an ethereal odor that burns in oxygen to form CO_2 and H_2O. Because the combustion of acetylene releases more energy per mole of product formed than other hydrocarbons, it burns with a very hot flame, making it an excellent fuel for welding torches.

Ethynylestradiol, the molecule that opened Chapter 11, and **norethindrone** are two components of oral contraceptives that contain a carbon–carbon triple bond (Figure 11.2). Both molecules are synthetic analogues of the naturally occurring female hormones estradiol and progesterone, but are more potent so they can be administered in lower doses. Most oral contraceptives contain two of these synthetic hormones. They act by artificially elevating hormone levels in a woman, thereby preventing pregnancy.

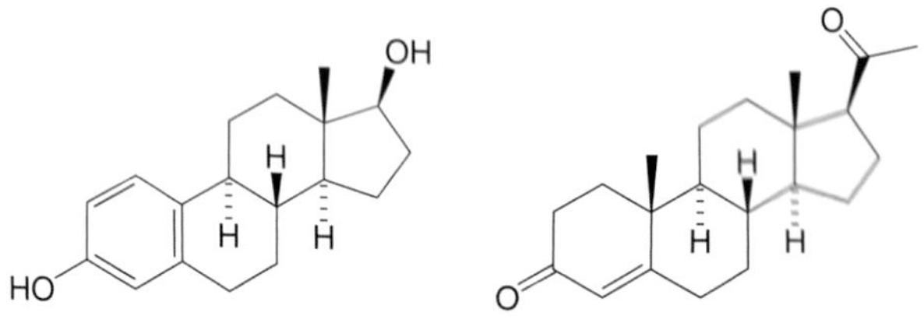

Figure 11.2 How oral contraceptives work

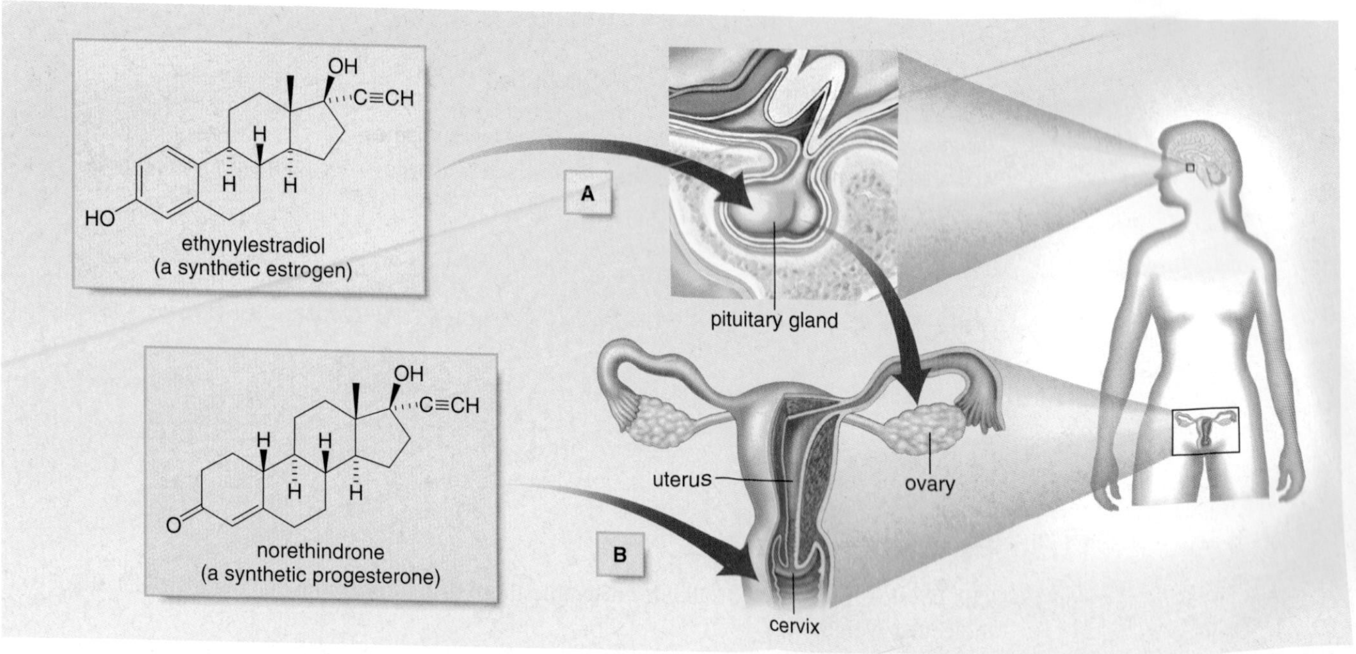

Monthly cycles of hormones from the pituitary gland cause ovulation, the release of an egg from an ovary. To prevent pregnancy, the two synthetic hormones in many oral contraceptives have different effects on the female reproductive system.

A: The elevated level of **ethynylestradiol,** a synthetic estrogen, "fools" the pituitary gland into thinking a woman is pregnant, so ovulation does not occur.

B: The elevated level of **norethindrone,** a synthetic progesterone, stimulates the formation of a thick layer of mucus in the cervix, making it difficult for sperm to reach the uterus.

Two other synthetic hormones with alkynyl appendages are **RU 486** and **levonorgestrel.** RU 486 blocks the effects of progesterone, and because of this, prevents implantation of a fertilized egg. RU 486 is used to induce abortions within the first few weeks of pregnancy. Levonorgestrel interferes with ovulation, and so it prevents pregnancy if taken within a few days of unprotected sex.

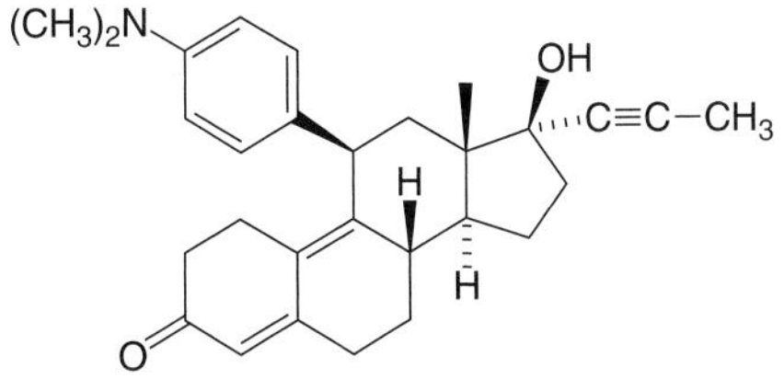

RU 486
(Trade name: Mifepristone)

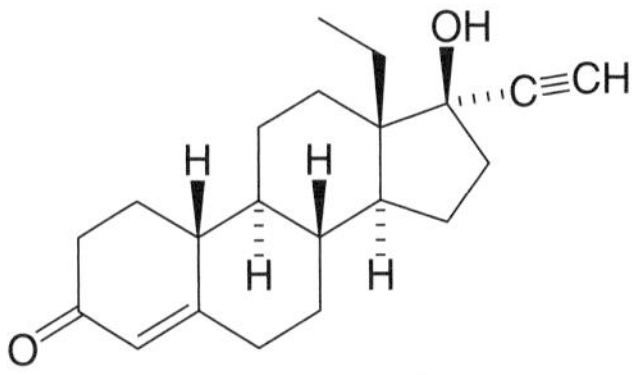

levonorgestrel
(Trade name: Plan B)

Histrionicotoxin is a diyne isolated in small quantities from the skin of *Dendrobates histrionicus,* a colorful South American frog (Figure 11.3). This toxin, secreted by the frog as a natural defense mechanism, was used as a poison on arrow tips by the Choco tribe of South America.

Figure 11.3
Histrionicotoxin

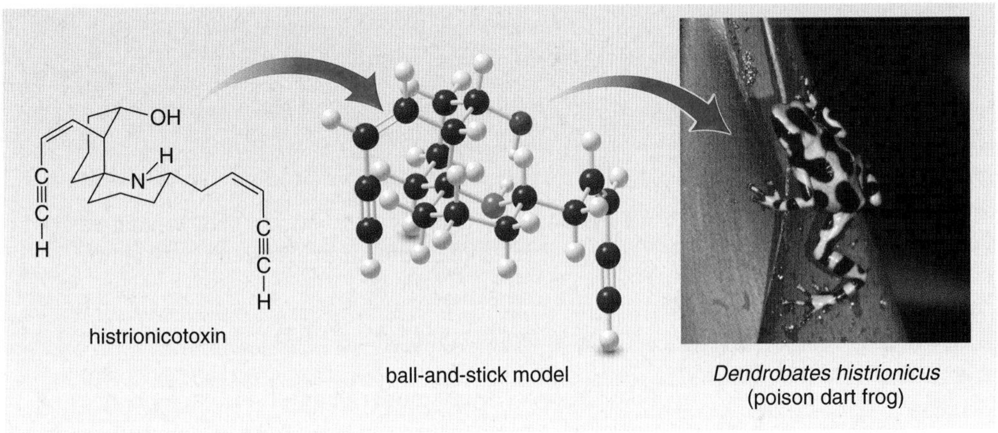
histrionicotoxin
ball-and-stick model
Dendrobates histrionicus
(poison dart frog)

- Histrionicotoxin is a defensive toxin that protects *Dendrobates histrionicus* from potential predators. These small "poison dart" frogs inhabit the moist humid floor of tropical rainforests, and are commonly found in western Ecuador and Colombia. Histrionicotoxin acts by interfering with nerve transmission in mammals, resulting in prolonged muscle contraction.

11.5 Preparation of Alkynes

Alkynes are prepared by elimination reactions, as discussed in Section 8.10. **A strong base removes two equivalents of HX from a vicinal or geminal dihalide to yield an alkyne** by two successive E2 eliminations.

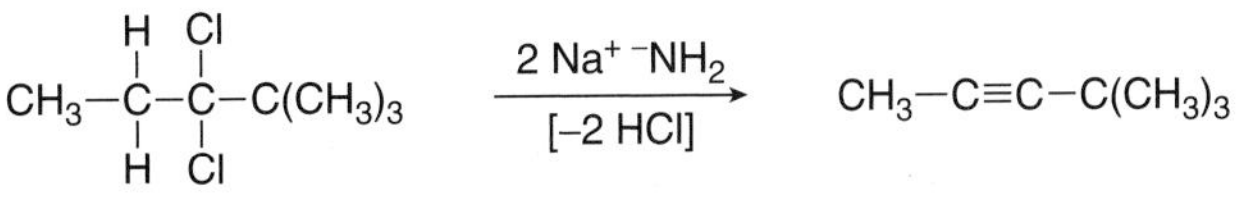
2 Na+ −NH2
[−2 HCl]

geminal dichloride

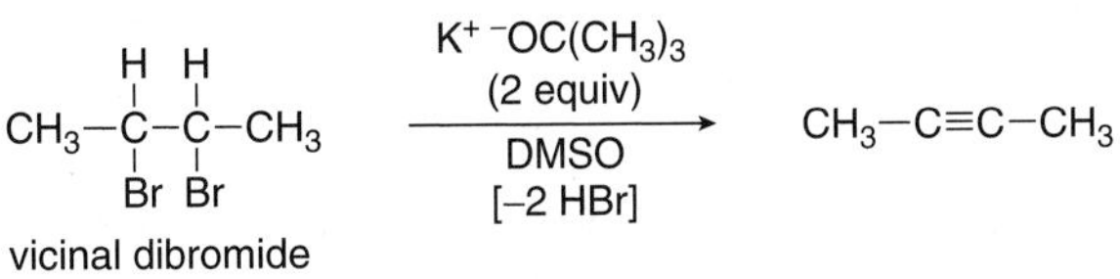
K+ −OC(CH3)3
(2 equiv)
DMSO
[−2 HBr]

vicinal dibromide

Because vicinal dihalides are synthesized by adding halogens to alkenes, an alkene can be converted to an alkyne by the two-step process illustrated in Sample Problem 11.2.

Sample Problem 11.2 Convert alkene **A** into alkyne **B** by a stepwise method.

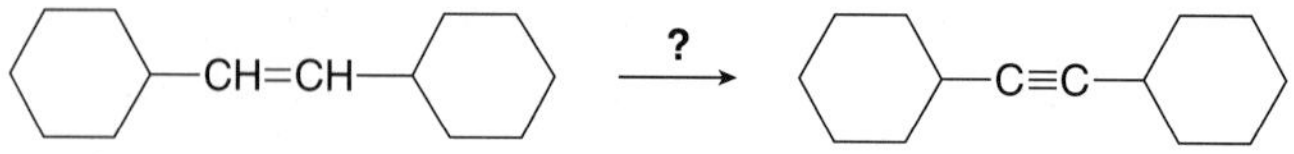

Solution

A two-step method is needed:

- **Addition of X_2** forms a vicinal dihalide.
- **Elimination** of two equivalents of HX forms two π bonds.

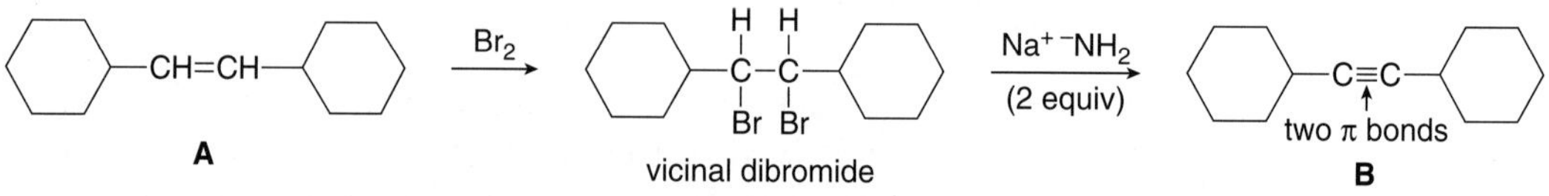

- **This two-step process introduces one degree of unsaturation:** an alkene with one π bond is converted to an alkyne with two π bonds.

Problem 11.6 Convert each compound to 1-hexyne, $HC{\equiv}CCH_2CH_2CH_2CH_3$.

a. $Br_2CH(CH_2)_4CH_3$ b. $CH_2{=}CCl(CH_2)_3CH_3$ c. $CH_2{=}CH(CH_2)_3CH_3$

11.6 Introduction to Alkyne Reactions

All reactions of alkynes occur because they contain **easily broken π bonds** or, in the case of terminal alkynes, an **acidic, *sp* hybridized C–H bond.**

11.6A Addition Reactions

Like alkenes, **alkynes undergo addition reactions because they contain weak π bonds.** Two sequential reactions take place: addition of one equivalent of reagent forms an alkene, which then adds a second equivalent of reagent to yield a product having **four new bonds.**

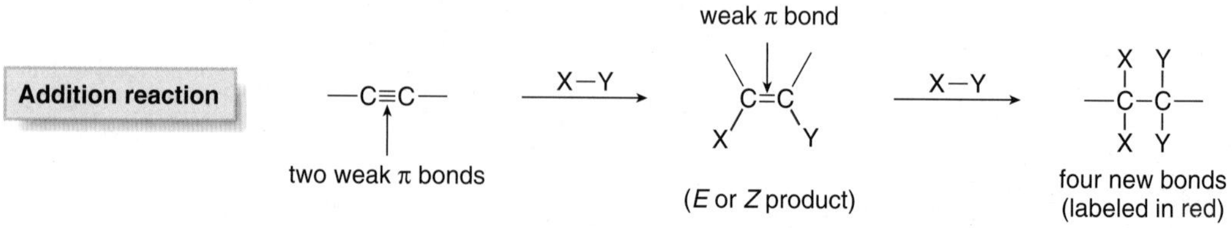

The oxidation and reduction of alkynes, reactions that also involve addition, are discussed in Chapter 12.

Alkynes are electron rich, as shown in the electrostatic potential map of acetylene in Figure 11.4. The two π bonds form a cylinder of electron density between the two *sp* hybridized carbon atoms, and this exposed electron density makes a triple bond nucleophilic. As a result, **alkynes react with electrophiles.** Four addition reactions are discussed in Chapter 11 and illustrated in Figure 11.5 with 1-butyne as the starting material.

Figure 11.4 Electrostatic potential map of acetylene

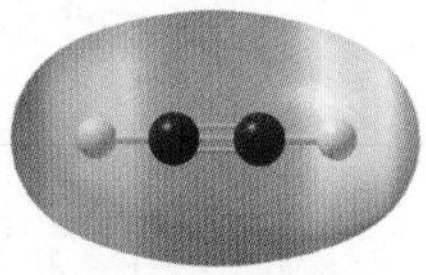

- The red electron-rich region is located between the two carbon atoms, forming a cylinder of electron density.

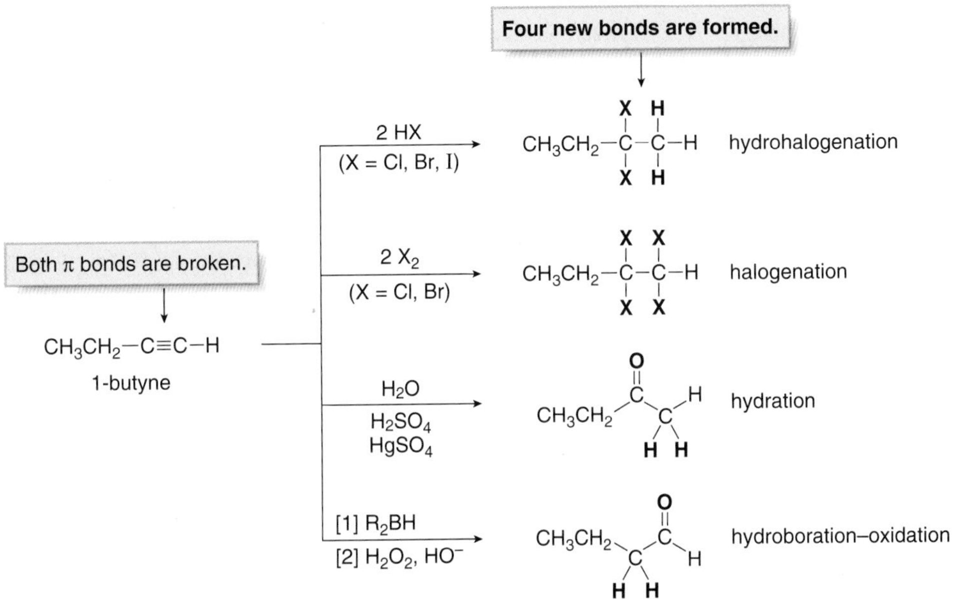

Figure 11.5 Four addition reactions of 1-butyne

11.6B Terminal Alkynes—Reaction as an Acid

Because ***sp*** **hybridized C – H bonds are more acidic than** ***sp***^{2} **and** ***sp***^{3} **hybridized C – H bonds,** terminal alkynes are readily deprotonated with strong base in a Brønsted–Lowry acid–base reaction. The resulting anion is called an **acetylide anion.**

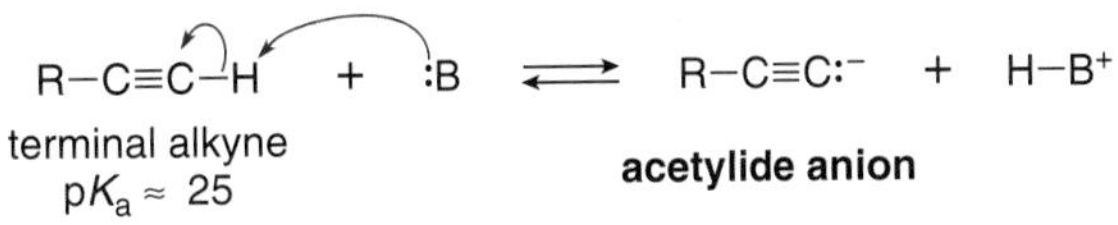

Recall from Section 2.5D that the acidity of a C – H bond increases as the percent *s*-character of C increases. Thus, the following order of relative acidity results: $C_{sp^3}-H < C_{sp^2}-H < C_{sp}-H$.

What bases can be used for this reaction? Because an acid–base equilibrium favors the weaker acid and base, only **bases having conjugate acids with p*K*$_a$ values *higher* than the terminal alkyne—that is, p*K*$_a$ values > 25—are strong enough** to form a significant concentration of acetylide anion. As shown in Table 11.1, $^-NH_2$ and H^- are strong enough to deprotonate a terminal alkyne, but ^-OH and ^-OR are not.

Why is this reaction useful? The acetylide anions formed by deprotonating terminal alkynes are **strong nucleophiles** that can react with a variety of electrophiles, as shown in Section 11.11.

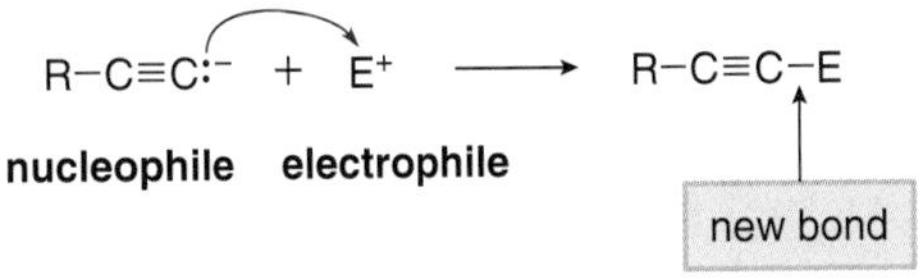

Table 11.1 A Comparison of Bases for Alkyne Deprotonation

	Base	pK_a of the conjugate acid
These bases are **strong** enough to deprotonate an alkyne.	$^-NH_2$	38
	H^-	35
These bases are ***not*** strong enough to deprotonate an alkyne.	^-OH	15.7
	^-OR	15.5–18

Problem 11.7 Which bases can deprotonate acetylene? The pK_a values of the conjugate acids are given in parentheses.

a. CH_3NH^- (pK_a = 40) b. CO_3^{2-} (pK_a = 10.2) c. $CH_2{=}CH^-$ (pK_a = 44) d. $(CH_3)_3CO^-$ (pK_a = 18)

11.7 Addition of Hydrogen Halides

Alkynes undergo **hydrohalogenation, the addition of hydrogen halides, HX** (X = Cl, Br, I). Two equivalents of HX are usually used: addition of one mole forms a **vinyl halide,** which then reacts with a second mole of HX to form a **geminal dihalide.**

Hydrohalogenation

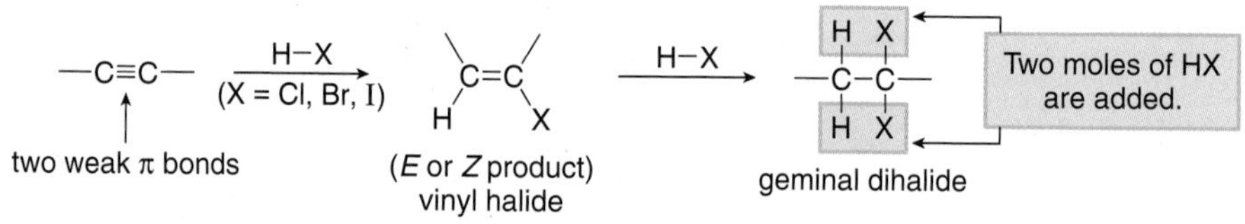

—C≡C—
H–X
(X = Cl, Br, I)
H–X
two weak π bonds
(E or Z product)
vinyl halide
geminal dihalide
Two moles of HX are added.

Addition of HX to an alkyne is another example of **electrophilic addition,** because the electrophilic (H) end of the reagent is attracted to the electron-rich triple bond.

- **With two equivalents of HX, both H atoms bond to the *same* carbon.**
- **With a terminal alkyne, both H atoms bond to the *terminal* carbon; that is, the hydrohalogenation of alkynes follows Markovnikov's rule.**

Examples

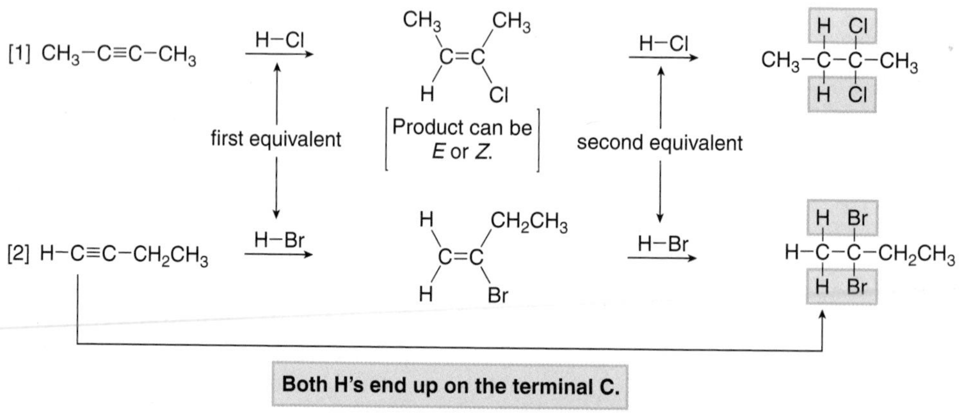

[1] CH3–C≡C–CH3
H–Cl
first equivalent
Product can be E or Z.
H–Cl
second equivalent
[2] H–C≡C–CH2CH3
H–Br
H–Br
Both H's end up on the terminal C.

- **With only one equivalent of HX, the reaction stops with formation of the vinyl halide.**

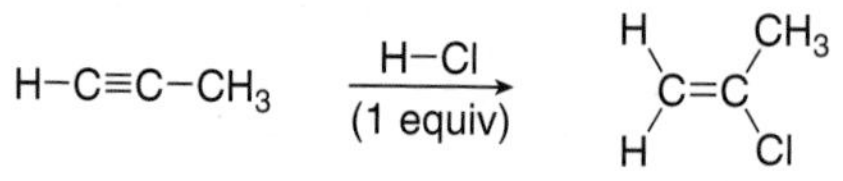

H–C≡C–CH3
H–Cl
(1 equiv)

a vinyl chloride
(2-chloropropene)

One currently accepted mechanism for the addition of two equivalents of HX to an alkyne involves **two steps for each addition of HX:** addition of H^+ (from HX) to form a carbocation, followed by nucleophilic attack of X^-. Mechanism 11.1 illustrates the addition of HBr to 1-butyne to yield 2,2-dibromobutane. Each two-step mechanism is similar to the two-step addition of HBr to *cis*-2-butene discussed in Section 10.9.

Because of the instability of a vinyl carbocation, other mechanisms for HX addition that avoid formation of a discrete carbocation have been proposed. It is likely that more than one mechanism occurs, depending in part on the identity of the alkyne substrate.

The formation of both carbocations (in Steps [1] and [3]) deserves additional scrutiny. **The vinyl carbocation formed in Step [1] is *sp* hybridized and therefore less stable than a 2° sp^2 hybridized carbocation** (Section 7.18). This makes electrophilic addition of HX to an alkyne ***slower*** than electrophilic addition of HX to an alkene, even though alkynes are more polarizable and have more loosely held π electrons than alkenes.

Mechanism 11.1 Electrophilic Addition of HX to an Alkyne

Part [1] Addition of HBr to form a vinyl halide

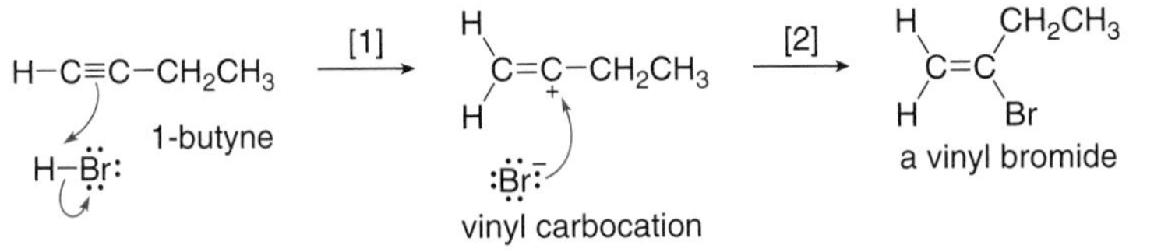

- The π bond attacks the H atom of HBr to form a new C – H bond, generating a **vinyl carbocation.** Addition follows Markovnikov's rule: H^+ adds to the less substituted carbon atom to form the **more substituted, more stable carbocation.** Nucleophilic attack of Br^- then forms a vinyl bromide; one mole of HBr has now been added.

Part [2] Addition of HBr to form a geminal dihalide

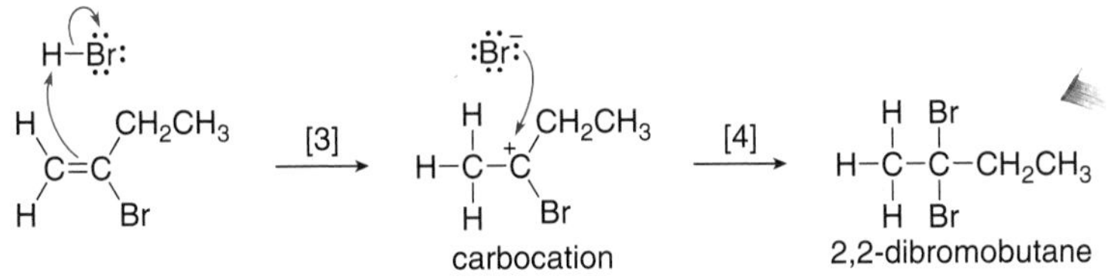

- **The second addition of HBr occurs in the same two-step manner.** Addition of H^+ to the π bond of the vinyl bromide generates a carbocation. Nucleophilic attack of Br^- then forms a geminal dibromide (2,2-dibromobutane), and two moles of HBr have now been added.

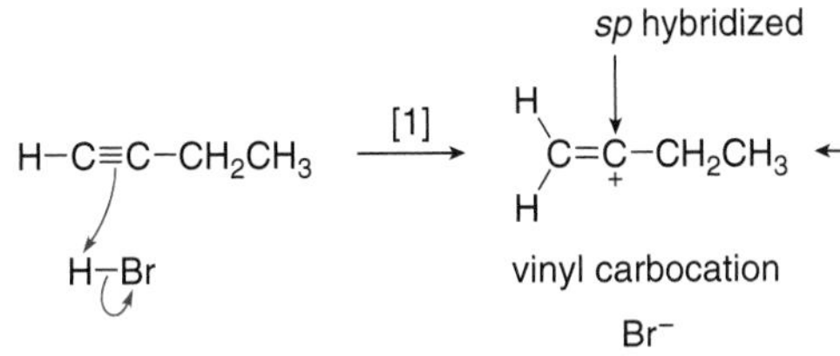

This unstable carbocation slows the first step, making **an alkyne less reactive than an alkene** towards HX.

In Step [3] two carbocations are possible but only one is formed. Markovnikov addition in Step [3] places the H on the terminal carbon (C1) to form the more substituted carbocation **A,** rather than the less substituted carbocation **B.** Because the more stable carbocation is formed faster—another example of the Hammond postulate—carbocation **A** must be more stable than carbocation **B.**

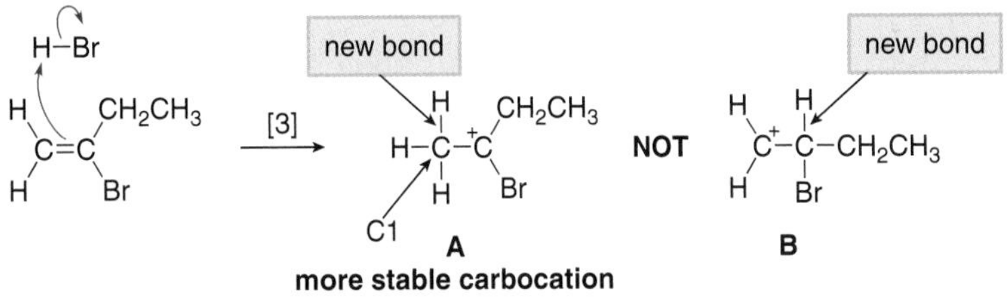

Why is carbocation **A,** having a positive charge on a carbon that also has a Br atom, more stable? Shouldn't the electronegative Br atom withdraw electron density from the positive charge, and thus destabilize it? It turns out that **A is stabilized by resonance** but **B** is not. Two resonance structures can be drawn for carbocation **A,** but only one Lewis structure can be drawn for carbocation **B.**

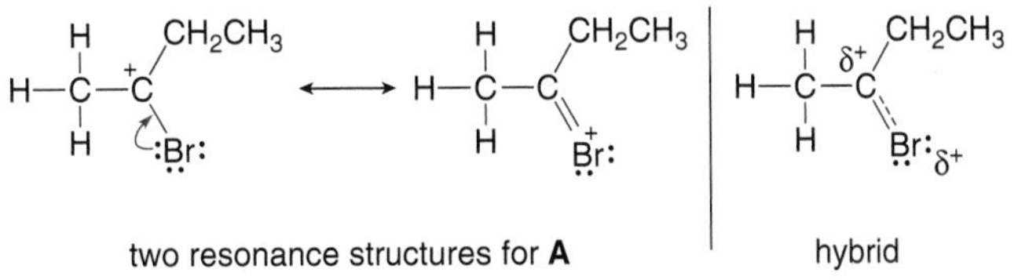

The positive charge is delocalized.

- **Resonance stabilizes a molecule by delocalizing charge and electron density.**
- **Thus, halogens stabilize an adjacent positive charge by resonance.**

Markovnikov's rule applies to the addition of HX to vinyl halides because **addition of H^+ forms a resonance-stabilized carbocation.** As a result, addition of each equivalent of HX to a triple bond forms the more stable carbocation, so that both H atoms bond to the less substituted C.

Problem 11.8 Draw the organic products formed when each alkyne is treated with two equivalents of HBr.

a. $CH_3CH_2CH_2CH_2{-}C{\equiv}C{-}H$ b. $CH_3{-}C{\equiv}C{-}CH_2CH_3$ c. 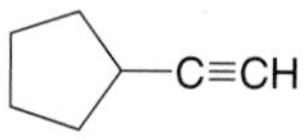
C≡CH

Problem 11.9 Draw an additional resonance structure for each cation.

a. 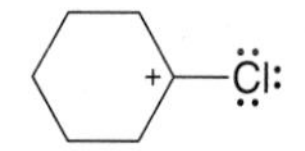
Cl:

b. $CH_3{-}\ddot{O}{-}\overset{+}{C}H_2$

c. 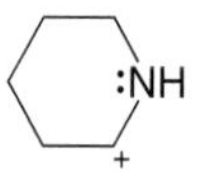
:NH

11.8 Addition of Halogen

Halogens, X_2 (X = Cl or Br), add to alkynes in much the same way they add to alkenes (Section 10.13). Addition of one mole of X_2 forms a **trans dihalide,** which can then react with a second mole of X_2 to yield a **tetrahalide.**

Halogenation

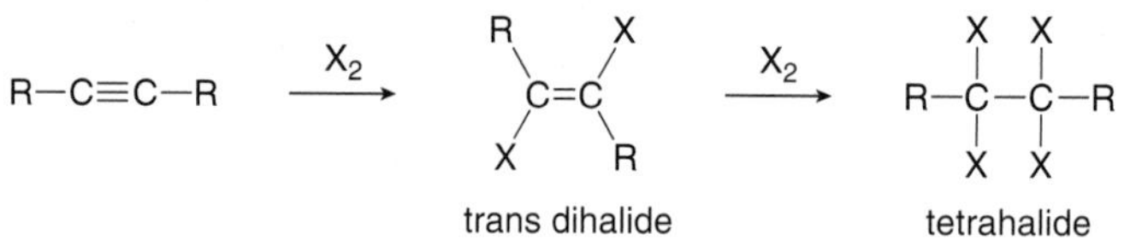
R—C≡C—R
X2
R
X
C=C
X
R
trans dihalide
X2
X X
R—C—C—R
X X
tetrahalide

Example

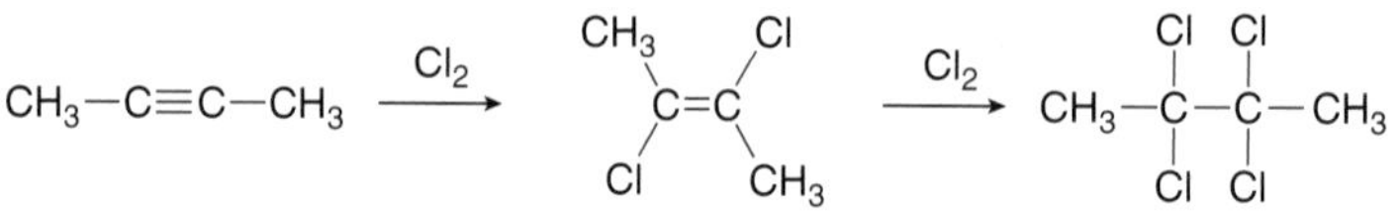
CH3—C≡C—CH3
Cl2
CH3
Cl
C=C
Cl
CH3
Cl2
Cl Cl
CH3—C—C—CH3
Cl Cl

Each addition of X_2 involves a two-step process with a **bridged halonium ion** intermediate, reminiscent of the addition of X_2 to alkenes (Section 10.13). A trans dihalide is formed after addition of one equivalent of X_2 because the intermediate **halonium ion ring is opened upon backside attack of the nucleophile.** Mechanism 11.2 illustrates the addition of two equivalents of Cl_2 to $CH_3C{\equiv}CCH_3$ to form $CH_3CCl_2CCl_2CH_3$.

Mechanism 11.2 Addition of X_2 to an Alkyne—Halogenation

Part [1] Addition of X_2 to form a trans dihalide

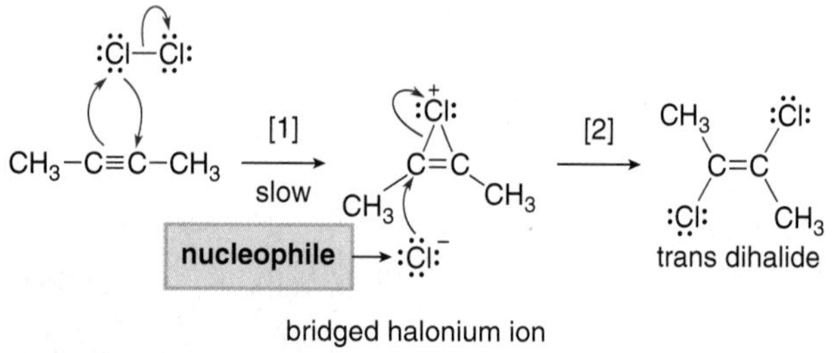
:Cl—Cl:
CH3—C≡C—CH3
[1]
slow
:Cl:
C=C
CH3
CH3
nucleophile
:Cl:⁻
bridged halonium ion
[2]
CH3
:Cl:
C=C
:Cl:
CH3
trans dihalide

- Two bonds are broken and two are formed in Step [1] to generate a **bridged halonium ion.** This strained three-membered ring is highly unstable, making it amenable to opening of the ring in the second step.
- Nucleophilic attack by Cl^- from the back side forms the trans dihalide in Step [2].

Part [2] Addition of X_2 to form a tetrahalide

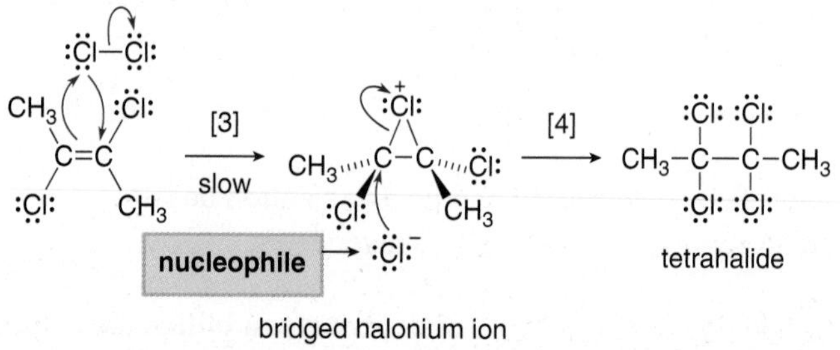
:Cl—Cl:
CH3
:Cl:
C=C
:Cl:
CH3
[3]
slow
:Cl:
CH3
C—C
:Cl:
:Cl:
CH3
nucleophile
:Cl:⁻
bridged halonium ion
[4]
:Cl: :Cl:
CH3—C—C—CH3
:Cl: :Cl:
tetrahalide

- **Electrophilic addition** of Cl^+ in Step [3] forms the bridged halonium ion ring, which is opened with Cl^- to form the tetrahalide in Step [4].

Problem 11.10 Draw the products formed when $CH_3CH_2C{\equiv}CCH_2CH_3$ is treated with each reagent: (a) Br_2 (2 equiv); (b) Cl_2 (1 equiv).

Problem 11.11 Explain the following result. Although alkenes are generally more reactive than alkynes towards electrophiles, the reaction of Cl_2 with 2-butyne can be stopped after one equivalent of Cl_2 has been added.

11.9 Addition of Water

Although the addition of H_2O to an alkyne resembles the acid-catalyzed addition of H_2O to an alkene in some ways, an important difference exists. In the presence of strong acid or Hg^{2+} catalyst, the **elements of H_2O add to the triple bond,** but the initial addition product, an **enol,** is unstable and rearranges to a product containing a **carbonyl group**—that is, a **C=O.** A carbonyl compound having two alkyl groups bonded to the C=O carbon is called a **ketone.**

Hydration

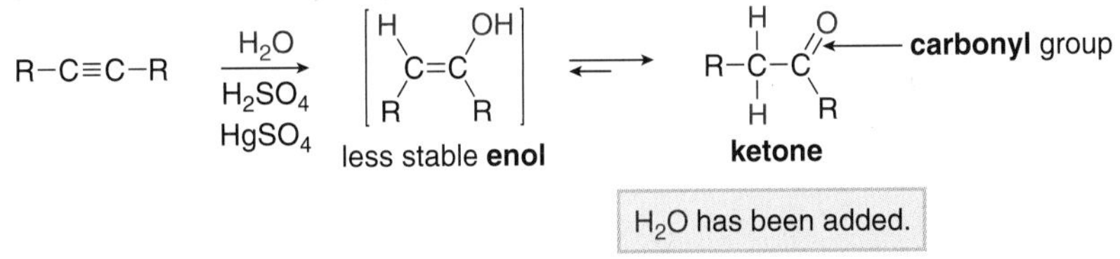

Internal alkynes undergo hydration with concentrated acid, whereas terminal alkynes require the presence of an additional Hg^{2+} catalyst—usually $HgSO_4$—to yield methyl ketones by **Markovnikov addition of H_2O.**

Because an enol contains both a C=C and a hydroxy group, the name **enol** comes from alk**ene** + alcoh**ol.**

$HgSO_4$ is often used in the hydration of internal alkynes as well, because hydration can be carried out under milder reaction conditions.

Examples

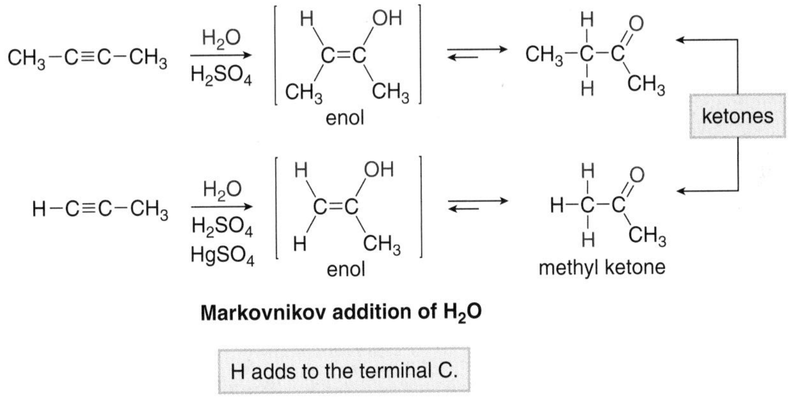

Let's first examine the conversion of a general enol **A** to the carbonyl compound **B. A** and **B** are called **tautomers: A is the *enol form* and B is the *keto form* of the tautomer.**

- ***Tautomers*** **are constitutional isomers that differ in the location of a double bond and a hydrogen atom. Two tautomers are in equilibrium with each other.**

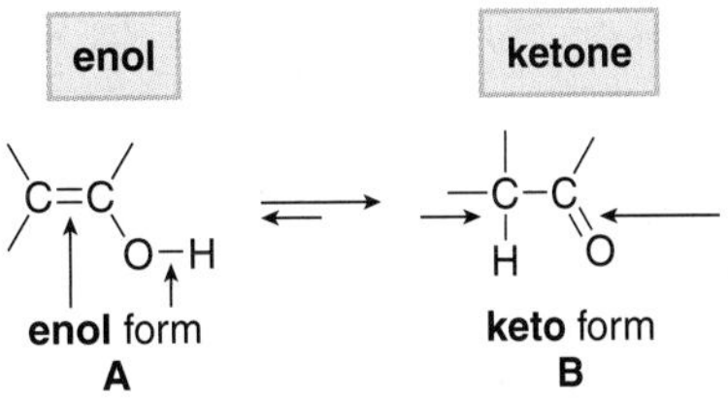

Tautomers differ in the position of a double bond and a hydrogen atom. In Chapter 23 an in-depth discussion of keto–enol tautomers is presented.

- **An enol tautomer has an O–H group bonded to a C=C.**
- **A keto tautomer has a C=O and an additional C–H bond.**

Equilibrium favors the keto form largely because a C=O is much stronger than a C=C. Tautomerization, the process of converting one tautomer into another, is catalyzed by both acid and base. Under the strongly acidic conditions of hydration, tautomerization of the enol to the keto form occurs rapidly by a two-step process: **protonation,** followed by **deprotonation** as shown in Mechanism 11.3.

Mechanism 11.3 Tautomerization in Acid

Step [1] Protonation of the enol double bond

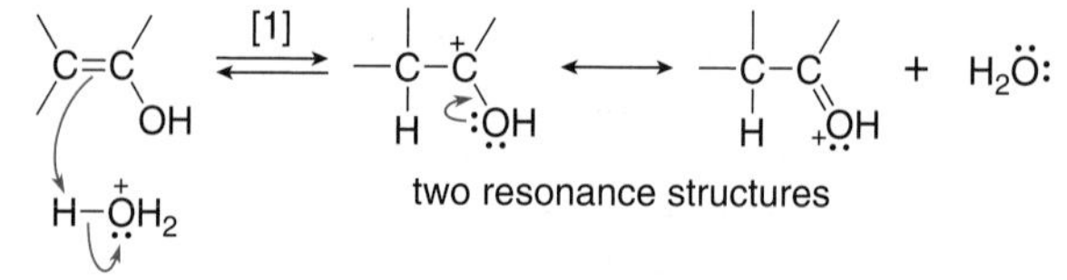
[1]
two resonance structures

- **Protonation** of the enol C=C with acid (H_3O^+) adds H^+ to form a **resonance-stabilized carbocation.**

Step [2] Deprotonation of the OH group

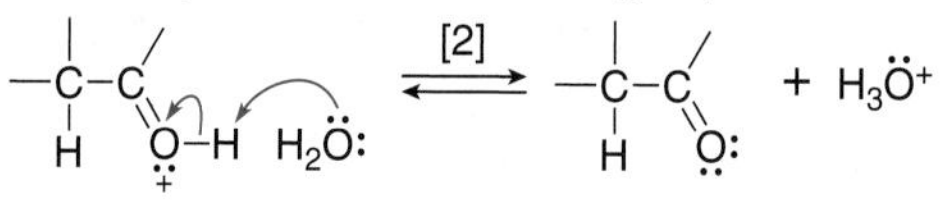
[2]

- **Loss of a proton** forms the carbonyl group. This step can be drawn with either resonance structure as starting material. Because the acid used in Step [1] is re-formed in Step [2], tautomerization is **acid catalyzed.**

Hydration of an internal alkyne with strong acid forms an enol by a mechanism similar to that of the acid-catalyzed hydration of an alkene (Section 10.12). Mechanism 11.4 illustrates the hydration of 2-butyne with H_2O and H_2SO_4. Once formed, the enol then tautomerizes to the more stable keto form by protonation followed by deprotonation.

Mechanism 11.4 Hydration of an Alkyne

Step [1] Addition of the electrophile (H^+) to a π bond

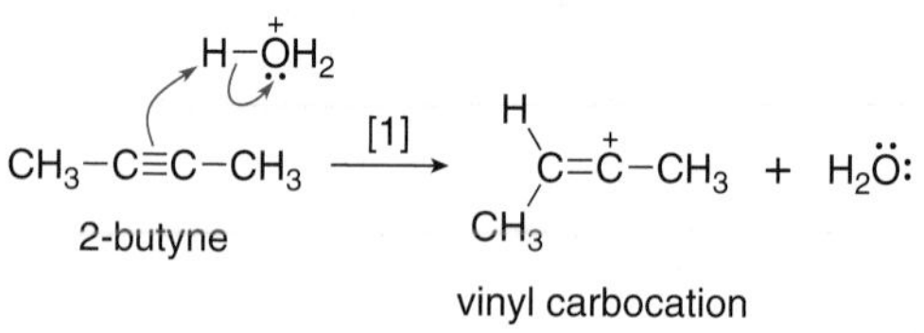
[1]
2-butyne
vinyl carbocation

- Addition of H^+ (from H_3O^+) forms an *sp* hybridized **vinyl carbocation.**

Steps [2] and [3] Nucleophilic attack of H_2O and loss of a proton

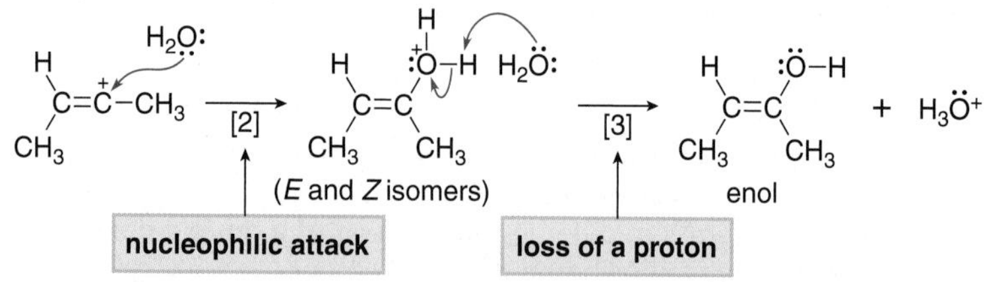
[2]
[3]
(*E* and *Z* isomers)
enol
nucleophilic attack
loss of a proton

- **Nucleophilic attack of H_2O** on the carbocation followed by loss of a proton forms the enol.

Steps [4] and [5] Tautomerization

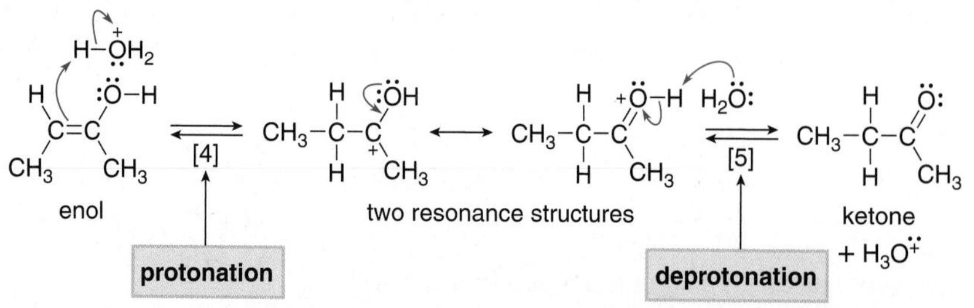
[4]
[5]
enol
two resonance structures
ketone
protonation
deprotonation

- **Tautomerization of the enol to the keto form** occurs by protonation of the double bond to form a carbocation. Loss of a proton from this **resonance-stabilized carbocation** generates the more stable keto form.

Sample Problem 11.3 Draw the enol intermediate and the ketone product formed in the following reaction.

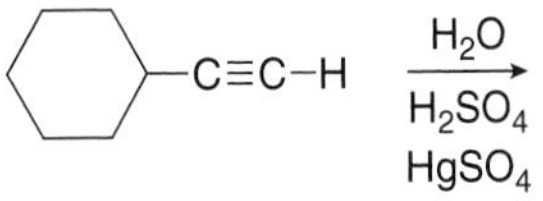
C≡C–H
H_2O
H_2SO_4
$HgSO_4$

Solution

First, form the enol by adding H_2O to the triple bond with the **H bonded to the less substituted terminal carbon.**

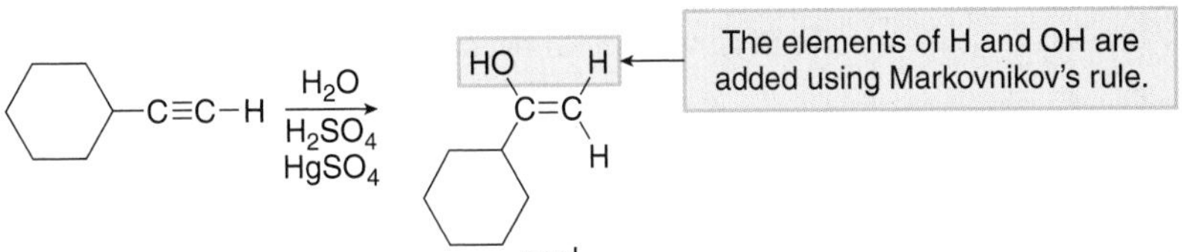
H_2O
H_2SO_4
$HgSO_4$
The elements of H and OH are added using Markovnikov's rule.

enol

To convert the enol to the keto tautomer, add a proton to the C=C and remove a proton from the OH group. In tautomerization, the C–OH bond is converted to a C=O, and a new C–H bond is formed on the other enol carbon.

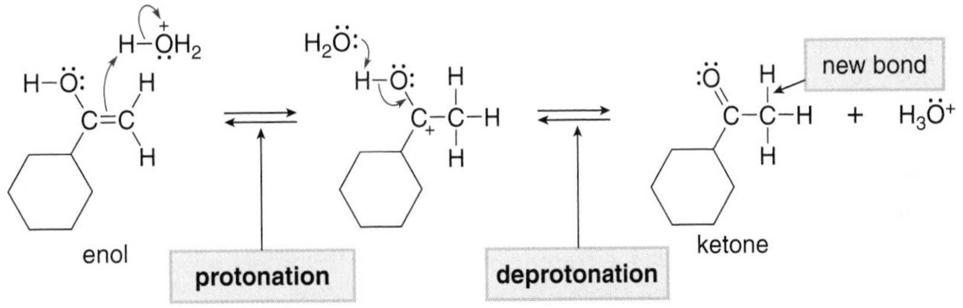
enol
protonation
deprotonation
ketone
new bond
$H_3\ddot{O}^+$

- **The overall result is the addition of H_2O to a triple bond to form a ketone.**

Problem 11.12 Draw the keto tautomer of each enol.

a. 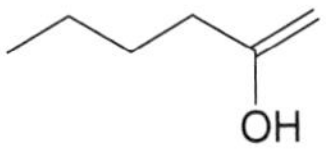

b. 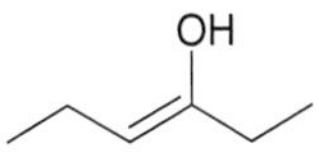

c. 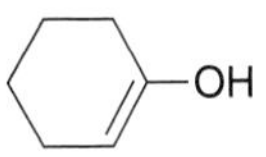

Problem 11.13 What two enols are formed when 2-pentyne is treated with H_2O, H_2SO_4, and $HgSO_4$? Draw the ketones formed from these enols after tautomerization.

Problem 11.14 (a) Draw two different enol tautomers of 2-methylcyclohexanone. (b) Draw two constitutional isomers that are not tautomers, but contain a C=C and an OH group.

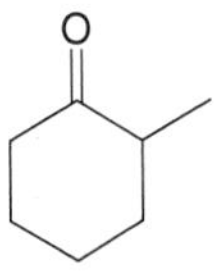

2-methylcyclohexanone

11.10 Hydroboration–Oxidation

Hydroboration–oxidation is a two-step reaction sequence that converts an alkyne to a carbonyl compound.

Hydroboration–oxidation

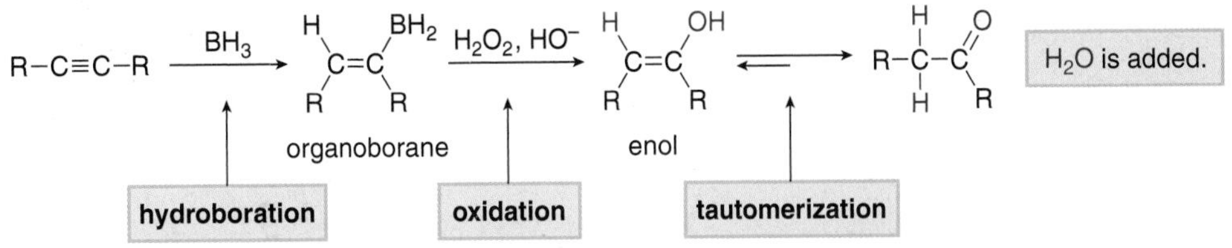
R–C≡C–R
BH_3
organoborane
H_2O_2, HO^-
enol
hydroboration
oxidation
tautomerization
H_2O is added.

- Addition of borane forms an organoborane.
- Oxidation with basic H_2O_2 forms an enol.
- Tautomerization of the enol forms a carbonyl compound.
- The overall result is addition of H_2O to a triple bond.

Hydroboration–oxidation of an *internal* alkyne forms a **ketone. Hydroboration of a *terminal* alkyne adds boron to the less substituted, terminal carbon.** After oxidation to the enol, tautomerization yields an **aldehyde,** a carbonyl compound having a hydrogen atom bonded to the carbonyl carbon. Hydroboration of a terminal alkyne is generally carried out with a dialkylborane (R_2BH), which has been prepared from BH_3 (Section 10.16).

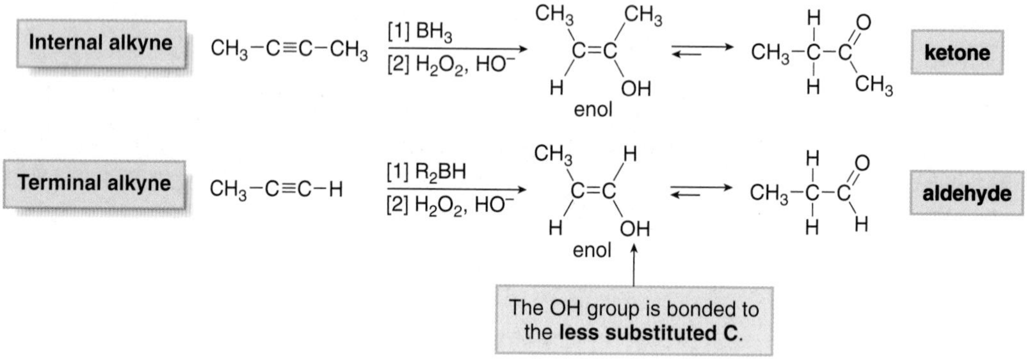

Hydration (H_2O, H_2SO_4, and $HgSO_4$) and **hydroboration–oxidation** (BH_3 or R_2BH followed by H_2O_2, HO^-) both **add the elements of H_2O across a triple bond.** Sample Problem 11.4 shows that different constitutional isomers are formed from terminal alkynes in these two reactions despite their similarities.

Sample Problem 11.4 Draw the product formed when $CH_3CH_2C{\equiv}CH$ is treated with each of the following sets of reagents: (a) H_2O, H_2SO_4, $HgSO_4$; and (b) R_2BH, followed by H_2O_2, HO^-.

Solution

(a) With $H_2O + H_2SO_4 + HgSO_4$, electrophilic addition of H and OH places the **H atom on the less substituted carbon** of the alkyne to form a **ketone** after tautomerization. (b) In contrast, addition of R_2BH places the **R_2B group on the less substituted terminal carbon** of the alkyne. Oxidation and tautomerization yield an **aldehyde.**

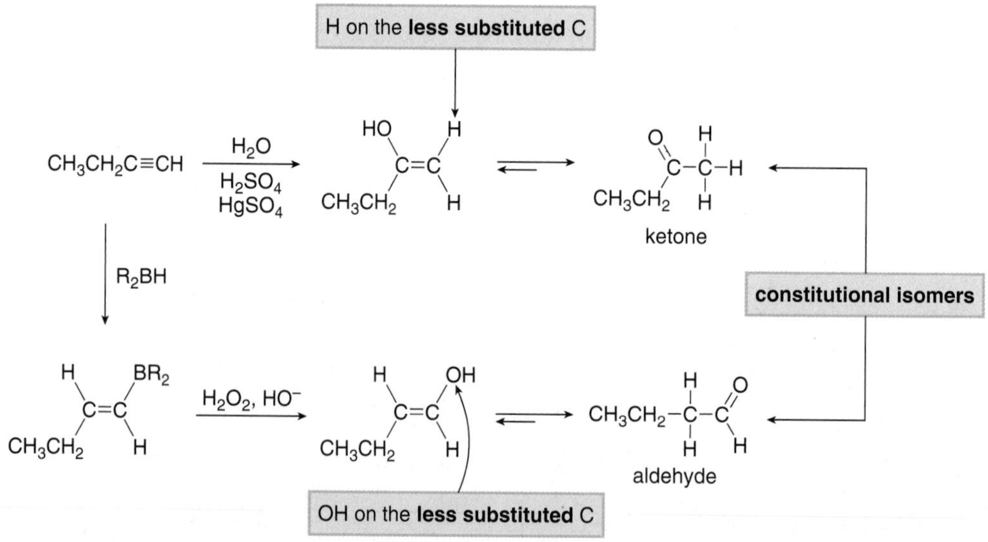

- **Addition of H_2O using H_2O, H_2SO_4, and $HgSO_4$ forms methyl ketones from terminal alkynes.**
- **Addition of H_2O using an organoborane, then H_2O_2, HO^- forms aldehydes from terminal alkynes.**

Problem 11.15 Draw the products formed when the following alkynes are treated with each set of reagents: [1] H_2O, H_2SO_4, $HgSO_4$; or [2] R_2BH followed by H_2O_2, ^-OH.

a. $(CH_3)_2CHCH_2-C{\equiv}CH$ b. 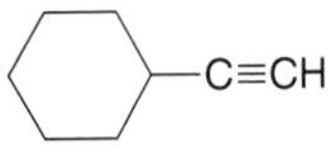

11.11 Reaction of Acetylide Anions

Terminal alkynes are readily converted to acetylide anions with strong bases such as $NaNH_2$ and NaH. These anions are strong nucleophiles, capable of reacting with electrophiles such as alkyl halides and epoxides.

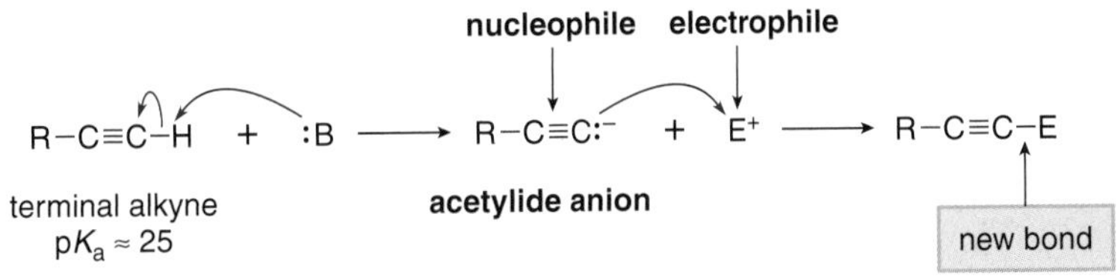

11.11A Reaction of Acetylide Anions with Alkyl Halides

Acetylide anions react with unhindered alkyl halides to yield products of nucleophilic substitution.

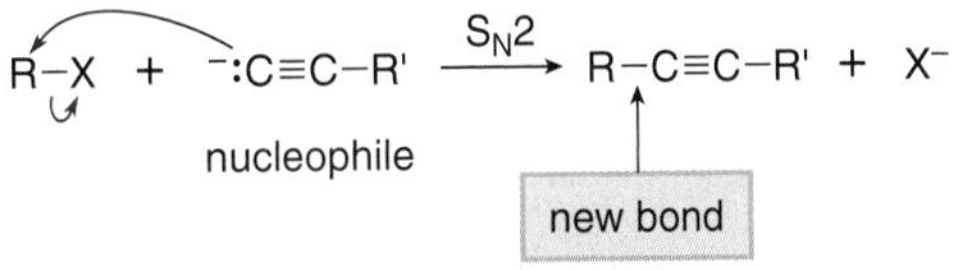

Because acetylide anions are strong nucleophiles, the mechanism of nucleophilic substitution is **S_N2,** and thus the **reaction is fastest with CH_3X and 1° alkyl halides.** Terminal alkynes (Reaction [1]) or internal alkynes (Reaction [2]) can be prepared depending on the identity of the acetylide anion.

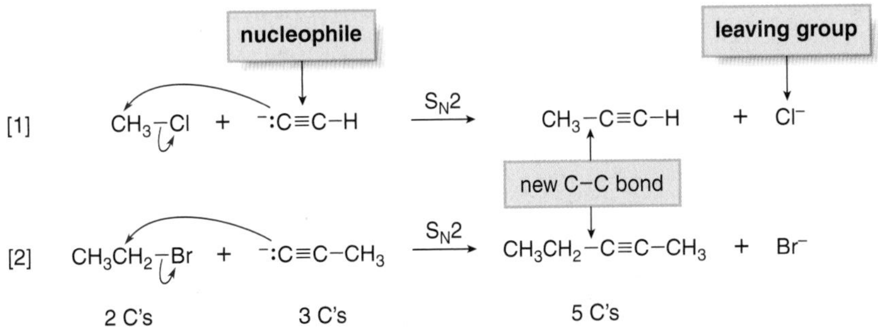

- **Nucleophilic substitution with acetylide anions forms new carbon–carbon bonds.**

Because organic compounds consist of a carbon framework, reactions that form carbon–carbon bonds are especially useful. In Reaction [2], for example, nucleophilic attack of a three-carbon acetylide anion on a two-carbon alkyl halide yields a five-carbon alkyne as product.

Although nucleophilic substitution with acetylide anions is a very valuable carbon–carbon bond-forming reaction, it has the same limitations as any S_N2 reaction. **Steric hindrance around the leaving group causes 2° and 3° alkyl halides to undergo elimination by an E2 mechanism,** as shown with 2-bromo-2-methylpropane. Thus, nucleophilic substitution with acetylide anions forms new carbon–carbon bonds in high yield only with unhindered CH_3X and 1° alkyl halides.

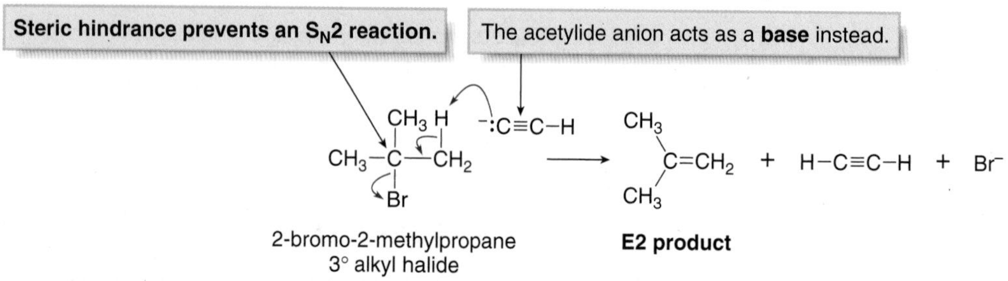

Sample Problem 11.5 Draw the organic products formed in each reaction.

a. $CH_3CH_2CH_2CH_2$–Cl + $^-$:C≡C–H ⟶

b. 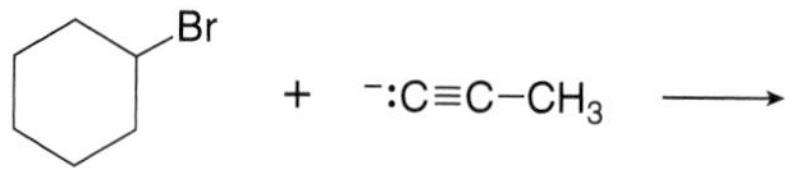

Solution

a. Because the alkyl halide is **1°** and the acetylide anion is a strong nucleophile, substitution occurs by an **S_N2** mechanism, resulting in a new C–C bond.

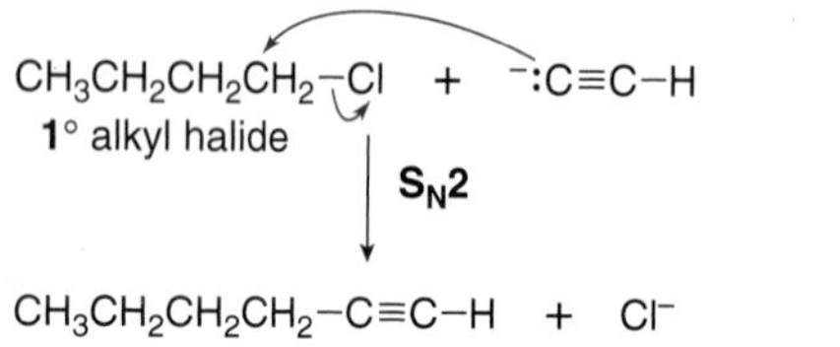

b. Because the alkyl halide is **2°,** the major product is formed from elimination by an **E2** mechanism.

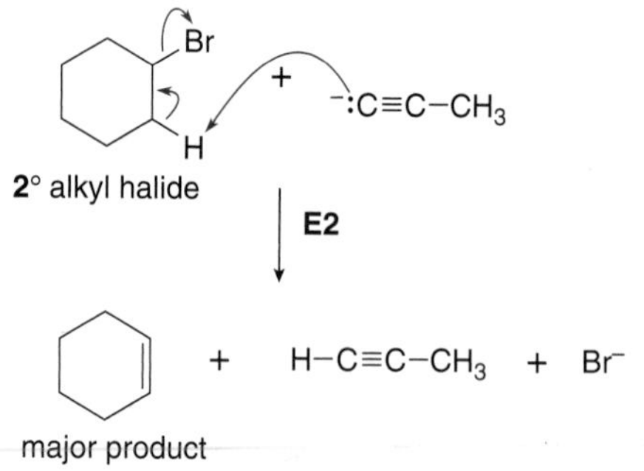

Problem 11.16 Draw the organic products formed in each reaction.

a. H–C≡C–H $\xrightarrow[\text{[2] (CH}_3)_2\text{CHCH}_2\text{Cl}]{\text{[1] NaH}}$

b. 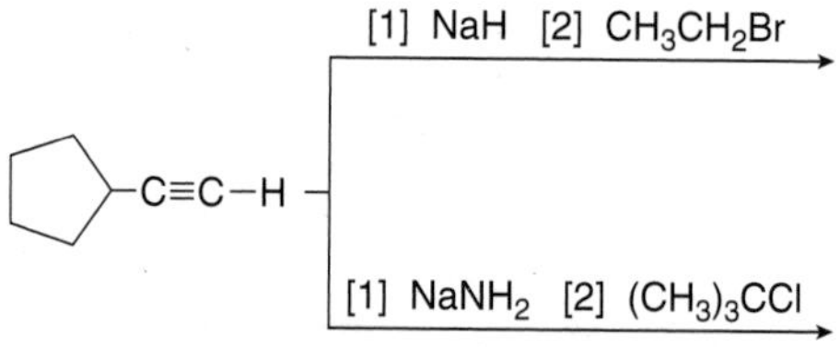

Problem 11.17 What acetylide anion and alkyl halide can be used to prepare each alkyne? Indicate all possibilities when more than one route will work.

a. $(CH_3)_2CHCH_2C{\equiv}CH$ b. $CH_3C{\equiv}CCH_2CH_2CH_2CH_3$ c. $(CH_3)_3CC{\equiv}CCH_2CH_3$

Because acetylene has two *sp* hybridized C–H bonds, two sequential reactions can occur to form **two new carbon–carbon bonds,** as shown in Sample Problem 11.6.

Sample Problem 11.6 Identify the terminal alkyne **A** and the internal alkyne **B** in the following reaction sequence.

$$\text{H–C≡C–H} \xrightarrow[\text{[2] CH}_3\text{Br}]{\text{[1] NaNH}_2} \textbf{A} \xrightarrow[\text{[2] CH}_3\text{CH}_2\text{Cl}]{\text{[1] NaNH}_2} \textbf{B}$$

Solution

In each step, the base $^{-}NH_2$ removes a proton on an *sp* hybridized carbon, and the resulting acetylide anion reacts as a nucleophile with an alkyl halide to yield an S_N2 product. The first two-step reaction sequence forms the **terminal alkyne A** by nucleophilic attack of the acetylide anion on CH_3Br.

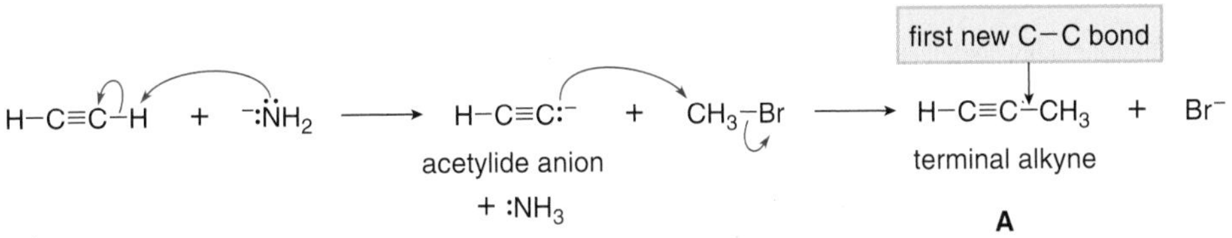

first new C–C bond
H–C≡C–H + ⁻:NH2 → H–C≡C:⁻ + CH3–Br → H–C≡C–CH3 + Br⁻
acetylide anion
+ :NH3
terminal alkyne
A

The second two-step reaction sequence forms the **internal alkyne B** by nucleophilic attack of the acetylide anion on CH_3CH_2Cl.

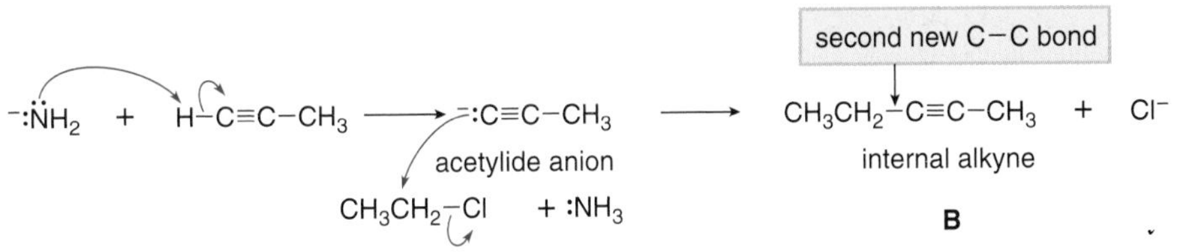

second new C–C bond
⁻:NH2 + H–C≡C–CH3 → ⁻:C≡C–CH3 → CH3CH2–C≡C–CH3 + Cl⁻
acetylide anion
CH3CH2–Cl + :NH3
internal alkyne
B

The soft coral *Capnella imbricata* is the source of the natural product capnellene.

Sample Problem 11.6 illustrates how a five-carbon product can be prepared from three smaller molecules by forming two new carbon–carbon bonds.

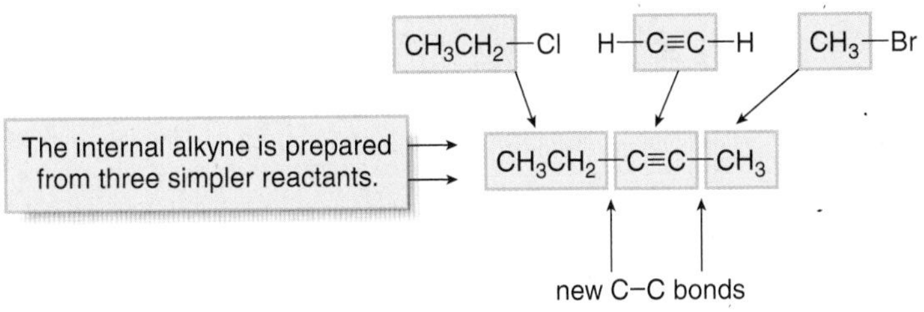

CH3CH2–Cl
H–C≡C–H
CH3–Br
The internal alkyne is prepared from three simpler reactants.
CH3CH2–C≡C–CH3
new C–C bonds

Carbon–carbon bond formation with acetylide anions is a valuable reaction used in the synthesis of numerous natural products. Two examples include **capnellene,** isolated from the soft coral *Capnella imbricata,* and **niphatoxin B,** isolated from a red sea sponge, as shown in Figure 11.6.

Figure 11.6 Use of acetylide anion reactions in the synthesis of two marine natural products

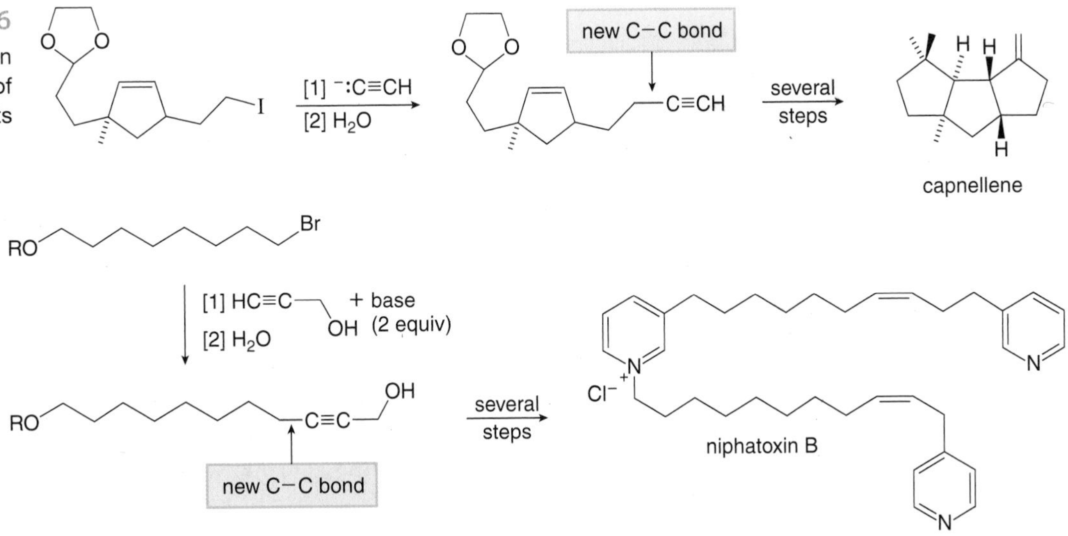

[1] ⁻:C≡CH
[2] H2O
new C–C bond
C≡CH
several steps
capnellene
RO
Br
[1] HC≡C–CH2OH + base (2 equiv)
[2] H2O
OH
C≡C
new C–C bond
several steps
Cl⁻
niphatoxin B

Problem 11.18 Show how $HC\equiv CH$, CH_3CH_2Br, and $(CH_3)_2CHCH_2CH_2Br$ can be used to prepare $CH_3CH_2C\equiv CCH_2CH_2CH(CH_3)_2$. Show all reagents, and use curved arrows to show movement of electron pairs.

Problem 11.19 Explain why 2,2,5,5-tetramethyl-3-hexyne can't be made using acetylide anions.

11.11B Reaction of Acetylide Anions with Epoxides

Acetylide anions are strong nucleophiles that open epoxide rings by an S_N2 mechanism. This reaction also results in the formation of a **new carbon–carbon bond.** Backside attack occurs at the less substituted end of the epoxide.

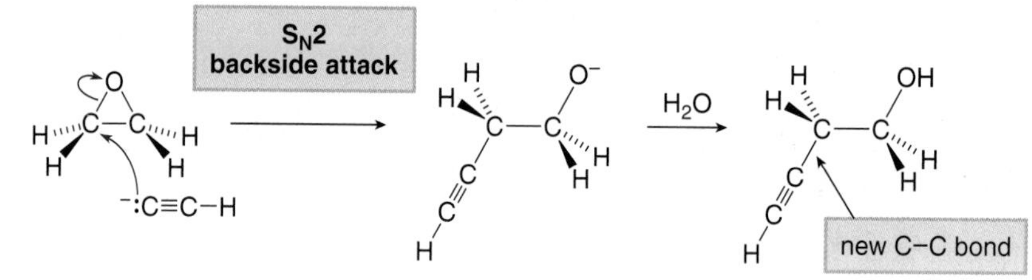

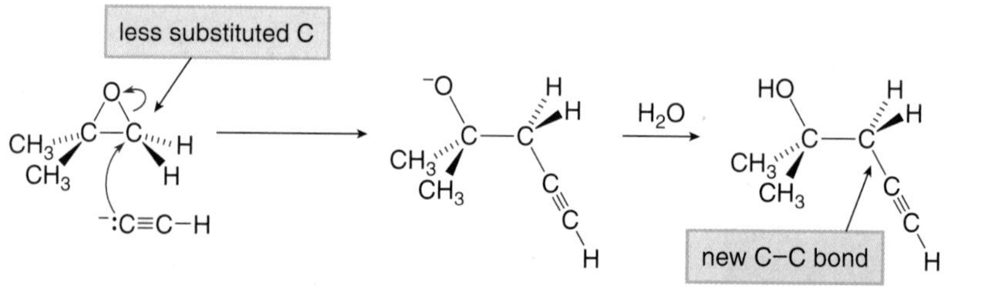

Opening of epoxide rings with strong nucleophiles was first discussed in Section 9.15A.

Problem 11.20 Draw the products of each reaction.

a. 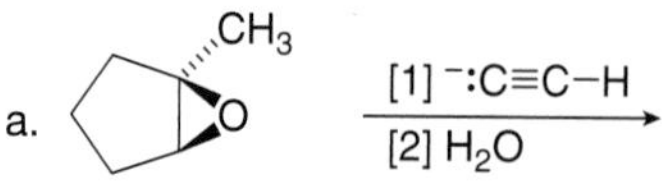

b. 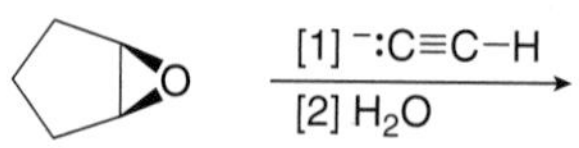

Problem 11.21 Draw the products formed when $CH_3CH_2C\equiv C^-Na^+$ reacts with each compound.

a. $CH_3CH_2CH_2Br$
b. $(CH_3)_2CHCH_2CH_2Cl$
c. $(CH_3CH_2)_3CCl$
d. $BrCH_2CH_2CH_2CH_2OH$
e. ethylene oxide followed by H_2O
f. propene oxide followed by H_2O

11.12 Synthesis

The reactions of acetylide anions give us an opportunity to examine organic synthesis more systematically. Performing a multistep synthesis can be difficult. Not only must you know the reactions for a particular functional group, but you must also put these reactions in a logical order, a process that takes much practice to master.

11.12A General Terminology and Conventions

To plan a synthesis of more than one step, we use the process of **retrosynthetic analysis**—that is, working backwards from the desired product to determine the starting materials from which it is made (Section 10.18). To write a synthesis working backwards from the product to the starting material, an **open arrow** (⇒) is used to indicate that the product is drawn on the left and the starting material on the right.

Carefully read the directions for each synthesis problem. Sometimes a starting material is specified, whereas at other times you must begin with a compound that meets a particular criterion; for example, you may be asked to synthesize a compound from alcohols having five or fewer carbon atoms. These limitations are meant to give you some direction in planning a multistep synthesis.

The product of a synthesis is often called the **target compound.** Using retrosynthetic analysis, we must determine what compound can be converted to the target compound by a single reaction. That is, **what is the immediate precursor of the target compound?** After an appropriate precursor is identified, this process is continued until we reach a specified starting material. Sometimes multiple retrosynthetic pathways are examined before a particular route is decided upon.

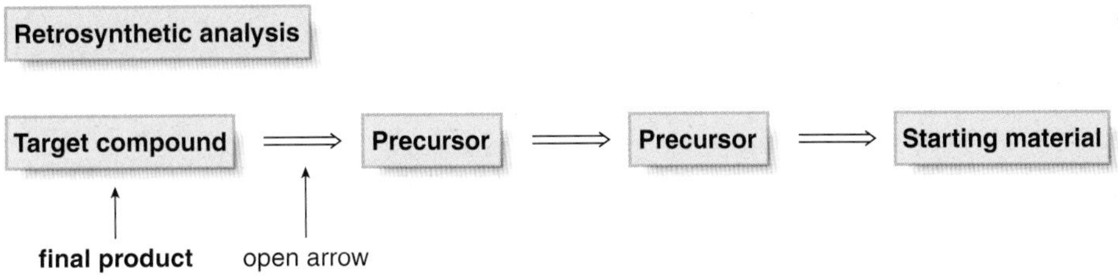

In designing a synthesis, reactions are often divided into two categories:

- **Those that form new carbon–carbon bonds.**
- **Those that convert one functional group into another—that is, functional group interconversions.**

Appendix D lists the carbon–carbon bond-forming reactions encountered in this text.

Carbon–carbon bond-forming reactions are central to organic synthesis because simpler and less valuable starting materials can be converted to more complex products. Keep in mind that whenever the product of a synthesis has more carbon–carbon bonds than the starting material, the synthesis must contain at least one of these reactions.

How To Develop a Retrosynthetic Analysis

Step [1] **Compare the carbon skeletons of the starting material and product.**

- If the product has more carbon–carbon σ bonds than the starting material, the synthesis must form one or more C–C bonds. If not, only functional group interconversion occurs.
- Match the carbons in the starting material with those in the product, to see where new C–C bonds must be added or where functional groups must be changed.

Step [2] **Concentrate on the functional groups in the starting material and product and ask:**

- What methods introduce the functional groups in the product?
- What kind of reactions does the starting material undergo?

Step [3] **Work backwards from the product and forwards from the starting material.**

- Ask: What is the immediate precursor of the product?
- Compare each precursor to the starting material to determine if there is a one-step reaction that converts one to the other. Continue this process until the starting material is reached.
- Always generate simpler precursors when working backwards.
- Use fewer steps when multiple routes are possible.
- Keep in mind that you may need to evaluate several different precursors for a given compound.

Step [4] **Check the synthesis by writing it in the synthetic direction.**

- To check a retrosynthetic analysis, write out the steps beginning with the starting material, indicating all necessary reagents.

11.12B Examples of Multistep Synthesis

Retrosynthetic analysis with acetylide anions is illustrated in Sample Problems 11.7 and 11.8.

Sample Problem 11.7 Devise a synthesis of $HC{\equiv}CCH_2CH_2CH_3$ from $HC{\equiv}CH$ and any other organic or inorganic reagents.

Retrosynthetic Analysis

The two C's in the starting material match up with the two *sp* hybridized C's in the product, so a three-carbon unit must be added.

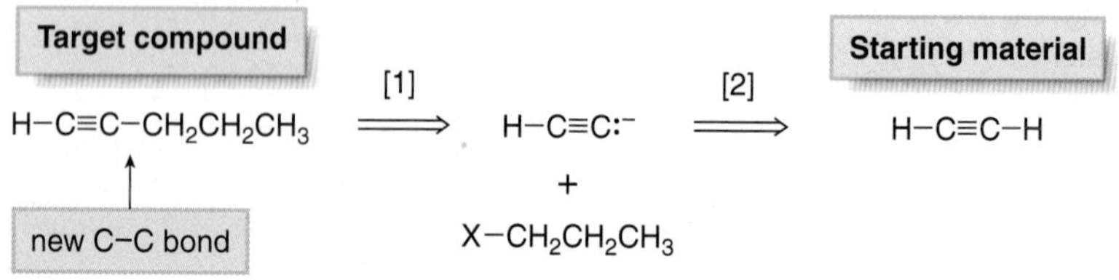
Target compound
H–C≡C–CH2CH2CH3
new C–C bond
[1]
H–C≡C:⁻
+
X–CH2CH2CH3
[2]
Starting material
H–C≡C–H

Thinking backwards . . .

[1] Form a new C–C bond using an acetylide anion and a 1° alkyl halide.
[2] Prepare the acetylide anion from acetylene by treatment with base.

Synthesis

Deprotonation of $HC{\equiv}CH$ with NaH forms the acetylide anion, which undergoes S_N2 reaction with an alkyl halide to form the target compound, a five-carbon alkyne.

A two-step process:

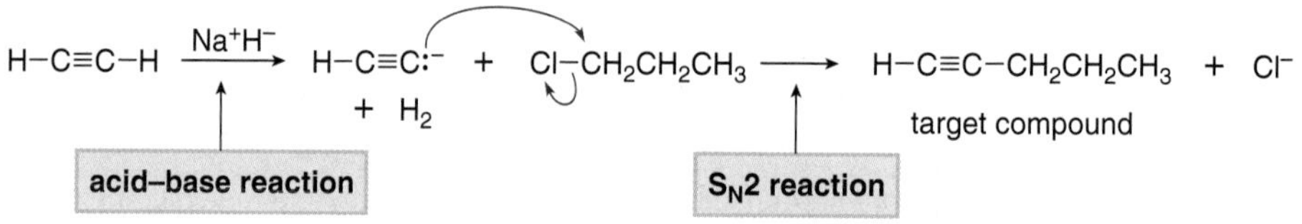
H–C≡C–H
Na+H⁻
H–C≡C:⁻ + H2
+ Cl–CH2CH2CH3
H–C≡C–CH2CH2CH3 + Cl⁻
target compound
acid–base reaction
SN2 reaction

Sample Problem 11.8 Devise a synthesis of the following compound from starting materials having two carbons or fewer.

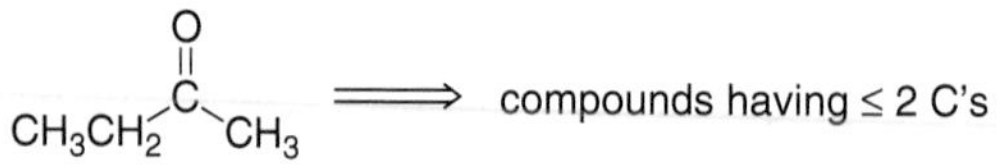
CH3CH2COCH3
compounds having ≤ 2 C's

Retrosynthetic Analysis

A carbon–carbon bond-forming reaction must be used to convert the two-carbon starting materials to the four-carbon product.

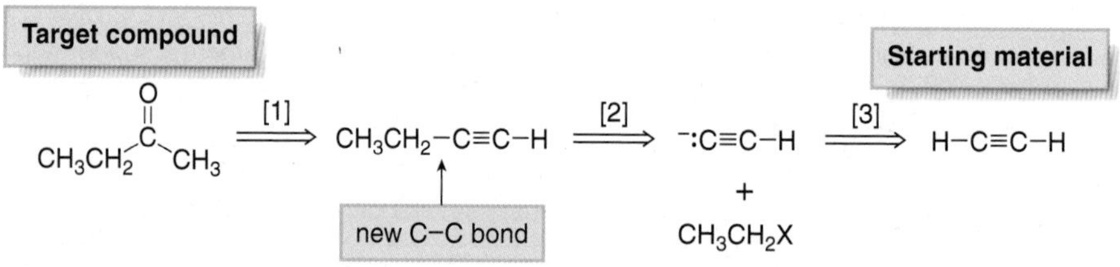
Target compound
CH3CH2COCH3
[1]
CH3CH2–C≡C–H
new C–C bond
[2]
⁻:C≡C–H
+
CH3CH2X
[3]
Starting material
H–C≡C–H

Thinking backwards . . .

[1] Form the carbonyl group by hydration of a triple bond.
[2] Form a new C–C bond using an acetylide anion and a 1° alkyl halide.
[3] Prepare the acetylide anion from acetylene by treatment with base.

Synthesis

Three steps are needed to complete the synthesis. Treatment of HC≡CH with NaH forms the acetylide anion, which undergoes an S_N2 reaction with an alkyl halide to form a four-carbon terminal alkyne. Hydration of the alkyne with H_2O, H_2SO_4, and $HgSO_4$ yields the target compound.

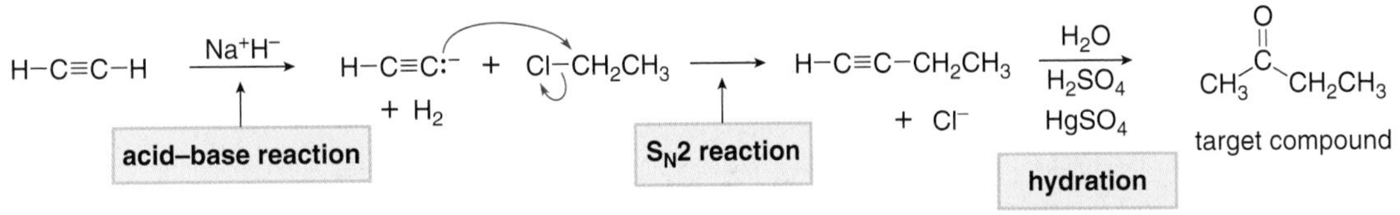

These examples illustrate the synthesis of organic compounds by multistep routes. In Chapter 12 we will learn other useful reactions that expand our capability to do synthesis.

Problem 11.22 Use retrosynthetic analysis to show how 3-hexyne can be prepared from acetylene and any other organic and inorganic compounds. Then draw the synthesis in the synthetic direction, showing all needed reagents.

Problem 11.23 Devise a synthesis of $CH_3CH_2CH_2CHO$ from two-carbon starting materials.

KEY CONCEPTS

Alkynes

General Facts About Alkynes

- Alkynes contain a carbon–carbon triple bond consisting of a strong σ bond and two weak π bonds. Each carbon is *sp* hybridized and linear (11.1).
- Alkynes are named using the suffix ***-yne*** (11.2).
- Alkynes have weak intermolecular forces, giving them low mp's and low bp's, and making them water insoluble (11.3).
- Because its weaker π bonds make an alkyne electron rich, alkynes undergo addition reactions with electrophiles (11.6).

Addition Reactions of Alkynes

[1] Hydrohalogenation—Addition of HX (X = Cl, Br, I) (11.7)

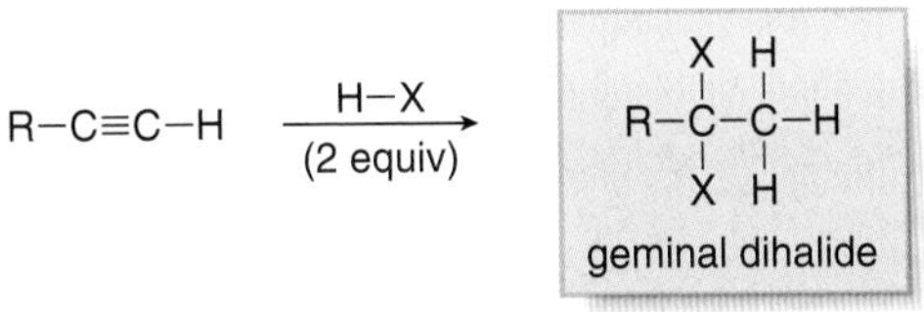

- Markovnikov's rule is followed. H bonds to the less substituted C to form the more stable carbocation.

[2] Halogenation—Addition of X_2 (X = Cl or Br) (11.8)

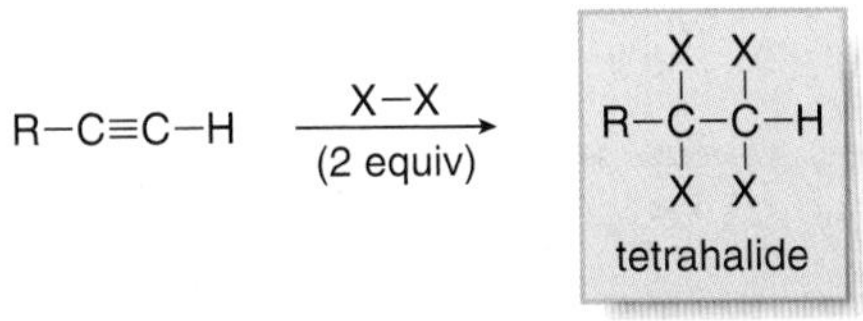

- Bridged halonium ions are formed as intermediates.
- Anti addition of X_2 occurs.

[3] Hydration—Addition of H_2O (11.9)

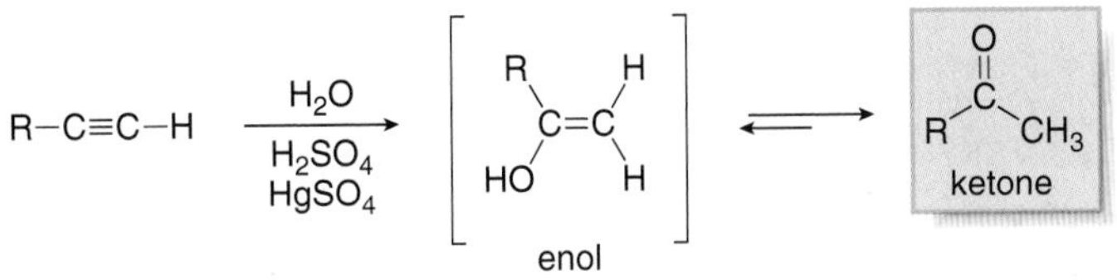

- Markovnikov's rule is followed. H bonds to the less substituted C to form the more stable carbocation.
- An unstable enol is first formed, which rearranges to a carbonyl group.

[4] Hydroboration–oxidation—Addition of H_2O (11.10)

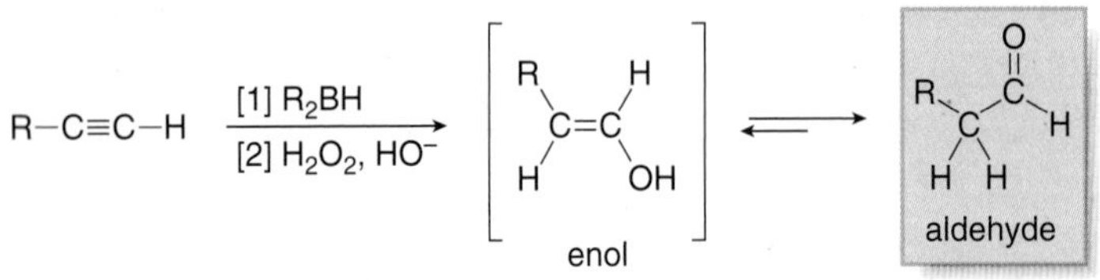
R–C≡C–H
[1] R2BH
[2] H2O2, HO−
enol
aldehyde

- The unstable enol, first formed after oxidation, rearranges to a carbonyl group.

Reactions Involving Acetylide Anions

[1] Formation of acetylide anions from terminal alkynes (11.6B)

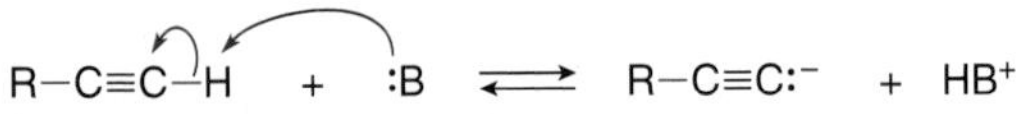
R–C≡C–H + :B ⇌ R–C≡C:− + HB+

- Typical bases used for the reaction are $NaNH_2$ and NaH.

[2] Reaction of acetylide anions with alkyl halides (11.11A)

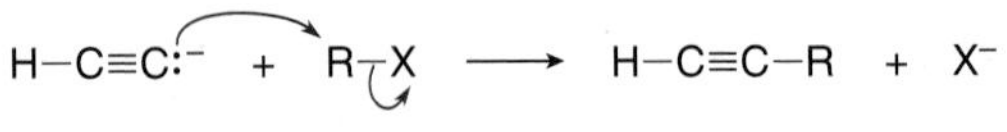
H–C≡C:− + R–X → H–C≡C–R + X−

- The reaction follows an S_N2 mechanism.
- The reaction works best with CH_3X and RCH_2X.

[3] Reaction of acetylide anions with epoxides (11.11B)

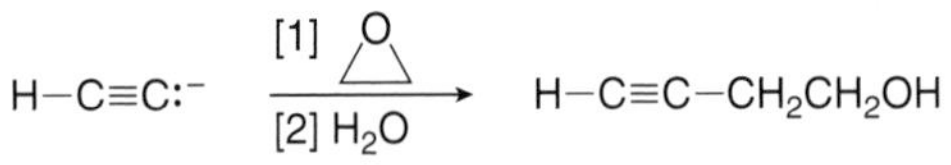
H–C≡C:−
[1]
[2] H2O
H–C≡C–CH2CH2OH

- The reaction follows an S_N2 mechanism.
- Opening of the ring occurs from the back side at the less substituted end of the epoxide.

PROBLEMS

Problems Using Three-Dimensional Models

11.24 Give the IUPAC name for each compound.

a. 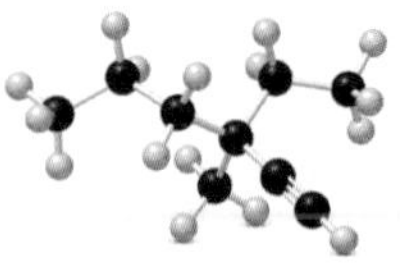

b. 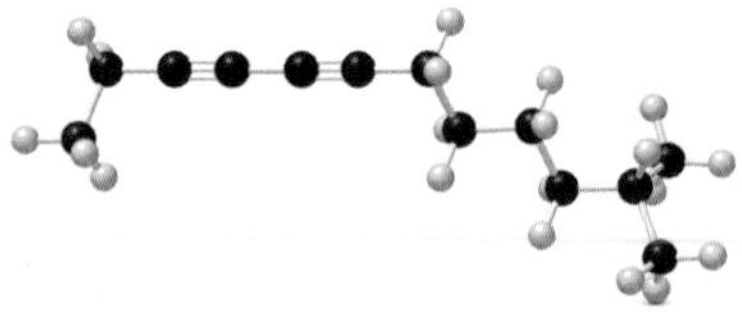

11.25 Draw the enol tautomer of (a) and the keto tautomer of (b).

a. 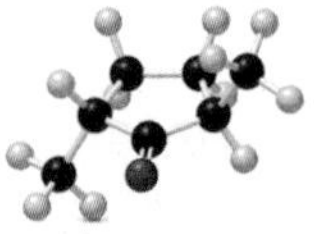

b. 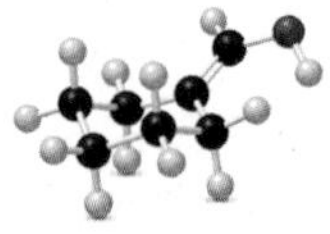

Structure and Nomenclature

11.26 Answer the following questions about erlotinib and phomallenic acid C. Erlotinib, sold under the trade name Tarceva, was introduced in 2004 for the treatment of lung cancer. Phomallenic acid C is an inhibitor of bacterial fatty acid synthesis.

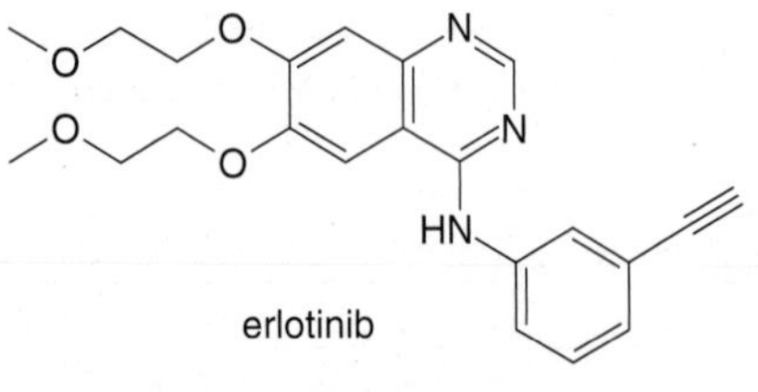
O
O
O
O
N
N
HN

erlotinib

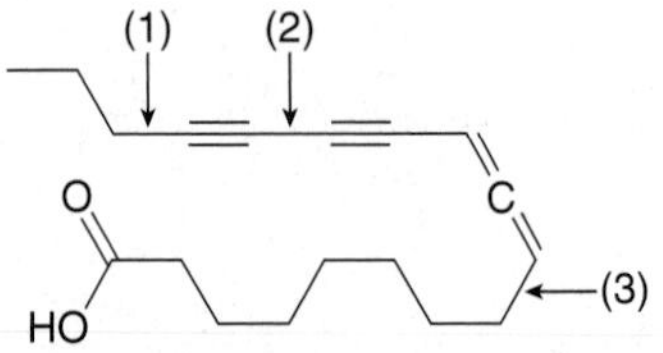
(1)
(2)
(3)
C
O
HO

phomallenic acid C

a. Which C–H bond in erlotinib is most acidic?
b. What orbitals are used to form the shortest C–C single bond in erlotinib?
c. Which H atom in phomallenic acid C is most acidic?
d. How many *sp* hybridized carbons are contained in phomallenic acid C?
e. Rank the labeled bonds in phomallenic acid C in order of increasing bond strength.

11.27 Draw the seven isomeric alkynes having molecular formula C_6H_{10}, and give the IUPAC name for each compound. Consider constitutional isomers only.

11.28 Give the IUPAC name for each alkyne.

a. $CH_3CH_2CH(CH_3)C{\equiv}CCH_2CH_3$

b. $(CH_3)_2CHC{\equiv}CCH(CH_3)_2$

c. $(CH_3CH_2)_2CHC{\equiv}CCH(CH_2CH_3)CH(CH_3)CH_2CH_3$

d. $HC{\equiv}C{-}CH(CH_2CH_3)CH_2CH_2CH_3$

e. $CH_3CH_2C{\equiv}CCH_2C{\equiv}CCH_3$

f. 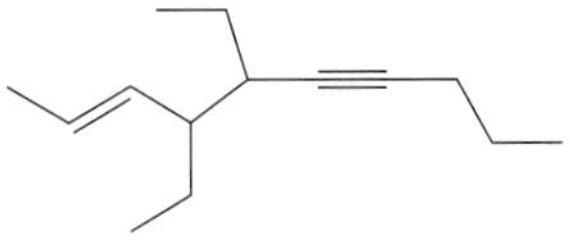

g. 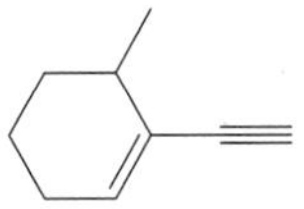

11.29 Give the structure corresponding to each name.

a. 5,6-dimethyl-2-heptyne
b. 5-*tert*-butyl-6,6-dimethyl-3-nonyne
c. (4*S*)-4-chloro-2-pentyne
d. *cis*-1-ethynyl-2-methylcyclopentane
e. 3,4-dimethyl-1,5-octadiyne
f. (6*Z*)-6-methyl-6-octen-1-yne

Tautomers

11.30 Which of the following pairs of compounds represent keto–enol tautomers?

a. 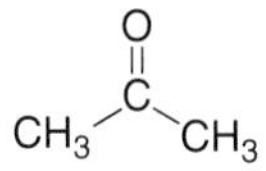

and 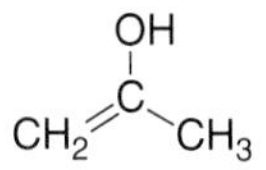

b. 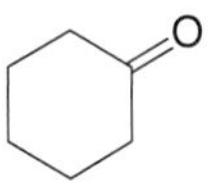

and 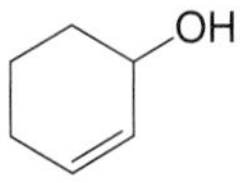

c. 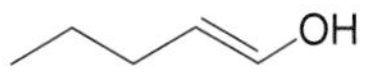

and 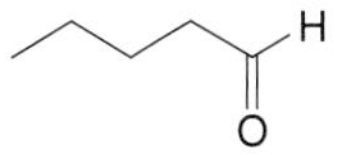

d. 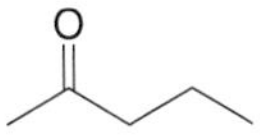

and 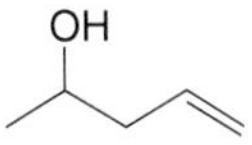

11.31 Draw the enol form of each keto tautomer in parts (a) and (b), and the keto form of each enol tautomer in parts (c) and (d).

a. CH_3CH_2CHO

b. 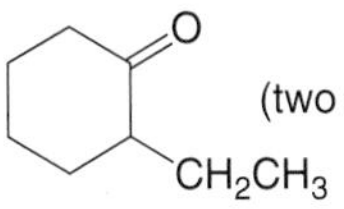

(two different enols)

c. 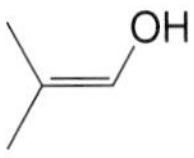

d. 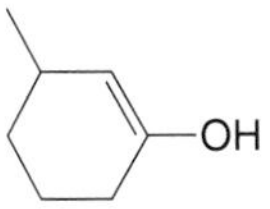

11.32 How is each compound related to **A**? Choose from tautomers, constitutional isomers but not tautomers, or neither.

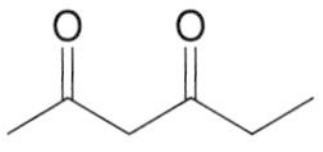

A

a. 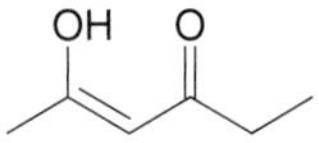

b. 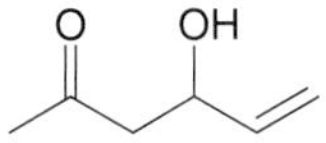

c. 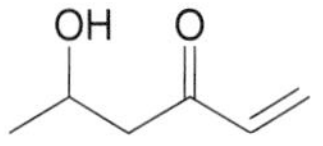

d. 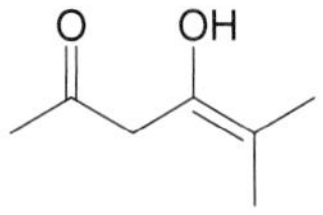

11.33 Ignoring stereoisomers, draw the two possible enols for 2-butanone ($CH_3COCH_2CH_3$), and predict which one is more stable.

11.34 Conversion of an enol to a ketone also occurs in the presence of base. Draw a stepwise mechanism for the following tautomerization.

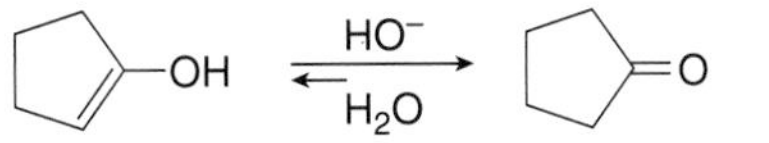

11.35 Enamines and imines are tautomers that contain N atoms. Draw a stepwise mechanism for the acid-catalyzed conversion of enamine **X** to imine **Y**.

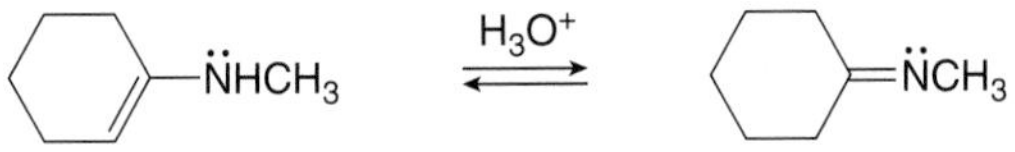

X enamine　　**Y** imine

Reactions

11.36 Draw the products formed when 1-hexyne is treated with each reagent.

a. HCl (2 equiv)
b. HBr (2 equiv)
c. Cl_2 (2 equiv)
d. $H_2O + H_2SO_4 + HgSO_4$
e. [1] R_2BH; [2] H_2O_2, HO^-
f. NaH
g. [1] $^-NH_2$; [2] CH_3CH_2Br
h. [1] $^-NH_2$; [2] ; [3] H_2O

11.37 Draw the products formed when 3-hexyne is treated with each reagent.

a. HBr (2 equiv)
b. Br_2 (2 equiv)
c. H_2O, H_2SO_4
d. [1] R_2BH; [2] H_2O_2, HO^-

11.38 What reagents are needed to convert $(CH_3CH_2)_3CC\equiv CH$ to each compound?

a. $(CH_3CH_2)_3CCOCH_3$
b. $(CH_3CH_2)_3CCH_2CHO$
c. $(CH_3CH_2)_3CCCl_2CH_3$
d. $(CH_3CH_2)_3CC\equiv CCH_2CH_3$

11.39 Explain the apparent paradox. Although the addition of one equivalent of HX to an alkyne is more exothermic than the addition of HX to an alkene, an alkene reacts faster with HX.

11.40 What alkyne gives each of the following ketones as the only product after hydration with H_2O, H_2SO_4, and $HgSO_4$?

a. 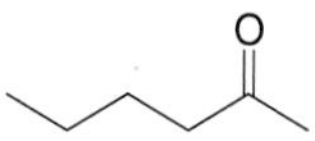

b. 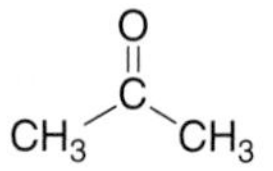

c. 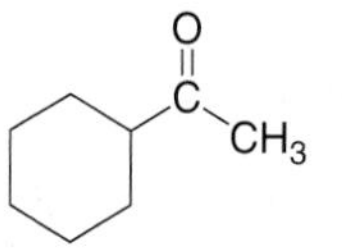

d. 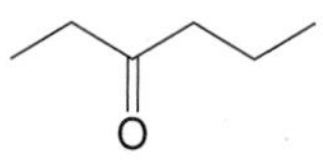

11.41 What two different alkynes yield 2-butanone from hydration with H_2O, H_2SO_4, and $HgSO_4$?

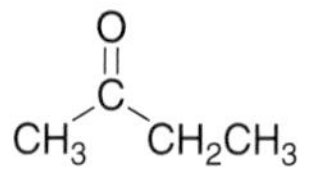

2-butanone

11.42 What alkyne gives each compound as the only product after hydroboration–oxidation?

a. 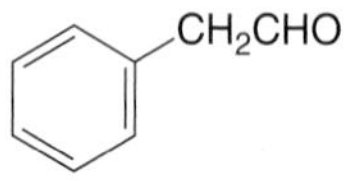

b. 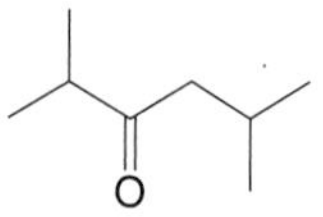

11.43 Draw the organic products formed in each reaction.

a. 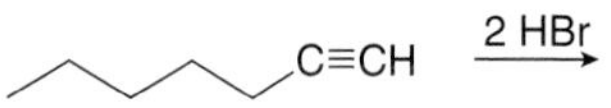

b. $(CH_3)_3CC\equiv CH \xrightarrow{2\,Cl_2}$

c. 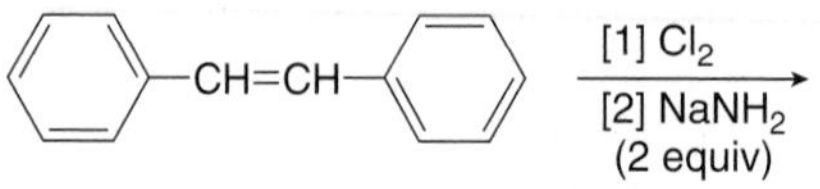

d. 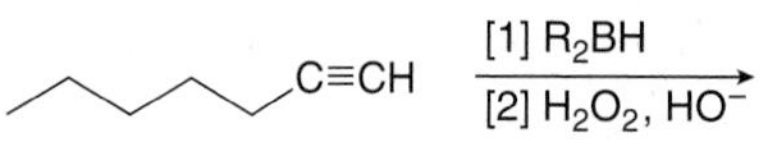

e. $HC\equiv C^- + D_2O \longrightarrow$

f. 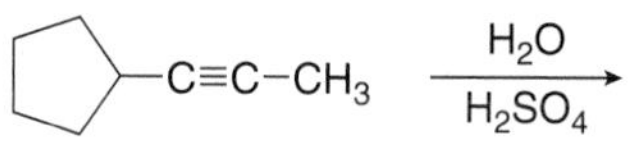

g. $CH_3CH_2C\equiv C^- + CH_3CH_2CH_2OTs \longrightarrow$

h. 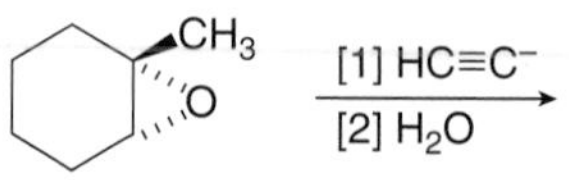

i. 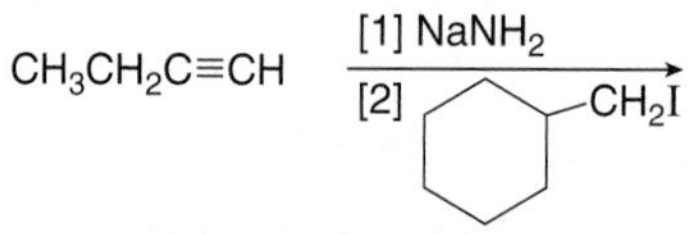

j. 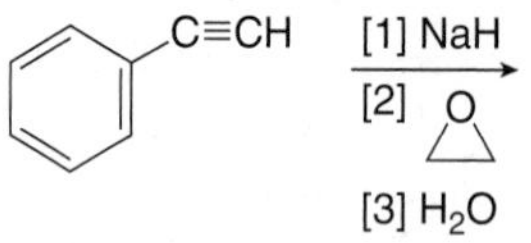

11.44 Draw the structure of compounds **A–E** in the following reaction scheme.

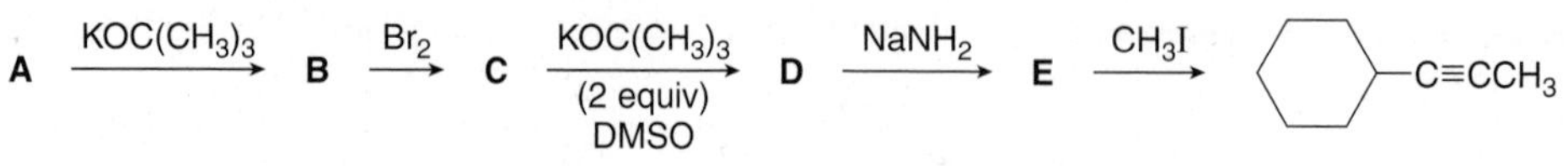

11.45 When alkyne **A** is treated with $NaNH_2$ followed by CH_3I, a product having molecular formula $C_6H_{10}O$ is formed, but it is *not* compound **B**. What is the structure of the product and why is it formed?

$$\underset{\mathbf{A}}{H-C\equiv C-CH_2CH_2CH_2OH} \xrightarrow[\text{[1] } NaNH_2 \text{ [2] } CH_3I]{\times} \underset{\mathbf{B}}{CH_3-C\equiv C-CH_2CH_2CH_2OH}$$

11.46 Draw the products formed in each reaction and indicate stereochemistry.

a. 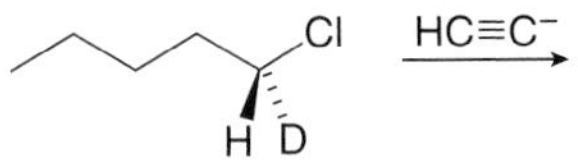

b. 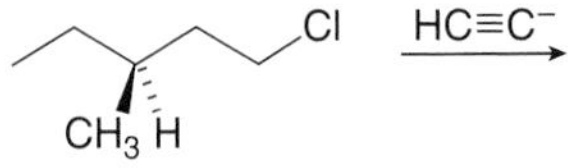

c. 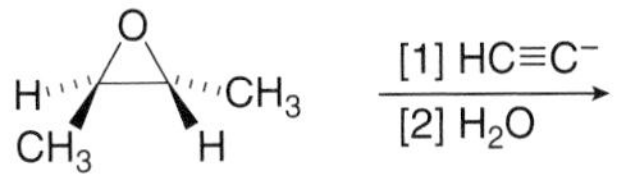

d. 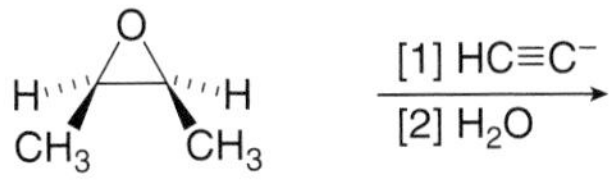

11.47 What reactions are needed to convert alcohol **A** into either alkyne **B** or alkyne **C?**

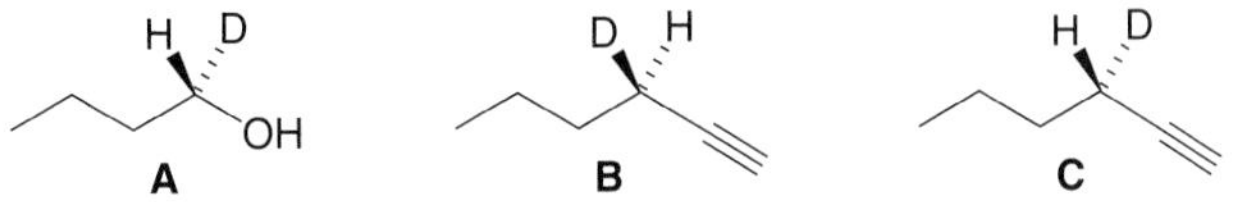

A **B** **C**

11.48 Identify the lettered compounds in the following reaction schemes. Each reaction sequence was used in the synthesis of a natural product.

a. 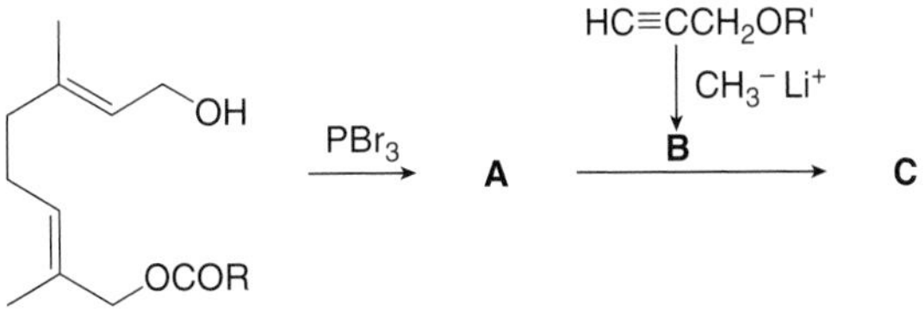

b. 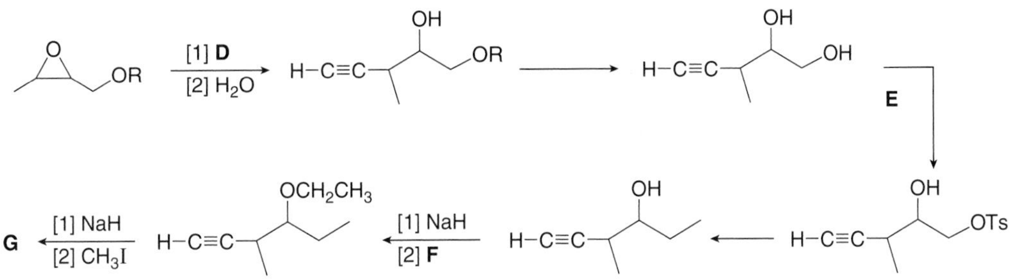

Mechanisms

11.49 Treatment of 2,2-dibromobutane with two equivalents of strong base affords 1-butyne and 2-butyne, as well as a small amount of 1,2-butadiene. Draw a mechanism showing how each compound is formed. Which alkyne should be the major product?

$$\underset{\text{2,2-dibromobutane}}{CH_3CBr_2CH_2CH_3} \xrightarrow[\text{(2 equiv)}]{Na^+\ ^-NH_2} \underset{\text{1-butyne}}{H{-}C{\equiv}C{-}CH_2CH_3} + \underset{\text{2-butyne}}{CH_3{-}C{\equiv}C{-}CH_3} + \underset{\text{1,2-butadiene}}{CH_2{=}C{=}CHCH_3}$$

11.50 Explain the following statement. Although $HC{\equiv}C^-$ is more stable than $CH_2{=}CH^-$, $HC{\equiv}C^+$ is less stable than $CH_2{=}CH^+$.

11.51 Draw a stepwise mechanism for the following reaction and explain why a mixture of *E* and *Z* isomers is formed.

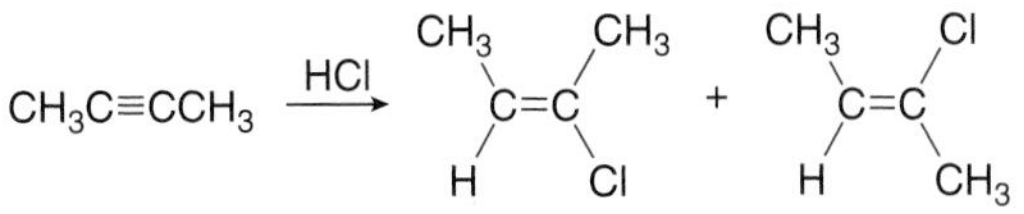

11.52 Draw a stepwise mechanism for each reaction.

a. 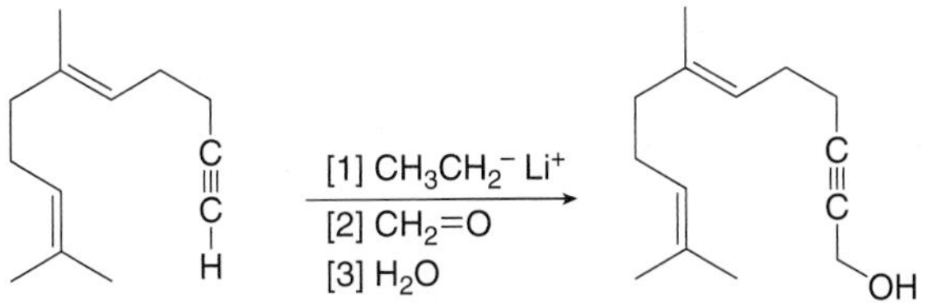

b. $$CH_3{-}\overset{OH}{\underset{H}{C}}{-}C{\equiv}CH \xrightarrow[H_2SO_4]{H_2O} CH_3{-}CH{=}CH{-}CHO$$

11.53 From what you have learned about enols and the hydration of alkynes, predict what product is formed by the acid-catalyzed hydration of $CH_3CH_2CH_2C{\equiv}COCH_3$. Draw a stepwise mechanism that illustrates how it is formed.

Synthesis

11.54 What steps are needed to prepare phenylacetylene, $C_6H_5C\equiv CH$, from each compound: (a) $C_6H_5CH_2CHBr_2$; (b) $C_6H_5CHBrCH_3$; (c) $C_6H_5CH_2CH_2OH$?

11.55 What acetylide anion and alkyl halide are needed to synthesize each alkyne?

a. $HC\equiv CCH_2CH_2CH(CH_3)_2$

b. 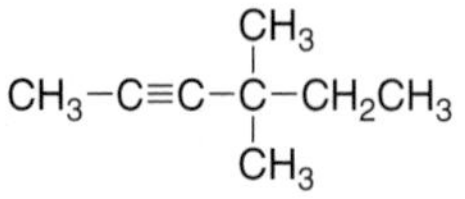

c. 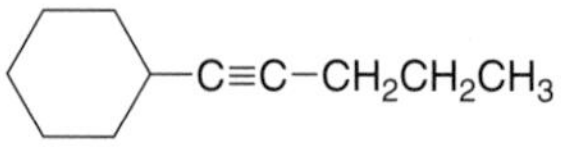

11.56 Synthesize each compound from acetylene. You may use any other organic or inorganic reagents.

a. $(CH_3)_2CHCH_2C\equiv CH$

b. $CH_3CH_2CH_2C\equiv CCH_2CH_2CH_3$

c. $CH_3CH_2CH_2CH_2CHO$

d. 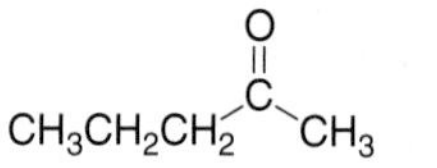

e. $CH_3CH_2CH_2CCl_2CH_3$

f. 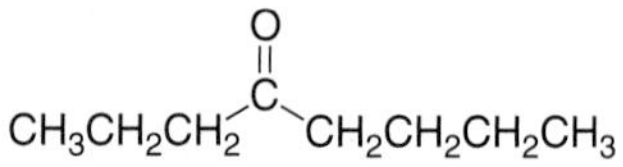

11.57 Devise a synthesis of each compound using $CH_3CH_2CH=CH_2$ as the starting material. You may use any other organic compounds or inorganic reagents.

a. $CH_3CH_2C\equiv CH$

b. $CH_3CH_2CBr_2CH_3$

c. $CH_3CH_2CCl_2CHCl_2$

d. $CH_3CH_2CHBrCH_2Br$

e. $CH_3CH_2C\equiv CCH_2CH_2CH_3$

f. $CH_3CH_2C\equiv CCH_2CH_2OH$

g. 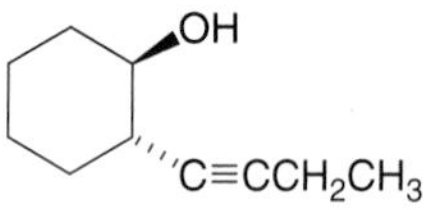

(+ enantiomer)

11.58 Devise a synthesis of each compound. You may use $HC\equiv CH$, ethylene oxide, and alkyl halides as organic starting materials and any inorganic reagents.

a. $CH_3CH_2CH_2CH_2CH_2CH_2C\equiv CH$

b. $CH_3CH_2CH_2CH_2CH_2CH_2C\equiv CCH_2CH_3$

c. $CH_3CH_2CH_2CH_2CH_2CH_2C\equiv CCH_2CH_2OH$

d. $CH_3CH_2CH_2CH_2CH_2CH_2C\equiv CCH_2CH_2OCH_2CH_3$

11.59 Devise a synthesis of the ketone 3-hexanone, $CH_3CH_2COCH_2CH_2CH_3$, from CH_3CH_2Br as the only organic starting material; that is, all the carbon atoms in 3-hexanone must come from CH_3CH_2Br. You may use any other needed reagents.

11.60 Devise a synthesis of each compound using $CH_3CH_2CH_2OH$ as the only organic starting material: (a) $CH_3C\equiv CCH_2CH_2CH_3$; (b) $CH_3C\equiv CCH_2CH(OH)CH_3$. You may use any other needed inorganic reagents.

11.61 Devise a synthesis of each compound from CH_3CH_2OH as the only organic starting material: (a) $CH_3CH_2C\equiv CCH_2CH_2OH$; (b) $CH_3CH_2C\equiv CCH_2CH_2OCH_2CH_3$. You may use any other needed reagents.

Challenge Problems

11.62 Explain why the C=C of an enol is more nucleophilic than the C=C of an alkene, despite the fact that the electronegative oxygen atom of the enol inductively withdraws electron density from the carbon–carbon double bond.

11.63 Draw a stepwise mechanism for the following reaction.

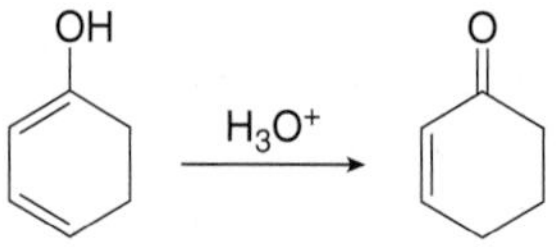

11.64 Draw a stepwise mechanism for the following reaction.

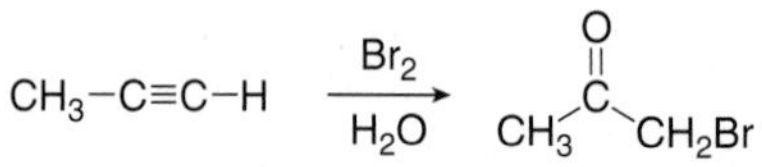

11.65 Why is compound **X** formed in the following reaction, instead of its constitutional isomer **Y?**

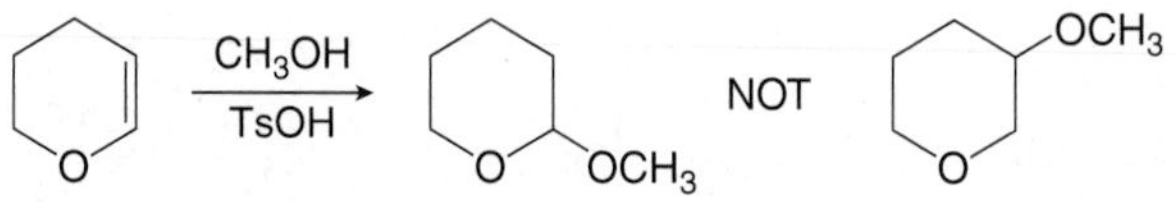

X **Y**

11.66 Write a stepwise mechanism for each of the following reactions. Explain why a more stable alkyne (2-butyne) is isomerized to a less stable alkyne (1-butyne), but under similar conditions, 2,5-dimethyl-3-hexyne forms 2,5-dimethyl-2,3-hexadiene.

$$\underset{\text{2-butyne}}{CH_3-C\equiv C-CH_3} \xrightarrow[\text{[2] } H_2O]{\text{[1] } KNH_2,\ NH_3} \underset{\text{1-butyne}}{HC\equiv C-CH_2CH_3}$$

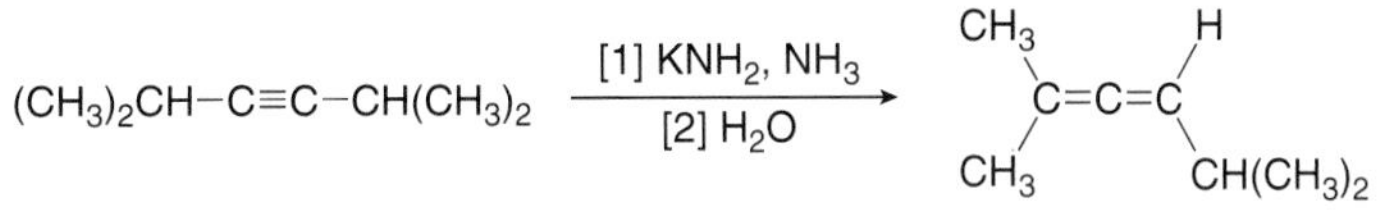

2,5-dimethyl-3-hexyne 2,5-dimethyl-2,3-hexadiene

11.67 Draw a stepwise mechanism for the following intramolecular reaction.

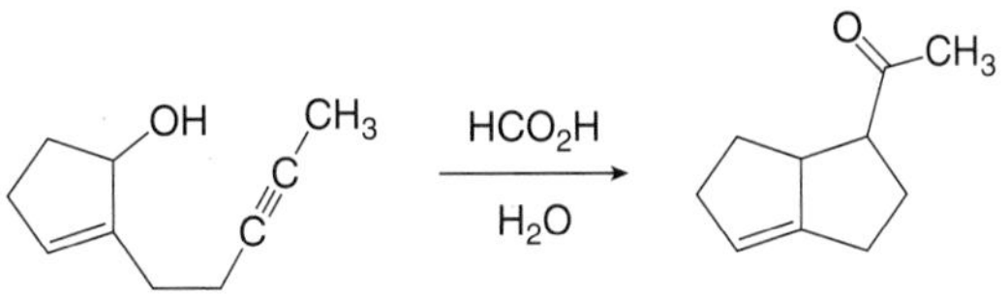

11.68 Explain why an optically active solution of (*R*)-α-methylbutyrophenone loses its optical activity when dilute acid is added to the solution.

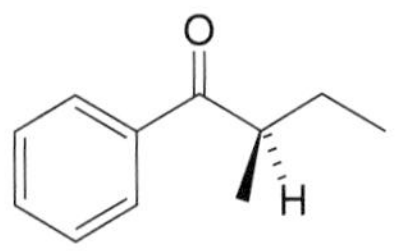

(*R*)-α-methylbutyrophenone

12 Oxidation and Reduction

12.1 Introduction
12.2 Reducing agents
12.3 Reduction of alkenes
12.4 Application: Hydrogenation of oils
12.5 Reduction of alkynes
12.6 The reduction of polar C – X σ bonds
12.7 Oxidizing agents
12.8 Epoxidation
12.9 Dihydroxylation
12.10 Oxidative cleavage of alkenes
12.11 Oxidative cleavage of alkynes
12.12 Oxidation of alcohols
12.13 Green chemistry
12.14 Application: The oxidation of ethanol
12.15 Sharpless epoxidation

Throughout history, humans have ingested alcoholic beverages for their pleasant taste and the feeling of euphoria they impart. Wine, beer, and similar products contain **ethanol** (CH_3CH_2OH), a 1° alcohol that is quickly absorbed in the stomach and small intestines and rapidly transported in the bloodstream to other organs. Like other 1° alcohols, ethanol is easily oxidized, and as a result, ethanol is metabolized in the body by a series of enzyme-catalyzed oxidation reactions that take place in the liver. In Chapter 12, we learn about oxidation and reduction reactions of organic molecules like ethanol.

In Chapter 12, we discuss the oxidation and reduction of **alkenes** and **alkynes,** as well as compounds with **polar C–X σ bonds**—alcohols, alkyl halides, and epoxides. Although there will be many different reagents and mechanisms, discussing these reactions as a group allows us to more easily compare and contrast them.

The word *mechanism* will often be used loosely here. In contrast to the S_N1 reaction of alkyl halides or the electrophilic addition reactions of alkenes, the details of some of the mechanisms presented in Chapter 12 are known with less certainty. For example, although the identity of a particular intermediate might be confirmed by experiment, other details of the mechanism are suggested by the structure or stereochemistry of the final product.

Oxidation and reduction reactions are very versatile, and knowing them allows us to design many more complex organic syntheses.

12.1 Introduction

Recall from Section 4.14 that the way to determine whether an organic compound has been oxidized or reduced is to compare the **relative number of C–H and C–Z bonds** (Z = an element *more electronegative* than carbon) in the starting material and product.

- *Oxidation* results in an *increase* in the number of C–Z bonds (usually C–O bonds) *or* a *decrease* in the number of C–H bonds.
- *Reduction* results in a *decrease* in the number of C–Z bonds (usually C–O bonds) *or* an *increase* in the number of C–H bonds.

Two components are always present in an oxidation or reduction reaction—**one component is oxidized and one is reduced.** When an organic compound is *oxidized* by a reagent, the reagent itself must be *reduced.* Similarly, when an organic compound is *reduced* by a reagent, the reagent becomes *oxidized.*

Thus, an organic compound such as CH_4 can be oxidized by replacing C–H bonds with C–O bonds, as shown in Figure 12.1. Reduction is the opposite of oxidation, so Figure 12.1 also shows how a compound can be reduced by replacing C–O bonds with C–H bonds. The symbols **[O]** and **[H]** indicate oxidation and reduction, respectively.

Sometimes two carbon atoms are involved in a single oxidation or reduction reaction, and the net change in the number of C–H or C–Z bonds at *both* atoms must be taken into account. The conversion of an **alkyne to an alkene** and an **alkene to an alkane** are examples of reduction, because each process adds two new C–H bonds to the starting material, as shown in Figure 12.2.

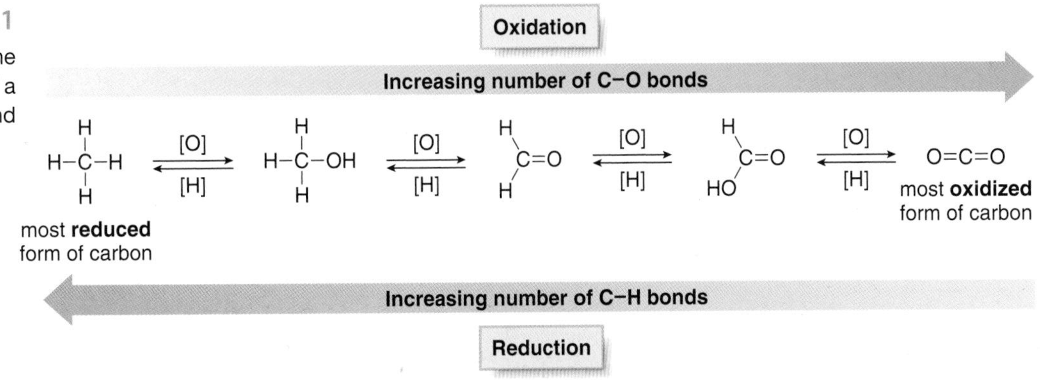

Figure 12.1
A general scheme for the oxidation and reduction of a carbon compound

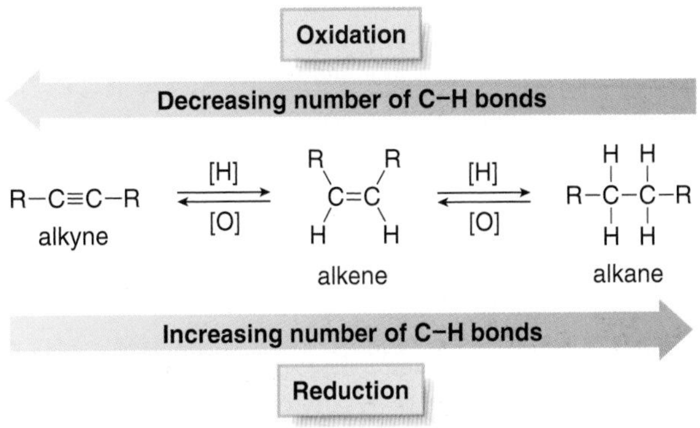

Figure 12.2
Oxidation and reduction of hydrocarbons

Problem 12.1 Classify each reaction as oxidation, reduction, or neither.

a. 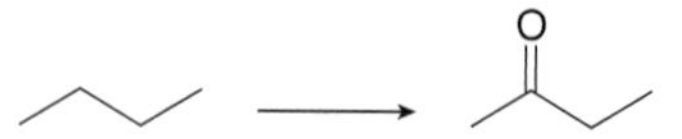

b. 

c. 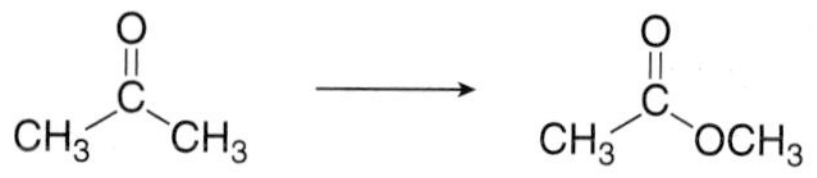

d. $CH_2{=}CH_2 \longrightarrow CH_3CH_2Cl$

12.2 Reducing Agents

Reducing agents provide the equivalent of two hydrogen atoms, but **there are three types of reductions,** differing in how H_2 is added. The simplest reducing agent is molecular $\mathbf{H_2}$. Reductions of this sort are carried out in the presence of a metal catalyst that acts as a surface on which the reaction occurs.

The second way to deliver H_2 in a reduction is to add two protons and two electrons to a substrate—that is, $\mathbf{H_2 = 2\ H^+ + 2\ e^-}$. Reducing agents of this sort use alkali metals as a source of electrons and liquid ammonia (NH_3) as a source of protons. Reductions with **Na in NH_3** are called **dissolving metal reductions.**

$$2\ Na \longrightarrow 2\ Na^+ + \boxed{2\ e^-}$$

$$2\ NH_3 \longrightarrow 2\ ^-NH_2 + \boxed{2\ H^+}$$

an equivalent of H_2 for reduction

The third way to deliver the equivalent of two hydrogen atoms is to add **hydride (H^-)** and a **proton (H^+).** The most common hydride reducing agents contain a hydrogen atom bonded to boron or aluminum. Simple examples include **sodium borohydride ($NaBH_4$)** and **lithium aluminum hydride ($LiAlH_4$).** These reagents deliver H^- to a substrate, and then a proton is added from H_2O or an alcohol.

$NaBH_4$ **$LiAlH_4$**

sodium borohydride lithium aluminum hydride

- **Metal hydride reagents act as a source of H^- because they contain polar metal–hydrogen bonds that place a partial negative charge on hydrogen.**

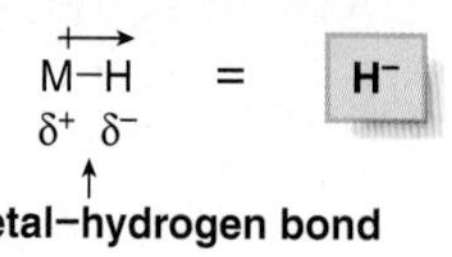

a polar metal–hydrogen bond

M = B or Al

12.3 Reduction of Alkenes

Reduction of an alkene forms an alkane by addition of H_2. Two bonds are broken—the **weak π bond** of the alkene and the H_2 σ bond—and two new C–H σ bonds are formed.

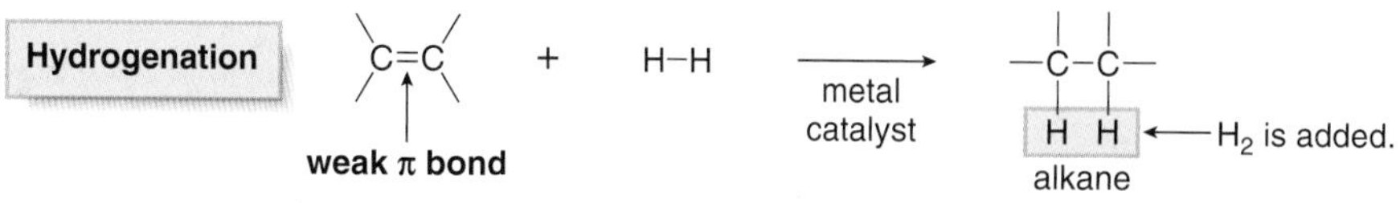
Hydrogenation
weak π bond
H–H
metal catalyst
H₂ is added.
alkane

Hydrogenation catalysts are insoluble in common solvents, thus creating a **heterogeneous** reaction mixture. This insolubility has a practical advantage. These catalysts contain expensive metals, but they can be filtered away from the other reactants after the reaction is complete, and then reused.

The addition of H_2 occurs only in the presence of a **metal catalyst,** and thus, the reaction is called **catalytic hydrogenation.** The catalyst consists of a metal—usually Pd, Pt, or Ni—adsorbed onto a finely divided inert solid, such as charcoal. For example, the catalyst 10% Pd on carbon is composed of 10% Pd and 90% carbon, by weight. H_2 adds in a **syn** fashion, as shown in Equation [2].

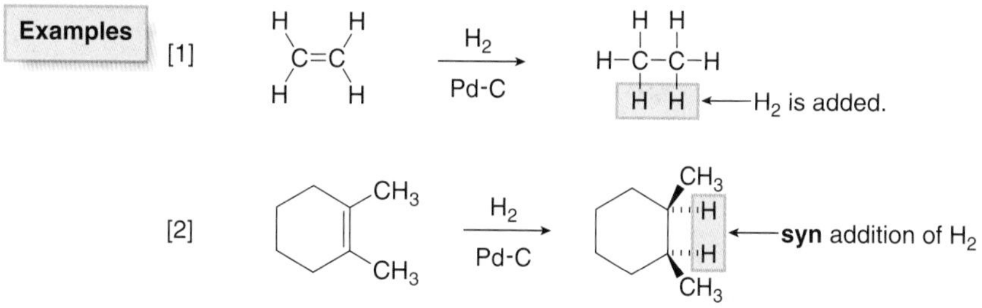
Examples
[1]
H₂
Pd-C
H₂ is added.
[2]
CH₃
H₂
Pd-C
syn addition of H₂

Problem 12.2 What alkane is formed when each alkene is treated with H_2 and a Pd catalyst?

a. 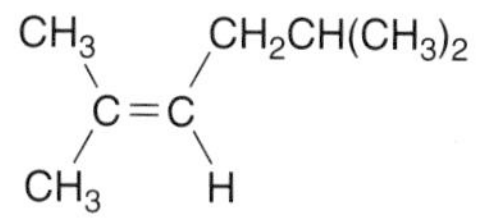
b. 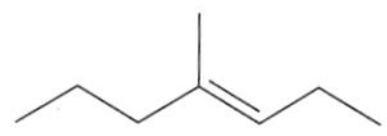
c. 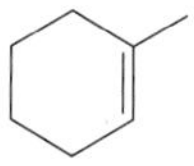

Problem 12.3 Draw all alkenes that react with one equivalent of H_2 in the presence of a palladium catalyst to form each alkane. Consider constitutional isomers only.

a. 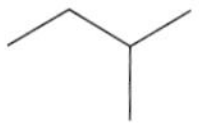
b. 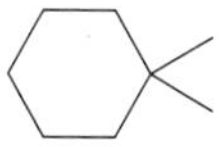
c. 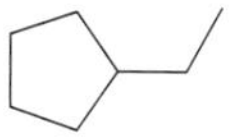

12.3A Hydrogenation and Alkene Stability

Hydrogenation reactions are **exothermic** because the bonds in the product are stronger than the bonds in the starting materials, making them similar to other alkene addition reactions. The $\Delta H°$ for hydrogenation, called the **heat of hydrogenation,** can be used as a measure of the relative stability of two different alkenes that are hydrogenated to the same alkane.

Recall from Chapter 8 that **trans alkenes are generally more stable than cis alkenes.**

For example, both *cis*- and *trans*-2-butene are hydrogenated to butane, and the heat of hydrogenation for the trans isomer is less than that for the cis isomer. **Because less energy is released in converting the trans alkene to butane, it must be lower in energy (more stable) to begin with.** The relative energies of the butene isomers are illustrated in Figure 12.3.

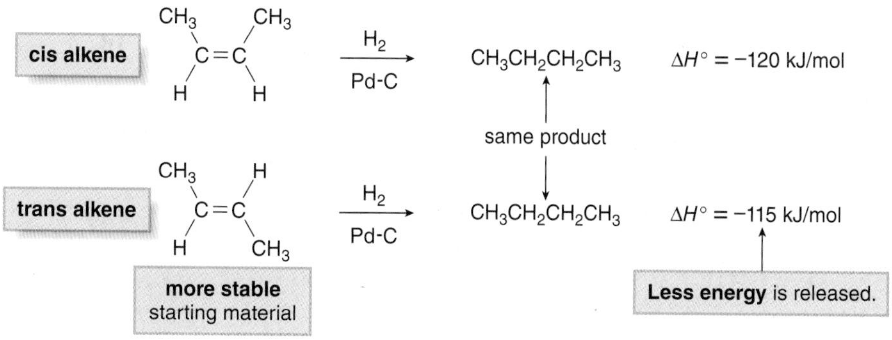
cis alkene
H₂
Pd-C
CH₃CH₂CH₂CH₃
ΔH° = –120 kJ/mol
same product
trans alkene
H₂
Pd-C
CH₃CH₂CH₂CH₃
ΔH° = –115 kJ/mol
more stable starting material
Less energy is released.

Figure 12.3

Relative energies of *cis*- and *trans*-2-butene

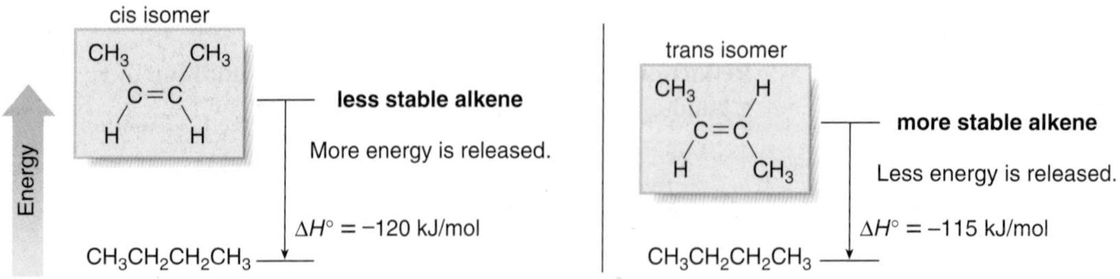

- **When hydrogenation of two alkenes gives the same alkane, the more stable alkene has the *smaller* heat of hydrogenation.**

Problem 12.4 Which alkene in each pair has the larger heat of hydrogenation?

a.  or 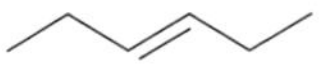 b. 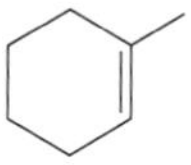 or 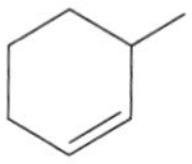

Problem 12.5 Explain why heats of hydrogenation cannot be used to determine the relative stability of 2-methyl-2-pentene and 3-methyl-1-pentene.

12.3B The Mechanism of Catalytic Hydrogenation

In the generally accepted mechanism for catalytic hydrogenation, the surface of the metal catalyst binds both H_2 and the alkene, and H_2 is transferred to the π bond in a rapid but stepwise process (Mechanism 12.1).

Mechanism 12.1 Addition of H_2 to an Alkene—Hydrogenation

Steps [1] and [2] Complexation of H_2 and the alkene to the catalyst

- **H_2 adsorbs to the catalyst surface** with partial or complete cleavage of the H–H bond.
- The π bond of the alkene complexes with the metal.

Steps [3] and [4] Sequential addition of the elements of H_2

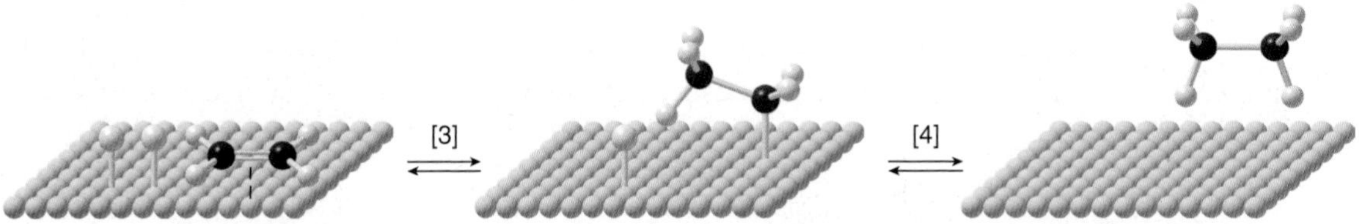

- **Two H atoms are transferred sequentially** to the π bond in Steps [3] and [4], forming the alkane.
- Because the product alkane no longer has a π bond with which to complex to the metal, it is released from the catalyst surface.

The mechanism explains two facts about hydrogenation:

- **Rapid, sequential addition of H_2 occurs from the side of the alkene complexed to the metal surface, resulting in syn addition.**
- **Less crowded double bonds complex more readily to the catalyst surface, resulting in faster reaction.**

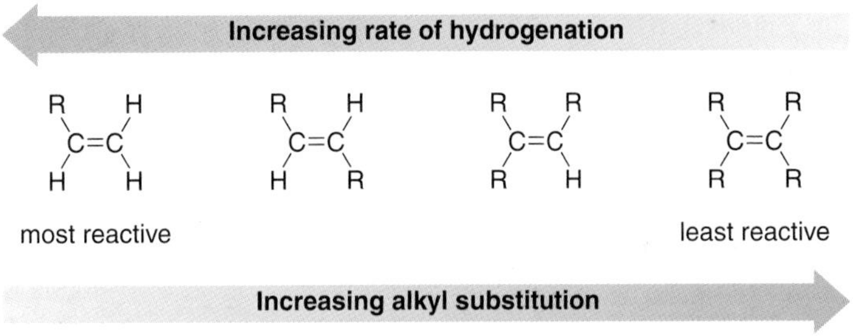

Problem 12.6 Given that syn addition of H_2 occurs from both sides of a trigonal planar double bond, draw all stereoisomers formed when each alkene is treated with H_2.

a. 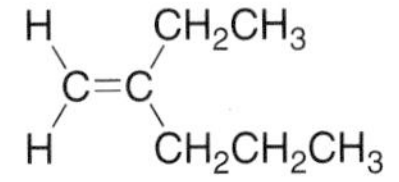

b. 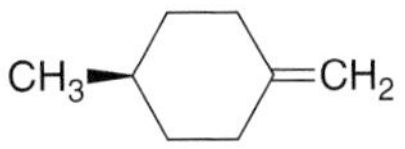

c. 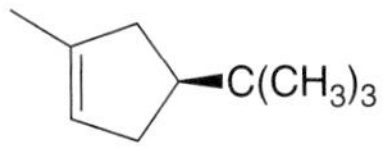

12.3C Hydrogenation Data and Degrees of Unsaturation

Recall from Section 10.2 that the **number of degrees of unsaturation gives the *total* number of rings and π bonds in a molecule.** Because H_2 adds to π bonds but does *not* add to the C–C σ bonds of rings, hydrogenation allows us to determine how many degrees of unsaturation are due to π bonds and how many are due to rings. This is done by comparing the number of degrees of unsaturation before and after a molecule is treated with H_2, as illustrated in Sample Problem 12.1.

Sample Problem 12.1 How many rings and π bonds are contained in a compound of molecular formula C_8H_{12} that is hydrogenated to a compound of molecular formula C_8H_{14}?

Solution

[1] Determine the number of degrees of unsaturation in the compounds before and after hydrogenation.

Before H_2 addition—C_8H_{12}

- The maximum number of H's possible for n C's is $2n + 2$; in this example, $2n + 2 = 2(8) + 2 = 18$.
- 18 H's (maximum) – 12 H's (actual) = 6 H's fewer than the maximum number.

$$\frac{\text{6 H's fewer than the maximum}}{\text{2 H's removed for each degree of unsaturation}} =$$

three degrees of unsaturation

After H_2 addition—C_8H_{14}

- The maximum number of H's possible for n C's is $2n + 2$; in this example, $2n + 2 = 2(8) + 2 = 18$.
- 18 H's (maximum) – 14 H's (actual) = 4 H's fewer than the maximum number.

$$\frac{\text{4 H's fewer than the maximum}}{\text{2 H's removed for each degree of unsaturation}} =$$

two degrees of unsaturation

[2] Assign the number of degrees of unsaturation to rings or π bonds as follows:

- The number of degrees of unsaturation that remain in the product after H_2 addition = the **number of rings** in the starting material.
- The number of degrees of unsaturation that react with H_2 = the **number of π bonds.**

In this example, **two** degrees of unsaturation remain after hydrogenation, so the starting material has **two** rings. Thus:

Before H_2 addition:		After H_2 addition:		
three degrees of unsaturation	−	**two** degrees of unsaturation	=	**one** degree of unsaturation that reacted with H_2
three rings or π bonds in C_8H_{12}	=	**two rings**	+	**one π bond** **ANSWER**

Problem 12.7 Complete the missing information for compounds **A, B,** and **C,** each subjected to hydrogenation. The number of rings and π bonds refers to the reactant (**A, B,** or **C**) prior to hydrogenation.

Compound	Molecular formula before hydrogenation	Molecular formula after hydrogenation	Number of rings	Number of π bonds
A	$C_{10}H_{12}$	$C_{10}H_{16}$	?	?
B	?	C_4H_{10}	0	1
C	C_6H_8	?	1	?

12.3D Hydrogenation of Other Double Bonds

Compounds that contain a carbonyl group also react with H_2 and a metal catalyst. For example, **aldehydes and ketones are reduced to 1° and 2° alcohols,** respectively. We return to this reaction in Chapter 20.

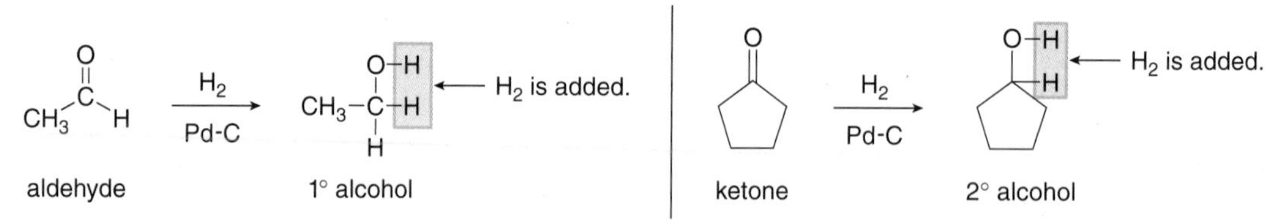

H2
Pd-C
H2 is added.
aldehyde
1° alcohol
H2
Pd-C
H2 is added.
ketone
2° alcohol

12.4 Application: Hydrogenation of Oils

Many processed foods, such as peanut butter, margarine, and some brands of crackers, contain *partially hydrogenated* vegetable oils. These oils are produced by hydrogenating the long hydrocarbon chains of triacylglycerols.

In Section 10.6 we learned that **fats and oils are triacylglycerols that differ in the number of degrees of unsaturation** in their long alkyl side chains.

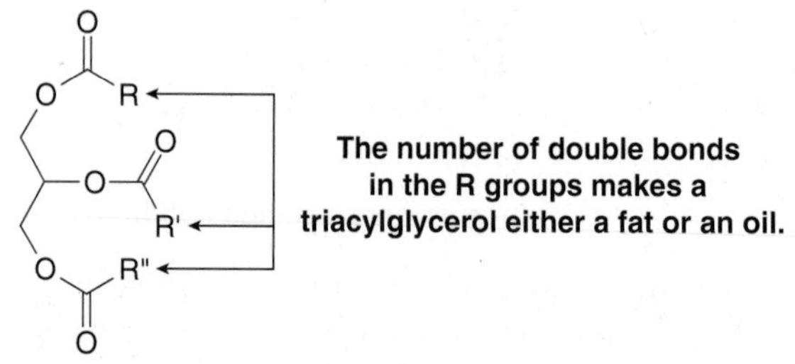

The number of double bonds in the R groups makes a triacylglycerol either a fat or an oil.

triacylglycerol

Peanut butter is a common consumer product that contains partially hydrogenated vegetable oil.

- **Fats—usually animal in origin—are solids with triacylglycerols having few degrees of unsaturation.**
- **Oils—usually vegetable in origin—are liquids with triacylglycerols having a larger number of degrees of unsaturation.**

When an unsaturated vegetable oil is treated with hydrogen, some (or all) of the π bonds add H_2, decreasing the number of degrees of unsaturation (Figure 12.4). This increases the melting point of the oil. For example, margarine is prepared by partially hydrogenating vegetable oil to give a product having a semi-solid consistency that more closely resembles butter. This process is sometimes called ***hardening.***

If unsaturated oils are healthier than saturated fats, why does the food industry hydrogenate oils? There are two reasons—aesthetics and shelf life. Consumers prefer the semi-solid consistency of margarine to a liquid oil. Imagine pouring vegetable oil on a piece of toast or pancakes.

Furthermore, unsaturated oils are more susceptible than saturated fats to oxidation at the **allylic carbon atoms**—the carbons adjacent to the double bond carbons—a process discussed in Chapter 15. Oxidation makes the oil rancid and inedible. Hydrogenating the double bonds reduces the number of allylic carbons (also illustrated in Figure 12.4), thus reducing the likelihood of oxidation and increasing the shelf life of the food product. This process reflects a delicate balance between providing consumers with healthier food products, while maximizing shelf life to prevent spoilage.

One other fact is worthy of note. Because the steps in hydrogenation are reversible and H atoms are added in a sequential rather than concerted fashion, a cis double bond can be isomerized to a trans double bond. After addition of one H atom (Step [3] in Mechanism 12.1), an intermediate can lose a hydrogen atom to re-form a double bond with either the cis or trans configuration.

As a result, some of the cis double bonds in vegetable oils are converted to trans double bonds during hydrogenation, forming so-called "trans fats." The shape of the resulting fatty acid chain is very different, closely resembling the shape of a *saturated* fatty acid chain. Consequently, trans

Figure 12.4 Partial hydrogenation of the double bonds in a vegetable oil

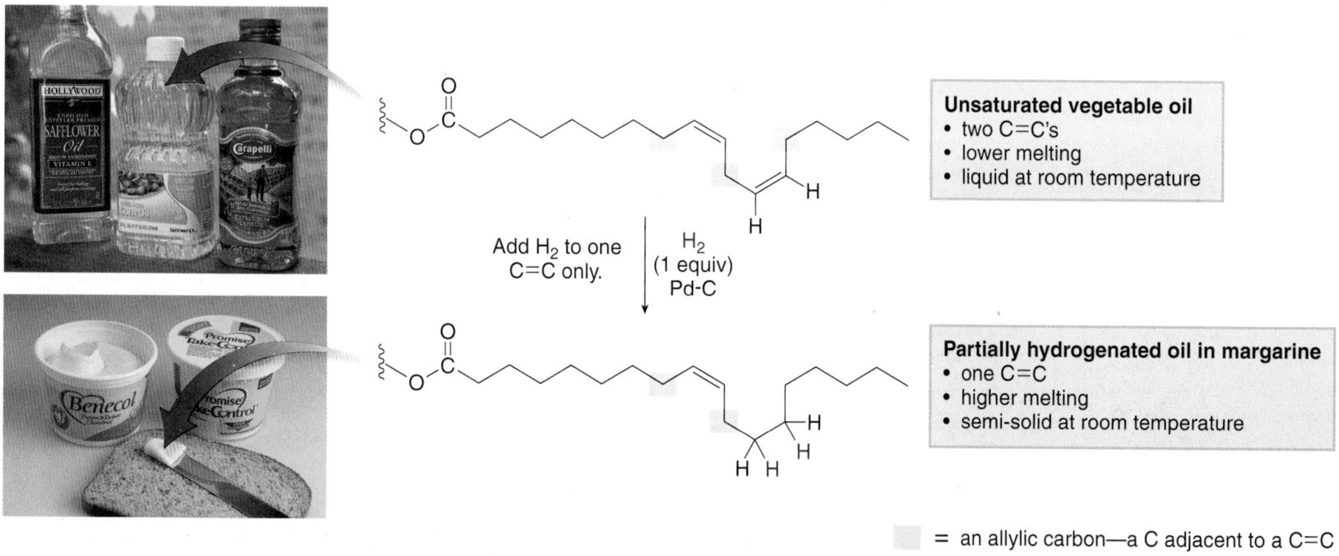

- **Decreasing** the number of degrees of unsaturation **increases** the melting point. Only one long chain of the triacylglycerol is drawn.
- When an oil is *partially* hydrogenated, some double bonds react with H_2, whereas some double bonds remain in the product.
- Partial hydrogenation **decreases** the number of allylic sites (shown in blue), making a triacylglycerol **less** susceptible to oxidation, thereby increasing its shelf life.

fats are thought to have the same negative effects on blood cholesterol levels as saturated fats; that is, trans fats stimulate cholesterol synthesis in the liver, thus increasing blood cholesterol levels, a factor linked to increased risk of heart disease.

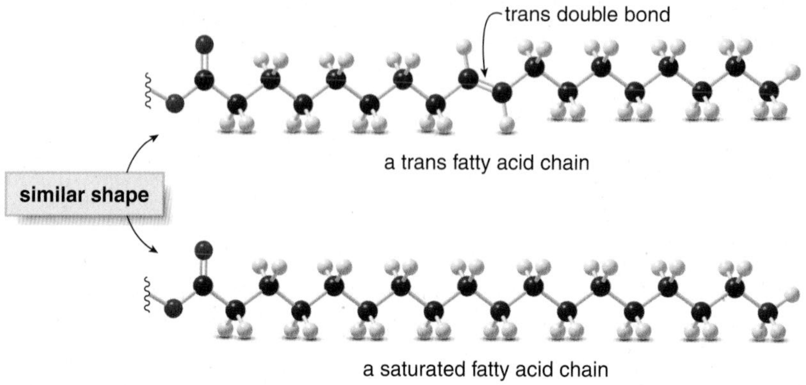

Problem 12.8 Draw the products formed when triacylglycerol **A** is treated with each reagent, forming compounds **B** and **C**. Rank **A, B,** and **C** in order of increasing melting point.

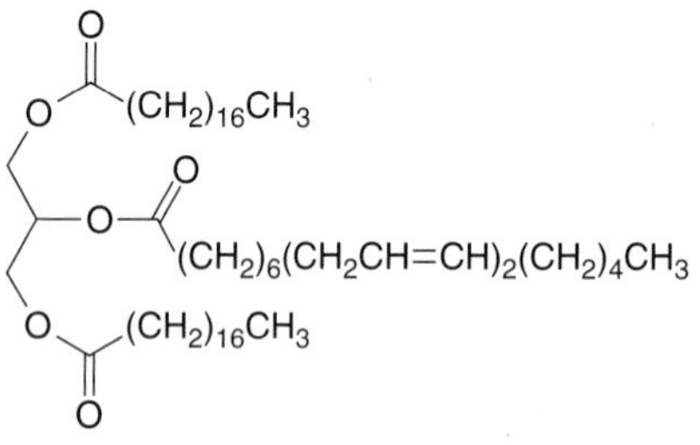

A

a. H_2 (excess), Pd-C (Compound **B**)
b. H_2 (1 equiv), Pd-C (Compound **C**)

12.5 Reduction of Alkynes

Reduction of an alkyne adds H_2 to one or both of the π bonds. There are three different ways by which the elements of H_2 can be added to a triple bond.

- **Adding two equivalents of H_2 forms an alkane.**

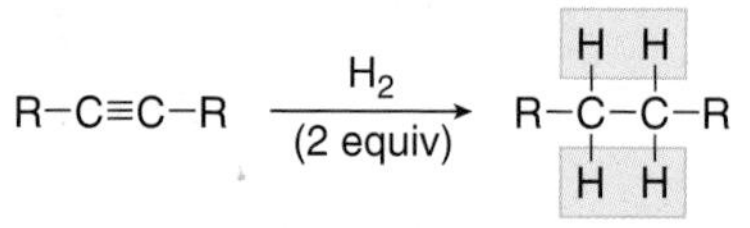

alkane

- **Adding one equivalent of H_2 in a syn fashion forms a cis alkene.**

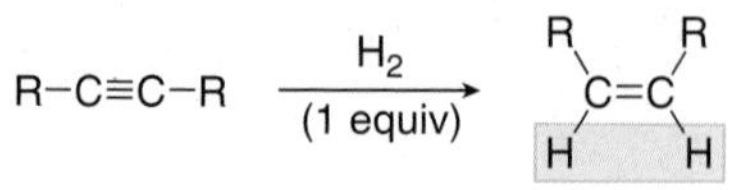

syn addition

cis alkene

- **Adding one equivalent of H_2 in an anti fashion forms a trans alkene.**

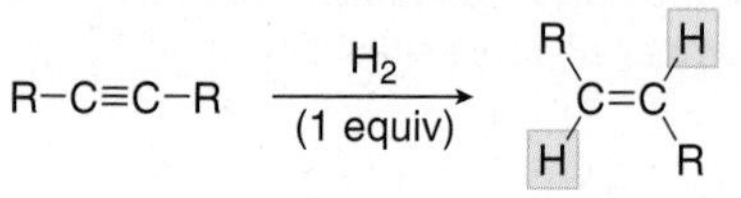

anti addition

trans alkene

12.5A Reduction of an Alkyne to an Alkane

When an alkyne is treated with two or more equivalents of H_2 and a Pd catalyst, reduction of *both* π bonds occurs. **Syn addition** of one equivalent of H_2 forms a cis alkene, which adds a second equivalent of H_2 to form an **alkane. Four new C–H bonds are formed.** By using a Pd-C catalyst, it is not possible to stop the reaction after addition of only one equivalent of H_2.

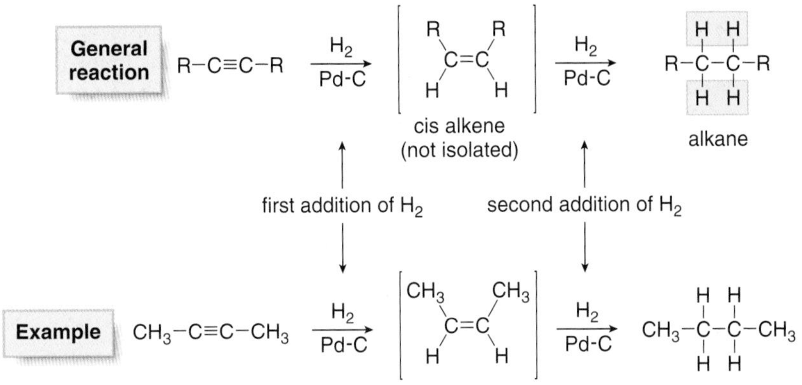
General reaction
R–C≡C–R
H2
Pd-C
cis alkene
(not isolated)
alkane
first addition of H2
second addition of H2
Example
CH3–C≡C–CH3

Problem 12.9 Which alkyne has the smaller heat of hydrogenation, $HC{\equiv}CCH_2CH_2CH_3$ or $CH_3C{\equiv}CCH_2CH_3$? Explain your choice.

12.5B Reduction of an Alkyne to a Cis Alkene

Palladium metal is too active a catalyst to allow the hydrogenation of an alkyne to stop after one equivalent of H_2. To prepare a cis alkene from an alkyne and H_2, a less active Pd catalyst is used—Pd adsorbed onto $CaCO_3$ with added lead(II) acetate and quinoline. This catalyst is called the **Lindlar catalyst** after the chemist who first prepared it. Compared to Pd metal, the **Lindlar catalyst is deactivated or "poisoned."**

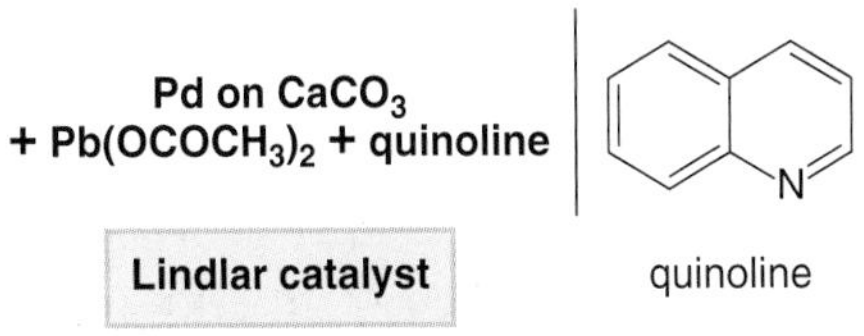
Pd on CaCO3
+ Pb(OCOCH3)2 + quinoline
Lindlar catalyst
quinoline

Reduction of an alkyne to a cis alkene is a **stereoselective reaction,** because only one stereoisomer is formed.

With the Lindlar catalyst, one equivalent of H_2 adds to an alkyne, and the cis alkene product is unreactive to further reduction.

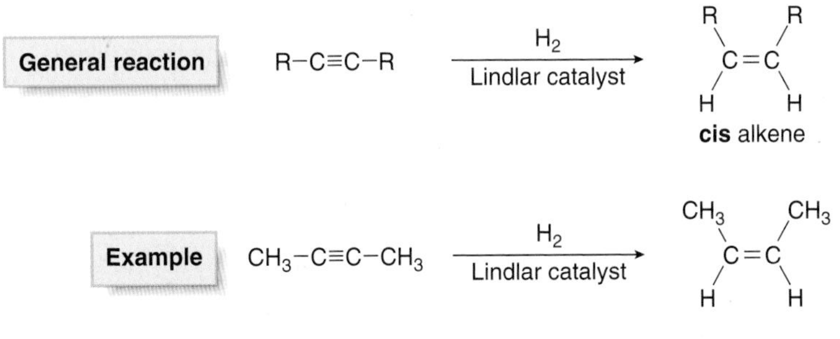
General reaction
R–C≡C–R
H2
Lindlar catalyst
cis alkene
Example
CH3–C≡C–CH3

Jasmine flowers are the source of *cis*-jasmone, a perfume component.

Problem 12.10 What is the structure of *cis*-jasmone, a natural product isolated from jasmine flowers, formed by treatment of alkyne **A** with H_2 in the presence of the Lindlar catalyst?

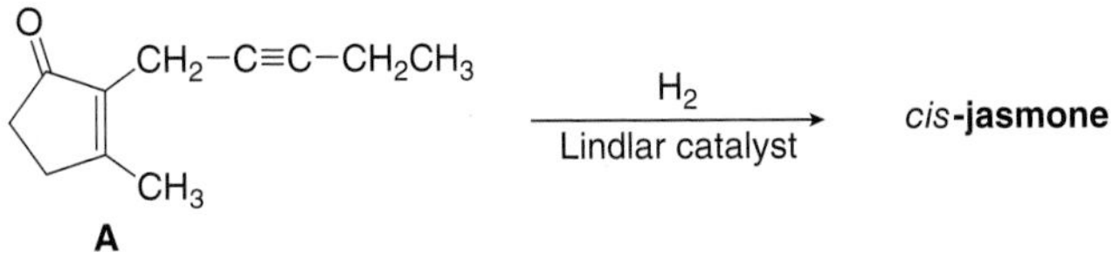
CH2–C≡C–CH2CH3
CH3
A
H2
Lindlar catalyst
cis-jasmone

Problem 12.11 (a) Draw the structure of a compound of molecular formula C_6H_{10} that reacts with H_2 in the presence of Pd-C but does not react with H_2 in the presence of Lindlar catalyst. (b) Draw the structure of a compound of molecular formula C_6H_{10} that reacts with H_2 when either catalyst is present.

12.5C Reduction of an Alkyne to a Trans Alkene

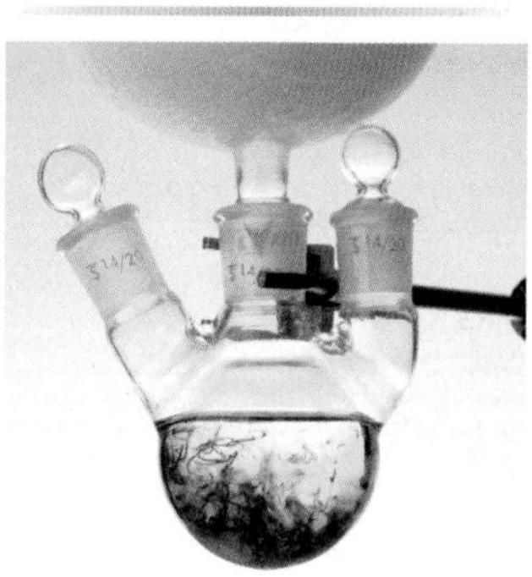

NH_3 has a boiling point of –33 °C, making it a gas at room temperature. To carry out a Na, NH_3 reduction, NH_3 gas is condensed into a flask kept at –78 °C by a cooling bath of solid CO_2 in acetone. When Na is added to the liquid NH_3, a brilliant blue solution is formed.

Although catalytic hydrogenation is a convenient method for preparing cis alkenes from alkynes, it cannot be used to prepare trans alkenes. With a dissolving metal reduction (such as Na in NH_3), however, the elements of H_2 are added in an **anti** fashion to the triple bond, thus forming a **trans alkene.** For example, 2-butyne reacts with Na in NH_3 to form *trans*-2-butene.

General reaction

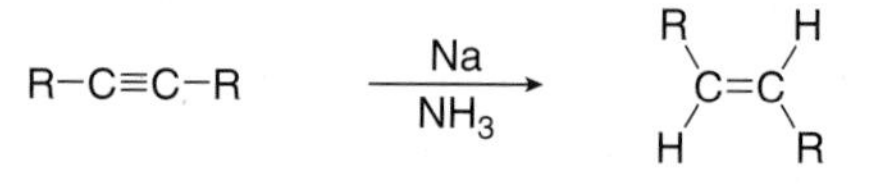

trans alkene

Example

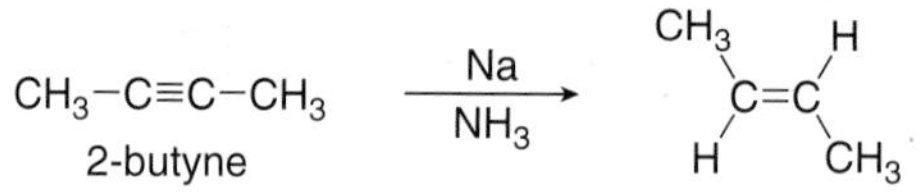

trans-2-butene

The **mechanism** for the dissolving metal reduction using Na in NH_3 features sequential addition of electrons and protons to the triple bond. Half-headed arrows denoting the movement of a single electron must be used in two steps when Na donates *one* electron. The mechanism can be divided conceptually into two parts, each of which consists of two steps: **addition of an electron followed by protonation of the resulting negative charge,** as shown in Mechanism 12.2.

Mechanism 12.2 Dissolving Metal Reduction of an Alkyne to a Trans Alkene

Steps [1] and [2] Addition of one electron and one proton to form a radical

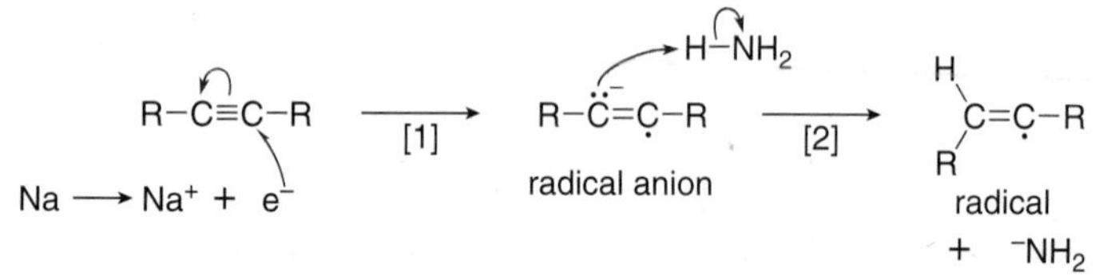

- Addition of an electron to the triple bond in Step [1] forms a **radical anion,** a species containing *both* a negative charge and an unpaired electron.
- Protonation of the anion with the solvent NH_3 in Step [2] yields a **radical.** The net effect of Steps [1] and [2] is to add one hydrogen atom (H•) to the triple bond.

Steps [3] and [4] Addition of one electron and one proton to form the trans alkene

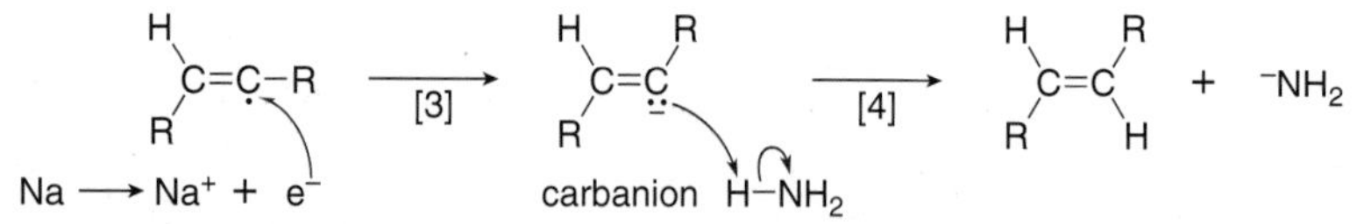

- Addition of a second electron to the radical in Step [3] forms a **carbanion.**
- Protonation of the carbanion in Step [4] forms the trans alkene. These last two steps add the second hydrogen atom (H•) to the triple bond.

Although the vinyl carbanion formed in Step [3] could have two different arrangements of its R groups, only the trans alkene is formed from the more stable vinyl carbanion; this carbanion has the larger R groups farther away from each other to avoid steric interactions. Protonation of this anion leads to the more stable trans product.

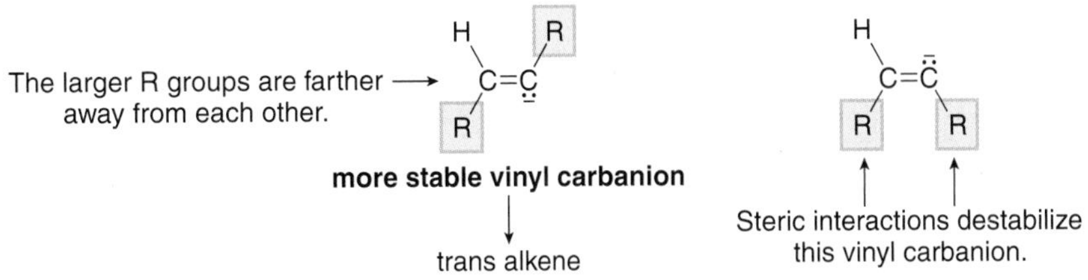
The larger R groups are farther away from each other.
H
R
C=C
R
more stable vinyl carbanion
trans alkene
H
C=C
R
R
Steric interactions destabilize this vinyl carbanion.

Dissolving metal reduction of a triple bond with Na in NH_3 is a **stereoselective reaction** because it forms a trans product exclusively.

- **Dissolving metal reductions always form the more stable trans product preferentially.**

The three methods to reduce a triple bond are summarized in Figure 12.5 using 3-hexyne as starting material.

Figure 12.5

Summary: Three methods to reduce a triple bond

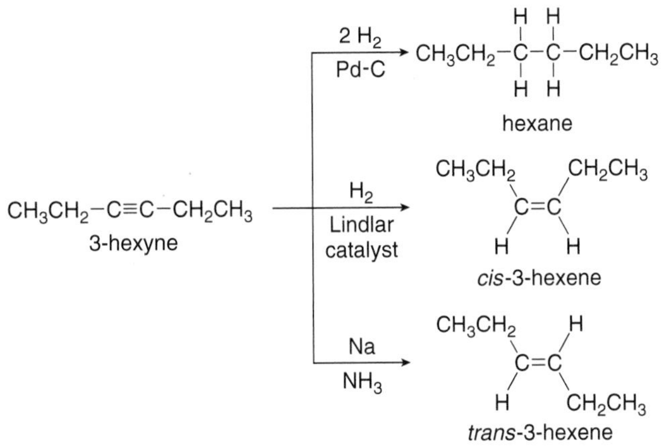
CH3CH2–C≡C–CH2CH3
3-hexyne
2 H2
Pd-C
CH3CH2–C–C–CH2CH3
hexane
H2
Lindlar catalyst
cis-3-hexene
Na
NH3
trans-3-hexene

Problem 12.12 What product is formed when $CH_3OCH_2CH_2C{\equiv}CCH_2CH(CH_3)_2$ is treated with each reagent: (a) H_2 (excess), Pd-C; (b) H_2 (1 equiv), Lindlar catalyst; (c) H_2 (excess), Lindlar catalyst; (d) Na, NH_3?

Problem 12.13 A chiral alkyne **A** with molecular formula C_6H_{10} is reduced with H_2 and Lindlar catalyst to **B** having the *R* configuration at its stereogenic center. What are the structures of **A** and **B?**

12.6 The Reduction of Polar C–X σ Bonds

Compounds containing polar C–X σ bonds that react with strong nucleophiles are reduced with metal hydride reagents, most commonly lithium aluminum hydride. Two functional groups possessing both of these characteristics are **alkyl halides** and **epoxides.** Alkyl halides are reduced to alkanes with loss of X^- as the leaving group. Epoxide rings are opened to form alcohols.

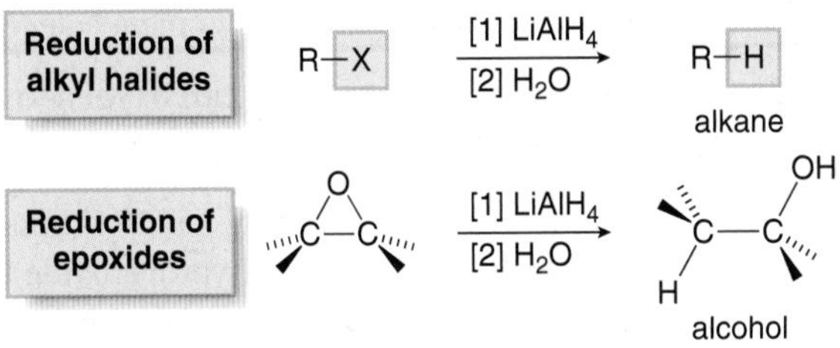
Reduction of alkyl halides
R–X
[1] LiAlH4
[2] H2O
R–H
alkane
Reduction of epoxides
[1] LiAlH4
[2] H2O
OH
H
alcohol

Reduction of these C–X σ bonds is another example of nucleophilic substitution, in which $LiAlH_4$ serves as a source of a hydride nucleophile (H^-). Because H^- is a strong nucleophile, the reaction follows an **S_N2 mechanism,** illustrated for the one-step reduction of an alkyl halide in Mechanism 12.3.

Mechanism 12.3 Reduction of RX with $LiAlH_4$

One step The nucleophile H^- substitutes for X^- in a single step.

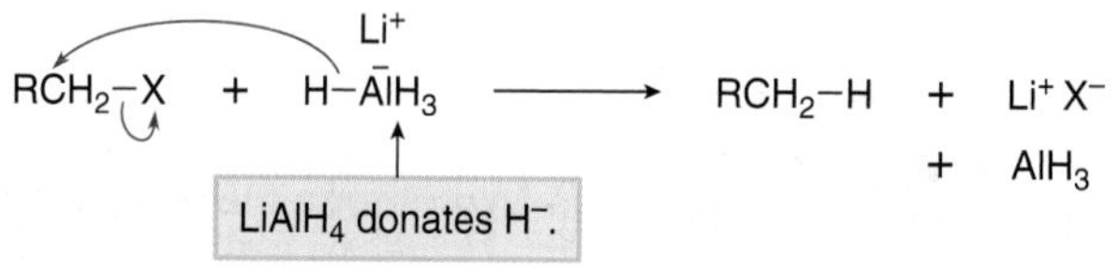
Li+
RCH2–X + H–AlH3
RCH2–H + Li+ X–
+ AlH3
LiAlH4 donates H–.

Because the reaction follows an S_N2 mechanism:

- **Unhindered CH_3X and 1° alkyl halides are more easily reduced than more substituted 2° and 3° halides.**
- **In unsymmetrical epoxides, nucleophilic attack of H^- (from $LiAlH_4$) occurs at the less substituted carbon atom.**

Examples are shown in Figure 12.6.

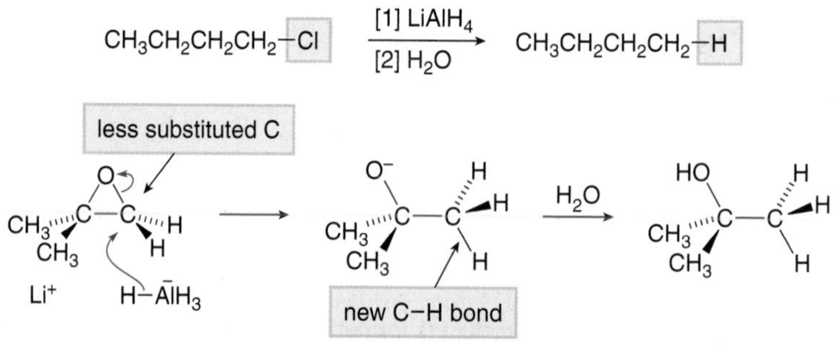
CH3CH2CH2CH2–Cl
[1] LiAlH4
[2] H2O
CH3CH2CH2CH2–H
less substituted C
CH3
CH3
Li+
H–AlH3
O–
H2O
HO
new C–H bond

Figure 12.6 Examples of reduction of C–X σ bonds with $LiAlH_4$

Problem 12.14 Draw the products of each reaction.

a. 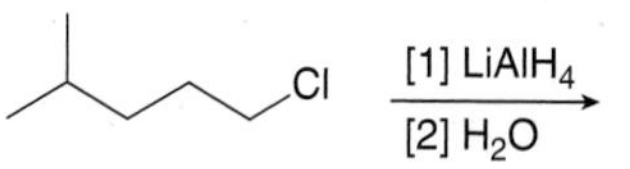 b. 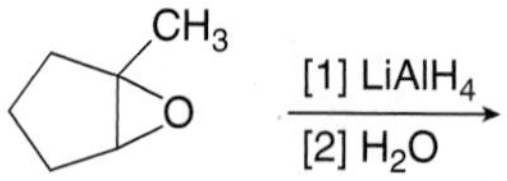
Cl
[1] LiAlH4
[2] H2O
CH3
O
[1] LiAlH4
[2] H2O

12.7 Oxidizing Agents

Oxidizing agents fall into two main categories:

- **Reagents that contain an oxygen–oxygen bond**
- **Reagents that contain metal–oxygen bonds**

Oxidizing agents containing an O–O bond include $\mathbf{O_2}$, $\mathbf{O_3}$ (ozone), $\mathbf{H_2O_2}$ (hydrogen peroxide), $\mathbf{(CH_3)_3COOH}$ (*tert*-butyl hydroperoxide), and peroxyacids. **Peroxyacids,** a group of reagents with the general structure $\mathbf{RCO_3H}$, have one more O atom than carboxylic acids (RCO_2H). Some peroxyacids are commercially available whereas others are prepared and used without isolation.

Figure 12.7
Common peroxyacids

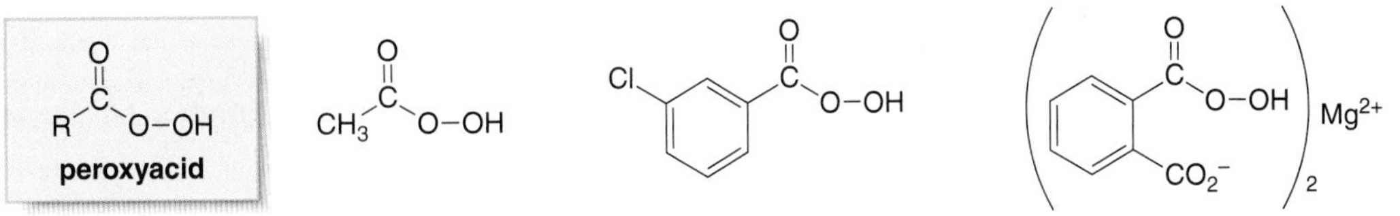
peroxyacid
Mg2+

peroxyacetic acid | *meta*-chloroperoxybenzoic acid **mCPBA** | magnesium monoperoxyphthalate **MMPP**

Examples are shown in Figure 12.7. All of these reagents contain a weak O–O bond that is cleaved during oxidation.

The most common oxidizing agents with metal–oxygen bonds contain either chromium in the +6 oxidation state (six Cr–O bonds) or manganese in the +7 oxidation state (seven Mn–O bonds). Common Cr^{6+} reagents include chromium(VI) oxide (**CrO_3**) and sodium or potassium dichromate (**$Na_2Cr_2O_7$** and **$K_2Cr_2O_7$**). **These reagents are strong oxidants** used in the presence of a strong aqueous acid such as H_2SO_4. **Pyridinium chlorochromate (PCC),** a Cr^{6+} reagent that is soluble in halogenated organic solvents, can be used without strong acid present. This makes it a **more selective Cr^{6+} oxidant,** as described in Section 12.12.

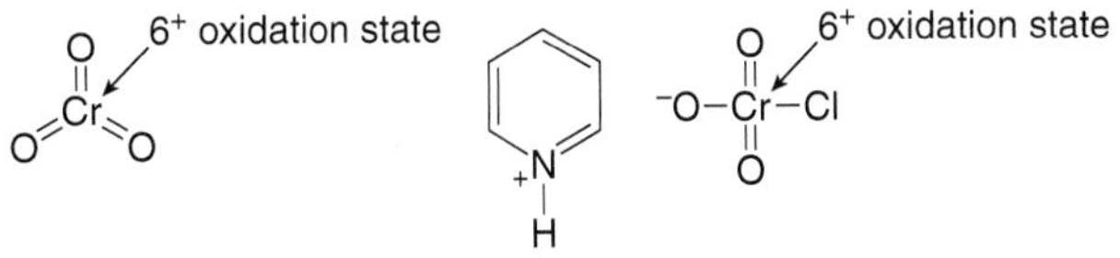
6+ oxidation state
6+ oxidation state

chromium(VI) oxide
CrO_3

pyridinium chlorochromate
PCC

The most common Mn^{7+} reagent is **$KMnO_4$** (potassium permanganate), a strong, water-soluble oxidant. Other oxidizing agents that contain metals include **OsO_4** (osmium tetroxide) and **Ag_2O** [silver(I) oxide].

In the remainder of Chapter 12, the oxidation of alkenes, alkynes, and alcohols—three functional groups already introduced in this text—is presented (Figure 12.8). Addition reactions to alkenes and alkynes that increase the number of C–O bonds are described in Sections 12.8–12.11. Oxidation of alcohols to carbonyl compounds appears in Sections 12.12–12.14.

Figure 12.8
Oxidation reactions of alkenes, alkynes, and alcohols

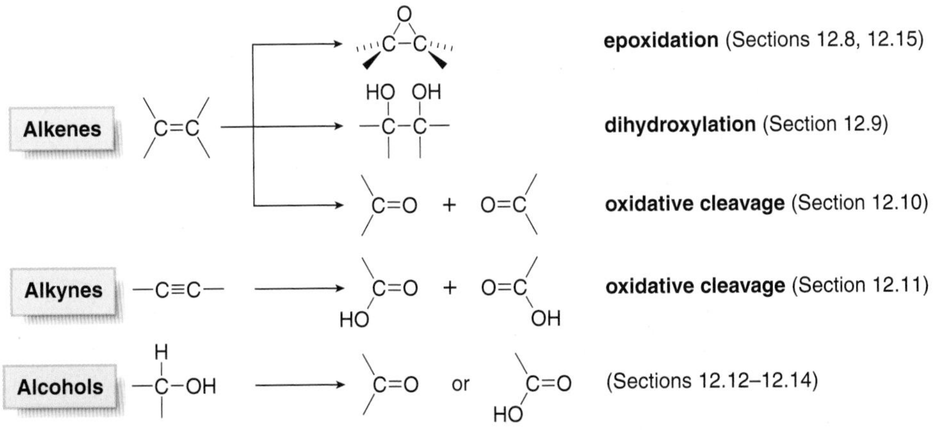
Alkenes
Alkynes
Alcohols
epoxidation (Sections 12.8, 12.15)
dihydroxylation (Section 12.9)
oxidative cleavage (Section 12.10)
oxidative cleavage (Section 12.11)
(Sections 12.12–12.14)

12.8 Epoxidation

Epoxidation is the addition of a single oxygen atom to an alkene to form an **epoxide.**

Epoxidation

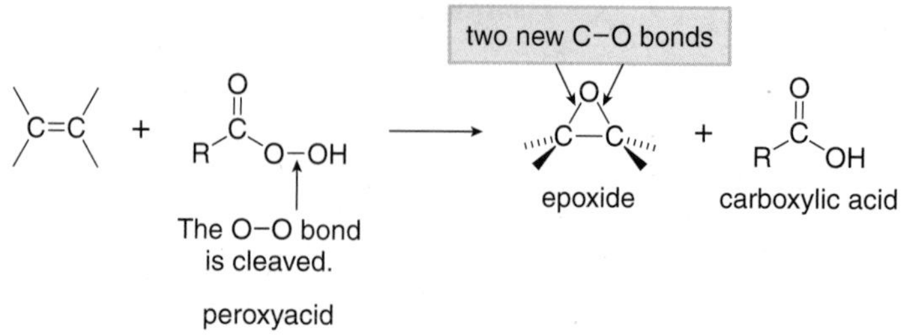

The weak π bond of the alkene is broken and two new C–O σ bonds are formed. Epoxidation is typically carried out with a peroxyacid, resulting in cleavage of the weak O–O bond of the reagent.

Examples

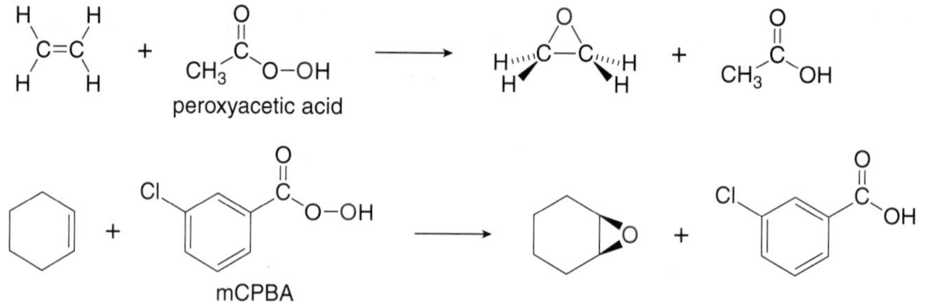

Epoxidation occurs via the concerted addition of one oxygen atom of the peroxyacid to the π bond as shown in Mechanism 12.4. Epoxidation resembles the formation of the bridged halonium ion in Section 10.13, in that two bonds in a three-membered ring are formed in one step.

Mechanism 12.4 Epoxidation of an Alkene with a Peroxyacid

One step All bonds are broken or formed in a single step.

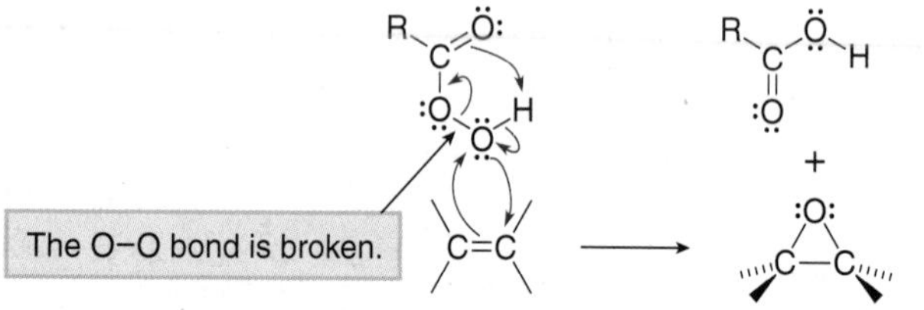

- Two C–O bonds are formed to one O atom with one electron pair from the peroxyacid and one from the π bond.
- The weak O–O bond is broken.

Problem 12.15 What epoxide is formed when each alkene is treated with mCPBA?

a. $(CH_3)_2C{=}CH_2$ b. $(CH_3)_2C{=}C(CH_3)_2$ c. 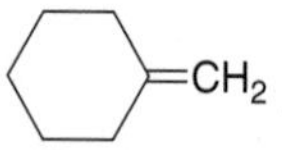

12.8A The Stereochemistry of Epoxidation

Epoxidation occurs via **syn addition** of an O atom from either side of the planar double bond, so that both C–O bonds are formed on the same side. The relative position of substituents in the alkene reactant is **retained** in the epoxide product.

- **A cis alkene gives an epoxide with cis substituents. A trans alkene gives an epoxide with trans substituents.**

Epoxidation is a **stereospecific** reaction because cis and trans alkenes yield different stereoisomers as products, as illustrated in Sample Problem 12.2.

Sample Problem 12.2 Draw the stereoisomers formed when *cis*- and *trans*-2-butene are epoxidized with mCPBA.

Solution

To draw each product of epoxidation, add an O atom from either side of the alkene, and keep all substituents in their *original* orientations. The **cis** methyl groups in *cis*-2-butene become **cis** substituents in the epoxide. Addition of an O atom from either side of the trigonal planar alkene leads to the same compound—an **achiral meso compound that contains two stereogenic centers.**

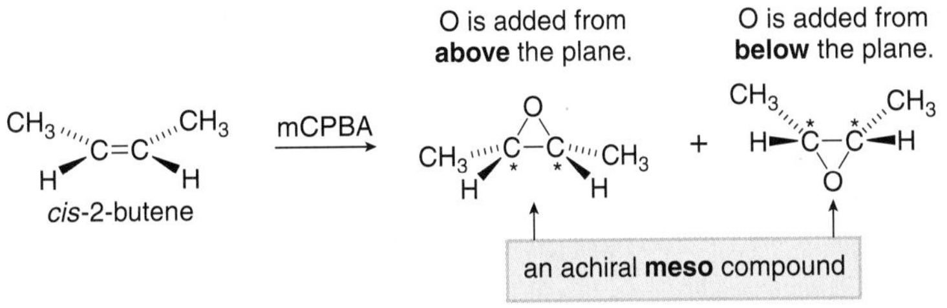

[* denotes a stereogenic center]

The **trans** methyl groups in *trans*-2-butene, become **trans** substituents in the epoxide. Addition of an O atom from either side of the trigonal planar alkene yields an equal mixture of two enantiomers—a **racemic mixture.**

Epoxidation of *cis*- and *trans*-2-butene illustrates the general rule about the stereochemistry of reactions: **an achiral starting material gives achiral or racemic products.**

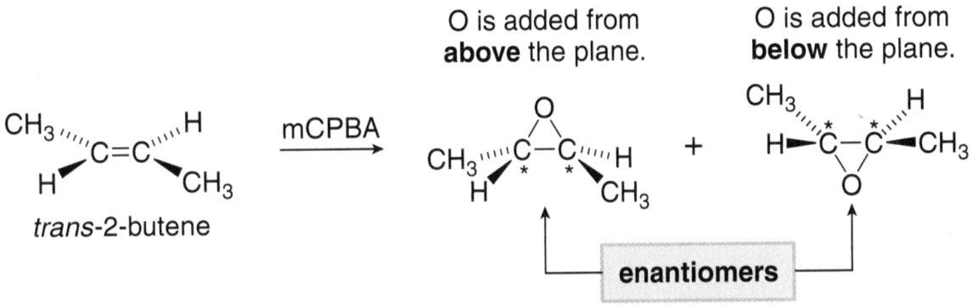

[* denotes a stereogenic center]

Problem 12.16 Draw all stereoisomers formed when each alkene is treated with mCPBA.

a. 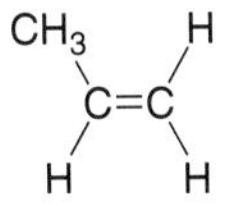

b. 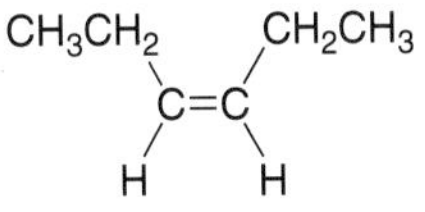

c. 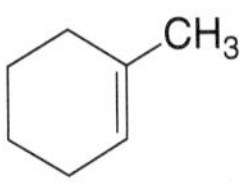

12.8B The Synthesis of Disparlure

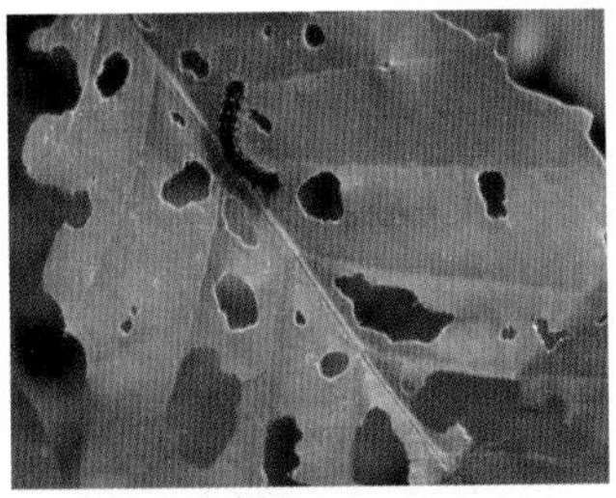

In 1869, the gypsy moth was introduced into New England in an attempt to develop a silk industry. Some moths escaped into the wild and the population flourished. Mature gypsy moth caterpillars eat an average of one square foot of leaf surface per day, defoliating shade trees and entire forests. Many trees die after a single defoliation.

Disparlure, the sex pheromone of the female gypsy moth, is synthesized by a stepwise reaction sequence that uses an epoxidation reaction as the final step. Retrosynthetic analysis of disparlure illustrates three key operations:

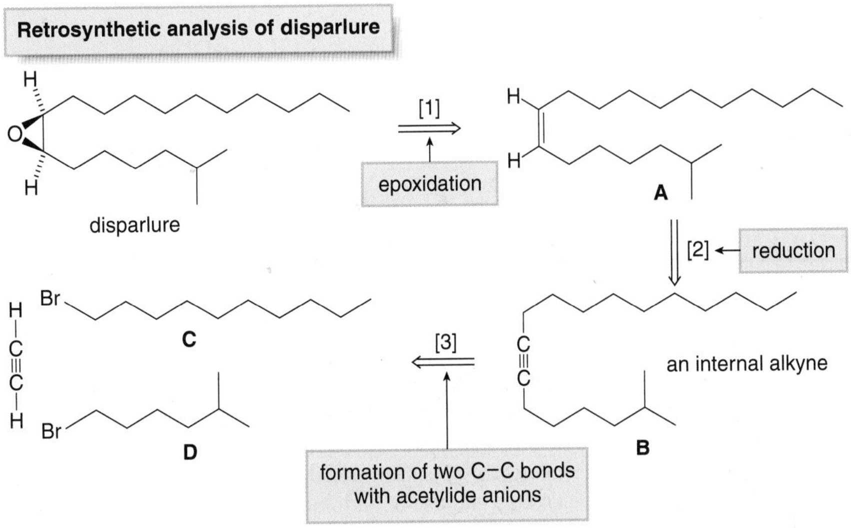

- **Step [1]** The cis epoxide in disparlure is prepared from a cis alkene **A** by epoxidation.
- **Step [2]** **A** is prepared from an internal alkyne **B** by reduction.
- **Step [3]** **B** is prepared from acetylene and two 1° alkyl halides (**C** and **D**) by using S_N2 reactions with acetylide anions.

Figure 12.9 illustrates the synthesis of disparlure beginning with acetylene. The synthesis is conceptually divided into three parts:

- **Part [1]** Acetylene is converted to an internal alkyne **B** by forming two C–C bonds. Each bond is formed by treating an alkyne with base ($NaNH_2$) to form an acetylide anion, which reacts with an alkyl halide (**C** or **D**) in an S_N2 reaction (Section 11.11).
- **Part [2]** The internal alkyne **B** is reduced to a cis alkene **A** by syn addition of H_2 using the Lindlar catalyst (Section 12.5B).
- **Part [3]** The cis alkene **A** is epoxidized to disparlure using a peroxyacid such as mCPBA.

Figure 12.9 The synthesis of disparlure

Part [1] Formation of two C–C bonds using acetylide anions

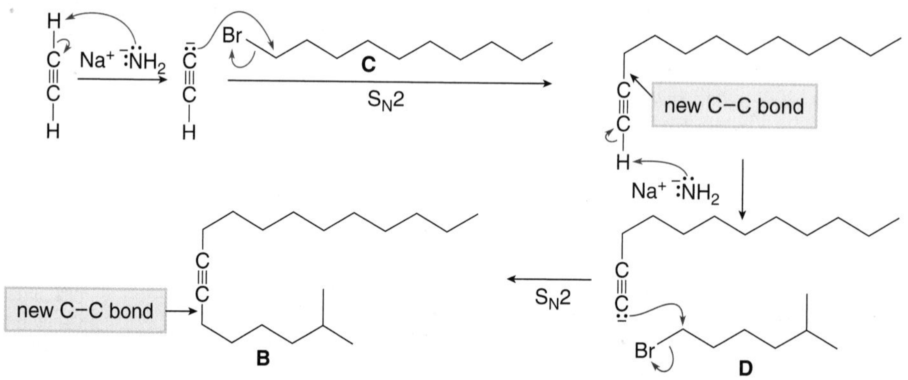

Part [2] Reduction of alkyne **B** to form cis alkene **A**

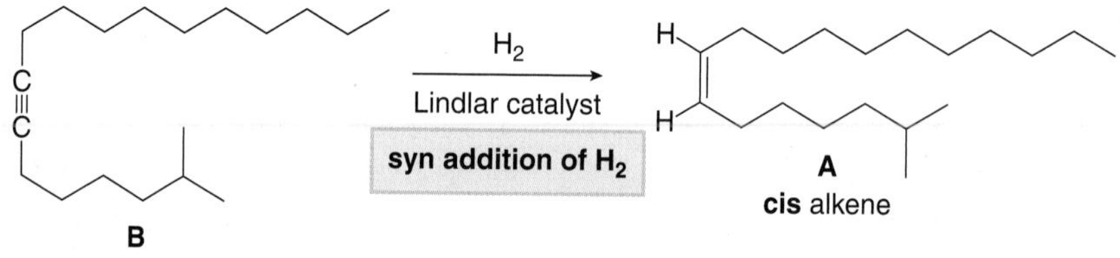

Part [3] Epoxidation of **A** to form disparlure

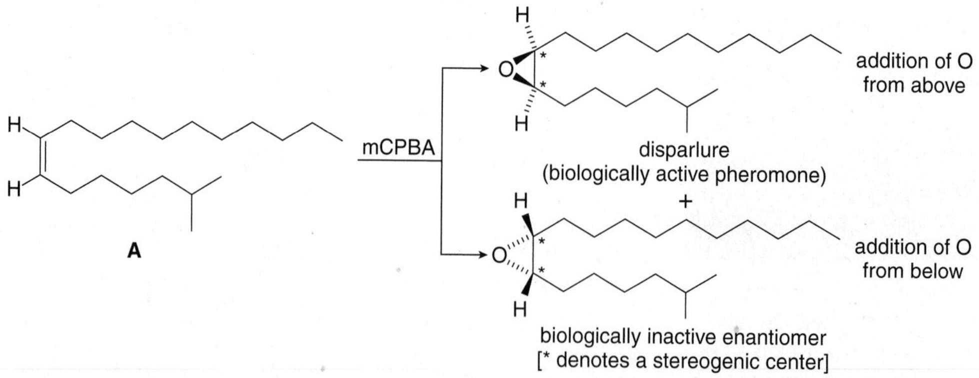

- Disparlure has been used to control the spread of the gypsy moth caterpillar, a pest that has periodically devastated forests in the northeastern United States by defoliating many shade and fruit-bearing trees. The active pheromone is placed in a trap containing a poison or sticky substance, and the male moth is lured to the trap by the pheromone. Alternatively, thousands of disparlure-baited traps are placed along the edges of infestation. When the pheromone permeates the air, males are confused and can't locate individual females so that mating is disrupted. Such a species-specific method presents a new way of controlling an insect population that avoids the widespread use of harmful, nonspecific pesticides.

How to separate a racemic mixture into its component enantiomers is discussed in Section 29.3.

Epoxidation of the cis alkene **A** from two different sides of the double bond affords two cis epoxides in the last step—a racemic mixture of two enantiomers. Thus, half of the product is the desired pheromone disparlure, but the other half is its biologically inactive enantiomer. Separating the desired from the undesired enantiomer is difficult and expensive, because both compounds have identical physical properties. A reaction that affords a chiral epoxide from an achiral precursor without forming a racemic mixture is discussed in Section 12.15.

12.9 Dihydroxylation

Dihydroxylation is the addition of two hydroxy groups to a double bond, forming a **1,2-diol** or **glycol.** Depending on the reagent, the two new OH groups can be added to the opposite sides (**anti** addition) or the same side (**syn** addition) of the double bond.

Dihydroxylation—General reaction

1,2-diol or glycol

Stereochemistry

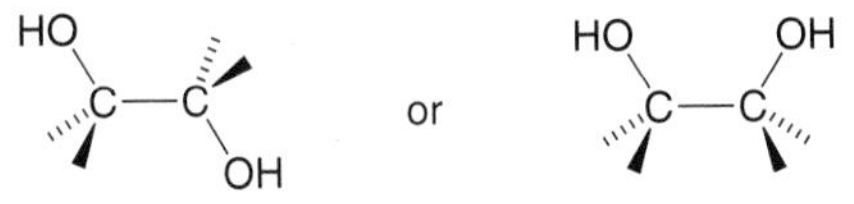

anti addition product

2 OH's added on **opposite** sides of the C=C

syn addition product

2 OH's added on the **same** side of the C=C

12.9A Anti Dihydroxylation

Anti dihydroxylation is achieved in two steps—epoxidation followed by opening of the ring with ^-OH or H_2O. Cyclohexene, for example, is converted to a racemic mixture of two *trans*-1,2-cyclohexanediols by anti addition of two OH groups.

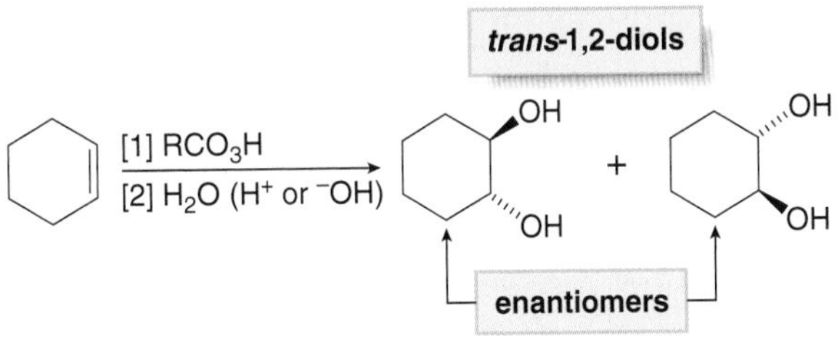

The stereochemistry of the products can be understood by examining the stereochemistry of each step.

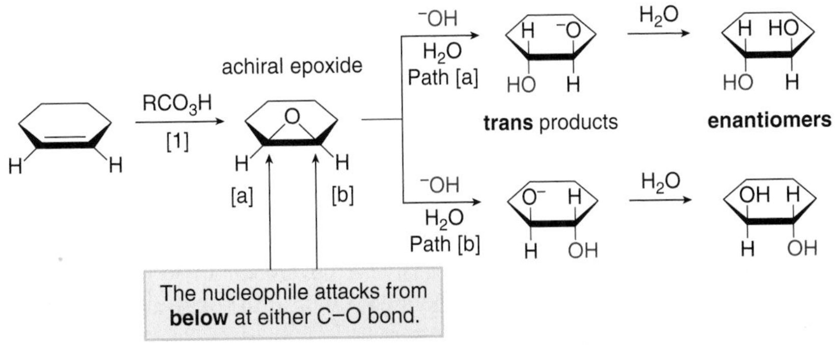

Epoxidation of cyclohexene adds an O atom from either above or below the plane of the double bond to form a single **achiral epoxide,** so only one representation is shown. Opening of the epoxide ring then occurs with **backside attack at either C–O bond.** Because the epoxide is drawn above the plane of the six-membered ring, nucleophilic attack occurs from **below** the plane. This reaction is a specific example of the opening of epoxide rings with strong nucleophiles, first presented in Section 9.15.

Because one OH group of the 1,2-diol comes from the epoxide and one OH group comes from the nucleophile (^-OH), the overall result is **anti addition of two OH groups** to an alkene.

Problem 12.17 Draw the products formed when both *cis*- and *trans*-2-butene are treated with a peroxyacid followed by ^-OH (in H_2O). Explain how these reactions illustrate that anti dihydroxylation is stereospecific.

12.9B Syn Dihydroxylation

Syn dihydroxylation results when an alkene is treated with either $\mathbf{KMnO_4}$ or $\mathbf{OsO_4}$.

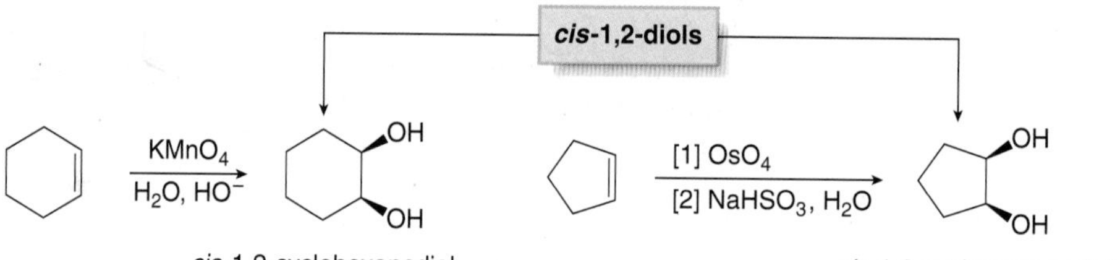

cis-1,2-cyclohexanediol *cis*-1,2-cyclopentanediol

Each reagent adds two oxygen atoms to the same side of the double bond—that is, in a **syn** fashion—to yield a cyclic intermediate. Hydrolysis of the cyclic intermediate cleaves the metal–oxygen bonds, forming the *cis*-1,2-diol. With OsO_4, sodium bisulfite ($NaHSO_3$) is also added in the hydrolysis step.

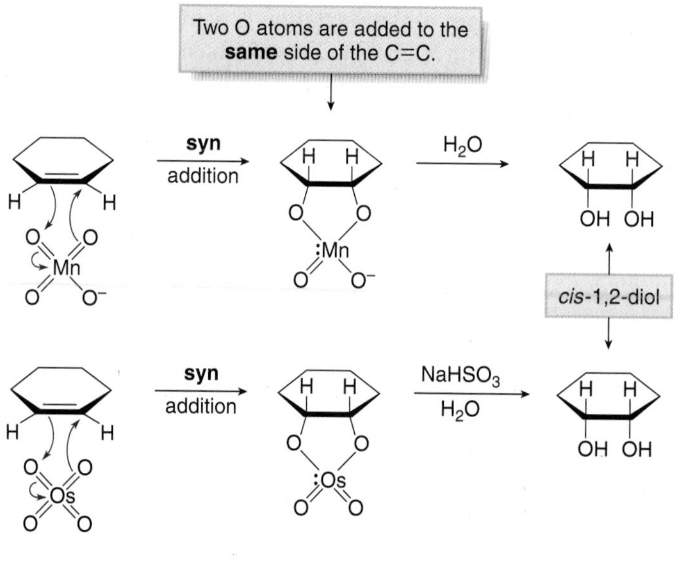

Although $KMnO_4$ is inexpensive and readily available, its use is limited by its insolubility in organic solvents. To prevent further oxidation of the product 1,2-diol, the reaction mixture must be kept basic with added ^-OH.

Although OsO_4 is a more selective oxidant than $KMnO_4$ and is soluble in organic solvents, it is toxic and expensive. To overcome these limitations, dihydroxylation can be carried out by using a *catalytic* amount of OsO_4, if the oxidant ***N*-methylmorpholine *N*-oxide** (**NMO**) is also added.

NMO is an **amine oxide.** It is not possible to draw a Lewis structure of an amine oxide having only neutral atoms.

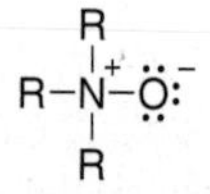

amine oxide

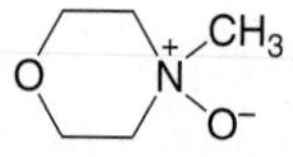

N-methylmorpholine *N*-oxide

NMO

In the catalytic process, dihydroxylation of the double bond converts the Os^{8+} oxidant into an Os^{6+} product, which is then re-oxidized by NMO to Os^{8+}. This Os^{8+} reagent can then be used for dihydroxylation once again, and the catalytic cycle continues.

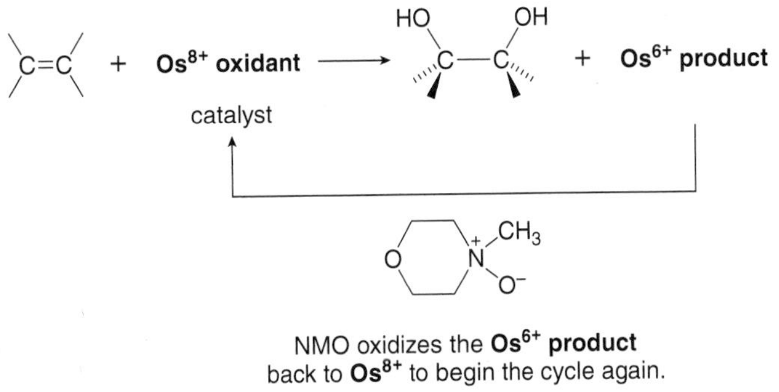

Problem 12.18 Draw the products formed when both *cis*- and *trans*-2-butene are treated with OsO_4, followed by hydrolysis with $NaHSO_3 + H_2O$. Explain how these reactions illustrate that syn dihydroxylation is stereospecific.

12.10 Oxidative Cleavage of Alkenes

Lightning produces O_3 from O_2 during an electrical storm. Moreover, the pungent odor around a heavily used photocopy machine is O_3 produced from O_2 during the process. O_3 at ground level is an unwanted atmospheric pollutant. In the stratosphere, however, it protects us from harmful ultraviolet radiation, as discussed in Chapter 15.

Oxidative cleavage of an alkene breaks both the σ and π bonds of the double bond to form two carbonyl groups. Depending on the number of R groups bonded to the double bond, oxidative cleavage yields either **ketones** or **aldehydes.**

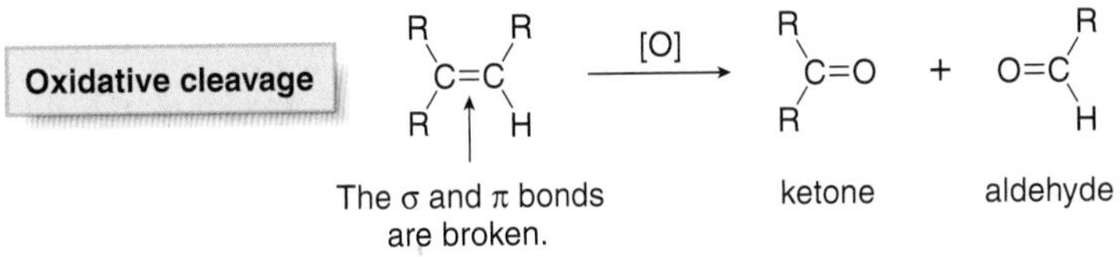

One method of oxidative cleavage relies on a two-step procedure using **ozone (O_3) as the oxidant** in the first step. Cleavage with ozone is called **ozonolysis.**

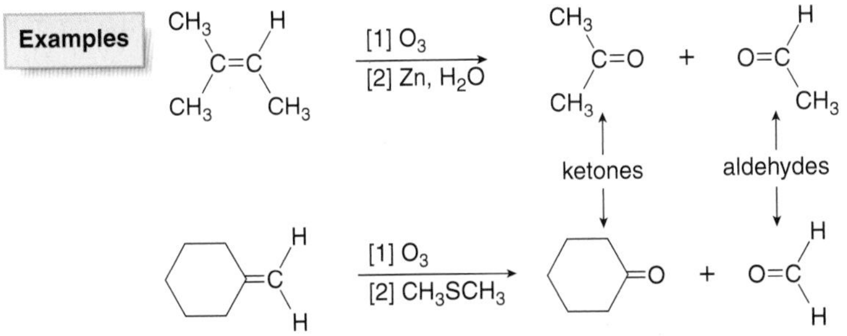

Addition of ozone to the π bond of the alkene forms an unstable intermediate called a **molozonide,** which then rearranges to an **ozonide** by a stepwise process. The unstable ozonide is then reduced without isolation to afford carbonyl compounds. **Zn (in H_2O) or dimethyl sulfide (CH_3SCH_3)** are two common reagents used to convert the ozonide to carbonyl compounds.

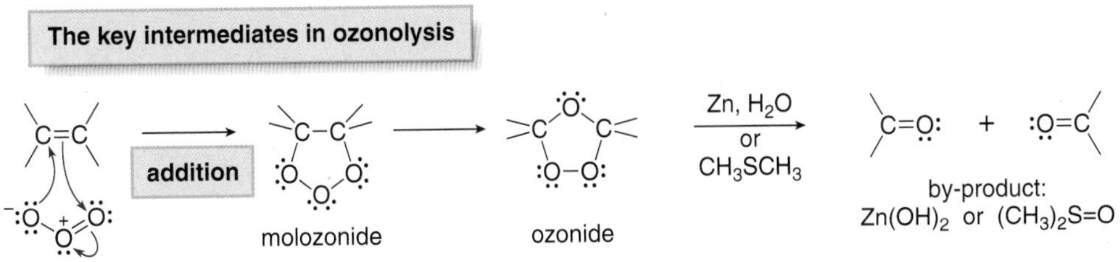

To draw the product of any oxidative cleavage:

- **Locate all π bonds in the molecule.**
- **Replace each C=C by two C=O bonds.**

Sample Problem 12.3 Draw the products when each alkene is treated with O_3 followed by CH_3SCH_3.

a. 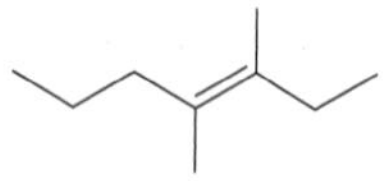 b. 

Solution

a. Cleave the double bond and replace it with two carbonyl groups.

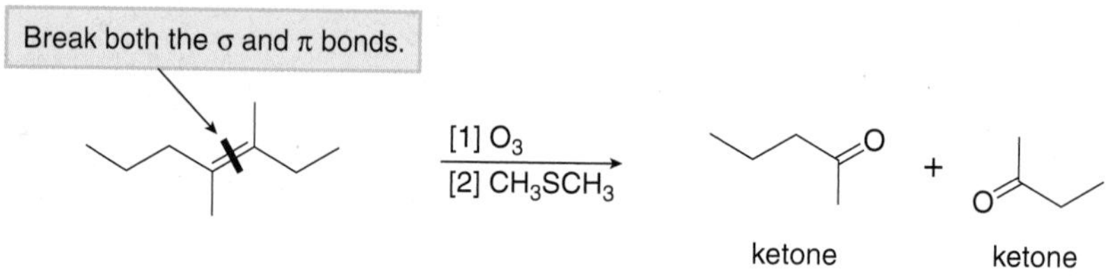
Break both the σ and π bonds.
[1] O3
[2] CH3SCH3
O
+
O
ketone
ketone

b. For a cycloalkene, oxidative cleavage results in a **single molecule with two carbonyl groups—a dicarbonyl compound.**

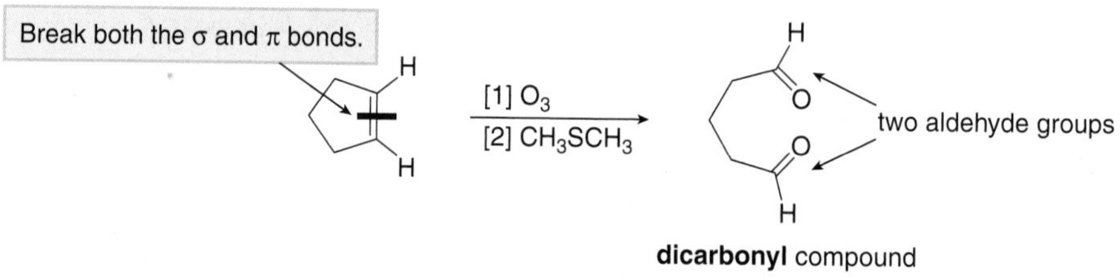
Break both the σ and π bonds.
H
H
[1] O3
[2] CH3SCH3
H
O
O
H
two aldehyde groups
dicarbonyl compound

Problem 12.19 Draw the products formed when each alkene is treated with O_3 followed by Zn, H_2O.

a. $(CH_3)_2C{=}CHCH_2CH_2CH_2CH_3$ b. 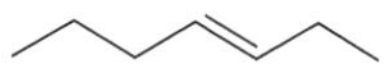 c. 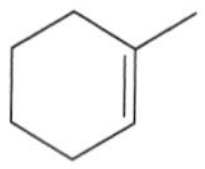

Ozonolysis of dienes (and other polyenes) results in oxidative cleavage of all C=C bonds. The number of carbonyl groups formed in the products is *twice* the number of double bonds in the starting material.

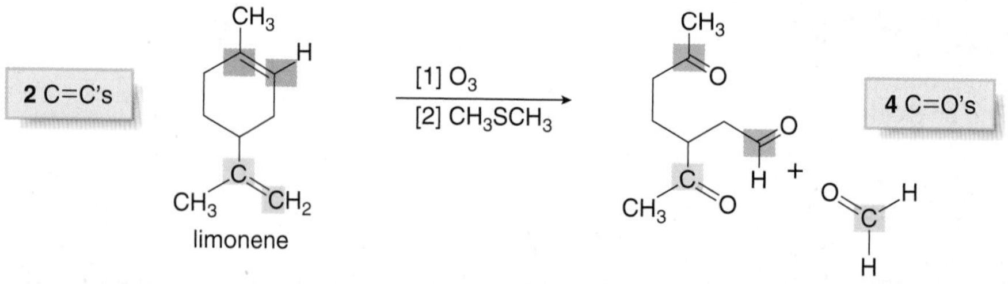
2 C=C's
CH3
H
C
CH3
CH2
limonene
[1] O3
[2] CH3SCH3
CH3
O
O
H
C
CH3
O
+
O
C
H
H
4 C=O's

Oxidative cleavage is a valuable tool for structure determination of unknown compounds. The ability to determine what alkene gives rise to a particular set of oxidative cleavage products is thus a useful skill, illustrated in Sample Problem 12.4.

Sample Problem 12.4 What alkene forms the following products after reaction with O_3 followed by CH_3SCH_3?

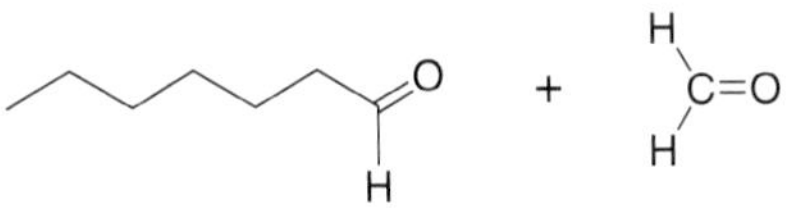

Solution

To draw the starting material, ignore the O atoms in the carbonyl groups and join the carbonyl carbons together by a C=C.

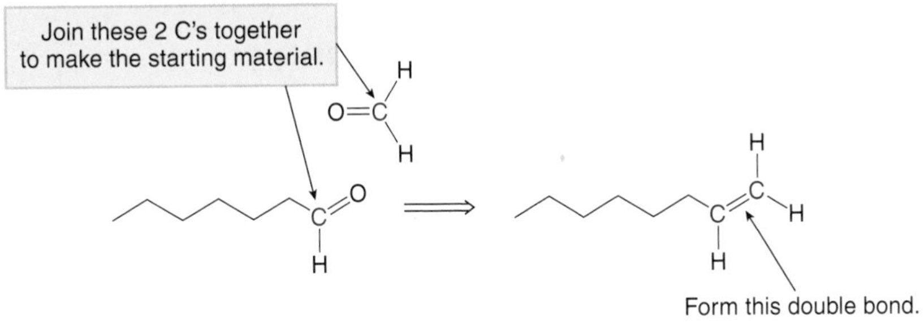
Join these 2 C's together
to make the starting material.
Form this double bond.

Problem 12.20 What alkene yields each set of oxidative cleavage products?

a. $(CH_3)_2C{=}O$ + $(CH_3CH_2)_2C{=}O$

b. 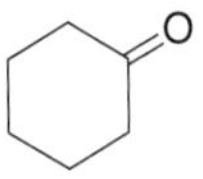 + CH_3CHO

c. 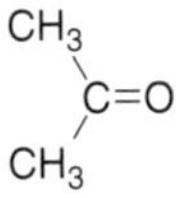 only

Problem 12.21 Draw the products formed when each diene is treated with O_3 followed by CH_3SCH_3.

a. 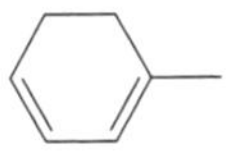

b. 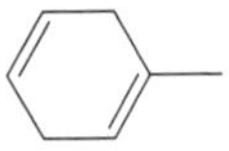

c. 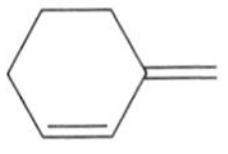

12.11 Oxidative Cleavage of Alkynes

Alkynes also undergo oxidative cleavage of the σ bond and both π bonds of the triple bond. Internal alkynes are oxidized to **carboxylic acids (RCOOH),** whereas terminal alkynes afford carboxylic acids and $\mathbf{CO_2}$ from the *sp* hybridized C–H bond.

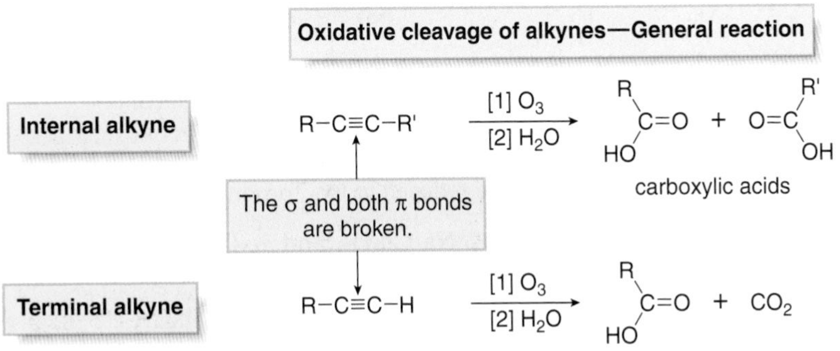
Oxidative cleavage of alkynes—General reaction
Internal alkyne
R–C≡C–R'
[1] O3
[2] H2O
carboxylic acids
The σ and both π bonds are broken.
Terminal alkyne
R–C≡C–H
[1] O3
[2] H2O
+ CO2

Oxidative cleavage is commonly carried out with O_3, followed by cleavage of the intermediate ozonide with H_2O.

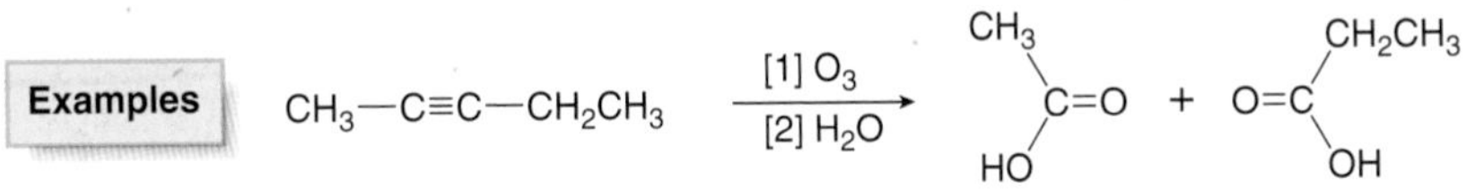
Examples
CH3–C≡C–CH2CH3
[1] O3
[2] H2O

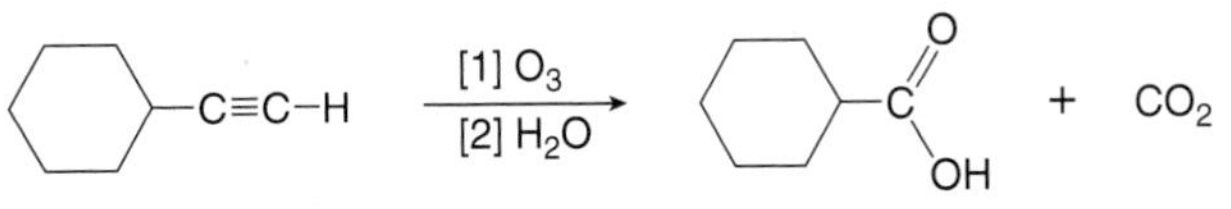
[1] O3
[2] H2O
+ CO2

Problem 12.22 Draw the products formed when each alkyne is treated with O_3 followed by H_2O.

a. $CH_3CH_2-C{\equiv}C-CH_2CH_2CH_3$

b. 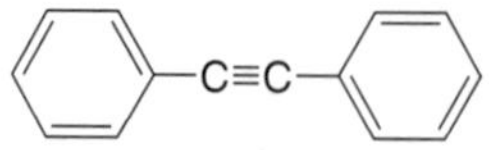

c. $HC{\equiv}C-CH_2CH_2-C{\equiv}C-CH_3$

Problem 12.23 What alkyne (or diyne) yields each set of oxidative cleavage products?

a. $CO_2 + CH_3(CH_2)_8CO_2H$

b. $CH_3CH_2CH(CH_3)CO_2H$ only

c. $CH_3CH_2CO_2H$, $HO_2CCH_2CO_2H$, CH_3CO_2H

d. $HO_2C(CH_2)_{14}CO_2H$

12.12 Oxidation of Alcohols

Alcohols are oxidized to a variety of carbonyl compounds, depending on the type of alcohol and reagent. Oxidation occurs by replacing the C–H bonds *on the carbon bearing the OH group* by C–O bonds.

- **1° Alcohols** are oxidized to either **aldehydes** or **carboxylic acids** by replacing either one or two C–H bonds by C–O bonds.

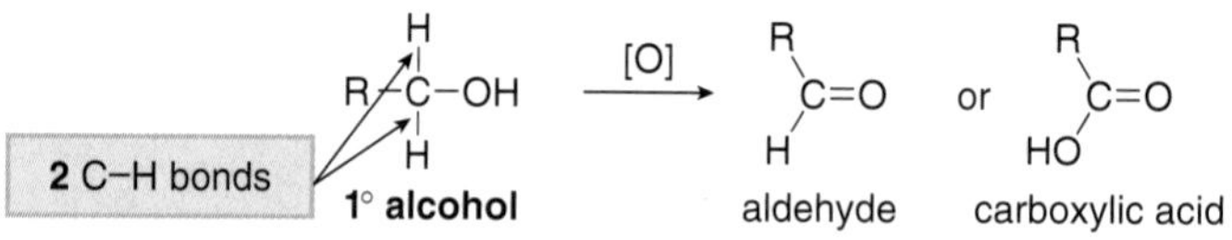

- **2° Alcohols** are oxidized to **ketones** by replacing the one C–H bond by a C–O bond.

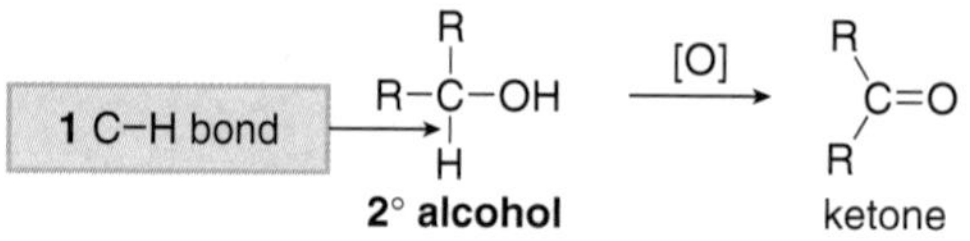

- **3° Alcohols have no H atoms on the carbon with the OH group,** so they are not easily oxidized.

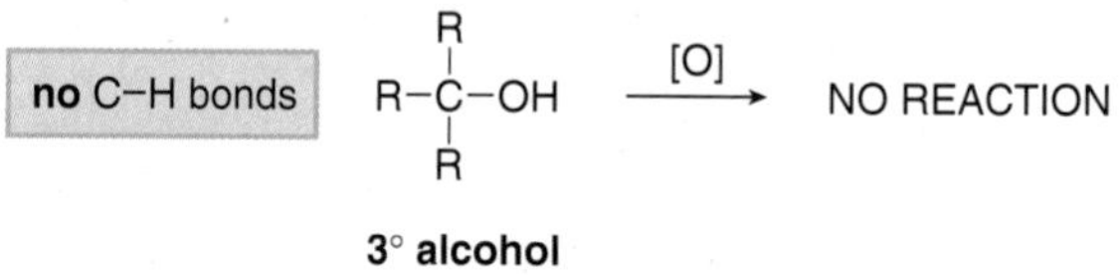

The oxidation of alcohols to carbonyl compounds is typically carried out with Cr^{6+} oxidants, which are reduced to Cr^{3+} products.

- **CrO_3, $Na_2Cr_2O_7$, and $K_2Cr_2O_7$** are **strong, nonselective oxidants** used in aqueous acid ($H_2SO_4 + H_2O$).
- **PCC** (Section 12.7) is soluble in CH_2Cl_2 (dichloromethane), and can be used without strong acid present, making it a **more selective, milder oxidant.**

12.12A Oxidation of 2° Alcohols

Any of the Cr^{6+} oxidants effectively oxidizes 2° alcohols to ketones.

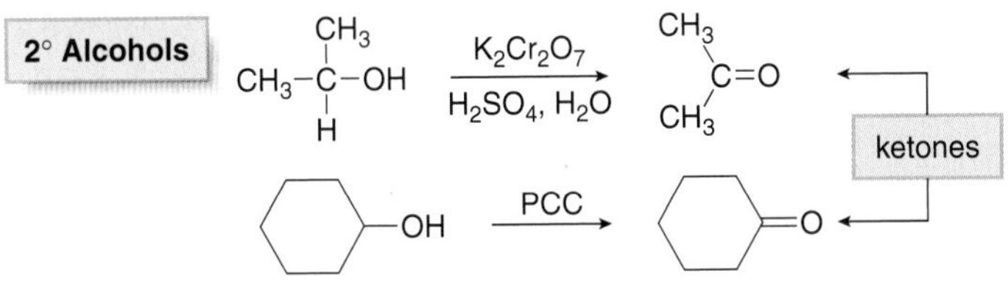

The mechanism for alcohol oxidation has two key parts: **formation of a chromate ester and loss of a proton.** Mechanism 12.5 is drawn for the oxidation of a general 2° alcohol with CrO_3.

Mechanism 12.5 Oxidation of an Alcohol with CrO_3

Steps [1] and [2] Formation of the chromate ester

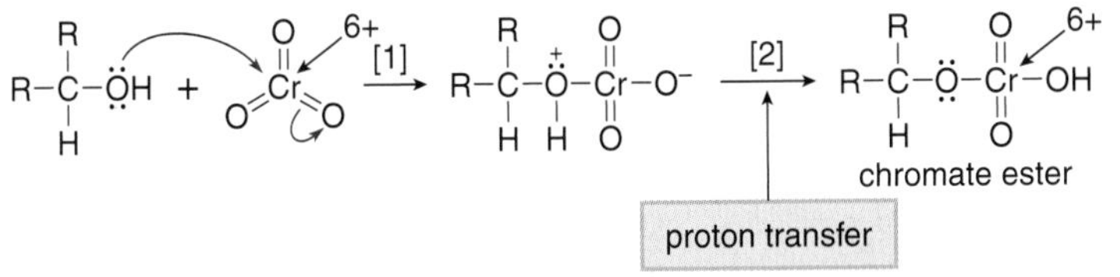

- Nucleophilic attack of the alcohol on the electrophilic metal followed by proton transfer forms a **chromate ester.** The C–H bond in the starting material (the 2° alcohol) is still present in the chromate ester, so there is no net oxidation in Steps [1] and [2].

Step [3] Removal of a proton to form the carbonyl group

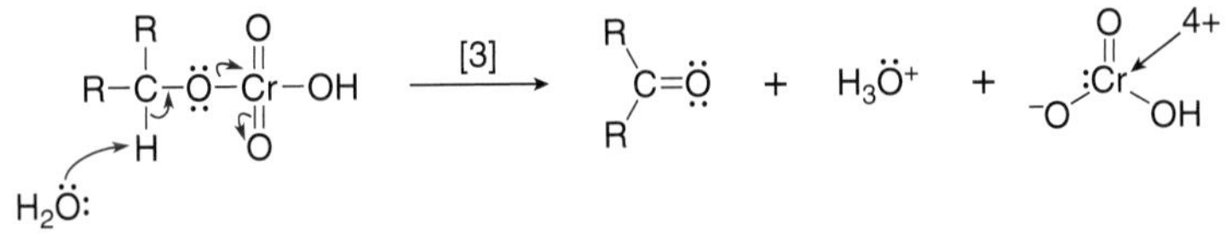

- In Step [3], a base (H_2O or a molecule of the starting alcohol) removes a proton, with the electron pair in the C–H bond forming the new π bond of the C=O. **Oxidation at carbon occurs in this step** because the number of C–H bonds decreases and the number of C–O bonds increases.

These three steps convert the Cr^{6+} oxidant to a Cr^{4+} product, which is then further reduced to a Cr^{3+} product by a series of steps.

12.12B Oxidation of 1° Alcohols

1° Alcohols are oxidized to either aldehydes or carboxylic acids, depending on the reagent.

- **1° Alcohols are oxidized to aldehydes (RCHO) under mild reaction conditions—using PCC in CH_2Cl_2.**
- **1° Alcohols are oxidized to carboxylic acids (RCOOH) under harsher reaction conditions: $Na_2Cr_2O_7$, $K_2Cr_2O_7$, or CrO_3 in the presence of H_2O and H_2SO_4.**

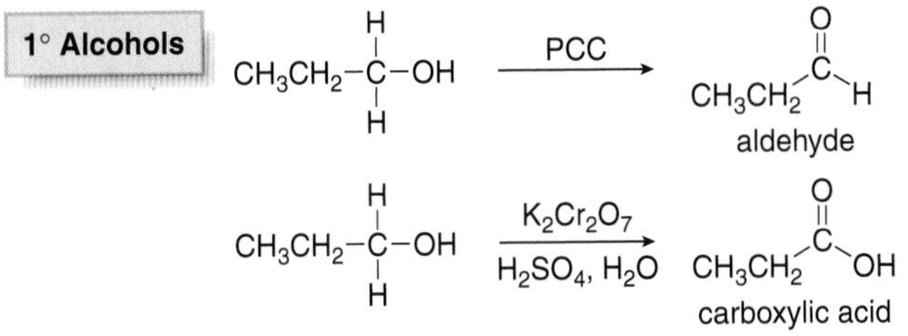

The mechanism for the oxidation of 1° alcohols to aldehydes parallels the oxidation of 2° alcohols to ketones detailed in Section 12.12A. Oxidation of a 1° alcohol to a carboxylic acid requires three operations: **oxidation first to the aldehyde, reaction with water,** and then further **oxidation to the carboxylic acid,** as shown in Mechanism 12.6.

Mechanism 12.6 Oxidation of a 1° Alcohol to a Carboxylic Acid

Part [1] Oxidation of a 1° alcohol to an aldehyde

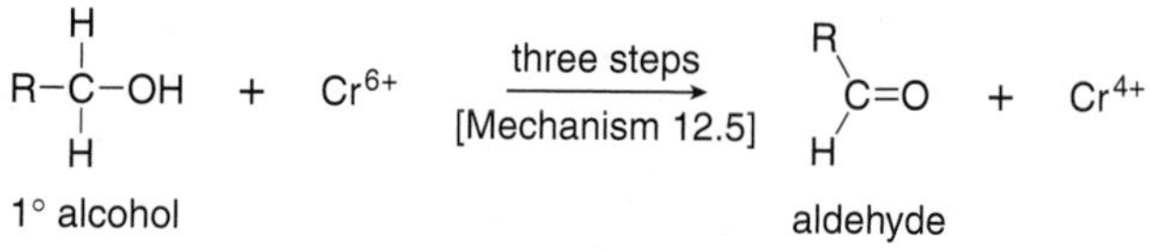

- Oxidation of a 1° alcohol to an aldehyde occurs by the three-step mechanism detailed in Mechanism 12.5.

Part [2] Addition of H_2O to form a hydrate

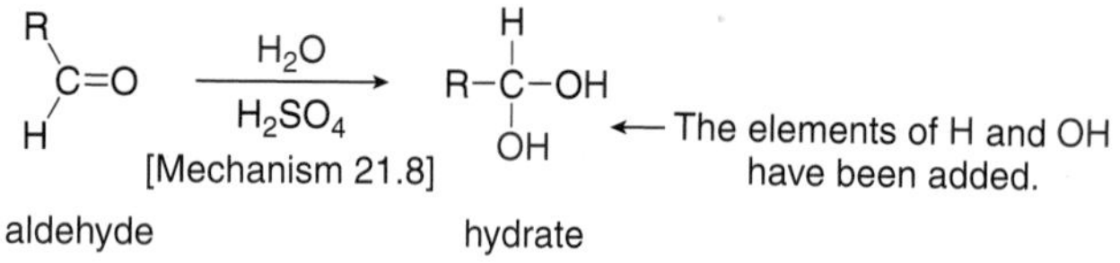

- The aldehyde reacts with H_2O to form a **hydrate,** a compound with two OH groups on the same carbon atom. Hydrates are discussed in greater detail in Section 21.13.

Part [3] Oxidation of the hydrate to a carboxylic acid

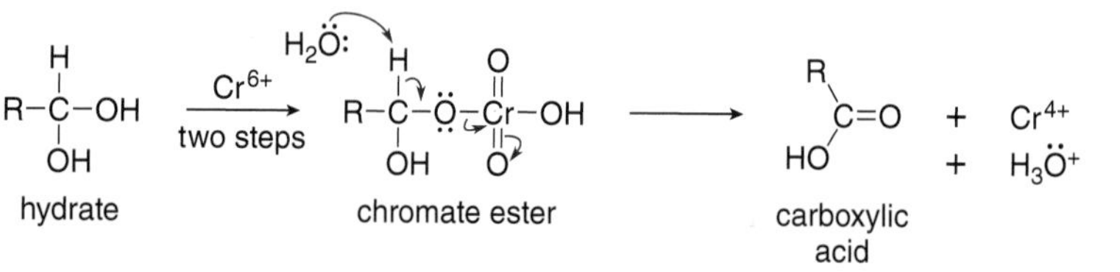

- The C–H bond of the hydrate is then oxidized with the Cr^{6+} reagent, following Mechanism 12.5. Because the hydrate contains two OH groups, the product of oxidation is a carboxylic acid.

Cr^{6+} oxidations are characterized by a color change, as the **red-orange Cr^{6+} reagent** is reduced to **green Cr^{3+}.** The first devices used to measure blood alcohol content in individuals suspected of "driving under the influence" made use of this color change. Oxidation of CH_3CH_2OH, the 1° alcohol in alcoholic beverages, with orange $K_2Cr_2O_7$ forms CH_3COOH and green Cr^{3+}.

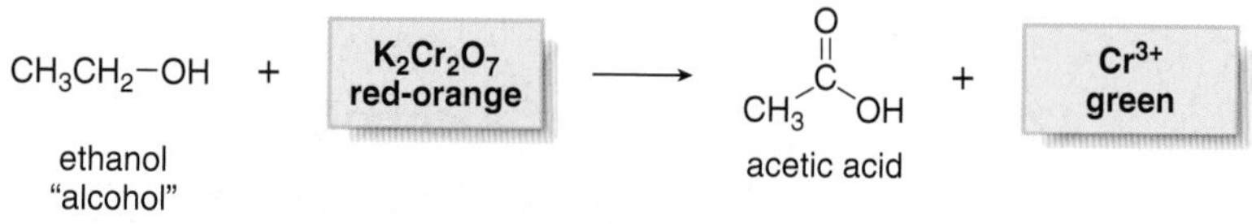

Blood alcohol level can be determined by having an individual blow into a tube containing $K_2Cr_2O_7$, H_2SO_4, and an inert solid. The alcohol in the exhaled breath is oxidized by the Cr^{6+} reagent, which turns green in the tube (Figure 12.10). The higher the concentration of CH_3CH_2OH in the breath, the more Cr^{6+} is reduced, and the farther the green Cr^{3+} color extends down the length of the sample tube. This value is then correlated with blood alcohol content to determine if an individual has surpassed the legal blood alcohol limit.

Problem 12.24 Draw the organic products in each of the following reactions.

a. 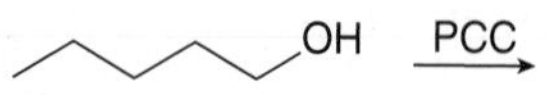

c. 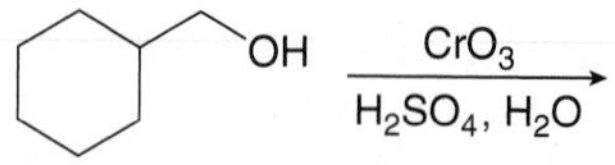

b. 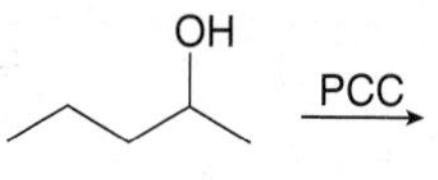

d. 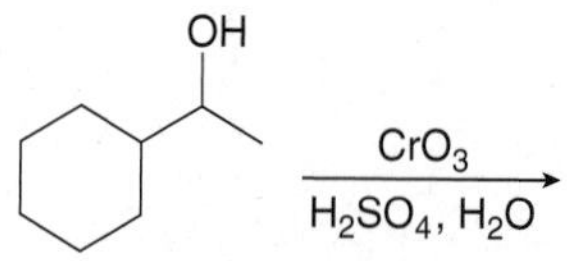

Figure 12.10
Blood alcohol screening

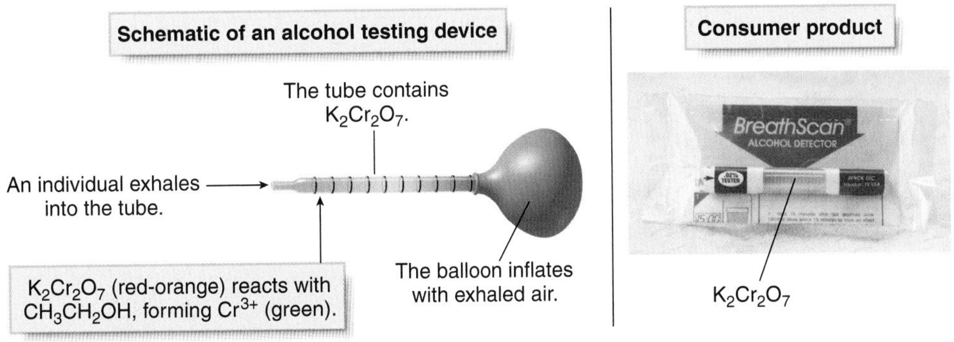
Schematic of an alcohol testing device
The tube contains $K_2Cr_2O_7$.
An individual exhales into the tube.
$K_2Cr_2O_7$ (red-orange) reacts with CH_3CH_2OH, forming Cr^{3+} (green).
The balloon inflates with exhaled air.
Consumer product
BreathScan®
ALCOHOL DETECTOR
$K_2Cr_2O_7$

- The oxidation of CH_3CH_2OH with $K_2Cr_2O_7$ to form CH_3COOH and Cr^{3+} was the first available method for the routine testing of alcohol concentration in exhaled air. Some consumer products for alcohol screening are still based on this technology.

12.13 Green Chemistry

Several new methods of oxidation are based on green chemistry. ***Green chemistry* is the use of environmentally benign methods to synthesize compounds.** Its purpose is to use safer reagents and less solvent, and develop reactions that form fewer by-products and generate less waste. Although the concept of designing green chemical processes was only formally established by the Environmental Protection Agency in the early 1990s, developing new chemical methods that minimize environmental impact has been in practice much longer.

Green polymer synthesis using starting materials derived from renewable resources (rather than petroleum) is discussed in Section 31.8.

Since many oxidation methods use toxic reagents (such as OsO_4 and O_3) and corrosive acids (such as H_2SO_4), or they generate carcinogenic by-products (such as Cr^{3+}), alternative reactions have been developed. One method uses a polymer-supported Cr^{6+} reagent—$HCrO_4^-$–Amberlyst A-26 resin—that avoids the use of strong acid, and forms a Cr^{3+} by-product that can be easily removed from the product by filtration.

The Amberlyst A-26 resin consists of a complex hydrocarbon network with cationic ammonium ion appendages that serve as counterions to the anionic chromium oxidant, $HCrO_4^-$. Heating the insoluble polymeric reagent with an alcohol results in oxidation to a carbonyl compound, with formation of an insoluble Cr^{3+} by-product. Not only can the metal by-product be removed by filtration without added solvent, it can also be regenerated and reused in a subsequent reaction.

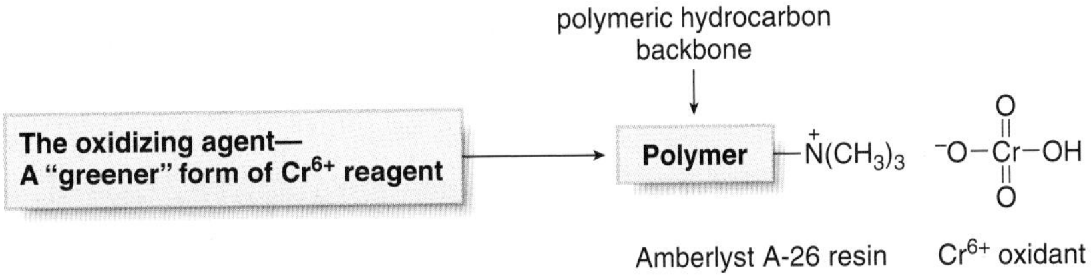
polymeric hydrocarbon backbone
The oxidizing agent—
A "greener" form of Cr^{6+} reagent
Polymer
Amberlyst A-26 resin
Cr^{6+} oxidant

With $HCrO_4^-$–Amberlyst A-26 resin, 1° alcohols are oxidized to aldehydes and 2° alcohols are oxidized to ketones.

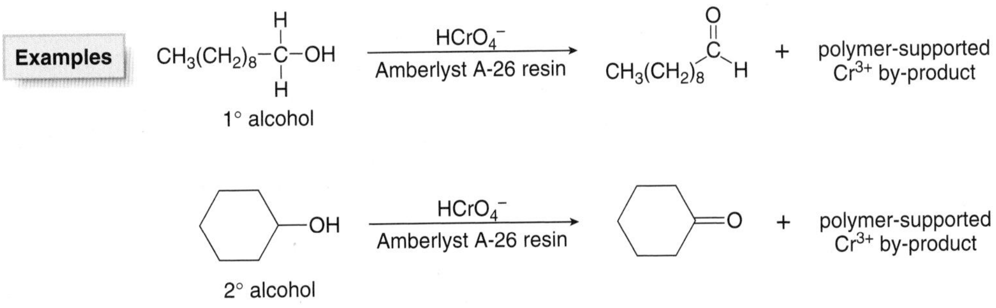
Examples
$HCrO_4^-$
Amberlyst A-26 resin
polymer-supported Cr^{3+} by-product
1° alcohol
2° alcohol

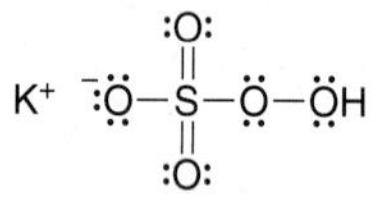

potassium peroxymonosulfate

Many other green approaches to oxidation that avoid the generation of metal by-products entirely are also under active investigation. For example, potassium peroxymonosulfate, $KHSO_5$, is a sulfate derivative of hydrogen peroxide, sold as a triple salt (2 $KHSO_5$•$KHSO_4$•K_2SO_4) under the trade name of Oxone. Oxone oxidizes a variety of substrates without the presence of a heavy metal like chromium or manganese, and in some cases, oxidation reactions can be carried out in water or aqueous solutions. The weak oxygen–oxygen bond of the reagent is cleaved during oxidation, and a sulfate salt (K_2SO_4) is formed as by-product. Two examples of oxidations of alcohols are shown.

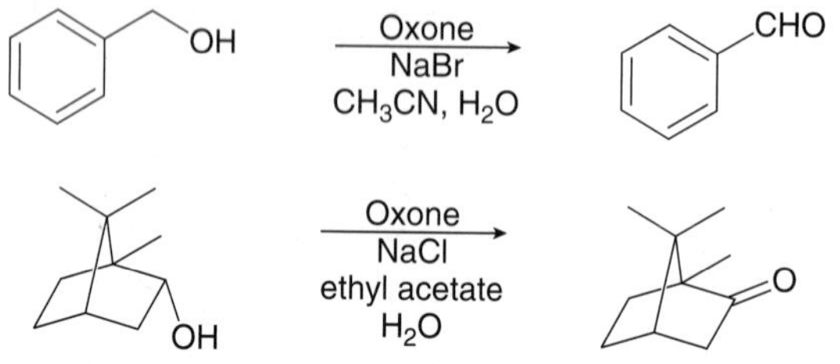

Problem 12.25 What carbonyl compound is formed when each alcohol is treated with $HCrO_4^-$–Amberlyst A-26 resin?

a. 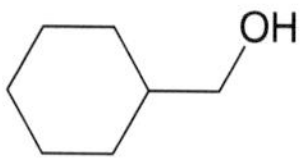

b. 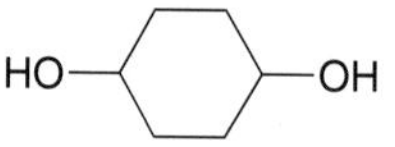

c. 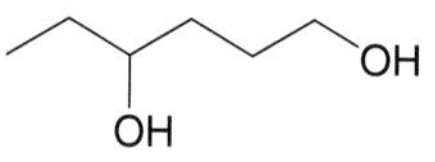

Problem 12.26 Sodium hypochlorite (NaOCl, the oxidant in household bleach) in aqueous CH_3COOH is also touted as a "green" oxidizing agent. For example, oxidation of $(CH_3)_2CHOH$ with NaOCl forms $(CH_3)_2C{=}O$ along with NaCl and H_2O. (a) What advantages and/or disadvantages does this method have over oxidation with $HCrO_4^-$–Amberlyst A-26 resin? (b) What advantages and/or disadvantages does this method have over oxidation with CrO_3, H_2SO_4, H_2O?

12.14 Application: The Oxidation of Ethanol

Many reactions in biological systems involve oxidation or reduction. Instead of using Cr^{6+} reagents for oxidation, cells use two organic compounds—a high molecular weight **enzyme** and a simpler **coenzyme** that serves as the oxidizing agent.

For example, when CH_3CH_2OH (ethanol) is ingested, it is oxidized in the liver first to CH_3CHO (acetaldehyde), and then to CH_3COO^- (acetate anion, the conjugate base of acetic acid). Acetate is the starting material for the synthesis of fatty acids and cholesterol. Both oxidations are catalyzed by a dehydrogenase enzyme.

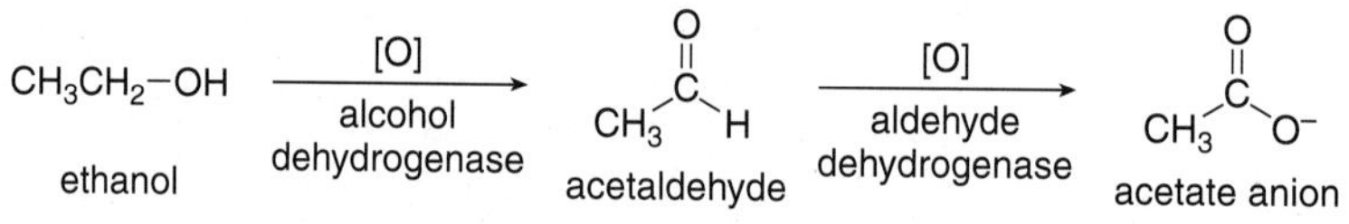

If more ethanol is ingested than can be metabolized in a given time, the concentration of acetaldehyde builds up. This toxic compound is responsible for the feelings associated with a hangover.

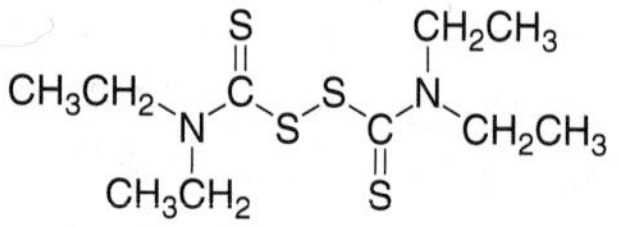

antabuse

Antabuse, a drug given to alcoholics to prevent them from consuming alcoholic beverages, acts by interfering with the normal oxidation of ethanol. Antabuse inhibits the oxidation of acetaldehyde to the acetate anion. Because the first step in ethanol metabolism occurs but the second does not, the concentration of acetaldehyde rises, causing an individual to become violently ill.

Like ethanol, methanol is oxidized by the same enzymes to give an aldehyde and an acid: formaldehyde and formic acid. These oxidation products are extremely toxic because they cannot be used by the body. As a result, the pH of the blood decreases, and blindness and death can follow.

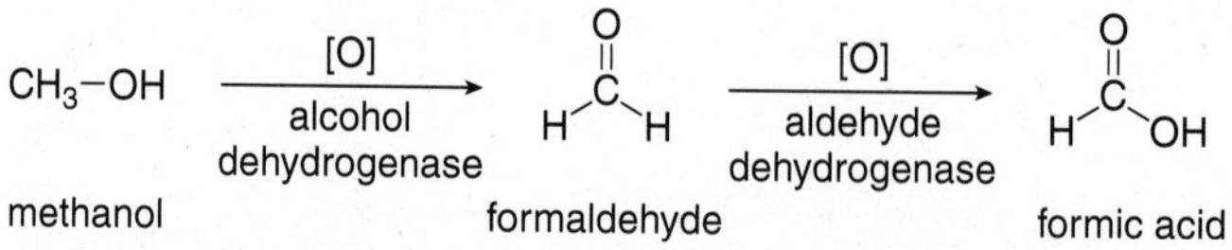

Because the enzymes have a higher affinity for ethanol than methanol, methanol poisoning is treated by giving ethanol to the afflicted individual. With both methanol and ethanol in the patient's system, the enzymes react more readily with ethanol, allowing the methanol to be excreted unchanged without the formation of methanol's toxic oxidation products.

12.15 Sharpless Epoxidation

In all of the reactions discussed so far, an **achiral starting material has reacted with an achiral reagent to give either an achiral product or a racemic mixture of two enantiomers.** If you are trying to make a chiral product, this means that only half of the product mixture is the desired enantiomer and the other half is the undesired one. The synthesis of disparlure, outlined in Figure 12.9, exemplifies this dilemma.

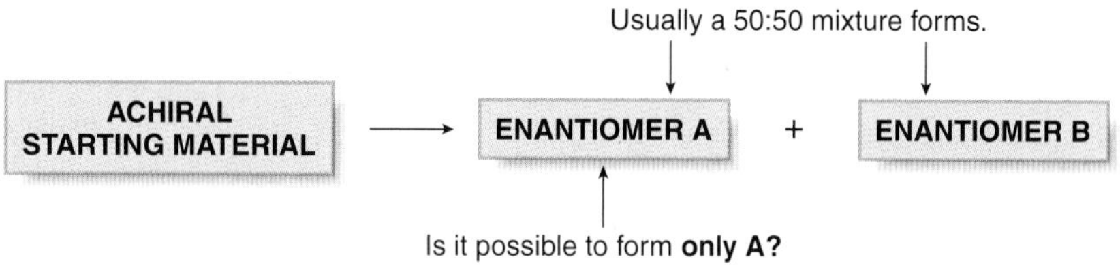
Usually a 50:50 mixture forms.
ACHIRAL STARTING MATERIAL
ENANTIOMER A
+
ENANTIOMER B
Is it possible to form **only A?**

K. Barry Sharpless shared the 2001 Nobel Prize in Chemistry for his work on chiral oxidation reactions.

K. Barry Sharpless, currently at The Scripps Research Institute, reasoned that using a chiral reagent might make it possible to favor the formation of one enantiomer over the other.

- An *enantioselective* reaction affords predominantly or exclusively one enantiomer.
- A reaction that converts an achiral starting material into predominantly one enantiomer is also called an *asymmetric reaction.*

The Sharpless asymmetric epoxidation is an enantioselective reaction that oxidizes alkenes to epoxides. Only the double bonds of **allylic alcohols**—that is, alcohols having a hydroxy group on the carbon adjacent to a C=C—are oxidized in this reaction.

Sharpless epoxidation

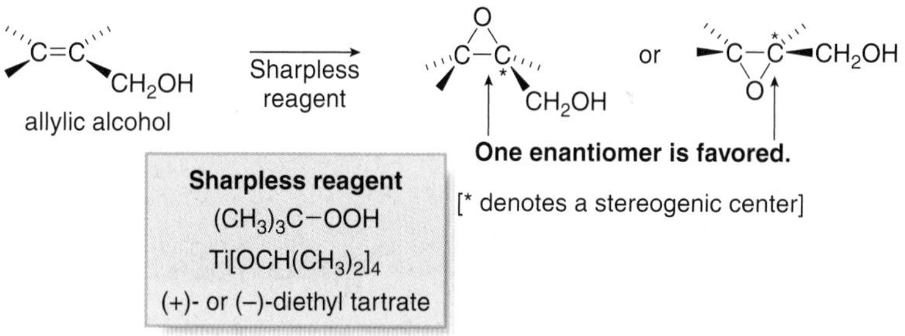
CH2OH
allylic alcohol
Sharpless reagent
O
CH2OH
or
CH2OH
O
One enantiomer is favored.
[* denotes a stereogenic center]
Sharpless reagent
(CH3)3C−OOH
Ti[OCH(CH3)2]4
(+)- or (−)-diethyl tartrate

The **Sharpless reagent** consists of three components: *tert*-butyl hydroperoxide, **$(CH_3)_3COOH$;** a titanium catalyst—usually titanium(IV) isopropoxide, **$Ti[OCH(CH_3)_2]_4$;** and **diethyl tartrate (DET).** There are two different chiral diethyl tartrate isomers, labeled as (+)-DET or (−)-DET to indicate the direction in which they rotate polarized light.

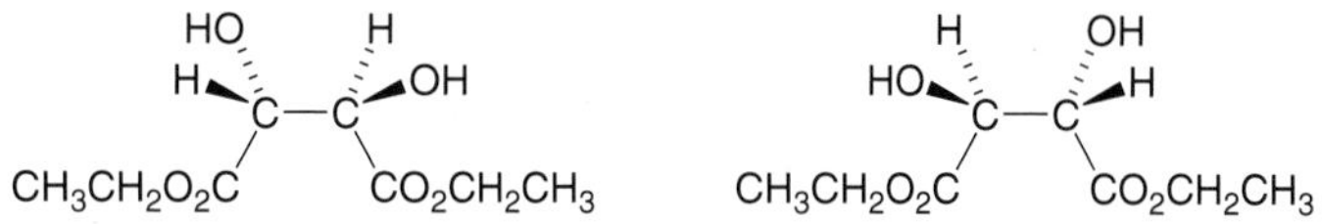
HO H
H OH
C−C
CH3CH2O2C CO2CH2CH3
H OH
HO H
C−C
CH3CH2O2C CO2CH2CH3

(+)-(*R,R*)-diethyl tartrate

(+)-DET

(−)-(*S,S*)-diethyl tartrate

(−)-DET

(+)-DET is prepared from (+)-(*R,R*)-tartaric acid [$HO_2CCH(OH)CH(OH)CO_2H$], a naturally occurring carboxylic acid found in grapes and sold as a by-product of the wine industry.

The identity of the DET isomer determines which enantiomer is the major product obtained in the epoxidation of an allylic alcohol with the Sharpless reagent.

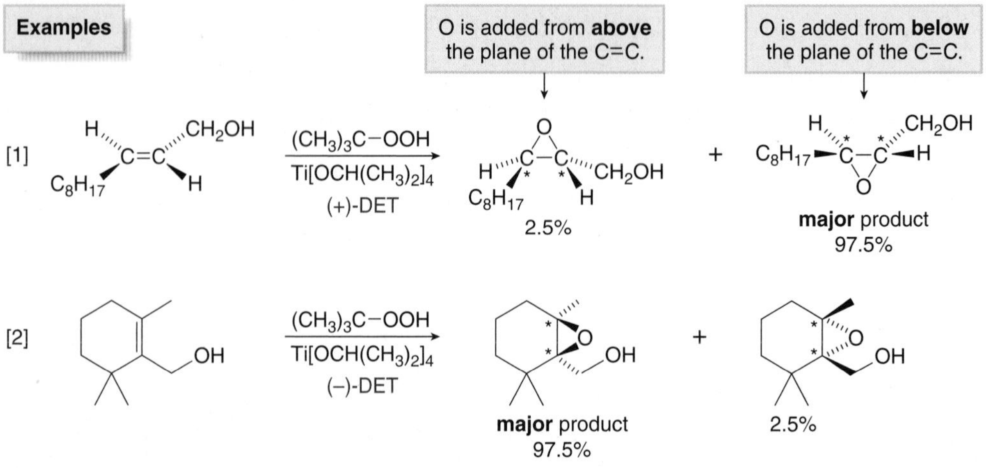
Examples
O is added from **above** the plane of the C=C.
O is added from **below** the plane of the C=C.
[1]
(CH3)3C–OOH
Ti[OCH(CH3)2]4
(+)-DET
2.5%
major product
97.5%
[2]
(CH3)3C–OOH
Ti[OCH(CH3)2]4
(–)-DET
major product
97.5%
2.5%

[* denotes a stereogenic center]

The degree of enantioselectivity of a reaction is measured by its enantiomeric excess (***ee***) (Section 5.12D). Reactions [1] and [2] are highly enantioselective because each has an enantiomeric excess of 95% (97.5% of the major enantiomer – 2.5% of the minor enantiomer).

Enantiomeric excess = ***ee*** = % of one enantiomer – % of the other enantiomer.

To determine which enantiomer is formed for a given isomer of DET, draw the allylic alcohol in a plane, with the **C=C horizontal and the OH group in the upper right corner;** then:

- **Epoxidation with (–)-DET adds an oxygen atom from above the plane.**
- **Epoxidation with (+)-DET adds an oxygen atom from below the plane.**

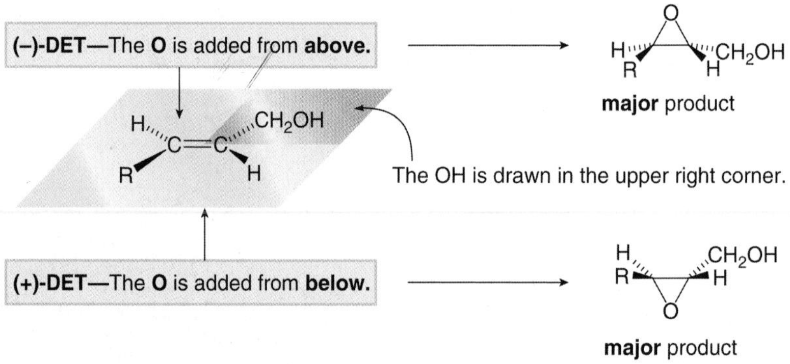
(–)-DET—The **O** is added from **above.**
major product
The OH is drawn in the upper right corner.
(+)-DET—The **O** is added from **below.**
major product

Sample Problem 12.5

Predict the major product in each epoxidation.

a. 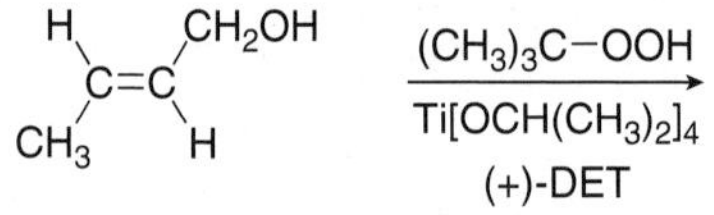

b. 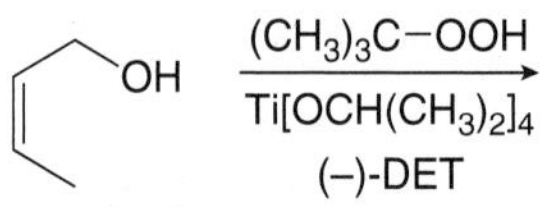

Solution

To draw an epoxidation product:

- Draw the allylic alcohol with the **C=C horizontal and the OH group in the upper right corner of the alkene.** Re-draw the alkene if necessary.
- **(+)-DET** adds the O atom from **below,** and **(–)-DET** adds the O atom from **above.**

a. Since the C=C is drawn horizontal with the OH group in the upper right corner, it is not necessary to re-draw the alkene. With **(+)-DET,** the O atom is added from **below.**

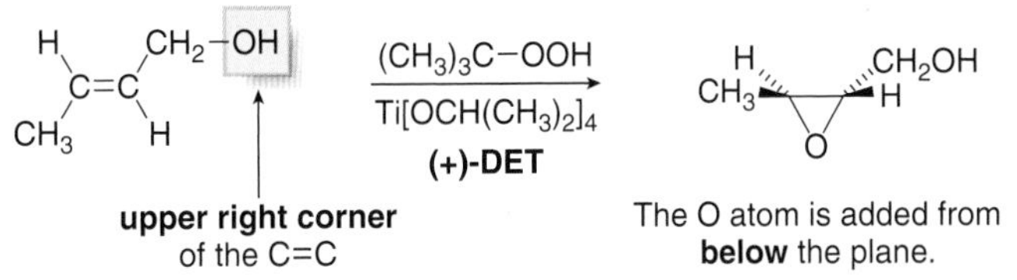

$(CH_3)_3C-OOH$
$Ti[OCH(CH_3)_2]_4$
(+)-DET
upper right corner of the C=C
The O atom is added from below the plane.

b. The allylic alcohol must be re-drawn with the C=C horizontal and the OH group in the upper right corner. Because **(–)-DET** is used, the O atom is then added from **above.**

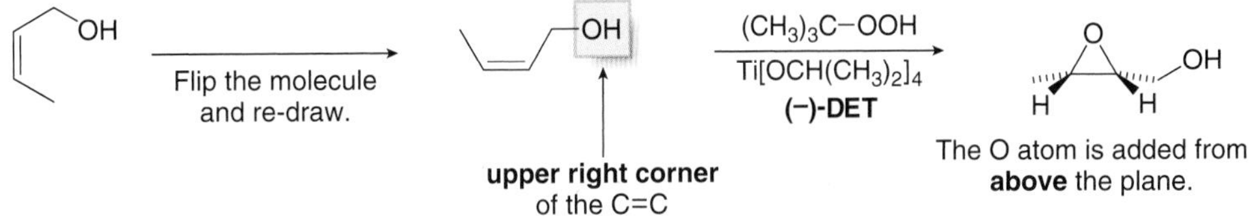

Flip the molecule and re-draw.
$(CH_3)_3C-OOH$
$Ti[OCH(CH_3)_2]_4$
(–)-DET
upper right corner of the C=C
The O atom is added from above the plane.

Problem 12.27 Draw the products of each Sharpless epoxidation.

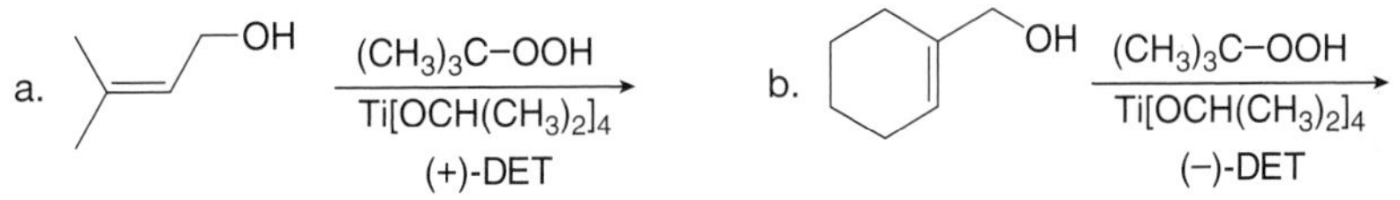

a.
$(CH_3)_3C-OOH$
$Ti[OCH(CH_3)_2]_4$
(+)-DET
b.
$(CH_3)_3C-OOH$
$Ti[OCH(CH_3)_2]_4$
(–)-DET

The Sharpless epoxidation has been used to synthesize many chiral natural products, including two insect pheromones—(+)-α-multistriatin and (–)-frontalin, as shown in Figure 12.11.

Figure 12.11 The synthesis of chiral insect pheromones using asymmetric epoxidation

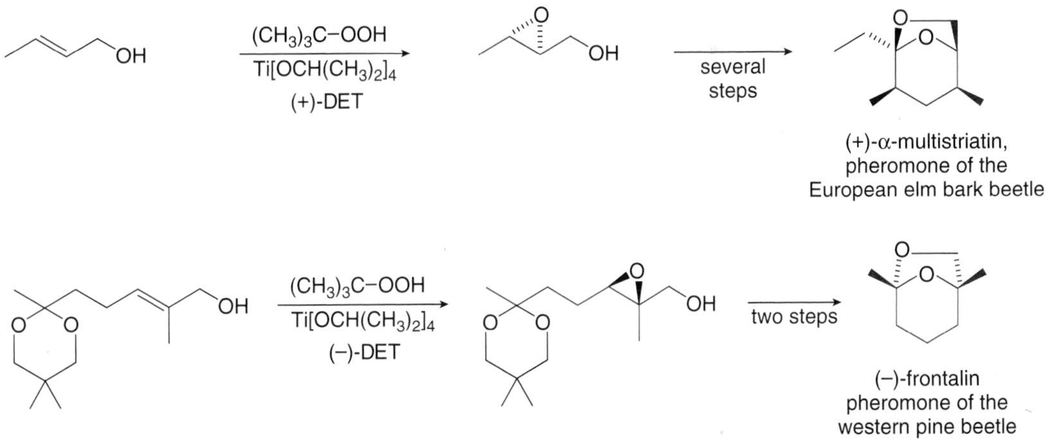

$(CH_3)_3C-OOH$
$Ti[OCH(CH_3)_2]_4$
(+)-DET
several steps
(+)-α-multistriatin, pheromone of the European elm bark beetle
$(CH_3)_3C-OOH$
$Ti[OCH(CH_3)_2]_4$
(–)-DET
two steps
(–)-frontalin pheromone of the western pine beetle

- The bonds in the products that originate from the epoxide intermediate are indicated in red.

Problem 12.28 Explain why only one C=C of geraniol is epoxidized with the Sharpless reagent.

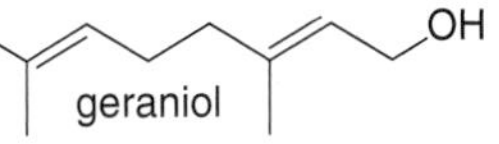
geraniol

KEY CONCEPTS

Oxidation and Reduction

Summary: Terms that Describe Reaction Selectivity

- A **regioselective reaction** forms predominantly or exclusively one constitutional isomer (Section 8.5).
- A **stereoselective reaction** forms predominantly or exclusively one stereoisomer (Section 8.5).
- An **enantioselective reaction** forms predominantly or exclusively one enantiomer (Section 12.15).

Definitions of Oxidation and Reduction (12.1)

Oxidation reactions result in:
- an increase in the number of C–Z bonds, *or*
- a decrease in the number of C–H bonds

Reduction reactions result in:
- a decrease in the number of C–Z bonds, *or*
- an increase in the number of C–H bonds

Reduction Reactions

[1] Reduction of alkenes—Catalytic hydrogenation (12.3)

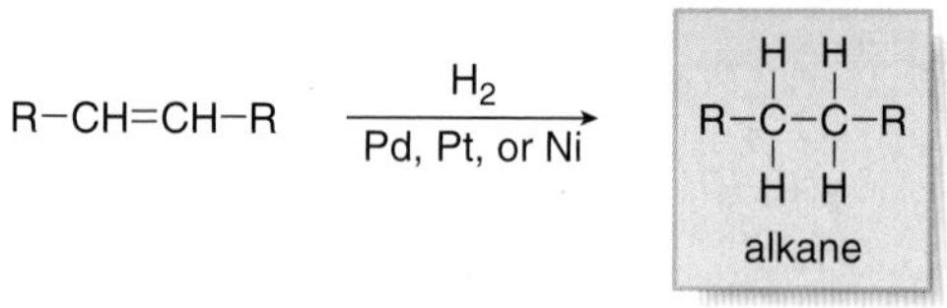

- **Syn addition** of H_2 occurs.
- Increasing alkyl substitution on the C=C decreases the rate of reaction.

[2] Reduction of alkynes

a.

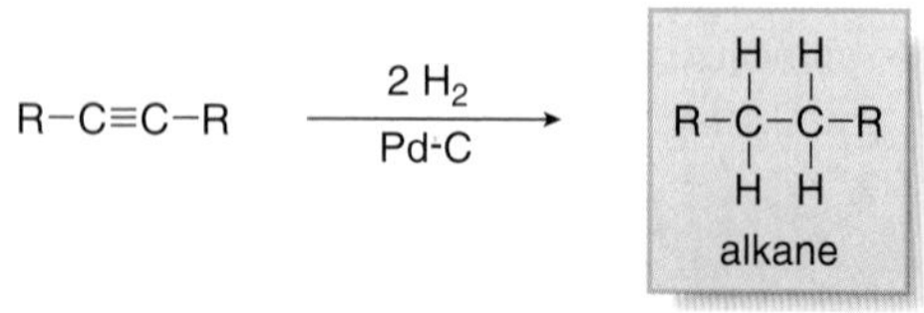

- Two equivalents of H_2 are added and four new C–H bonds are formed (12.5A).

b.

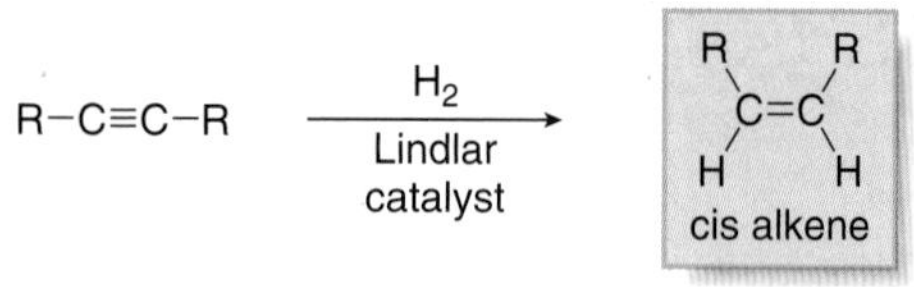

- **Syn addition** of H_2 occurs, forming a **cis** alkene (12.5B).
- The Lindlar catalyst is deactivated; reaction stops after one equivalent of H_2 has added.

c.

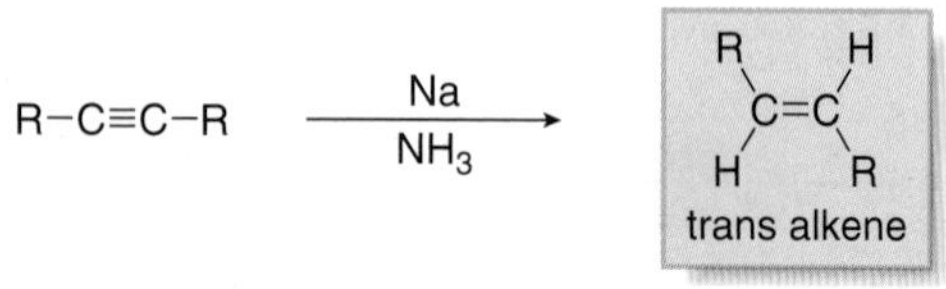

- **Anti addition** of H_2 occurs, forming a **trans** alkene (12.5C).

[3] Reduction of alkyl halides (12.6)

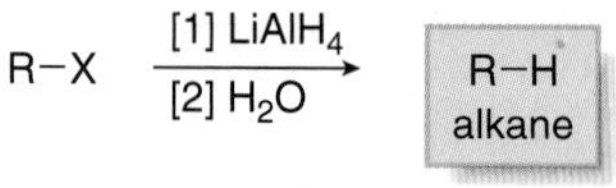

- The reaction follows an **S_N2** mechanism.
- CH_3X and RCH_2X react faster than a more substituted RX.

[4] Reduction of epoxides (12.6)

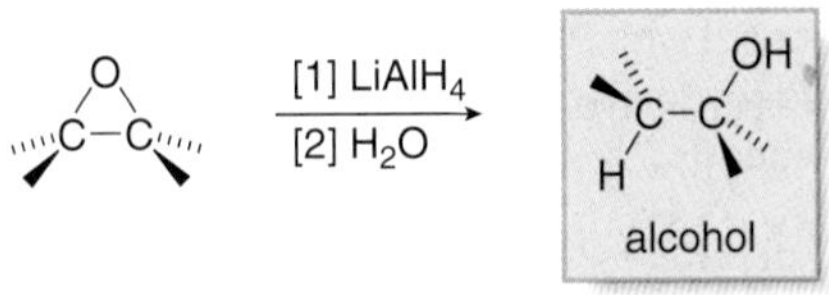

- The reaction follows an **S_N2** mechanism.
- In unsymmetrical epoxides, H$^-$ (from LiAlH$_4$) attacks at the less substituted carbon.

Oxidation Reactions

[1] Oxidation of alkenes

a. Epoxidation (12.8)

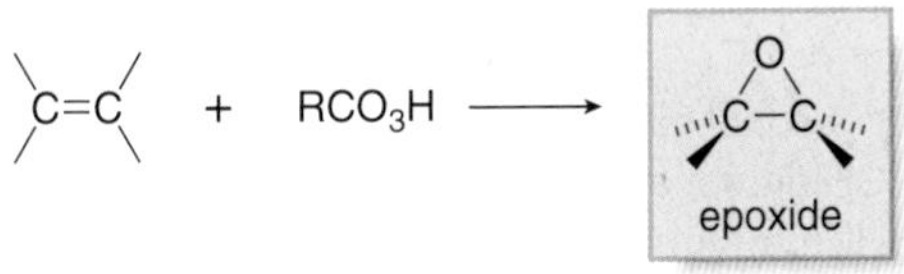

- The mechanism has **one step.**
- **Syn addition** of an O atom occurs.
- The reaction is stereospecific.

b. Anti dihydroxylation (12.9A)

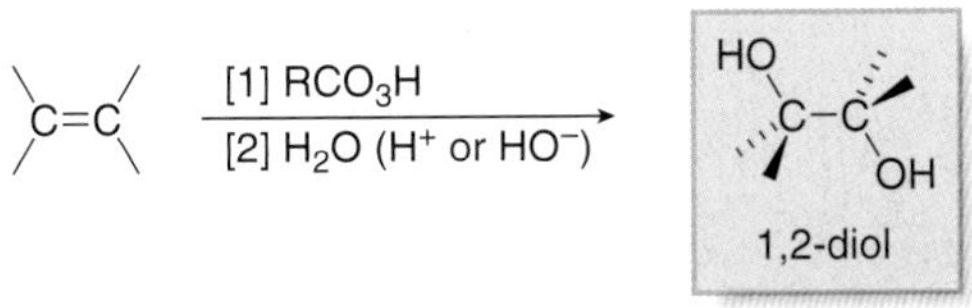

- Opening of an epoxide ring intermediate with $^-$OH or H$_2$O forms a 1,2-diol with two OH groups added in an **anti** fashion.

c. Syn dihydroxylation (12.9B)

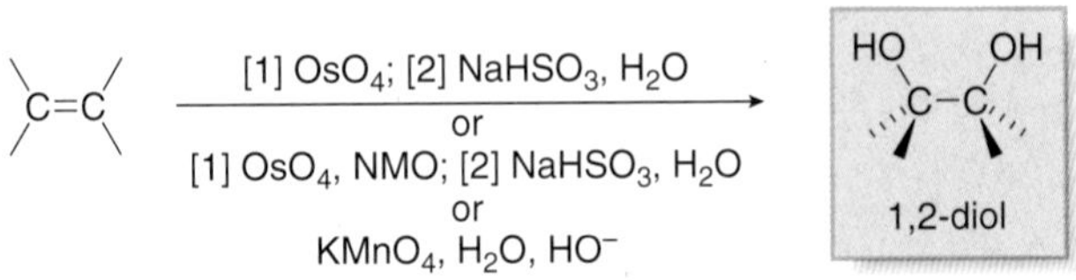

- Each reagent adds two new C–O bonds to the C=C in a **syn** fashion.

d. Oxidative cleavage (12.10)

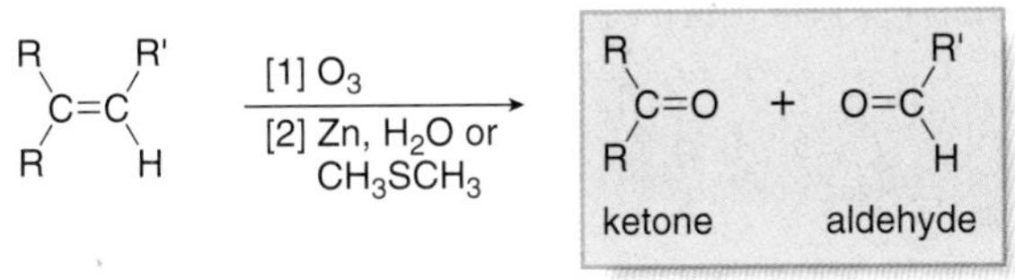

- Both the σ and π bonds of the alkene are cleaved to form two carbonyl groups.

[2] Oxidative cleavage of alkynes (12.11)

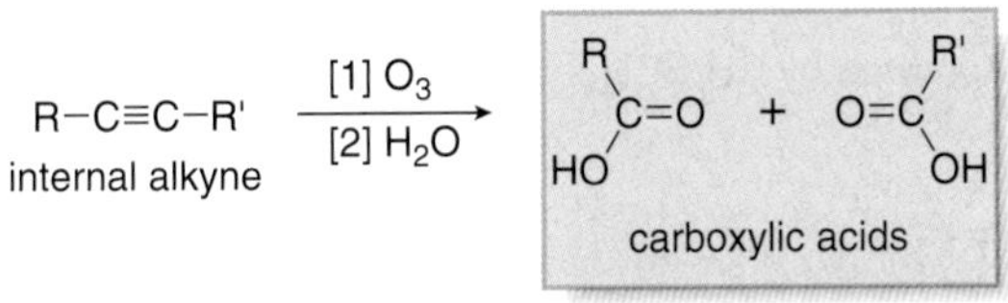

- The σ bond and both π bonds of the alkyne are cleaved.

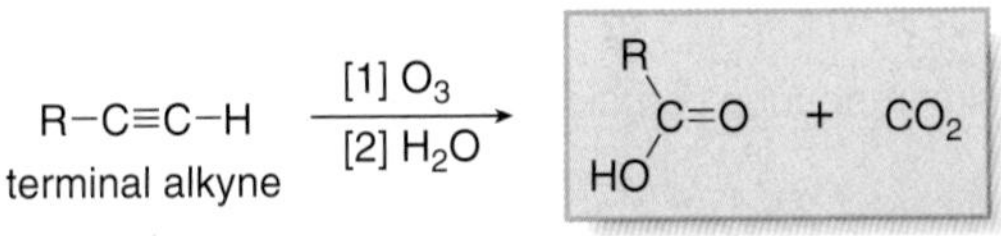

[3] Oxidation of alcohols (12.12, 12.13)

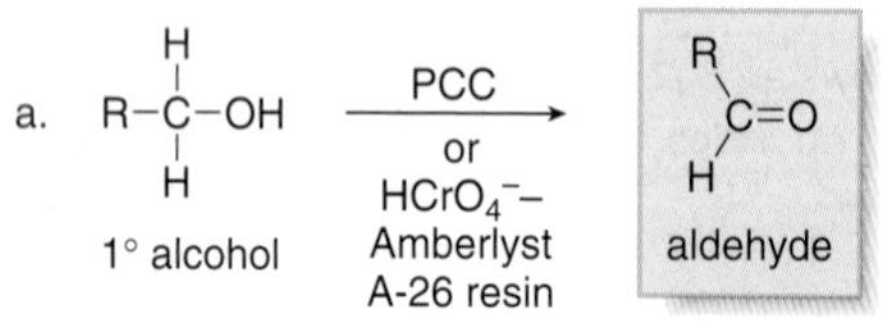

- Oxidation of a 1° alcohol with PCC or $HCrO_4^-$–Amberlyst A-26 resin stops at the aldehyde stage. Only one C–H bond is replaced by a C–O bond.

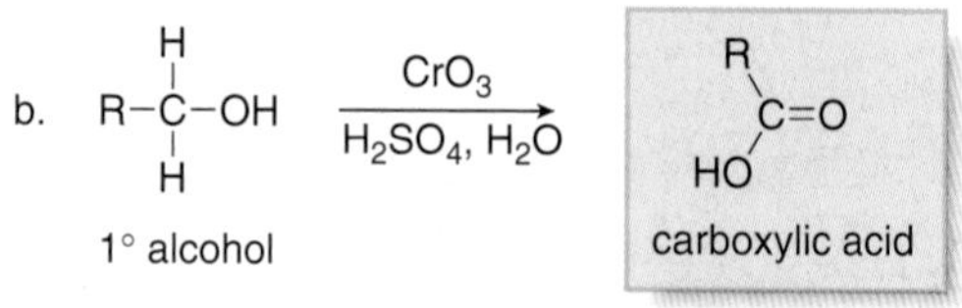

- Oxidation of a 1° alcohol under harsher reaction conditions—CrO_3 (or $Na_2Cr_2O_7$ or $K_2Cr_2O_7$) + H_2O + H_2SO_4—leads to a RCOOH. Two C–H bonds are replaced by two C–O bonds.

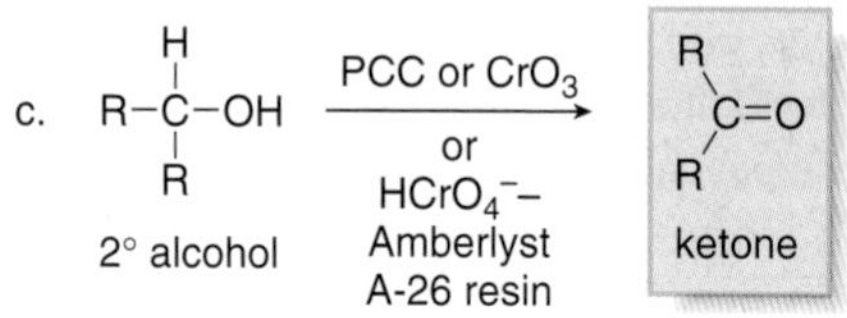

- Because a 2° alcohol has only one C–H bond on the carbon bearing the OH group, all Cr^{6+} reagents—PCC, CrO_3, $Na_2Cr_2O_7$, $K_2Cr_2O_7$, or $HCrO_4^-$ (Amberlyst A-26 resin)—oxidize a 2° alcohol to a ketone.

[4] Asymmetric epoxidation of allylic alcohols (12.15)

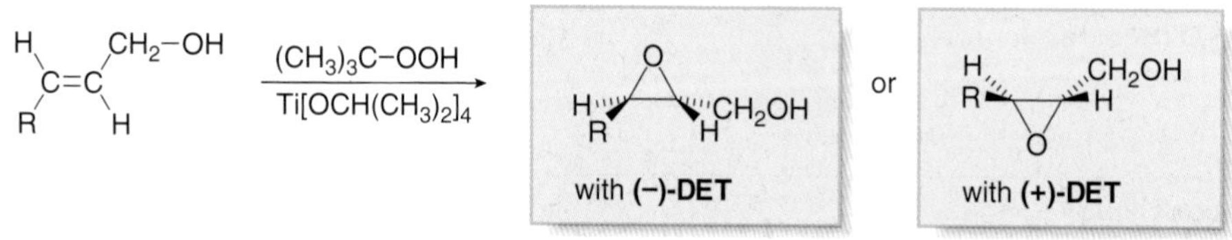

PROBLEMS

Problems Using Three-Dimensional Models

12.29 Draw the products formed when **A** is treated with each reagent: (a) H_2 + Pd-C; (b) mCPBA; (c) PCC; (d) CrO_3, H_2SO_4, H_2O; (e) Sharpless reagent with (+)-DET.

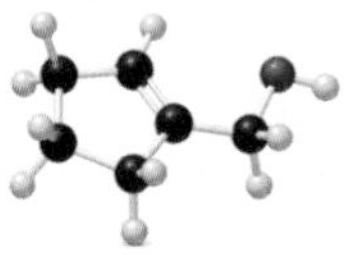

A

12.30 Draw the products formed when the following diene is treated with O_3 followed by CH_3SCH_3.

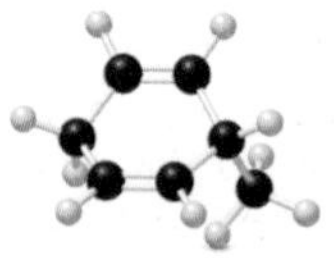

12.31 Devise a synthesis of the following compound from acetylene and organic compounds containing two carbons or fewer. You may use any other required reagents.

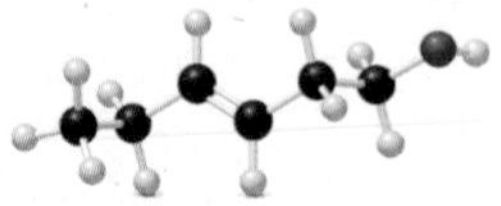

Classifying Reactions as Oxidation or Reduction

12.32 Label each reaction as oxidation, reduction, or neither.

a. 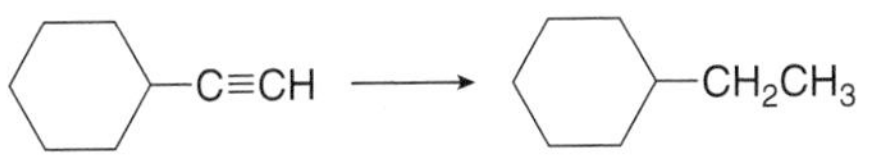

c. 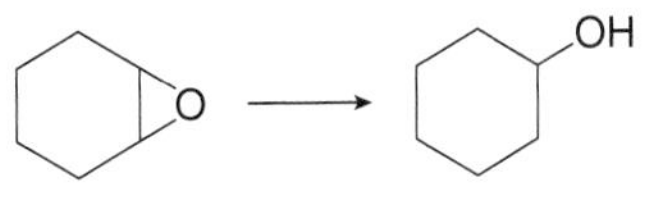

b. $CH_3CH_2Br \longrightarrow CH_2{=}CH_2$

d. 

Hydrogenation

12.33 Draw the organic products formed when each alkene is treated with H_2, Pd-C. Indicate the three-dimensional structure of all stereoisomers formed.

a. 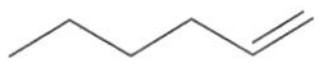

b. 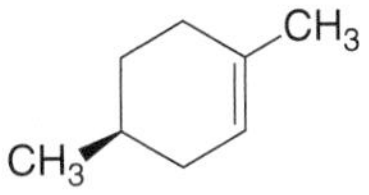

c. 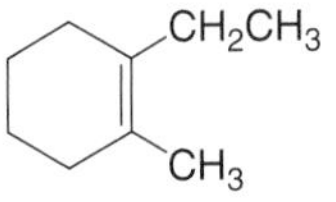

d. 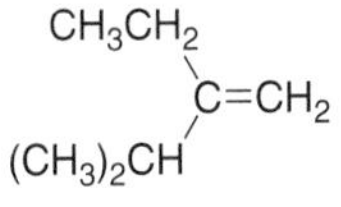

12.34 Match each alkene to its heat of hydrogenation.
Alkenes: 3-methyl-1-butene, 2-methyl-1-butene, 2-methyl-2-butene
$\Delta H°$ (hydrogenation) kJ/mol: –119, –127, –112

12.35 How many rings and π bonds are contained in compounds **A–C?** Draw one possible structure for each compound.

a. Compound **A** has molecular formula C_5H_8 and is hydrogenated to a compound having molecular formula C_5H_{10}.
b. Compound **B** has molecular formula $C_{10}H_{16}$ and is hydrogenated to a compound having molecular formula $C_{10}H_{18}$.
c. Compound **C** has molecular formula C_8H_8 and is hydrogenated to a compound having molecular formula C_8H_{16}.

12.36 For alkenes **A, B,** and **C:** (a) Rank **A, B,** and **C** in order of increasing heat of hydrogenation; (b) rank **A, B,** and **C** in order of increasing rate of reaction with H_2, Pd-C; (c) draw the products formed when each alkene is treated with ozone, followed by Zn, H_2O.

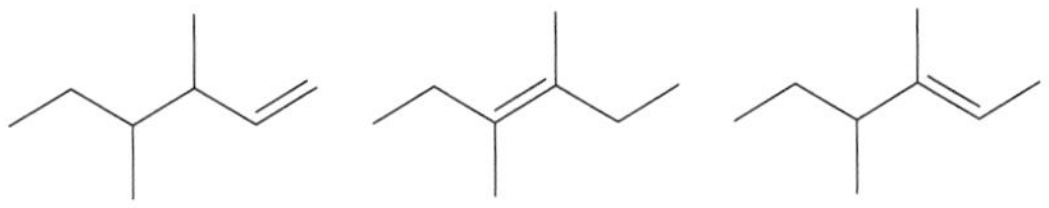

A **B** **C**

12.37 Stearidonic acid ($C_{18}H_{28}O_2$) is an unsaturated fatty acid obtained from oils isolated from hemp and blackcurrant (see also Problem 10.11).

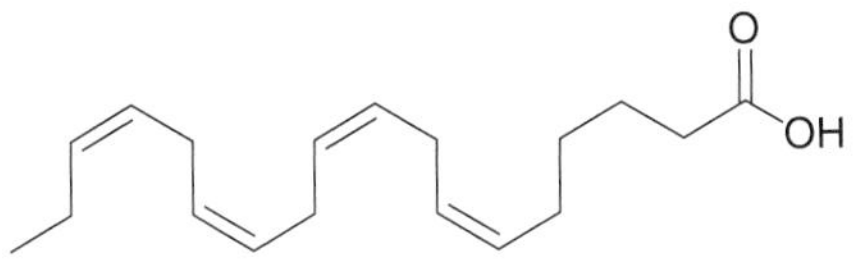

stearidonic acid

a. What fatty acid is formed when stearidonic acid is hydrogenated with excess H_2 and a Pd catalyst?
b. What fatty acids are formed when stearidonic acid is hydrogenated with one equivalent of H_2 and a Pd catalyst?
c. Draw the structure of a possible product formed when stearidonic acid is hydrogenated with one equivalent of H_2 and a Pd catalyst, and one double bond is isomerized to a trans isomer.
d. How do the melting points of the following fatty acids compare: stearidonic acid; one of the products formed in part (b); the product drawn in part (c)?

Reactions—General

12.38 Draw the organic products formed when cyclopentene is treated with each reagent. With some reagents, no reaction occurs.

a. H_2 + Pd-C
b. H_2 + Lindlar catalyst
c. Na, NH_3
d. CH_3CO_3H
e. [1] CH_3CO_3H; [2] H_2O, HO^-
f. [1] OsO_4 + NMO; [2] $NaHSO_3$, H_2O
g. $KMnO_4$, H_2O, HO^-
h. [1] $LiAlH_4$; [2] H_2O
i. [1] O_3; [2] CH_3SCH_3
j. $(CH_3)_3COOH$, $Ti[OCH(CH_3)_2]_4$, (–)-DET
k. mCPBA
l. Product in (k); then [1] $LiAlH_4$; [2] H_2O

12.39 Draw the organic products formed when 4-octyne is treated with each reagent.

a. H_2 (excess) + Pd-C
b. H_2 + Lindlar catalyst
c. Na, NH_3
d. [1] O_3; [2] H_2O

12.40 Draw the organic products formed when allylic alcohol **A** is treated with each reagent.

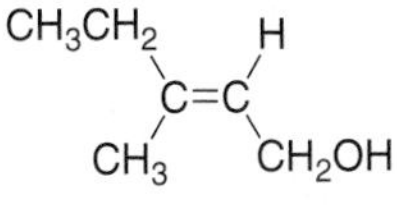

A

a. H_2 + Pd-C
b. mCPBA
c. PCC
d. CrO_3, H_2SO_4, H_2O
e. $(CH_3)_3COOH$, $Ti[OCH(CH_3)_2]_4$, (+)-DET
f. $(CH_3)_3COOH$, $Ti[OCH(CH_3)_2]_4$, (–)-DET
g. [1] PBr_3; [2] $LiAlH_4$; [3] H_2O
h. $HCrO_4^-$–Amberlyst A-26 resin

12.41 Draw the organic products formed in each reaction.

a. 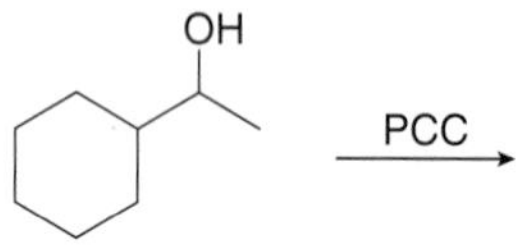

b. $CH_3CH_2CH_2CH_2OH$ $\xrightarrow{\text{PCC}}$

c. 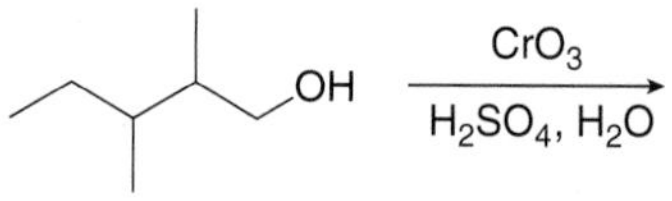

12.42 Draw the organic products formed in each reaction.

a. 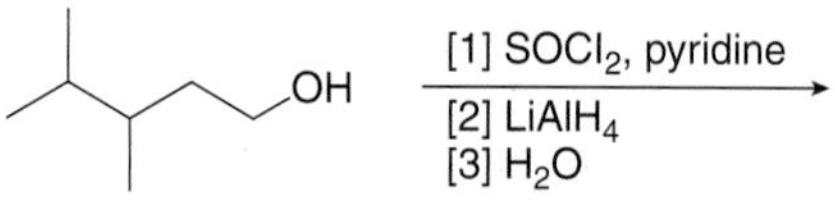

b. 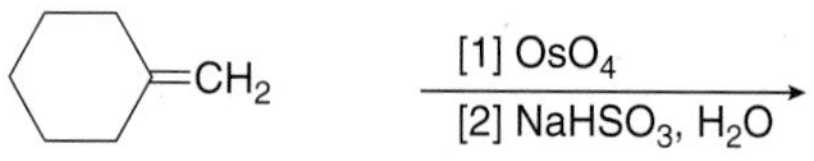

c. 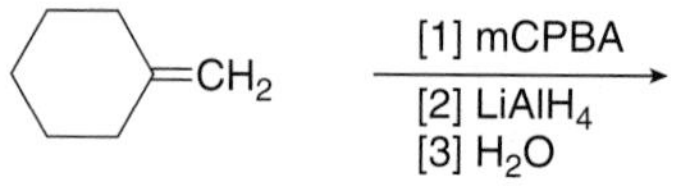

d. 

12.43 Identify the reagents needed to carry out each transformation.

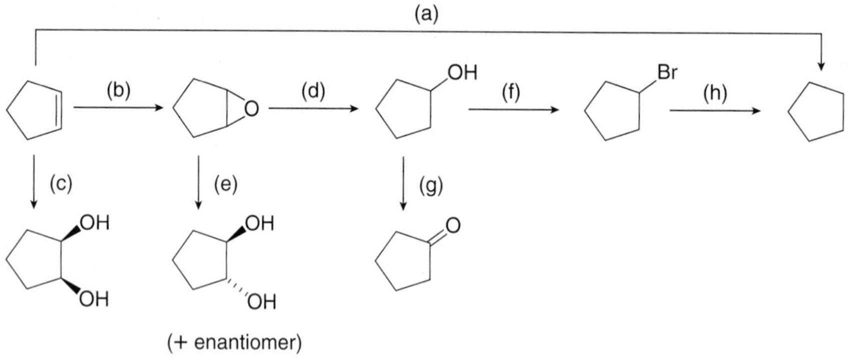

12.44 Draw the structure of two different epoxides that would yield 2-methyl-2-pentanol [$(CH_3)_2C(OH)CH_2CH_2CH_3$] when reduced with $LiAlH_4$.

12.45 Hydrogenation of alkene **A** with D_2 in the presence of Pd-C affords a single product **B.** Keeping this result in mind, what compound is formed when **A** is treated with each reagent: (a) mCPBA; (b) Br_2, H_2O followed by base? Explain these results.

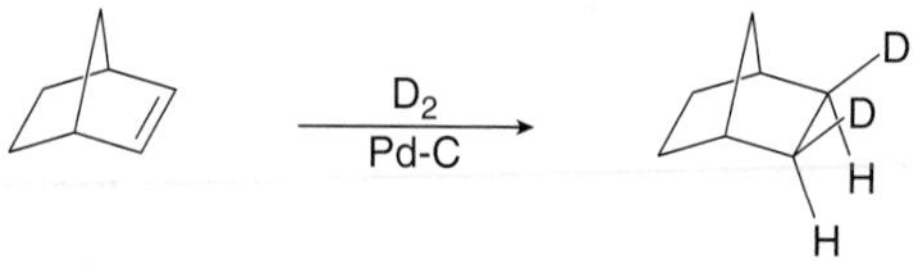

A **B**

12.46 What alkene is needed to synthesize each 1,2-diol using [1] OsO_4 followed by $NaHSO_3$ in H_2O; or [2] CH_3CO_3H followed by ^-OH in H_2O?

a. 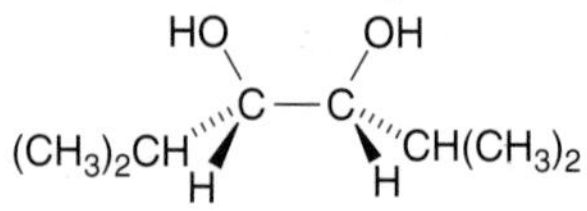

b. 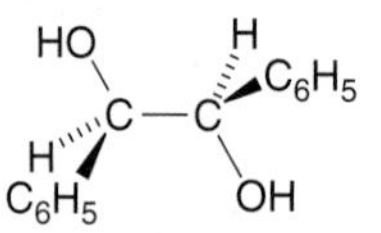

+ enantiomer

c. 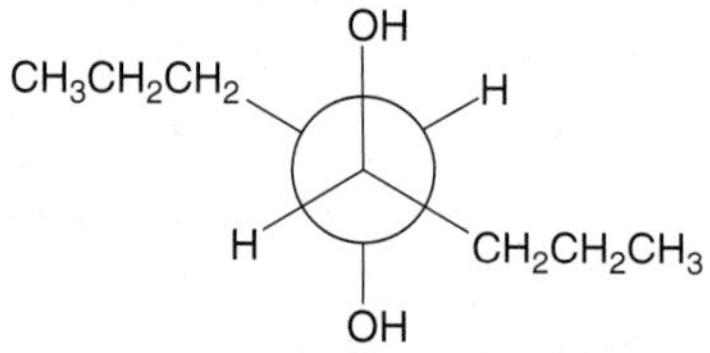

12.47 Draw a stepwise mechanism for the reduction of epoxide **A** to alcohol **B** using $LiAlH_4$. What product would be formed if $LiAlD_4$ were used as reagent? Indicate the stereochemistry of all stereogenic centers in the product using wedges and dashes.

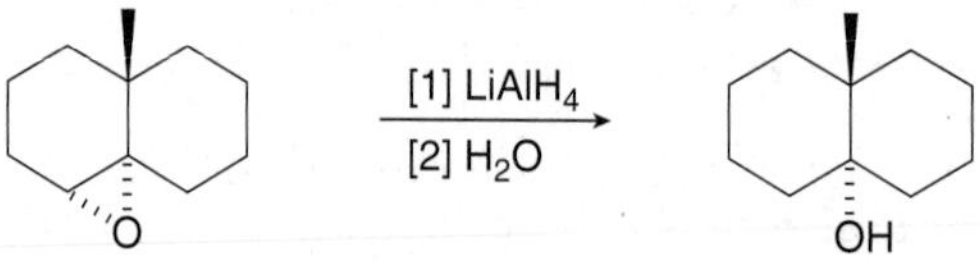

A **B**

12.48 Draw the products formed after Steps [1] and [2] in the following three-step sequence. Then draw stepwise mechanisms for each step.

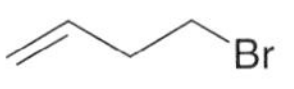
[1] mCPBA → [2] ^{-}OH, H_2O [3] NaH
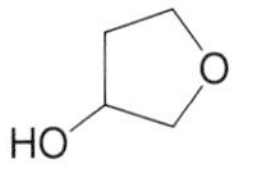

Oxidative Cleavage

12.49 Draw the products formed in each oxidative cleavage.

a. $(CH_3CH_2)_2C{=}CHCH_2CH_3$ → [1] O_3 [2] CH_3SCH_3

b. 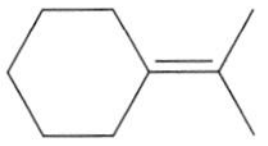 → [1] O_3 [2] Zn, H_2O

c. 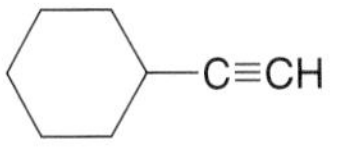 → [1] O_3 [2] H_2O

d. 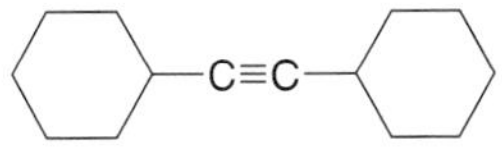 → [1] O_3 [2] H_2O

12.50 What alkene yields each set of products after treatment with O_3 followed by CH_3SCH_3?

a. $(CH_3)_2C{=}O$ and $CH_2{=}O$

b. 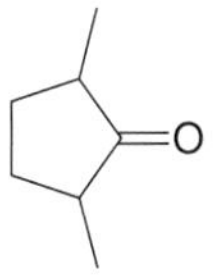 and 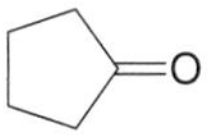

c. $CH_3CH_2CH_2CHO$ only

d. 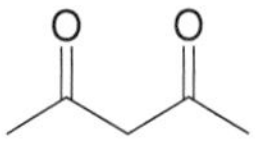 and two equivalents of $CH_2{=}O$

12.51 Identify the starting material in each reaction.

a. $C_{10}H_{18}$ → [1] O_3 [2] CH_3SCH_3 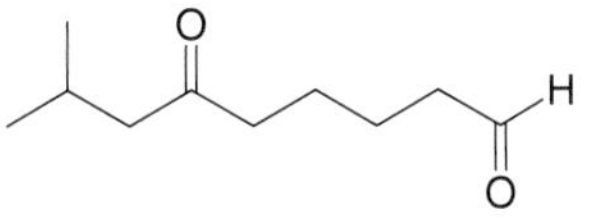

b. $C_{10}H_{16}$ → [1] O_3 [2] CH_3SCH_3 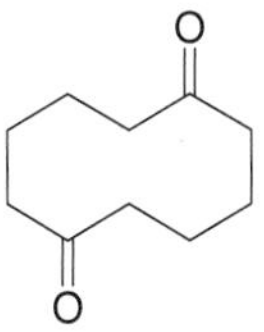

12.52 What alkyne gives each set of products after treatment with O_3 followed by H_2O?

a. $CH_3CH_2CH_2CH_2COOH$ and CO_2

b. CH_3CH_2COOH and $CH_3CH_2CH_2COOH$

c. 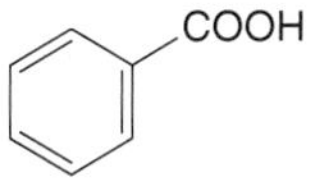 and CH_3COOH

12.53 Draw the products formed when each naturally occurring compound is treated with O_3 followed by Zn, H_2O.

a. 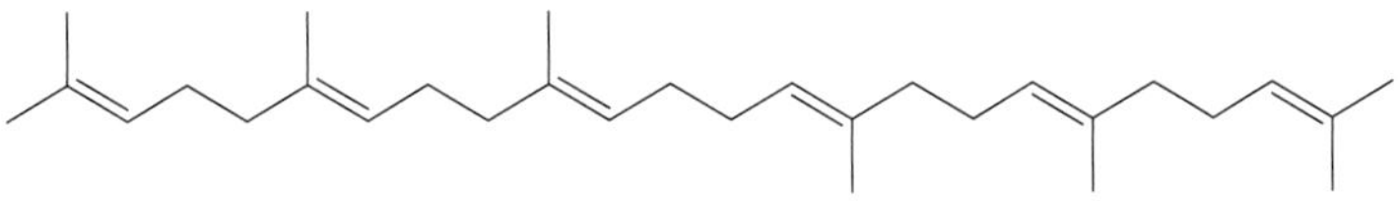
squalene

b. 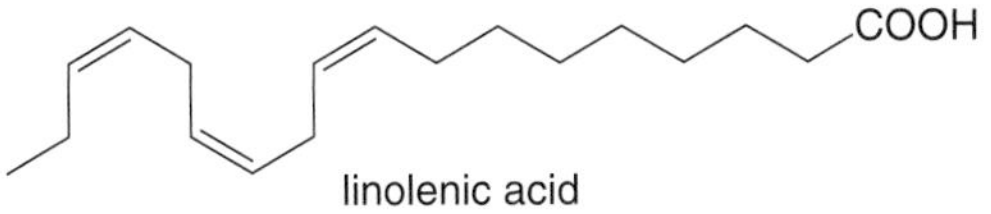
linolenic acid

c. 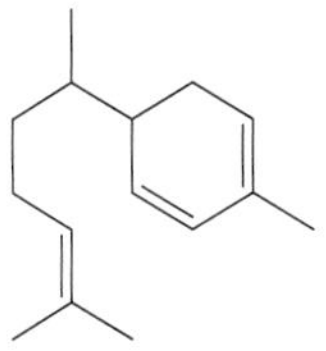
zingiberene

Identifying Compounds from Reactions

12.54 Identify compounds **A, B,** and **C.**

a. Compound **A** has molecular formula C_8H_{12} and reacts with two equivalents of H_2. **A** gives $HCOCH_2CH_2CHO$ as the only product of oxidative cleavage with O_3 followed by CH_3SCH_3.

b. Compound **B** has molecular formula C_6H_{10} and gives $(CH_3)_2CHCH_2CH_2CH_3$ when treated with excess H_2 in the presence of Pd. **B** reacts with $NaNH_2$ and CH_3I to form compound **C** (molecular formula C_7H_{12}).

12.55 Oximene and myrcene, two hydrocarbons isolated from alfalfa that have the molecular formula $C_{10}H_{16}$, both yield 2,6-dimethyloctane when treated with H_2 and a Pd catalyst. Ozonolysis of oximene forms $(CH_3)_2C{=}O$, $CH_2{=}O$, $CH_2(CHO)_2$, and CH_3COCHO. Ozonolysis of myrcene yields $(CH_3)_2C{=}O$, $CH_2{=}O$ (two equiv), and $HCOCH_2CH_2COCHO$. Identify the structures of oximene and myrcene.

12.56 An unknown compound **A** of molecular formula $C_{10}H_{18}O$ reacts with H_2SO_4 to form two compounds (**B** and **C**) of molecular formula $C_{10}H_{16}$. **B** and **C** both react with H_2 in the presence of Pd-C to form decalin. Ozonolysis of **B** forms **D,** and ozonolysis of **C** forms a diketone **E** of molecular formula $C_{10}H_{16}O_2$. Identify the structures of compounds **A, B, C,** and **E.**

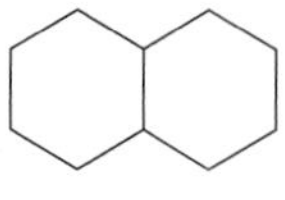

decalin

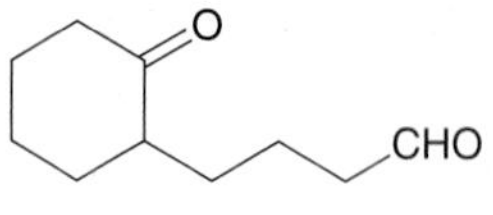

D

12.57 DHA is a fatty acid derived from fish oil and an abundant fatty acid in vertebrate brains. Hydrogenation of DHA forms docosanoic acid [$CH_3(CH_2)_{20}CO_2H$] and ozonolysis forms CH_3CH_2CHO, $CH_2(CHO)_2$ (five equivalents), and $OHCCH_2CH_2CO_2H$. What is the structure of DHA if all double bonds have the *Z* configuration?

12.58 One compound that contributes to the "seashore smell" at beaches in Hawai'i is dictyopterene D', a component of a brown edible seaweed called limu lipoa. Hydrogenation of dictyopterene D' with excess H_2 in the presence of a Pd catalyst forms butylcycloheptane. Ozonolysis with O_3 followed by $(CH_3)_2S$ forms $CH_2(CHO)_2$, $OHCCH_2CH(CHO)_2$, and CH_3CH_2CHO. What are possible structures of dictyopterene D'?

Sharpless Asymmetric Epoxidation

12.59 Draw the product of each asymmetric epoxidation reaction.

a. 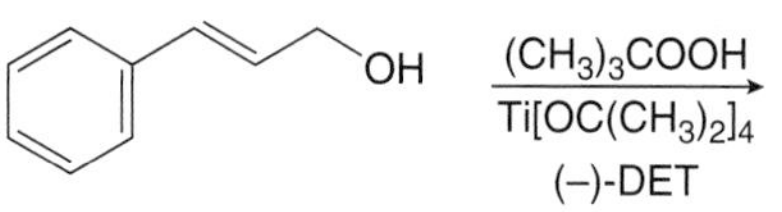

b. 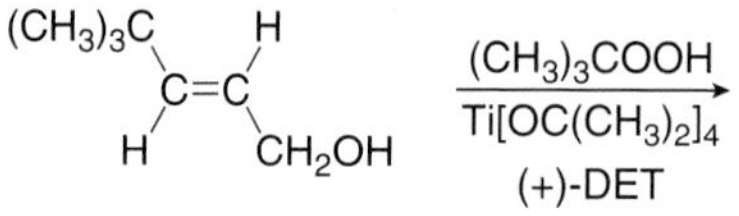

12.60 Epoxidation of the following allylic alcohol using the Sharpless reagent with (–)-DET gives two epoxy alcohols in a ratio of 87:13.

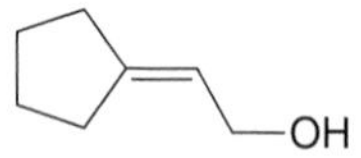

a. Assign structures to the major and minor product.

b. What is the enantiomeric excess in this reaction?

12.61 What allylic alcohol and DET isomer are needed to make each chiral epoxide using a Sharpless asymmetric epoxidation reaction?

a. 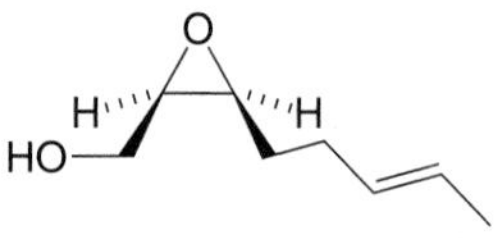

b. 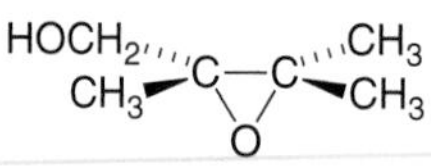

c. 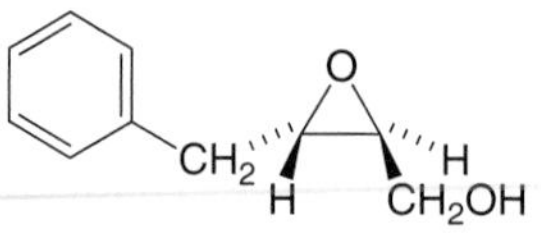

Synthesis

12.62 Devise a synthesis of each hydrocarbon from acetylene, and any other needed reagents.

a. 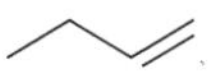

b. 

c. 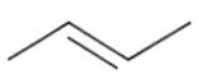

d. 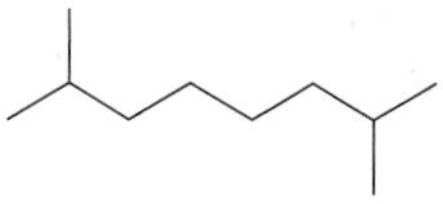

12.63 Devise a synthesis of muscalure, the sex pheromone of the common housefly, from acetylene and any other required reagents.

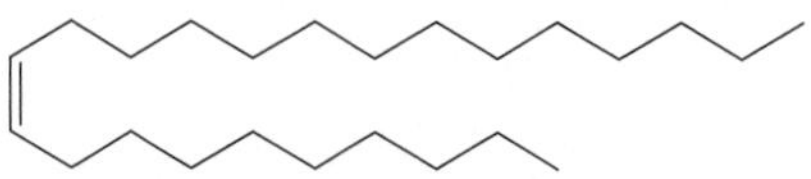

muscalure

12.64 It is sometimes necessary to isomerize a cis alkene to a trans alkene in a synthesis, a process that cannot be accomplished in a single step. Using the reactions you have learned in Chapters 8–12, devise a stepwise method to convert *cis*-2-butene to *trans*-2-butene.

12.65 Devise a synthesis of each compound from acetylene and any other required reagents.

a. 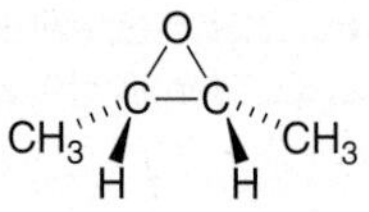

b. 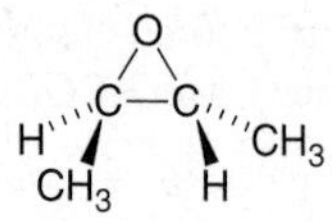

(+ enantiomer)

c. 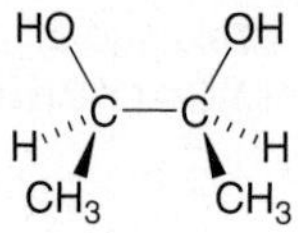

d. 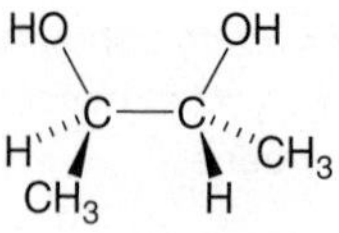

(+ enantiomer)

12.66 Devise a synthesis of each compound from styrene ($C_6H_5CH{=}CH_2$). You may use any inorganic or organic reagents. More than one step is required.

a. $C_6H_5CH_2CHO$ b. $C_6H_5COCH_3$ c. $C_6H_5CH_2COOH$ d. $C_6H_5CH(OH)CH_2C{\equiv}CH$

12.67 Devise a synthesis of compound **A** from the given starting materials. You may use any other inorganic reagents or organic alcohols. **A** was used to prepare aliskiren, a drug used to treat hypertension (see also Problem 5.7).

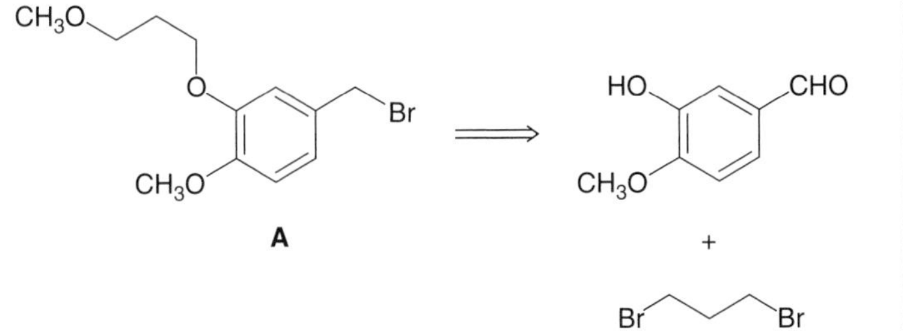

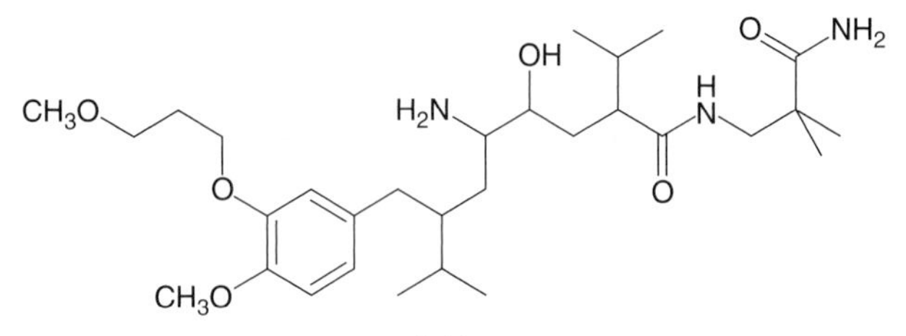

aliskiren

12.68 Devise a synthesis of (2*E*)-2-hexene from 1-pentene and any needed organic compounds or inorganic reagents.

12.69 Devise a synthesis of each compound from the indicated starting material and any other required reagents.

a. $CH_3CH_2CH{=}CH_2 \longrightarrow CH_3CH_2CH_2COOH$

c. 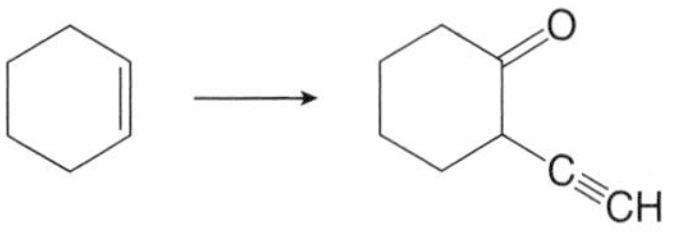

b. $CH_3CH_2CH_2CH_2OH \longrightarrow$ 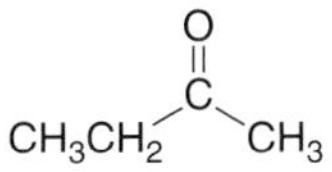

d. 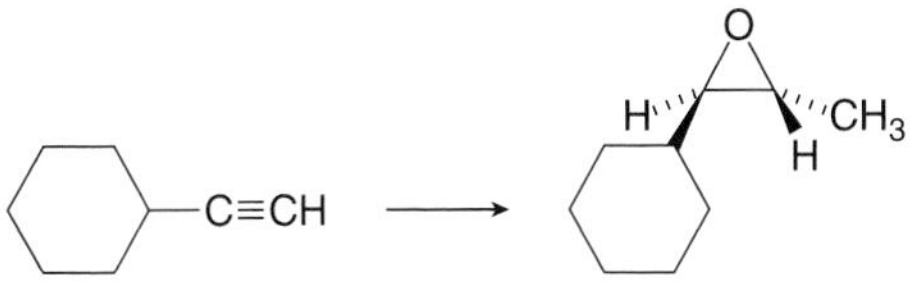

(+ enantiomer)

12.70 Devise a synthesis of each compound from acetylene and organic compounds containing two carbons or fewer. You may use any other required reagents.

a. 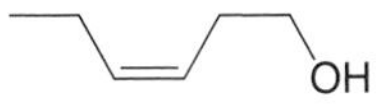

b. 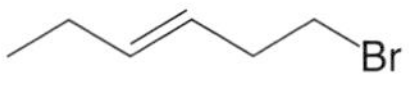

c. 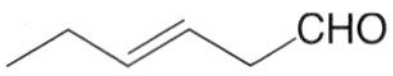

12.71 Devise a synthesis of 1-phenyl-5-methylhexane [$C_6H_5(CH_2)_4CH(CH_3)_2$] from acetylene, alkyl halides, and any required inorganic reagents.

12.72 Devise a stepwise method to convert 1-methylcyclopentene oxide to methylcyclopentane.

12.73 Devise a synthesis of (3*R*,4*S*)-3,4-dichlorohexane from acetylene and any needed organic compounds or inorganic reagents.

12.74 Devise a synthesis of each compound from CH_3CH_2OH as the only organic starting material; that is, every carbon in the product must come from a molecule of ethanol. You may use any other needed inorganic reagents.

a. 
b. 

c. 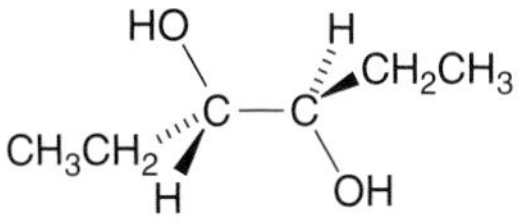

Challenge Problems

12.75 The Birch reduction is a dissolving metal reaction that converts substituted benzenes to 1,4-cyclohexadienes using Li and liquid ammonia in the presence of an alcohol. Draw a stepwise mechanism for the following Birch reduction.

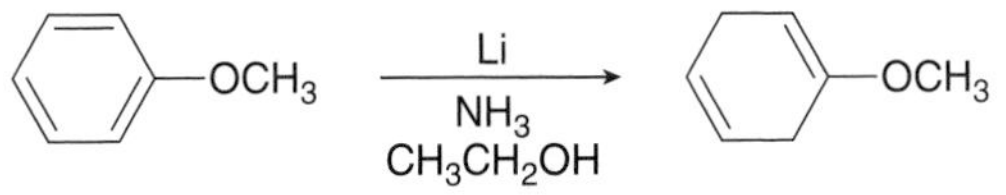

12.76 In the Cr^{6+} oxidation of cyclohexanols, it is generally true that sterically hindered alcohols react faster than unhindered alcohols. Which of the following alcohols should be oxidized more rapidly?

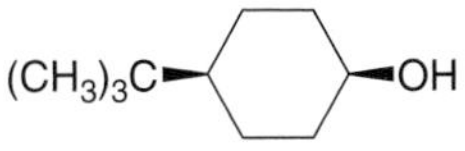

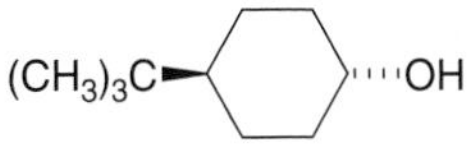

12.77 Draw a stepwise mechanism for the following reaction.

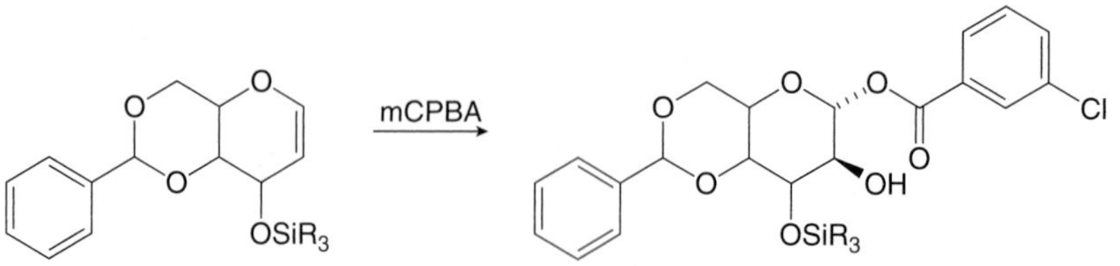

R = alkyl group R = alkyl group

12.78 Although reagents can always add to an alkene from either side, sometimes one side of the double bond is more sterically hindered, so an unequal mixture of addition products results. For example, when **X** is treated with H_2 in the presence of a Pd catalyst, 80% of the product mixture contains the cis isomer **Y** and only 20% is the trans isomer **Z.** Thus, addition of H_2 occurs predominantly on the side opposite to the bulky *tert*-butyl group, resulting in a new equatorial C–H bond. Keeping this in mind, what is the major epoxidation product formed from **X** under each of the following reaction conditions: (a) mCPBA; or (b) Br_2, H_2O followed by NaH?

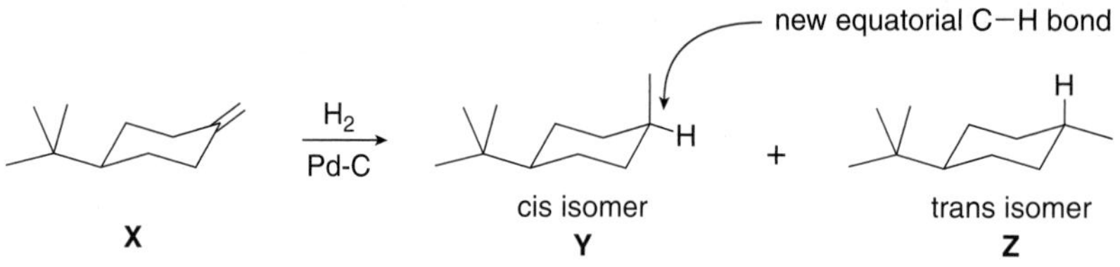

12.79 Dihydroxylation of an alkene can be carried out with H_2O_2 in HCO_2H. In this reaction, *trans*-2-butene affords (2*R*,3*S*)-2,3-butanediol, whereas *cis*-2-butene affords a mixture of (2*R*,3*R*)-2,3-butanediol and (2*S*,3*S*)-2,3-butanediol. Does dihydroxylation by this method occur with syn or anti addition?

12.80 Draw a stepwise mechanism for the following reaction.

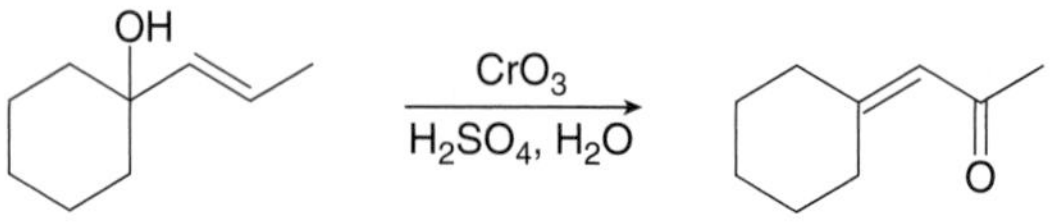

12.81 Sharpless epoxidation of allylic alcohol **X** forms compound **Y.** Treatment of **Y** with NaOH and C_6H_5SH in an alcohol–water mixture forms **Z.** Identify the structure of **Y** and draw a mechanism for the conversion of **Y** to **Z.** Account for the stereochemistry of the stereogenic centers in **Z. Z** has been used as an intermediate in the synthesis of chiral carbohydrates.

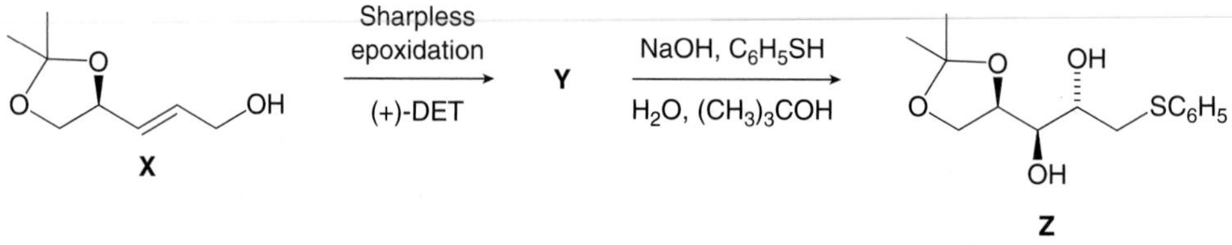

Mass Spectrometry and Infrared Spectroscopy

13

13.1 Mass spectrometry
13.2 Alkyl halides and the M + 2 peak
13.3 Fragmentation
13.4 Other types of mass spectrometry
13.5 Electromagnetic radiation
13.6 Infrared spectroscopy
13.7 IR absorptions
13.8 IR and structure determination

The serendipitous discovery of **penicillin** by Scottish bacteriologist Sir Alexander Fleming in 1928 is considered one of the single most important events in the history of medicine. Penicillin G and related compounds are members of the β-lactam family of antibiotics, all of which contain a strained four-membered amide ring that is responsible for their biological activity. Penicillin was first used to cure a streptococcal infection in 1942, and by 1944 penicillin production was given high priority by the United States government, because it was needed to treat the many injured soldiers in World War II. The unusual structure of penicillin was elucidated by modern instrumental methods in the 1940s. In Chapter 13, we learn about mass spectrometry and infrared spectroscopy, two techniques for characterizing organic compounds like penicillin.

Whether a compound is prepared in the laboratory or isolated from a natural source, a chemist must determine its identity. Seventy years ago, determining the structure of an organic compound involved a series of time-consuming operations: measuring physical properties (melting point, boiling point, solubility, and density), identifying the functional groups using a series of chemical tests, and converting an unknown compound into another compound whose physical and chemical properties were then characterized as well.

Although still a challenging task, structure determination has been greatly simplified by modern instrumental methods. These techniques have both decreased the time needed for compound characterization, and increased the complexity of compounds whose structures can be completely determined.

In Chapter 13 we examine **mass spectrometry (MS),** which is used to determine the molecular weight and molecular formula of a compound, and **infrared (IR) spectroscopy,** a tool used to identify a compound's functional groups. Chapter 14 is devoted to **nuclear magnetic resonance (NMR) spectroscopy,** which is used to identify the carbon–hydrogen framework in a compound, making it the most powerful spectroscopic tool for organic structure analysis. **Each of these methods relies on the interaction of an energy source with a molecule to produce a change that is recorded in a spectrum.**

13.1 Mass Spectrometry

***Mass spectrometry* is a technique used for measuring the molecular weight and determining the molecular formula of an organic molecule.**

13.1A General Features

In the most common type of **mass spectrometer,** a molecule is vaporized and ionized, usually by bombardment with a beam of high-energy electrons, as shown in Figure 13.1. The energy of these electrons is typically about 6400 kJ, or 70 electron volts (eV). Because it takes ~400 kJ of energy to cleave a typical σ bond, 6400 kJ is an enormous amount of energy to come into contact with a molecule. This electron beam ionizes a molecule by causing it to eject an electron.

Figure 13.1
Schematic of a mass spectrometer

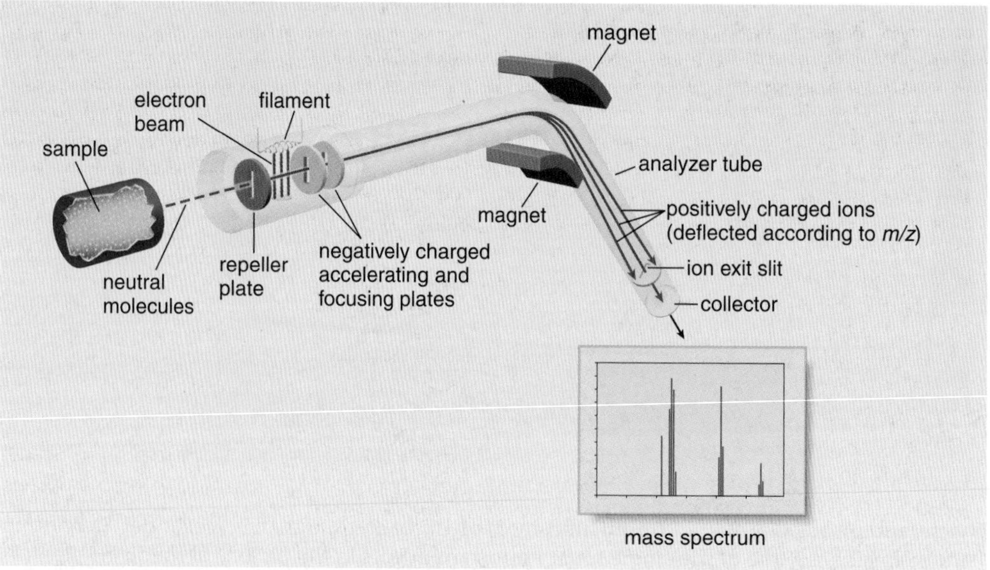

In a mass spectrometer, a sample is vaporized and bombarded by a beam of electrons to form an unstable radical cation, which then decomposes to smaller fragments. The positively charged ions are accelerated toward a negatively charged plate, and then passed through a curved analyzer tube in a magnetic field, where they are deflected by different amounts depending on their ratio of mass to charge (*m/z*). A mass spectrum plots the intensity of each ion versus its *m/z* ratio.

The term **spectroscopy** is usually used for techniques that use electromagnetic radiation as an energy source. Because the energy source in MS is a beam of electrons, the term **mass spectrometry** is used instead.

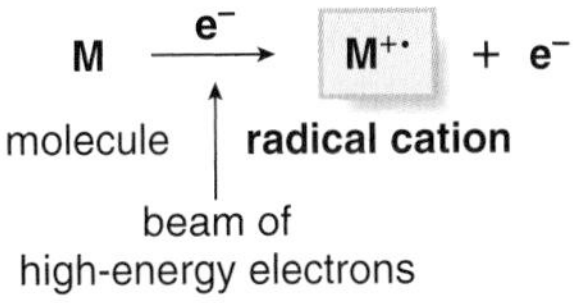

The species formed is a **radical cation,** symbolized **M$^{+\cdot}$.** It is a radical because it has an unpaired electron, and it is a cation because it has one fewer electron than it started with.

- **The radical cation M$^{+\cdot}$ is called the *molecular ion* or the *parent ion.***

A single electron has a negligible mass, so the **mass of M$^{+\cdot}$ represents the molecular weight** of M. Because the molecular ion **M$^{+\cdot}$** is inherently unstable, it decomposes. Single bonds break to form ***fragments,*** **radicals and cations having a lower molecular weight than the molecular ion.** A mass spectrometer analyzes the masses of cations only. The cations are accelerated in an electric field and deflected in a curved path in a magnetic field, thus sorting the molecular ion and its fragments by their **mass-to-charge (*m/z*) ratio.** Because *z* is almost always +1, *m/z* actually measures the mass (*m*) of the individual ions.

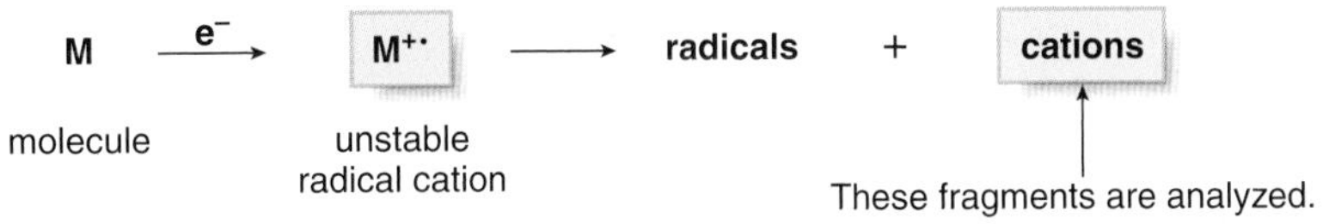

- **A *mass spectrum* plots the amount of each cation (its relative abundance) versus its mass.**

The whole-number mass of CH_4 is (1 C × 12 amu) + (4 H × 1 amu) = 16 amu; amu = atomic mass unit.

A mass spectrometer analyzes the masses of *individual* molecules, not the weighted average mass of a group of molecules, so the whole-number masses of the most common individual isotopes must be used to calculate the mass of the molecular ion. Thus, the mass of the molecular ion for CH_4 should be 16. As a result, the mass spectrum of CH_4 shows a line for the molecular ion—the parent peak or **M** peak—at $m/z = 16$.

Mass spectrum of CH_4

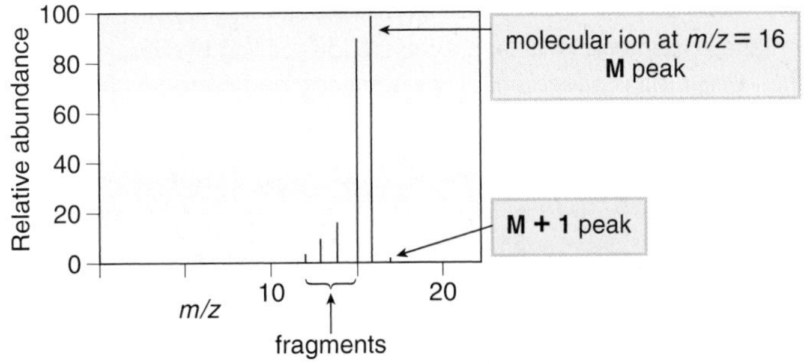

m/z	relative abundance	
17	1.2	
16	100.0	← base peak
15	85.9	
14	16.1	
13	8.1	
12	2.8	

The tallest peak in a mass spectrum is called the **base peak.** For CH_4, the base peak is also the M peak, although this may *not* always be the case for all organic compounds.

The mass spectrum of CH_4 consists of more peaks than just the M peak. What is responsible for the peaks at $m/z < 16$? Because the molecular ion is unstable, it fragments into other cations and radical cations containing one, two, three, or four fewer hydrogen atoms than methane itself. Thus, the peaks at m/z = 15, 14, 13, and 12, are due to these lower molecular weight fragments. The decomposition of a molecular ion into lower molecular weight fragments is called **fragmentation.**

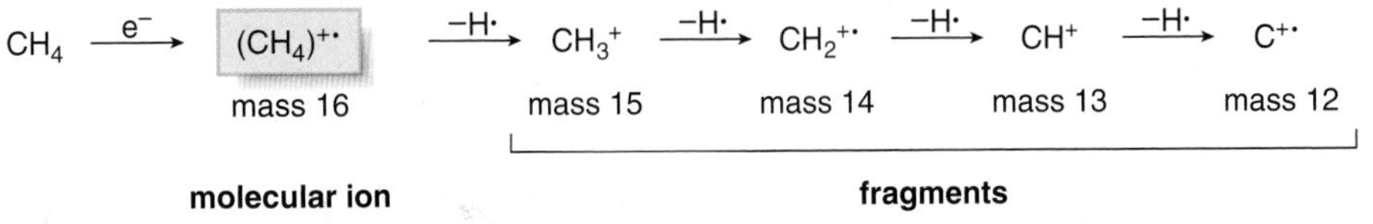

What is responsible for the small peak at $m/z = 17$ in the mass spectrum of CH_4? Although most carbon atoms have an atomic mass of 12, 1.1% of them have an additional neutron in the nucleus, giving them an atomic mass of 13. When one of these carbon-13 isotopes forms methane, it gives a molecular ion peak at $m/z = 17$ in the mass spectrum. This peak is called the **M + 1** peak.

These key features—the molecular ion, the base peak, and the M + 1 peak—are illustrated in the mass spectrum of hexane in Figure 13.2.

Figure 13.2
Mass spectrum of hexane ($CH_3CH_2CH_2CH_2CH_2CH_3$)

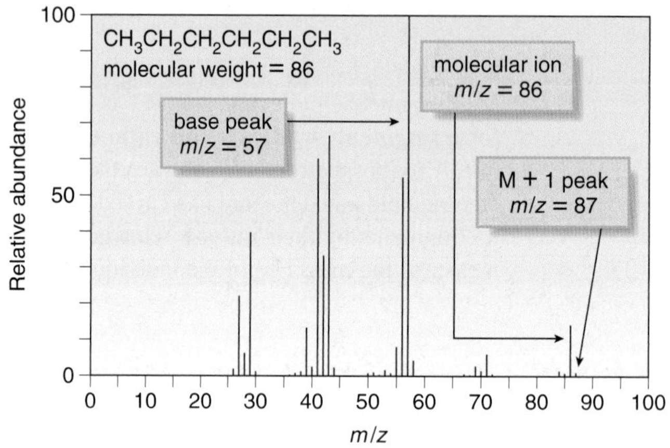

- The molecular ion for hexane (molecular formula C_6H_{14}) is at $m/z = 86$.
- The base peak (relative abundance = 100) occurs at $m/z = 57$.
- A small M + 1 peak occurs at $m/z = 87$.

13.1B Analyzing Unknowns Using the Molecular Ion

Because the **mass of the molecular ion equals the molecular weight of a compound,** a mass spectrum can be used to distinguish between compounds that have similar physical properties but different molecular weights, as illustrated in Sample Problem 13.1.

Sample Problem 13.1 Pentane, 1-pentene, and 1-pentyne are low-boiling hydrocarbons that have different molecular ions in their mass spectra. Match each hydrocarbon to its mass spectrum.

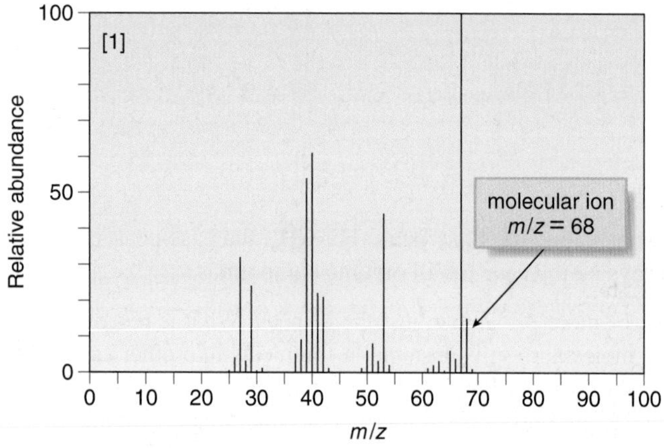

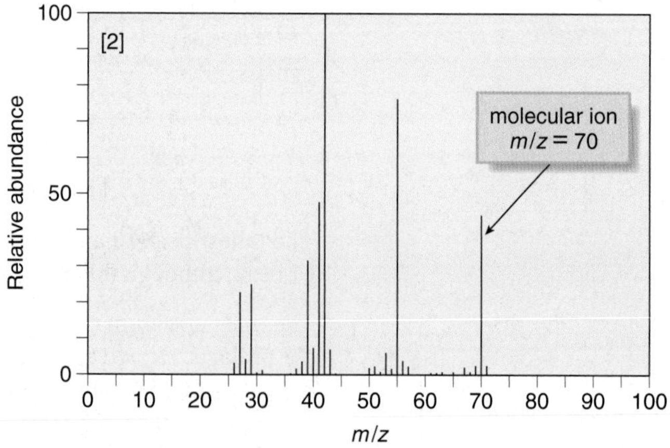

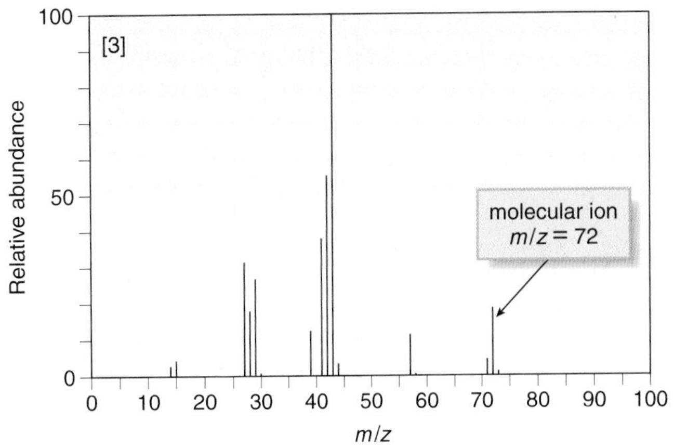

Solution

To solve this problem, first determine the molecular formula and molecular weight of each compound. Then, because the molecular weight of the compound equals the mass of the molecular ion, match the molecular weight to *m/z* for the molecular ion:

Compound	Molecular formula	Molecular weight = *m/z* of molecular ion	Spectrum
pentane, $CH_3CH_2CH_2CH_2CH_3$	C_5H_{12}	72	[3]
1-pentene, $CH_2{=}CHCH_2CH_2CH_3$	C_5H_{10}	70	[2]
1-pentyne, $HC{\equiv}CCH_2CH_2CH_3$	C_5H_8	68	[1]

Problem 13.1 What is the mass of the molecular ion formed from compounds having each molecular formula: (a) C_3H_6O; (b) $C_{10}H_{20}$; (c) $C_8H_8O_2$; (d) methamphetamine ($C_{10}H_{15}N$)?

How to use the mass of the molecular ion to propose molecular formulas for an unknown is shown in Sample Problem 13.2. In this process, keep in mind the following useful fact. Hydrocarbons like methane (CH_4) and hexane (C_6H_{14}), as well as compounds that contain only C, H, and O atoms, always have a molecular ion with an *even* mass. An odd molecular ion generally indicates that a compound contains nitrogen.

Sample Problem 13.2 Propose possible molecular formulas for a compound with a molecular ion at *m/z* = 86.

Solution

Because the molecular ion has an **even** mass, the compound likely contains C, H, and possibly O atoms. Begin by determining the molecular formula for a hydrocarbon having a molecular ion at 86. Then, because the mass of an O atom is 16 (the mass of CH_4), replace CH_4 by O to give a molecular formula containing one O atom. Repeat this last step to give possible molecular formulas for compounds with two or more O atoms.

For a molecular ion at *m/z* = 86:

Possible hydrocarbons:

- Divide 86 by 12 (mass of 1 C atom). This gives the maximum number of C's possible.

$$\frac{86}{12} = 7 \text{ C's maximum (remainder} = 2) \longrightarrow \boxed{C_7H_2}$$

- Replace 1 C by 12 H's for another possible molecular formula.

$$C_7H_2 \xrightarrow[+\,12\text{ H's}]{-\,1\text{ C}} \boxed{C_6H_{14}}$$

Possible compounds with C, H, and O:

- Substitute 1 O for CH_4. (This can't be done for C_7H_2.)

$$C_6H_{14} \xrightarrow[+\,1\text{ O}]{-\,CH_4} \boxed{C_5H_{10}O}$$

- Repeat the process.

$$C_5H_{10}O \xrightarrow[+\,1\text{ O}]{-\,CH_4} \boxed{C_4H_6O_2}$$

The effect of N atoms on the mass of the molecular ion in a mass spectrum is called the **nitrogen rule: A compound that contains an *odd* number of N atoms gives an odd molecular ion.** Conversely, a compound that contains an *even* number of N atoms (including *zero*) gives an *even* molecular ion. Two "street" drugs that mimic the effects of heroin illustrate this principle: 3-methylfentanyl (two N atoms, even molecular weight) and MPPP (one N atom, odd molecular weight).

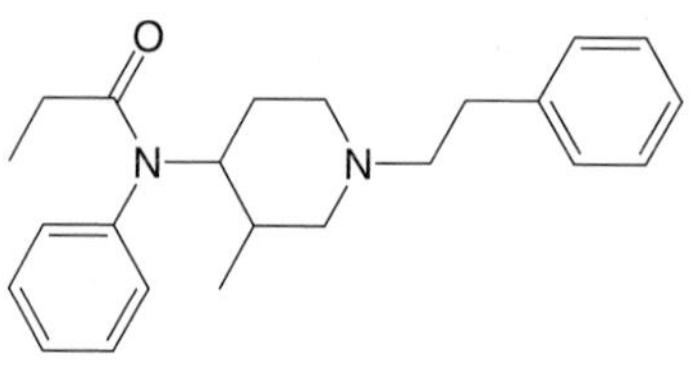

3-methylfentanyl
$C_{23}H_{30}N_2O$
molecular weight = 350

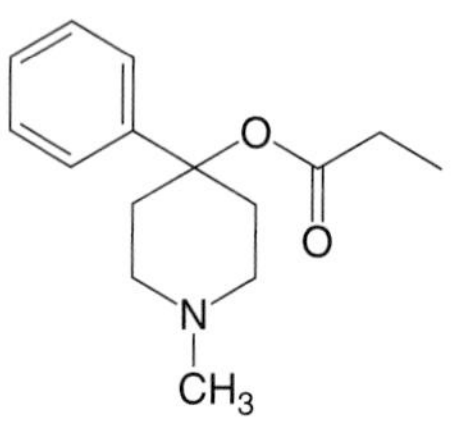

MPPP
(1-methyl-4-phenyl-4-propionoxypiperidine)
$C_{15}H_{21}NO_2$
molecular weight = 247

Problem 13.2 Propose two molecular formulas for each of the following molecular ions: (a) 72; (b) 100; (c) 73.

13.2 Alkyl Halides and the M + 2 Peak

Most of the elements found in organic compounds, such as carbon, hydrogen, oxygen, nitrogen, sulfur, phosphorus, fluorine, and iodine, have one major isotope. **Chlorine** and **bromine,** on the other hand, have two, giving characteristic patterns to the mass spectra of their compounds.

Chlorine has two common isotopes, ^{35}**Cl** and ^{37}**Cl,** which occur naturally in a 3:1 ratio. Thus, **there are two peaks in a 3:1 ratio for the molecular ion of an alkyl chloride.** The larger peak—the **M** peak—corresponds to the compound containing ^{35}Cl, and the smaller peak—the **M + 2** peak—corresponds to the compound containing ^{37}Cl.

- **When the molecular ion consists of two peaks (M and M + 2) in a 3:1 ratio, a Cl atom is present.**

Sample Problem 13.3 What molecular ions will be present in a mass spectrum of 2-chloropropane, $(CH_3)_2CHCl$?

Solution

Calculate the molecular weight using each of the common isotopes of Cl.

Molecular formula	Mass of molecular ion (*m/z*)
$C_3H_7{}^{35}Cl$	78 (M peak)
$C_3H_7{}^{37}Cl$	80 (M + 2 peak)

There should be two peaks in a ratio of 3:1, at *m/z* = 78 and 80, as illustrated in the mass spectrum of 2-chloropropane in Figure 13.3.

Figure 13.3 Mass spectrum of 2-chloropropane [$(CH_3)_2CHCl$]

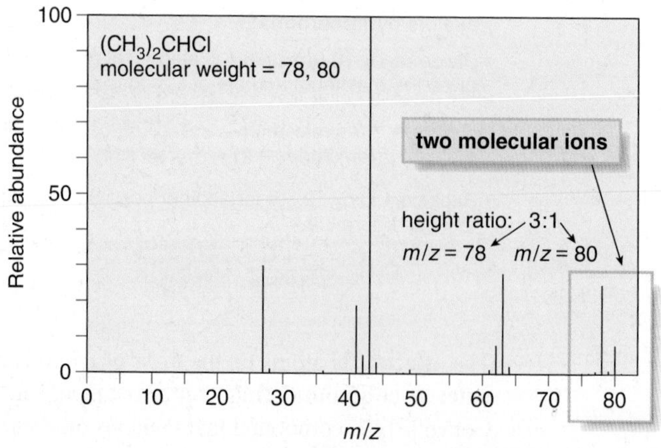

Figure 13.4
Mass spectrum of 2-bromopropane [$(CH_3)_2CHBr$]

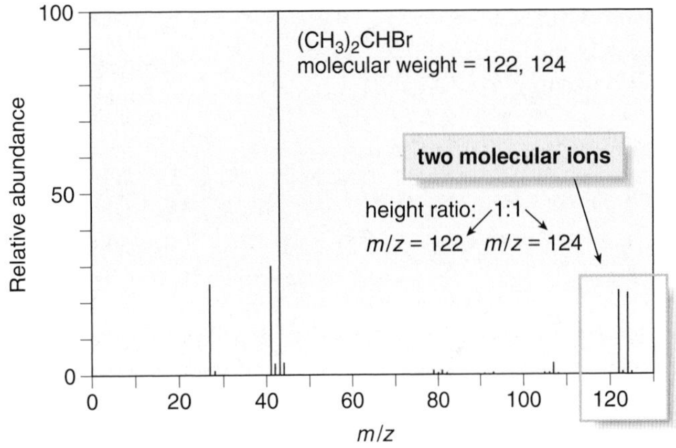

Bromine has two common isotopes, ^{79}**Br** and ^{81}**Br,** which occur naturally in a 1:1 ratio. Thus, **there are two peaks in a 1:1 ratio for the molecular ion of an alkyl bromide.** In the mass spectrum of 2-bromopropane (Figure 13.4), for example, there is an M peak at m/z = 122 and an M + 2 peak at m/z = 124.

- **When the molecular ion consists of two peaks (M and M + 2) in a 1:1 ratio, a Br atom is present in the molecule.**

Problem 13.3 What molecular ions would you expect for compounds having each of the following molecular formulas: (a) C_4H_9Cl; (b) C_3H_7F; (c) $C_4H_{11}N$; (d) $C_4H_4N_2$?

Problem 13.4 What molecular ions would you expect for the compound depicted in the ball-and-stick model?

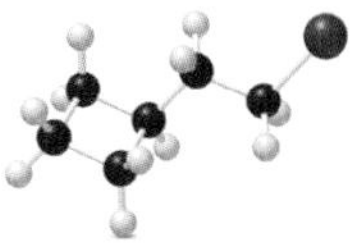

13.3 Fragmentation

While many chemists use a mass spectrum to determine only a compound's molecular weight and molecular formula, additional useful structural information can be obtained from fragmentation patterns. Although each organic compound fragments in a unique way, a particular functional group exhibits common fragmentation patterns.

13.3A General Features of Fragmentation

As an example, consider hexane, whose mass spectrum was shown in Figure 13.2. When hexane is bombarded by an electron beam, it forms a highly unstable radical cation (m/z = 86) that can decompose by cleavage of any of the C–C bonds. Thus, cleavage of the terminal C–C bond forms $CH_3CH_2CH_2CH_2CH_2^+$ and $CH_3\cdot$. Fragmentation generates a cation and a radical, and cleavage generally yields the more stable, more substituted carbocation.

Cleave this bond.

$$CH_3CH_2CH_2CH_2CH_2CH_3 \xrightarrow{e^-} (CH_3CH_2CH_2CH_2CH_2{-}CH_3)^{+\cdot} \longrightarrow CH_3CH_2CH_2CH_2\overset{+}{C}H_2 + \cdot CH_3$$

radical cation $m/z = 86$ | cation $m/z = 71$ | radical

- **Loss of a CH_3 group always forms a fragment with a mass 15 units less than the molecular ion.**

Figure 13.5
Identifying fragments in the mass spectrum of hexane

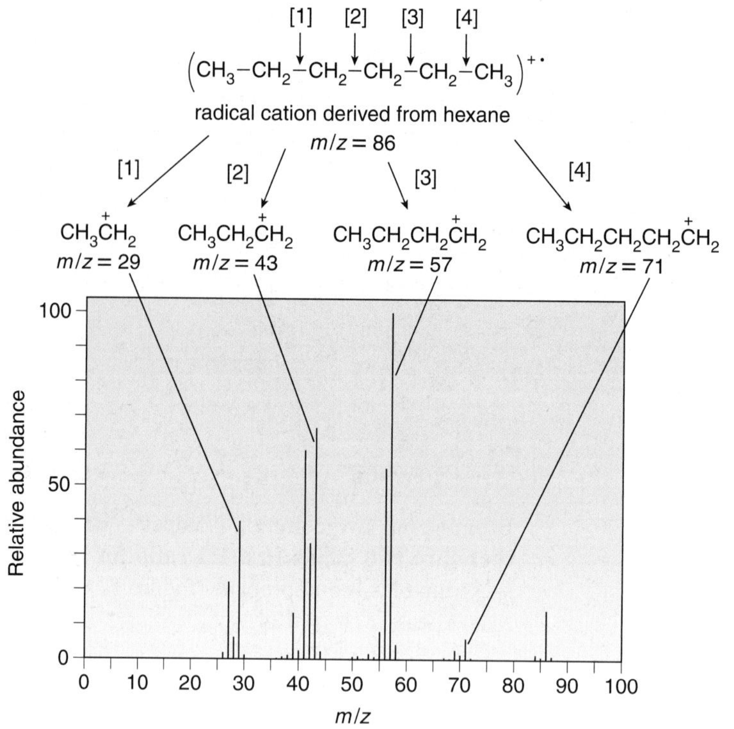

- Cleavage of C–C bonds (labeled [1]–[4]) in hexane forms lower molecular weight fragments that correspond to lines in the mass spectrum. Although the mass spectrum is complex, possible structures can be assigned to some of the fragments, as shown.

As a result, the mass spectrum of hexane shows a peak at $m/z = 71$ due to $CH_3CH_2CH_2CH_2CH_2^+$. Figure 13.5 illustrates how cleavage of other C–C bonds in hexane gives rise to other fragments that correspond to peaks in its mass spectrum.

Sample Problem 13.4 The mass spectrum of 2,3-dimethylpentane [$(CH_3)_2CHCH(CH_3)CH_2CH_3$] shows fragments at m/z = 85 and 71. Propose possible structures for the ions that give rise to these peaks.

Solution

To solve a problem of this sort, first calculate the mass of the molecular ion. Draw out the structure of the compound, break a C–C bond, and calculate the mass of the resulting fragments. Repeat this process on different C–C bonds until fragments of the desired mass-to-charge ratio are formed.

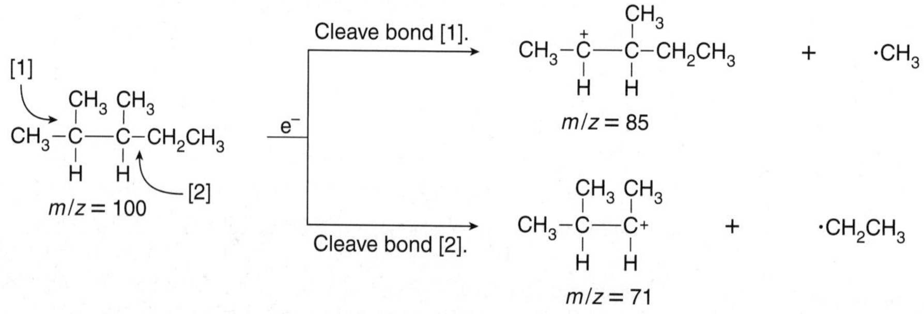

In this example, 2,3-dimethylpentane has a molecular ion at m/z = 100. Cleavage of bond [1] forms a 2° carbocation with m/z = 85 and $CH_3\bullet$. Cleavage of bond [2] forms another 2° carbocation with m/z = 71 and $CH_3CH_2\bullet$. Thus, the fragments at m/z = 85 and 71 are possibly due to the two carbocations drawn.

Problem 13.5 The mass spectrum of 2,3-dimethylpentane also shows peaks at m/z = 57 and 43. Propose possible structures for the ions that give rise to these peaks.

Problem 13.6 The base peak in the mass spectrum of 2,2,4-trimethylpentane [$(CH_3)_3CCH_2CH(CH_3)_2$] occurs at m/z = 57. What ion is responsible for this peak and why is this ion the most abundant fragment?

13.3B Fragmentation Patterns of Some Common Functional Groups

Each functional group exhibits characteristic fragmentation patterns that help to analyze a mass spectrum. For example, aldehydes and ketones often undergo the process of **α cleavage, breaking the bond between the carbonyl carbon and the carbon adjacent to it.** Cleavage yields a neutral radical and a resonance-stabilized acylium ion.

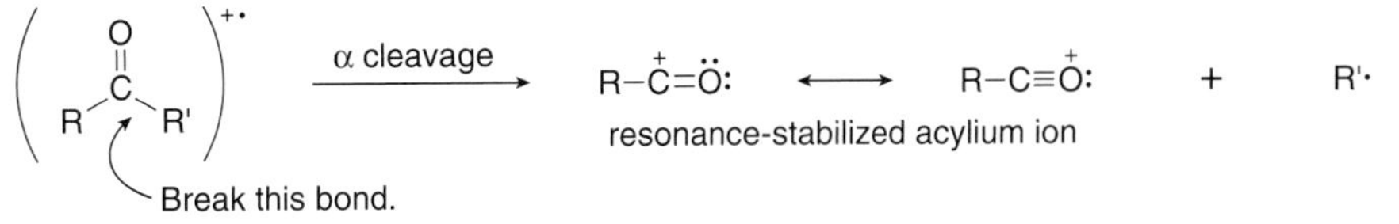

R = H or alkyl

Alcohols undergo fragmentation in two different ways—α cleavage and dehydration. Alpha (α) cleavage occurs by breaking a bond between an alkyl group and the carbon that bears the OH group, resulting in an alkyl radical and a resonance-stabilized carbocation.

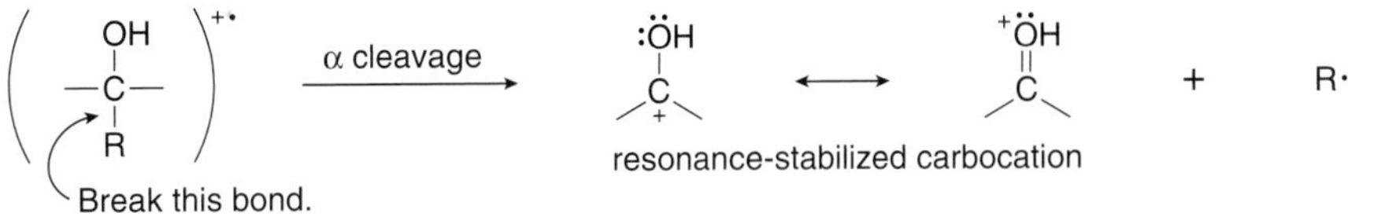

Likewise, alcohols undergo dehydration, the elimination of H_2O, from two adjacent atoms. Unlike fragmentations discussed thus far, dehydration results in the cleavage of two bonds and forms H_2O and the radical cation derived from an alkene.

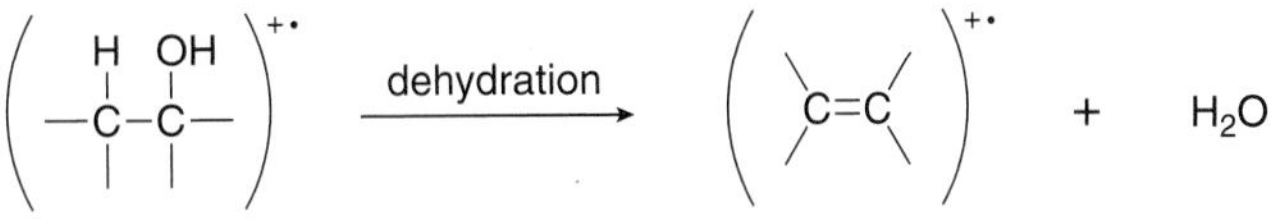

- **Loss of H_2O from an alcohol always forms a fragment with a mass 18 units less than the molecular ion.**

Sample Problem 13.5 What mass spectral fragments are formed from α cleavage of 2-pentanone, $CH_3COCH_2CH_2CH_3$?

Solution

Alpha (α) cleavage breaks the bond between the carbonyl carbon and the carbon adjacent to it, yielding a neutral radical and a resonance-stabilized acylium ion. A ketone like 2-pentanone with two different alkyl groups bonded to the carbonyl carbon has two different pathways for α cleavage.

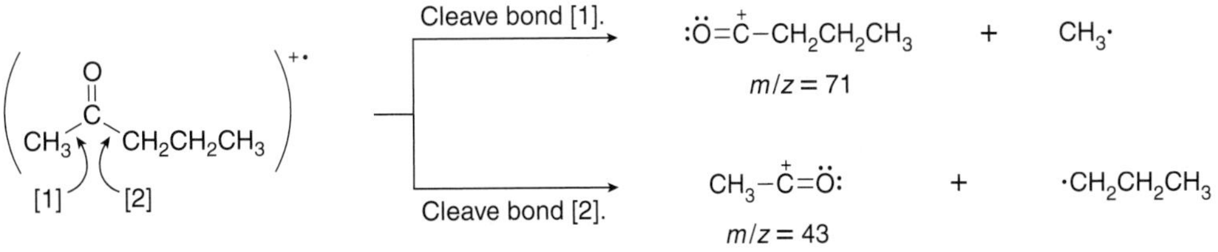

As a result, two fragments are formed by α cleavage of 2-pentanone, giving peaks at m/z = 71 and 43.

Problem 13.7 (a) What mass spectral fragments are formed by α cleavage of 2-butanol, $CH_3CH(OH)CH_2CH_3$?
(b) What fragments are formed by dehydration of 2-butanol?

Problem 13.8 What cations are formed in the mass spectrometer by α cleavage of each of the following compounds?

a. 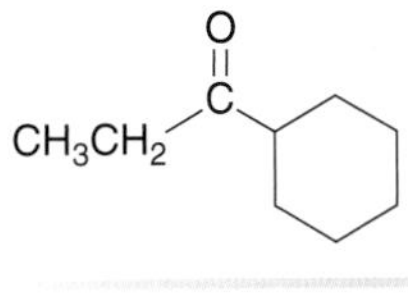

b. $CH_3CH_2CH_2CH_2CH_2CH_2OH$

c. $CH_3CH_2CH_2CHO$

13.4 Other Types of Mass Spectrometry

Recent advances have greatly expanded the information obtained from mass spectrometry.

13.4A High-Resolution Mass Spectrometry

The mass spectra described thus far have been low-resolution spectra; that is, they report *m/z* values to the nearest whole number. As a result, the mass of a given molecular ion can correspond to many different molecular formulas, as shown in Sample Problem 13.2.

Table 13.1 Exact Masses of Some Common Isotopes

Isotope	Mass
^{12}C	12.0000
^{1}H	1.00783
^{16}O	15.9949
^{14}N	14.0031

High-resolution mass spectrometers measure *m/z* ratios to four (or more) decimal places. This is valuable because except for carbon-12, whose mass is defined as 12.0000, the masses of all other nuclei are very close to—but not exactly—whole numbers. Table 13.1 lists the exact mass values of a few common nuclei. Using these values it is possible to determine the single molecular formula that gives rise to a molecular ion.

For example, a compound having a molecular ion at $m/z = 60$ using a low-resolution mass spectrometer could have the following molecular formulas:

Formula	Exact mass
C_3H_8O	60.0575
$C_2H_4O_2$	60.0211
$C_2H_8N_2$	60.0688

If the molecular ion had an exact mass of 60.0578, the compound's molecular formula is C_3H_8O, because its mass is closest to the observed value.

Problem 13.9 The low-resolution mass spectrum of an unknown analgesic **X** had a molecular ion of 151. Possible molecular formulas include $C_7H_5NO_3$, $C_8H_9NO_2$, and $C_{10}H_{17}N$. High-resolution mass spectrometry gave an exact mass of 151.0640. What is the molecular formula of **X**?

13.4B Gas Chromatography–Mass Spectrometry (GC–MS)

Two analytical tools—**gas chromatography (GC)** and **mass spectrometry (MS)**—can be combined into a single instrument **(GC–MS)** to analyze mixtures of compounds (Figure 13.6a). The gas chromatograph separates the mixture, and then the mass spectrometer records a spectrum of the individual components.

Like other controlled substances, the tetrahydrocannabinol from marijuana leaves can be detected in minute amounts by GC–MS.

A gas chromatograph consists of a thin capillary column containing a viscous, high-boiling liquid, all housed in an oven. When a sample is injected into the GC, it is vaporized and swept by an inert gas through the column. The components of the mixture travel through the column at different rates, often separated by boiling point, with lower boiling compounds exiting the column before higher boiling compounds. Each compound then enters the mass spectrometer, where it is ionized to form its molecular ion and lower molecular weight fragments. The GC–MS records a gas chromatogram for the mixture, which plots the amount of each component versus its **retention time**—that is, the time required to travel through the column. Each component of a mixture is characterized by its retention time in the gas chromatogram and its molecular ion in the mass spectrum (Figure 13.6b).

GC–MS is widely used for characterizing mixtures containing environmental pollutants. It is also used to analyze urine and hair samples for the presence of illegal drugs or banned substances thought to improve athletic performance.

To analyze a urine sample for THC (tetrahydrocannabinol), the principal psychoactive component of marijuana, the organic compounds are extracted from urine, purified, concentrated, and injected into the GC–MS. THC appears as a GC peak with a characteristic retention time (for a given set of experimental parameters), and gives a molecular ion at 314, its molecular weight, as shown in Figure 13.7.

Figure 13.6
Compound analysis using GC–MS

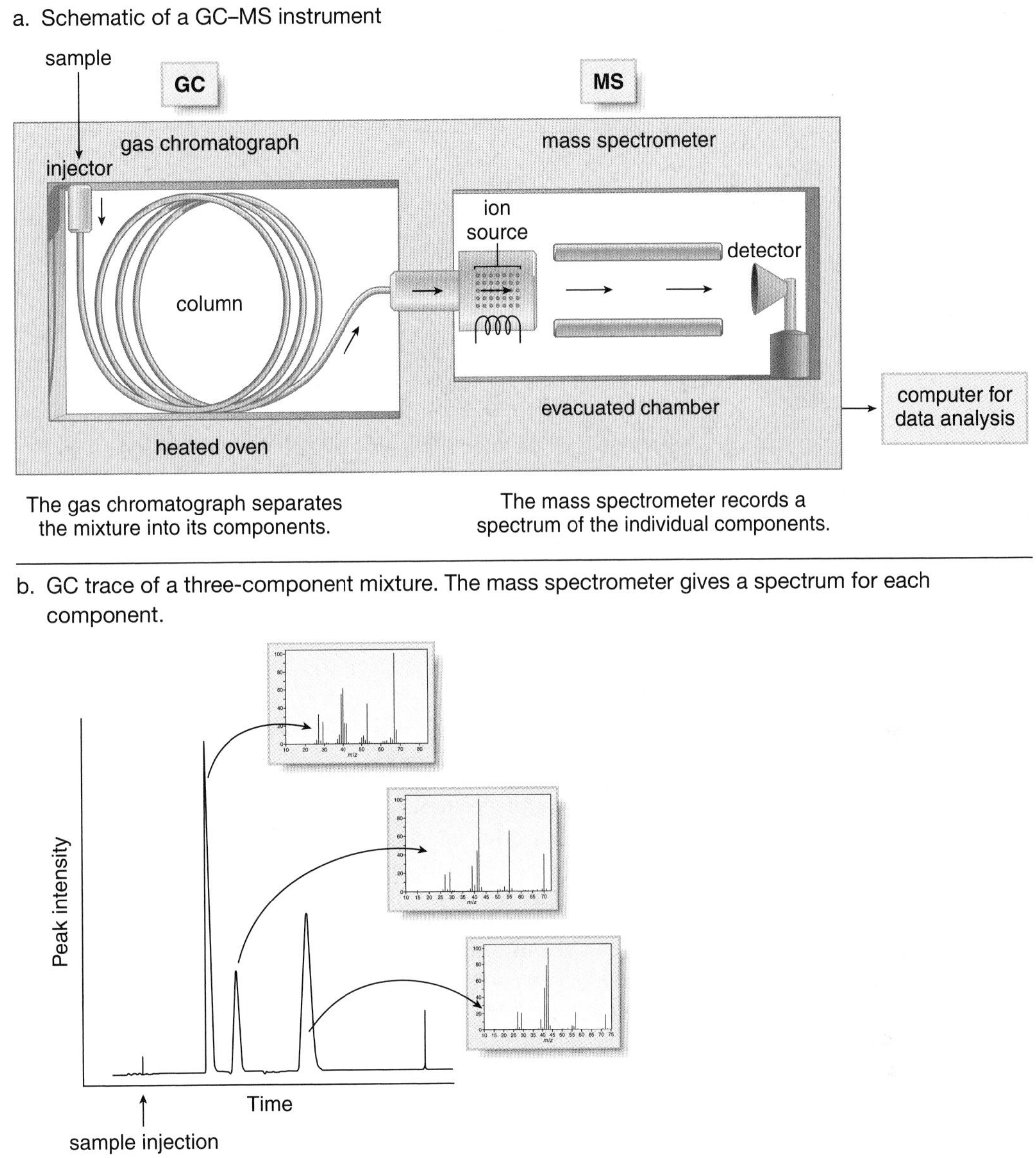

Figure 13.7
Mass spectrum of tetrahydrocannabinol (THC)

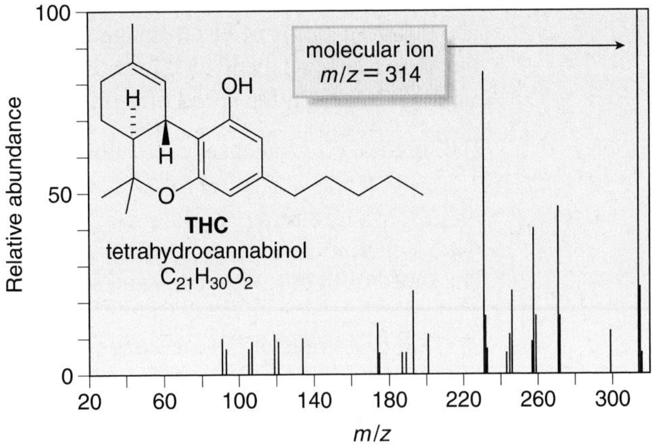

Problem 13.10 Benzene, toluene, and *p*-xylene (BTX) are often added to gasoline to boost octane ratings. What would be observed if a mixture of these three compounds were subjected to GC–MS analysis? How many peaks would be present in the gas chromatogram? What would be the relative order of the peaks? What molecular ions would be observed in the mass spectra?

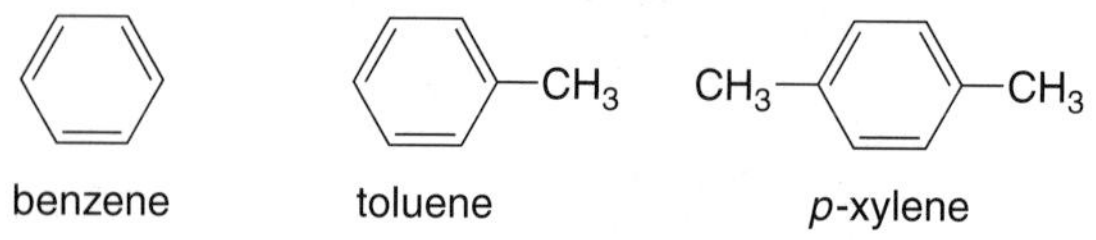

13.4C Mass Spectra of High Molecular Weight Biomolecules

Dr. John Fenn shared the 2002 Nobel Prize in Chemistry for his development of ESI mass spectrometry.

Until the 1980s mass spectra were limited to molecules that could be readily vaporized with heat under vacuum, and thus had molecular weights of < 800. In the last 25 years, new methods have been developed to generate gas phase ions of large molecules, allowing mass spectra to be recorded for large biomolecules such as proteins and carbohydrates. **Electrospray ionization (ESI),** for example, forms ions by creating a fine spray of charged droplets in an electric field. Evaporation of the charged droplets forms gaseous ions that are then analyzed by their *m/z* ratio. ESI and related techniques have extended mass spectrometry into the analysis of nonvolatile compounds with molecular weights greater than 100,000 daltons (atomic mass units).

13.5 Electromagnetic Radiation

Infrared (IR) spectroscopy and **nuclear magnetic resonance (NMR)** spectroscopy (Chapter 14) both use a form of electromagnetic radiation as their energy source. To understand IR and NMR, therefore, you need to understand some of the properties of **electromagnetic radiation**—radiant energy having dual properties of both waves and particles.

The particles of electromagnetic radiation are called **photons,** each having a discrete amount of energy called a **quantum.** Because electromagnetic radiation also has wave properties, it can be characterized by its **wavelength** and **frequency.**

- **Wavelength (λ) is the distance from one point on a wave (e.g., the peak or trough) to the same point on the adjacent wave. A variety of different length units are used for λ, depending on the type of radiation.**
- **Frequency (ν) is the number of waves passing a point per unit time. Frequency is reported in cycles per second (s^{-1}), which is also called hertz (Hz).**

Length units used to report wavelength include:

Unit	Length
meter (m)	1 m
centimeter (cm)	10^{-2} m
micrometer (μm)	10^{-6} m
nanometer (nm)	10^{-9} m
Angstrom (Å)	10^{-10} m

You come into contact with many different kinds of electromagnetic radiation in your daily life. For example, you use visible light to see the words on this page, you may cook with microwaves, and you should use sunscreen to protect your skin from the harmful effects of ultraviolet radiation.

The different forms of electromagnetic radiation make up the **electromagnetic spectrum.** The spectrum is arbitrarily divided into different regions, as shown in Figure 13.8. All electromagnetic radiation travels at the speed of light (*c*), 3.0×10^8 m/s.

The speed of electromagnetic radiation (*c*) is directly proportional to its wavelength and frequency:

$$c = \lambda\nu$$

The speed of light (*c*) is a constant, so wavelength and frequency are *inversely* related:

- **$\lambda = c/\nu$: Wavelength increases as frequency decreases.**
- **$\nu = c/\lambda$: Frequency increases as wavelength decreases.**

The energy (*E*) of a photon is directly proportional to its frequency:

$$E = h\nu \qquad h = \text{Planck's constant } (6.63 \times 10^{-34}\ \text{J·s})$$

Figure 13.8
The electromagnetic spectrum

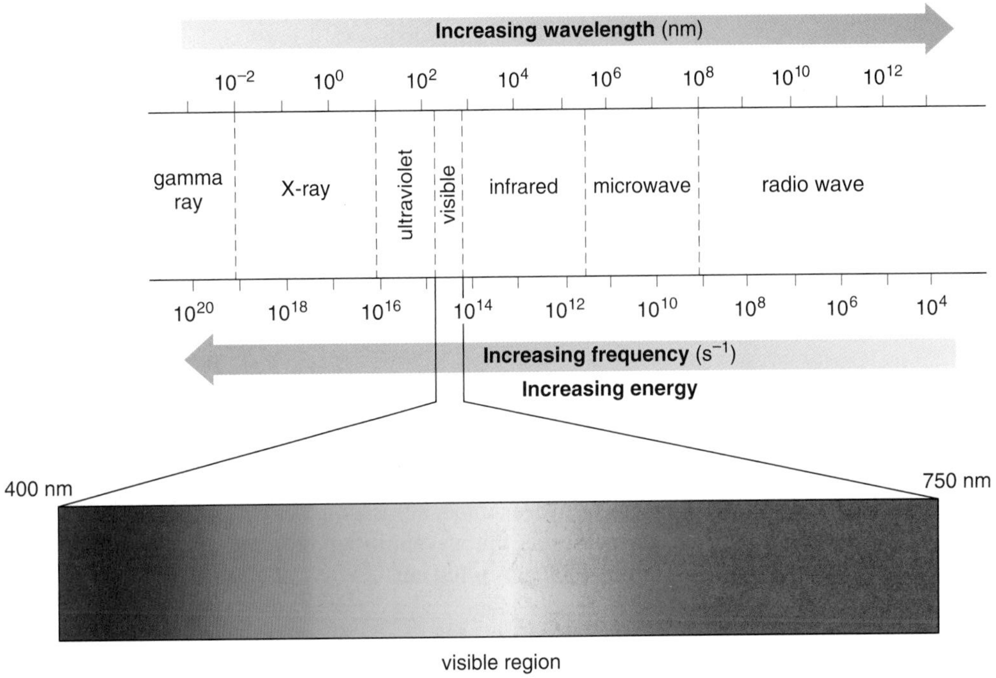

- Visible light occupies only a small region of the electromagnetic spectrum.

Frequency and wavelength are *inversely* proportional ($\nu = c/\lambda$), however, so energy and wavelength are *inversely* proportional:

$$E = h\nu = \frac{hc}{\lambda}$$

- E increases as ν increases.
- E decreases as λ increases.

When electromagnetic radiation strikes a molecule, some wavelengths—but not all—are absorbed. Only some wavelengths are absorbed because molecules have discrete energy levels. The energies of their electronic, vibrational, and nuclear spin states are *quantized,* not *continuous.*

- **For absorption to occur, the energy of the photon must match the difference between two energy states in a molecule.**

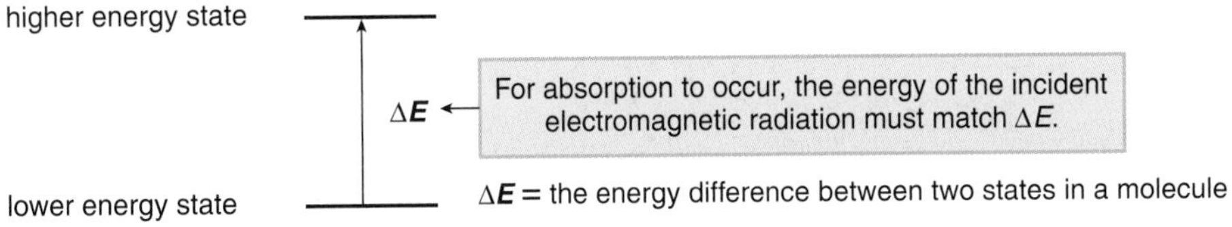

- **The *larger* the energy difference between two states, the *higher* the energy of radiation needed for absorption, the *higher* the frequency, and the *shorter* the wavelength.**

Problem 13.11 Which of the following has the higher frequency: (a) light having a wavelength of 10^2 or 10^4 nm; (b) light having a wavelength of 100 nm or 100 μm; (c) red light or blue light?

Problem 13.12 Which of the following has the higher energy: (a) light having a ν of 10^4 Hz or 10^8 Hz; (b) light having a λ of 10 nm or 1000 nm; (c) red light or blue light?

13.6 Infrared Spectroscopy

Organic chemists use infrared (IR) spectroscopy to identify the functional groups in a compound.

13.6A Background

Using the wavenumber scale results in IR values in a numerical range that is easier to report than the corresponding frequencies given in hertz (4000–400 cm^{-1} compared to 1.2×10^{14}–1.2×10^{15} Hz).

Infrared radiation (λ = 2.5–25 μm) is the energy source in infrared spectroscopy. These are somewhat longer wavelengths than visible light, so they are lower in frequency and lower in energy than visible light. Frequencies in IR spectroscopy are reported using a unit called the **wavenumber** ($\tilde{\nu}$):

$$\tilde{\nu} = \frac{1}{\lambda}$$

Wavenumber is *inversely* proportional to wavelength and reported in reciprocal centimeters **(cm^{-1})**. Wavenumber ($\tilde{\nu}$) is *proportional* to frequency (ν). **Frequency (and therefore energy) increases as the wavenumber increases.** Using the wavenumber scale, IR absorptions occur from **4000 cm^{-1}–400 cm^{-1}.**

- **Absorption of IR light causes changes in the vibrational motions of a molecule.**

Covalent bonds are not static. They are more like springs with weights on each end. When two atoms are bonded to each other, the bond stretches back and forth. When three or more atoms are joined together, bonds can also bend. These bond stretching and bending vibrations represent the different vibrational modes available to a molecule.

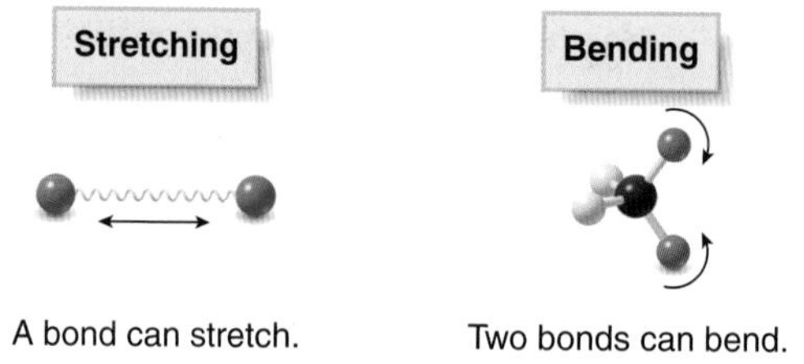
Stretching
Bending
A bond can stretch.
Two bonds can bend.

These vibrations are quantized, so they occur only at specific frequencies, which correspond to the frequency of IR light. When the frequency of IR light matches the frequency of a particular vibrational mode, the IR light is absorbed, causing the amplitude of the particular bond stretch or bond bend to increase.

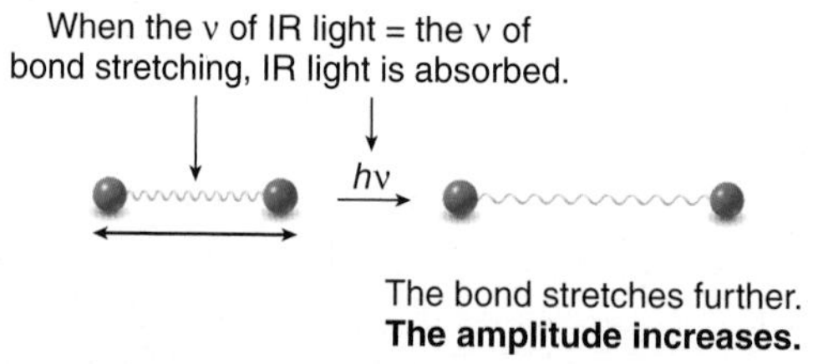
When the ν of IR light = the ν of bond stretching, IR light is absorbed.
hν
The bond stretches further.
The amplitude increases.

- **Different kinds of bonds vibrate at different frequencies, so they absorb different frequencies of IR light.**
- **IR spectroscopy distinguishes between the different kinds of bonds in a molecule, so it is possible to determine the functional groups present.**

Problem 13.13 Which of the following has higher energy: (a) IR light of 3000 cm^{-1} or 1500 cm^{-1} in wavenumber; (b) IR light having a wavelength of 10 μm or 20 μm?

13.6B Characteristics of an IR Spectrum

In an IR spectrometer, light passes through a sample. Frequencies that match vibrational frequencies are absorbed, and the remaining light is transmitted to a detector. A spectrum plots the amount of transmitted light versus its wavenumber. The IR spectrum of 1-propanol, $CH_3CH_2CH_2OH$, illustrates several important features of IR spectroscopy.

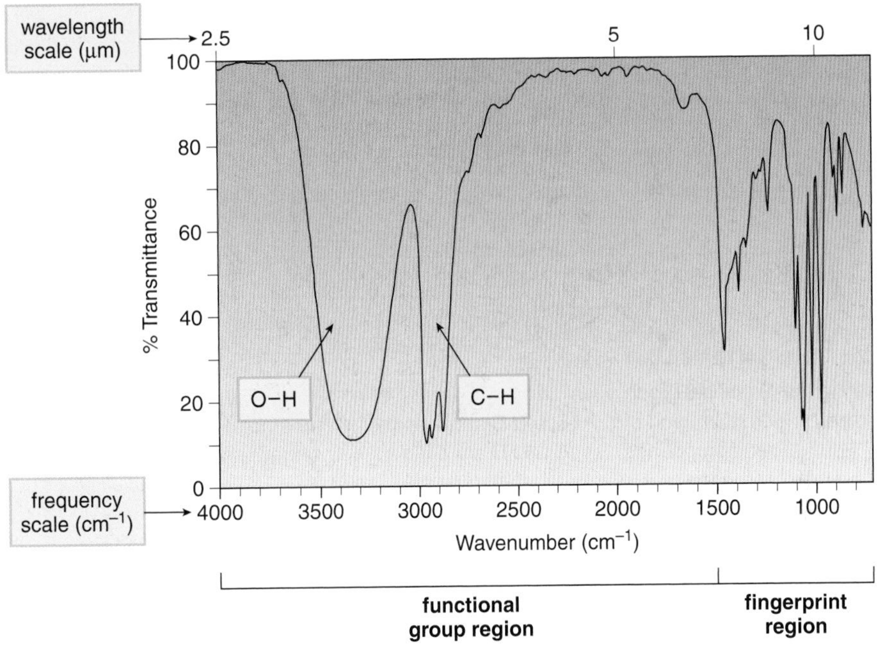

- An IR spectrum has broad lines.
- The absorption peaks go *down* on a page. The *y* axis measures **percent transmittance:** 100% transmittance means that all the light shone on a sample is transmitted and none is absorbed; 0% transmittance means that none of the light shone on a sample is transmitted and all is absorbed. Most absorptions lie between these two extremes.
- **Each peak corresponds to a particular kind of bond, and each bond type (such as O–H and C–H) occurs at a characteristic frequency.**
- IR spectra have both a wavelength and a wavenumber scale on the *x* axis. Wavelengths are recorded in μm (2.5–25). Wavenumber, frequency, and energy *decrease* from left to right. Where a peak occurs is reported in reciprocal centimeters (cm^{-1}).

Conceptually, the IR spectrum is divided into two regions:

- **The functional group region occurs at ≥ 1500 cm^{-1}. Common functional groups give one or two peaks in this region, at a characteristic frequency.**
- **The fingerprint region occurs at < 1500 cm^{-1}. This region often contains a complex set of peaks and is unique for every compound.**

Compare, for example, the IR spectra of 5-methyl-2-hexanone (**A**) and ethyl propanoate (**B**) in Figure 13.9. The IR spectra look similar in their functional group regions because both compounds contain a carbonyl group (C=O) and several sp^3 hybridized C–H bonds. Since **A** and **B** are different compounds, however, their fingerprint regions look very different.

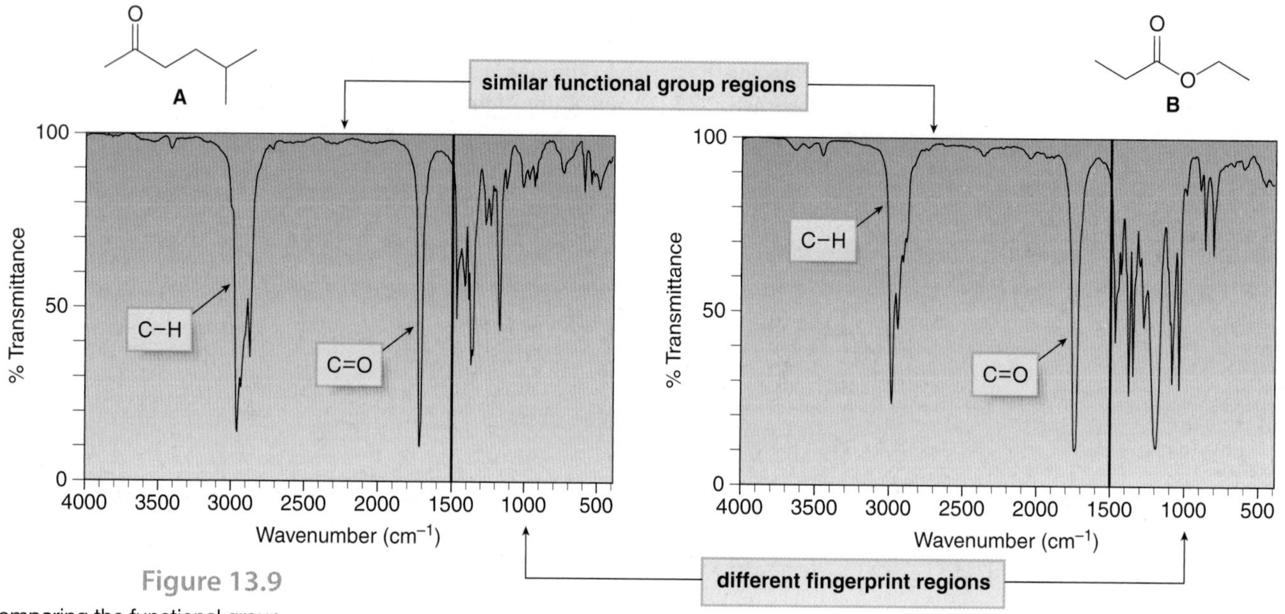

Figure 13.9
Comparing the functional group region and fingerprint region of two compounds

- **A** and **B** show peaks in the same regions for their C=O group and sp^3 hybridized C–H bonds.
- **A** and **B** are different compounds, so their fingerprint regions are quite different.

13.7 IR Absorptions

13.7A Where Particular Bonds Absorb in the IR

Where a particular bond absorbs in the IR depends on **bond strength** and **atom mass.**

- **Bond strength: stronger bonds vibrate at higher frequency, so they absorb at higher $\tilde{\nu}$.**
- **Atom mass: bonds with lighter atoms vibrate at higher frequency, so they absorb at higher $\tilde{\nu}$.**

Thinking of bonds as springs with weights on each end illustrates these trends. The strength of the spring is analogous to bond strength, and the mass of the weights is analogous to atomic mass. For two springs with the same weights on each end, the **stronger spring vibrates at a higher frequency.** For two springs of the same strength, **springs with lighter weights vibrate at higher frequency** than those with heavier weights. Hooke's law, as shown in Figure 13.10, describes the relationship of frequency to mass and bond strength.

Figure 13.10
Hooke's law: How the frequency of bond vibration depends on atom mass and bond strength

The frequency of bond vibration can be derived from Hooke's law, which describes the motion of a vibrating spring:

stronger bond ---→ higher frequency

Hooke's law $$\tilde{\nu} = k\sqrt{\frac{f}{m}}$$

f = force constant
m = mass
k = constant

smaller mass ---→ higher frequency

- The force constant (f) is the strength of the bond (or spring). The larger the value of f, the stronger the bond, and the higher the $\tilde{\nu}$ of vibration.
- The mass (m) is the mass of atoms (or weights). The smaller the value of m, the higher the $\tilde{\nu}$ of vibration.

Figure 13.11
Summary: The four regions of the IR spectrum

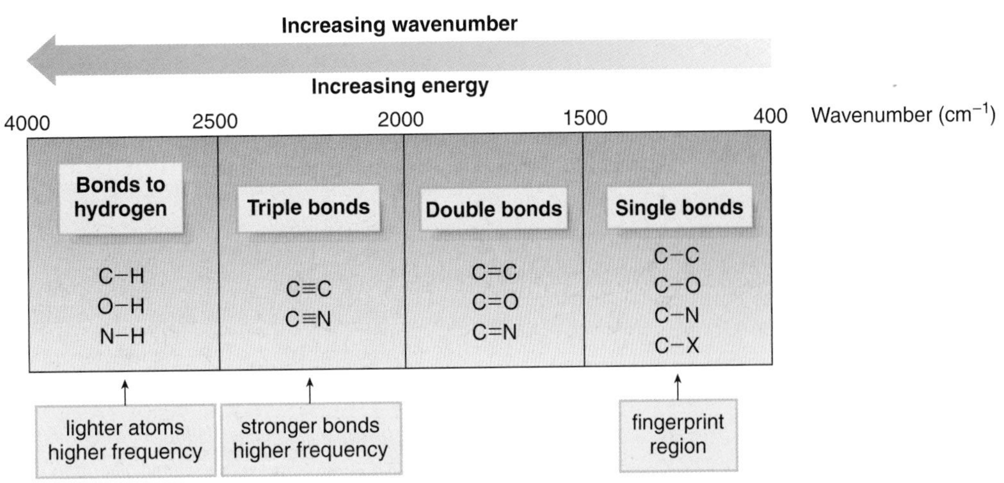

As a result, **bonds absorb in four predictable regions in an IR spectrum.** These four regions, and the bonds that absorb there, are summarized in Figure 13.11. Remembering the information in this figure will help you analyze the spectra of unknown compounds. To help you remember it, keep in mind the following two points:

- **Absorptions for bonds to hydrogen always occur on the left side of the spectrum (the high wavenumber region). H has so little mass that H–Z bonds (where Z = C, O, and N) vibrate at high frequencies.**
- **Bond strength decreases in going from C≡C → C=C → C–C, so the frequency of vibration decreases—that is, the absorptions for these bonds move farther to the right side of the spectrum.**

The functional group region consists of absorptions for single bonds to hydrogen (all H–Z bonds), as well as absorptions for all multiple bonds. Most absorptions in the functional group region are due to bond stretching (rather than bond bending). The fingerprint region consists of absorptions due to all other single bonds (except H–Z bonds), often making it a complex region that is very difficult to analyze.

Besides learning the general regions of the IR spectrum, it is also important to learn the specific absorption values for common bonds. Table 13.2 lists the most important IR absorptions in the functional group region. Other details of IR absorptions will be presented in later chapters when

Table 13.2 Important IR Absorptions

Bond type	Approximate $\tilde{\nu}$ (cm^{-1})	Intensity
O–H	3600–3200	strong, broad
N–H	3500–3200	medium
C–H	~3000	
• C_{sp^3}–H	3000–2850	strong
• C_{sp^2}–H	3150–3000	medium
• C_{sp}–H	3300	medium
C≡C	2250	medium
C≡N	2250	medium
C=O	1800–1650 (often ~1700)	strong
C=C	1650	medium
	1600, 1500	medium

new functional groups are introduced. Appendix E contains a detailed list of the characteristic IR absorption frequencies for common bonds.

Even subtle differences that affect bond strength affect the frequency of an IR absorption. Recall from Section 1.11 that the strength of a C–H bond increases as the percent *s*-character of the hybrid orbital on the carbon increases; thus:

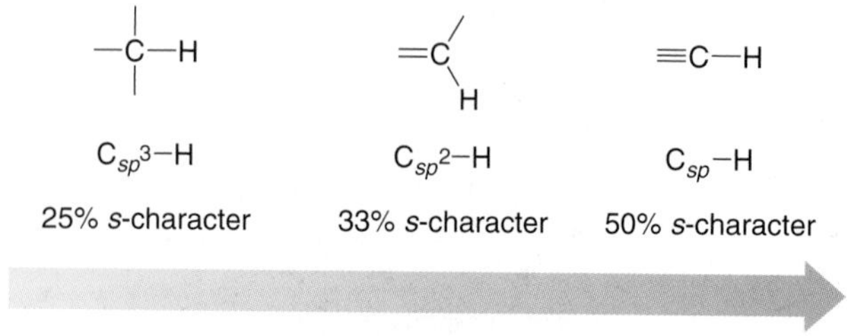
C–H
=C
H
≡C–H
C_{sp^3}–H
C_{sp^2}–H
C_{sp}–H
25% *s*-character
33% *s*-character
50% *s*-character

Increasing percent *s*-character
Increasing $\tilde{\nu}$

- **The higher the percent *s*-character, the stronger the bond and the higher the wavenumber of absorption.**

Problem 13.14 Which bond in each pair absorbs at higher wavenumber?

a. CH_3–C≡C–CH_2CH_3 or CH_2=C(CH_3)$_2$ (↑ indicates the C≡C and C=C bonds)

b. CH_3–H or CH_3–D (↑ indicates the C–H and C–D bonds)

Finally, almost all bonds in a molecule give rise to an absorption peak in an IR spectrum, but a few do not. **For a bond to absorb in the IR, there must be a change in dipole moment during the vibration.** Thus, symmetrical, nonpolar bonds do not absorb in the IR. The carbon–carbon triple bond of 2-butyne, for example, does not have an IR stretching absorption at 2250 cm^{-1} because the C≡C bond is nonpolar and there is no change in dipole moment when the bond stretches along its axis. This type of vibration is said to be **IR inactive.**

Stretching along the bond axis
does not change the dipole moment.

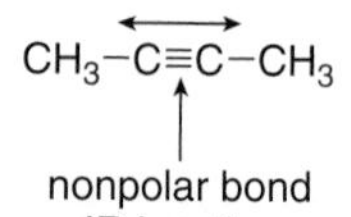
CH3–C≡C–CH3

nonpolar bond
IR inactive

13.7B IR Absorptions in Hydrocarbons

The IR spectra of hexane, 1-hexene, and 1-hexyne illustrate the important differences that characterize the IR spectra of hydrocarbons above 1500 cm^{-1}. Although all three compounds contain C–C bonds and sp^3 hybridized C–H bonds, the absorption peaks due to C=C and C≡C readily distinguish the alkene and alkyne.

Note, too, that the C–H absorptions in alkanes, alkenes, and alkynes have a characteristic appearance and position. The sp^3 hybridized C–H bonds are often seen as a broad, strong absorption at < 3000 cm^{-1}, whereas sp^2 and sp hybridized C–H bonds absorb at somewhat higher frequency.

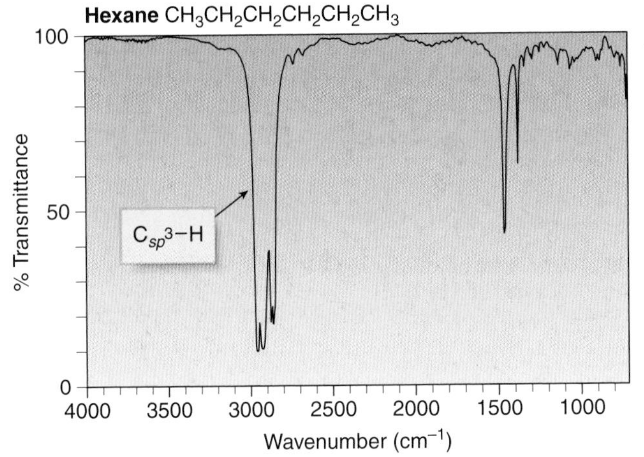

- The **alkane** $CH_3CH_2CH_2CH_2CH_2CH_3$ has only C–C single bonds and sp^3 hybridized C atoms. Therefore, it has only one major absorption above 1500 cm^{-1}, its C_{sp^3}–H absorption at 3000–2850 cm^{-1}.

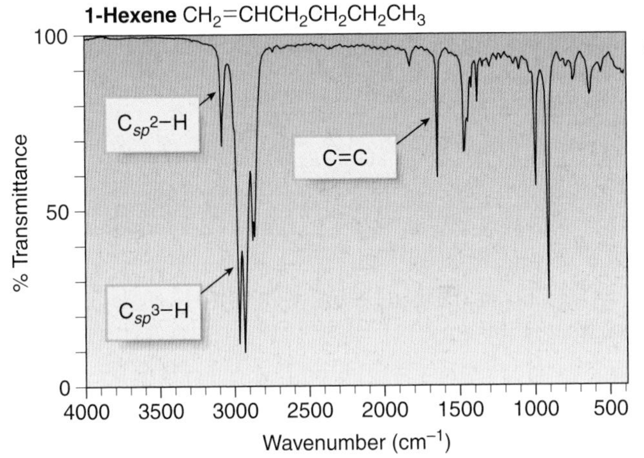

- The **alkene** $CH_2{=}CHCH_2CH_2CH_2CH_3$ has a C=C and C_{sp^2}–H, in addition to its sp^3 hybridized C atoms. Therefore, there are three major absorptions above 1500 cm^{-1}:
  - C_{sp^2}–H at 3150–3000 cm^{-1}
  - C_{sp^3}–H at 3000–2850 cm^{-1}
  - C=C at 1650 cm^{-1}

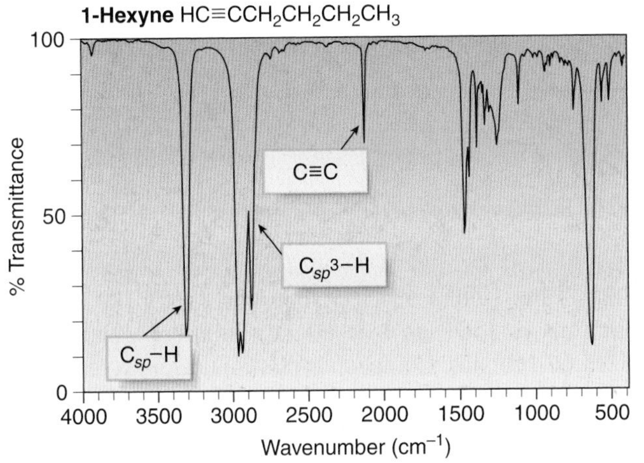

- The **alkyne** $HC{\equiv}CCH_2CH_2CH_2CH_3$ has a C≡C and C_{sp}–H, in addition to its sp^3 hybridized C atoms. Therefore, there are three major absorptions:
  - C_{sp}–H at 3300 cm^{-1}
  - C_{sp^3}–H at 3000–2850 cm^{-1}
  - C≡C at ~2250 cm^{-1}

Problem 13.15 How do the IR spectra of the isomers cyclopentane and 1-pentene differ?

13.7C IR Absorptions in Oxygen-Containing Compounds

The most important IR absorptions for oxygen-containing compounds occur at **3600–3200 cm^{-1} for an OH group,** and at approximately **1700 cm^{-1} for a C=O,** as illustrated in the IR spectra of an **alcohol** (2-butanol), a **ketone** (2-butanone), and an **ether** (diethyl ether). The peak at ~3000 cm^{-1} in each spectrum is due to C_{sp^3}–H bonds.

2-Butanol $CH_3CH(OH)CH_2CH_3$

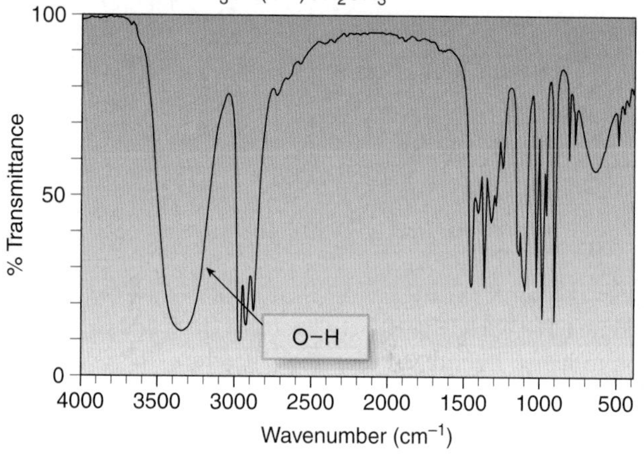

- The **OH** group in the alcohol $CH_3CH(OH)CH_2CH_3$ shows a strong absorption at 3600–3200 cm^{-1}.

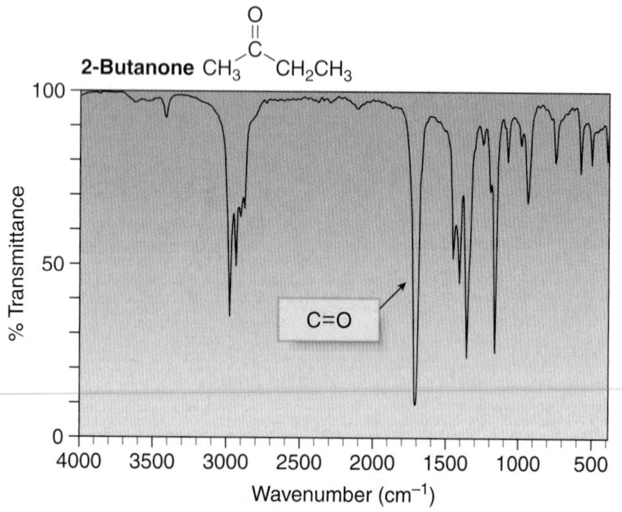

- The **C=O** group in the ketone $CH_3COCH_2CH_3$ shows a strong absorption at ~1700 cm^{-1}.
- The exact location of the C=O absorption depends on the particular type of carbonyl group, whether the carbonyl carbon is part of a ring, and whether there are nearby double bonds. These details are discussed in Chapters 21 and 22.

Diethyl ether $CH_3CH_2OCH_2CH_3$

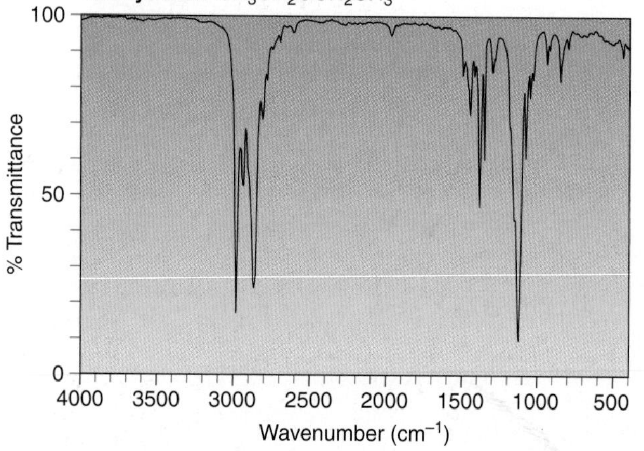

- $(CH_3CH_2)_2O$ has neither an OH group nor a C=O, so its only absorption above 1500 cm^{-1} occurs at ~3000 cm^{-1}, due to sp^3 hybridized C–H bonds. Compounds that contain an oxygen atom but do not show an OH or C=O absorption are **ethers.**

13.7D IR Absorptions in Nitrogen-Containing Compounds

Common functional groups that contain nitrogen atoms are also distinguishable by their IR absorptions above 1500 cm^{-1}, as illustrated by the IR spectra of an **amine** (octylamine), an **amide** (propanamide), and a **nitrile** (octanenitrile). Additional details on the IR spectra of these compounds are given in Chapters 22 and 25.

Octylamine $CH_3CH_2CH_2CH_2CH_2CH_2CH_2CH_2NH_2$

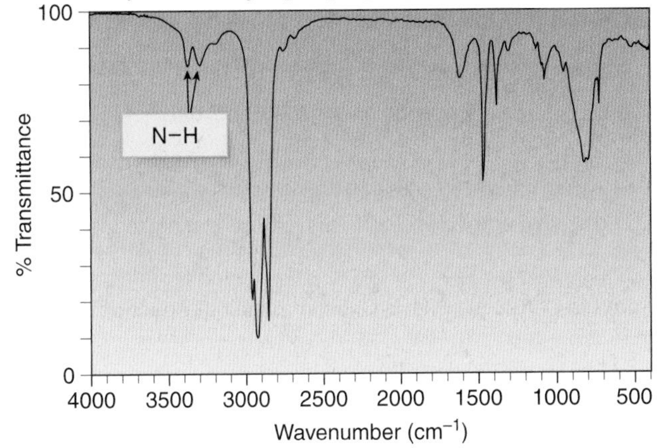

- The **N–H** bonds in the amine $CH_3(CH_2)_7NH_2$ give rise to two weak absorptions at 3300 and 3400 cm^{-1}.

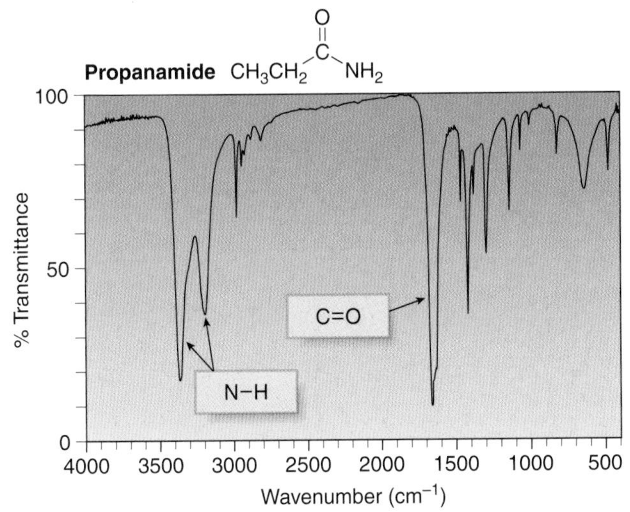

- The **amide** $CH_3CH_2CONH_2$ exhibits absorptions above 1500 cm^{-1} for both its **N–H** and **C=O** groups:
  - N–H (two peaks) at 3200 and 3400 cm^{-1}
  - C=O at 1660 cm^{-1}

Octanenitrile $CH_3CH_2CH_2CH_2CH_2CH_2CH_2C{\equiv}N$

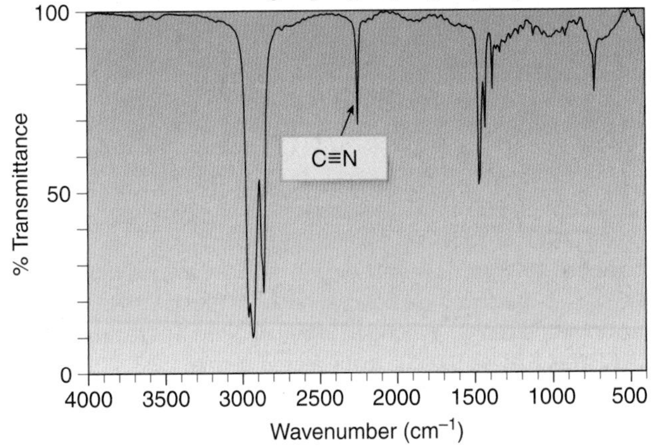

- The **C≡N** group of the **nitrile** $CH_3(CH_2)_6CN$ absorbs in the triple bond region at ~2250 cm^{-1}.

Sample Problem 13.6

How can the two isomers having molecular formula C_2H_6O be distinguished by IR spectroscopy?

Solution

First, draw the structures of the compounds and then locate the functional groups. One compound is an alcohol and one is an ether.

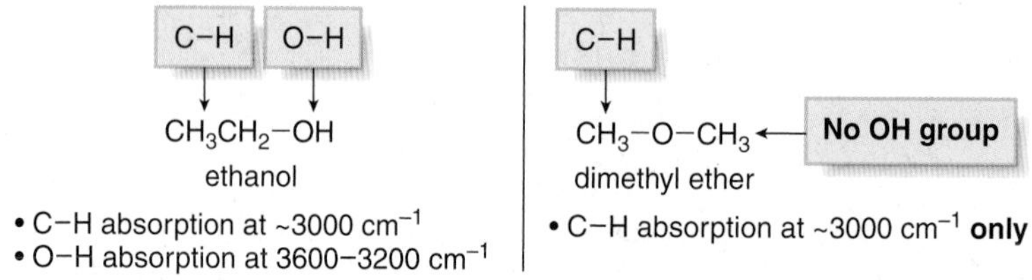

Although both compounds have sp^3 hybridized C–H bonds, ethanol has an OH group that gives a strong absorption at 3600–3200 cm^{-1}, and dimethyl ether does not. This feature distinguishes the two isomers.

Problem 13.16

How do the three isomers of molecular formula C_3H_6O (**A, B,** and **C**) differ in their IR spectra?

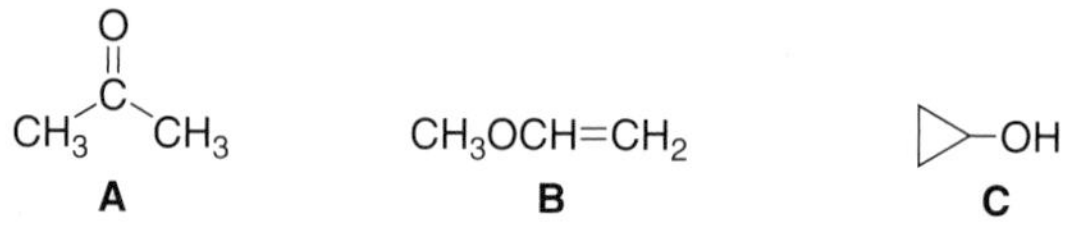

Sample Problem 13.7 shows how the region above 1500 cm^{-1} in an IR spectrum can be used for functional group identification.

Sample Problem 13.7

What functional groups are responsible for the absorptions above 1500 cm^{-1} in compounds **A** and **B?**

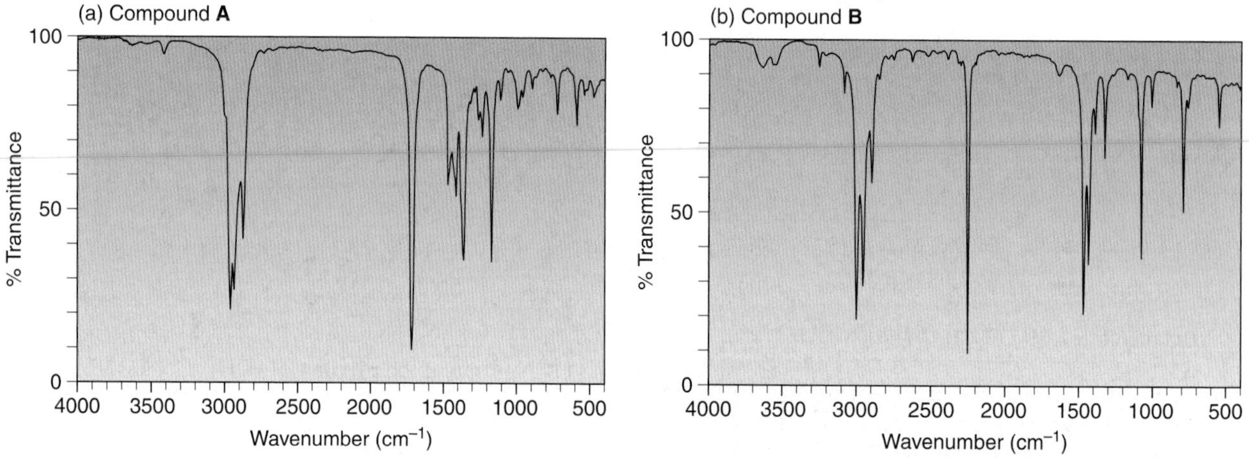

Solution

a. Compound **A** has two major absorptions above 1500 cm^{-1}: The absorption at ~3000 cm^{-1} is due to C–H bonds and the absorption at ~1700 cm^{-1} is due to a C=O group.

b. Compound **B** has two major absorptions above 1500 cm^{-1}: The absorption at ~3000 cm^{-1} is due to C–H bonds and the absorption at ~2250 cm^{-1} is due to a triple bond, either a C≡C or a C≡N. Because there is no absorption due to an *sp* hybridized C–H bond at 3300 cm^{-1}, this IR spectrum can*not* be due to a terminal alkyne (HC≡CR) but may still be due to an internal alkyne.

Problem 13.17 What functional groups are responsible for the absorptions above 1500 cm^{-1} in the IR spectra for compounds **A** and **B?**

(a) Compound **A**

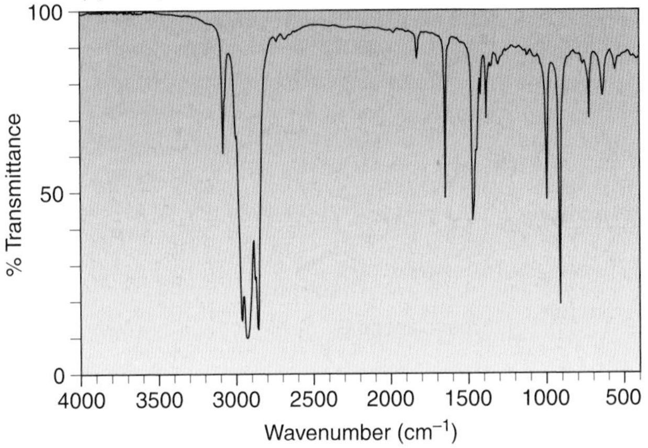

(b) Compound **B**

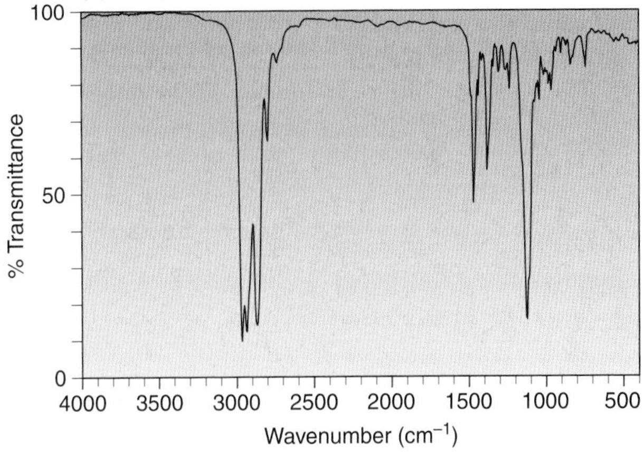

Problem 13.18 What are the major IR absorptions in the functional group region for each compound?

a. 

b. 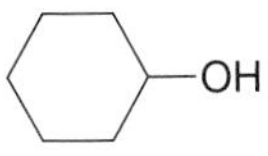

c. 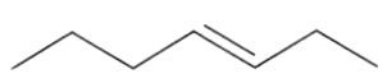

d. 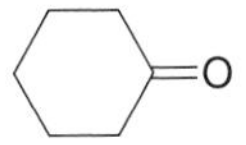

e. 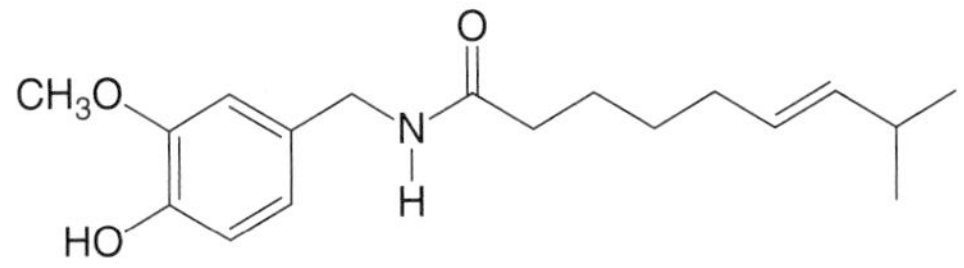

capsaicin
(spicy component of hot peppers)

Problem 13.19 What are the major IR absorptions in the functional group region for oleic acid, a common unsaturated fatty acid (Section 10.6A)?

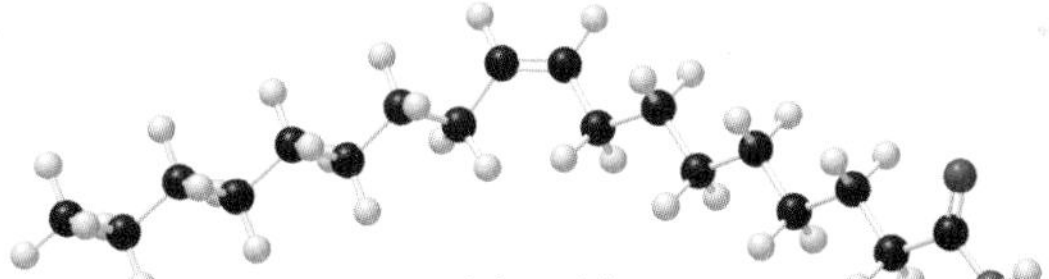

oleic acid

The antibiotic properties of penicillin were discovered when Sir Alexander Fleming noticed that a mold of the genus *Penicillium* inhibited the growth of certain bacteria. Penicillin was used as an antibiotic before its structure was determined conclusively.

13.8 IR and Structure Determination

Since its introduction, IR spectroscopy has proven to be a valuable tool for determining the functional groups in organic molecules.

In the 1940s, IR spectroscopy played a key role in elucidating the structure of the antibiotic penicillin G, the chapter-opening molecule. **β-Lactams,** four-membered rings that contain an amide, have a carbonyl group that absorbs at ~1760 cm^{-1}, a much higher frequency than that observed for most amides and many other carbonyl groups. Because penicillin G had an IR absorption at this frequency, **A** became the leading candidate for the structure of penicillin rather than **B,** a possibility originally considered more likely. Structure **A** was later confirmed by X-ray analysis.

Correct structure

Incorrect structure, ruled out using IR spectroscopy

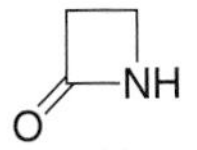

β-lactam

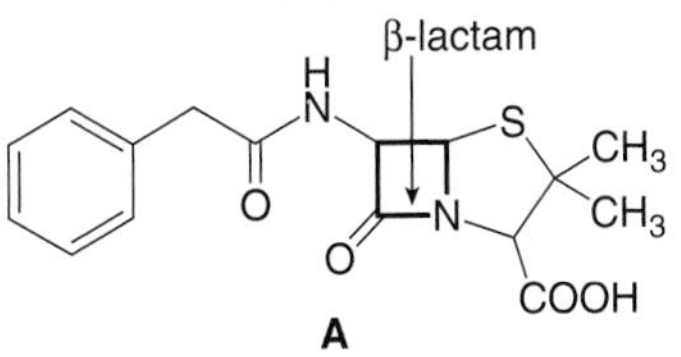

A
penicillin G

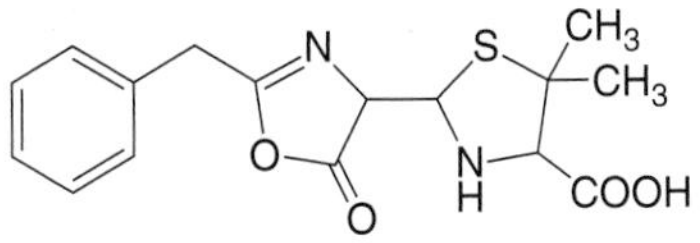

B

New instruments for determining blood alcohol concentration use IR spectroscopy for analyzing the C–H absorption of CH_3CH_2OH in exhaled air. Figure 12.10 illustrated an earlier method based on oxidation chemistry.

IR spectroscopy is often used to determine the outcome of a chemical reaction. For example, oxidation of the hydroxy group in **C** to form the carbonyl group in periplanone B is accompanied by the disappearance of the OH absorption (3600–3200 cm^{-1}) and the appearance of a carbonyl absorption near 1700 cm^{-1} in the IR spectrum of the product. Periplanone B is the sex pheromone of the female American cockroach.

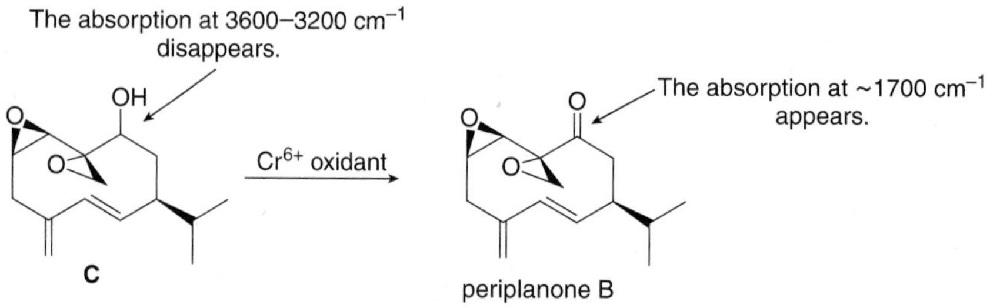

The combination of IR and mass spectral data provides key information on the structure of an unknown compound. The mass spectrum reveals the molecular weight of the unknown (and the molecular formula if an exact mass is available), and the IR spectrum helps to identify the important functional groups.

How To Use MS and IR for Structure Determination

Example What information is obtained from the mass spectrum and IR spectrum of an unknown compound **X**? Assume **X** contains the elements C, H, and O.

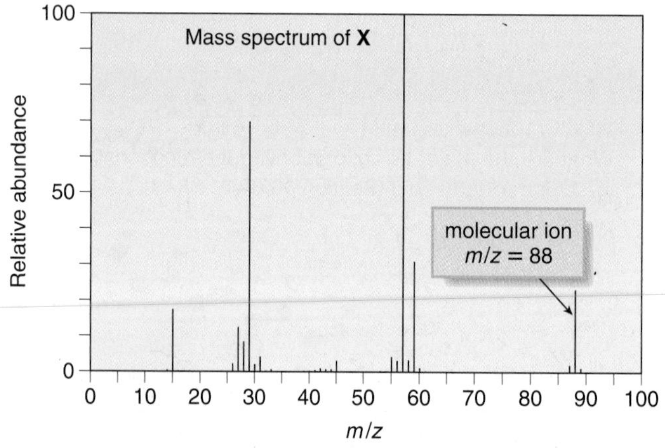

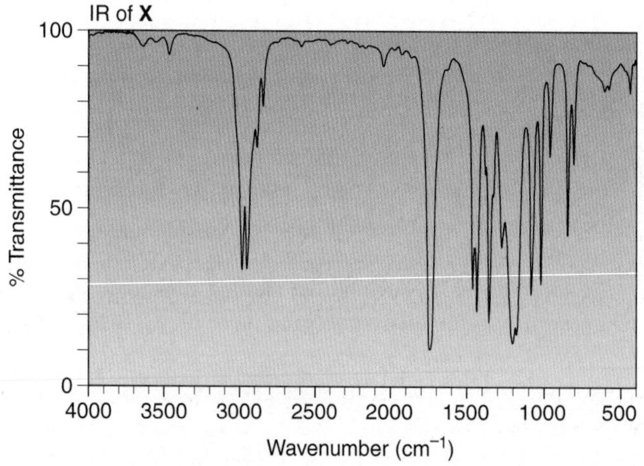

How To, continued . . .

Step [1] **Use the molecular ion to determine possible molecular formulas. Use an exact mass (when available) to determine a molecular formula.**

- Use the procedure outlined in Sample Problem 13.2 to calculate possible molecular formulas. For a molecular ion at m/z = 88:

$$\frac{88}{12} = 7 \text{ C's (maximum, remainder = 4)} \dashrightarrow C_7H_4 \xrightarrow[+1\,O]{-CH_4} C_6O \xrightarrow[+12\text{ H's}]{-1\,C} \boxed{C_5H_{12}O} \xrightarrow[+1\,O]{-CH_4} \boxed{C_4H_8O_2} \xrightarrow[+1\,O]{-CH_4} \boxed{C_3H_4O_3}$$

three possible formulas

- Discounting C_7H_4 (a hydrocarbon) and C_6O (because it contains no H's) gives three possible formulas for **X.**
- If high-resolution mass spectral data are available, the molecular formula can be determined directly. If the molecular ion had an exact mass of 88.0580, the molecular formula of **X** is $\mathbf{C_4H_8O_2}$ (exact mass = 88.0524) rather than $C_5H_{12}O$ (exact mass = 88.0888) or $C_3H_4O_3$ (exact mass = 88.0160).

Step [2] **Calculate the number of degrees of unsaturation (Section 10.2).**

- For a compound of molecular formula $C_4H_8O_2$, the maximum number of H's = $2n + 2 = 2(4) + 2 = 10$.
- Because the compound contains only 8 H's, it has 10 – 8 = 2 H's fewer than the maximum number.
- Because each degree of unsaturation removes 2 H's, **X** has one degree of unsaturation. **X has one ring or one π bond.**

Step [3] **Determine what functional group is present from the IR spectrum.**

- The two major absorptions in the IR spectrum above 1500 cm^{-1} are due to sp^3 hybridized C–H bonds (~3000–2850 cm^{-1}) and a C=O group (1740 cm^{-1}). Thus, the one degree of unsaturation in **X** is due to the presence of the **C=O.**

Mass spectrometry and IR spectroscopy give valuable but limited information on the identity of an unknown. Although the mass spectral and IR data reveal that **X** has a molecular formula of $C_4H_8O_2$ and contains a carbonyl group, more data are needed to determine its complete structure. In Chapter 14, we will learn how other spectroscopic data can be used for that purpose.

Problem 13.20 Which of the following possible structures for **X** can be excluded on the basis of its IR spectrum: (a) $CH_3COOCH_2CH_3$; (b) $HOCH_2CH_2CH_2CHO$; (c) $CH_3CH_2COOCH_3$; (d) $CH_3CH_2CH_2COOH$?

Problem 13.21 Propose structures consistent with each set of data: (a) a hydrocarbon with a molecular ion at m/z = 68 and IR absorptions at 3310, 3000–2850, and 2120 cm^{-1}; (b) a compound containing C, H, and O with a molecular ion at m/z = 60 and IR absorptions at 3600–3200 and 3000–2850 cm^{-1}.

KEY CONCEPTS

Mass Spectrometry and Infrared Spectroscopy

Mass Spectrometry (MS; 13.1–13.4)

- Mass spectrometry measures the molecular weight of a compound (13.1A).
- The mass of the molecular ion (**M**) = the molecular weight of a compound. Except for isotope peaks at M + 1 and M + 2, the molecular ion has the highest mass in a mass spectrum (13.1A).
- The base peak is the tallest peak in a mass spectrum (13.1A).
- A compound with an odd number of N atoms gives an odd molecular ion. A compound with an even number of N atoms (including zero) gives an even molecular ion (13.1B).
- Organic monochlorides show two peaks for the molecular ion (M and M + 2) in a 3:1 ratio (13.2).
- Organic monobromides show two peaks for the molecular ion (M and M + 2) in a 1:1 ratio (13.2).
- The fragmentation of radical cations formed in a mass spectrometer gives lower molecular weight fragments, often characteristic of a functional group (13.3).
- High-resolution mass spectrometry gives the molecular formula of a compound (13.4A).

Electromagnetic Radiation (13.5)

- The wavelength and frequency of electromagnetic radiation are *inversely* related by the following equations: $\lambda = c/\nu$ or $\nu = c/\lambda$ (13.5).
- The energy of a photon is proportional to its frequency; the higher the frequency, the higher the energy: $E = h\nu$ (13.5).

Infrared Spectroscopy (IR; 13.6 and 13.7)

- Infrared spectroscopy identifies functional groups.
- IR absorptions are reported in wavenumbers, $\tilde{\nu} = 1/\lambda$.
- The functional group region from **4000–1500 cm^{-1}** is the most useful region of an IR spectrum.
- C–H, O–H, and N–H bonds absorb at high frequency, $\geq$ 2500 cm^{-1}.
- As bond strength increases, the $\tilde{\nu}$ of absorption increases; thus, triple bonds absorb at higher $\tilde{\nu}$ than double bonds.

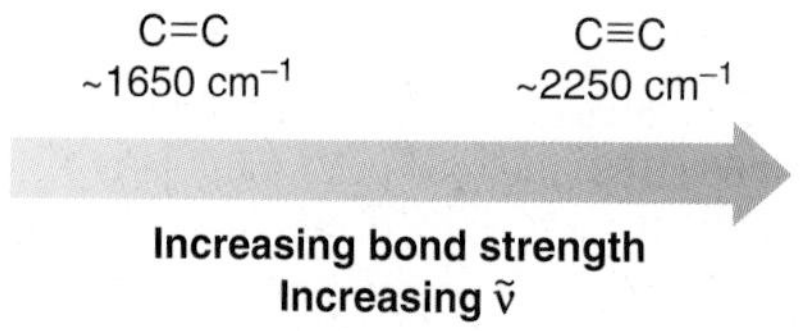
C=C
~1650 cm^{-1}
C≡C
~2250 cm^{-1}
Increasing bond strength
Increasing $\tilde{\nu}$

- The higher the percent *s*-character, the stronger the bond, and the higher the $\tilde{\nu}$ of an IR absorption.

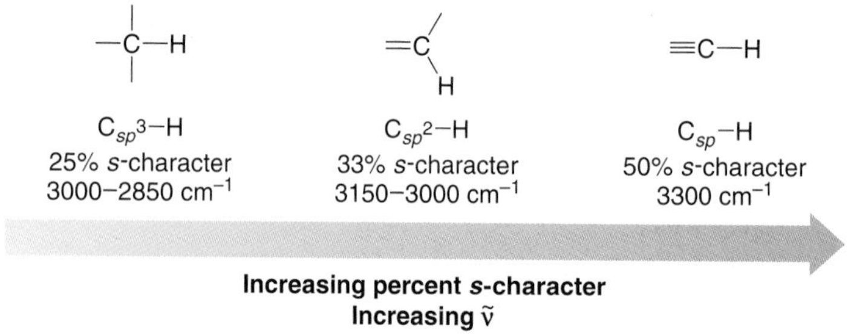
C_{sp^3}–H
25% *s*-character
3000–2850 cm^{-1}
C_{sp^2}–H
33% *s*-character
3150–3000 cm^{-1}
C_{sp}–H
50% *s*-character
3300 cm^{-1}
Increasing percent *s*-character
Increasing $\tilde{\nu}$

PROBLEMS

Problems Using Three-Dimensional Models

13.22 What major IR absorptions are present above 1500 cm^{-1} for each compound?

a. 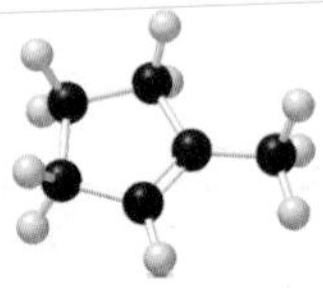 b. 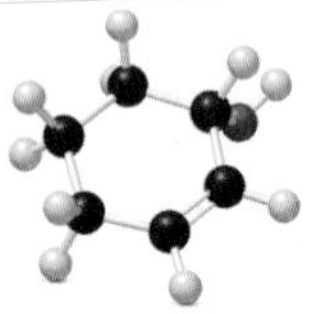

13.23 The mass spectrum of the following compound shows fragments at m/z = 127, 113, and 85. Propose structures for the ions that give rise to these peaks.

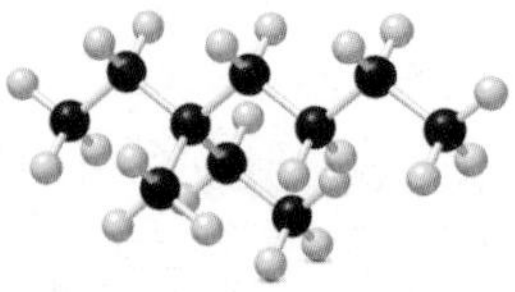

Mass Spectrometry

13.24 What molecular ion is expected for each compound?

a.  b. 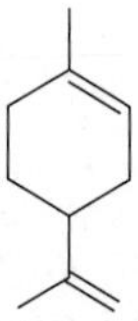 c. 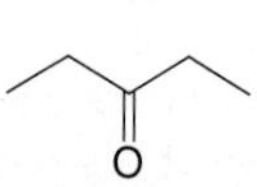 d. 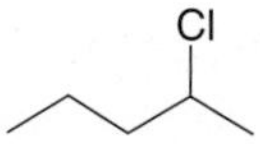 e. $(CH_3)_3CCH(Br)CH(CH_3)_2$

13.25 Which compound gives a molecular ion at m/z = 122: $C_6H_5CH_2CH_2CH_3$, $C_6H_5COCH_2CH_3$, or $C_6H_5OCH_2CH_3$?

13.26 Propose two molecular formulas for each molecular ion: (a) 102; (b) 98; (c) 119; (d) 74.

13.27 Propose four possible structures for a hydrocarbon with a molecular ion at m/z = 112.

13.28 Match each structure to its mass spectrum.

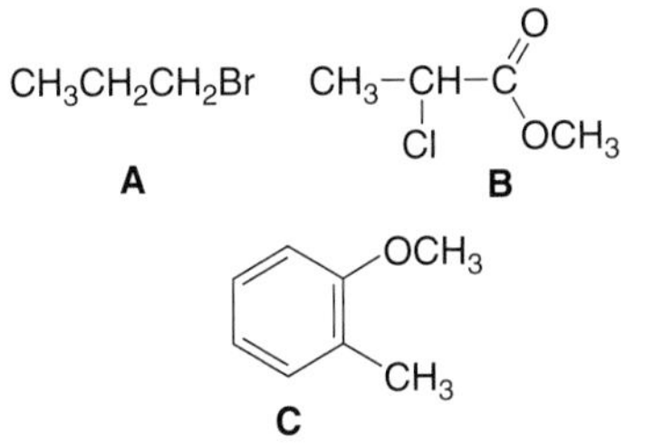

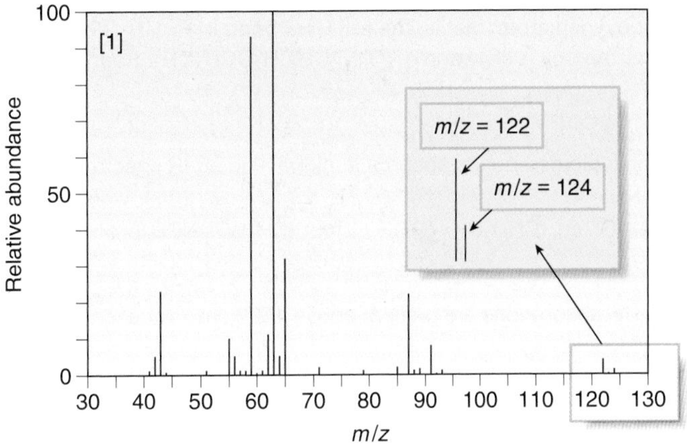

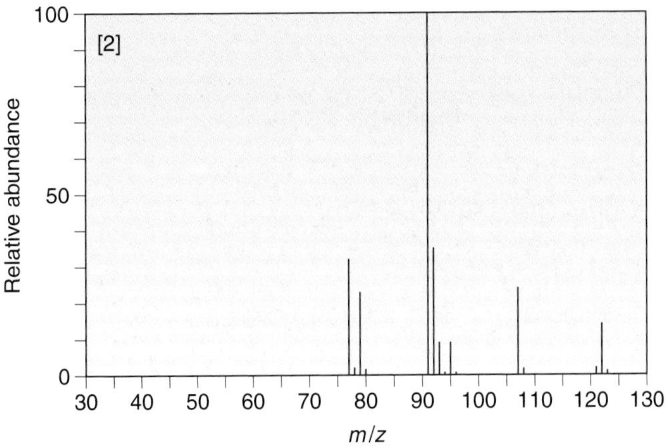

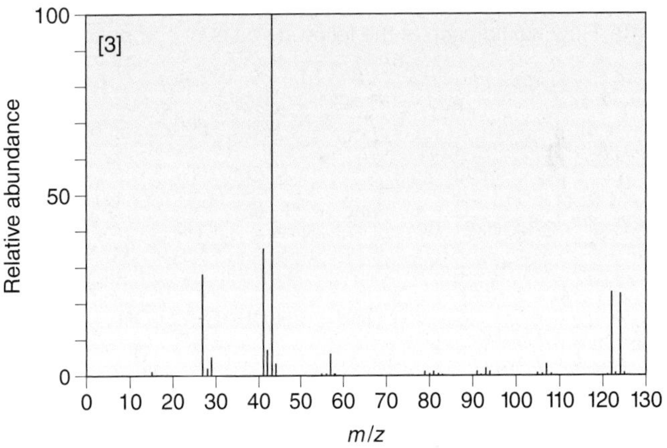

13.29 Propose two possible structures for a hydrocarbon having an exact mass of 96.0939 that forms ethylcyclopentane upon hydrogenation with H_2 and Pd-C.

13.30 What cations are formed in the mass spectrometer by α cleavage of each of the following compounds?

a. 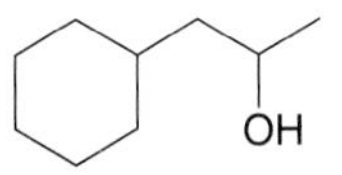

b. 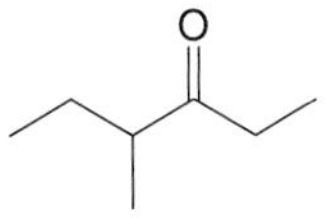

c. 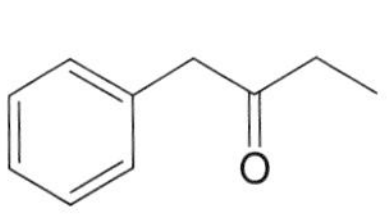

13.31 For each compound, assign likely structures to the fragments at each m/z value, and explain how each fragment is formed.

a. $C_6H_5CH_2CH_2OH$: peaks at m/z = 104, 91

b. $CH_2=C(CH_3)CH_2CH_2OH$: peaks at m/z = 71, 68, 41, 31

13.32 Suppose you have two bottles, labeled ketone **A** and ketone **B.** You know that one bottle contains $CH_3CO(CH_2)_5CH_3$ and one contains $CH_3CH_2CO(CH_2)_4CH_3$, but you do not know which ketone is in which bottle. Ketone **A** gives a fragment at m/z = 99 and ketone **B** gives a fragment at m/z = 113. What are the likely structures of ketones **A** and **B** from these fragmentation data?

13.33 Propose a structure consistent with each set of data.

a. a compound that contains a benzene ring and has a molecular ion at m/z = 107

b. a hydrocarbon that contains only sp^3 hybridized carbons and a molecular ion at m/z = 84

c. a compound that contains a carbonyl group and gives a molecular ion at m/z = 114

d. a compound that contains C, H, N, and O and has an exact mass for the molecular ion at 101.0841

13.34 A low-resolution mass spectrum of the neurotransmitter dopamine gave a molecular ion at m/z = 153. Two possible molecular formulas for this molecular ion are $C_8H_{11}NO_2$ and $C_7H_{11}N_3O$. A high-resolution mass spectrum provided an exact mass at 153.0680. Which of the possible molecular formulas is the correct one?

13.35 Can the exact mass obtained in a high-resolution mass spectrum distinguish between two isomers such as $CH_2{=}CHCH_2CH_2CH_2CH_3$ and $(CH_3)_2C{=}CHCH_2CH_3$?

13.36 Primary (1°) alcohols often show a peak in their mass spectra at $m/z = 31$. Suggest a structure for this fragment.

13.37 Like alcohols, ethers undergo α cleavage by breaking a carbon–carbon bond between an alkyl group and the carbon bonded to the ether oxygen atom; that is, the red C–C bond in $R{-}CH_2OR'$ is broken. With this in mind, propose structures for the fragments formed by α cleavage of $(CH_3)_2CHCH_2OCH_2CH_3$. Suggest a reason why an ether fragments by α cleavage.

Infrared Spectroscopy

13.38 Which of the indicated bonds absorbs at higher $\tilde{\nu}$ in an IR spectrum?

a. $(CH_3)_2C{=}O$ or $(CH_3)_2CH{-}OH$

b. $(CH_3)_2C{=}NCH_3$ or $(CH_3)_2CH{-}NHCH_3$

c. 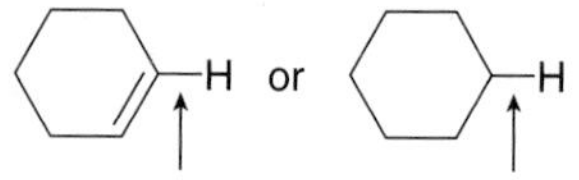

13.39 What major IR absorptions are present above 1500 cm^{-1} for each compound?

a. 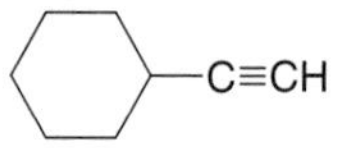

b. 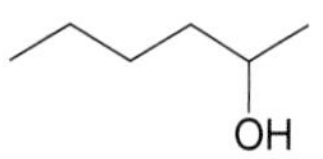

c. 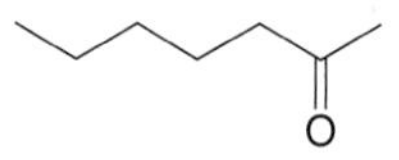

d. 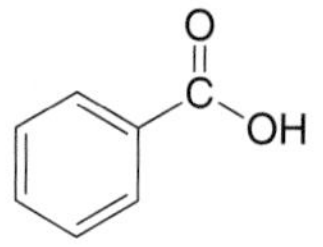

13.40 How would each of the following pairs of compounds differ in their IR spectra?

a.  and $HC{\equiv}CCH_2CH_2CH_3$

b. 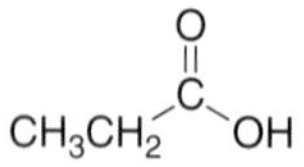 and 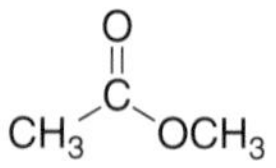

c. 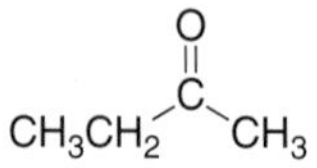 and $CH_3CH{=}CHCH_2OH$

d. 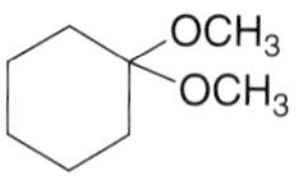 and 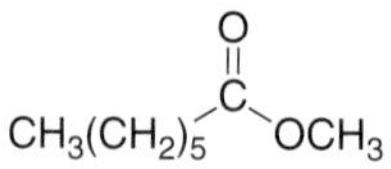

e. $CH_3C{\equiv}CCH_3$ and $CH_3CH_2C{\equiv}CH$

f. $HC{\equiv}CCH_2N(CH_2CH_3)_2$ and $CH_3(CH_2)_5C{\equiv}N$

13.41 Morphine, heroin, and oxycodone are three addicting analgesic narcotics. How could IR spectroscopy be used to distinguish these three compounds from each other?

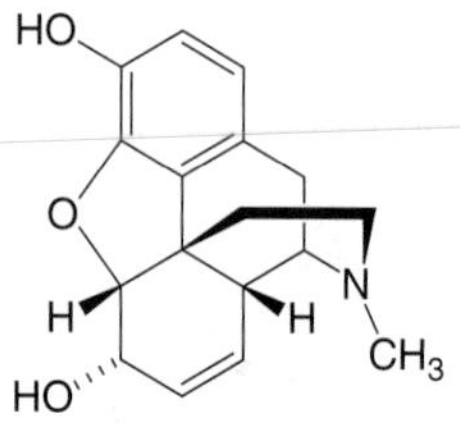

morphine

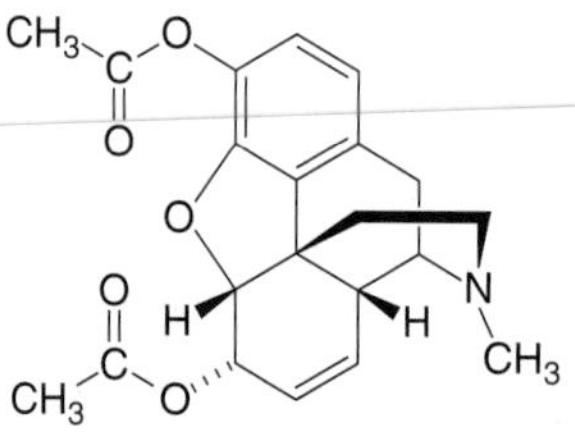

heroin

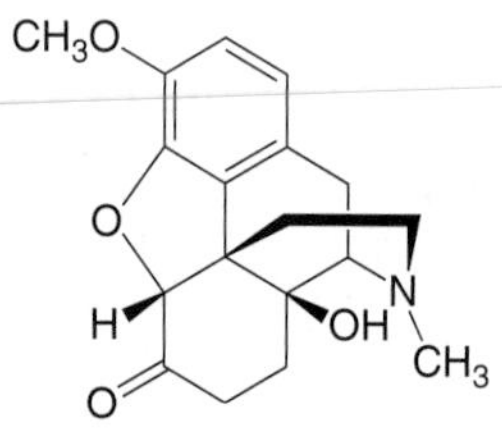

oxycodone

13.42 Tell how IR spectroscopy could be used to determine when each reaction is complete.

a. 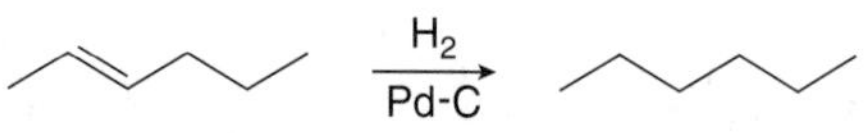

b. 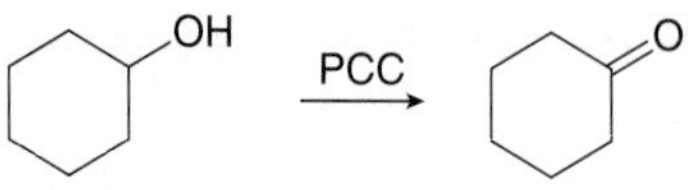

c. 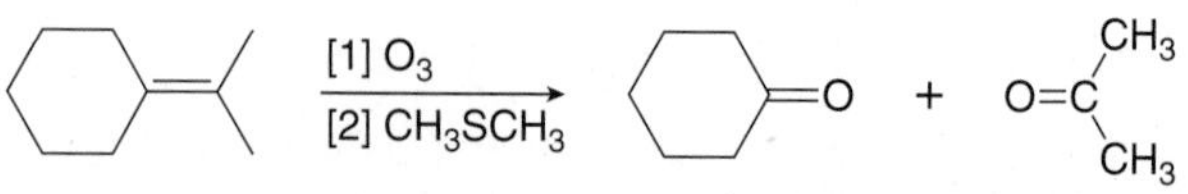

d. 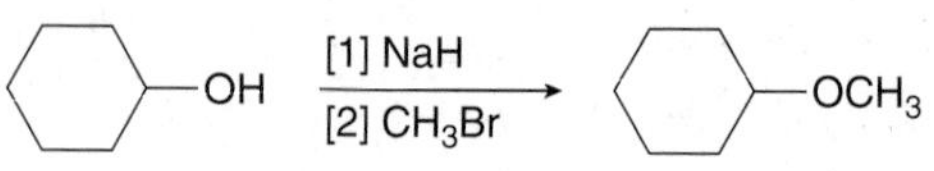

13.43 Match each compound to its IR spectrum.

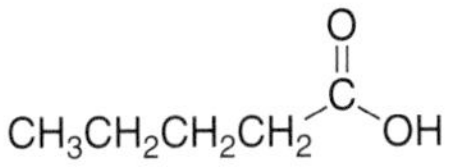

A

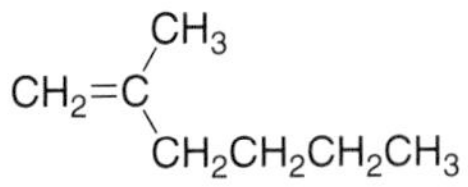

B

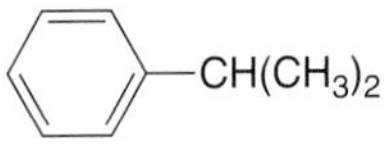

C

$(CH_3)_2CHOCH(CH_3)_2$
D

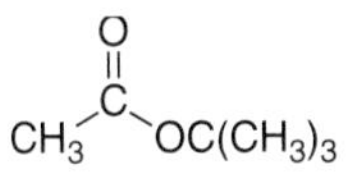

E

$(CH_3CH_2)_3COH$
F

Spectrum [1]

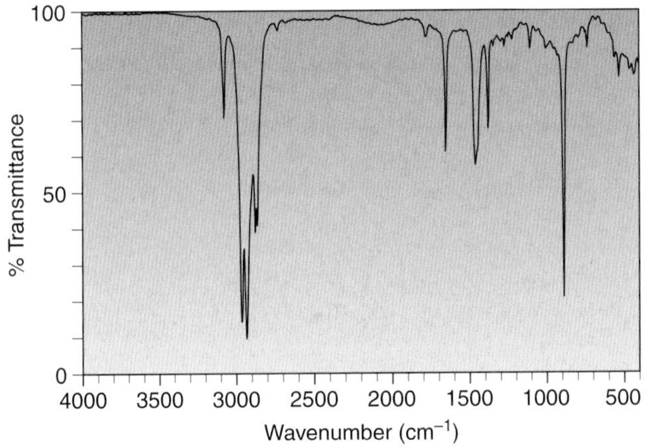

Spectrum [2]

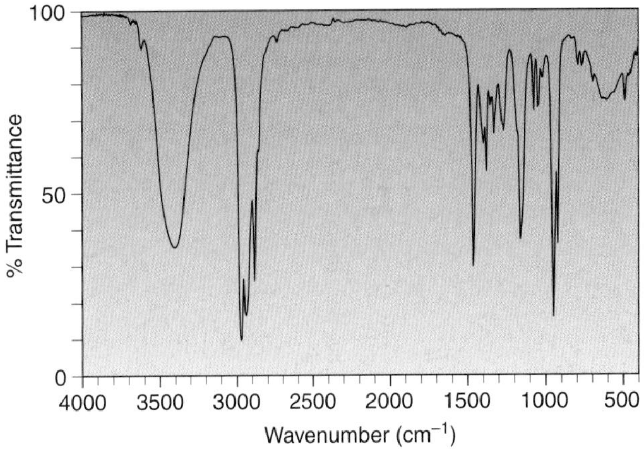

Spectrum [3]

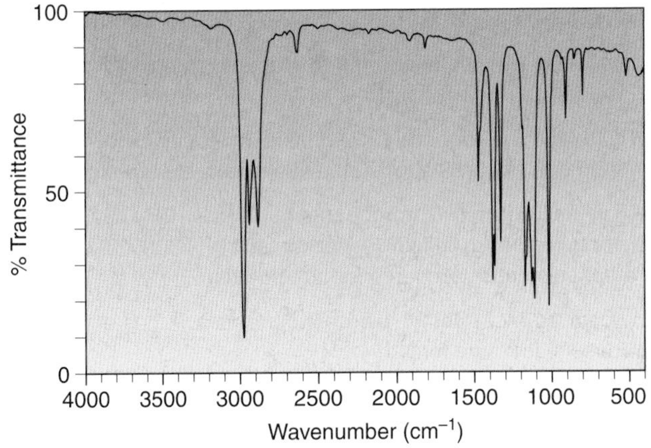

Spectrum [4]

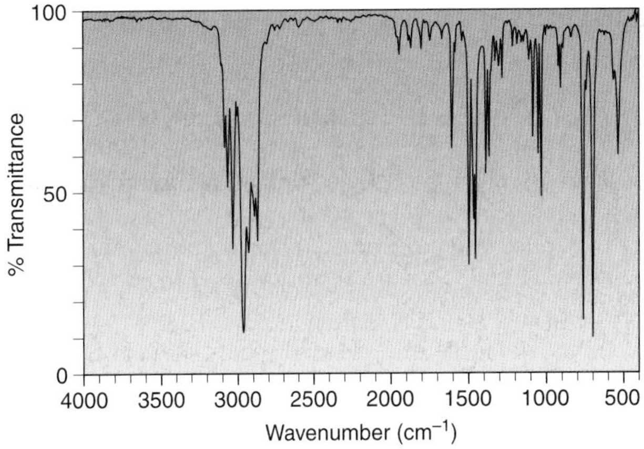

Spectrum [5]

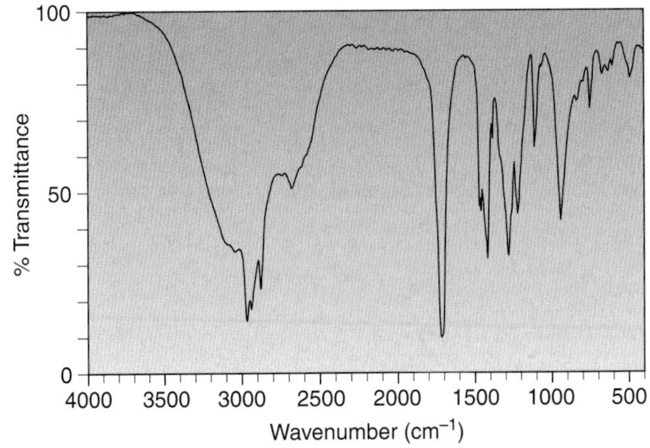

Spectrum [6]

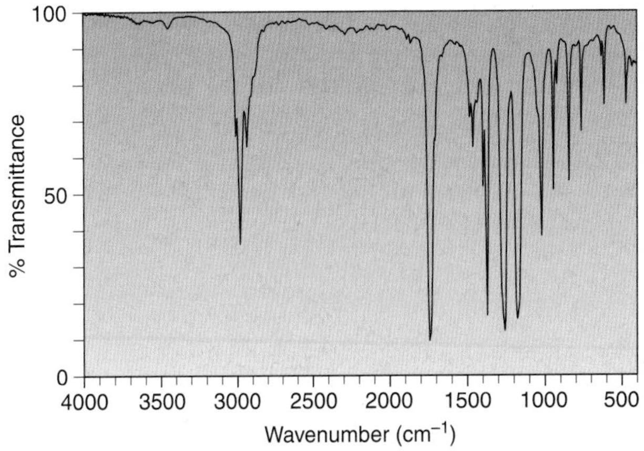

Combined Spectroscopy Problems

13.44 Propose possible structures consistent with each set of data. Assume each compound has an sp^3 hybridized C–H absorption in its IR spectrum, and that other major IR absorptions above 1500 cm^{-1} are listed.

a. a compound having a molecular ion at 72 and an absorption in its IR spectrum at 1725 cm^{-1}

b. a compound having a molecular ion at 55 and an absorption in its IR spectrum at ~2250 cm^{-1}

c. a compound having a molecular ion of 74 and an absorption in its IR spectrum at 3600–3200 cm^{-1}

13.45 A chiral hydrocarbon **X** exhibits a molecular ion at 82 in its mass spectrum. The IR spectrum of **X** shows peaks at 3300, 3000–2850, and 2250 cm^{-1}. Propose a structure for **X.**

13.46 A chiral compound **Y** has a strong absorption at 2970–2840 cm^{-1} in its IR spectrum and gives the following mass spectrum. Propose a structure for **Y.**

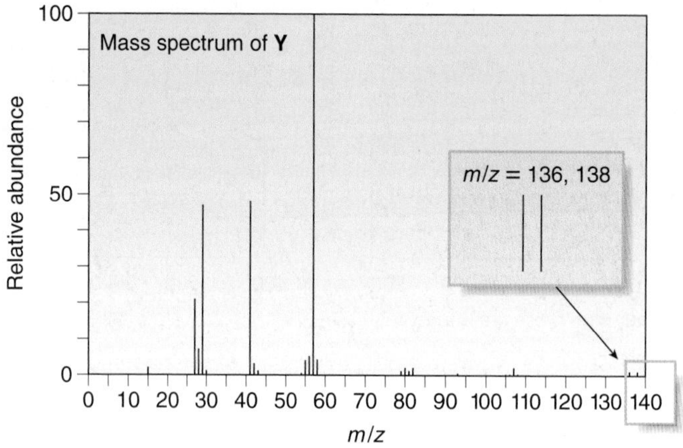

13.47 Treatment of benzoic acid ($C_6H_5CO_2H$) with NaOH followed by 1-iodo-3-methylbutane forms **H. H** has a molecular ion at 192 and IR absorptions at 3064, 3035, 2960–2872, and 1721 cm^{-1}. Propose a structure for **H.**

13.48 Treatment of benzaldehyde (C_6H_5CHO) with Zn(Hg) in aqueous HCl forms a compound **Z** that has a molecular ion at 92 in its mass spectrum. **Z** shows absorptions at 3150–2950, 1605, and 1496 cm^{-1} in its IR spectrum. Give a possible structure for **Z.**

13.49 Reaction of *tert*-butyl pentyl ether [$CH_3CH_2CH_2CH_2CH_2OC(CH_3)_3$] with HBr forms 1-bromopentane ($CH_3CH_2CH_2CH_2CH_2Br$) and compound **B. B** has a molecular ion in its mass spectrum at 56 and gives peaks in its IR spectrum at 3150–3000, 3000–2850, and 1650 cm^{-1}. Propose a structure for **B** and draw a stepwise mechanism that accounts for its formation.

13.50 Reaction of 2-methylpropanoic acid [$(CH_3)_2CHCO_2H$] with $SOCl_2$ followed by 2-methyl-1-propanol forms **X. X** has a molecular ion at 144 and IR absorptions at 2965, 2940, and 1739 cm^{-1}. Propose a structure for **X.**

13.51 Reaction of pentanoyl chloride ($CH_3CH_2CH_2CH_2COCl$) with lithium dimethyl cuprate [$LiCu(CH_3)_2$] forms a compound **J** that has a molecular ion in its mass spectrum at 100, as well as fragments at m/z = 85, 57, and 43 (base). The IR spectrum of **J** has strong peaks at 2962 and 1718 cm^{-1}. Propose a structure for **J.**

13.52 Benzonitrile (C_6H_5CN) is reduced to two different products depending on the reducing agent used. Treatment with lithium aluminum hydride followed by water forms **K,** which has a molecular ion in its mass spectrum at 107 and the following IR absorptions: 3373, 3290, 3062, 2920, and 1600 cm^{-1}. Treatment with a milder reducing agent forms **L,** which has a molecular ion in its mass spectrum at 106 and the following IR absorptions: 3086, 2850, 2820, 2736, 1703, and 1600 cm^{-1}. **L** shows fragments in its mass spectrum at m/z = 105 and 77. Propose structures for **K** and **L** and explain how you arrived at your conclusions.

13.53 Treatment of anisole ($CH_3OC_6H_5$) with Cl_2 and $FeCl_3$ forms **P,** which has peaks in its mass spectrum at m/z = 142 (M), 144 (M + 2), 129, and 127. **P** has absorptions in its IR spectrum at 3096–2837 (several peaks), 1582, and 1494 cm^{-1}. Propose possible structures for **P.**

13.54 Reaction of $BrCH_2CH_2CH_2CH_2NH_2$ with NaH forms compound **W,** which gives the IR and mass spectra shown below. Propose a structure for **W** and draw a stepwise mechanism that accounts for its formation.

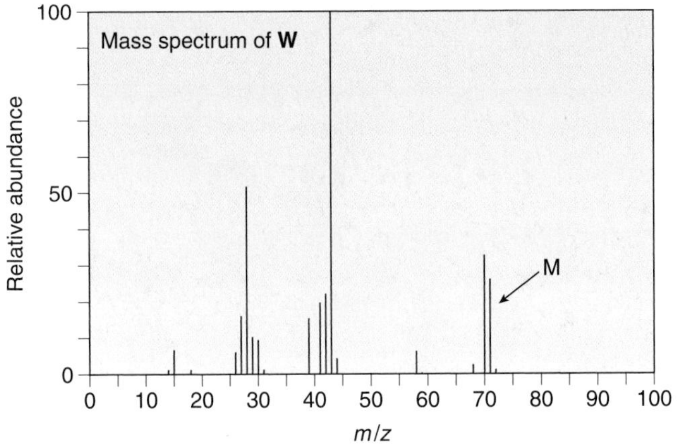

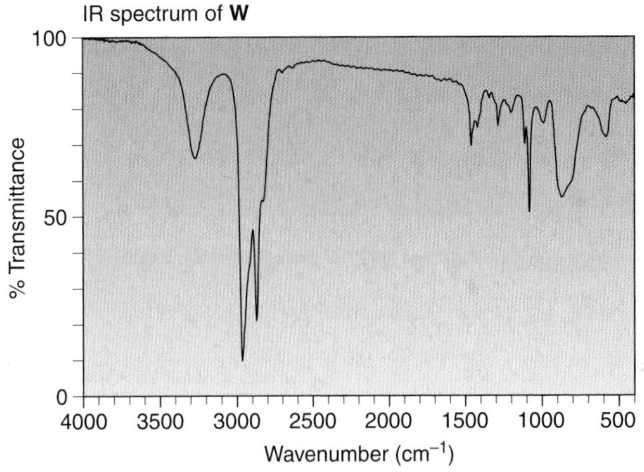

Challenge Problems

13.55 The carbonyl absorption of an amide typically occurs in the 1630–1680 cm^{-1} range, while the carbonyl absorption of an ester occurs at much higher wavenumber, typically 1735–1745 cm^{-1}. Account for this difference.

13.56 Explain why a carbonyl absorption shifts to lower frequency in an α,β-unsaturated carbonyl compound—a compound having a carbonyl group bonded directly to a carbon–carbon double bond. For example, the carbonyl absorption occurs at 1720 cm^{-1} for cyclohexanone, and at 1685 cm^{-1} for 2-cyclohexenone.

cyclohexanone

2-cyclohexenone (an α,β-unsaturated carbonyl compound)

13.57 Explain why a ketone carbonyl typically absorbs at a lower wavenumber than an aldehyde carbonyl (1715 versus 1730 cm^{-1}).

13.58 Oxidation of citronellol, a constituent of rose and geranium oils, with PCC in the presence of added $NaOCOCH_3$ forms compound **A. A** has a molecular ion in its mass spectrum at 154 and a strong peak in its IR spectrum at 1730 cm^{-1}, in addition to C–H stretching absorptions. Without added $NaOCOCH_3$, oxidation of citronellol with PCC yields isopulegone, which is then converted to **B** with aqueous base. **B** has a molecular ion at 152, and a peak in its IR spectrum at 1680 cm^{-1} in addition to C–H stretching absorptions.

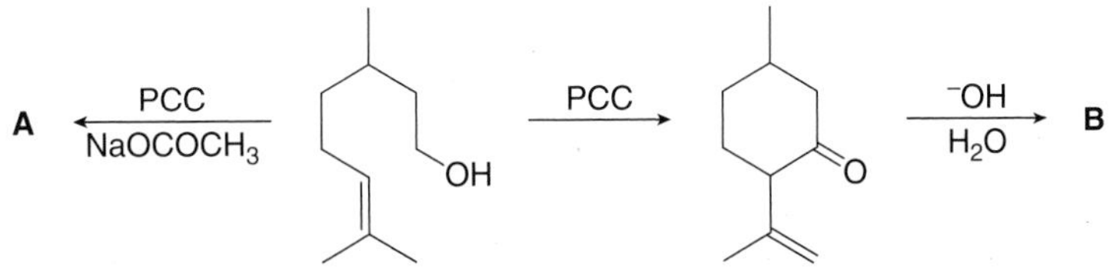

a. Identify the structures of **A** and **B.**
b. Draw a mechanism for the conversion of citronellol to isopulegone.
c. Draw a mechanism for the conversion of isopulegone to **B.**

14 Nuclear Magnetic Resonance Spectroscopy

14.1 An introduction to NMR spectroscopy
14.2 ^{1}H NMR: Number of signals
14.3 ^{1}H NMR: Position of signals
14.4 The chemical shift of protons on sp^2 and sp hybridized carbons
14.5 ^{1}H NMR: Intensity of signals
14.6 ^{1}H NMR: Spin–spin splitting
14.7 More complex examples of splitting
14.8 Spin–spin splitting in alkenes
14.9 Other facts about ^{1}H NMR spectroscopy
14.10 Using ^{1}H NMR to identify an unknown
14.11 ^{13}C NMR spectroscopy
14.12 Magnetic resonance imaging (MRI)

Palau'amine is a complex natural product isolated from the sea sponge *Stylotella agminata* collected in the Pacific Ocean near the Republic of Palau. The initial structure proposed for palau'amine in 1993 was revised in 2007 using a variety of modern spectroscopic techniques, including nuclear magnetic resonance spectroscopy. The dense array of functional groups in palau'amine and its antitumor and immunosuppressive properties attracted the attention of dozens of organic chemists, leading to its total synthesis in the laboratory in early 2010. In Chapter 14, we learn how nuclear magnetic resonance spectroscopy plays a key role in structure determination.

In Chapter 14 we continue our study of organic structure determination by learning about **nuclear magnetic resonance (NMR)** spectroscopy. NMR spectroscopy is the most powerful tool for characterizing organic molecules, because it can be used to identify the carbon–hydrogen framework in a compound.

14.1 An Introduction to NMR Spectroscopy

Two common types of NMR spectroscopy are used to characterize organic structure:

- **^{1}H NMR (proton NMR)** is used to determine the number and type of hydrogen atoms in a molecule; and
- **^{13}C NMR (carbon NMR)** is used to determine the type of carbon atoms in a molecule.

Before you can learn how to use NMR spectroscopy to determine the structure of a compound, you need to understand a bit about the physics behind it. Keep in mind, though, that NMR stems from the same basic principle as all other forms of spectroscopy. Energy interacts with a molecule, and absorptions occur only when the incident energy matches the energy difference between two states.

14.1A The Basis of NMR Spectroscopy

The source of energy in NMR is radio waves. Radiation in the radiofrequency region of the electromagnetic spectrum (so-called **RF** radiation) has very long wavelengths, so its corresponding frequency and energy are both low. **When these low-energy radio waves interact with a molecule, they can change the nuclear spins of some elements, including ^{1}H and ^{13}C.**

When a charged particle such as a proton spins on its axis, it creates a magnetic field. For the purpose of this discussion, therefore, a nucleus is a tiny bar magnet, symbolized by ↕. Normally these nuclear magnets are randomly oriented in space, but in the presence of an external magnetic field, B_0, they are oriented with or against this applied field. More nuclei are oriented *with* the applied field because this arrangement is lower in energy, but the **energy difference between these two states is very small** (< 0.4 J/mol).

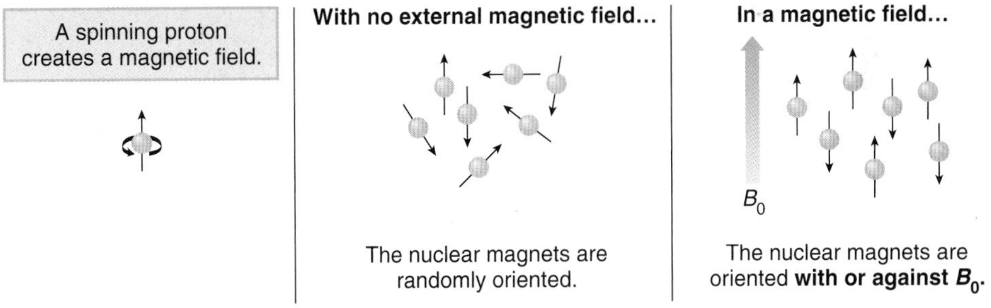

In a magnetic field, there are now two different energy states for a proton:

- **In the *lower energy state* the nucleus is aligned in the *same direction* as B_0.**
- **In the *higher energy state* the nucleus is aligned *opposed* to B_0.**

When an external energy source ($h\nu$) that matches the energy difference (ΔE) between these two states is applied, energy is absorbed, causing the **nucleus to "spin flip" from one orientation to another.** The energy difference between these two nuclear spin states corresponds to the low-frequency radiation in the RF region of the electromagnetic spectrum.

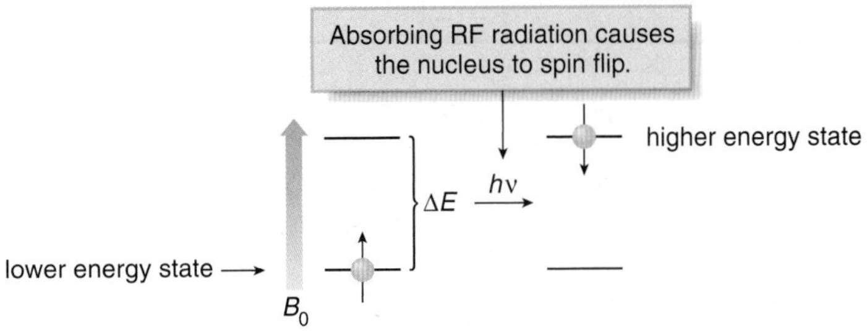

- **A nucleus is in *resonance* when it absorbs RF radiation and "spin flips" to a higher energy state.**

Thus, two variables characterize NMR:

- **An applied magnetic field, B_0.** Magnetic field strength is measured in tesla (T).
- **The frequency ν of radiation used for resonance,** measured in hertz (Hz) or megahertz (MHz); (1 MHz = 10^6 Hz).

The frequency needed for resonance and the applied magnetic field strength are proportionally related:

$$\nu \propto B_0$$

- **The stronger the magnetic field, the larger the energy difference between the two nuclear spin states, and the higher the ν needed for resonance.**

NMR spectrometers are referred to as 300 MHz instruments, 500 MHz instruments, and so forth, depending on the frequency of RF radiation used for resonance.

Early NMR spectrometers used a magnetic field strength of ~1.4 T, which required RF radiation of 60 MHz for resonance. Modern NMR spectrometers use stronger magnets, thus requiring higher frequencies of RF radiation for resonance. For example, a magnetic field strength of 7.05 T requires a frequency of 300 MHz for a proton to be in resonance. These spectrometers use very powerful magnetic fields to create a small, but measurable energy difference between the two possible spin states. A schematic of an NMR spectrometer is shown in Figure 14.1.

If all protons absorbed at the same frequency in a given magnetic field, the spectra of all compounds would consist of a single absorption, rendering NMR useless for structure determination. Fortunately, however, this is not the case.

Figure 14.1 Schematic of an NMR spectrometer

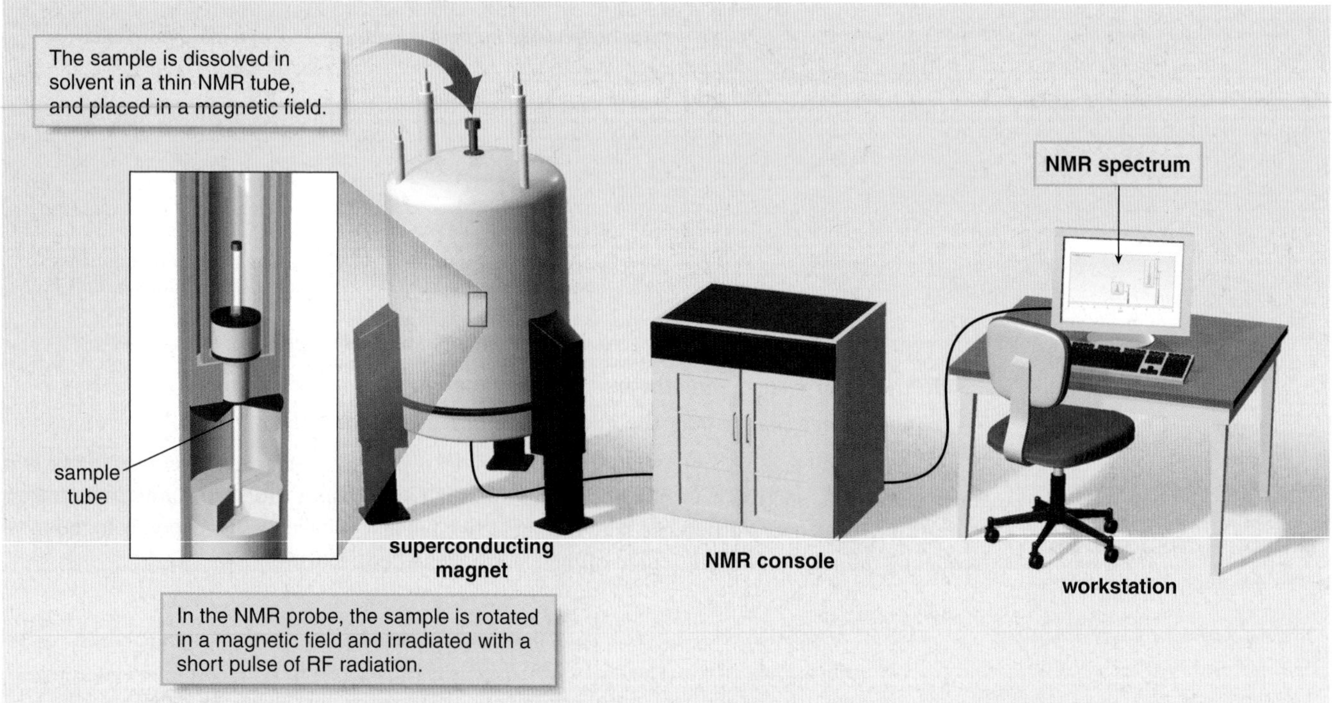

The sample is dissolved in solvent in a thin NMR tube, and placed in a magnetic field.
NMR spectrum
sample tube
superconducting magnet
NMR console
workstation
In the NMR probe, the sample is rotated in a magnetic field and irradiated with a short pulse of RF radiation.

An NMR spectrometer. The sample is dissolved in a solvent, usually $CDCl_3$ (deuterochloroform), and placed in a magnetic field. A radiofrequency generator then irradiates the sample with a short pulse of radiation, causing resonance. When the nuclei fall back to their lower energy state, the detector measures the energy released, and a spectrum is recorded. The superconducting magnets in modern NMR spectrometers have coils that are cooled in liquid helium and conduct electricity with essentially no resistance.

- **All protons do *not* absorb at the same frequency. Protons in different environments absorb at slightly different frequencies, and so they are distinguishable by NMR.**

The frequency at which a particular proton absorbs is determined by its electronic environment, as discussed in Section 14.3. Because electrons are moving charged particles, they create a magnetic field opposed to the applied field B_0, and the size of the magnetic field generated by the electrons around a proton determines where it absorbs. Modern NMR spectrometers use a constant magnetic field strength B_0, and then a narrow range of frequencies is applied to achieve the resonance of all protons.

Only nuclei that contain odd mass numbers (such as ^1H, ^{13}C, ^{19}F, and ^{31}P) or odd atomic numbers (such as ^2H and ^{14}N) give rise to NMR signals. Because both ^1H and ^{13}C, the less abundant isotope of carbon, are NMR active, NMR allows us to map the carbon and hydrogen framework of an organic molecule.

14.1B A ^{1}H NMR Spectrum

An NMR spectrum plots the **intensity of a signal** against its **chemical shift** measured in **parts per million (ppm).** The common scale of chemical shifts is called the **δ (delta) scale.** The proton NMR spectrum of *tert*-butyl methyl ether [$CH_3OC(CH_3)_3$] illustrates several important features:

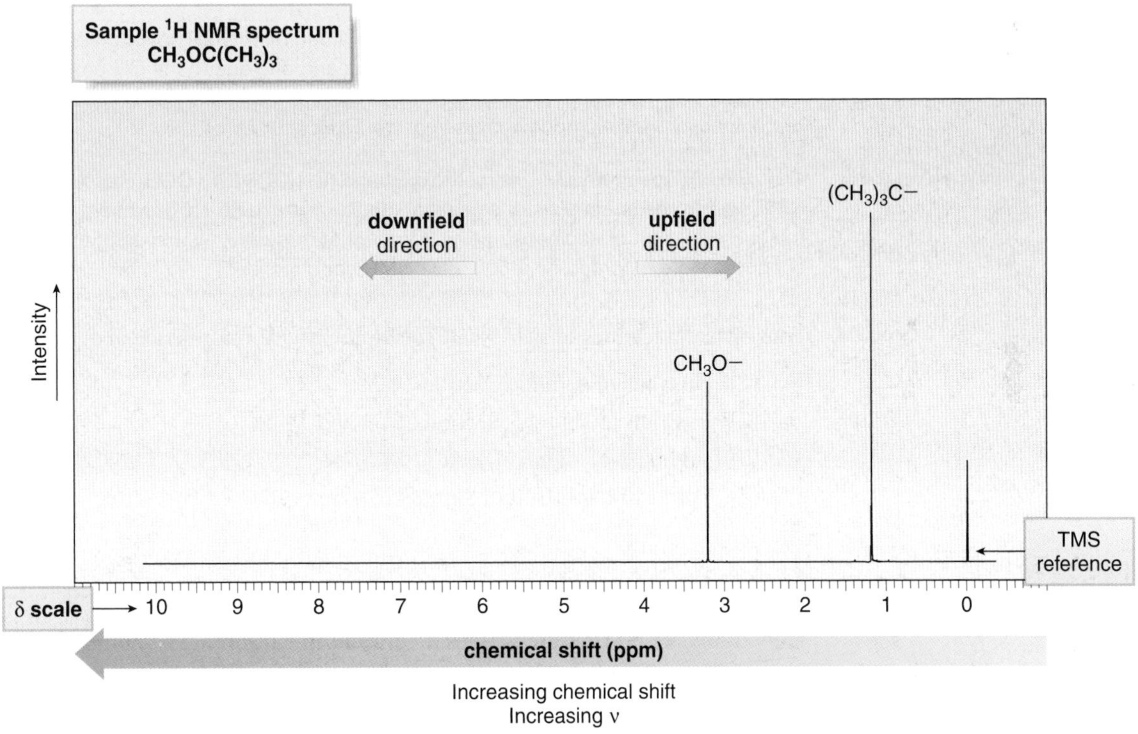

tert-Butyl methyl ether (MTBE) is the high-octane gasoline additive that has contaminated the water supply in some areas (Section 3.4).

- NMR absorptions generally appear as sharp signals. The ^{1}H NMR spectrum of $CH_3OC(CH_3)_3$ consists of two signals: a tall peak at 1.2 ppm due to the $(CH_3)_3C-$ group, and a smaller peak at 3.2 ppm due to the CH_3O- group.
- **Increasing chemical shift is plotted from *right to left.*** Most protons absorb somewhere from 0–12 ppm.
- The terms **upfield** and **downfield** describe the relative location of signals. Upfield means to the *right.* The $(CH_3)_3C-$ peak is upfield from the CH_3O- peak. Downfield means to the *left.* The CH_3O- peak is downfield from the $(CH_3)_3C-$ peak.

$(CH_3)_4Si$
tetramethylsilane
TMS

NMR absorptions are measured relative to the position of a reference signal at 0 ppm on the δ scale due to **tetramethylsilane (TMS). TMS** is a volatile and inert compound that gives a single peak upfield from other typical NMR absorptions.

Although chemical shifts are measured relative to the TMS signal at 0 ppm, this reference is often not plotted on a spectrum.

The *positive* direction of the δ scale is *downfield* from TMS. A very small number of absorptions occur upfield from the TMS signal, which is defined as the negative direction of the δ scale. (See Problem 14.76.)

The **chemical shift** on the *x* axis gives the position of an NMR signal, measured in ppm, according to the following equation:

$$\begin{array}{c}\textbf{chemical shift}\\ \text{(in ppm on the } \delta \text{ scale)}\end{array} = \frac{\text{observed chemical shift (in Hz) downfield from TMS}}{\nu \text{ of the NMR spectrometer (in MHz)}}$$

A chemical shift gives absorptions as a fraction of the NMR operating frequency, making it independent of the spectrometer used to record a spectrum. Because the frequency of the radiation required for resonance is proportional to the strength of the applied magnetic field, B_0, reporting NMR absorptions in frequency is meaningless unless the value of B_0 is also reported. By reporting the absorption as a fraction of the NMR operating frequency, though, we get units—ppm—that are independent of the spectrometer.

Sample Problem 14.1 Calculate the chemical shift of an absorption that occurs at 1500 Hz downfield from TMS using a 300 MHz NMR spectrometer.

Solution

Use the equation that defines the chemical shift in ppm:

$$\text{chemical shift} = \frac{\text{1500 Hz downfield from TMS}}{\text{300 MHz operating frequency}} = \text{5 ppm}$$

Problem 14.1 The ^1H NMR spectrum of CH_3OH recorded on a 500 MHz NMR spectrometer consists of two signals, one due to the CH_3 protons at 1715 Hz and one due to the OH proton at 1830 Hz, both measured downfield from TMS. (a) Calculate the chemical shift of each absorption. (b) Do the CH_3 protons absorb upfield or downfield from the OH proton?

Problem 14.2 The ^1H NMR spectrum of 1,2-dimethoxyethane ($CH_3OCH_2CH_2OCH_3$) recorded on a 300 MHz NMR spectrometer consists of signals at 1017 Hz and 1065 Hz downfield from TMS. (a) Calculate the chemical shift of each absorption. (b) At what frequency would each absorption occur if the spectrum were recorded on a 500 MHz NMR spectrometer?

Four different features of a ^1H NMR spectrum provide information about a compound's structure:

[1] **Number of signals** (Section 14.2)
[2] **Position of signals** (Sections 14.3 and 14.4)
[3] **Intensity of signals** (Section 14.5)
[4] **Spin–spin splitting of signals** (Sections 14.6–14.8)

14.2 ^1H NMR: Number of Signals

How many ^1H NMR signals does a compound exhibit? The number of NMR signals *equals* the number of different types of protons in a compound.

14.2A General Principles

- **Protons in different environments give different NMR signals. Equivalent protons give the same NMR signal.**

In many compounds, deciding whether two protons are in identical or different environments is intuitive.

Any CH_3 group is different from any CH_2 group, which is different from any CH group in a molecule. Two CH_3 groups may be identical (as in CH_3OCH_3) or different (as in $CH_3OCH_2CH_3$), depending on what each CH_3 group is bonded to.

tert-Butyl methyl ether [$CH_3OC(CH_3)_3$] (Section 14.1) exhibits two NMR signals because it contains two different kinds of protons: one CH_3 group is bonded to $-OC(CH_3)_3$, whereas the other three CH_3 groups are each bonded to the same group, [$-C(CH_3)_2$]OCH_3.

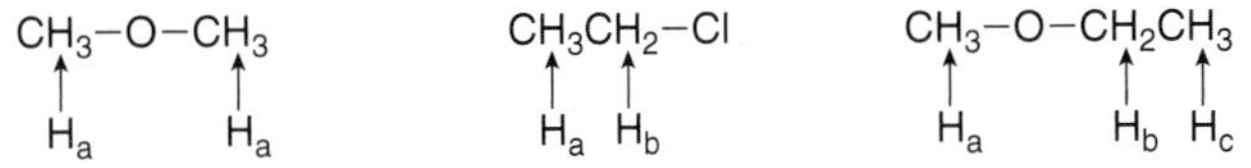
CH3–O–CH3
Ha Ha
CH3CH2–Cl
Ha Hb
CH3–O–CH2CH3
Ha Hb Hc

All equivalent H's 1 NMR signal | 2 types of H's 2 NMR signals | 3 types of H's 3 NMR signals

- **CH_3OCH_3:** Each CH_3 group is bonded to the same group ($-OCH_3$), making both CH_3 groups equivalent.
- **CH_3CH_2Cl:** The protons of the CH_3 group are different from those of the CH_2 group.
- **$CH_3OCH_2CH_3$:** The protons of the CH_2 group are different from those in each CH_3 group. The two CH_3 groups are also different from each other; one CH_3 group is bonded to $-OCH_2CH_3$ and the other is bonded to $-CH_2OCH_3$.

In some cases, it is less obvious by inspection if two protons are equivalent or different. To rigorously determine whether two protons are in identical environments (and therefore give rise to one NMR signal), replace each H atom in question by another atom Z (for example, Z = Cl). If substitution by Z yields the same compound or enantiomers, the two protons are equivalent, as shown in Sample Problem 14.2.

Sample Problem 14.2 How many different kinds of H atoms does $CH_3CH_2CH_2CH_2CH_3$ contain?

Solution

In comparing two H atoms, replace each H by Z (for example, Z = Cl), and examine the substitution products that result. The two CH_3 groups are identical because substitution of one H by Cl gives $CH_3CH_2CH_2CH_2CH_2Cl$ (1-chloropentane). There are two different types of CH_2 groups, because substitution of one H by Cl gives two different products:

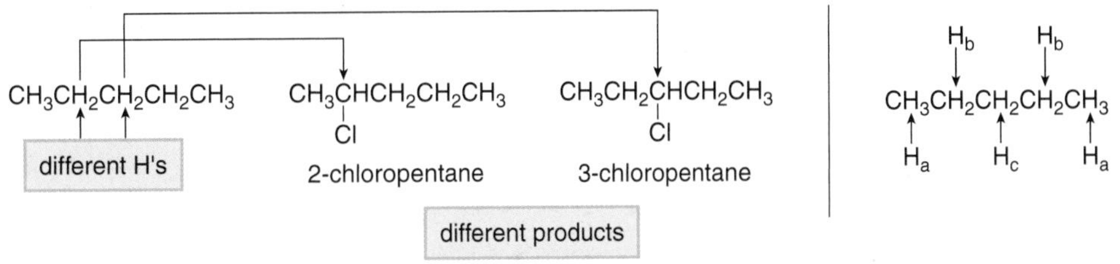
CH3CH2CH2CH2CH3
different H's
CH3CHCH2CH2CH3
Cl
2-chloropentane
CH3CH2CHCH2CH3
Cl
3-chloropentane
different products
Hb Hb
CH3CH2CH2CH2CH3
Ha Hc Ha

Thus, $CH_3CH_2CH_2CH_2CH_3$ has **three** different types of protons and gives **three** NMR signals.

Figure 14.2 gives the number of NMR signals exhibited by four additional molecules. All protons—not just protons bonded to carbon atoms—give rise to NMR signals. Ethanol (CH_3CH_2OH), for example, gives three NMR signals, one of which is due to its OH proton.

Problem 14.3 How many ¹H NMR signals does each compound show?

a. CH_3CH_3
b. $CH_3CH_2CH_3$
c. $CH_3CH_2CH_2CH_3$
d. $(CH_3)_2CHCH(CH_3)_2$
e. $CH_3CH_2CO_2CH_2CH_3$
f. $CH_3OCH_2CH(CH_3)_2$
g. $CH_3(CH_2)_7Cl$
h. $CH_3CH_2CH_2OH$

Figure 14.2 The number of ¹H NMR signals of some representative organic compounds

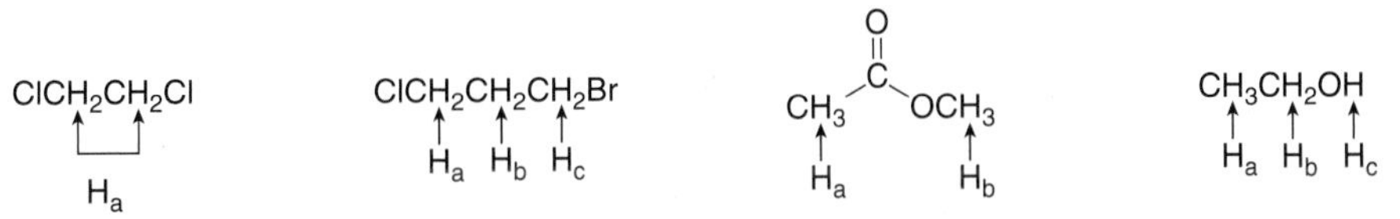
ClCH2CH2Cl
Ha
ClCH2CH2CH2Br
Ha Hb Hc
O
C
CH3 OCH3
Ha Hb
CH3CH2OH
Ha Hb Hc

1 type of H 1 NMR signal | 3 types of H's 3 NMR signals | 2 types of H's 2 NMR signals | 3 types of H's 3 NMR signals

14.2B Determining Equivalent Protons in Alkenes and Cycloalkanes

To determine equivalent protons in cycloalkanes and alkenes that have restricted bond rotation, always draw in all bonds to hydrogen.

Draw 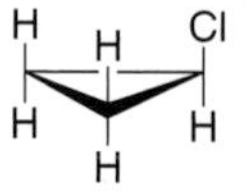 NOT 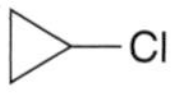 | Draw 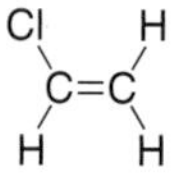 NOT $ClCH{=}CH_2$

Then, in comparing two H atoms on a ring or double bond, **two protons are equivalent only if they are cis (or trans) to the same groups,** as illustrated with 1,1-dichloroethylene, 1-bromo-1-chloroethylene, and chloroethylene.

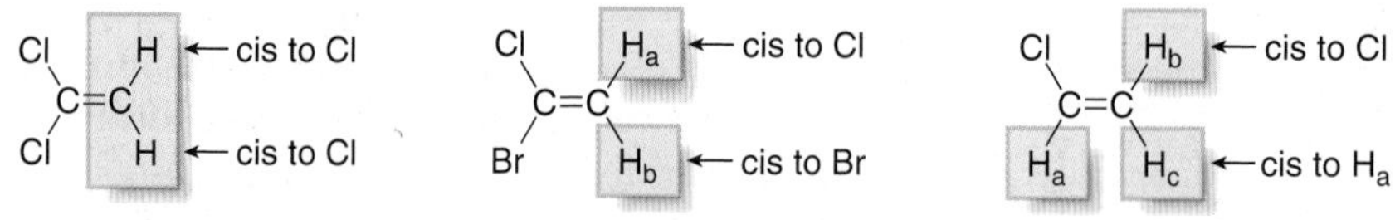

1,1-dichloroethylene	1-bromo-1-chloroethylene	chloroethylene
1 type of H 1 NMR signal	2 types of H's 2 NMR signals	3 types of H's 3 NMR signals

- **1,1-Dichloroethylene:** The two H atoms on the C=C are both cis to a Cl atom. Thus, both H atoms are equivalent.
- **1-Bromo-1-chloroethylene:** H_a is cis to a Cl atom and H_b is cis to a Br atom. Thus, H_a and H_b are different, giving rise to two NMR signals.
- **Chloroethylene:** H_a is bonded to the carbon with the Cl atom, making it different from H_b and H_c. Of the remaining two H atoms, H_b is cis to a Cl atom and H_c is cis to a H atom, making them different. All three H atoms in this compound are different.

Proton equivalency in cycloalkanes can be determined similarly.

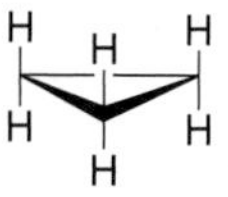

cyclopropane

All H's are equivalent.
1 NMR signal

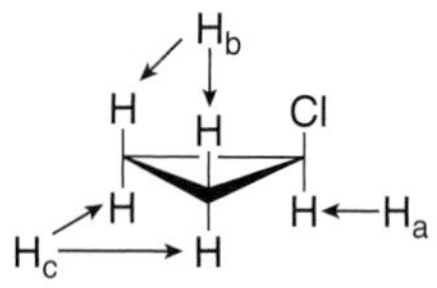

chlorocyclopropane

3 types of H's
3 NMR signals

- **Cyclopropane:** All H atoms are equivalent, so there is only one NMR signal.
- **Chlorocyclopropane:** There are now three kinds of H atoms: H_a is bonded to a carbon bonded to a Cl; both H_b protons are cis to the Cl whereas both H_c protons are cis to another H.

Problem 14.4 How many ^1H NMR signals does each dimethylcyclopropane show?

a. 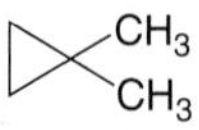 b.  c. 

14.2C Enantiotopic and Diastereotopic Protons

Let's look more closely at the protons of a single *sp*^{3} hybridized CH_2 group to determine whether these two protons are always equivalent to *each other.* Two examples illustrate different outcomes.

CH_3CH_2Br has two different types of protons—those of the CH_3 group and those of the CH_2 group—meaning that the two H atoms of the CH_2 group are *equivalent to each other.* To confirm this fact, we replace each H of the CH_2 group by an atom Z and examine the products of substitution. In this case, substitution of each H by Z creates a new stereogenic center, forming two products that are **enantiomers.**

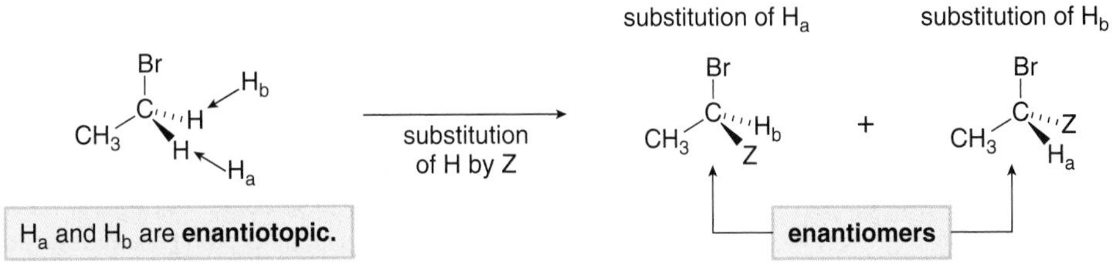

- **When substitution of two H atoms by Z forms enantiomers, the two H atoms are equivalent and give a single NMR signal. These two H atoms are called *enantiotopic* protons.**

In contrast, the two H atoms of the CH_2 group in (2*R*)-2-chlorobutane, which contains one stereogenic center, are *not* equivalent to each other. Substitution of each H by Z forms two **diastereomers,** and thus, these two H atoms give *different* NMR signals.

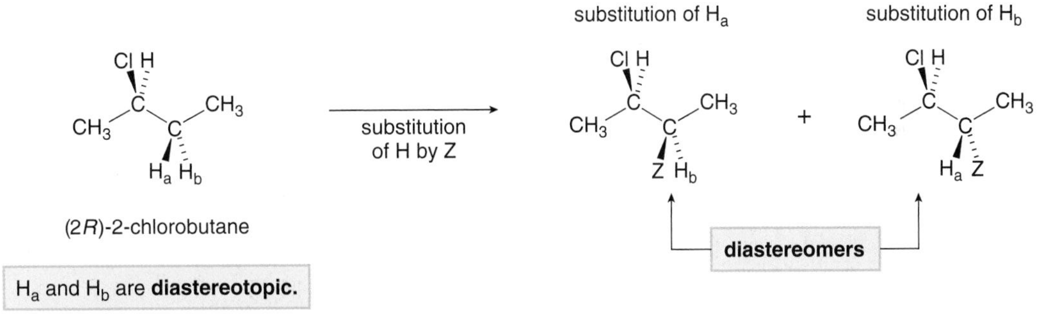

- **When substitution of two H atoms by Z forms diastereomers, the two H atoms are not equivalent, and give two NMR signals. These two H atoms are called *diastereotopic* protons.**

Sample Problem 14.3 Label the protons in each indicated CH_2 group as enantiotopic, diastereotopic, or neither.

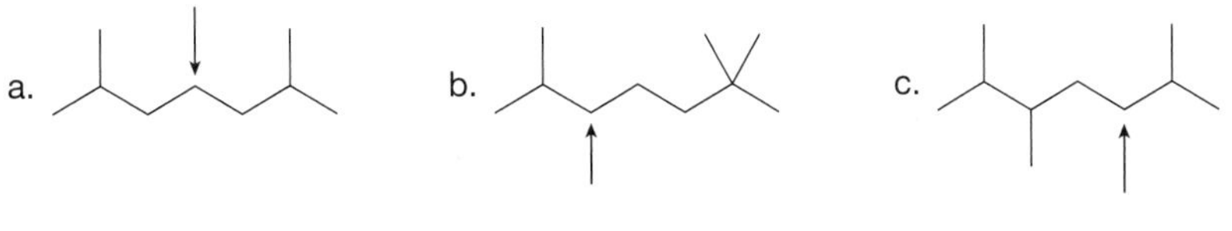

Solution

To determine equivalency in these cases, look for whether the compound has a stereogenic center to begin with and whether a new stereogenic center is formed when H is replaced by Z.

a. The compound is achiral and has no stereogenic center. Since no new stereogenic center is formed on substitution of H by Z, the protons are **neither** enantiotopic nor diastereotopic. The H's within the CH_2 group are *equivalent* to each other and give *one* NMR signal.

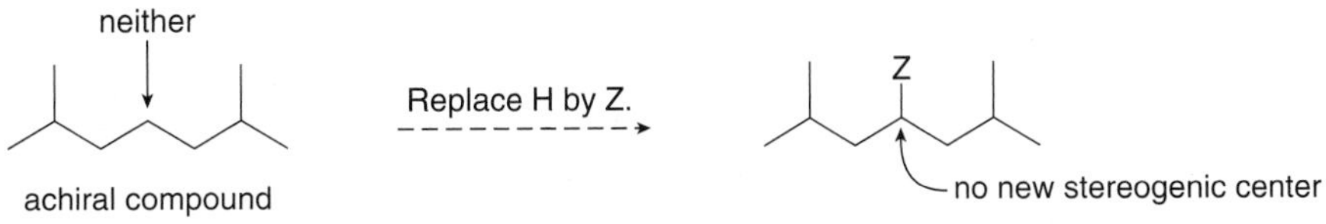

b. The compound is achiral and has no stereogenic center. Since a new stereogenic center is formed on substitution of H by Z, the protons are **enantiotopic.** The H's within the CH_2 group are *equivalent* to each other and give *one* NMR signal.

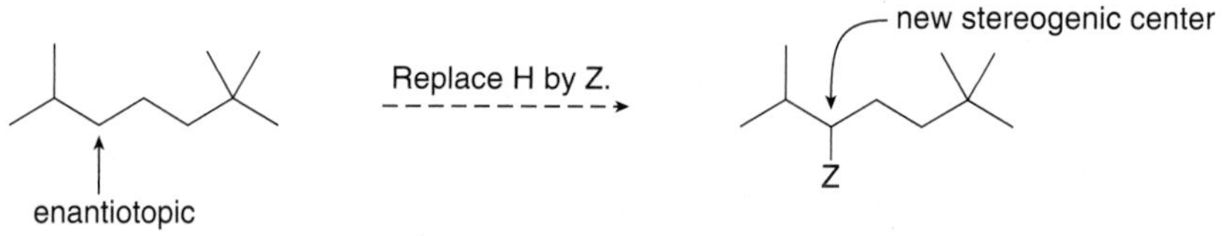

new stereogenic center
Replace H by Z.
Z
enantiotopic

c. The compound has one stereogenic center to begin with. Since a new stereogenic center is formed on substitution of H by Z, the protons are **diastereotopic.** The H's within the CH_2 group are *different* from each other and give *different* NMR signals.

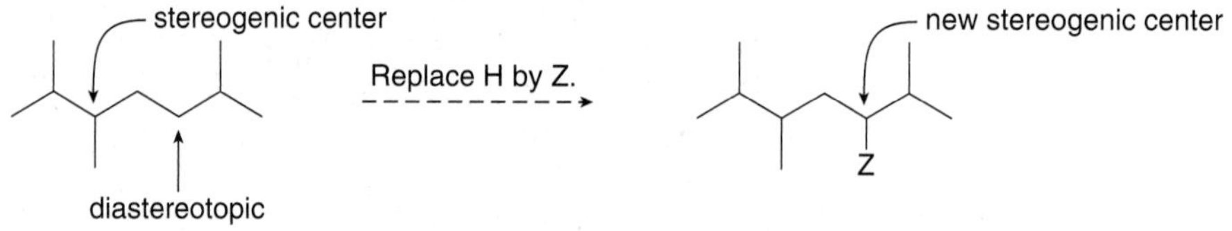

stereogenic center
new stereogenic center
Replace H by Z.
Z
diastereotopic

Problem 14.5 Label the protons in each indicated CH_2 group as enantiotopic, diastereotopic, or neither.

a. $CH_3CH_2CH_2CH_2CH_2CH_3$ (↑ at the second carbon) b. $CH_3CH_2CH_2CH_2CH_3$ (↑ at the third carbon) c. $CH_3CH(OH)CH_2CH_2CH_3$ (↑ at the fourth carbon)

Problem 14.6 How many ^1H NMR signals would you expect for each compound: (a) $CH_3CH(Cl)CH_2CH_3$; (b) $ClCH_2CH(CH_3)OCH_3$; (c) $CH_3CH(Br)CH_2CH_2CH_3$?

14.3 ^1H NMR: Position of Signals

In the NMR spectrum of *tert*-butyl methyl ether in Section 14.1B, why does the CH_3O- group absorb downfield from the $-C(CH_3)_3$ group?

- **Where a particular proton absorbs depends on its electronic environment.**

14.3A Shielding and Deshielding Effects

To understand how the electronic environment around a nucleus affects its chemical shift, recall that in a magnetic field, an electron creates a small magnetic field that opposes the applied magnetic field, B_0. **Electrons are said to *shield* the nucleus from B_0.**

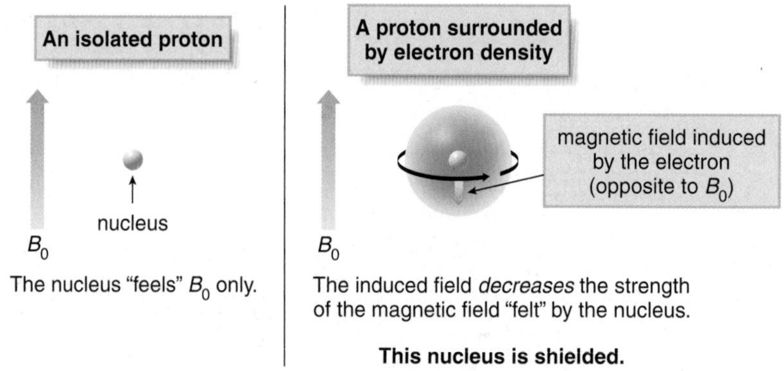

An isolated proton
nucleus
B0
The nucleus "feels" B0 only.
A proton surrounded by electron density
magnetic field induced by the electron (opposite to B0)
B0
The induced field decreases the strength of the magnetic field "felt" by the nucleus.
This nucleus is shielded.

In the vicinity of the nucleus, therefore, the magnetic field generated by the circulating electron *decreases* the external magnetic field that the proton "feels." Because the proton experiences a lower magnetic field strength, it needs a lower frequency to achieve resonance. Lower frequency is to the right in an NMR spectrum, toward lower chemical shift, so **shielding shifts an absorption *upfield,*** as shown in Figure 14.3a.

What happens if the electron density around a nucleus is *decreased,* instead? For example, how do the chemical shifts of the protons in CH_4 and CH_3Cl compare?

Figure 14.3 How chemical shift is affected by electron density around a nucleus

a. Shielding effects
- An electron shields the nucleus.
- The absorption shifts *upfield.*

b. Deshielding effects
- Decreased electron density deshields a nucleus.
- The absorption shifts *downfield.*

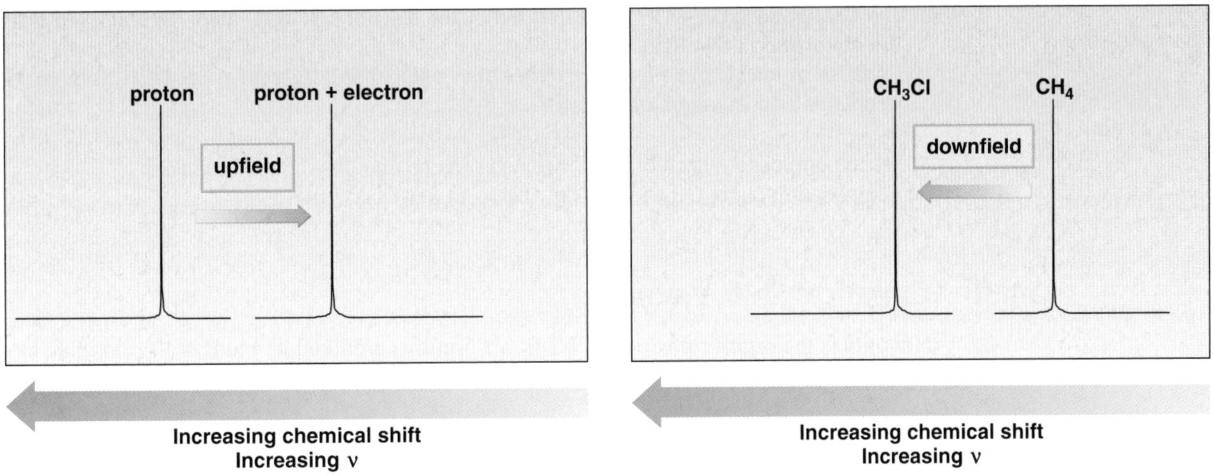

The less shielded the nucleus becomes, the more of the applied magnetic field (B_0) it feels. This *deshielded* nucleus experiences a higher magnetic field strength, so it needs a higher frequency to achieve resonance. Higher frequency is to the *left* in an NMR spectrum, toward higher chemical shift, so **deshielding shifts an absorption downfield,** as shown in Figure 14.3b for CH_3Cl versus CH_4. The electronegative Cl atom withdraws electron density from the carbon and hydrogen atoms in CH_3Cl, thus deshielding them relative to those in CH_4.

Remember the trend: ***D**ecreased electron density **d**eshields a nucleus and an absorption moves **d**ownfield.*

- **Protons near electronegative atoms are deshielded, so they absorb downfield.**

Figure 14.4 summarizes the effects of shielding and deshielding.

These electron density arguments explain the relative position of NMR signals in many compounds.

CH_3CH_2Cl (H_a on CH_3, H_b on CH_2)
- The H_b protons are **deshielded** because they are closer to the electronegative Cl atom, so they absorb **downfield** from H_a.

$BrCH_2CH_2F$ (H_a on $BrCH_2$, H_b on CH_2F)
- Because F is more electronegative than Br, the H_b protons are more **deshielded** than the H_a protons and absorb farther **downfield.**

$ClCH_2CHCl_2$ (H_a on $ClCH_2$, H_b on $CHCl_2$)
- The larger number of electronegative Cl atoms (two versus one) **deshields** H_b more than H_a, so it absorbs **downfield** from H_a.

Figure 14.4 Shielding and deshielding effects

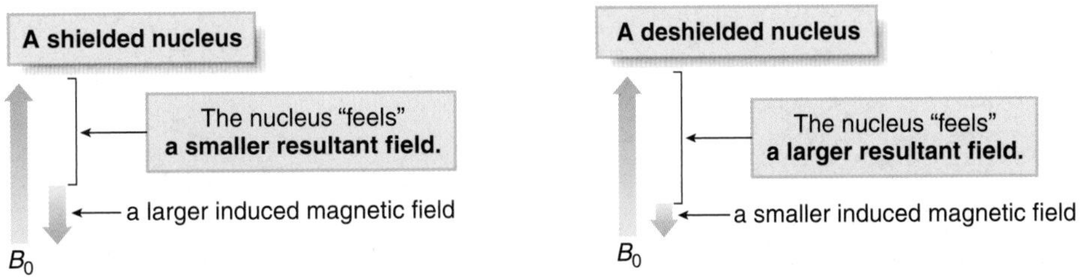

- As the electron density around the nucleus increases, the nucleus feels a smaller resultant magnetic field, so a lower frequency is needed to achieve resonance.
- **The absorption shifts upfield.**

- As the electron density around the nucleus decreases, the nucleus feels a larger resultant magnetic field, so a higher frequency is needed to achieve resonance.
- **The absorption shifts downfield.**

Sample Problem 14.4 Which of the underlined protons in each pair absorbs farther downfield: (a) $CH_3CH_2C\underline{H}_3$ or $CH_3OC\underline{H}_3$; (b) $CH_3OC\underline{H}_3$ or $CH_3SC\underline{H}_3$?

Solution

a. The CH_3 group in CH_3OCH_3 is deshielded by the electronegative O atom. **Deshielding shifts the absorption downfield.**

b. Because oxygen is more electronegative than sulfur, the CH_3 group in CH_3OCH_3 is more **deshielded** and absorbs **downfield.**

Problem 14.7 For each compound, which of the underlined protons absorbs farther downfield: (a) $FC\underline{H}_2CH_2C\underline{H}_2Cl$; (b) $CH_3C\underline{H}_2CH_2C\underline{H}_2OCH_3$; (c) $C\underline{H}_3OC(C\underline{H}_3)_3$?

14.3B Chemical Shift Values

Not only is the *relative* position of NMR absorptions predictable, but it is also possible to predict the approximate chemical shift value for a given type of proton.

- **Protons in a given environment absorb in a predictable region in an NMR spectrum.**

A more detailed list of characteristic chemical shift values is found in Appendix F.

Table 14.1 lists the typical chemical shift values for the most common bonds encountered in organic molecules.

Table 14.1 also illustrates that absorptions for a given type of C–H bond occur in a narrow range of chemical shift values, usually 1–2 ppm. For example, all sp^3 hybridized C–H bonds in alkanes and cycloalkanes absorb between 0.9 and 2.0 ppm. By contrast, absorptions due to N–H and O–H protons can occur over a broader range. For example, the OH proton of an alcohol is found anywhere in the 1–5 ppm range. The position of these absorptions is affected by the extent of hydrogen bonding, making it more variable.

Table 14.1 Characteristic Chemical Shifts of Common Types of Protons

Type of proton	Chemical shift (ppm)	Type of proton	Chemical shift (ppm)
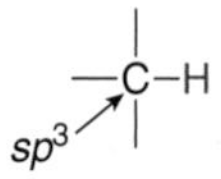	0.9–2	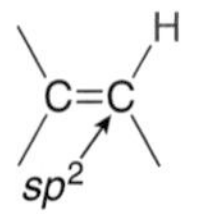	4.5–6
• RCH_3 • R_2CH_2 • R_3CH	~0.9 ~1.3 ~1.7	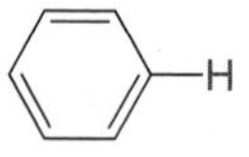	6.5–8
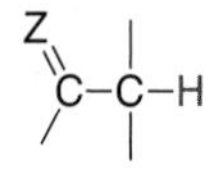 Z = C, O, N	1.5–2.5	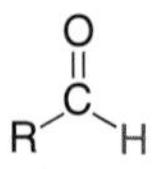	9–10
—C≡C–H	~2.5	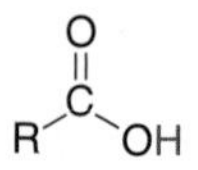	10–12
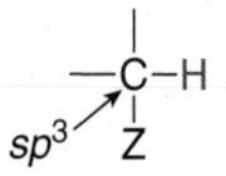 Z = N, O, X	2.5–4	RO–H or R–N–H	1–5

The chemical shift of a particular type of C−H bond is also affected by the number of R groups bonded to the carbon atom.

RCH_2—H	R_2CH—H	R_3C—H
~ 0.9 ppm	~ 1.3 ppm	~ 1.7 ppm

Increasing alkyl substitution
Increasing chemical shift

- **The chemical shift of a C−H bond increases with increasing alkyl substitution.**

Problem 14.8 For each compound, first label each different type of proton and then rank the protons in order of increasing chemical shift.

a. $ClCH_2CH_2CH_2Br$ b. $CH_3OCH_2OC(CH_3)_3$ c. 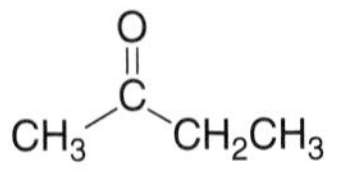

O
C
CH3
CH2CH3

14.4 The Chemical Shift of Protons on sp^2 and *sp* Hybridized Carbons

The chemical shift of protons bonded to benzene rings, C−C double bonds, and C−C triple bonds merits additional comment.

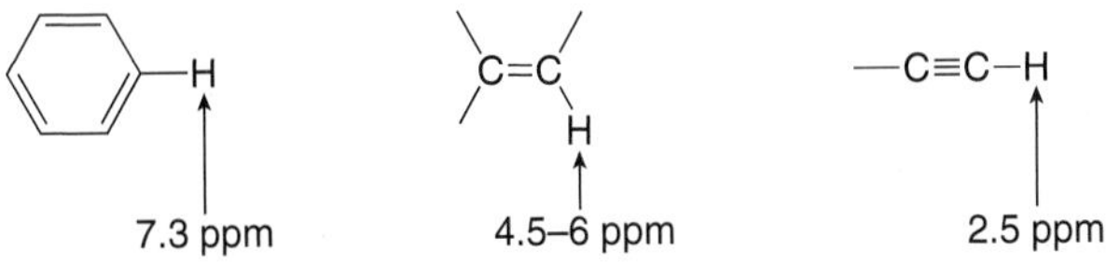

H
7.3 ppm
C=C
H
4.5–6 ppm
—C≡C—H
2.5 ppm

Each of these functional groups contains π bonds with **loosely held π electrons.** When placed in a magnetic field, these π electrons move in a circular path, inducing a new magnetic field. How this induced magnetic field affects the chemical shift of a proton depends on the direction of the induced field *in the vicinity of the absorbing proton.*

Protons on Benzene Rings

In a magnetic field, the six π electrons in **benzene** circulate around the ring, creating a ring current. The magnetic field induced by these moving electrons *reinforces* the applied magnetic field in the vicinity of the protons. The protons thus feel a stronger magnetic field and a higher frequency is needed for resonance, so the **protons are deshielded and the absorption is *downfield.***

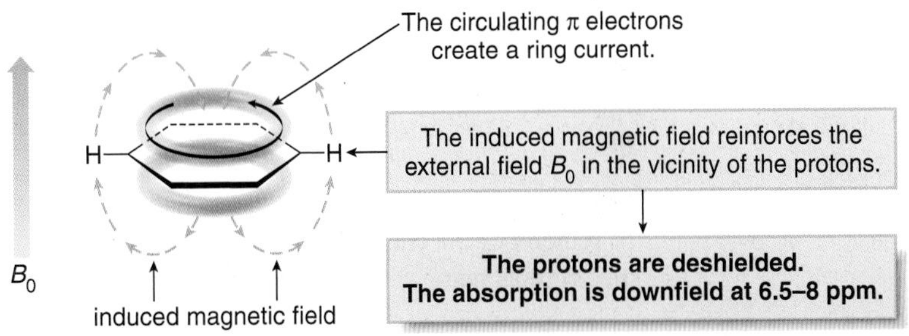

The circulating π electrons create a ring current.
H
H
The induced magnetic field reinforces the external field B_0 in the vicinity of the protons.
The protons are deshielded.
The absorption is downfield at 6.5–8 ppm.
B_0
induced magnetic field

Protons on Carbon–Carbon Double Bonds

A similar phenomenon occurs with protons on carbon–carbon double bonds. In a magnetic field, the loosely held π electrons create a magnetic field that *reinforces* the applied field in the vicinity of the protons. Because the protons now feel a stronger magnetic field, they require a higher frequency for resonance. **The protons are deshielded and the absorption is *downfield.***

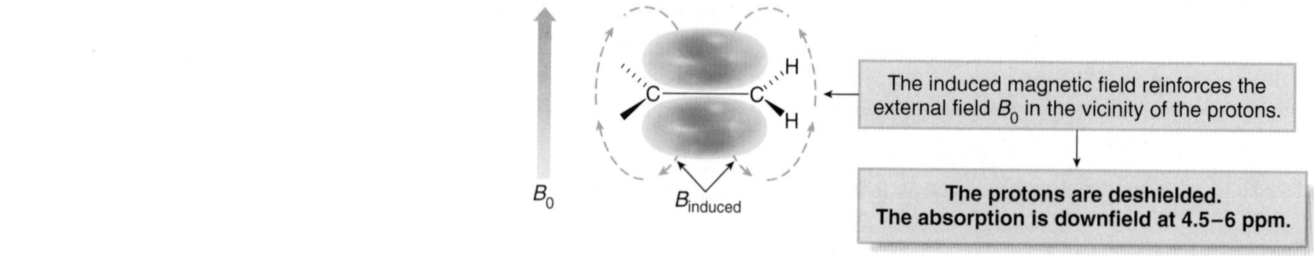

Protons on Carbon–Carbon Triple Bonds

In a magnetic field, the π electrons of a carbon–carbon triple bond are induced to circulate, but in this case the induced magnetic field *opposes* the applied magnetic field (B_0). The proton thus feels a weaker magnetic field, so a lower frequency is needed for resonance. **The nucleus is shielded and the absorption is *upfield.***

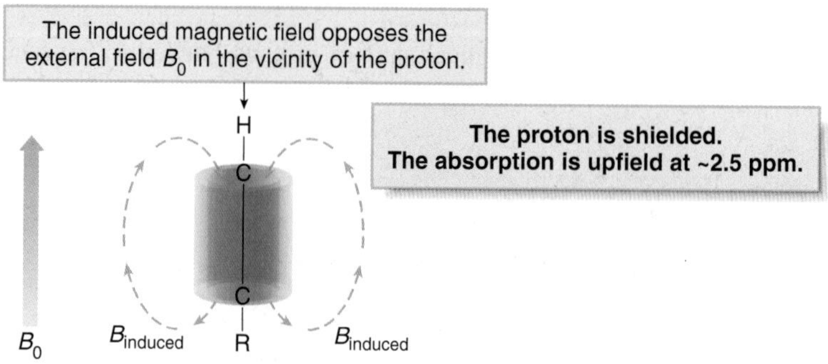

Table 14.2 summarizes the shielding and deshielding effects due to circulating π electrons.

Table 14.2 Effect of π Electrons on Chemical Shift Values

Proton type	Effect	Chemical shift (ppm)
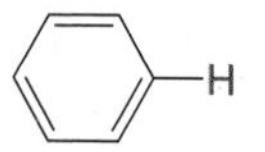	highly deshielded	6.5–8
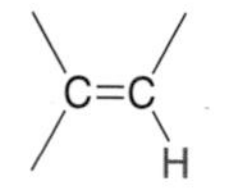	deshielded	4.5–6
—C≡C—H	shielded	~2.5

To remember the chemical shifts of some common bond types, it is helpful to think of a ^{1}H NMR spectrum as being divided into six different regions (Figure 14.5).

Figure 14.5
Regions in the ¹H NMR spectrum

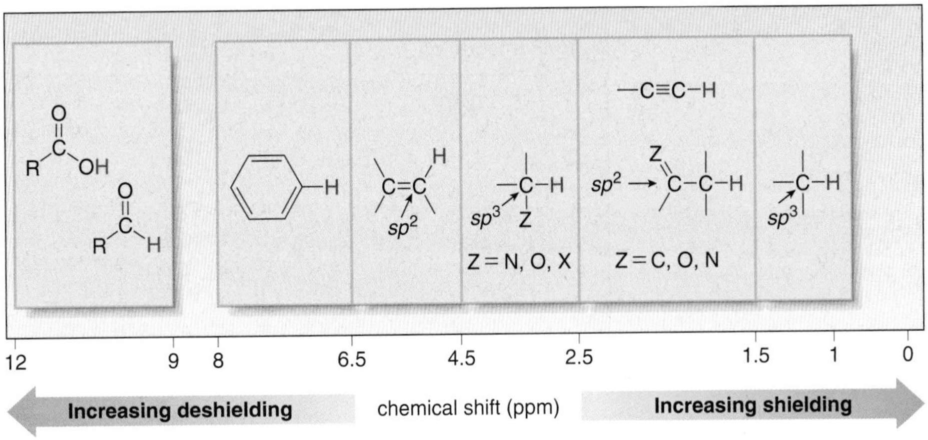

- Shielded protons absorb at lower chemical shift (to the right).
- Deshielded protons absorb at higher chemical shift (to the left).
- Note: The drawn chemical shift scale is not linear.

Sample Problem 14.5 Rank H_a, H_b, and H_c in order of increasing chemical shift.

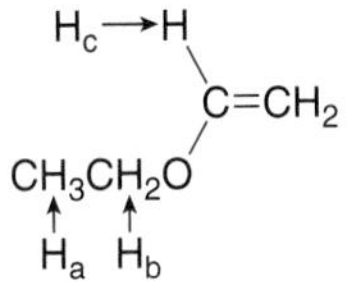

Solution

The H_a protons are bonded to an sp^3 hybridized carbon, so they are shielded and absorb upfield compared to H_b and H_c. Because the H_b protons are deshielded by the electronegative oxygen atom on the C to which they are bonded, they absorb downfield from H_a. The H_c proton is deshielded by two factors. The electronegative O atom withdraws electron density from H_c. Moreover, because H_c is bonded directly to a C=C, the magnetic field induced by the π electrons causes further deshielding. Thus, in order of increasing chemical shift, $H_a < H_b < H_c$.

Problem 14.9 Rank each group of protons in order of increasing chemical shift.

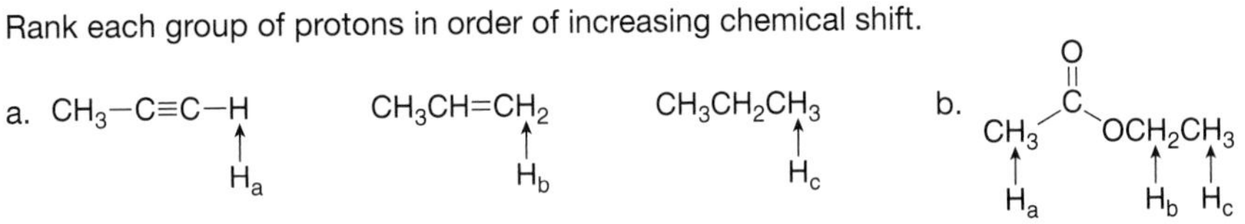

14.5 ¹H NMR: Intensity of Signals

The relative intensity of ¹H NMR signals also provides information about a compound's structure.

- **The area under an NMR signal is proportional to the number of absorbing protons.**

For example, in the ¹H NMR spectrum of $CH_3OC(CH_3)_3$, the ratio of the area under the downfield peak (due to the CH_3O- group) to the upfield peak [due to the $-C(CH_3)_3$ group] is 1:3. An NMR spectrometer automatically integrates the area under the peaks, and prints out a stepped curve (an **integral**) on the spectrum. **The height of each step is proportional to the area under the peak, which is in turn proportional to the number of absorbing protons.**

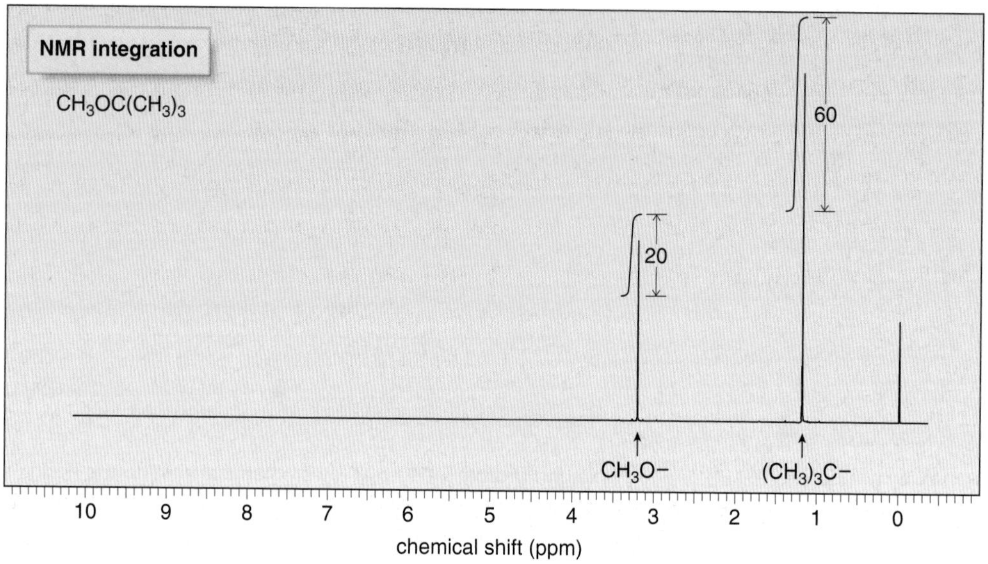

Integrals can be manually measured, but modern NMR spectrometers automatically calculate and plot the value of each integral in arbitrary units. If the heights of two integrals are 20 units and 60 units, the ratio of absorbing protons is 20:60, or 1:3, or 2:6, or 3:9, and so forth. This tells the *ratio,* not the absolute number of protons. Integration ratios are approximate, and often values must be rounded to the nearest whole number.

Problem 14.10 Which compounds give a ^1H NMR spectrum with two signals in a ratio of 2:3?

a. CH_3CH_2Cl b. $CH_3CH_2CH_3$ c. $CH_3CH_2OCH_2CH_3$ d. $CH_3OCH_2CH_2OCH_3$

Knowing the molecular formula of a compound and integration values from its ^1H NMR spectrum gives the *actual number* of protons responsible for a particular signal.

How To Determine the Number of Protons Giving Rise to an NMR Signal

Example A compound of molecular formula $C_9H_{10}O_2$ gives the following integrated ^1H NMR spectrum. How many protons give rise to each signal?

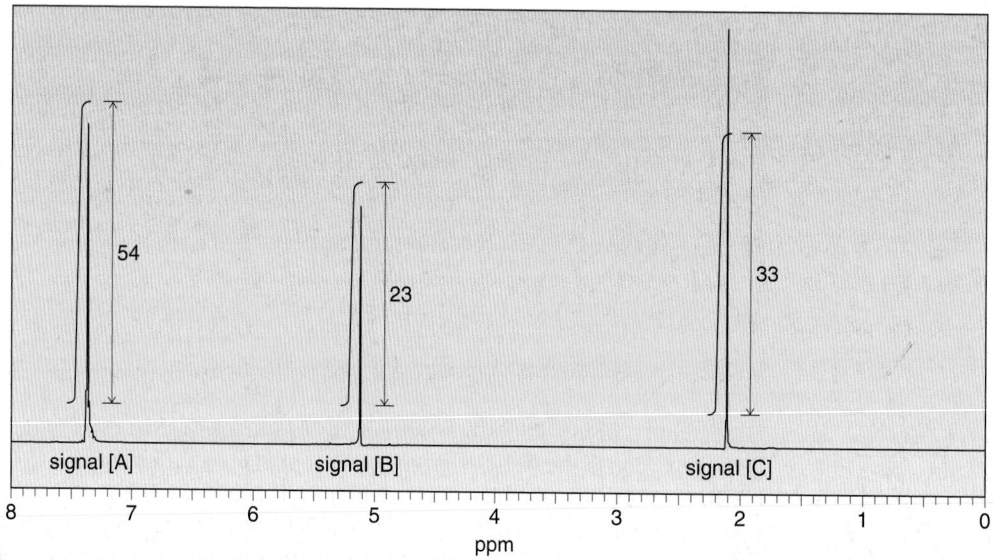

—Continued

How To, continued . . .

Step [1] **Determine the number of integration units per proton by dividing the total number of integration units by the total number of protons.**

- Total number of integration units: 54 + 23 + 33 = 110 units
- Total number of protons = 10
- Divide: 110 units/10 protons = **11 units per proton**

Step [2] **Determine the number of protons giving rise to each signal.**

- To determine the number of H atoms giving rise to each signal, divide each integration value by the answer of Step [1] and round to the nearest whole number.

Answer:

Signal [A]: $\frac{54}{11} = 4.9 \approx$ **5 H**

Signal [B]: $\frac{23}{11} = 2.1 \approx$ **2 H**

Signal [C]: $\frac{33}{11} =$ **3 H**

Problem 14.11 A compound of molecular formula $C_8H_{14}O_2$ gives three NMR signals having the indicated integration values: signal [A] 14 units, signal [B] 12 units, and signal [C] 44 units. How many protons give rise to each signal?

Problem 14.12 Compound **A** exhibits two signals in its ^1H NMR spectrum at 2.64 and 3.69 ppm and the ratio of the absorbing signals is 2:3. Compound **B** exhibits two signals in its ^1H NMR spectrum at 2.09 and 4.27 ppm and the ratio of the absorbing signals is 3:2. Which compound corresponds to $CH_3O_2CCH_2CH_2CO_2CH_3$ (dimethyl succinate) and which compound corresponds to $CH_3CO_2CH_2CH_2O_2CCH_3$ (ethylene diacetate)?

14.6 ^1H NMR: Spin–Spin Splitting

The ^1H NMR spectra you have seen up to this point have been limited to one or more single absorptions called **singlets.** In the ^1H NMR spectrum of $BrCH_2CHBr_2$, however, the two signals for the two different kinds of protons are each split into more than one peak. The splitting patterns, the result of **spin–spin splitting,** can be used to determine how many protons reside on the carbon atoms near the absorbing proton.

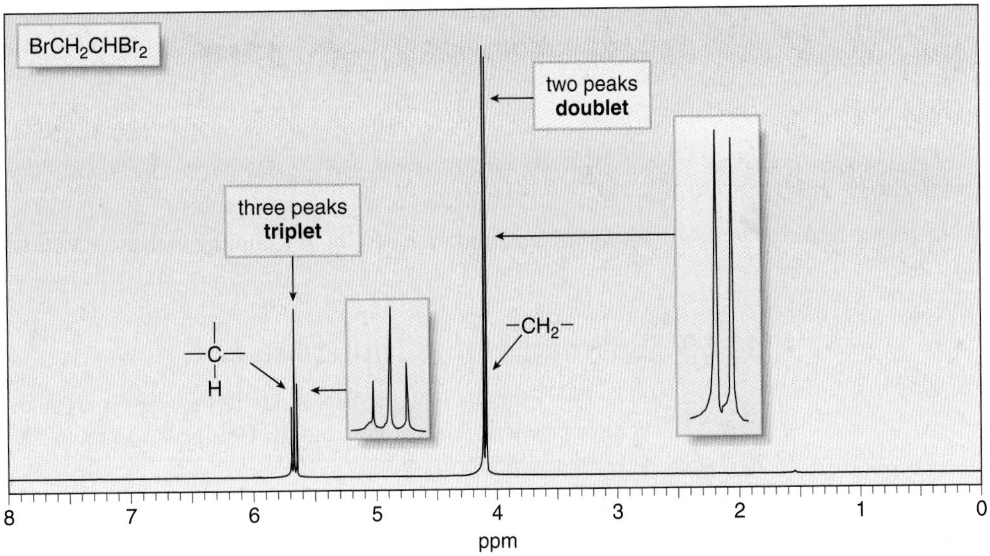

To understand spin–spin splitting, we must distinguish between the **absorbing protons** that give rise to an NMR signal, and the **adjacent protons** that cause the signal to split. **The number of adjacent protons determines the observed splitting pattern.**

- The CH_2 signal appears as **two peaks,** called a ***doublet.*** The relative area under the peaks of a doublet is 1:1.
- The CH signal appears as **three peaks,** called a ***triplet.*** The relative area under the peaks of a triplet is 1:2:1.

Spin–spin splitting occurs between nonequivalent protons on the same carbon or adjacent carbons. To illustrate how spin–spin splitting arises, we'll examine nonequivalent protons on adjacent carbons, the more common example. Spin–spin splitting arises because protons are little magnets that can be aligned with or against an applied magnetic field, and this affects the magnetic field that a nearby proton feels.

14.6A Splitting: How a Doublet Arises

First, let's examine how the doublet due to the CH_2 group in $BrCH_2CHBr_2$ arises. The CH_2 group contains the absorbing protons and the CH group contains the adjacent proton that causes the splitting.

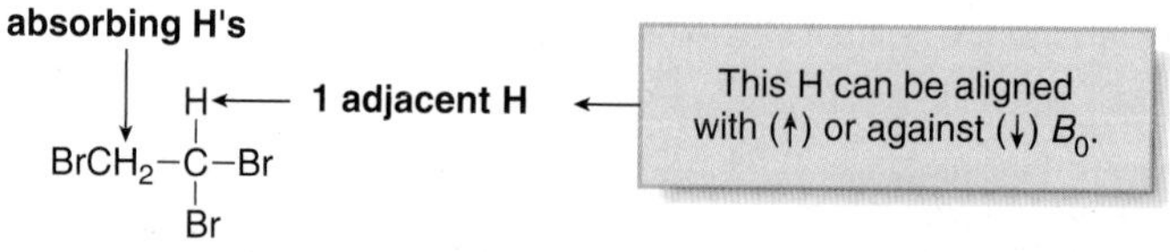
absorbing H's
H
1 adjacent H
BrCH2–C–Br
Br
This H can be aligned with (↑) or against (↓) B0.

When placed in an applied magnetic field (B_0), the adjacent proton ($CHBr_2$) can be aligned with (↑) or against (↓) B_0. As a result, the absorbing protons (CH_2Br) feel two slightly different magnetic fields—one slightly larger than B_0 and one slightly smaller than B_0. Because the absorbing protons feel two different magnetic fields, they absorb at two different frequencies in the NMR spectrum, thus splitting a single absorption into a doublet.

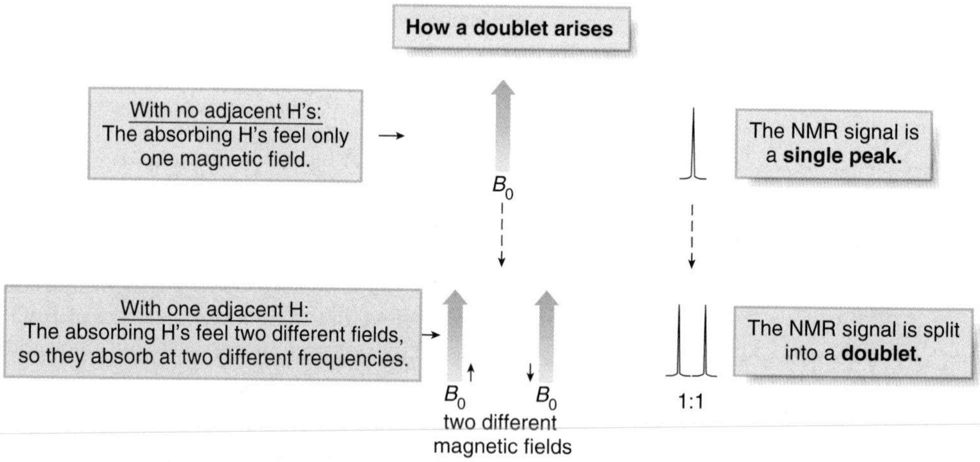
How a doublet arises
With no adjacent H's:
The absorbing H's feel only one magnetic field.
B0
The NMR signal is a single peak.
With one adjacent H:
The absorbing H's feel two different fields, so they absorb at two different frequencies.
B0
B0
two different magnetic fields
1:1
The NMR signal is split into a doublet.

Keep in mind the difference between an **NMR signal** and an **NMR peak.** An NMR signal is the entire absorption due to a particular kind of proton. NMR peaks are contained within a signal. A doublet constitutes one signal that is split into two peaks.

- **One adjacent proton splits an NMR signal into a doublet.**

The two peaks of a doublet are approximately equal in area. The area under both peaks—the entire NMR signal—is due to both protons of the CH_2 group of $BrCH_2CHBr_2$.

coupling constant, ***J***, in Hz

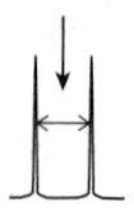

The frequency difference (measured in Hz) between the two peaks of the doublet is called the **coupling constant,** denoted by ***J***. Coupling constants are usually in the range of 0–18 Hz, and are independent of the strength of the applied magnetic field B_0.

14.6B Splitting: How a Triplet Arises

Now let's examine how the triplet due to the CH group in $BrCH_2CHBr_2$ arises. The CH group contains the absorbing proton and the CH_2 group contains the adjacent protons (H_a and H_b) that cause the splitting.

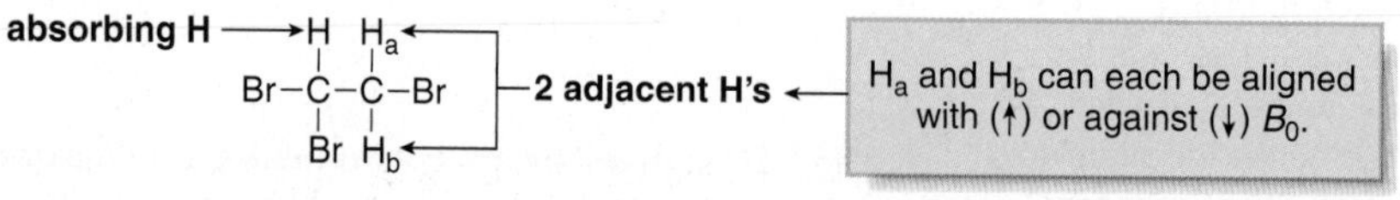
absorbing H
H Ha
Br–C–C–Br
Br Hb
2 adjacent H's
Ha and Hb can each be aligned with (↑) or against (↓) B0.

When placed in an applied magnetic field (B_0), the adjacent protons H_a and H_b can each be aligned with (↑) or against (↓) B_0. As a result, the absorbing proton feels three slightly different magnetic fields—one slightly larger than B_0, one slightly smaller than B_0, and one the same strength as B_0.

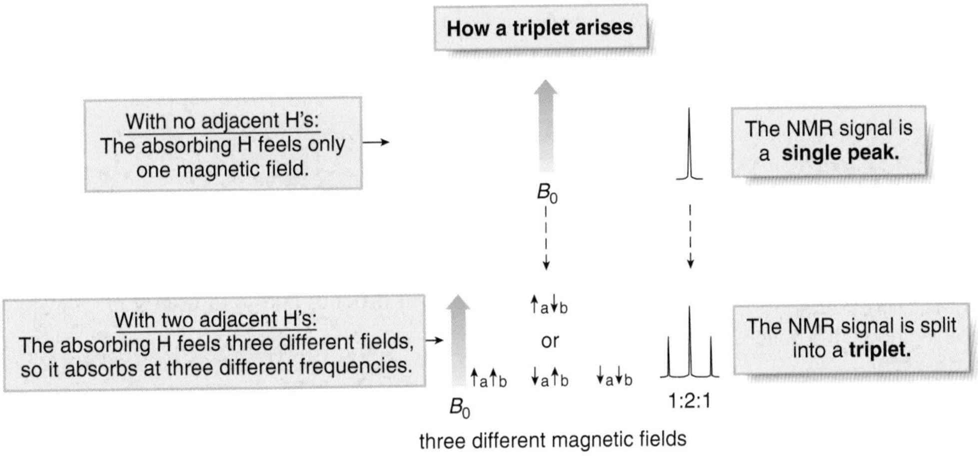

Because the absorbing proton feels three different magnetic fields, it absorbs at three different frequencies in the NMR spectrum, thus splitting a single absorption into a triplet. Because there are two different ways to align one proton with B_0 and one proton against B_0—that is, $\uparrow_a\downarrow_b$ and $\downarrow_a\uparrow_b$—the middle peak of the triplet is twice as intense as the two outer peaks, making the ratio of the areas under the three peaks 1:2:1.

- **Two adjacent protons split an NMR signal into a triplet.**

When two protons split each other's NMR signals, they are said to be ***coupled.*** In $BrCH_2CHBr_2$, the CH proton is coupled to the CH_2 protons. The spacing between peaks in a split NMR signal, measured by the J value, is *equal* for coupled protons.

14.6C Splitting: The Rules and Examples

Three general rules describe the splitting patterns commonly seen in the ^{1}H NMR spectra of organic compounds.

Rule [1] **Equivalent protons don't split each other's signals.**

Rule [2] **A set of *n* nonequivalent protons splits the signal of a nearby proton into *n* + 1 peaks.**

- In $BrCH_2CHBr_2$, for example, *one* adjacent CH proton splits an NMR signal into *two* peaks (a doublet), and *two* adjacent CH_2 protons split an NMR signal into *three* peaks (a triplet). Names for split NMR signals containing two to seven peaks are given in Table 14.3. An NMR signal having more than seven peaks is called a **multiplet.**
- The inside peaks of a split NMR signal are always most intense, with the area under the peaks decreasing from the inner to the outer peaks in a given splitting pattern.

Table 14.3 Names for a Given Number of Peaks in an NMR Signal

Number of peaks	Name	Number of peaks	Name
1	singlet	5	quintet
2	doublet	6	sextet
3	triplet	7	septet
4	quartet	> 7	multiplet

Rule [3] Splitting is observed for nonequivalent protons on the same carbon or adjacent carbons.

If H_a and H_b are not equivalent, splitting is observed when:

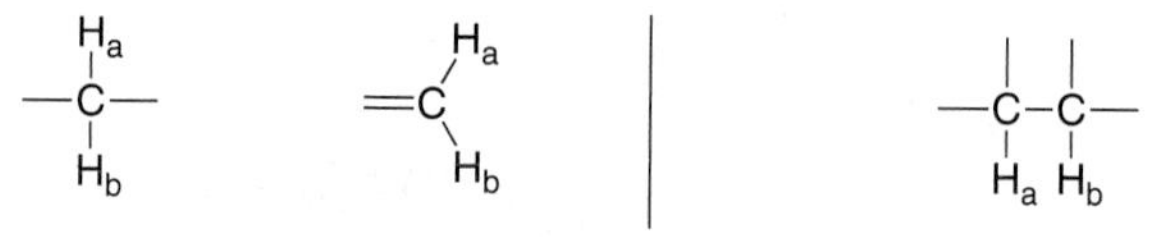

H_a and H_b are on the **same** carbon. H_a and H_b are on **adjacent** carbons.

The splitting of an NMR signal reveals the number of nearby nonequivalent protons. It tells nothing about the absorbing proton itself.

Splitting is not generally observed between protons separated by more than three σ bonds. Although H_a and H_b are not equivalent to each other in 2-butanone and ethyl methyl ether, H_a and H_b are separated by four σ bonds and so they are too far away to split each other's NMR signals.

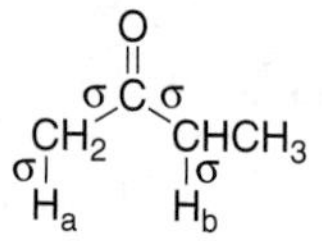

2-butanone

H_a and H_b are separated by four σ bonds.

no splitting between H_a and H_b

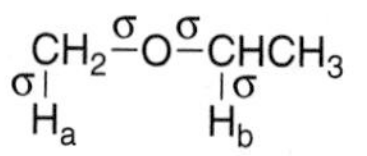

ethyl methyl ether

H_a and H_b are separated by four σ bonds.

no splitting between H_a and H_b

Table 14.4 illustrates common splitting patterns observed for adjacent nonequivalent protons.

Table 14.4 Common Splitting Patterns Observed in ^{1}H NMR

Example	Pattern	Analysis (H_a and H_b are not equivalent.)				
[1] 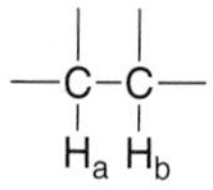	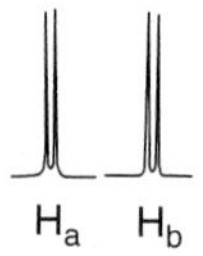	• H_a: one adjacent H_b proton • H_b: one adjacent H_a proton	---→ ---→	two peaks two peaks	---→ ---→	a **doublet** a **doublet**
[2] 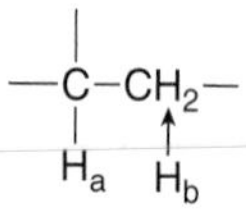	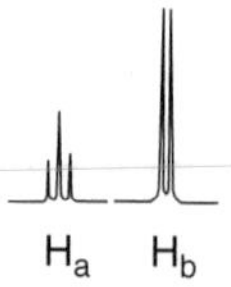	• H_a: two adjacent H_b protons • H_b: one adjacent H_a proton	---→ ---→	three peaks two peaks	---→ ---→	a **triplet** a **doublet**
[3] 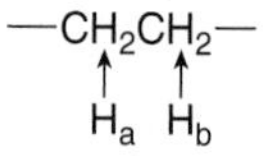	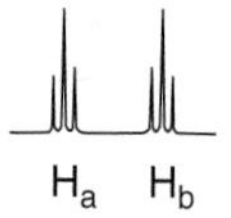	• H_a: two adjacent H_b protons • H_b: two adjacent H_a protons	---→ ---→	three peaks three peaks	---→ ---→	a **triplet** a **triplet**
[4] 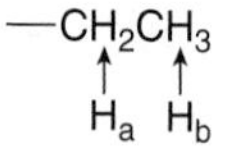	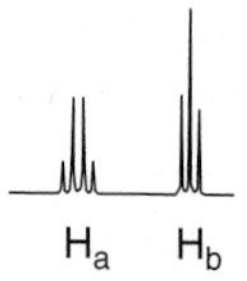	• H_a: three adjacent H_b protons • H_b: two adjacent H_a protons	---→ ---→	four peaks three peaks	---→ ---→	a **quartet*** a **triplet**
[5] 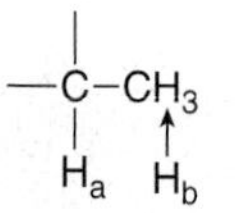	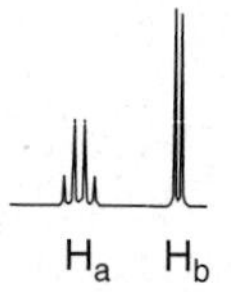	• H_a: three adjacent H_b protons • H_b: one adjacent H_a proton	---→ ---→	four peaks two peaks	---→ ---→	a **quartet*** a **doublet**

*The relative area under the peaks of a quartet is 1:3:3:1.

Predicting splitting is always a two-step process:

- **Determine if two protons are equivalent or different.** Only nonequivalent protons split each other.
- **Determine if two nonequivalent protons are close enough to split each other's signals.** Splitting is observed only for nonequivalent protons on the *same* carbon or *adjacent* carbons.

Several examples of spin–spin splitting in specific compounds illustrate the result of this two-step strategy.

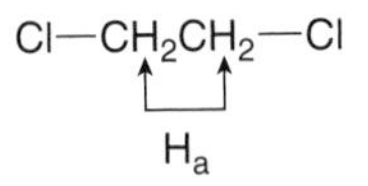

- All protons are equivalent (H_a), so there is no splitting and the NMR signal is one singlet.

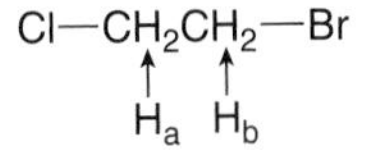

- There are two NMR signals. H_a and H_b are nonequivalent protons bonded to adjacent C atoms, so they are close enough to split each other's NMR signals. The H_a signal is split into a triplet by the two H_b protons. The H_b signal is split into a triplet by the two H_a protons.

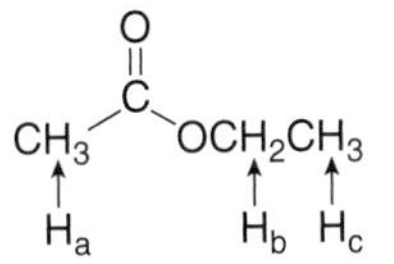

- There are three NMR signals. H_a has no adjacent nonequivalent protons, so its signal is a singlet. The H_b signal is split into a quartet by the three H_c protons. The H_c signal is split into a triplet by the two H_b protons.

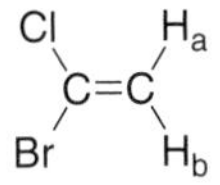

- There are two NMR signals. H_a and H_b are nonequivalent protons on the same carbon, so they are close enough to split each other's NMR signals. The H_a signal is split into a doublet by H_b. The H_b signal is split into a doublet by H_a.

Problem 14.13 Into how many peaks will each indicated proton be split?

a. 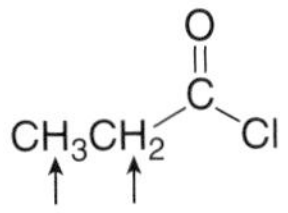

c. 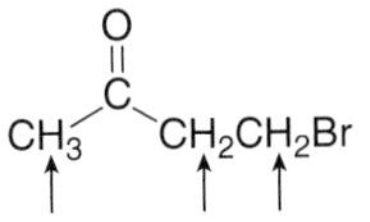

e. 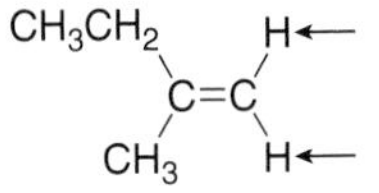

b. 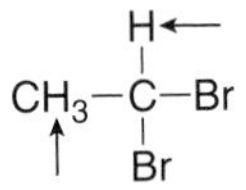

d. 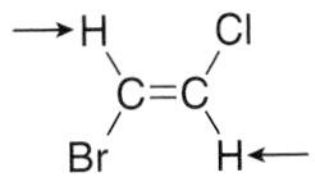

f. 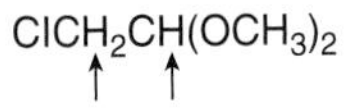

Problem 14.14 For each compound give the number of ^1H NMR signals, and then determine how many peaks are present for each NMR signal.

a. 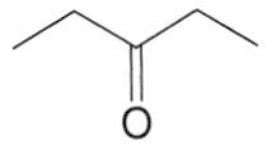

b. 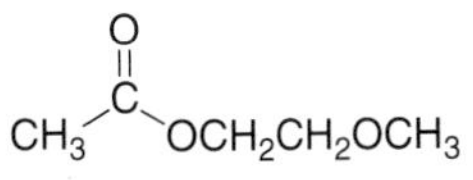

c. 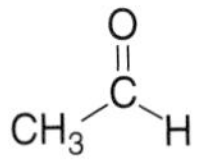

d. $Cl_2CHCH_2CO_2CH_3$

Problem 14.15 Sketch the NMR spectrum of CH_3CH_2Cl, giving the approximate location of each NMR signal.

14.7 More Complex Examples of Splitting

Up to now you have studied examples of spin–spin splitting where the absorbing proton has nearby protons on *one* adjacent carbon only. What happens when the absorbing proton has nonequivalent protons on *two* adjacent carbons? Different outcomes are possible, depending on whether the adjacent nonequivalent protons are *equivalent to* or *different from* each other.

For example, 2-bromopropane [$(CH_3)_2CHBr$] has two types of protons—H_a and H_b—so it exhibits two NMR signals, as shown in Figure 14.6.

- The H_a protons have only one adjacent nonequivalent proton (H_b), so they are split into two peaks, a **doublet.**
- H_b has three H_a protons on each side. Because the six H_a protons are *equivalent to each other,* the ***n* + 1** rule can be used to determine splitting: 6 + 1 = 7 peaks, a **septet.**

Figure 14.6
The ^{1}H NMR spectrum of 2-bromopropane, [$(CH_3)_2CHBr$]

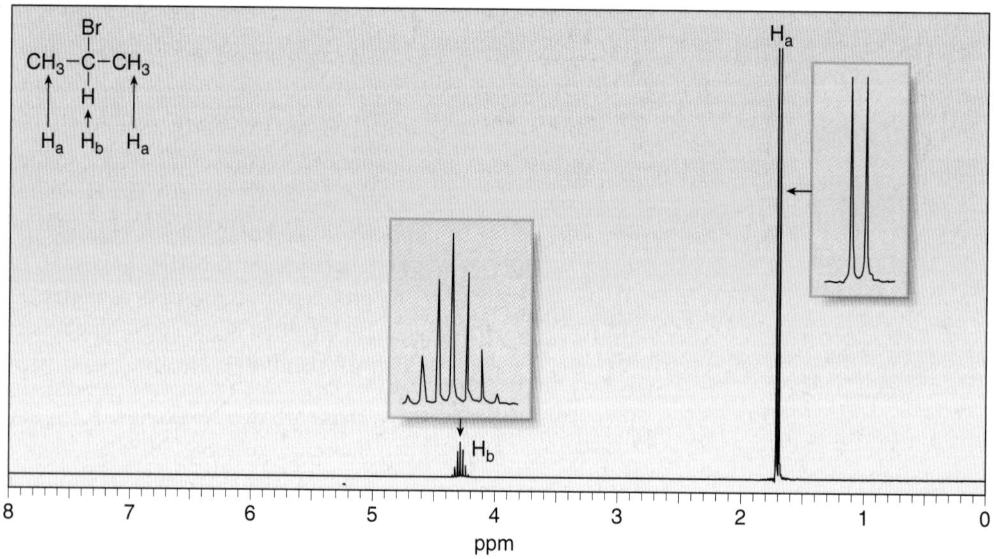
Br
CH3–C–CH3
H
Ha Hb Ha
Ha
Hb
8
7
6
5
4
3
2
1
0
ppm

This is a specific example of a general rule:

- **Whenever two (or three) sets of adjacent protons are equivalent to each other, use the *n* + 1 rule to determine the splitting pattern.**

A different outcome results when an absorbing proton is flanked by adjacent protons that are *not equivalent to each other.* Consider the splitting pattern expected for the H_b protons in the ^{1}H NMR spectrum of $CH_3CH_2CH_2Z$. H_b has protons on both adjacent carbons, but since H_a and H_c are *not equivalent to each other,* we cannot merely add them together and use the $n + 1$ rule.

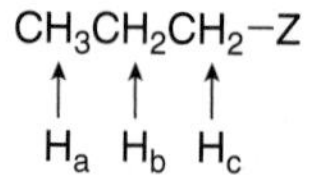
CH3CH2CH2–Z
Ha Hb Hc

Instead, to determine the splitting of H_b, we must consider the effect of the H_a protons and the H_c protons *separately.* The three H_a protons split the H_b signal into four peaks, and the two H_c protons split each of these four peaks into three peaks—that is, the NMR signal due to H_b consists of 4×3 = **12 peaks.** Figure 14.7 shows a splitting diagram illustrating how these 12 peaks arise.

- **When two sets of adjacent protons are *different from each other* (*n* protons on one adjacent carbon and *m* protons on the other), the number of peaks in an NMR signal = (*n* + 1)(*m* + 1).**

It is only possible to see 12 peaks in an NMR spectrum when the coupling constants between each set of nonequivalent protons—that is, J_{ab} and J_{bc} in this example—are different; in other words, $J_{ab} \neq J_{bc}$. Such is the case with the nonequivalent protons on carbon–carbon double bonds, which is discussed in Section 14.8. **In practice, with flexible alkyl chains it is more common for J_{ab} and J_{bc} to be very similar or identical.** In this case, peaks overlap and many fewer than 12 peaks are observed.

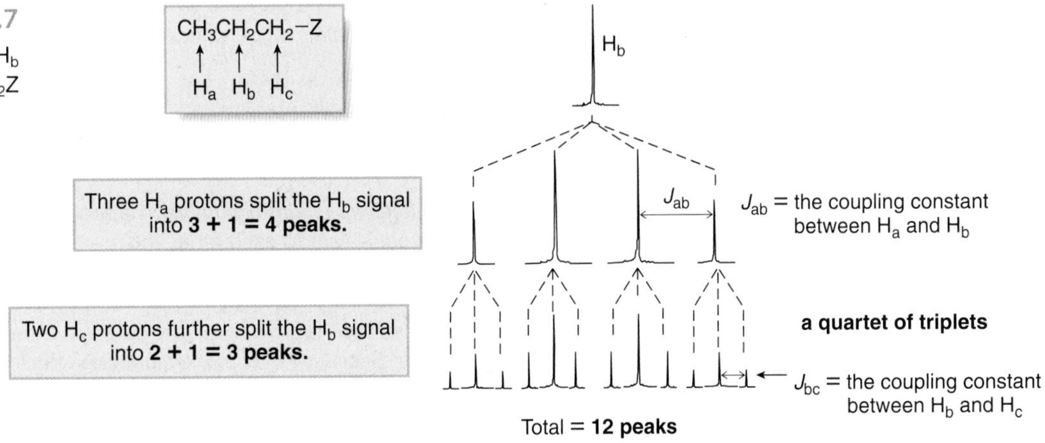
CH3CH2CH2–Z
Ha Hb Hc
Hb
Three Ha protons split the Hb signal into 3 + 1 = 4 peaks.
Jab
Jab = the coupling constant between Ha and Hb
Two Hc protons further split the Hb signal into 2 + 1 = 3 peaks.
a quartet of triplets
Jbc = the coupling constant between Hb and Hc
Total = 12 peaks

Figure 14.7
A splitting diagram for the H_b protons in $CH_3CH_2CH_2Z$

- The H_b signal is split into 12 peaks, a quartet of triplets. The number of peaks actually seen for the signal depends on the relative size of the coupling constants, J_{ab} and J_{bc}. When $J_{ab} >> J_{bc}$, as drawn in this diagram, all 12 lines of the pattern are visible. When J_{ab} and J_{bc} are similar in magnitude, peaks overlap and fewer lines are observed.

The ^{1}H NMR spectrum of 1-bromopropane ($CH_3CH_2CH_2Br$) illustrates the result of peak overlap (Figure 14.8).

$$\underset{H_a}{CH_3}\underset{H_b}{CH_2}\underset{H_c}{CH_2}-Br$$

$CH_3CH_2CH_2Br$ has three different types of protons—H_a, H_b, and H_c—so it exhibits three NMR signals. H_a and H_c are each triplets because they are adjacent to two H_b protons. H_b has protons on both adjacent carbons, and H_a and H_c are *not equivalent to each other.* The three H_a protons should split the H_b signal into four peaks, and the two H_c protons should split each of these four peaks into three peaks—that is, the NMR signal due to H_b should once again consist of $4 \times 3 =$ **12 peaks.** However, since $J_{ab} = J_{bc}$ in this case, peak overlap occurs and a multiplet of only six peaks is observed.

In $CH_3CH_2CH_2Br$, **the *n* protons on one adjacent carbon and the *m* protons on the other adjacent carbon split the observed signal into *n* + *m* + 1 peaks.** In other words, the 3 H_a protons and 2 H_c protons split the NMR signal into 3 + 2 + 1 = 6 peaks, as shown in the sextet in Figure 14.8.

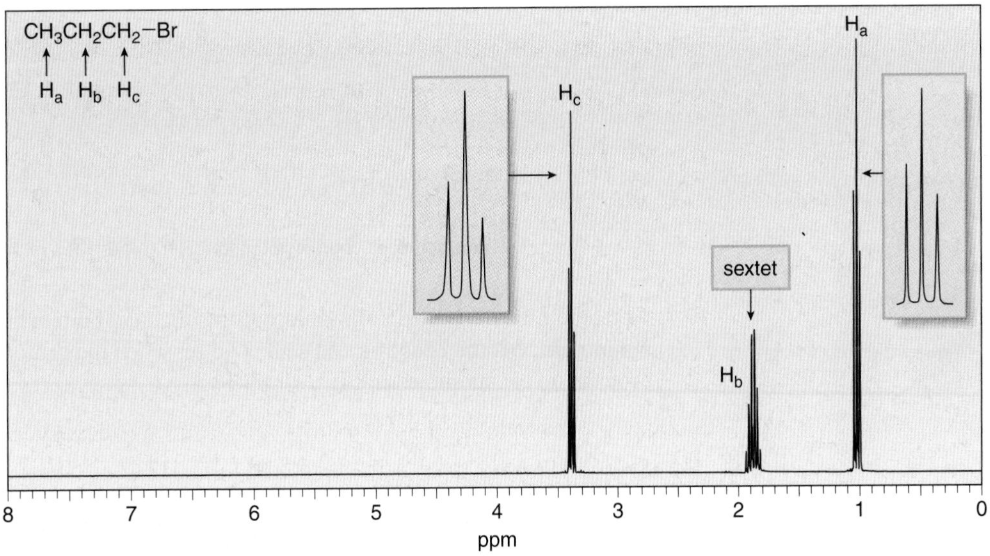
CH3CH2CH2–Br
Ha Hb Hc
Ha
Hc
sextet
Hb
8
7
6
5
4
3
2
1
0
ppm

Figure 14.8
The ^{1}H NMR spectrum of 1-bromopropane, $CH_3CH_2CH_2Br$

- H_a and H_c are both triplets.
- The signal for H_b appears as a multiplet of six peaks (a sextet), due to peak overlap.

Sample Problem 14.6 How many peaks are present in the NMR signal of each indicated proton?

a. $ClCH_2CH_2CH_2Cl$ b. $ClCH_2CH_2CH_2Br$

Solution

a. $ClCH_2CH_2CH_2Cl$
H_a H_b H_a

- H_b has two H_a protons on each adjacent C. Because the four H_a protons are equivalent to each other, the $n + 1$ rule can be used to determine splitting: 4 + 1 = **5 peaks,** a quintet.

b. $ClCH_2CH_2CH_2Br$
H_a H_b H_c

- H_b has two H_a protons on one adjacent C and two H_c protons on the other. Because H_a and H_c are not equivalent to each other, the maximum number of peaks for $H_b = (n + 1)(m + 1) = (2 + 1)(2 + 1) =$ **9 peaks.** However, since this molecule has a flexible alkyl chain, it is likely that J_{ab} and J_{bc} are very similar, so that peak overlap occurs. In this case, the number of peaks for $H_b = n + m + 1 = 2 + 2 + 1 =$ **5 peaks.**

Problem 14.16 How many peaks are present in the NMR signal of each indicated proton?

a. $(CH_3)_2CHCO_2CH_3$ b. $CH_3CH_2CH_2CH_2CH_3$ c. 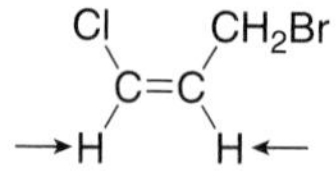 d. 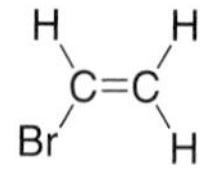 (all H atoms)

Problem 14.17 Describe the ^{1}H NMR spectrum of each compound. State how many NMR signals are present, the splitting pattern for each signal, and the approximate chemical shift.

a. $CH_3OCH_2CH_3$ c. $CH_3OCH_2CH_2CH_2OCH_3$

b. 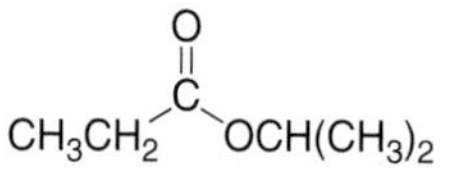 d. 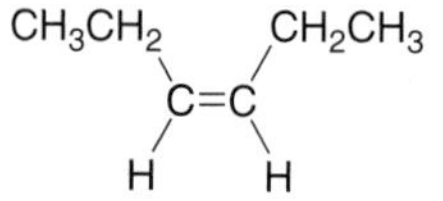

14.8 Spin–Spin Splitting in Alkenes

Protons on carbon–carbon double bonds often give characteristic splitting patterns. A disubstituted double bond can have two **geminal protons** (on the same carbon atom), two **cis protons,** or two **trans protons.** When these protons are different, each proton splits the NMR signal of the other, so that each proton appears as a doublet. **The magnitude of the coupling constant *J* for these doublets depends on the arrangement of hydrogen atoms.**

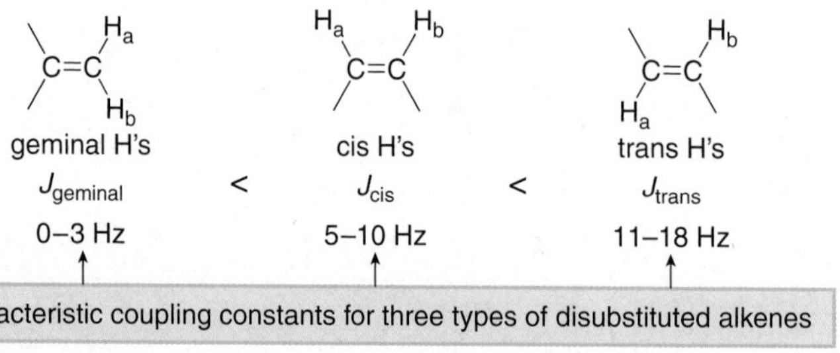
geminal H's
cis H's
trans H's
$J_{geminal}$ < J_{cis} < J_{trans}
0–3 Hz
5–10 Hz
11–18 Hz
characteristic coupling constants for three types of disubstituted alkenes

Thus, the *E* and *Z* isomers of 3-chloropropenoic acid both exhibit two doublets for the two alkenyl protons, but the coupling constant is larger when the protons are trans compared to when the protons are cis, as shown in Figure 14.9.

Figure 14.9
^1H NMR spectra for the alkenyl protons of (*E*)- and (*Z*)-3-chloropropenoic acid

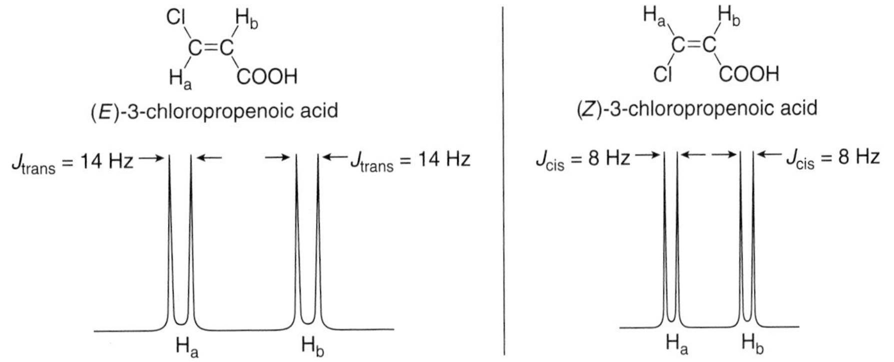

- Although both (*E*)- and (*Z*)-3-chloropropenoic acid show two doublets in their ^1H NMR spectra for their alkenyl protons, $J_{trans} > J_{cis}$.

When a double bond is monosubstituted, there are three nonequivalent protons, and the pattern is more complicated because all three protons are coupled to each other. For example, vinyl acetate ($CH_2{=}CHOCOCH_3$) has four different types of protons, three of which are bonded to the double bond. Besides the singlet for the CH_3 group, each proton on the double bond is coupled to two other different protons on the double bond, giving the spectrum in Figure 14.10.

- H_b has two nearby nonequivalent protons that split its signal, the geminal proton H_c and the trans proton H_d. H_d splits the H_b signal into a doublet, and the H_c proton splits the doublet into two doublets. This pattern of four peaks is called a **doublet of doublets.**
- H_c has two nearby nonequivalent protons that split its signal, the geminal proton H_b and the cis proton H_d. H_d splits the H_c signal into a doublet, and the H_b proton splits the doublet into two doublets, forming another **doublet of doublets.**
- H_d has two nearby nonequivalent protons that split its signal, the trans proton H_b and the cis proton H_c. H_b splits the H_d signal into a doublet, and the H_c proton splits the doublet into two doublets, forming another **doublet of doublets.**

Figure 14.10
The ^1H NMR spectrum of vinyl acetate ($CH_2{=}CHOCOCH_3$)

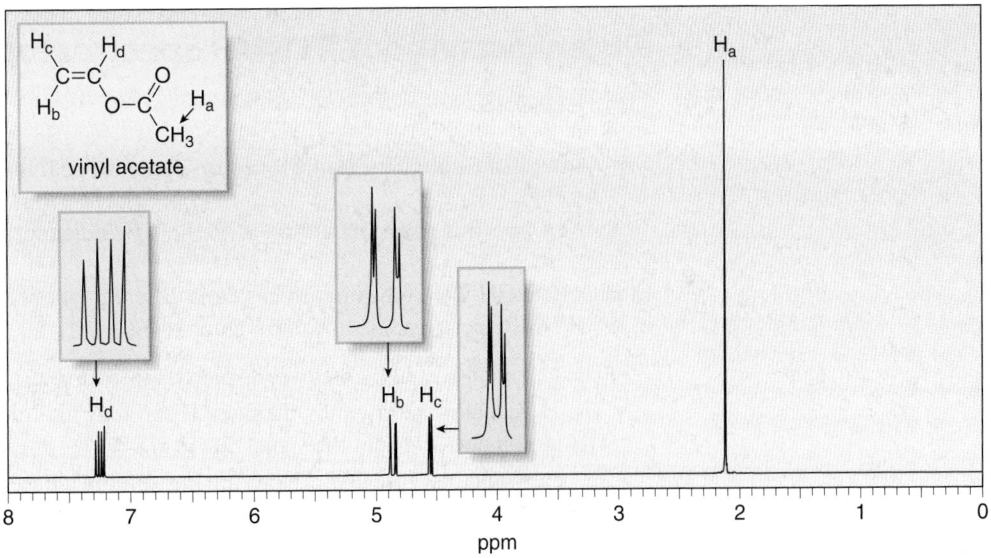

Vinyl acetate is polymerized to poly(vinyl acetate) (Problem 15.28), a polymer used in paints, glues, and adhesives.

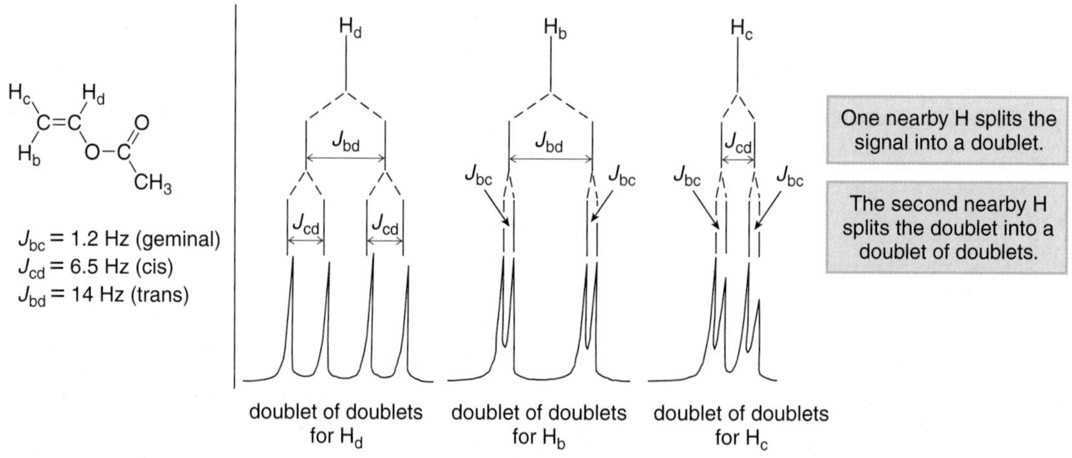

J_{bc} = 1.2 Hz (geminal)
J_{cd} = 6.5 Hz (cis)
J_{bd} = 14 Hz (trans)
One nearby H splits the signal into a doublet.
The second nearby H splits the doublet into a doublet of doublets.
doublet of doublets for H_d
doublet of doublets for H_b
doublet of doublets for H_c

Figure 14.11 Splitting diagram for the alkenyl protons in vinyl acetate (CH_2=CHOCOCH$_3$)

Splitting diagrams for the three alkenyl protons in vinyl acetate are drawn in Figure 14.11. Note that each pattern is different in appearance because the magnitude of the coupling constants forming them is different.

Problem 14.18 Draw a splitting diagram for H_b in *trans*-1,3-dichloropropene, given that J_{ab} = 13.1 Hz and J_{bc} = 7.2 Hz.

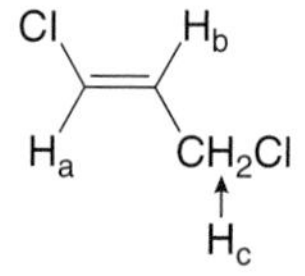

trans-1,3-dichloropropene

Problem 14.19 Identify **A** and **B,** isomers of molecular formula $C_3H_4Cl_2$, from the given ^{1}H NMR data: Compound **A** exhibits signals at 1.75 (doublet, 3 H, J = 6.9 Hz) and 5.89 (quartet, 1 H, J = 6.9 Hz) ppm. Compound **B** exhibits signals at 4.16 (singlet, 2 H), 5.42 (doublet, 1 H, J = 1.9 Hz), and 5.59 (doublet, 1 H, J = 1.9 Hz) ppm.

14.9 Other Facts About ^{1}H NMR Spectroscopy

14.9A OH Protons

- **Under usual conditions, an OH proton does not split the NMR signal of adjacent protons.**
- **The signal due to an OH proton is not split by adjacent protons.**

Ethanol (CH_3CH_2OH), for example, has three different types of protons, so there are three signals in its ^{1}H NMR spectrum, as shown in Figure 14.12.

- The H_a signal is split by the two H_b protons into three peaks, a **triplet.**
- The H_b signal is split by only the three H_a protons into four peaks, a **quartet.** The adjacent OH proton does *not* split the signal due to H_b.
- H_c is a **singlet** because OH protons are *not* split by adjacent protons.

Why is a proton bonded to an oxygen atom a singlet in a ^{1}H NMR spectrum? Protons on electronegative elements rapidly **exchange** between molecules in the presence of trace amounts of

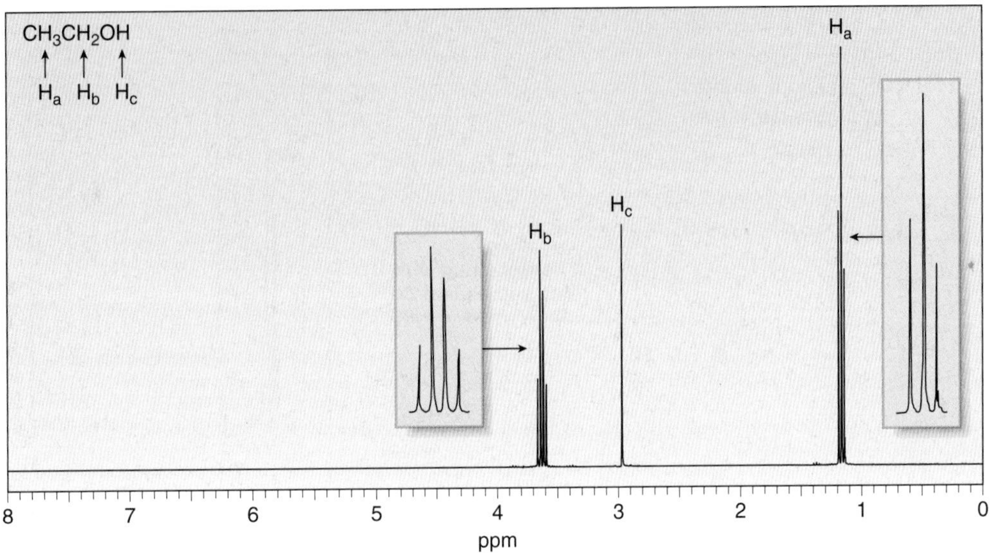

Figure 14.12 The ¹H NMR spectrum of ethanol (CH_3CH_2OH)

acid or base. It is as if the CH_2 group in ethanol never "feels" the presence of the OH proton, because the OH proton is rapidly moving from one molecule to another. We therefore see a peak due to the OH proton, but it is a single peak with no splitting. This phenomenon usually occurs with NH and OH protons.

Problem 14.20 How many signals are present in the ¹H NMR spectrum for each molecule? What splitting is observed in each signal: (a) $(CH_3)_3CCH_2OH$; (b) $CH_3CH_2CH_2OH$; (c) $(CH_3)_2CHNH_2$?

14.9B Cyclohexane Conformations

How does the rotation around carbon–carbon σ bonds and the ring flip of cyclohexane rings affect an NMR spectrum? Because these processes are rapid at room temperature, an NMR spectrum records an **average** of all conformations that interconvert.

Thus, even though each cyclohexane carbon has two different types of hydrogens—one axial and one equatorial—the two chair forms of cyclohexane rapidly interconvert them, and an **NMR spectrum shows a single signal for the average environment** that it "sees."

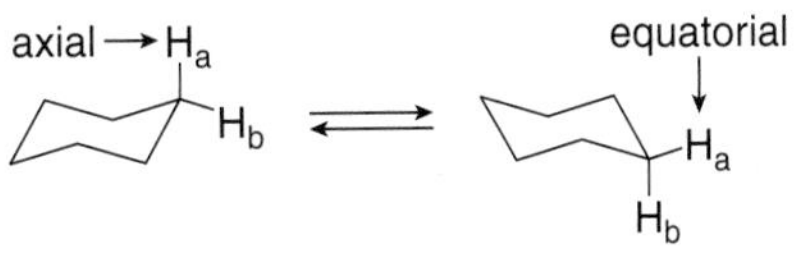

Axial and equatorial H's rapidly interconvert. NMR sees an average environment and shows one signal.

14.9C Protons on Benzene Rings

We will learn more about the spectroscopic absorptions of benzene derivatives in Chapter 17.

Benzene has six equivalent, deshielded protons and exhibits a single peak in its ¹H NMR spectrum at 7.27 ppm. Monosubstituted benzene derivatives—that is, benzene rings with one H atom replaced by another substituent Z—contain five deshielded protons that are no longer all equivalent to each other. The identity of Z determines the appearance of this region of a ¹H NMR spectrum (6.5–8 ppm), as shown in Figure 14.13. We will not analyze the splitting patterns observed for the ring protons of monosubstituted benzenes.

Figure 14.13
The 6.5–8 ppm region of the ^1H NMR spectrum of three benzene derivatives

A benzene ring with one substituent Z

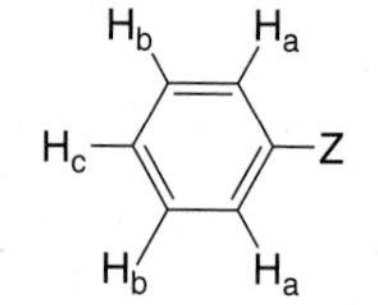

A monosubstituted benzene ring has three different types of H atoms: H_a, H_b, and H_c.

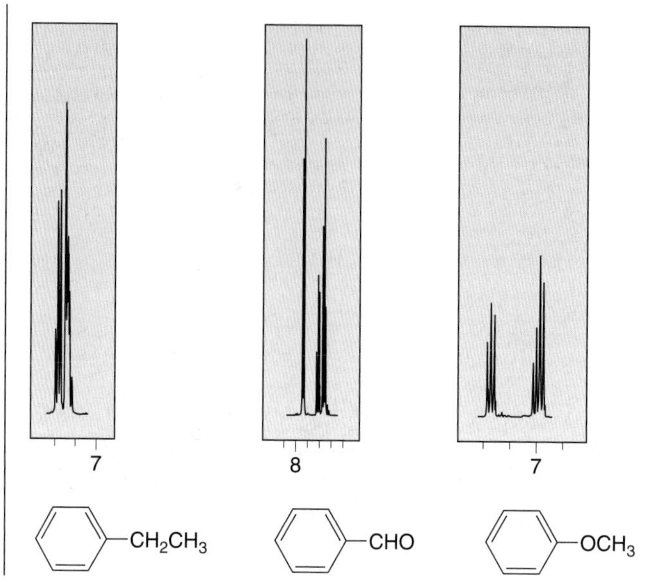

- The appearance of the signals in the 6.5–8 ppm region of the ^1H NMR spectrum depends on the identity of Z in C_6H_5Z.

Problem 14.21 What protons in alcohol **A** give rise to each signal in its ^1H NMR spectrum? Explain all splitting patterns observed for absorptions between 0–7 ppm.

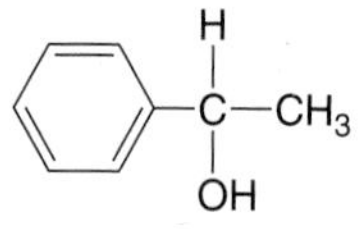

A

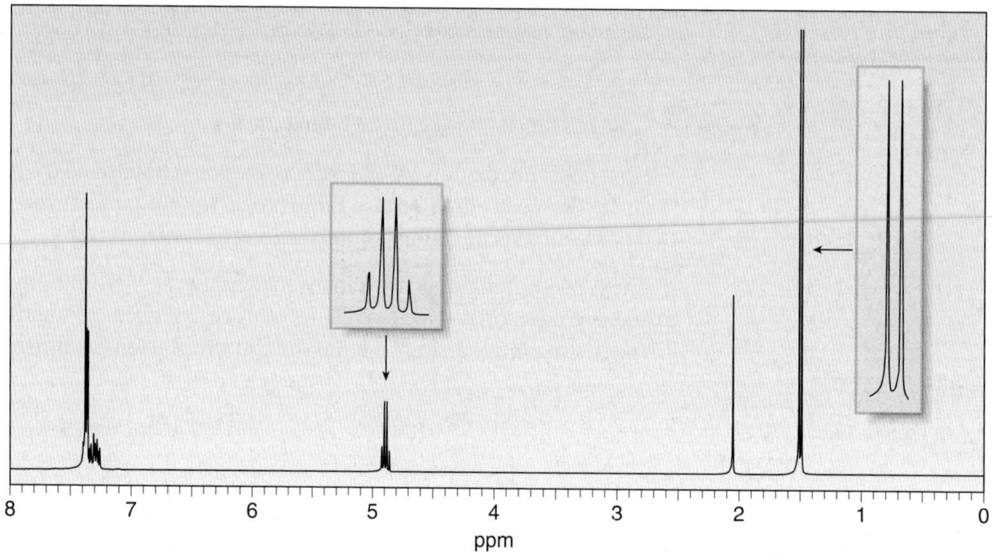

Problem 14.22 How many peaks are observed in the ^1H NMR signal for each proton shown in red in palau'amine, the complex chapter-opening molecule?

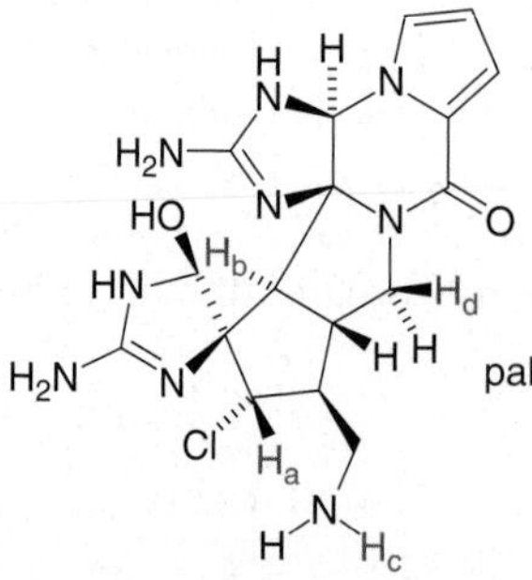

palau'amine

14.10 Using ^{1}H NMR to Identify an Unknown

Once we know a compound's molecular formula from its mass spectral data and the identity of its functional group from its IR spectrum, we can then use its ^{1}H NMR spectrum to determine its structure. A suggested procedure is illustrated for compound **X,** whose molecular formula ($C_4H_8O_2$) and functional group (C=O) were determined in Section 13.8.

How To Use ^{1}H NMR Data to Determine a Structure

Example **Using its ^{1}H NMR spectrum, determine the structure of an unknown compound X that has molecular formula $C_4H_8O_2$ and contains a C=O absorption in its IR spectrum.**

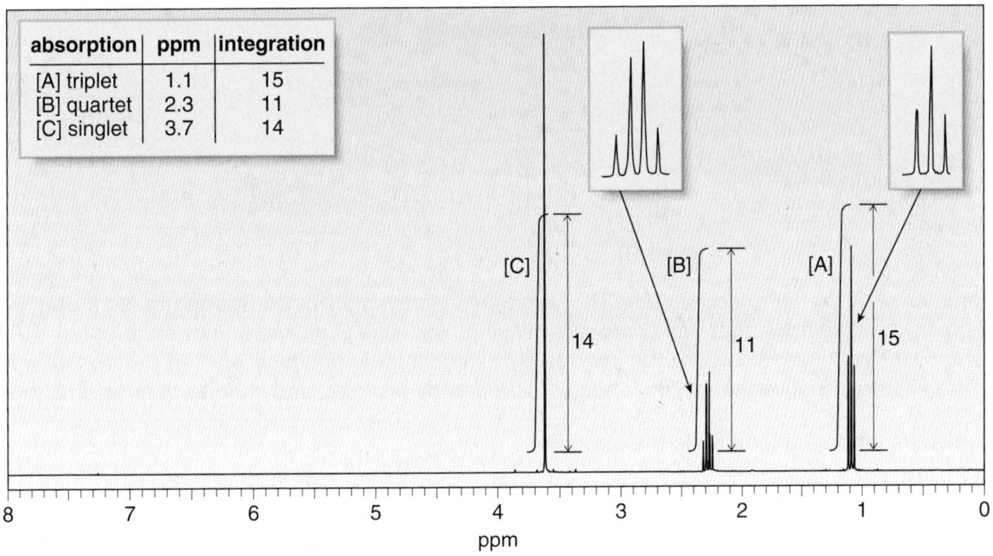
absorption | ppm | integration
[A] triplet | 1.1 | 15
[B] quartet | 2.3 | 11
[C] singlet | 3.7 | 14
[C]
[B]
[A]
14
11
15
8
7
6
5
4
3
2
1
0
ppm

Step [1] **Determine the number of different kinds of protons.**

- The number of NMR signals equals the number of different types of protons.
- This molecule has three NMR signals ([A], [B], and [C]) and therefore **three** types of protons (H_a, H_b, and H_c).

Step [2] **Use the integration data to determine the number of H atoms giving rise to each signal (Section 14.5).**

- Total number of integration units: 14 + 11 + 15 = 40 units
- Total number of protons = 8
- Divide: 40 units/8 protons = **5 units per proton**
- Then, divide each integration value by this answer (5 units per proton) and round to the nearest whole number.

$\frac{15}{5}$ = 3 H_a protons — signal [A] → Three equivalent H's usually means a **CH_3** group.

$\frac{11}{5}$ = 2.2 ≈ 2 H_b protons — signal [B] → Two equivalent H's usually means a **CH_2** group.

$\frac{14}{5}$ = 2.8 ≈ 3 H_c protons — signal [C] → Three equivalent H's usually means a **CH_3** group.

—Continued

How To, continued . . .

Step [3] Use individual splitting patterns to determine what carbon atoms are bonded to each other.

- Start with the singlets. Signal [C] is due to a CH_3 group with no adjacent nonequivalent H atoms. Possible structures include:

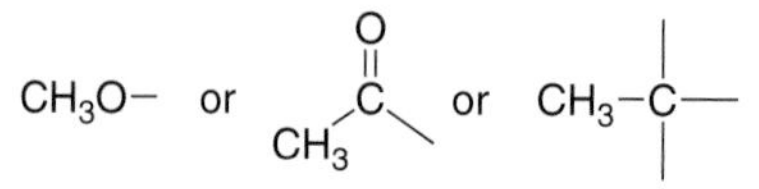

- Because signal [A] is a **triplet,** there must be **2 H's** (CH_2 group) on the adjacent carbon.
- Because signal [B] is a **quartet,** there must be **3 H's** (CH_3 group) on the adjacent carbon.
- This information suggests that **X** has an **ethyl** group ---→ CH_3CH_2–.

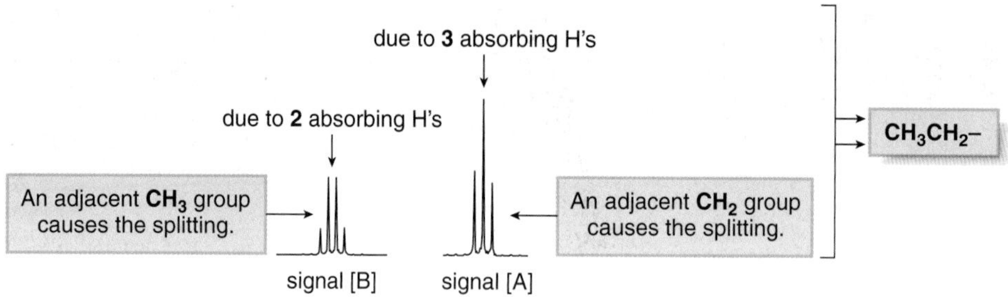

To summarize, **X** contains CH_3–, CH_3CH_2–, and C=O (from the IR). Comparing these atoms with the molecular formula shows that one O atom is missing. Because O atoms do not absorb in a ^{1}H NMR spectrum, their presence can only be inferred by examining the chemical shift of protons near them. O atoms are more electronegative than C, thus deshielding nearby protons, and shifting their absorption downfield.

Step [4] Use chemical shift data to complete the structure.

- Put the structure together in a manner that preserves the splitting data and is consistent with the reported chemical shifts.
- In this example, two isomeric structures (**A** and **B**) are possible for **X** considering the splitting data only:

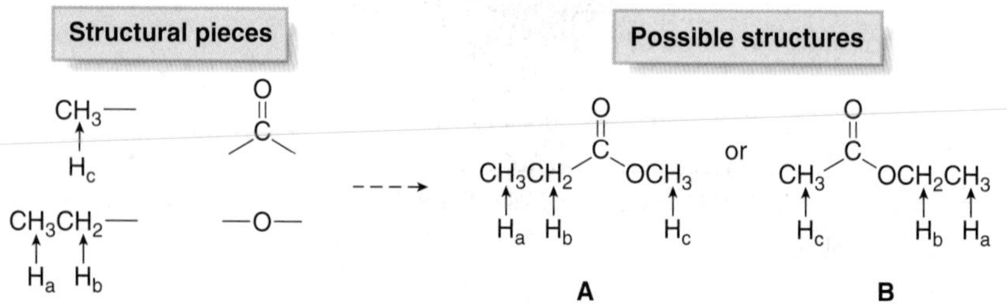

- Chemical shift information distinguishes the two possibilities. The electronegative O atom deshields adjacent H's, shifting them downfield between 3 and 4 ppm. If **A** is the correct structure, the singlet due to the CH_3 group (H_c) should occur downfield, whereas if **B** is the correct structure, the quartet due to the CH_2 group (H_b) should occur downfield.
- Because the NMR of **X** has a singlet (not a quartet) at 3.7, **A is the correct structure.**

Problem 14.23 Propose a structure for a compound of molecular formula $C_7H_{14}O_2$ with an IR absorption at 1740 cm^{-1} and the following ^1H NMR data:

Absorption	ppm	Integration value
singlet	1.2	26
triplet	1.3	10
quartet	4.1	6

Problem 14.24 Propose a structure for a compound of molecular formula C_3H_8O with an IR absorption at 3600–3200 cm^{-1} and the following NMR spectrum:

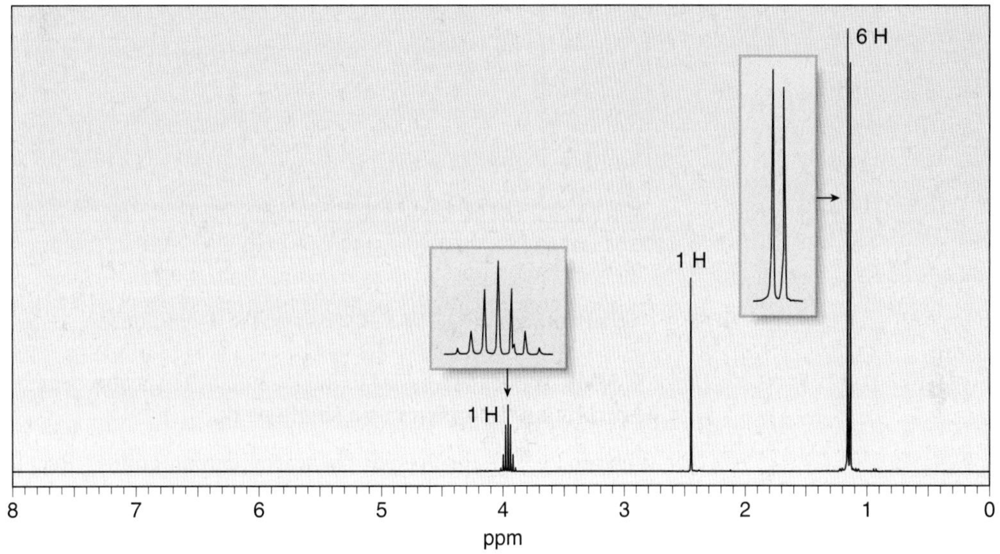

Problem 14.25 Identify products **A** and **B** from the given ^1H NMR data.

a. Treatment of $CH_2{=}CHCOCH_3$ with one equivalent of HCl forms compound **A. A** exhibits the following absorptions in its ^1H NMR spectrum: 2.2 (singlet, 3 H), 3.05 (triplet, 2 H), and 3.6 (triplet, 2 H) ppm. What is the structure of **A?**

b. Treatment of acetone [$(CH_3)_2C{=}O$] with dilute aqueous base forms **B.** Compound **B** exhibits four singlets in its ^1H NMR spectrum at 1.3 (6 H), 2.2 (3 H), 2.5 (2 H), and 3.8 (1 H) ppm. What is the structure of **B?**

14.11 ^{13}C NMR Spectroscopy

^{13}C NMR spectroscopy is also an important tool for organic structure analysis. The physical basis for ^{13}C NMR is the same as for ^1H NMR. When placed in a magnetic field, B_0, ^{13}C nuclei can align themselves with or against B_0. More nuclei are aligned with B_0 because this arrangement is lower in energy, but these nuclei can be made to spin flip against the applied field by applying RF radiation of the appropriate frequency.

^{13}C NMR spectra, like ^1H NMR spectra, plot peak intensity versus chemical shift, using TMS as the reference signal at 0 ppm. ^{13}C occurs in only 1.1% natural abundance, however, so ^{13}C NMR signals are much weaker than ^1H NMR signals. To overcome this limitation, modern spectrometers irradiate samples with many pulses of RF radiation and use mathematical tools to increase signal sensitivity and decrease background noise. The spectrum of acetic acid (CH_3COOH) illustrates the general features of a ^{13}C NMR spectrum.

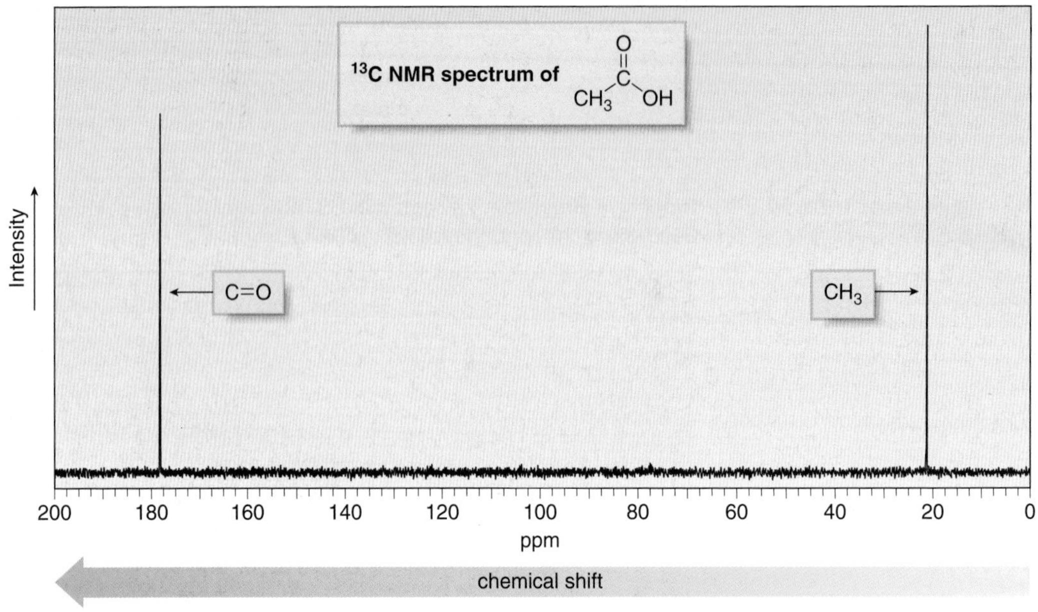

^{13}C NMR spectra are easier to analyze than ^{1}H spectra because signals are not split. **Each type of carbon atom appears as a single peak.**

Why aren't ^{13}C signals split by nearby carbon atoms? Recall from Section 14.6 that splitting occurs when two NMR active nuclei—like two protons—are close to each other. Because of the low natural abundance of ^{13}C nuclei (1.1%), the chance of two ^{13}C nuclei being bonded to each other is very small (0.01%), and so no carbon–carbon splitting is observed.

A ^{13}C NMR signal can also be split by nearby protons. This $^{1}H-^{13}C$ splitting is usually eliminated from a spectrum, however, by using an instrumental technique that decouples the proton–carbon interactions, so that every signal in a ^{13}C NMR spectrum is a singlet.

Two features of ^{13}C NMR spectra provide the most structural information: the **number of signals** observed and the **chemical shifts** of those signals.

14.11A ^{13}C NMR: Number of Signals

- **The number of signals in a ^{13}C spectrum gives the number of different types of carbon atoms in a molecule.**

Carbon atoms in the same environment give the same NMR signal, whereas carbons in different environments give different NMR signals. The ^{13}C NMR spectrum of CH_3COOH has two signals because there are two different types of carbon atoms—the C of the CH_3 group and the C of the carbonyl (C=O).

- **Because ^{13}C NMR signals are not split, the number of signals equals the number of lines in the ^{13}C NMR spectrum.**

Thus, the ^{13}C NMR spectra of dimethyl ether, chloroethane, and methyl acetate exhibit one, two, and three lines, respectively, because these compounds contain one, two, and three different types of carbon atoms.

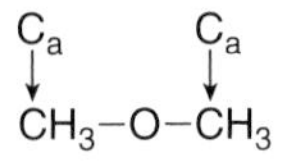
Ca
Ca
CH3–O–CH3
dimethyl ether

1 ^{13}C NMR signal
Both C's are equivalent.

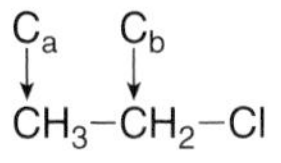
Ca
Cb
CH3–CH2–Cl
chloroethane

2 ^{13}C NMR signals

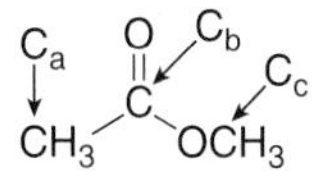
Ca
O
Cb
Cc
C
CH3
OCH3
methyl acetate

3 ^{13}C NMR signals

In contrast to what occurs in proton NMR, peak intensity is not proportional to the number of absorbing carbons, so ^{13}C NMR signals are not integrated.

Sample Problem 14.7 How many lines are observed in the ^{13}C NMR spectrum of each compound?

a. $CH_3CH_2CH_2CH_2CH_3$

b. 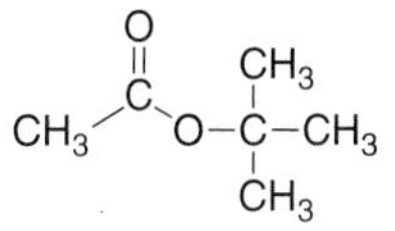
O
C
CH3
CH3
O–C–CH3
CH3

c. 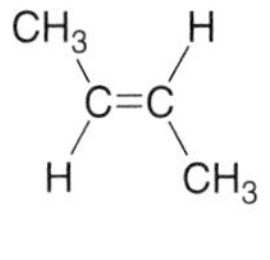
CH3
H
C=C
H
CH3

Solution

The number of different types of carbons equals the number of lines in a ^{13}C NMR spectrum.

a. 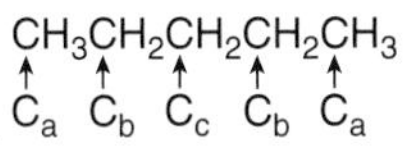
CH3CH2CH2CH2CH3
Ca Cb Cc Cb Ca

3 types of C's
3 ^{13}C NMR signals

b. 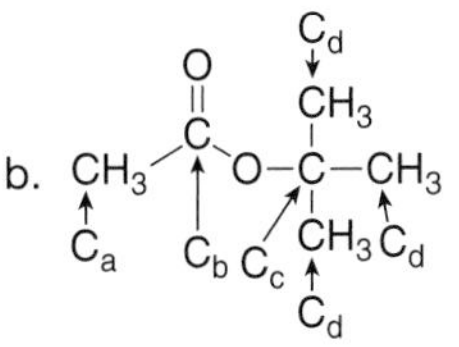
Cd
O
CH3
C
CH3
O–C–CH3
CH3
Ca
Cb
Cc
Cd
Cd

4 types of C's
4 ^{13}C NMR signals

c. 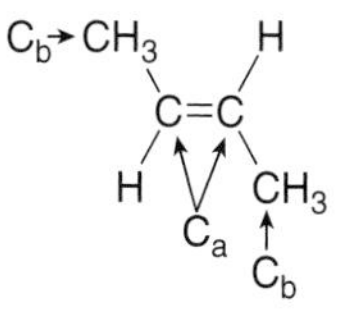
Cb
CH3
H
C=C
H
CH3
Ca
Cb

2 types of C's
2 ^{13}C NMR signals

Problem 14.26 How many lines are observed in the ^{13}C NMR spectrum of each compound?

a. $CH_3CH_2CH_2CH_3$

b. 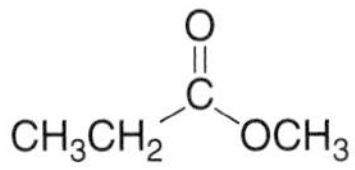
O
C
CH3CH2
OCH3

c. $CH_3CH_2CH_2{-}O{-}CH_2CH_2CH_3$

d. 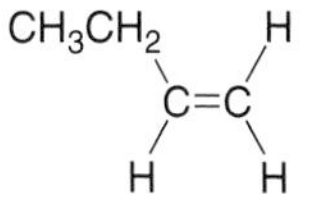
CH3CH2
H
C=C
H
H

Esters of chrysanthemic acid are obtained from the flowers of *Chrysanthemum cinerariifolium*. Because they are biodegradable and active against numerous insect species, these esters are widely used insecticides (see also Section 26.4).

Problem 14.27 Draw all constitutional isomers of molecular formula $C_3H_6Cl_2$.

a. How many signals does each isomer exhibit in its ^1H NMR spectrum?
b. How many lines does each isomer exhibit in its ^{13}C NMR spectrum?
c. When only the number of signals in both ^1H and ^{13}C NMR spectroscopy is considered, is it possible to distinguish all of these constitutional isomers?

Problem 14.28 Esters of chrysanthemic acid are naturally occurring insecticides. How many lines are present in the ^{13}C NMR spectrum of chrysanthemic acid?

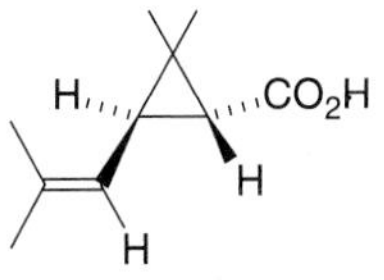
H
CO2H
H
H
chrysanthemic acid

14.11B ^{13}C NMR: Position of Signals

In contrast to the small range of chemical shifts in ^{1}H NMR (0–12 ppm usually), ^{13}C NMR absorptions occur over a much broader range, 0–220 ppm. The chemical shifts of carbon atoms in ^{13}C NMR depend on the same effects as the chemical shifts of protons in ^{1}H NMR:

- The sp^3 hybridized C atoms of alkyl groups are shielded and absorb upfield.
- Electronegative elements like halogen, nitrogen, and oxygen shift absorptions downfield.
- The sp^2 hybridized C atoms of alkenes and benzene rings absorb downfield.
- Carbonyl carbons are highly deshielded, and absorb farther downfield than other carbon types.

Table 14.5 lists common ^{13}C chemical shift values. The ^{13}C NMR spectra of 1-propanol ($CH_3CH_2CH_2OH$) and methyl acetate ($CH_3CO_2CH_3$) in Figure 14.14 illustrate these principles.

Table 14.5 Common ^{13}C Chemical Shift Values

Type of carbon	Chemical shift (ppm)	Type of carbon	Chemical shift (ppm)
—C—H (sp^3)	5–45	C=C	100–140
—C—Z (sp^3) Z = N, O, X	30–80	benzene ring C—	120–150
—C≡C—	65–100	C=O	160–210

Figure 14.14 Representative ^{13}C NMR spectra

a. 1-Propanol

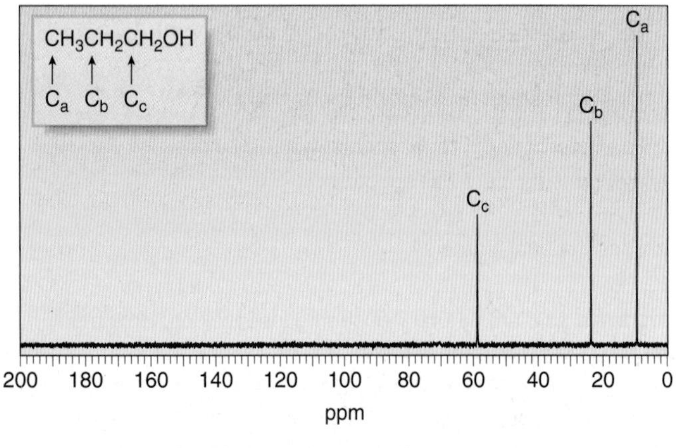

b. Methyl acetate

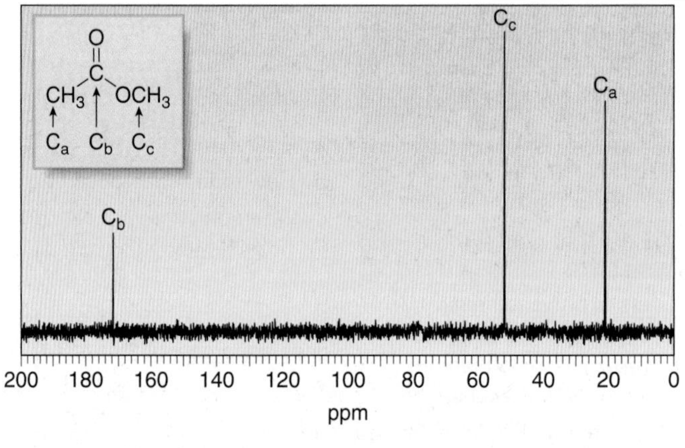

- The three types of C's in 1-propanol—identified as C_a, C_b, and C_c—give rise to three ^{13}C NMR signals.
- Deshielding increases with increasing proximity to the electronegative O atom, and the absorption shifts downfield; thus, in order of increasing chemical shift: $C_a < C_b < C_c$.

- The three types of C's in methyl acetate—identified as C_a, C_b, and C_c—give rise to three ^{13}C NMR signals.
- The carbonyl carbon (C_b) is highly deshielded, so it absorbs farthest downfield.
- C_a, an sp^3 hybridized C that is not bonded to an O atom, is the most shielded, and so it absorbs farthest upfield.
- Thus, in order of increasing chemical shift: $C_a < C_c < C_b$.

Problem 14.29 Which of the indicated carbon atoms in each molecule absorbs farther downfield?

a. CH3CH2OCH2CH3
b. BrCH2CHBr2
c.
O
C
H
OCH3
d. CH3CH=CH2

Problem 14.30 Identify the carbon atoms that give rise to each NMR signal.

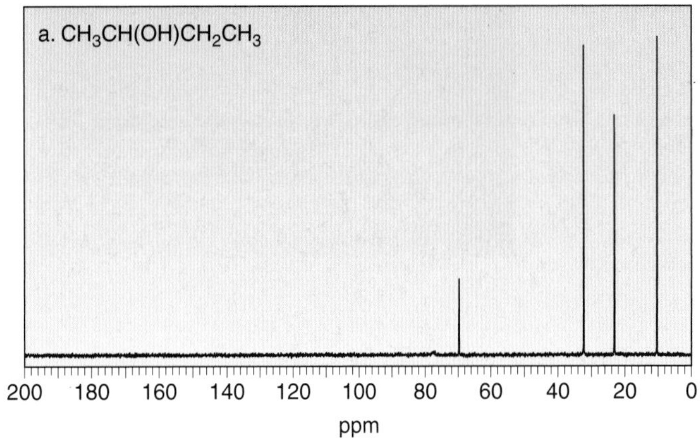
a. CH3CH(OH)CH2CH3
200 180 160 140 120 100 80 60 40 20 0
ppm

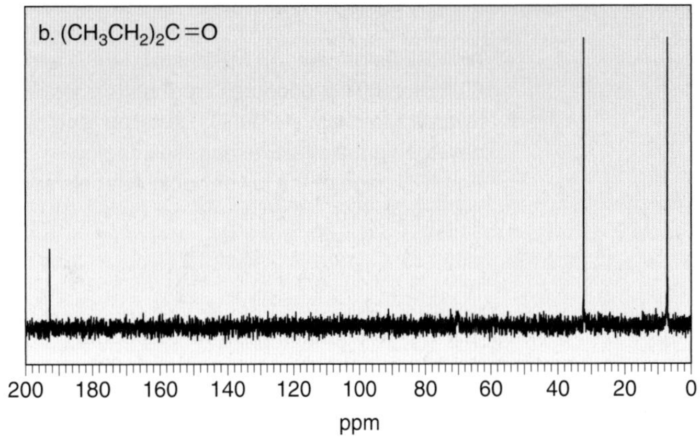
b. (CH3CH2)2C=O
200 180 160 140 120 100 80 60 40 20 0
ppm

Problem 14.31 A compound of molecular formula $C_4H_8O_2$ shows no IR peaks at 3600–3200 or 1700 cm^{-1}. It exhibits one singlet in its ^1H NMR spectrum at 3.69 ppm, and one line in its ^{13}C NMR spectrum at 67 ppm. What is the structure of this unknown?

Problem 14.32 Draw the structure of a compound of molecular formula C_4H_8O that has a signal in its ^{13}C NMR spectrum at > 160 ppm. Then draw the structure of an isomer of molecular formula C_4H_8O that has all of its ^{13}C NMR signals at < 160 ppm.

14.12 Magnetic Resonance Imaging (MRI)

Magnetic resonance imaging (MRI)—NMR spectroscopy in medicine—is a powerful diagnostic technique (Figure 14.15a). The "sample" is the patient, who is placed in a large cavity in a magnetic field, and then irradiated with RF energy. Because RF energy has very low frequency and low energy, the method is safer than X-rays or computed tomography (CT) scans that employ high-frequency, high-energy radiation that is known to damage living cells.

Figure 14.15 Magnetic resonance imaging

(a) (b)

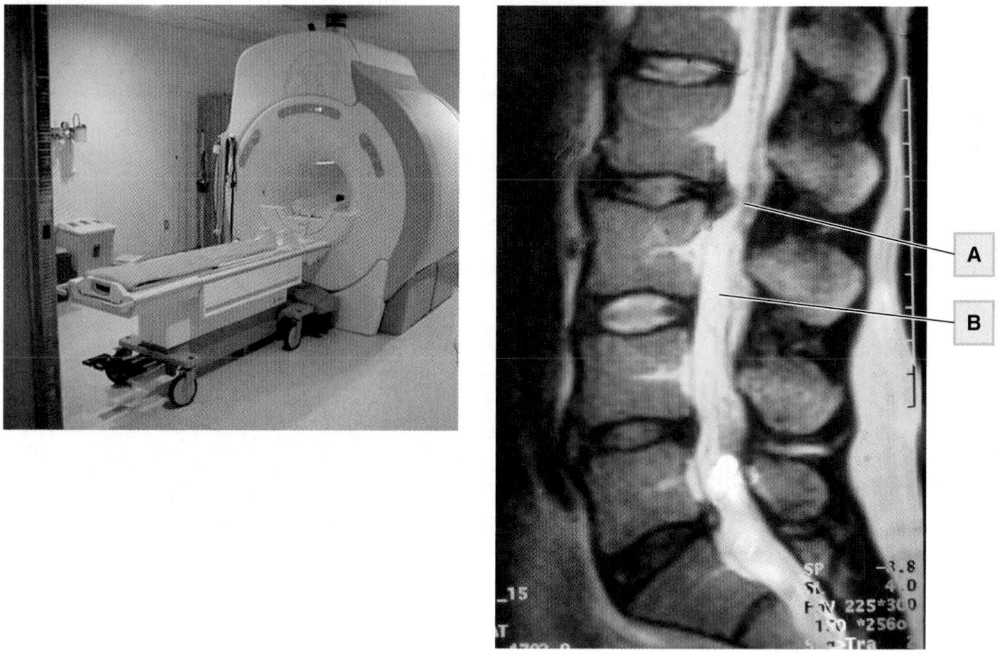
A
B

a. An MRI instrument: An MRI instrument is especially useful for visualizing soft tissue. In 2002, 60 million MRI procedures were performed. The 2003 Nobel Prize in Physiology or Medicine was awarded to chemist Paul C. Lauterbur and physicist Sir Peter Mansfield for their contributions in developing magnetic resonance imaging.
b. An MRI image of the lower back: **A** labels spinal cord compression from a herniated disc. **B** labels the spinal cord, which would not be visualized with conventional X-rays.

Living tissue contains protons (especially the H atoms in H_2O) in different concentrations and environments. When irradiated with RF energy, these protons are excited to a higher energy spin state, and then fall back to the lower energy spin state. These data are analyzed by a computer that generates a plot that delineates tissues of different proton density (Figure 14.15b). MRIs can be recorded in any plane. Moreover, because the calcium present in bones is not NMR active, an MRI instrument can "see through" bones such as the skull and visualize the soft tissue underneath.

KEY CONCEPTS

Nuclear Magnetic Resonance Spectroscopy

^{1}H NMR Spectroscopy

[1] The **number of signals** equals the number of different types of protons (14.2).

[2] The **position of a signal** (its chemical shift) is determined by shielding and deshielding effects.

- Shielding shifts an absorption upfield; deshielding shifts an absorption downfield.
- Electronegative atoms withdraw electron density, deshield a nucleus, and shift an absorption downfield (14.3).

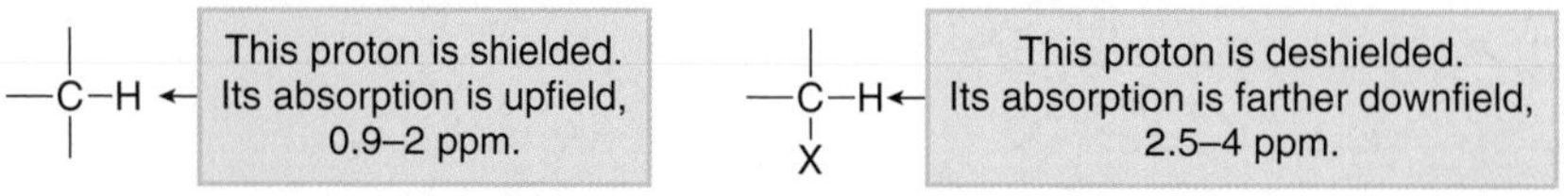
C–H
This proton is shielded.
Its absorption is upfield,
0.9–2 ppm.
C–H
X
This proton is deshielded.
Its absorption is farther downfield,
2.5–4 ppm.

- Loosely held π electrons can either shield or deshield a nucleus. Protons on benzene rings and double bonds are deshielded and absorb downfield, whereas protons on triple bonds are shielded and absorb upfield (14.4).

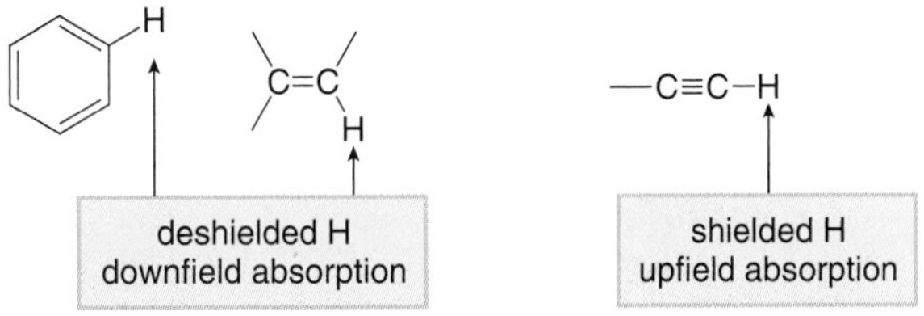
H
C=C
H
—C≡C—H
deshielded H
downfield absorption
shielded H
upfield absorption

[3] The **area under an NMR signal** is proportional to the number of absorbing protons (14.5).

[4] **Spin–spin splitting** tells about nearby nonequivalent protons (14.6–14.8).

- Equivalent protons do not split each other's signals.
- A set of n nonequivalent protons on the same carbon or adjacent carbons splits an NMR signal into $n + 1$ peaks.
- OH and NH protons do not cause splitting (14.9).
- When an absorbing proton has two sets of nearby nonequivalent protons that are equivalent to each other, use the $n + 1$ rule to determine splitting.
- When an absorbing proton has two sets of nearby nonequivalent protons that are not equivalent to each other, the number of peaks in the NMR signal = $(n + 1)(m + 1)$. In flexible alkyl chains, peak overlap often occurs, resulting in $n + m + 1$ peaks in an NMR signal.

^{13}C NMR Spectroscopy (14.11)

[1] **The number of signals equals the number of different types of carbon atoms.** All signals are **single peaks.**

[2] The relative position of ^{13}C signals is determined by shielding and deshielding effects.

- Carbons that are sp^3 hybridized are shielded and absorb upfield.
- Electronegative elements (N, O, and halogen) shift absorptions downfield.
- The carbons of alkenes and benzene rings absorb downfield.
- Carbonyl carbons are highly deshielded, and absorb farther downfield than other carbon types.

PROBLEMS

Problems Using Three-Dimensional Models

14.33 (a) How many ^{1}H NMR signals does each of the following compounds exhibit? (b) How many ^{13}C NMR signals does each compound exhibit?

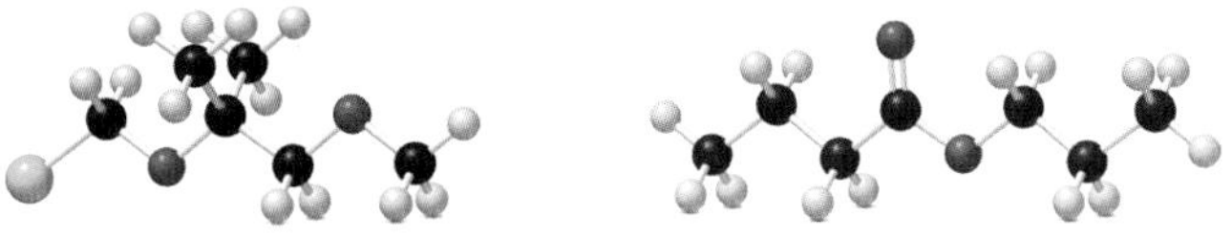

A B

14.34 (a) How many ^{1}H NMR signals does each compound show? (b) Into how many peaks is each signal split?

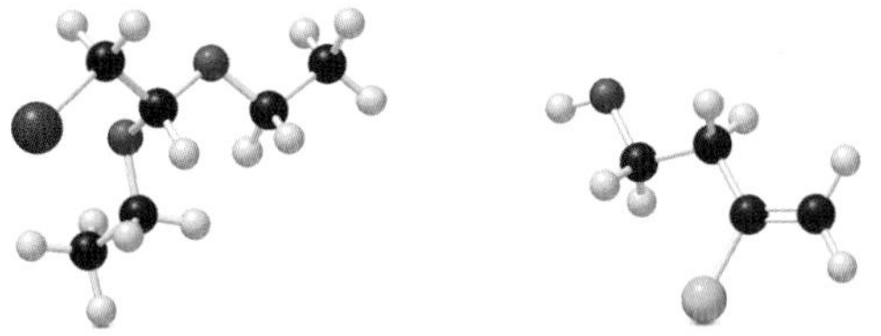

C D

¹H NMR Spectroscopy—Determining Equivalent Protons

14.35 How many different types of protons are present in each compound?

a. $(CH_3)_3CH$

b. $(CH_3)_3CC(CH_3)_3$

c. $CH_3CH_2OCH_2CH_2CH_2CH_2CH_3$

d. $CH_3CH{=}CH_2$

e. 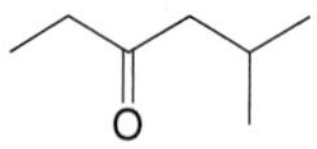

f. 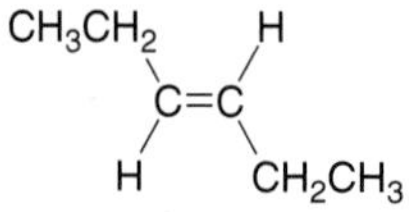

g. $CH_3CH_2CH_2OCH_2CH_2CH_3$

h. 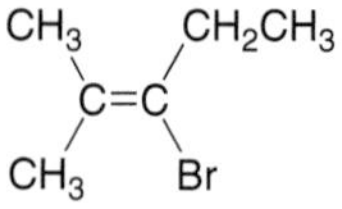

i. $CH_3CH(OH)CH_2CH_3$

j. 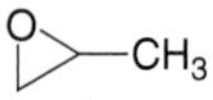

14.36 How many ¹H NMR signals does each compound give?

a. 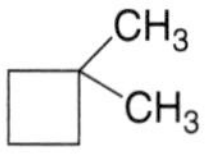

b. 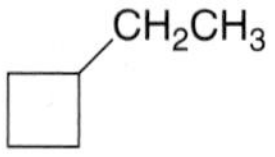

c. 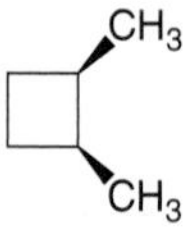

d. 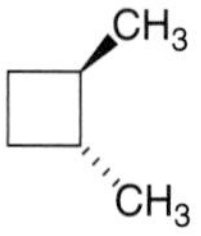

14.37 How many ¹H NMR signals does each natural product exhibit?

a. 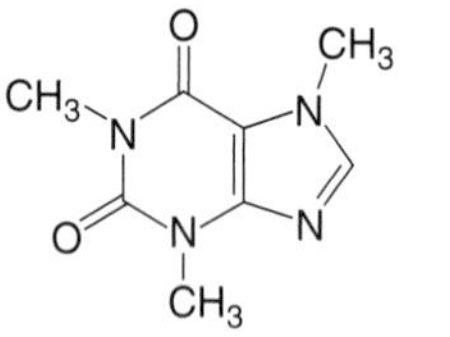

caffeine
(from coffee beans and tea leaves)

b. 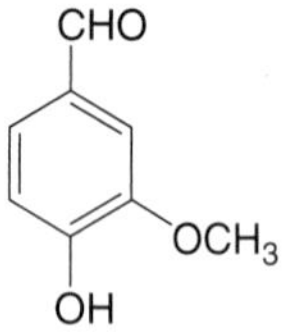

vanillin
(from the vanilla bean)

c. 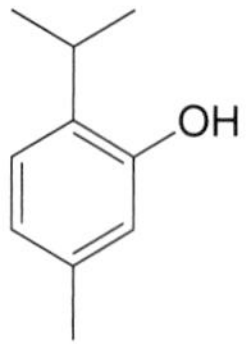

thymol
(from thyme)

d. 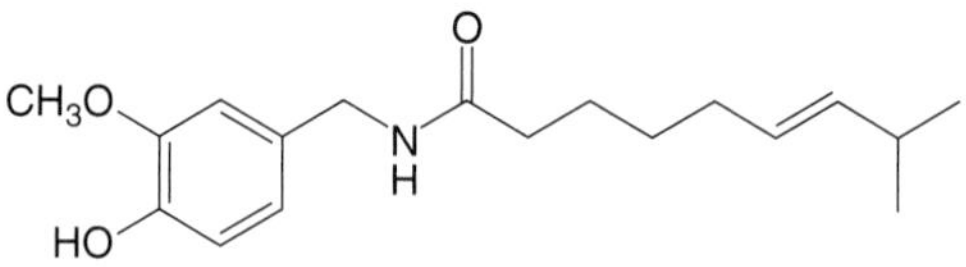

capsaicin
(from hot peppers)

¹H NMR—Chemical Shift and Integration

14.38 Using a 300 MHz NMR instrument:

a. How many Hz downfield from TMS is a signal at 2.5 ppm?

b. If a signal comes at 1200 Hz downfield from TMS, at what ppm does it occur?

c. If two peaks are separated by 2 ppm, how many Hz does this correspond to?

14.39 Acetone exhibits a singlet in its ¹H NMR spectrum at 2.16 ppm. If CH_2Cl_2 exhibits a singlet 1570 Hz downfield from acetone on a 500 MHz NMR spectrometer, what is the chemical shift of the singlet due to CH_2Cl_2?

14.40 Which of the indicated protons in each pair absorbs farther downfield?

a. $CH_3CH_2CH_2CH_2CH_3$ or $CH_3CH_2CH_2OCH_3$

b. $CH_3CH_2CH_2I$ or $CH_3CH_2CH_2F$

c. $CH_3OCH_2CH_3$ (↑ or ↑)

d. $CH_3CH_2CHBr_2$ or $CH_3CH_2CH_2Br$

14.41 A compound of molecular formula C_6H_{10} gives three signals in its ¹H NMR spectrum with the following integration units: 13, 33, 73 units. How many protons are responsible for each signal?

14.42 How could you use chemical shift and integration data in ¹H NMR spectroscopy to distinguish between each pair of compounds? The ¹H NMR spectrum of each compound contains only singlets.

a. $CH_3CO_2C(CH_3)_3$ and $CH_3CO_2CH_3$

b. $CH_3OCH_2CH_2OCH_3$ and $CH_3OCH_2OCH_3$

c. 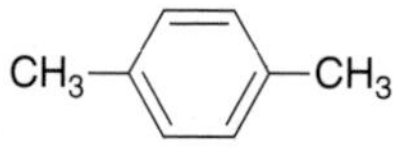

and

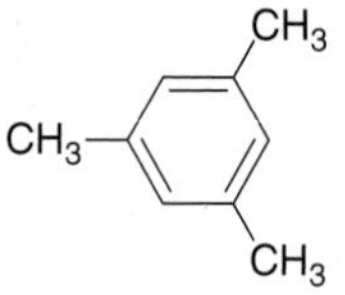

^{1}H NMR—Splitting

14.43 Which compounds give one singlet in the ^{1}H NMR spectrum?

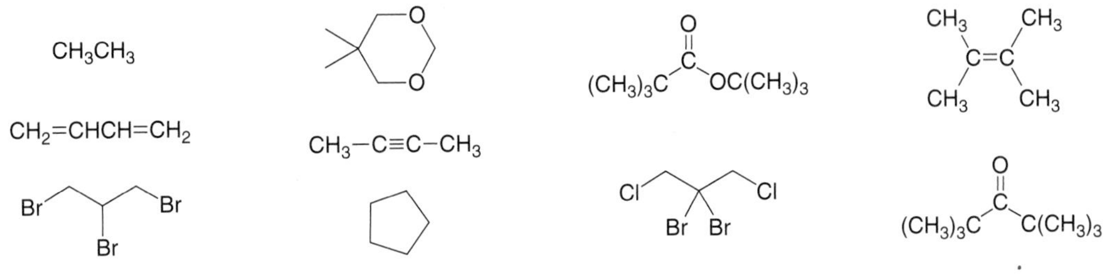

14.44 Into how many peaks will the signal for each of the indicated protons be split?

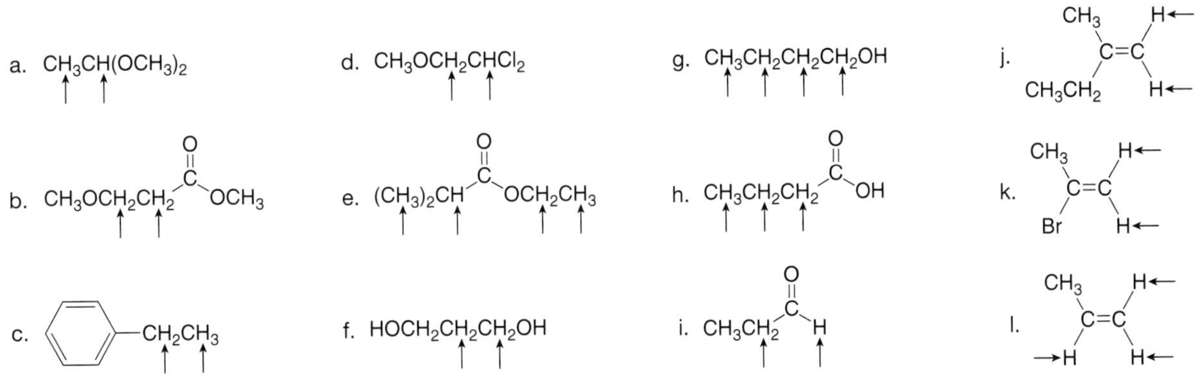

14.45 How can you use ^{1}H NMR spectroscopy to distinguish between $CH_2=C(Br)CO_2CH_3$ and methyl (2*E*)-3-bromo-2-propenoate, $BrCH=CHCO_2CH_3$?

14.46 Label the signals due to H_a, H_b, and H_c in the ^{1}H NMR spectrum of acrylonitrile ($CH_2=CHCN$). Draw a splitting diagram for the absorption due to the H_a proton.

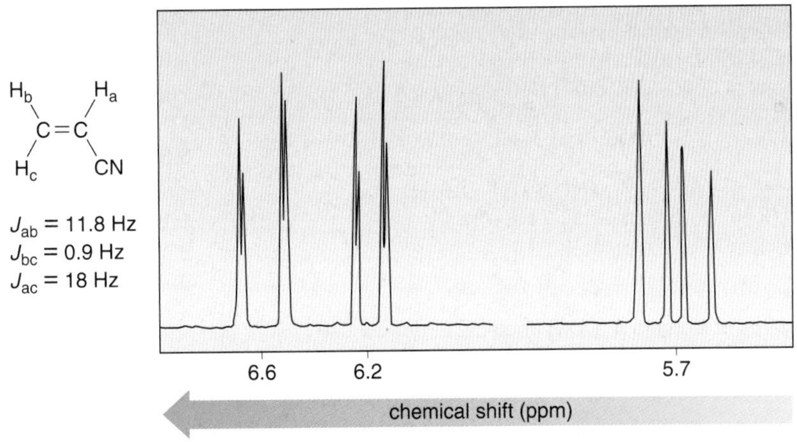
Hb
Ha
C=C
Hc
CN
Jab = 11.8 Hz
Jbc = 0.9 Hz
Jac = 18 Hz
6.6
6.2
5.7
chemical shift (ppm)

^{13}C NMR

14.47 Draw the four constitutional isomers having molecular formula C_4H_9Br and indicate how many different kinds of carbon atoms each has.

14.48 Which compounds in Problem 14.43 give one signal in their ^{13}C NMR spectra?

14.49 Explain why the carbonyl carbon of an aldehyde or ketone absorbs farther downfield than the carbonyl carbon of an ester in a ^{13}C NMR spectrum.

14.50 How many ^{13}C NMR signals does each compound exhibit?

a. $HC(CH_3)_3$

b. 

c. $CH_3OCH(CH_3)_2$

d. 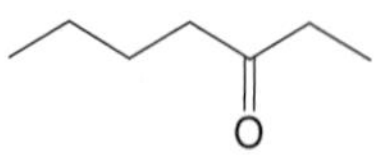

e. 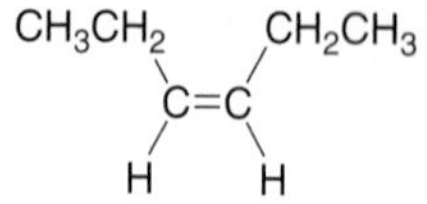

f. 

g. 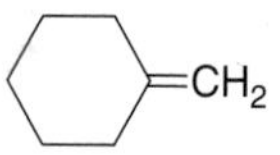

h. 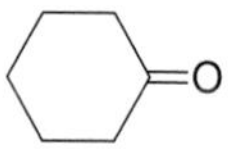

i. 

14.51 Rank the indicated carbon atoms in each compound in order of increasing chemical shift.

a. 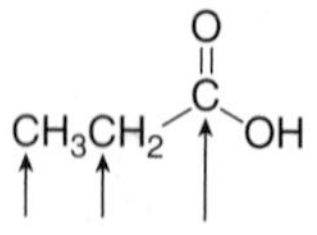

b. 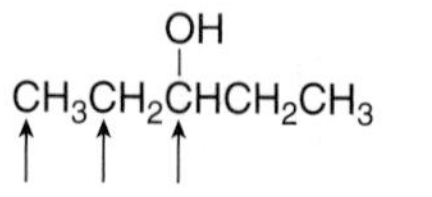

c. 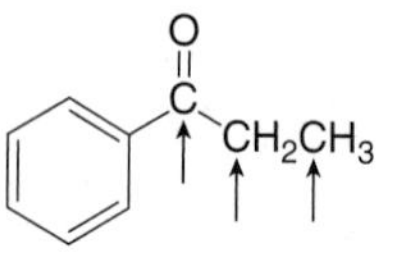

d. 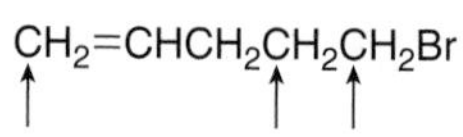

14.52 Identify the carbon atoms that give rise to the signals in the ^{13}C NMR spectrum of each compound.

a. $CH_3CH_2CH_2CH_2OH$; ^{13}C NMR: 14, 19, 35, and 62 ppm

b. $(CH_3)_2CHCHO$; ^{13}C NMR: 16, 41, and 205 ppm

c. $CH_2=CHCH(OH)CH_3$; ^{13}C NMR: 23, 69, 113, and 143 ppm

14.53 a. How many signals does dimethyl fumarate ($CH_3O_2CCH=CHCO_2CH_3$, with a trans C=C) exhibit in its ^{13}C NMR spectrum?

b. Draw the structure of an isomer of dimethyl fumarate that has each of the following number of signals in its ^{13}C NMR spectrum: [1] three; [2] four; [5] five.

Combined Spectroscopy Problems

Additional spectroscopy problems are located at the end of Chapters 15–23 and 25.

14.54 Propose a structure consistent with each set of spectral data:

a. $C_4H_8Br_2$: IR peak at 3000–2850 cm^{-1}; NMR (ppm):
1.87 (singlet, 6 H)
3.86 (singlet, 2 H)

b. $C_3H_6Br_2$: IR peak at 3000–2850 cm^{-1}; NMR (ppm):
2.4 (quintet)
3.5 (triplet)

c. $C_5H_{10}O_2$: IR peak at 1740 cm^{-1}; NMR (ppm):
1.15 (triplet, 3 H) 2.30 (quartet, 2 H)
1.25 (triplet, 3 H) 4.72 (quartet, 2 H)

d. $C_6H_{14}O$: IR peak at 3600–3200 cm^{-1}; NMR (ppm):
0.8 (triplet, 6 H) 1.5 (quartet, 4 H)
1.0 (singlet, 3 H) 1.6 (singlet, 1 H)

e. $C_6H_{14}O$: IR peak at 3000–2850 cm^{-1}; NMR (ppm):
1.10 (doublet, 30 units)
3.60 (septet, 5 units)

f. C_3H_6O: IR peak at 1730 cm^{-1}; NMR (ppm):
1.11 (triplet)
2.46 (multiplet)
9.79 (triplet)

14.55 Identify the structures of isomers **A** and **B** (molecular formula $C_9H_{10}O$).

Compound **A**: IR peak at 1742 cm^{-1}; ^1H NMR data (ppm) at 2.15 (singlet, 3 H), 3.70 (singlet, 2 H), and 7.20 (broad singlet, 5 H).

Compound **B**: IR peak at 1688 cm^{-1}; ^1H NMR data (ppm) at 1.22 (triplet, 3 H), 2.98 (quartet, 2 H), and 7.28–7.95 (multiplet, 5 H).

14.56 Reaction of $C_6H_5CH_2CH_2OH$ with CH_3COCl affords compound **W**, which has molecular formula $C_{10}H_{12}O_2$. **W** shows prominent IR absorptions at 3088–2897, 1740, and 1606 cm^{-1}. **W** exhibits the following signals in its ^1H NMR spectrum: 2.02 (singlet), 2.91 (triplet), 4.25 (triplet), and 7.20–7.35 (multiplet) ppm. What is the structure of **W?** We will learn about this reaction in Chapter 22.

14.57 Treatment of 2-methylpropanenitrile [$(CH_3)_2CHCN$] with $CH_3CH_2CH_2MgBr$, followed by aqueous acid, affords compound **V**, which has molecular formula $C_7H_{14}O$. **V** has a strong absorption in its IR spectrum at 1713 cm^{-1}, and gives the following ^1H NMR data: 0.91 (triplet, 3 H), 1.09 (doublet, 6 H), 1.6 (multiplet, 2 H), 2.43 (triplet, 2 H), and 2.60 (septet, 1 H) ppm. What is the structure of **V?** We will learn about this reaction in Chapter 22.

14.58 Compound **C** has a molecular ion in its mass spectrum at 146 and a prominent absorption in its IR spectrum at 1762 cm^{-1}. **C** shows the following ^1H NMR spectral data: 1.47 (doublet, 3 H), 2.07 (singlet, 6 H), and 6.84 (quartet, 1 H) ppm. What is the structure of **C?**

14.59 As we will learn in Chapter 20, reaction of $(CH_3)_2CO$ with $LiC\equiv CH$ followed by H_2O affords compound **D**, which has a molecular ion in its mass spectrum at 84 and prominent absorptions in its IR spectrum at 3600–3200, 3303, 2938, and 2120 cm^{-1}. **D** shows the following ^1H NMR spectral data: 1.53 (singlet, 6 H), 2.37 (singlet, 1 H), and 2.43 (singlet, 1 H) ppm. What is the structure of **D?**

14.60 Identify the structures of isomers **E** and **F** (molecular formula $C_4H_8O_2$).

Compound E: IR absorption at 1743 cm^{-1}

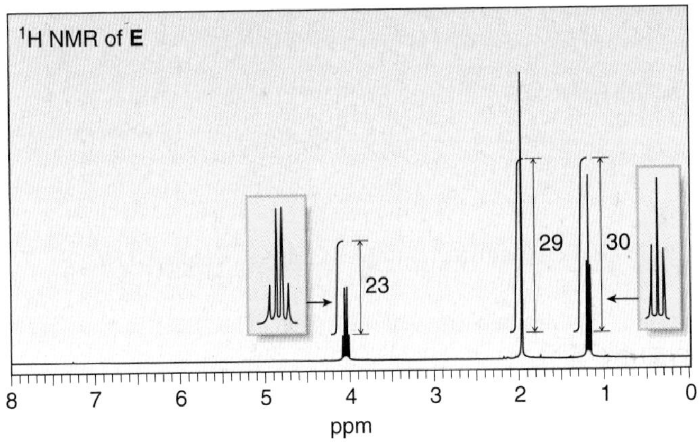

Compound F: IR absorption at 1730 cm^{-1}

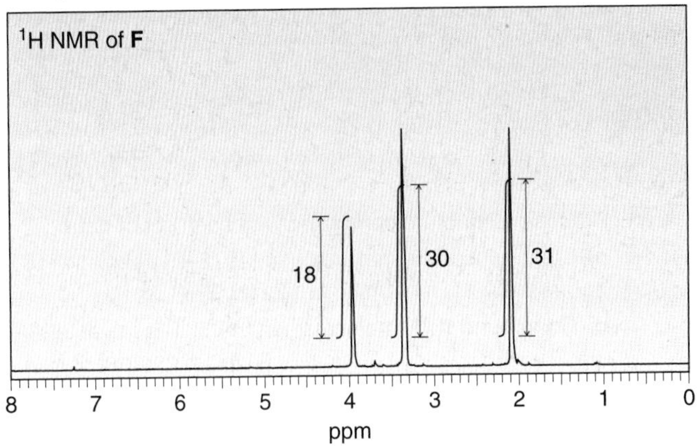

14.61 Identify the structures of isomers **H** and **I** (molecular formula $C_8H_{11}N$).

a. **Compound H:** IR absorptions at 3365, 3284, 3026, 2932, 1603, and 1497 cm^{-1}

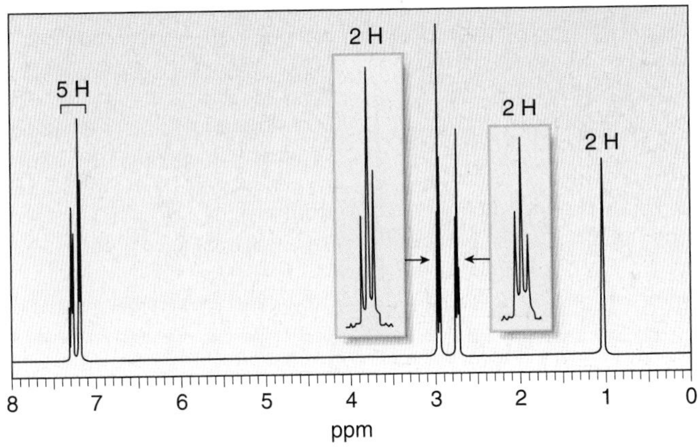

b. **Compound I:** IR absorptions at 3367, 3286, 3027, 2962, 1604, and 1492 cm^{-1}

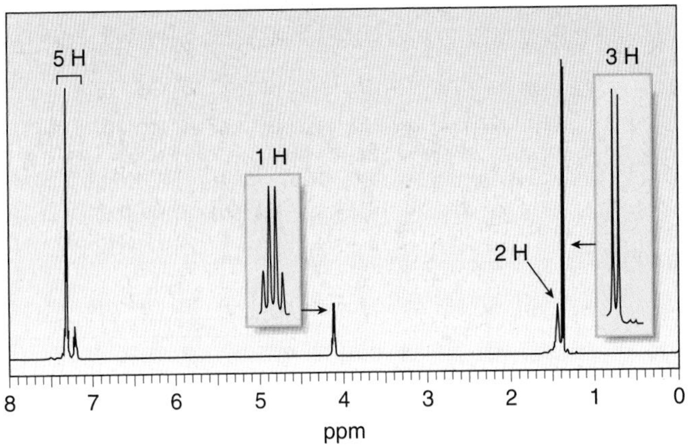

14.62 Propose a structure consistent with each set of data.

a. $C_9H_{10}O_2$: IR absorption at 1718 cm^{-1}

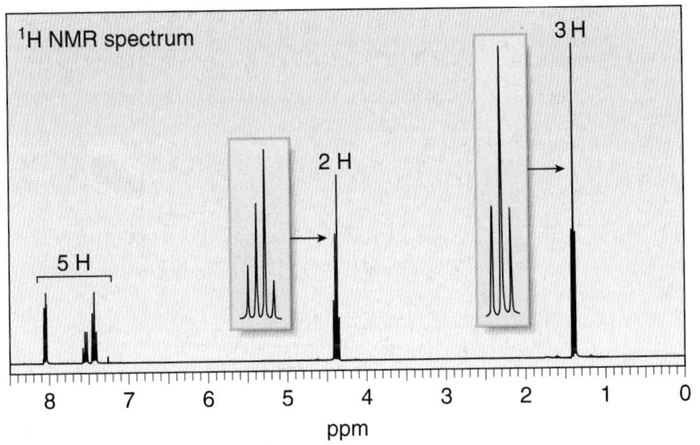

b. C_9H_{12}: IR absorption at 2850–3150 cm^{-1}

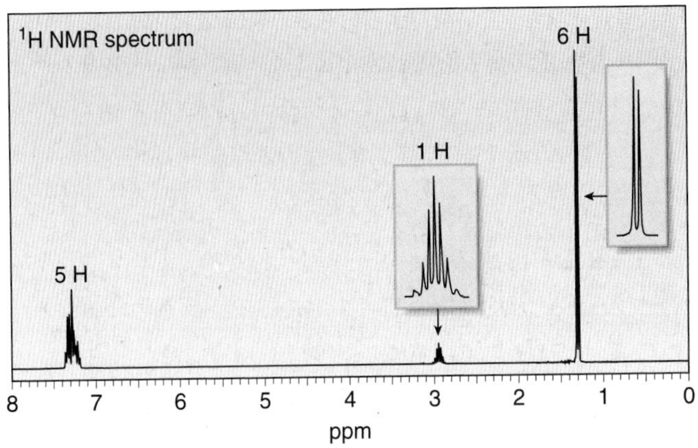

14.63 Reaction of $(CH_3)_3CCHO$ with $(C_6H_5)_3P{=}C(CH_3)OCH_3$, followed by treatment with aqueous acid, affords **R** ($C_7H_{14}O$). **R** has a strong absorption in its IR spectrum at 1717 cm^{-1} and three singlets in its ^1H NMR spectrum at 1.02 (9 H), 2.13 (3 H), and 2.33 (2 H) ppm. What is the structure of **R?** We will learn about this reaction in Chapter 21.

14.64 Reaction of aldehyde **D** with amino alcohol **E** in the presence of NaH forms **F** (molecular formula $C_{11}H_{15}NO_2$). **F** absorbs at 1730 cm^{-1} in its IR spectrum. **F** also shows eight lines in its ^{13}C NMR spectrum, and gives the following ^1H NMR spectrum: 2.32 (singlet, 6 H), 3.05 (triplet, 2 H), 4.20 (triplet, 2 H), 6.97 (doublet, 2 H), 7.82 (doublet, 2 H), and 9.97 (singlet, 1 H) ppm. Propose a structure for **F.** We will learn about this reaction in Chapter 18.

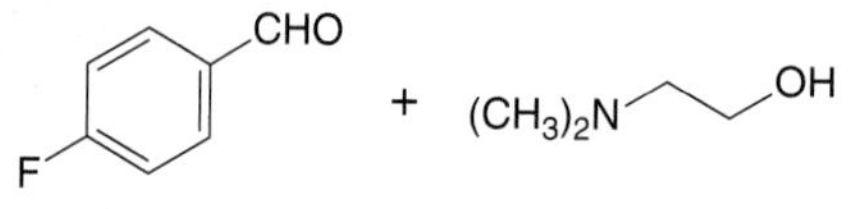

D **E**

14.65 Propose a structure consistent with each set of data.

a. Compound **J:** molecular ion at 72; IR peak at 1710 cm^{-1}; ^1H NMR data (ppm) at 1.0 (triplet, 3 H), 2.1 (singlet, 3 H), and 2.4 (quartet, 2 H)

b. Compound **K:** molecular ion at 88; IR peak at 3600–3200 cm^{-1}; ^1H NMR data (ppm) at 0.9 (triplet, 3 H), 1.2 (singlet, 6 H), 1.5 (quartet, 2 H), and 1.6 (singlet, 1 H)

14.66 In the presence of a small amount of acid, a solution of acetaldehyde (CH_3CHO) in methanol (CH_3OH) was allowed to stand and a new compound **L** was formed. **L** has a molecular ion in its mass spectrum at 90 and IR absorptions at 2992 and 2941 cm^{-1}. **L** shows three signals in its ^{13}C NMR at 19, 52, and 101 ppm. The ^1H NMR spectrum of **L** is given below. What is the structure of **L?**

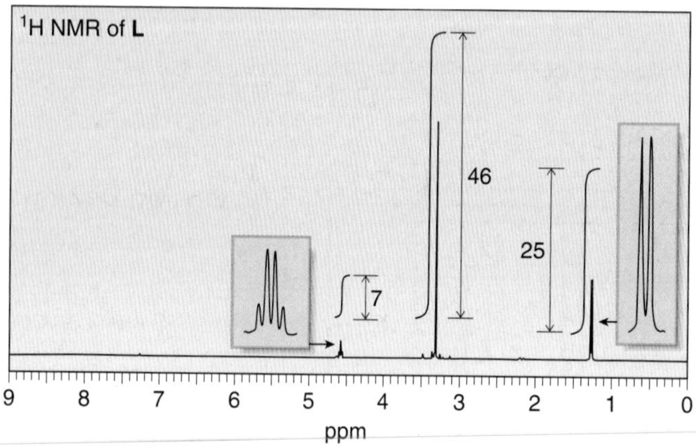

14.67 Treatment of $(CH_3)_2CHCH(OH)CH_2CH_3$ with TsOH affords two products (**M** and **N**) with molecular formula C_6H_{12}. The ^1H NMR spectra of **M** and **N** are given below. Propose structures for **M** and **N** and draw a mechanism to explain their formation.

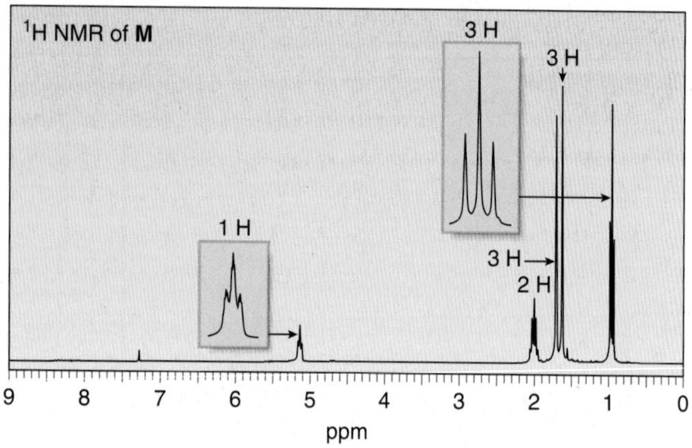

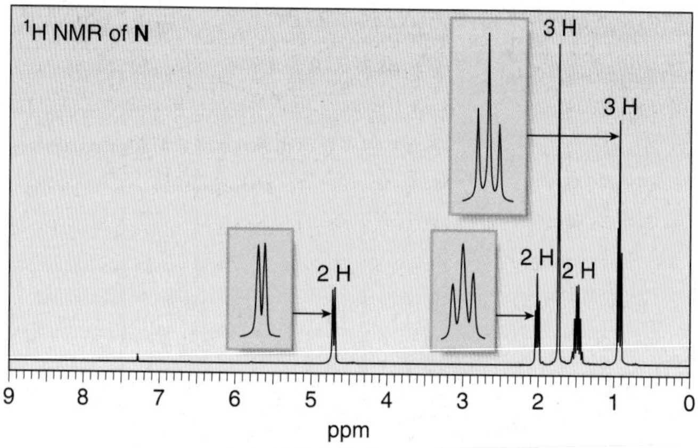

14.68 Compound **O** has molecular formula $C_{10}H_{12}O$ and shows an IR absorption at 1687 cm^{-1}. The ^1H NMR spectrum of **O** is given below. What is the structure of **O?**

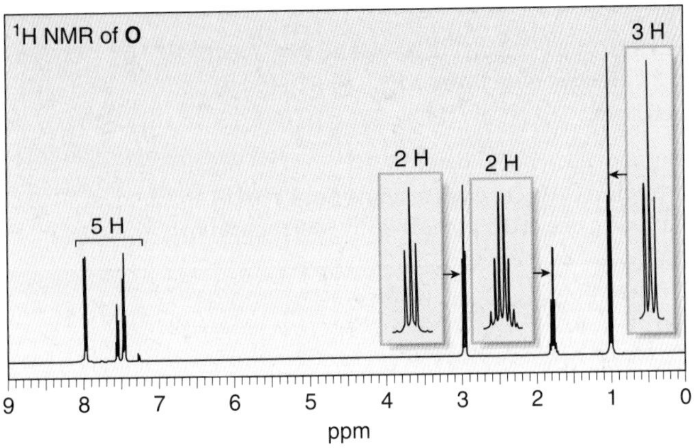

14.69 Compound **P** has molecular formula $C_5H_9ClO_2$. Deduce the structure of **P** from its ^1H and ^{13}C NMR spectra.

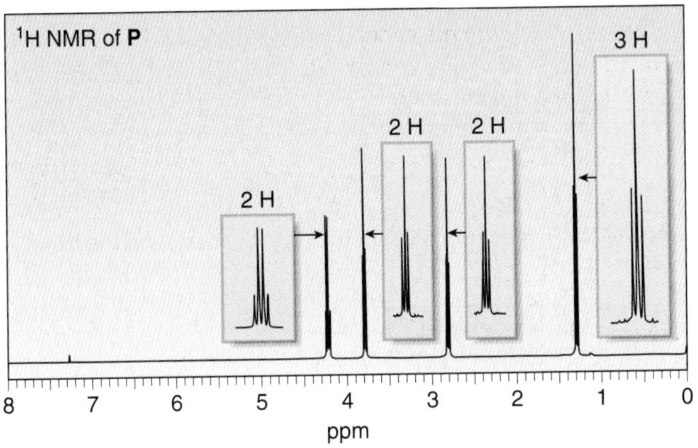

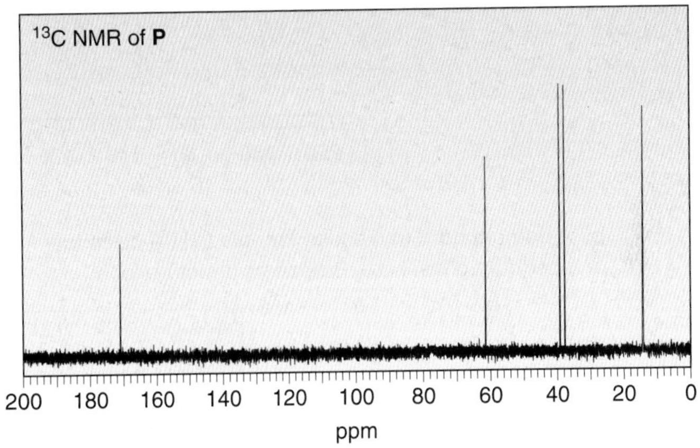

14.70 Treatment of 2-butanone ($CH_3COCH_2CH_3$) with strong base followed by CH_3I forms a compound **Q,** which gives a molecular ion in its mass spectrum at 86. The IR (> 1500 cm^{-1} only) and ^1H NMR spectrum of **Q** are given below. What is the structure of **Q?**

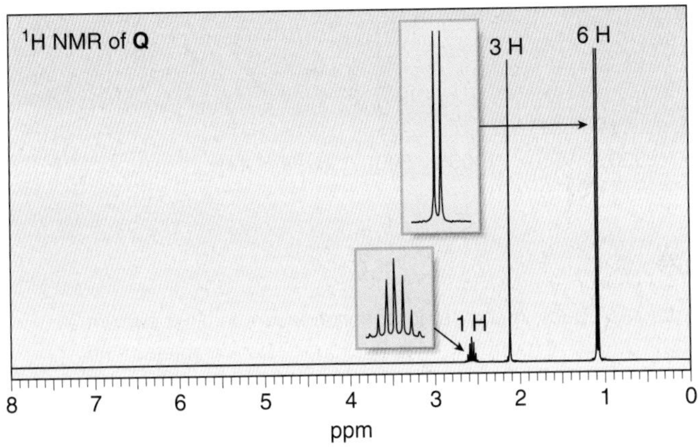

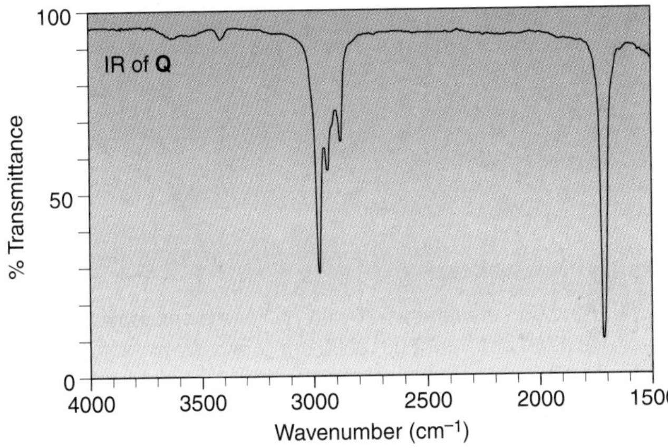

14.71 Low molecular weight esters (RCO_2R) often have characteristic odors. Using its molecular formula and ^1H NMR spectral data, identify each ester.

a. Compound **R,** the odor of banana: $C_7H_{14}O_2$; ^1H NMR: 0.93 (doublet, 6 H), 1.52 (multiplet, 2 H), 1.69 (multiplet, 1 H), 2.04 (singlet, 3 H), and 4.10 (triplet, 2 H) ppm

b. Compound **S,** the odor of rum: $C_7H_{14}O_2$; ^1H NMR: 0.94 (doublet, 6 H), 1.15 (triplet, 3 H), 1.91 (multiplet, 1 H), 2.33 (quartet, 2 H), and 3.86 (doublet, 2 H) ppm

14.72 When 2-bromo-3,3-dimethylbutane is treated with $K^+ \ ^-OC(CH_3)_3$, a single product **T** having molecular formula C_6H_{12} is formed. When 3,3-dimethyl-2-butanol is treated with H_2SO_4, the major product **U** has the same molecular formula. Given the following ^1H NMR data, what are the structures of **T** and **U?** Explain in detail the splitting patterns observed for the three split signals in **T.**

^1H NMR of **T:** 1.01 (singlet, 9 H), 4.82 (doublet of doublets, 1 H, J = 10, 1.7 Hz), 4.93 (doublet of doublets, 1 H, J = 18, 1.7 Hz), and 5.83 (doublet of doublets, 1 H, J = 18, 10 Hz) ppm

^1H NMR of **U:** 1.60 (singlet) ppm

14.73 Propose a structure consistent with each set of data.

a. A compound **X** (molecular formula $C_6H_{12}O_2$) gives a strong peak in its IR spectrum at 1740 cm^{-1}. The ^1H NMR spectrum of **X** shows only two singlets, including one at 3.5 ppm. The ^{13}C NMR spectrum is given below. Propose a structure for **X.**

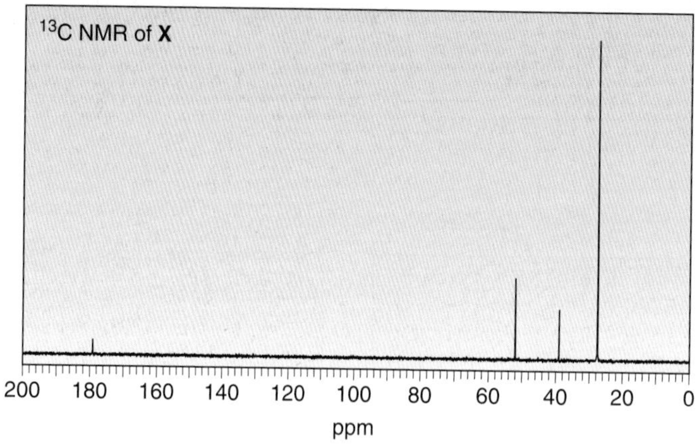

b. A compound **Y** (molecular formula C_6H_{10}) gives four lines in its ^{13}C NMR spectrum (27, 30, 67, and 93 ppm), and the IR spectrum given here. Propose a structure for **Y.**

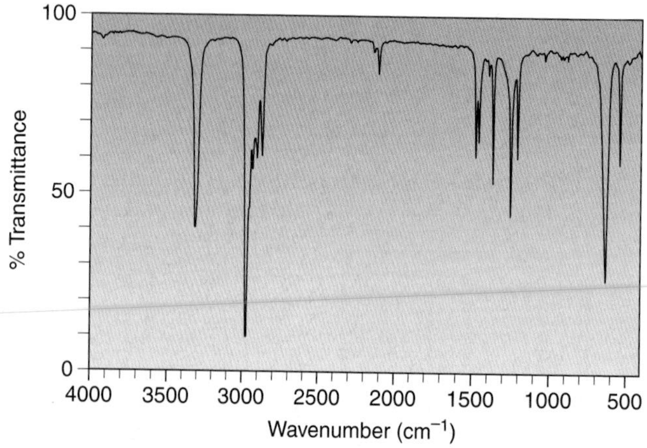

Challenge Problems

14.74 Reaction of unknown **A** with HCl forms chlorohydrin **B** as the major product. **A** shows no absorptions in its IR spectrum at 1700 cm^{-1} or 3600–3200 cm^{-1}, and gives the following ^1H NMR data: 1.4 (doublet, 3 H), 3.0 (quartet of doublets, 1 H), 3.5 (doublet, 1 H), 3.8 (singlet, 3 H), 6.9 (doublet, 2 H), and 7.2 (doublet, 2 H) ppm. (a) Propose a structure for **A,** including stereochemistry. (b) Explain why **B** is the major product in this reaction.

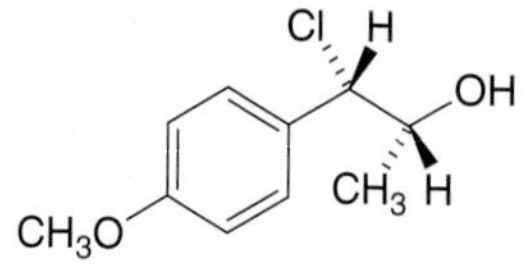

B

14.75 The ^{1}H NMR spectrum of *N,N*-dimethylformamide shows three singlets at 2.9, 3.0, and 8.0 ppm. Explain why the two CH_3 groups are not equivalent to each other, thus giving rise to two NMR signals.

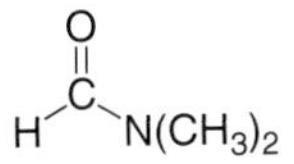

N,N-dimethylformamide

14.76 18-Annulene shows two signals in its ^{1}H NMR spectrum, one at 8.9 (12 H) and one at –1.8 (6 H) ppm. Using a similar argument to that offered for the chemical shift of benzene protons, explain why both shielded and deshielded values are observed for 18-annulene.

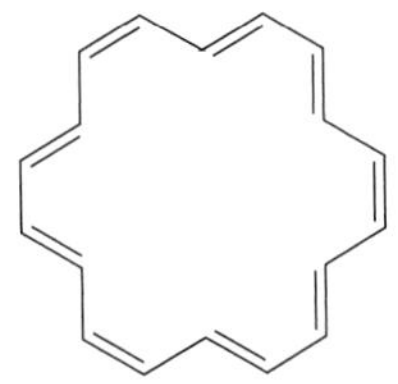

18-annulene

14.77 Explain why the ^{13}C NMR spectrum of 3-methyl-2-butanol shows five signals.

14.78 Since ^{31}P has an odd mass number, ^{31}P nuclei absorb in the NMR and, in many ways, these nuclei behave similarly to protons in NMR spectroscopy. With this in mind, explain why the ^{1}H NMR spectrum of methyl dimethylphosphonate, $CH_3PO(OCH_3)_2$, consists of two doublets at 1.5 and 3.7 ppm.

14.79 2-Cyclohexenone has two protons on its carbon–carbon double bond (labeled H_a and H_b) and two protons on the carbon adjacent to the double bond (labeled H_c). (a) If J_{ab} = 11 Hz and J_{bc} = 4 Hz, sketch the splitting pattern observed for each proton on the sp^2 hybridized carbons. (b) Despite the fact that H_a is located adjacent to an electron-withdrawing C=O, its absorption occurs upfield from the signal due to H_b (6.0 vs. 7.0 ppm). Offer an explanation.

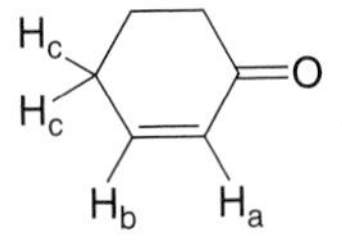

2-cyclohexenone

15 Radical Reactions

15.1 Introduction
15.2 General features of radical reactions
15.3 Halogenation of alkanes
15.4 The mechanism of halogenation
15.5 Chlorination of other alkanes
15.6 Chlorination versus bromination
15.7 Halogenation as a tool in organic synthesis
15.8 The stereochemistry of halogenation reactions
15.9 Application: The ozone layer and CFCs
15.10 Radical halogenation at an allylic carbon
15.11 Application: Oxidation of unsaturated lipids
15.12 Application: Antioxidants
15.13 Radical addition reactions to double bonds
15.14 Polymers and polymerization

Polystyrene, an inexpensive polymer synthesized from the monomer styrene, $C_6H_5CH{=}CH_2$, is one of the six compounds—called the "Big Six"—that account for three-quarters of the synthetic polymers produced in the United States. The polystyrene foam used in packaging materials and drinking cups for hot beverages is called Styrofoam, a trademark of the Dow Chemical Company. Polystyrene is also used to form the housings of small kitchen appliances, televisions, computers, and CD cases. Although recycled polystyrene can be molded into trays and trash cans, the polystyrene used in food packaging and beverage cups is contaminated with food, making it difficult to clean and recycle. In Chapter 15, we learn about the synthesis of polymers like polystyrene.

A small but significant group of reactions involves the homolysis of nonpolar bonds to form highly reactive **radical intermediates.** Although they are unlike other organic reactions, radical transformations are important in many biological and industrial processes. The gases O_2 and NO (nitric oxide) are both radicals. This means that many oxidation reactions with O_2 involve radical intermediates, and biological processes mediated by NO such as blood clotting and neurotransmission may involve radicals. Many useful industrial products such as Styrofoam and polyethylene are prepared by radical processes.

In Chapter 15 we examine the cleavage of nonpolar bonds by radical reactions.

15.1 Introduction

Radicals were first discussed in Section 6.3.

- A *radical* is a reactive intermediate with a single unpaired electron, formed by homolysis of a covalent bond.

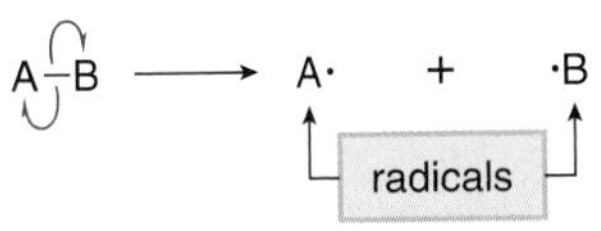

A radical contains an atom that does not have an octet of electrons, making it reactive and unstable. Radical processes involve single electrons, so half-headed arrows are used to show the movement of electrons. **One half-headed arrow is used for each electron.**

Carbon radicals are classified as **primary (1°), secondary (2°),** or **tertiary (3°)** by the number of R groups bonded to the carbon with the unpaired electron. A carbon radical is ***sp*²** hybridized and **trigonal planar,** like sp^2 hybridized carbocations. The unhybridized *p* orbital contains the unpaired electron and extends above and below the trigonal planar carbon.

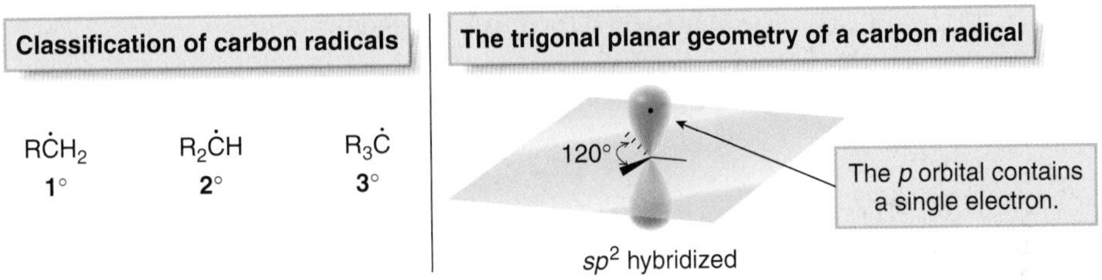

Bond dissociation energies for the cleavage of C–H bonds are used as a measure of radical stability. For example, two different radicals can be formed by cleavage of the C–H bonds in $CH_3CH_2CH_3$.

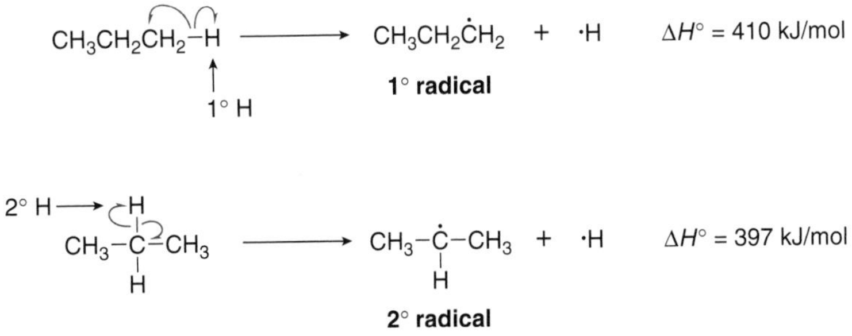

Cleavage of the stronger 1° C–H bond to form the 1° radical ($CH_3CH_2CH_2\cdot$) requires more energy than cleavage of the weaker 2° C–H bond to form the 2° radical [$(CH_3)_2CH\cdot$]—410 versus 397 kJ/mol. This makes the 2° radical more stable, because less energy is required for its

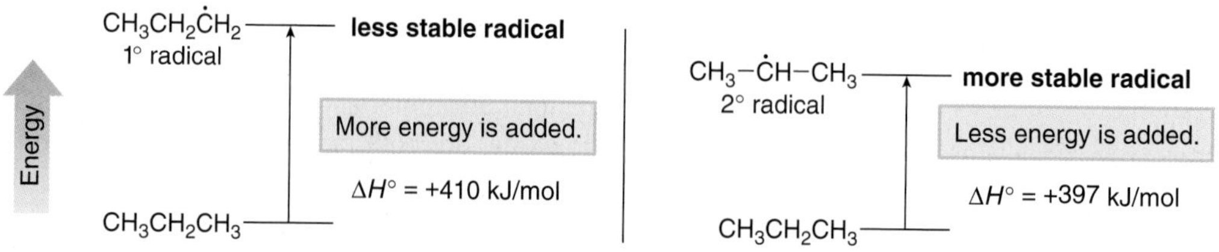

Figure 15.1 The relative stability of 1° and 2° carbon radicals

formation, as illustrated in Figure 15.1. Thus, **cleavage of the weaker bond forms the more stable radical.** This is a specific example of a general trend.

- **The stability of a radical increases as the number of alkyl groups bonded to the radical carbon increases.**

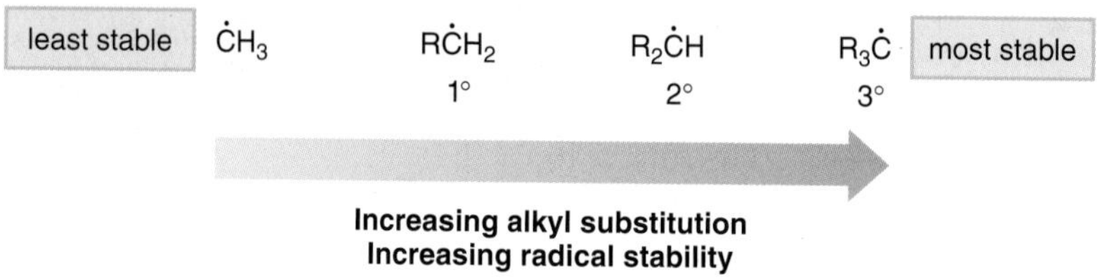

The **lower** the bond dissociation energy for a C–H bond, the **more stable** the resulting carbon radical.

Thus, a 3° radical is more stable than a 2° radical, and a 2° radical is more stable than a 1° radical. Increasing alkyl substitution increases radical stability in the same way it increases carbocation stability. Alkyl groups are more polarizable than hydrogen atoms, so they can more easily donate electron density to the electron-deficient carbon radical, thus increasing stability.

Unlike carbocations, however, **less stable radicals generally do *not* rearrange to more stable radicals.** This difference can be used to distinguish between reactions involving radical intermediates and those involving carbocations.

Problem 15.1 Classify each radical as 1°, 2°, or 3°.

a. $CH_3CH_2-\dot{C}HCH_2CH_3$ b. 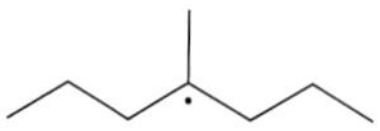 c.  d. 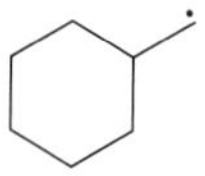

Problem 15.2 Draw the most stable radical that can result from cleavage of a C–H bond in each molecule.

a. $(CH_3)_2CHCH_2CH_3$ b. $(CH_3)_3CCH_2CH_3$ c. $(CH_3)_4C$ d. 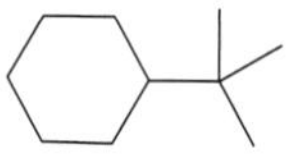

15.2 General Features of Radical Reactions

Radicals are formed from covalent bonds by adding energy in the form of **heat (Δ)** or **light (*hν*).** Some radical reactions are carried out in the presence of a **radical initiator,** a compound that contains an especially weak bond that serves as a source of radicals. **Peroxides,** compounds with the general structure **RO–OR,** are the most commonly used radical initiators. Heating a peroxide readily causes homolysis of the weak O–O bond, forming two RO· radicals.

15.2A Two Common Reactions of Radicals

Radicals undergo two main types of reactions: **they react with σ bonds,** and **they add to π bonds,** in both cases achieving an octet of electrons.

[1] Reaction of a Radical X· with a C–H Bond

A radical X· abstracts a hydrogen atom from a C–H σ bond to form H–X and a carbon radical. One electron from the C–H bond is used to form the new H–X bond, and the other electron in the C–H bond remains on carbon. The result is that the original radical X· is now surrounded by an octet of electrons, and a new radical is formed.

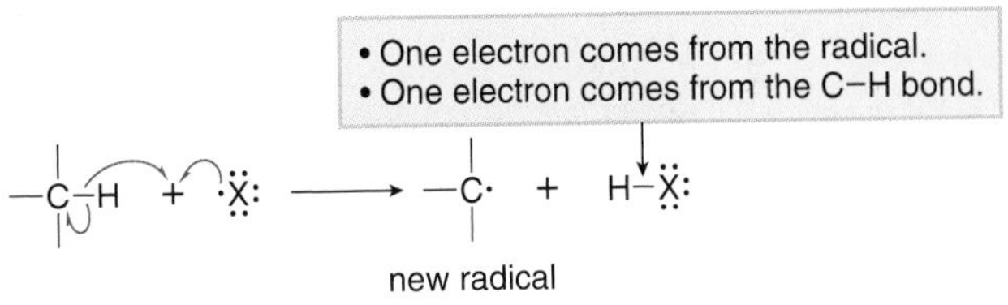
• One electron comes from the radical.
• One electron comes from the C–H bond.
new radical

This radical reaction is typically seen with the nonpolar C–H bonds of **alkanes,** which cannot react with polar or ionic electrophiles and nucleophiles.

[2] Reaction of a Radical X· with a C=C

A radical X· also adds to the π bond of a carbon–carbon double bond. One electron from the double bond is used to form a new C–X bond, and the other electron remains on the other carbon originally part of the double bond.

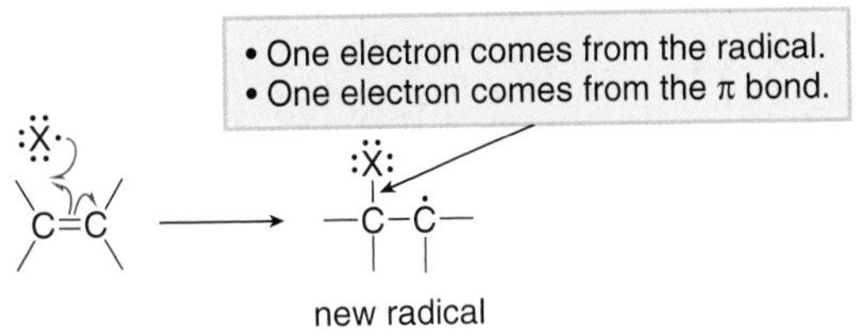
• One electron comes from the radical.
• One electron comes from the π bond.
new radical

Whenever a radical reacts with a stable single or double bond, a new radical is formed in the products.

Although the electron-rich double bond of an **alkene** reacts with electrophiles by ionic addition mechanisms, it also reacts with radicals because these reactive intermediates are also electron deficient.

15.2B Two Radicals Reacting with Each Other

A radical, once formed, rapidly reacts with whatever is available. Usually that means a stable σ or π bond. Occasionally, however, two radicals come into contact with each other, and they react to form a σ bond.

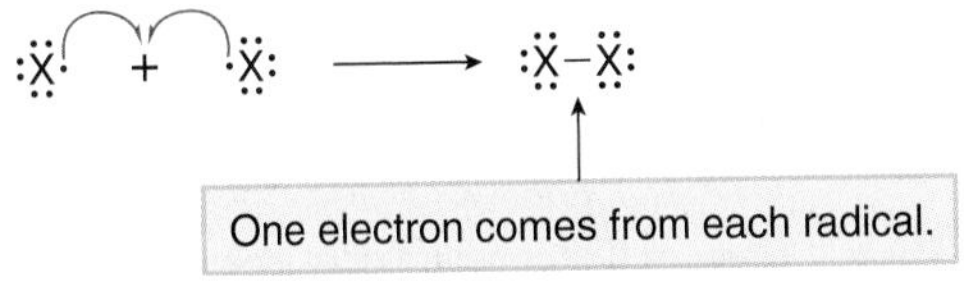
One electron comes from each radical.

The reaction of a radical with oxygen, a diradical in its ground state electronic configuration, is another example of two radicals reacting with each other. In this case, the reaction of O_2 with X· forms a new radical, thus preventing X· from reacting with an organic substrate.

O_2 is a radical inhibitor.

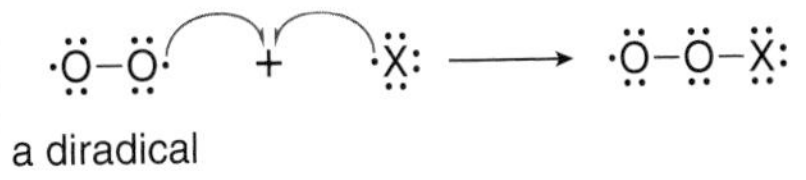
a diradical

Compounds that prevent radical reactions from occurring are called *radical inhibitors* or *radical scavengers*. Besides O_2, vitamin E and related compounds, discussed in Section 15.12, are radical scavengers, too. The fact that these compounds inhibit a reaction often suggests that the reaction occurs via radical intermediates.

Problem 15.3 Draw the products formed when a chlorine atom (Cl·) reacts with each species.

a. $CH_3–CH_3$ b. $CH_2=CH_2$ c. :C̈l· d. O_2

15.3 Halogenation of Alkanes

In the presence of light or heat, alkanes react with halogens to form alkyl halides. Halogenation is a **radical substitution reaction,** because a halogen atom X replaces a hydrogen via a mechanism that involves radical intermediates.

General reaction—Halogenation of alkanes

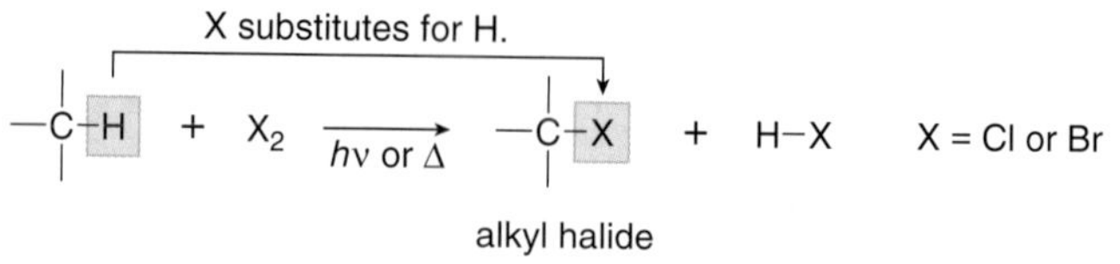
X substitutes for H.
hν or Δ
alkyl halide
X = Cl or Br

Halogenation of alkanes is useful only with Cl_2 and Br_2. Reaction with F_2 is too violent and reaction with I_2 is too slow to be useful. With an alkane that has more than one type of hydrogen atom, a mixture of alkyl halides may result (Reaction [3]).

When asked to draw the products of halogenation of an alkane, **draw the products of monohalogenation only,** unless specifically directed to do otherwise.

Examples

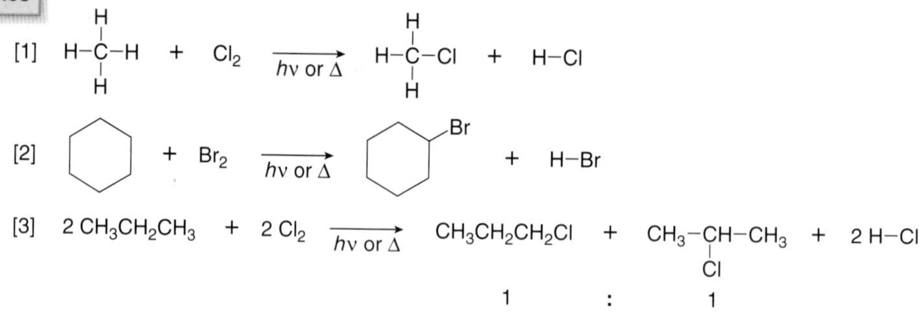
[1]
[2]
[3]
hν or Δ
1 : 1

In these examples of halogenation, a halogen has replaced a single hydrogen atom on the alkane. Can the other hydrogen atoms be replaced, too? Figure 15.2 shows that when CH_4 is treated with excess Cl_2, all four hydrogen atoms can be successively replaced by Cl to form CCl_4. **Monohalogenation**—the substitution of a single H by X—can be achieved experimentally by adding halogen X_2 to an excess of alkane.

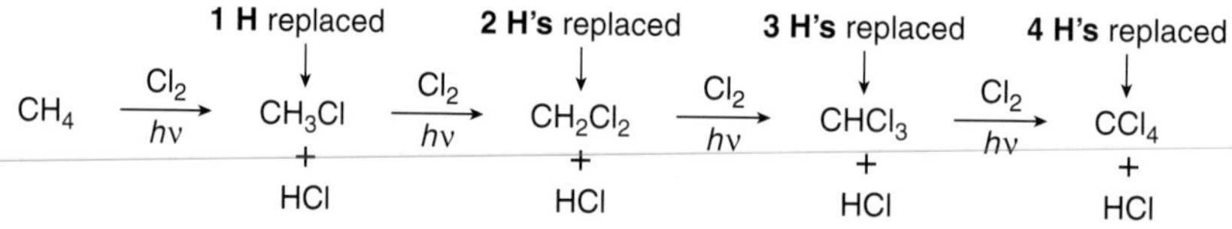
1 H replaced
2 H's replaced
3 H's replaced
4 H's replaced

Figure 15.2
Complete halogenation of CH_4 using excess Cl_2

Sample Problem 15.1 Draw all the constitutional isomers formed by monohalogenation of $(CH_3)_2CHCH_2CH_3$ with Cl_2 and $h\nu$.

Solution

Substitute Cl for H on every carbon, and then check to see if any products are identical. The starting material has five C's, but replacement of one H atom on two C's gives the same product. Thus, **$(CH_3)_2CHCH_2CH_3$ affords four monochloro substitution products.**

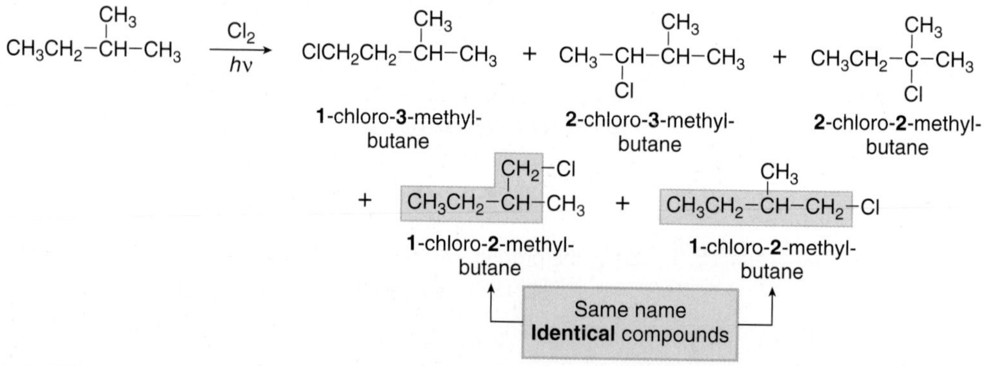
1-chloro-3-methylbutane
2-chloro-3-methylbutane
2-chloro-2-methylbutane
1-chloro-2-methylbutane
1-chloro-2-methylbutane
Same name
Identical compounds

Problem 15.4 Draw all constitutional isomers formed by monochlorination of each alkane.

a. 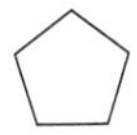 b. $CH_3CH_2CH_2CH_2CH_2CH_3$ c. $(CH_3)_3CH$

Problem 15.5 Compounds **A** and **B** are isomers having molecular formula C_5H_{12}. Heating **A** with Cl_2 gives a single product of monohalogenation, whereas heating **B** under the same conditions forms three constitutional isomers. What are the structures of **A** and **B?**

15.4 The Mechanism of Halogenation

Unlike nucleophilic substitution, which proceeds by two different mechanisms depending on the starting material and reagent, all halogenation reactions of alkanes—regardless of the halogen and alkane used—proceed by the *same* mechanism. Three facts about halogenation suggest that the mechanism involves radical, not ionic, intermediates.

Fact	Explanation
[1] Light, heat, or added peroxide is necessary for the reaction.	• Light or heat provides the energy needed for homolytic bond cleavage to form radicals. Breaking the weak O–O bond of peroxides initiates radical reactions as well.
[2] O_2 inhibits the reaction.	• The diradical O_2 removes radicals from a reaction mixture, thus preventing reaction.
[3] No rearrangements are observed.	• Radicals do not rearrange.

15.4A The Steps of Radical Halogenation

The chlorination of ethane illustrates the **three distinct parts of radical halogenation** (Mechanism 15.1):

Overall reaction

$$CH_3CH_3 + Cl_2 \xrightarrow[h\nu \text{ or } \Delta]{} CH_3CH_2Cl + HCl$$

- *Initiation:* Two radicals are formed by homolysis of a σ bond and this begins the reaction.
- *Propagation:* A radical reacts with another reactant to form a new σ bond and another radical.
- *Termination:* Two radicals combine to form a stable bond. Removing radicals from the reaction mixture without generating any new radicals stops the reaction.

Mechanism 15.1 Radical Halogenation of Alkanes

Initiation

Step [1] Bond cleavage forms two radicals.

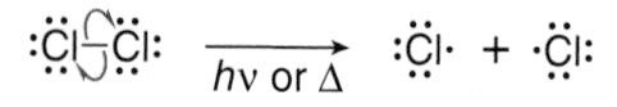

- Homolysis of the weakest bond in the starting materials requires energy from light or heat.
- Thus, the Cl–Cl bond ($\Delta H°$ = 242 kJ/mol), which is weaker than either the C–C or C–H bond in ethane ($\Delta H°$ = 368 and 410 kJ/mol, respectively), is broken to form two chlorine radicals.

Propagation

Steps [2] and [3] One radical reacts and a new radical is formed.

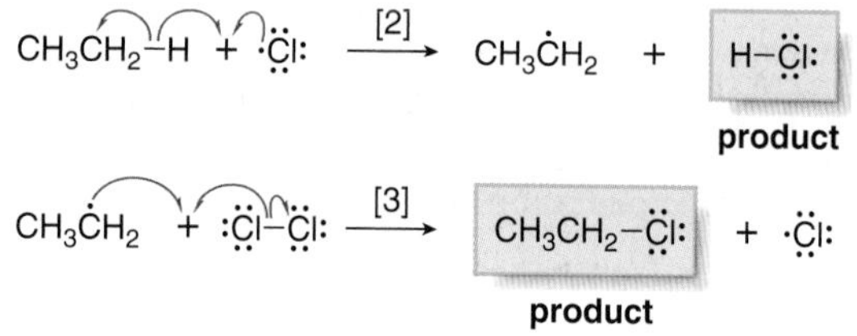

Repeat Steps [2], [3], [2], [3], again and again.

- The Cl· radicals abstract a hydrogen atom from ethane (Step [2]). This forms H–Cl and leaves one unpaired electron on carbon, generating the ethyl radical (CH_3CH_2·).
- CH_3CH_2· abstracts a chlorine atom from Cl_2 (Step [3]), forming CH_3CH_2Cl and a new chlorine radical (Cl·).
- The Cl· radical formed in Step [3] is a reactant in Step [2], so Steps [2] and [3] can occur repeatedly without an additional initiation reaction (Step [1]).
- In each propagation step, one radical is consumed and one radical is formed. The two products—CH_3CH_2Cl and HCl—are formed during propagation.

Termination

Step [4] Two radicals react to form a σ bond.

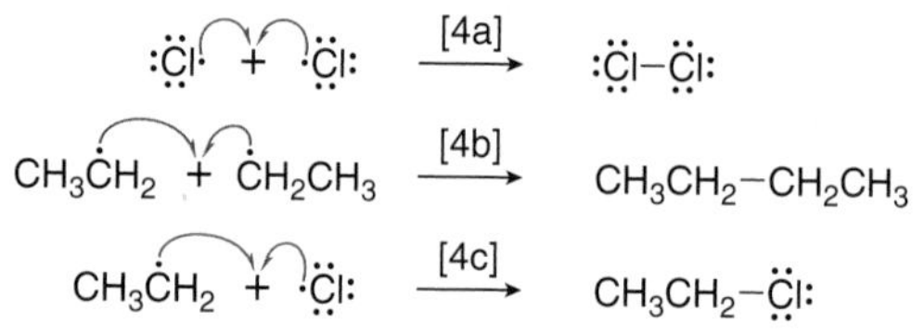

- To terminate the chain, two radicals react with each other in one of three ways (Steps [4a, b, and c]) to form stable bonds.

Although initiation generates the Cl· radicals needed to begin the reaction, the propagation steps ([2] and [3]) form the two reaction products—$\mathbf{CH_3CH_2Cl}$ and **HCl.** Once the process has begun, propagation occurs over and over without the need for Step [1] to occur. **A mechanism such as radical halogenation that involves two or more repeating steps is called a *chain mechanism.*** Each propagation step involves a reactive radical abstracting an atom from a stable bond to form a new bond and another radical that continues the chain.

Usually a radical reacts with a stable bond to propagate the chain, but occasionally two radicals combine, and this reaction terminates the chain. Depending on the reaction and the reaction conditions, some radical chain mechanisms can repeat thousands of times before termination occurs.

Termination Step [4a] forms Cl_2, a reactant, whereas Step [4c] forms CH_3CH_2Cl, one of the reaction products. Termination Step [4b] forms $CH_3CH_2-CH_2CH_3$, which is neither a reactant nor a desired product. The formation of a small quantity of $CH_3CH_2-CH_2CH_3$, however, is evidence that ethyl radicals are formed in the reaction.

The most important steps of radical halogenation are those that lead to product formation—the propagation steps—so subsequent discussion of this reaction concentrates on these steps only.

Problem 15.6 Using Mechanism 15.1 as a guide, write the mechanism for the reaction of CH_4 with Br_2 to form CH_3Br and HBr. Classify each step as initiation, propagation, or termination.

15.4B Energy Changes During the Chlorination of Ethane

Figure 15.3 shows how bond dissociation energies (Section 6.4) can be used to calculate $\Delta H°$ for the two propagation steps in the chlorination of ethane. Because the overall $\Delta H°$ is negative, the reaction is **exothermic.** Moreover, because the transition state for the first propagation step is higher in energy than the transition state for the second propagation step, the **first step is rate-determining.** Both of these facts are illustrated in the energy diagram in Figure 15.4.

Problem 15.7 Calculate $\Delta H°$ for the two propagation steps in the reaction of CH_4 with Br_2 to form CH_3Br and HBr (Problem 15.6).

Problem 15.8 Calculate $\Delta H°$ for the rate-determining step of the reaction of CH_4 with I_2. Explain why this result illustrates that this reaction is extremely slow.

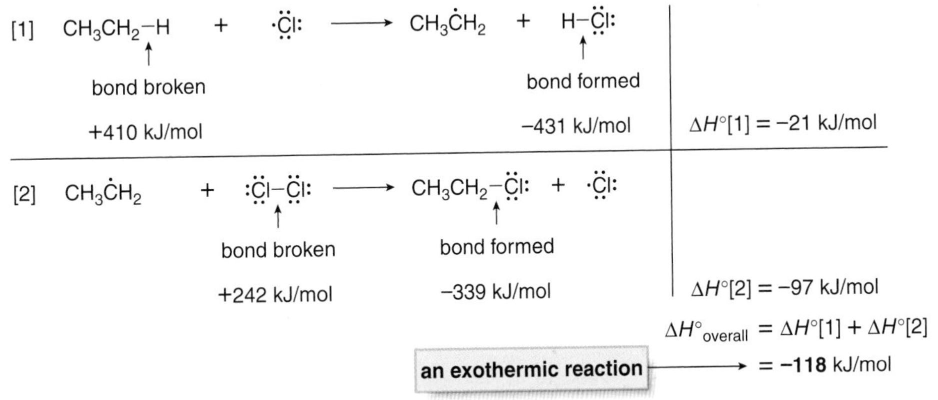
[1] CH3CH2–H + ·Cl: → CH3CH2· + H–Cl:
bond broken
bond formed
+410 kJ/mol
–431 kJ/mol
ΔH°[1] = –21 kJ/mol
[2] CH3CH2· + :Cl–Cl: → CH3CH2–Cl: + ·Cl:
bond broken
bond formed
+242 kJ/mol
–339 kJ/mol
ΔH°[2] = –97 kJ/mol
ΔH°overall = ΔH°[1] + ΔH°[2]
an exothermic reaction
= –118 kJ/mol

Figure 15.3 Energy changes in the propagation steps during the chlorination of ethane

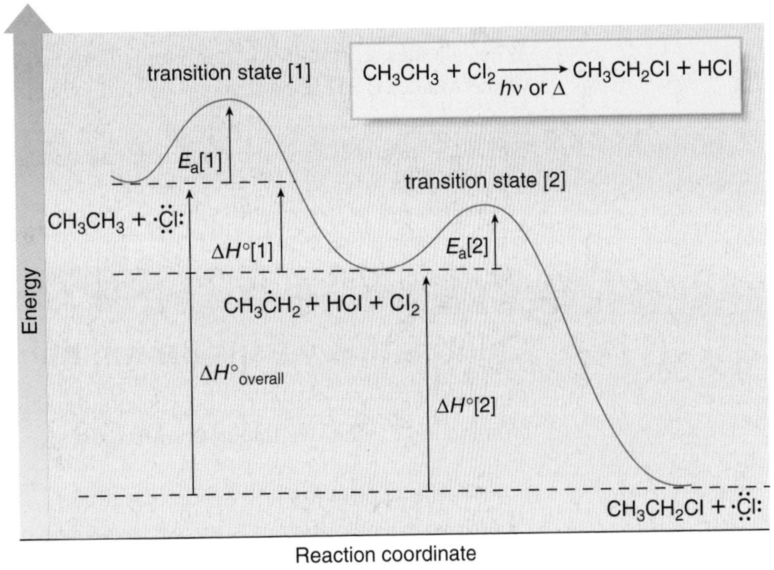
transition state [1]
CH3CH3 + Cl2 → CH3CH2Cl + HCl
hν or Δ
Ea[1]
transition state [2]
CH3CH3 + ·Cl:
ΔH°[1]
Ea[2]
CH3CH2· + HCl + Cl2
Energy
ΔH°overall
ΔH°[2]
CH3CH2Cl + ·Cl:
Reaction coordinate

Figure 15.4 Energy diagram for the propagation steps in the chlorination of ethane

- Because radical halogenation consists of two propagation steps, the energy diagram has two energy barriers.
- The first step is rate-determining because its transition state is at higher energy.
- The reaction is exothermic because $\Delta H°_{overall}$ is negative.

15.5 Chlorination of Other Alkanes

Recall from Section 15.3 that the chlorination of $CH_3CH_2CH_3$ affords a 1:1 mixture of $CH_3CH_2CH_2Cl$ (formed by removal of a 1° hydrogen) and $(CH_3)_2CHCl$ (formed by removal of a 2° hydrogen).

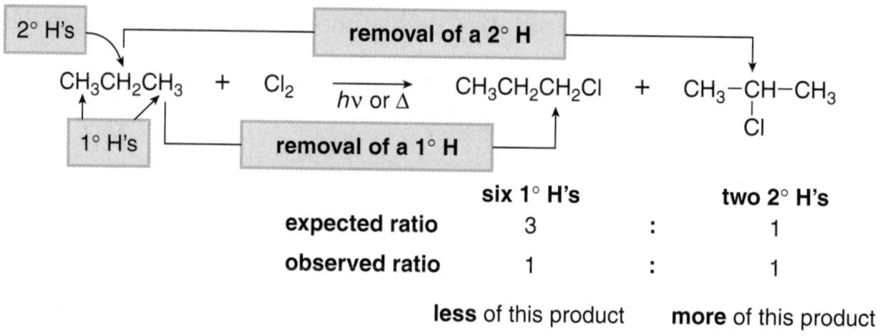

$CH_3CH_2CH_3$ has six 1° hydrogen atoms and only two 2° hydrogens, so the expected product ratio of $CH_3CH_2CH_2Cl$ to $(CH_3)_2CHCl$ (assuming all hydrogens are *equally* reactive) is 3:1. Because the observed ratio is 1:1, however, the 2° C–H bonds must be more reactive; that is, **it must be easier to homolytically cleave a 2° C–H bond than a 1° C–H bond.** Recall from Section 15.2 that 2° C–H bonds are weaker than 1° C–H bonds. Thus,

- **The weaker the C–H bond, the more readily the hydrogen atom is removed in radical halogenation.**

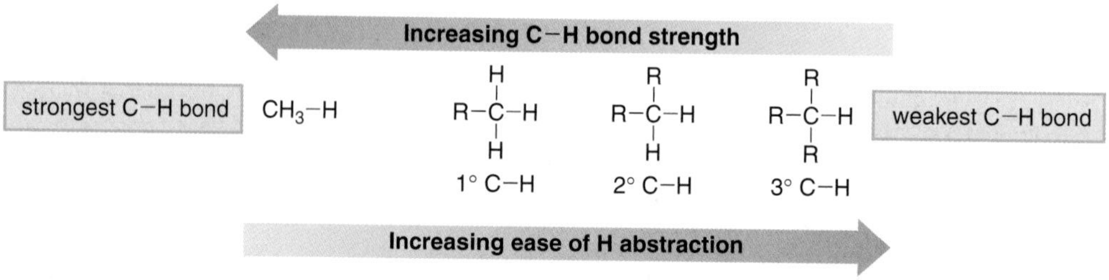

When alkanes react with Cl_2, a mixture of products results, with more product formed by cleavage of the weaker C–H bond than you would expect on statistical grounds.

Problem 15.9 Which C–H bond in each compound is most readily broken during radical halogenation?

a. 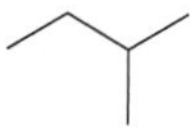 b. 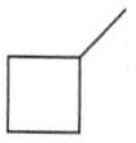 c. $CH_3CH_2CH_2CH_3$

15.6 Chlorination versus Bromination

Although alkanes undergo radical substitution reactions with both Cl_2 and Br_2, chlorination and bromination exhibit two important differences:

- **Chlorination is *faster* than bromination.**
- **Although chlorination is *unselective*, yielding a mixture of products, bromination is often *selective*, yielding one major product.**

For example, propane reacts rapidly with Cl_2 to form a 1:1 mixture of 1° and 2° alkyl chlorides. On the other hand, propane reacts with Br_2 much more slowly and forms 99% $(CH_3)_2CHBr$.

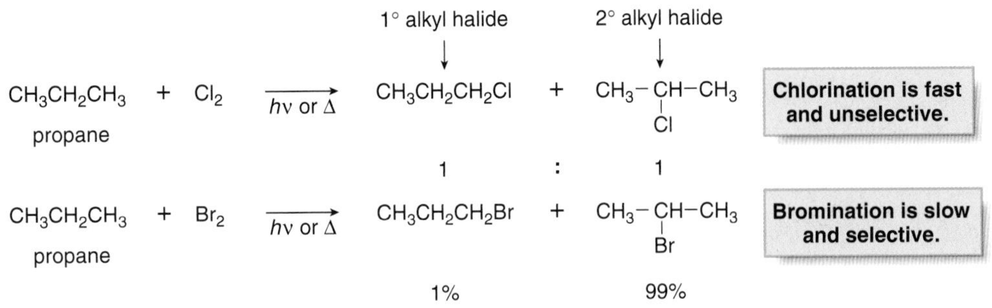

- **In bromination, the major (and sometimes exclusive) product results from cleavage of the *weakest* C–H bond.**

Sample Problem 15.2 Draw the major product formed when 3-ethylpentane is heated with Br_2.

Solution

Keep in mind: **the more substituted the carbon atom, the weaker the C–H bond.** The major bromination product in 3-ethylpentane is formed by cleavage of the sole **3° C–H bond,** its weakest C–H bond.

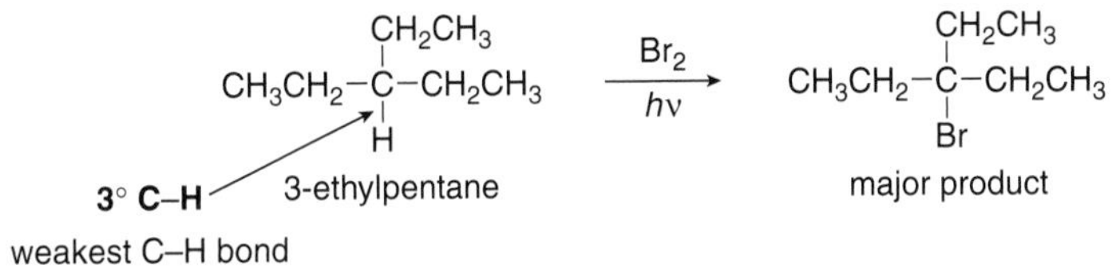

Problem 15.10 Draw the major product formed when each cycloalkane is heated with Br_2.

To explain the difference between chlorination and bromination, we return to the Hammond postulate (Section 7.15) to estimate the relative energy of the transition states of the rate-determining steps of these reactions. The **rate-determining step is the abstraction of a hydrogen atom by the halogen radical,** so we must compare these steps for bromination and chlorination. Keep in mind:

- **Transition states in endothermic reactions resemble the products. The more stable product is formed faster.**
- **Transition states in exothermic reactions resemble the starting materials. The relative stability of the products does not greatly affect the relative energy of the transition states, so a mixture of products often results.**

Bromination: $CH_3CH_2CH_3 + Br_2$

A bromine radical can abstract either a 1° or a 2° hydrogen from propane, generating either a 1° radical or a 2° radical. Calculating $\Delta H°$ using bond dissociation energies reveals that both reactions are **endothermic,** but **it takes less energy to form the more stable 2° radical.**

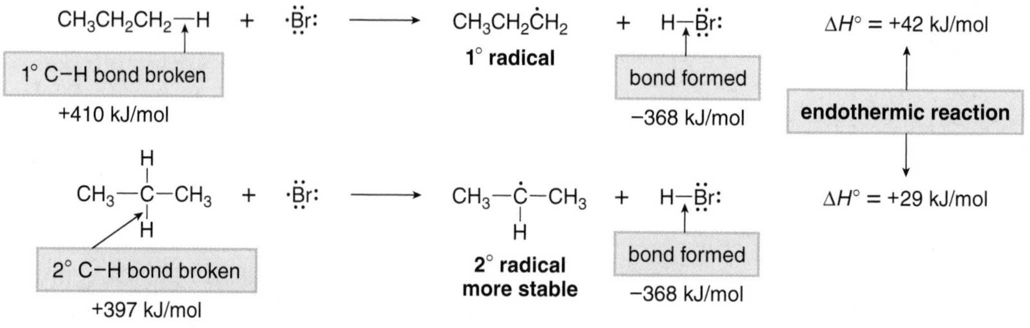

According to the Hammond postulate, the transition state of an endothermic reaction resembles the products, so the energy of activation to form the more stable 2° radical is lower and it is formed faster, as shown in the energy diagram in Figure 15.5. Because the 2° radical $[(CH_3)_2CH\cdot]$ is converted to 2-bromopropane $[(CH_3)_2CHBr]$ in the second propagation step, this **2° alkyl halide is the major product of bromination.**

- **Conclusion: Because the rate-determining step in bromination is endothermic, the more stable radical is formed faster, and often a single radical halogenation product predominates.**

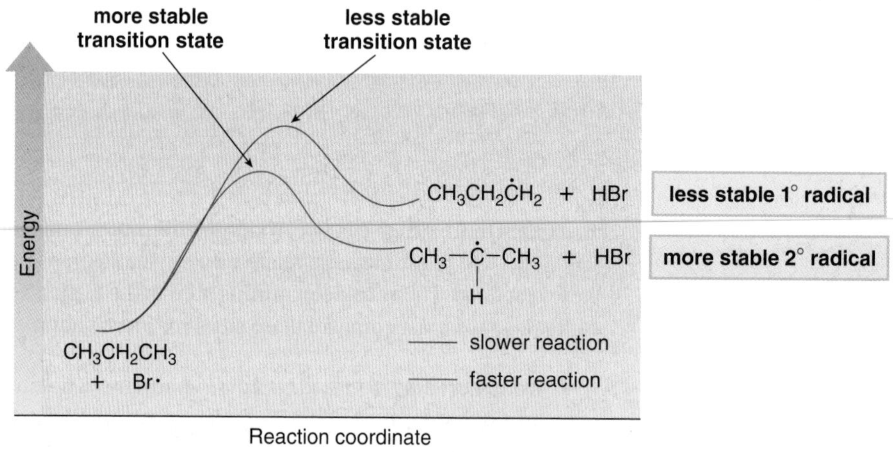

Figure 15.5
Energy diagram for a selective endothermic reaction: $CH_3CH_2CH_3 + Br\cdot \rightarrow CH_3CH_2CH_2\cdot$ or $(CH_3)_2CH\cdot + HBr$

- The transition state to form the less stable 1° radical $(CH_3CH_2CH_2\cdot)$ is higher in energy than the transition state to form the more stable 2° radical $[(CH_3)_2CH\cdot]$. Thus, **the 2° radical is formed faster.**

Chlorination: $CH_3CH_2CH_3 + Cl_2$

A chlorine radical can also abstract either a 1° or a 2° hydrogen from propane, generating either a 1° radical or a 2° radical. Calculating $\Delta H°$ using bond dissociation energies reveals that both reactions are **exothermic.**

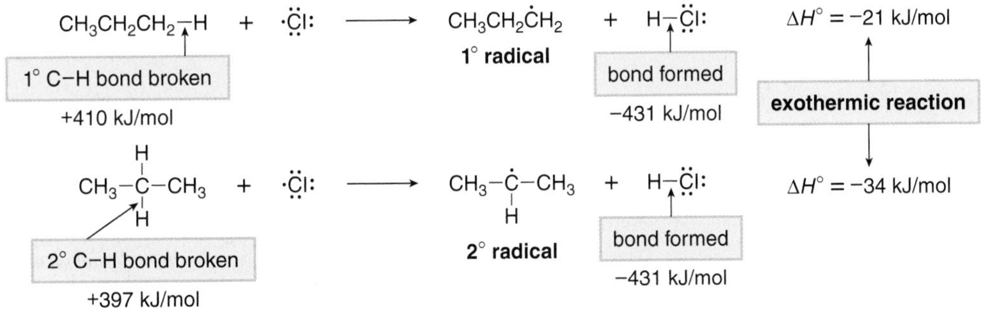
1° C–H bond broken
+410 kJ/mol
1° radical
bond formed
−431 kJ/mol
ΔH° = −21 kJ/mol
exothermic reaction
ΔH° = −34 kJ/mol
2° C–H bond broken
+397 kJ/mol
2° radical
bond formed
−431 kJ/mol

Because chlorination has an *exothermic* rate-determining step, the transition state to form both radicals resembles the same starting material, $CH_3CH_2CH_3$. As a result, the relative stability of the two radicals is much less important and both radicals are formed. An energy diagram for these processes is drawn in Figure 15.6. Because the 1° and 2° radicals are converted to 1-chloropropane ($CH_3CH_2CH_2Cl$) and 2-chloropropane [$(CH_3)_2CHCl$], respectively, in the second propagation step, **both alkyl halides are formed in chlorination.**

- **Conclusion: Because the rate-determining step in chlorination is exothermic, the transition state resembles the starting material, both radicals are formed, and a mixture of products results.**

Problem 15.11 Reaction of $(CH_3)_3CH$ with Cl_2 forms two products: $(CH_3)_2CHCH_2Cl$ (63%) and $(CH_3)_3CCl$ (37%). Why is the major product formed by cleavage of the stronger 1° C–H bond?

Figure 15.6 Energy diagram for a nonselective exothermic reaction: $CH_3CH_2CH_3 + Cl\cdot \rightarrow CH_3CH_2CH_2\cdot$ or $(CH_3)_2CH\cdot + HCl$

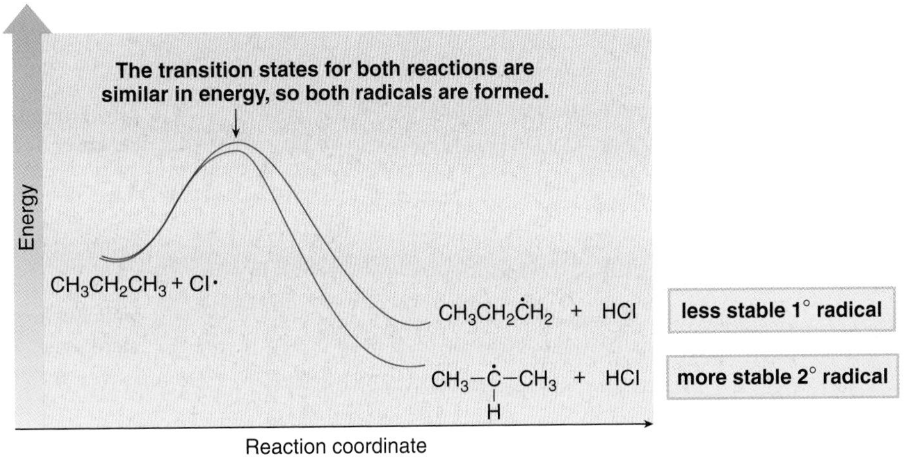
The transition states for both reactions are similar in energy, so both radicals are formed.
Energy
CH3CH2CH3 + Cl·
CH3CH2ĊH2 + HCl
less stable 1° radical
more stable 2° radical
Reaction coordinate

15.7 Halogenation as a Tool in Organic Synthesis

Halogenation is a useful tool because it adds a functional group to a previously unfunctionalized molecule, making an **alkyl halide.** These alkyl halides can then be converted to alkenes by elimination, and to alcohols and ethers by nucleophilic substitution.

Sample Problem 15.3 Show how cyclohexane can be converted to cyclohexene by a stepwise sequence.

Solution

There is no one-step method to convert an alkane to an alkene. A two-step method is needed:

[1] **Radical halogenation** produces an alkyl halide.

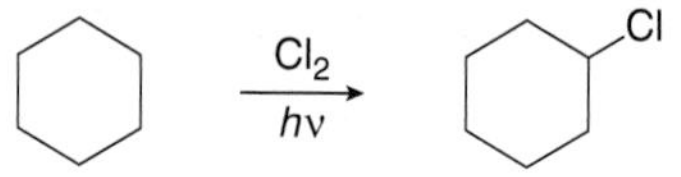

[2] **Elimination of HCl** with a strong base produces cyclohexene.

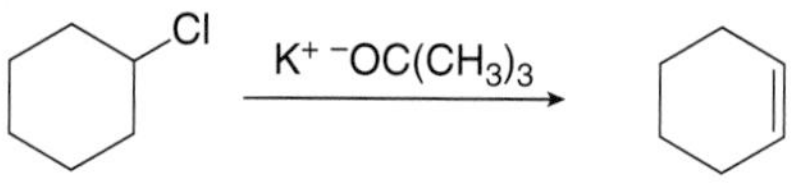

Problem 15.12 Synthesize each compound from $(CH_3)_3CH$.

a. $(CH_3)_3CBr$ b. $(CH_3)_2C{=}CH_2$ c. $(CH_3)_3COH$ d. $(CH_3)_2C(Cl)CH_2Cl$

Problem 15.13 Show all steps and reagents needed to convert cyclohexane into each compound: (a) the two enantiomers of *trans*-1,2-dibromocyclohexane; and (b) 1,2-epoxycyclohexane.

15.8 The Stereochemistry of Halogenation Reactions

The stereochemistry of a reaction product depends on whether the reaction occurs at a stereogenic center or at another atom, and whether a new stereogenic center is formed. The rules predicting the stereochemistry of reaction products are summarized in Table 15.1.

Table 15.1 Rules for Predicting the Stereochemistry of Reaction Products

Starting material	Result
Achiral	• An achiral starting material always gives either an achiral or a racemic product.
Chiral	• If a reaction does not occur at a stereogenic center, the configuration at a stereogenic center is retained in the product. • If a reaction occurs at a stereogenic center, we must know the mechanism to predict the stereochemistry of the product.

15.8A Halogenation of an Achiral Starting Material

Halogenation of the **achiral starting material $CH_3CH_2CH_2CH_3$** forms two constitutional isomers by replacement of either a 1° or 2° hydrogen.

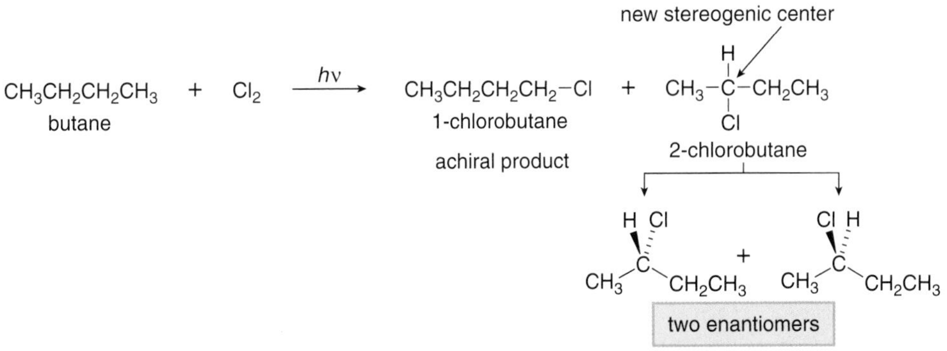

- 1-Chlorobutane ($CH_3CH_2CH_2CH_2Cl$) has no stereogenic center and thus it is an **achiral** compound.
- 2-Chlorobutane [$CH_3CH(Cl)CH_2CH_3$] has a new stereogenic center, and so an **equal amount of two enantiomers** must form—**a racemic mixture.**

A racemic mixture results when a new stereogenic center is formed because the first propagation step generates a **planar, sp^2 hybridized radical.** Cl_2 then reacts with the planar radical from either the front or back side to form an equal amount of two enantiomers.

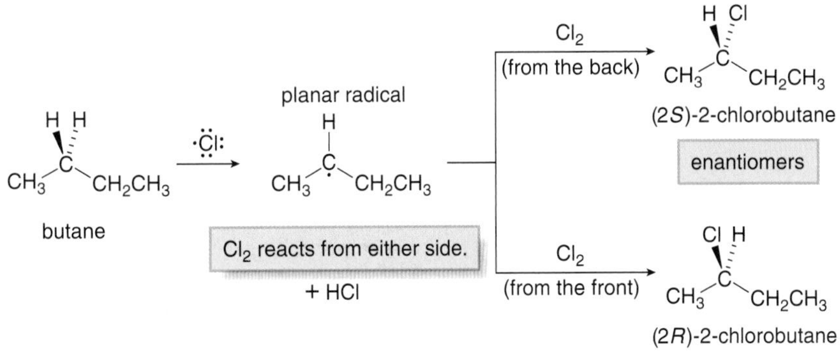

Thus, the achiral starting material butane forms an achiral product (1-chlorobutane) and a racemic mixture of two enantiomers [(2*R*)- and (2*S*)-2-chlorobutane].

15.8B Halogenation of a Chiral Starting Material

Let's now examine chlorination of the chiral starting material (2*R*)-2-bromobutane at C2 and C3.

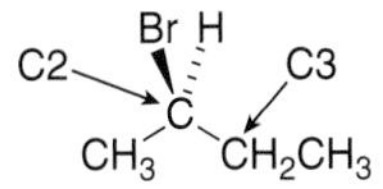

(2*R*)-2-bromobutane

Chlorination at C2 occurs at the stereogenic center. Abstraction of a hydrogen atom at C2 forms a trigonal planar sp^2 hybridized radical that is now achiral. This achiral radical then reacts with Cl_2 from either side to form a new stereogenic center, resulting in an **equal amount of two enantiomers—a racemic mixture.**

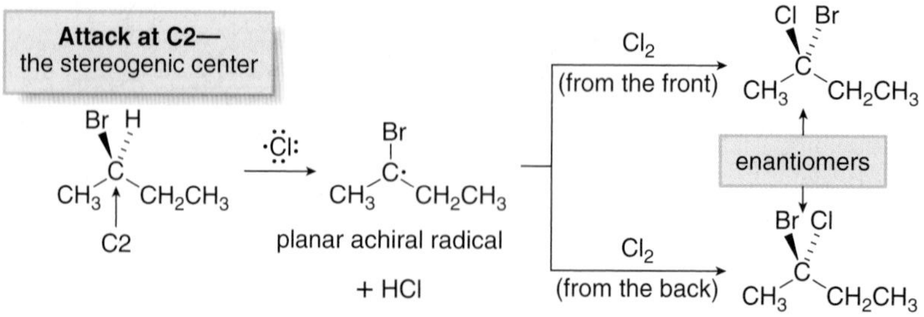

- **Radical halogenation reactions occur with racemization at a stereogenic center.**

Chlorination at C3 does *not* occur at the stereogenic center, but it forms a new stereogenic center. Because no bond is broken to the stereogenic center at C2, **its configuration is retained** during the reaction. Abstraction of a hydrogen atom at C3 forms a trigonal planar sp^2 hybridized radical that still contains this stereogenic center. Reaction of the radical with Cl_2 from either side forms a new stereogenic center, so the products have two stereogenic centers: the configuration at C2 is the same in both compounds, but the configuration at C3 is different, making them **diastereomers.**

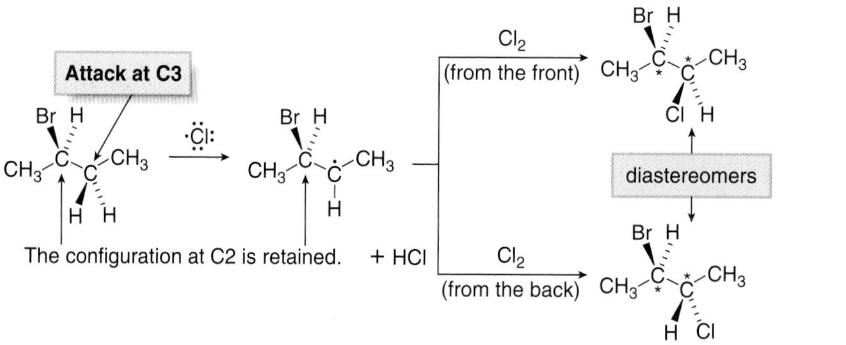

[* denotes a stereogenic center]

Thus, four isomers are formed by chlorination of (2*R*)-2-bromobutane at C2 and C3. Attack at the stereogenic center (C2) gives a product with one stereogenic center, resulting in a mixture of enantiomers. Attack at C3 forms a new stereogenic center, giving a mixture of diastereomers.

Problem 15.14 What products are formed from monochlorination of (2*R*)-2-bromobutane at C1 and C4? Assign *R* and *S* designations to each stereogenic center.

Problem 15.15 Draw the monochlorination products formed when each compound is heated with Cl_2. Include the stereochemistry at any stereogenic center.

a. $CH_3CH_2CH_2CH_2CH_3$

b. 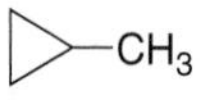

c. $(CH_3CH_2)_3CH$

d. 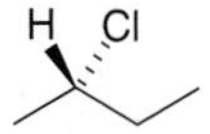

(Consider attack at C2 and C3 only.)

15.9 Application: The Ozone Layer and CFCs

The 1995 Nobel Prize in Chemistry was awarded to Mario Molina, Paul Crutzen, and F. Sherwood Rowland for their work in elucidating the interaction of ozone with CFCs. What began as a fundamental research project turned out to have important implications in the practical world.

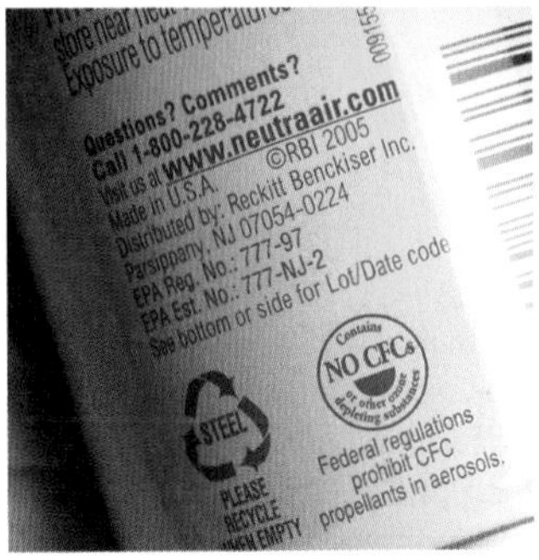

Propane and butane are now used as propellants in spray cans in place of CFCs.

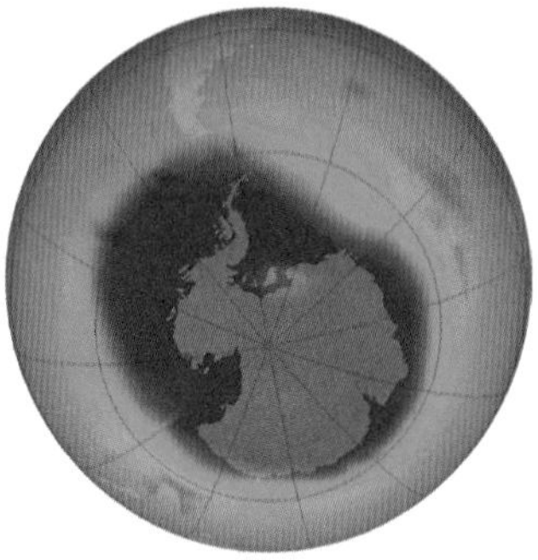

Sept. 12, 2011
Ozone (Dobson Units)
100 200 300 400 500

O_3 destruction is most severe in the region of the South Pole, where a large ozone hole is visible with satellite imaging.

Ozone is formed in the upper atmosphere by reaction of oxygen molecules with oxygen atoms. Ozone is also decomposed with sunlight back to these same two species. The overall result of these reactions is to convert high-energy ultraviolet light into heat.

The synthesis and decomposition of O_3 in the upper atmosphere

$$O_2 + \cdot\ddot{\underset{\cdot\cdot}{O}}\cdot \longrightarrow \underset{\text{ozone}}{O_3} + \text{heat}$$

$$\underset{\text{ozone}}{O_3} \xrightarrow{h\nu} O_2 + \cdot\ddot{\underset{\cdot\cdot}{O}}\cdot$$

Ozone is vital to life; it acts like a shield, protecting the earth's surface from destructive ultraviolet radiation. A decrease in ozone concentration in this protective layer would have some immediate consequences, including an increase in the incidence of skin cancer and eye cataracts. Other long-term effects include a reduced immune response, interference with photosynthesis in plants, and harmful effects on the growth of plankton, the mainstay of the ocean food chain.

Current research suggests that **chlorofluorocarbons (CFCs)** are responsible for destroying ozone in the upper atmosphere. **CFCs** are simple halogen-containing organic compounds manufactured under the trade name Freons.

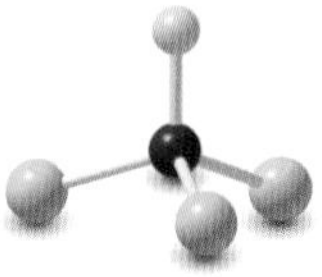

$CFCl_3$
trichlorofluoromethane
CFC 11
Freon 11

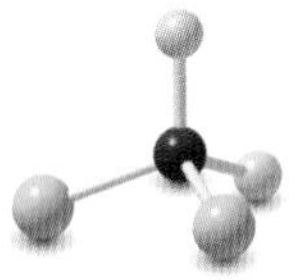

CF_2Cl_2
dichlorodifluoromethane
CFC 12
Freon 12

CFCs are inert, odorless, and nontoxic, and they have been used as refrigerants, solvents, and aerosol propellants. Because CFCs are volatile and water insoluble, they readily escape into the upper atmosphere, where they are decomposed by high-energy sunlight to form radicals that destroy ozone by the radical chain mechanism shown in Figure 15.7.

The overall result is that O_3 is consumed as a reactant and O_2 molecules are formed. In this way, a small amount of CFC can destroy a large amount of O_3. These findings led to a ban on the use of CFCs in aerosol propellants in the United States in 1978 and to the phasing out of their use in refrigeration systems.

Newer alternatives to CFCs are **hydrochlorofluorocarbons (HCFCs)** and **hydrofluorocarbons (HFCs)** such as CH_2FCF_3. These compounds have many properties in common with CFCs, but they are largely decomposed by HO· before they reach the stratosphere and therefore they have little impact on stratospheric O_3.

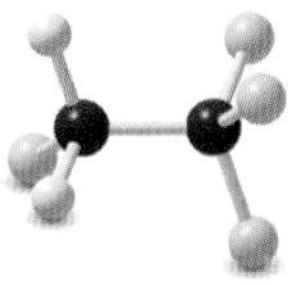

CH_2FCF_3
HFC-134a

$$H{-}\ddot{\underset{\cdot\cdot}{O}}\cdot + H{-}CHFCF_3 \longrightarrow H{-}\ddot{\underset{\cdot\cdot}{O}}{-}H + \cdot CHFCF_3$$

This HFC is decomposed before it reaches the stratosphere.

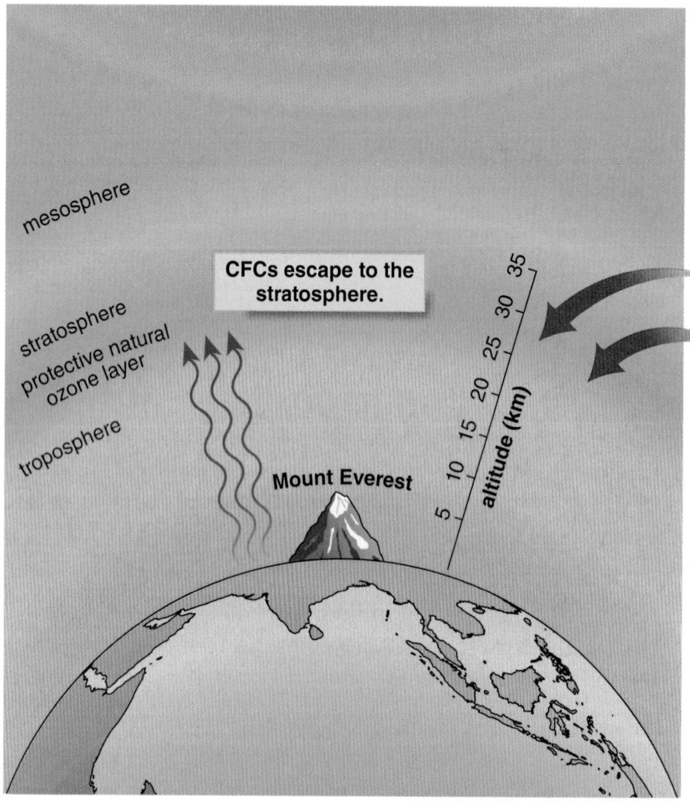

Figure 15.7 CFCs and the destruction of the ozone layer

Initiation: CFCs are decomposed by sunlight to form chlorine radicals.

$$CFCl_3 \xrightarrow{h\nu} \cdot CFCl_2 + \cdot\ddot{\underset{\cdot\cdot}{Cl}}:$$

Propagation: Ozone is destroyed by a chain reaction with radical intermediates.

$$\cdot\ddot{\underset{\cdot\cdot}{Cl}}: + O_3 \longrightarrow :\ddot{\underset{\cdot\cdot}{Cl}}-\ddot{\underset{\cdot\cdot}{O}}\cdot + O_2$$

$$:\ddot{\underset{\cdot\cdot}{Cl}}-\ddot{\underset{\cdot\cdot}{O}}\cdot + \cdot\ddot{\underset{\cdot\cdot}{O}}\cdot \longrightarrow \cdot\ddot{\underset{\cdot\cdot}{Cl}}: + O_2$$

- The chain reaction is initiated by homolysis of a C–Cl bond in $CFCl_3$.
- Propagation consists of two steps. Reaction of Cl· with O_3 forms chlorine monoxide (ClO·), which reacts with oxygen atoms to form O_2 and Cl·.

Problem 15.16 Nitric oxide, NO·, is another radical also thought to cause ozone destruction by a similar mechanism. One source of NO· in the stratosphere is supersonic aircraft whose jet engines convert small amounts of N_2 and O_2 to NO·. Write the propagation steps for the reaction of O_3 with NO·.

15.10 Radical Halogenation at an Allylic Carbon

Now let's examine radical halogenation at an ***allylic carbon*****—the carbon adjacent to a double bond.** Homolysis of the allylic C–H bond of propene generates the **allyl radical,** which has an unpaired electron on the carbon adjacent to the double bond.

$$CH_2{=}CH{-}CH_2{-}H \longrightarrow CH_2{=}CH{-}\dot{C}H_2 + \cdot H \qquad \Delta H^\circ = +364\ \text{kJ/mol}$$

(allylic C–H bond) (allyl radical)

The bond dissociation energy for this process (364 kJ/mol) is even less than that for a 3° C–H bond (381 kJ/mol). Because the weaker the C–H bond, the more stable the resulting radical, an **allyl radical is more stable than a 3° radical,** and the following order of radical stability results:

least stable: $\dot{C}H_3$ < $R\dot{C}H_2$ (1°) < $R_2\dot{C}H$ (2°) < $R_3\dot{C}$ (3°) < $CH_2{=}CH{-}\dot{C}H_2$ (allyl radical) : most stable

Increasing radical stability →

The position of the atoms and the σ bonds stays the same in drawing resonance structures. Resonance structures differ in the location of only π bonds and nonbonded electrons.

The allyl radical is more stable than other radicals because two resonance structures can be drawn for it.

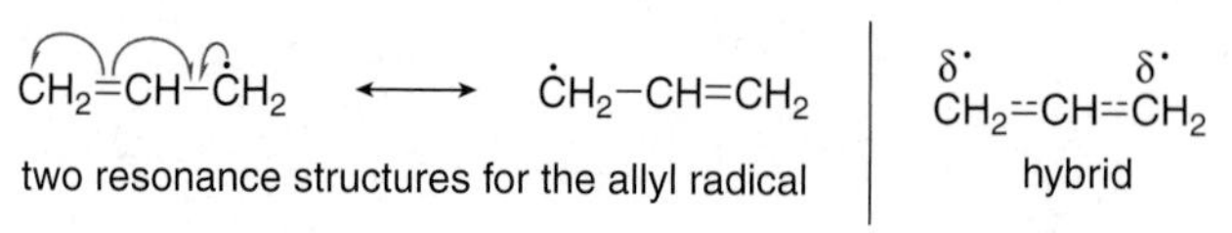

- **The "true" structure of the allyl radical is a hybrid of the two resonance structures. In the hybrid, the π bond and the unpaired electron are delocalized.**
- **Delocalizing electron density lowers the energy of the hybrid, thus stabilizing the allyl radical.**

Problem 15.17 Draw a second resonance structure for each radical. Then draw the hybrid.

a. $CH_3CH{=}CH{-}\dot{C}H_2$

b. 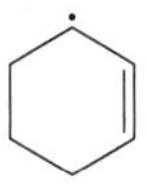

c. 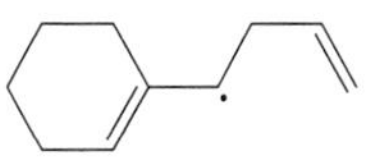

d. 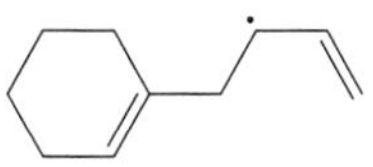

15.10A Selective Bromination at Allylic C–H Bonds

Because allylic C–H bonds are weaker than other sp^3 hybridized C–H bonds, the **allylic carbon can be selectively halogenated** by using *N*-bromosuccinimide (**NBS,** Section 10.15) in the presence of light or peroxides. Under these conditions only the allylic C–H bond in cyclohexene reacts to form an allylic halide.

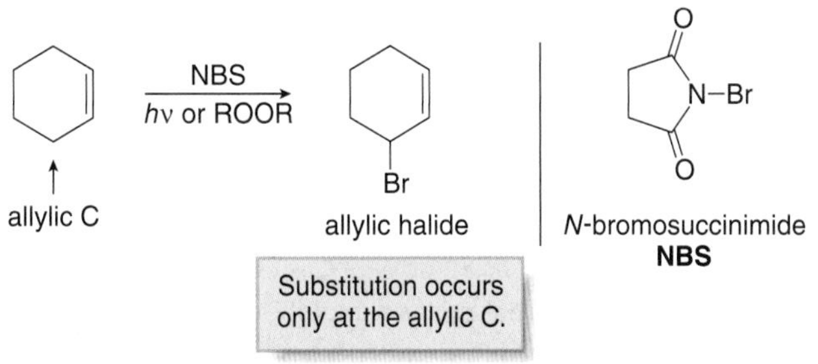
NBS
hν or ROOR
allylic C
Br
allylic halide
N–Br
O
O
N-bromosuccinimide
NBS
Substitution occurs only at the allylic C.

NBS contains a weak N–Br bond that is homolytically cleaved with light to generate a bromine radical, initiating an allylic halogenation reaction. Propagation then consists of the usual two steps of radical halogenation as shown in Mechanism 15.2.

Mechanism 15.2 Allylic Bromination with NBS

Initiation

Step [1] Cleavage of the N–Br bond forms two radicals.

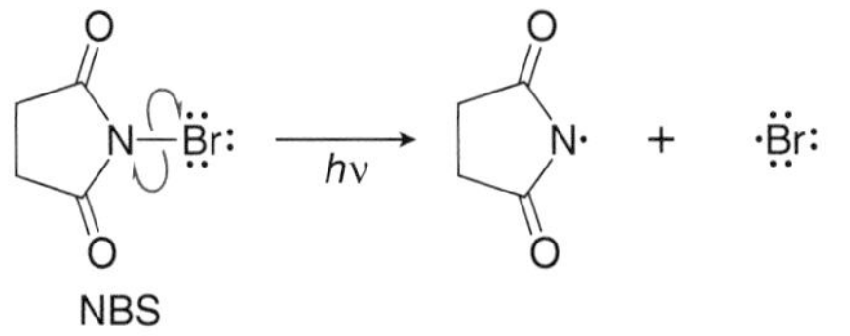
O
N
Br:
O
NBS
hν
N·
+
·Br:

- The reaction begins with homolysis of the weak N–Br bond in NBS using light energy. This generates a Br· radical that begins the radical halogenation process.

Propagation

Steps [2] and [3] One radical reacts and a new radical is formed in each step.

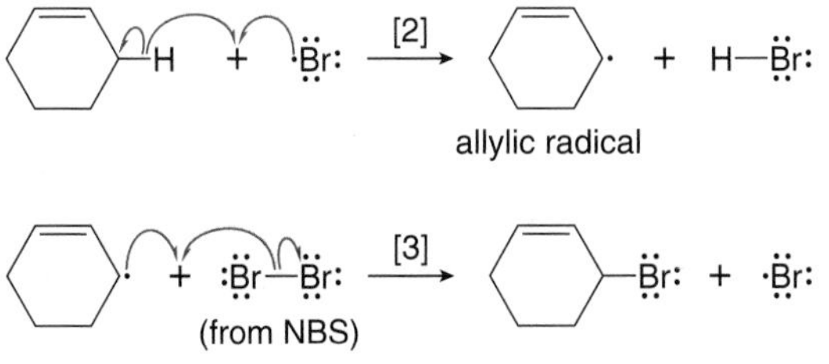
H
+
·Br:
[2]
+ H–Br:
allylic radical
+ :Br–Br:
(from NBS)
[3]
Br:
+ ·Br:

- The Br· radical abstracts an allylic hydrogen atom to afford an allylic radical in Step [2]. (Only one Lewis structure of the allylic radical is drawn.)
- The allylic radical reacts with Br_2 in the second propagation step to form the product of allylic halogenation. Because the Br· radical formed in Step [3] is also a reactant in Step [2], Steps [2] and [3] repeatedly occur without the need for Step [1].

Besides acting as a source of Br· to initiate the reaction, NBS generates a low concentration of Br_2 needed in the second chain propagation step (Step [3] of the mechanism). The HBr formed in Step [2] reacts with NBS to form Br_2, which is then used for halogenation in Step [3] of the mechanism.

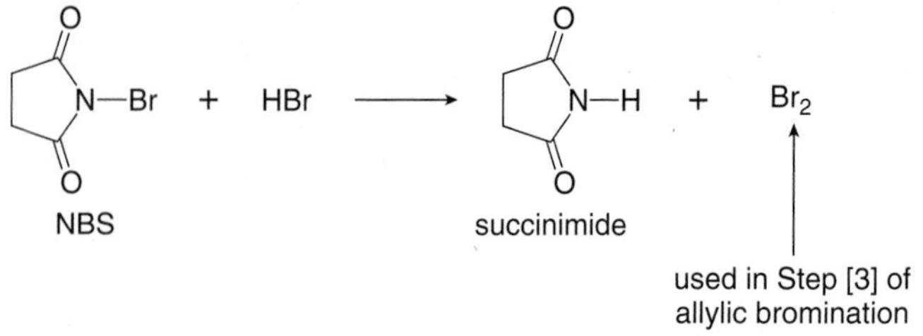

A **low concentration of Br_2** (from NBS) **favors allylic substitution** (over addition) in part because bromine is needed for only *one* step of the mechanism. When Br_2 adds to a double bond, a low Br_2 concentration would first form a low concentration of bridged bromonium ion (Section 10.13), which must then react with more bromine (in the form of Br^-) in a second step to form a dibromide. **If concentrations of both intermediates—bromonium ion and Br^-—are low, the overall rate of addition is very slow.**

Thus, an alkene with allylic C–H bonds undergoes two different reactions depending on the reaction conditions.

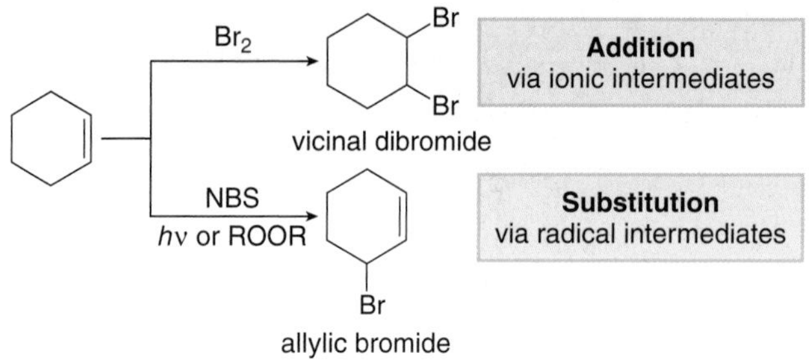

- Treatment of cyclohexene with Br_2 (in an organic solvent like CCl_4) leads to **addition** via **ionic intermediates** (Section 10.13).
- Treatment of cyclohexene with NBS (+ *h*ν or ROOR) leads to **allylic substitution,** via **radical intermediates.**

Problem 15.18 Draw the products of each reaction.

a.  $\xrightarrow[h\nu]{\text{NBS}}$ b. $CH_2{=}CH{-}CH_3 \xrightarrow[h\nu]{\text{NBS}}$ c. $CH_2{=}CH{-}CH_3 \xrightarrow{Br_2}$

15.10B Product Mixtures in Allylic Halogenation

Halogenation at an allylic carbon often results in a mixture of products. For example, bromination of 1-butene under radical conditions forms a mixture of 3-bromo-1-butene and 1-bromo-2-butene.

$$\underset{\text{1-butene}}{CH_2{=}CHCH_2CH_3} \xrightarrow[h\nu \text{ or ROOR}]{\text{NBS}} \underset{\text{3-bromo-1-butene}}{CH_2{=}CH\underset{Br}{C}HCH_3} + \underset{\text{1-bromo-2-butene}}{BrCH_2CH{=}CHCH_3}$$

A mixture is obtained because the reaction proceeds by way of a **resonance-stabilized radical.** Abstraction of an allylic hydrogen from 1-butene with a Br· radical (from NBS) forms an allylic radical for which **two different Lewis structures** can be drawn.

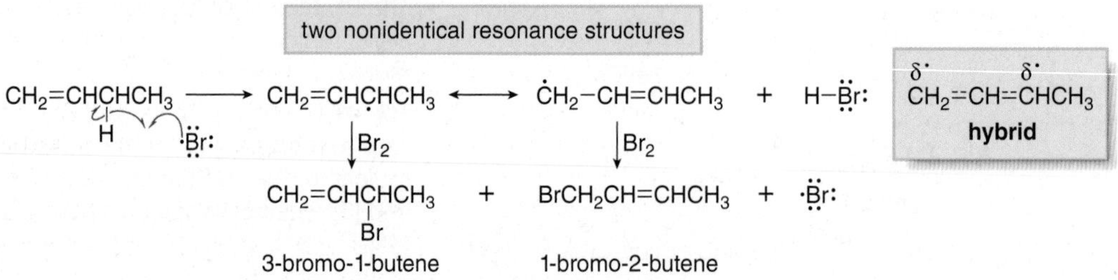

As a result, two different C atoms have partial radical character (indicated by $\delta^{\bullet}$), so that Br_2 reacts at two different sites and two allylic halides are formed.

- **Whenever two different resonance structures can be drawn for an allylic radical, two different allylic halides are formed by radical substitution.**

Sample Problem 15.4 Draw the products formed when **A** is treated with NBS + *hν*.

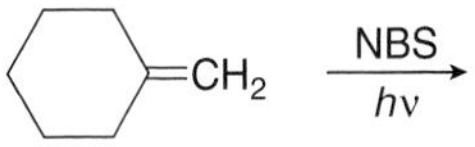

A

Solution

Hydrogen abstraction at the allylic C forms a resonance-stabilized radical (with two different resonance structures) that reacts with Br_2 to form two constitutional isomers as products.

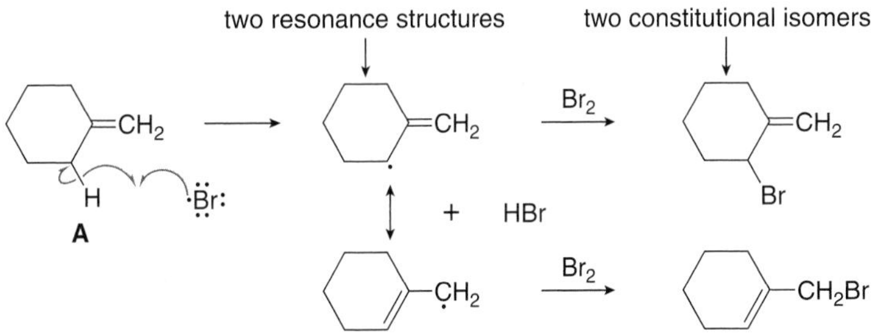

Problem 15.19 Draw all constitutional isomers formed when each alkene is treated with NBS + *hν*.

a. $CH_3CH{=}CHCH_3$ b. 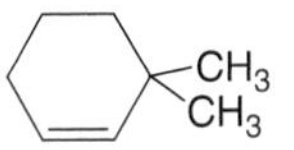

c. $CH_2{=}C(CH_2CH_3)_2$

Problem 15.20 Draw the structure of the four allylic halides formed when 3-methylcyclohexene undergoes allylic halogenation with NBS + *hν*.

Problem 15.21 Which compounds can be prepared in good yield by allylic halogenation of an alkene?

a. 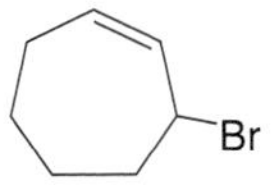

b. $CH_3CH_2CH{=}CHCH_2Br$ c. 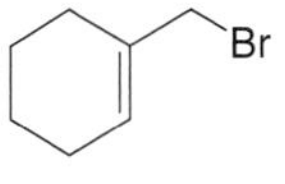

15.11 Application: Oxidation of Unsaturated Lipids

Oils—triacylglycerols having one or more sites of unsaturation in their long carbon chains—are susceptible to oxidation at their allylic carbon atoms. Oxidation occurs by way of a radical chain mechanism, as shown in Figure 15.8.

- **Step [1]** Oxygen in the air abstracts an allylic hydrogen atom to form an allylic radical because the allylic C–H bond is weaker than the other C–H bonds.
- **Step [2]** The allylic radical reacts with another molecule of O_2 to form a peroxy radical.
- **Step [3]** The peroxy radical abstracts an allylic hydrogen from another lipid molecule to form a hydroperoxide and another allylic radical that continues the chain. Steps [2] and [3] can repeat again and again until some other radical terminates the chain.

The hydroperoxides formed by this process are unstable and decompose to other oxidation products, many of which have a disagreeable odor and taste. **This process turns an oil rancid. Unsaturated lipids are more easily oxidized than saturated ones** because they contain weak allylic C–H bonds that are readily cleaved in Step [1] of this reaction, forming resonance-stabilized allylic radicals. Because saturated fats have no double bonds and thus no weak allylic C–H bonds, they are much less susceptible to air oxidation, resulting in increased shelf life of products containing them.

Figure 15.8
The oxidation of unsaturated lipids with O_2

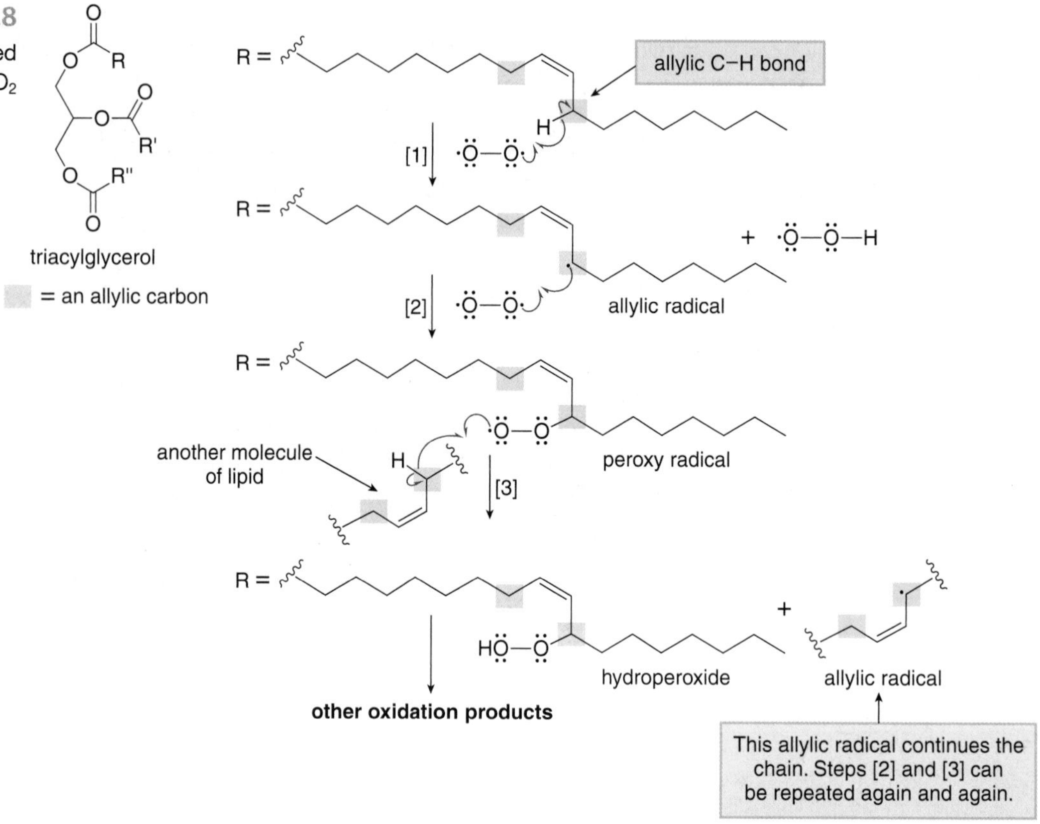

- Oxidation is shown at one allylic carbon only. Reaction at the other labeled allylic carbon is also possible.

Problem 15.22 Which C–H bond is most readily cleaved in linoleic acid? Draw all possible resonance structures for the resulting radical. Draw all the hydroperoxides formed by reaction of this resonance-stabilized radical with O_2.

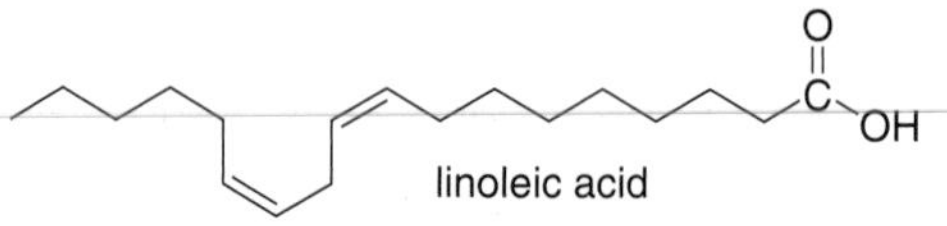

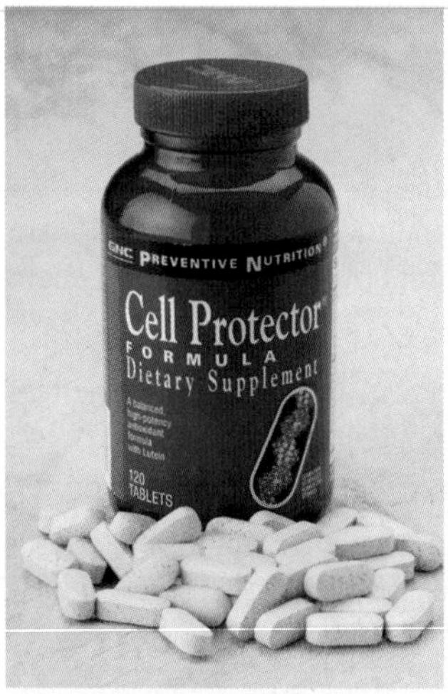

The purported health benefits of antioxidants have made them a popular component in anti-aging formulations.

15.12 Application: Antioxidants

An *antioxidant* is a compound that stops an oxidation reaction from occurring.

- Naturally occurring antioxidants such as **vitamin E** prevent radical reactions that can cause cell damage.
- Synthetic antioxidants such as **BHT—b**utylated **h**ydroxy **t**oluene—are added to packaged and prepared foods to prevent oxidation and spoilage.

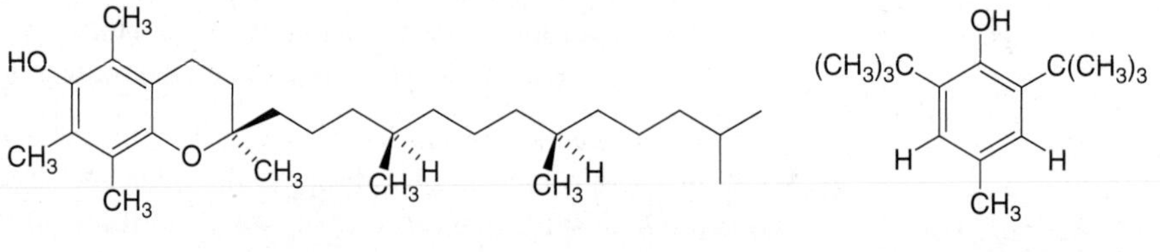

vitamin E

BHT
(**b**utylated **h**ydroxy **t**oluene)

Hazelnuts, almonds, and many other types of nuts are an excellent source of the natural antioxidant vitamin E.

Vitamin E and BHT are radical inhibitors, so they terminate radical chain mechanisms by reacting with radicals. How do they trap radicals? Both vitamin E and BHT use a hydroxy group bonded to a benzene ring—a general structure called a **phenol.**

Radicals (R·) abstract a hydrogen atom from the OH group of an antioxidant, forming a new resonance-stabilized radical. **This new radical does not participate in chain propagation,** but rather terminates the chain and halts the oxidation process. All phenols (including vitamin E and BHT) inhibit oxidation by this radical process.

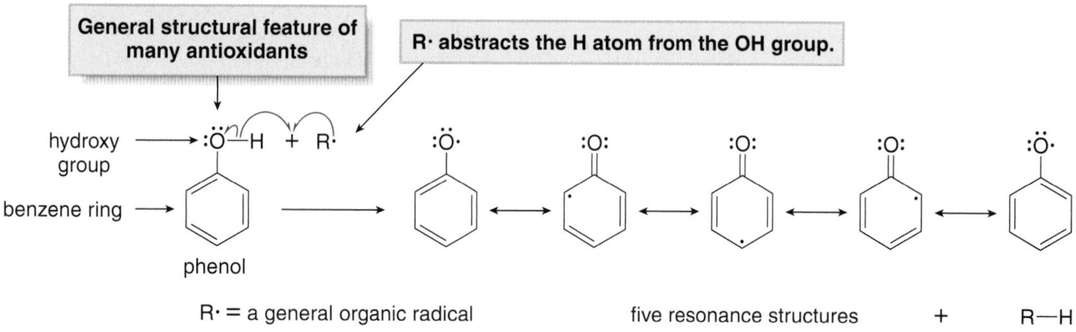

The many nonpolar C–C and C–H bonds of vitamin E make it fat soluble, and thus it dissolves in the nonpolar interior of the cell membrane, where it is thought to inhibit the oxidation of the unsaturated fatty acid residues in the phospholipids. Oxidative damage to lipids in cells via radical mechanisms is thought to play an important role in the aging process. For this reason, many anti-aging formulas with antioxidants like vitamin E are now popular consumer products.

Problem 15.23 Which of the following compounds might be an antioxidant?

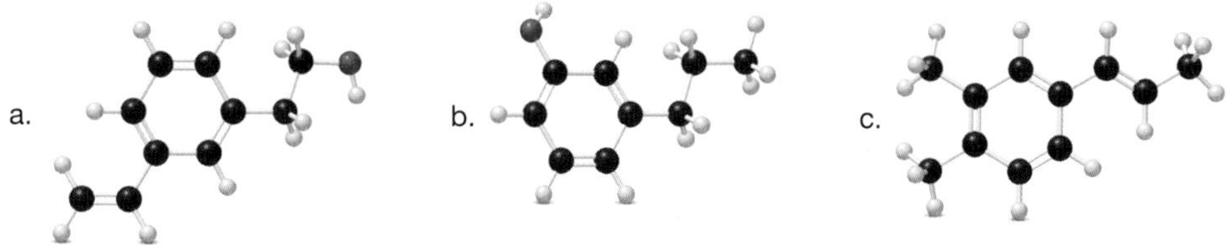

15.13 Radical Addition Reactions to Double Bonds

We now turn our attention to the second common reaction of radicals, addition to double bonds. Because an alkene contains an electron-rich, easily broken π bond, it reacts with an electron-deficient radical.

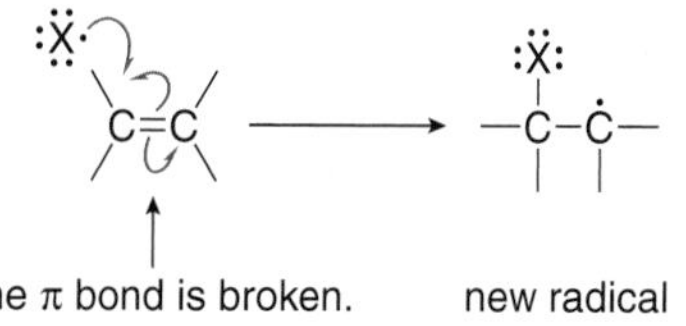

Radicals react with alkenes via a radical chain mechanism that consists of initiation, propagation, and termination steps analogous to those discussed previously for radical substitution.

15.13A Addition of HBr

HBr adds to alkenes to form alkyl bromides in the presence of light, heat, or peroxides.

General reaction—Radical addition of HBr

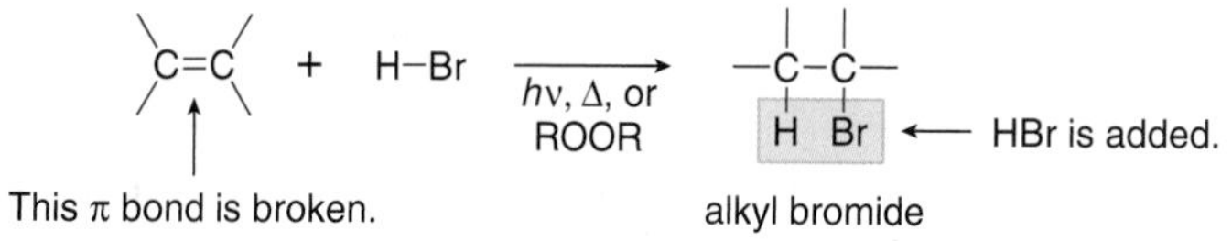

The regioselectivity of addition to an unsymmetrical alkene is *different* from the addition of HBr without added light, heat, or peroxides.

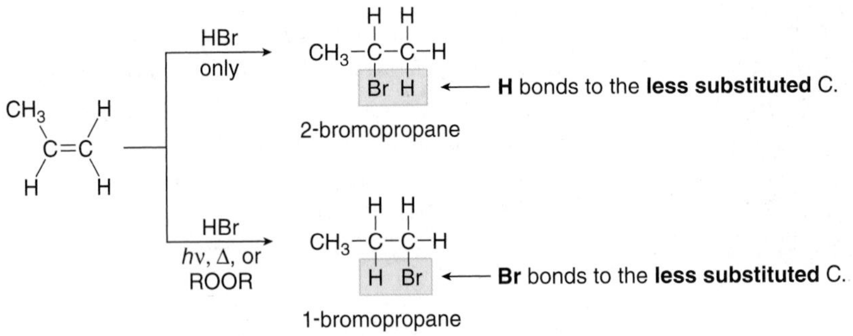

- HBr addition to propene *without* added light, heat, or peroxides gives 2-bromopropane: the **H atom is added to the less substituted carbon.** This reaction occurs via **carbocation** intermediates (Section 10.10).
- HBr addition to propene *with* added light, heat, or peroxides gives 1-bromopropane: the **Br atom is added to the less substituted carbon.** This reaction occurs via **radical** intermediates.

Problem 15.24 Draw the product(s) formed when each alkene is treated with either [1] HBr alone; or [2] HBr in the presence of peroxides.

a. $CH_2{=}CHCH_2CH_2CH_2CH_3$ b. 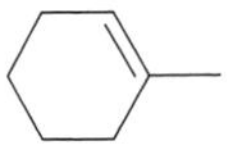 c. $CH_3CH{=}CHCH_2CH_2CH_3$

15.13B The Mechanism of the Radical Addition of HBr to an Alkene

In the presence of added light, heat, or peroxides, HBr addition to an alkene forms radical intermediates, and like other radical reactions, proceeds by a mechanism with three distinct parts: initiation, propagation, and termination. Mechanism 15.3 is written for the reaction of $CH_3CH{=}CH_2$ with HBr and ROOR to form $CH_3CH_2CH_2Br$.

The first propagation step (Step [3] of the mechanism, the addition of Br· to the double bond) is worthy of note. With propene there are two possible paths for this step, depending on which carbon atom of the double bond forms the new bond to bromine. Path [A] forms a less stable 1° radical whereas Path [B] forms a more stable 2° radical. **The more stable 2° radical forms faster,** so Path [B] is preferred.

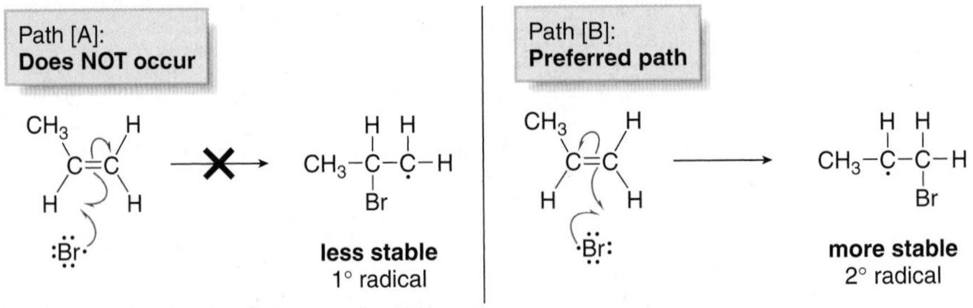

Mechanism 15.3 Radical Addition of HBr to an Alkene

Initiation

Steps [1] and [2] Abstraction of H from HBr occurs by a two-step process.

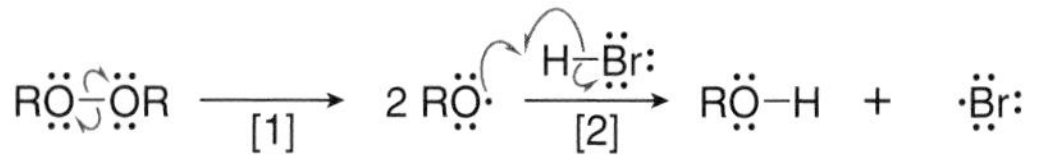

- With ROOR to initiate the reaction, two steps are needed to form Br·. Homolysis of the weak O – O bond of the peroxide forms RO·, which abstracts a hydrogen atom from HBr to form Br·.

Propagation

Steps [3] and [4] The π bond is broken and the C – H and C – Br σ bonds are formed.

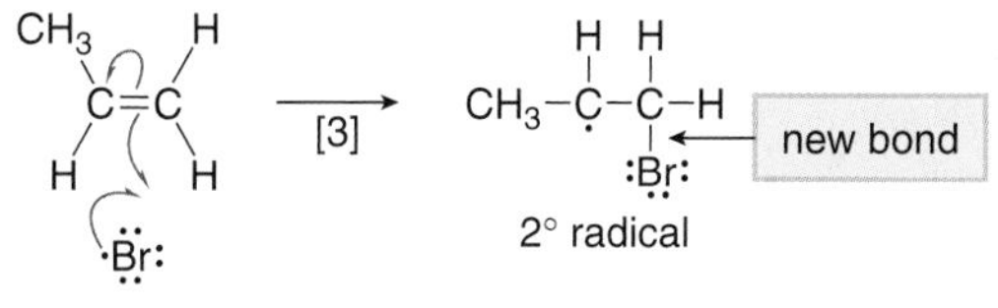

- The first step of propagation forms the C – Br bond when the Br· radical adds to the terminal carbon, leading to a 2° carbon radical.

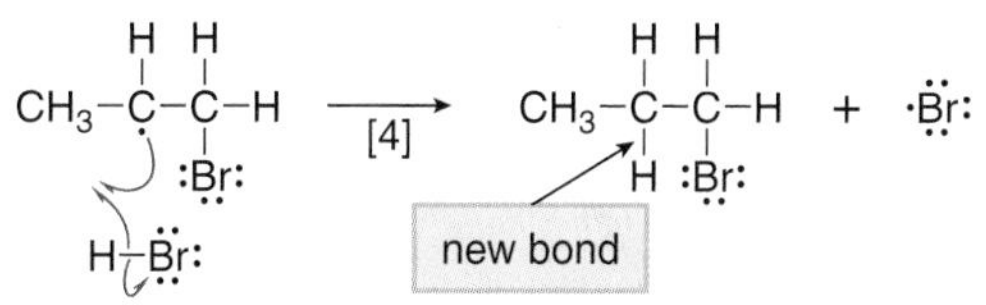

- The 2° radical abstracts a H atom from HBr, forming the new C – H bond and completing the addition reaction. Because a new Br· radical is also formed in this step, Steps [3] and [4] occur repeatedly.

Repeat Steps [3], [4], [3], [4], and so forth.

Termination

Step [5] Two radicals react to form a bond.

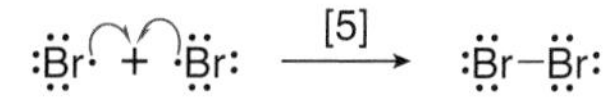

- To terminate the chain, two radicals (for example two Br· radicals) react with each other to form a stable bond, preventing further propagation via Steps [3] and [4].

The mechanism also illustrates why the regioselectivity of HBr addition is different depending on the reaction conditions. In both reactions, H and Br add to the double bond, but the *order* of addition depends on the mechanism.

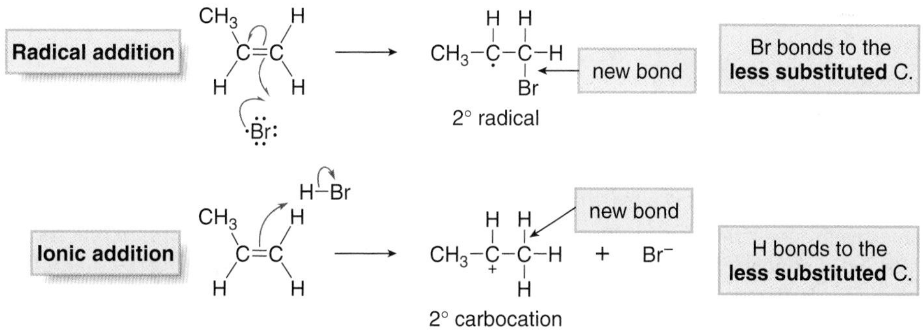

- **In radical addition (HBr with added light, heat, or ROOR), *Br· adds first* to generate the more stable radical.**
- **In ionic addition (HBr alone), *H⁺ adds first* to generate the more stable carbocation.**

Problem 15.25 When HBr adds to $(CH_3)_2C=CH_2$ under radical conditions, two radicals are possible products in the first step of chain propagation. Draw the structure of both radicals and indicate which one is formed. Then draw the preferred product from HBr addition under radical conditions.

Problem 15.26 What reagents are needed to convert 1-ethylcyclohexene into (a) 1-bromo-2-ethylcyclohexane; (b) 1-bromo-1-ethylcyclohexane; (c) 1,2-dibromo-1-ethylcyclohexane?

15.13C Energy Changes in the Radical Addition of HBr

The energy changes during propagation in the radical addition of HBr to $CH_2{=}CH_2$ can be calculated from bond dissociation energies, as shown in Figure 15.9.

Both propagation steps for the addition of HBr are exothermic, so propagation is exothermic (energetically favorable) overall. For the addition of HCl or HI, however, one of the chain-propagating steps is quite endothermic, and thus too difficult to be part of a repeating chain mechanism. Thus, **HBr adds to alkenes under radical conditions, but HCl and HI do not.**

Problem 15.27 Draw an energy diagram for the two propagation steps in the radical addition of HBr to propene. Draw the transition state for each step.

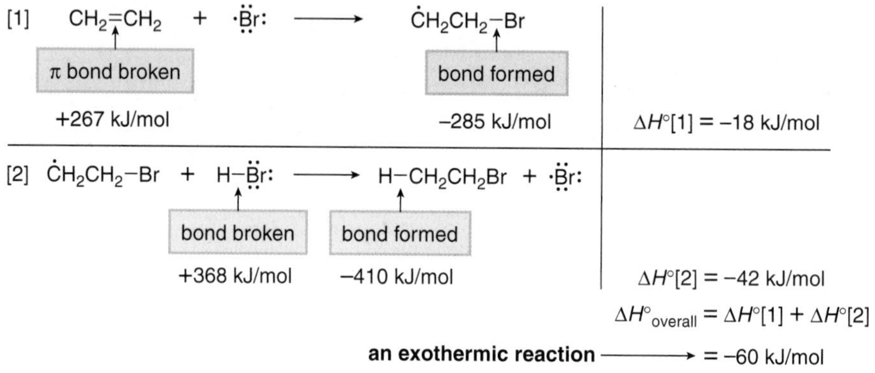

Figure 15.9 Energy changes during the propagation steps: $CH_2{=}CH_2 + HBr \rightarrow CH_3CH_2Br$

15.14 Polymers and Polymerization

HDPE (high-density polyethylene) and **LDPE** (low-density polyethylene) are two common types of polyethylene prepared under different reaction conditions and having different physical properties. HDPE is opaque and rigid, and is used in milk containers and water jugs. LDPE is less opaque and more flexible, and is used in plastic bags and electrical insulation. Products containing HDPE and LDPE (and other plastics) are often labeled with a symbol indicating recycling ease: the lower the number, the easier to recycle.

Polymers*—large molecules made up of repeating units of smaller molecules called *monomers—include such biologically important compounds as proteins and carbohydrates. They also include such industrially important plastics as polyethylene, poly(vinyl chloride) (PVC), and polystyrene.

15.14A Synthetic Polymers

Many synthetic polymers—that is, those synthesized in the lab—are among the most widely used organic compounds in modern society. Although some synthetic polymers resemble natural substances, many have different and unusual properties that make them more useful than naturally occurring materials. Soft drink bottles, plastic bags, food wrap, compact discs, Teflon, and Styrofoam are all made of synthetic polymers. In this section we examine polymers derived from alkene monomers. Chapter 31 is devoted to a detailed discussion of the synthesis and properties of several different types of synthetic polymers.

- ***Polymerization*** **is the joining together of monomers to make polymers.**

For example, joining **ethylene monomers** together forms the polymer **polyethylene,** a plastic used in milk containers and sandwich bags.

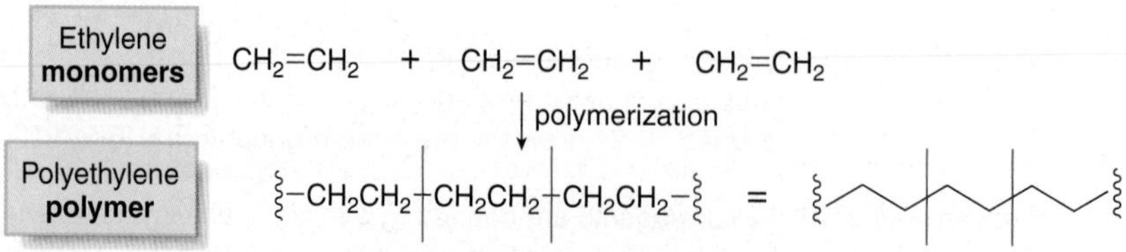

three monomer units joined together

Many ethylene derivatives having the general structure **$CH_2{=}CHZ$** are also used as monomers for polymerization. The identity of Z affects the physical properties of the resulting polymer, making some polymers more suitable for one consumer product (e.g., plastic bags or food wrap) than another (e.g., soft drink bottles or compact discs). Polymerization of $CH_2{=}CHZ$ usually affords polymers with the Z groups on every other carbon atom in the chain. Table 15.2 lists some common monomers and polymers used in medicine or dentistry.

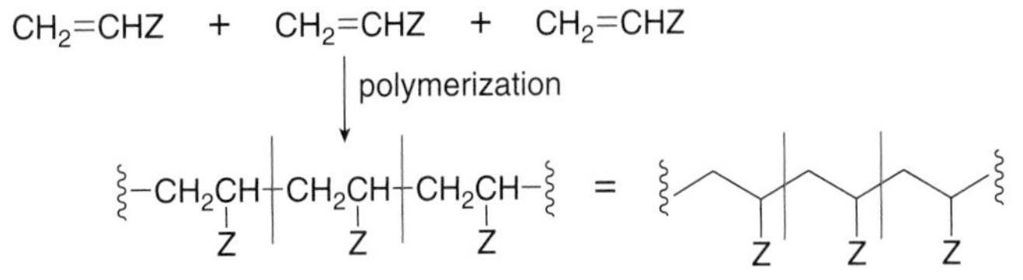

three monomer units joined together

Sample Problem 15.5 What polymer is formed when $CH_2{=}CHCO_2H$ (acrylic acid) is polymerized? The resulting polymer, poly(acrylic acid), is used in disposable diapers because it absorbs 30 times its weight in water.

Solution

Draw three or more alkene monomers, break one bond of each double bond, and join the alkenes together with single bonds. With unsymmetrical alkenes, substituents are bonded to every other carbon.

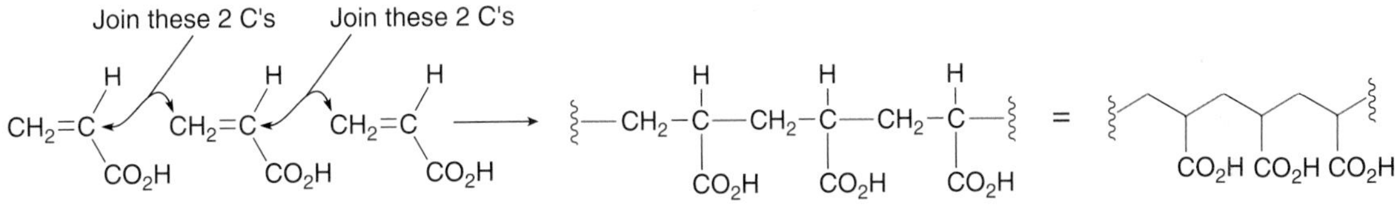

[New bonds are drawn in red.]

poly(acrylic acid)

Table 15.2 Common Monomers and Polymers Used in Medicine and Dentistry

Monomer →	Polymer	Consumer product
$CH_2{=}CHCl$ → vinyl chloride	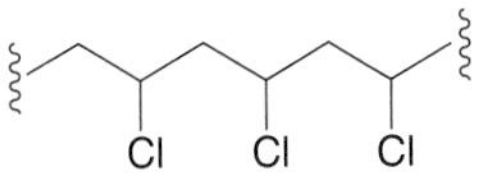 **poly(vinyl chloride) PVC**	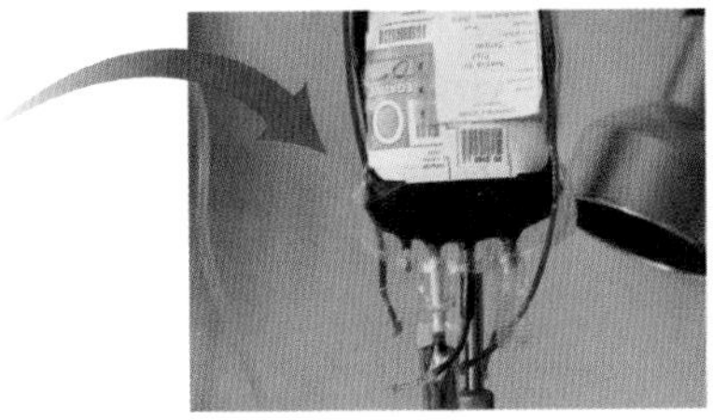 PVC blood bags and tubing
$CH_2{=}CHCH_3$ → propene	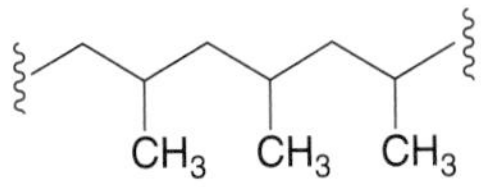 **polypropylene**	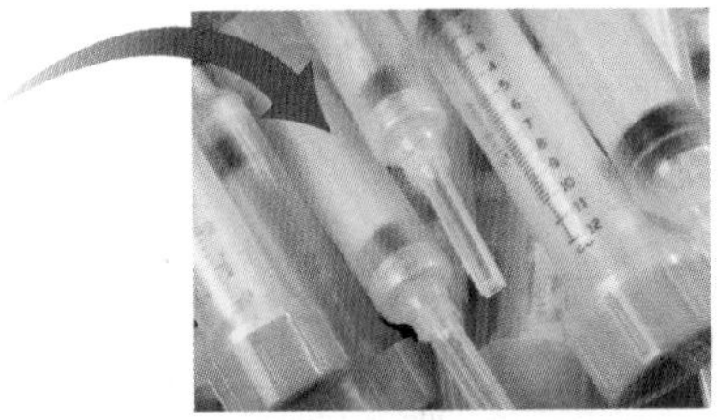 polypropylene syringes
$CF_2{=}CF_2$ → tetrafluoroethylene	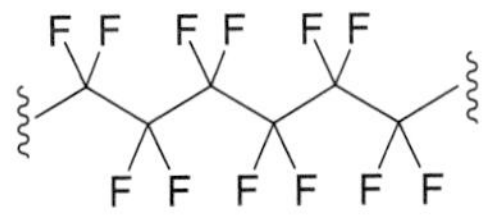 **polytetrafluoroethylene Teflon**	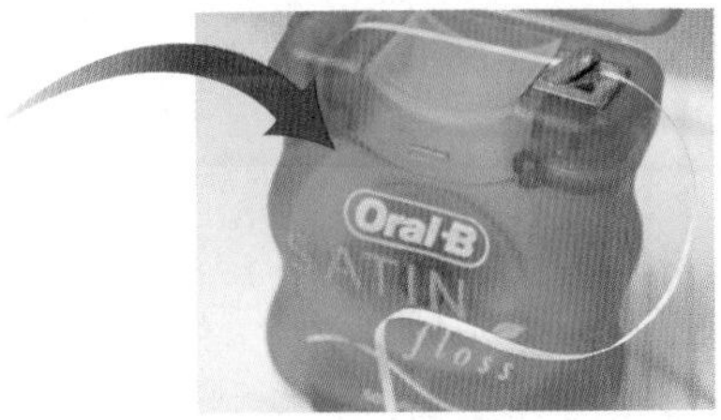 dental floss

Problem 15.28 (a) Draw the structure of polystyrene, the chapter-opening molecule, which is formed by polymerizing the monomer styrene, $C_6H_5CH{=}CH_2$. (b) What monomer is used to form poly(vinyl acetate), a polymer used in paints and adhesives?

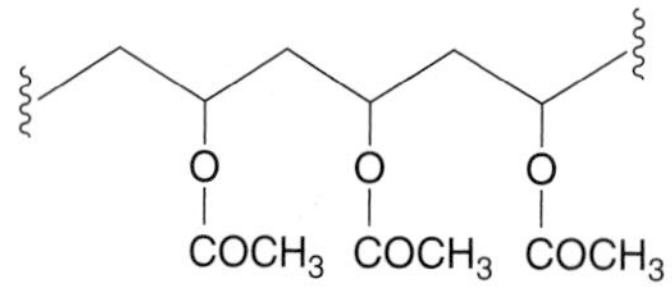

poly(vinyl acetate)

15.14B Radical Polymerization

The alkene monomers used in polymerization are prepared from petroleum.

The polymers described in Section 15.14A are prepared by polymerization of alkene monomers by **adding a radical to a π bond.** The mechanism resembles the radical addition of HBr to an alkene, except that a **carbon radical rather than a bromine atom is added to the double bond.** Mechanism 15.4 is written with the general monomer $CH_2{=}CHZ$, and again has three parts: initiation, propagation, and termination.

Mechanism 15.4 Radical Polymerization of $CH_2{=}CHZ$

Initiation

Steps [1] and [2] A carbon radical is formed by a two-step process.

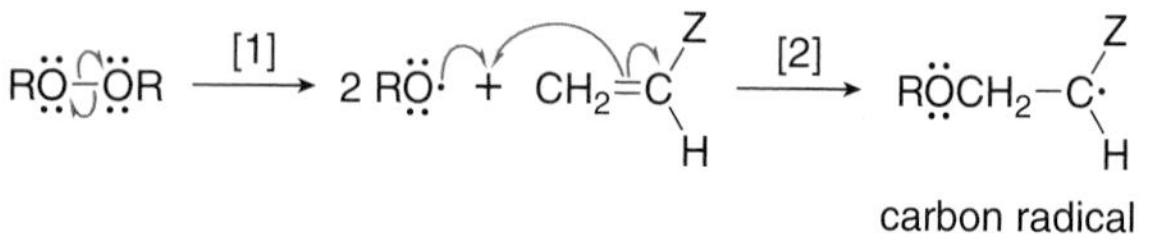

- Chain initiation begins with homolysis of the weak O–O bond of the peroxide to form RO·, which then adds to a molecule of monomer to form a carbon radical.

Propagation

Step [3] The polymer chain grows.

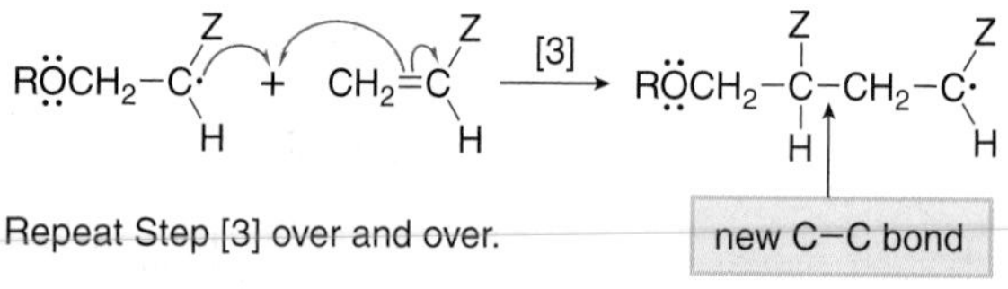

Repeat Step [3] over and over.

- Chain propagation consists of a single step that joins monomer units together.
- In Step [3], the carbon radical formed during initiation adds to another alkene molecule to form a new C–C bond and another carbon radical. Addition always forms the more substituted carbon radical—that is, the **unpaired electron is always located on the carbon atom having the Z substituent.**
- This carbon radical reacts with more monomer, so that Step [3] occurs repeatedly, and the polymer chain grows.

Termination

Step [4] Two radicals combine to form a bond.

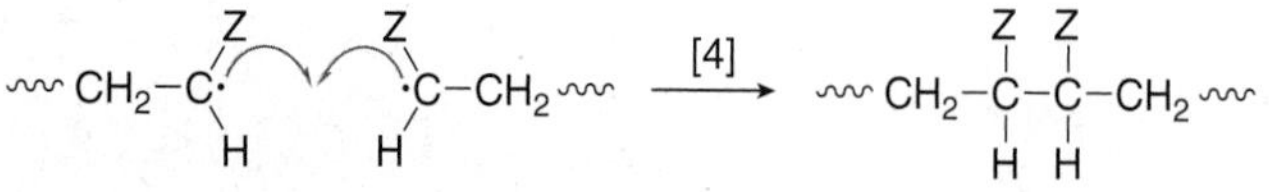

- To terminate the chain, two radicals combine to form a stable bond, thus ending the polymerization process.

In radical polymerization, the more substituted radical always adds to the less substituted end of the monomer, a process called **head-to-tail polymerization.**

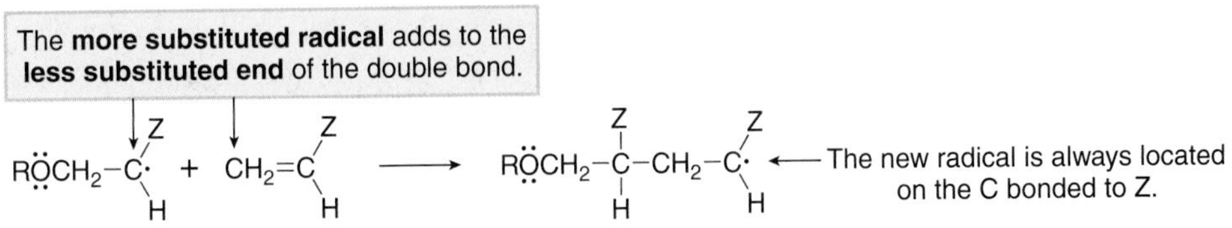
The more substituted radical adds to the less substituted end of the double bond.
The new radical is always located on the C bonded to Z.

Problem 15.29 Draw the steps of the mechanism that converts vinyl chloride ($CH_2{=}CHCl$) into poly(vinyl chloride).

KEY CONCEPTS

Radical Reactions

General Features of Radicals

- A radical is a reactive intermediate with a single unpaired electron (15.1).
- A carbon radical is sp^2 hybridized and trigonal planar (15.1).
- The stability of a radical increases as the number of C atoms bonded to the radical carbon increases (15.1).
- Allylic radicals are stabilized by resonance, making them more stable than 3° radicals (15.10).

Radical Reactions

[1] Halogenation of alkanes (15.4)

$$R{-}H \xrightarrow[h\nu \text{ or } \Delta]{X_2} R{-}X \text{ (alkyl halide)}$$

X = Cl or Br

- The reaction follows a radical chain mechanism.
- The weaker the C–H bond, the more readily the hydrogen is replaced by X.
- Chlorination is faster and less selective than bromination (15.6).
- Radical substitution at a stereogenic center results in racemization (15.8).

[2] Allylic halogenation (15.10)

$$CH_2{=}CH{-}CH_3 \xrightarrow[h\nu \text{ or ROOR}]{NBS} CH_2{=}CHCH_2Br \text{ (allylic halide)}$$

- The reaction follows a radical chain mechanism.

[3] Radical addition of HBr to an alkene (15.13)

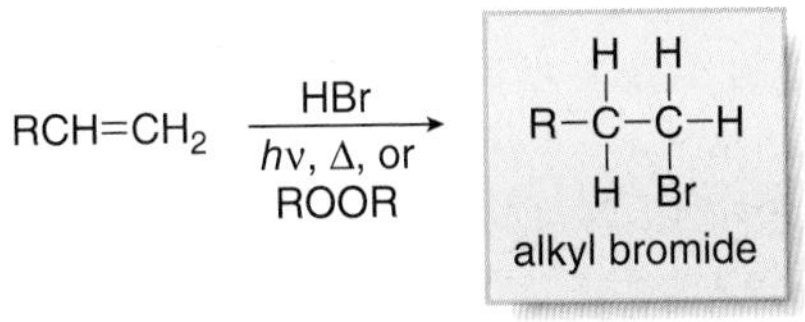
RCH=CH2
HBr
hν, Δ, or ROOR
alkyl bromide

- A radical addition mechanism is followed.
- Br bonds to the less substituted carbon atom to form the more substituted, more stable radical.

[4] Radical polymerization of alkenes (15.14)

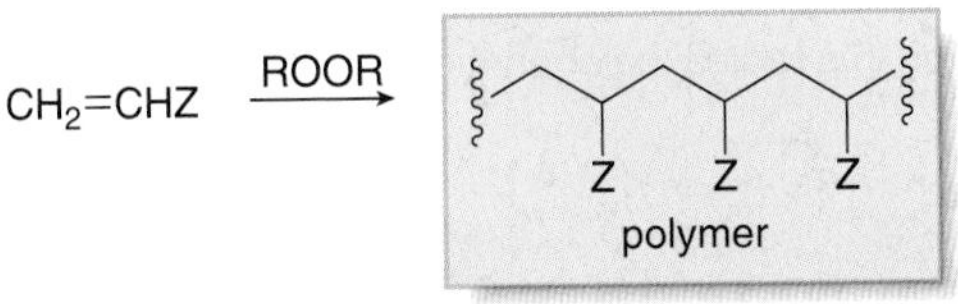
CH2=CHZ
ROOR
Z Z Z
polymer

- A radical addition mechanism is followed.

PROBLEMS

Problems Using Three-Dimensional Models

15.30 (a) Draw all constitutional isomers formed by monochlorination of each alkane with Cl_2 and *hν*. (b) Draw the major monobromination product formed by heating each alkane with Br_2.

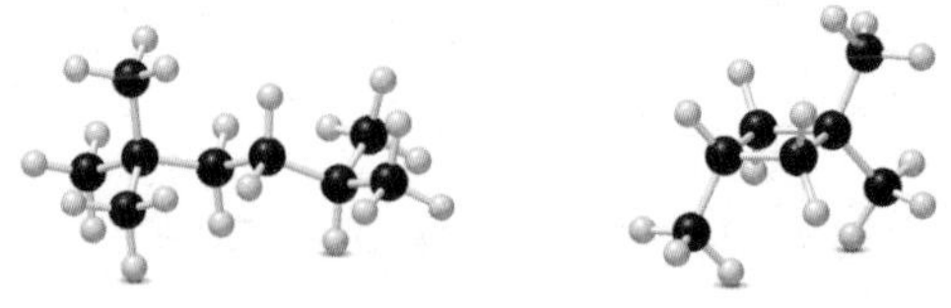

A B

15.31 Draw all resonance structures of the radical that results from abstraction of a hydrogen atom from the antioxidant BHA (**b**utylated **h**ydroxy **a**nisole).

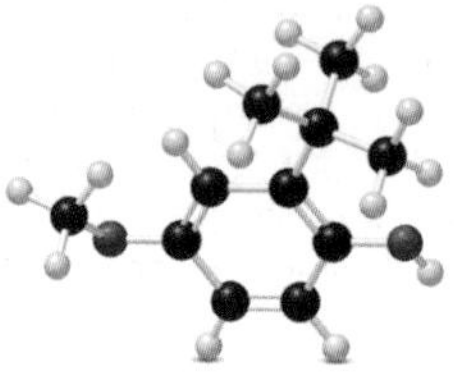

BHA

Radicals and Bond Strength

15.32 With reference to the indicated C – H bonds in 2-methylbutane:

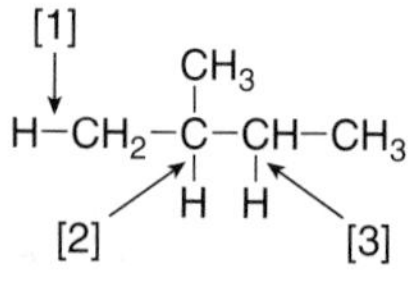

2-methylbutane

a. Rank the C – H bonds in order of increasing bond strength.
b. Draw the radical resulting from cleavage of each C – H bond, and classify it as 1°, 2°, or 3°.
c. Rank the radicals in order of increasing stability.
d. Rank the C – H bonds in order of increasing ease of H abstraction in a radical halogenation reaction.

15.33 Rank each group of radicals in order of increasing stability.

a. $(CH_3)_2\dot{C}CH_2CH(CH_3)_2$ $(CH_3)_2CH\dot{C}HCH(CH_3)_2$ $(CH_3)_2CHCH_2CH(CH_3)\dot{C}H_2$

b. 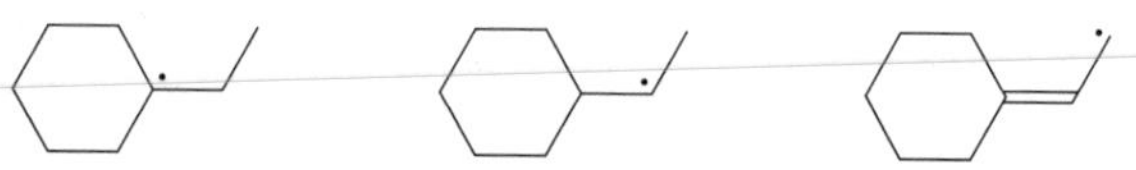

15.34 Why is a benzylic C – H bond unusually weak?

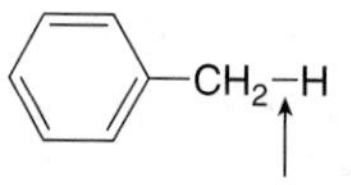

benzylic C—H bond

Halogenation of Alkanes

15.35 Rank the indicated hydrogen atoms in order of increasing ease of abstraction in a radical halogenation reaction.

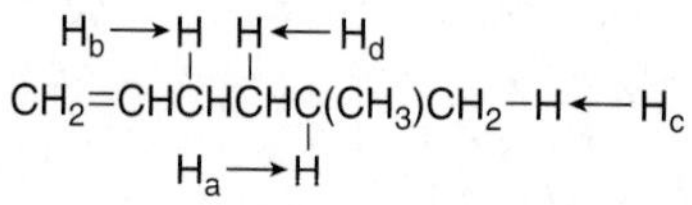

15.36 Draw all constitutional isomers formed by monochlorination of each alkane with Cl_2 and *hν*.

a.  b. $(CH_3)_3CCH_2CH_2CH_2CH_3$ c.  d. 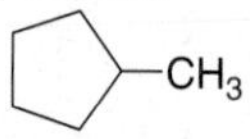

15.37 What is the major monobromination product formed by heating each alkane with Br_2?

a. 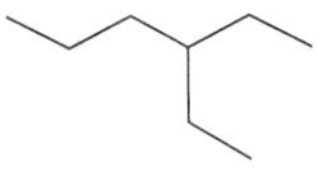 b. $(CH_3)_3CCH_2CH(CH_3)_2$ c. 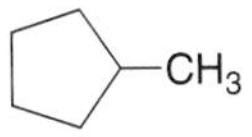 d. $(CH_3)_3CCH_2CH_3$

15.38 Five isomeric alkanes (**A–E**) having the molecular formula C_6H_{14} are each treated with $Cl_2 + h\nu$ to give alkyl halides having molecular formula $C_6H_{13}Cl$. **A** yields five constitutional isomers. **B** yields four constitutional isomers. **C** yields two constitutional isomers. **D** yields three constitutional isomers, two of which possess stereogenic centers. **E** yields three constitutional isomers, only one of which possesses a stereogenic center. Identify the structures of **A–E.**

15.39 What alkane is needed to make each alkyl halide by radical halogenation?

a. 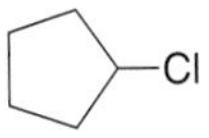 b. 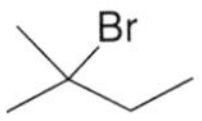 c. 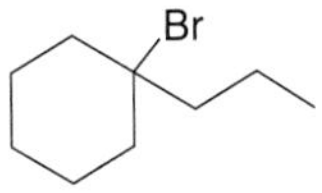 d. $(CH_3)_3CCH_2Cl$

15.40 Which alkyl halides can be prepared in good yield by radical halogenation of an alkane?

a. 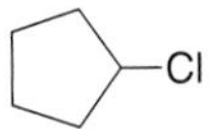 b. 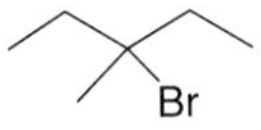 c. 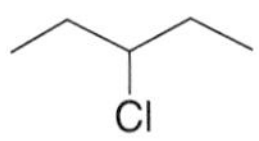 d. 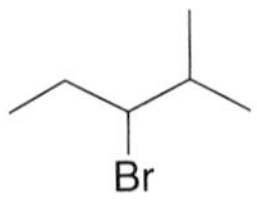

15.41 Draw the products of radical chlorination and bromination of each compound. For which compounds is a single constitutional isomer formed for both reactions? What must be true about the structure of a reactant for both reactions to form a single product?

a. 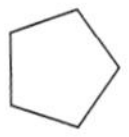 b.  c. 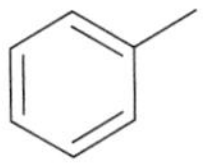 d.  e. 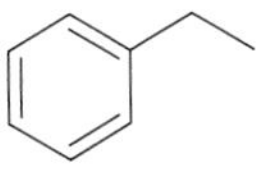

15.42 Explain why radical bromination of *p*-xylene forms **C** rather than **D.**

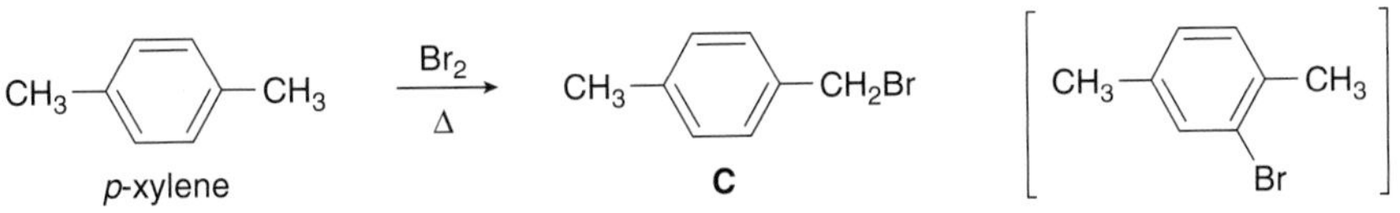

p-xylene **C** **D** NOT formed

15.43 a. What product(s) (excluding stereoisomers) are formed when **Y** is heated with Cl_2?
b. What product(s) (excluding stereoisomers) are formed when **Y** is heated with Br_2?
c. What steps are needed to convert **Y** to the alkene **Z**?

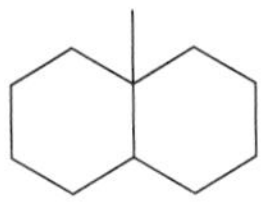

Y

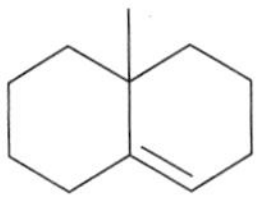

Z

Resonance

15.44 Draw resonance structures for each radical.

a. 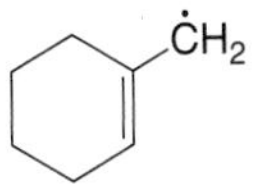 b.  c. 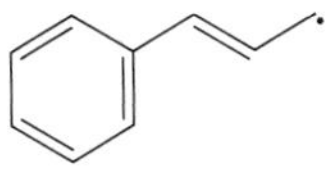

Allylic Halogenation

15.45 Draw the products formed when each alkene is treated with NBS + $h\nu$.

a.  b. $CH_3CH_2CH{=}CHCH_2CH_3$ c. $(CH_3)_2C{=}CHCH_3$ d. 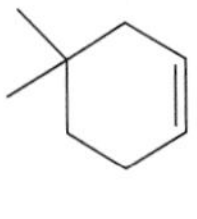

15.46 Is it possible to prepare 5-bromo-1-methylcyclopentene in good yield by allylic bromination of 1-methylcyclopentene? Explain.

15.47 Draw all constitutional isomers formed when **X** is treated with NBS + *hν*.

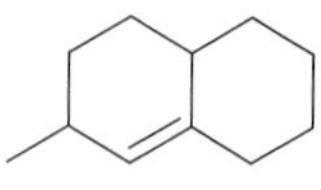

X

Reactions

15.48 Draw the organic products formed in each reaction.

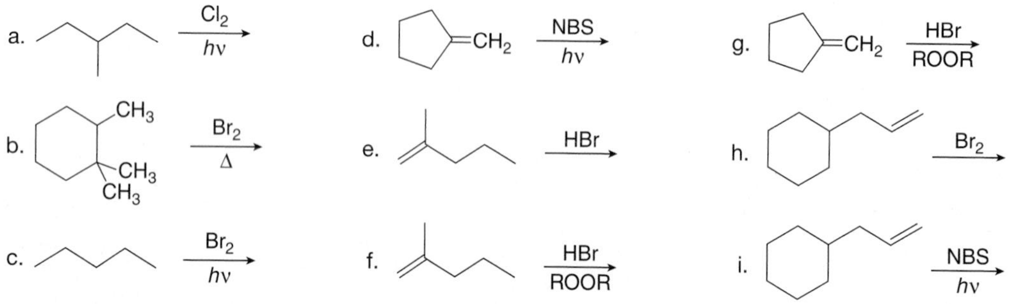

15.49 What reagents are needed to convert cyclopentene into (a) bromocyclopentane; (b) *trans*-1,2-dibromocyclopentane; (c) 3-bromocyclopentene?

15.50 Treatment of a hydrocarbon **A** (molecular formula C_9H_{18}) with Br_2 in the presence of light forms alkyl halides **B** and **C,** both having molecular formula $C_9H_{17}Br$. Reaction of either **B** or **C** with $KOC(CH_3)_3$ forms compound **D** (C_9H_{16}) as the major product. Ozonolysis of **D** forms cyclohexanone and acetone. Identify the structures of **A–D.**

cyclohexanone acetone

Stereochemistry and Reactions

15.51 Draw the products formed in each reaction and include the stereochemistry around any stereogenic centers.

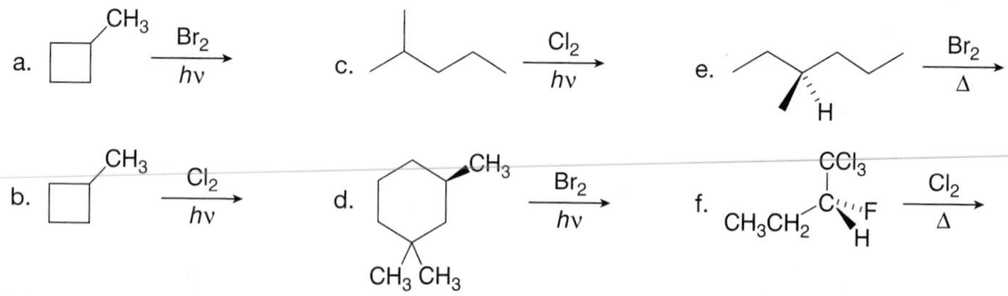

15.52 (a) Draw all stereoisomers of molecular formula $C_5H_{10}Cl_2$ formed when (2*R*)-2-chloropentane is heated with Cl_2. (b) Assuming that products having different physical properties can be separated into fractions by some physical method (such as fractional distillation), how many different fractions would be obtained? (c) Which of these fractions would be optically active?

15.53 (a) Draw all stereoisomers of molecular formula $C_7H_{15}Cl$ formed when (3*S*)-3-methylhexane is heated with Cl_2. (b) Assuming that products having different physical properties can be separated by fractional distillation, how many different fractions would be obtained? (c) How many fractions would be optically active?

15.54 Draw the six products (including stereoisomers) formed when **A** is treated with NBS + *hν*.

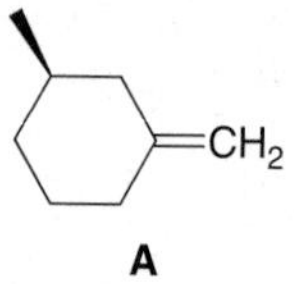

A

Mechanisms

15.55 Consider the following bromination: $(CH_3)_3CH + Br_2 \xrightarrow{\Delta} (CH_3)_3CBr + HBr$.

a. Calculate $\Delta H°$ for this reaction by using the bond dissociation energies in Table 6.2.

b. Draw out a stepwise mechanism for the reaction, including the initiation, propagation, and termination steps.

c. Calculate $\Delta H°$ for each propagation step.

d. Draw an energy diagram for the propagation steps.

e. Draw the structure of the transition state of each propagation step.

15.56 Draw a stepwise mechanism for the following reaction.

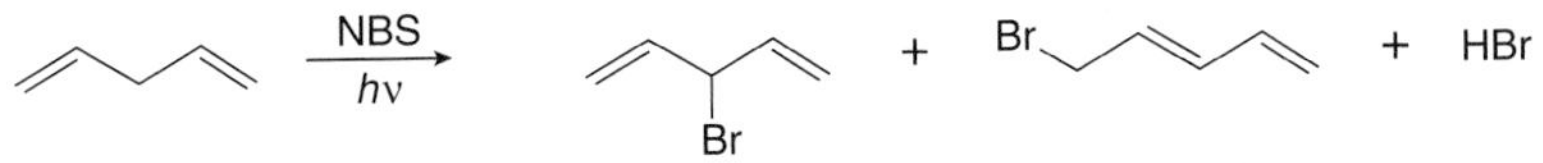

15.57 Although CH_4 reacts with Cl_2 to form CH_3Cl and HCl, the corresponding reaction of CH_4 with I_2 does not occur at an appreciable rate, even though the I–I bond is much weaker than the Cl–Cl bond. Explain why this is so.

15.58 An alternative mechanism for the propagation steps in the radical chlorination of CH_4 is drawn below. Calculate $\Delta H°$ for these steps and explain why this pathway is unlikely.

$$CH_4 + :\ddot{\underset{..}{Cl}}\cdot \longrightarrow CH_3Cl + H\cdot$$

$$H\cdot + Cl_2 \longrightarrow HCl + :\ddot{\underset{..}{Cl}}\cdot$$

15.59 When 3,3-dimethyl-1-butene is treated with HBr alone, the major product is 2-bromo-2,3-dimethylbutane. When the same alkene is treated with HBr and peroxide, the sole product is 1-bromo-3,3-dimethylbutane. Explain these results by referring to the mechanisms.

15.60 Write out the two propagation steps for the addition of HCl to propene and calculate $\Delta H°$ for each step. Which step prohibits chain propagation from repeatedly occurring?

Synthesis

15.61 Devise a synthesis of each compound from cyclopentane and any other required organic or inorganic reagents.

a. 

c. 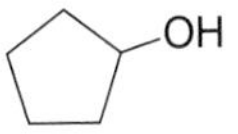

e. 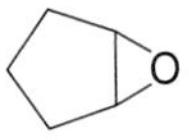

g. 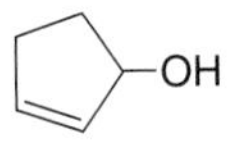

b. 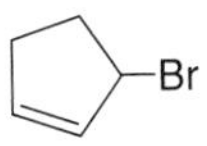

d. 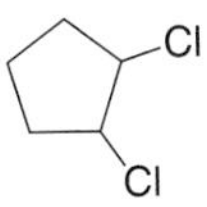

f. 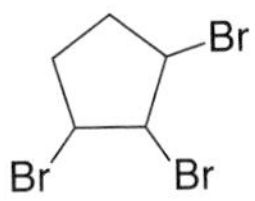

h. 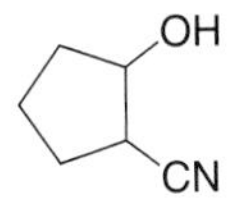

15.62 Devise a synthesis of each target compound from methylcyclohexane. You may use any other required organic or inorganic reagents.

a. 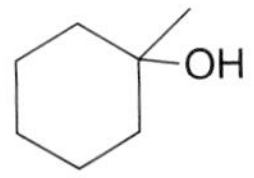

b. 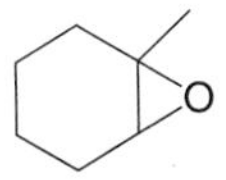

c. 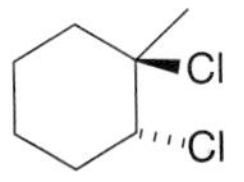

+ enantiomer

15.63 Devise a synthesis of each target compound from the indicated starting material. You may use any other required organic or inorganic reagents.

a. $CH_3C\equiv CH \Longrightarrow CH_3CH_2CH_3$

b. 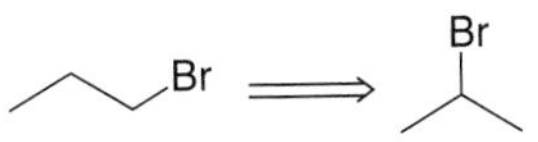

c. 

$\Longrightarrow$ HC≡CH

15.64 Devise a synthesis of each compound using CH_3CH_3 as the only source of carbon atoms. You may use any other required organic or inorganic reagents.

a. HC≡CH b. $HC\equiv CCH_2CH_3$ c. $HC\equiv CCH_2CH_2OH$ d. 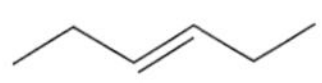 e. 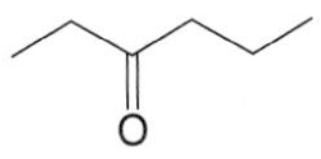

15.65 Devise a synthesis of $OHC(CH_2)_4CHO$ from cyclohexane using any required organic or inorganic reagents.

Radical Oxidation Reactions

15.66 As described in Section 9.16, the leukotrienes, important components in the asthmatic response, are synthesized from arachidonic acid via the hydroperoxide 5-HPETE. Write a stepwise mechanism for the conversion of arachidonic acid to 5-HPETE with O_2.

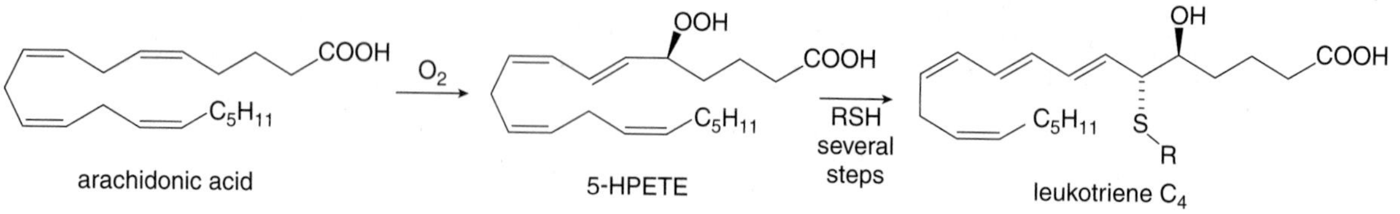
COOH
C5H11
arachidonic acid
O2
OOH
COOH
C5H11
5-HPETE
RSH
several
steps
OH
COOH
C5H11
S
R
leukotriene C4

15.67 Ethers are oxidized with O_2 to form hydroperoxides that decompose violently when heated. Draw a stepwise mechanism for this reaction.

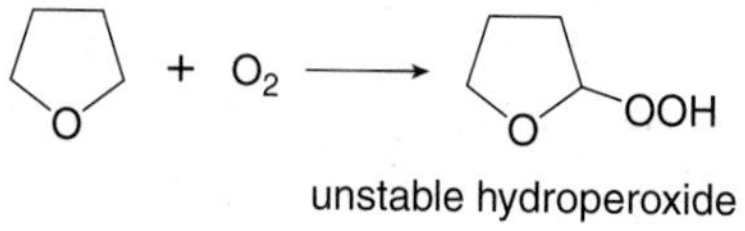
O
+ O2
O
OOH
unstable hydroperoxide

15.68 (a) Ignoring stereoisomers, what two allylic hydroperoxides are formed by the oxidation of 1-hexene with O_2? (b) Draw a stepwise mechanism that shows how these hydroperoxides are formed.

Antioxidants

15.69 Resveratrol is an antioxidant found in the skin of red grapes. Its anticancer, anti-inflammatory, and various cardiovascular effects are under active investigation. (a) Draw all resonance structures for the radical that results from homolysis of the OH bond shown in red. (b) Explain why homolysis of this OH bond is preferred to homolysis of either OH bond in the other benzene ring.

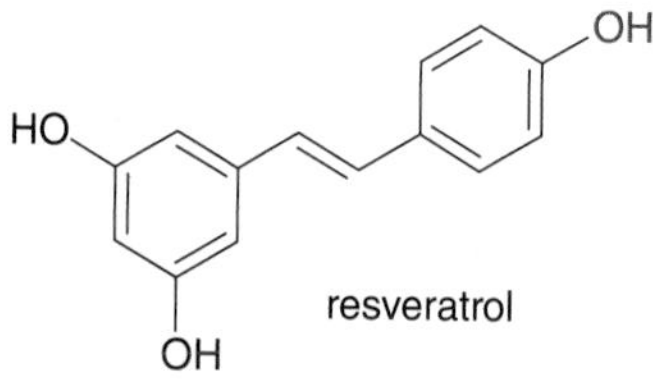
OH
HO
OH
resveratrol

15.70 In cells, vitamin C exists largely as its conjugate base **X**. **X** is an antioxidant because radicals formed in oxidation processes abstract the indicated H atom, forming a new radical that halts oxidation. Draw the structure of the radical formed by H abstraction, and explain why this H atom is most easily removed.

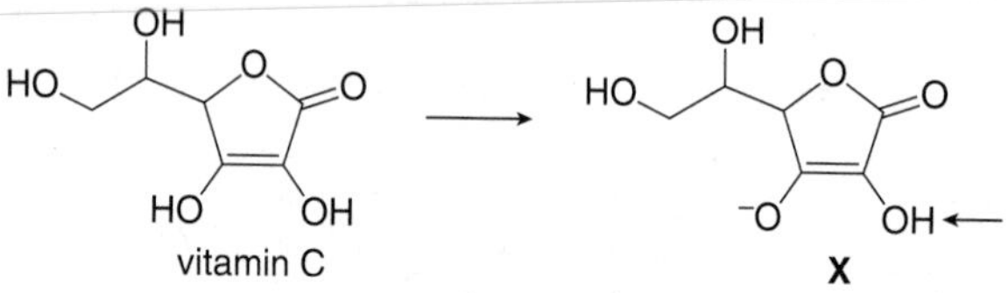
OH
HO
O
O
HO
OH
vitamin C
OH
HO
O
O
-O
OH
X

Polymers and Polymerization

15.71 What monomer is needed to form each polymer?

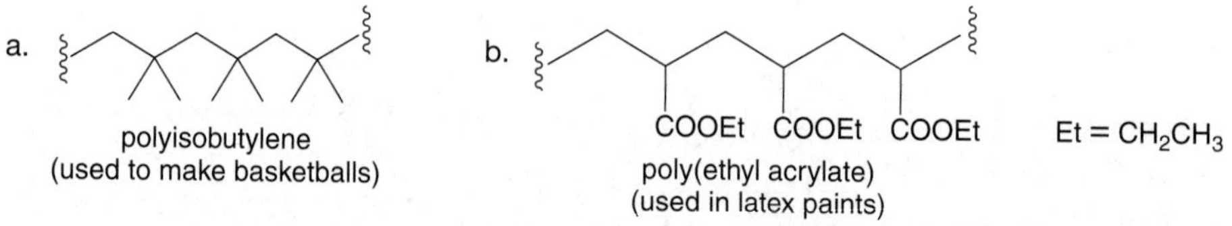
a.
polyisobutylene
(used to make basketballs)
b.
COOEt
COOEt
COOEt
Et = CH2CH3
poly(ethyl acrylate)
(used in latex paints)

15.72 (a) Hard contact lenses, which first became popular in the 1960s, were made by polymerizing methyl methacrylate [$CH_2{=}C(CH_3)CO_2CH_3$] to form poly(methyl methacrylate) (PMMA). Draw the structure of PMMA. (b) More comfortable softer contact lenses introduced in the 1970s were made by polymerizing hydroxyethyl methacrylate [$CH_2{=}C(CH_3)CO_2CH_2CH_2OH$] to form poly(hydroxyethyl methacrylate) (poly-HEMA). Draw the structure of poly-HEMA. Since neither polymer allows oxygen from the air to pass through to the retina, newer contact lenses that are both comfortable and oxygen-permeable have now been developed.

15.73 Explain why polystyrene is much more readily oxidized by O_2 in the air than polyethylene is. Which H's in polystyrene are most easily abstracted and why?

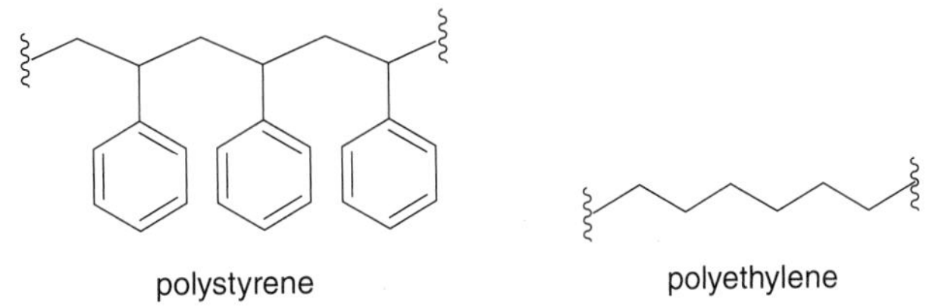
polystyrene
polyethylene

15.74 Draw a stepwise mechanism for the following polymerization reaction.

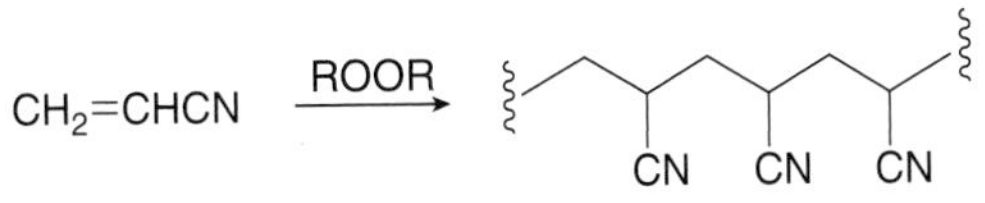
CH2=CHCN
ROOR
CN CN CN

15.75 As we will learn in Section 31.2C, styrene derivatives such as **A** can be polymerized by way of cationic rather than radical intermediates. Cationic polymerization is an example of electrophilic addition to an alkene involving carbocations.

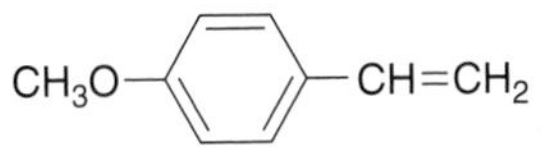
CH3O
CH=CH2

A

a. Draw a short segment of the polymer formed by the polymerization of **A.**
b. Why does **A** react faster than styrene ($C_6H_5CH=CH_2$) in a cationic polymerization?

15.76 When two monomers (**X** and **Y**) are polymerized together, a copolymer results. An alternating copolymer is formed when the two monomers **X** and **Y** alternate regularly in the polymer chain. Draw the structure of the alternating copolymer formed when the two monomers, $CH_2=CCl_2$ and $CH_2=CHC_6H_5$, are polymerized together.

Spectroscopy

15.77 **A** and **B,** isomers of molecular formula $C_3H_5Cl_3$, are formed by the radical chlorination of a dihalide **C** of molecular formula $C_3H_6Cl_2$.

a. Identify the structures of **A** and **B** from the following ^1H NMR data:
   Compound **A:** singlet at 2.23 and singlet at 4.04 ppm
   Compound **B:** doublet at 1.69, multiplet at 4.34, and doublet at 5.85 ppm
b. What is the structure of **C?**

15.78 Identify the structure of a minor product formed from the radical chlorination of propane, which has molecular formula $C_3H_6Cl_2$ and exhibits the given ^1H NMR spectrum.

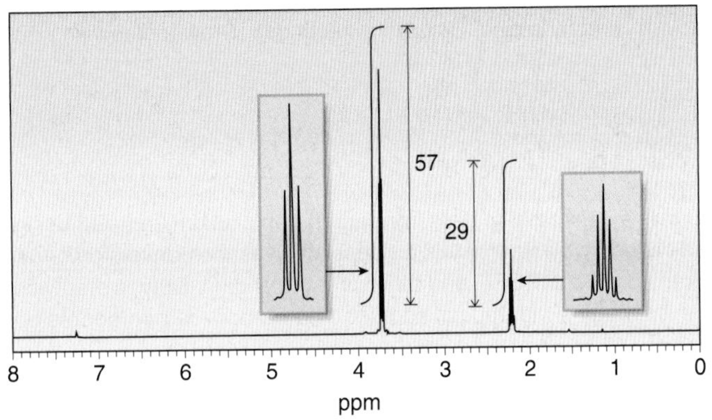
57
29
8
7
6
5
4
3
2
1
0
ppm

15.79 Radical chlorination of CH_3CH_3 forms two minor products **X** and **Y** of molecular formula $C_2H_4Cl_2$.

a. Identify the structures of **X** and **Y** from the following ^1H NMR data:
   Compound **X:** singlet at 3.7 ppm
   Compound **Y:** doublet at 2.1 and quartet at 5.9 ppm
b. Draw a stepwise mechanism that shows how each product is formed from CH_3CH_3.

Challenge Problems

15.80 Draw a stepwise mechanism for the following addition reaction to an alkene.

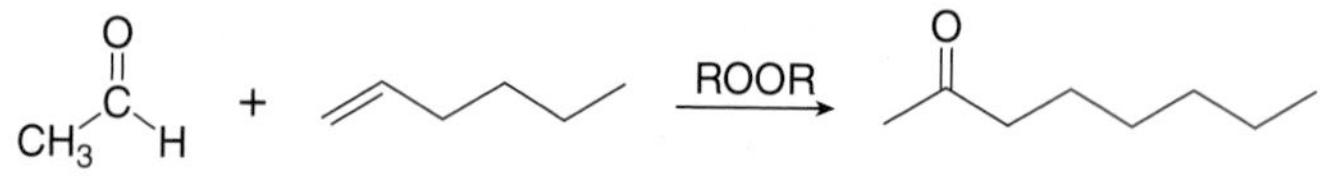

15.81 The triphenylmethyl radical is an unusual persistent radical present in solution in equilibrium with its dimer. For 70 years the dimer was thought to be hexaphenylethane, but in 1970, NMR data showed it to be **A.**

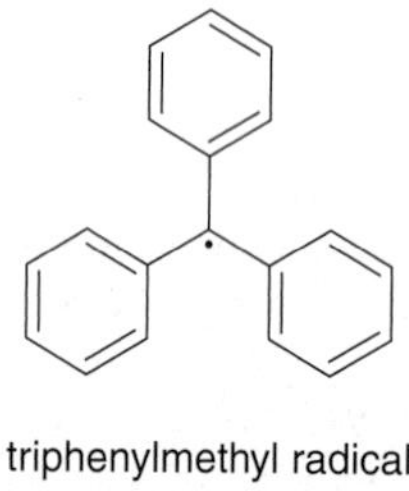
triphenylmethyl radical

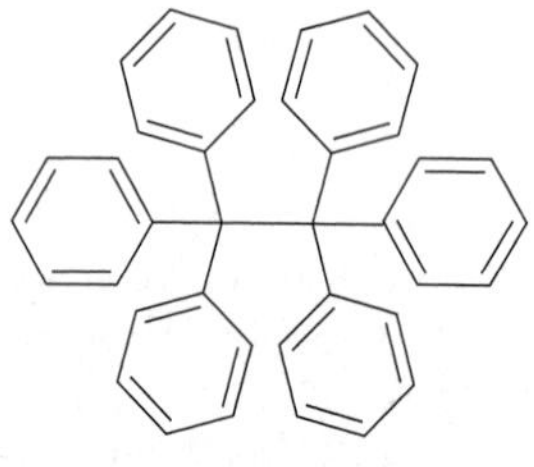
hexaphenylethane

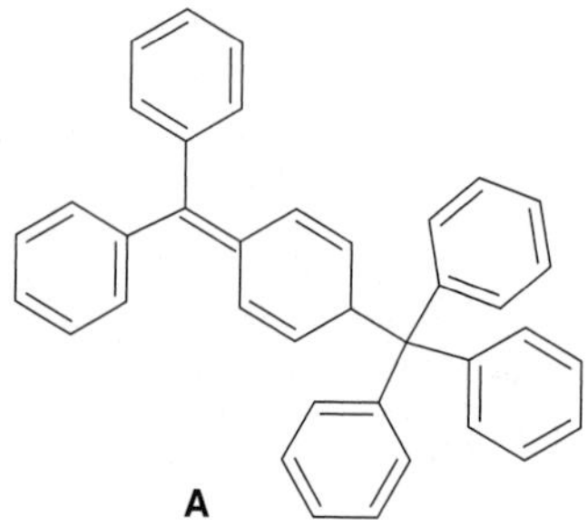
A

a. Why is the triphenylmethyl radical more stable than most other radicals?

b. Use curved arrow notation to show how two triphenylmethyl radicals dimerize to form **A.**

c. Propose a reason for the formation of **A** rather than hexaphenylethane.

d. How could ^{1}H and ^{13}C NMR spectroscopy be used to distinguish between hexaphenylethane and **A?**

15.82 In the presence of a radical initiator (Z·), tributyltin hydride (R_3SnH, R = $CH_3CH_2CH_2CH_2$) reduces alkyl halides to alkanes: $R'X + R_3SnH \rightarrow R'H + R_3SnX$. The mechanism consists of a radical chain process with an intermediate tin radical:

Initiation: $R_3SnH + Z\cdot \longrightarrow R_3Sn\cdot + HZ$

Propagation:

$R'{-}Br + R_3Sn\cdot \longrightarrow R'\cdot + R_3SnBr$

$R'\cdot + R_3SnH \longrightarrow R'{-}H + R_3Sn\cdot$

This reaction has been employed in many radical cyclization reactions. Draw a stepwise mechanism for the following reaction.

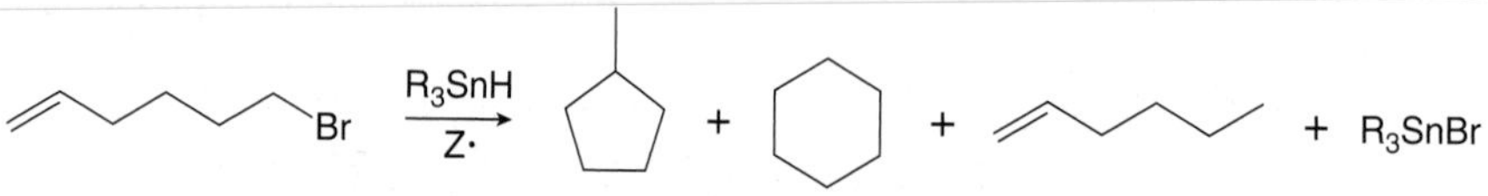

15.83 PGF$_{2\alpha}$ (Sections 4.15 and 30.6) is synthesized in cells from arachidonic acid ($C_{20}H_{32}O_2$) using a cyclooxygenase enzyme that catalyzes a multistep radical pathway. Part of this process involves the conversion of radical **A** to PGG$_2$, an unstable intermediate, which is then transformed to PGF$_{2\alpha}$ and other prostaglandins. Draw a stepwise mechanism for the conversion of **A** to PGG$_2$. (Hint: The mechanism begins with radical addition to a carbon–carbon double bond to form a resonance-stabilized radical.)

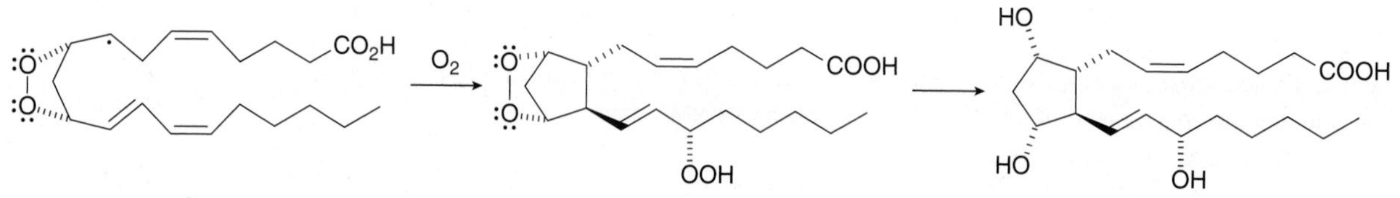

A PGG$_2$ unstable intermediate PGF$_{2\alpha}$

Conjugation, Resonance, and Dienes

16

16.1 Conjugation
16.2 Resonance and allylic carbocations
16.3 Common examples of resonance
16.4 The resonance hybrid
16.5 Electron delocalization, hybridization, and geometry
16.6 Conjugated dienes
16.7 Interesting dienes and polyenes
16.8 The carbon–carbon σ bond length in 1,3-butadiene
16.9 Stability of conjugated dienes
16.10 Electrophilic addition: 1,2- versus 1,4-addition
16.11 Kinetic versus thermodynamic products
16.12 The Diels–Alder reaction
16.13 Specific rules governing the Diels–Alder reaction
16.14 Other facts about the Diels–Alder reaction
16.15 Conjugated dienes and ultraviolet light

Morphine is an analgesic and narcotic isolated from the opium poppy *Papaver somniferum*. Opium has been widely used as a recreational drug and pain-killing remedy for centuries, and poppy seed tea, which contains morphine, was used as a folk remedy in parts of England until World War II. A key step in a laboratory synthesis of morphine involves the Diels–Alder reaction, a powerful reaction of conjugated dienes discussed in Chapter 16.

Chapter 16 is the first of three chapters that discuss the chemistry of conjugated molecules—molecules with overlapping *p* orbitals on three or more adjacent atoms. Chapter 16 focuses mainly on acyclic conjugated compounds, whereas Chapters 17 and 18 discuss the chemistry of benzene and related compounds that have a *p* orbital on every atom in a ring.

Much of Chapter 16 is devoted to the properties and reactions of 1,3-dienes. To understand these compounds, however, we must first learn about the consequences of having *p* orbitals on three or more adjacent atoms. Because the ability to draw resonance structures is also central to mastering this material, the key aspects of resonance theory are presented in detail.

16.1 Conjugation

***Conjugation* occurs whenever *p* orbitals can overlap on three or more adjacent atoms.** Two common conjugated systems are 1,3-dienes and allylic carbocations.

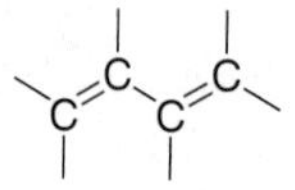

1,3-diene

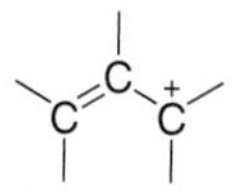

allylic carbocation

16.1A 1,3-Dienes

1,3-Dienes such as 1,3-butadiene contain two carbon–carbon double bonds joined by a single σ bond. Each carbon atom of a 1,3-diene is bonded to three other atoms and has no nonbonded electron pairs, so each carbon atom is sp^2 hybridized and has one *p* orbital containing an electron. **The four *p* orbitals on adjacent atoms make a 1,3-diene a conjugated system.**

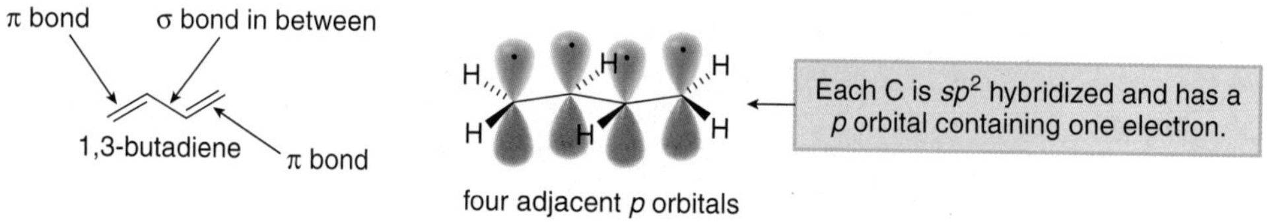

What is special about conjugation? Having three or more *p* orbitals on adjacent atoms allows *p* orbitals to overlap and electrons to delocalize.

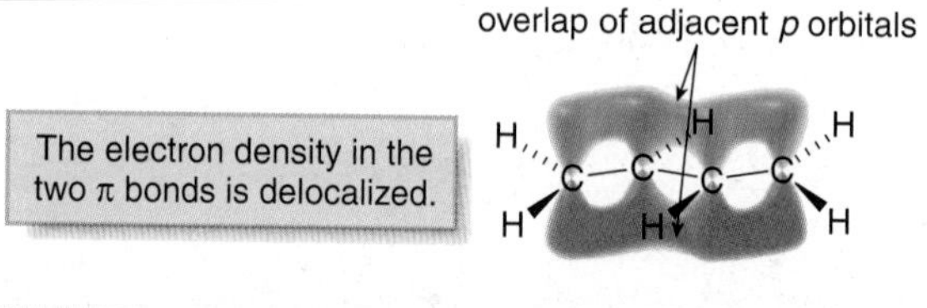

- **When *p* orbitals overlap, the electron density in each of the π bonds is spread out over a larger volume, thus lowering the energy of the molecule and making it more stable.**

Conjugation makes 1,3-butadiene inherently different from 1,4-pentadiene, a compound having two double bonds separated by more than one σ bond. The π bonds in 1,4-pentadiene are too far apart to be conjugated.

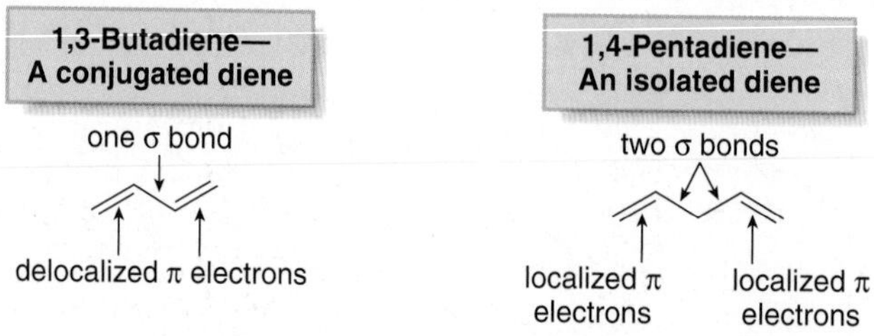

Figure 16.1
Electrostatic potential plots for a conjugated and an isolated diene

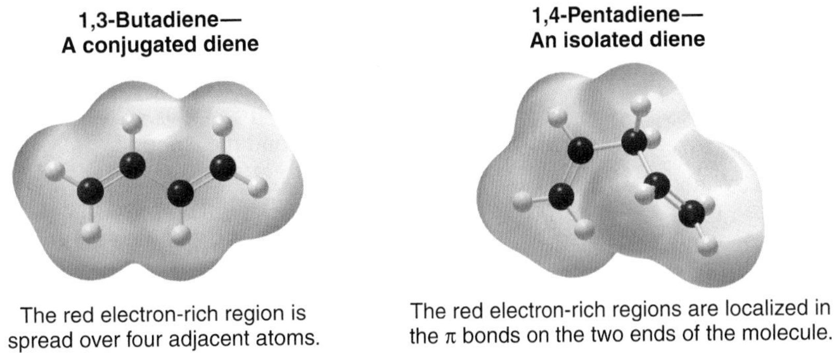
1,3-Butadiene—
A conjugated diene
1,4-Pentadiene—
An isolated diene
The red electron-rich region is spread over four adjacent atoms.
The red electron-rich regions are localized in the π bonds on the two ends of the molecule.

1,4-Pentadiene is an **isolated diene.** The electron density in each π bond of an isolated diene is *localized* between two carbon atoms. In 1,3-butadiene, however, the electron density of both π bonds is *delocalized* over the four atoms of the diene. Electrostatic potential maps in Figure 16.1 clearly indicate the difference between these localized and delocalized π bonds.

Problem 16.1 Classify each diene as isolated or conjugated.

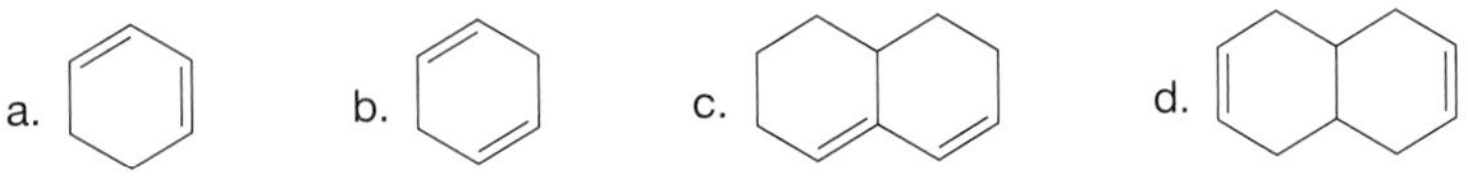
a.
b.
c.
d.

16.1B Allylic Carbocations

The **allyl carbocation** is another example of a conjugated system. The three carbon atoms of the allyl carbocation—the positively charged carbon atom and the two that form the double bond—are sp^2 hybridized with a *p* orbital. The *p* orbitals for the double bond carbons each contain an electron, whereas the *p* orbital for the carbocation is empty.

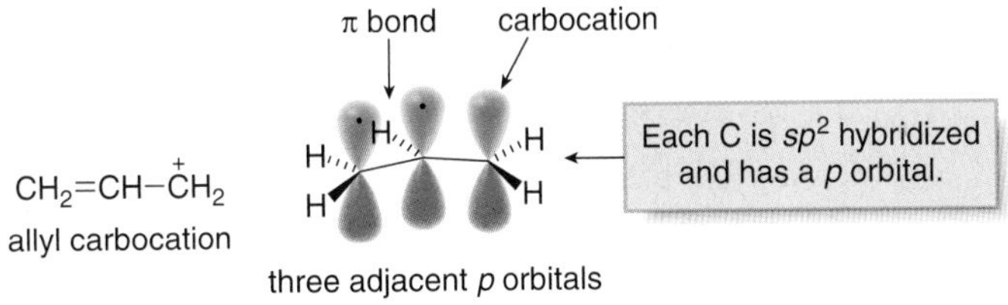
$CH_2{=}CH{-}\overset{+}{C}H_2$
allyl carbocation
π bond
carbocation
Each C is sp^2 hybridized and has a *p* orbital.
three adjacent *p* orbitals

- **Three *p* orbitals on three adjacent atoms, even if one of the *p* orbitals is empty, make the allyl carbocation conjugated.**

Conjugation stabilizes the allyl carbocation because overlap of three adjacent *p* orbitals delocalizes the electron density of the π bond over three atoms.

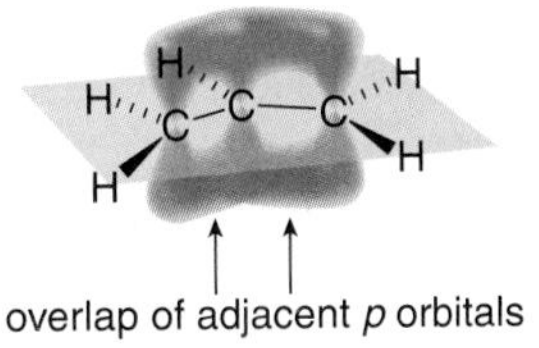
overlap of adjacent *p* orbitals

Problem 16.2 Which of the following species are conjugated?

a. $CH_2{=}CH{-}CH{=}CH{-}CH{=}CH_2$

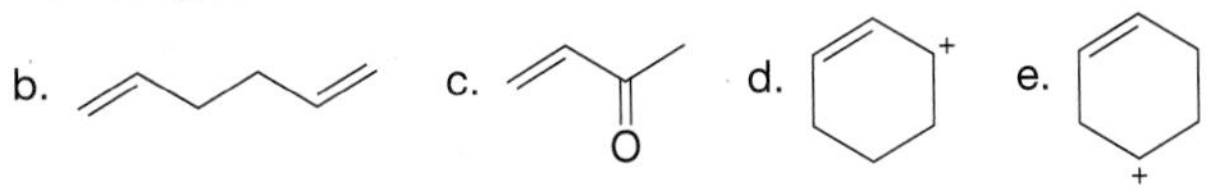
b.
c.
d.
e.

16.2 Resonance and Allylic Carbocations

The word *resonance* is used in two different contexts. In NMR spectroscopy, a nucleus is ***in resonance*** when it absorbs energy, promoting it to a higher energy state. In drawing molecules, there is ***resonance*** when two different Lewis structures can be drawn for the same arrangement of atoms.

Recall from Section 1.6 that resonance structures are two or more different Lewis structures for the same arrangement of atoms. Being able to draw correct resonance structures is crucial to understanding conjugation and the reactions of conjugated dienes.

- **Two resonance structures differ in the placement of π bonds and nonbonded electrons. The placement of atoms and σ bonds stays the same.**

We have already drawn resonance structures for the acetate anion (Section 2.5C) and the allyl radical (Section 15.10). The **conjugated allyl carbocation** is another example of a species for which two resonance structures can be drawn. Drawing resonance structures for the allyl carbocation is a way to use Lewis structures to illustrate how conjugation delocalizes electrons.

two resonance structures for the allyl carbocation

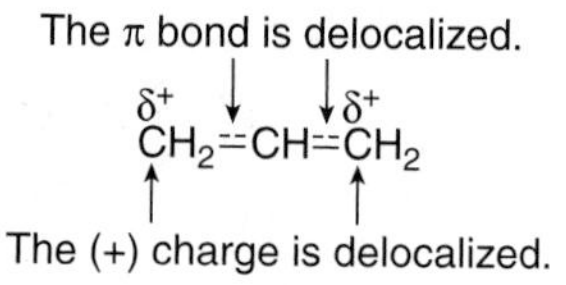

hybrid

The true structure of the allyl carbocation is a hybrid of the two resonance structures. In the hybrid, the π bond is delocalized over all three atoms. As a result, the positive charge is also delocalized over the two terminal carbons. Delocalizing electron density lowers the energy of the hybrid, thus stabilizing the allyl carbocation and making it more stable than a normal 1° carbocation. Experimental data show that its stability is comparable to a more highly substituted 2° carbocation.

Relative carbocation stability

$\overset{+}{C}H_3$ < $R\overset{+}{C}H_2$ (1°) < $R_2\overset{+}{C}H$ (2°) ≈ $CH_2{=}CH{-}\overset{+}{C}H_2$ (allyl) < $R_3\overset{+}{C}$ (3°)

least stable → most stable

Increasing stability

The electrostatic potential maps in Figure 16.2 compare the resonance-stabilized allyl carbocation with $CH_3CH_2CH_2^+$, a localized 1° carbocation. The electron-deficient region—the site of the positive charge—is concentrated on a single carbon atom in the 1° carbocation $CH_3CH_2CH_2^+$. In the allyl carbocation, however, the electron-poor region is spread out on both terminal carbons.

Problem 16.3 Draw a second resonance structure for each carbocation. Then draw the hybrid.

a. b. c.

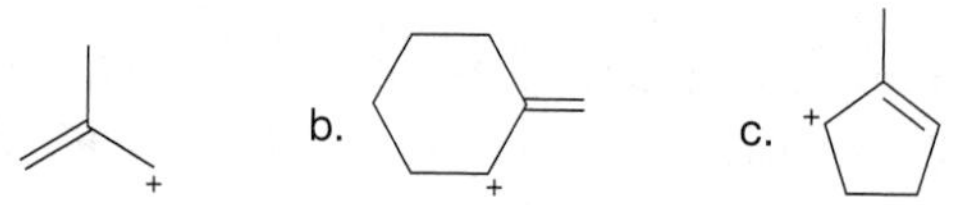

Figure 16.2 Electrostatic potential maps for a localized and a delocalized carbocation

$CH_3CH_2CH_2^+$
a localized carbocation

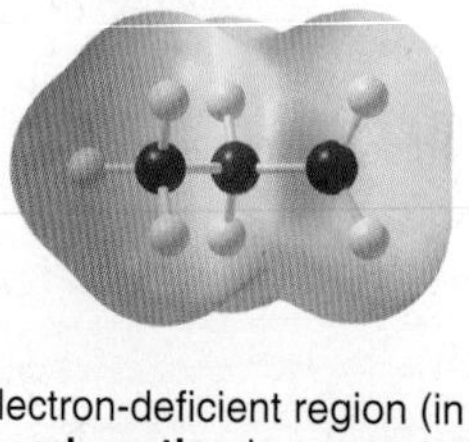

The electron-deficient region (in blue) of a **1° carbocation** is concentrated on a single carbon atom.

$CH_2{=}CHCH_2^+$ ⟷ $^+CH_2CH{=}CH_2$
a delocalized carbocation

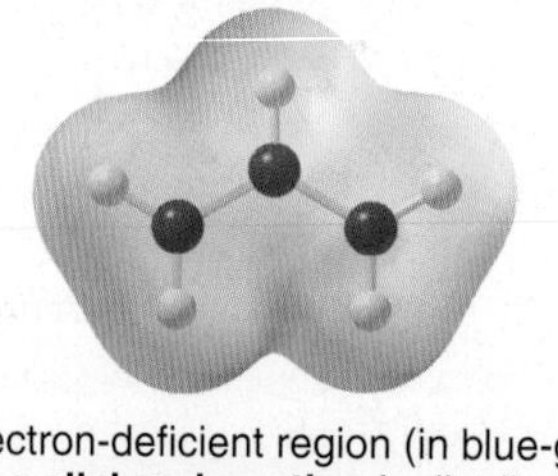

The electron-deficient region (in blue-green) of the **allyl carbocation** is distributed over both terminal carbons.

Figure 16.3
^{13}C chemical shifts for a localized and a resonance-stabilized carbocation

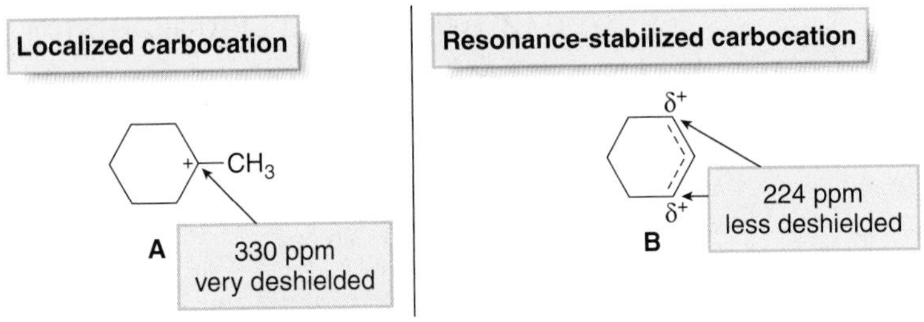

- The absorption shifts *upfield* as the amount of positive charge *decreases*.

How "real" is the delocalization of charge and electron density in the allyl carbocation? Recall from the discussion of NMR spectroscopy in Chapter 14 that an NMR absorption shifts downfield (to higher chemical shift) as the electron density around the nucleus decreases (is deshielded). Thus, a positively charged carbocation, such as **A** in Figure 16.3, is highly deshielded, so its ^{13}C NMR absorption is far downfield at 330 ppm. A resonance-stabilized carbocation, however, such as **B** in Figure 16.3, has less positive charge concentrated on any given carbon atom (because the charge is delocalized), so its ^{13}C NMR absorption is farther upfield at 224 ppm.

Problem 16.4 Use resonance theory and the Hammond postulate to explain why 3-chloro-1-propene ($CH_2{=}CHCH_2Cl$) is more reactive than 1-chloropropane ($CH_3CH_2CH_2Cl$) in S_N1 reactions.

16.3 Common Examples of Resonance

When are resonance structures drawn for a molecule or reactive intermediate? Because resonance involves delocalizing π bonds and nonbonded electrons, one or both of these structural features must be present to draw additional resonance forms. There are four common bonding patterns for which more than one Lewis structure can be drawn.

Type [1] The Three Atom "Allyl" System, X=Y–Z*

- **For any group of three atoms having a double bond X=Y and an atom Z that contains a *p* orbital with zero, one, or two electrons, two resonance structures are possible:**

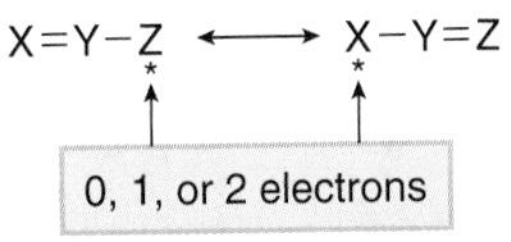

The asterisk [*] corresponds to a charge, a radical, or a lone pair.

* = +, –, ·, or ··

This is called **allyl** type resonance because it can be drawn for allylic carbocations, allylic carbanions, and allylic radicals.

X, Y, and Z may all be carbon atoms, as in the case of an allylic carbocation (resonance structures **A** and **B**), or they may be heteroatoms, as in the case of the acetate anion (resonance structures **C** and **D**). The atom Z bonded to the multiple bond can be charged (a net positive or negative charge) or neutral (having zero, one, or two nonbonded electrons). **The two resonance structures differ in the location of the double bond, and either the charge, the radical, or the lone pair, generalized by [*].**

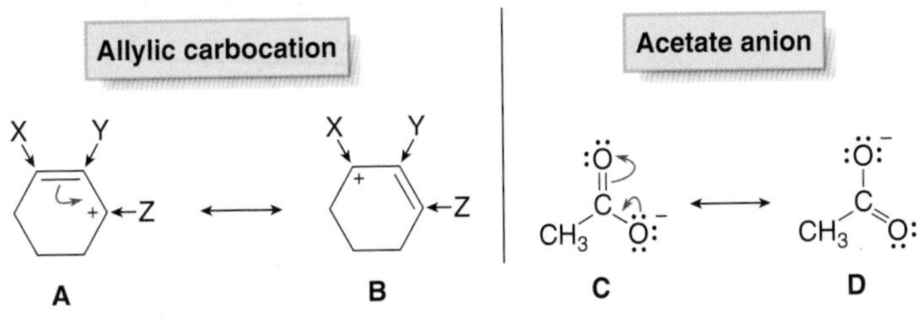

Type [2] Conjugated Double Bonds

Cyclic, completely conjugated rings like benzene have two resonance structures, drawn by moving the electrons in a cyclic manner around the ring. Three resonance structures can be drawn for conjugated dienes, two of which involve charge separation.

Two resonance structures for benzene

Three resonance structures for 1,3-butadiene

Or, moving electrons in the opposite direction:

Type [3] Cations Having a Positive Charge Adjacent to a Lone Pair

- **When a lone pair and a positive charge are located on adjacent atoms, two resonance structures can be drawn.**

General case

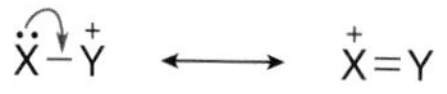

Specific example

The overall charge is the same in both resonance structures. Based on formal charge, a neutral X in one structure must bear a (+) charge in the other.

Type [4] Double Bonds Having One Atom More Electronegative Than the Other

- **For a double bond X=Y in which the electronegativity of Y > X, a second resonance structure can be drawn by moving the π electrons onto Y.**

General case

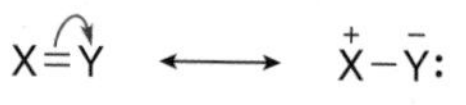

Electronegativity of Y > X.

Specific example

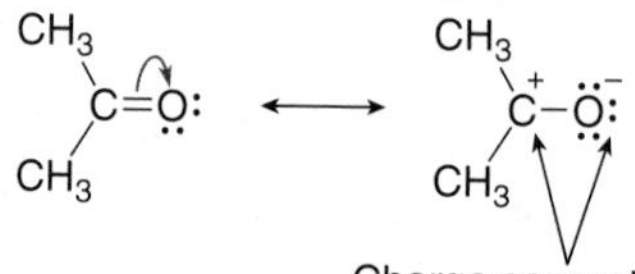

Charge separation results.

Sample Problem 16.1 illustrates how to apply these different types of resonance to actual molecules.

Sample Problem 16.1 Draw two more resonance structures for each species.

a.  b. 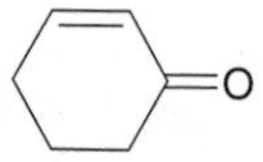

Solution

Mentally breaking a molecule into two- or three-atom units can make it easier to draw additional resonance structures.

a. Think of the top three atoms of the six-membered ring in **A** as an "allyl" unit. Moving the π bond forms a new "allyl" unit in **B,** and moving the π bond in **B** generates a third resonance structure **C.** No new valid resonance structures are generated by moving electrons in **C.**

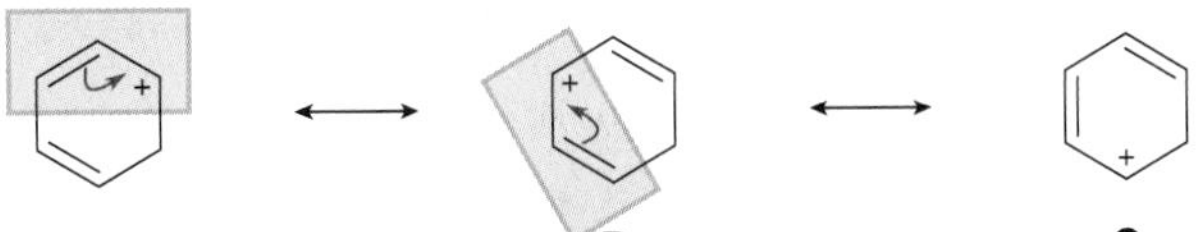

A — a three-atom "allyl" unit; **B** — another three-atom "allyl" unit; **C**

b. Compound **D** contains a carbonyl group, so moving the electron pair in the double bond to the more electronegative oxygen atom separates the charge and generates structure **E. E** now has a three-atom "allyl" unit, so the remaining π bond can be moved to form structure **F.**

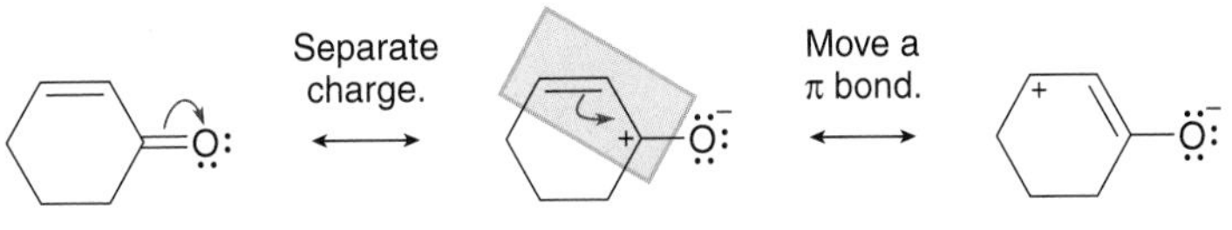
Separate charge.
Move a π bond.

D **E** **F**

a three-atom "allyl" unit

Problem 16.5 Draw additional resonance structures for each ion.

a. $CH_2{=}CH{-}\ddot{C}H^{-}{-}CH{=}CH_2$ b. 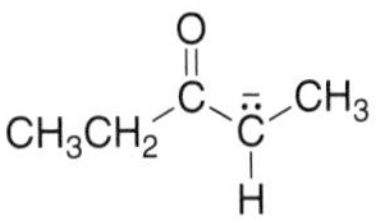 c. $CH_3{-}\overset{+}{C}H{-}\ddot{C}l{:}$ d. 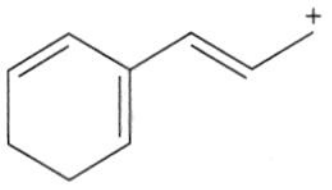

16.4 The Resonance Hybrid

The lower its energy, the more a resonance structure contributes to the overall structure of the hybrid.

Although the resonance hybrid is some combination of all of its valid resonance structures, the **hybrid more closely resembles the most stable resonance structure.** Recall from Section 1.6C that the most stable resonance structure is called the **major contributor** to the hybrid, and the less stable resonance structures are called the **minor contributors.** Two identical resonance structures are equal contributors to the hybrid.

Use the following three rules to evaluate the relative stabilities of two or more valid resonance structures.

Rule [1] **Resonance structures with more bonds and fewer charges are more stable.**

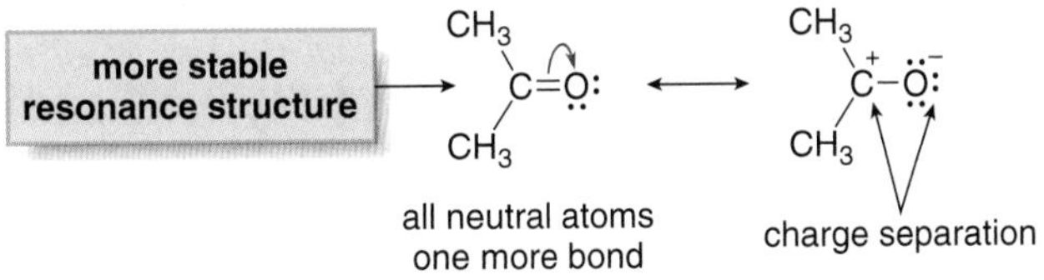
more stable resonance structure
all neutral atoms
one more bond
charge separation

Rule [2] **Resonance structures in which every atom has an octet are more stable.**

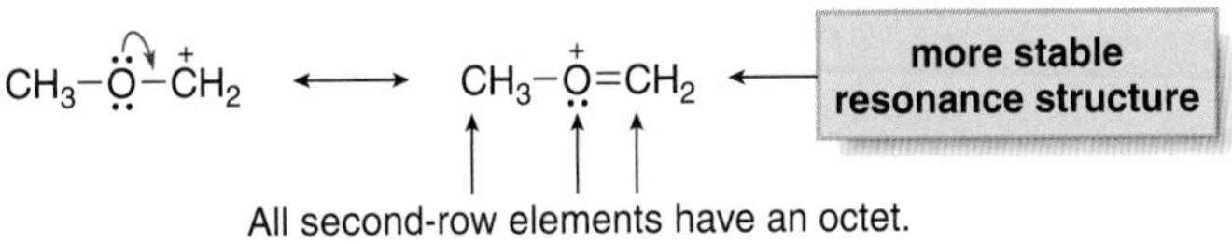
more stable resonance structure
All second-row elements have an octet.

In this example, the resonance structure in which all atoms have octets is better, even though it places a (+) charge on a more electronegative O atom.

Rule [3] **Resonance structures that place a negative charge on a more electronegative atom are more stable.**

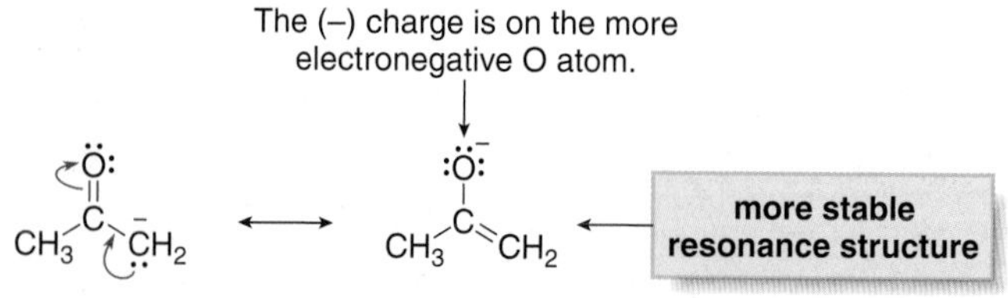
The (–) charge is on the more
electronegative O atom.
more stable
resonance structure

Sample Problem 16.2 illustrates how to determine the relative energy of contributing resonance structures and the hybrid.

Sample Problem 16.2

Draw a second resonance structure for carbocation **A,** as well as the hybrid of both resonance structures. Then use Rules [1]–[3] to rank the relative stability of both resonance structures and the hybrid.

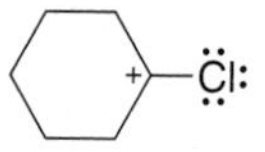

A

Solution

Because **A** contains a positive charge and a lone pair on adjacent atoms, a second resonance structure **B** can be drawn. Because **B** has more bonds and all second-row atoms have octets, **B** is more stable than **A,** making it the major contributor to the hybrid **C.** Because the hybrid is more stable than either resonance contributor, the order of stability is:

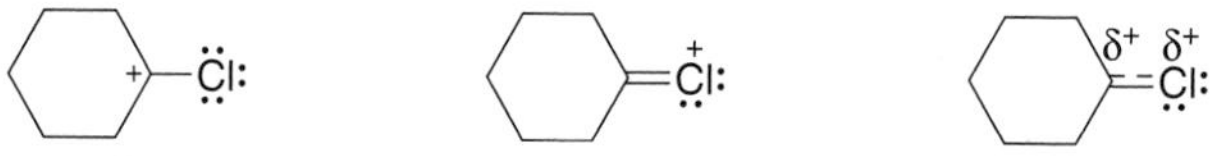

A minor contributor — **B** major contributor — **C** hybrid

Increasing stability →

Problem 16.6

Draw a second resonance structure and the hybrid for each species, and then rank the two resonance structures and the hybrid in order of increasing stability.

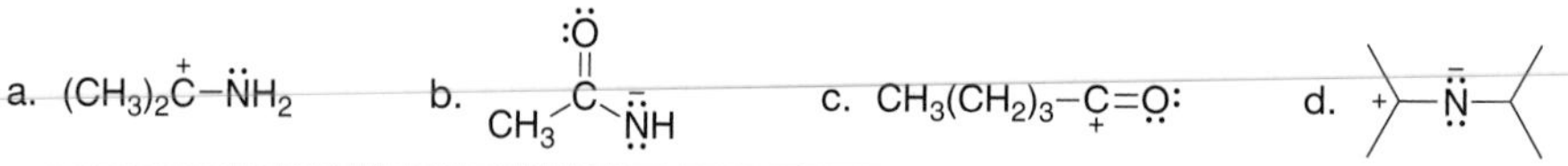
a.
b.
c.
d.

Problem 16.7

Draw all possible resonance structures for the following cation and indicate which structure makes the largest contribution to the resonance hybrid.

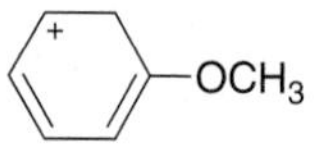

16.5 Electron Delocalization, Hybridization, and Geometry

To delocalize nonbonded electrons or electrons in π bonds, there must be *p* orbitals that can overlap. This may mean that the hybridization of an atom is different than would have been predicted using the rules first outlined in Chapter 1.

For example, there are two Lewis structures (**A** and **B**) for the resonance-stabilized anion $(CH_3COCH_2)^-$.

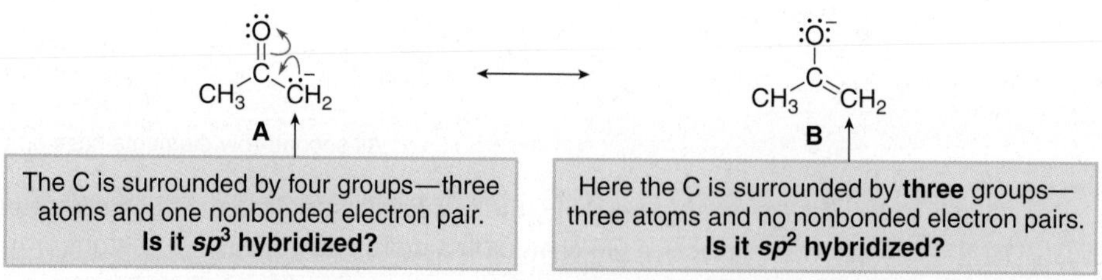
A
B
The C is surrounded by four groups—three atoms and one nonbonded electron pair.
Is it sp3 hybridized?
Here the C is surrounded by three groups—three atoms and no nonbonded electron pairs.
Is it sp2 hybridized?

Based on structure **A,** the indicated carbon is sp^3 hybridized, with the lone pair of electrons in an sp^3 hybrid orbital. Based on structure **B,** though, it is sp^2 hybridized with the unhybridized p orbital forming the π portion of the double bond.

Delocalizing electrons stabilizes a molecule. The electron pair on the carbon atom adjacent to the C=O can only be delocalized, though, if it has a p orbital that can overlap with two other p orbitals on two adjacent atoms. Thus, the terminal carbon atom is sp^2 hybridized with trigonal planar geometry. **Three adjacent *p* orbitals make the anion conjugated.**

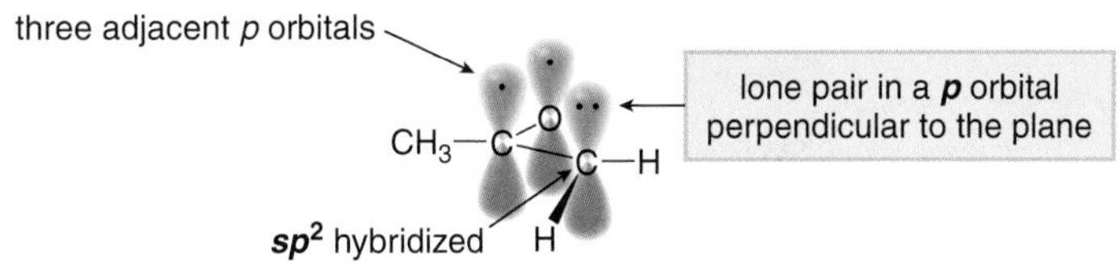

- **In a system X=Y−Z:, Z is generally sp^2 hybridized, and the nonbonded electron pair occupies a p orbital to make the system conjugated.**

Sample Problem 16.3 Determine the hybridization around the indicated carbon atom in the following anion.

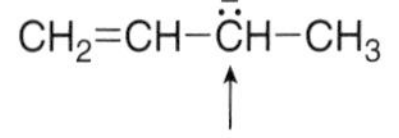

Solution

Because this is an example of an allyl-type system (X=Y−Z*), a second resonance structure can be drawn that "moves" the lone pair and the π bond. To delocalize the lone pair and make the system conjugated, the indicated carbon atom must be sp^2 hybridized with the lone pair occupying a p orbital.

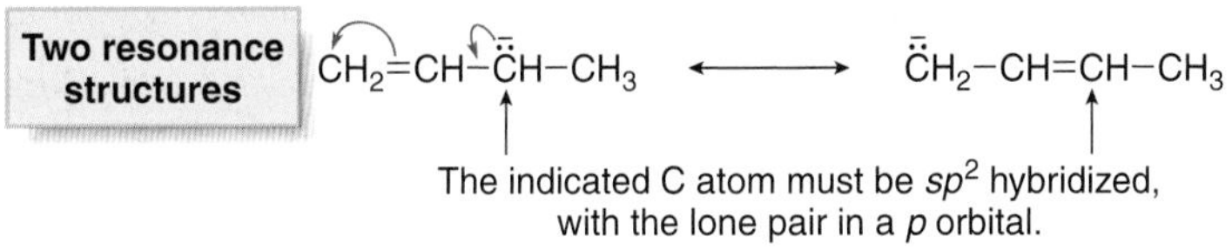

Problem 16.8 Determine the hybridization of the indicated atom in each species.

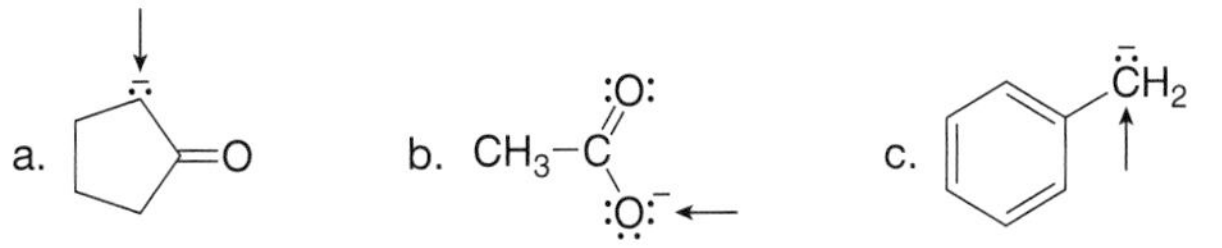

16.6 Conjugated Dienes

Compounds with many π bonds are called **polyenes.**

In the remainder of Chapter 16 we examine **conjugated dienes,** compounds having two double bonds joined by one σ bond. Conjugated dienes are also called **1,3-dienes.** 1,3-Butadiene ($CH_2{=}CH{-}CH{=}CH_2$) is the simplest conjugated diene.

Three stereoisomers are possible for 1,3-dienes with alkyl groups bonded to each end carbon of the diene (RCH=CH−CH=CHR).

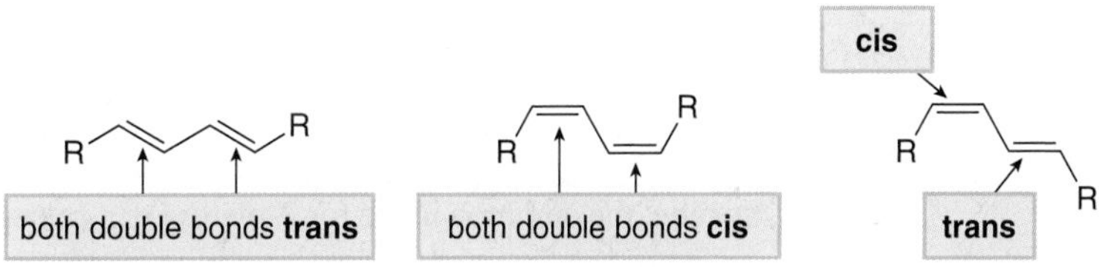

trans,trans-1,3-diene or (*E,E*)-1,3-diene	*cis,cis*-1,3-diene or (*Z,Z*)-1,3-diene	*cis,trans*-1,3-diene or (*Z,E*)-1,3-diene

Two possible conformations result from rotation around the C–C bond that joins the two double bonds.

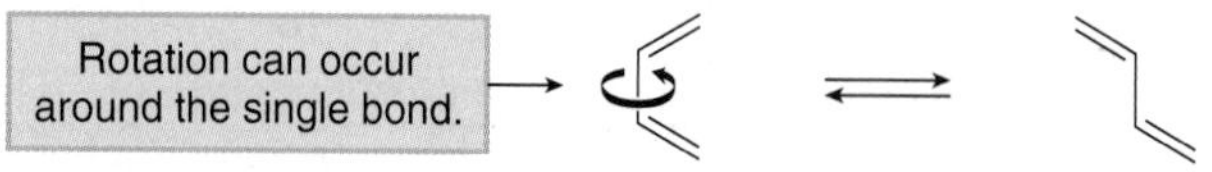
Rotation can occur around the single bond.

s-cis conformation **s-trans** conformation

- **The *s*-cis conformation has two double bonds on the *same* side of the single bond.**
- **The *s*-trans conformation has two double bonds on *opposite* sides of the single bond.**

Keep in mind that stereoisomers are discrete molecules, whereas conformations interconvert. Three structures drawn for 2,4-hexadiene illustrate the differences between stereoisomers and conformations in a 1,3-diene:

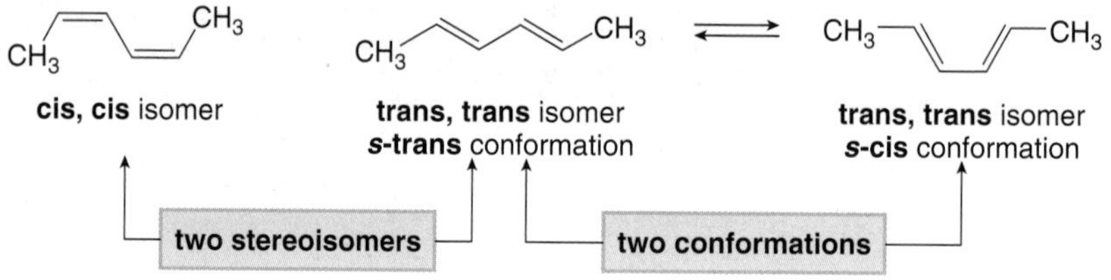
CH_3
CH_3
cis, cis isomer
trans, trans isomer
s-trans conformation
trans, trans isomer
s-cis conformation
two stereoisomers
two conformations

Problem 16.9 Draw the structure consistent with each description.

a. (2*E*,4*E*)-2,4-octadiene in the *s*-trans conformation
b. (3*E*,5*Z*)-3,5-nonadiene in the *s*-cis conformation
c. (3*Z*,5*Z*)-4,5-dimethyl-3,5-decadiene. Draw both the *s*-cis and *s*-trans conformations.

Problem 16.10 Neuroprotectin D1 (NPD1) is synthesized in the body from highly unsaturated essential fatty acids. NPD1 is a potent natural anti-inflammatory agent.

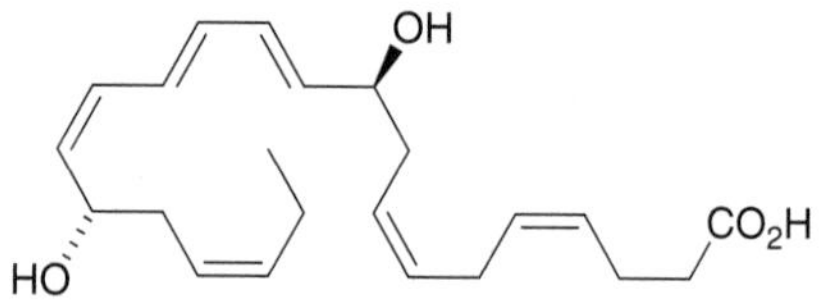
OH
CO_2H
HO

NPD1

a. Label each double bond as conjugated or isolated.
b. Label each double bond as *E* or *Z*.
c. For each conjugated system, label the given conformation as *s*-cis or *s*-trans.

16.7 Interesting Dienes and Polyenes

Isoprene is a component of the blue haze seen above forested hillsides, such as Virginia's Blue Ridge Mountains.

Isoprene and **lycopene** are two naturally occurring compounds with conjugated double bonds.

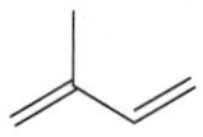

isoprene
(2-methyl-1,3-butadiene)

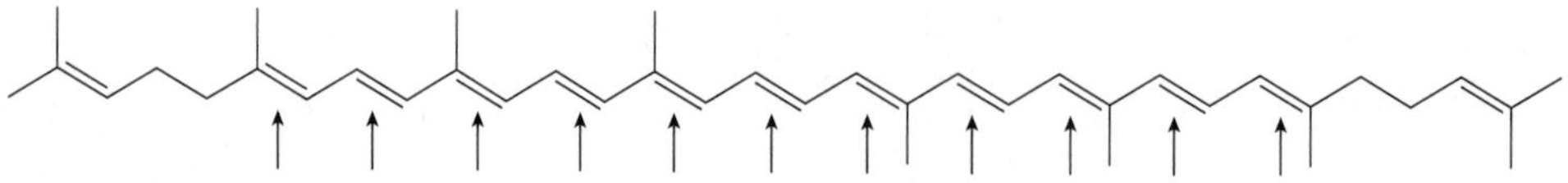
11 conjugated double bonds

lycopene

Isoprene, the common name for 2-methyl-1,3-butadiene, is given off by plants as the temperature rises, a process thought to increase a plant's tolerance for heat stress.

Lycopene, a naturally occurring molecule responsible for the red color of tomatoes and other fruits, is an antioxidant like vitamin E. The 11 conjugated double bonds of lycopene cause its red color, a phenomenon discussed in Section 16.15.

Figure 16.4
Biologically active organic compounds that contain conjugated double bonds

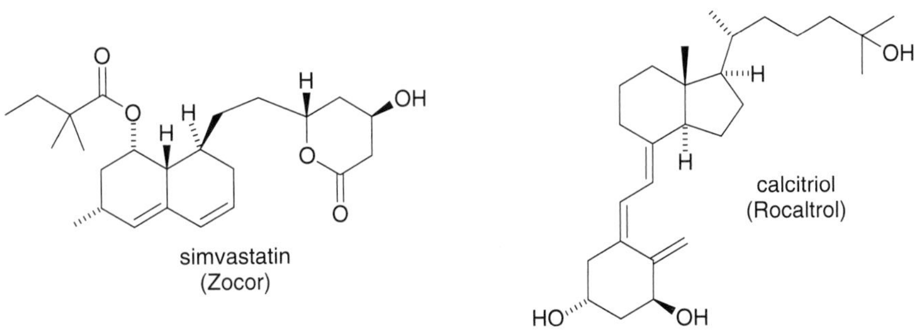

Simvastatin and calcitriol are two drugs that contain conjugated double bonds in addition to other functional groups (Figure 16.4). Simvastatin is the generic name of the widely used cholesterol-lowering medicine Zocor. Calcitriol, a biologically active hormone formed from vitamin D_3 obtained in the diet, is responsible for regulating calcium and phosphorus metabolism. Sold under the trade name of Rocaltrol, calcitriol is used to treat patients who are unable to convert vitamin D_3 to the active hormone. Since calcitriol promotes the absorption of calcium ions, it is also used to treat hypocalcemia, the presence of low calcium levels in the blood.

16.8 The Carbon–Carbon σ Bond Length in 1,3-Butadiene

Four features distinguish conjugated dienes from isolated dienes.

[1] **The C–C single bond joining the two double bonds is unusually short.**

[2] **Conjugated dienes are more stable than similar isolated dienes.**

[3] **Some reactions of conjugated dienes are different than reactions of isolated double bonds.**

[4] **Conjugated dienes absorb longer wavelengths of ultraviolet light.**

The bond length of the carbon–carbon double bonds in 1,3-butadiene is similar to an isolated double bond, but the central carbon–carbon single bond is shorter than the C–C bond in ethane.

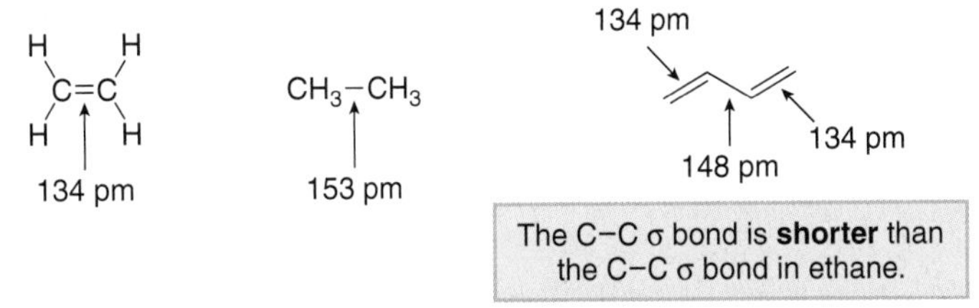

The observed bond distances can be explained by looking at hybridization. Each carbon atom in 1,3-butadiene is sp^2 hybridized, so the central C–C single bond is formed by the overlap of two sp^2 hybridized orbitals, rather than the sp^3 hybridized orbitals used to form the C–C bond in CH_3CH_3.

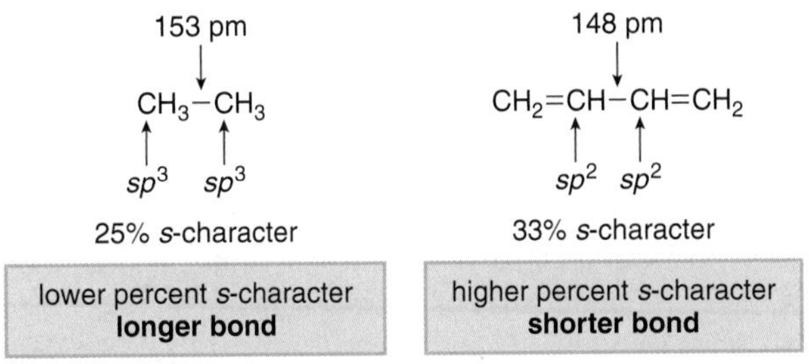

Recall from Section 1.11B that increasing percent *s*-character decreases bond length.

- **Based on hybridization, a $C_{sp^2}–C_{sp^2}$ bond should be shorter than a $C_{sp^3}–C_{sp^3}$ bond because it is formed from orbitals having a higher percent *s*-character.**

A resonance argument can also be used to explain the shorter C–C σ bond length of 1,3-butadiene. 1,3-Butadiene can be represented by three resonance structures:

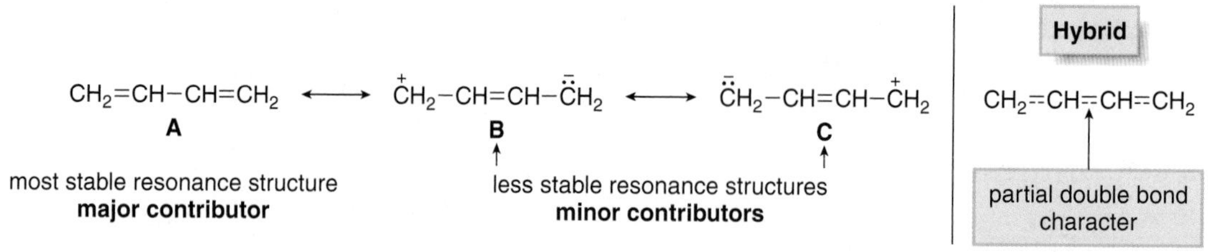
Hybrid
A
B
C
most stable resonance structure
major contributor
less stable resonance structures
minor contributors
partial double bond character

Structures **B** and **C** have charge separation and fewer bonds than **A,** making them less stable resonance structures and only minor contributors to the resonance hybrid. **B** and **C** both contain a double bond between the central carbon atoms, however, so the hybrid must have a partial double bond there. This makes the central C–C bond shorter than a C–C single bond in an alkane.

- **Based on resonance, the central C–C bond in 1,3-butadiene is shorter because it has partial double bond character.**

Finally, 1,3-butadiene is a conjugated molecule with four overlapping *p* orbitals on adjacent atoms. As a result, the π electrons are not localized between the carbon atoms of the double bonds, but rather delocalized over four atoms. This places more electron density between the central two carbon atoms of 1,3-butadiene than would normally be present. This *shortens* the bond. Drawing resonance structures illustrates this delocalization.

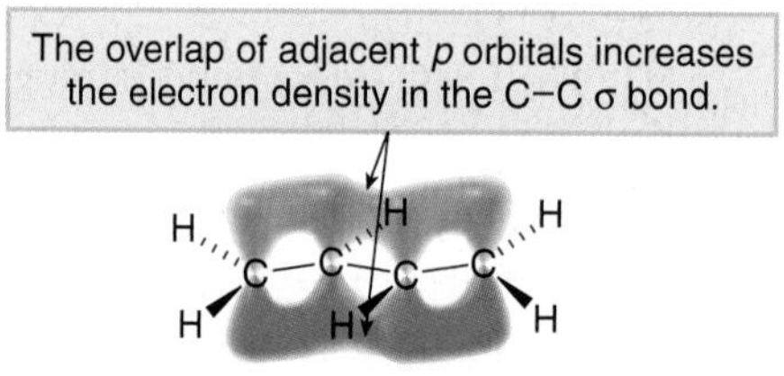
The overlap of adjacent p orbitals increases the electron density in the C–C σ bond.

Problem 16.11 Using hybridization, predict how the bond length of the C–C σ bond in HC≡C–C≡CH should compare with the C–C σ bonds in CH_3CH_3 and $CH_2{=}CH{-}CH{=}CH_2$.

Problem 16.12 Use resonance theory to explain why both C–O bond lengths are equal in the acetate anion.

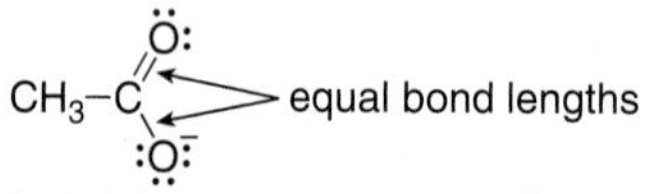
equal bond lengths
acetate

16.9 Stability of Conjugated Dienes

In Section 12.3 we learned that hydrogen adds to alkenes to form alkanes, and that the heat released in this reaction, the **heat of hydrogenation,** can be used as a measure of alkene stability.

Recall:

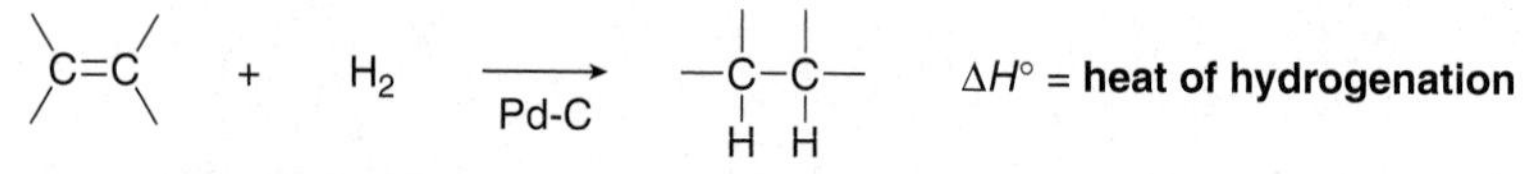
H2
Pd-C
ΔH° = heat of hydrogenation

The relative stability of conjugated and isolated dienes can also be determined by comparing their heats of hydrogenation.

- **When hydrogenation gives the same alkane from two dienes, the more stable diene has the smaller heat of hydrogenation.**

Figure 16.5
Relative energies of an isolated and conjugated diene

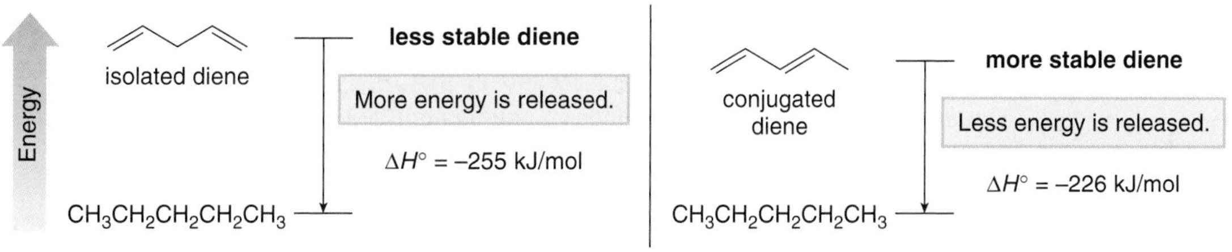

For example, both 1,4-pentadiene (an isolated diene) and (3*E*)-1,3-pentadiene (a conjugated diene) are hydrogenated to pentane with two equivalents of H_2. Because less energy is released in converting the conjugated diene to pentane, it must be lower in energy (more stable) to begin with. The relative energies of these isomeric pentadienes are illustrated in Figure 16.5.

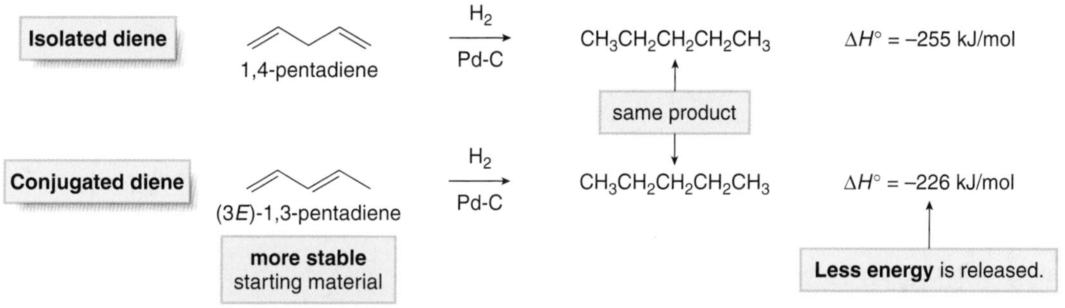

- **A conjugated diene has a smaller heat of hydrogenation and is more stable than a similar isolated diene.**

Why is a conjugated diene more stable than an isolated diene? Because a conjugated diene has overlapping *p* orbitals on four adjacent atoms, its π electrons are delocalized over four atoms. This delocalization, which cannot occur in an isolated diene, is illustrated by drawing resonance structures.

No resonance structures can be drawn for 1,4-pentadiene, but three can be drawn for (3*E*)-1,3-pentadiene (or any other conjugated diene). The hybrid of these resonance structures illustrates that the two adjacent π bonds are delocalized in a conjugated diene, making it lower in energy than an isolated diene.

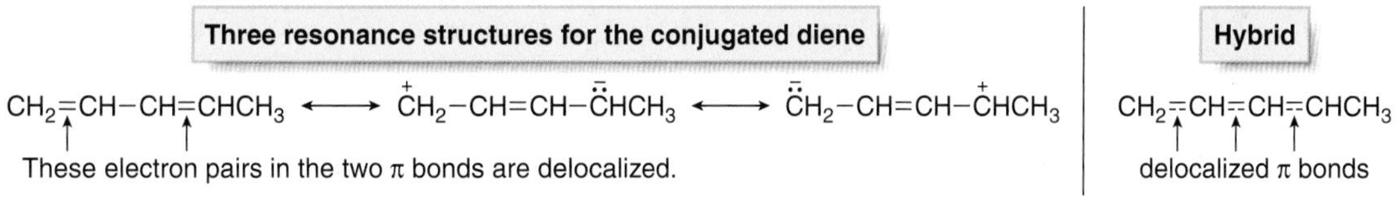

Problem 16.13 Which diene in each pair has the larger heat of hydrogenation?

a. 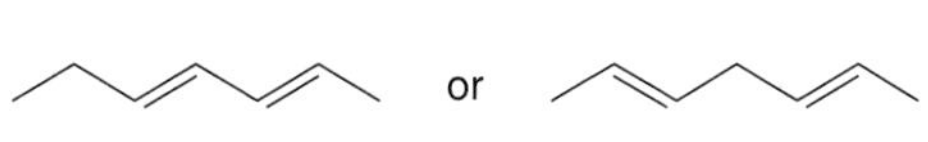

b. 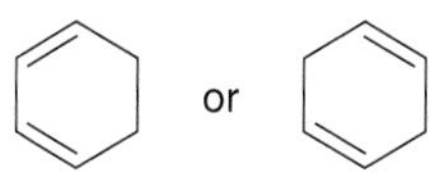

Problem 16.14 Rank the following compounds in order of increasing stability.

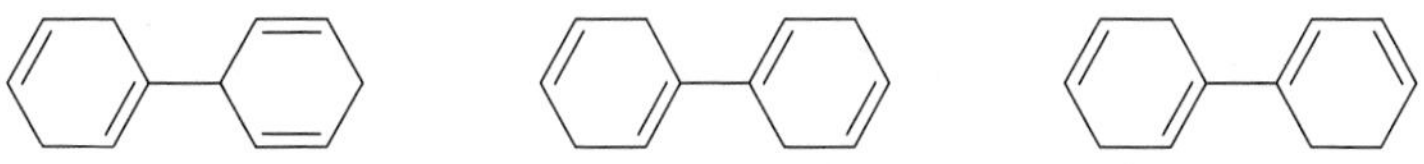

16.10 Electrophilic Addition: 1,2- Versus 1,4-Addition

Recall from Chapters 10 and 11 that the characteristic reaction of compounds with π bonds is **addition.** The π bonds in conjugated dienes undergo addition reactions, too, but they differ in two ways from the addition reactions to isolated double bonds.

- **Electrophilic addition in conjugated dienes gives a mixture of products.**
- **Conjugated dienes undergo a unique addition reaction not seen in alkenes or isolated dienes.**

We learned in Chapter 10 that HX adds to the π bond of alkenes to form alkyl halides.

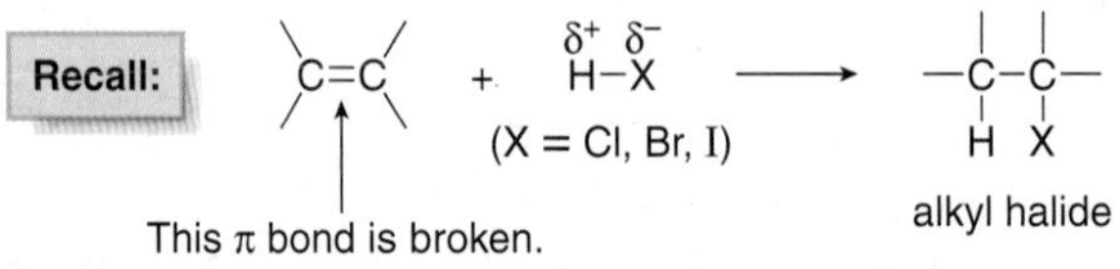
Recall:
δ+ δ−
H−X
(X = Cl, Br, I)
This π bond is broken.
alkyl halide

With an **isolated diene,** electrophilic addition of one equivalent of HBr yields *one* product and Markovnikov's rule is followed. The H atom bonds to the less substituted carbon—that is, the carbon atom of the double bond that had more H atoms to begin with.

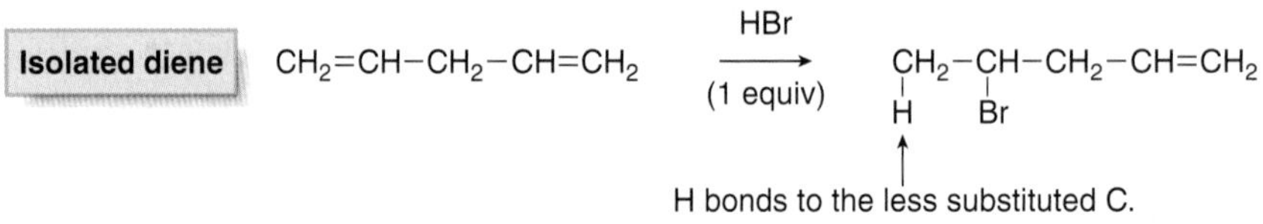
Isolated diene
CH2=CH−CH2−CH=CH2
HBr
(1 equiv)
CH2−CH−CH2−CH=CH2
H Br
H bonds to the less substituted C.

With a **conjugated diene,** electrophilic addition of one equivalent of HBr affords *two* products.

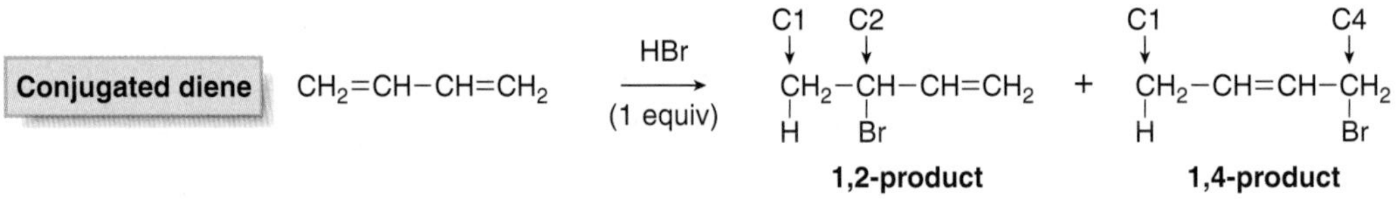
Conjugated diene
CH2=CH−CH=CH2
HBr
(1 equiv)
C1 C2
CH2−CH−CH=CH2
H Br
1,2-product
C1 C4
CH2−CH=CH−CH2
H Br
1,4-product

The ends of the 1,3-diene are called C1 and C4 arbitrarily, without regard to IUPAC numbering.

- The **1,2-addition product** results from Markovnikov addition of HBr across two adjacent carbon atoms (C1 and C2) of the diene.
- The **1,4-addition product** results from addition of HBr to the two end carbons (C1 and C4) of the diene. 1,4-Addition is also called **conjugate addition.**

The mechanism of electrophilic addition of HX involves **two steps:** addition of H^+ (from HX) to form a resonance-stabilized carbocation, followed by nucleophilic attack of X^- at either electrophilic end of the carbocation to form two products. Mechanism 16.1 illustrates the reaction of 1,3-butadiene with HBr.

Like the electrophilic addition of HX to an alkene, the addition of HBr to a conjugated diene forms the more stable carbocation in Step [1], the rate-determining step. In this case, however, the carbocation is both 2° and **allylic,** and thus two Lewis structures can be drawn for it. In the second step, nucleophilic attack of Br^- can then occur at two different electrophilic sites, forming two different products.

- **Addition of HX to a conjugated diene forms 1,2- and 1,4-products because of the resonance-stabilized allylic carbocation intermediate.**

Mechanism 16.1 Electrophilic Addition of HBr to a 1,3-Diene—1,2- and 1,4-Addition

Step [1] Addition of the electrophile (H^+) to the π bond

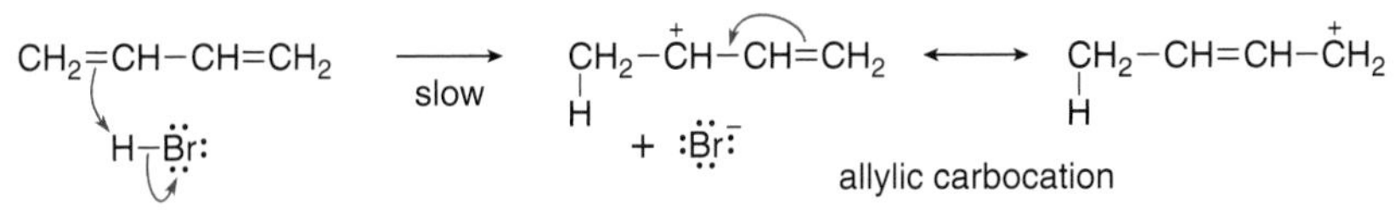

- H^+ (from HBr) always adds to a terminal C of the 1,3-diene to form a resonance-stabilized carbocation. This is the slow step of the mechanism because two bonds are broken and only one is formed.

Step [2] Nucleophilic attack of Br^-

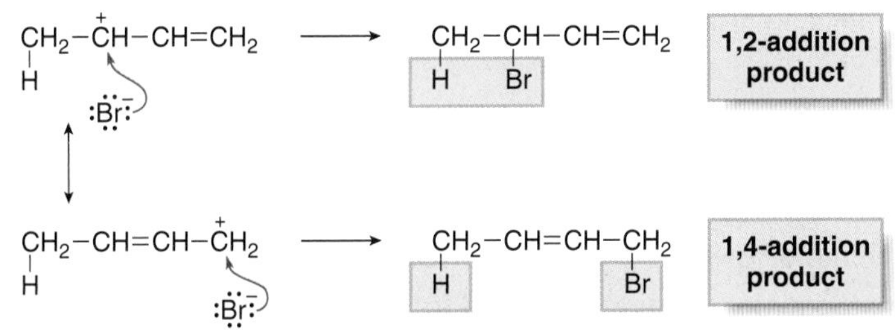

- **Nucleophilic attack of Br^-** can occur at either site of the resonance-stabilized carbocation that bears a (+) charge, forming either the 1,2-addition product or the 1,4-addition product.

Sample Problem 16.4

Draw the products of the following reaction.

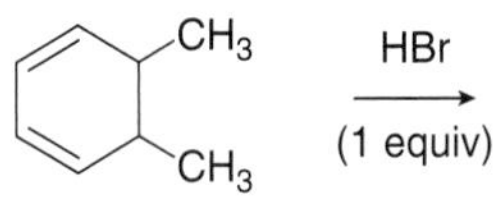

Solution

Write the steps of the mechanism to determine the structure of the products. Addition of H^+ forms the more stable 2° allylic carbocation, for which two resonance structures can be drawn. Nucleophilic attack of Br^- at either end of the allylic carbocation gives two constitutional isomers, formed by 1,2-addition and 1,4-addition to the diene.

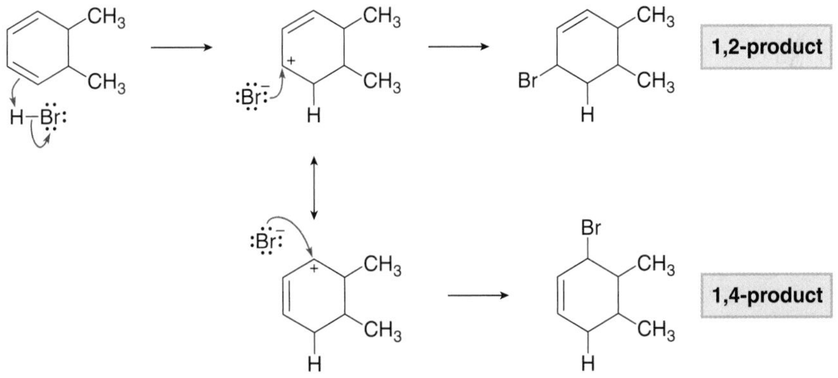

2° allylic carbocation

Problem 16.15

Draw the products formed when each diene is treated with one equivalent of HCl.

a. $CH_3CH{=}CH{-}CH{=}CHCH_3$

b. 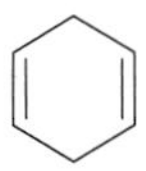

c. 

d. 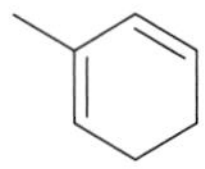

Problem 16.16

Draw a stepwise mechanism for the following reaction.

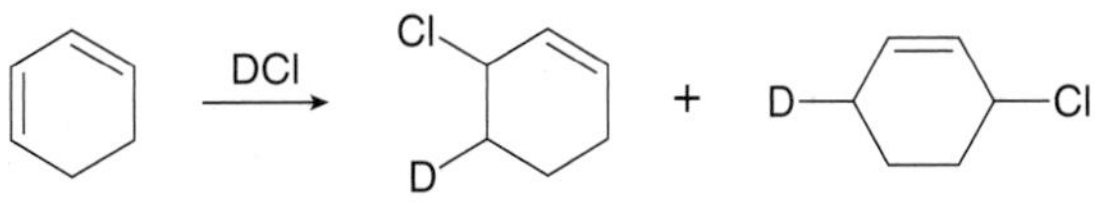

16.11 Kinetic Versus Thermodynamic Products

The amount of 1,2- and 1,4-addition products formed in the electrophilic addition reactions of 1,3-butadiene, a conjugated diene, depends greatly on the reaction conditions.

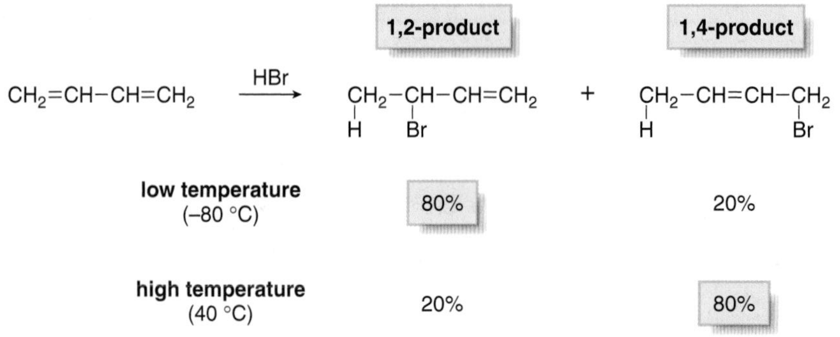

- **At low temperature the major product is formed by 1,2-addition.**
- **At higher temperature the major product is formed by 1,4-addition.**

Moreover, when a mixture containing predominately the 1,2-product is heated, the 1,4-addition product becomes the major product at equilibrium.

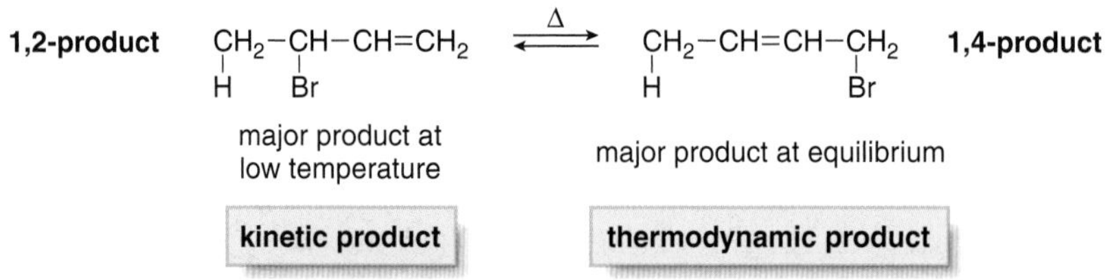

- The 1,2-product is formed faster because it predominates at low temperature. The product that is formed faster is called the *kinetic product.*
- The 1,4-product must be more stable because it predominates at equilibrium. The product that predominates at equilibrium is called the *thermodynamic product.*

In many of the reactions we have learned thus far, the more stable product is formed faster—that is, the kinetic and thermodynamic products are the same. The electrophilic addition of HBr to 1,3-butadiene is different, in that **the more stable product is formed more slowly**—that is, the kinetic and thermodynamic products are *different.* Why is the more stable product formed more slowly?

To answer this question, recall that the rate of a reaction is determined by its energy of activation (E_a), whereas the amount of product present at equilibrium is determined by its stability (Figure 16.6). When a single starting material **A** forms two different products (**B** and **C**) by two exothermic pathways, the relative height of the energy barriers determines how fast **B** and **C** are formed, whereas the relative energies of **B** and **C** determine the amount of each at equilibrium. In an exothermic reaction, the relative energies of **B** and **C** do not determine the relative energies of activation to form **B** and **C.**

Why, in the addition of HBr to 1,3-butadiene, is the 1,2-product formed faster, but the 1,4-product more stable? The 1,4-product (1-bromo-2-butene) is more stable because it has two alkyl groups bonded to the carbon–carbon double bond, whereas the 1,2-product (3-bromo-1-butene) has only one.

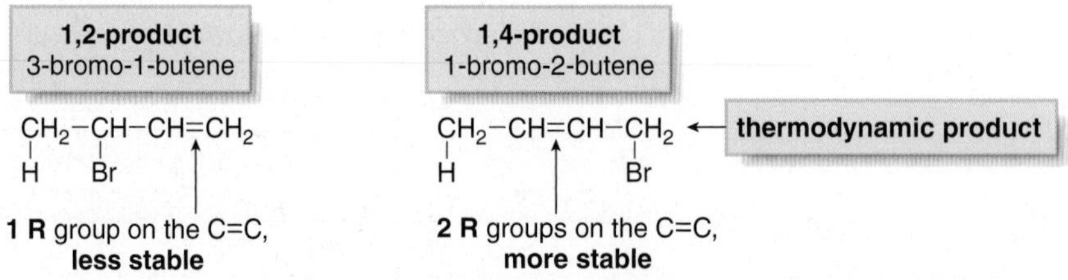

Figure 16.6
How kinetic and thermodynamic products form in a reaction: **A** → **B** + **C**

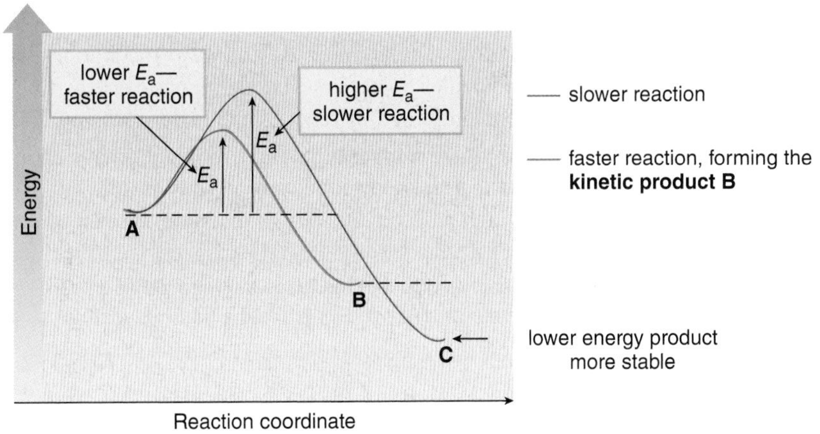

- The conversion of **A** → **B** is a faster reaction because the energy of activation leading to **B** is lower. **B** is the kinetic product.
- Because **C** is lower in energy, **C** is the thermodynamic product.

- **The more substituted alkene—1-bromo-2-butene in this case—is the thermodynamic product.**

The 1,2-product is the kinetic product because of a **proximity effect.** When H^+ (from HBr) adds to the double bond, Br^- is closer to the adjacent carbon (C2) than it is to C4. Even though the resonance-stabilized carbocation bears a partial positive charge on both C2 and C4, attack at C2 is faster simply because Br^- is closer to this carbon.

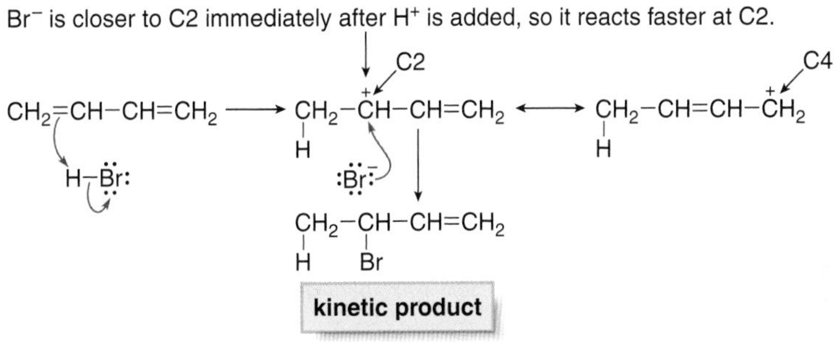

A **proximity effect** occurs because one species is close to another.

- **The 1,2-product forms faster because of the proximity of Br^- to C2.**

The overall two-step mechanism for addition of HBr to 1,3-butadiene, forming a 1,2-addition product and 1,4-addition product, is illustrated with the energy diagram in Figure 16.7.

Figure 16.7
Energy diagram for the two-step mechanism: $CH_2{=}CH{-}CH{=}CH_2 + HBr \rightarrow CH_3CH(Br)CH{=}CH_2 + CH_3CH{=}CHCH_2Br$

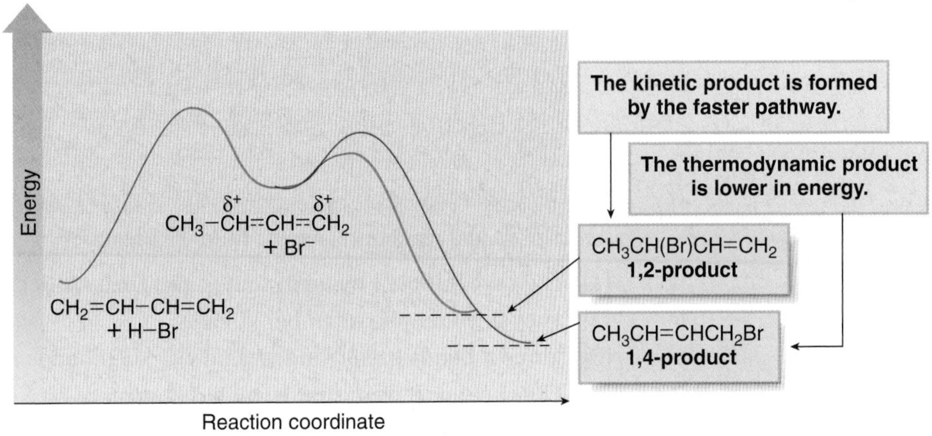

Why is the ratio of products temperature dependent?

- At low temperature, the energy of activation is the more important factor. Because most molecules do not have enough kinetic energy to overcome the higher energy barrier at lower temperature, they react by the faster pathway, forming the kinetic product.
- At higher temperature, most molecules have enough kinetic energy to reach either transition state. The two products are in equilibrium with each other, and the more stable compound—which is lower in energy—becomes the major product.

Problem 16.17 Label each product in the following reaction as a 1,2-product or 1,4-product, and decide which is the kinetic product and which is the thermodynamic product.

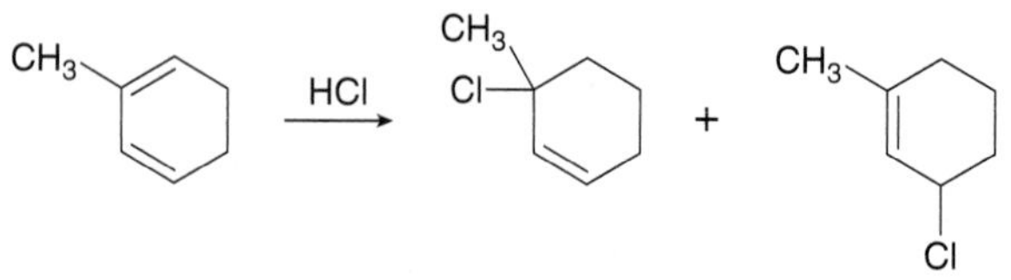

16.12 The Diels–Alder Reaction

Diels and Alder shared the 1950 Nobel Prize in Chemistry for unraveling the intricate details of this remarkable reaction.

The arrows may be drawn in a clockwise or counterclockwise direction to show the flow of electrons in a Diels–Alder reaction.

The **Diels–Alder reaction,** named for German chemists Otto Diels and Kurt Alder, is an addition reaction between a **1,3-diene** and an alkene called a **dienophile,** to form a new six-membered ring.

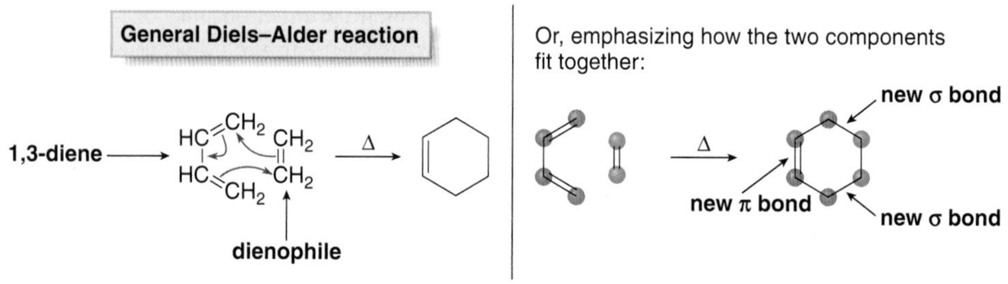

Three curved arrows are needed to show the cyclic movement of electron pairs because three π bonds break and two σ bonds and one π bond form. Because each new σ bond is ~100 kJ/mol stronger than a π bond that is broken, a typical Diels–Alder reaction releases ~200 kJ/mol of energy. The following equations illustrate three examples of the Diels–Alder reaction:

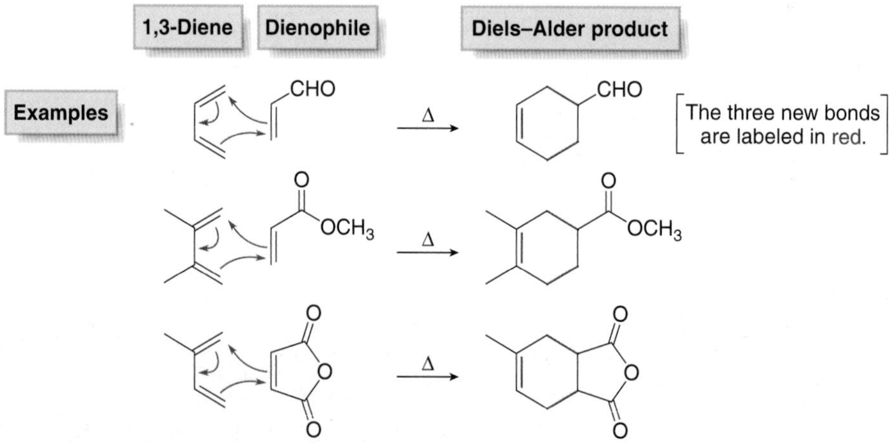

All Diels–Alder reactions have the following features in common:

[1] They are initiated by heat; that is, the Diels–Alder reaction is a *thermal* reaction.

[2] They form new six-membered rings.

[3] Three π bonds break, and two new C–C σ bonds and one new C–C π bond form.

[4] They are concerted; that is, all old bonds are broken and all new bonds are formed in a single step.

Figure 16.8
Synthesis of a natural product using the Diels–Alder reaction

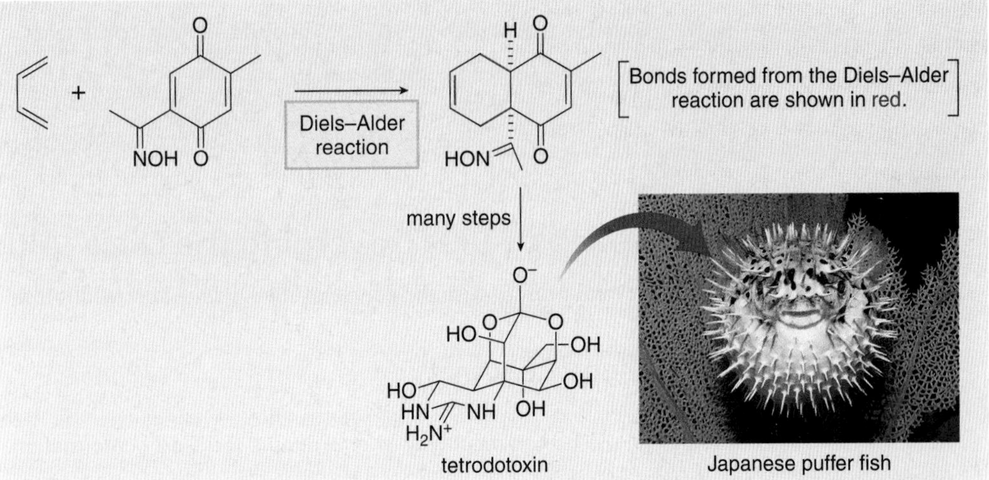
Diels–Alder reaction
Bonds formed from the Diels–Alder reaction are shown in red.
many steps
tetrodotoxin
Japanese puffer fish

- Tetrodotoxin, a complex natural product containing several six-membered rings joined together, is a poison isolated from the ovaries and liver of the puffer fish, so named because the fish inflates itself into a ball when alarmed. One step in the synthesis of tetrodotoxin involves forming a six-membered ring by a Diels–Alder reaction.

The Diels–Alder reaction forms new carbon–carbon bonds, so it can be used to synthesize larger, more complex molecules from smaller ones. For example, Figure 16.8 illustrates a Diels–Alder reaction used in the synthesis of tetrodotoxin, a toxin isolated from many different types of puffer fish and first mentioned in the Prologue.

Diels–Alder reactions may seem complicated at first, but they are really less complicated than many of the reactions you have already learned, especially those with multistep mechanisms and carbocation intermediates. The key is to learn how to arrange the starting materials to more easily visualize the structure of the product.

How To Draw the Product of a Diels–Alder Reaction

Example Draw the product of the following Diels–Alder reaction:

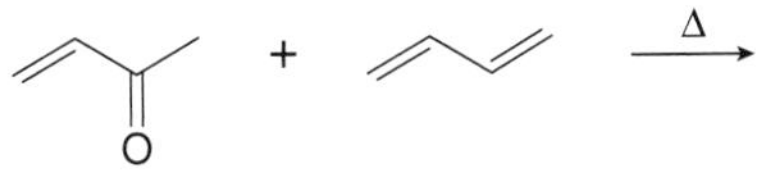

Step [1] Arrange the 1,3-diene and the dienophile next to each other, with the diene drawn in the *s*-cis conformation.

- This step is key: **Rotate the diene** so that it is drawn in the **s-cis** conformation, and place the end C's of the diene close to the double bond of the dienophile.

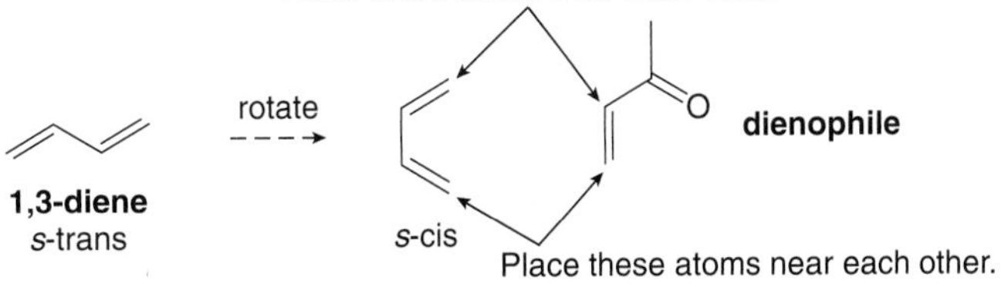
Place these atoms near each other.
rotate
1,3-diene
s-trans
s-cis
dienophile
Place these atoms near each other.

Step [2] Cleave the three π bonds and use arrows to show where the new bonds will be formed.

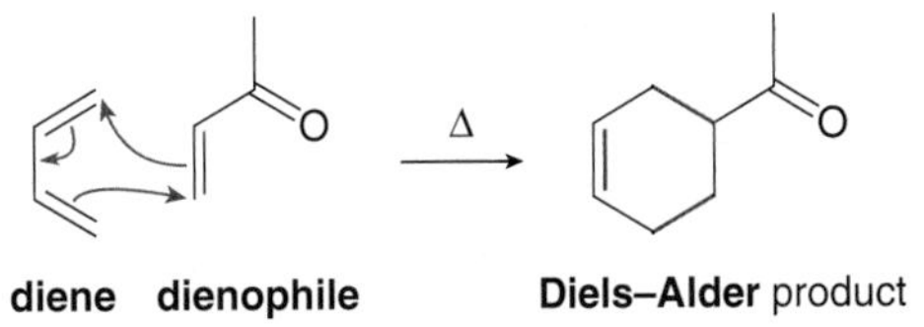
diene
dienophile
Diels–Alder product

Problem 16.18 Draw the product formed when each diene and dienophile react in a Diels–Alder reaction.

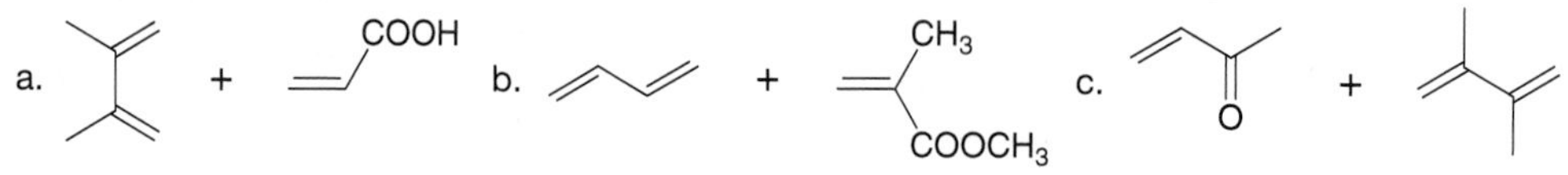

16.13 Specific Rules Governing the Diels–Alder Reaction

Several rules govern the course of the Diels–Alder reaction.

16.13A Diene Reactivity

Rule [1] **The diene can react only when it adopts the s-cis conformation.**

Both ends of the conjugated diene must be close to the π bond of the dienophile for reaction to occur. Thus, an acyclic diene in the *s*-trans conformation must rotate about the central C–C σ bond to form the *s*-cis conformation before reaction can take place.

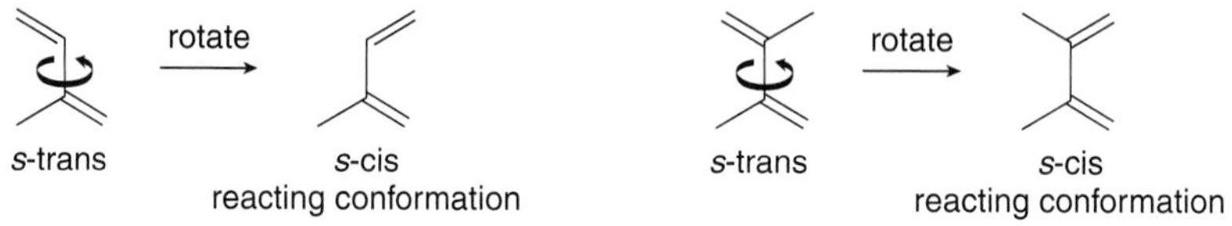

This rotation is prevented in cyclic dienes. As a result:

- When the two double bonds are constrained in the **s-cis** conformation, the diene is unusually *reactive.*
- When the two double bonds are constrained in the **s-trans** conformation, the diene is *unreactive.*

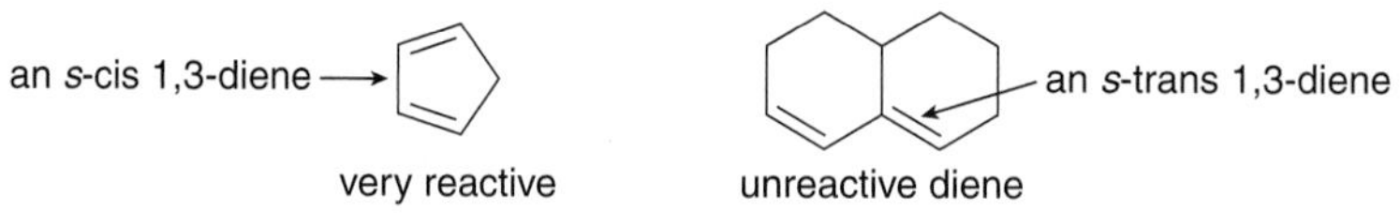

Zingiberene and β-sesquiphellandrene are trienes obtained from ginger root. Ginger is used as a spice in Indian and Chinese cooking. Ginger candy is sometimes used to treat nausea resulting from seasickness.

Problem 16.19 Rank the following dienes in order of increasing reactivity in a Diels–Alder reaction.

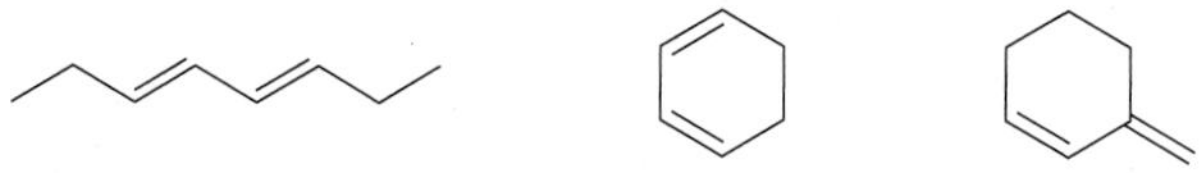

Problem 16.20 Zingiberene and β-sesquiphellandrene, natural products obtained from ginger root, contain conjugated diene units. Which diene reacts faster in the Diels–Alder reaction and why?

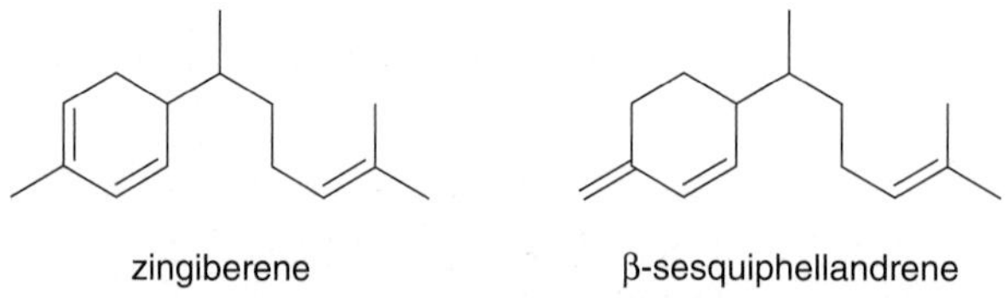

16.13B Dienophile Reactivity

Rule [2] **Electron-withdrawing substituents in the dienophile increase the reaction rate.**

In a Diels–Alder reaction, the conjugated diene acts as a nucleophile and the dienophile acts as an electrophile. As a result, electron-withdrawing groups make the dienophile more electrophilic (and, thus, more reactive) by withdrawing electron density from the carbon–carbon double bond. If Z is an electron-withdrawing group, then the reactivity of the dienophile increases as follows:

$CH_2{=}CH_2$ $\quad$ $CH_2{=}CHZ$ $\quad$ $ZCH{=}CHZ$

A carbonyl group is an effective electron-withdrawing group because the carbonyl carbon bears a partial positive charge (δ^+), which withdraws electron density from the carbon–carbon double bond of the dienophile. Common dienophiles that contain a carbonyl group are shown in Figure 16.9.

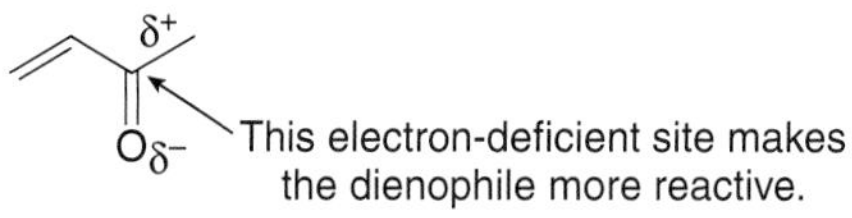

Problem 16.21 Rank the following dienophiles in order of increasing reactivity.

$CH_2{=}CHCOOH$

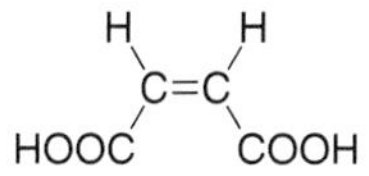

$CH_2{=}CH_2$

Figure 16.9
Common dienophiles in the Diels–Alder reaction

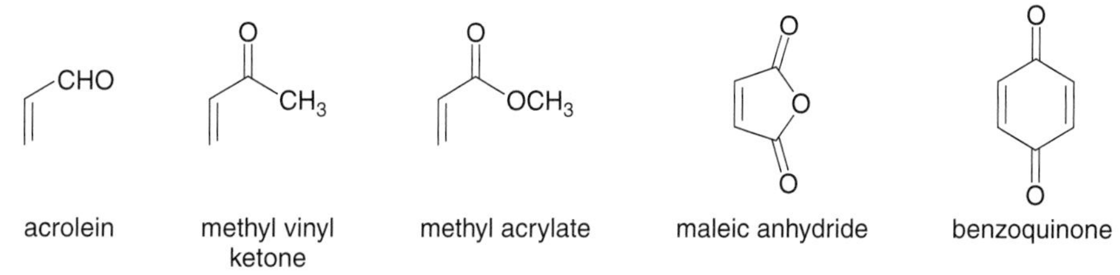

16.13C Stereospecificity

Rule [3] The stereochemistry of the dienophile is retained in the product.

- **A cis dienophile forms a cis-substituted cyclohexene.**
- **A trans dienophile forms a trans-substituted cyclohexene.**

The two **cis** COOH groups of maleic acid become two **cis** substituents in a Diels–Alder adduct. The COOH groups can be drawn both above or both below the plane to afford a single achiral **meso** compound. The **trans dienophile** fumaric acid yields two enantiomers with **trans** COOH groups.

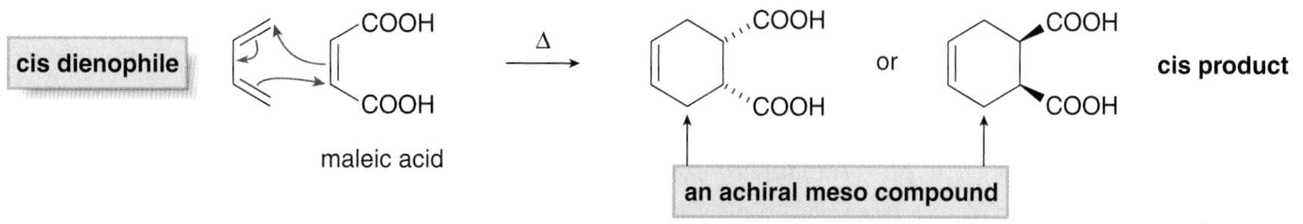

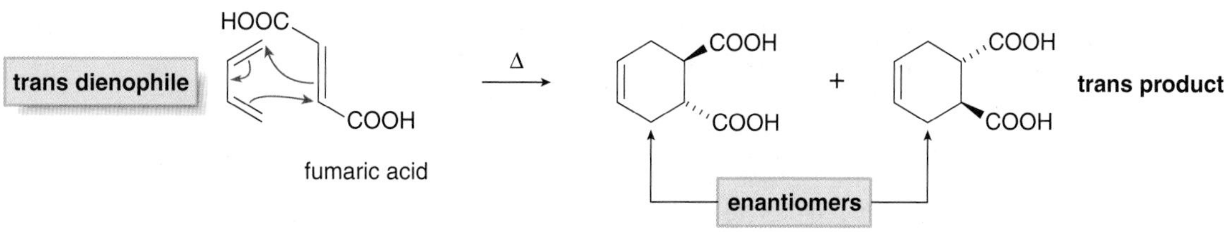

A **cyclic dienophile** forms a **bicyclic product.** A bicyclic system in which the two rings share a common C–C bond is called a **fused ring system.** The two H atoms at the ring fusion must be cis, because they were cis in the starting dienophile. A bicyclic system of this sort is said to be **cis-fused.**

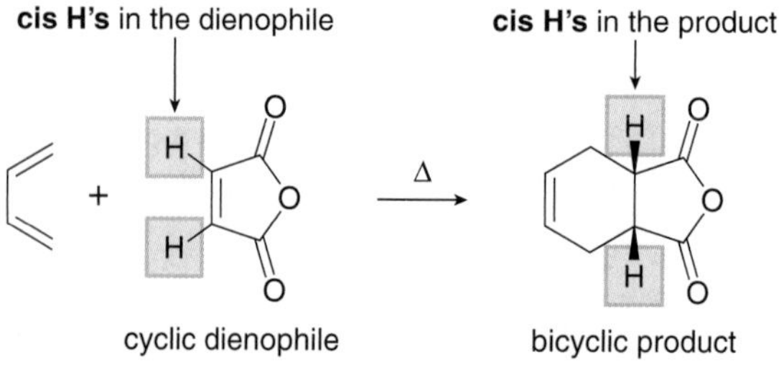

Problem 16.22 Draw the products of each Diels–Alder reaction, and indicate the stereochemistry.

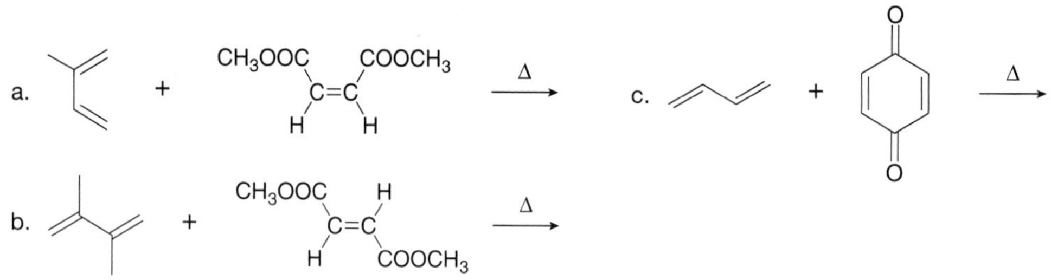

16.13D The Rule of Endo Addition

Rule [4] **When endo and exo products are possible, the endo product is preferred.**

To understand the rule of endo addition, we must first examine Diels–Alder products that result from cyclic 1,3-dienes. When cyclopentadiene reacts with a dienophile such as ethylene, a new six-membered ring forms, and above the ring there is a one atom "bridge." This carbon atom originated as the sp^3 hybridized carbon of the diene that was not involved in the reaction.

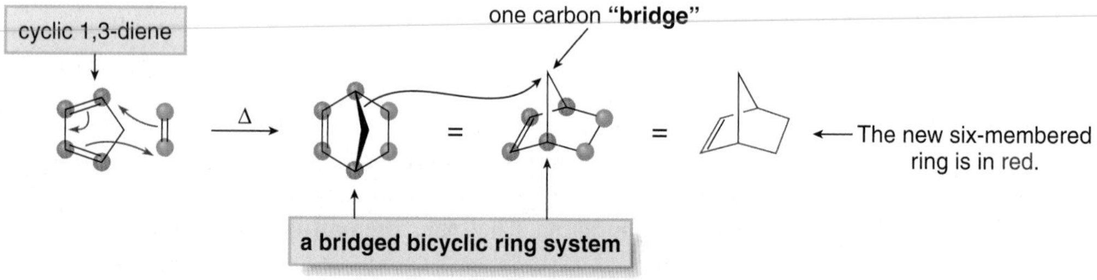

The product of the Diels–Alder reaction of a cyclic 1,3-diene is bicyclic, but the carbon atoms shared by both rings are *non-adjacent.* Thus, this bicyclic product differs from the fused ring system obtained when the dienophile is cyclic.

- **A bicyclic ring system in which the two rings share non-adjacent carbon atoms is called a *bridged* ring system.**

Fused and bridged bicyclic ring systems are compared in Figure 16.10.

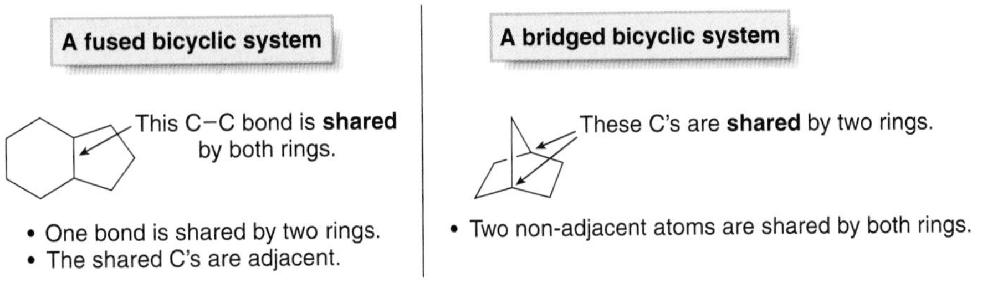
A fused bicyclic system
This C–C bond is **shared** by both rings.
• One bond is shared by two rings.
• The shared C's are adjacent.
A bridged bicyclic system
These C's are **shared** by two rings.
• Two non-adjacent atoms are shared by both rings.

Figure 16.10
Fused and bridged bicyclic ring systems compared

When cyclopentadiene reacts with a substituted alkene as the dienophile ($CH_2{=}CHZ$), the substituent Z can be oriented in one of two ways in the product. The terms **endo** and **exo** are used to indicate the position of Z.

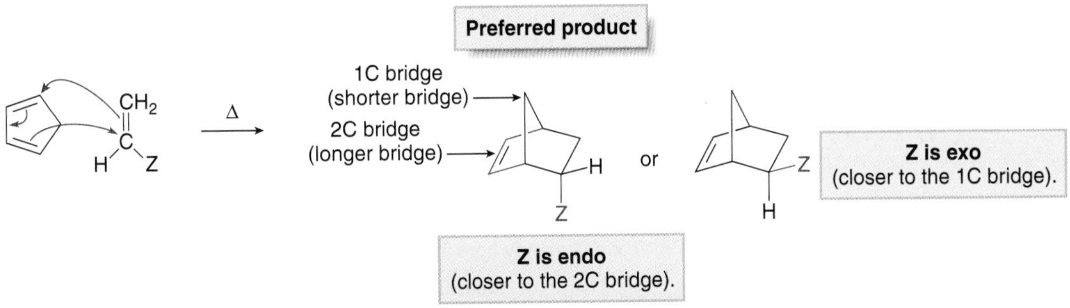
Preferred product
CH2
H
Z
Δ
1C bridge
(shorter bridge)
2C bridge
(longer bridge)
H
Z
or
Z
H
Z is exo
(closer to the 1C bridge).
Z is endo
(closer to the 2C bridge).

- **A substituent on one bridge is *endo* if it is closer to the *longer* bridge that joins the two carbons common to both rings.**
- **A substituent is *exo* if it is closer to the *shorter* bridge that joins the carbons together.**

In a Diels–Alder reaction, the **endo** product is preferred, as shown in two examples.

To help you distinguish endo and exo, remember that en*d*o is u*n*der the newly formed six-membered ring.

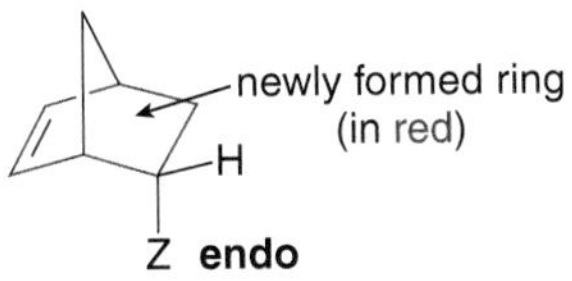
newly formed ring
(in red)
H
Z endo

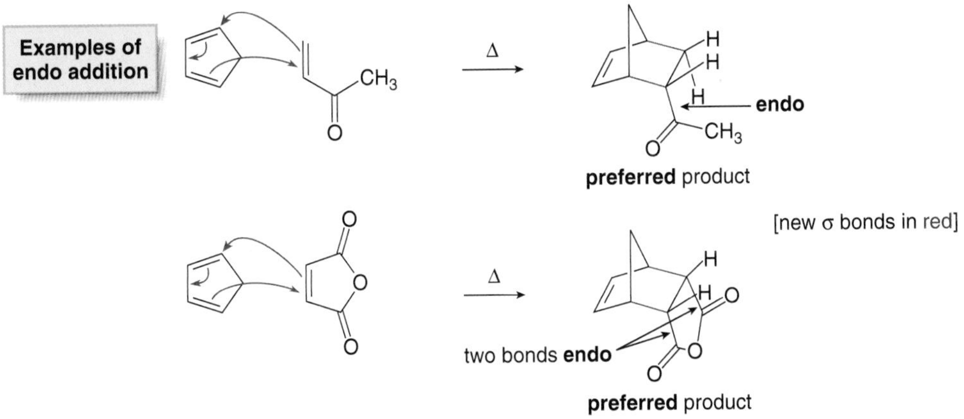
Examples of endo addition
CH3
O
Δ
H
H
H
endo
CH3
O
preferred product
[new σ bonds in red]
O
O
O
Δ
H
H
O
two bonds endo
O
O
preferred product

More details on the Diels–Alder reaction are given in Section 27.4.

The Diels–Alder reaction is concerted, and the reaction occurs with the diene and the dienophile arranged one above the other, as shown in Figure 16.11, not side-by-side. In theory, the substituent Z can be oriented either directly under the diene to form the endo product (Pathway [1] in Figure 16.11) or away from the diene to form the exo product (Pathway [2] in Figure 16.11). In practice, though, the **endo product is the major product.** The transition state leading to the endo product allows more interaction between the electron-rich diene and the electron-withdrawing substituent Z on the dienophile, an energetically favorable arrangement.

Figure 16.11 How endo and exo products are formed in the Diels–Alder reaction

Pathway [1] With Z oriented under the diene, the endo product is formed.

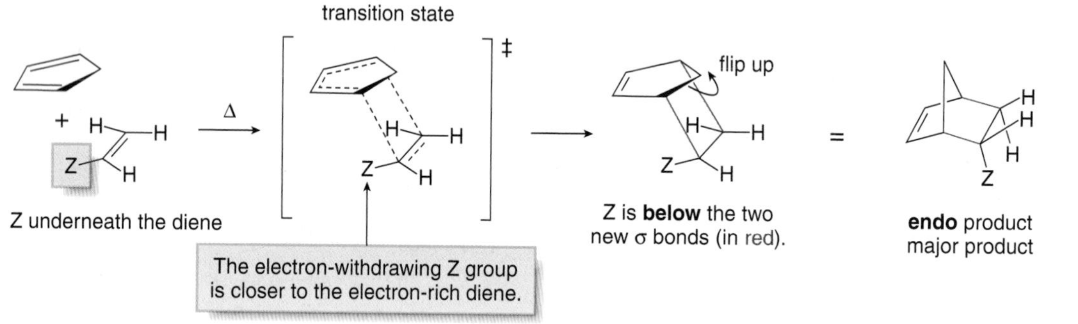

Pathway [2] With Z oriented away from the diene, the exo product is formed.

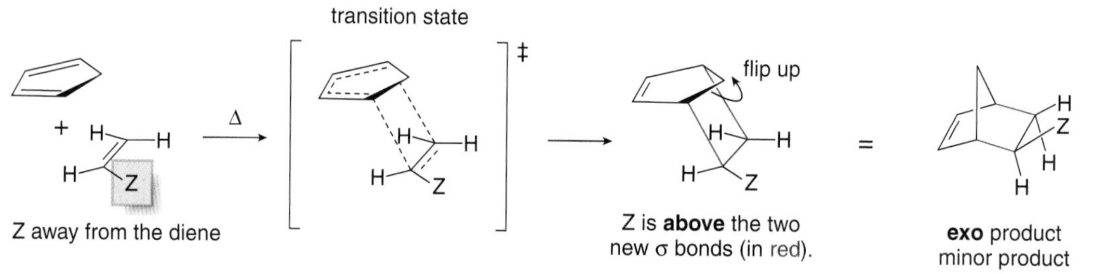

Problem 16.23 Draw the product of each Diels–Alder reaction.

a. 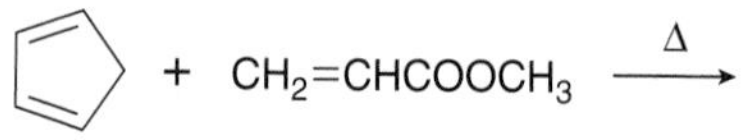

b. 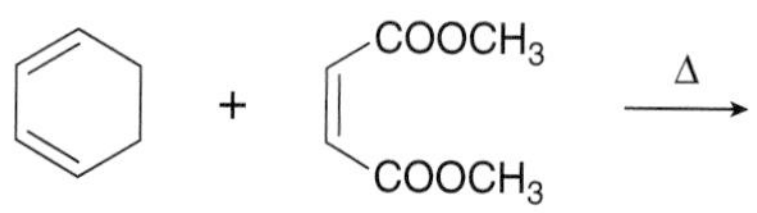

16.14 Other Facts About the Diels–Alder Reaction

16.14A Retrosynthetic Analysis of a Diels–Alder Product

The Diels–Alder reaction is used widely in organic synthesis, so you must be able to look at a compound and determine what conjugated diene and what dienophile were used to make it. To draw the starting materials from a given Diels–Alder adduct:

- **Locate the six-membered ring that contains the C=C.**
- **Draw three arrows around the cyclohexene ring, beginning with the π bond. Each arrow moves two electrons to the adjacent bond, cleaving one π bond and two σ bonds, and forming three π bonds.**
- **Retain the stereochemistry of substituents on the C=C of the dienophile. Cis substituents on the six-membered ring give a cis dienophile.**

This stepwise retrosynthetic analysis gives the 1,3-diene and dienophile needed for any Diels–Alder reaction, as shown in the two examples in Figure 16.12.

Figure 16.12

Finding the diene and dienophile needed for a Diels–Alder reaction

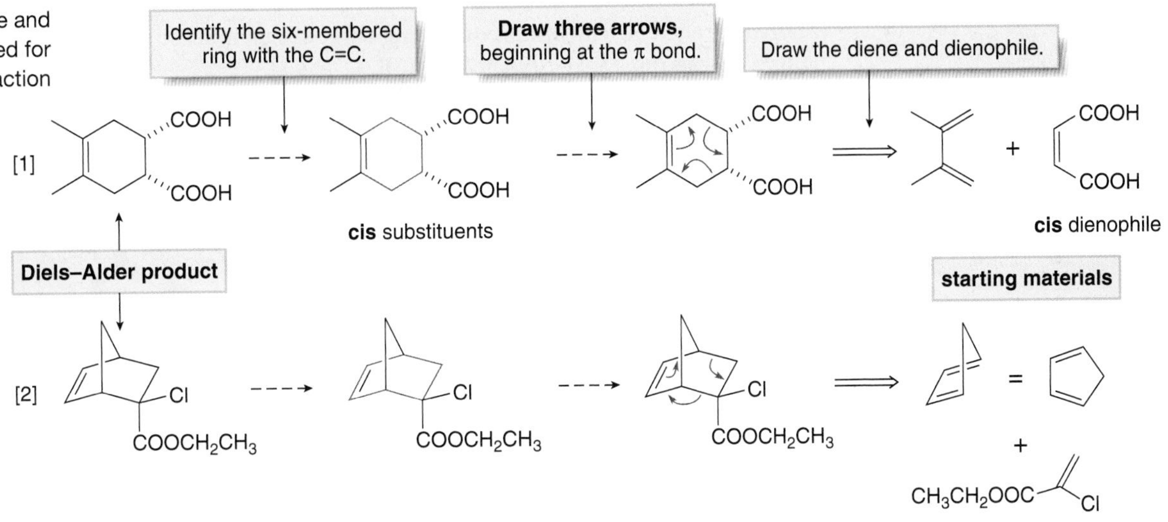

Problem 16.24 What diene and dienophile are needed to prepare each product?

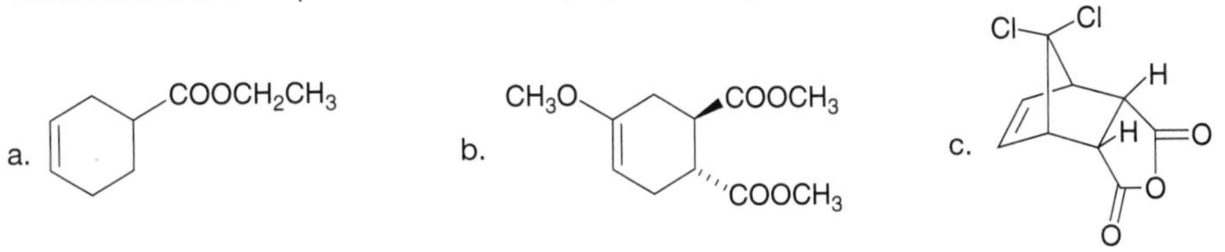

16.14B Retro Diels–Alder Reaction

A reactive diene like 1,3-cyclopentadiene readily undergoes a Diels–Alder reaction with *itself;* that is, **1,3-cyclopentadiene dimerizes because one molecule acts as the diene and another acts as the dienophile.**

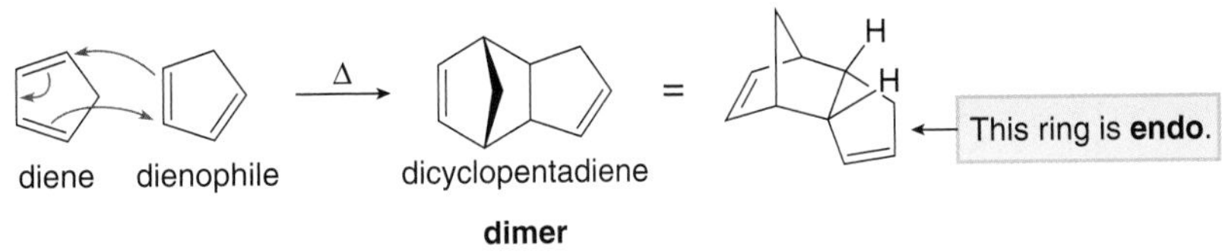

The formation of dicyclopentadiene is so rapid that it takes only a few hours at room temperature for cyclopentadiene to completely dimerize. How, then, can cyclopentadiene be used in a Diels–Alder reaction if it really exists as a dimer?

When heated, dicyclopentadiene undergoes a **retro Diels–Alder reaction,** and two molecules of cyclopentadiene are re-formed. If cyclopentadiene is immediately treated with a different dienophile, it reacts to form a new Diels–Alder adduct with this dienophile.

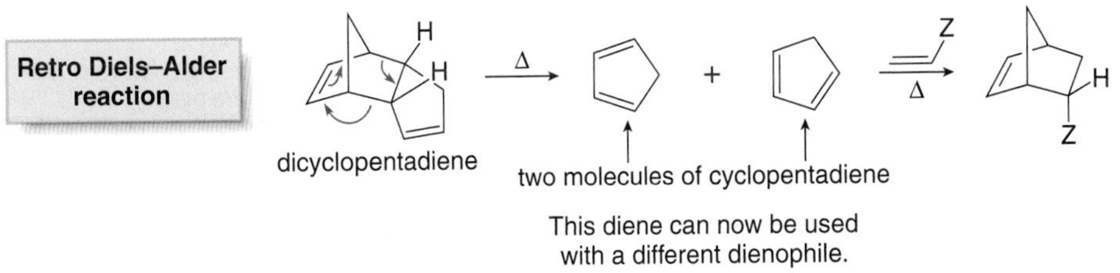

16.14C Application: Diels–Alder Reaction in the Synthesis of Steroids

Recall from Section 4.15 that lipids are water-insoluble biomolecules that have diverse structures.

***Steroids* are tetracyclic lipids containing three six-membered rings and one five-membered ring.** The four rings are designated as **A, B, C,** and **D.**

The steroid skeleton

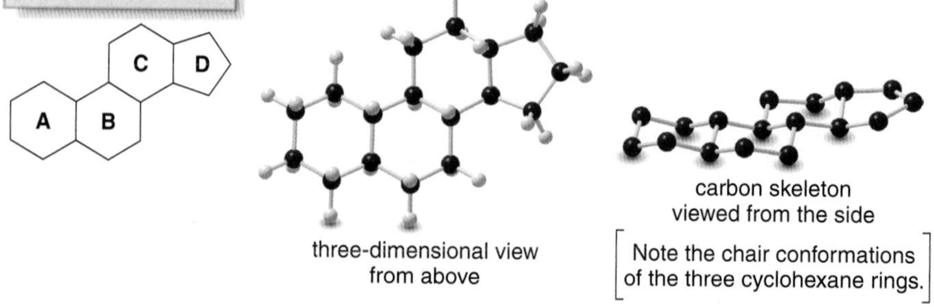
A
B
C
D
three-dimensional view from above
carbon skeleton viewed from the side
Note the chair conformations of the three cyclohexane rings.

Steroids exhibit a wide range of biological properties, depending on the substitution pattern of functional groups on the rings. They include **cholesterol** (a component of cell membranes that is implicated in cardiovascular disease), **estrone** (a female sex hormone responsible for the regulation of the menstrual cycle), and **cortisone** (a hormone responsible for the control of inflammation and the regulation of carbohydrate metabolism).

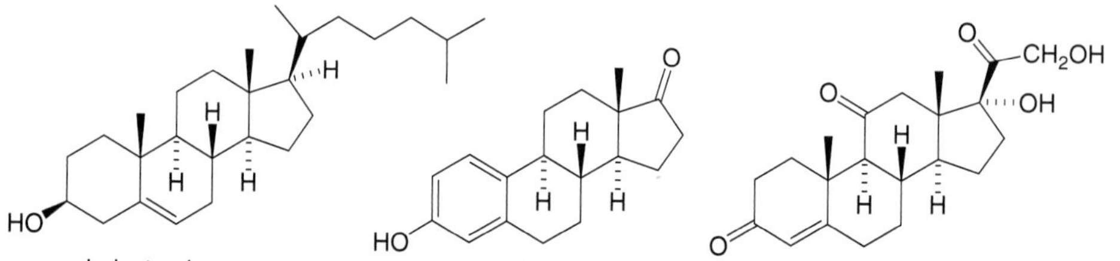
HO
H
H
H
O
HO
H
H
H
O
CH₂OH
OH
O
O
H
H
H

cholesterol estrone cortisone

Diels–Alder reactions have been used widely in the laboratory syntheses of steroids. The key Diels–Alder reactions used to prepare the C ring of estrone and the B ring of cortisone are as follows:

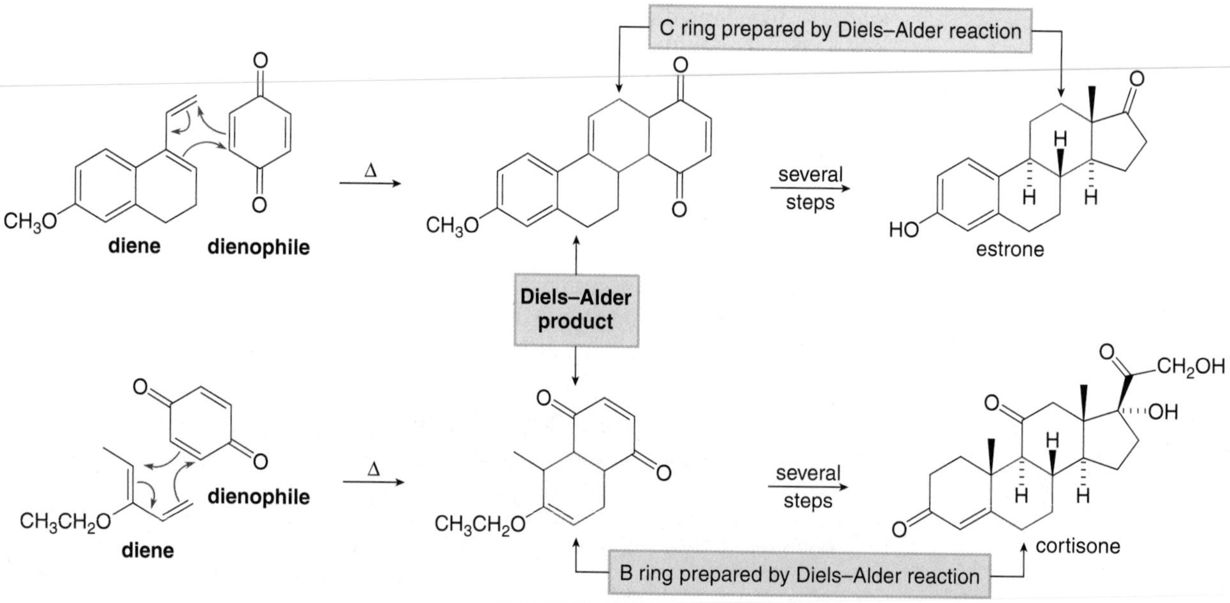
C ring prepared by Diels–Alder reaction
CH₃O
diene
dienophile
O
O
Δ
CH₃O
several steps
HO
estrone
Diels–Alder product
CH₃CH₂O
diene
dienophile
Δ
CH₃CH₂O
several steps
cortisone
CH₂OH
OH
B ring prepared by Diels–Alder reaction

Problem 16.25 Draw the product (**A**) of the following Diels–Alder reaction. **A** was a key intermediate in the synthesis of the addicting pain reliever morphine, the chapter-opening molecule.

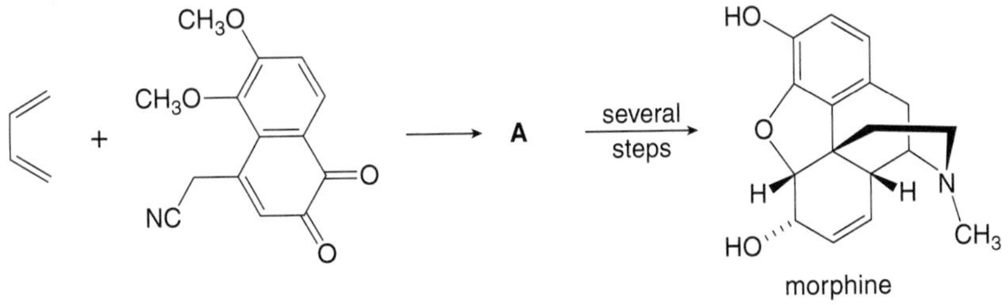
CH3O
CH3O
NC
O
O
A
several steps
HO
O
H
H
N
CH3
HO
morphine

16.15 Conjugated Dienes and Ultraviolet Light

Recall from Chapter 13 that the absorption of infrared energy can promote a molecule from a lower vibrational state to a higher one. In a similar fashion, the absorption of ultraviolet (UV) light can promote an electron from a lower electronic state to a higher one. Ultraviolet light has a slightly shorter wavelength (and, thus, higher frequency) than visible light. The most useful region of UV light for this purpose is **200–400 nm.**

The UV region of the electromagnetic spectrum

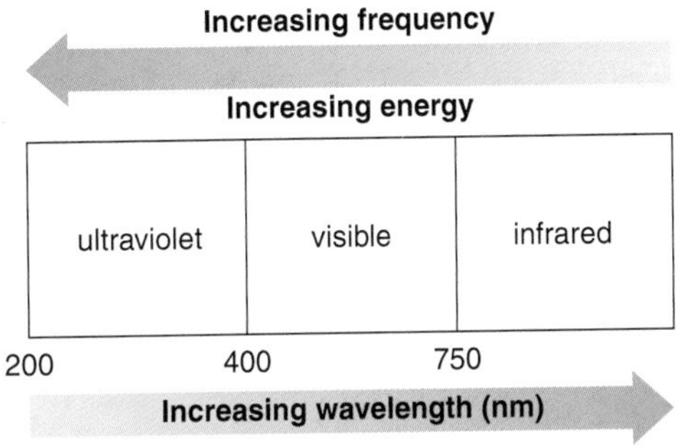
Increasing frequency
Increasing energy
ultraviolet
visible
infrared
200
400
750
Increasing wavelength (nm)

16.15A General Principles

When electrons in a lower energy state (the **ground state**) absorb light having the appropriate energy, an electron is promoted to a higher electronic state (the **excited state**).

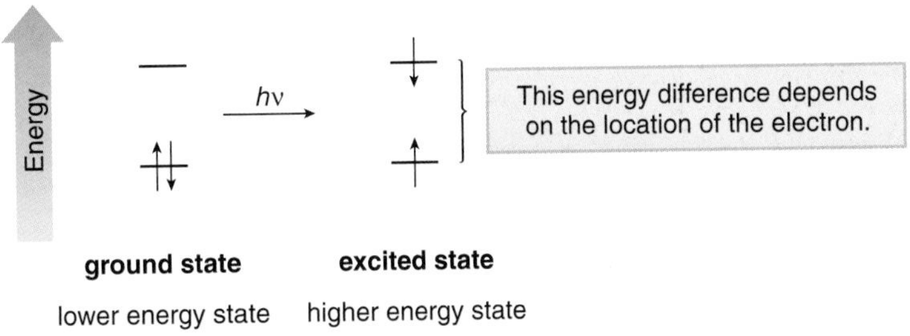
Energy
hν
This energy difference depends on the location of the electron.
ground state
excited state
lower energy state
higher energy state

The energy difference between the two states depends on the location of the electron. The promotion of electrons in σ bonds and unconjugated π bonds requires light having a wavelength of < 200 nm; that is, it has a shorter wavelength and higher energy than light in the UV region of the electromagnetic spectrum. With conjugated dienes, however, the energy difference between the ground and excited states decreases, so longer wavelengths of light can be used to promote electrons. The wavelength of UV light absorbed by a compound is often referred to as its λ_{max}. 1,3-Butadiene, for example, absorbs UV light at λ_{max} = 217 nm and 1,3-cyclohexadiene has a λ_{max} of 256 nm.

λ_{max} = 217 nm λ_{max} = 256 nm

Lycopene is the red pigment found in tomatoes, watermelon, papaya, guava, and pink grapefruit. Lycopene is not destroyed when fruits and vegetables are processed, so tomato juice and ketchup are high in lycopene.

- **Conjugated dienes and polyenes absorb light in the UV region of the electromagnetic spectrum (200–400 nm).**

As the number of conjugated π bonds increases, the energy difference between the ground and excited state decreases, shifting the absorption to longer wavelengths.

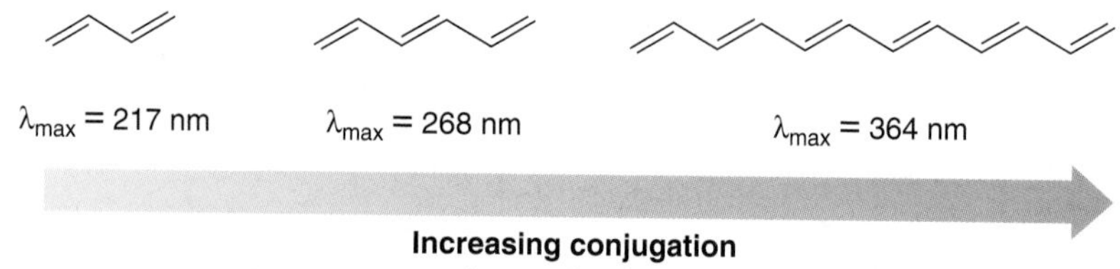
λ_{max} = 217 nm
λ_{max} = 268 nm
λ_{max} = 364 nm
Increasing conjugation
Increasing λ_{max}

With molecules having eight or more conjugated π bonds, the absorption shifts from the UV to the visible region and the compound takes on the color of those wavelengths of visible light it does *not* absorb. For example, lycopene absorbs visible light at λ_{max} = 470 nm, in the blue-green region of the visible spectrum. Because it does not absorb light in the red region, lycopene appears bright red (Figure 16.13).

Problem 16.26 Which compound in each pair absorbs UV light at longer wavelength?

a. 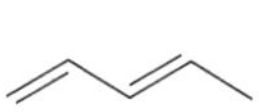 or 

b. 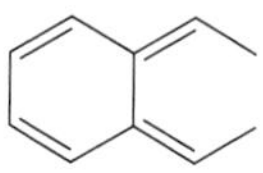 or 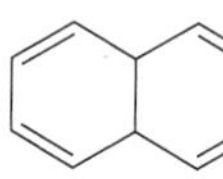

Figure 16.13
Why lycopene appears red

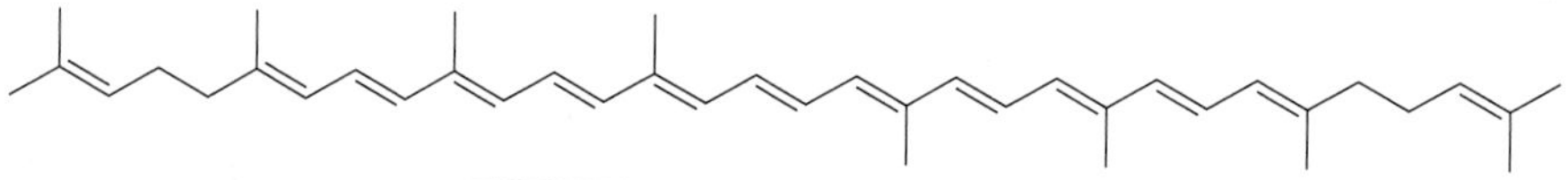

Lycopene—11 conjugated π bonds

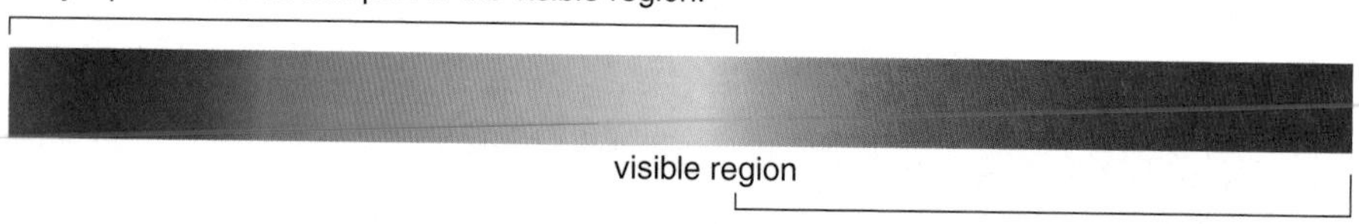
Lycopene absorbs this part of the visible region.
visible region
This part of the spectrum is *not* absorbed.
Lycopene appears red.

16.15B Sunscreens

Ultraviolet radiation from the sun is high enough in energy to cleave bonds, forming radicals that can prematurely age skin and cause skin cancers. The ultraviolet region is often subdivided, based on the wavelength of UV light: UV-A (320–400 nm), UV-B (290–320 nm), and UV-C (< 290 nm). Fortunately, much of the highest energy UV light (UV-C) is filtered out by the ozone layer, so that only UV light having wavelengths > 290 nm reaches the skin's surface. Much of this UV light is absorbed by **melanin,** the highly conjugated colored pigment in the skin that serves as the body's natural protection against the harmful effects of UV radiation.

Prolonged exposure to the sun can allow more UV radiation to reach your skin than melanin can absorb. A commercial sunscreen can offer added protection, however, because it contains conjugated compounds that absorb UV light, thus shielding your skin (for a time) from the

Commercial sunscreens are given an **SPF** rating (sun protection factor), according to the amount of sunscreen present. The higher the number, the greater the protection.

harmful effects of UV radiation. Two sunscreens that have been used for this purpose are *para*-aminobenzoic acid (PABA) and padimate O.

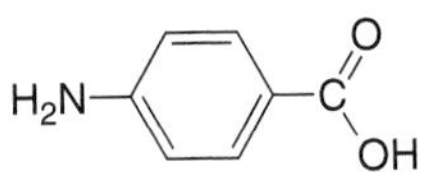

para-aminobenzoic acid (PABA)

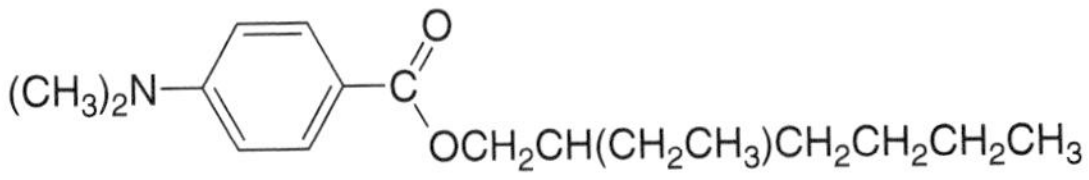

padimate O

Many sunscreens contain more than one component to filter out different regions of the UV spectrum. Conjugated compounds generally shield the skin from UV-B radiation, but often have little effect on longer-wavelength UV-A radiation, which does not burn the skin, but can still cause long-term damage to skin cells.

Problem 16.27 Which of the following compounds might be an ingredient in a commercial sunscreen? Explain why or why not.

a. 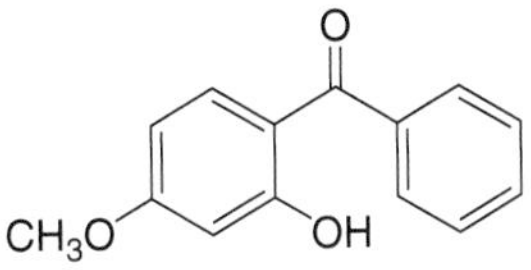

c. 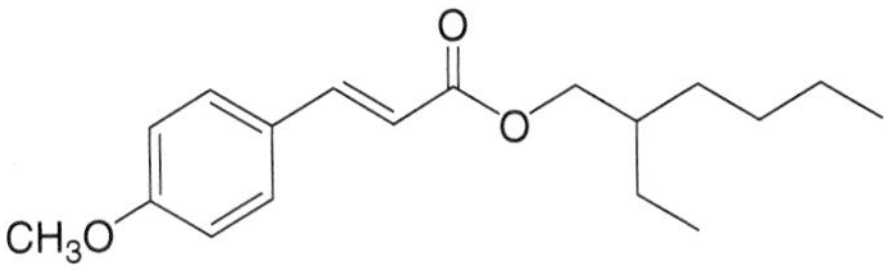

b. 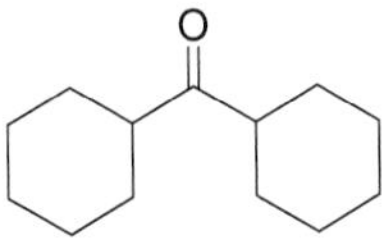

KEY CONCEPTS

Conjugation, Resonance, and Dienes

Conjugation and Delocalization of Electron Density

- The overlap of *p* orbitals on three or more adjacent atoms allows electron density to delocalize, thus adding stability (16.1).
- An allyl carbocation ($CH_2=CHCH_2^+$) is more stable than a 1° carbocation because of *p* orbital overlap (16.2).
- In a system X=Y−Z:, Z is generally sp^2 hybridized to allow the lone pair to occupy a *p* orbital, making the system conjugated (16.5).

Four Common Examples of Resonance (16.3)

[1] The three-atom "allyl" system: $X=Y-\underset{*}{Z} \longleftrightarrow \underset{*}{X}-Y=Z$ * = +, −, ·, or ··

[2] Conjugated double bonds:

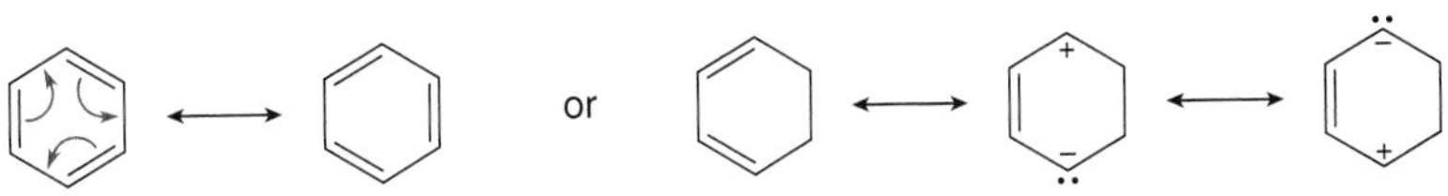

[3] Cations having a positive charge adjacent to a lone pair: $\ddot{X}-\overset{+}{Y} \longleftrightarrow \overset{+}{X}=Y$

[4] Double bonds involving one atom more electronegative than the other: $X=Y \longleftrightarrow \overset{+}{X}-\overset{-}{\ddot{Y}}:$ [electronegativity of Y > X]

Rules on Evaluating the Relative "Stability" of Resonance Structures (16.4)

[1] Structures with more bonds and fewer charges are more stable.
[2] Structures in which every atom has an octet are more stable.
[3] Structures that place a negative charge on a more electronegative atom are more stable.

The Unusual Properties of Conjugated Dienes

[1] The C−C σ bond joining the two double bonds is unusually short (16.8).
[2] Conjugated dienes are more stable than the corresponding isolated dienes. $\Delta H°$ of hydrogenation is smaller for a conjugated diene than for an isolated diene converted to the same product (16.9).
[3] The reactions are unusual:
- Electrophilic addition affords products of 1,2-addition and 1,4-addition (16.10, 16.11).
- Conjugated dienes undergo the Diels–Alder reaction, a reaction that does not occur with isolated dienes (16.12–16.14).

[4] Conjugated dienes absorb UV light in the 200–400 nm region. As the number of conjugated π bonds increases, the absorption shifts to longer wavelength (16.15).

Reactions of Conjugated Dienes

[1] Electrophilic addition of HX (X = halogen) (16.10–16.11)

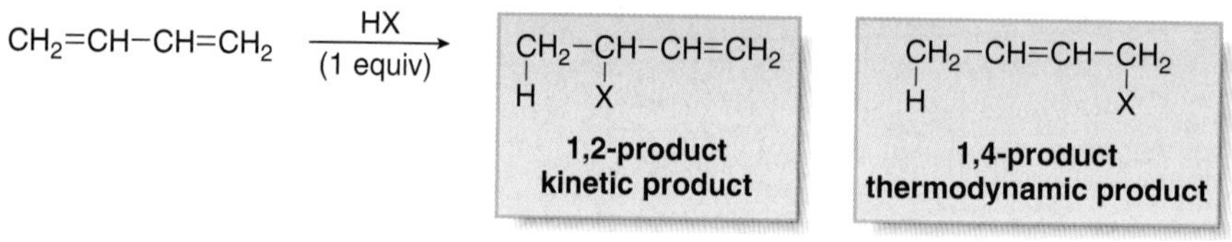
$CH_2=CH-CH=CH_2$
HX
(1 equiv)
$CH_2-CH-CH=CH_2$
H X
1,2-product
kinetic product
$CH_2-CH=CH-CH_2$
H X
1,4-product
thermodynamic product

- The mechanism has two steps.
- Markovnikov's rule is followed. Addition of H^+ forms the more stable allylic carbocation.
- The 1,2-product is the kinetic product. When H^+ adds to the double bond, X^- adds to the end of the allylic carbocation to which it is closer (C2 not C4). The kinetic product is formed faster at low temperature.
- The thermodynamic product has the more substituted, more stable double bond. The thermodynamic product predominates at equilibrium. With 1,3-butadiene, the thermodynamic product is the 1,4-product.

[2] Diels–Alder reaction (16.12–16.14)

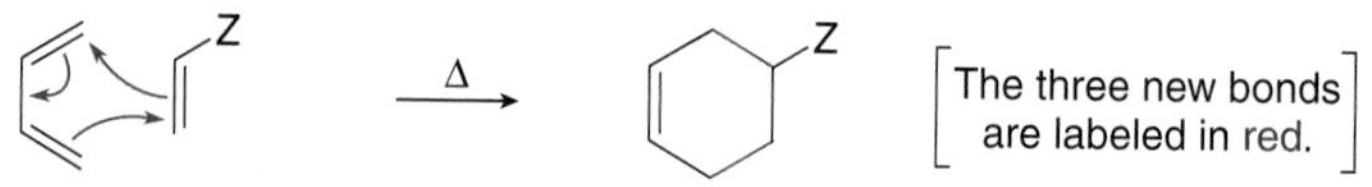
Z
Δ
Z
The three new bonds are labeled in red.

1,3-diene dienophile

- The reaction forms two σ and one π bond in a six-membered ring.
- The reaction is initiated by heat.
- The mechanism is concerted: All bonds are broken and formed in a single step.
- The diene must react in the *s*-cis conformation (16.13A).
- Electron-withdrawing groups in the dienophile increase the reaction rate (16.13B).
- The stereochemistry of the dienophile is retained in the product (16.13C).
- Endo products are preferred (16.13D).

PROBLEMS

Problems Using Three-Dimensional Models

16.28 Name each diene and state whether the ball-and-stick model shows the diene in the *s*-cis or *s*-trans conformation.

a. 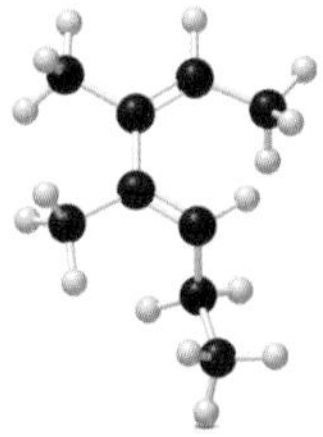

b. 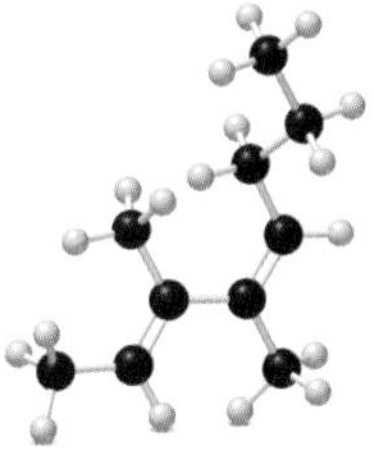

16.29 What diene and dienophile are needed to prepare each compound by a Diels–Alder reaction?

a. 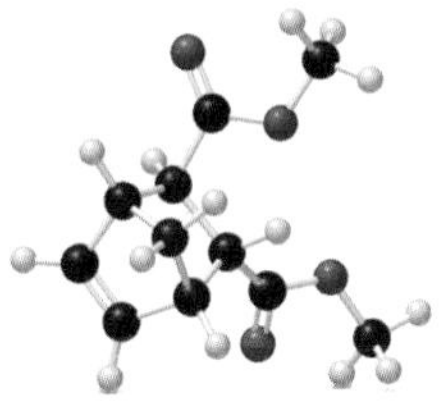

b. 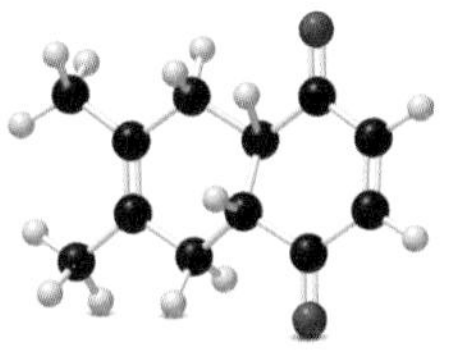

Conjugation

16.30 Which of the following systems are conjugated?

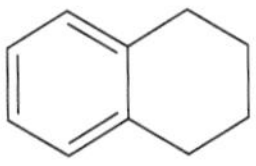

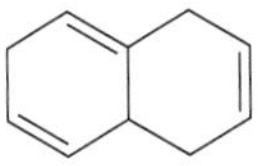

$CH_2{=}CHCN$

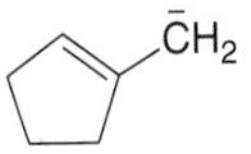

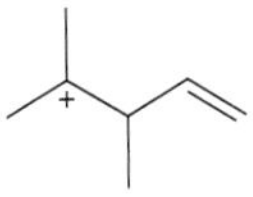

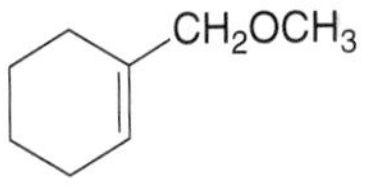

16.31 Label each double bond in 5-HPETE (5-hydroperoxyeicosatetraenoic acid) as isolated or conjugated. 5-HPETE is an intermediate in the biological conversion of arachidonic acid to leukotrienes, potent molecules that contribute to the asthmatic response (Section 9.16).

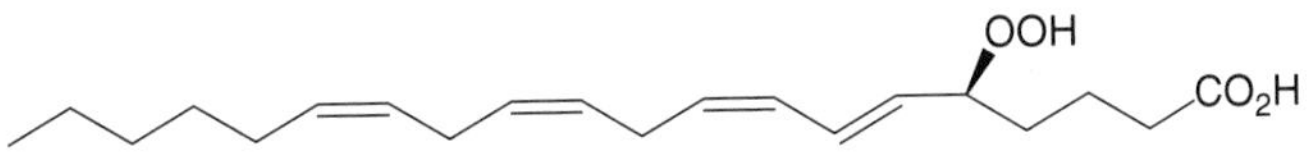

5-HPETE

Resonance and Hybridization

16.32 Draw all reasonable resonance structures for each species.

a. 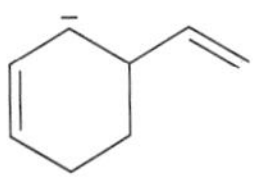

c. 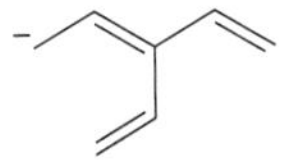

e. 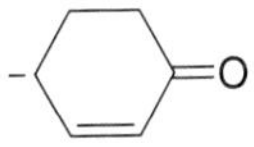

b. 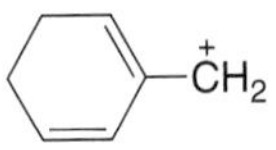

d. $CH_3OCH{=}CH\overset{+}{C}H_2$

f. 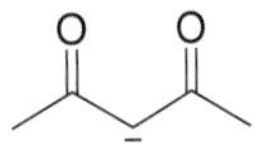

16.33 Draw all reasonable resonance structures for each species.

a. 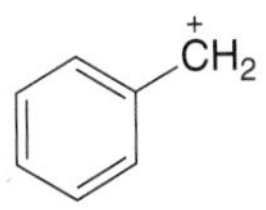

b. 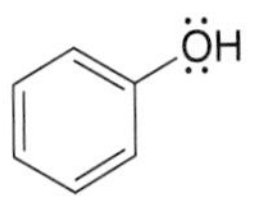

c. 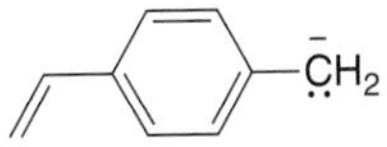

d. 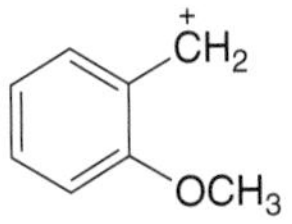

16.34 For which compounds can a second resonance structure be drawn? Draw an additional resonance structure for each resonance-stabilized compound.

a. 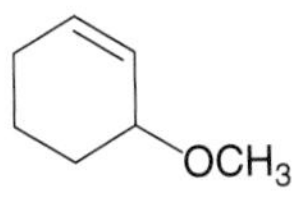

b. 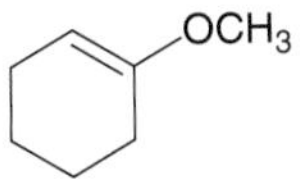

c. 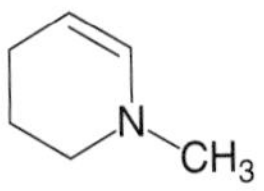

d. 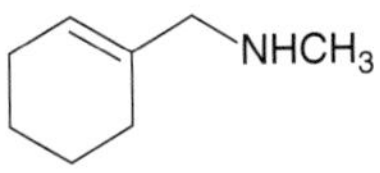

16.35 Explain why the cyclopentadienide anion **A** gives only one signal in its ^{13}C NMR spectrum.

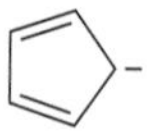
= **A**

16.36 Explain each statement using resonance theory.

a. The indicated C–H bond in propene is more acidic than the indicated C–H bond in propane.

more acidic	less acidic
$CH_2{=}CHCH_2{-}H$	$CH_3CH_2CH_2{-}H$
propene	propane

b. The bond dissociation energy for the C–C bond in ethane is much higher than the bond dissociation energy for the indicated C–C bond in 1-butene.

+368 kJ/mol	+301 kJ/mol
$CH_3{-}CH_3$	$CH_3{-}CH_2CH{=}CH_2$
ethane	1-butene

Nomenclature and Stereoisomers in Conjugated Dienes

16.37 Draw the structure of each compound.

a. (3*Z*)-1,3-pentadiene in the *s*-trans conformation
b. (2*E*,4*Z*)-1-bromo-3-methyl-2,4-hexadiene
c. (2*E*,4*E*,6*E*)-2,4,6-octatriene
d. (2*E*,4*E*)-3-methyl-2,4-hexadiene in the *s*-cis conformation

16.38 Draw and name all dienes of molecular formula C_5H_8. When *E* and *Z* isomers are possible, draw and name each stereoisomer.

16.39 Draw all possible stereoisomers of 2,4-heptadiene and label each double bond as *E* or *Z*.

16.40 Label each pair of compounds as stereoisomers or conformations.

a. 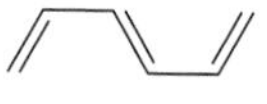 and 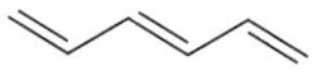

c.  and 

b.  and 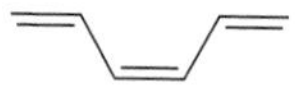

16.41 Rank the following dienes in order of increasing heat of hydrogenation.

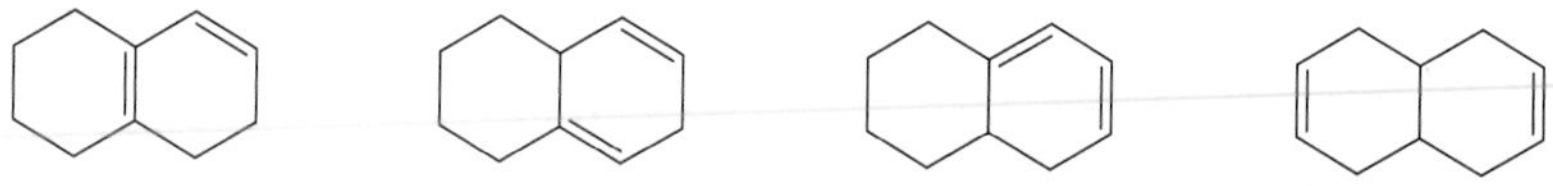

Electrophilic Addition

16.42 Draw the products formed when each compound is treated with one equivalent of HBr.

a. 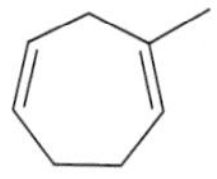

b. 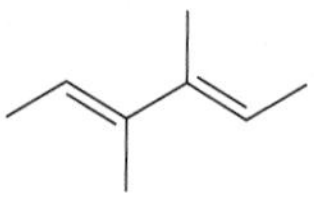

c. 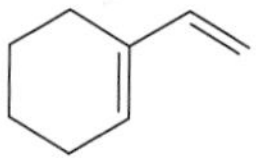

16.43 Ignoring stereoisomers, draw all products that form by addition of HBr to (3*E*)-1,3,5-hexatriene.

16.44 Treatment of alkenes **A** and **B** with HBr gives the same alkyl halide **C.** Draw a mechanism for each reaction, including all reasonable resonance structures for any intermediate.

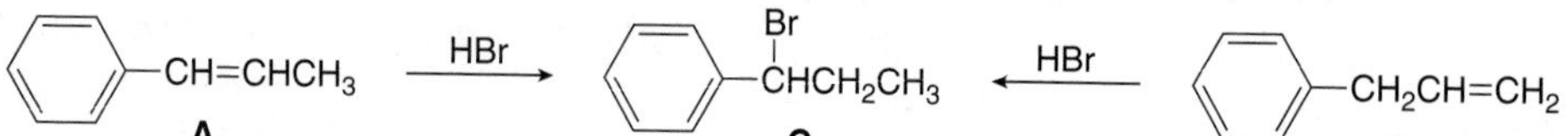

CH=CHCH3
HBr
Br
CHCH2CH3
HBr
CH2CH=CH2

A **C** **B**

16.45 Draw a stepwise mechanism for the following reaction.

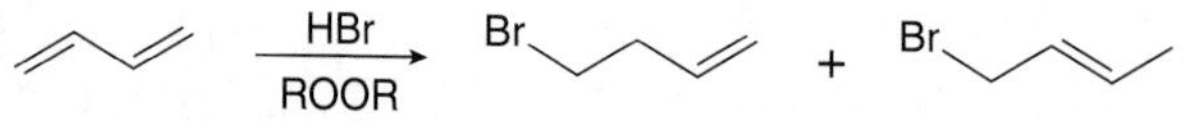

HBr
ROOR
Br
+
Br

16.46 Addition of HCl to alkene **X** forms two alkyl halides **Y** and **Z**.

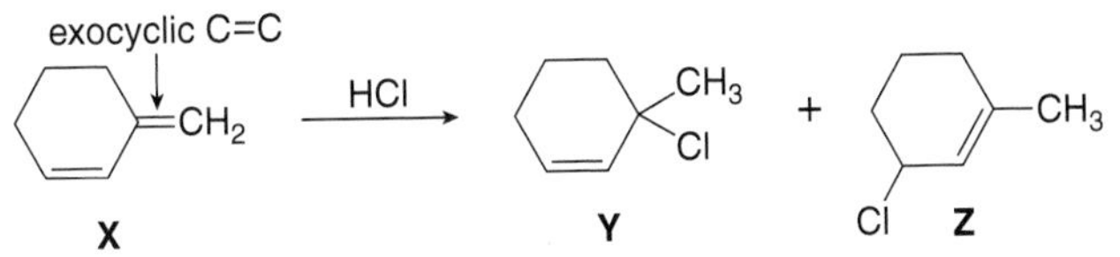

a. Label **Y** and **Z** as a 1,2-addition product or a 1,4-addition product.
b. Label **Y** and **Z** as the kinetic or thermodynamic product and explain why.
c. Explain why addition of HCl occurs at the indicated C=C (called an exocyclic double bond), rather than the other C=C (called an endocyclic double bond).

16.47 Explain, with reference to the mechanism, why addition of one equivalent of HCl to diene **A** forms only two products of electrophilic addition, even though four constitutional isomers are possible.

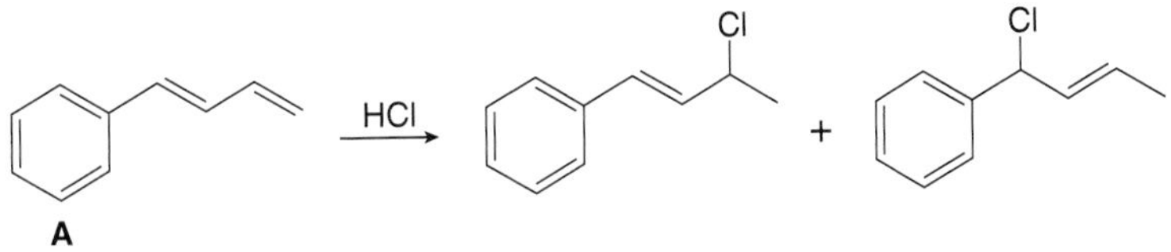

16.48 The major product formed by addition of HBr to $(CH_3)_2C{=}CH{-}CH{=}C(CH_3)_2$ is the same at low and high temperature. Draw the structure of the major product and explain why the kinetic and thermodynamic products are the same in this reaction.

Diels–Alder Reaction

16.49 Explain why methyl vinyl ether ($CH_2{=}CHOCH_3$) is not a reactive dienophile in the Diels–Alder reaction.

16.50 Draw the products of the following Diels–Alder reactions. Indicate stereochemistry where appropriate.

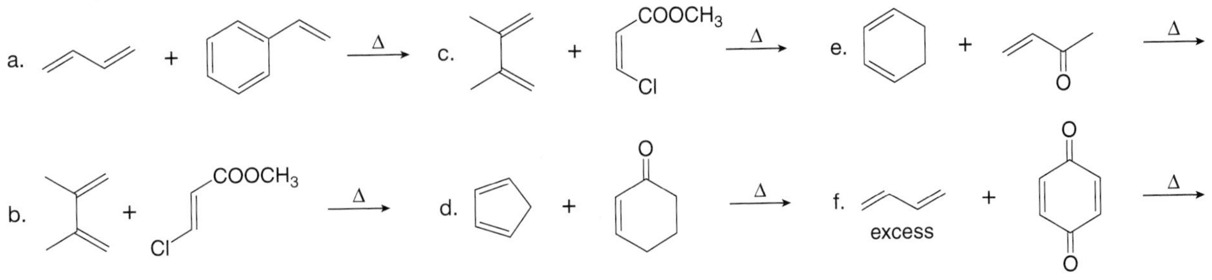

16.51 What diene and dienophile are needed to prepare each Diels–Alder product?

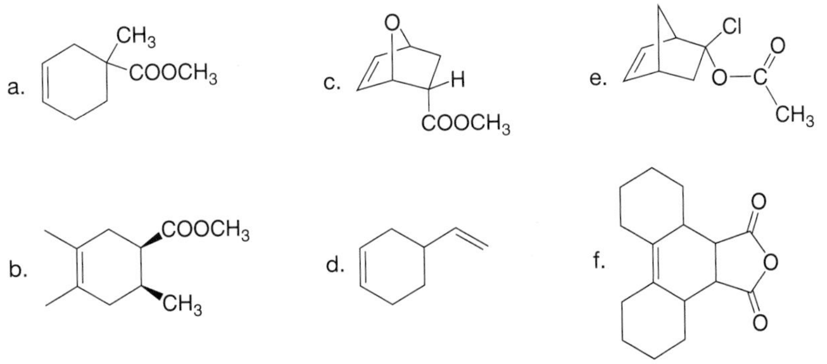

16.52 Give two different ways to prepare the following compound by the Diels–Alder reaction. Explain which method is preferred.

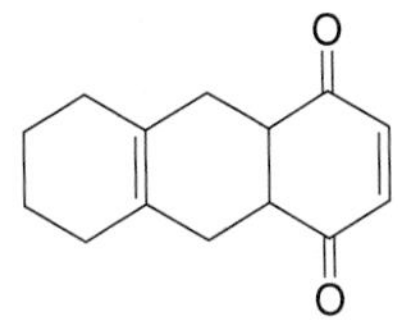

16.53 Compounds containing triple bonds are also Diels–Alder dienophiles. With this in mind, draw the products of each reaction.

a. 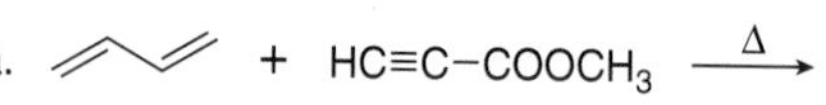
+ HC≡C−COOCH3
Δ

b. 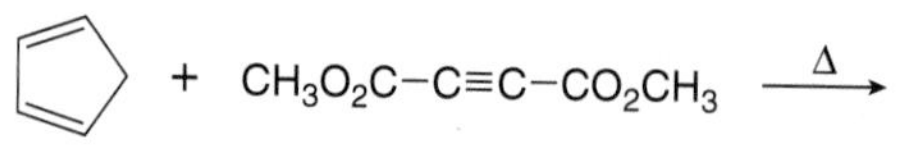
+ CH3O2C−C≡C−CO2CH3
Δ

16.54 Diels–Alder reaction of a monosubstituted diene (such as $CH_2{=}CH-CH{=}CHOCH_3$) with a monosubstituted dienophile (such as $CH_2{=}CHCHO$) gives a mixture of products, but the 1,2-disubstituted product often predominates. Draw the resonance hybrid for each reactant and use the charge distribution of the hybrids to explain why the 1,2-disubstituted product is the major product.

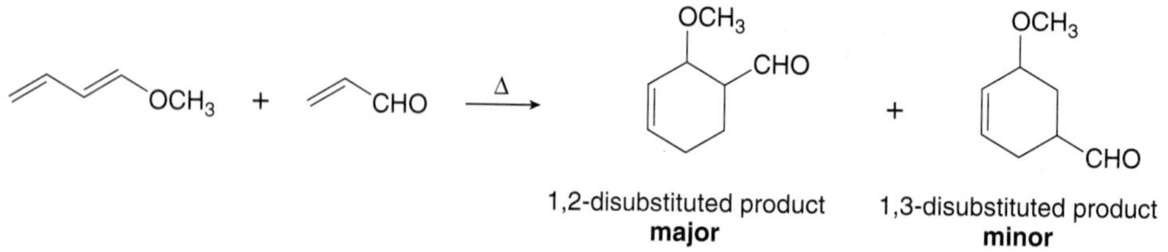
OCH3
+
CHO
Δ
OCH3
CHO
+
OCH3
CHO
1,2-disubstituted product
major
1,3-disubstituted product
minor

16.55 What is the structure of the product formed when **A** is heated in the presence of maleic acid? Explain why only one product is formed even though **A** has four double bonds.

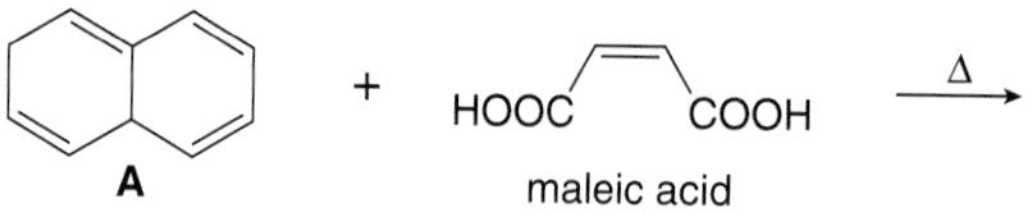
A
+
HOOC
COOH
maleic acid
Δ

16.56 The following reactions have been used to synthesize dieldrin and aldrin (named for Diels and Alder), two pesticides having a similar story to DDT (Section 7.4). Identify the lettered compounds in this reaction scheme.

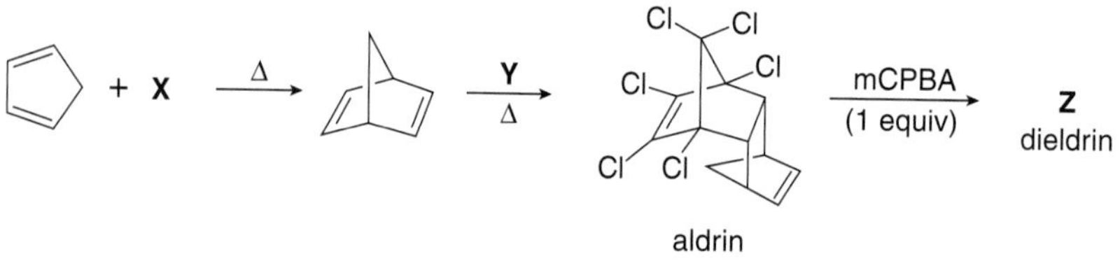
+ X
Δ
Y
Δ
Cl
Cl
Cl
Cl
Cl
Cl
mCPBA
(1 equiv)
Z
dieldrin
aldrin

16.57 Devise a stepwise synthesis of each compound from dicyclopentadiene using a Diels–Alder reaction as one step. You may also use organic compounds having ≤ 4 C's, and any required organic or inorganic reagents.

a. 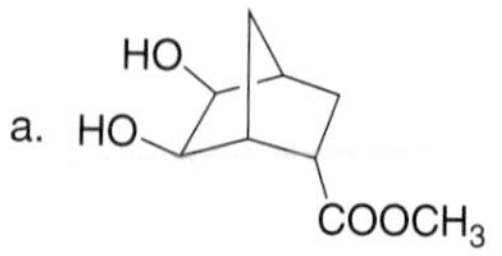
HO
HO
COOCH3

b. 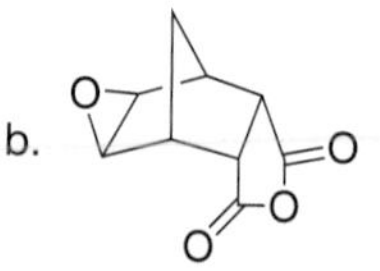
O
O
O
O

c. 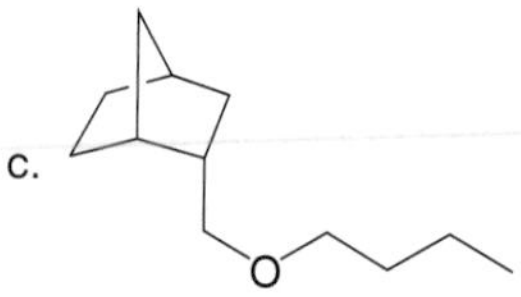
O

16.58 Intramolecular Diels–Alder reactions are possible when a substrate contains both a 1,3-diene and a dienophile, as shown in the following general reaction.

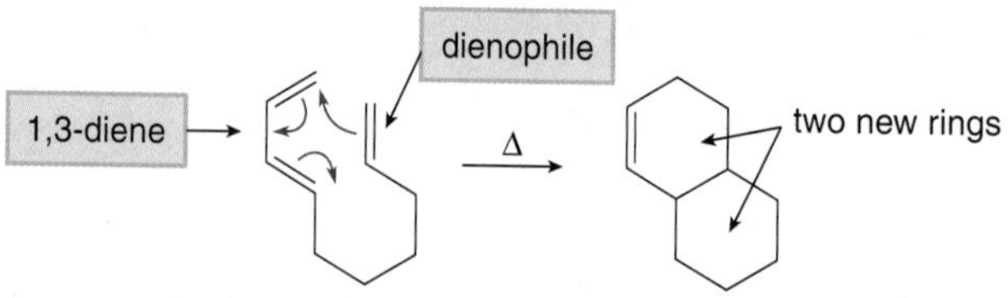
dienophile
1,3-diene
Δ
two new rings

With this in mind, draw the product of each intramolecular Diels–Alder reaction.

a. 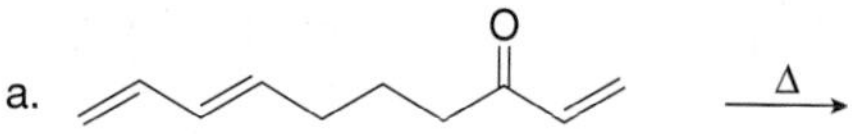
O
Δ

b. 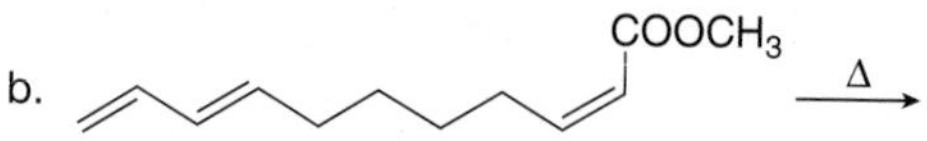
COOCH3
Δ

16.59 A transannular Diels–Alder reaction is an intramolecular reaction that occurs when the diene and dienophile are contained in one ring, resulting in the formation of a tricyclic ring system. Draw the product formed when the following triene undergoes a transannular Diels–Alder reaction.

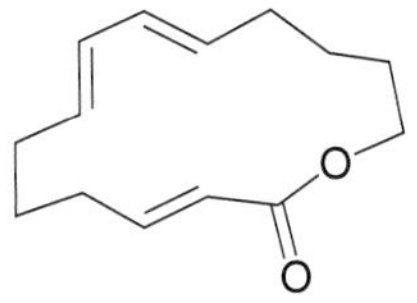

General Reactions

16.60 Draw a stepwise mechanism for the following reaction.

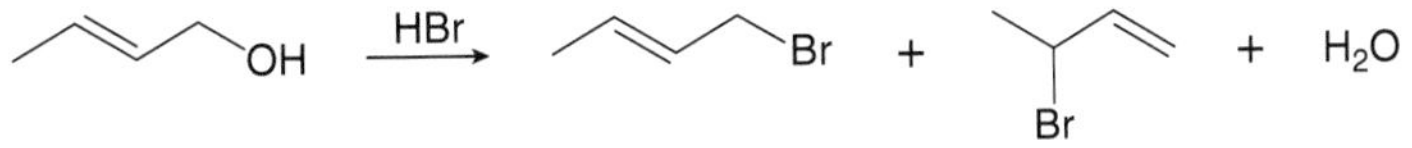

16.61 Draw the products of each reaction. Indicate the stereochemistry of Diels–Alder products.

a. $(CH_3)_2C{=}CHCH_2CH_2CH{=}CH_2 \xrightarrow[\text{(1 equiv)}]{\text{HCl}}$

b. 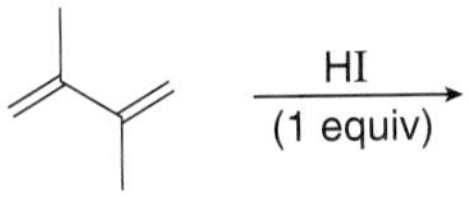

c. 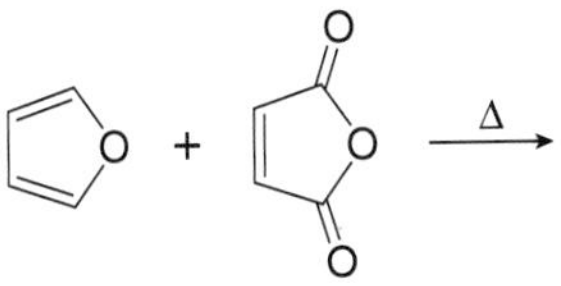

d. 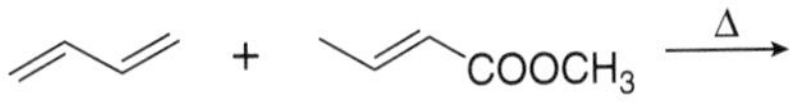

e. 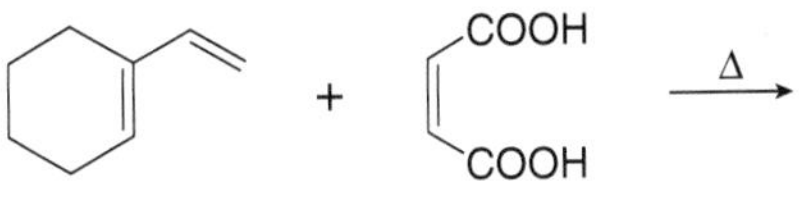

f. 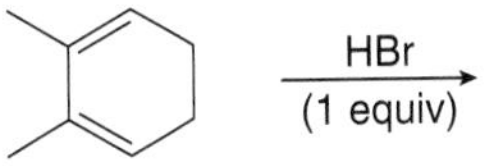

16.62 Which benzylic halide reacts faster in an S_N1 reaction? Explain.

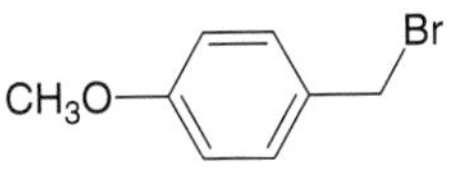

A

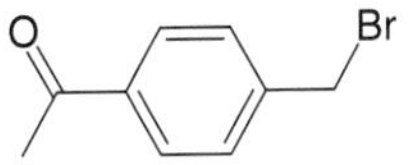

B

16.63 Like alkenes, conjugated dienes can be prepared by elimination reactions. Draw a stepwise mechanism for the acid-catalyzed dehydration of 3-methyl-2-buten-1-ol [$(CH_3)_2C{=}CHCH_2OH$] to isoprene [$CH_2{=}C(CH_3)CH{=}CH_2$].

16.64 (a) Draw the two isomeric dienes formed when $CH_2{=}CHCH_2CH(Cl)CH(CH_3)_2$ is treated with an alkoxide base. (b) Explain why the major product formed in this reaction does not contain the more highly substituted alkene.

Spectroscopy

16.65 The treatment of isoprene [$CH_2{=}C(CH_3)CH{=}CH_2$] with one equivalent of mCPBA forms **A** as the major product. **A** gives a molecular ion at 84 in its mass spectrum, and peaks at 2850–3150 cm^{-1} in its IR spectrum. The ^1H NMR spectrum of **A** is given below. What is the structure of **A**?

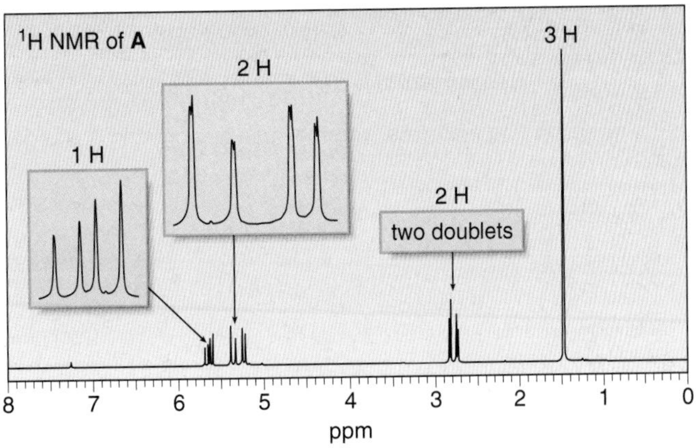

16.66 The treatment of $(CH_3)_2C{=}CHCH_2Br$ with H_2O forms **B** (molecular formula $C_5H_{10}O$) as one of the products. Determine the structure of **B** from its ^1H NMR and IR spectra.

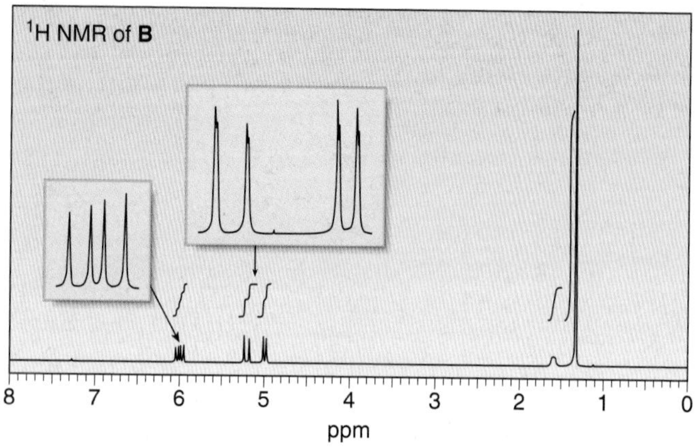

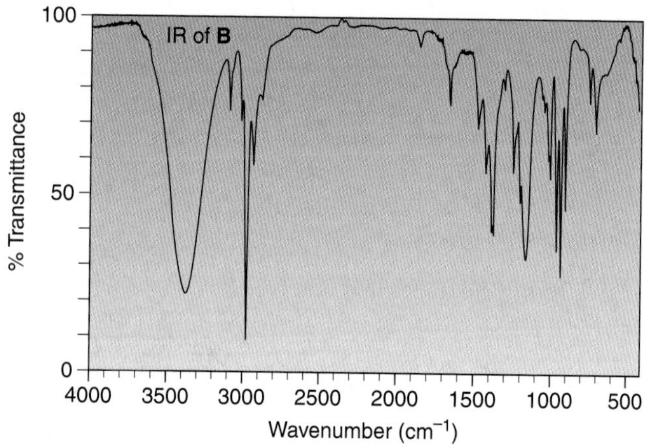

UV Absorption

16.67 Rank the following compounds in the order of increasing λ_{max}.

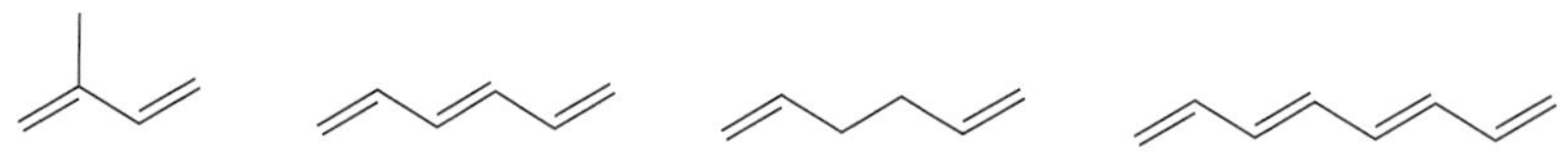

16.68 Explain why ferulic acid, a natural product found in rice, oats, and other plants, is both an antioxidant and a sunscreen.

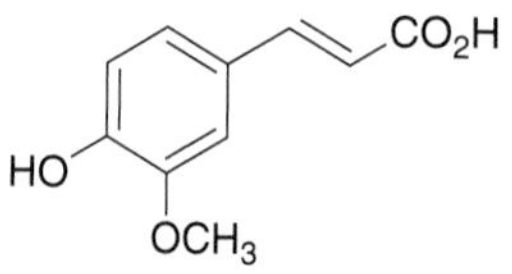

ferulic acid

Challenge Problems

16.69 Addition of HBr to allene ($CH_2{=}C{=}CH_2$) forms 2-bromo-1-propene rather than 3-bromo-1-propene, even though 3-bromo-1-propene is formed from an allylic carbocation. Considering the arrangement of orbitals in the allene reactant, explain this result.

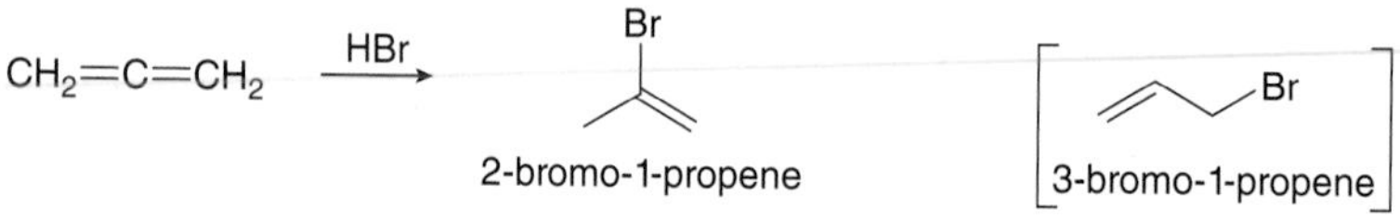

NOT formed

16.70 Determine the hybridization around the N atom in each amine and explain why cyclohexanamine is 10^6 times more basic than aniline.

cyclohexanamine aniline

16.71 Devise a synthesis of **X** from the given starting materials. You may use any organic or inorganic reagents. Account for the stereochemistry observed in **X.**

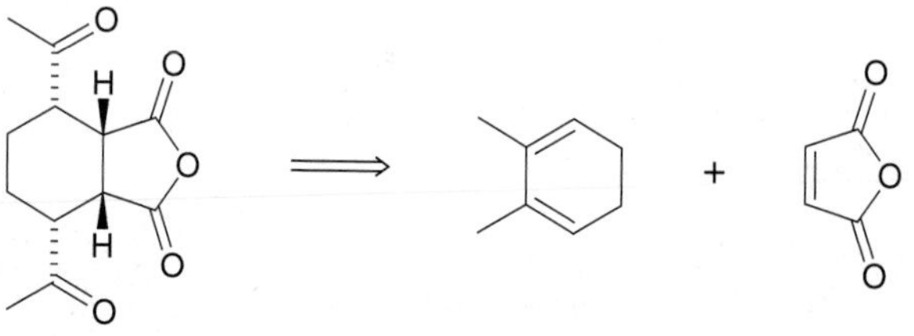

X

16.72 One step in the synthesis of occidentalol, a natural product isolated from the eastern white cedar tree, involved the following reaction. Identify the structure of **A** and show how **A** is converted to **B.**

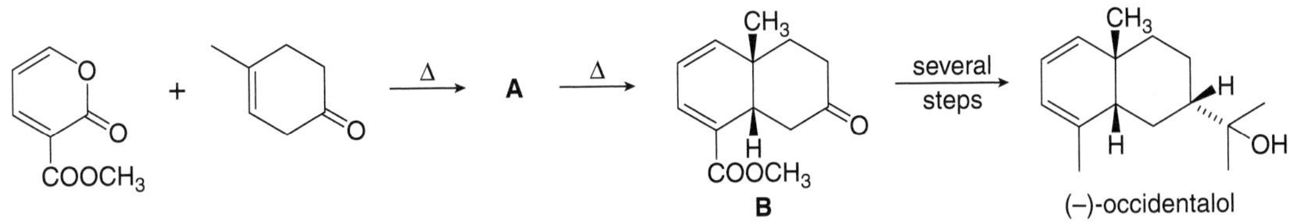

16.73 One step in the synthesis of dodecahedrane (Section 4.11) involved reaction of the tetraene **C** with dimethylacetylene dicarboxylate (**D**) to afford two compounds having molecular formula $C_{16}H_{16}O_4$. This reaction has been called a domino Diels–Alder reaction. Identify the two products formed.

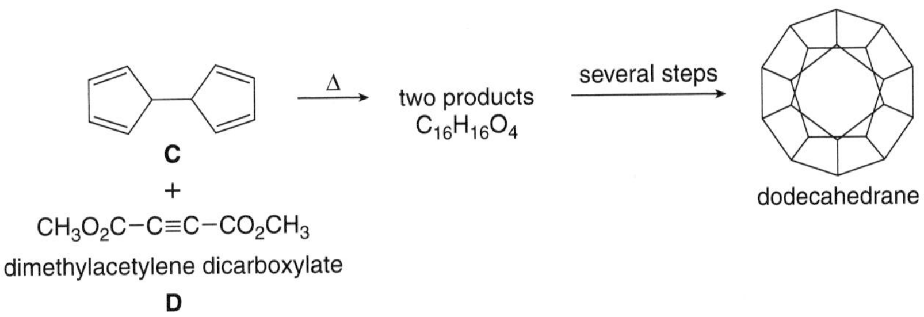

16.74 Devise a stepwise mechanism for the conversion of **M** to **N. N** has been converted in several steps to lysergic acid, a naturally occurring precursor of the hallucinogen LSD (Figure 18.4).

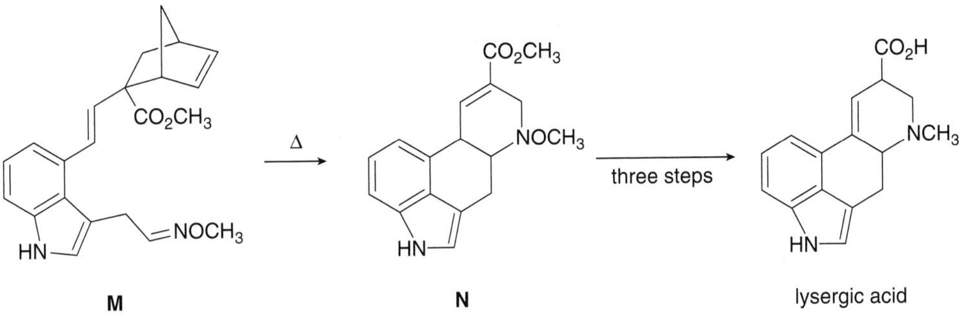

17 Benzene and Aromatic Compounds

17.1 Background
17.2 The structure of benzene
17.3 Nomenclature of benzene derivatives
17.4 Spectroscopic properties
17.5 Interesting aromatic compounds
17.6 Benzene's unusual stability
17.7 The criteria for aromaticity—Hückel's rule
17.8 Examples of aromatic compounds
17.9 What is the basis of Hückel's rule?
17.10 The inscribed polygon method for predicting aromaticity
17.11 Buckminsterfullerene—Is it aromatic?

Capsaicin is responsible for the characteristic spicy flavor of jalapeño and habañero peppers. Although it first produces a burning sensation on contact with the mouth or skin, repeated application desensitizes the area to pain. This property has made it the active ingredient in several topical creams for the treatment of chronic pain. Capsaicin has also been used as an animal deterrent in pepper sprays, and as an additive to make birdseed squirrel-proof. Capsaicin is an aromatic compound because it contains a benzene ring. In this chapter, we learn about the characteristics of aromatic compounds like capsaicin.

The hydrocarbons we have examined thus far—including the alkanes, alkenes, and alkynes, as well as the conjugated dienes and polyenes of Chapter 16—have been aliphatic hydrocarbons. In Chapter 17, we continue our study of conjugated systems with **aromatic hydrocarbons.**

We begin with **benzene** and then examine other cyclic, planar, and conjugated ring systems to learn the modern definition of what it means to be aromatic. Then, in Chapter 18, we will learn about the reactions of aromatic compounds, highly unsaturated hydrocarbons that do not undergo addition reactions like other unsaturated compounds. An explanation of this behavior relies on an understanding of the structure of aromatic compounds presented in Chapter 17.

17.1 Background

For 6 C's, the maximum number of H's = $2n + 2$ = 2(6) + 2 = 14. Because benzene contains only 6 H's, it has 14 – 6 = 8 H's fewer than the maximum number. This corresponds to 8 H's/2 H's for each degree of unsaturation = **four degrees of unsaturation in benzene.**

Benzene (C_6H_6) is the simplest aromatic hydrocarbon (or arene). Since its isolation by Michael Faraday from the oily residue remaining in the illuminating gas lines in London in 1825, it has been recognized as an unusual compound. Based on the calculation introduced in Section 10.2, **benzene has four degrees of unsaturation, making it a highly unsaturated hydrocarbon.** But, whereas unsaturated hydrocarbons such as alkenes, alkynes, and dienes readily undergo addition reactions, *benzene does not.* For example, bromine adds to ethylene to form a dibromide, but benzene is inert under similar conditions.

Ethylene (an alkene)

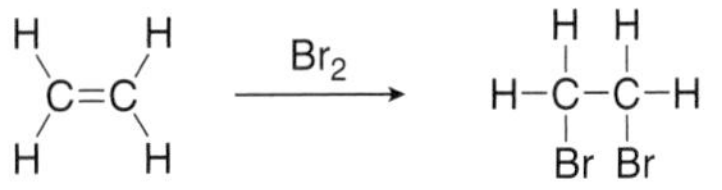

addition product

Benzene (an arene)

$$C_6H_6 \xrightarrow{Br_2} \textbf{No reaction}$$

Benzene *does* react with bromine, but only in the presence of $FeBr_3$ (a Lewis acid), and the reaction is a **substitution,** *not* an addition.

$$C_6H_6 \xrightarrow[FeBr_3]{Br_2} C_6H_5Br$$

substitution
Br replaces H

Thus, any structure proposed for benzene must account for its high degree of unsaturation and its lack of reactivity towards electrophilic addition.

In the last half of the nineteenth century August Kekulé proposed structures that were close to the modern description of benzene. In the Kekulé model, benzene was thought to be a rapidly equilibrating mixture of two compounds, each containing a six-membered ring with three alternating π bonds. These structures are now called **Kekulé structures.** In the Kekulé description, the bond between any two carbon atoms is sometimes a single bond and sometimes a double bond.

Kekulé description: An equilibrium

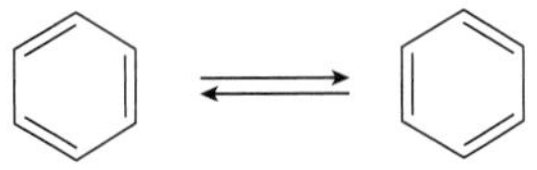

Although benzene is still drawn as a six-membered ring with three alternating π bonds, in reality **there is no equilibrium between two different kinds of benzene molecules.** Instead, current descriptions of benzene are based on resonance and electron delocalization due to orbital overlap, as detailed in Section 17.2.

In the nineteenth century, many other compounds having properties similar to those of benzene were isolated from natural sources. Because these compounds possessed strong and characteristic odors, they were called ***aromatic*** **compounds.** It is their chemical properties, though, not their odor that make these compounds special.

- **Aromatic compounds resemble benzene—they are unsaturated compounds that do not undergo the addition reactions characteristic of alkenes.**

17.2 The Structure of Benzene

Any structure for benzene must account for the following:

- **Benzene contains a six-membered ring and three additional degrees of unsaturation.**
- **Benzene is planar.**
- **All C–C bond lengths are equal.**

Although the Kekulé structures satisfy the first two criteria, they break down with the third, because having three alternating π bonds means that benzene should have three short double bonds alternating with three longer single bonds.

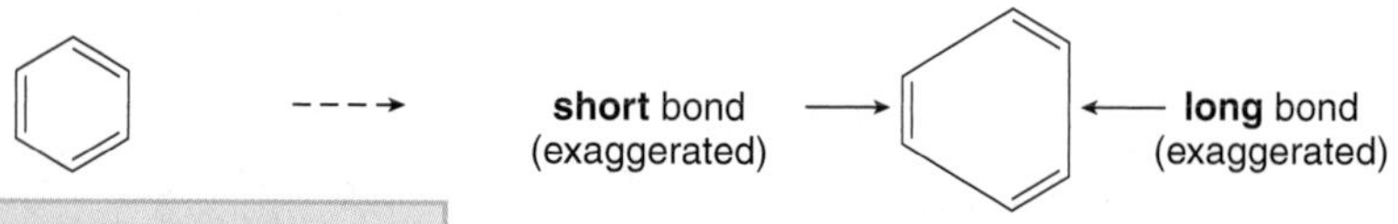
short bond
(exaggerated)
long bond
(exaggerated)

This structure implies that the C–C bonds should have **two different lengths.**

- three short bonds
- three long bonds

Resonance

Some texts draw benzene as a hexagon with an inner circle:

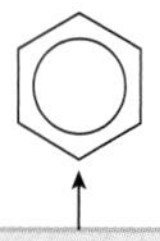

The circle represents the **six π electrons,** distributed over the six atoms of the ring.

Benzene is conjugated, so we must use resonance and orbitals to describe its structure. The resonance description of benzene consists of two equivalent Lewis structures, each with three double bonds that alternate with three single bonds.

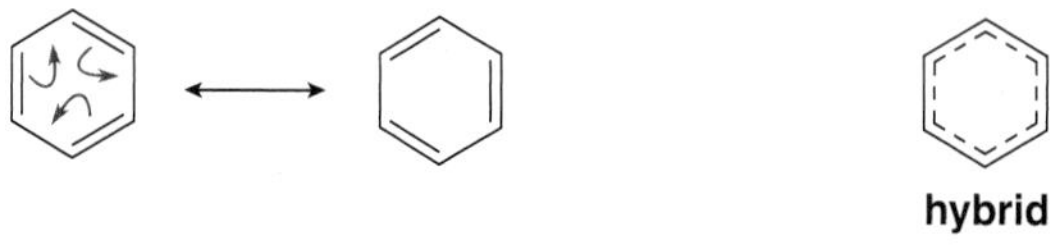
hybrid

The electrons in the π bonds are **delocalized** around the ring.

The resonance description of benzene matches the Kekulé description with one important exception. **The two Kekulé representations are *not* in equilibrium with each other.** Instead, the true structure of benzene is a resonance **hybrid** of the two Lewis structures, with the dashed lines of the hybrid indicating the position of the π bonds.

We will use one of the two Lewis structures and not the hybrid in drawing benzene, because it is easier to keep track of the electron pairs in the π bonds (the π electrons).

- **Because each π bond has two electrons, benzene has six π electrons.**

The resonance hybrid of benzene explains why all C–C bond lengths are the same. Each C–C bond is single in one resonance structure and double in the other, so the actual bond length (139 pm) is intermediate between a carbon–carbon single bond (153 pm) and a carbon–carbon double bond (134 pm).

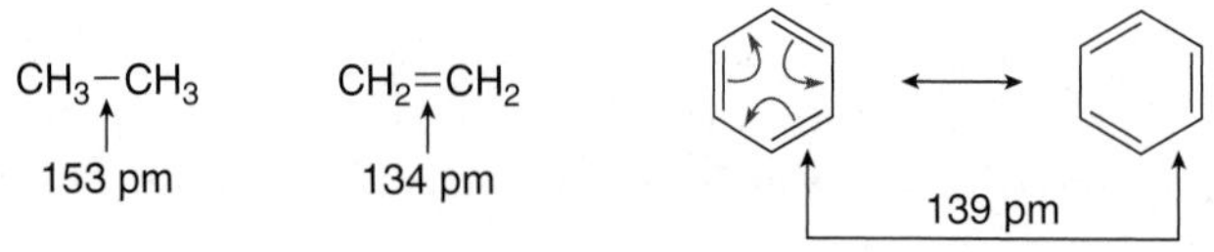
CH3–CH3
153 pm
CH2=CH2
134 pm
139 pm

The C–C bonds in benzene are equal and intermediate in length.

Hybridization and Orbitals

Each carbon atom in a benzene ring is surrounded by three atoms and no lone pairs of electrons, making it ***sp*² hybridized and trigonal planar with all bond angles 120°.** Each carbon also has a *p* orbital with one electron that extends above and below the plane of the molecule.

Benzene—A planar molecule

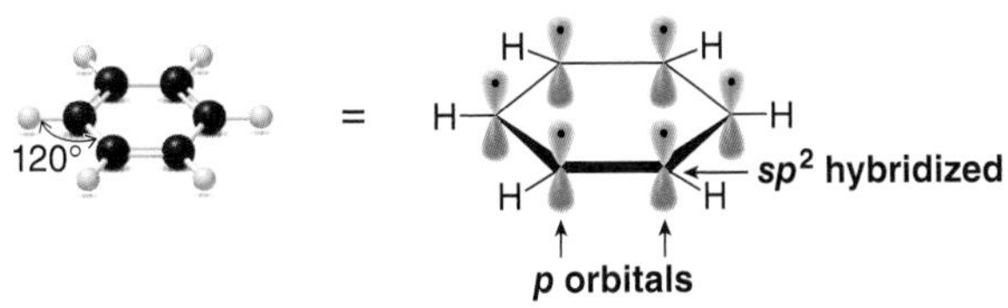

The six adjacent *p* orbitals overlap, delocalizing the six electrons over the six atoms of the ring and making benzene a conjugated molecule. Because each *p* orbital has two lobes, one above and one below the plane of the benzene ring, the overlap of the *p* orbitals creates two "doughnuts" of electron density, as shown in Figure 17.1a. The electrostatic potential plot in Figure 17.1b also shows that the electron-rich region is concentrated above and below the plane of the molecule, where the six π electrons are located.

- **Benzene's six π electrons make it electron rich, so it reacts with electrophiles.**

Problem 17.1 Draw all possible resonance structures for the antihistamine diphenhydramine, the active ingredient in Benadryl.

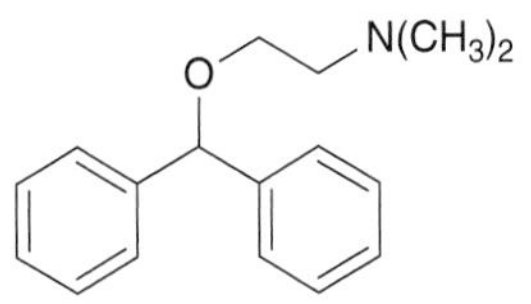

diphenhydramine

Problem 17.2 What orbitals are used to form the bonds indicated in each molecule? Of the indicated C–C bonds, which is the shortest?

a.

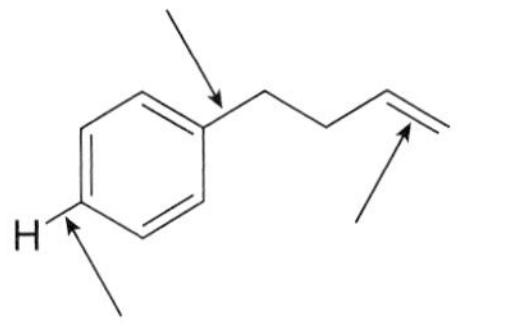

b.

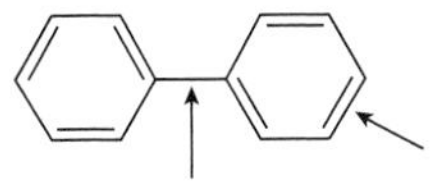

Figure 17.1 Two views of the electron density in a benzene ring

a. View of the *p* orbital overlap

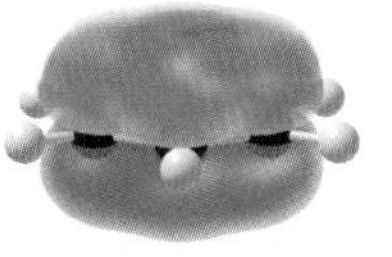

- Overlap of six adjacent *p* orbitals creates two rings of electron density, one above and one below the plane of the benzene ring.

b. Electrostatic potential plot

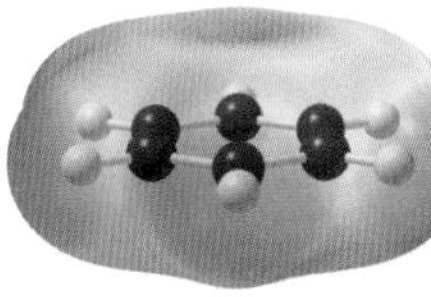

- The electron-rich region (in red) is concentrated above and below the ring carbons, where the six π electrons are located. (The electron-rich region below the plane is hidden from view.)

17.3 Nomenclature of Benzene Derivatives

Many organic molecules contain a benzene ring with one or more substituents, so we must learn how to name them. Many common names are recognized by the IUPAC system, however, so this complicates the nomenclature of benzene derivatives somewhat.

17.3A Monosubstituted Benzenes

To name a benzene ring with one substituent, **name the substituent and add the word *benzene*.** Carbon substituents are named as alkyl groups.

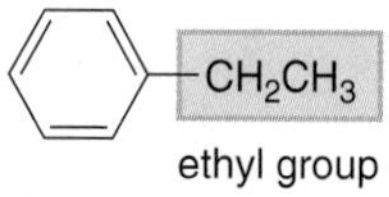
ethyl group

ethylbenzene

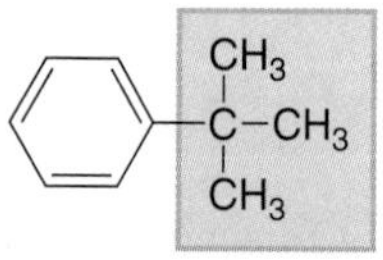
tert-butyl group

tert-butylbenzene

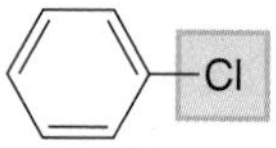
chloro group

chlorobenzene

Many monosubstituted benzenes, such as those with methyl (CH_3-), hydroxy ($-OH$), and amino ($-NH_2$) groups, have common names that you must learn, too.

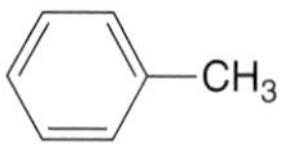
toluene
(methylbenzene)

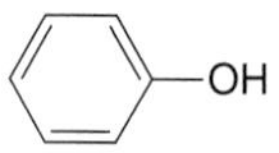
phenol
(hydroxybenzene)

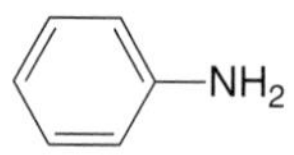
aniline
(aminobenzene)

17.3B Disubstituted Benzenes

There are three different ways that two groups can be attached to a benzene ring, so a prefix—**ortho, meta,** or **para**—can be used to designate the relative position of the two substituents. Ortho, meta, and para are also abbreviated as ***o, m,*** and ***p,*** respectively.

1,2-Disubstituted benzene
ortho isomer

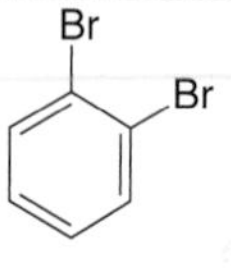

o-dibromobenzene
or
1,2-dibromobenzene

1,3-Disubstituted benzene
meta isomer

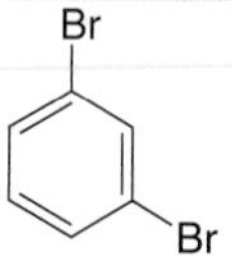

m-dibromobenzene
or
1,3-dibromobenzene

1,4-Disubstituted benzene
para isomer

p-dibromobenzene
or
1,4-dibromobenzene

If the two groups on the benzene ring are different, **alphabetize the names of the substituents** preceding the word *benzene.* If one of the substituents is part of a **common root,** name the **molecule as a derivative of that monosubstituted benzene.**

Alphabetize two different substituent names:

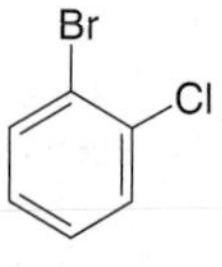

***o*-bromochloro-**
benzene

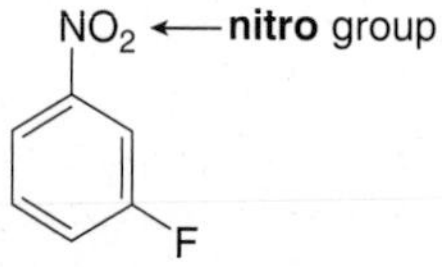

***m*-fluoronitro-**
benzene

Use a common root name:

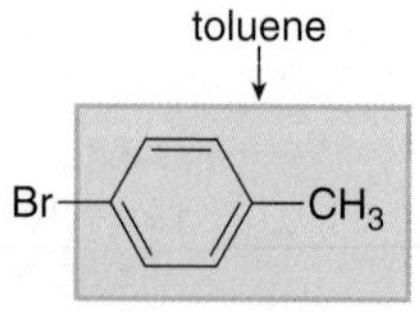

p-bromo**toluene**

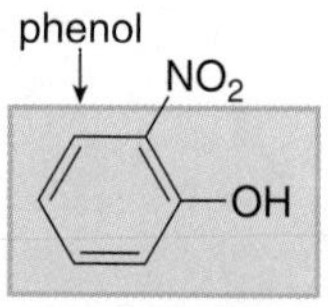

o-nitro**phenol**

17.3C Polysubstituted Benzenes

For three or more substituents on a benzene ring:

[1] Number to give the lowest possible numbers around the ring.

[2] Alphabetize the substituent names.

[3] When substituents are part of common roots, name the molecule as a derivative of that monosubstituted benzene. The substituent that comprises the common root is located at C1.

Examples of naming polysubstituted benzenes

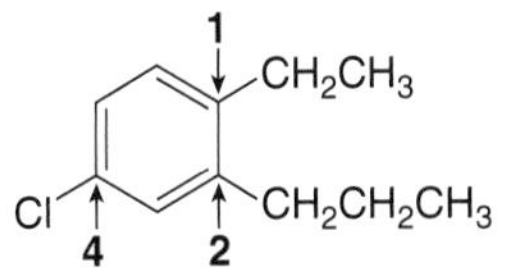
1
CH_2CH_3
$CH_2CH_2CH_3$
Cl
4
2

- Assign the lowest set of numbers.
- Alphabetize the names of all the substituents.

4-chloro-1-ethyl-2-propylbenzene

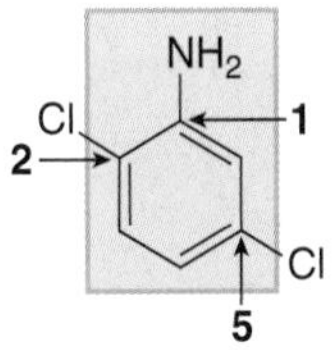
NH_2
Cl
1
2
Cl
5

- Name the molecule as a derivative of the common root **aniline.**
- Designate the position of the NH_2 group as "1," and then assign the lowest possible set of numbers to the other substituents.

2,5-dichloroaniline

17.3D Naming Aromatic Rings as Substituents

A benzene substituent (C_6H_5-) is called a **phenyl group,** and it can be abbreviated in a structure as **Ph–.**

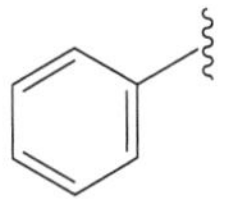

abbreviated as Ph–

phenyl group
C_6H_5-

- **A phenyl group (C_6H_5-) is formed by removing one hydrogen from benzene (C_6H_6).**

Benzene, therefore, can be represented as PhH, and phenol would be PhOH.

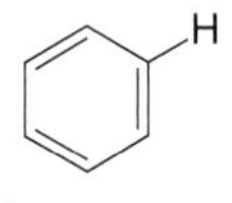
H

= C_6H_5-H **PhH**

benzene

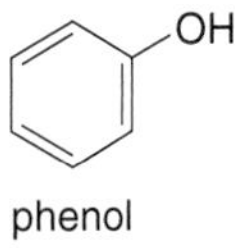
OH

= C_6H_5-OH **PhOH**

phenol

The **benzyl** group, another common substituent that contains a benzene ring, differs from a phenyl group.

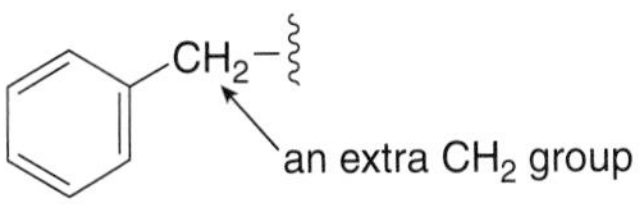
CH_2-
an extra CH_2 group

benzyl group
$C_6H_5CH_2-$

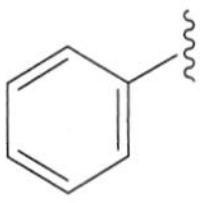

phenyl group
C_6H_5-

Finally, substituents derived from benzene, as well as all other substituted aromatic rings, are collectively called **aryl groups.**

Examples of aryl groups

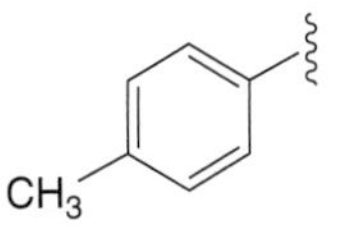
CH_3

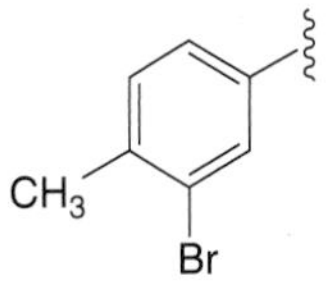
CH_3
Br

Problem 17.3 Give the IUPAC name for each compound.

a. $PhCH(CH_3)_2$

b. 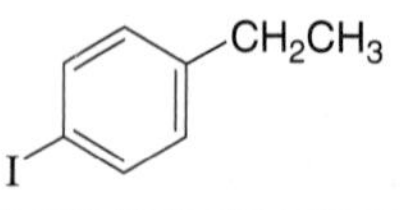
CH2CH3
I

c. 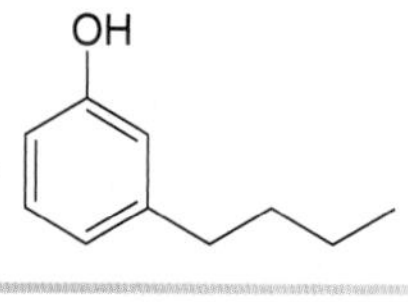
OH

d. 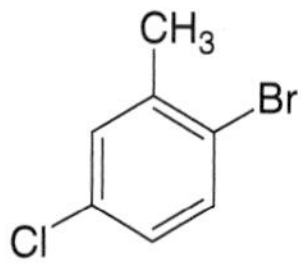
CH3
Br
Cl

Problem 17.4 Draw the structure corresponding to each name:

a. isobutylbenzene
b. *o*-dichlorobenzene
c. *cis*-1,2-diphenylcyclohexane
d. *m*-bromoaniline
e. 4-chloro-1,2-diethylbenzene
f. 3-*tert*-butyl-2-ethyltoluene

Problem 17.5 What is the structure of propofol, which has the IUPAC name 2,6-diisopropylphenol? Propofol is an intravenous medication used to induce and maintain anesthesia.

17.4 Spectroscopic Properties

The important IR and NMR absorptions of aromatic compounds are summarized in Table 17.1.

Table 17.1 Characteristic Spectroscopic Absorptions of Benzene Derivatives

Type of spectroscopy	Type of C, H	Absorption
IR absorptions	C_{sp^2}–H C=C (arene)	3150–3000 cm^{-1} 1600, 1500 cm^{-1}
^{1}H NMR absorptions	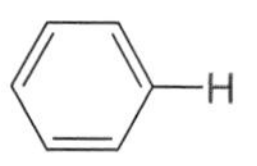 H (aryl H)	6.5–8 ppm (highly deshielded protons)
	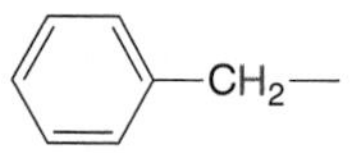 CH2 (benzylic H)	1.5–2.5 ppm (somewhat deshielded C_{sp^3}–H)
^{13}C NMR absorption	C_{sp^2} of arenes	120–150 ppm

The absorption at 6.5–8.0 ppm in the ^{1}H NMR spectrum is particularly characteristic of compounds containing benzene rings. **All aromatic compounds have highly deshielded protons due to the ring current effect of the circulating π electrons,** as discussed in Section 14.4. Observing whether a new compound absorbs in this region of a ^{1}H NMR spectrum is one piece of data used to determine if it is aromatic.

^{13}C NMR spectroscopy is used to determine the substitution patterns in disubstituted benzenes, because each line in a spectrum corresponds to a different kind of carbon atom. For example, *o*-, *m*-, and *p*-dibromobenzene each exhibit a different number of lines in its ^{13}C NMR spectrum, as shown in Figure 17.2.

Problem 17.6 What is the structure of a compound of molecular formula $C_{10}H_{14}O_2$ that shows a strong IR absorption at 3150–2850 cm^{-1} and gives the following ^{1}H NMR absorptions: 1.4 (triplet, 6 H), 4.0 (quartet, 4 H), and 6.8 (singlet, 4 H) ppm?

Problem 17.7 How many ^{13}C NMR signals does each compound exhibit?

a. 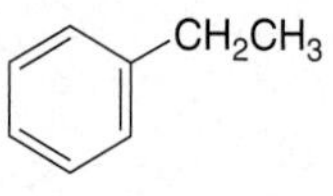
CH2CH3

b. 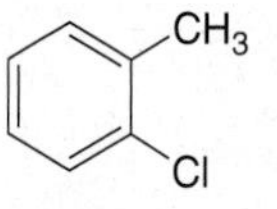
CH3
Cl

c. 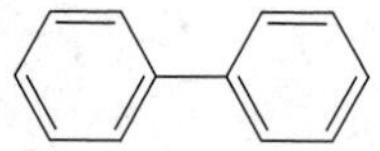

Figure 17.2
^{13}C NMR absorptions of the three isomeric dibromobenzenes

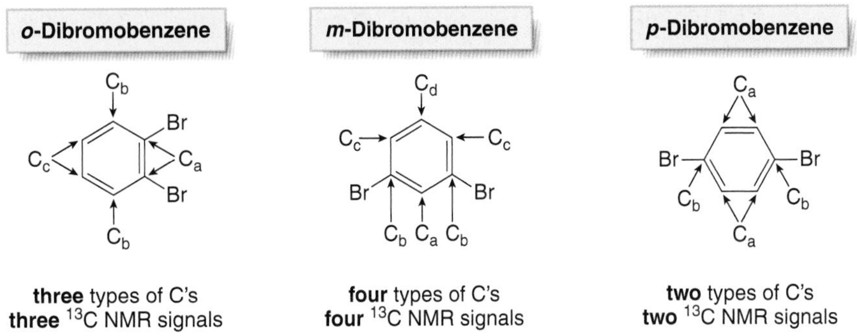

- The number of signals (lines) in the ^{13}C NMR spectrum of a disubstituted benzene with two identical groups indicates whether they are ortho, meta, or para to each other.

17.5 Interesting Aromatic Compounds

BTX contains **b**enzene, **t**oluene, and **x**ylene (the common name for dimethylbenzene).

Benzene and **toluene,** the simplest aromatic hydrocarbons obtained from petroleum refining, are useful starting materials for synthetic polymers. They are two components of the **BTX** mixture added to gasoline to boost octane ratings.

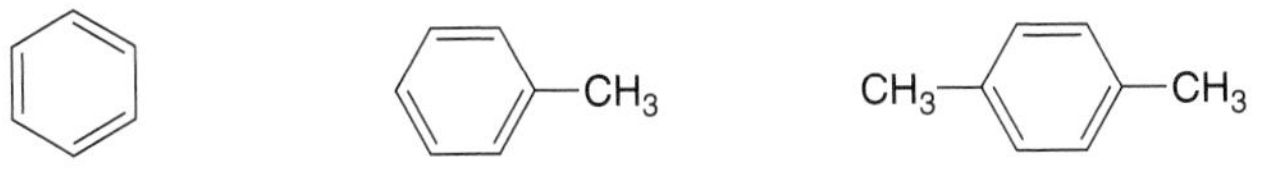

benzene toluene *p*-xylene

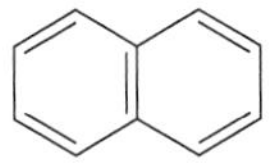

naphthalene
(used in mothballs)

Compounds containing two or more benzene rings that share carbon–carbon bonds are called **polycyclic aromatic hydrocarbons (PAHs).** Naphthalene, the simplest PAH, is the active ingredient in mothballs.

Benzo[*a*]pyrene, a more complicated PAH shown in Figure 17.3, is formed by the incomplete combustion of organic materials. It is found in cigarette smoke, automobile exhaust, and the fumes from charcoal grills. When ingested or inhaled, benzo[*a*]pyrene and other similar PAHs are oxidized to carcinogenic products, as discussed in Section 9.17.

Figure 17.3
Benzo[*a*]pyrene, a common PAH

- Benzo[*a*]pyrene, produced by the incomplete oxidation of organic compounds in tobacco, is found in cigarette smoke.

Figure 17.4 Helicene and twistoflex—Two synthetic polycyclic aromatic hydrocarbons

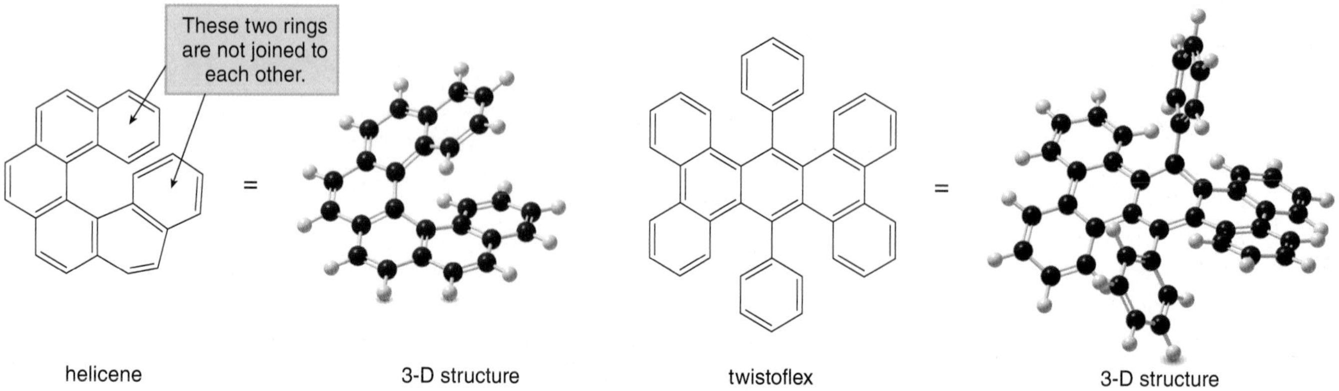

helicene   3-D structure   twistoflex   3-D structure

Helicene and **twistoflex** are two synthetic PAHs whose unusual shapes are shown in Figure 17.4. Helicene consists of six benzene rings. Because the rings at both ends are not bonded to each other, all of the rings twist slightly, creating a rigid helical shape that prevents the hydrogen atoms on both ends from crashing into each other. Similarly, to reduce steric hindrance between the hydrogen atoms on nearby benzene rings, twistoflex is also nonplanar.

Both helicene and twistoflex are chiral molecules—that is, they are not superimposable on their mirror images, even though neither of them contains a stereogenic center. It's their shape that makes them chiral, not the presence of carbon atoms bonded to four different groups. Each ring system is twisted into a shape that lacks a mirror plane, and each structure is rigid, thus creating the chirality.

Many widely used drugs contain a benzene ring. Six examples are shown in Figure 17.5.

Figure 17.5
Selected drugs that contain a benzene ring

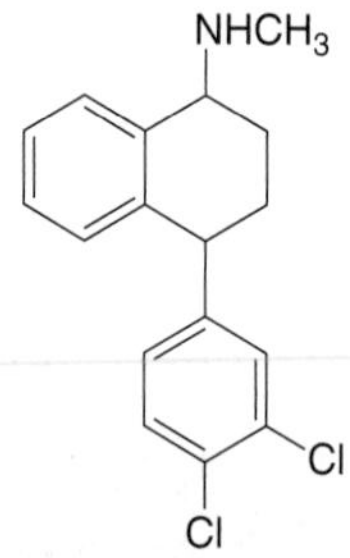

- Trade name: **Zoloft**
- Generic name: **sertraline**
- Use: a psychotherapeutic drug for depression and panic disorders

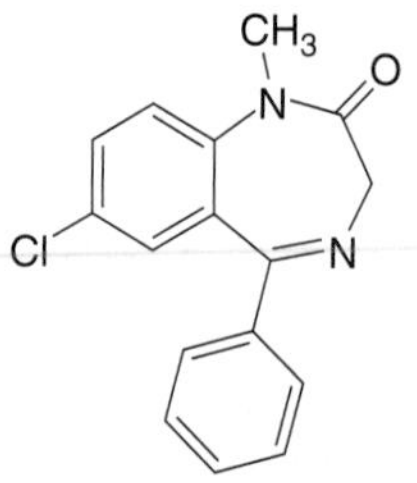

- Trade name: **Valium**
- Generic name: **diazepam**
- Use: a sedative

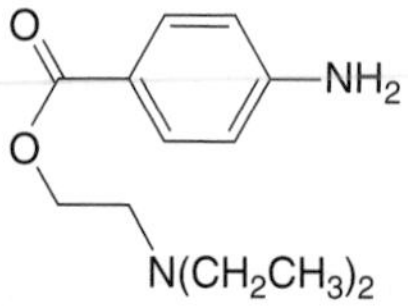

- Trade name: **Novocain**
- Generic name: **procaine**
- Use: a local anesthetic

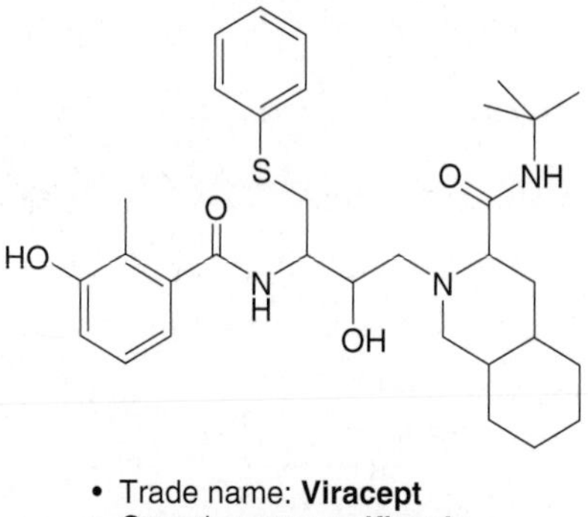

- Trade name: **Viracept**
- Generic name: **nelfinavir**
- Use: an antiviral drug used to treat HIV

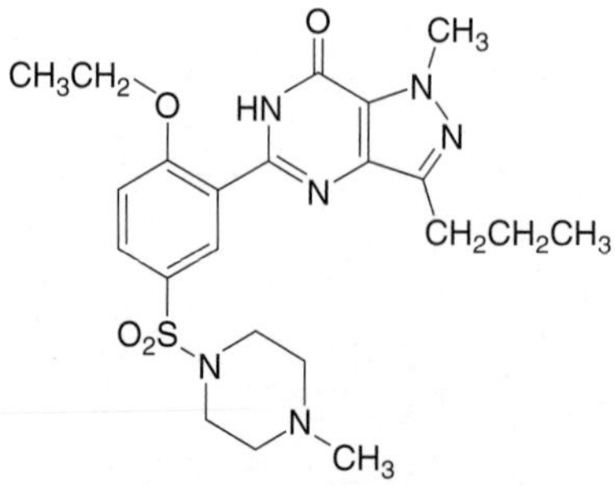

- Trade name: **Viagra**
- Generic name: **sildenafil**
- Use: a drug used to treat erectile dysfunction

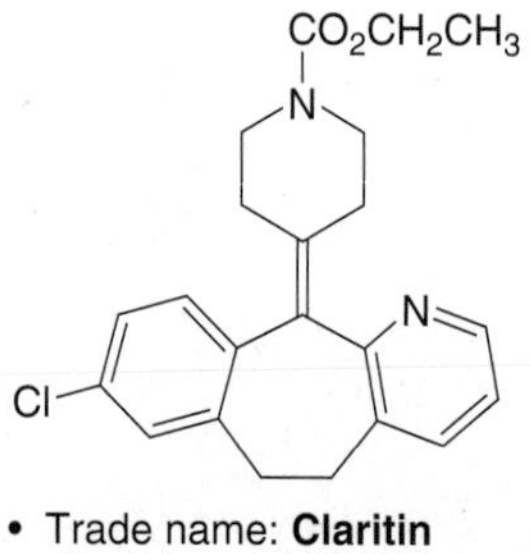

- Trade name: **Claritin**
- Generic name: **loratadine**
- Use: an antihistamine for seasonal allergies

17.6 Benzene's Unusual Stability

Considering benzene as the hybrid of two resonance structures adequately explains its equal C−C bond lengths, but does not account for its unusual stability and lack of reactivity toward addition.

Heats of hydrogenation, which were used in Section 16.9 to show that conjugated dienes are more stable than isolated dienes, can also be used to estimate the stability of benzene. Equations [1]–[3] compare the heats of hydrogenation of cyclohexene, 1,3-cyclohexadiene, and benzene, all of which give cyclohexane when treated with excess hydrogen in the presence of a metal catalyst.

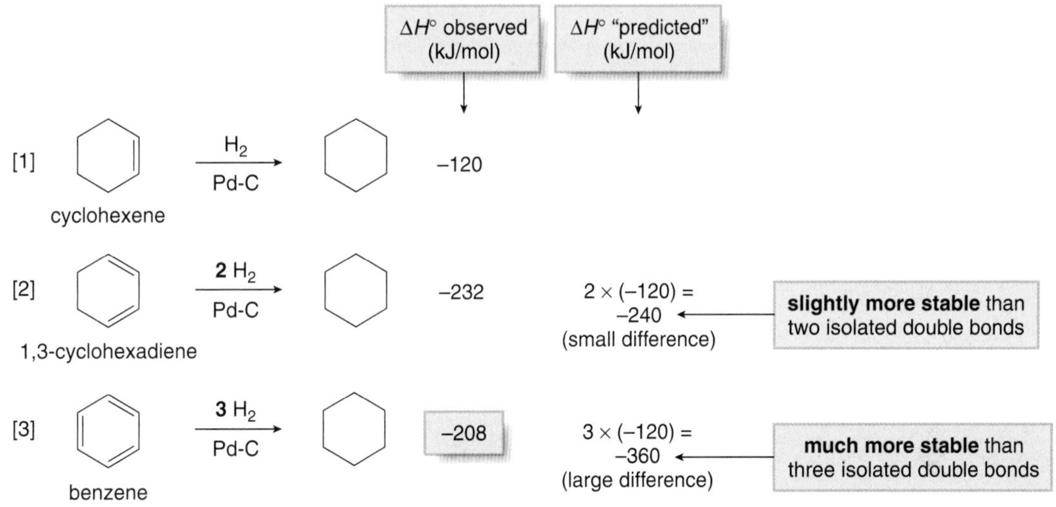
ΔH° observed (kJ/mol)
ΔH° "predicted" (kJ/mol)
[1]
H2
Pd-C
–120
cyclohexene
[2]
2 H2
Pd-C
–232
2 × (–120) = –240 (small difference)
slightly more stable than two isolated double bonds
1,3-cyclohexadiene
[3]
3 H2
Pd-C
–208
3 × (–120) = –360 (large difference)
much more stable than three isolated double bonds
benzene

The relative stability of conjugated dienes versus isolated dienes was first discussed in Section 16.9.

The addition of one mole of H_2 to cyclohexene releases –120 kJ/mol of energy (Equation [1]). If each double bond is worth –120 kJ/mol of energy, then the addition of two moles of H_2 to 1,3-cyclohexadiene (Equation [2]) should release 2 × –120 kJ/mol = –240 kJ/mol of energy. The observed value, however, is –232 kJ/mol. This is slightly smaller than expected because 1,3-cyclohexadiene is a conjugated diene, and conjugated dienes are more stable than two isolated carbon–carbon double bonds.

The hydrogenations of cyclohexene and 1,3-cyclohexadiene occur readily at room temperature, but benzene can be hydrogenated only under forcing conditions, and even then the reaction is extremely slow. If each double bond is worth –120 kJ/mol of energy, then the addition of three moles of H_2 to benzene should release 3 × –120 kJ/mol = –360 kJ/mol of energy. In fact, the observed heat of hydrogenation is only –208 kJ/mol, which is 152 kJ/mol less than predicted and even lower than the observed value for 1,3-cyclohexadiene. Figure 17.6 compares the hypothetical and observed heats of hydrogenation for benzene.

The huge difference between the hypothetical and observed heats of hydrogenation for benzene cannot be explained solely on the basis of resonance and conjugation.

Figure 17.6
A comparison between the observed and hypothetical heats of hydrogenation for benzene

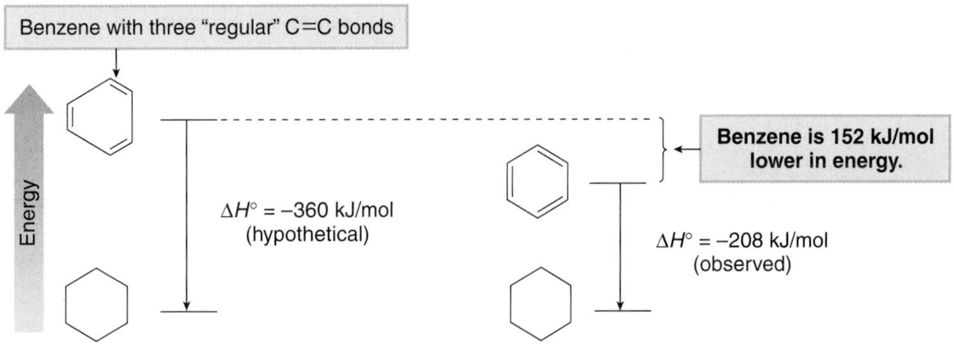
Benzene with three "regular" C=C bonds
Energy
ΔH° = –360 kJ/mol (hypothetical)
Benzene is 152 kJ/mol lower in energy.
ΔH° = –208 kJ/mol (observed)

- **The low heat of hydrogenation of benzene means that benzene is especially stable, even more so than the conjugated compounds introduced in Chapter 16. This unusual stability is characteristic of aromatic compounds.**

Benzene's unusual behavior in chemical reactions is not limited to hydrogenation. As mentioned in Section 17.1, **benzene does not undergo addition reactions typical of other highly unsaturated compounds, including conjugated dienes.** Benzene does not react with Br_2 to yield an addition product. Instead, in the presence of a Lewis acid, bromine *substitutes* for a hydrogen atom, thus yielding a product that retains the benzene ring.

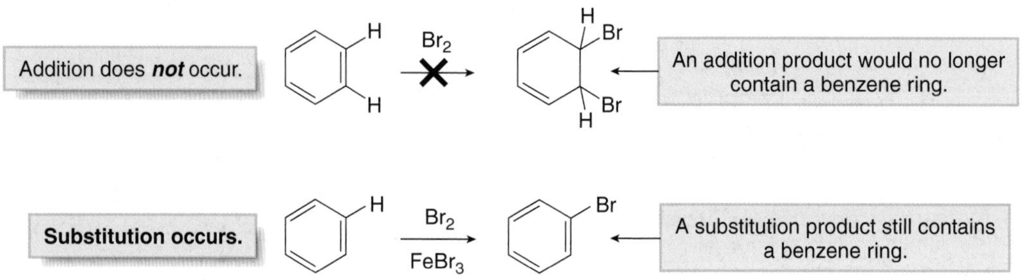

Addition does *not* occur.
H
H
Br_2
H
Br
Br
H
An addition product would no longer contain a benzene ring.
Substitution occurs.
H
Br_2
$FeBr_3$
Br
A substitution product still contains a benzene ring.

This behavior is characteristic of aromatic compounds. The structural features that distinguish aromatic compounds from the rest are discussed in Section 17.7.

Problem 17.8 Compounds **A** and **B** are both hydrogenated to methylcyclohexane. Which compound has the larger heat of hydrogenation? Which compound is more stable?

CH_3
CH_2

A **B**

17.7 The Criteria for Aromaticity—Hückel's Rule

Four structural criteria must be satisfied for a compound to be aromatic:

- **A molecule must be cyclic, planar, completely conjugated, and contain a particular number of π electrons.**

[1] A molecule must be cyclic.

- **To be aromatic, each *p* orbital must overlap with *p* orbitals on two adjacent atoms.**

The *p* orbitals on all six carbons of benzene continuously overlap, so benzene is aromatic. 1,3,5-Hexatriene has six *p* orbitals, too, but the two on the terminal carbons cannot overlap with each other, so **1,3,5-hexatriene is not aromatic.**

Cyclic compound

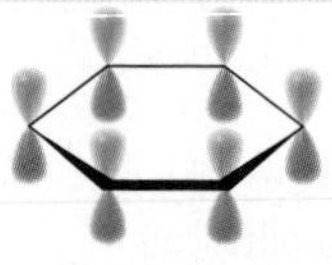

benzene

Every *p* orbital overlaps with two neighboring *p* orbitals.

aromatic

Acyclic compound

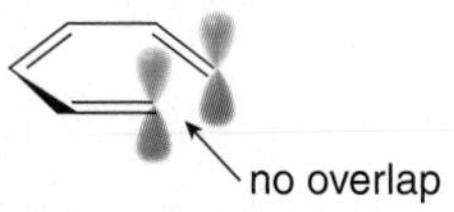

no overlap

1,3,5-hexatriene

There can be no overlap between the *p* orbitals on the two terminal C's.

not aromatic

[2] A molecule must be planar.

- **All adjacent *p* orbitals must be aligned so that the π electron density can be delocalized.**

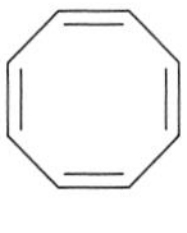

cyclooctatetraene
not aromatic

a tub-shaped,
eight-membered ring

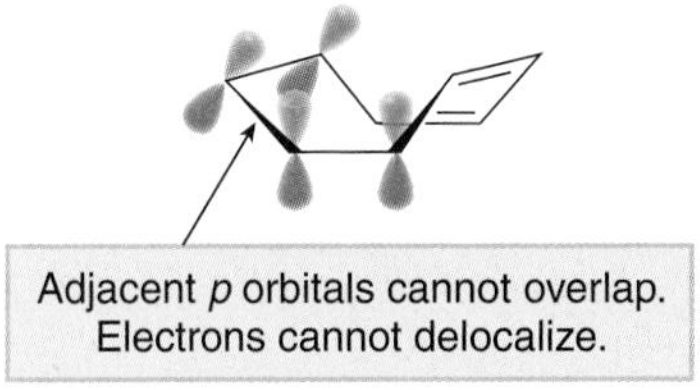
Adjacent *p* orbitals cannot overlap.
Electrons cannot delocalize.

For example, cyclooctatetraene resembles benzene in that it is a cyclic molecule with alternating double and single bonds. Cyclooctatetraene is tub shaped, however, **not planar,** so overlap between adjacent π bonds is impossible. **Cyclooctatetraene, therefore, is *not* aromatic,** so it undergoes addition reactions like those of other alkenes.

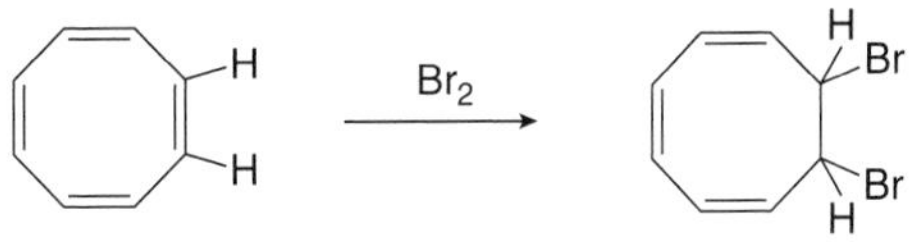
H
H
Br_2
H
Br
Br
H

cyclooctatetraene — **addition** product

[3] A molecule must be completely conjugated.

- **Aromatic compounds must have a *p* orbital on every atom in the ring.**

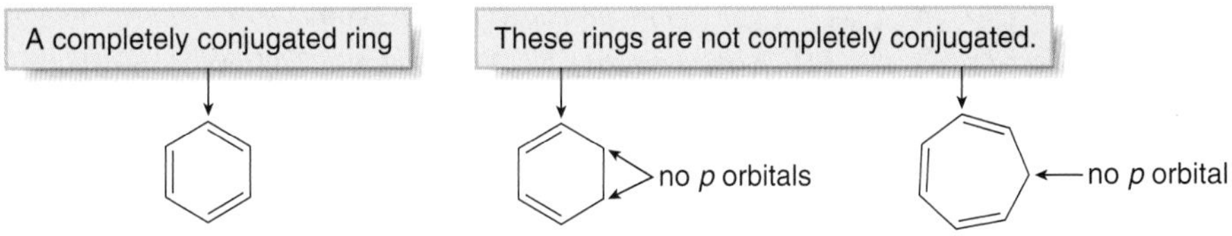
A completely conjugated ring
These rings are not completely conjugated.
no *p* orbitals
no *p* orbital

benzene
a *p* orbital on **every** C
aromatic

1,3-cyclohexadiene
not aromatic

1,3,5-cycloheptatriene
not aromatic

Both 1,3-cyclohexadiene and 1,3,5-cycloheptatriene contain at least one carbon atom that does not have a *p* orbital, and so they are not completely conjugated and therefore ***not* aromatic.**

[4] A molecule must satisfy Hückel's rule, and contain a particular number of π electrons.

Some compounds satisfy the first three criteria for aromaticity, but still they show none of the stability typical of aromatic compounds. For example, **cyclobutadiene** is so highly reactive that it can only be prepared at extremely low temperatures.

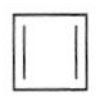

cyclobutadiene

a planar, cyclic, completely conjugated molecule that is *not* aromatic

Hückel's rule refers to the number of π electrons, *not* the number of atoms in a particular ring.

It turns out that in addition to being cyclic, planar, and completely conjugated, a compound needs a particular number of π electrons to be aromatic. Erich Hückel first recognized in 1931 that the following criterion, expressed in two parts and now known as **Hückel's rule,** had to be satisfied, as well:

- **An aromatic compound must contain 4*n* + 2 π electrons (*n* = 0, 1, 2, and so forth).**
- **Cyclic, planar, and completely conjugated compounds that contain 4*n* π electrons are especially unstable, and are said to be *antiaromatic.***

Thus, compounds that contain 2, 6, 10, 14, 18, and so forth π electrons are aromatic, as shown in Table 17.2. **Benzene is aromatic and especially stable because it contains 6 π electrons. Cyclobutadiene is antiaromatic and especially unstable because it contains 4 π electrons.**

Benzene
An aromatic compound

$\mathbf{4n + 2} = 4(1) + 2 =$
6 π electrons
aromatic

Cyclobutadiene
An antiaromatic compound

$\mathbf{4n} = 4(1) =$
4 π electrons
antiaromatic

Table 17.2 The Number of π Electrons That Satisfy Hückel's Rule

n	$4n + 2$
0	2
1	6
2	10
3	14
4, etc.	18

Considering aromaticity, all compounds can be classified in one of three ways:

[1] **Aromatic** • **A cyclic, planar, completely conjugated compound with $4n + 2$ π electrons.**

[2] **Antiaromatic** • **A cyclic, planar, completely conjugated compound with $4n$ π electrons.**

[3] **Not aromatic (or nonaromatic)** • **A compound that lacks one (or more) of the four requirements to be aromatic or antiaromatic.**

Note, too, the relationship between each compound type and a similar open-chained molecule having the same number of π electrons.

- **An aromatic compound is *more* stable than a similar acyclic compound having the same number of π electrons. Benzene is more stable than 1,3,5-hexatriene.**

- **An antiaromatic compound is *less* stable than an acyclic compound having the same number of π electrons. Cyclobutadiene is less stable than 1,3-butadiene.**

- **A compound that is not aromatic is *similar* in stability to an acyclic compound having the same number of π electrons. 1,3-Cyclohexadiene is similar in stability to *cis,cis*-2,4-hexadiene, so it is not aromatic.**

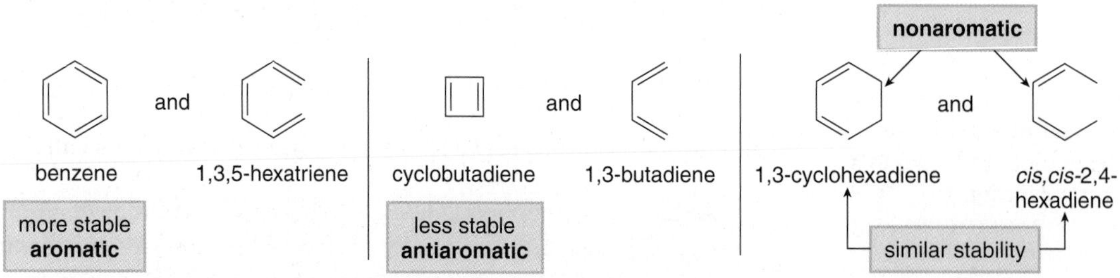

^{1}H NMR spectroscopy readily indicates whether a compound is aromatic. The protons on sp^2 hybridized carbons in aromatic hydrocarbons are highly deshielded and absorb at 6.5–8 ppm, whereas unsaturated hydrocarbons that are not aromatic absorb at 4.5–6 ppm, typical of protons bonded to the C=C of an alkene. Thus, benzene absorbs at 7.3 ppm, whereas cyclooctatetraene, which is not aromatic, absorbs farther upfield, at 5.8 ppm for the protons on its sp^2 hybridized carbons.

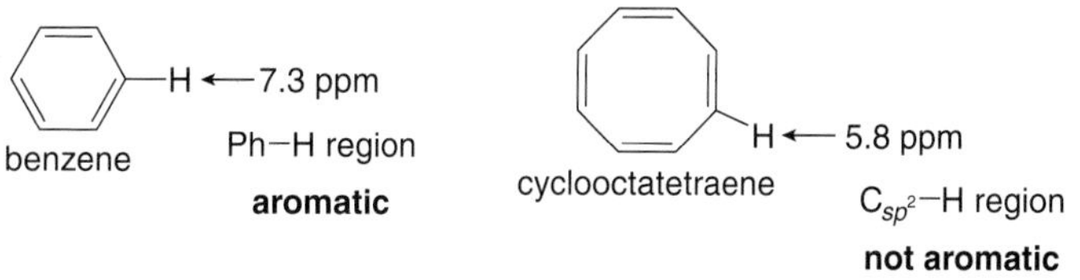

Many compounds in addition to benzene are aromatic. Several examples are presented in Section 17.8.

Problem 17.9 Estimate where the protons bonded to the sp^2 hybridized carbons will absorb in the ^{1}H NMR spectrum of each compound.

a. 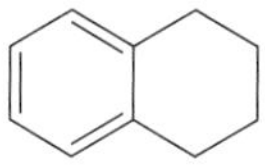 b.  c. 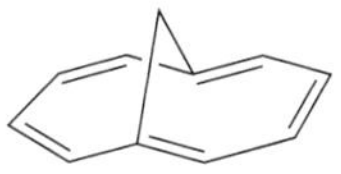

17.8 Examples of Aromatic Compounds

In Section 17.8 we look at many different types of aromatic compounds.

17.8A Aromatic Compounds with a Single Ring

Benzene is the most common aromatic compound having a single ring. **Completely conjugated rings larger than benzene are also aromatic if they are planar and have $4n + 2$ π electrons.**

- **Hydrocarbons containing a single ring with alternating double and single bonds are called *annulenes.***

To name an annulene, indicate the number of atoms in the ring in brackets and add the word *annulene.* Thus, benzene is [6]-annulene. Both **[14]-annulene** and **[18]-annulene** are cyclic, planar, completely conjugated molecules that follow Hückel's rule, and so they are aromatic.

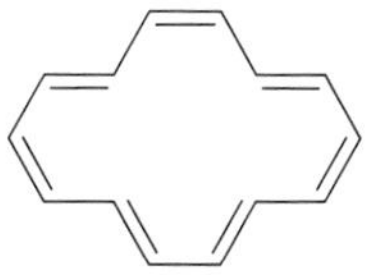

[14]-annulene
$4n + 2 = 4(3) + 2 =$
14 π electrons
aromatic

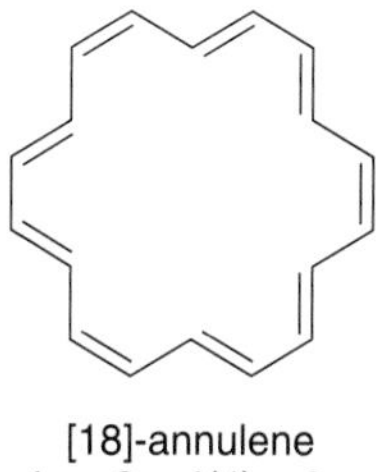

[18]-annulene
$4n + 2 = 4(4) + 2 =$
18 π electrons
aromatic

[10]-Annulene has 10 π electrons, which satisfies Hückel's rule, but a planar molecule would place the two H atoms inside the ring too close to each other, so the ring puckers to relieve this strain. Because **[10]-annulene is not planar,** the 10 π electrons can't delocalize over the entire ring and it is **not aromatic.**

[10]-Annulene fits Hückel's rule, but it's **not planar.**

The molecule puckers to keep these H's farther away from each other.

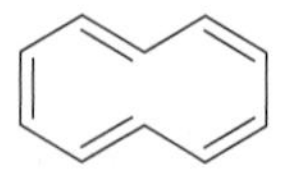

[10]-annulene
10 π electrons
not aromatic

=

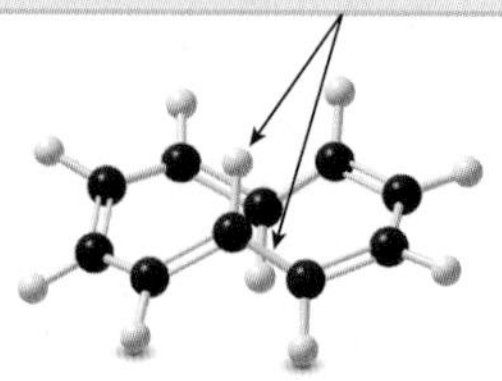

3-D representation

Problem 17.10 Would [16]-, [20]- or [22]-annulene be aromatic if each ring is planar?

17.8B Aromatic Compounds with More Than One Ring

Hückel's rule for determining aromaticity can be applied only to monocyclic systems, but many aromatic compounds containing several benzene rings joined together are also known. Two or more six-membered rings with alternating double and single bonds can be fused together to form **polycyclic aromatic hydrocarbons (PAHs).** Joining two benzene rings together forms **naphthalene.** There are two different ways to join three rings together, forming **anthracene** and **phenanthrene,** and many more complex hydrocarbons are known.

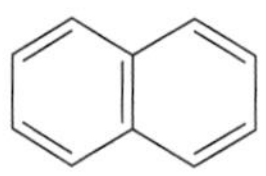

naphthalene
10 π electrons

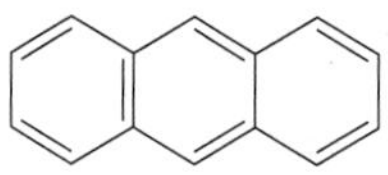

anthracene
14 π electrons

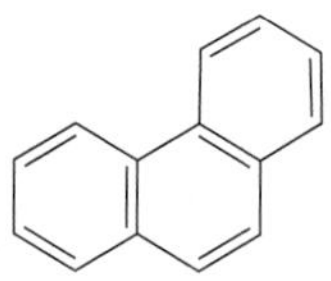

phenanthrene
14 π electrons

As the number of fused benzene rings increases, the number of resonance structures increases as well. Although two resonance structures can be drawn for benzene, naphthalene is a hybrid of three resonance structures.

Three resonance structures for naphthalene

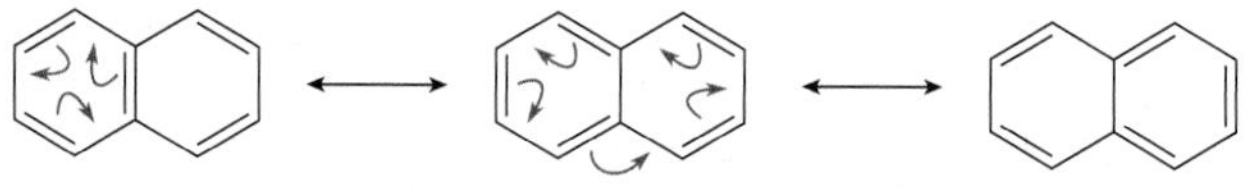

Problem 17.11 Draw the four resonance structures for anthracene.

17.8C Aromatic Heterocycles

Recall from Section 9.3 that a **heterocycle** is a ring that contains at least one heteroatom.

Heterocycles containing oxygen, nitrogen, or sulfur—atoms that also have at least one lone pair of electrons—can also be aromatic. With heteroatoms, we must always determine whether the lone pair is localized on the heteroatom or part of the delocalized π system. Two examples, **pyridine** and **pyrrole,** illustrate these different possibilities.

Pyridine

Pyridine is a heterocycle containing a six-membered ring with three π bonds and one nitrogen atom. Like benzene, two resonance structures (with all neutral atoms) can be drawn.

two resonance structures for pyridine
6 π electrons

Pyridine is cyclic, planar, and completely conjugated, because the three single and double bonds alternate around the ring. **Pyridine has six π electrons, two from each π bond, thus satisfying Hückel's rule and making pyridine aromatic.** The nitrogen atom of pyridine also has a nonbonded electron pair, which is localized on the N atom, so it is *not* part of the delocalized π electron system of the aromatic ring.

How is the nitrogen atom of the pyridine ring hybridized? The N atom is surrounded by three groups (two atoms and a lone electron pair), making it ***sp*^{2} hybridized,** and leaving one unhybridized *p* orbital with one electron that overlaps with adjacent *p* orbitals. The lone pair on N resides in an *sp*^{2} hybrid orbital that is perpendicular to the delocalized π electrons.

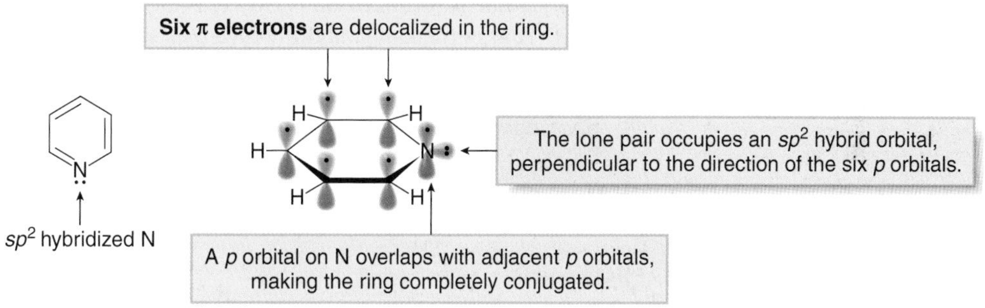

Pyrrole

Pyrrole contains a five-membered ring with two π bonds and one nitrogen atom. The N atom also has a lone pair of electrons.

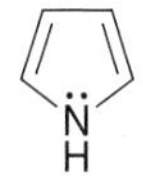

pyrrole

Pyrrole is cyclic and planar, with a total of four π electrons from the two π bonds. Is the nonbonded electron pair localized on N or part of a delocalized π electron system? The lone pair on N is *adjacent* to a double bond. Recall the following general rule from Section 16.5:

- **In a system X=Y−Z:, Z is generally *sp*^{2} hybridized and the lone pair occupies a *p* orbital to make the system conjugated.**

If the lone pair on the N atom occupies a *p* orbital:

- **Pyrrole has a *p* orbital on every adjacent atom, so it is completely conjugated.**
- **Pyrrole has six π electrons—four from the π bonds and two from the lone pair.**

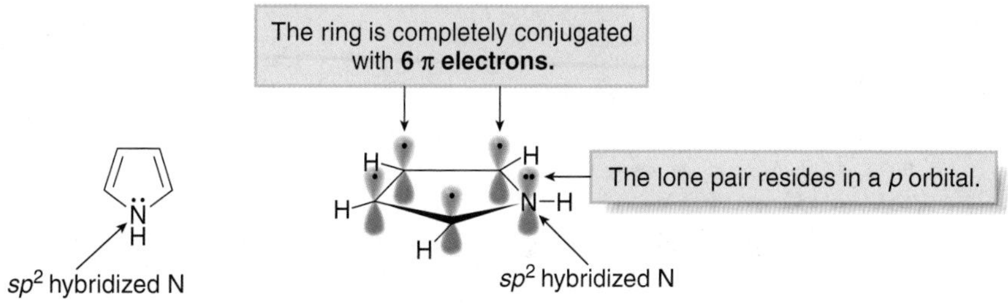

Figure 17.7
Electrostatic potential maps of pyridine and pyrrole

- In pyridine, the nonbonded electron pair is localized on the N atom in an sp^2 hybridized orbital, as shown by the region of high electron density (in red) on N.
- In pyrrole, the nonbonded electron pair is in a *p* orbital and is delocalized over the ring, so the entire ring is electron rich (red).

Because pyrrole is cyclic, planar, completely conjugated, and has $4n + 2$ π electrons, **pyrrole is aromatic. The number of electrons—not the size of the ring—determines whether a compound is aromatic.**

Electrostatic potential maps, shown in Figure 17.7 for pyridine and pyrrole, confirm that the **lone pair in pyridine is localized on N,** whereas the **lone pair in pyrrole is part of the delocalized π system.** Thus, a fundamental difference exists between the N atoms in pyridine and pyrrole.

- **When a heteroatom is already part of a double bond (as in the N of pyridine), its lone pair *cannot* occupy a *p* orbital and so it cannot be delocalized over the ring.**
- **When a heteroatom is *not* part of a double bond (as in the N of pyrrole), its lone pair can be located in a *p* orbital and *delocalized* over a ring to make it aromatic.**

Scombroid fish poisoning, associated with facial flushing, hives, and general itching, is caused by the ingestion of inadequately refrigerated fish, typically mahimahi (pictured) and tuna. Bacteria convert the amino acid histidine (Chapter 29) to histamine, which, when consumed in large amounts, results in this clinical syndrome.

Histamine

Histamine, a biologically active amine formed in many tissues, has an aromatic heterocycle with two N atoms, one of which is similar to the N atom of pyridine and one of which is similar to the N atom of pyrrole.

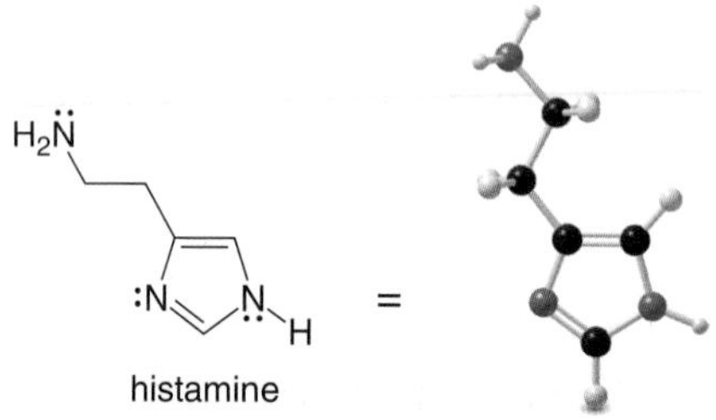

Histamine has a five-membered ring with two π bonds and two nitrogen atoms, each of which contains a lone pair of electrons. The heterocycle has four π electrons from the two double bonds. The lone pair on N1 also occupies a *p* orbital, making the heterocycle completely conjugated, and giving it a total of six π electrons. The lone pair on N1 is thus delocalized over the five-membered ring and the heterocycle is aromatic. The lone pair on N2 occupies an sp^2 hybrid orbital perpendicular to the delocalized π electrons.

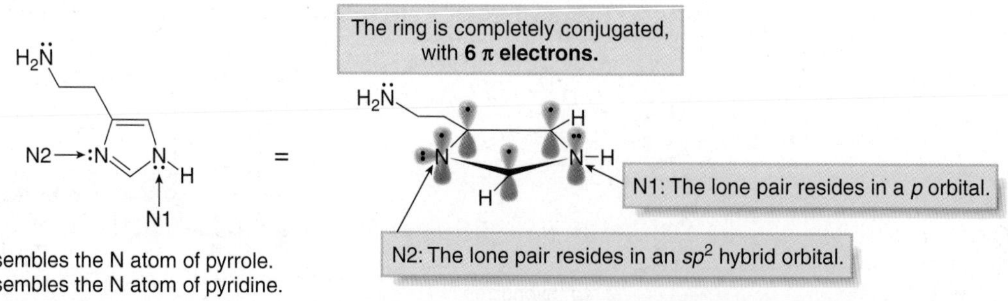

- N1 resembles the N atom of pyrrole.
- N2 resembles the N atom of pyridine.

Histamine produces a wide range of physiological effects in the body. Excess histamine is responsible for the runny nose and watery eyes symptomatic of hay fever. It also stimulates the overproduction of stomach acid, and contributes to the formation of hives. These effects result from the interaction of histamine with two different cellular receptors. We will learn more about antihistamines and antiulcer drugs, compounds that block the effects of histamine, in Section 25.6.

Problem 17.12 Which heterocycles are aromatic?

Quinine is isolated from the bark of the cinchona tree native to the Andes Mountains.

Problem 17.13 (a) How is each N atom in quinine, an effective antimalarial drug that reduces fever, hybridized? (b) In what type of orbital does the lone pair on each N reside?

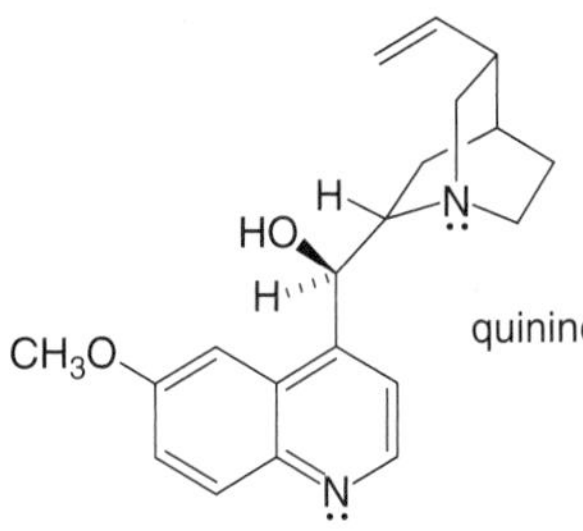

quinine

Problem 17.14 Januvia is the trade name for sitagliptin, a drug that increases the body's ability to lower blood sugar levels, and thus it was introduced in 2006 for the treatment of type 2 diabetes. (a) Explain why the five-membered ring in sitagliptin is aromatic. (b) Determine the hybridization of each N atom. (c) In what type of orbital does the lone pair on each N atom reside?

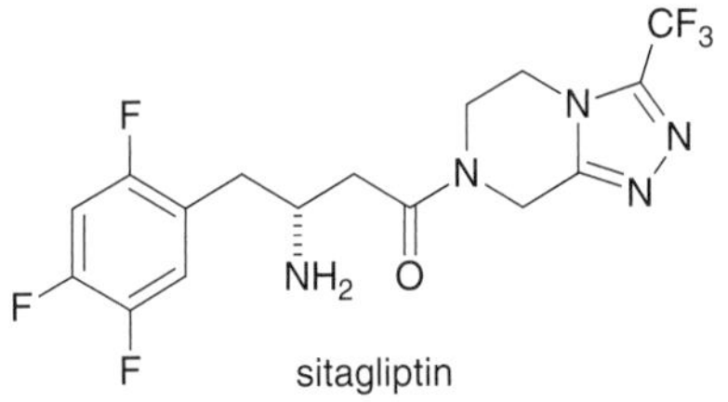

sitagliptin

Problem 17.15 Explain why a neutral aromatic heterocycle in a five-membered ring can have only one oxygen atom but two or more nitrogen atoms.

17.8D Charged Aromatic Compounds

Both negatively and positively charged ions can also be aromatic if they satisfy all the necessary criteria.

Cyclopentadienyl Anion

The **cyclopentadienyl anion** is a cyclic and planar anion with two double bonds and a nonbonded electron pair. In this way it resembles pyrrole. The two π bonds contribute four electrons and the lone pair contributes two more, for a total of six. By Hückel's rule, having **six π electrons confers aromaticity.** Like the N atom in pyrrole, the **negatively charged carbon atom must be**

***sp*² hybridized,** and the **nonbonded electron pair must occupy a *p* orbital** for the ring to be completely conjugated.

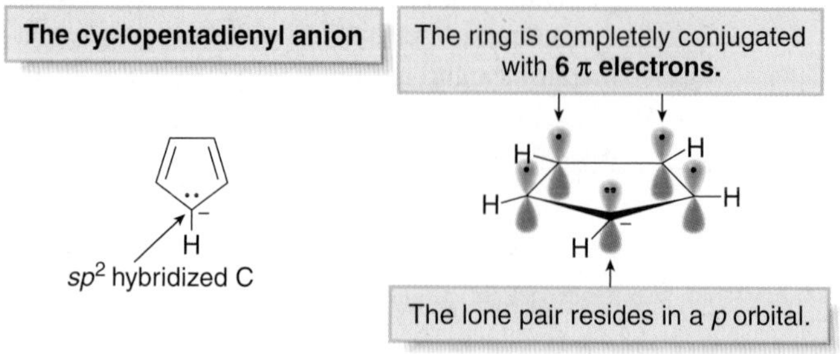

- **The cyclopentadienyl anion is aromatic because it is cyclic, planar, completely conjugated, and has six π electrons.**

We can draw **five equivalent resonance structures for the cyclopentadienyl anion,** delocalizing the negative charge over every carbon atom of the ring.

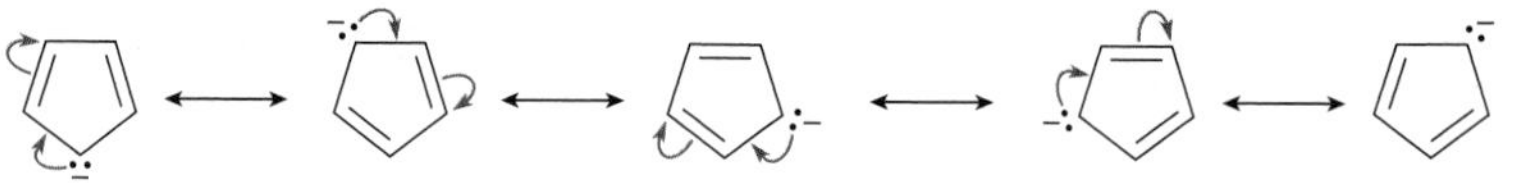

Although five resonance structures can also be drawn for both the **cyclopentadienyl cation** and **radical,** only the cyclopentadienyl anion has six π electrons, a number that satisfies Hückel's rule. The cyclopentadienyl cation has four π electrons, making it antiaromatic and especially unstable. The cyclopentadienyl radical has five π electrons, so it is neither aromatic nor antiaromatic. Having the "right" number of electrons is necessary for a species to be unusually stable by virtue of aromaticity.

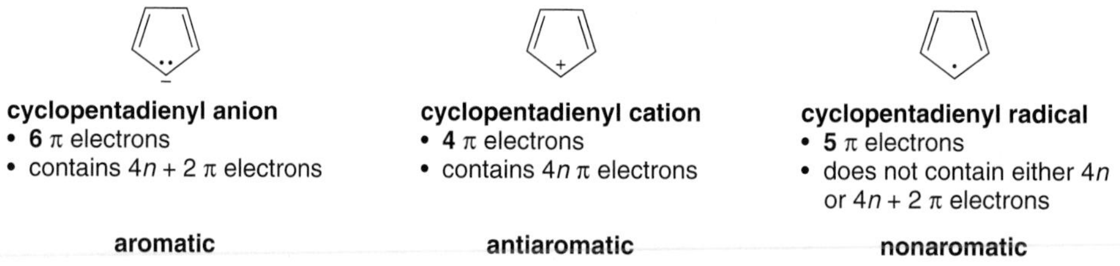

The cyclopentadienyl anion is readily formed from cyclopentadiene by a Brønsted–Lowry acid–base reaction.

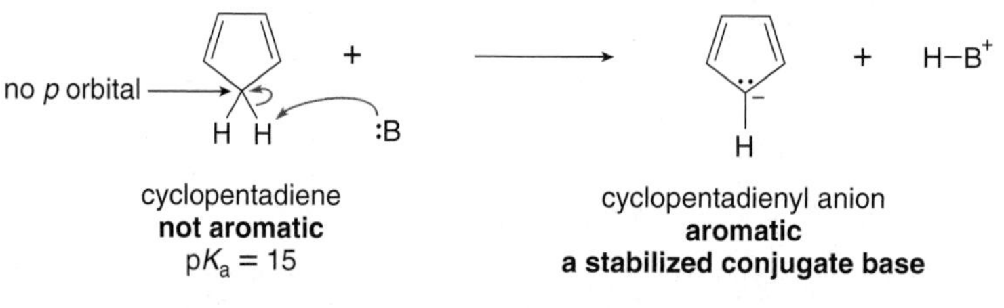

Cyclopentadiene itself is not aromatic because it is not fully conjugated. The cyclopentadienyl anion, however, is aromatic, so it is a very stable base. As such, it makes cyclopentadiene more acidic than other hydrocarbons. In fact, the pK_a of cyclopentadiene is 15, much lower (more acidic) than the pK_a of any C–H bond discussed thus far.

- **Cyclopentadiene is more acidic than many hydrocarbons because its conjugate base is aromatic.**

Problem 17.16 Draw the product formed when 1,3,5-cycloheptatriene ($pK_a = 39$) is treated with a strong base. Why is its pK_a so much higher than the pK_a of cyclopentadiene?

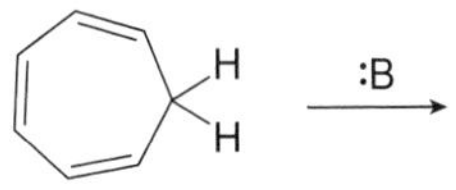
H
H
:B

1,3,5-cycloheptatriene
$pK_a = 39$

Problem 17.17 Rank the following compounds in order of increasing acidity.

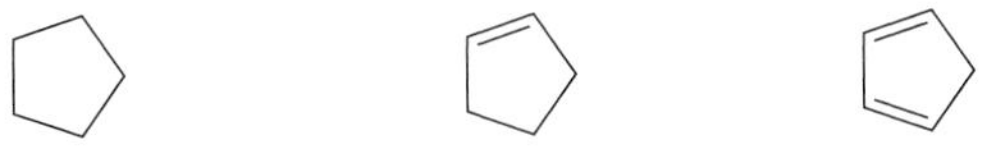

Tropylium Cation

The cyclopentadienyl anion and the tropylium cation both illustrate an important principle: The **number of π electrons determines aromaticity,** not the number of atoms in a ring or the number of *p* orbitals that overlap. The cyclopentadienyl anion and tropylium cation are aromatic because they each have six π electrons.

The **tropylium cation** is a planar carbocation with three double bonds and a positive charge contained in a seven-membered ring. This carbocation is completely conjugated, because the positively charged carbon is sp^2 hybridized and has a vacant *p* orbital that overlaps with the six *p* orbitals from the carbons of the three double bonds. **Because the tropylium cation has three π bonds and no other nonbonded electron pairs, it contains six π electrons,** thereby satisfying Hückel's rule.

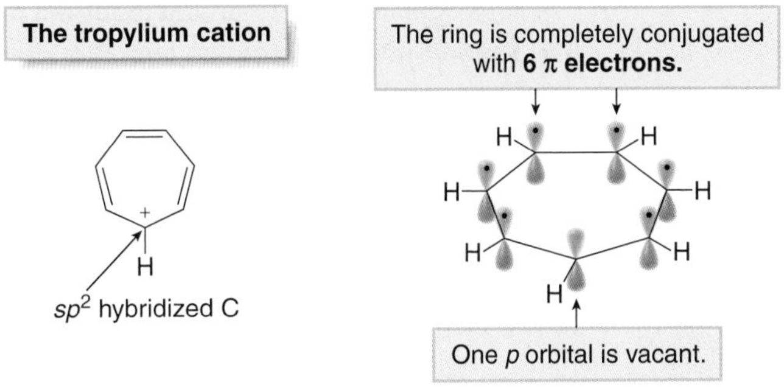
The tropylium cation
+
H
sp² hybridized C
The ring is completely conjugated with 6 π electrons.
H
H
H
H
H
H
H
One p orbital is vacant.

- **The tropylium cation is aromatic because it is cyclic, planar, completely conjugated, and has six π electrons delocalized over the seven atoms of the ring.**

Problem 17.18 Draw the seven resonance structures for the tropylium cation.

Problem 17.19 Assuming the rings are planar, which ions are aromatic?

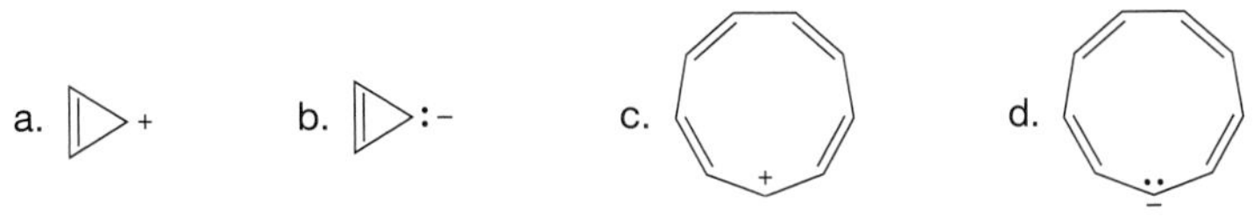
a.
+
b.
:–
c.
+
d.

Problem 17.20 Compound **A** exhibits a peak in its ^1H NMR spectrum at 7.6 ppm, indicating that it is aromatic. How are the carbon atoms of the triple bonds hybridized? In what type of orbitals are the π electrons of the triple bonds contained? How many π electrons are delocalized around the ring in **A**?

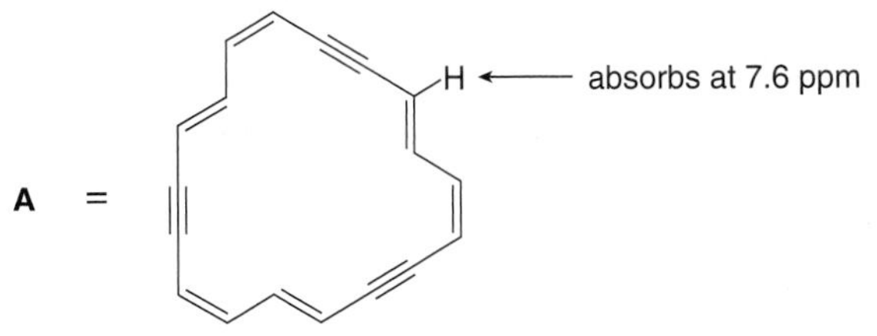
A =
H
absorbs at 7.6 ppm

17.9 What Is the Basis of Hückel's Rule?

Why does the number of π electrons determine whether a compound is aromatic? Cyclobutadiene is cyclic, planar, and completely conjugated, just like benzene, but why is benzene aromatic and cyclobutadiene antiaromatic?

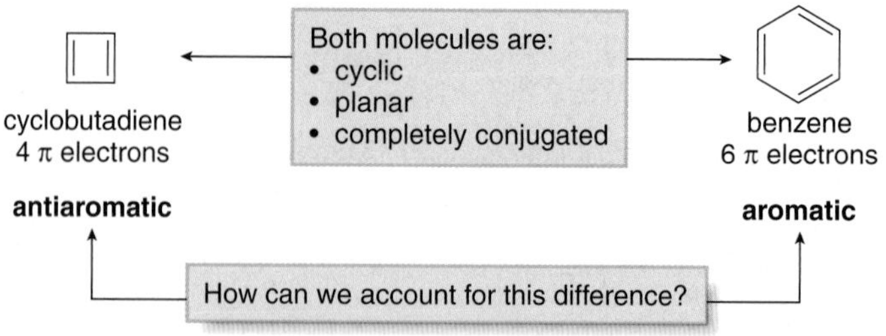

A complete explanation is beyond the scope of an introductory organic chemistry text, but nevertheless, you can better understand the basis of aromaticity by learning more about orbitals and bonding.

17.9A Bonding and Antibonding Orbitals

So far we have used the following basic concepts to describe how bonds are formed:

- **Hydrogen uses its 1*s* orbital to form σ bonds with other elements.**
- **Second-row elements use hybrid orbitals (*sp*, sp^2, or sp^3) to form σ bonds.**
- **Second-row elements use *p* orbitals to form π bonds.**

This description of bonding is called **valence bond theory.** In valence bond theory, a covalent bond is formed by the overlap of two atomic orbitals, and the electron pair in the resulting bond is shared by both atoms. Thus, a carbon–carbon double bond consists of a σ bond, formed by overlap of two sp^2 hybrid orbitals, each containing one electron, and a π bond, formed by overlap of two *p* orbitals, each containing one electron.

This description of bonding works well for most of the organic molecules we have encountered thus far. Unfortunately, it is inadequate for describing systems with many adjacent *p* orbitals that overlap, as there are in aromatic compounds. To more fully explain the bonding in these systems, we must utilize **molecular orbital (MO) theory.**

MO theory describes bonds as the mathematical combination of atomic orbitals that form a new set of orbitals called **molecular orbitals (MOs).** A molecular orbital occupies a region of space *in a molecule* where electrons are likely to be found. When forming molecular orbitals from atomic orbitals, keep in mind:

- **A set of *n* atomic orbitals forms *n* molecular orbitals.**

If *two* atomic orbitals combine, *two* molecular orbitals are formed. This is fundamentally different than valence bond theory. Because aromaticity is based on *p* orbital overlap, what does MO theory predict will happen when two *p* (atomic) orbitals combine?

The two lobes of each p orbital are opposite in phase, with a node of electron density at the nucleus. When two p orbitals combine, two molecular orbitals should form. The two p orbitals can add together constructively—that is, with like phases interacting—or destructively—that is, with opposite phases interacting.

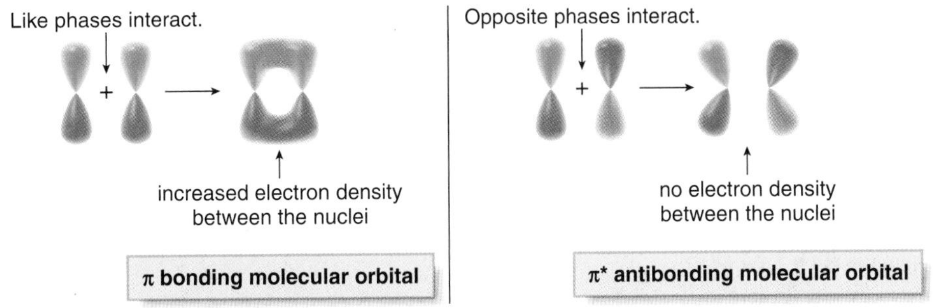

- **When two *p* orbitals of similar phase overlap side-by-side, a π bonding molecular orbital results.**
- **When two *p* orbitals of opposite phase overlap side-by-side, a π* antibonding molecular orbital results.**

A π bonding MO is lower in energy than the two atomic p orbitals from which it is formed because a stable bonding interaction results when orbitals of similar phase combine. A bonding interaction holds nuclei together. Similarly, a π* antibonding MO is higher in energy because a destabilizing node results when orbitals of opposite phase combine. A destabilizing interaction pushes nuclei apart.

If two atomic p orbitals each have one electron and then combine to form MOs, the two electrons will occupy the lower energy π bonding MO, as shown in Figure 17.8.

Figure 17.8
Combination of two p orbitals to form π and π* molecular orbitals

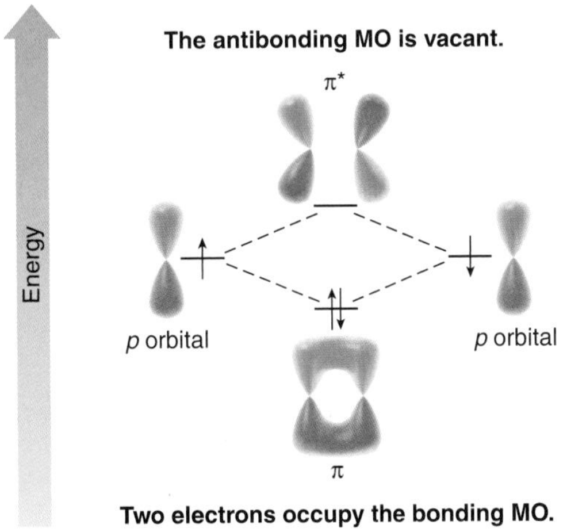

- Two atomic p orbitals combine to form two molecular orbitals. The bonding π MO is lower in energy than the two p orbitals from which it was formed, and the antibonding π* MO is higher in energy than the two p orbitals from which it was formed.
- Two electrons fill the lower energy bonding MO first.

17.9B Molecular Orbitals Formed When More Than Two *p* Orbitals Combine

The molecular orbital description of benzene is much more complex than the two MOs formed in Figure 17.8. Because each of the six carbon atoms of benzene has a *p* orbital, six atomic *p* orbitals combine to form six π molecular orbitals, as shown in Figure 17.9. A description of the exact appearance and energies of these six MOs requires more sophisticated mathematics and understanding of MO theory than is presented in this text. Nevertheless, note that the six MOs are labeled ψ_1–ψ_6, with ψ_1 being the lowest in energy and ψ_6 the highest.

Figure 17.9
How the six *p* orbitals of benzene overlap to form six molecular orbitals

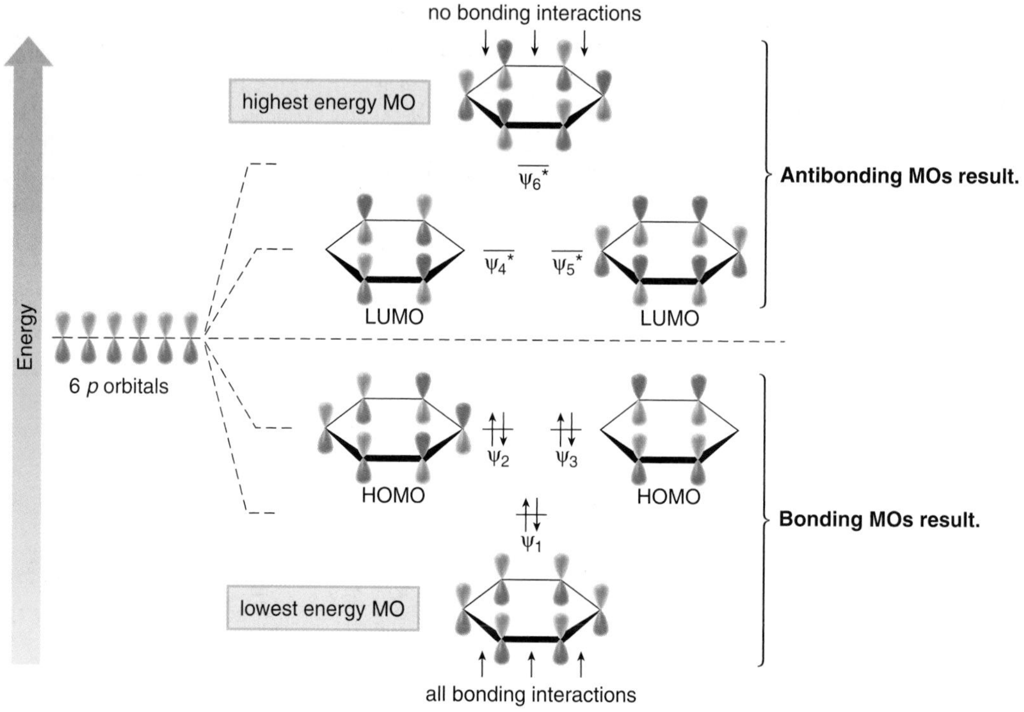

- Depicted in this diagram are the interactions of the six atomic *p* orbitals of benzene, which form six molecular orbitals. When orbitals of like phase combine, a bonding interaction results. When orbitals of opposite phase combine, a destabilizing node results.

The most important features of the six benzene MOs are as follows:

- **The larger the number of bonding interactions, the lower in energy the MO.** The lowest energy molecular orbital (ψ_1) has all bonding interactions between the *p* orbitals.
- **The larger the number of nodes, the higher in energy the MO.** The highest energy MO (ψ_6^*) has all nodes between the *p* orbitals.
- Three MOs are lower in energy than the starting *p* orbitals, making them bonding MOs (ψ_1, ψ_2, ψ_3), whereas three MOs are higher in energy than the starting *p* orbitals, making them antibonding MOs (ψ_4^*, ψ_5^*, ψ_6^*).
- The two pairs of MOs (ψ_2 and ψ_3; ψ_4^* and ψ_5^*) with the same energy are called **degenerate orbitals.**
- **The highest energy orbital that contains electrons is called the *highest occupied molecular orbital* (HOMO).** For benzene, the degenerate orbitals ψ_2 and ψ_3 are the HOMOs.
- **The lowest energy orbital that does *not* contain electrons is called the *lowest unoccupied molecular orbital* (LUMO).** For benzene, the degenerate orbitals ψ_4^* and ψ_5^* are the LUMOs.

To fill the MOs, the six electrons are added, two to an orbital, beginning with the lowest energy orbital. As a result, the six electrons completely fill the bonding MOs, leaving the antibonding MOs empty. This is what gives benzene and other aromatic compounds their special stability and this is why six π electrons satisfies Hückel's $4n + 2$ rule.

- **All bonding MOs (and HOMOs) are completely filled in aromatic compounds. No π electrons occupy antibonding MOs.**

17.10 The Inscribed Polygon Method for Predicting Aromaticity

An inscribed polygon is also called a **Frost circle.**

To predict whether a compound has π electrons completely filling bonding MOs, we must know how many bonding molecular orbitals and how many π electrons it has. It is possible to predict the relative energies of cyclic, completely conjugated compounds, without sophisticated math (or knowing what the resulting MOs look like) by using the **inscribed polygon method.**

How To Use the Inscribed Polygon Method to Determine the Relative Energies of MOs for Cyclic, Completely Conjugated Compounds

Example Plot the relative energies of the MOs of benzene

Step [1] Draw the polygon in question inside a circle with its vertices touching the circle and one of the vertices pointing down. Mark the points at which the polygon intersects the circle.

- Inscribe a hexagon inside a circle for benzene. The six vertices of the hexagon form six points of intersection, corresponding to the six MOs of benzene. The pattern—a single MO having the lowest energy, two degenerate pairs of MOs, and a single highest energy MO—matches that found in Figure 17.9.

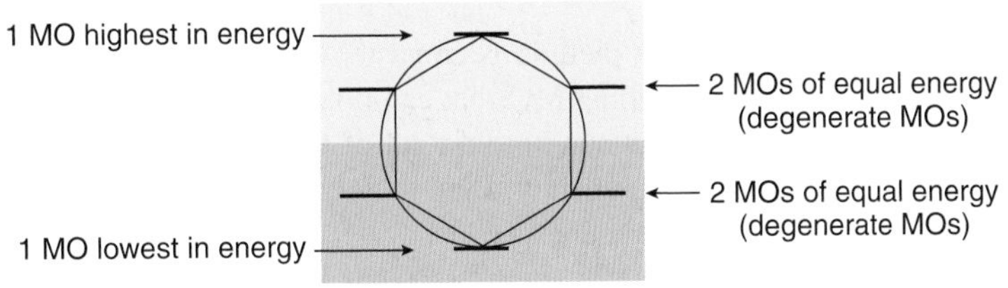

Step [2] Draw a line horizontally through the center of the circle and label MOs as bonding, nonbonding, or antibonding.

- **MOs below this line are bonding,** and lower in energy than the *p* orbitals from which they were formed. Benzene has three bonding MOs.
- **MOs at this line are nonbonding,** and equal in energy to the *p* orbitals from which they were formed. Benzene has no nonbonding MOs.
- **MOs above this line are antibonding,** and higher in energy than the *p* orbitals from which they were formed. Benzene has three antibonding MOs.

Step [3] Add the electrons, beginning with the lowest energy MO.

- **All the bonding MOs (and the HOMOs) are completely filled in aromatic compounds. No π electrons occupy antibonding MOs.**
- Benzene is aromatic because it has six π electrons that completely fill the bonding MOs.

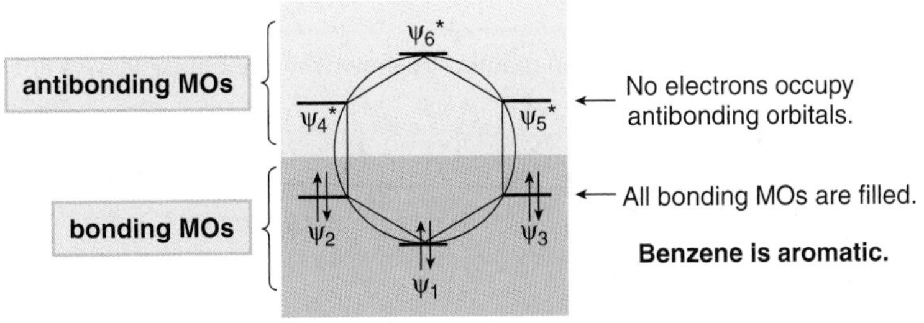

This method works for all monocyclic, completely conjugated hydrocarbons regardless of ring size. Figure 17.10 illustrates MOs for completely conjugated five- and seven-membered rings using this method. The total number of MOs always equals the number of vertices of the polygon. Because both systems have three bonding MOs, each needs six π electrons to fully occupy them, making the cyclopentadienyl anion and the tropylium cation aromatic, as we learned in Section 17.8D.

Figure 17.10
Using the inscribed polygon method for five- and seven-membered rings

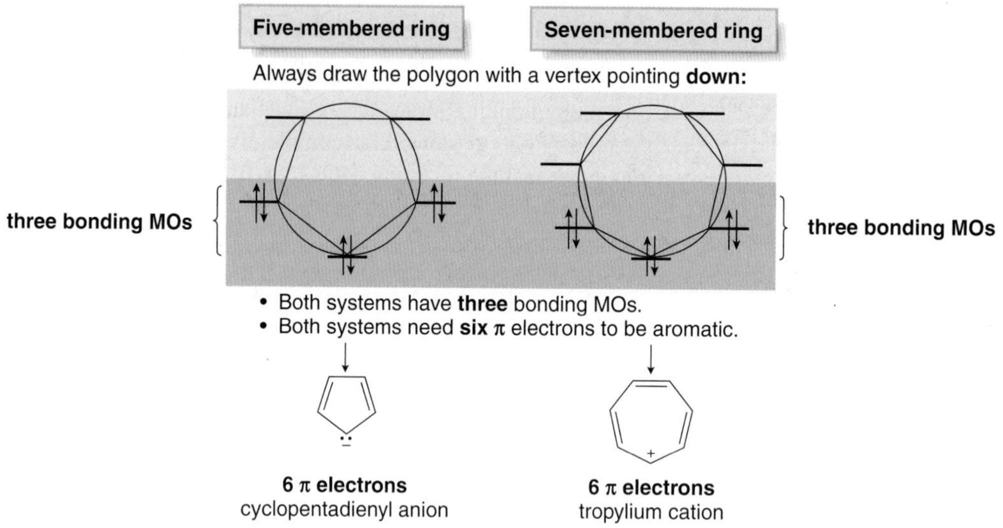

The inscribed polygon method is consistent with Hückel's $4n + 2$ rule; that is, there is always one lowest energy bonding MO that can hold two π electrons and the other bonding MOs come in degenerate pairs that can hold a total of four π electrons. For the compound to be aromatic, these MOs must be completely filled with electrons, so the "magic numbers" for aromaticity fit Hückel's $4n + 2$ rule (Figure 17.11).

Figure 17.11
MO patterns for cyclic, completely conjugated systems

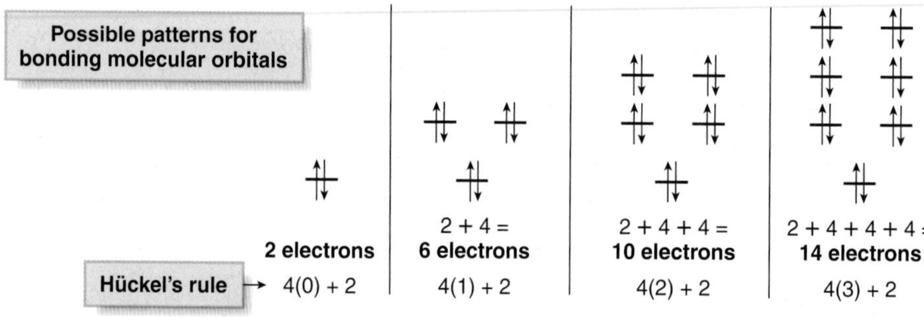

Sample Problem 17.1 Use the inscribed polygon method to show why cyclobutadiene is not aromatic.

cyclobutadiene
4 π electrons

Solution

Cyclobutadiene has four MOs (formed from its four *p* orbitals), to which its four π electrons must be added.

Step [1] Inscribe a square with a vertex down and mark its four points of intersection with the circle.

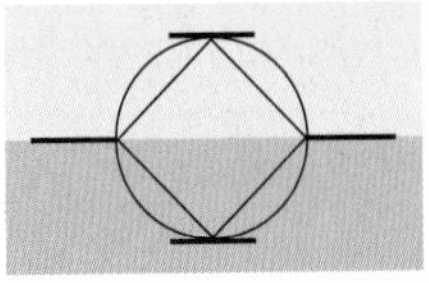

- The four points of intersection correspond to the four MOs of cyclobutadiene.

Steps [2] and [3] Draw a line through the center of the circle, label the MOs, and add the electrons.

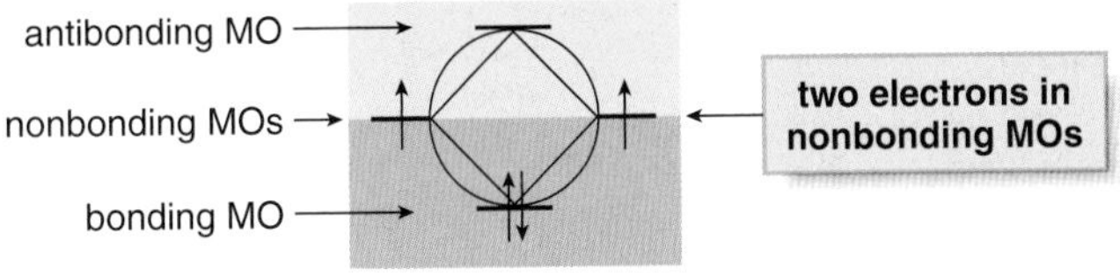

- Cyclobutadiene has four MOs—one bonding, two nonbonding, and one antibonding.
- Adding cyclobutadiene's four π electrons to these orbitals places two in the lowest energy bonding MO and one each in the two nonbonding MOs.
- Separating electrons in two degenerate MOs keeps like charges farther away from each other.

Conclusion: Cyclobutadiene is not aromatic because its HOMOs, two degenerate nonbonding MOs, are not completely filled.

The procedure followed in Sample Problem 17.1 also illustrates why cyclobutadiene is antiaromatic. Having the two unpaired electrons in nonbonding MOs suggests that cyclobutadiene should be a highly unstable diradical. In fact, antiaromatic compounds resemble cyclobutadiene because their HOMOs contain two unpaired electrons, making them especially unstable.

Problem 17.21 Use the inscribed polygon method to show why the following cation is aromatic:

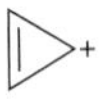

Problem 17.22 Use the inscribed polygon method to show why the cyclopentadienyl cation and radical are not aromatic.

17.11 Buckminsterfullerene—Is It Aromatic?

Diamond and graphite are two elemental forms of carbon.

The two most common elemental forms of carbon are diamond and graphite. Diamond, one of the hardest substances known, is used for industrial cutting tools, whereas graphite, a slippery black substance, is used as a lubricant. Their physical characteristics are so different because their molecular structures are very different.

The structure of diamond consists of a continuous tetrahedral network of sp^3 hybridized carbon atoms, thus creating an infinite array of chair cyclohexane rings (without the hydrogen atoms). The structure of graphite, on the other hand, consists of parallel sheets of sp^2 hybridized carbon atoms, thus creating an infinite array of benzene rings. The parallel sheets are then held together by weak intermolecular interactions.

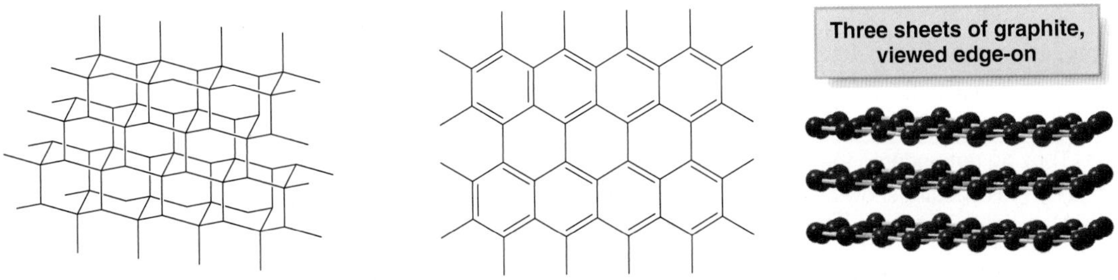

diamond
an "infinite" array of six-membered rings, covalently bonded in three dimensions

graphite
an "infinite" array of benzene rings, covalently bonded in two dimensions

Graphite exists in planar sheets of benzene rings, held together by weak intermolecular forces.

Buckminsterfullerene (C_{60}) is a third elemental form of carbon. Its structure consists of 20 hexagons and 12 pentagons of sp^2 hybridized carbon atoms joined in a spherical arrangement. It is completely conjugated because each carbon atom has a *p* orbital with an electron in it.

Buckminsterfullerene (or buckyball) was discovered by Smalley, Curl, and Kroto, who shared the 1996 Nobel Prize in Chemistry for their work. Its unusual name stems from its shape, which resembles the geodesic dome invented by R. Buckminster Fuller. The pattern of five- and six-membered rings also resembles the pattern of rings on a soccer ball.

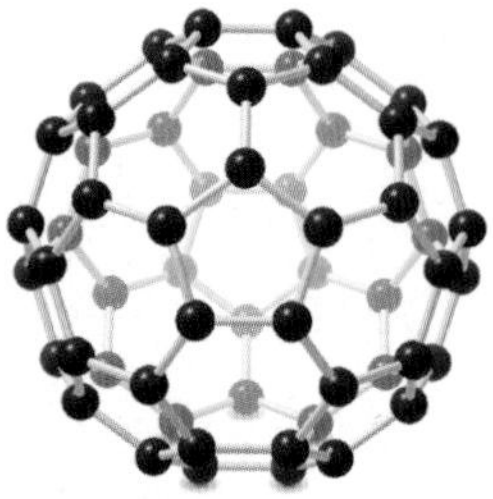

buckminsterfullerene, C_{60}

20 hexagons + 12 pentagons of carbon atoms joined together

The 60 C's of buckminsterfullerene are drawn. Each C also contains a *p* orbital with one electron, which is not drawn.

Is C_{60} aromatic? Although it is completely conjugated, it is not planar. Because of its curvature, it is not as stable as benzene. In fact, it undergoes addition reactions with electrophiles in much the same way as ordinary alkenes. Benzene, on the other hand, undergoes substitution reactions with electrophiles, which preserves the unusually stable benzene ring intact. These reactions are the subject of Chapter 18.

Problem 17.23 How many ^{13}C NMR signals does C_{60} exhibit?

KEY CONCEPTS

Benzene and Aromatic Compounds

Comparing Aromatic, Antiaromatic, and Nonaromatic Compounds (17.7)

- **Aromatic compound**
  - A cyclic, planar, completely conjugated compound that contains $4n + 2$ π electrons (n = 0, 1, 2, 3, and so forth).
  - An aromatic compound is more stable than a similar acyclic compound having the same number of π electrons.
- **Antiaromatic compound**
  - A cyclic, planar, completely conjugated compound that contains $4n$ π electrons (n = 0, 1, 2, 3, and so forth).
  - An antiaromatic compound is less stable than a similar acyclic compound having the same number of π electrons.
- **Nonaromatic compound**
  - A compound that lacks one (or more) of the four requirements to be aromatic or antiaromatic.

Properties of Aromatic Compounds

- Every atom in the ring has a *p* orbital to delocalize electron density (17.2).
- They are unusually stable. $\Delta H°$ for hydrogenation is much less than expected, given the number of degrees of unsaturation (17.6).
- They do not undergo the usual addition reactions of alkenes (17.6).
- ^1H NMR spectra show highly deshielded protons because of ring currents that reinforce the applied magnetic field (17.4).
- All bonding MOs and HOMOs are completely filled and no electrons occupy antibonding orbitals (17.9).

Examples of Aromatic Compounds with Six π Electrons (17.8)

 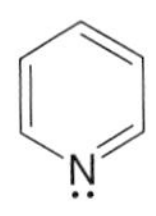 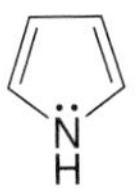  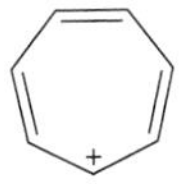

benzene | pyridine | pyrrole | cyclopentadienyl anion | tropylium cation

Examples of Compounds That Are Not Aromatic (17.8)

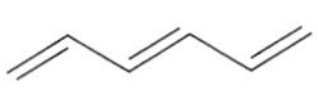  

not cyclic | not planar | not completely conjugated

PROBLEMS

Problems Using Three-Dimensional Models

17.24 Name each compound and state how many lines are observed in its ^{13}C NMR spectrum.

a. 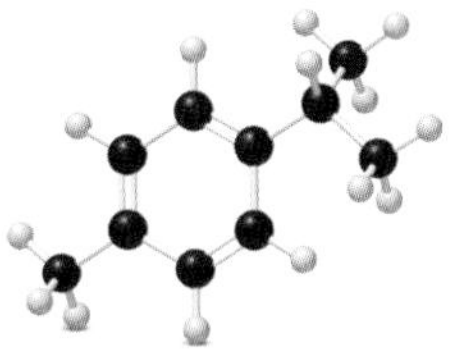

b. 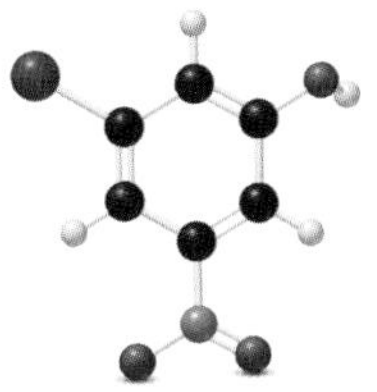

17.25 Classify each compound as aromatic, antiaromatic, or not aromatic.

a. 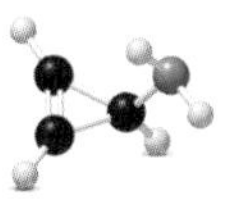

b. 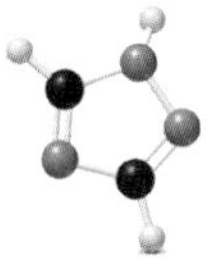

c. 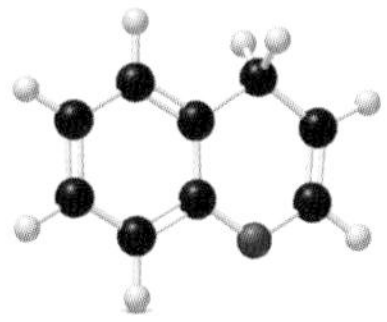

Benzene Structure and Nomenclature

17.26 Early structural studies on benzene had to explain the following experimental evidence. When benzene was treated with Br_2 (plus a Lewis acid), a single substitution product of molecular formula C_6H_5Br was formed. When this product was treated with another equivalent of Br_2, three different compounds of molecular formula $C_6H_4Br_2$ were formed.

a. Explain why a single Kekulé structure is consistent with the first result, but does not explain the second result.

b. Then explain why a resonance description of benzene is consistent with the results of both reactions.

17.27 Draw all aromatic hydrocarbons that have molecular formula C_8H_{10}. For each compound, determine how many isomers of molecular formula C_8H_9Br would be formed if one H atom on the benzene ring were replaced by a Br atom.

17.28 Give the IUPAC name for each compound.

a. 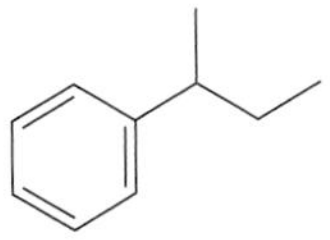

c. 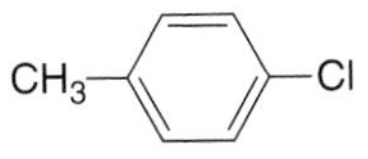

e. 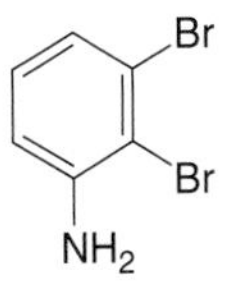

g. 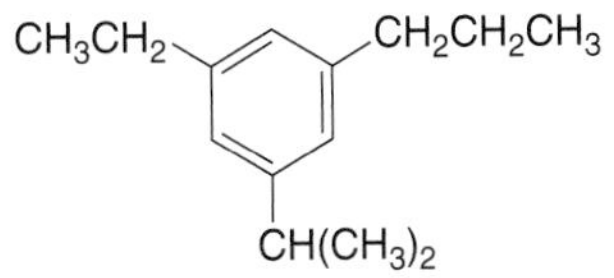

b. 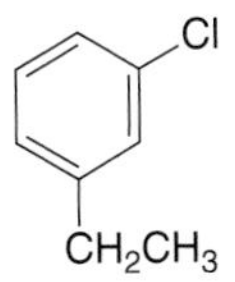

d. 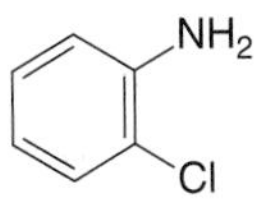

f. 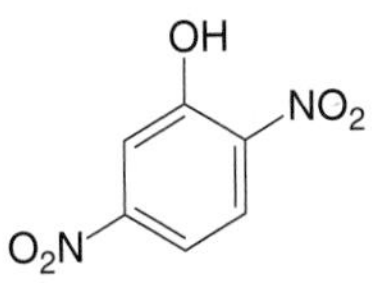

h. 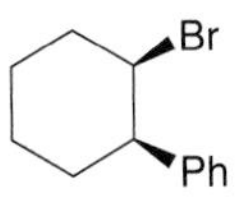

17.29 Draw a structure corresponding to each name.

a. *p*-dichlorobenzene
b. *m*-chlorophenol
c. *p*-iodoaniline
d. *o*-bromonitrobenzene
e. 2,6-dimethoxytoluene
f. 2-phenyl-1-butene
g. 2-phenyl-2-propen-1-ol
h. *trans*-1-benzyl-3-phenylcyclopentane

17.30 a. Draw the 14 constitutional isomers of molecular formula C_8H_9Cl that contain a benzene ring.
b. Name all compounds that contain a trisubstituted benzene ring.
c. For which compound(s) are stereoisomers possible? Draw all possible stereoisomers.

Aromaticity

17.31 How many π electrons are contained in each molecule?

a. 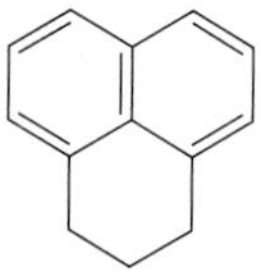
b. 
c. 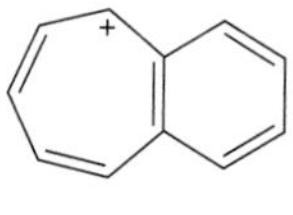
d. 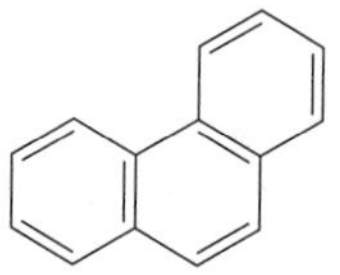
e. 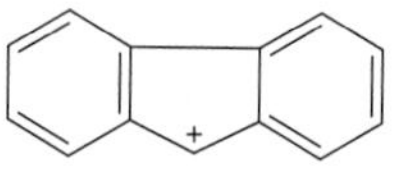

17.32 Which compounds are aromatic? For any compound that is not aromatic, state why this is so.

a. 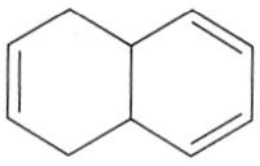
b. 
c. 
d. 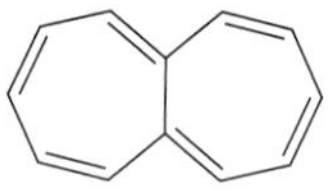

17.33 Which of the following heterocycles are aromatic?

a. 

c. 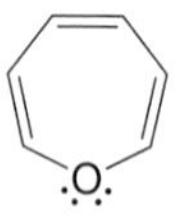

e. 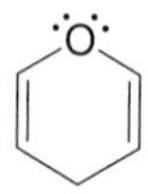

g. 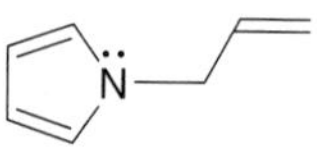

b. 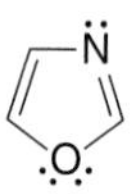

d. 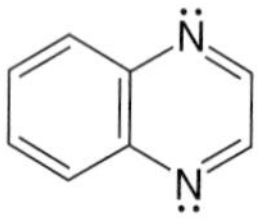

f. 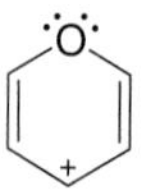

h. 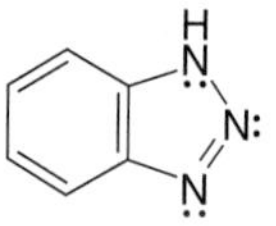

17.34 Label each compound as aromatic, antiaromatic, or not aromatic. Assume all completely conjugated rings are planar.

a. 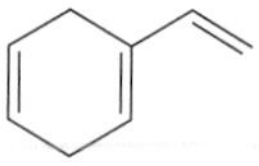
b. 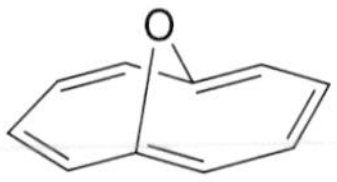

c. 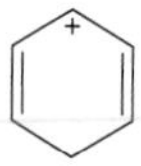
d. 

17.35 Hydrocarbon **A** possesses a significant dipole, even though it is composed of only C–C and C–H bonds. Explain why the dipole arises and use resonance structures to illustrate the direction of the dipole. Which ring is more electron rich?

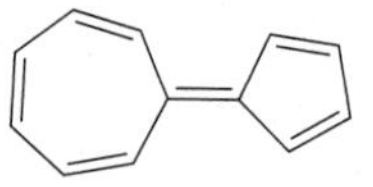

A

17.36 Pentalene, azulene, and heptalene are conjugated hydrocarbons that do not contain a benzene ring. Which hydrocarbons are especially stable or unstable based on the number of π electrons they contain? Explain your choices.

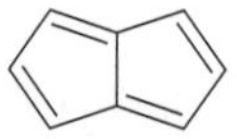
pentalene

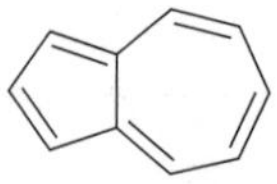
azulene

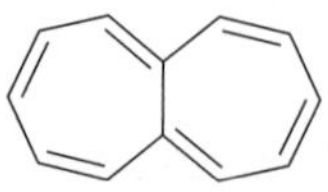
heptalene

17.37 The purine heterocycle occurs commonly in the structure of DNA.

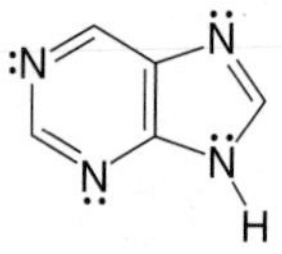

purine

a. How is each N atom hybridized?
b. In what type of orbital does each lone pair on a N atom reside?
c. How many π electrons does purine contain?
d. Why is purine aromatic?

17.38 

C

a. How many π electrons does **C** contain?
b. How many π electrons are delocalized in the ring?
c. Explain why **C** is aromatic.

17.39 AZT was the first drug approved to treat HIV, the virus that causes AIDS. Explain why the six-membered ring of AZT is aromatic.

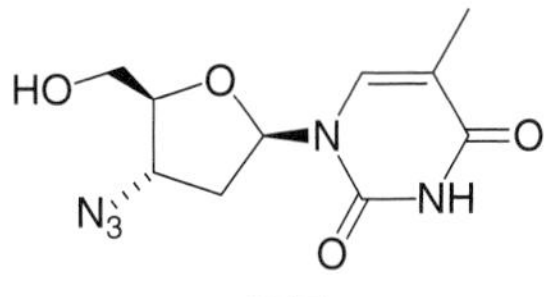

AZT

17.40 Explain the observed rate of reactivity of the following 2° alkyl halides in an S_N1 reaction.

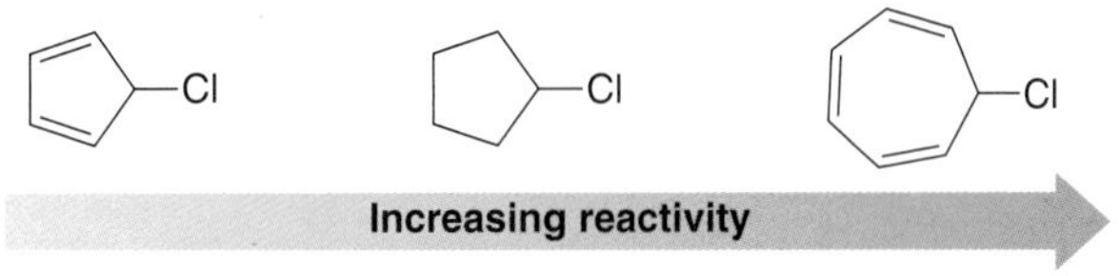

17.41 Draw a stepwise mechanism for the following reaction.

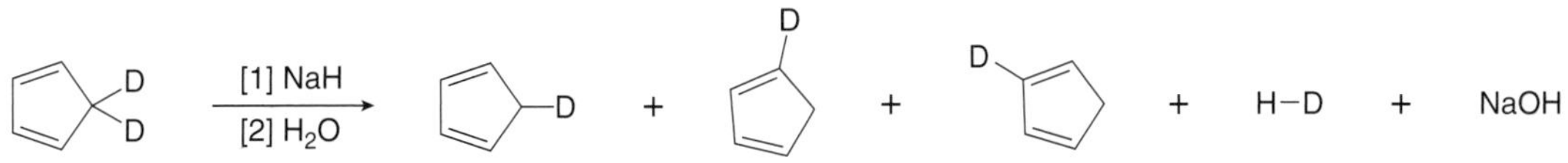

17.42 Explain why α-pyrone reacts with Br_2 to yield a substitution product (like benzene does), rather than an addition product to one of its C=C bonds.

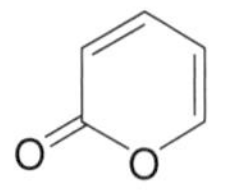

α-pyrone

Resonance

17.43 Draw additional resonance structures for each species.

a. 

cyclopropenyl radical

b. 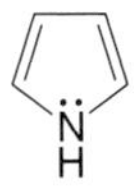

pyrrole

c. 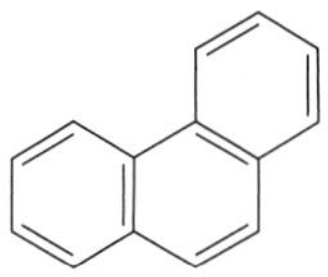

phenanthrene

17.44 The carbon–carbon bond lengths in naphthalene are not equal. Use a resonance argument to explain why bond (a) is shorter than bond (b).

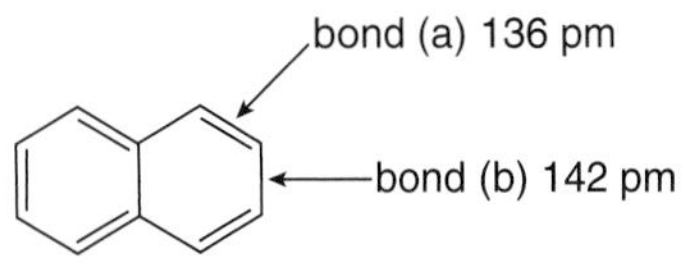

17.45 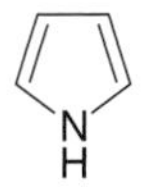

pyrrole

furan

a. Draw all reasonable resonance structures for pyrrole and explain why pyrrole is less resonance stabilized than benzene.
b. Draw all reasonable resonance structures for furan and explain why furan is less resonance stabilized than pyrrole.

Acidity

17.46 Which compound in each pair is the stronger acid?

a.  or 

b.  or 

17.47 Treatment of indene with $NaNH_2$ forms its conjugate base in a Brønsted–Lowry acid–base reaction. Draw all reasonable resonance structures for indene's conjugate base, and explain why the pK_a of indene is lower than the pK_a of most hydrocarbons.

indene
pK_a = 20

17.48 Considering both 5-methyl-1,3-cyclopentadiene (**A**) and 7-methyl-1,3,5-cycloheptatriene (**B**), which labeled H atom is most acidic? Which labeled H atom is least acidic? Explain your choices.

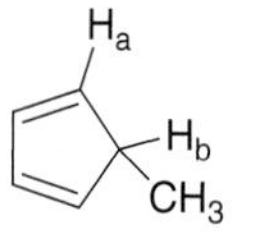

A

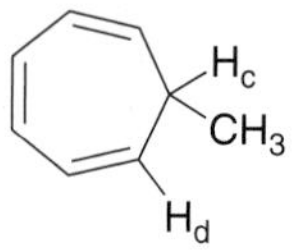

B

17.49 Draw the conjugate bases of pyrrole and cyclopentadiene. Explain why the sp^3 hybridized C–H bond of cyclopentadiene is more acidic than the N–H bond of pyrrole.

17.50 a. Explain why protonation of pyrrole occurs at C2 to form **A,** rather than on the N atom to form **B.**
b. Explain why **A** is more acidic than **C,** the conjugate acid of pyridine.

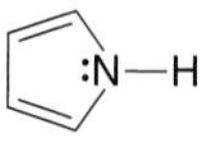

pyrrole

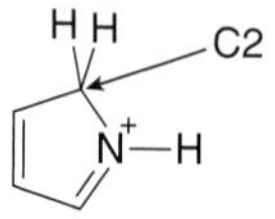

pK_a = 0.4

A

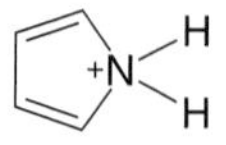

B

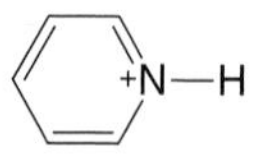

pK_a = 5.3

C

Inscribed Polygon Method

17.51 Use the inscribed polygon method to show the pattern of molecular orbitals in cyclooctatetraene.

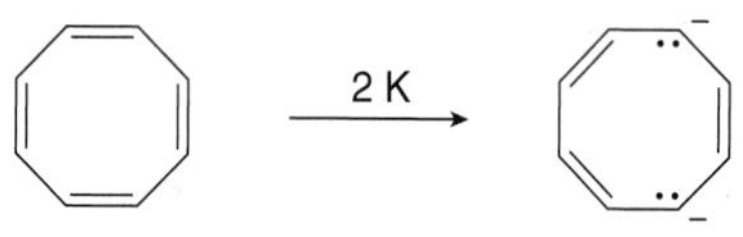

(one resonance structure) + 2 K^+

cyclooctatetraene — dianion of cyclooctatetraene

a. Label the MOs as bonding, antibonding, or nonbonding.
b. Indicate the arrangement of electrons in these orbitals for cyclooctatetraene, and explain why cyclooctatetraene is not aromatic.
c. Treatment of cyclooctatetraene with potassium forms a dianion. How many π electrons does this dianion contain?
d. How are the π electrons in this dianion arranged in the molecular orbitals?
e. Classify the dianion of cyclooctatetraene as aromatic, antiaromatic, or not aromatic, and explain why this is so.

17.52 Use the inscribed polygon method to show the pattern of molecular orbitals in 1,3,5,7-cyclononatetraene and use it to label its cation, radical, and anion as aromatic, antiaromatic, or not aromatic.

cyclononatetraenyl cation

cyclononatetraenyl radical

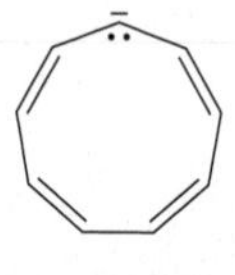

cyclononatetraenyl anion

Spectroscopy

17.53 How many ^{13}C NMR signals does each compound exhibit?

a. 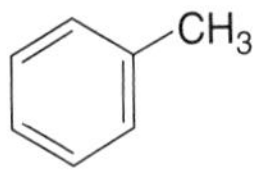

b. 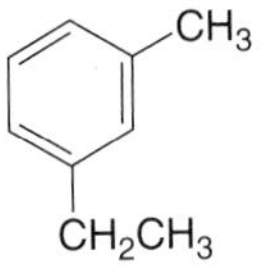

c. 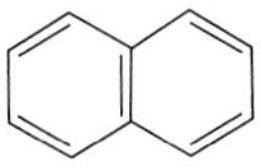

d. 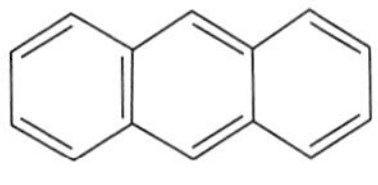

17.54 Which of the diethylbenzene isomers (ortho, meta, or para) corresponds to each set of ^{13}C NMR spectral data?

[A] ^{13}C NMR signals: 16, 29, 125, 127.5, 128.4, and 144 ppm

[B] ^{13}C NMR signals: 15, 26, 126, 128, and 142 ppm

[C] ^{13}C NMR signals: 16, 29, 128, and 141 ppm

17.55 Propose a structure consistent with each set of data.

a. $C_{10}H_{14}$: IR absorptions at 3150–2850, 1600, and 1500 cm^{-1}

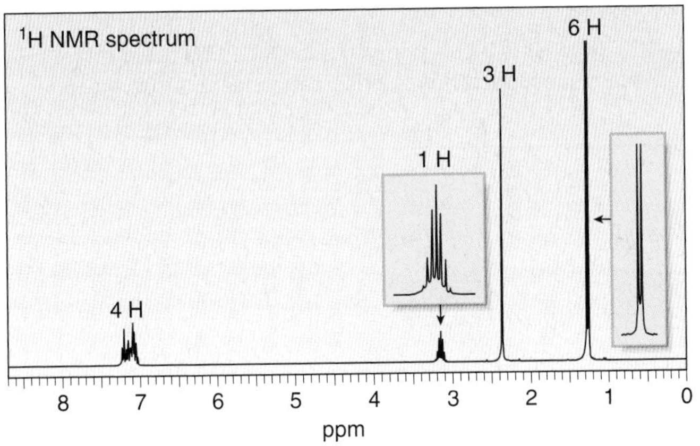

b. C_9H_{12}: ^{13}C NMR signals at 21, 127, and 138 ppm

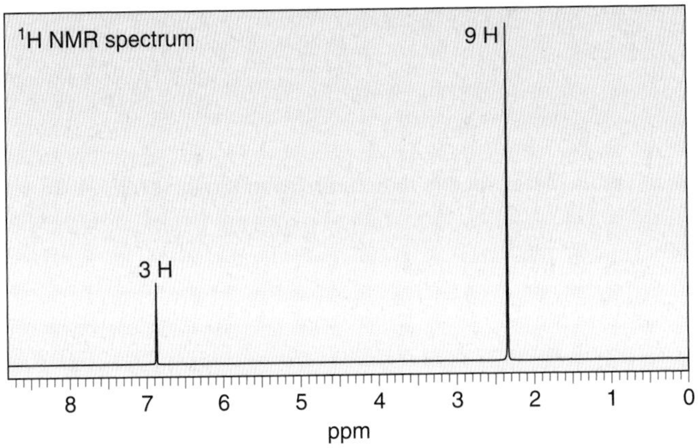

c. C_8H_{10}: IR absorptions at 3108–2875, 1606, and 1496 cm^{-1}

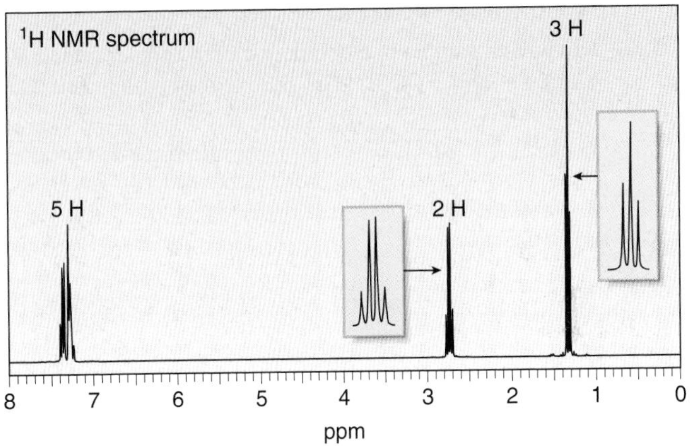

17.56 Propose a structure consistent with each set of data.

a. Compound **A:**

Molecular formula: $C_8H_{10}O$

IR absorption at 3150–2850 cm^{-1}

^{1}H NMR data: 1.4 (triplet, 3 H), 3.95 (quartet, 2 H), and 6.8–7.3 (multiplet, 5 H) ppm

b. Compound **B:**

Molecular formula: $C_9H_{10}O_2$

IR absorption at 1669 cm^{-1}

^{1}H NMR data: 2.5 (singlet, 3 H), 3.8 (singlet, 3 H), 6.9 (doublet, 2 H), and 7.9 (doublet, 2 H) ppm

17.57 Thymol (molecular formula $C_{10}H_{14}O$) is the major component of the oil of thyme. Thymol shows IR absorptions at 3500–3200, 3150–2850, 1621, and 1585 cm^{-1}. The ^{1}H NMR spectrum of thymol is given below. Propose a possible structure for thymol.

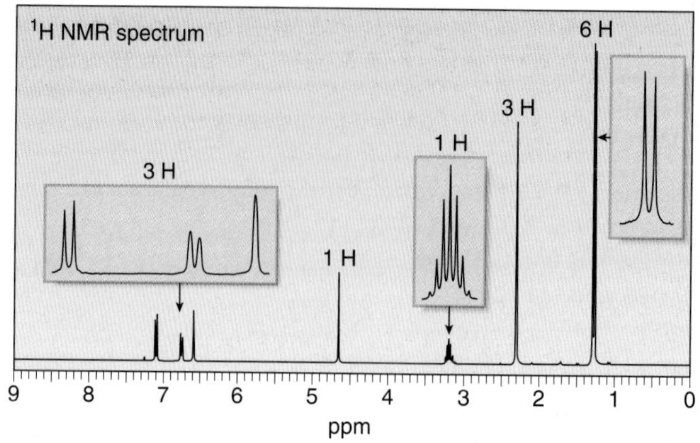

17.58 You have a sample of a compound of molecular formula $C_{11}H_{15}NO_2$, which has a benzene ring substituted by two groups, $(CH_3)_2N-$ and $-CO_2CH_2CH_3$, and exhibits the given ^{13}C NMR. What disubstituted benzene isomer corresponds to these ^{13}C data?

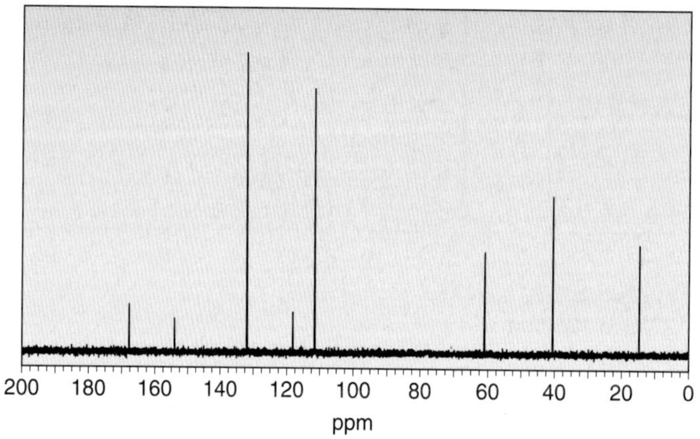

General Problems

17.59 Explain why tetrahydrofuran has a higher boiling point and is much more water soluble than furan, even though both compounds are cyclic ethers containing four carbons.

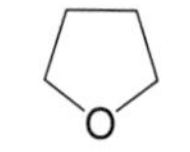

tetrahydrofuran

furan

17.60 Zolpidem (trade name Ambien) promotes the rapid onset of sleep, making it a widely prescribed drug for treating insomnia.

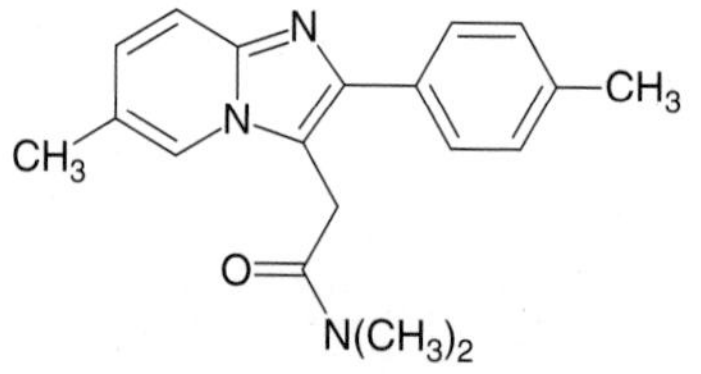

zolpidem

a. In what type of orbital does the lone pair on each N atom in the heterocycle reside?
b. Explain why the bicyclic ring system that contains both N atoms is aromatic.
c. Draw all reasonable resonance structures for the bicyclic ring system.

17.61 Answer the following questions about curcumin, a yellow pigment isolated from turmeric, a tropical perennial in the ginger family and a principal ingredient in curry powder.

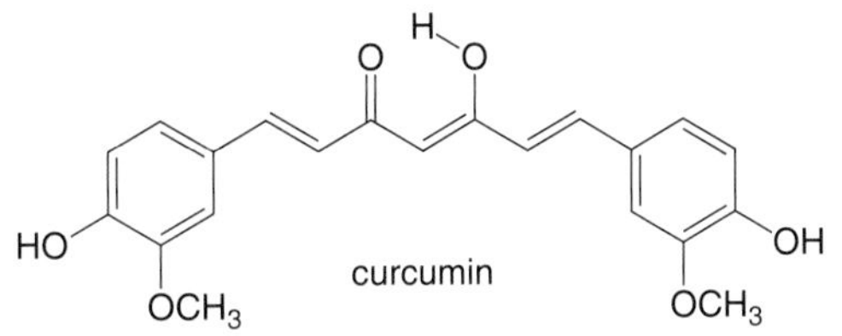

curcumin

a. In Chapter 11 we learned that most enols, compounds that contain a hydroxy group bonded to a C = C, are unstable and tautomerize to carbonyl groups. Draw the keto form of the enol of curcumin, and explain why the enol is more stable than many other enols.
b. Explain why the enol O – H proton is more acidic than an alcohol O – H proton.
c. Why is curcumin colored?
d. Explain why curcumin is an antioxidant.

17.62 Stanozolol is an anabolic steroid that promotes muscle growth. Although stanozolol has been used by athletes and body builders, many physical and psychological problems result from prolonged use and it is banned in competitive sports.

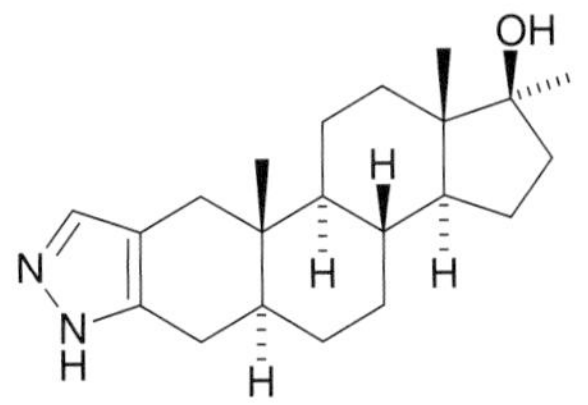

stanozolol

a. Explain why the nitrogen heterocycle—a pyrazole ring—is aromatic.
b. In what type of orbital is the lone pair on each N atom contained?
c. Draw all reasonable resonance structures for stanozolol.
d. Explain why the pK_a of the N – H bond in the pyrazole ring is comparable to the pK_a of the O – H bond, making it considerably more acidic than amines such as CH_3NH_2 (pK_a = 40).

Challenge Problems

17.63 Explain why **A** is aromatic but **B** is not aromatic.

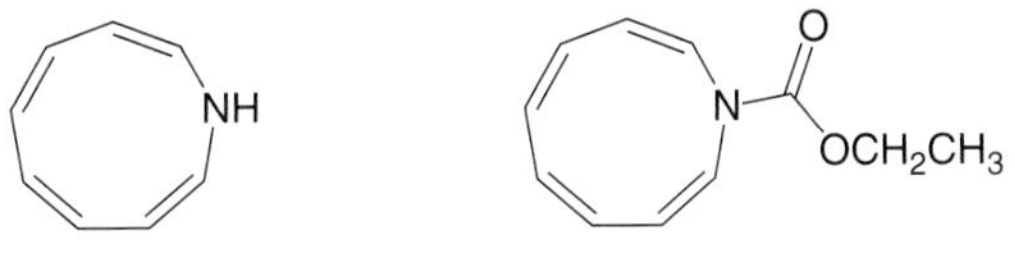

A **B**

17.64 Use the observed ^{1}H NMR data to decide whether **C** and its dianion are aromatic, antiaromatic, or not aromatic. **C** shows NMR signals at –4.25 (6 H) and 8.14–8.67 (10 H) ppm. The dianion of **C** shows NMR signals at –3 (10 H) and 21 (6 H) ppm. Why are the signals shifted upfield (or downfield) to such a large extent?

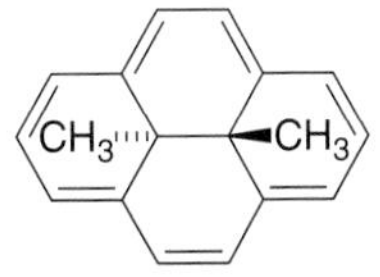

C

17.65 Explain why compound **A** is much more stable than compound **B.**

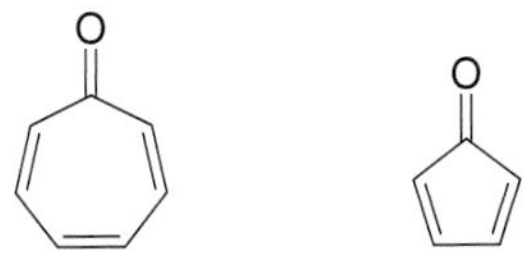

A **B**

17.66 (*R*)-Carvone, the major component of the oil of spearmint, undergoes acid-catalyzed isomerization to carvacrol, a major component of the oil of thyme. Draw a stepwise mechanism and explain why this isomerization occurs.

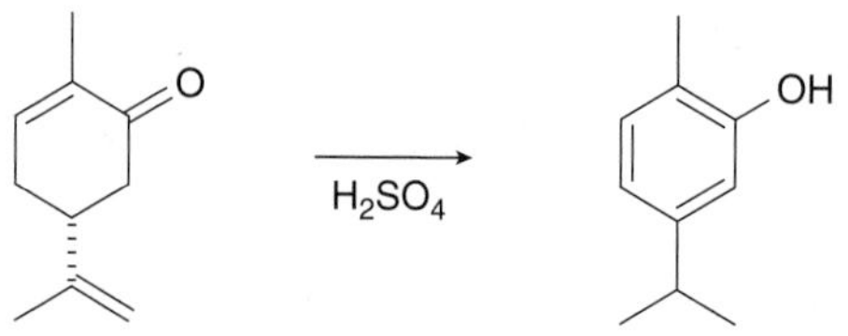

(*R*)-carvone   carvacrol

17.67 Explain why triphenylene resembles benzene in that it does not undergo addition reactions with Br_2, but phenanthrene reacts with Br_2 to yield the addition product drawn. (Hint: Draw resonance structures for both triphenylene and phenanthrene, and use them to determine how delocalized each π bond is.)

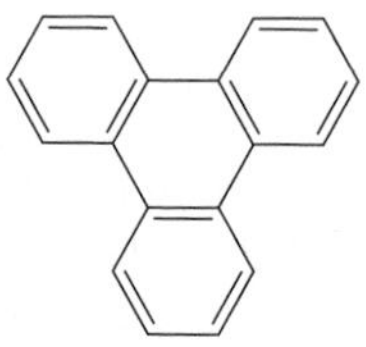

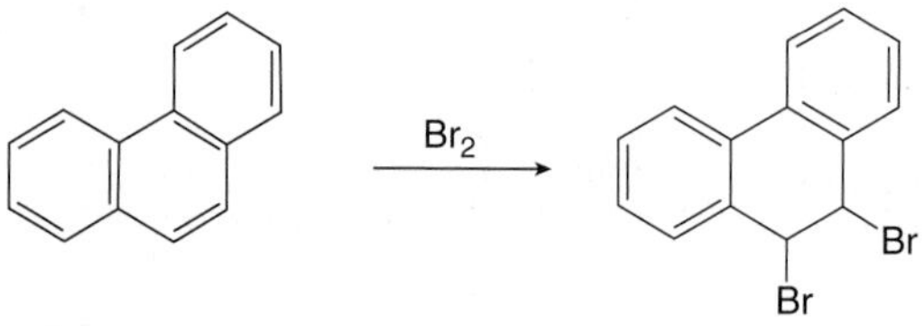

triphenylene   phenanthrene

17.68 Although benzene itself absorbs at 128 ppm in its ^{13}C NMR spectrum, the carbons of substituted benzenes absorb either upfield or downfield from this value depending on the substituent. Explain the observed values for the carbon ortho to the given substituent in the monosubstituted benzene derivatives **X** and **Y.**

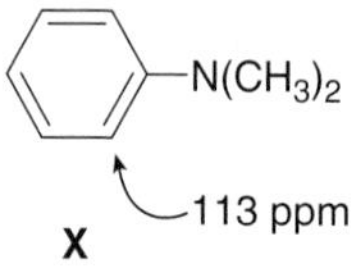

X

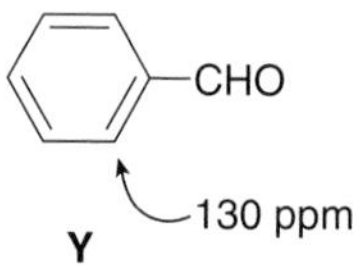

Y

Reactions of Aromatic Compounds

18

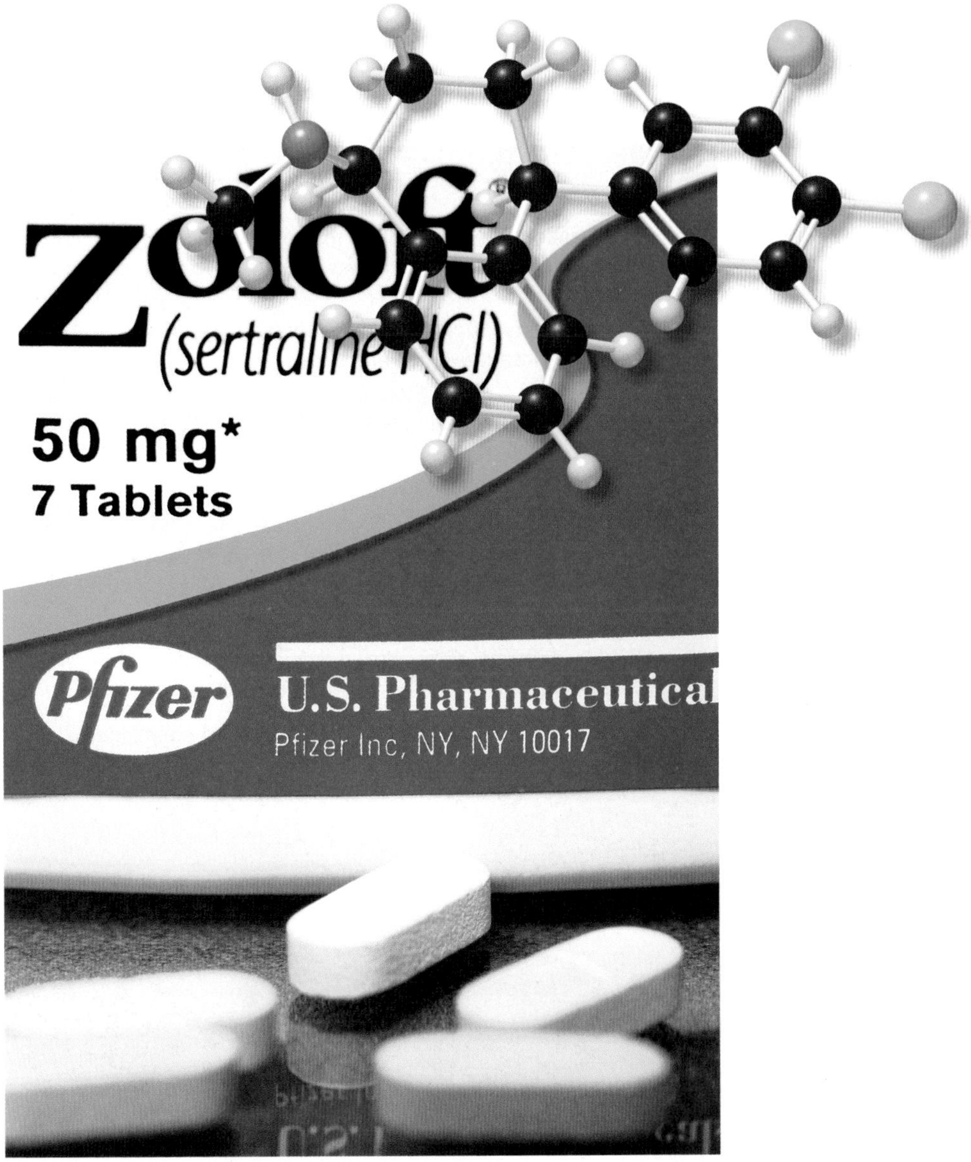

18.1 Electrophilic aromatic substitution
18.2 The general mechanism
18.3 Halogenation
18.4 Nitration and sulfonation
18.5 Friedel–Crafts alkylation and Friedel–Crafts acylation
18.6 Substituted benzenes
18.7 Electrophilic aromatic substitution of substituted benzenes
18.8 Why substituents activate or deactivate a benzene ring
18.9 Orientation effects in substituted benzenes
18.10 Limitations on electrophilic substitution reactions with substituted benzenes
18.11 Disubstituted benzenes
18.12 Synthesis of benzene derivatives
18.13 Nucleophilic aromatic substitution
18.14 Halogenation of alkyl benzenes
18.15 Oxidation and reduction of substituted benzenes
18.16 Multistep synthesis

Sertraline (trade name Zoloft) belongs to the class of antidepressants called SSRIs—selective serotonin reuptake inhibitors. Sertraline is effective because it increases the concentration of the neurotransmitter serotonin in the brain. Serotonin plays a key role in mood, sleep, and temperature regulation, and a deficiency of serotonin causes depression. A key step in the synthesis of sertraline involves carbon–carbon bond formation using electrophilic aromatic substitution, the most common reaction of aromatic compounds discussed in Chapter 18.

Chapter 18 discusses the chemical reactions of benzene and other aromatic compounds. Although aromatic rings are unusually stable, making benzene unreactive in most of the reactions discussed so far, benzene acts as a nucleophile with certain electrophiles, yielding substitution products with an intact aromatic ring.

We begin with the basic features and mechanism of electrophilic aromatic substitution (Sections 18.1–18.5), the most prevalent reaction of benzene. Next, we discuss the electrophilic aromatic substitution of substituted benzenes (Sections 18.6–18.12), and conclude with nucleophilic aromatic substitution and other useful reactions of benzene derivatives (Sections 18.13–18.15). The ability to interconvert resonance structures and evaluate their relative stabilities is crucial to understanding this material.

18.1 Electrophilic Aromatic Substitution

Based on its structure and properties, what kinds of reactions should benzene undergo? Are any of its bonds particularly weak? Does it have electron-rich or electron-deficient atoms?

- **Benzene has six π electrons delocalized in six *p* orbitals that overlap above and below the plane of the ring. These loosely held π electrons make the benzene ring electron rich, and so it reacts with electrophiles.**
- **Because benzene's six π electrons satisfy Hückel's rule, benzene is especially stable. Reactions that keep the aromatic ring intact are therefore favored.**

As a result, **the characteristic reaction of benzene is *electrophilic aromatic substitution*—a hydrogen atom is replaced by an electrophile.**

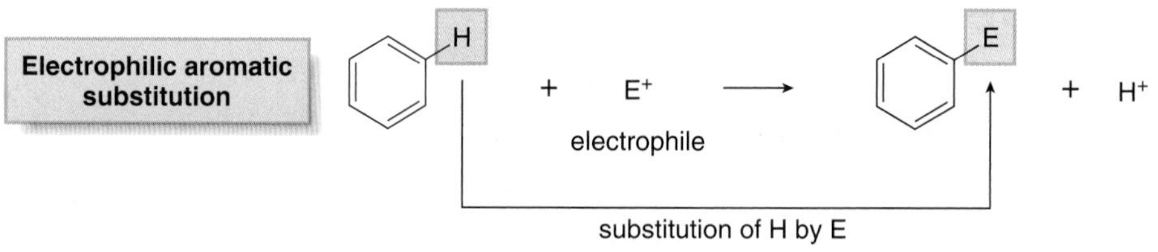

Benzene does *not* undergo addition reactions like other unsaturated hydrocarbons, because addition would yield a product that is not aromatic. Substitution of a hydrogen, on the other hand, keeps the aromatic ring intact.

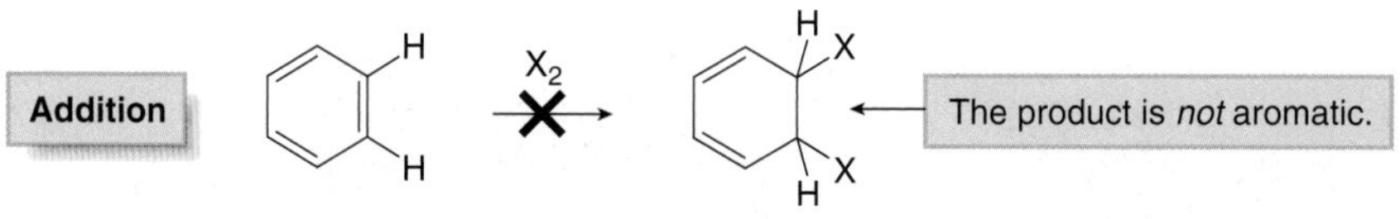

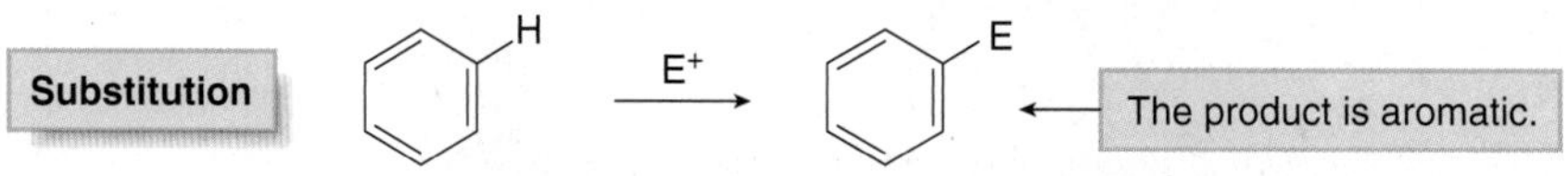

Five specific examples of electrophilic aromatic substitution are shown in Figure 18.1. The basic mechanism, discussed in Section 18.2, is the same in all five cases. The reactions differ only in the identity of the electrophile, E^+.

Problem 18.1 Why is benzene less reactive toward electrophiles than an alkene, even though it has more π electrons than an alkene (six versus two)?

Figure 18.1
Five examples of electrophilic aromatic substitution

Reaction	Electrophile

[1] Halogenation—Replacement of H by X (Cl or Br)

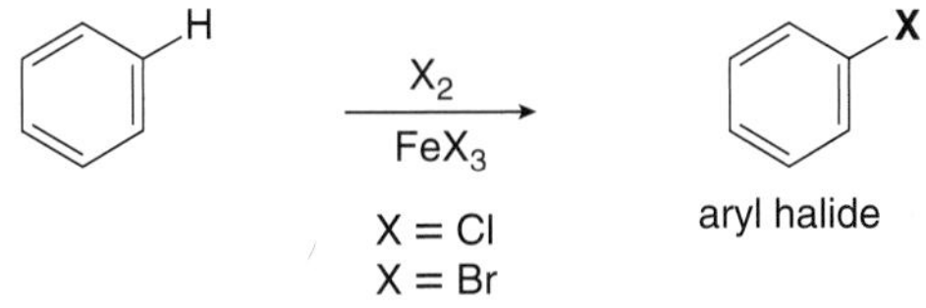

$E^+ = Cl^+$ or Br^+

[2] Nitration—Replacement of H by NO_2

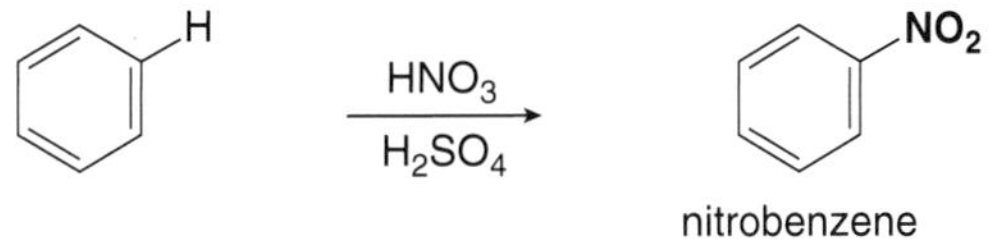

$E^+ = \overset{+}{N}O_2$

[3] Sulfonation—Replacement of H by SO_3H

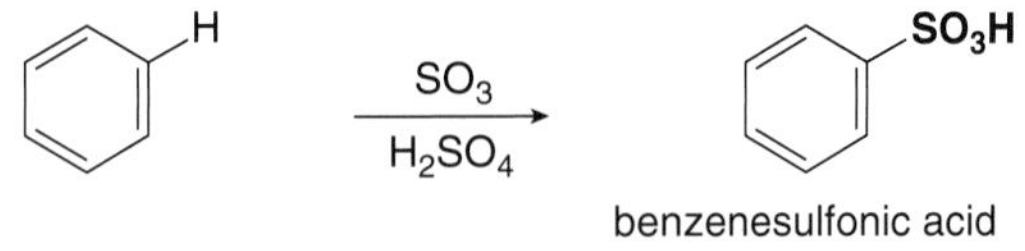

$E^+ = \overset{+}{S}O_3H$

[4] Friedel–Crafts alkylation—Replacement of H by R

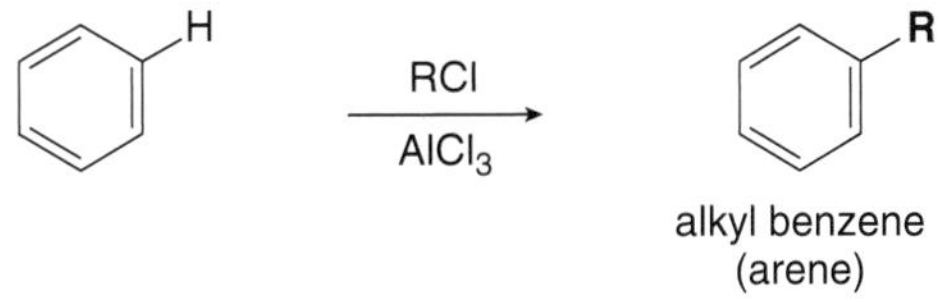

$E^+ = R^+$

[5] Friedel–Crafts acylation—Replacement of H by RCO

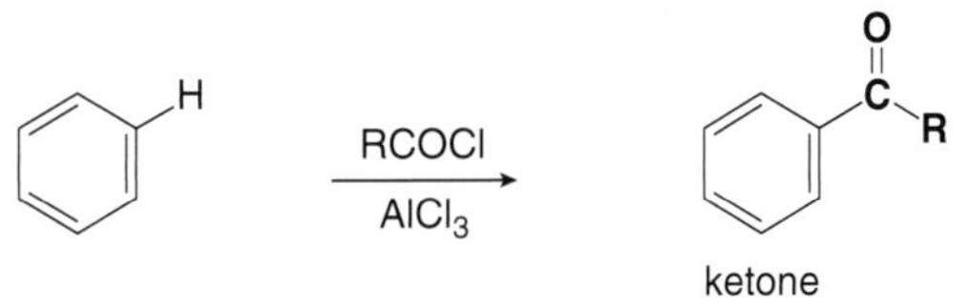

$E^+ = R\overset{+}{C}O$

Friedel–Crafts alkylation and acylation, named for Charles Friedel and James Crafts who discovered the reactions in the nineteenth century, form new carbon–carbon bonds.

18.2 The General Mechanism

No matter what electrophile is used, all electrophilic aromatic substitution reactions occur via a **two-step mechanism:** addition of the electrophile E^+ to form a resonance-stabilized carbocation, followed by deprotonation with base, as shown in Mechanism 18.1.

The first step in electrophilic aromatic substitution forms a carbocation, for which three resonance structures can be drawn. To help keep track of the location of the positive charge:

- **Always draw in the H atom on the carbon bonded to E. This serves as a reminder that it is the only sp^3 hybridized carbon in the carbocation intermediate.**

- **Notice that the positive charge in a given resonance structure is always located ortho or para to the new C–E bond. In the hybrid, therefore, the charge is delocalized over three atoms of the ring.**

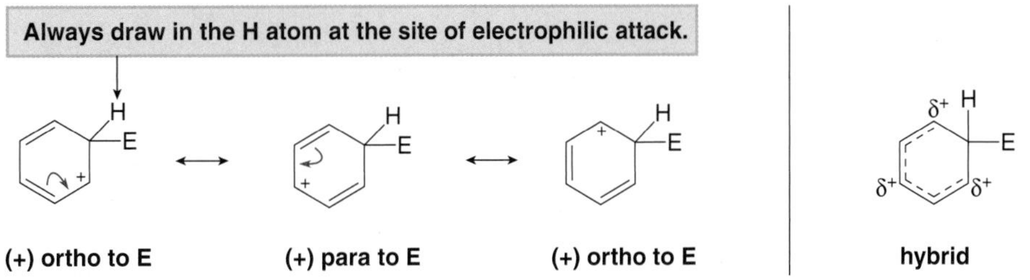

Mechanism 18.1 General Mechanism—Electrophilic Aromatic Substitution

Step [1] Addition of the electrophile (E^+) to form a carbocation

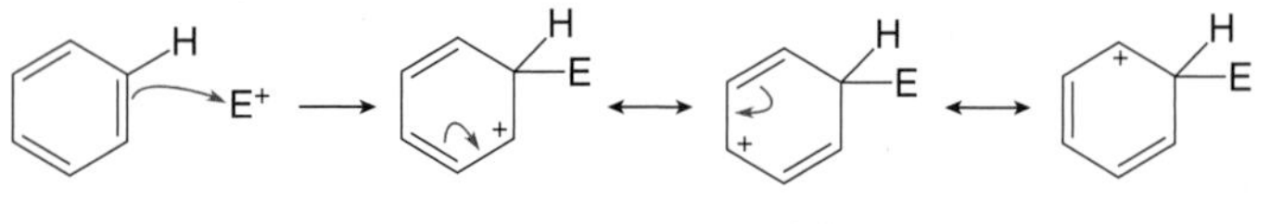

- Addition of the electrophile (E^+) forms a new C–E bond using two π electrons from the benzene ring, and generating a carbocation. This carbocation intermediate is not aromatic, but it is resonance stabilized—**three resonance structures can be drawn.**
- Step [1] is rate-determining because the aromaticity of the benzene ring is lost.

Step [2] Loss of a proton to re-form the aromatic ring

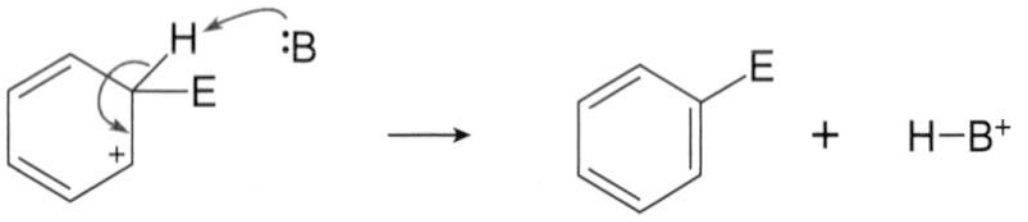

- In Step [2], a base (B:) removes the proton from the carbon bearing the electrophile, thus re-forming the aromatic ring. This step is fast because the aromaticity of the benzene ring is restored.
- Any of the three resonance structures of the carbocation intermediate can be used to draw the product. The choice of resonance structure affects how curved arrows are drawn, but not the identity of the product.

This two-step mechanism for electrophilic aromatic substitution applies to all of the electrophiles in Figure 18.1. **The net result of addition of an electrophile (E^+) followed by elimination of a proton (H^+) is substitution of E for H.**

The energy changes in electrophilic aromatic substitution are shown in Figure 18.2. The mechanism consists of two steps, so the energy diagram has two energy barriers. Because the transition state of the first step is higher in energy, it is rate-determining.

Problem 18.2 In Step [2] of Mechanism 18.1, loss of a proton to form the substitution product was drawn using one resonance structure only. Use curved arrows to show how the other two resonance structures can be converted to the substitution product (PhE) by removal of a proton with :B.

Figure 18.2
Energy diagram for electrophilic aromatic substitution: $PhH + E^+ \rightarrow PhE + H^+$

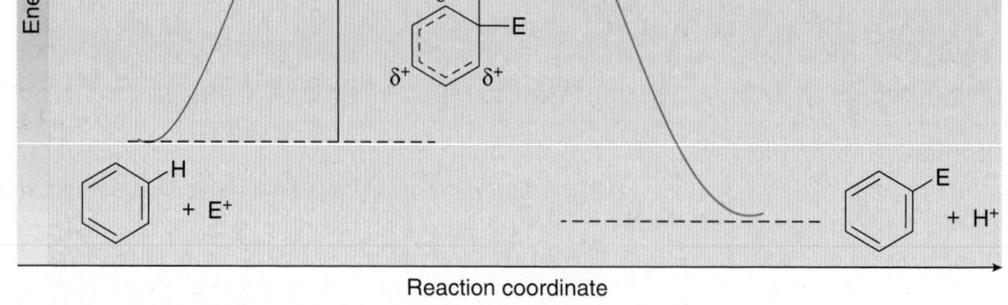

- The mechanism has two steps, so there are two energy barriers.
- Step [1] is rate-determining; its transition state is at higher energy.

18.3 Halogenation

The general mechanism outlined in Mechanism 18.1 can now be applied to each of the five specific examples of electrophilic aromatic substitution shown in Figure 18.1. For each mechanism we must learn how to generate a specific electrophile. This step is *different* with each electrophile. Then, the electrophile reacts with benzene by the two-step process of Mechanism 18.1. These two steps are the *same* for all five reactions.

In **halogenation,** benzene reacts with Cl_2 or Br_2 in the presence of a Lewis acid catalyst, such as $FeCl_3$ or $FeBr_3$, to give the **aryl halides** chlorobenzene or bromobenzene, respectively. Analogous reactions with I_2 and F_2 are not synthetically useful because I_2 is too unreactive and F_2 reacts too violently.

Chlorination

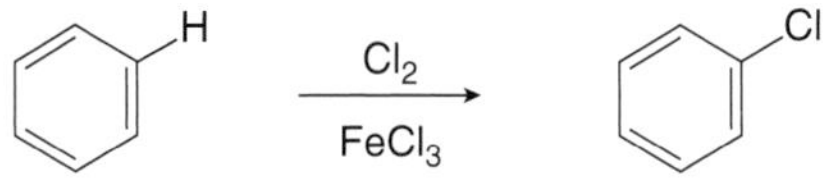

H
Cl2
FeCl3
Cl

chlorobenzene

Bromination

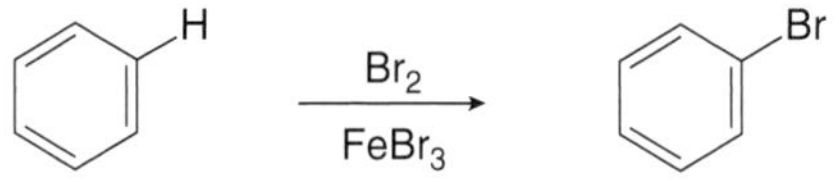

H
Br2
FeBr3
Br

bromobenzene

In bromination (Mechanism 18.2), the Lewis acid $FeBr_3$ reacts with Br_2 to form a Lewis acid–base complex that weakens and polarizes the Br–Br bond, making it more electrophilic. This reaction is Step [1] of the mechanism for the bromination of benzene. The remaining two steps follow directly from the general mechanism for electrophilic aromatic substitution: addition of the electrophile (Br^+ in this case) forms a resonance-stabilized carbocation, and loss of a proton regenerates the aromatic ring.

Mechanism 18.2 Bromination of Benzene

Step [1] Generation of the electrophile

:Br—Br: + FeBr3
:Br—Br—FeBr3

Lewis base Lewis acid electrophile (serves as a source of Br^+)

- Lewis acid–base reaction of Br_2 with $FeBr_3$ forms a species with a weakened and polarized Br–Br bond. This adduct serves as a source of Br^+ in the next step.

Step [2] Addition of the electrophile to form a carbocation

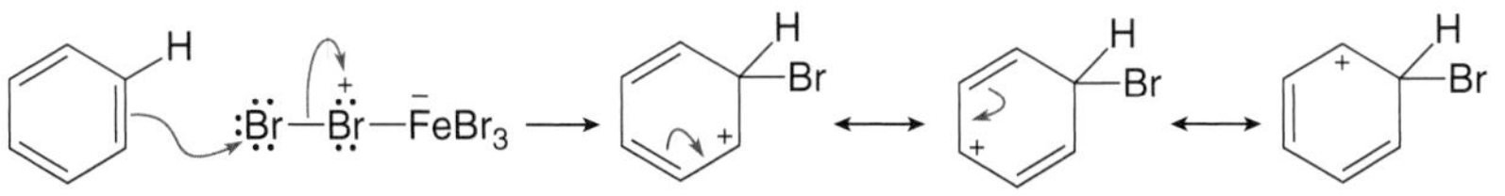

H
:Br—Br—FeBr3
H
Br
H
Br
H
Br

resonance-stabilized carbocation
+ $FeBr_4^-$

- Addition of the electrophile forms a new C–Br bond and generates a carbocation. This carbocation intermediate is resonance stabilized—**three resonance structures can be drawn.**
- The $FeBr_4^-$ also formed in this reaction is the base used in Step [3].

Step [3] Loss of a proton to re-form the aromatic ring

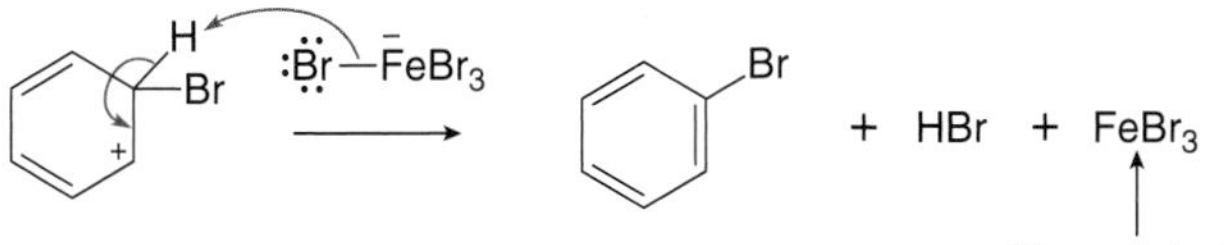

H
Br
:Br—FeBr3
Br
+ HBr + FeBr3

The catalyst is regenerated.

- $FeBr_4^-$ removes the proton from the carbon bearing the Br, thus re-forming the aromatic ring.
- $FeBr_3$, a catalyst, is also regenerated for another reaction cycle.

Figure 18.3 Examples of biologically active aryl chlorides

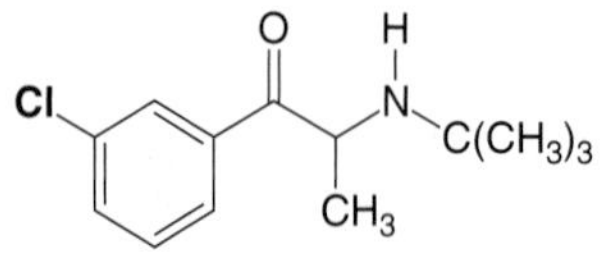

Generic name: **bupropion**
Trade names: **Wellbutrin, Zyban**
antidepressant,
also used to reduce nicotine cravings

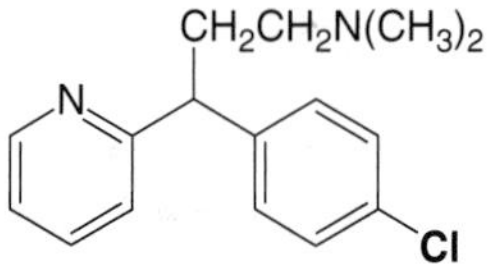

chlorpheniramine
antihistamine

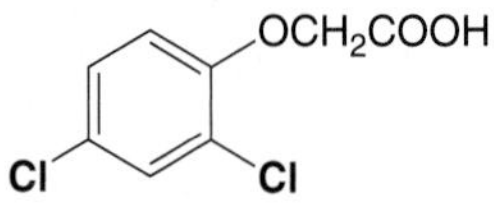

2,4-D
2,4-dichlorophenoxy-acetic acid
herbicide

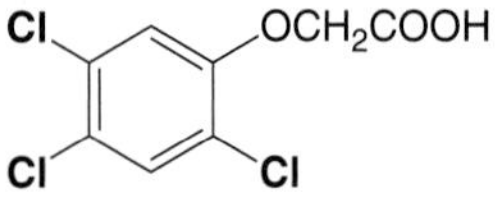

2,4,5-T
2,4,5-trichlorophenoxy-acetic acid
herbicide

the active components in **Agent Orange,** a defoliant used in the Vietnam War

Herbicides were used extensively during the Vietnam War to defoliate dense jungle areas. The concentration of certain herbicide by-products in the soil remains high today.

Chlorination proceeds by a similar mechanism. Reactions that introduce a halogen substituent on a benzene ring are widely used, and many halogenated aromatic compounds with a range of biological activity have been synthesized, as shown in Figure 18.3.

Problem 18.3 Draw a detailed mechanism for the chlorination of benzene using Cl_2 and $FeCl_3$.

18.4 Nitration and Sulfonation

Nitration and **sulfonation** of benzene introduce two different functional groups on an aromatic ring. Nitration is an especially useful reaction because a nitro group can then be reduced to an NH_2 group, a common benzene substituent, in a reaction discussed in Section 18.15.

Nitration

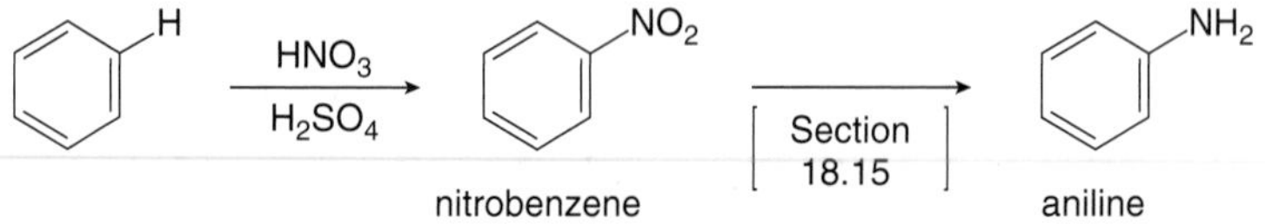

nitrobenzene
aniline

Sulfonation

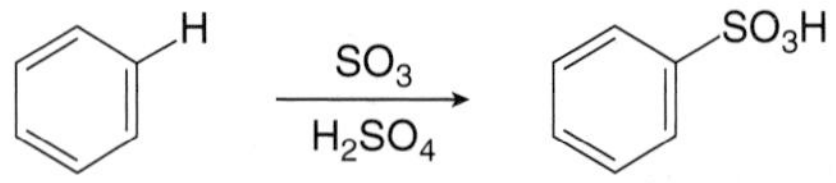

benzenesulfonic acid

Generation of the electrophile in both nitration and sulfonation requires strong acid. In **nitration,** the electrophile is $^+NO_2$ (the **nitronium ion**), formed by protonation of HNO_3 followed by loss of water (Mechanism 18.3).

Mechanism 18.3 Formation of the Nitronium Ion ($^+NO_2$) for Nitration

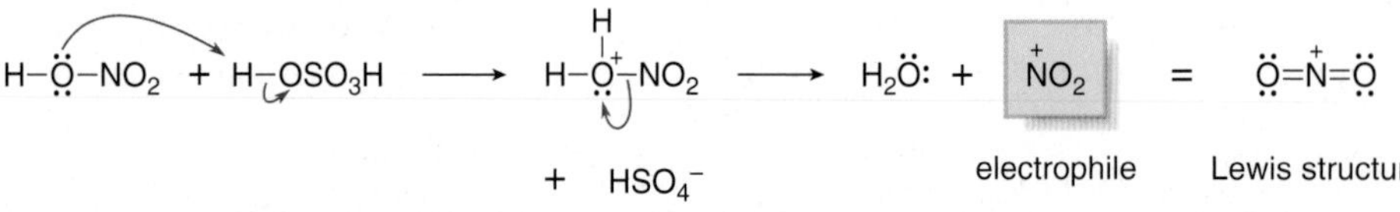

electrophile
Lewis structure

In **sulfonation,** protonation of sulfur trioxide, SO_3, forms a positively charged sulfur species ($^+SO_3H$) that acts as an electrophile (Mechanism 18.4).

Mechanism 18.4 Formation of the Electrophile $^+SO_3H$ for Sulfonation

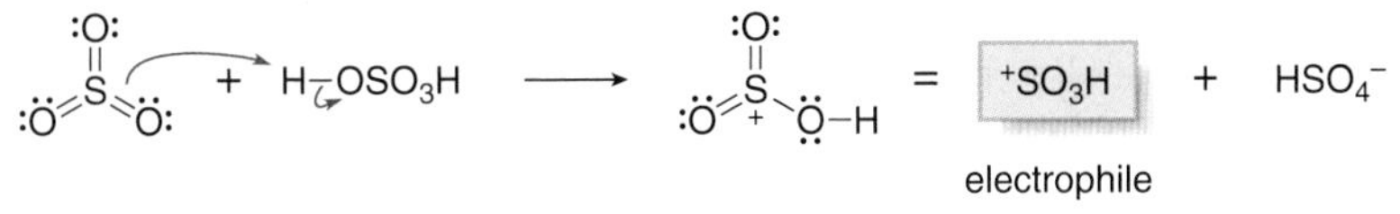

+ H–OSO3H
= +SO3H + HSO4–
electrophile

These steps illustrate how to generate the electrophile E^+ for nitration and sulfonation, the process that begins any mechanism for electrophilic aromatic substitution. To complete either of these mechanisms, you must replace the electrophile E^+ by either $^+NO_2$ or $^+SO_3H$ in the general mechanism (Mechanism 18.1). Thus, **the two-step sequence that replaces H by E is the same regardless of E^+.** This is shown in Sample Problem 18.1 using the reaction of benzene with the nitronium ion.

Sample Problem 18.1 Draw a stepwise mechanism for the nitration of a benzene ring.

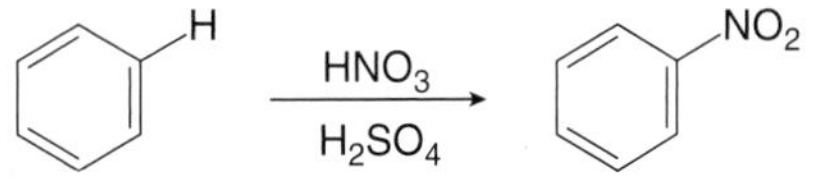

H
HNO3
H2SO4
NO2

nitrobenzene

Solution

We must first generate the electrophile and then write the two-step mechanism for electrophilic aromatic substitution using it.

Generation of the electrophile $^+NO_2$

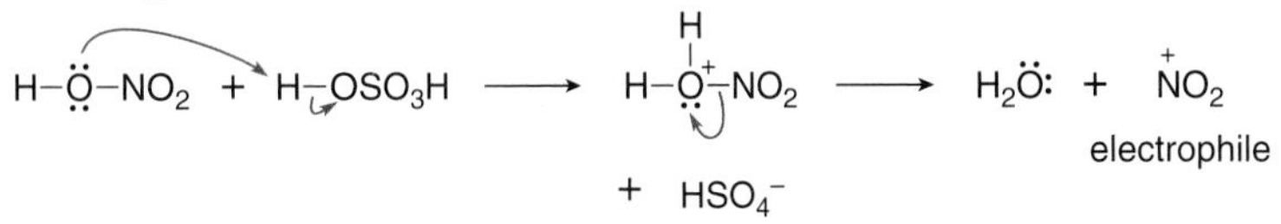

H–Ö–NO2 + H–OSO3H
H–O–NO2
+ HSO4–
H2Ö: + NO2
electrophile

Two-step mechanism for substitution

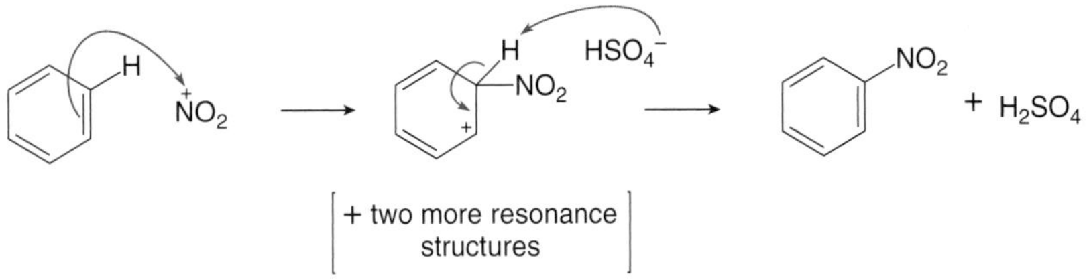

H
NO2
HSO4–
+ H2SO4
+ two more resonance structures

Any species with a lone pair of electrons can be used to remove the proton in the last step. In this case, the mechanism is drawn with HSO_4^-, formed when $^+NO_2$ is generated as the electrophile.

Problem 18.4 Draw a stepwise mechanism for the sulfonation of an alkyl benzene such as **A** to form a substituted benzenesulfonic acid **B.** Treatment of **B** with base forms a sodium salt **C** that can be used as a synthetic detergent to clean away dirt (see Problem 3.15).

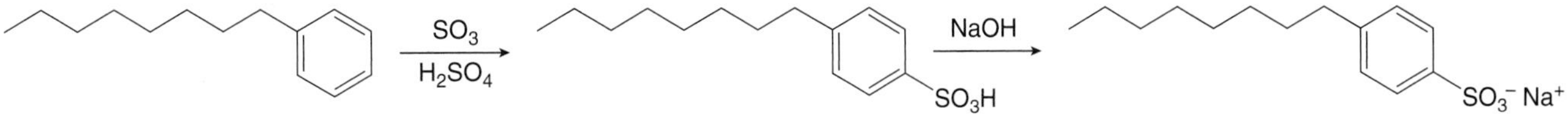

SO3
H2SO4
NaOH
SO3H
SO3– Na+

A **B** synthetic detergent **C**

18.5 Friedel–Crafts Alkylation and Friedel–Crafts Acylation

Friedel–Crafts alkylation and **Friedel–Crafts acylation** form new carbon–carbon bonds.

18.5A General Features

In **Friedel–Crafts alkylation,** treatment of benzene with an alkyl halide and a Lewis acid ($AlCl_3$) forms an alkyl benzene. This reaction is an **alkylation** because it results in transfer of an alkyl group from one atom to another (from Cl to benzene).

Friedel–Crafts alkylation

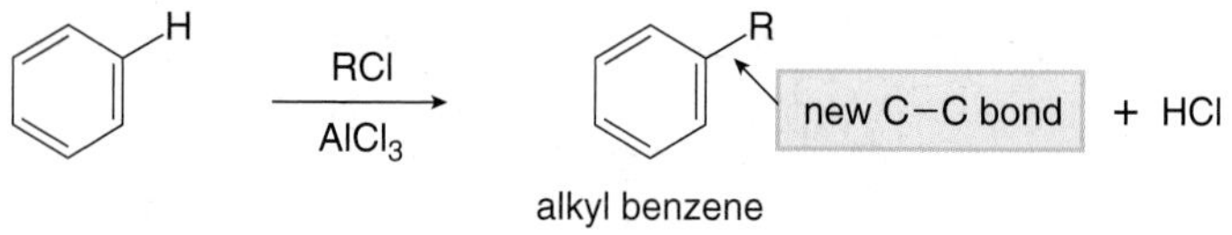

Examples

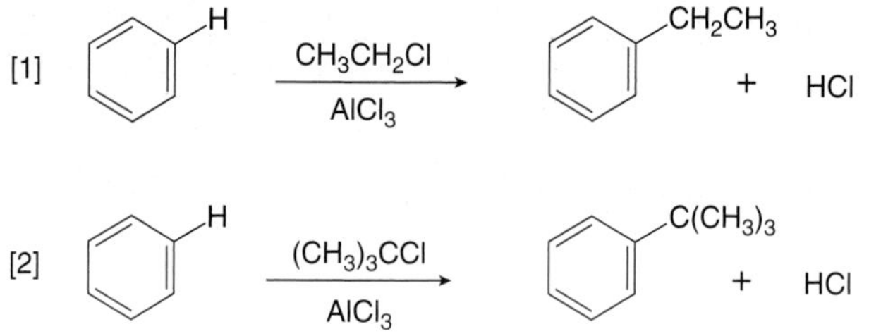

In **Friedel–Crafts acylation,** a benzene ring is treated with an **acid chloride** (RCOCl) and $AlCl_3$ to form a ketone. Because the new group bonded to the benzene ring is called an **acyl group,** the transfer of an acyl group from one atom to another is an **acylation.**

Friedel–Crafts acylation

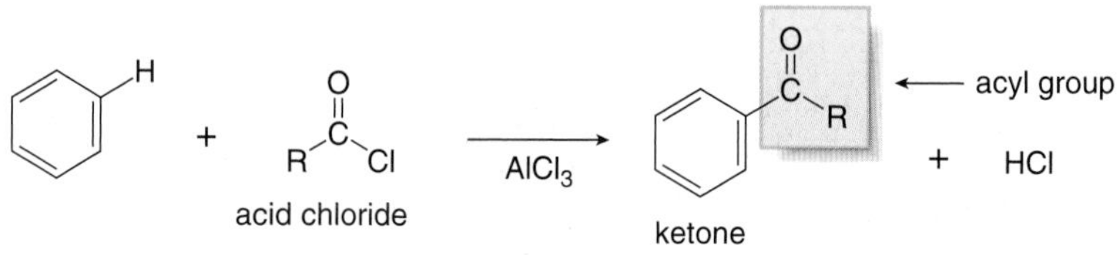

Example

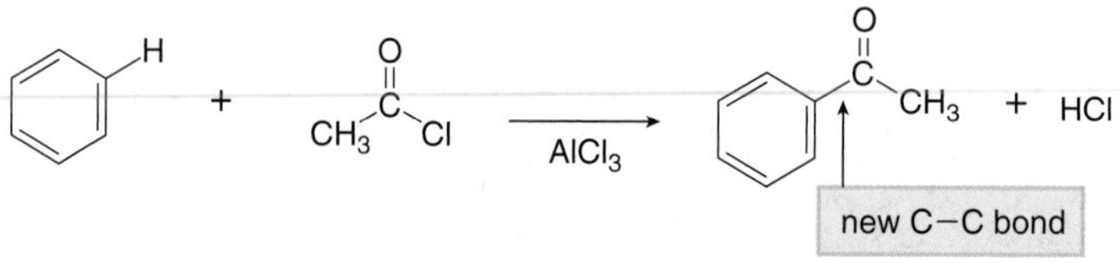

Acid chlorides are also called **acyl chlorides.**

Problem 18.5 What product is formed when benzene is treated with each organic halide in the presence of $AlCl_3$?

a. $(CH_3)_2CHCl$ b. 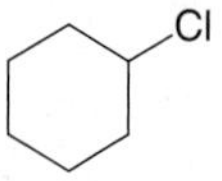

c. 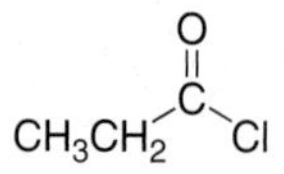

Problem 18.6 What acid chloride would be needed to prepare each of the following ketones from benzene using a Friedel–Crafts acylation?

a. 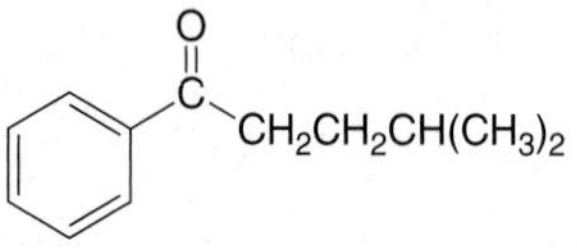

b. 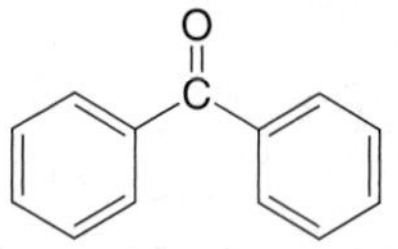

c. 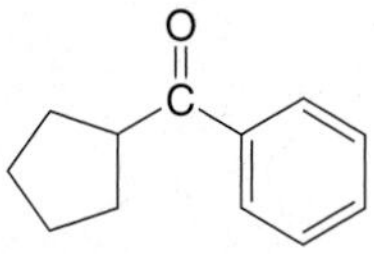

18.5B Mechanism

The mechanisms of alkylation and acylation proceed in a manner analogous to those for halogenation, nitration, and sulfonation. The unique feature in each reaction is how the electrophile is generated.

In **Friedel–Crafts alkylation,** the Lewis acid $AlCl_3$ reacts with the alkyl chloride to form a Lewis acid–base complex, illustrated with CH_3CH_2Cl and $(CH_3)_3CCl$ as alkyl chlorides. The identity of the alkyl chloride determines the exact course of the reaction as shown in Mechanism 18.5.

Mechanism 18.5 Formation of the Electrophile in Friedel–Crafts Alkylation—Two Possibilities

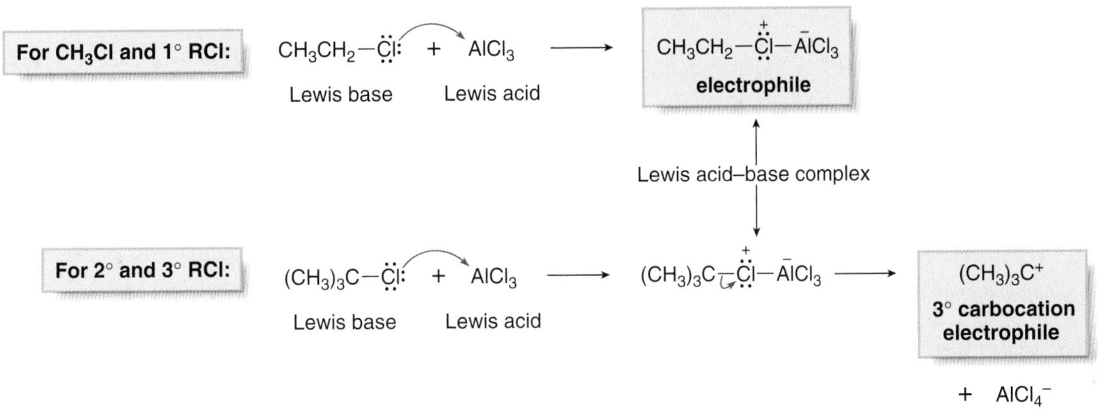

- **For CH_3Cl and 1° RCl, the Lewis acid–base complex itself serves as the electrophile for electrophilic aromatic substitution.**
- **With 2° and 3° RCl, the Lewis acid–base complex reacts further to give a 2° or 3° carbocation, which serves as the electrophile. Carbocation formation occurs only with 2° and 3° alkyl chlorides, because they afford more stable carbocations.**

In either case, the electrophile goes on to react with benzene in the two-step mechanism characteristic of electrophilic aromatic substitution, illustrated in Mechanism 18.6 using the 3° carbocation, $(CH_3)_3C^+$.

Mechanism 18.6 Friedel–Crafts Alkylation Using a 3° Carbocation

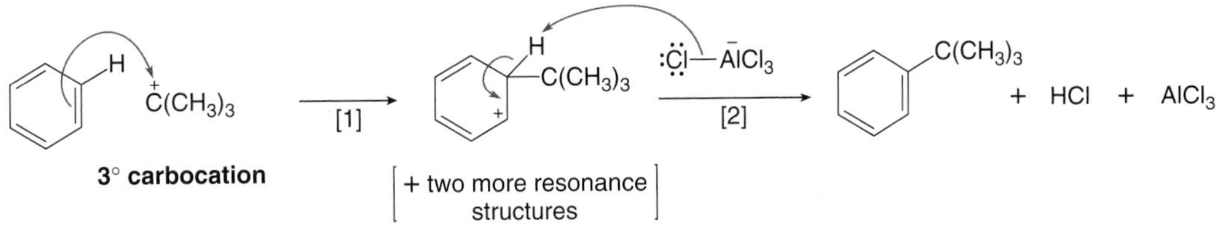

- Addition of the electrophile (a 3° carbocation) forms a new carbon–carbon bond in Step [1].
- $AlCl_4^-$ removes a proton on the carbon bearing the new substituent, thus re-forming the aromatic ring in Step [2].

In **Friedel–Crafts acylation,** the Lewis acid $AlCl_3$ ionizes the carbon–halogen bond of the acid chloride, thus forming a positively charged carbon electrophile called an **acylium ion,** which is resonance stabilized (Mechanism 18.7). The positively charged carbon atom of the acylium ion then goes on to react with benzene in the two-step mechanism of electrophilic aromatic substitution.

Mechanism 18.7 Formation of the Electrophile in Friedel–Crafts Acylation

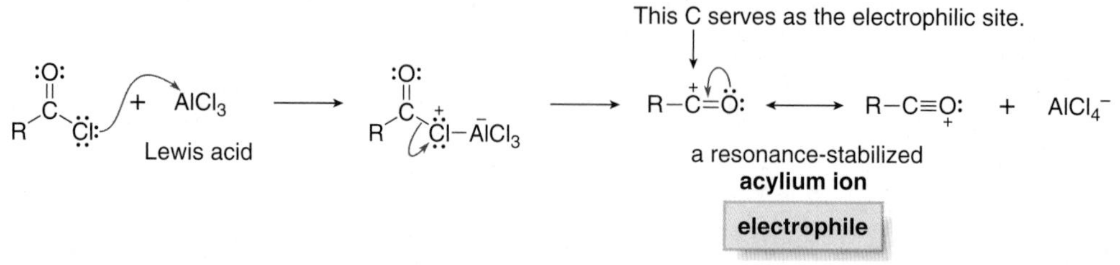
This C serves as the electrophilic site.
Lewis acid
a resonance-stabilized
acylium ion
electrophile

To complete the mechanism for acylation, insert the electrophile into the general mechanism and draw the last two steps, as illustrated in Sample Problem 18.2.

Sample Problem 18.2 Draw a stepwise mechanism for the following Friedel–Crafts acylation.

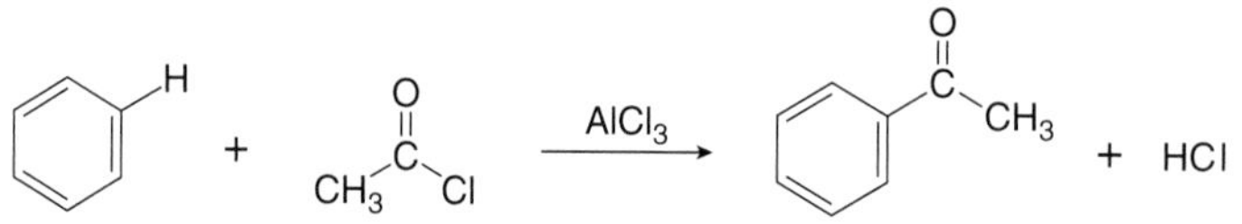

Solution

First generate the acylium ion, and then write the two-step mechanism for electrophilic aromatic substitution using it for the electrophile.

Generation of the electrophile ($(CH_3CO)^+$)

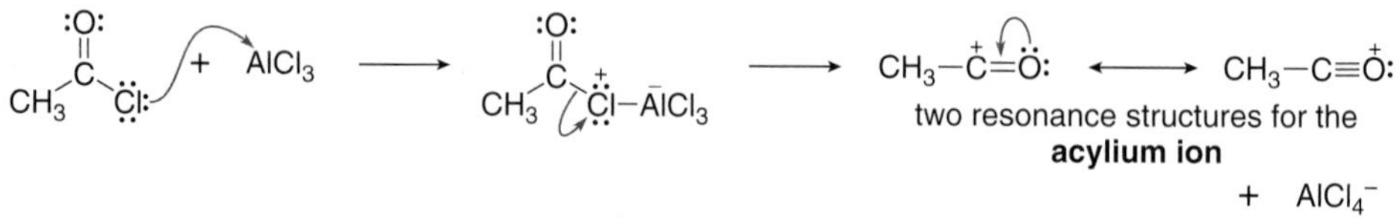
two resonance structures for the
acylium ion

Two-step mechanism for substitution

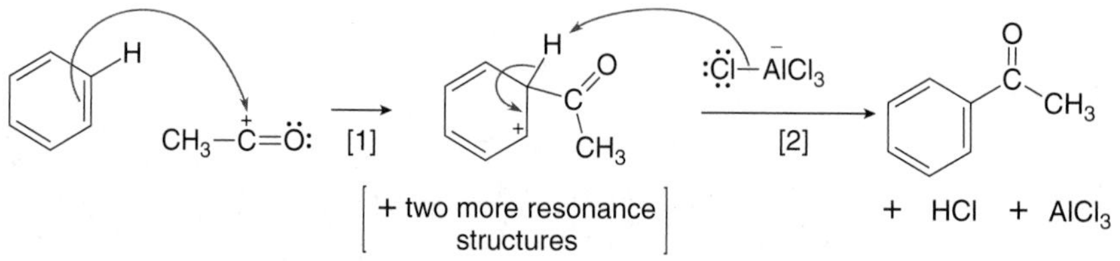
[1]
[2]
+ two more resonance structures
+ HCl + AlCl3

18.5C Other Facts About Friedel–Crafts Alkylation

Three additional facts about Friedel–Crafts alkylations must be kept in mind.

[1] Vinyl halides and aryl halides do *not* react in Friedel–Crafts alkylation.

Most Friedel–Crafts reactions involve carbocation electrophiles. Because the carbocations derived from vinyl halides and aryl halides are highly unstable and do not readily form, these organic halides do *not* undergo Friedel–Crafts alkylation.

Unreactive halides in the Friedel–Crafts alkylation

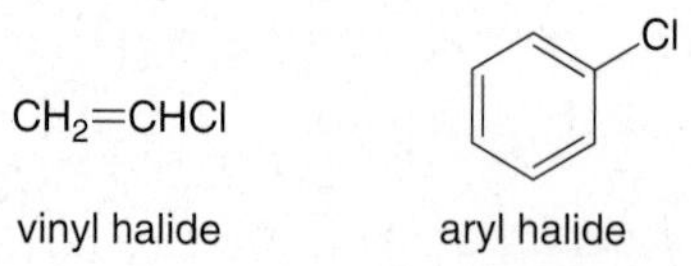
vinyl halide
aryl halide

Problem 18.7 Which halides are unreactive in a Friedel–Crafts alkylation reaction?

a. 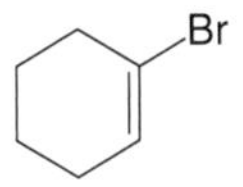
Br

b. 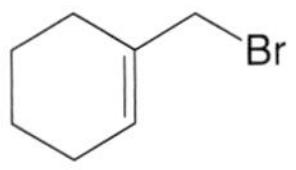
Br

c. 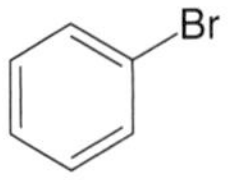
Br

d. 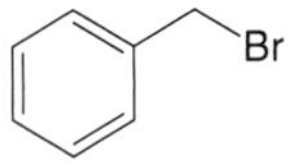
Br

[2] Rearrangements can occur.

The Friedel–Crafts reaction can yield products having rearranged carbon skeletons when 1° and 2° alkyl halides are used as starting materials, as shown in Equations [1] and [2]. In both reactions, the carbon atom bonded to the halogen in the starting material (labeled in red) is not bonded to the benzene ring in the product, thus indicating that a rearrangement has occurred.

Recall from Section 9.9 that a 1,2-shift converts a less stable carbocation to a more stable carbocation by shift of a hydrogen atom or an alkyl group.

[1] 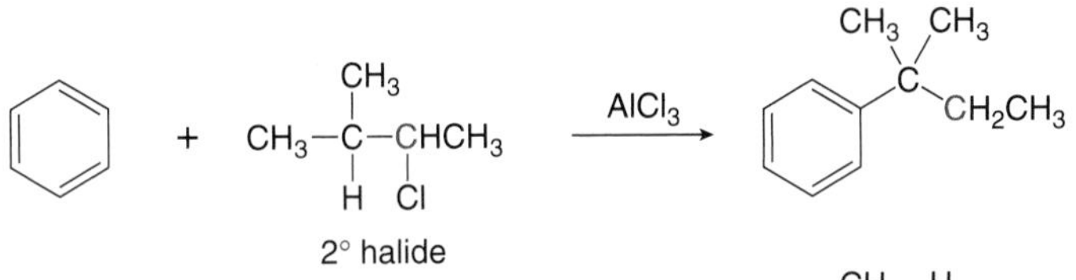
CH3
CH3–C–CHCH3
H Cl
2° halide
AlCl3
CH3 CH3
C
CH2CH3

[2] 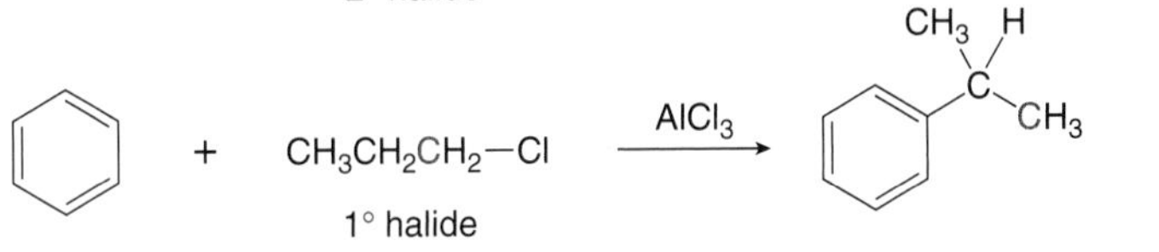
CH3CH2CH2–Cl
1° halide
AlCl3
CH3 H
C
CH3

The result in Equation [1] is explained by a carbocation rearrangement involving a 1,2-hydride shift: **the less stable 2° carbocation (formed from the 2° halide) rearranges to a more stable 3° carbocation,** as illustrated in Mechanism 18.8.

Mechanism 18.8 Friedel–Crafts Alkylation Involving Carbocation Rearrangement

Steps [1] and [2] Formation of a 2° carbocation

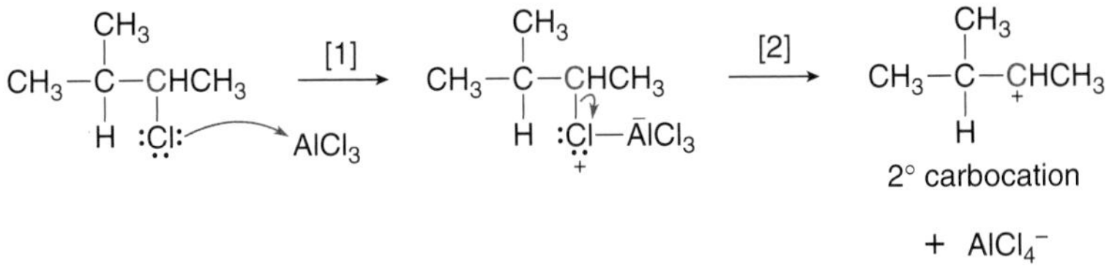
CH3
CH3–C–CHCH3
H :Cl:
[1]
AlCl3
CH3
CH3–C–CHCH3
H :Cl–AlCl3
[2]
CH3
CH3–C–CHCH3
H
2° carbocation
+ AlCl4−

- Reaction of the alkyl chloride with $AlCl_3$ forms a complex that decomposes in Step [2] to form a **2° carbocation.**

Step [3] Carbocation rearrangement

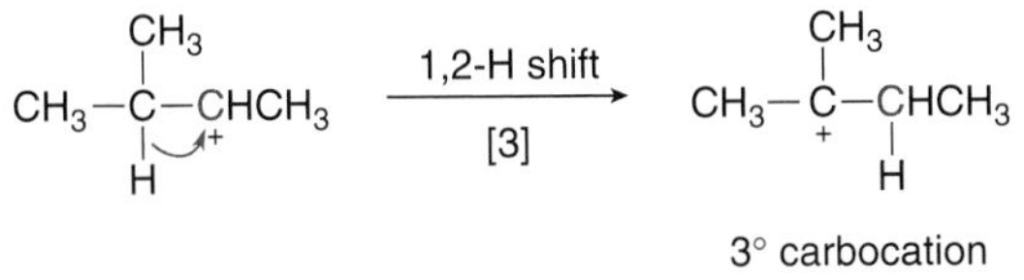
CH3
CH3–C–CHCH3
H
1,2-H shift
[3]
CH3
CH3–C–CHCH3
H
3° carbocation

- **1,2-Hydride shift** converts the less stable 2° carbocation to a more stable 3° carbocation.

Steps [4] and [5] Addition of the carbocation and loss of a proton

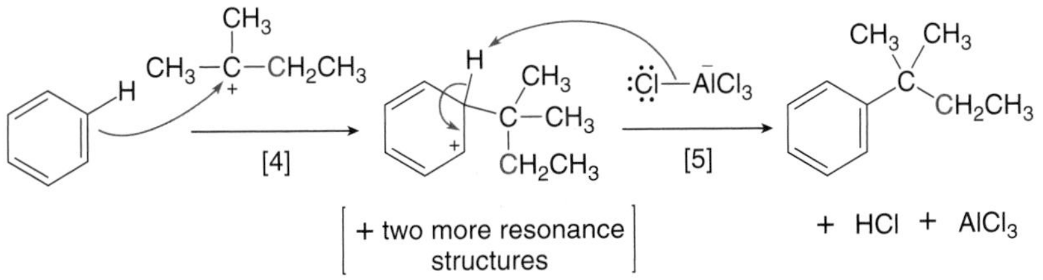
CH3
CH3–C–CH2CH3
H
[4]
H
CH3
C–CH3
CH2CH3
:Cl–AlCl3
[5]
CH3 CH3
C
CH2CH3
+ two more resonance structures
+ HCl + AlCl3

- Friedel–Crafts alkylation occurs by the usual two-step process: **addition of the carbocation** followed by **loss of a proton** to form the alkylated product.

Rearrangements can occur even when no free carbocation is formed initially. For example, the 1° alkyl chloride in Equation [2] forms a complex with $AlCl_3$, which does *not* decompose to an unstable 1° carbocation, as shown in Mechanism 18.9. Instead, a **1,2-hydride shift** forms a 2° carbocation, which then serves as the electrophile in the two-step mechanism for electrophilic aromatic substitution.

Mechanism 18.9 A Rearrangement Reaction Beginning with a 1° Alkyl Chloride

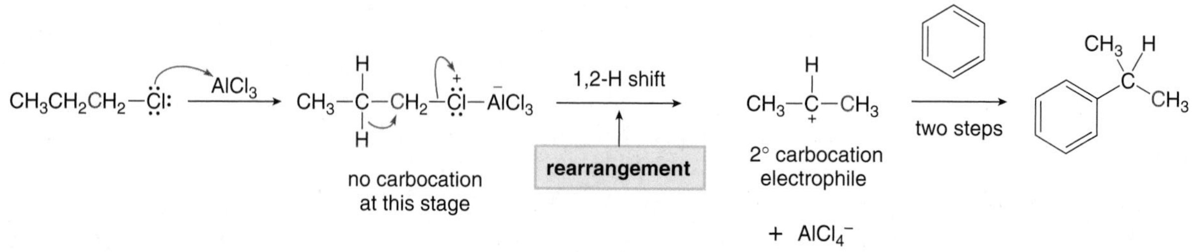

CH3CH2CH2—Cl:
AlCl3
CH3—C—CH2—Cl—AlCl3
no carbocation
at this stage
1,2-H shift
rearrangement
CH3—C—CH3
2° carbocation
electrophile
+ AlCl4−
two steps
CH3 H
CH3

Problem 18.8 Draw a stepwise mechanism for the following reaction.

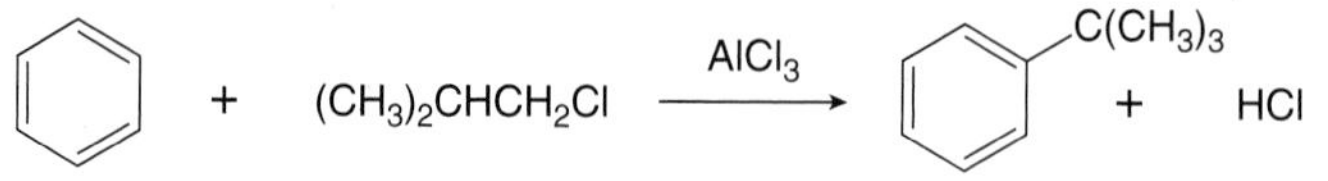

+ (CH3)2CHCH2Cl
AlCl3
C(CH3)3
+ HCl

[3] Other functional groups that form carbocations can also be used as starting materials.

Although Friedel–Crafts alkylation works well with alkyl halides, any compound that readily forms a carbocation can be used instead. The two most common alternatives are alkenes and alcohols, both of which afford carbocations in the presence of strong acid.

- **Protonation of an alkene forms a carbocation, which can then serve as an electrophile in a Friedel–Crafts alkylation.**

- **Protonation of an alcohol, followed by loss of water, likewise forms a carbocation.**

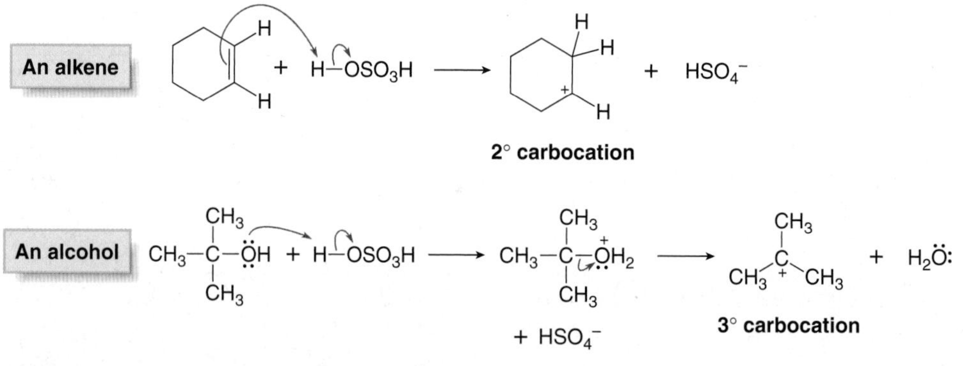

An alkene
+ H—OSO3H
+ HSO4−
2° carbocation
An alcohol
CH3—C—OH + H—OSO3H
CH3—C—OH2
+ HSO4−
+ H2O:
3° carbocation

Each carbocation can then go on to react with benzene to form a product of electrophilic aromatic substitution. For example:

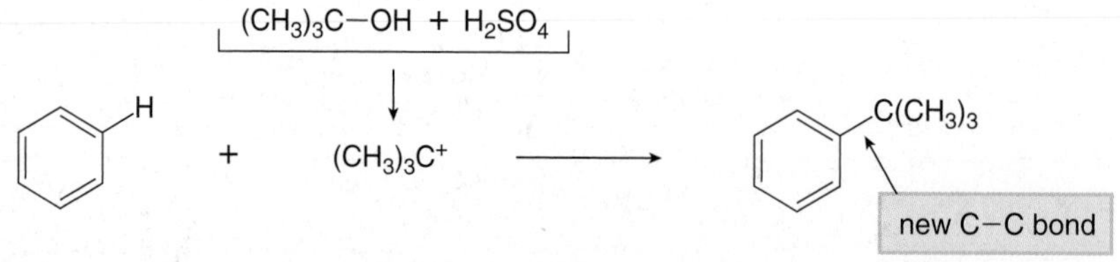

(CH3)3C—OH + H2SO4
+ (CH3)3C+
C(CH3)3
new C—C bond

Problem 18.9 Draw the product of each reaction.

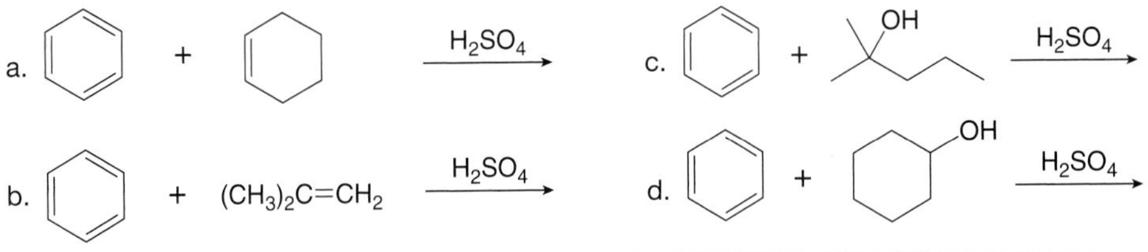
a.
+
H2SO4
b.
+ (CH3)2C=CH2
H2SO4
c.
+
OH
H2SO4
d.
+
OH
H2SO4

18.5D Intramolecular Friedel–Crafts Reactions

All of the Friedel–Crafts reactions discussed thus far have resulted from intermolecular reaction of a benzene ring with an electrophile. Starting materials that contain both units are capable of **intramolecular reaction,** and this forms a new ring. For example, treatment of compound **A,** which contains both a benzene ring and an acid chloride, with $AlCl_3$, forms α-tetralone by an intramolecular Friedel–Crafts acylation reaction.

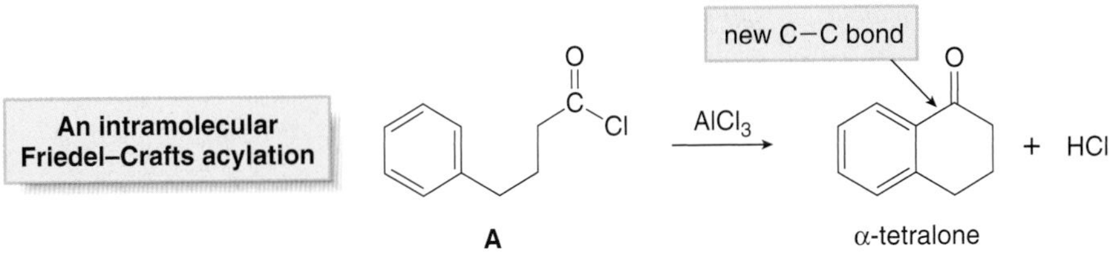
An intramolecular Friedel–Crafts acylation
O
C
Cl
AlCl3
new C–C bond
O
+ HCl
A
α-tetralone

Such an intramolecular Friedel–Crafts acylation was a key step in the synthesis of the hallucinogen LSD, as shown in Figure 18.4.

Figure 18.4 Intramolecular Friedel–Crafts acylation in the synthesis of LSD

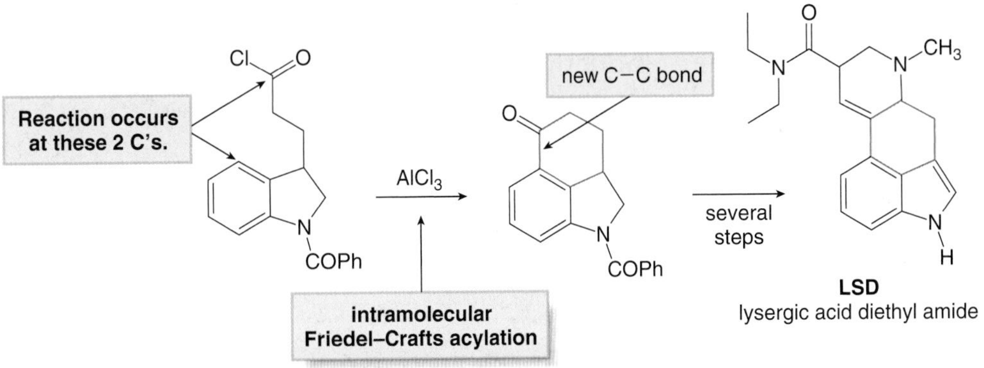
Reaction occurs at these 2 C's.
Cl
O
N
COPh
AlCl3
intramolecular Friedel–Crafts acylation
new C–C bond
O
N
COPh
several steps
O
N
N
CH3
N
H
LSD
lysergic acid diethyl amide

Ergot-infected grain, the source of lysergic acid

- Intramolecular Friedel–Crafts acylation formed a product containing a new six-membered ring (in red), which was converted to LSD in several steps.
- LSD was first prepared by Swiss chemist Albert Hoffman in 1938 from a related organic compound isolated from the ergot fungus that attacks rye and other grains. Ergot has a long history as a dreaded poison, affecting individuals who become ill from eating ergot-contaminated bread. The hallucinogenic effects of LSD were first discovered when Hoffman accidentally absorbed a small amount of the drug through his fingertips.

Problem 18.10 Draw a stepwise mechanism for the intramolecular Friedel–Crafts acylation of compound **A** to form **B**. **B** can be converted in one step to the antidepressant sertraline, the chapter-opening molecule.

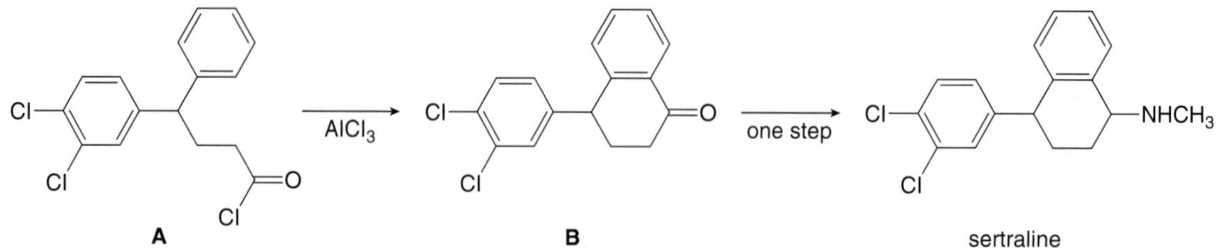

sertraline
(Zoloft)

Problem 18.11 Intramolecular reactions are also observed in Friedel–Crafts alkylation. Draw the intramolecular alkylation product formed from each of the following reactants. (Watch out for rearrangements!)

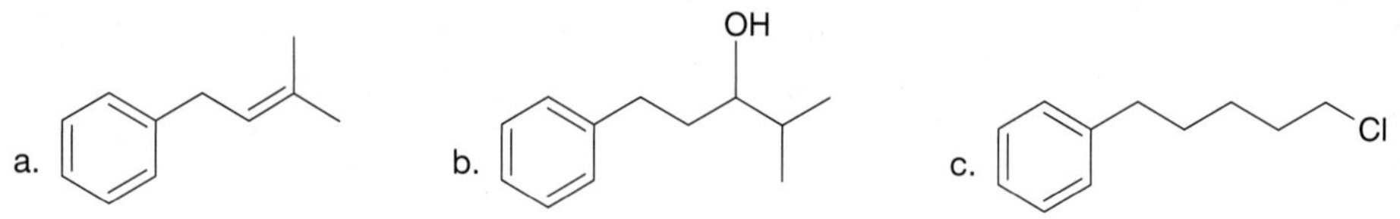

18.6 Substituted Benzenes

Many substituted benzene rings undergo electrophilic aromatic substitution. Common substituents include halogens, OH, NH_2, alkyl, and many functional groups that contain a carbonyl. Each substituent either increases or decreases the electron density in the benzene ring, and this affects the course of electrophilic aromatic substitution, as we will learn in Section 18.7.

What makes a substituent on a benzene ring electron donating or electron withdrawing? The answer is **inductive effects** and **resonance effects,** both of which can add or remove electron density.

Inductive Effects

Inductive effects stem from the **electronegativity** of the atoms in the substituent and the **polarizability** of the substituent group.

Inductive and resonance effects were first discussed in Sections 2.5B and 2.5C, respectively.

- **Atoms more electronegative than carbon—including N, O, and X—pull electron density away from carbon and thus exhibit an electron-withdrawing inductive effect.**
- **Polarizable alkyl groups donate electron density, and thus exhibit an electron-donating inductive effect.**

Considering inductive effects *only,* an NH_2 group withdraws electron density and CH_3 donates electron density.

Electron-withdrawing inductive effect

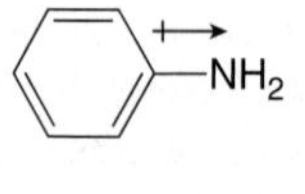

- N is **more electronegative** than C.
- N inductively withdraws electron density.

Electron-donating inductive effect

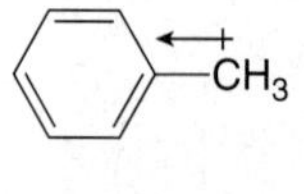

- Alkyl groups are **polarizable,** making them electron-donating groups.

Problem 18.12 Which substituents have an electron-withdrawing and which have an electron-donating inductive effect: (a) $CH_3CH_2CH_2CH_2-$; (b) $Br-$; (c) CH_3CH_2O-?

Resonance Effects

Resonance effects can either donate or withdraw electron density, depending on whether they place a positive or negative charge on the benzene ring.

- **A resonance effect is electron donating when resonance structures place a negative charge on carbons of the benzene ring.**
- **A resonance effect is electron withdrawing when resonance structures place a positive charge on carbons of the benzene ring.**

An electron-donating resonance effect is observed whenever an atom Z having a lone pair of electrons is directly bonded to a benzene ring (general structure—$\mathbf{C_6H_5-Z:}$). Common examples of Z include N, O, and halogen. For example, five resonance structures can be drawn for aniline ($C_6H_5NH_2$). Because three of them place a negative charge on a carbon atom of the benzene ring, an **$\mathbf{NH_2}$ group donates electron density to a benzene ring by a resonance effect.**

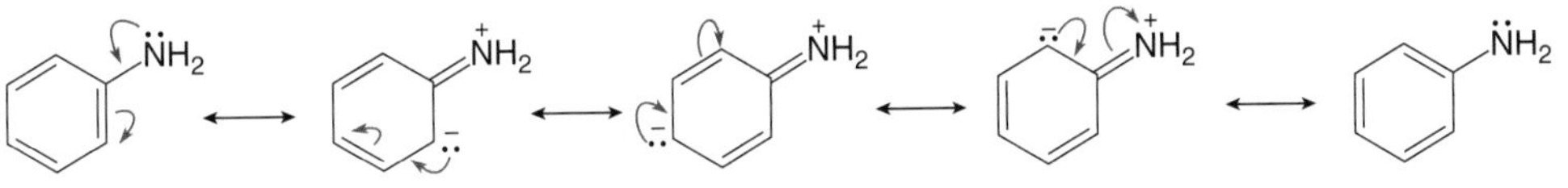

aniline

Three resonance structures place a (–) charge on atoms in the ring.

In contrast, **an electron-withdrawing resonance effect is observed in substituted benzenes having the general structure $\mathbf{C_6H_5-Y=Z}$,** where Z is more electronegative than Y. For example, seven resonance structures can be drawn for benzaldehyde (C_6H_5CHO). Because three of them place a positive charge on a carbon atom of the benzene ring, a CHO group withdraws electron density from a benzene ring by a resonance effect.

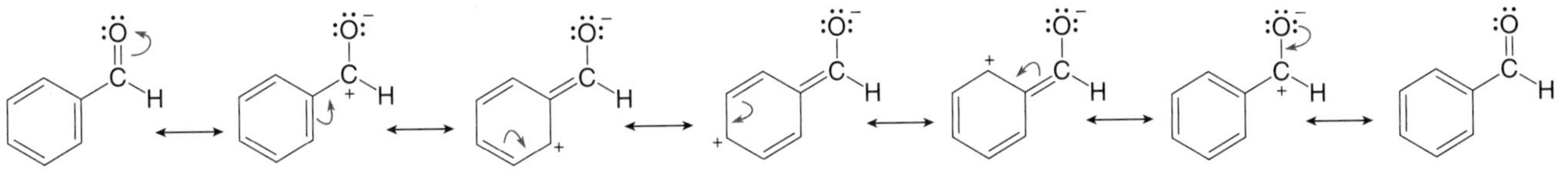

benzaldehyde

Three resonance structures place a (+) charge on atoms in the ring.

Problem 18.13 Draw all resonance structures for each compound and use the resonance structures to determine if the substituent has an electron-donating or electron-withdrawing resonance effect.

a. 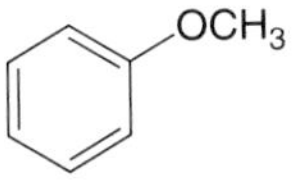

b. 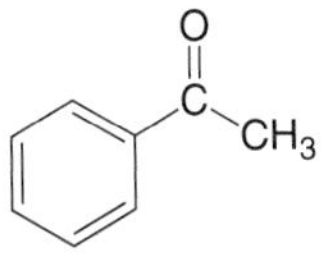

Considering Both Inductive and Resonance Effects

To predict whether a substituted benzene is more or less electron rich than benzene itself, we must consider the **net balance of *both* the inductive and the resonance effects.** Alkyl groups, for instance, donate electrons by an inductive effect, but they have no resonance effect because they lack nonbonded electron pairs or π bonds. As a result,

- **An alkyl group is an electron-donating group and an alkyl benzene is more electron rich than benzene.**

When electronegative atoms, such as N, O, or halogen, are bonded to the benzene ring, they inductively *withdraw* electron density from the ring. All of these groups also have a nonbonded pair of electrons, so they *donate* electron density to the ring by resonance. **The *identity of the element* determines the net balance of these opposing effects.**

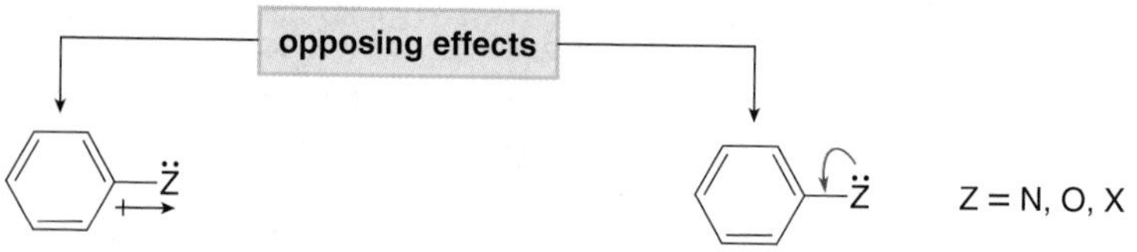

These elements are electronegative, so they **inductively withdraw electron density.**

These elements have a lone pair, so they can **donate electron density by resonance.**

- **When a neutral O or N atom is bonded directly to a benzene ring, the resonance effect dominates and the net effect is electron donation.**
- **When a halogen X is bonded to a benzene ring, the inductive effect dominates and the net effect is electron withdrawal.**

Thus, NH_2 and OH are electron-donating groups because the resonance effect predominates, whereas Cl and Br are electron-withdrawing groups because the inductive effect predominates.

Finally, the inductive and resonance effects in compounds having the general structure $\mathbf{C_6H_5{-}Y{=}Z}$ (with Z more electronegative than Y) are **both electron withdrawing;** in other words, the two effects *reinforce* each other. This is true for benzaldehyde (C_6H_5CHO) and all other compounds that contain a carbonyl group bonded directly to the benzene ring.

Thus, on balance, an **$\mathbf{NH_2}$ group is electron donating,** so the benzene ring of aniline ($C_6H_5NH_2$) has more electron density than benzene. An **aldehyde group (CHO), on the other hand, is electron withdrawing,** so the benzene ring of benzaldehyde (C_6H_5CHO) has less electron density than benzene. These effects are illustrated in the electrostatic potential maps in Figure 18.5. These compounds represent examples of the general structural features in electron-donating and electron-withdrawing substituents:

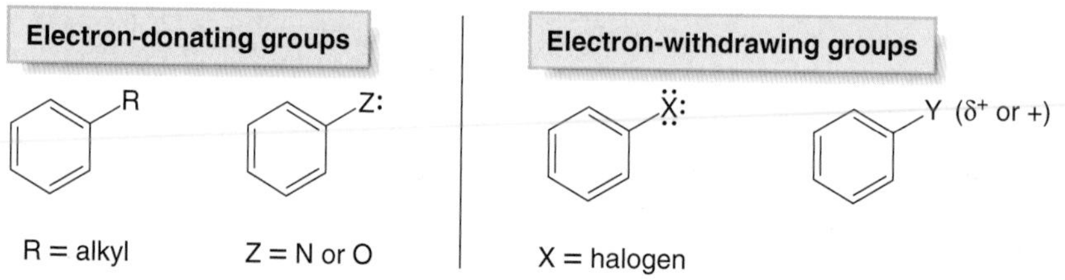

Figure 18.5
The effect of substituents on the electron density in substituted benzenes

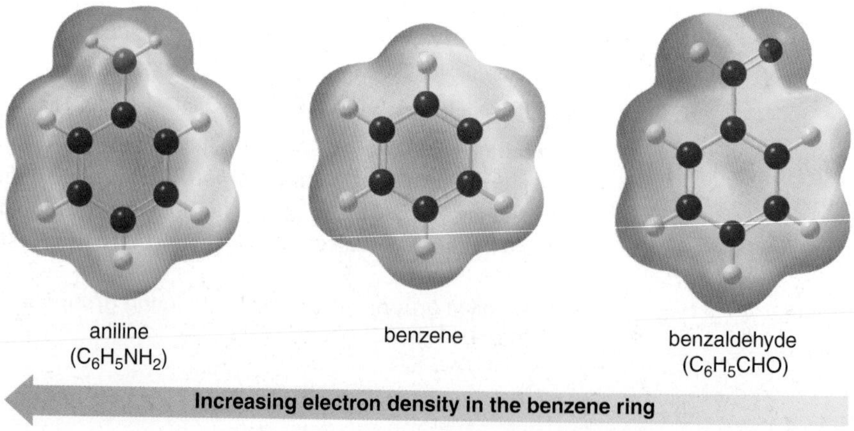

- The NH_2 group donates electron density, making the benzene ring more electron rich (redder), whereas the CHO group withdraws electron density, making the benzene ring less electron rich (greener).

- **Common electron-donating groups are alkyl groups or groups with an N or O atom (with a lone pair) bonded to the benzene ring.**

- **Common electron-withdrawing groups are halogens or groups with an atom Y bearing a full or partial positive charge (+ or δ^+) bonded to the benzene ring.**

The net effect of electron donation and withdrawal on the reactions of substituted aromatics is discussed in Sections 18.7–18.9.

Sample Problem 18.3 Classify each substituent as electron donating or electron withdrawing.

a. 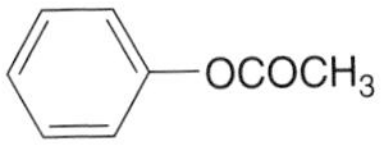

b. 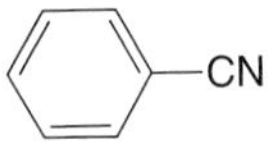

Solution

Draw out the atoms and bonds of the substituent to clearly see lone pairs and multiple bonds. Always look at the atom bonded directly to the benzene ring to determine electron-donating or electron-withdrawing effects. An O or N atom with a lone pair of electrons makes a substituent electron donating. A halogen or an atom with a partial positive charge makes a substituent electron withdrawing.

a. 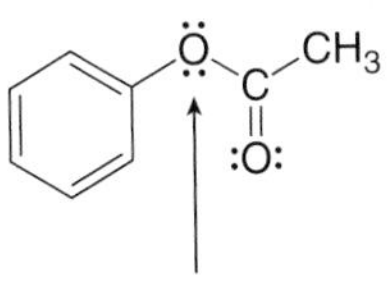

- An O atom with a lone pair bonded directly to the benzene ring

an electron-donating group

b. 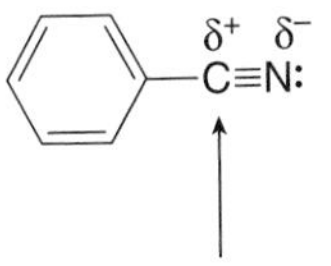

- An atom with a partial (+) charge bonded directly to the benzene ring

an electron-withdrawing group

Problem 18.14 Classify each substituent as electron donating or electron withdrawing.

a. 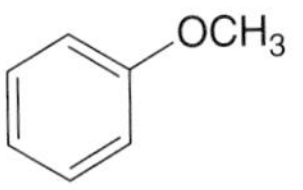

b. 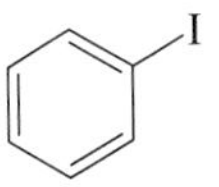

c. 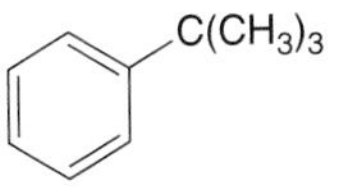

18.7 Electrophilic Aromatic Substitution of Substituted Benzenes

Electrophilic aromatic substitution is a general reaction of *all* aromatic compounds, including polycyclic aromatic hydrocarbons, heterocycles, and substituted benzene derivatives. A substituent affects two aspects of electrophilic aromatic substitution:

- **The rate of reaction:** A substituted benzene reacts faster or slower than benzene itself.
- **The orientation:** The new group is located either ortho, meta, or para to the existing substituent. The identity of the first substituent determines the position of the second substituent.

Toluene ($C_6H_5CH_3$) and nitrobenzene ($C_6H_5NO_2$) illustrate two possible outcomes.

[1] Toluene

Toluene reacts **faster** than benzene in all substitution reactions. Thus, its **electron-donating CH_3 group activates the benzene ring** to electrophilic attack. Although three products are possible, compounds with the new group ortho or para to the CH_3 group predominate. The CH_3 group is therefore called an **ortho, para director.**

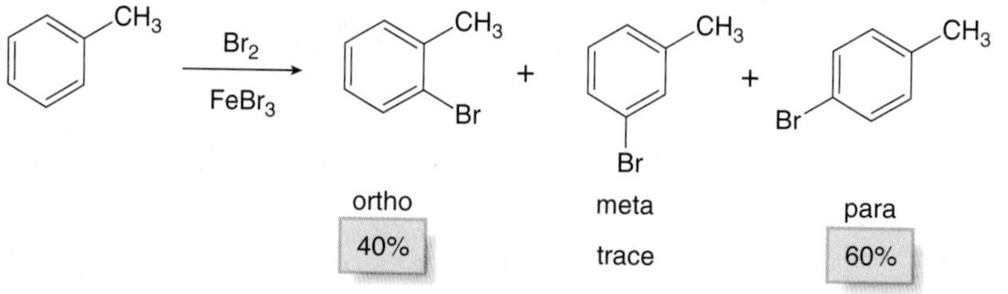

[2] Nitrobenzene

Nitrobenzene reacts **more slowly** than benzene in all substitution reactions. Thus, its **electron-withdrawing NO_2 group deactivates the benzene ring** to electrophilic attack. Although three products are possible, the compound with the new group meta to the NO_2 group predominates. The NO_2 group is called a **meta director.**

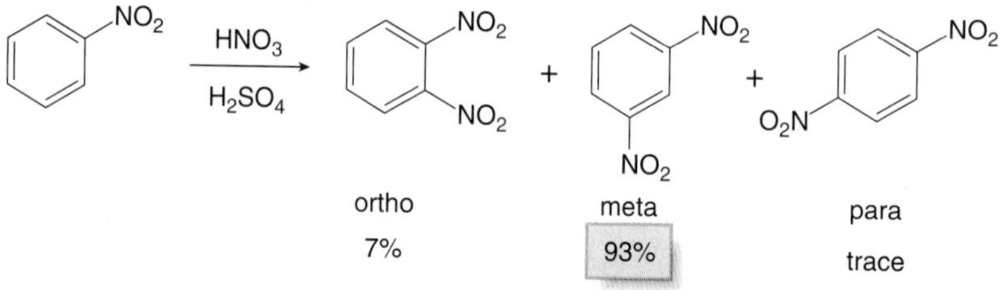

Substituents either activate or deactivate a benzene ring towards electrophiles, and direct selective substitution at specific sites on the ring. **All substituents can be divided into three general types.**

[1] Ortho, para directors and activators

- **Substituents that *activate* a benzene ring and direct substitution ortho and para.**

Increasing activation (↑)

$-\ddot{N}H_2$, $-\ddot{N}HR$, $-\ddot{N}R_2$

$-\ddot{O}H$

$-\ddot{O}R$

$-\ddot{N}HCOR$

$-R$

General structure
$-R$ or $-Z$:

[2] Ortho, para deactivators

- **Substituents that *deactivate* a benzene ring and direct substitution ortho and para.**

$-\ddot{F}:$ $-\ddot{Cl}:$ $-\ddot{Br}:$ $-\ddot{I}:$

[3] Meta directors

- **Substituents that direct substitution meta.**
- **All meta directors *deactivate* the ring.**

Increasing deactivation (↓)

–CHO
–COR
–COOR
–COOH
–CN
$–SO_3H$
$–NO_2$
$–\overset{+}{N}R_3$

General structure
–Y (δ^+ or +)

To learn these lists: **Keep in mind that the halogens are in a class by themselves.** Then learn the general structures for each type of substituent.

- All ortho, para directors are R groups or have a nonbonded electron pair on the atom bonded to the benzene ring.

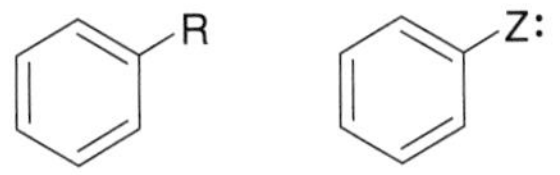
R
Z:

Z = N or O ---→ The ring is **activated.**
Z = halogen --→ The ring is **deactivated.**

- All meta directors have a full or partial positive charge on the atom bonded to the benzene ring.

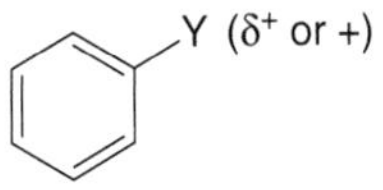
Y (δ^+ or +)

Sample Problem 18.4 shows how this information can be used to predict the products of electrophilic aromatic substitution reactions.

Sample Problem 18.4

Draw the products of each reaction and state whether the reaction is faster or slower than a similar reaction with benzene.

a. 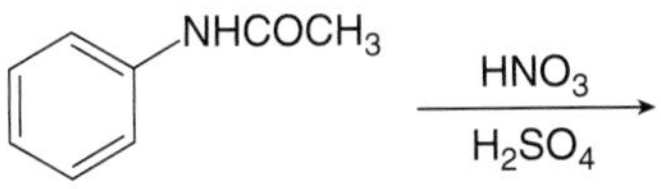
$NHCOCH_3$
HNO_3
H_2SO_4

b. 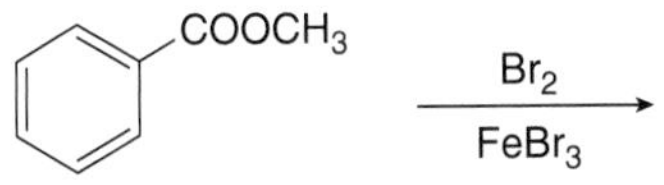
$COOCH_3$
Br_2
$FeBr_3$

Solution

To draw the products:

- Draw the Lewis structure for the substituent to see if it has a lone pair or partial positive charge on the atom bonded to the benzene ring.
- Classify the substituent—ortho, para activating, ortho, para deactivating, or meta deactivating—and draw the products.

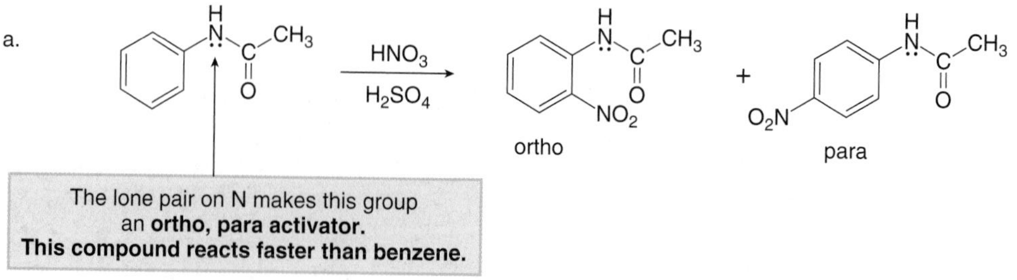
a.
HNO_3
H_2SO_4
ortho
para
The lone pair on N makes this group an **ortho, para activator.**
This compound reacts faster than benzene.

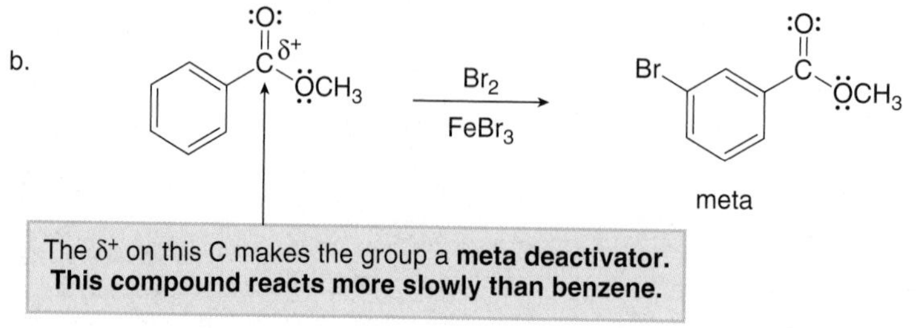
b.
Br_2
$FeBr_3$
meta
The δ+ on this C makes the group a **meta deactivator.**
This compound reacts more slowly than benzene.

Problem 18.15 Draw the products formed when each compound is treated with HNO_3 and H_2SO_4. State whether the reaction occurs faster or slower than a similar reaction with benzene.

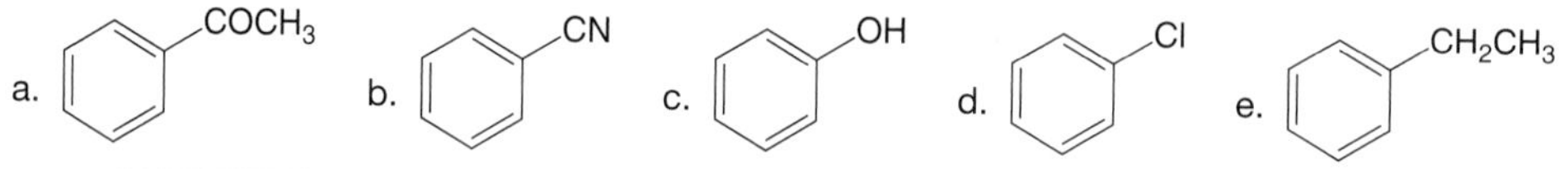
a.
$COCH_3$
b.
CN
c.
OH
d.
Cl
e.
CH_2CH_3

18.8 Why Substituents Activate or Deactivate a Benzene Ring

- **Why do substituents activate or deactivate a benzene ring?**
- **Why are particular orientation effects observed?** Why are some groups ortho, para directors and some groups meta directors?

To understand why some substituents make a benzene ring react faster than benzene itself (activators), whereas others make it react slower (deactivators), we must evaluate the rate-determining step (the first step) of the mechanism. Recall from Section 18.2 that the first step in electrophilic aromatic substitution is the addition of an electrophile (E^+) to form a resonance-stabilized carbocation. The Hammond postulate (Section 7.15) makes it possible to predict the relative rate of the reaction by looking at the stability of the carbocation intermediate.

- **The more stable the carbocation, the lower in energy the transition state that forms it, and the faster the reaction.**

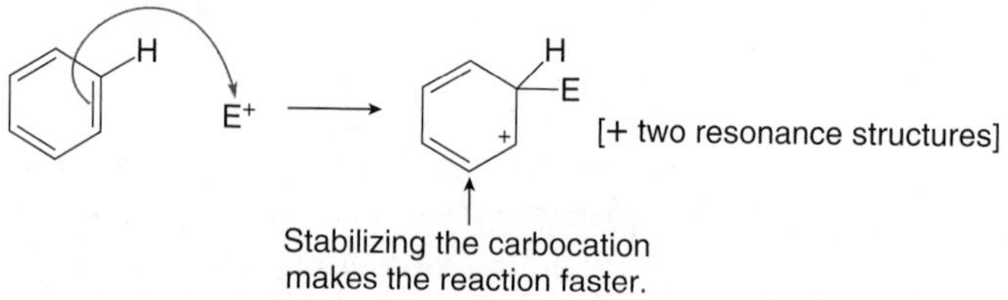
E^+
[+ two resonance structures]
Stabilizing the carbocation makes the reaction faster.

The principles of inductive effects and resonance effects, first introduced in Section 18.6, can now be used to predict carbocation stability.

- **Electron-donating groups stabilize the carbocation and activate a benzene ring toward electrophilic attack.**
- **Electron-withdrawing groups destabilize the carbocation and deactivate a benzene ring toward electrophilic attack.**

Figure 18.6 Energy diagrams comparing the rate of electrophilic aromatic substitution of substituted benzenes

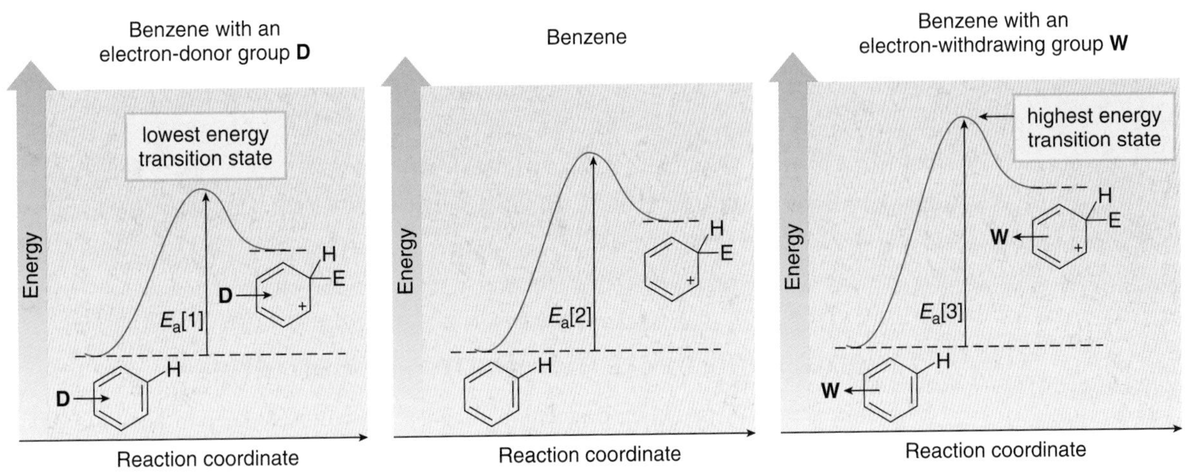

- Electron-donor groups **D** stabilize the carbocation intermediate, lower the energy of the transition state, and increase the rate of reaction.
- Electron-withdrawing groups **W** destabilize the carbocation intermediate, raise the energy of the transition state, and decrease the rate of reaction.

The energy diagrams in Figure 18.6 illustrate the effect of electron-donating and electron-withdrawing groups on the energy of the transition state of the rate-determining step in electrophilic aromatic substitution. From Section 18.6, we now know which groups increase or decrease the rate of reaction of substituted benzenes with electrophiles.

- **All activators are either R groups or they have an N or O atom with a lone pair bonded directly to the benzene ring. These are the electron-donor groups of Section 18.6.**

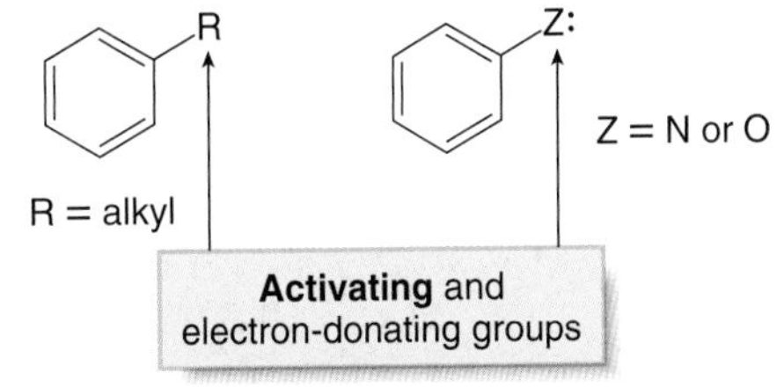

Activating groups:

$-\ddot{N}H_2$ $-\ddot{N}HR$ $-\ddot{N}R_2$

$-\ddot{O}H$ $-\ddot{O}R$

$-\ddot{N}HCOR$

$-R$

- **All deactivators are either halogens or they have an atom with a partial or full positive charge bonded directly to the benzene ring. These are the electron-withdrawing groups of Section 18.6.**

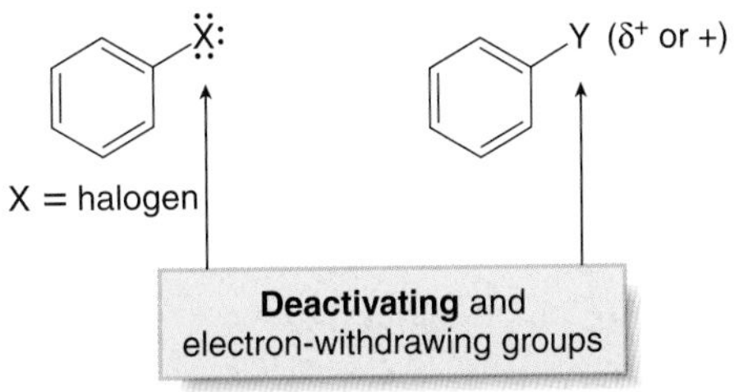

Deactivating groups:

$-\ddot{F}:$ $-\ddot{C}l:$ $-\ddot{B}r:$ $-\ddot{I}:$

$-CHO$ $-COR$

$-COOR$ $-COOH$

$-CN$ $-SO_3H$ $-NO_2$ $-\overset{+}{N}R_3$

Problem 18.16 Label each compound as more or less reactive than benzene in electrophilic aromatic substitution.

a. 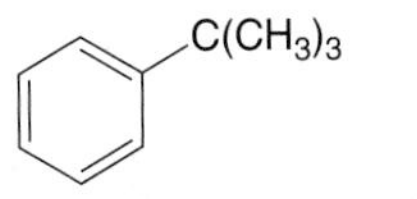

b. 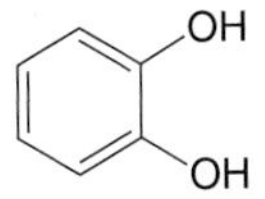

c. 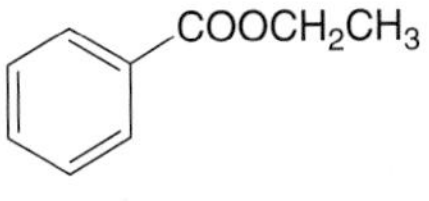

d. 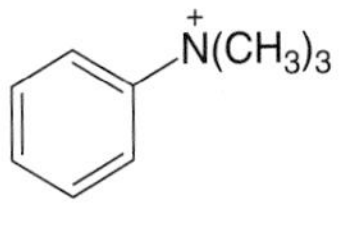

Problem 18.17 Rank the following compounds in order of increasing reactivity in electrophilic aromatic substitution: C_6H_6, C_6H_5Cl, $C_6H_5OCH_3$.

Problem 18.18 Rank the following compounds in order of increasing reactivity in electrophilic aromatic substitution.

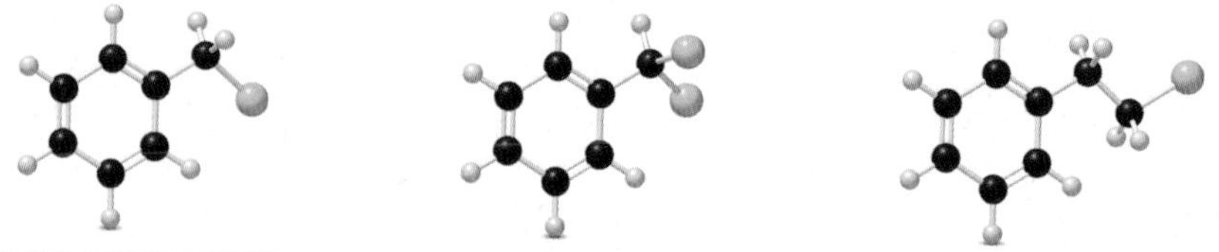

18.9 Orientation Effects in Substituted Benzenes

To understand why particular orientation effects arise, you must keep in mind the general structures for ortho, para directors and for meta directors already given in Section 18.7. There are two general types of ortho, para directors and one general type of meta director:

- **All ortho, para directors are R groups or have a nonbonded electron pair on the atom bonded to the benzene ring.**

- **All meta directors have a full or partial positive charge on the atom bonded to the benzene ring.**

To evaluate the directing effects of a given substituent, we can follow a stepwise procedure.

How To Determine the Directing Effects of a Particular Substituent

Step [1] **Draw all resonance structures for the carbocation formed from attack of an electrophile E^+ at the ortho, meta, and para positions of a substituted benzene (C_6H_5-A).**

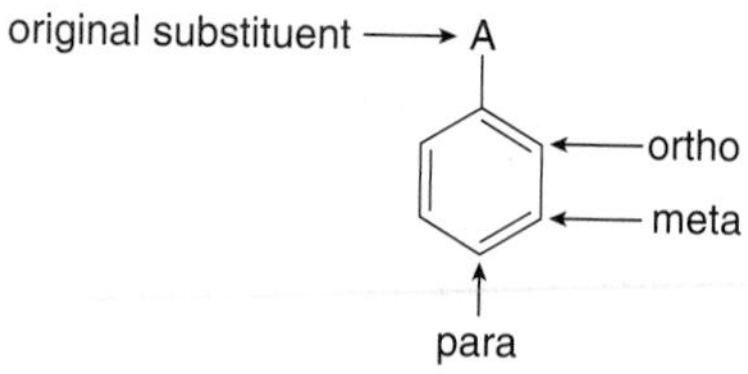

- There are at least three resonance structures for each site of reaction.
- Each resonance structure places a positive charge ortho or para to the new C–E bond.

Step [2] **Evaluate the stability of the intermediate resonance structures. The electrophile attacks at those positions that give the most stable carbocation.**

Sections 18.9A–C show how this two-step procedure can be used to determine the directing effects of the CH_3 group in toluene, the NH_2 group in aniline, and the NO_2 group in nitrobenzene, respectively.

18.9A The CH_3 Group—An ortho, para Director

To determine why a **CH_3 group directs electrophilic aromatic substitution to the ortho and para positions,** first draw all resonance structures that result from electrophilic attack at the ortho, meta, and para positions to the CH_3 group.

Always draw in the H atom at the site of electrophilic attack. This will help you keep track of where the charges go.

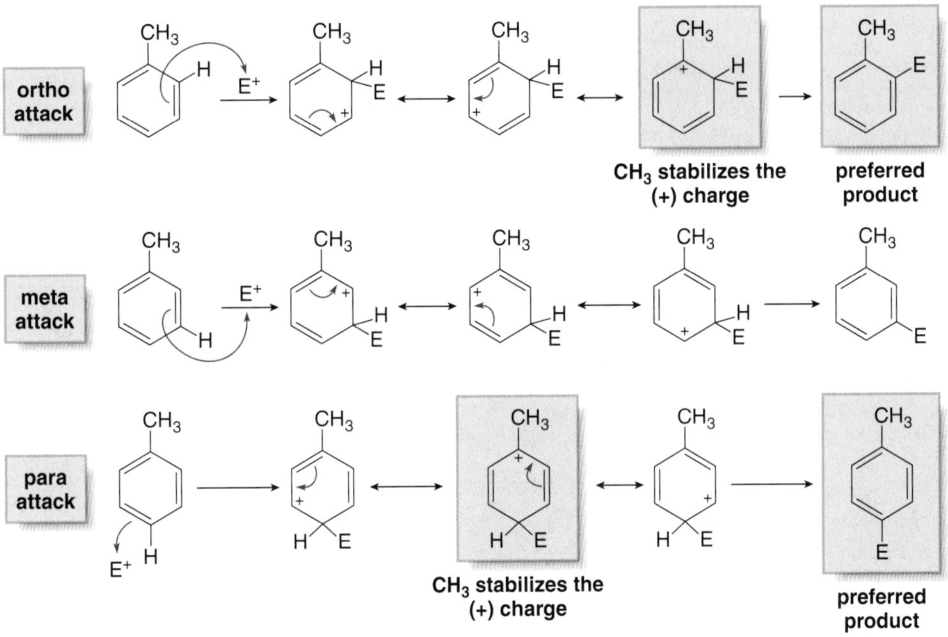

ortho attack
CH3
H
E+
E
CH3 stabilizes the (+) charge
preferred product
meta attack
para attack

Note that the positive charge in all resonance structures is always ortho or para to the new C–E bond. It is *not* necessarily ortho or para to the CH_3 group.

To evaluate the stability of the resonance structures, determine whether any are especially stable or unstable. In this example, **attack ortho or para to CH_3 generates a resonance structure that places a positive charge on a carbon atom with the CH_3 group.** The electron-donating CH_3 group *stabilizes* the adjacent positive charge. In contrast, attack meta to the CH_3 group does *not* generate any resonance structure stabilized by electron donation. Other alkyl groups are ortho, para directors for the same reason.

- **Conclusion: The CH_3 group directs electrophilic attack ortho and para to itself because an electron-donating inductive effect stabilizes the carbocation intermediate.**

18.9B The NH_2 Group—An ortho, para Director

To determine why an **amino group (NH_2) directs electrophilic aromatic substitution to the ortho and para positions,** follow the same procedure.

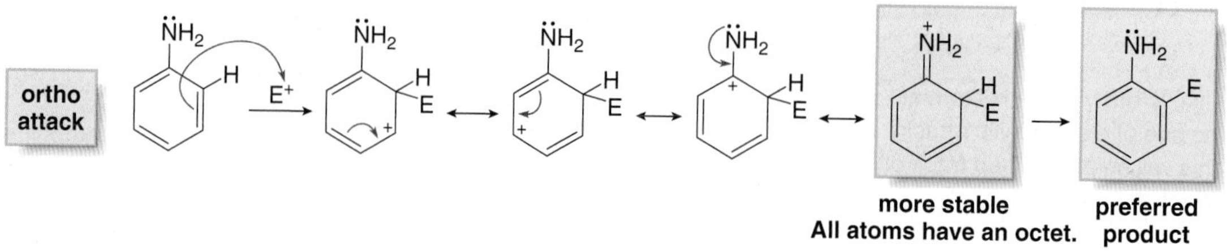
ortho attack
$\ddot{N}H_2$
H
E^+
E
+
more stable
All atoms have an octet.
preferred product

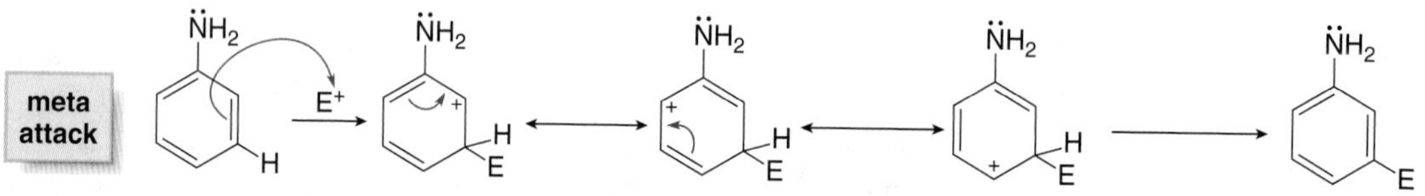
meta attack
$\ddot{N}H_2$
H
E^+
E
+

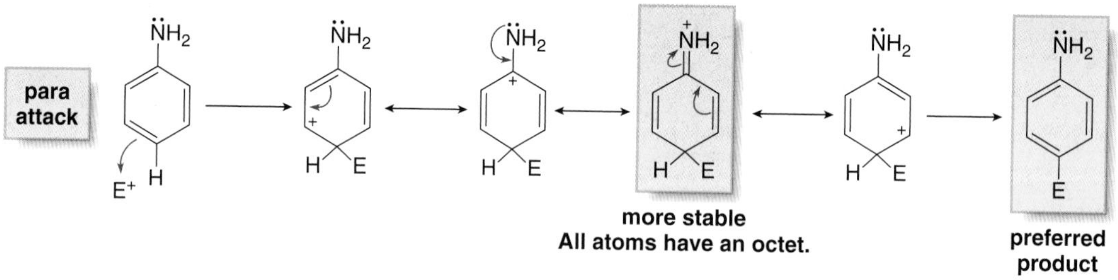
para attack
$\ddot{N}H_2$
E^+
H
E
+
more stable
All atoms have an octet.
preferred product

Attack at the meta position generates the usual three resonance structures. Because of the lone pair on the N atom, attack at the ortho and para positions generates a fourth resonance structure, which is stabilized because **every atom has an octet of electrons. This additional resonance structure can be drawn for all substituents that have an N, O, or halogen atom bonded directly to the benzene ring.**

- **Conclusion: The NH_2 group directs electrophilic attack ortho and para to itself because the carbocation intermediate has additional resonance stabilization.**

18.9C The NO_2 Group—A meta Director

To determine why a **nitro group (NO_2) directs electrophilic aromatic substitution to the meta position,** follow the same procedure.

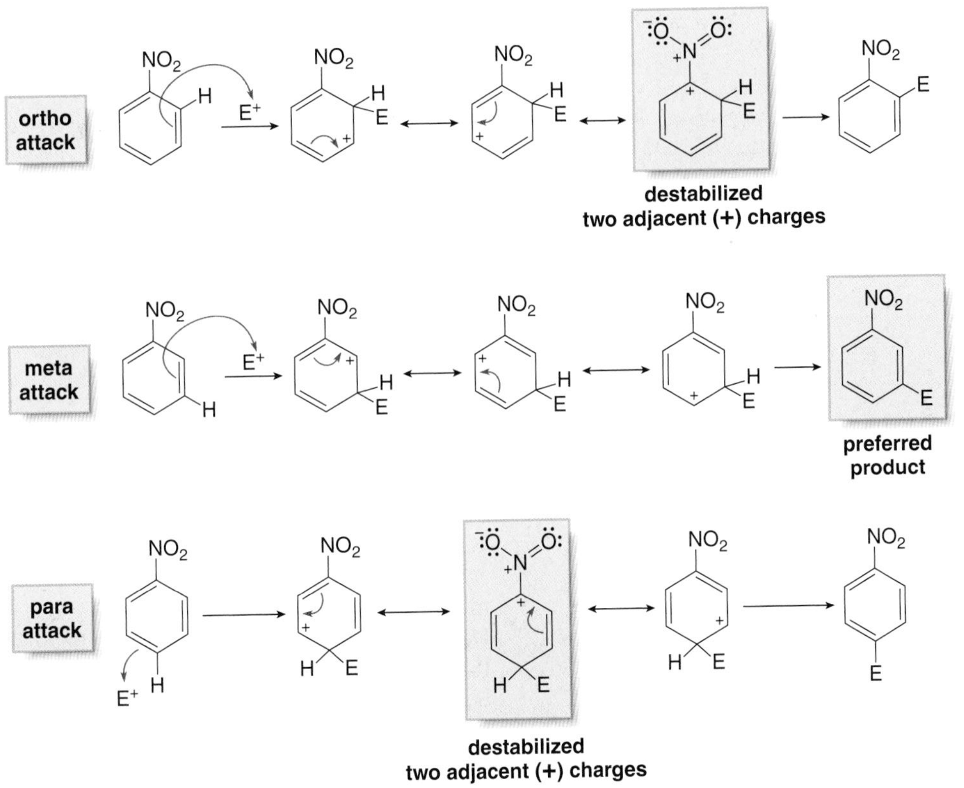
ortho attack
meta attack
para attack
destabilized
two adjacent (+) charges
preferred product
destabilized
two adjacent (+) charges

Attack at each position generates three resonance structures. One resonance structure resulting from attack at the ortho and para positions is especially *destabilized,* because it contains a positive charge on two adjacent atoms. Attack at the meta position does not generate any particularly unstable resonance structures.

- **Conclusion: With the NO_2 group (and all meta directors), meta attack occurs because attack at the ortho or para position gives a destabilized carbocation intermediate.**

Problem 18.19 Draw all resonance structures for the carbocation formed by ortho attack of the electrophile $^+NO_2$ on each starting material. Label any resonance structures that are especially stable or unstable.

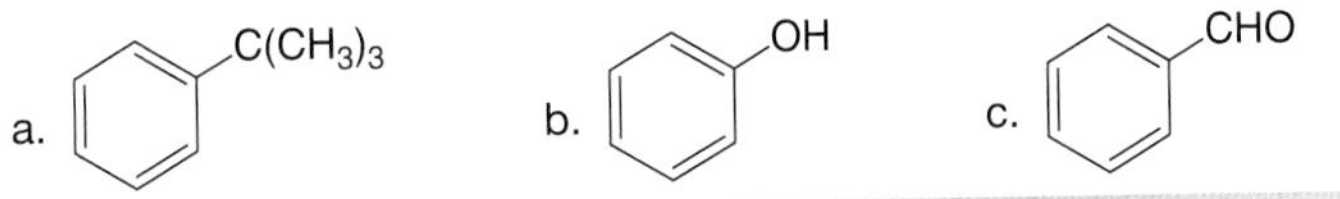
a.
C(CH3)3
b.
OH
c.
CHO

Figure 18.7
The reactivity and directing effects of common substituted benzenes

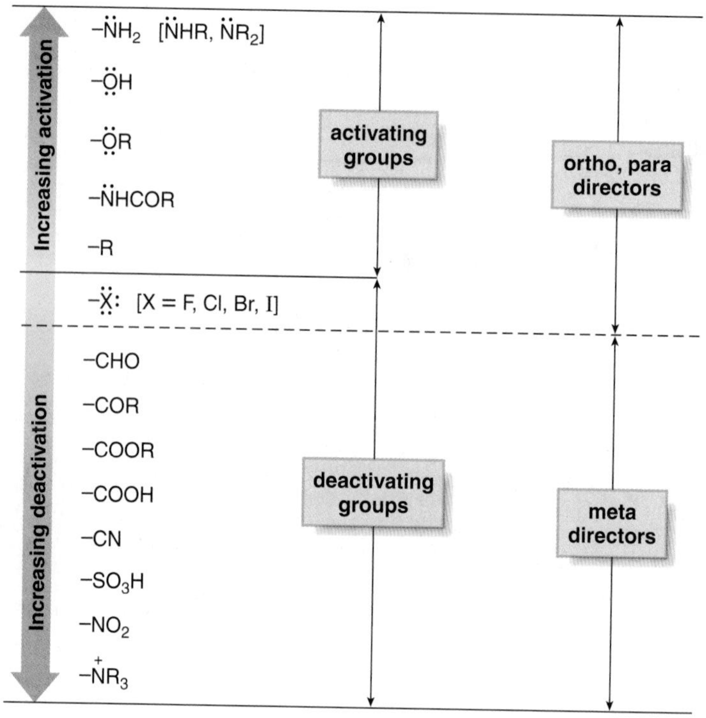

In summary:
[1] All ortho, para directors except the halogens activate the benzene ring.
[2] All meta directors deactivate the benzene ring.
[3] The halogens deactivate the benzene ring.

Figure 18.7 summarizes the reactivity and directing effects of the common substituents on benzene rings. You do not need to memorize this list. Instead, follow the general procedure outlined in Sections 18.9A–C to predict particular substituent effects.

18.10 Limitations on Electrophilic Substitution Reactions with Substituted Benzenes

Although electrophilic aromatic substitution works well with most substituted benzenes, halogenation and the Friedel–Crafts reactions have some additional limitations that must be kept in mind.

18.10A Halogenation of Activated Benzenes

Considering all electrophilic aromatic substitution reactions, halogenation occurs the most readily. As a result, benzene rings activated by strong electron-donating groups—OH, NH_2, and their alkyl derivatives (OR, NHR, and NR_2)—undergo **polyhalogenation** when treated with X_2 and FeX_3. For example, aniline ($C_6H_5NH_2$) and phenol (C_6H_5OH) both give a tribromo derivative when treated with Br_2 and $FeBr_3$. Substitution occurs at all hydrogen atoms ortho and para to the NH_2 and OH groups.

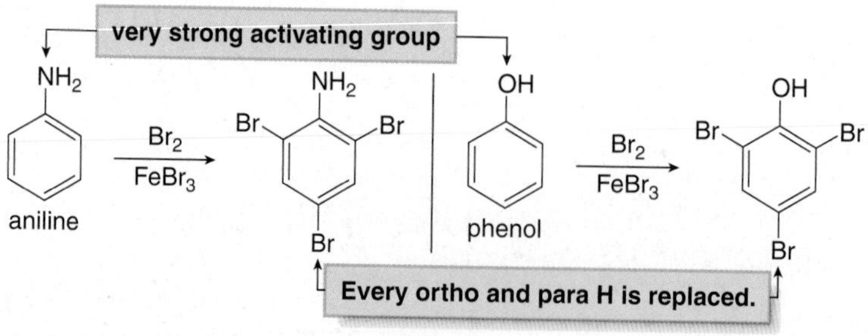

Monosubstitution of H by Br occurs with Br_2 *alone* without added catalyst to form a mixture of ortho and para products.

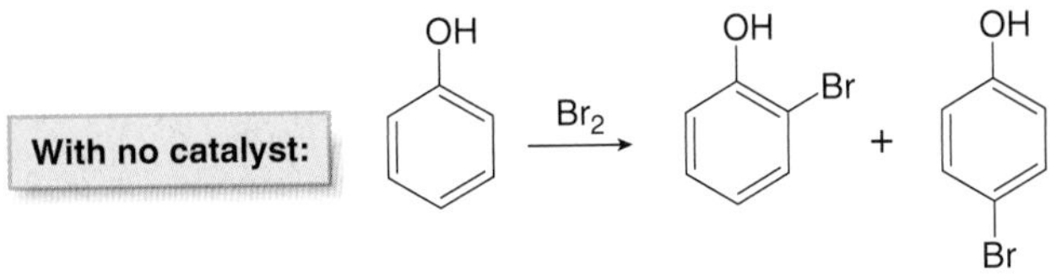
With no catalyst:
OH
Br2
OH
Br
+
OH
Br

Problem 18.20 Draw the products of each reaction.

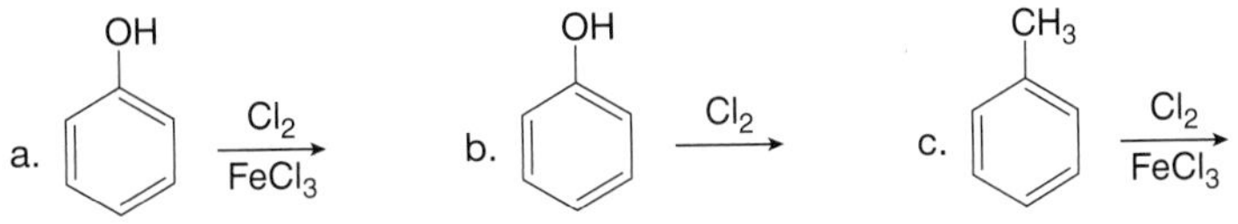
a.
OH
Cl2
FeCl3
b.
OH
Cl2
c.
CH3
Cl2
FeCl3

18.10B Limitations in Friedel–Crafts Reactions

Friedel–Crafts reactions are the most difficult electrophilic aromatic substitution reactions to carry out in the laboratory. For example, they do not occur when the benzene ring is substituted with NO_2 (a strong deactivator) or with NH_2, NHR, or NR_2 (strong activators).

A benzene ring deactivated by a strong electron-withdrawing group—that is, any of the meta directors—is not electron rich enough to undergo Friedel–Crafts reactions.

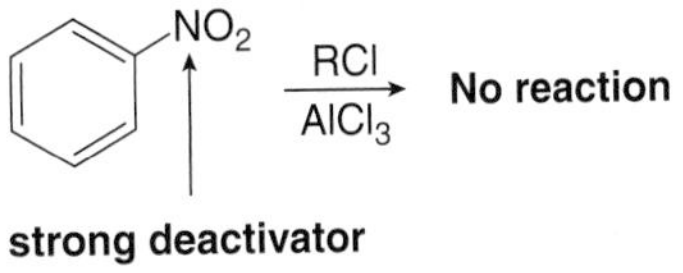
NO2
RCl
AlCl3
No reaction
strong deactivator

Friedel–Crafts reactions also do not occur with NH_2 groups, which are strong activating groups. NH_2 groups are strong Lewis bases (due to the nonbonded electron pair on N), so they react with $AlCl_3$, the Lewis acid needed for alkylation or acylation. The resulting product contains a positive charge adjacent to the benzene ring, so the ring is now strongly deactivated and therefore unreactive in Friedel–Crafts reactions.

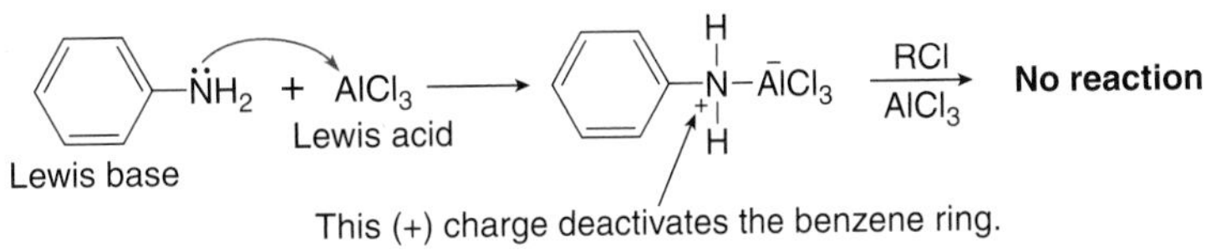
NH2
+
AlCl3
Lewis acid
Lewis base
H
N–AlCl3
H
RCl
AlCl3
No reaction
This (+) charge deactivates the benzene ring.

Problem 18.21 Which of the following compounds undergo Friedel–Crafts alkylation with CH_3Cl and $AlCl_3$? Draw the products formed when a reaction occurs.

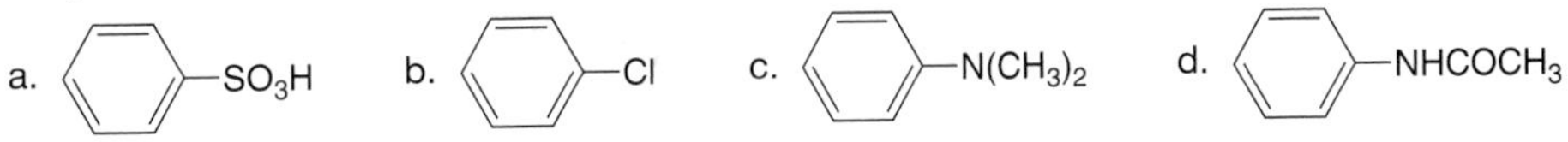
a.
SO3H
b.
Cl
c.
N(CH3)2
d.
NHCOCH3

Another limitation of the Friedel–Crafts alkylation arises because of **polyalkylation.** Treatment of benzene with an alkyl halide and $AlCl_3$ places an electron-donor R group on the ring. Because R groups activate a ring, the alkylated product (C_6H_5R) is now *more reactive* than benzene itself toward further substitution, and it reacts again with RCl to give products of polyalkylation.

To minimize polyalkylation a large excess of benzene is used relative to the amount of alkyl halide.

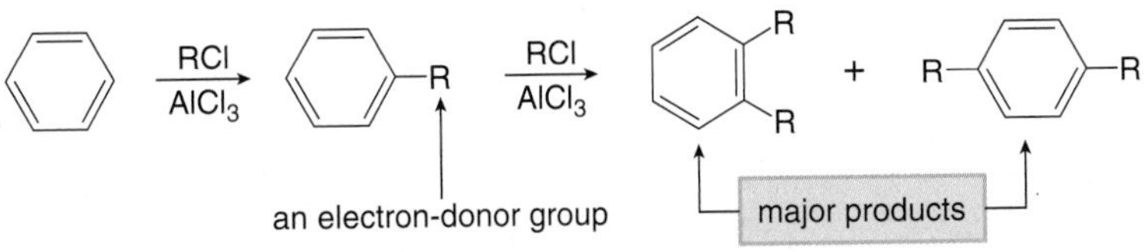
RCl
AlCl3
R
RCl
AlCl3
R
R
+
R
R
an electron-donor group
major products

Polysubstitution does not occur with Friedel–Crafts acylation, because the product now has an electron-withdrawing group that deactivates the ring toward another electrophilic substitution.

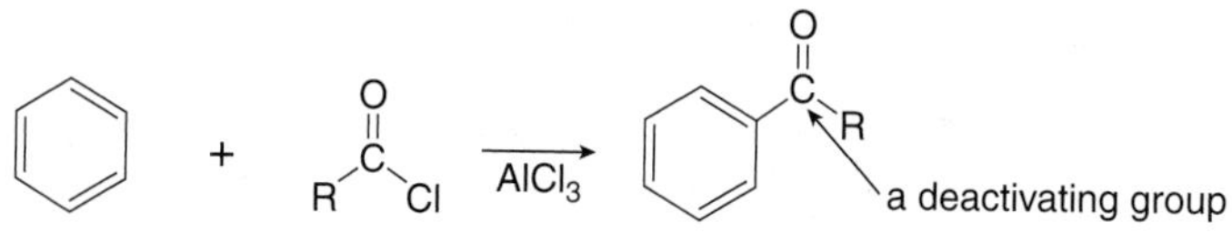

18.11 Disubstituted Benzenes

What happens in electrophilic aromatic substitution when a disubstituted benzene ring is used as starting material? **To predict the products, look at the directing effects of both substituents and then determine the net result,** using the following three guidelines.

Rule [1] **When the directing effects of two groups reinforce, the new substituent is located on the position directed by both groups.**

For example, the CH_3 group in *p*-nitrotoluene is an ortho, para director and the NO_2 group is a meta director. These two effects reinforce each other so that one product is formed on treatment with Br_2 and $FeBr_3$. Notice that the position para to the CH_3 group is "blocked" by a nitro group so no substitution can occur on that carbon.

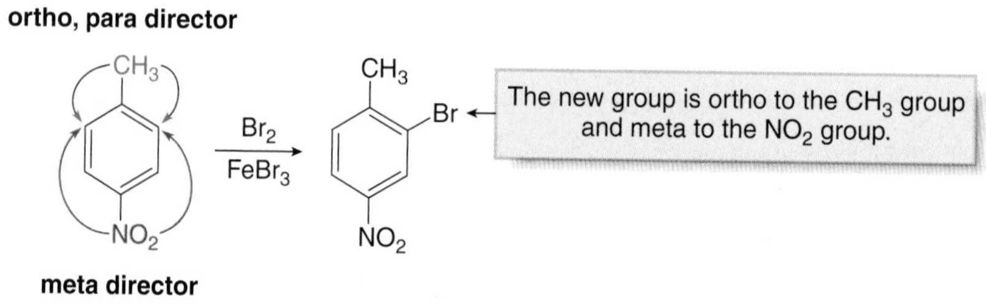

p-nitrotoluene

Rule [2] **If the directing effects of two groups oppose each other, the more powerful activator "wins out."**

In compound **A,** the $NHCOCH_3$ group activates its two ortho positions, and the CH_3 group activates its two ortho positions to reaction with electrophiles. Because the $NHCOCH_3$ is a stronger activator, substitution occurs ortho to it.

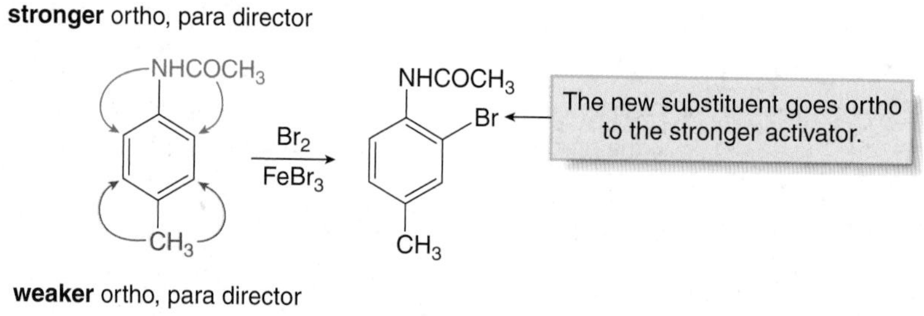

A

Rule [3] **No substitution occurs between two meta substituents because of crowding.**

For example, no substitution occurs at the carbon atom between the two CH_3 groups in *m*-xylene, even though two CH_3 groups activate that position.

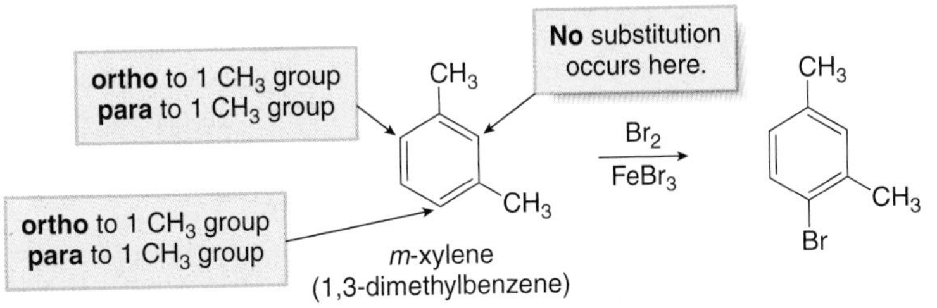

Sample Problem 18.5 Draw the products formed from nitration of each compound.

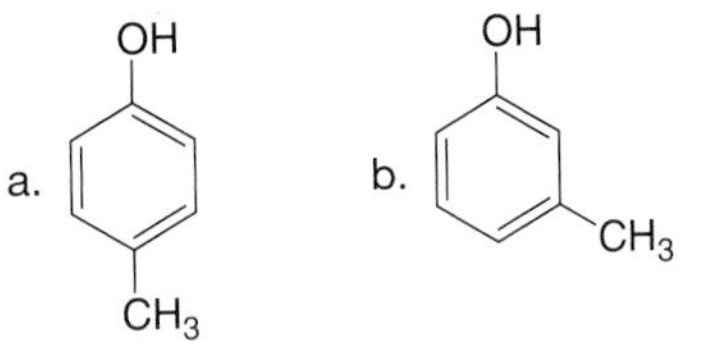

Solution

a. Both the OH and CH_3 groups are ortho, para directors. Because the OH group is a stronger activator, substitution occurs ortho to it.

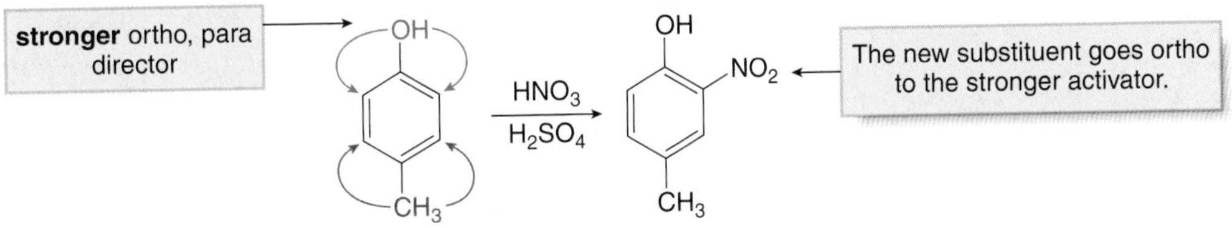

b. Both the OH and CH_3 groups are ortho, para directors whose directing effects reinforce each other in this case. No substitution occurs between the two meta substituents, however, so two products result.

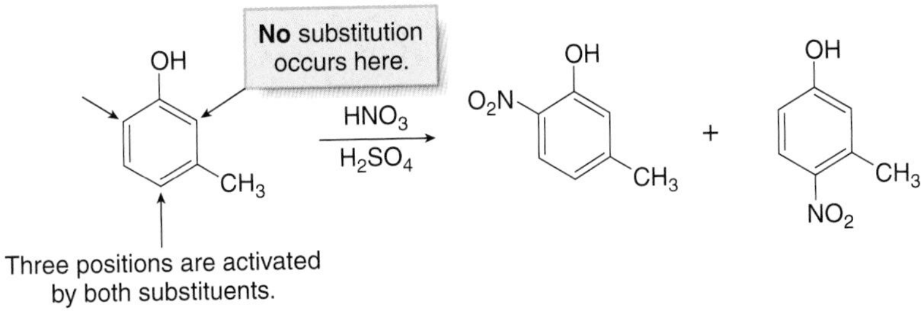

Problem 18.22 Draw the products formed when each compound is treated with HNO_3 and H_2SO_4.

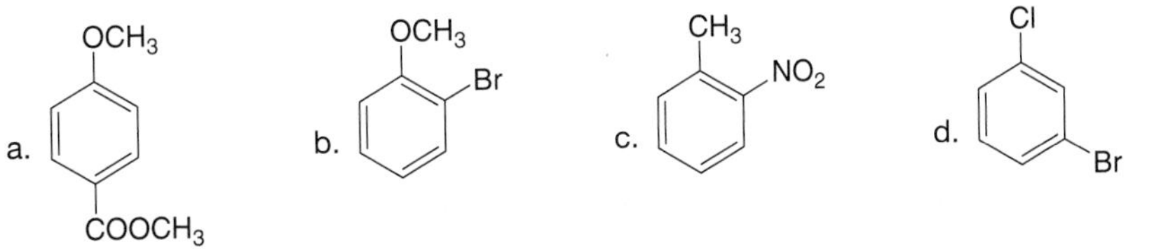

18.12 Synthesis of Benzene Derivatives

To synthesize benzene derivatives with more than one substituent, we must always take into account the directing effects of each substituent. In a disubstituted benzene, for example, **the directing effects indicate which substituent must be added to the ring first.**

For example, the Br group in *p*-bromonitrobenzene is an ortho, para director and the NO_2 group is a meta director. Because the two substituents are para to each other, the ortho, para director must be introduced *first* when synthesizing this compound from benzene.

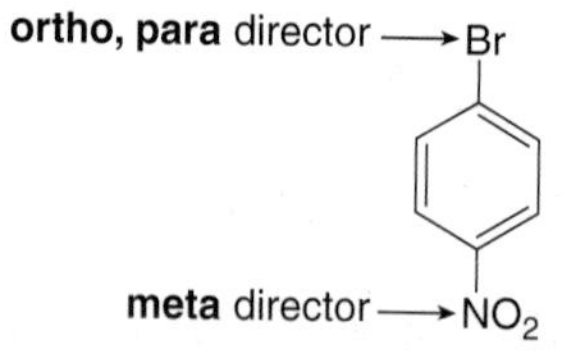

ortho, para director → Br
meta director → NO2

p-bromonitrobenzene

Because the two groups are para to each other, **add the ortho, para director first.**

Thus, Pathway [1], in which bromination precedes nitration, yields the desired para product, whereas Pathway [2], in which nitration precedes bromination, yields the undesired meta isomer.

Pathway [1]: Bromination before nitration

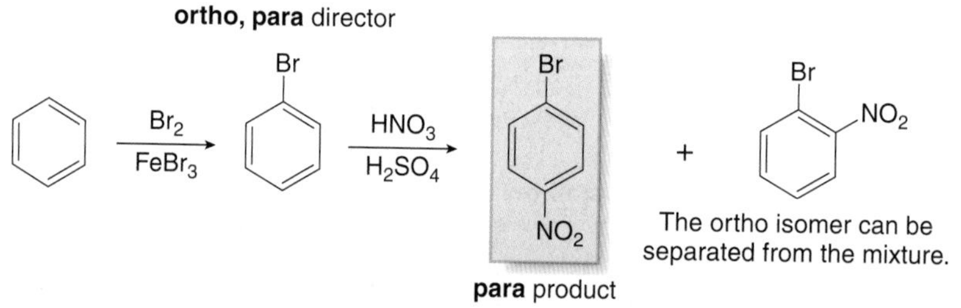

ortho, para director
Br2
FeBr3
Br
HNO3
H2SO4
Br
NO2
para product
+
Br
NO2
The ortho isomer can be separated from the mixture.

This pathway gives the desired product.

Pathway [2]: Nitration before bromination

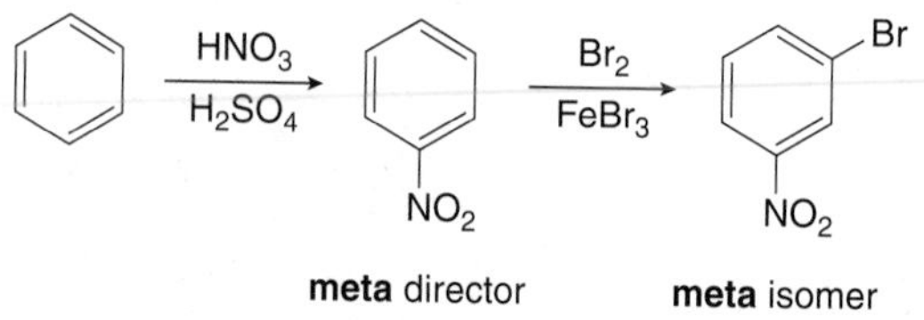

HNO3
H2SO4
NO2
meta director
Br2
FeBr3
Br
NO2
meta isomer

This pathway does NOT form the desired product.

Pathway [1] yields both the desired para product as well as the undesired ortho isomer. Because these compounds are constitutional isomers, they are separable. Obtaining such a mixture of ortho and para isomers is often unavoidable.

Sample Problem 18.6 Devise a synthesis of *o*-nitrotoluene from benzene.

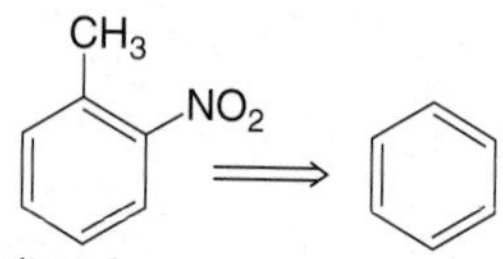

CH3
NO2

o-nitrotoluene

Solution

The CH_3 group in *o*-nitrotoluene is an ortho, para director and the NO_2 group is a meta director. Because the two substituents are ortho to each other, the **ortho, para director must be introduced first.** The synthesis thus involves two steps: Friedel–Crafts alkylation followed by nitration.

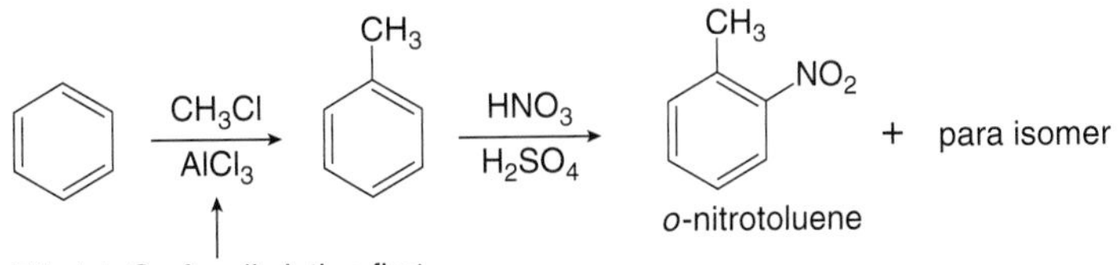

o-nitrotoluene

Friedel–Crafts alkylation first

Problem 18.23 Devise a synthesis of each compound from the indicated starting material.

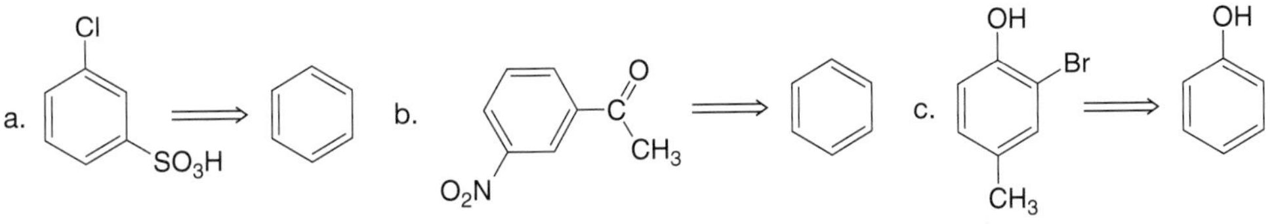

18.13 Nucleophilic Aromatic Substitution

Although most reactions of aromatic compounds occur by way of electrophilic aromatic substitution, aryl halides undergo a limited number of substitution reactions with strong nucleophiles.

Nucleophilic aromatic substitution

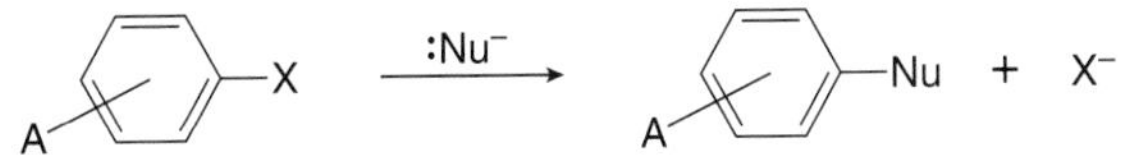

X = F, Cl, Br, I
A = H or electron-withdrawing group

- **Nucleophilic aromatic substitution results in the substitution of a halogen X on a benzene ring by a nucleophile (:Nu⁻).**

As we learned in Section 7.18, these reactions *cannot* occur by an S_N1 or S_N2 mechanism, which take place only at sp^3 hybridized carbons. Instead, two different mechanisms are proposed to explain the results: **addition–elimination** (Section 18.13A) and **elimination–addition** (Section 18.13B).

18.13A Nucleophilic Aromatic Substitution by Addition–Elimination

Aryl halides with strong electron-withdrawing groups (such as NO_2) on the ortho or para positions react with nucleophiles to afford substitution products. For example, treatment of *p*-chloronitrobenzene with hydroxide (^-OH) affords *p*-nitrophenol by replacement of Cl by OH.

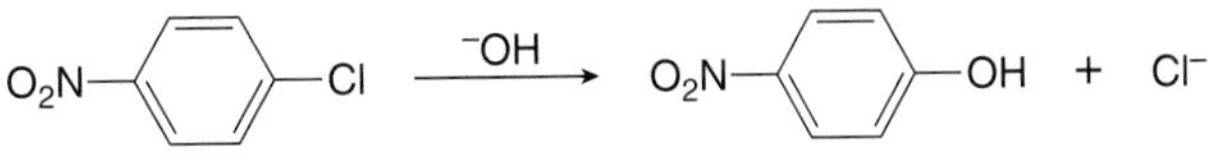

p-chloronitrobenzene *p*-nitrophenol

Nucleophilic aromatic substitution occurs with a variety of strong nucleophiles, including ^-OH, ^-OR, $^-NH_2$, ^-SR, and in some cases, neutral nucleophiles such as NH_3 and RNH_2. The mechanism of these reactions has two steps: **addition of the nucleophile** to form a resonance-stabilized carbanion, followed by **elimination of the halogen leaving group.** Mechanism 18.10 is drawn with an aryl chloride containing a general electron-withdrawing group W.

Mechanism 18.10 Nucleophilic Aromatic Substitution by Addition–Elimination

Step [1] Addition of the nucleophile (:Nu⁻) to form a carbanion

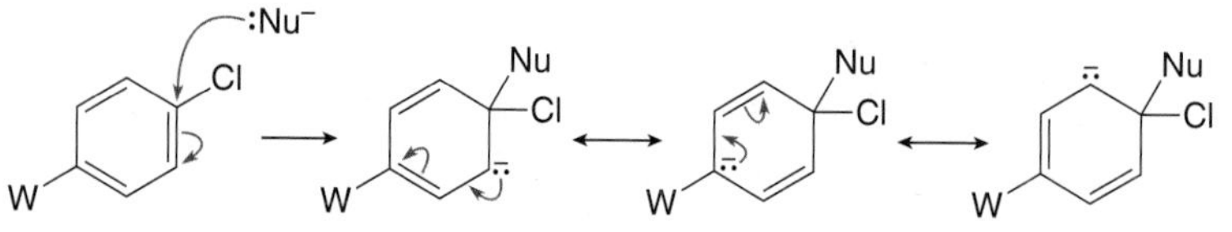

resonance-stabilized carbanion

- Addition of the nucleophile (:Nu⁻) forms a resonance-stabilized carbanion with a new C–Nu bond—**three resonance structures can be drawn.**
- Step [1] is rate-determining since the aromaticity of the benzene ring is lost.

Step [2] Loss of the leaving group to re-form the aromatic ring

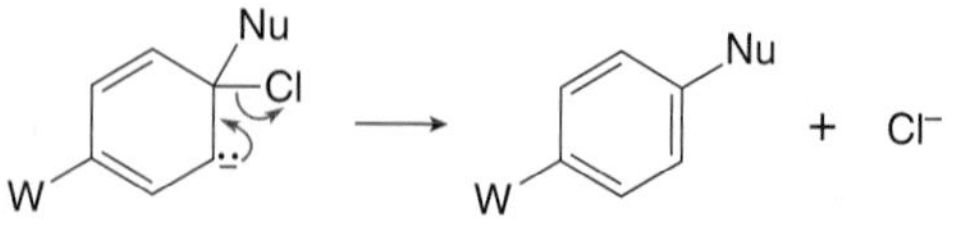

- In Step [2], loss of the leaving group re-forms the aromatic ring. This step is fast because the aromaticity of the benzene ring is restored.

In nucleophilic aromatic substitution, the following trends in reactivity are observed.

- **Increasing the number of electron-withdrawing groups increases the reactivity of the aryl halide. Electron-withdrawing groups stabilize the intermediate carbanion, and by the Hammond postulate, lower the energy of the transition state that forms it.**

- **Increasing the electronegativity of the halogen increases the reactivity of the aryl halide. A more electronegative halogen stabilizes the intermediate carbanion by an inductive effect, making aryl fluorides (ArF) much *more* reactive than other aryl halides, which contain less electronegative halogens.**

Thus, aryl chloride **B** is more reactive than *o*-chloronitrobenzene (**A**) because it contains two electron-withdrawing NO_2 groups. Aryl fluoride **C** is more reactive than **B** because **C** contains the more electronegative halogen, fluorine.

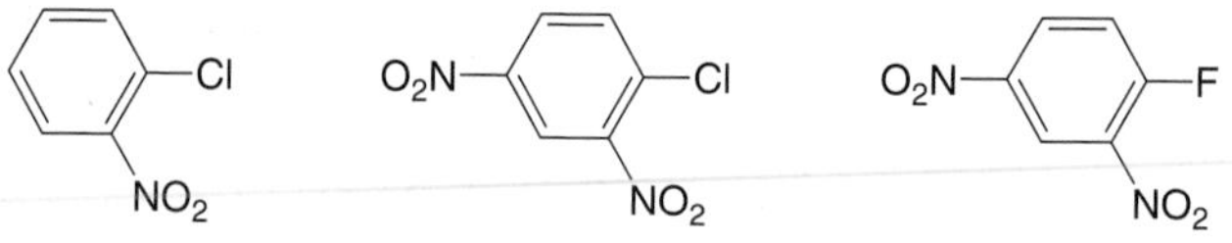

A **B** **C**

Note, too, that the location of the electron-withdrawing group greatly affects the rate of nucleophilic aromatic substitution. When a nitro group is located ortho or para to the halogen, the negative charge of the intermediate carbanion can be delocalized onto the NO_2 group, thus stabilizing it. With a meta NO_2 group, no such additional delocalization onto the NO_2 group occurs.

Para NO_2 group

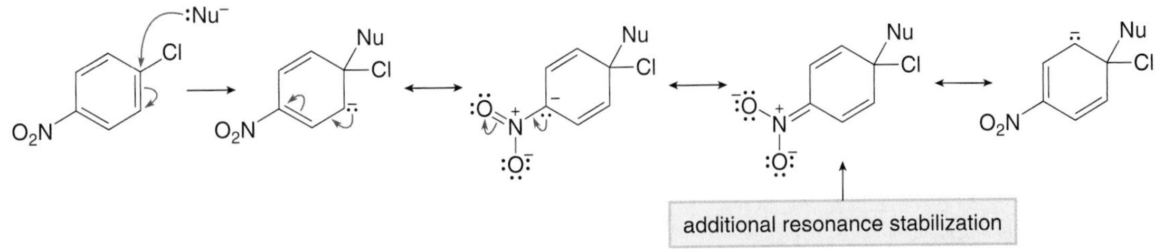

The negative charge is delocalized on the O atom of the NO_2 group.

Meta NO_2 group

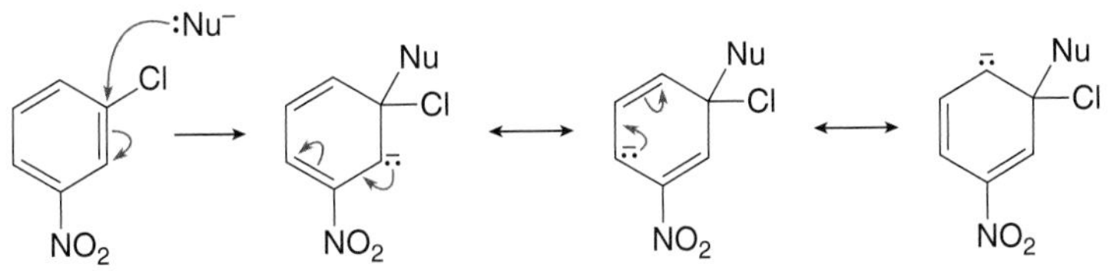

The negative charge is never delocalized on the NO_2 group.

Thus, nucleophilic aromatic substitution by an addition–elimination mechanism occurs only with aryl halides that contain electron-withdrawing substituents at the ortho or para position.

Problem 18.24 Draw the products of each reaction.

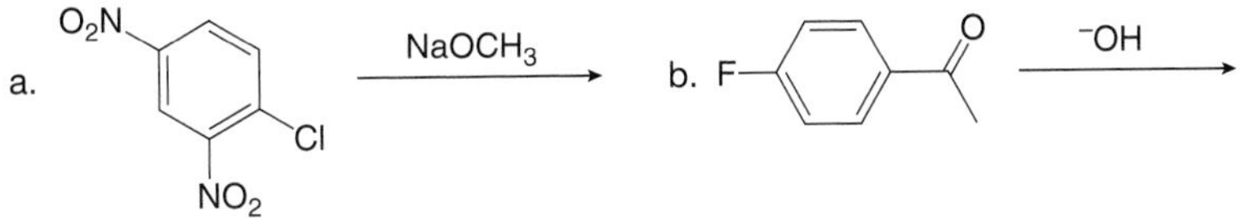

Problem 18.25 Draw a stepwise mechanism for the following reaction that forms ether **D. D** can be converted to the antidepressant fluoxetine (trade name Prozac) in a single step.

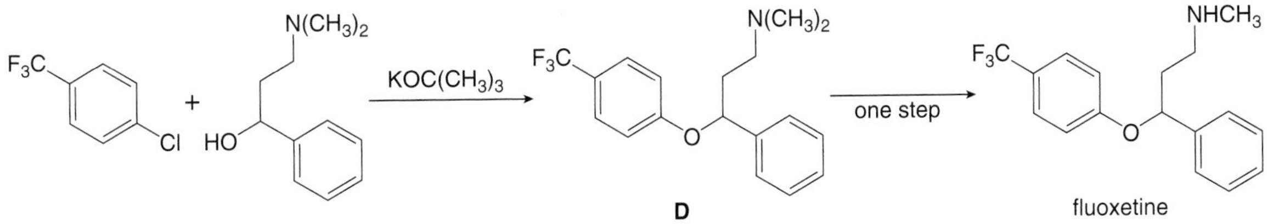

D fluoxetine

18.13B Nucleophilic Aromatic Substitution by Elimination–Addition: Benzyne

Aryl halides that do not contain an electron-withdrawing group generally do not react with nucleophiles. Under extreme reaction conditions, however, nucleophilic aromatic substitution can occur with aryl halides. For example, heating chlorobenzene with NaOH above 300 °C and 170 atmospheres of pressure affords phenol.

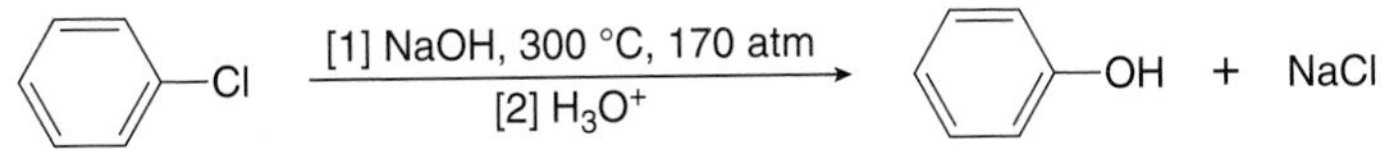

chlorobenzene phenol

The mechanism proposed to explain this result involves formation of a **benzyne** intermediate (C_6H_4) by elimination–addition. As shown in Mechanism 18.11, benzyne is a highly reactive, unstable intermediate formed by elimination of HX from an aryl halide.

Mechanism 18.11 Nucleophilic Aromatic Substitution by Elimination–Addition: Benzyne

Part [1] Elimination of HX to form benzyne

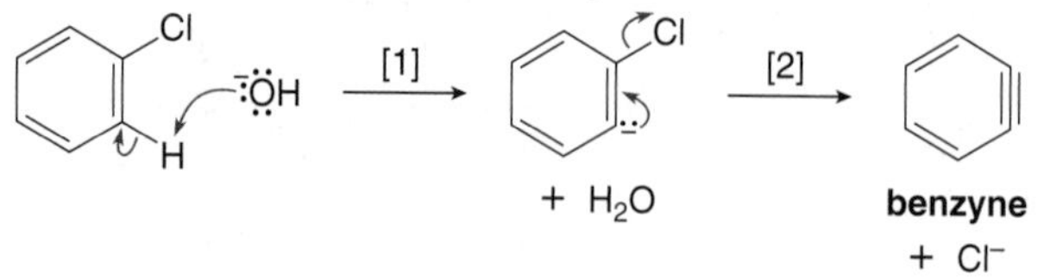

- Elimination of H and X from two adjacent carbons forms a reactive benzyne intermediate (Steps [1] and [2]).

Part [2] Nucleophilic addition to form the substitution product

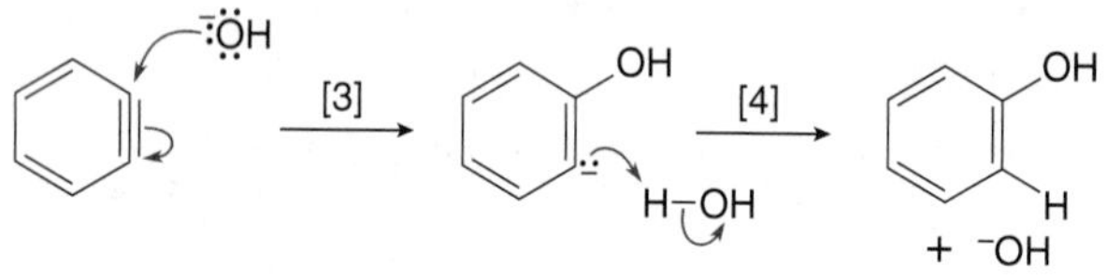

- Addition of the nucleophile (−OH in this case) and protonation form the substitution product (Steps [3] and [4]).

Formation of a benzyne intermediate explains why substituted aryl halides form mixtures of products. **Nucleophilic aromatic substitution by an elimination–addition mechanism affords substitution on the carbon directly bonded to the leaving group and the carbon adjacent to it.** As an example, treatment of *p*-chlorotoluene with $NaNH_2$ forms para- and meta-substitution products.

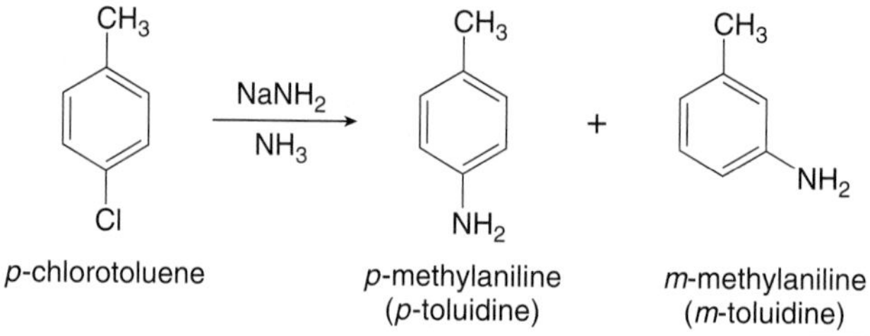

This result is explained by the fact that nucleophilic attack on the benzyne intermediate may occur at either C3 to form *m*-methylaniline, or C4 to form *p*-methylaniline.

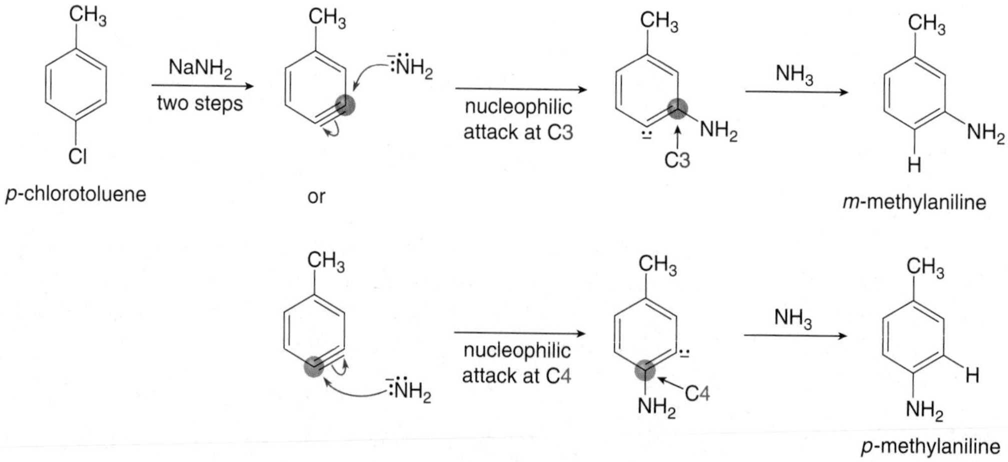

As you might expect, the triple bond in benzyne is unusual. Each carbon of the six-membered ring is sp^2 hybridized, and as a result, the σ bond and two π bonds of the triple bond are formed with the following orbitals.

- **The σ bond is formed by overlap of two sp^2 hybrid orbitals.**
- **One π bond is formed by overlap of two *p* orbitals perpendicular to the plane of the molecule.**
- **The second π bond is formed by overlap of two sp^2 hybrid orbitals.**

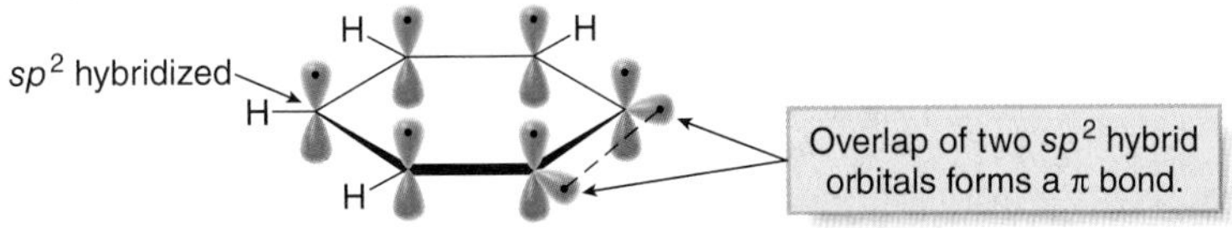

Thus, the second π bond of benzyne differs from all other π bonds seen thus far, because **it is formed by the side-by-side overlap of *sp^2 hybrid orbitals,* not *p* orbitals.** This π bond, located in the plane of the molecule, is extremely weak.

Problem 18.26 Draw the products of each reaction.

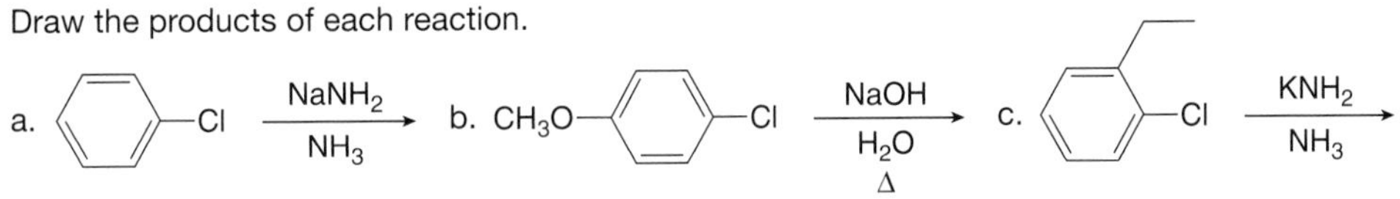

Problem 18.27 Draw all products formed when *m*-chlorotoluene is treated with KNH_2 in NH_3.

18.14 Halogenation of Alkyl Benzenes

Radical halogenation of alkanes was discussed in Chapter 15. The mechanism of radical halogenation at an allylic carbon was given in Section 15.10.

We finish Chapter 18 by learning some additional reactions of substituted benzenes that greatly expand the ability to synthesize benzene derivatives. In Section 18.14 we return to radical halogenation, and in Section 18.15 we examine useful oxidation and reduction reactions.

Benzylic C – H bonds are weaker than most other sp^3 hybridized C – H bonds, because homolysis forms a resonance-stabilized benzylic radical.

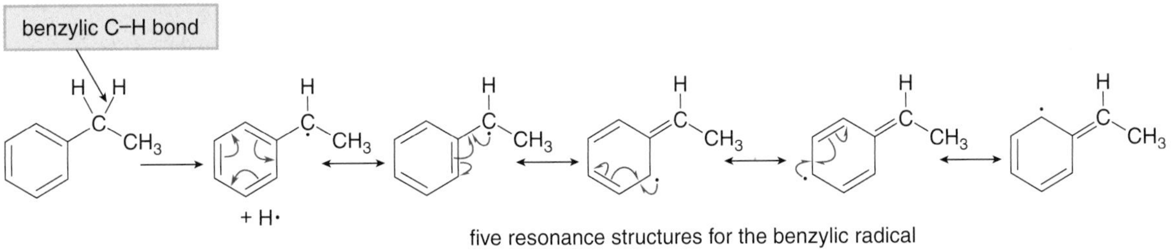

five resonance structures for the benzylic radical

The bond dissociation energy for a benzylic C – H bond (356 kJ/mol) is even less than the bond dissociation energy for a 3° C – H bond (381 kJ/mol).

As a result, an alkyl benzene undergoes selective bromination at the weak benzylic C – H bond under radical conditions to form a **benzylic halide.** For example, radical bromination of ethylbenzene using either Br_2 (in the presence of light or heat) or *N*-bromosuccinimide (NBS, in the presence of light or peroxides) forms a benzylic bromide as the sole product.

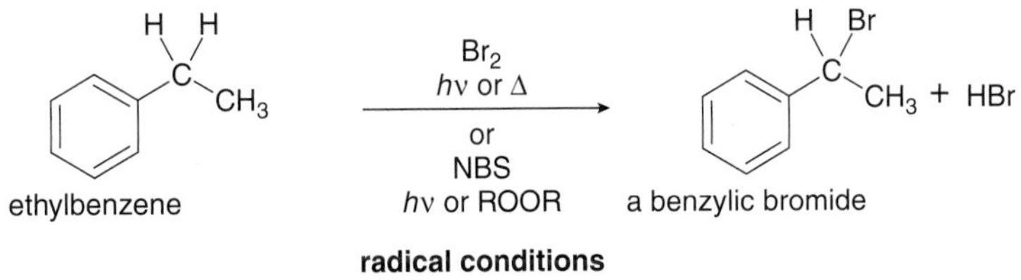

The mechanism for halogenation at the benzylic position resembles other radical halogenation reactions, and so it involves initiation, propagation, and termination. Mechanism 18.12 illustrates the radical bromination of ethylbenzene using Br_2 ($h\nu$ or Δ).

Mechanism 18.12 Benzylic Bromination

Initiation

Step [1] Bond cleavage forms two radicals.

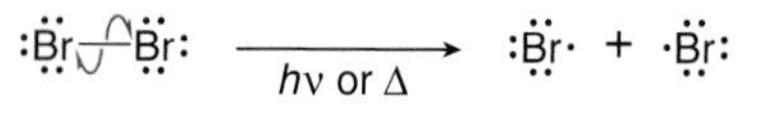

hν or Δ

- The reaction begins with homolysis of the Br–Br bond using energy from light or heat to form two Br• radicals.

Propagation

Steps [2] and [3] One radical reacts and a new radical is formed.

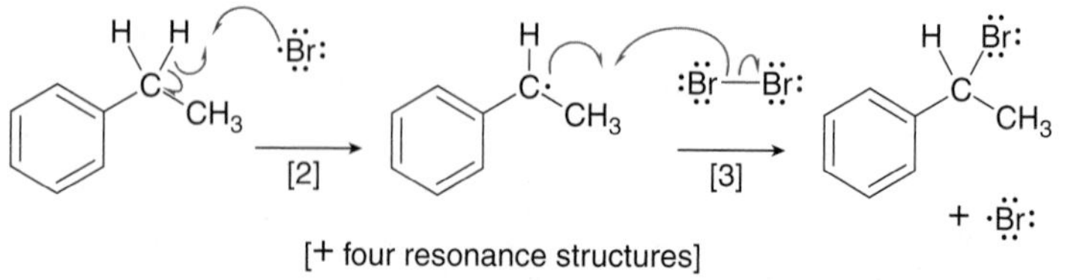

[2]
[3]

[+ four resonance structures]

+ HBr

Repeat Steps [2], [3], [2], [3], again and again.

- Abstraction of a benzylic hydrogen by a Br• radical forms the resonance-stabilized benzylic radical in Step [2], which reacts with Br_2 in Step [3] to form the bromination product.
- Because the Br• radical formed in Step [3] is a reactant in Step [2], Steps [2] and [3] can occur repeatedly without additional initiation.

Termination

Step [4] Two radicals react to form a bond.

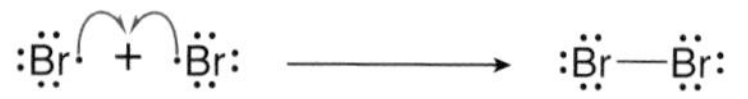

- To terminate the reaction, two radicals, for example two Br• radicals, react with each other to form a stable bond.

Thus, an alkyl benzene undergoes two different reactions with Br_2, depending on the reaction conditions.

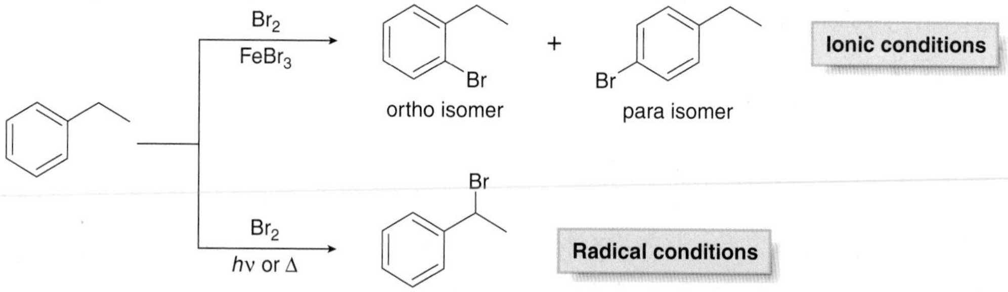

Br_2
$FeBr_3$
ortho isomer
para isomer
Ionic conditions
Br_2
hν or Δ
Radical conditions

- With Br_2 and $FeBr_3$ (**ionic conditions**), electrophilic aromatic substitution occurs, resulting in replacement of H by Br on the aromatic ring to form ortho and para isomers.
- With Br_2 and light or heat (**radical conditions**), substitution of H by Br occurs at the *benzylic* carbon of the alkyl group.

Problem 18.28 Explain why $C_6H_5CH_2CH_2Br$ is not formed during the radical bromination of $C_6H_5CH_2CH_3$.

The radical bromination of alkyl benzenes is a useful reaction because the resulting benzylic halide can serve as starting material for a variety of substitution and elimination reactions, thus making it possible to form many new substituted benzenes. Sample Problem 18.7 illustrates one possibility.

Sample Problem 18.7 Design a synthesis of styrene from ethylbenzene.

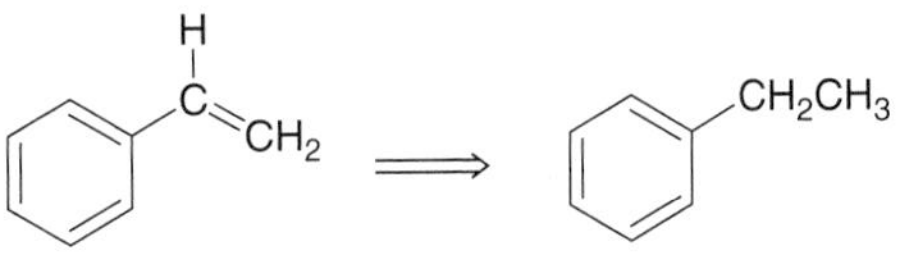

styrene ethylbenzene

Solution

The double bond can be introduced by a two-step reaction sequence: bromination at the benzylic position under radical conditions, followed by elimination of HBr with strong base to form the π bond.

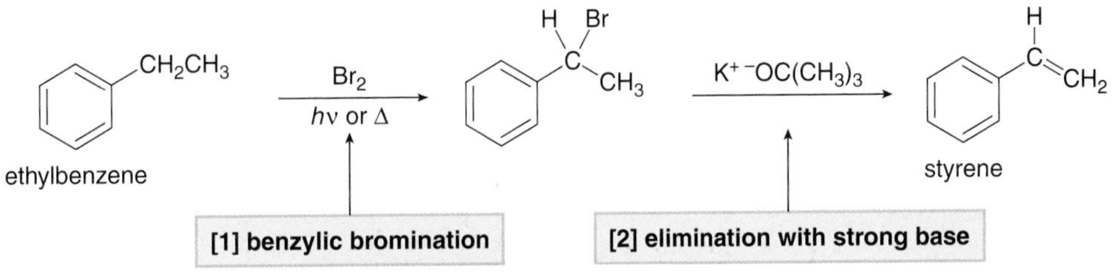
ethylbenzene
Br2
hν or Δ
K+ −OC(CH3)3
styrene
[1] benzylic bromination
[2] elimination with strong base

Problem 18.29 How could you use ethylbenzene to prepare each compound? More than one step is required.

a. 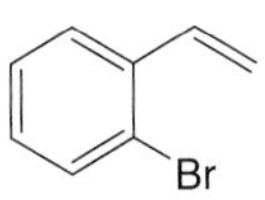
b. 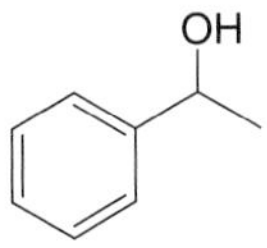
c. 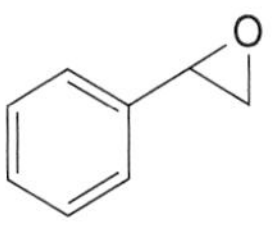
d. 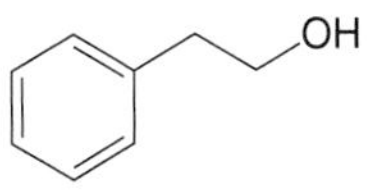

18.15 Oxidation and Reduction of Substituted Benzenes

Oxidation and reduction reactions are valuable tools for preparing many other benzene derivatives. Because the mechanisms are complex and do not have general applicability, reagents and reactions are presented only, without reference to the detailed mechanism.

18.15A Oxidation of Alkyl Benzenes

Arenes containing at least one benzylic C–H bond are oxidized with $KMnO_4$ to benzoic acid, a carboxylic acid with the carboxy group (COOH) bonded directly to the benzene ring. With some alkyl benzenes, this also results in the cleavage of carbon–carbon bonds, so the product has fewer carbon atoms than the starting material.

Examples

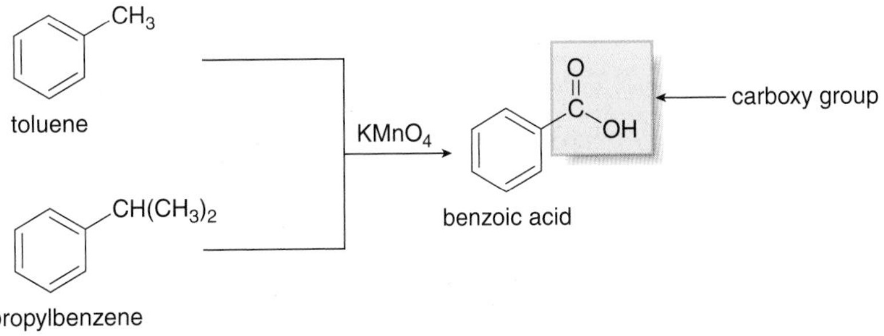
toluene
isopropylbenzene
KMnO4
benzoic acid
carboxy group

Substrates with more than one alkyl group are oxidized to dicarboxylic acids. Compounds without a benzylic C–H bond are inert to oxidation.

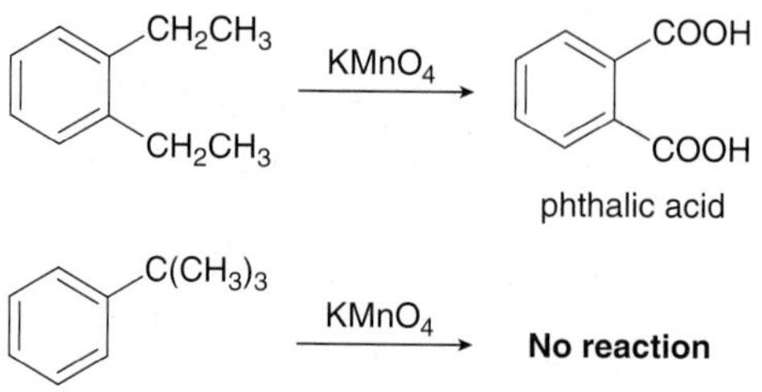

18.15B Reduction of Aryl Ketones to Alkyl Benzenes

Ketones formed as products in Friedel–Crafts acylation can be reduced to alkyl benzenes by two different methods.

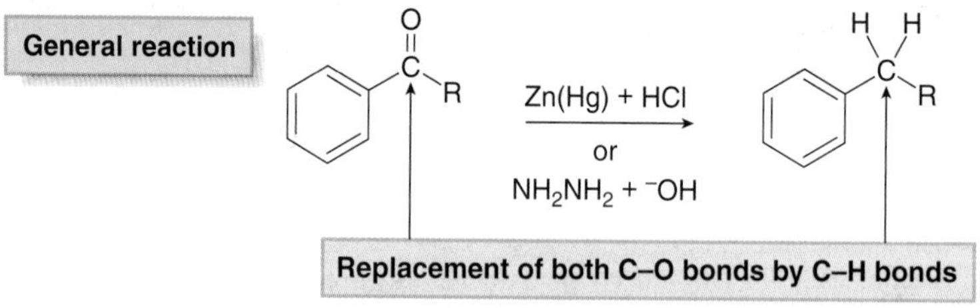

- The **Clemmensen reduction** uses zinc and mercury in the presence of strong acid.
- The **Wolff–Kishner reduction** uses hydrazine (NH_2NH_2) and strong base (KOH).

Because both C–O bonds in the starting material are converted to C–H bonds in the product, the reduction is difficult and the reaction conditions must be harsh.

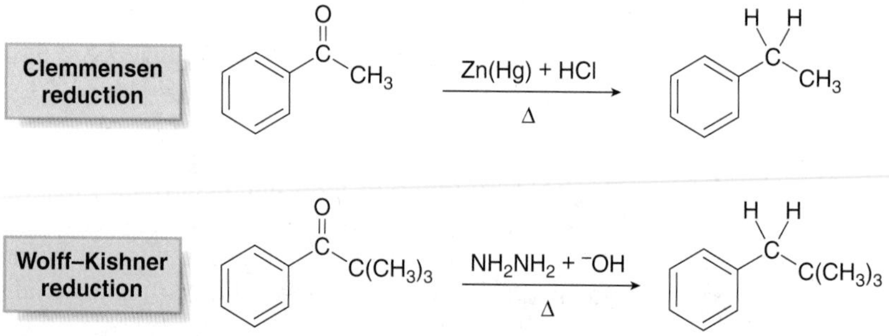

We now know two different ways to introduce an alkyl group on a benzene ring (Figure 18.8):

- **A one-step method using Friedel–Crafts alkylation**
- **A two-step method using Friedel–Crafts acylation to form a ketone, followed by reduction**

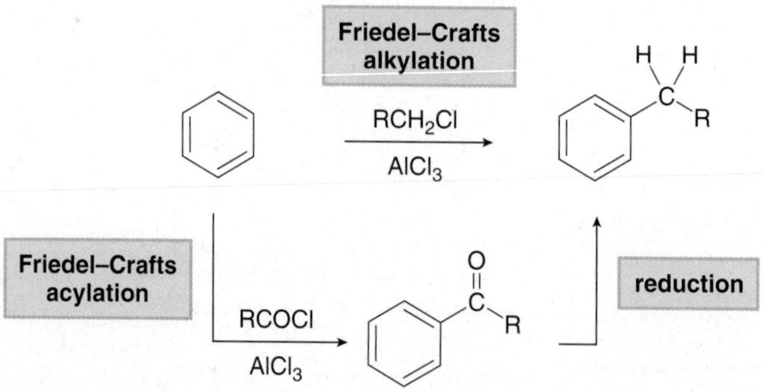

Figure 18.8 Two methods to prepare an alkyl benzene

Although the two-step method seems more roundabout, it must be used to synthesize certain alkyl benzenes that cannot be prepared by the one-step Friedel–Crafts alkylation because of rearrangements.

Recall from Section 18.5C that propylbenzene cannot be prepared by a Friedel–Crafts alkylation. Instead, when benzene is treated with 1-chloropropane and $AlCl_3$, isopropylbenzene is formed by a rearrangement reaction. Propylbenzene can be made, however, by a two-step procedure using Friedel–Crafts acylation followed by reduction.

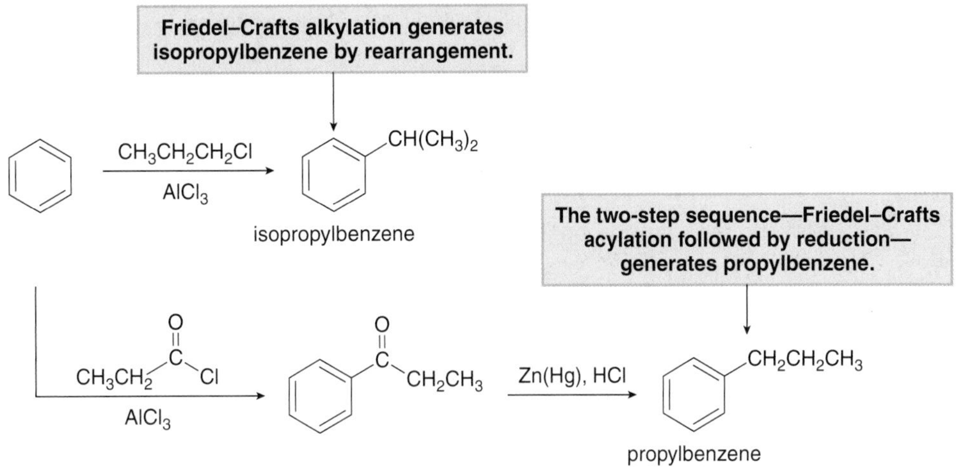

Problem 18.30 Write out the two-step sequence that converts benzene to each compound: (a) $C_6H_5CH_2CH_2CH_2CH_2CH_3$; (b) $C_6H_5CH_2C(CH_3)_3$.

Problem 18.31 What steps are needed to convert benzene into *p*-isobutylacetophenone, a synthetic intermediate used in the synthesis of the anti-inflammatory agent ibuprofen.

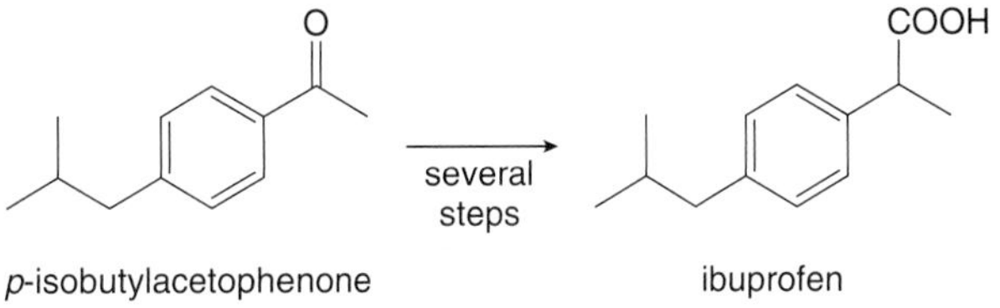

18.15C Reduction of Nitro Groups

A nitro group (NO_2) is easily introduced on a benzene ring by nitration with strong acid (Section 18.4). This process is useful because the nitro group is readily reduced to an amino group (NH_2) under a variety of conditions. The most common methods use H_2 and a catalyst, or a metal (such as Fe or Sn) and a strong acid like HCl.

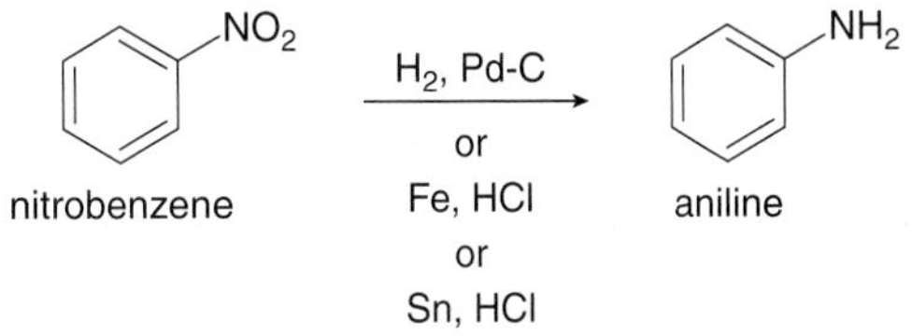

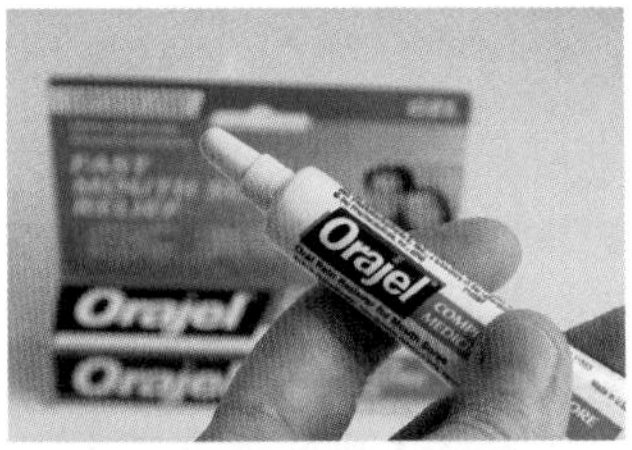

Benzocaine is the active ingredient in the over-the-counter topical anesthetic Orajel.

For example, reduction of ethyl *p*-nitrobenzoate with H_2 and a palladium catalyst forms ethyl *p*-aminobenzoate, a local anesthetic commonly called benzocaine.

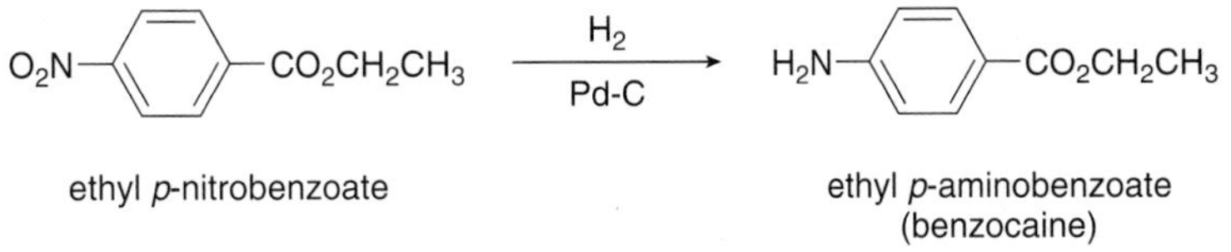

Sample Problem 18.8 illustrates the utility of this process in a short synthesis.

Sample Problem 18.8 Design a synthesis of *m*-bromoaniline from benzene.

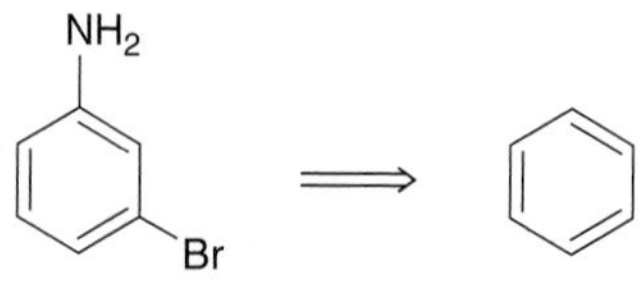

m-bromoaniline

Solution

To devise a retrosynthetic plan, keep in mind:

- The NH_2 group cannot be introduced directly on the ring by electrophilic aromatic substitution. It must be added by a two-step process: nitration followed by reduction.
- Both the Br and NH_2 groups are ortho, para directors, but they are located meta to each other on the ring. However, an NO_2 group (from which an NH_2 group is made) *is* a meta director, and we can use this fact to our advantage.

Retrosynthetic Analysis

Working backward gives the following **three-step retrosynthetic analysis:**

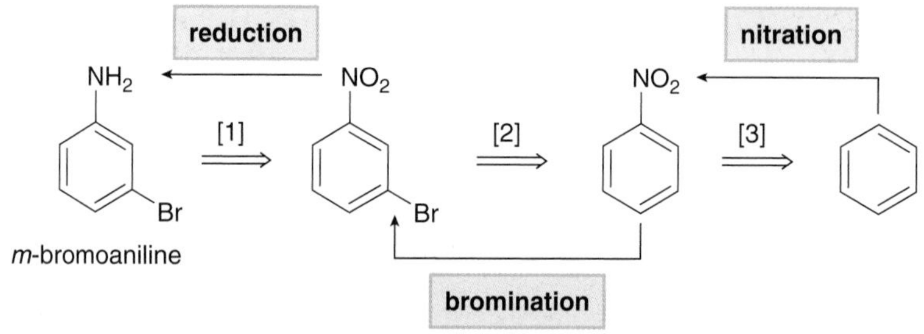

- [1] Form the NH_2 group by reduction of NO_2.
- [2] Introduce the Br group meta to the NO_2 group by halogenation.
- [3] Add the NO_2 group by nitration.

Synthesis

The synthesis then involves three steps, and the order is crucial for success. Halogenation (Step [2] of the synthesis) must occur *before* reduction (Step [3]) in order to form the meta substitution product.

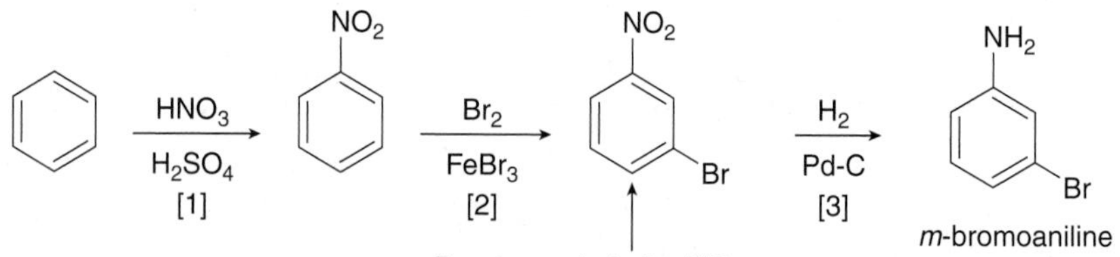

Problem 18.32 Synthesize each compound from benzene.

a. 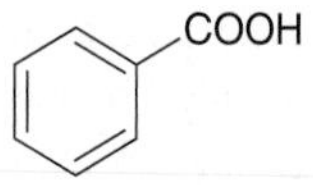

b. 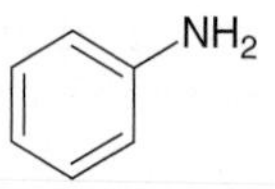

c. 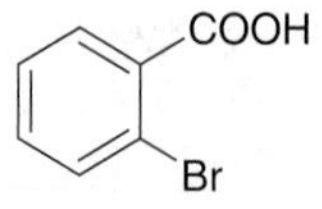

18.16 Multistep Synthesis

The reactions learned in Chapter 18 make it possible to synthesize a wide variety of substituted benzenes, as shown in Sample Problems 18.9–18.11.

Sample Problem 18.9 Synthesize *p*-nitrobenzoic acid from benzene.

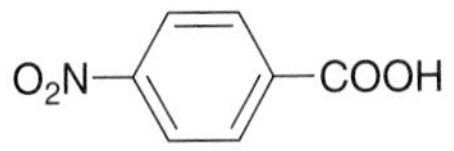

p-nitrobenzoic acid

Solution

Both groups on the ring (NO_2 and COOH) are meta directors. To place these two groups para to each other, remember that the COOH group is prepared by oxidizing an alkyl group, which is an ortho, para director.

Retrosynthetic Analysis

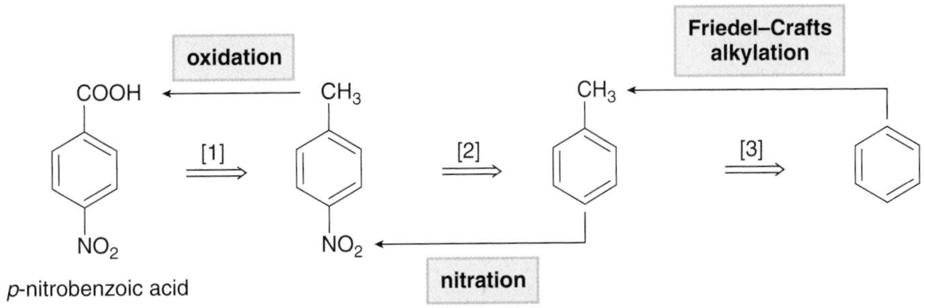

Working backwards:

- [1] Form the COOH group by oxidation of an alkyl group.
- [2] Introduce the NO_2 group para to the CH_3 group (an ortho, para director) by nitration.
- [3] Add the CH_3 group by Friedel–Crafts alkylation.

Synthesis

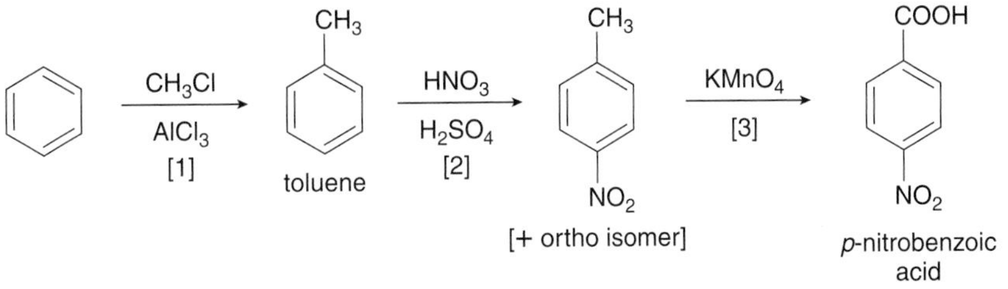

- Friedel–Crafts alkylation with CH_3Cl and $AlCl_3$ forms toluene in Step [1]. Because CH_3 is an ortho, para director, nitration yields the desired para product, which can be separated from its ortho isomer (Step [2]).
- Oxidation with $KMnO_4$ converts the CH_3 group into a COOH group, giving the desired product in Step [3].

Sample Problem 18.10 Synthesize *p*-chlorostyrene from benzene.

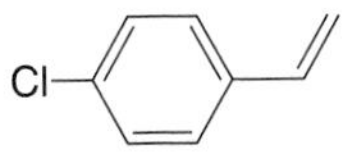

p-chlorostyrene

Solution

Both groups on the ring are ortho, para directors located para to each other. To introduce the double bond in the side chain, we must follow the two-step sequence in Sample Problem 18.7.

Retrosynthetic Analysis

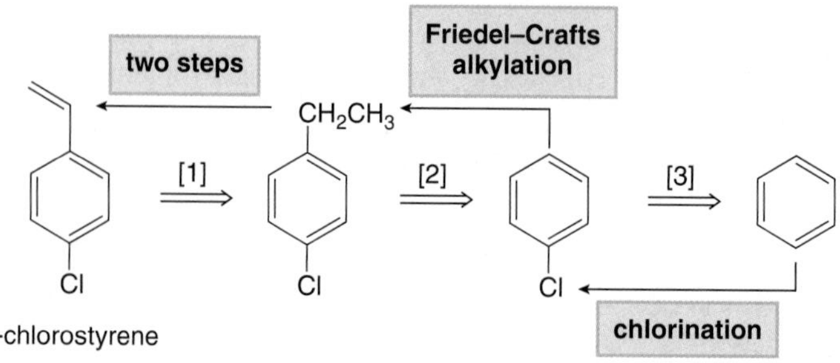

p-chlorostyrene

Working backwards:

- [1] Form the double bond by two steps: benzylic halogenation followed by elimination.
- [2] Introduce the CH_3CH_2 group by Friedel–Crafts alkylation.
- [3] Add the Cl atom by chlorination.

Synthesis

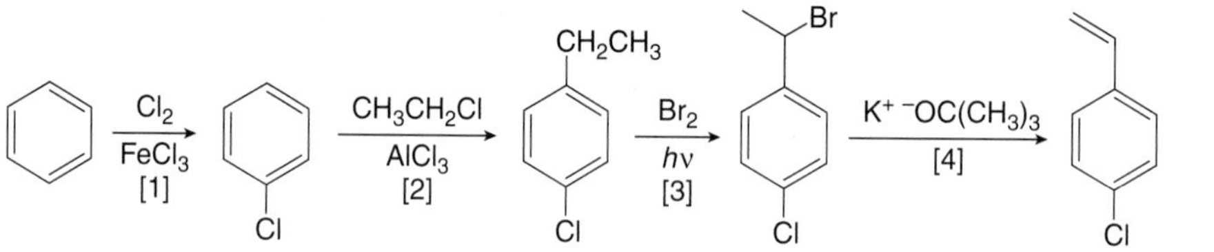

[+ ortho isomer]

p-chlorostyrene

- Chlorination in Step [1] followed by Friedel–Crafts alkylation in Step [2] forms the desired para product, which can be separated from its ortho isomer.
- Benzylic bromination followed by elimination with strong base [$KOC(CH_3)_3$] (Steps [3] and [4]) forms the double bond of the target compound, *p*-chlorostyrene.

Sample Problem 18.11

Synthesize the trisubstituted benzene **A** from benzene.

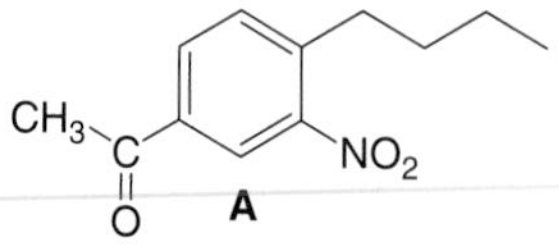

A

Solution

Two groups (CH_3CO and NO_2) in **A** are meta directors located meta to each other, and the third substituent, an alkyl group, is an ortho, para director.

Retrosynthetic Analysis

With three groups on the benzene ring, begin by determining the possible disubstituted benzenes that are immediate precursors of the target compound, and then eliminate any that cannot be converted to the desired product. For example, three different disubstituted benzenes (**B–D**) can theoretically be precursors to **A.** However, conversion of compounds **B** or **D** to **A** would require a Friedel–Crafts reaction on a deactivated benzene ring, a reaction that does not occur. Thus, only **C** is a feasible precursor of **A.**

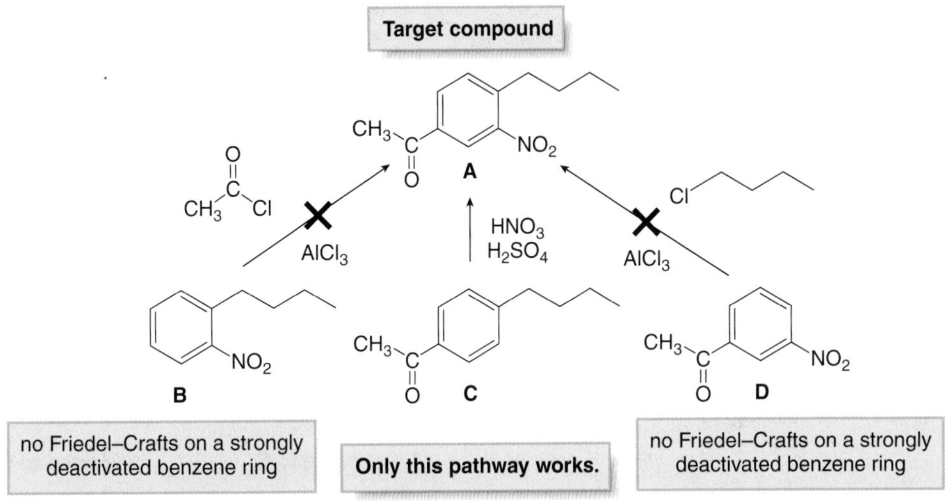

To complete the retrosynthetic analysis, prepare **C** from benzene:

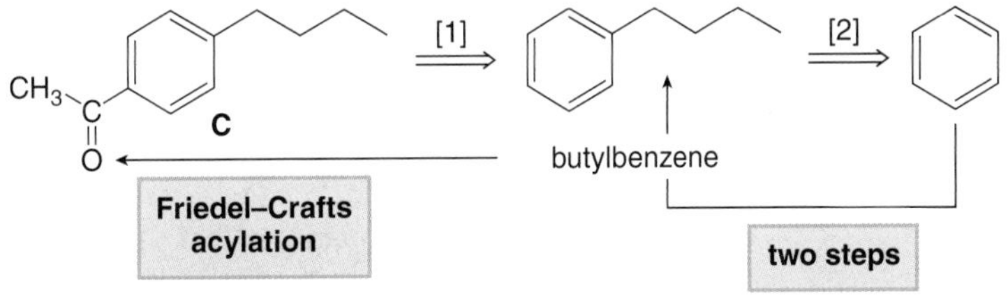

- [1] Add the ketone by Friedel–Crafts acylation.
- [2] Add the alkyl group by the two-step process—Friedel–Crafts acylation followed by reduction. It is not possible to prepare butylbenzene by a one-step Friedel–Crafts alkylation because of a rearrangement reaction (Section 18.15B).

Synthesis

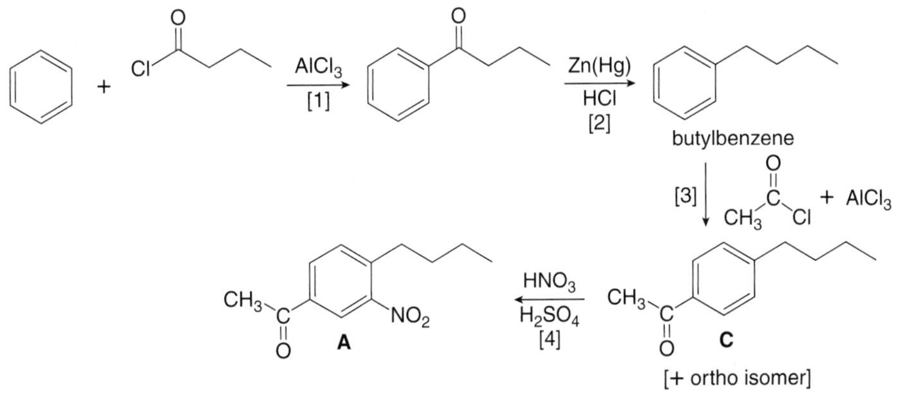

- Friedel–Crafts acylation followed by reduction with Zn(Hg), HCl yields butylbenzene (Steps [1]–[2]).
- Friedel–Crafts acylation gives the para product **C,** which can be separated from its ortho isomer (Step [3]).
- Nitration in Step [4] introduces the NO_2 group ortho to the alkyl group (an ortho, para director) and meta to the CH_3CO group (a meta director).

Problem 18.33 Synthesize each compound from benzene.

a. 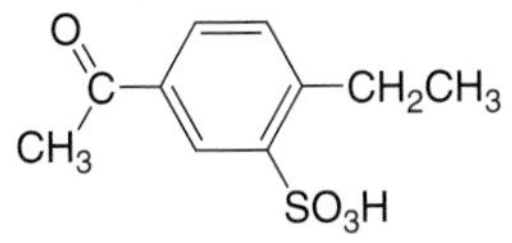

b. 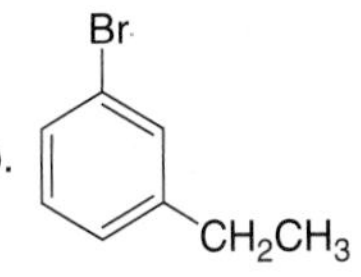

c. 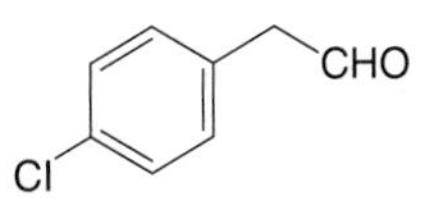

KEY CONCEPTS

Reactions of Aromatic Compounds

Mechanism of Electrophilic Aromatic Substitution (18.2)

- Electrophilic aromatic substitution follows a two-step mechanism. Reaction of the aromatic ring with an electrophile forms a carbocation, and loss of a proton regenerates the aromatic ring.
- The first step is rate-determining.
- The intermediate carbocation is stabilized by resonance; a minimum of three resonance structures can be drawn. The positive charge is always located ortho or para to the new C – E bond.

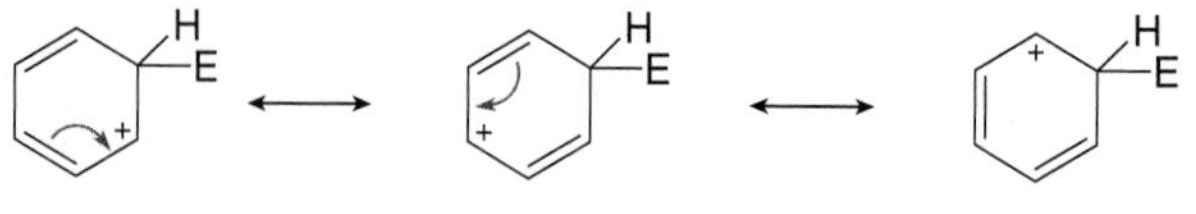
H
E
(+) ortho to E
(+) para to E
(+) ortho to E

Three Rules Describing the Reactivity and Directing Effects of Common Substituents (18.7–18.9)

[1] All ortho, para directors except the halogens activate the benzene ring.
[2] All meta directors deactivate the benzene ring.
[3] The halogens deactivate the benzene ring and direct ortho, para.

Summary of Substituent Effects in Electrophilic Aromatic Substitution (18.6–18.9)

	Substituent	Inductive effect	Resonance effect	Reactivity	Directing effect
[1]	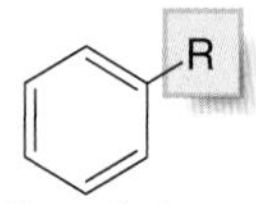 R = alkyl	donating	none	activating	ortho, para
[2]	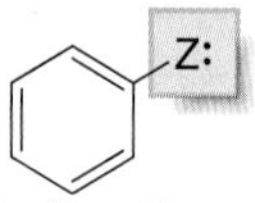 Z = N or O	withdrawing	donating	activating	ortho, para
[3]	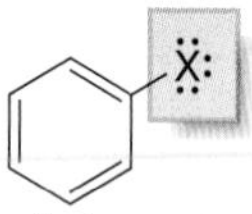 X = halogen	withdrawing	donating	deactivating	ortho, para
[4]	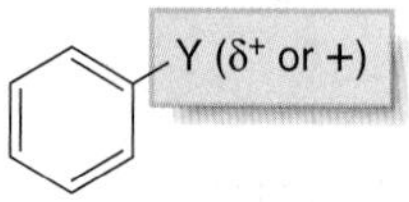	withdrawing	withdrawing	deactivating	meta

Five Examples of Electrophilic Aromatic Substitution

[1] Halogenation—Replacement of H by Cl or Br (18.3)

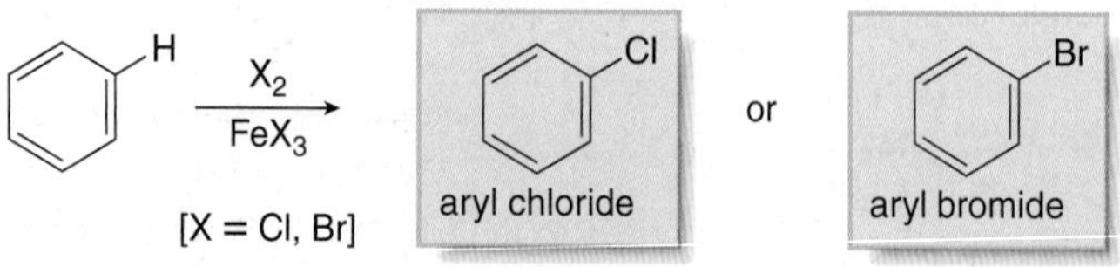
H
X_2
FeX_3
[X = Cl, Br]
Cl
aryl chloride
or
Br
aryl bromide

- Polyhalogenation occurs on benzene rings substituted by OH and NH_2 (and related substituents) (18.10A).

---

[2] Nitration—Replacement of H by NO_2 (18.4)

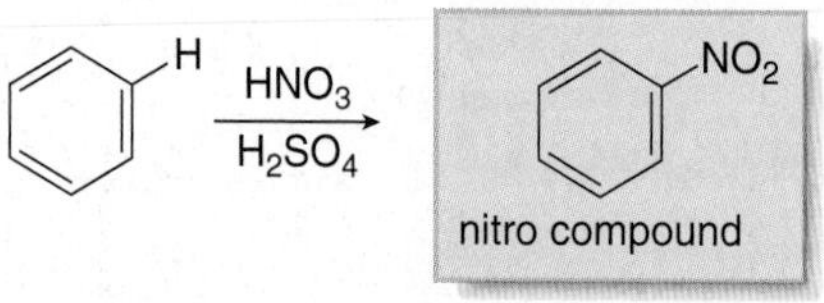
H
HNO_3
H_2SO_4
NO_2
nitro compound

---

[3] Sulfonation—Replacement of H by SO_3H (18.4)

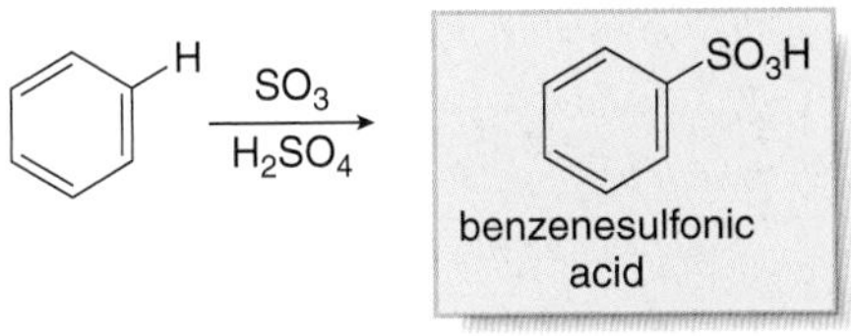

[4] Friedel–Crafts alkylation—Replacement of H by R (18.5)

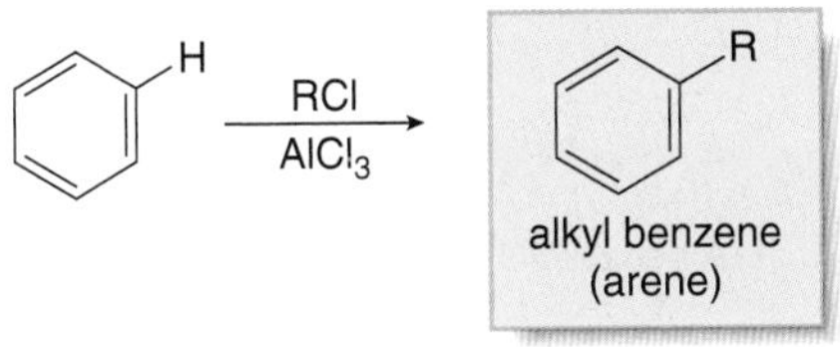

- Rearrangements can occur.
- Vinyl halides and aryl halides are unreactive.
- The reaction does not occur on benzene rings substituted by meta deactivating groups or NH_2 groups (18.10B).
- Polyalkylation can occur.

Variations:

[1] with alcohols

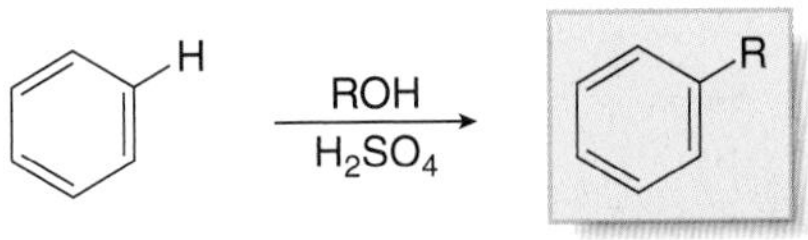

[2] with alkenes

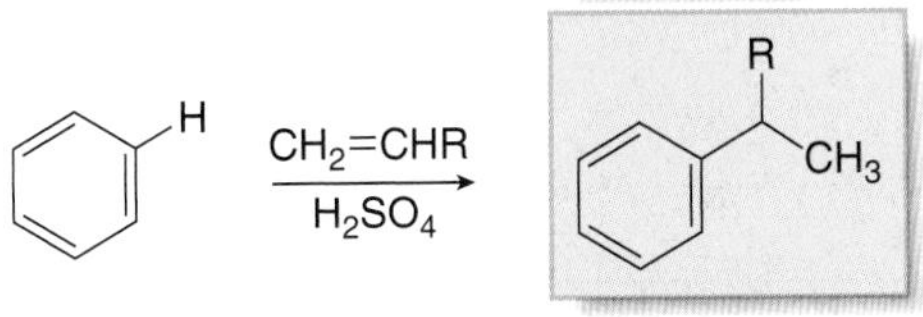

[5] Friedel–Crafts acylation—Replacement of H by RCO (18.5)

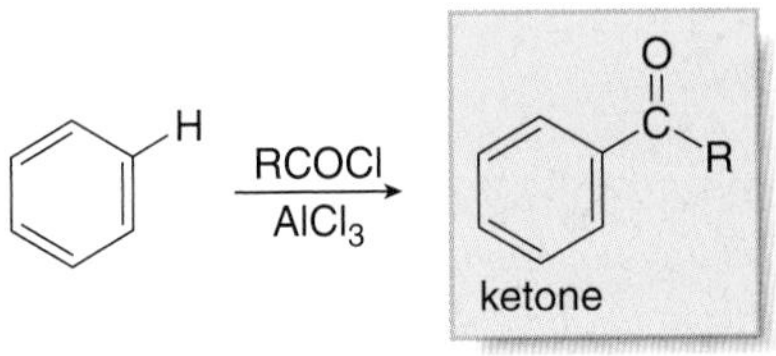

- The reaction does not occur on benzene rings substituted by meta deactivating groups or NH_2 groups (18.10B).

Nucleophilic Aromatic Substitution (18.13)

[1] Nucleophilic substitution by an addition–elimination mechanism

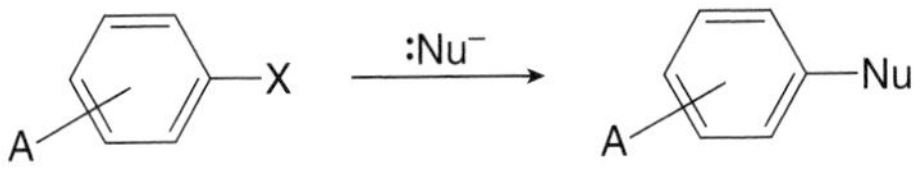

X = F, Cl, Br, I
A = electron-withdrawing group

- The mechanism has two steps.
- Strong electron-withdrawing groups at the ortho or para positions are required.
- Increasing the number of electron-withdrawing groups increases the rate.
- Increasing the electronegativity of the halogen increases the rate.

[2] Nucleophilic substitution by an elimination–addition mechanism

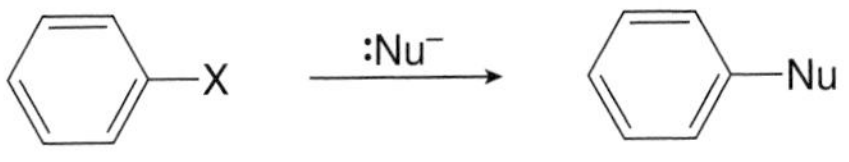

X = halogen

- Reaction conditions are harsh.
- Benzyne is formed as an intermediate.
- Product mixtures may result.

Other Reactions of Benzene Derivatives

[1] Benzylic halogenation (18.14)

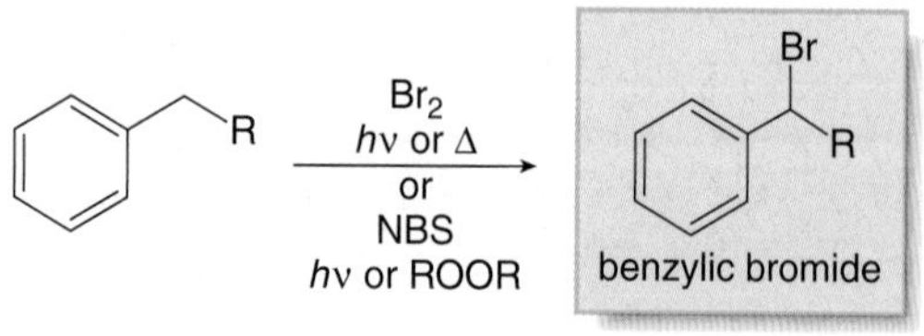
R
Br2
hν or Δ
or
NBS
hν or ROOR
Br
R
benzylic bromide

[2] Oxidation of alkyl benzenes (18.15A)

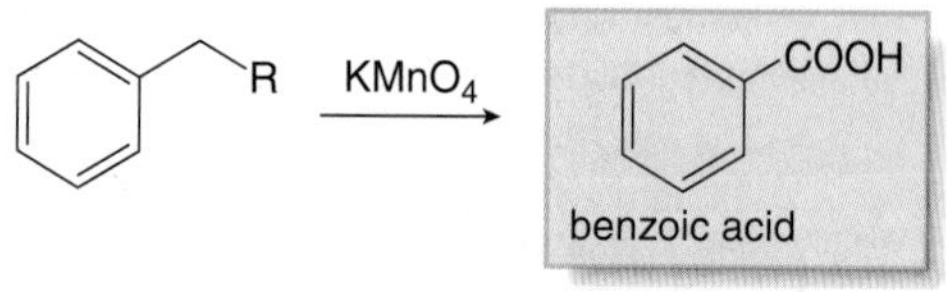
R
KMnO4
COOH
benzoic acid

- A benzylic C–H bond is needed for reaction.

[3] Reduction of ketones to alkyl benzenes (18.15B)

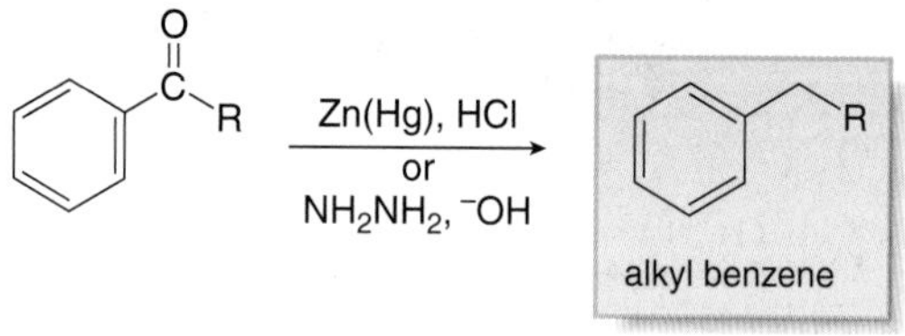
O
C
R
Zn(Hg), HCl
or
NH2NH2, −OH
R
alkyl benzene

[4] Reduction of nitro groups to amino groups (18.15C)

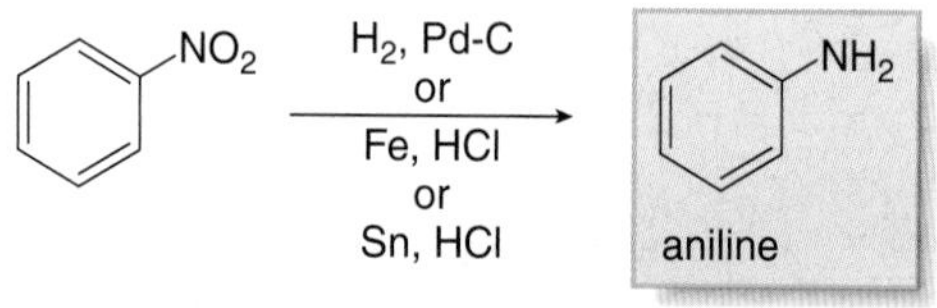
NO2
H2, Pd-C
or
Fe, HCl
or
Sn, HCl
NH2
aniline

PROBLEMS

Problems Using Three-Dimensional Models

18.34 Draw the products formed when **A** and **B** are treated with each of the following reagents: (a) Br_2, $FeBr_3$; (b) HNO_3, H_2SO_4; (c) CH_3CH_2COCl, $AlCl_3$.

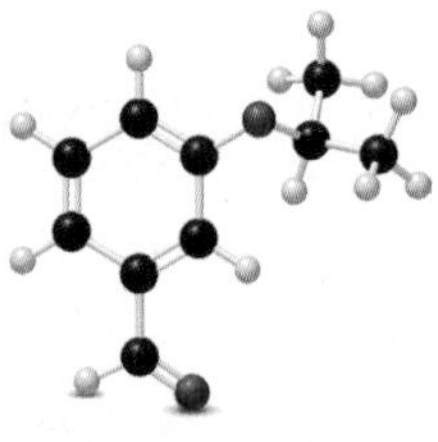

A

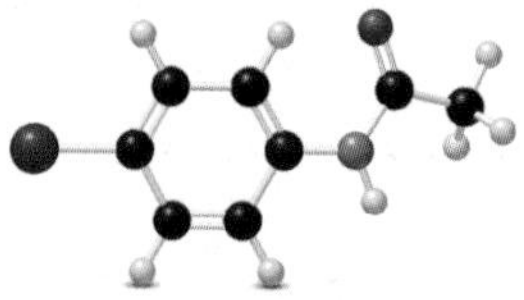

B

18.35 What is the major product formed by an intramolecular Friedel–Crafts acylation of the following compound?

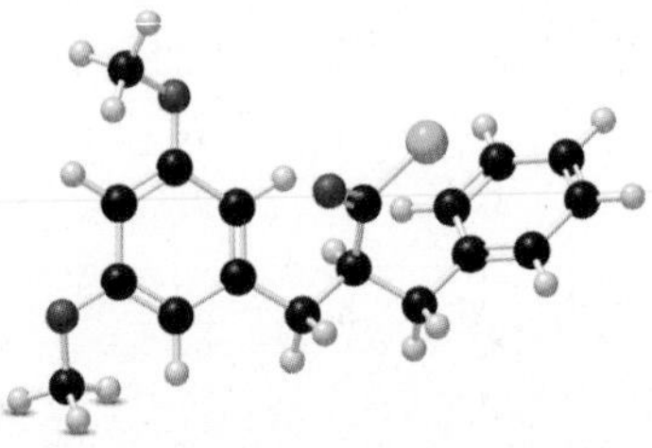

Reactions

18.36 Draw the products formed when phenol (C_6H_5OH) is treated with each reagent.

a. HNO_3, H_2SO_4
b. SO_3, H_2SO_4
c. CH_3CH_2Cl, $AlCl_3$
d. $(CH_3CH_2)_2CHCOCl$, $AlCl_3$
e. Br_2, $FeBr_3$
f. Br_2
g. Cl_2, $FeCl_3$
h. product in (a), then Sn, HCl
i. product in (d), then Zn(Hg), HCl
j. product in (d), then NH_2NH_2, ^{-}OH
k. product in (c), then Br_2, $h\nu$
l. product in (c), then $KMnO_4$

18.37 Draw the products formed when each compound is treated with CH_3CH_2COCl, $AlCl_3$.

a. 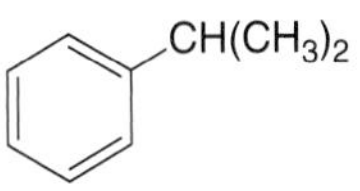

b. 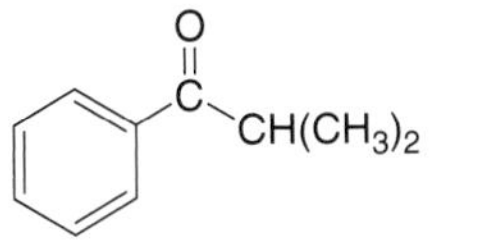

c. 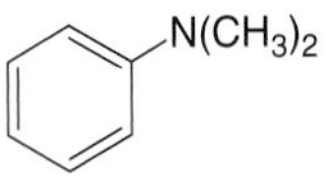

d. 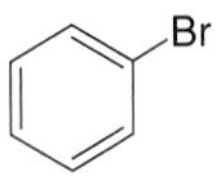

e. 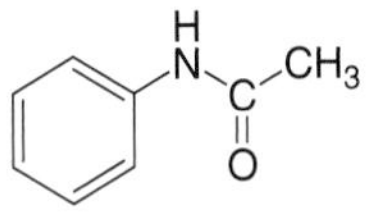

18.38 Draw the products of each reaction.

a. 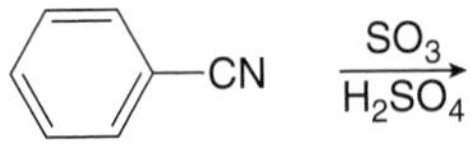

b. 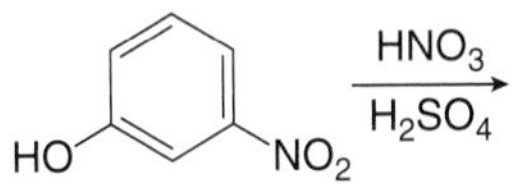

c. 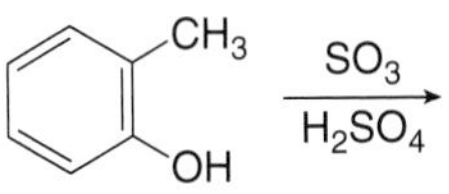

d. 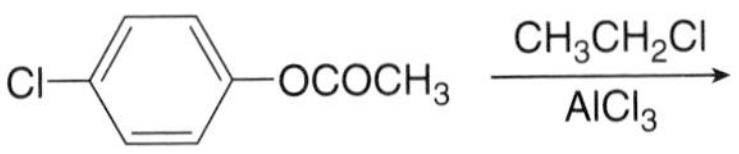

e. 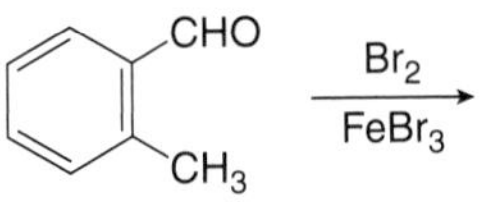

f. 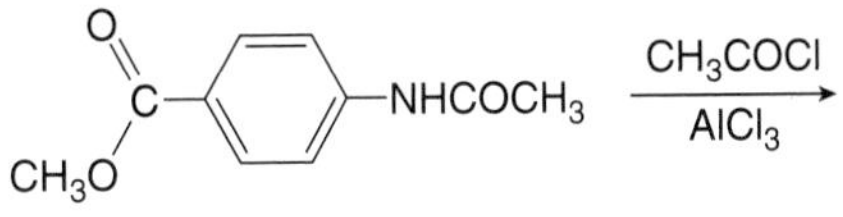

g. 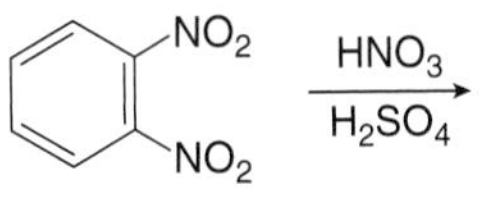

h. 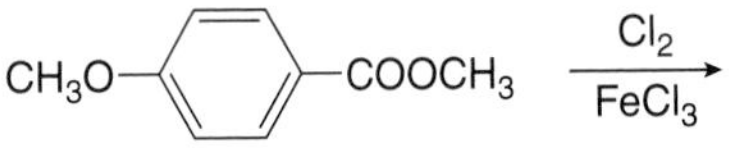

i. 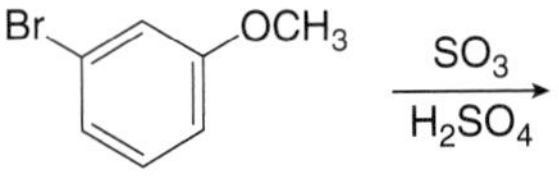

j. 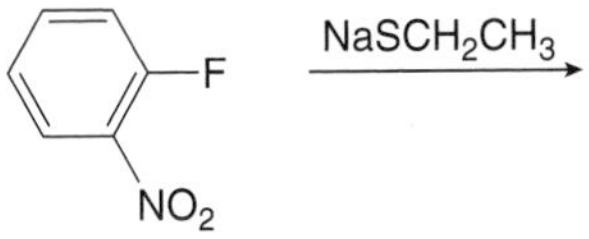

18.39 What products are formed when benzene is treated with each alkyl chloride and $AlCl_3$?

a. 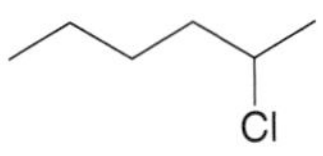

b. 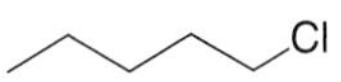

c. 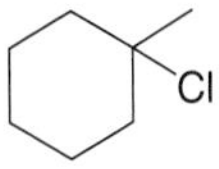

d. 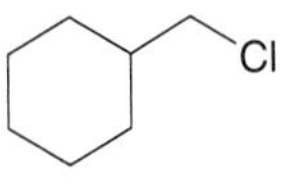

18.40 Draw the products of each reaction.

a. 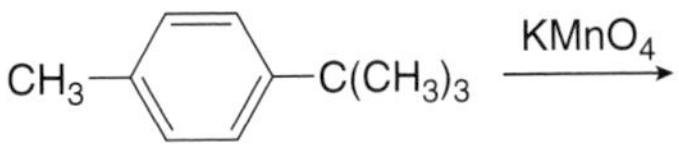

b. 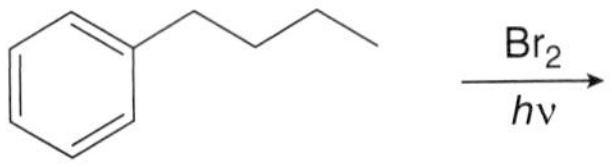

c. 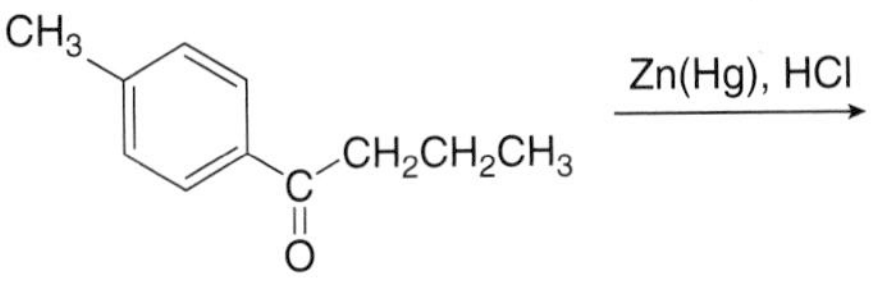

d. 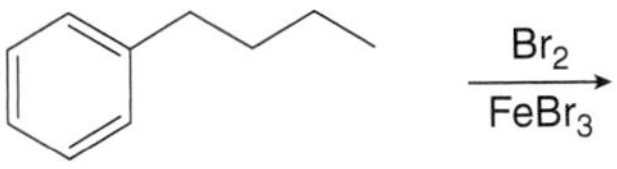

e. 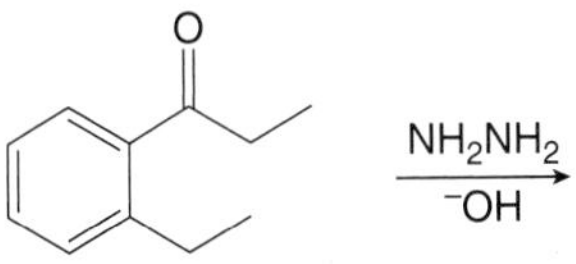

f. 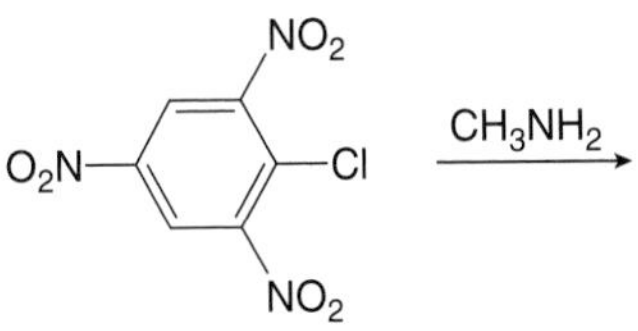

18.41 You have learned two ways to make an alkyl benzene: Friedel–Crafts alkylation, and Friedel–Crafts acylation followed by reduction. Although some alkyl benzenes can be prepared by both methods, it is often true that only one method can be used to prepare a given alkyl benzene. Which method(s) can be used to prepare each of the following compounds from benzene? Show the steps that would be used.

a. 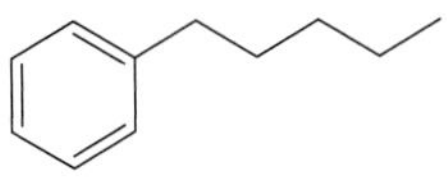
b. 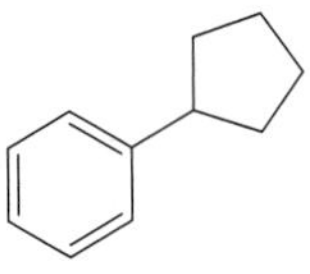
c. 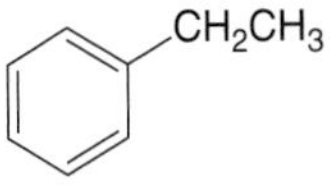

d. 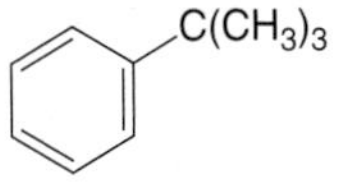

18.42 One step in the synthesis of pioglitazone (trade name Actos), a drug used to treat type 2 diabetes, involves the reaction of **A** with **B** in the presence of NaH to afford **C.** What is the structure of **C?**

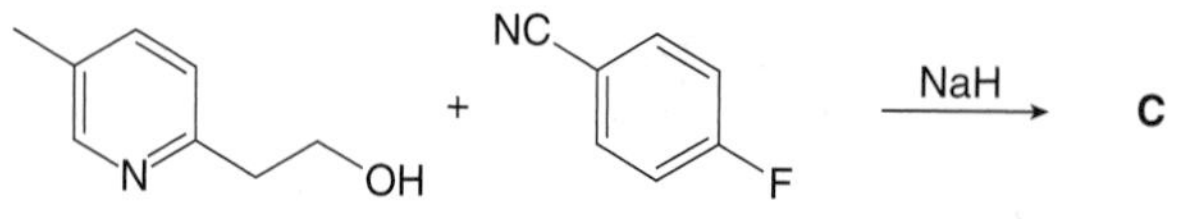

A B

18.43 **D** is an intermediate in the synthesis of rosiglitazone (trade name Avandia), a drug used for type 2 diabetes. Suggest two different methods to prepare the ether in **D** by substitution reactions.

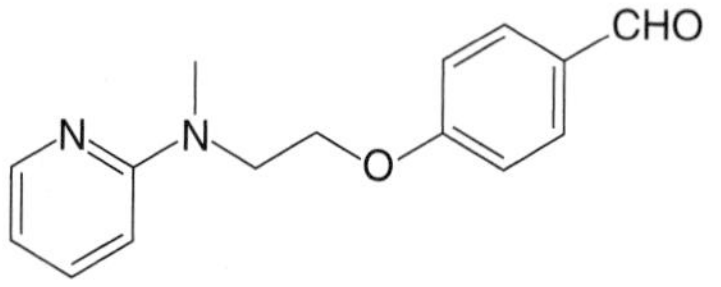

D

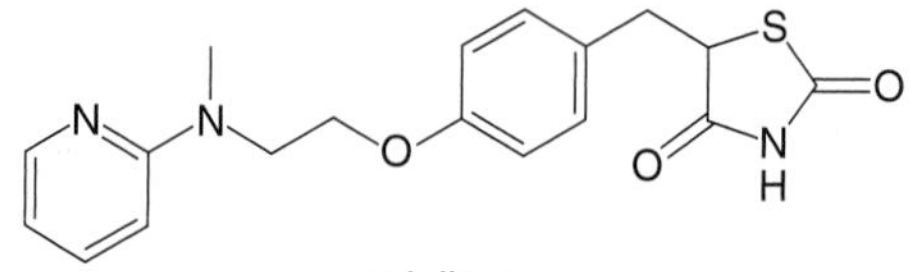

rosiglitazone

18.44 Explain why each of the following reactions will not form the given product. Then, design a synthesis of **A** from benzene and **B** from phenol (C_6H_5OH).

a. 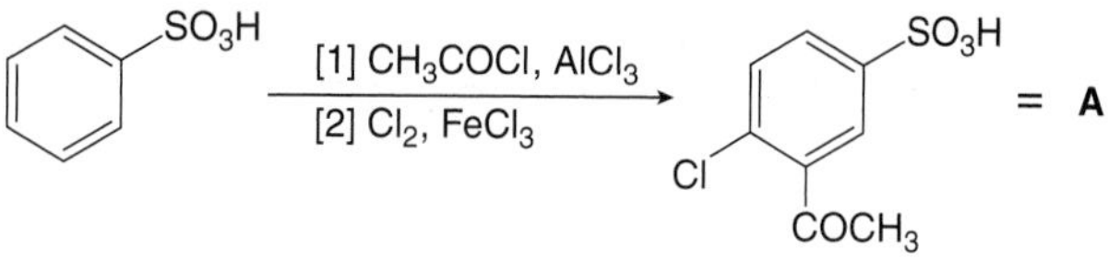

b. 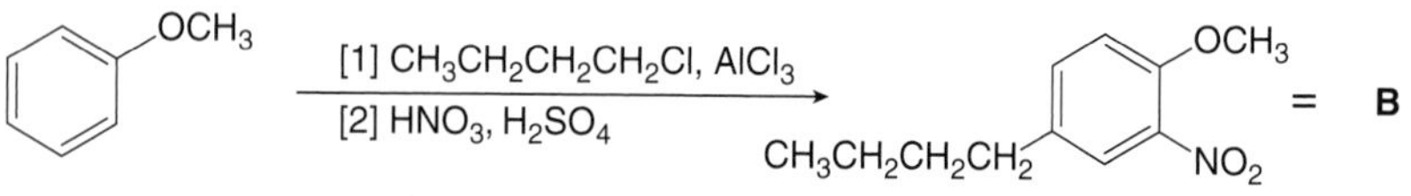

Substituent Effects

18.45 Rank the compounds in each group in order of increasing reactivity in electrophilic aromatic substitution.

a. $C_6H_5NO_2$, C_6H_6, C_6H_5OH

b. C_6H_6, C_6H_5Cl, C_6H_5CHO

c. C_6H_6, $C_6H_5NO_2$, $C_6H_5NH_2$

d. $C_6H_5CH_3$, $C_6H_5NH_2$, $C_6H_5CH_2NH_2$

18.46 For each of the following substituted benzenes: [1] C_6H_5Br; [2] C_6H_5CN; [3] $C_6H_5OCOCH_3$:

a. Does the substituent donate or withdraw electron density by an inductive effect?

b. Does the substituent donate or withdraw electron density by a resonance effect?

c. On balance, does the substituent make a benzene ring more or less electron rich than benzene itself?

d. Does the substituent activate or deactivate the benzene ring in electrophilic aromatic substitution?

18.47 Which benzene ring in each compound is more reactive in electrophilic aromatic substitution?

a. 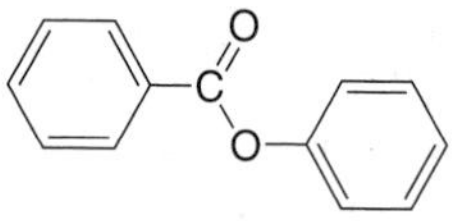

b. 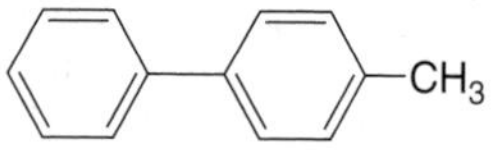

c. 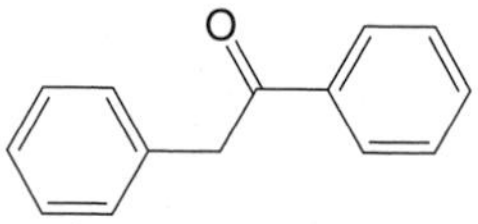

18.48 For each N-substituted benzene, predict whether the compound reacts faster than, slower than, or at a similar rate to benzene in electrophilic aromatic substitution. Then draw the major product(s) formed when each compound reacts with a general electrophile E^+.

a. 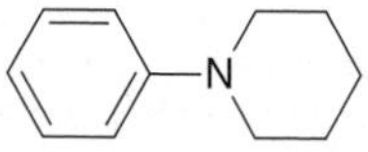

b. 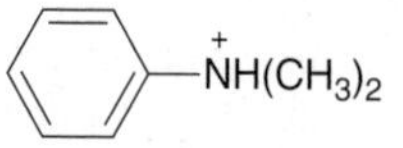

c. 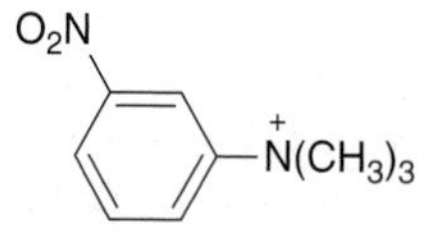

d. 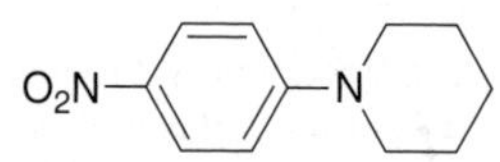

18.49 Explain each statement in detail using resonance structures.

a. A phenyl group (C_6H_5-) is an ortho, para director that activates a benzene ring toward electrophilic attack.

b. A nitroso group ($-NO$) is an ortho, para director that deactivates a benzene ring toward electrophilic attack.

18.50 Explain the following observation. Ethyl 3-phenylpropanoate ($C_6H_5CH_2CH_2CO_2CH_2CH_3$) reacts with electrophiles to afford ortho- and para-disubstituted arenes, but ethyl 3-phenyl-2-propenoate ($C_6H_5CH{=}CHCO_2CH_2CH_3$) reacts with electrophiles to afford meta-disubstituted arenes.

18.51 Explain why the meta product is formed in the following reaction despite the fact that $-N(CH_3)_2$ is usually an ortho, para director.

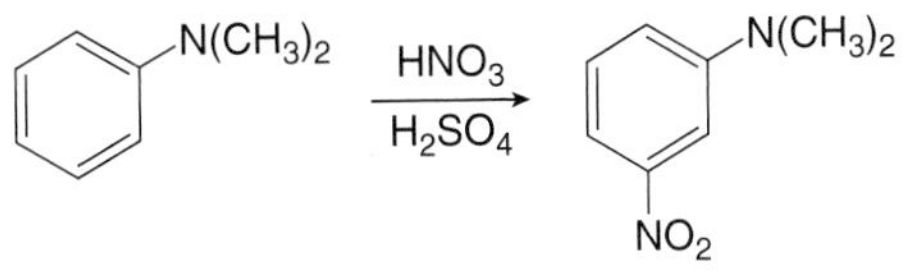

18.52 Rank the aryl halides in each group in order of increasing reactivity in nucleophilic aromatic substitution by an addition–elimination mechanism.

a. chlorobenzene, *p*-fluoronitrobenzene, *m*-fluoronitrobenzene

b. 1-fluoro-2,4-dinitrobenzene, 1-fluoro-3,5-dinitrobenzene, 1-fluoro-3,4-dinitrobenzene

c. 1-fluoro-2,4-dinitrobenzene, 4-chloro-3-nitrotoluene, 4-fluoro-3-nitrotoluene

18.53 Explain why a methoxy group (CH_3O) increases the rate of electrophilic aromatic substitution, but decreases the rate of nucleophilic aromatic substitution.

Mechanisms

18.54 Draw a stepwise mechanism for the following reaction.

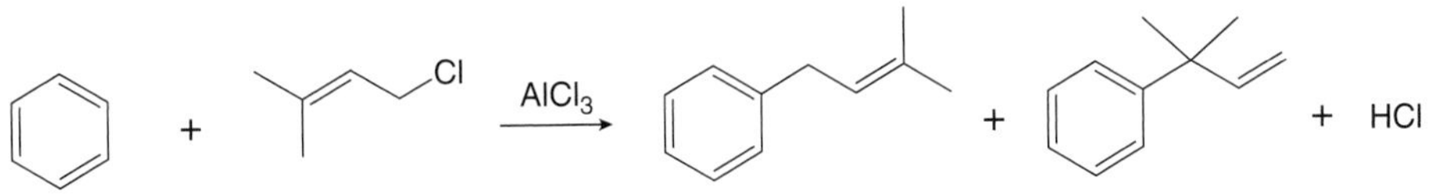

18.55 Draw a stepwise, detailed mechanism for the following intramolecular reaction.

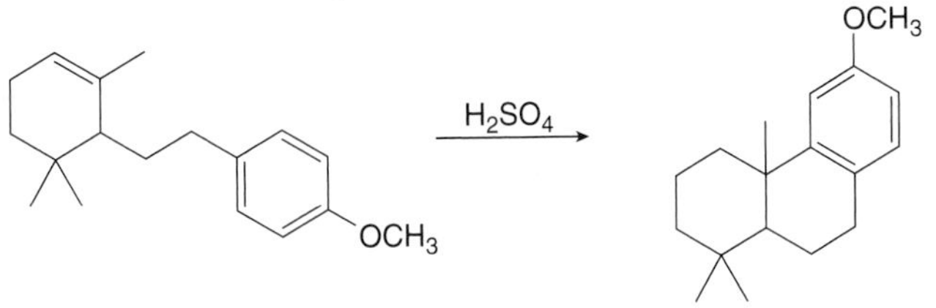

18.56 Draw a stepwise, detailed mechanism for the following reaction.

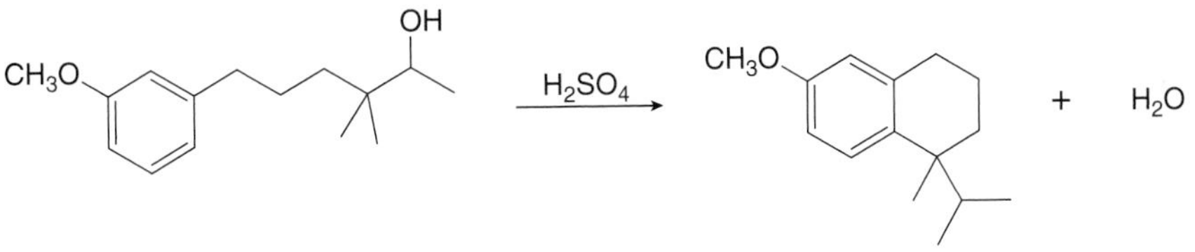

18.57 Friedel–Crafts alkylation of benzene with (2*R*)-2-chlorobutane and $AlCl_3$ affords *sec*-butylbenzene.

a. How many stereogenic centers are present in the product?

b. Would you expect the product to exhibit optical activity? Explain, with reference to the mechanism.

18.58 Draw a stepwise mechanism for the following substitution. Explain why 2-chloropyridine reacts faster than chlorobenzene in this type of reaction.

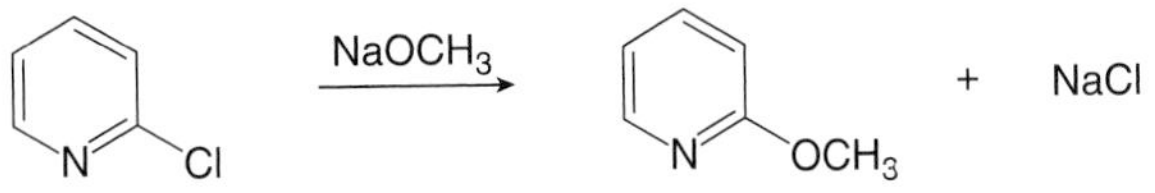

2-chloropyridine

18.59 Draw a stepwise mechanism for the following reaction.

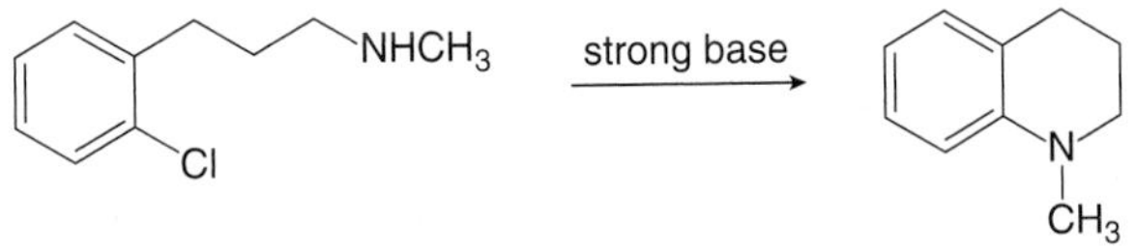

18.60 Although two products (**A** and **B**) are possible when naphthalene undergoes electrophilic aromatic substitution, only **A** is formed. Draw resonance structures for the intermediate carbocation to explain why this is observed.

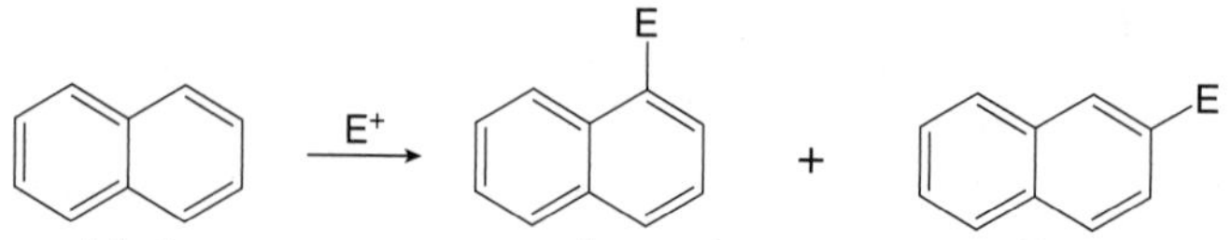

naphthalene **A** This product is formed. **B** This product is *not* formed.

18.61 Draw a stepwise mechanism for the following reaction, which is used to prepare the pesticide DDT.

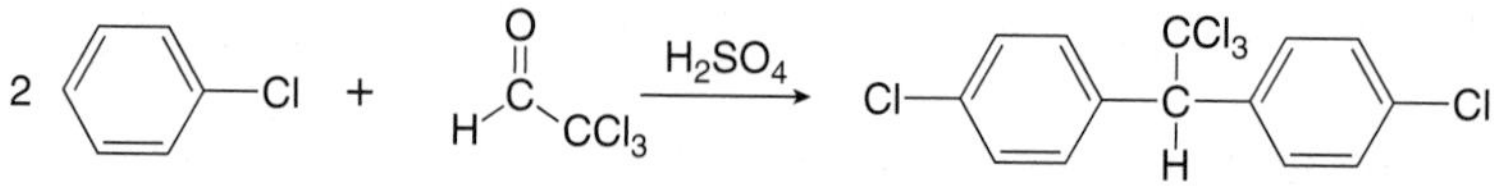

DDT

18.62 Benzene undergoes electrophilic aromatic substitution with anhydrides, compounds having the general structure $(RCO)_2O$, in a reaction that resembles Friedel–Crafts acylation. Draw a stepwise mechanism for the reaction of benzene with glutaric anhydride in the presence of $AlCl_3$.

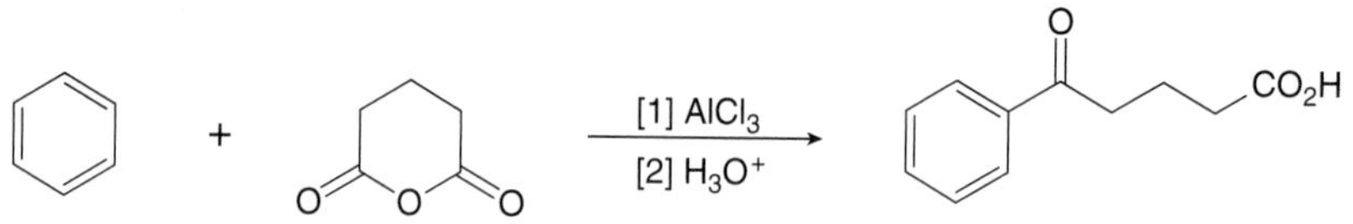

glutaric anhydride

18.63 Benzyl bromide ($C_6H_5CH_2Br$) reacts rapidly with CH_3OH to afford benzyl methyl ether ($C_6H_5CH_2OCH_3$). Draw a stepwise mechanism for the reaction, and explain why this 1° alkyl halide reacts rapidly with a weak nucleophile under conditions that favor an S_N1 mechanism. Would you expect the para-substituted benzylic halides $CH_3OC_6H_4CH_2Br$ and $O_2NC_6H_4CH_2Br$ to each be more or less reactive than benzyl bromide in this reaction? Explain your reasoning.

Synthesis

18.64 Synthesize each compound from benzene and any other organic or inorganic reagents.

a. *o*-butylchlorobenzene

b. *m*-bromonitrobenzene

c. 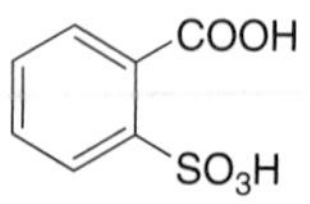

d. 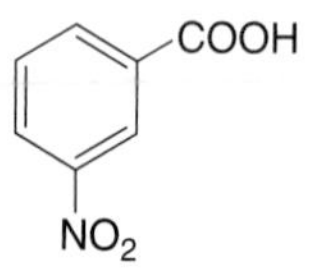

e. 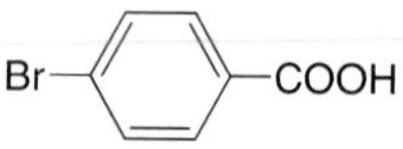

f. 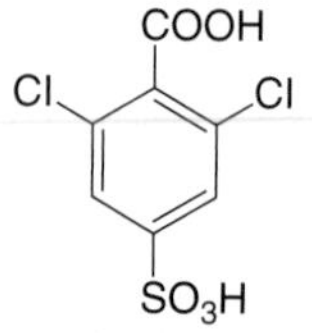

g. 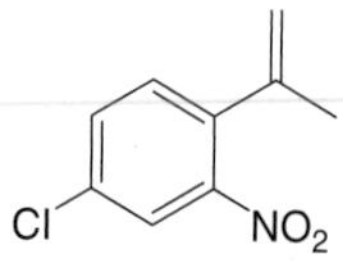

18.65 Synthesize each compound from benzene and any other organic or inorganic reagents.

a. 

c. 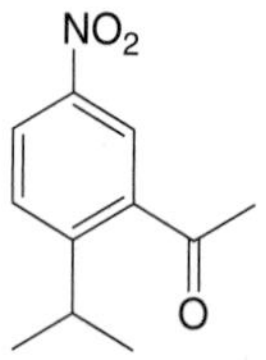

e. 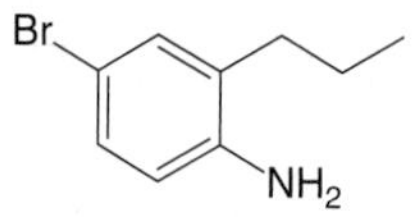

b. 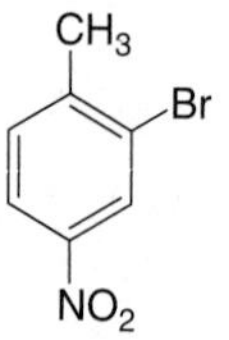

d. 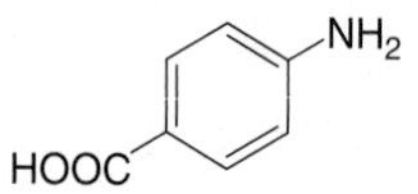

(PABA)
sunscreen component

f. 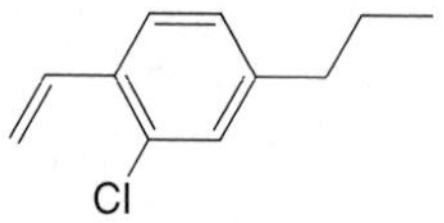

18.66 Synthesize each compound from toluene ($C_6H_5CH_3$) and any other organic or inorganic reagents.

a. $C_6H_5CH_2OC(CH_3)_3$

b. C_6H_5CHO

c. 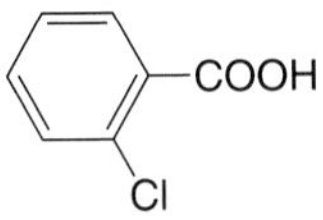

d. 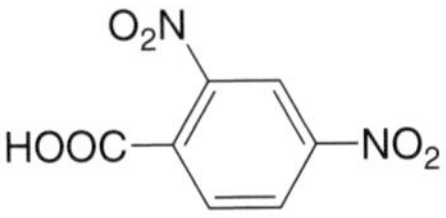

e. 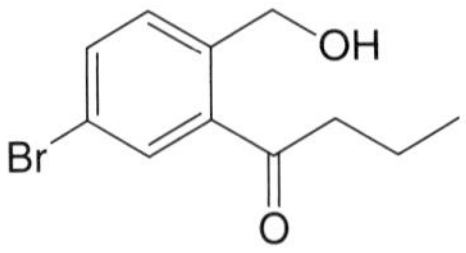

f. 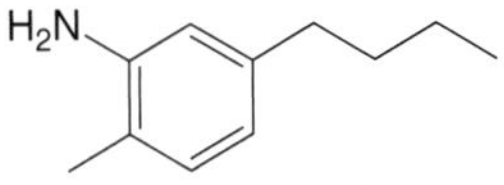

g. 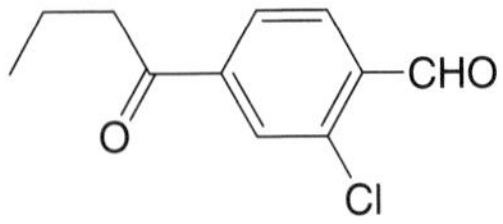

18.67 Devise a synthesis of each compound from phenol (C_6H_5OH) and any other organic or inorganic reagents.

a. 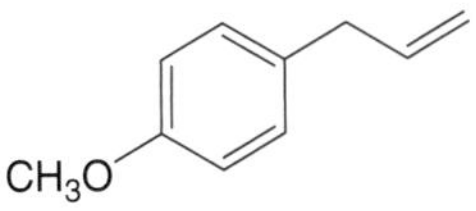

estragole
(isolated from basil)

b. 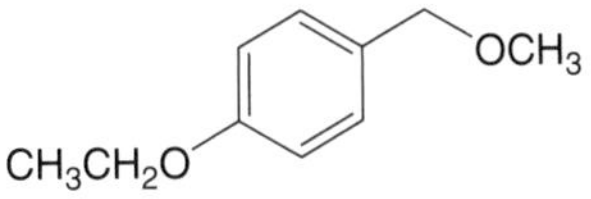

c. 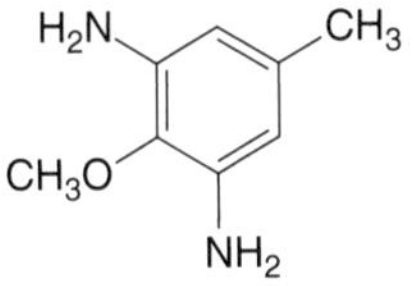

18.68 Use the reactions in this chapter along with those learned in Chapters 11 and 12 to synthesize each compound. You may use benzene, acetylene (HC≡CH), two-carbon alcohols, ethylene oxide, and any inorganic reagents.

a. $C_6H_5C{\equiv}CH$

b. $C_6H_5C{\equiv}CCH_2CH_2OH$

c. 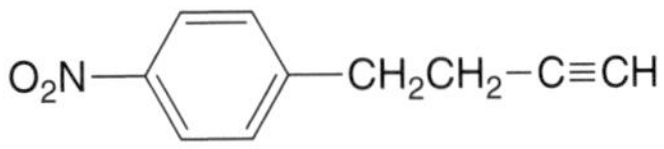

d. 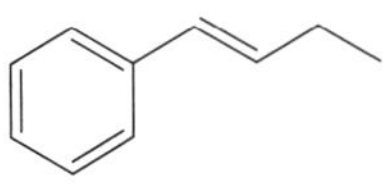

e. 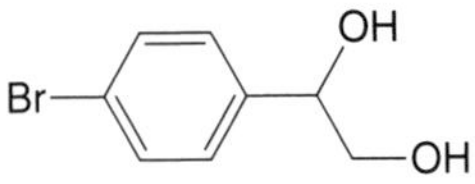

f. 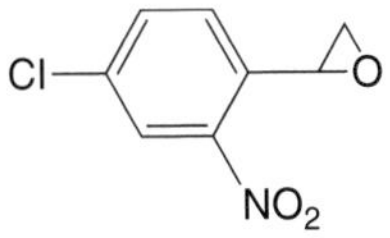

18.69 Ibufenac, a para-disubstituted arene with the structure $HO_2CCH_2C_6H_4CH_2CH(CH_3)_2$, is a much more potent analgesic than aspirin, but it was never sold commercially because it caused liver toxicity in some clinical trials. Devise a synthesis of ibufenac from benzene and organic halides having fewer than five carbons.

18.70 Carboxylic acid **X** is an intermediate in the multistep synthesis of proparacaine, a local anesthetic. Devise a synthesis of **X** from phenol and any needed organic or inorganic reagents.

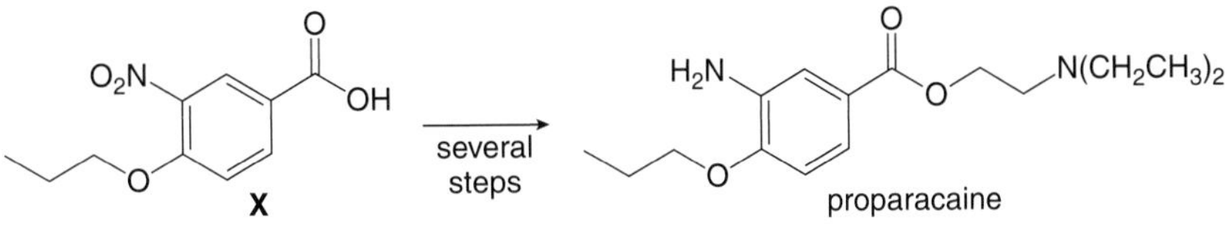

Spectroscopy

18.71 Identify the structures of isomers **A** and **B** (molecular formula C_8H_9Br).

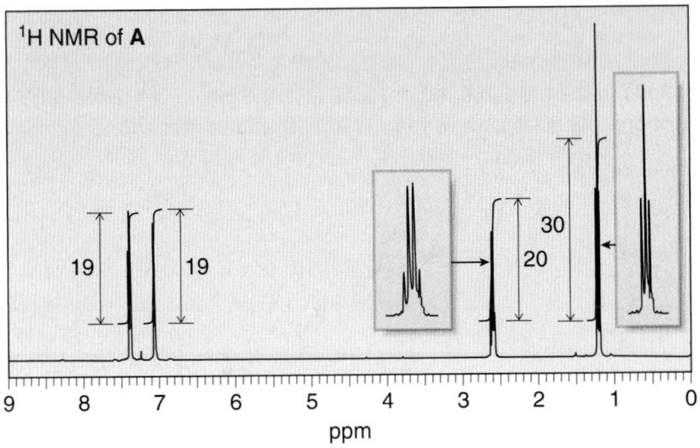

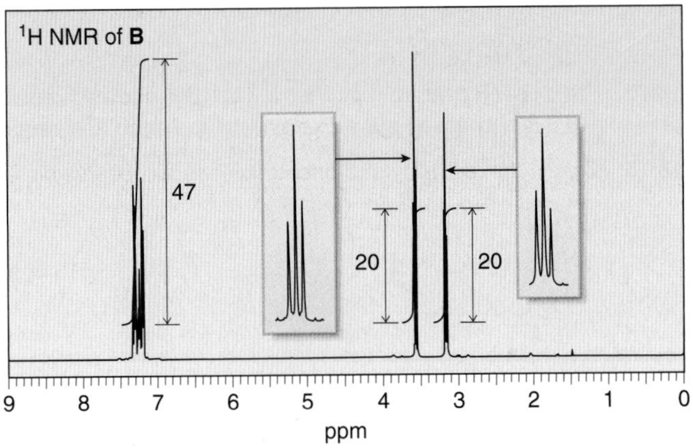

18.72 Propose a structure of compound **C** (molecular formula $C_{10}H_{12}O$) consistent with the following data. **C** is partly responsible for the odor and flavor of raspberries.

Compound **C:** IR absorption at 1717 cm^{-1}

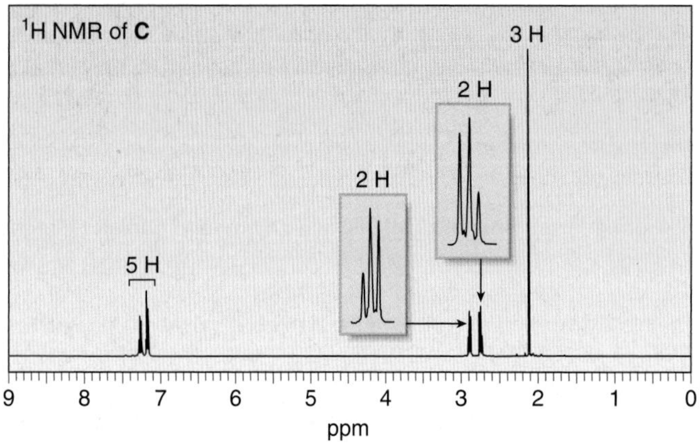

18.73 Compound **X** (molecular formula $C_{10}H_{12}O$) was treated with NH_2NH_2, ^-OH to yield compound **Y** (molecular formula $C_{10}H_{14}$). Based on the ^{1}H NMR spectra of **X** and **Y** given below, what are the structures of **X** and **Y?**

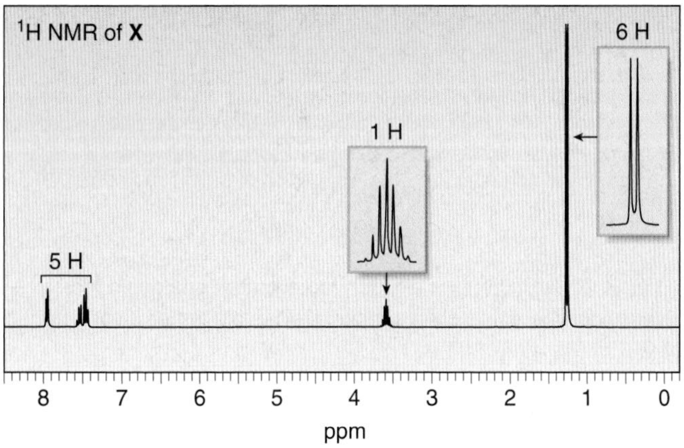

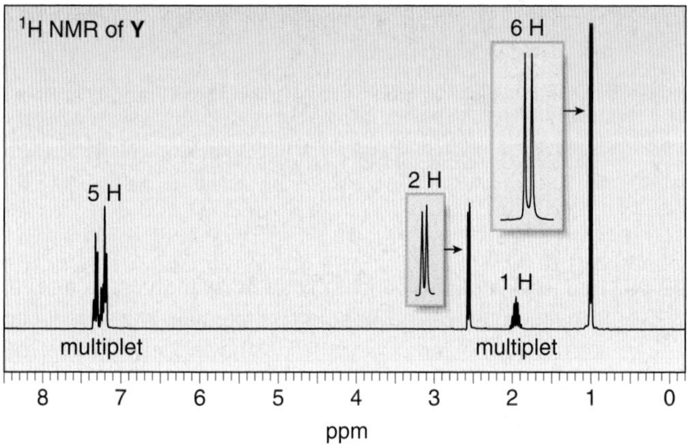

18.74 Reaction of *p*-cresol with two equivalents of 2-methyl-1-propene affords BHT, a preservative with molecular formula $C_{15}H_{24}O$. BHT gives the following ^{1}H NMR spectral data: 1.4 (singlet, 18 H), 2.27 (singlet, 3 H), 5.0 (singlet, 1 H), and 7.0 (singlet, 2 H) ppm. What is the structure of BHT? Draw a stepwise mechanism illustrating how it is formed.

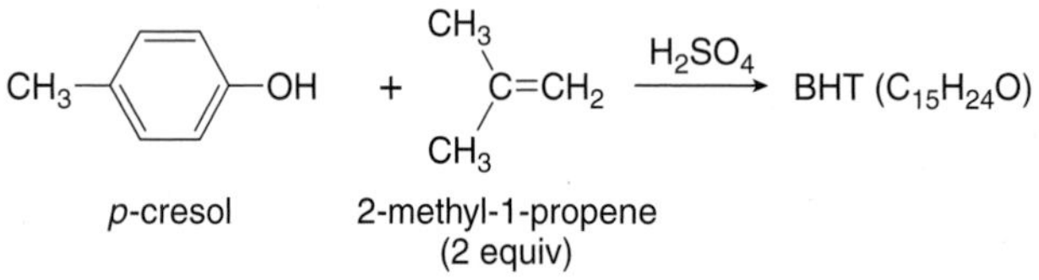

Challenge Problems

18.75 The ^{1}H NMR spectrum of phenol (C_6H_5OH) shows three absorptions in the aromatic region: 6.70 (2 ortho H's), 7.14 (2 meta H's), and 6.80 (1 para H) ppm. Explain why the ortho and para absorptions occur at lower chemical shift than the meta absorption.

18.76 Explain the reactivity and orientation effects observed in each heterocycle.

a. Pyridine is less reactive than benzene in electrophilic aromatic substitution and yields 3-substituted products.
b. Pyrrole is more reactive than benzene in electrophilic aromatic substitution and yields 2-substituted products.

18.77 Draw a stepwise, detailed mechanism for the dienone–phenol rearrangement, a reaction that forms alkyl-substituted phenols from cyclohexadienones.

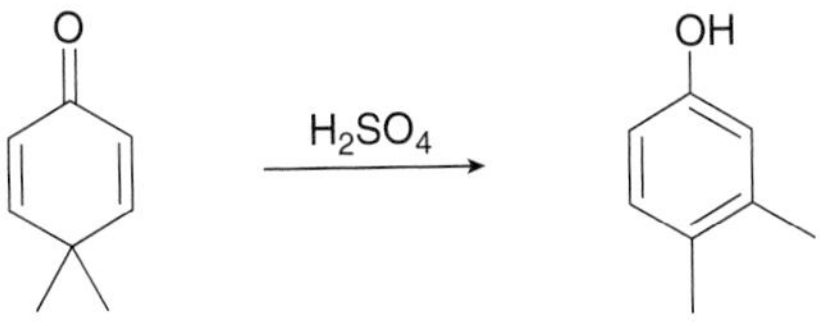

18.78 Draw a stepwise mechanism for the following intramolecular reaction, which is used in the synthesis of the female sex hormone estrone.

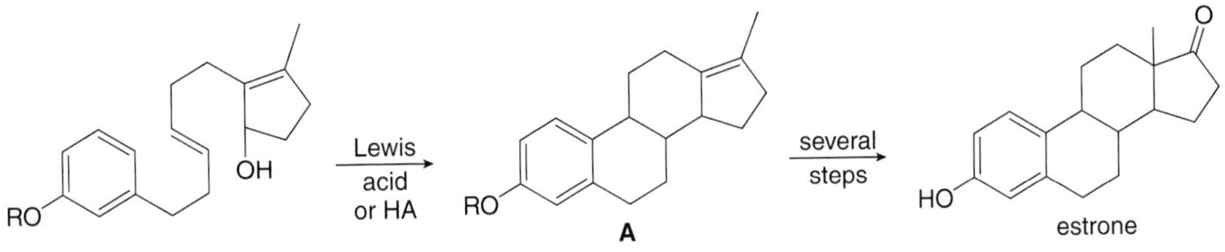

18.79 The bicyclic heterocycles quinoline and indole undergo electrophilic aromatic substitution to give the products shown. (a) Explain why electrophilic substitution occurs on the ring without the N atom for quinoline, but occurs on the ring with the N atom in indole. (b) Explain why electrophilic substitution occurs more readily at C8 than C7 in quinoline. (c) Explain why electrophilic substitution occurs more readily at C3 rather than C2 of indole.

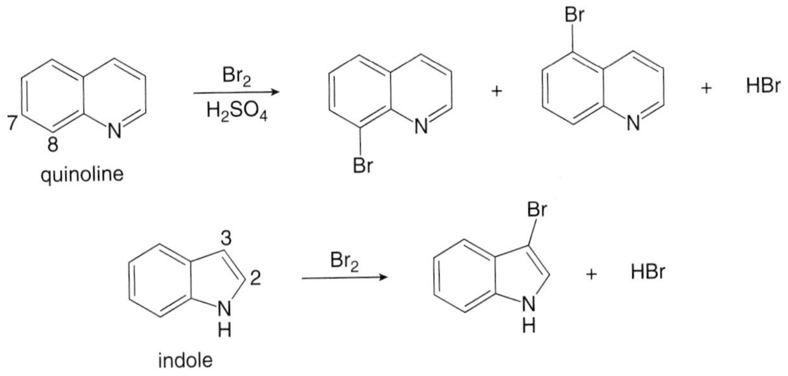

18.80 Devise a stepwise mechanism for the following reaction. The reaction does not take place by direct electrophilic aromatic substitution at C2. (Hint: The mechanism begins with addition of an electrophile at C3.)

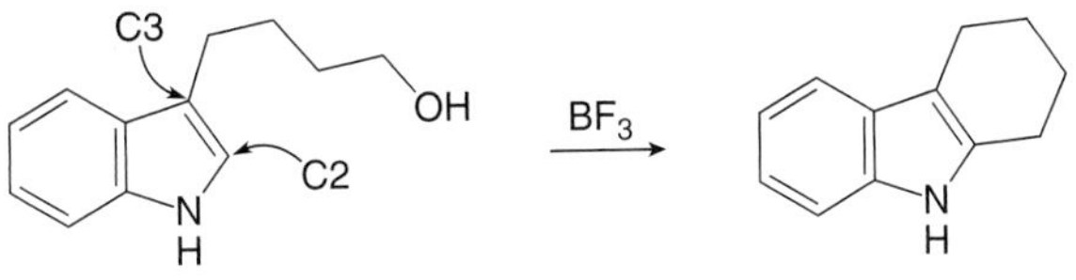

19 Carboxylic Acids and the Acidity of the O–H Bond

19.1 Structure and bonding
19.2 Nomenclature
19.3 Physical properties
19.4 Spectroscopic properties
19.5 Interesting carboxylic acids
19.6 Aspirin, arachidonic acid, and prostaglandins
19.7 Preparation of carboxylic acids
19.8 Reactions of carboxylic acids—General features
19.9 Carboxylic acids—Strong organic Brønsted–Lowry acids
19.10 Inductive effects in aliphatic carboxylic acids
19.11 Substituted benzoic acids
19.12 Extraction
19.13 Sulfonic acids
19.14 Amino acids

Hexanoic acid is a low molecular weight carboxylic acid with the foul odor associated with dirty socks and locker rooms. Its common name, caproic acid, is derived from the Latin word *caper,* meaning "goat." The fleshy coat of ginkgo seeds contains hexanoic acid, giving the seeds an unpleasant and even repulsive odor. It is likely that this foul odor served as an attractant for seed dispersal at some time during the 280 million years that *Ginkgo biloba* has existed on earth. Since only female ginkgo trees produce seeds, male trees, which are propagated by cuttings and grafts, are generally planted by landscapers in the United States. In Chapter 19 we learn about the properties of hexanoic acid and other carboxylic acids.

Chapter 19 serves as a transition between the preceding discussion of resonance and aromaticity, and the subsequent treatment of carbonyl chemistry. We pause to study the chemistry of the OH group by examining **carboxylic acids (RCOOH)**, and to a lesser extent, **phenols (PhOH)** and **alcohols (ROH)**.

In Chapter 19 we concentrate on the acidity of carboxylic acids, and revisit some of the factors that determine acidity, a topic first discussed in Chapter 2. Then, in Chapters 20 and 22 we will learn other reactions of carboxylic acids that occur at the carbonyl group.

19.1 Structure and Bonding

The word **carboxy** (for a COOH group) is derived from ***carb***onyl (C=O) + hydr***oxy*** (OH).

***Carboxylic acids* are organic compounds containing a carboxy group (COOH).** Although the structure of a carboxylic acid is often abbreviated as **RCOOH** or **RCO_2H,** keep in mind that the central carbon atom of the functional group is doubly bonded to one oxygen atom and singly bonded to another.

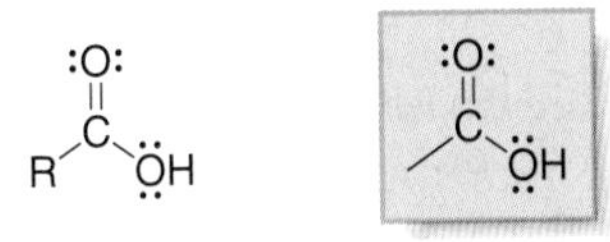

carboxylic acid carboxy group

The carbon atom of a carboxy group is surrounded by three groups, making it ***sp^2* hybridized** and **trigonal planar,** with bond angles of approximately 120°. The C=O of a carboxylic acid is shorter than its C–O.

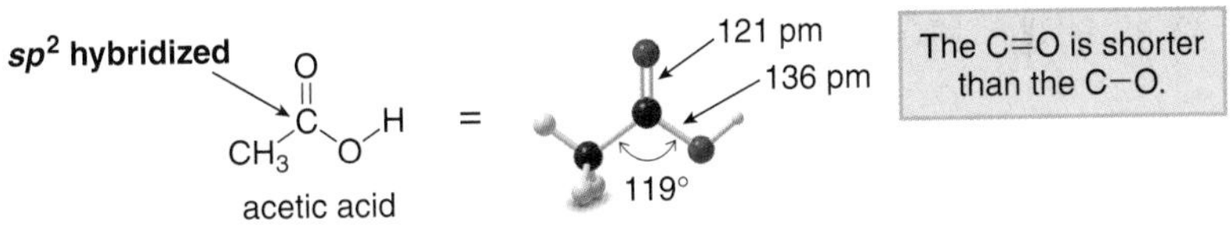

*sp*² hybridized
CH₃ C O H
=
121 pm
136 pm
119°
The C=O is shorter than the C–O.

acetic acid

The C–O single bond of a carboxylic acid is shorter than the C–O single bond of an alcohol. This can be explained by looking at the hybridization of the respective carbon atoms. In the alcohol, the carbon is sp^3 hybridized, whereas in the carboxylic acid the carbon is sp^2 hybridized. As a result, the higher percent *s*-character in the sp^2 hybrid orbital shortens the C–O bond in the carboxylic acid.

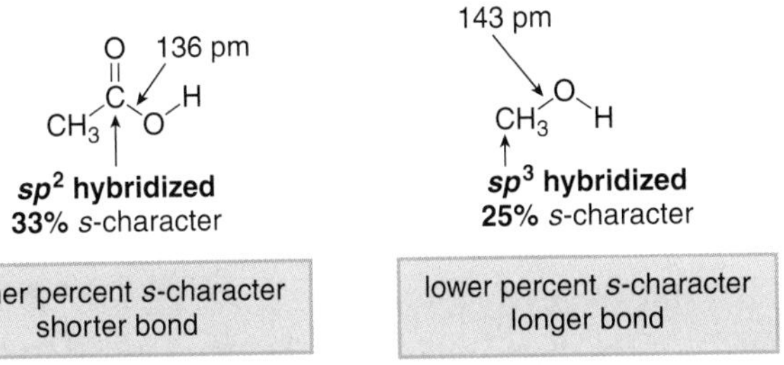

136 pm
143 pm
*sp*² hybridized
33% *s*-character
*sp*³ hybridized
25% *s*-character
higher percent *s*-character
shorter bond
lower percent *s*-character
longer bond

Because oxygen is more electronegative than either carbon or hydrogen, **the C–O and O–H bonds are polar.** The electrostatic potential plot of acetic acid in Figure 19.1 shows that the carbon and hydrogen atoms are electron poor and the oxygen atoms are electron rich.

Figure 19.1 Electrostatic potential plot of acetic acid (CH_3COOH)

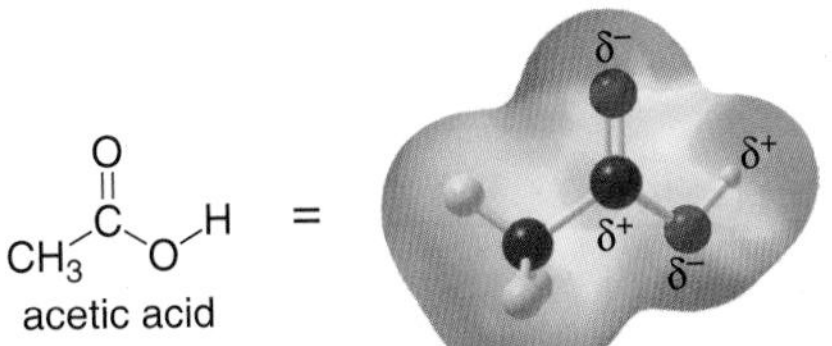

acetic acid
=
δ−
δ+
δ+
δ−

Acetic acid contains two electron-rich oxygen atoms (in red). Its carbonyl carbon and hydroxy hydrogen are both electron deficient.

19.2 Nomenclature

Both IUPAC and common names are used for carboxylic acids.

19.2A IUPAC System

In IUPAC nomenclature, carboxylic acids are identified by a suffix added to the parent name of the longest chain, and two different endings are used depending on whether the carboxy group is bonded to a chain or ring.

To name a carboxylic acid using the IUPAC system:

[1] If the COOH is bonded to a chain of carbons, find the longest chain containing the COOH group, and change the ***-e*** ending of the parent alkane to the suffix ***-oic acid.*** If the COOH group is bonded to a ring, name the ring and add the words ***carboxylic acid.***

[2] Number the carbon chain or ring to put the **COOH group at C1,** but omit this number from the name. Apply all of the other usual rules of nomenclature.

Sample Problem 19.1 Give the IUPAC name of each compound.

a. 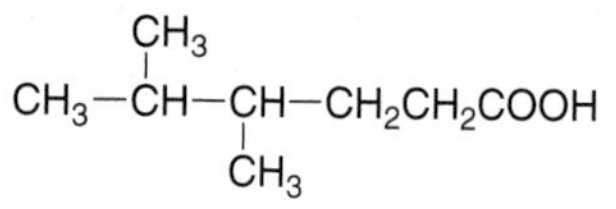

b. 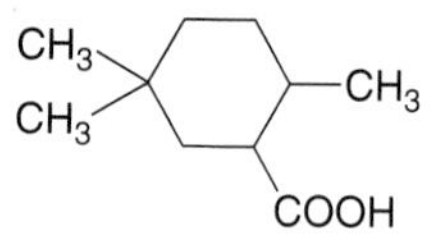

Solution

a. [1] Find and name the longest chain containing COOH:

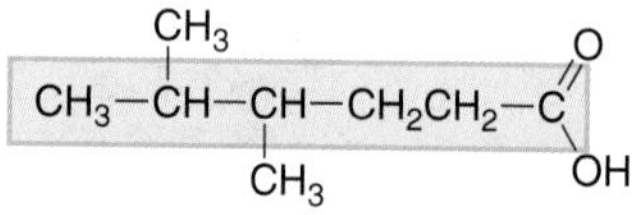

hexane ⟶ **hexan*oic acid***
(6 C's)

The COOH contributes one C to the longest chain.

[2] Number and name the substituents:

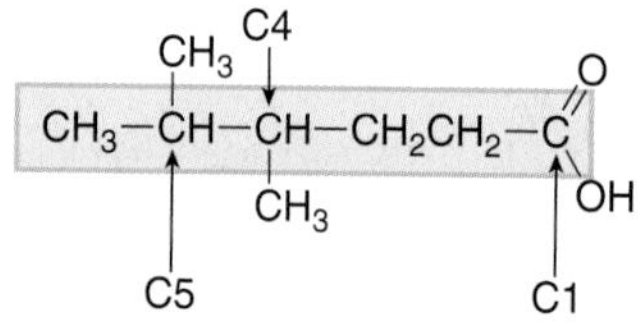

two methyl substituents on C4 and C5

Answer: 4,5-dimethylhexanoic acid

b. [1] Find and name the ring bonded to COOH.

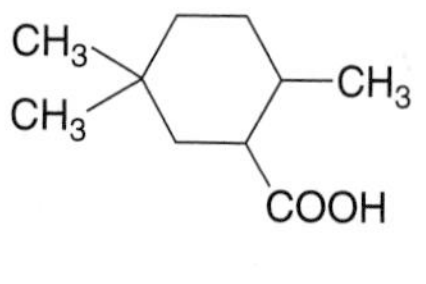

cyclohexane + carboxylic acid
(6 C's)

[2] Number and name the substituents:

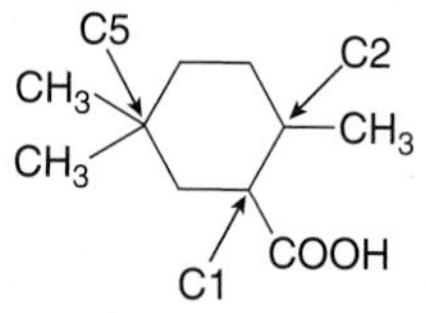

Number to put COOH at C1 and give the second substituent (CH_3) the lower number (C2).

Answer: 2,5,5-trimethylcyclohexanecarboxylic acid

Problem 19.1 Give the IUPAC name for each compound.

a. $CH_3CH_2CH_2C(CH_3)_2CH_2COOH$
b. $CH_3CH(Cl)CH_2CH_2COOH$
c. $(CH_3CH_2)_2CHCH_2CH(CH_2CH_3)COOH$
d. 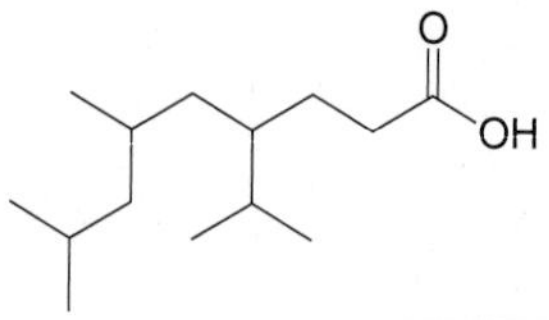

Problem 19.2 Give the structure corresponding to each IUPAC name.

a. 2-bromobutanoic acid
b. 2,3-dimethylpentanoic acid
c. 3,3,4-trimethylheptanoic acid
d. 2-*sec*-butyl-4,4-diethylnonanoic acid
e. 3,4-diethylcyclohexanecarboxylic acid
f. 1-isopropylcyclobutanecarboxylic acid

19.2B Common Names

Most simple carboxylic acids have common names that are more widely used than their IUPAC names.

- **A common name is formed by using a common parent name followed by the suffix *-ic acid*.**

Table 19.1 lists common parent names for some simple carboxylic acids. These parent names are used in the nomenclature of many other compounds with carbonyl groups (Chapters 21 and 22).

Greek letters are used to designate the location of substituents in common names.

- **The carbon adjacent to the COOH is called the α carbon.**
- **The carbon bonded to the α carbon is the β carbon, followed by the γ (gamma) carbon, the δ (delta) carbon, and so forth down the chain. The last carbon in the chain is sometimes called the Ω (omega) carbon.**

Table 19.1 Common Names for Some Simple Carboxylic Acids

Number of C atoms	Structure	Parent name	Common name
1	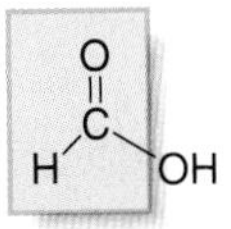	**form-**	formic acid
2	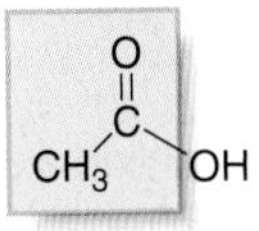	**acet-**	acetic acid
3	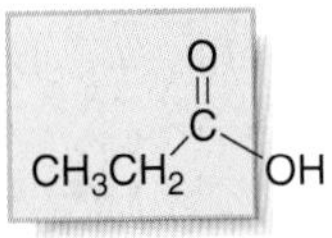	**propion-**	propionic acid
4	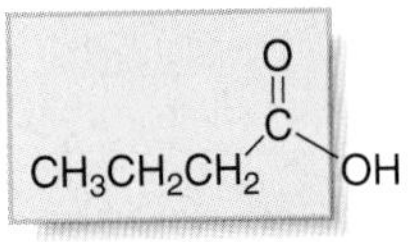	**butyr-**	butyric acid
5	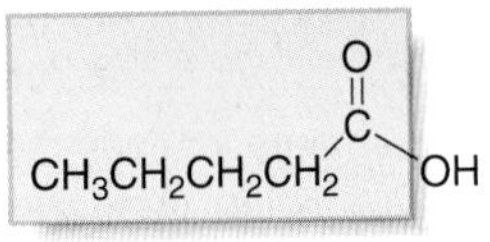	**valer-**	valeric acid
6	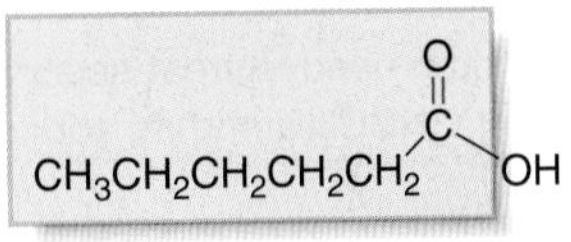	**capro-**	caproic acid
	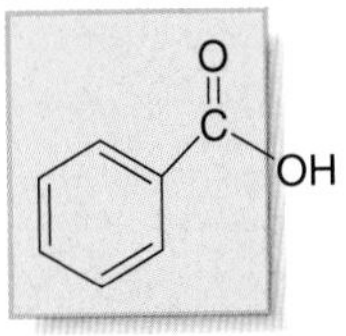	**benzo-**	benzoic acid

The α carbon in the common system is numbered C2 in the IUPAC system.

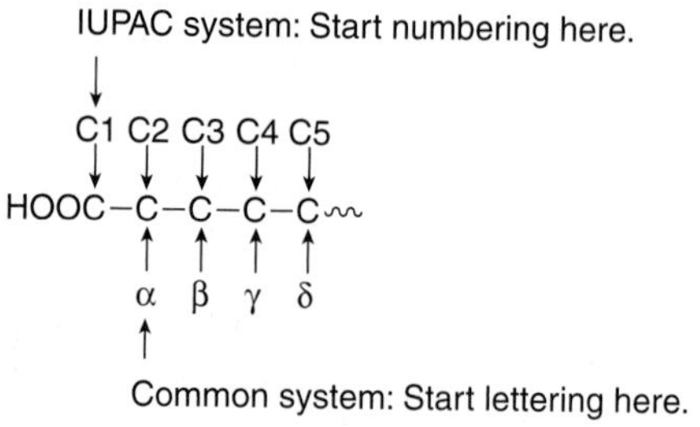
IUPAC system: Start numbering here.
C1 C2 C3 C4 C5
HOOC–C–C–C–C
α β γ δ
Common system: Start lettering here.

Problem 19.3 Draw the structure corresponding to each common name:

a. α-methoxyvaleric acid
b. β-phenylpropionic acid
c. α,β-dimethylcaproic acid
d. α-chloro-β-methylbutyric acid

19.2C Other Nomenclature Facts

Many compounds containing two carboxy groups are also known. In the IUPAC system, **diacids** are named by adding the suffix ***-dioic acid*** to the name of the parent alkane. The three simplest diacids are most often identified by their common names, as shown.

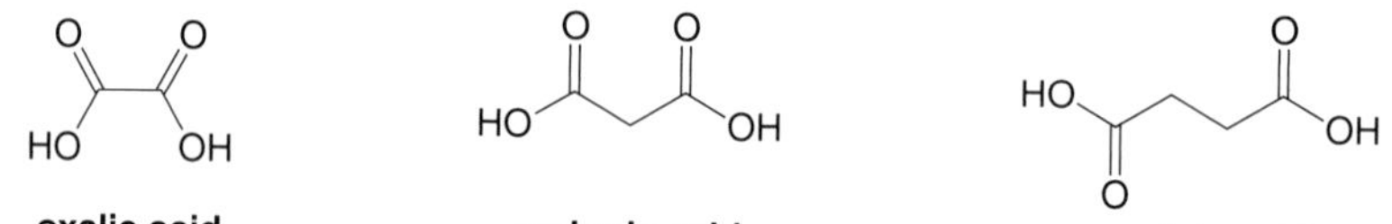
HO
OH
O

oxalic acid (ethanedioic acid) | **malonic acid** (propanedioic acid) | **succinic acid** (butanedioic acid)

Metal salts of carboxylate anions are formed from carboxylic acids in many reactions in Chapter 19. To name the **metal salt of a carboxylate anion,** change the *-ic acid* ending of the carboxylic acid to the suffix ***-ate*** and put three parts together:

name of the metal cation + parent (common or IUPAC) + suffix (***-ate***)

Two examples are shown in Figure 19.2.

Problem 19.4 Give the IUPAC name for each metal salt of a carboxylate anion: (a) $C_6H_5CO_2^-\ Li^+$; (b) $HCO_2^-\ Na^+$; (c) $(CH_3)_2CHCO_2^-\ K^+$; (d) $(CH_3CH_2)_2CHCH_2CH(Br)CH_2CH_2CO_2^-\ Na^+$.

Problem 19.5 Depakote, a drug used to treat seizures and bipolar disorder, consists of a mixture of valproic acid $[(CH_3CH_2CH_2)_2CHCO_2H]$ and its sodium salt. Give IUPAC names for each of these compounds.

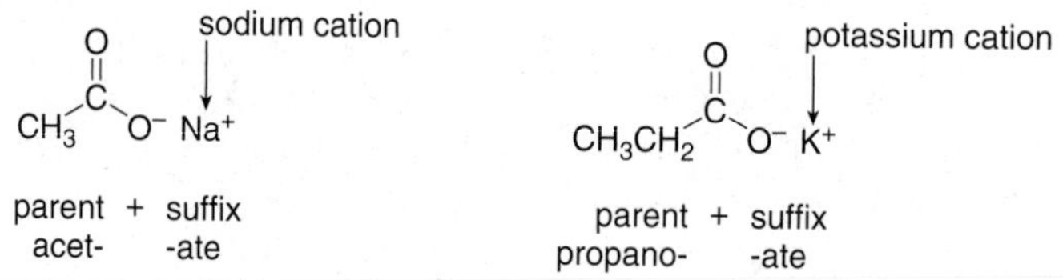
sodium cation
CH_3 O⁻ Na⁺
parent + suffix
acet- -ate
potassium cation
CH_3CH_2 O⁻ K⁺
parent + suffix
propano- -ate

sodium acetate | **potassium propanoate**

Figure 19.2 Naming the metal salts of carboxylate anions

19.3 Physical Properties

Carboxylic acids exhibit **dipole–dipole** interactions because they have polar C–O and O–H bonds. They also exhibit intermolecular **hydrogen bonding** because they possess a hydrogen atom bonded to an electronegative oxygen atom. Carboxylic acids often exist as **dimers,** held together by *two* intermolecular hydrogen bonds between the carbonyl oxygen atom of one molecule and the OH hydrogen atom of another molecule (Figure 19.3). Carboxylic acids are the **most polar** organic compounds we have studied so far.

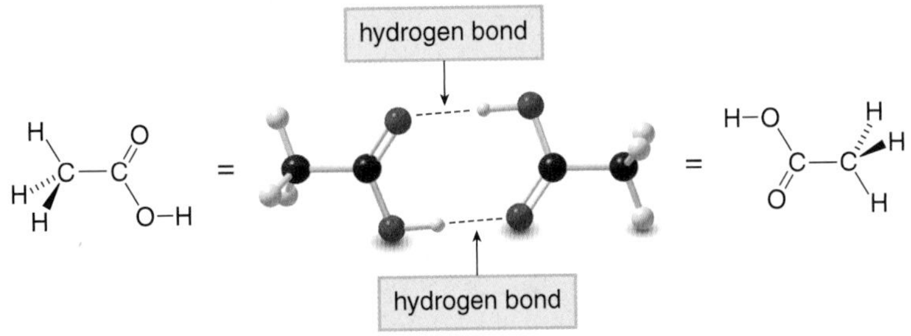

Figure 19.3
Two molecules of acetic acid (CH_3COOH) held together by two hydrogen bonds

How these intermolecular forces affect the physical properties of carboxylic acids is summarized in Table 19.2.

Table 19.2 Physical Properties of Carboxylic Acids

Property	Observation
Boiling point and melting point	• Carboxylic acids have higher boiling points and melting points than other compounds of comparable molecular weight. $CH_3CH_2CH_2CH_3$ VDW, MW = 58, bp 0 °C CH_3CH_2CHO VDW, DD, MW = 58, bp 48 °C $CH_3CH_2CH_2OH$ VDW, DD, HB, MW = 60, bp 97 °C CH_3COOH VDW, DD, two HB, MW = 60, bp 118 °C **Increasing strength of intermolecular forces** **Increasing boiling point**
Solubility	• Carboxylic acids are soluble in organic solvents regardless of size. • Carboxylic acids having ≤ 5 C's are water soluble because they can hydrogen bond with H_2O (Section 3.4C). • Carboxylic acids having > 5 C's are water insoluble because the nonpolar alkyl portion is too large to dissolve in the polar H_2O solvent. These "fatty" acids dissolve in a nonpolar fat-like environment but do not dissolve in water.

Key: VDW = van der Waals, DD = dipole–dipole, HB = hydrogen bonding, MW = molecular weight

Problem 19.6 Rank the following compounds in order of increasing boiling point. Which compound is the most water soluble? Which compound is the least water soluble?

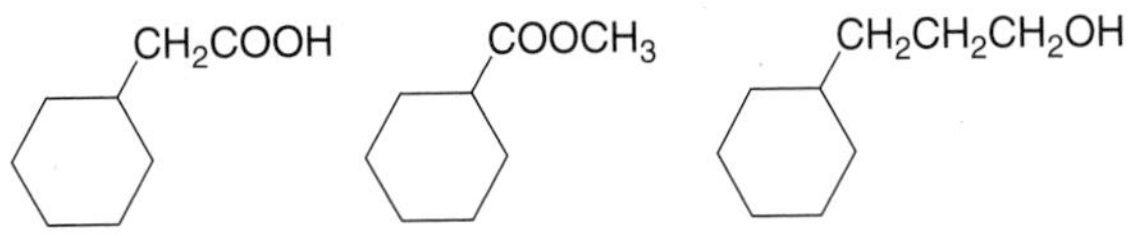

19.4 Spectroscopic Properties

Carboxylic acids have very characteristic IR and NMR absorptions. In the IR, carboxylic acids show two strong absorptions.

- The **C=O group absorbs at about 1710 cm^{-1},** in the usual region for a carbonyl.
- The **O–H absorption** occurs from **2500–3500 cm^{-1}.** This very broad absorption sometimes obscures the C–H peak at 3000 cm^{-1}.

The IR spectrum of butanoic acid in Figure 19.4 illustrates these characteristic peaks.

Figure 19.4
The IR spectrum of butanoic acid, $CH_3CH_2CH_2COOH$

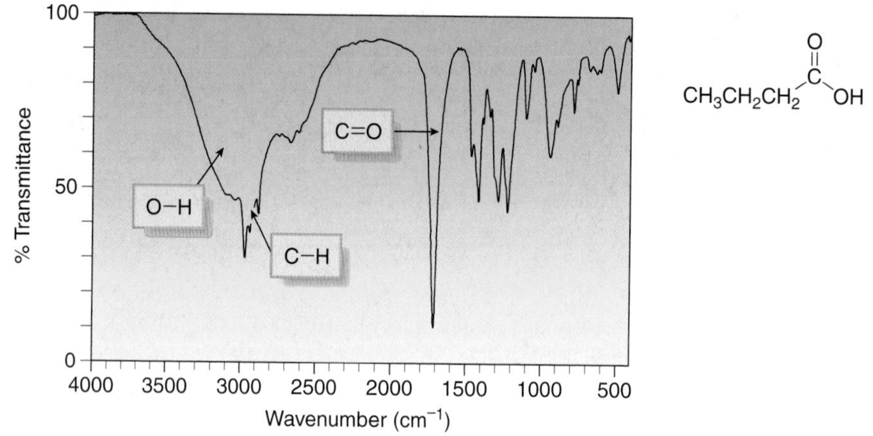

- A strong C=O absorption occurs at 1712 cm^{-1}.
- The broad O–H absorption (2500–3500 cm^{-1}) nearly obscures the C–H peak at ~3000 cm^{-1}.

Carboxylic acids have two noteworthy ^{1}H NMR absorptions and one noteworthy ^{13}C NMR absorption.

- **The highly deshielded OH proton absorbs in the ^{1}H NMR spectrum somewhere between 10 and 12 ppm,** farther *downfield* than all other absorptions of common organic compounds. Like the OH signal of an alcohol, the exact location depends on the degree of hydrogen bonding and the concentration of the sample.
- The protons on the α carbon to the carboxy group are somewhat deshielded, absorbing at 2–2.5 ppm.
- In the ^{13}C NMR spectrum, the carbonyl absorption is highly deshielded, appearing at 170–210 ppm.

Sometimes the OH absorption of a carboxylic acid is very broad, so that it is almost buried in the baseline of the ^{1}H NMR spectrum, making it difficult to see (Figure 19.5).

Figure 19.5 illustrates the ^{1}H and ^{13}C NMR spectra of propanoic acid.

Problem 19.7 Explain how you could use IR spectroscopy to distinguish among the following three compounds.

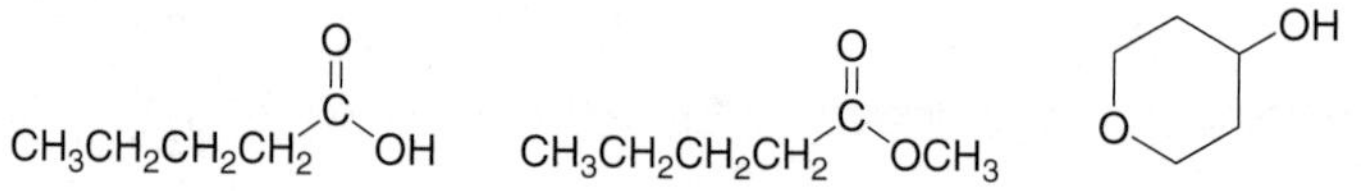

Problem 19.8 Identify the structure of a compound of molecular formula $C_4H_8O_2$ that gives the following ^{1}H NMR data: 0.95 (triplet, 3 H), 1.65 (multiplet, 2 H), 2.30 (triplet, 2 H), and 11.8 (singlet, 1 H) ppm.

Figure 19.5
The ^1H and ^{13}C NMR spectra of propanoic acid

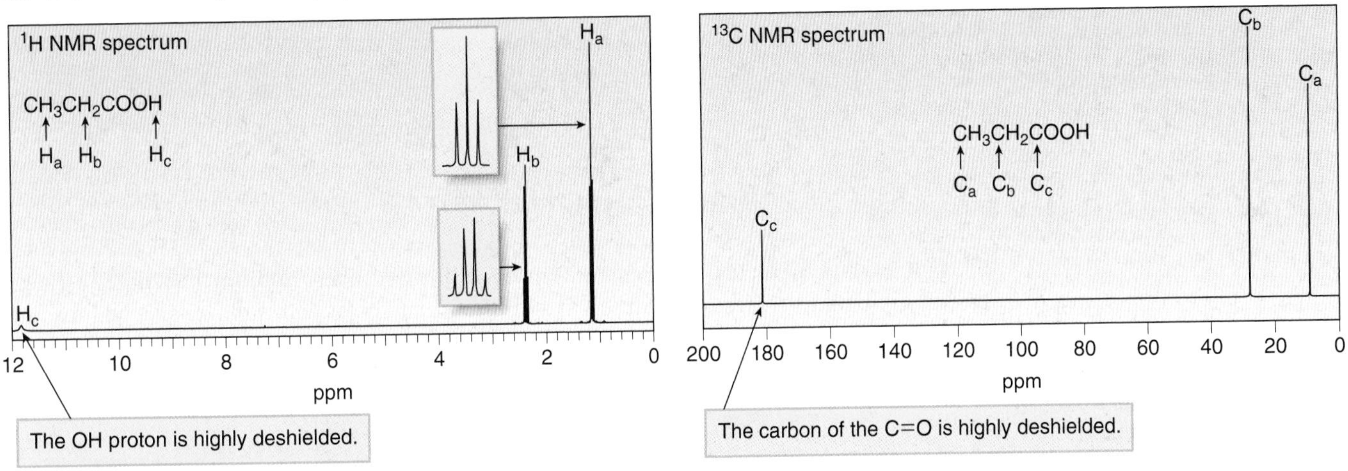

- **^{1}H NMR spectrum:** There are three signals due to three different kinds of H atoms. The H_a and H_b signals are split into a triplet and quartet, respectively, but the H_c signal is a singlet.
- **^{13}C NMR spectrum:** There are three signals due to three different kinds of carbon atoms.

19.5 Interesting Carboxylic Acids

Several simple carboxylic acids have characteristic odors and flavors.

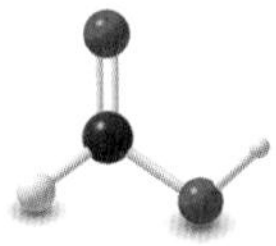
formic acid

- **Formic acid (HCOOH),** a carboxylic acid with an acrid odor and a biting taste, is responsible for the sting of some types of ants. The name is derived from the Latin word formica, meaning "ant."

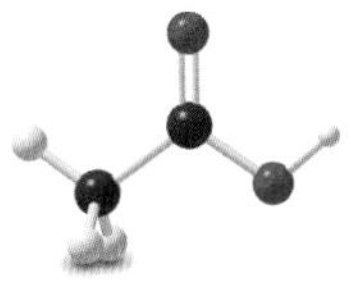
acetic acid

- **Acetic acid (CH_3COOH)** is the sour-tasting component of vinegar. The name comes from the Latin *acetum,* meaning "vinegar." The air oxidation of ethanol to acetic acid is the process that makes "bad" wine taste sour. Acetic acid is an industrial starting material for polymers used in paints and adhesives. Pure acetic acid is often called *glacial* acetic acid, because it freezes just below room temperature (mp = 17 °C), forming white crystals reminiscent of the ice in a glacier.

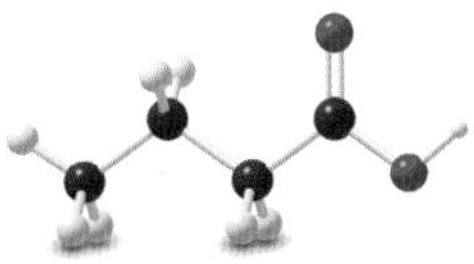
butanoic acid

- **Butanoic acid ($CH_3CH_2CH_2COOH$)** is an oxidation product that contributes to the disagreeable smell of body odor. Its common name, butyric acid, is derived from the Latin word *butyrum,* meaning "butter," because butyric acid gives rancid butter its peculiar odor and taste.

Although oxalic acid is toxic, you would have to eat about nine pounds of spinach at one time to ingest a fatal dose.

Oxalic acid and **lactic acid** are simple carboxylic acids quite prevalent in nature. Oxalic acid occurs naturally in spinach and rhubarb. Lactic acid gives sour milk its distinctive taste.

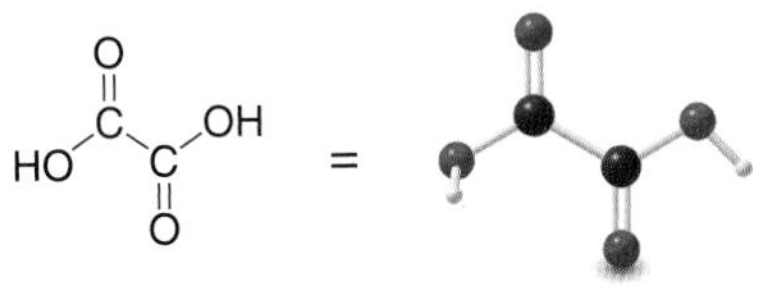

oxalic acid

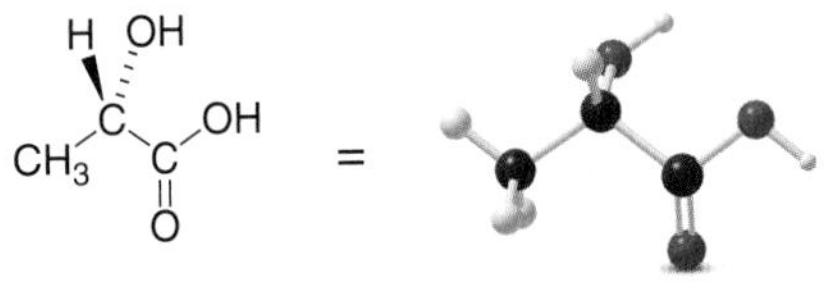

lactic acid

4-Hydroxybutanoic acid, known by its common name γ-hydroxybutyric acid (GHB), is an illegal recreational drug that depresses the central nervous system and results in intoxication. GHB is highly addictive and widely abused, and because its taste can be easily masked in an alcoholic beverage, it has been used as a "date rape" drug.

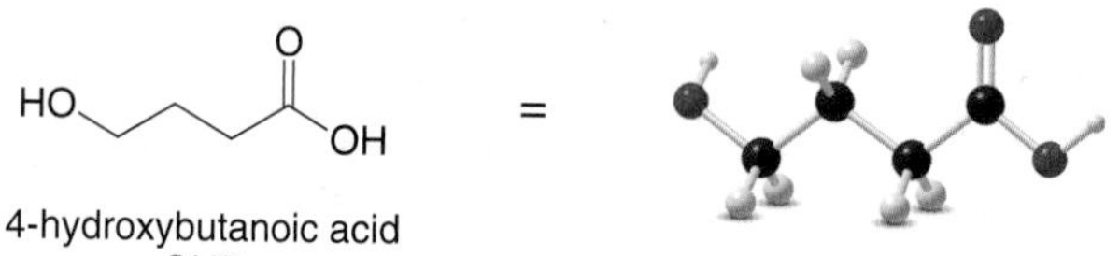

4-hydroxybutanoic acid
GHB

Salts of carboxylic acids are commonly used as preservatives. **Sodium benzoate,** a fungal growth inhibitor, is a preservative used in soft drinks, and potassium sorbate is an additive that prolongs the shelf-life of baked goods and other foods.

Soaps, the sodium salts of fatty acids, were discussed in Section 3.6.

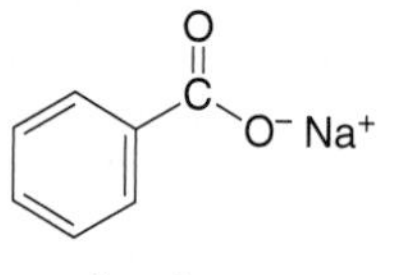

sodium benzoate

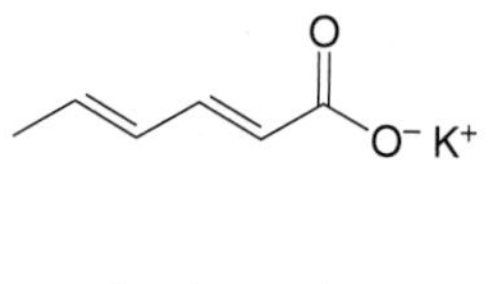

potassium sorbate

19.6 Aspirin, Arachidonic Acid, and Prostaglandins

The word *aspirin* is derived from the prefix ***a-*** for *acetyl* + ***spir*** from the Latin name *spirea* for the meadowsweet plant.

Recall from Chapter 2 that **aspirin (acetylsalicylic acid)** is a synthetic carboxylic acid, similar in structure to **salicin,** a naturally occurring compound isolated from willow bark, and **salicylic acid,** found in meadowsweet.

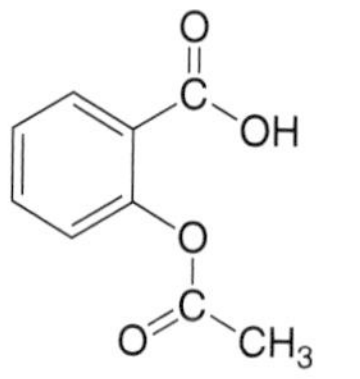

aspirin
(acetylsalicylic acid)

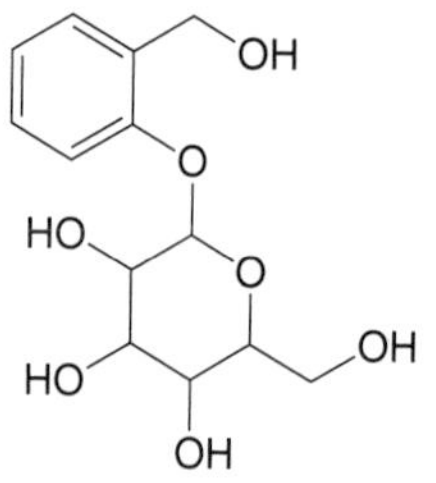

salicin
(isolated from
willow bark)

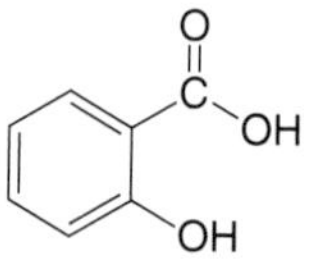

salicylic acid
(isolated from
meadowsweet)

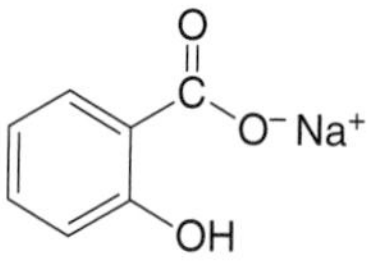

sodium salicylate
(sweet carboxylate salt)

Both salicylic acid and sodium salicylate (its sodium salt) were widely used analgesics in the nineteenth century, but both had undesirable side effects. Salicylic acid irritated the mucous membranes of the mouth and stomach, and sodium salicylate was too sweet for most patients. Aspirin, a synthetic compound, was first sold in 1899 after Felix Hoffman, a German chemist at Bayer Company, developed a feasible commercial synthesis. Hoffman's work was motivated by personal reasons; his father suffered from rheumatoid arthritis and was unable to tolerate the sweet taste of sodium salicylate.

How does aspirin relieve pain and reduce inflammation? Aspirin blocks the synthesis of **prostaglandins,** 20-carbon fatty acids with a five-membered ring that are responsible for pain, inflammation, and a wide variety of other biological functions. **PGF$_{2\alpha}$** contains the typical carbon skeleton of a prostaglandin.

Aspirin is the most widely used pain reliever and anti-inflammatory agent in the world, yet its mechanism of action remained unknown until the 1970s. John Vane, Bengt Samuelsson, and Sune Bergstrom shared the 1982 Nobel Prize in Physiology or Medicine for unraveling the details of its mechanism.

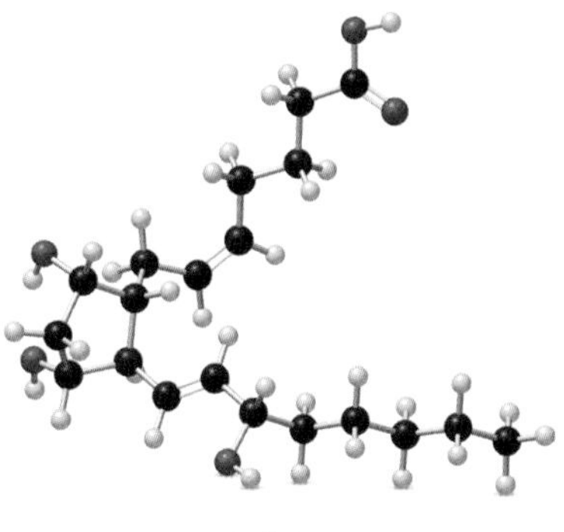

$PGF_{2\alpha}$
a prostaglandin

Prostaglandins are not stored in cells. Rather they are synthesized from arachidonic acid, a polyunsaturated fatty acid having four cis double bonds. Unlike hormones, which are transported in the bloodstream to their sites of action, prostaglandins act where they are synthesized. Aspirin acts by blocking the synthesis of prostaglandins from arachidonic acid. Aspirin inactivates cyclooxygenase, an enzyme that converts arachidonic acid to PGG_2, an unstable precursor of $PGF_{2\alpha}$ and other prostaglandins. **Aspirin lessens pain and decreases inflammation because it prevents the synthesis of prostaglandins, the compounds responsible for both of these physiological responses.**

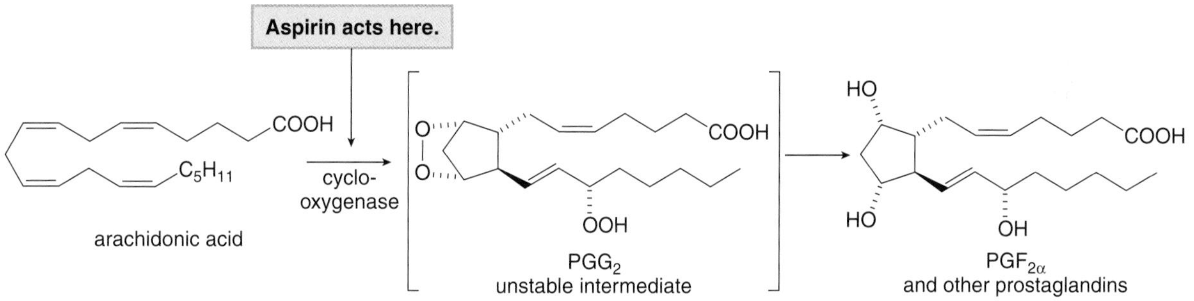

Although prostaglandins have a wide range of biological activity, their inherent instability often limits their usefulness as drugs. Consequently, more stable analogues with useful medicinal properties have been synthesized. For example, latanoprost (trade name Xalatan) and bimatoprost (trade name Lumigan) are prostaglandin analogues used to reduce eye pressure in individuals with glaucoma.

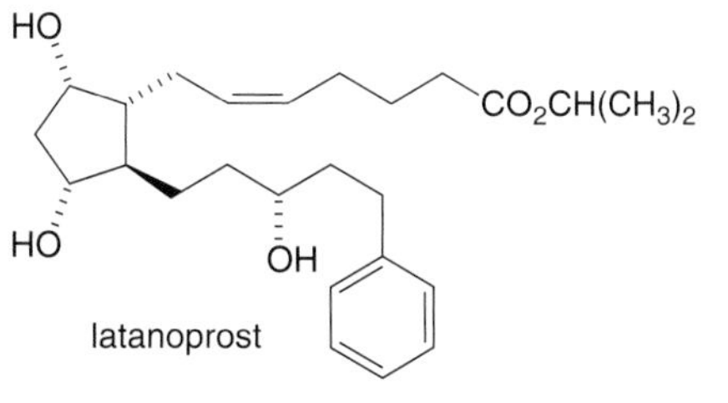

latanoprost

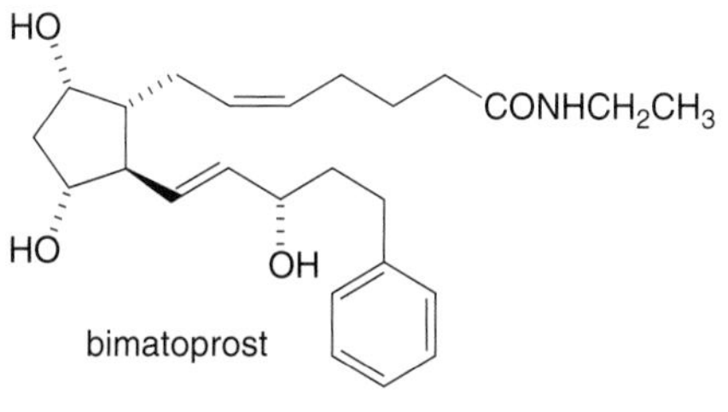

bimatoprost

Problem 19.9 How many tetrahedral stereogenic centers does $PGF_{2\alpha}$ contain? Draw its enantiomer. How many of its double bonds can exhibit cis-trans isomerism? Considering both its double bonds and its tetrahedral stereogenic centers, how many stereoisomers are possible for $PGF_{2\alpha}$?

19.7 Preparation of Carboxylic Acids

Our discussion of the reactions involving carboxylic acids begins with a brief list of reactions that synthesize them. This list serves as a reminder of where you have seen this functional group before. In these reactions, the carboxy group is formed in the *product,* and many different functional groups serve as starting materials. Reactions that produce a particular functional group are called **preparations.**

In the remainder of Chapter 19 (and Chapters 20 and 22) we discuss reactions in which a carboxylic acid is a *starting material* that may be converted to a variety of different products. Keep in mind that **reactions of a particular functional group follow a common theme.** For example, alkenes undergo addition reactions. As a result, these reactions are easier to learn than the list of preparations, in which vastly different functional groups undergo a wide variety of reactions to form the same kind of product.

Where have we encountered carboxylic acids as reaction products before? The carbonyl carbon is highly oxidized, because it has three C–O bonds, so **carboxylic acids are typically prepared by oxidation reactions.** Three oxidation methods are summarized below. Two other useful methods to prepare carboxylic acids are presented in Chapter 20.

[1] By oxidation of 1° alcohols (Section 12.12B)

1° Alcohols are converted to carboxylic acids with $Na_2Cr_2O_7$, $K_2Cr_2O_7$, or CrO_3 in the presence of H_2O and H_2SO_4.

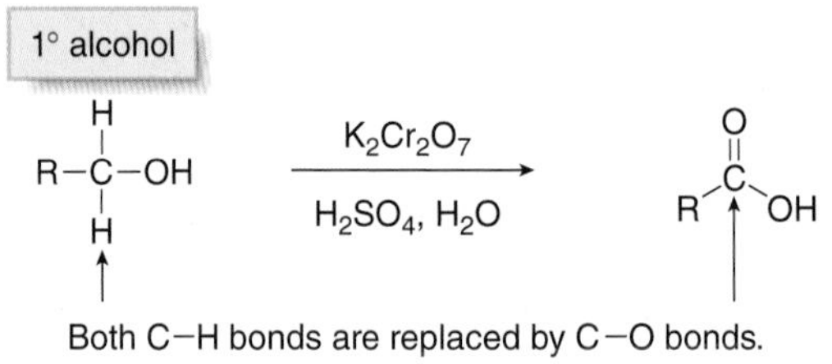

[2] By oxidation of alkyl benzenes (Section 18.15A)

Alkyl benzenes having at least one benzylic C–H bond are oxidized with $KMnO_4$ to benzoic acid.

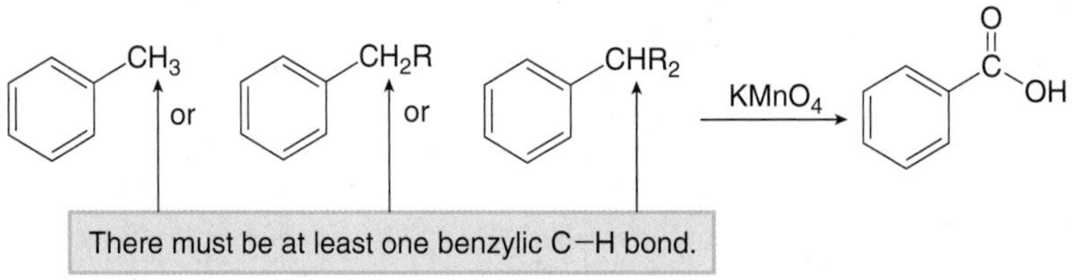

Benzoic acid is *always* the product regardless of the alkyl benzene used as starting material.

[3] By oxidative cleavage of alkynes (Section 12.11)

Both internal and terminal alkynes are oxidatively cleaved with ozone to give carboxylic acids.

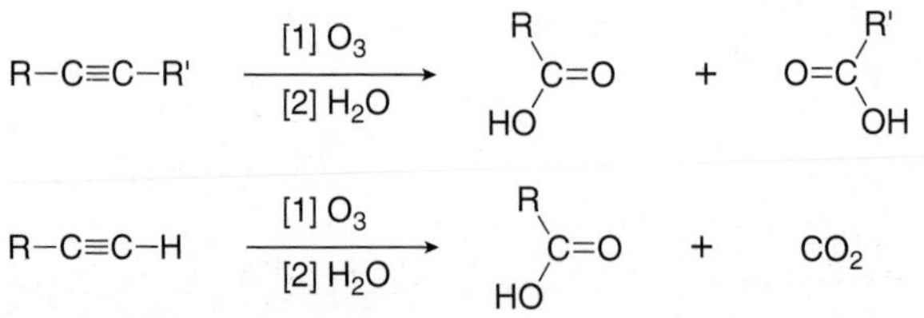

With internal alkynes two carboxylic acids are formed as products. With terminal alkynes, the *sp* hybridized C–H bond is converted to CO_2.

Problem 19.10 What alcohol can be oxidized to each carboxylic acid?

a. 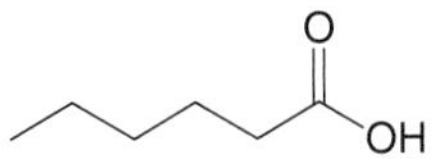
b. $(CH_3)_2CHCOOH$
c. 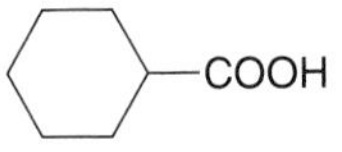

Problem 19.11 Identify **A–D** in the following reactions.

a. **A** 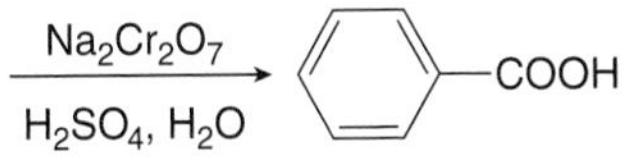
c. **C** 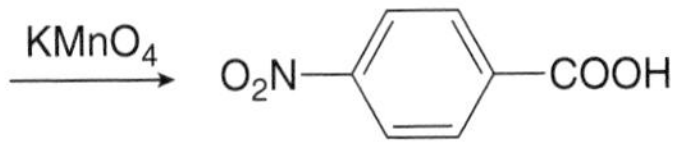
b. **B** 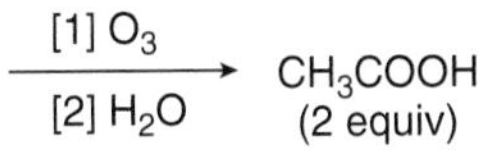
d. **D** 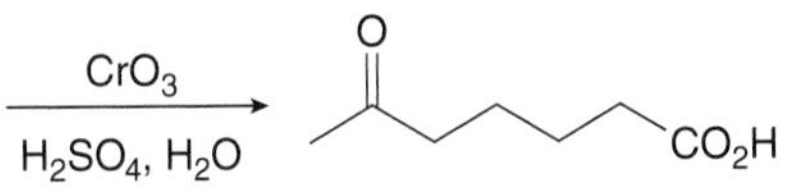

19.8 Reactions of Carboxylic Acids—General Features

The polar C–O and O–H bonds, nonbonded electron pairs on oxygen, and the π bond give a carboxylic acid many reactive sites, complicating its chemistry somewhat. By far, **the most important reactive feature of a carboxylic acid is its polar O–H bond, which is readily cleaved with base.**

- **Carboxylic acids react as Brønsted–Lowry acids—that is, as proton donors.**

A Brønsted–Lowry acid–base reaction

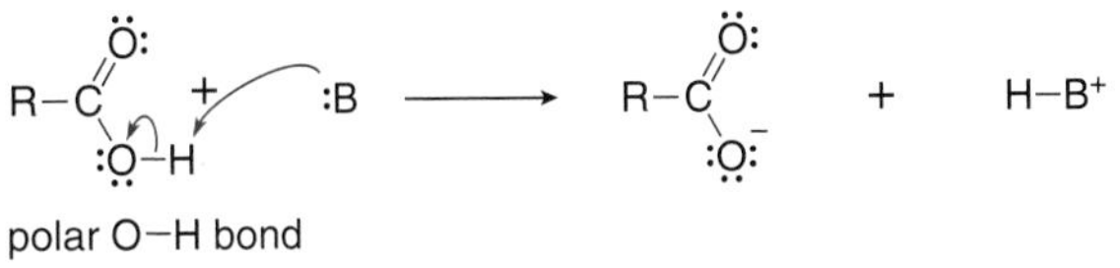
polar O–H bond

Much of the rest of Chapter 19 is devoted to the acidity of carboxylic acids, as well as some related acid–base reactions. Two other structural features are less important in the reactions of carboxylic acids, but they play a role in the reactions of Chapters 20 and 22.

The nonbonded electron pairs on oxygen create electron-rich sites that can be protonated by strong acids (H–A). Protonation occurs at the carbonyl oxygen because the resulting conjugate acid is resonance stabilized (Possibility [1]). The product of protonation of the OH group (Possibility [2]) cannot be resonance stabilized. As a result, **carboxylic acids are weakly basic—they react with strong acids by protonation of the carbonyl oxygen.** This reaction plays an important role in several mechanisms in Chapter 22.

Possibility [1]
Protonation of the C=O

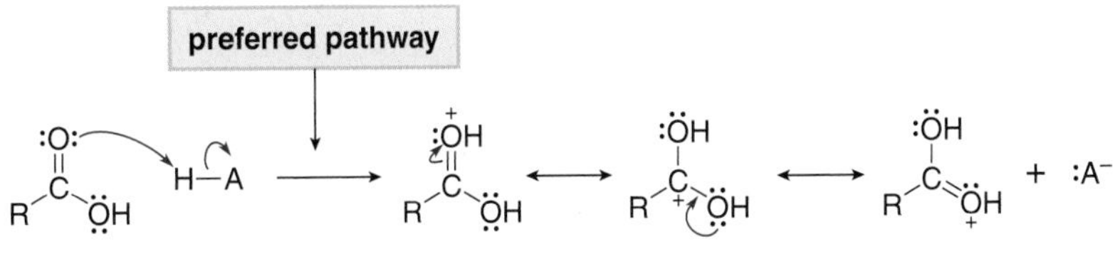
preferred pathway

three resonance structures for the conjugate acid

Possibility [2]
Protonation of the OH group

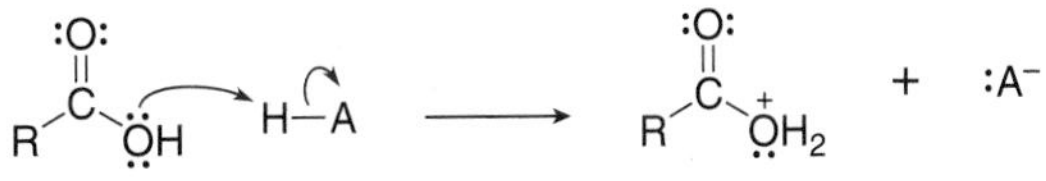

not resonance stabilized

Finally, the polar C–O bonds make the carboxy carbon electrophilic, so carboxylic acids react with nucleophiles. Nucleophilic attack occurs at an sp^2 hybridized carbon atom, so it results in the cleavage of the π bond, as well. This reaction is also discussed in Chapter 22.

Nucleophilic attack at the carboxy carbon

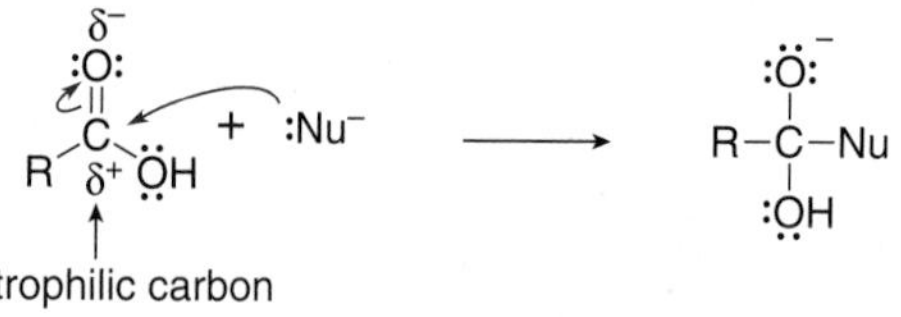

19.9 Carboxylic Acids—Strong Organic Brønsted–Lowry Acids

Carboxylic acids are strong organic acids, and as such, readily react with Brønsted–Lowry bases to form carboxylate anions.

Recall from Section 2.3 that **the lower the pK_a, the stronger the acid.**

General acid–base reaction

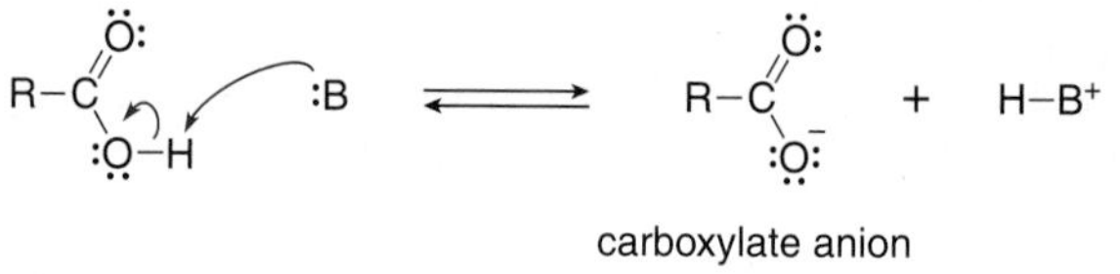

What bases are used to deprotonate a carboxylic acid? As we learned in Section 2.3, equilibrium favors the products of an acid–base reaction when the weaker base and acid are formed. Because a weaker acid has a higher pK_a, the following general rule results:

- **An acid can be deprotonated by a base that has a conjugate acid with a higher pK_a.**

Because the pK_a values of many carboxylic acids are ~5, bases that have conjugate acids with pK_a values higher than 5 are strong enough to deprotonate them. Thus, acetic acid (pK_a = 4.8) and benzoic acid (pK_a = 4.2) can be deprotonated with NaOH and $NaHCO_3$, as shown in the following equations.

Examples

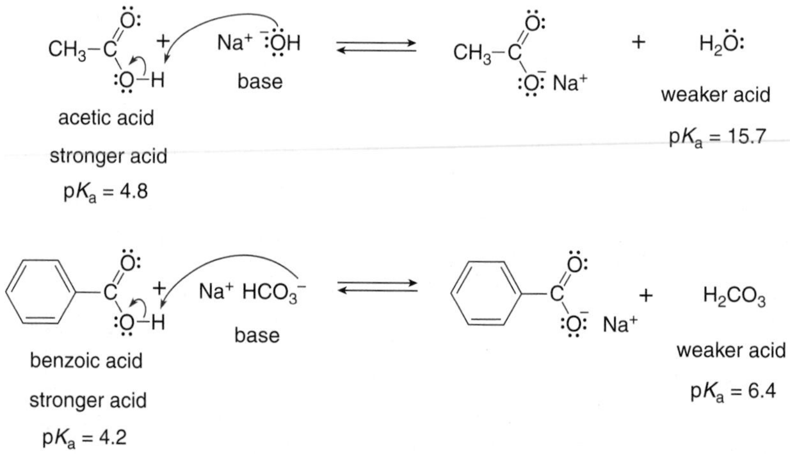

Table 19.3 lists common bases that can be used to deprotonate carboxylic acids. It is noteworthy that even a weak base like $NaHCO_3$ is strong enough to remove a proton from RCOOH.

Table 19.3 Common Bases Used to Deprotonate Carboxylic Acids

	Base	Conjugate acid (pK_a)
Increasing basicity ↓	$Na^+\ HCO_3^-$	H_2CO_3 (6.4)
	NH_3	NH_4^+ (9.4)
	Na_2CO_3	HCO_3^- (10.2)
	$Na^+\ ^-OCH_3$	CH_3OH (15.5)
	$Na^+\ ^-OH$	H_2O (15.7)
	$Na^+\ ^-OCH_2CH_3$	CH_3CH_2OH (16)
	$Na^+\ H^-$	H_2 (35)

Why are carboxylic acids such strong organic acids? Remember that a strong acid has a weak, stabilized conjugate base. **Deprotonation of a carboxylic acid forms a resonance-stabilized conjugate base—a carboxylate anion.** For example, two equivalent resonance structures can be drawn for acetate (the conjugate base of acetic acid), both of which place a negative charge on an electronegative O atom. In the resonance hybrid, therefore, the negative charge is delocalized over two oxygen atoms.

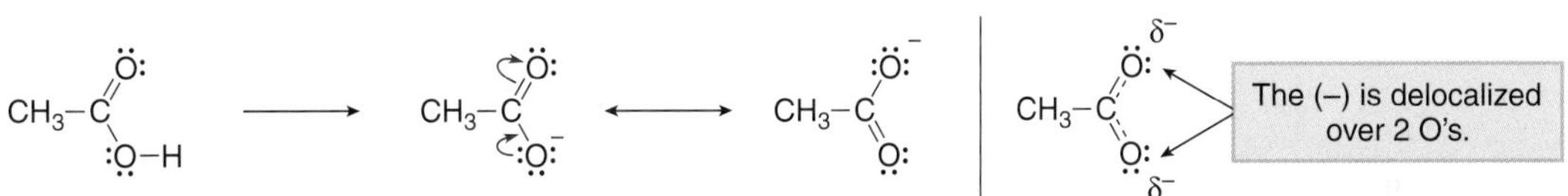
The (–) is delocalized over 2 O's.

acetic acid — **two resonance structures for acetate,** the conjugate base — **hybrid**

How resonance affects acidity was first discussed in Section 2.5C.

Experimental data support this resonance description of acetate. **The acetate anion has two C–O bonds of equal length** (127 pm) and intermediate between the length of a C–O single bond (136 pm) and C=O (121 pm).

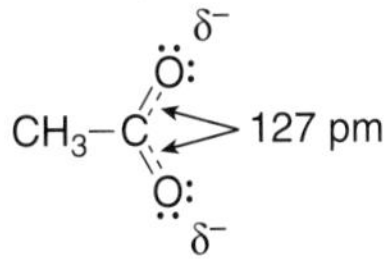
127 pm

acetate hybrid

Resonance stabilization accounts for why carboxylic acids are more acidic than other compounds with O–H bonds—namely, alcohols and phenols. For example, the pK_a values of ethanol (CH_3CH_2OH) and phenol (C_6H_5OH) are 16 and 10, respectively, both higher than the pK_a of acetic acid (4.8).

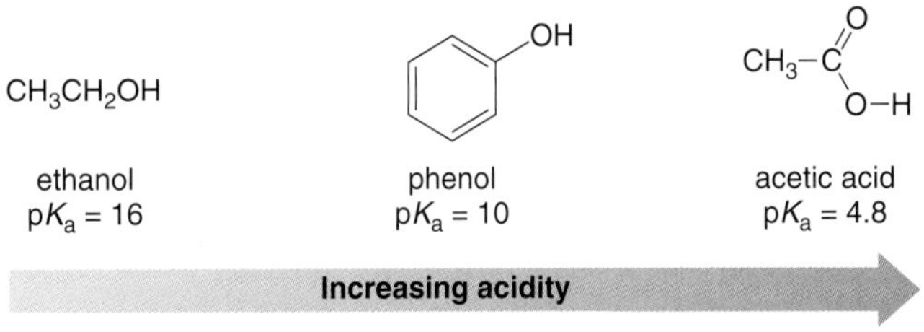
CH3CH2OH
ethanol
pKa = 16
phenol
pKa = 10
acetic acid
pKa = 4.8
Increasing acidity

To understand the relative acidity of ethanol, phenol, and acetic acid, we must compare the stability of their conjugate bases and use the following rule:

- **Anything that stabilizes a conjugate base A:⁻ makes the starting acid H–A more acidic.**

Ethoxide, the conjugate base of ethanol, bears a negative charge on an oxygen atom, but there are no additional factors to further stabilize the anion. Because ethoxide is less stable than acetate, **ethanol is a weaker acid than acetic acid.**

$CH_3CH_2\ddot{O}H \longrightarrow CH_3CH_2\ddot{O}:^-$ — no additional resonance stabilization

ethanol → ethoxide

The resonance hybrid of phenoxide illustrates that its negative charge is dispersed over four atoms—three C atoms and one O atom.

Like acetate, **phenoxide** ($C_6H_5O^-$, the conjugate base of phenol) is also resonance stabilized. In the case of phenoxide, however, there are five resonance structures that disperse the negative charge over a total of four different atoms (three different carbons and the oxygen).

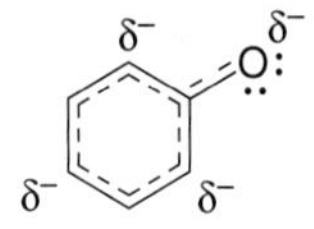
δ−
δ−
δ−
δ−

hybrid

Phenoxide, the conjugate base

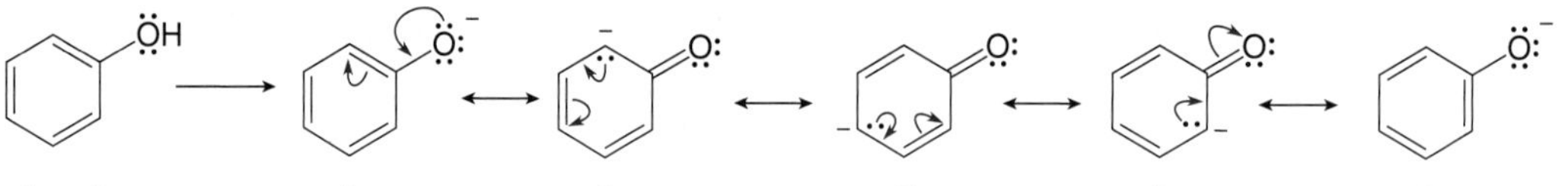

phenol 1 2 3 4 5

Five resonance structures delocalize the negative charge over four atoms.

Phenoxide is more stable than ethoxide, but less stable than acetate, because acetate has two electronegative oxygen atoms upon which to delocalize the negative charge, whereas phenoxide has only one. Additionally, phenoxide resonance structures **2–4** have the negative charge on a carbon, a less electronegative element than oxygen. As a result, structures **2–4** are less stable than structures **1** and **5,** which have the negative charge on oxygen.

Moreover, resonance structures **1** and **5** have intact aromatic rings, whereas structures **2–4** do not. This, too, makes structures **2–4** less stable than **1** and **5.** Figure 19.6 summarizes this information about phenoxide by displaying the approximate relative energies of its five resonance structures and its hybrid.

As a result, resonance stabilization of the conjugate base is important in determining acidity, but **the absolute number of resonance structures alone is not what's important.** We must evaluate their relative contributions to predict the relative stability of the conjugate bases.

Figure 19.6 The relative energies of the five resonance structures for phenoxide and its hybrid

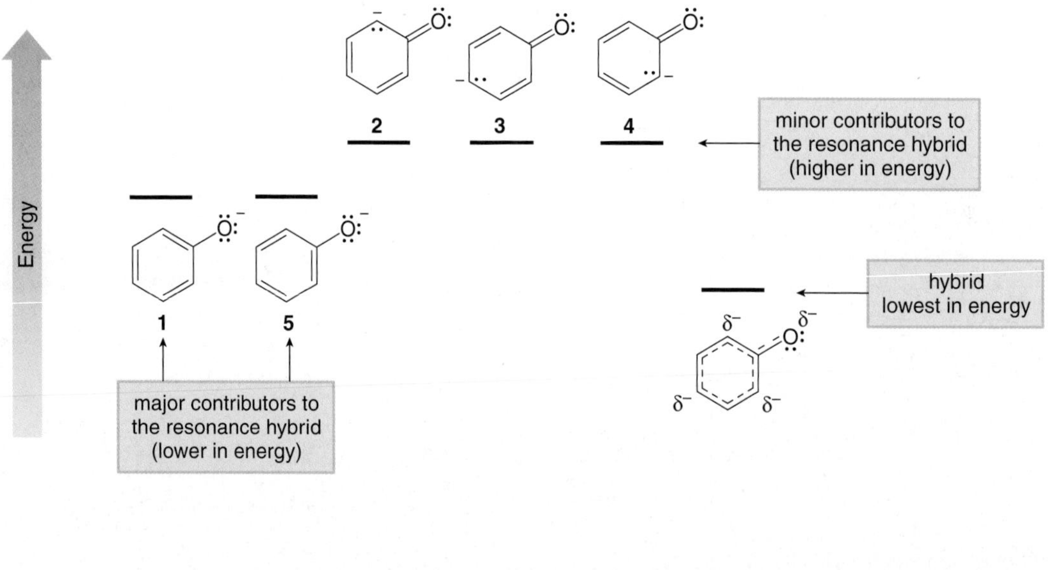
Energy
2
3
4
minor contributors to the resonance hybrid (higher in energy)
1
5
major contributors to the resonance hybrid (lower in energy)
hybrid lowest in energy
δ−
δ−
δ−
δ−

Keep in mind that although carboxylic acids are strong organic acids, they are still much weaker than strong inorganic acids like HCl and H_2SO_4, which have pK_a values < 0.

- **Because of their O–H bond, RCOOH, ROH, and C_6H_5OH are more acidic than most organic hydrocarbons.**

- **A carboxylic acid is a stronger acid than an alcohol or phenol because its conjugate base is most effectively resonance stabilized.**

The relationship between acidity and stability of the conjugate base is summarized for acetic acid, phenol, and ethanol in Figure 19.7.

Figure 19.7

Summary: The relationship between acidity and conjugate base stability for acetic acid, phenol, and ethanol

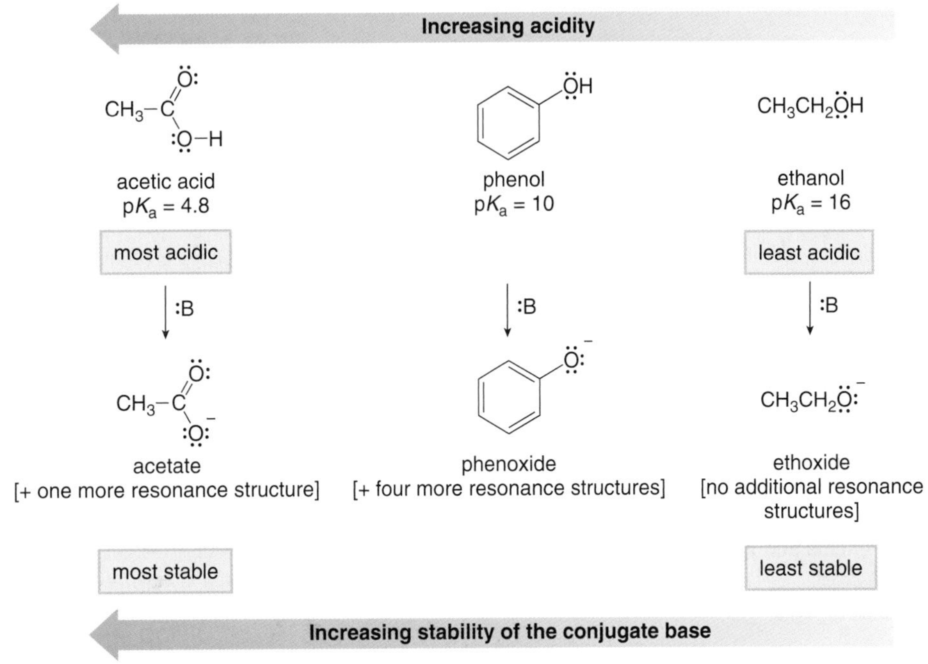

- **Acetate is the most stable conjugate base** because it has two equivalent resonance structures, both of which place a negative charge on an O atom.
- **Phenoxide** has only one O atom to accept the negative charge. The two resonance structures that contain an intact aromatic ring and place a negative charge on an O atom are major contributors to the hybrid. Resonance stabilizes phenoxide but not as much as resonance stabilizes acetate.
- **Ethoxide is the least stable conjugate base** because it has no additional resonance stabilization.

Because alcohols and phenols are weaker acids than carboxylic acids, stronger bases are needed to deprotonate them. To deprotonate C_6H_5OH (pK_a = 10), a base whose conjugate acid has a pK_a > 10 is needed. Thus, of the bases listed in Table 19.3, $NaOCH_3$, NaOH, $NaOCH_2CH_3$, and NaH are strong enough. To deprotonate CH_3CH_2OH (pK_a = 16), only NaH is strong enough.

Problem 19.12 Draw the products of each acid–base reaction.

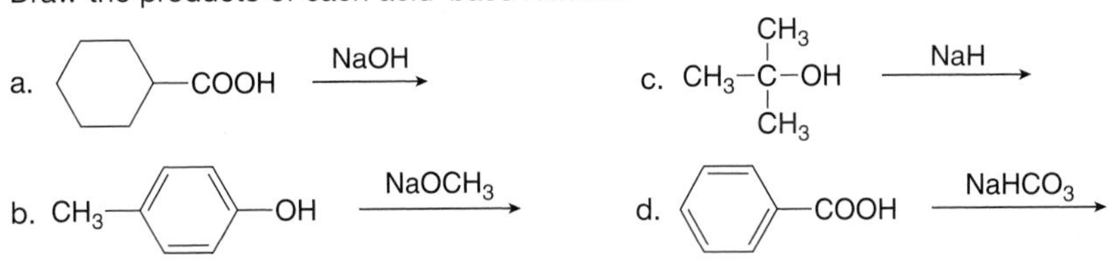

Problem 19.13 Given the pK_a values in Appendix A, which of the following bases are strong enough to deprotonate CH_3COOH: (a) F^-; (b) $(CH_3)_3CO^-$; (c) CH_3^-; (d) $^-NH_2$; (e) Cl^-?

Problem 19.14 Rank the labeled protons (H_a–H_c) in mandelic acid, a naturally occurring carboxylic acid in plums and peaches, in order of increasing acidity. Explain in detail why you chose this order.

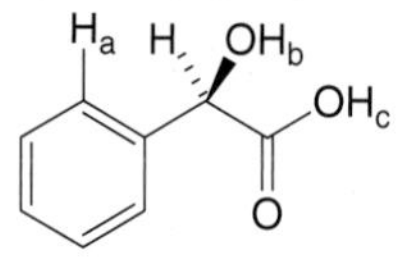

mandelic acid

19.10 Inductive Effects in Aliphatic Carboxylic Acids

The pK_a of a carboxylic acid is affected by nearby groups that inductively donate or withdraw electron density.

- **Electron-withdrawing groups stabilize a conjugate base, making a carboxylic acid more acidic.**
- **Electron-donating groups destabilize the conjugate base, making a carboxylic acid less acidic.**

The relative acidity of CH_3COOH, $ClCH_2COOH$, and $(CH_3)_3CCOOH$ illustrates these principles in the following equations.

We first learned about inductive effects and acidity in Section 2.5B.

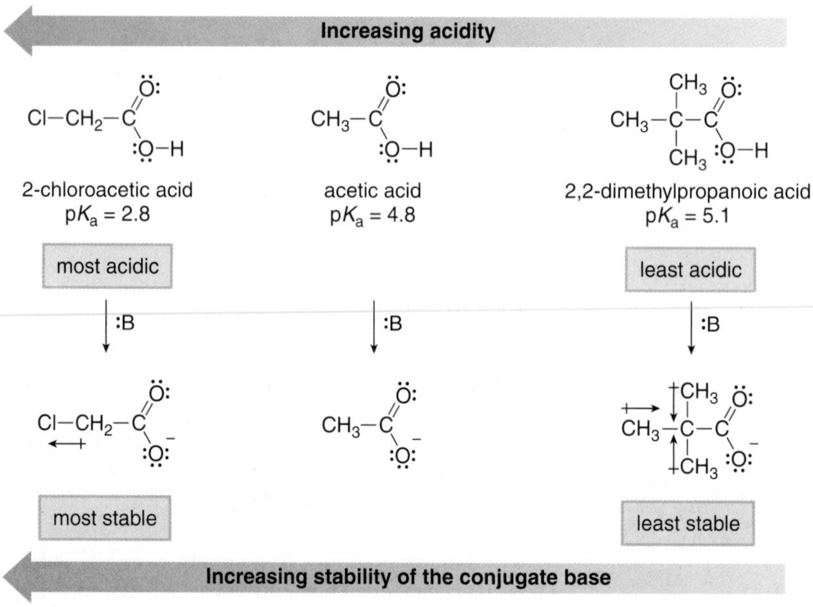

- $ClCH_2COOH$ is more acidic (pK_a = 2.8) than CH_3COOH (pK_a = 4.8) because its conjugate base is stabilized by the electron-withdrawing inductive effect of the electronegative Cl.
- $(CH_3)_3CCOOH$ is less acidic (pK_a = 5.1) than CH_3COOH because the three polarizable CH_3 groups donate electron density and destabilize the conjugate base.

The number, electronegativity, and location of substituents also affect acidity.

- **The larger the number of electronegative substituents, the stronger the acid.**

$ClCH_2{-}COOH$	$Cl_2CH{-}COOH$	$Cl_3C{-}COOH$
$pK_a = 2.8$	$pK_a = 1.3$	$pK_a = 0.9$

Increasing acidity
Increasing number of electronegative Cl atoms

- **The more electronegative the substituent, the stronger the acid.**

$ClCH_2{-}COOH$	$FCH_2{-}COOH$
$pK_a = 2.8$	$pK_a = 2.6$
	stronger acid

F is more electronegative than Cl.

- **The closer the electron-withdrawing group to the COOH, the stronger the acid.**

$ClCH_2CH_2CH_2COOH$	$CH_3CH(Cl)CH_2COOH$	$CH_3CH_2CH(Cl)COOH$
4-chlorobutanoic acid	3-chlorobutanoic acid	2-chlorobutanoic acid
$pK_a = 4.5$	$pK_a = 4.1$	$pK_a = 2.9$

Increasing acidity
Increasing proximity of Cl to COOH

Problem 19.15 Match each of the following pK_a values (3.2, 4.9, and 0.2) to the appropriate carboxylic acid: (a) CH_3CH_2COOH; (b) CF_3COOH; (c) ICH_2COOH.

Problem 19.16 Rank the compounds in each group in order of increasing acidity.

a. CH_3COOH, $HSCH_2COOH$, $HOCH_2COOH$ b. ICH_2COOH, $I_2CHCOOH$, ICH_2CH_2COOH

19.11 Substituted Benzoic Acids

Recall from Chapter 18 that substituents on a benzene ring either donate or withdraw electron density, depending on the balance of their inductive and resonance effects. These same effects also determine the acidity of substituted benzoic acids. There are two rules to keep in mind.

Rule [1] **Electron-donor groups destabilize a conjugate base, making an acid less acidic.**

An electron-donor group destabilizes a conjugate base by donating electron density onto a negatively charged carboxylate anion. A benzoic acid substituted by an electron-donor group has a higher pK_a than benzoic acid ($pK_a = 4.2$).

D = Electron-donor group

This acid is less acidic than benzoic acid.

$pK_a > 4.2$

D destabilizes the carboxylate anion.

Rule [2] **Electron-withdrawing groups stabilize a conjugate base, making an acid more acidic.**

An electron-withdrawing group stabilizes a conjugate base by removing electron density from the negatively charged carboxylate anion. A benzoic acid substituted by an electron-withdrawing group has a lower pK_a than benzoic acid ($pK_a = 4.2$).

W = Electron-withdrawing group

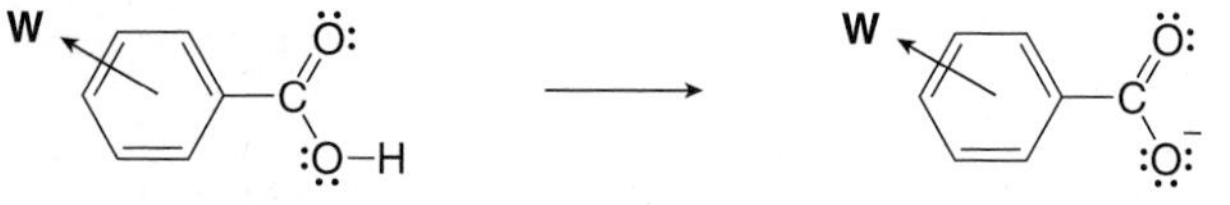

W
:Ö:
C
:O–H
W
:Ö:
C
:O:⁻

This acid is more acidic than benzoic acid.

$pK_a < 4.2$

W stabilizes the carboxylate anion.

How do we know which groups are electron donating or electron withdrawing on a benzene ring? We already learned the characteristics of electron-donating and electron-withdrawing groups in Chapter 18, and how they affect the rate of electrophilic aromatic substitution. These principles can now be extended to substituted benzoic acids.

Electron-donor groups D →
- **activate benzene to electrophilic attack**
- **make a benzoic acid less acidic**

Electron-withdrawing groups W →
- **deactivate benzene to electrophilic attack**
- **make a benzoic acid more acidic**

Figure 19.8 illustrates how common electron-donating and electron-withdrawing groups affect both the rate of reaction of a benzene ring towards electrophiles and the acidity of substituted benzoic acids.

Sample Problem 19.2

Rank the following three carboxylic acids in order of increasing acidity.

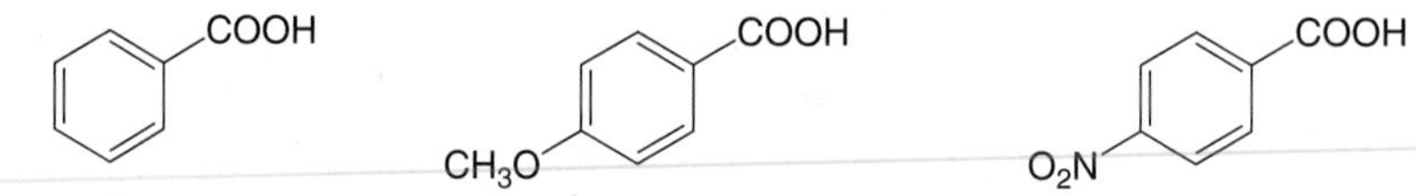

COOH
COOH
CH3O
COOH
O2N

A	B	C
benzoic acid	*p*-methoxybenzoic acid	*p*-nitrobenzoic acid

Solution

***p*-Methoxybenzoic acid (B):** The CH_3O group is an electron-donor group because its electron-donating resonance effect is stronger than its electron-withdrawing inductive effect (Section 18.6). This destabilizes the conjugate base by donating electron density to the negatively charged carboxylate anion, making **B** less acidic than benzoic acid **A.**

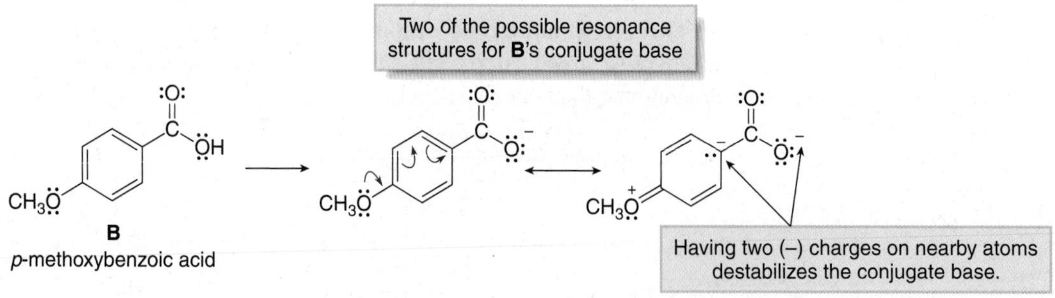

Two of the possible resonance structures for B's conjugate base
:O:
C
ÖH
CH3Ö
B
p-methoxybenzoic acid
:O:
C
Ö:⁻
CH3Ö
:O:
C
Ö:⁻
CH3O
Having two (–) charges on nearby atoms destabilizes the conjugate base.

***p*-Nitrobenzoic acid (C):** The NO_2 group is an electron-withdrawing group because of both inductive effects and resonance (Section 18.6). This stabilizes the conjugate base by removing electron density from the negatively charged carboxylate anion, making **C** more acidic than benzoic acid **A.**

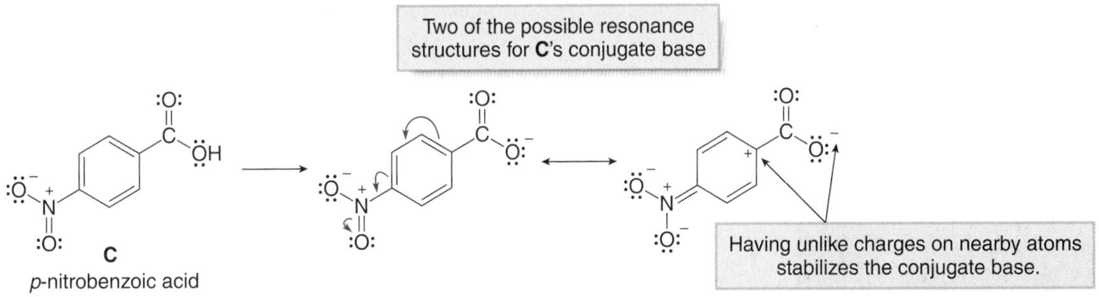
Two of the possible resonance structures for C's conjugate base
C
p-nitrobenzoic acid
Having unlike charges on nearby atoms stabilizes the conjugate base.

By this analysis, the order of acidity is **B < A < C.**

Problem 19.17 Rank the compounds in each group in order of increasing acidity.

a. 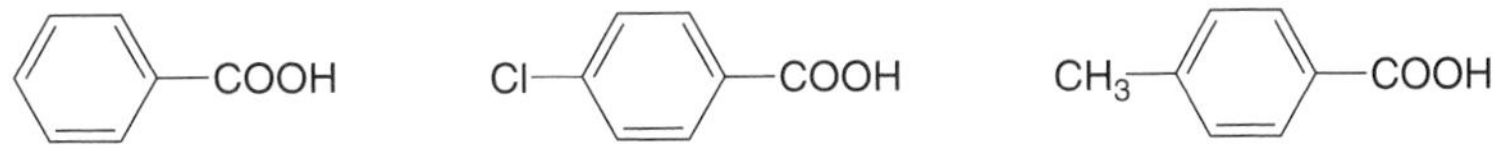
COOH
Cl
COOH
CH3
COOH

b. 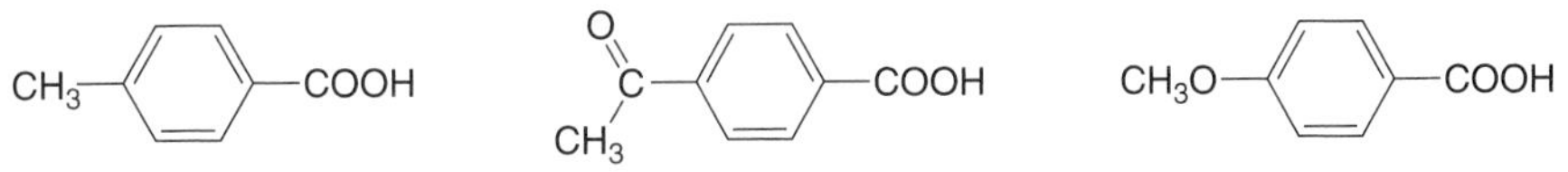
CH3
COOH
O
C
CH3
COOH
CH3O
COOH

Figure 19.8 How common substituents affect the reactivity of a benzene ring towards electrophiles and the acidity of substituted benzoic acids

	Substituent	Effect in electrophilic substitution	Effect on acidity of substituted benzoic acids
electron-donating groups	$-\ddot{N}H_2$ [$\ddot{N}HR$, $\ddot{N}R_2$]	activating groups	These groups make a benzoic acid **less acidic**.
	$-\ddot{O}H$		
	$-\ddot{O}R$		
	$-\ddot{N}HCOR$		
	$-R$		
electron-withdrawing groups	$-\ddot{X}:$ [X = F, Cl, Br, I]	deactivating groups	These groups make a benzoic acid **more acidic**.
	$-CHO$		
	$-COR$		
	$-COOR$		
	$-COOH$		
	$-CN$		
	$-SO_3H$		
	$-NO_2$		
	$-\overset{+}{N}R_3$		

Increasing acidity (downward)

- **Groups that donate electron density activate a benzene ring towards electrophilic attack and make a benzoic acid *less* acidic.** Common electron-donating groups are R groups, or groups that have an N or O atom (with a lone pair) bonded to the benzene ring.
- **Groups that withdraw electron density deactivate a benzene ring towards electrophilic attack, and make a benzoic acid *more* acidic.** Common electron-withdrawing groups are the halogens, or groups with an atom Y (with a full or partial positive charge) bonded to the benzene ring.

Problem 19.18 Substituted phenols show substituent effects similiar to substituted benzoic acids. Should the pK_a of phenol **A,** one of the naturally occurring phenols called urushiols isolated from poison ivy, be higher or lower than the pK_a of phenol (C_6H_5OH, pK_a = 10)? Explain.

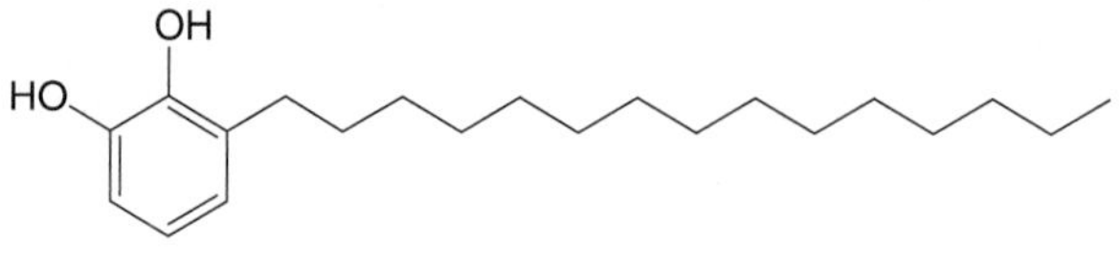
OH
HO

A

Poison ivy contains the irritant urushiol.

Extraction has long been and remains the first step in isolating a natural product from its source.

19.12 Extraction

An organic chemist in the laboratory must separate and purify mixtures of compounds. One particularly useful technique is **extraction,** which uses solubility differences and acid–base principles to separate and purify compounds.

Two solvents are used in extraction: water or an aqueous solution such as 10% $NaHCO_3$ or 10% NaOH; and an organic solvent such as dichloromethane (CH_2Cl_2), diethyl ether, or hexane. **Compounds are separated by their solubility differences in an aqueous and organic solvent.**

An item of glassware called a **separatory funnel,** depicted in Figure 19.9, is used for the extraction. When two insoluble liquids are added to the separatory funnel, two layers form, with the less dense liquid on top and the more dense liquid on the bottom.

Suppose a mixture of benzoic acid (C_6H_5COOH) and NaCl is added to a separatory funnel containing H_2O and CH_2Cl_2. The benzoic acid would dissolve in the organic layer and the NaCl would dissolve in the water layer. Separating the organic and aqueous layers and placing them in different flasks separates the benzoic acid and NaCl from each other.

Figure 19.9
Using a separatory funnel for extraction

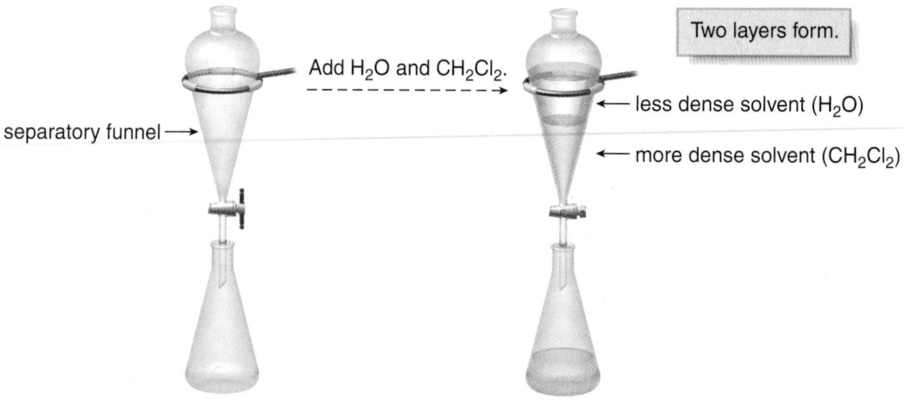
Add H2O and CH2Cl2.
separatory funnel
Two layers form.
less dense solvent (H2O)
more dense solvent (CH2Cl2)

- When two insoluble liquids are added to a separatory funnel, two layers are visible, and the less dense liquid forms the upper layer.
- To separate the layers, the lower layer can be drained from the bottom of the separatory funnel by opening the stopcock. The top layer can then be poured out the top neck of the funnel.

How could we separate a mixture of benzoic acid and cyclohexanol? Both compounds are organic, and as a result, both are soluble in an organic solvent such as CH_2Cl_2 and insoluble in water. If a mixture of benzoic acid and cyclohexanol were added to a separatory funnel with CH_2Cl_2 and water, both would dissolve in the CH_2Cl_2 layer, and the two compounds would *not* be separated from each other. Is it possible to use extraction to separate two compounds of this sort that have similar solubility properties?

Recall from Tables 9.1 and 19.2 that alcohols and carboxylic acids having more than five carbons are water insoluble.

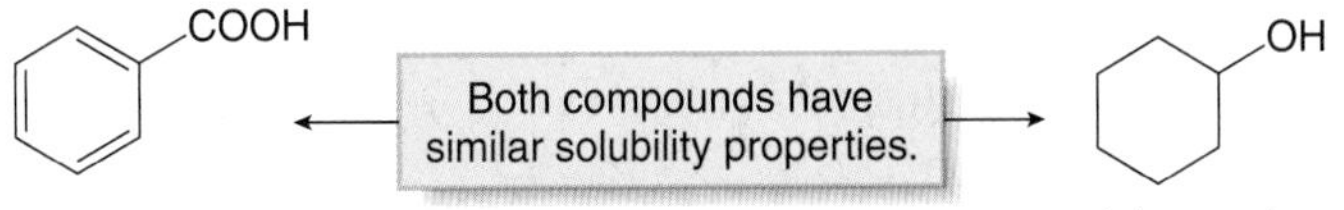

benzoic acid
- insoluble in water
- soluble in CH_2Cl_2

cyclohexanol
- insoluble in water
- soluble in CH_2Cl_2

If a carboxylic acid is one of the compounds, the answer is *yes,* because we can use acid–base chemistry to change its solubility properties.

When benzoic acid (a strong organic acid) is treated with aqueous NaOH, benzoic acid is deprotonated, forming sodium benzoate. Because sodium benzoate is ionic, it is soluble in water, but insoluble in organic solvents.

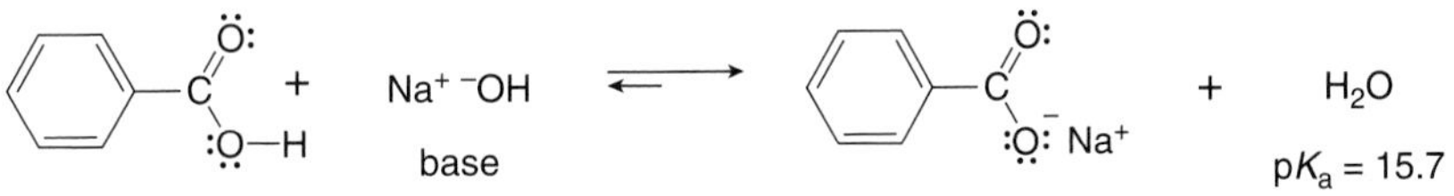

benzoic acid
pK_a = 4.2
- insoluble in water
- soluble in CH_2Cl_2

sodium benzoate
- soluble in water
- insoluble in CH_2Cl_2

The solubility properties of the conjugate base are *different* from those of the starting acid.

A similar acid–base reaction does *not* occur when cyclohexanol is treated with NaOH because organic alcohols are much weaker organic acids, so they can be deprotonated only by a *very strong base* such as NaH. NaOH is not strong enough to form significant amounts of the sodium alkoxide.

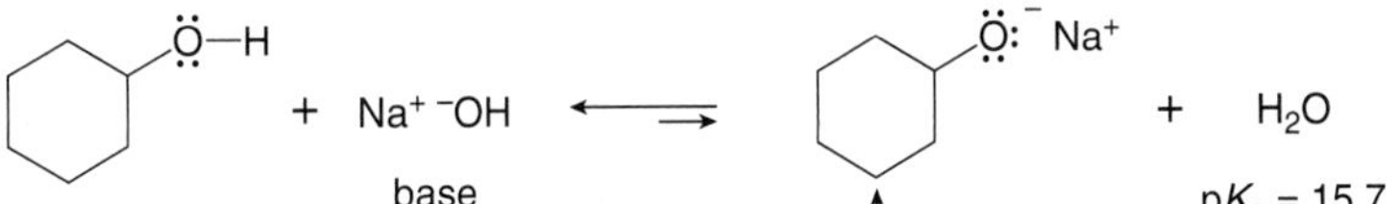

cyclohexanol
pK_a ~ 17

Since equilibrium favors the starting materials, little alkoxide is formed.

Figure 19.10 Separation of benzoic acid and cyclohexanol by an extraction procedure

Step [1] Dissolve benzoic acid and cyclohexanol in CH_2Cl_2.

Step [2] Add 10% NaOH solution to form two layers.

Step [3] Separate the layers.

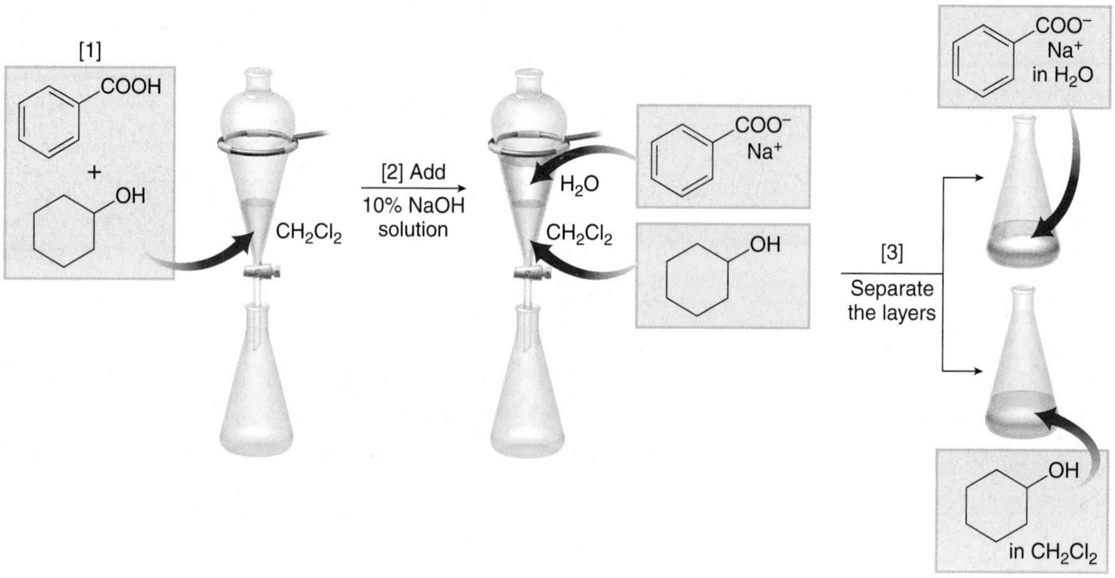

- Both compounds dissolve in the organic solvent CH_2Cl_2.

- Adding 10% aqueous NaOH solution forms two layers. When the two layers are mixed, the NaOH deprotonates C_6H_5COOH to form $C_6H_5COO^-Na^+$, which dissolves in the aqueous layer.
- The cyclohexanol remains in the CH_2Cl_2 layer.

- Draining the lower layer out the bottom stopcock separates the two layers, and the separation process is complete.
- Cyclohexanol (dissolved in CH_2Cl_2) is in one flask. The sodium salt of benzoic acid, $C_6H_5COO^-Na^+$ (dissolved in water) is in another flask.

This difference in acid–base chemistry can be used to separate benzoic acid and cyclohexanol by the stepwise extraction procedure illustrated in Figure 19.10. This extraction scheme relies on two principles:

- **Extraction can separate only compounds having different solubility properties. One compound must dissolve in the aqueous layer and one must dissolve in the organic layer.**

- **A carboxylic acid can be separated from other organic compounds by converting it to a water-soluble carboxylate anion by an acid–base reaction.**

Thus, the water-soluble salt, $C_6H_5COO^-Na^+$ (derived from C_6H_5COOH by an acid–base reaction) can be separated from water-insoluble cyclohexanol by an extraction procedure.

Problem 19.19 Which of the following pairs of compounds can be separated from each other by an extraction procedure?

a. $CH_3(CH_2)_6COOH$ and $CH_3CH_2CH_2CH_2CH{=}CH_2$
b. $CH_3CH_2CH_2CH_2CH{=}CH_2$ and $(CH_3CH_2CH_2)_2O$
c. $CH_3(CH_2)_6COOH$ and NaCl
d. NaCl and KCl

19.13 Sulfonic Acids

Although much less common than carboxylic acids, **sulfonic acids** constitute a useful group of organic acids. Sulfonic acids have the general structure **RSO_3H.** The most widely used sulfonic acid, ***p*-toluenesulfonic acid,** was first discussed in Section 2.6.

Recall from Section 9.13 that **$CH_3C_6H_4SO_2$–** is called a **tosyl group,** abbreviated by the letters **Ts.** For this reason, *p*-toluenesulfonic acid (also called tosic acid) is abbreviated as **TsOH.**

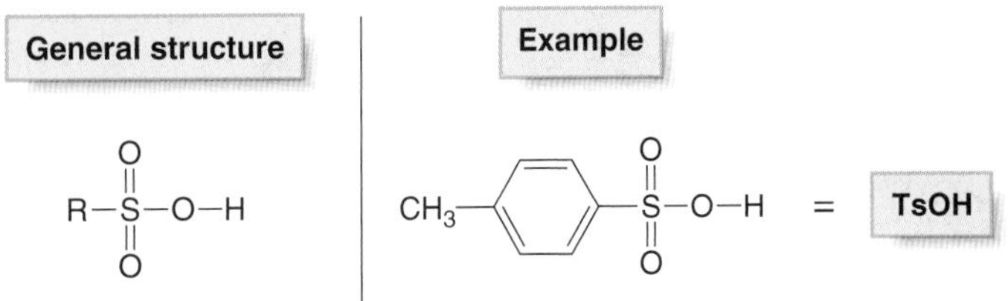

sulfonic acid | *p*-toluenesulfonic acid

Sulfonic acids are very strong acids (pK_a values ≈ –7) because their conjugate bases are resonance stabilized, and all the resonance structures delocalize a negative charge on oxygen. The conjugate base of a sulfonic acid is called a **sulfonate anion.**

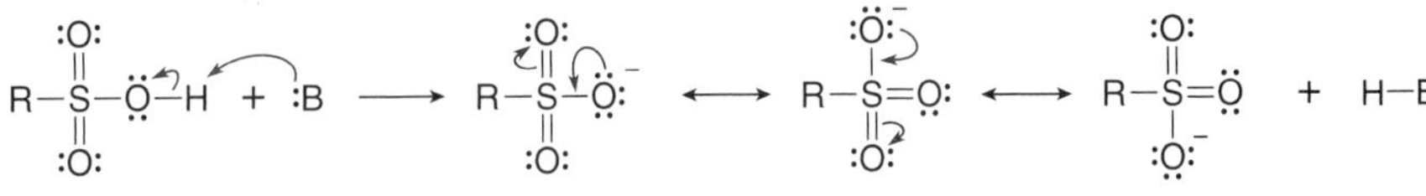

strong acid
pK_a ≈ –7

Three resonance structures—
All have a negative charge on oxygen.

Because sulfonate anions are such weak bases, they make **good leaving groups** in nucleophilic substitution reactions, as we learned in Section 9.13.

Problem 19.20 Two other commonly used sulfonic acids are methanesulfonic acid (CH_3SO_3H) and trifluoromethanesulfonic acid (CF_3SO_3H). Which has the weaker conjugate base? Which conjugate base is the better leaving group? Which of these acids has the higher pK_a?

19.14 Amino Acids

Amino acids, one of four kinds of small biomolecules that have important biological functions in the cell (Section 3.9), also undergo proton transfer reactions.

19.14A Introduction

Chapter 29 discusses the synthesis of amino acids and their conversion to proteins.

Amino acids contain two functional groups—an amino group (NH_2) and a carboxy group (COOH). In most naturally occurring amino acids, the amino group is bonded to the α carbon, and so they are called **α-amino acids.** Amino acids are the building blocks of proteins, biomolecules that comprise muscle, hair, fingernails, and many other biological tissues.

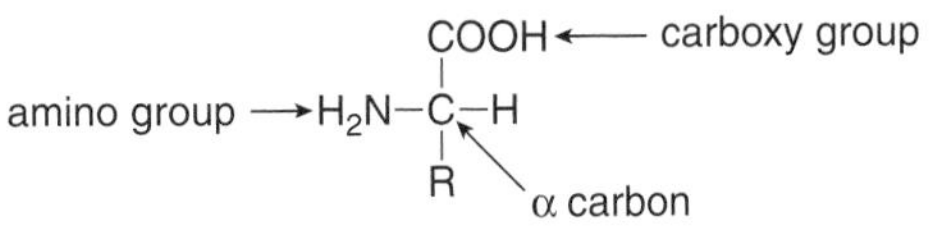

α-amino acid

Humans can synthesize only 10 of the 20 amino acids needed for protein synthesis. The remaining 10, called **essential amino acids,** must be obtained from the diet and consumed on a regular, almost daily basis. Because plant sources generally do not have sufficient amounts of all the essential amino acids, vegetarian diets must be carefully balanced. Grains—wheat, rice, and corn—are low in lysine, and legumes—beans, peas, and peanuts—are low in methionine, but a combination of these foods provides all the needed amino acids. Thus, a diet of corn tortillas and beans, or rice and tofu, provides all essential amino acids. A peanut butter sandwich on wheat bread does, too.

The 20 amino acids that occur naturally in proteins differ in the identity of the R group bonded to the α carbon. **The simplest amino acid, called glycine, has R = H.** When the R group is any other substituent, **the α carbon is a stereogenic center,** and there are two possible enantiomers.

Simplest amino acid, R = H

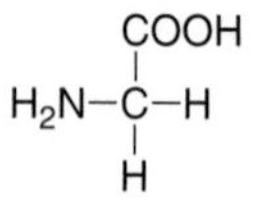

glycine
no stereogenic centers

Two possible enantiomers when R ≠ H

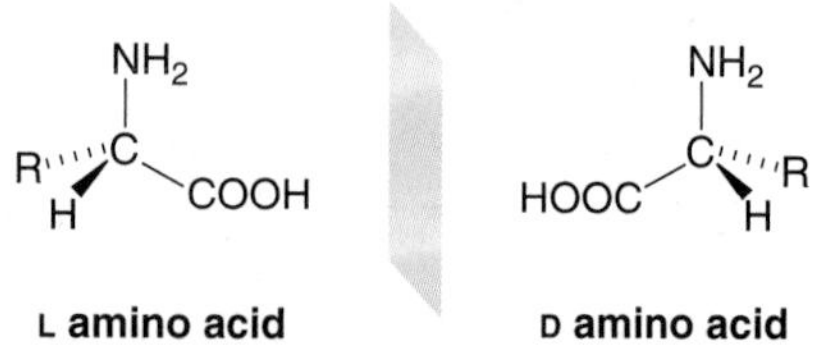

L amino acid — Only this isomer occurs in proteins.

D amino acid

Amino acids exist in nature as only one of these enantiomers. Except when the R group is CH_2SH, the stereogenic center on the α carbon has the *S* configuration. An older system of nomenclature names the **naturally occurring enantiomer of an amino acid as the L isomer, and its unnatural enantiomer the D isomer.**

The R group of an amino acid can be H, alkyl, aryl, or an alkyl chain containing an N, O, or S atom. Representative examples are listed in Table 19.4. All amino acids have common names, which are abbreviated by a three-letter or one-letter designation. For example, glycine is often written as the three-letter abbreviation **Gly,** or the one-letter abbreviation **G.** These abbreviations are also given in Table 19.4. A complete list of the 20 naturally occurring amino acids is found in Figure 29.2.

Table 19.4 Representative Amino Acids

General structure:

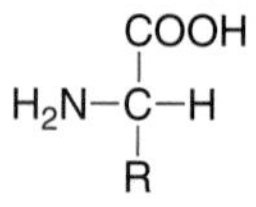

R group	Name	Three-letter abbreviation	One-letter abbreviation
H	glycine	Gly	G
CH_3	alanine	Ala	A
$CH_2C_6H_5$	phenylalanine	Phe	F
CH_2OH	serine	Ser	S
CH_2SH	cysteine	Cys	C
$CH_2CH_2SCH_3$	methionine	Met	M
CH_2CH_2COOH	glutamic acid	Glu	E
$(CH_2)_4NH_2$	lysine	Lys	K

Problem 19.21 Draw both enantiomers of each amino acid and label them as *R* or *S:* (a) phenylalanine; (b) methionine.

19.14B Acid–Base Properties

An amino acid is both an acid and a base.

- **The NH_2 group has a nonbonded electron pair, making it a base.**
- **The COOH group has an acidic proton, making it an acid.**

Amino acids are never uncharged neutral compounds. They exist as salts, so they have very high melting points and are very soluble in water.

- **Proton transfer from the acidic carboxy group to the basic amino group forms a salt called a *zwitterion*, which contains both a positive and a negative charge.**

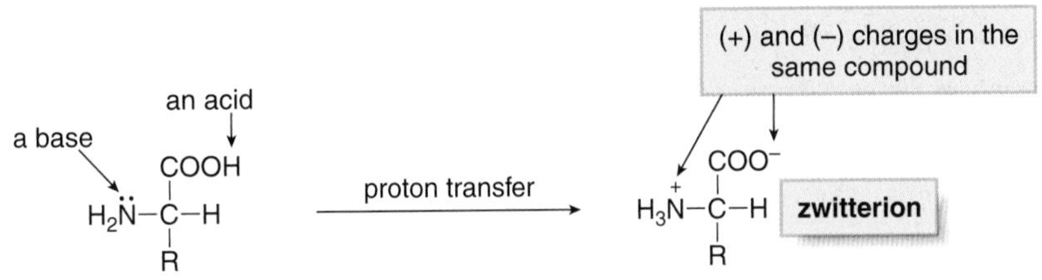

This neutral form of an amino acid does *not* exist.

a salt

This salt is the neutral form of an amino acid.

In actuality, an amino acid can exist in three different forms, depending on the pH of the aqueous solution in which it is dissolved.

When the pH of a solution is ~6, alanine (R = CH_3) exists in its zwitterionic form (**A**), having no net charge. In this form the carboxy group bears a negative charge—it is a **carboxylate anion**—and the amino group bears a net positive charge (an **ammonium cation**).

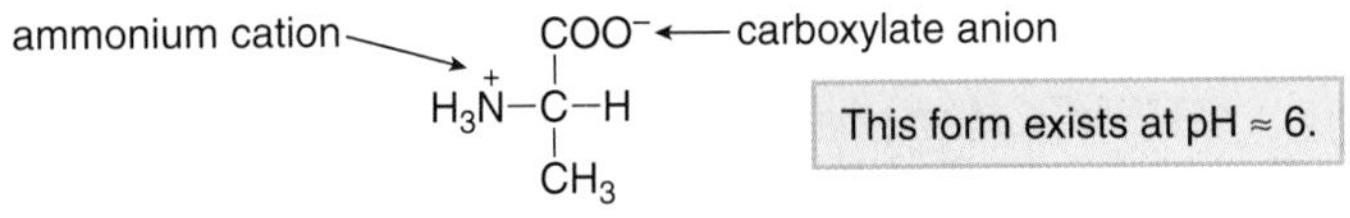

alanine
A
a neutral zwitterion

When strong acid is added to lower the pH (≤ 2), the carboxylate anion is protonated and the **amino acid has a net positive charge** (form **B**).

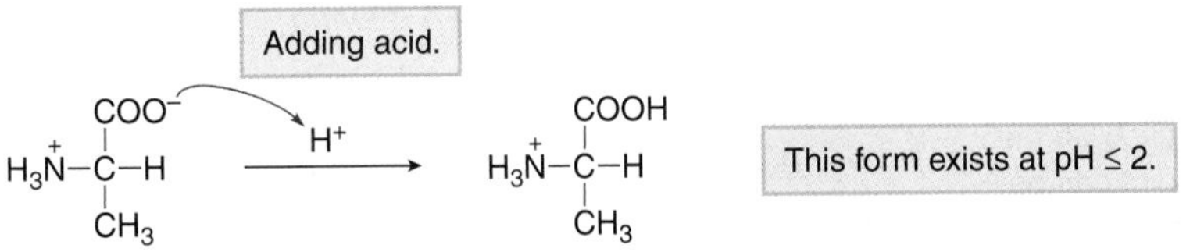

A **B**
overall (+1) charge

When strong base is added to **A** to raise the pH (≥ 10), the ammonium cation is deprotonated and the **amino acid has a net negative charge** (form **C**).

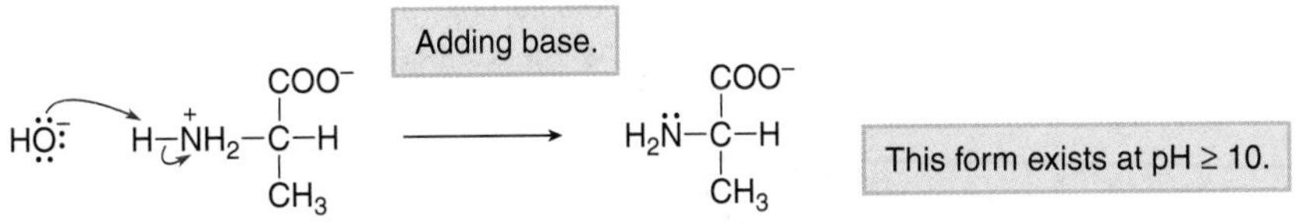

A **C**
overall (–1) charge

Thus, **alanine exists in one of three different forms depending on the pH of the solution in which it is dissolved.** If the pH of a solution is gradually increased from 2 to 10, the following process occurs.

- **At low pH alanine has a net (+) charge (form B).**
- **As the pH is increased to ~6, the carboxy group is deprotonated, and the amino acid exists as a zwitterion with no overall charge (form A).**
- **At high pH, the ammonium cation is deprotonated, and the amino acid has a net (–) charge (form C).**

These reactions are summarized in Figure 19.11.

Figure 19.11
Summary of the acid–base reactions of alanine

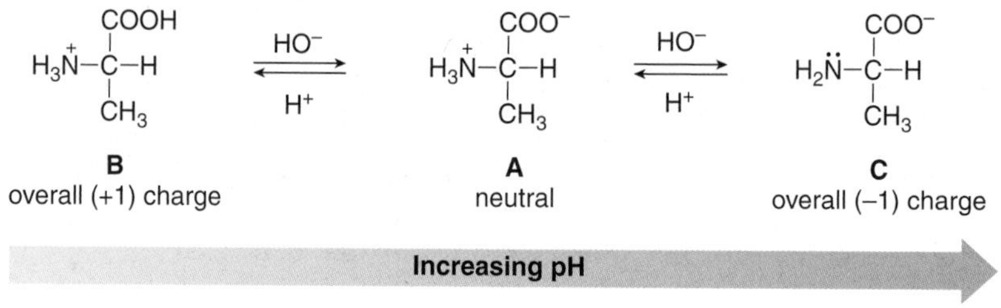

Problem 19.22 Explain why amino acids, unlike most other organic compounds, are insoluble in organic solvents like diethyl ether.

Problem 19.23 Draw the positively charged, neutral, and negatively charged forms for the amino acid glycine. Which species predominates at pH 11? Which species predominates at pH 1?

19.14C Isoelectric Point

Because a protonated amino acid has at least two different protons that can be removed, a pK_a value is reported for each of these protons. For example, the pK_a of the carboxy proton of alanine is 2.35 and the pK_a of the ammonium proton is 9.87. Table 29.1 lists these values for all 20 amino acids.

- **The pH at which the amino acid exists primarily in its neutral form is called its *isoelectric point,* abbreviated as p*I*.**

More information on the isoelectric point can be found in Section 29.1 and Problem 29.36.

Generally, the isoelectric point is the average of both pK_a values of an amino acid:

$$\text{Isoelectric point} = pI = \frac{pK_a\,(COOH) + pK_a\,(NH_3^+)}{2}$$

$$\text{For alanine:} \quad pI = \frac{2.35 + 9.87}{2} = \underset{pI\text{ (alanine)}}{6.12}$$

Problem 19.24 The pK_a values for the carboxy and ammonium protons of phenylalanine are 2.58 and 9.24, respectively. What is the isoelectric point of phenylalanine? Draw the structure of phenylalanine at its isoelectric point.

Problem 19.25 Explain why the pK_a of the COOH group of glycine is much lower than the pK_a of the COOH of acetic acid (2.35 compared to 4.8).

KEY CONCEPTS

Carboxylic Acids and the Acidity of the O–H Bond

General Facts

- Carboxylic acids contain a carboxy group (COOH). The central carbon is sp^2 hybridized and trigonal planar (19.1).
- Carboxylic acids are identified by the suffixes *-oic acid, carboxylic acid,* or *-ic acid* (19.2).
- Carboxylic acids are polar compounds that exhibit hydrogen bonding interactions (19.3).

Summary of Spectroscopic Absorptions (19.4)

IR absorptions	C=O	~1710 cm^{-1}
	O–H	3500–2500 cm^{-1} (very broad and strong)
^{1}H NMR absorptions	O–H	10–12 ppm (highly deshielded proton)
	C–H α to COOH	2–2.5 ppm (somewhat deshielded C_{sp^3}–H)
^{13}C NMR absorption	C=O	170–210 ppm (highly deshielded carbon)

General Acid–Base Reaction of Carboxylic Acids (19.9)

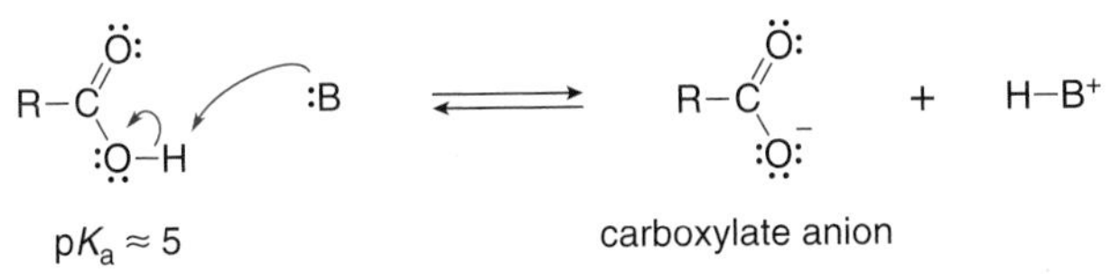

R–C
:B
+
H–B+
pKa ≈ 5
carboxylate anion

- Carboxylic acids are especially acidic because carboxylate anions are resonance stabilized.
- For equilibrium to favor the products, the base must have a conjugate acid with a $pK_a > 5$. Common bases are listed in Table 19.3.

Factors That Affect Acidity

Resonance effects

- A carboxylic acid is more acidic than an alcohol or phenol because its conjugate base is more effectively stabilized by resonance (19.9).

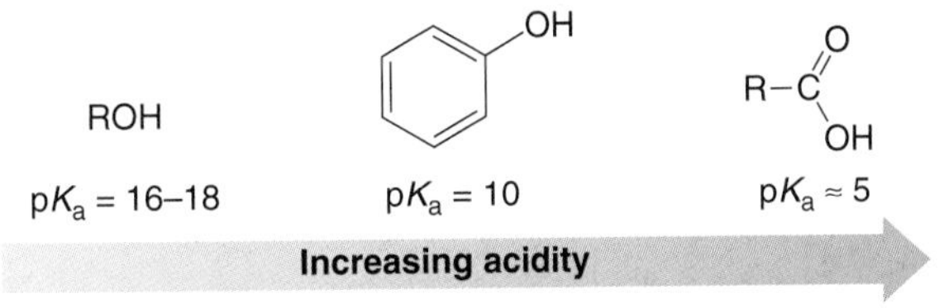

ROH
OH
R–C
OH
pKa = 16–18
pKa = 10
pKa ≈ 5
Increasing acidity

Inductive effects

- Acidity increases with the presence of electron-withdrawing groups (like the electronegative halogens) and decreases with the presence of electron-donating groups (like polarizable alkyl groups) (19.10).

Substituted benzoic acids

- Electron-donor groups **(D)** make a substituted benzoic acid less acidic than benzoic acid.
- Electron-withdrawing groups **(W)** make a substituted benzoic acid more acidic than benzoic acid.

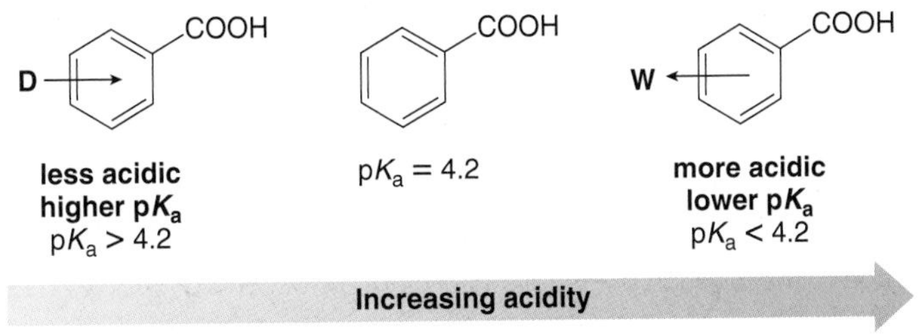

COOH
D
COOH
COOH
W
less acidic
higher pKa
pKa > 4.2
pKa = 4.2
more acidic
lower pKa
pKa < 4.2
Increasing acidity

Other Facts

- Extraction is a useful technique for separating compounds having different solubility properties. Carboxylic acids can be separated from other organic compounds by extraction, because aqueous base converts a carboxylic acid into a water-soluble carboxylate anion (19.12).
- A sulfonic acid (RSO_3H) is a strong acid because it forms a weak, resonance-stabilized conjugate base on deprotonation (19.13).
- Amino acids have an amino group on the α carbon to the carboxy group [$RCH(NH_2)COOH$]. Amino acids exist as zwitterions at pH ≈ 6. Adding acid forms a species with a net (+1) charge [$RCH(NH_3)COOH]^+$. Adding base forms a species with a net (–1) charge [$RCH(NH_2)COO]^-$ (19.14).

PROBLEMS

Problems Using Three-Dimensional Models

19.26 Answer each question for **A** and **B** depicted in the ball-and-stick models.

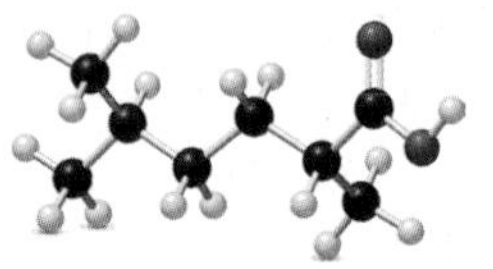

A

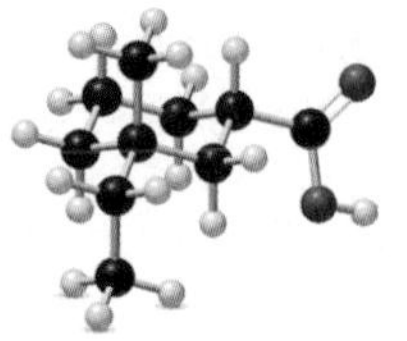

B

a. What is the IUPAC name for each compound?
b. What product is formed when each compound is treated with NaOH?
c. Name the products formed in part (b).
d. Draw the structure of an isomer that is at least 10^5 times less acidic than each compound.

19.27 Rank the carboxylic acids in order of increasing acidity.

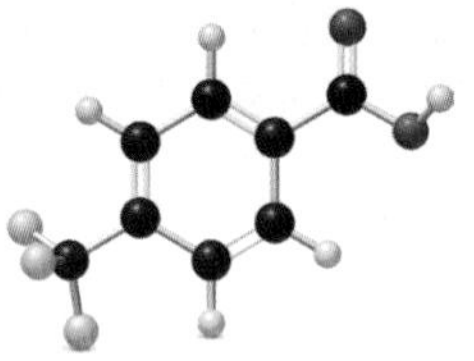

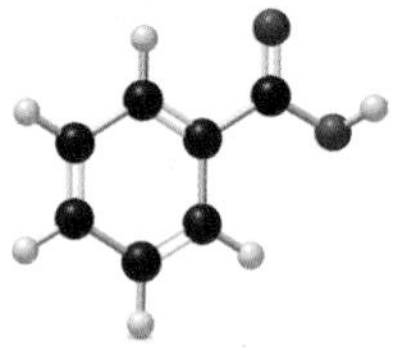

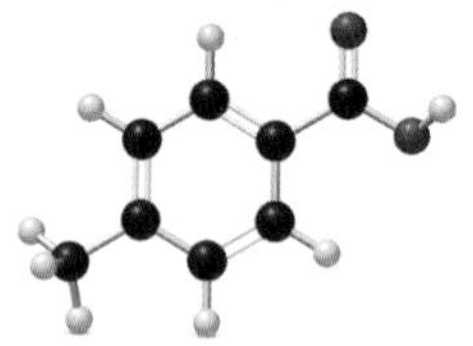

Nomenclature

19.28 Give the IUPAC name for each compound.

a. $(CH_3)_2CHCH_2CH_2CO_2H$
b. $BrCH_2COOH$
c. 

d. $CH_3CH_2CH_2COO^{-}Li^{+}$
e. 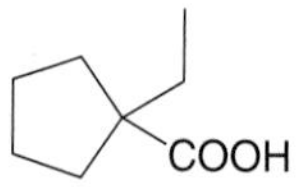

f. 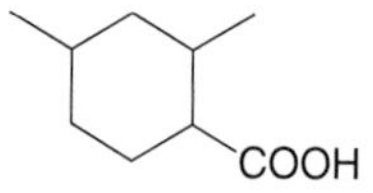

g. 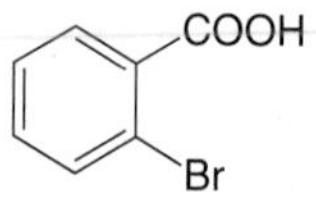

h. 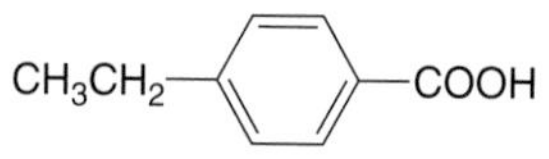

i. 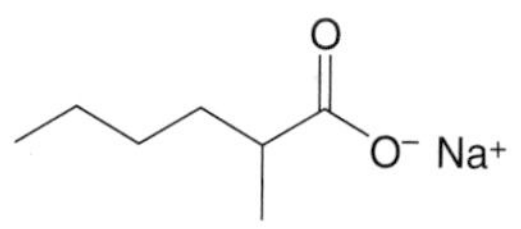

j. 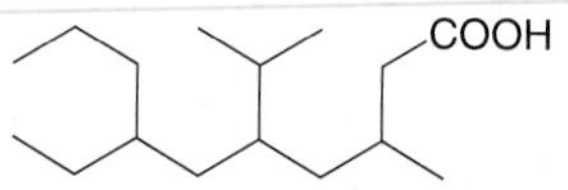

19.29 Draw the structure corresponding to each name.
a. 3,3-dimethylpentanoic acid
b. 4-chloro-3-phenylheptanoic acid
c. (2*R*)-2-chloropropanoic acid
d. β,β-dichloropropionic acid
e. *m*-hydroxybenzoic acid
f. *o*-chlorobenzoic acid
g. potassium acetate
h. sodium α-bromobutyrate
i. 2,2-dichloropentanedioic acid
j. 4-isopropyl-2-methyloctanedioic acid

19.30 Draw the structures and give the IUPAC names for the carboxylic acids having molecular formula $C_5H_{10}O_2$. Then give the IUPAC names for the sodium salts that result from treatment of each carboxylic acid with NaOH.

19.31 Give an IUPAC and common name for each of the following naturally occurring carboxylic acids: (a) $CH_3CH(OH)CO_2H$ (lactic acid); (b) $HOCH_2CH_2C(OH)(CH_3)CH_2CO_2H$ (mevalonic acid).

Physical Properties

19.32 Rank the compounds in each group in order of increasing boiling point.

a. $CH_3CH_2CH_2CH_2COOH$, $(CH_3CH_2CH_2)_2O$, $CH_3(CH_2)_5OH$

b. $CH_3COCH_2CH(CH_3)_2$, $(CH_3)_2CHCH_2COOH$, $(CH_3)_2CHCH_2CH(OH)CH_3$

Preparation of Carboxylic Acids

19.33 Draw the organic products formed in each reaction.

a. 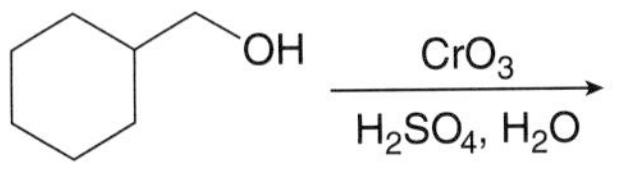

c. 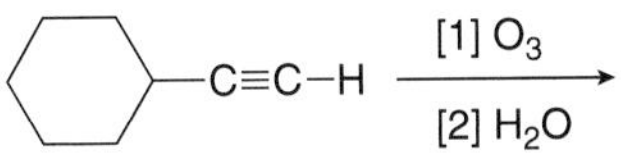

b. 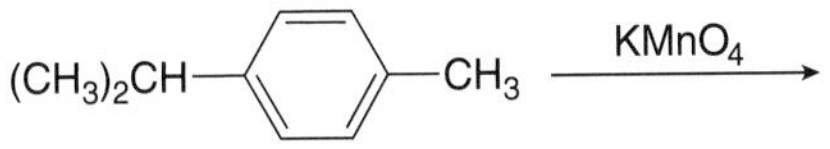

d. $CH_3(CH_2)_6CH_2OH \xrightarrow[H_2SO_4,\ H_2O]{Na_2Cr_2O_7}$

19.34 Identify the lettered compounds in each reaction sequence.

a. 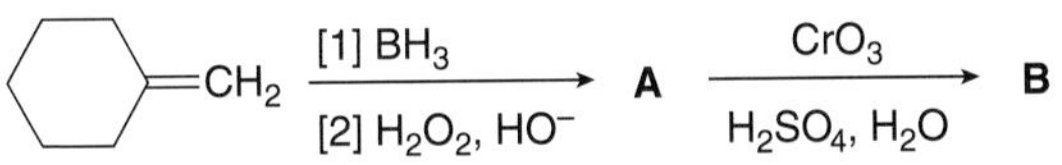

c. 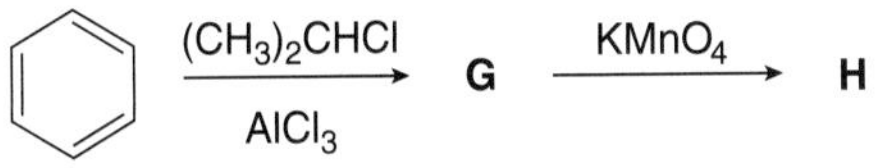

b. $HC{\equiv}CH \xrightarrow[[2]\ CH_3I]{[1]\ NaNH_2} \textbf{C} \xrightarrow[[2]\ CH_3CH_2I]{[1]\ NaNH_2} \textbf{D} \xrightarrow[[2]\ H_2O]{[1]\ O_3} \textbf{E} + \textbf{F}$

Acid–Base Reactions; General Questions on Acidity

19.35 Using the pK_a table in Appendix A, determine whether each of the following bases is strong enough to deprotonate the three compounds listed below. Bases: [1] ^-OH; [2] $CH_3CH_2^-$; [3] $^-NH_2$; [4] NH_3; [5] $HC{\equiv}C^-$.

a. 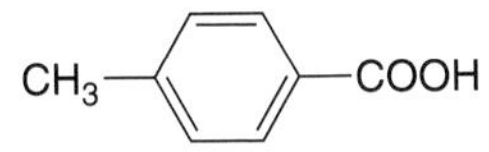

pK_a = 4.3

b. 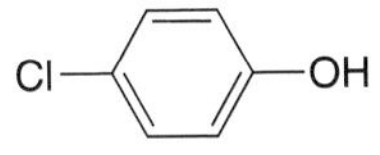

pK_a = 9.4

c. $(CH_3)_3COH$

pK_a = 18

19.36 Draw the products of each acid–base reaction, and using the pK_a table in Appendix A, determine if equilibrium favors the reactants or products.

a. 

d. 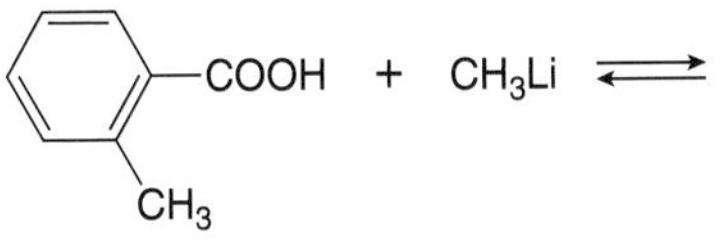

b. 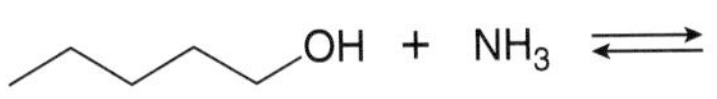

e. $(CH_3)_2CHCH_2OH + NaH \rightleftharpoons$

c. 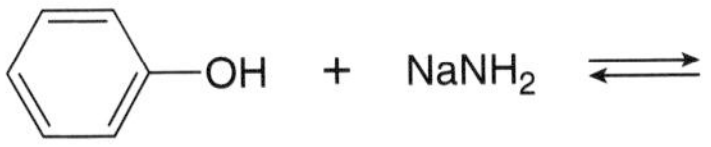

f. 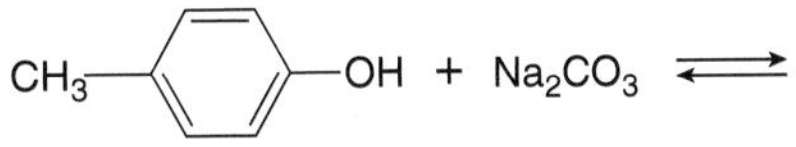

19.37 Which compound in each pair has the lower pK_a? Which compound in each pair has the stronger conjugate base?

a. 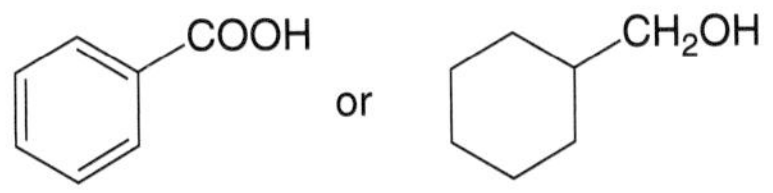

c. 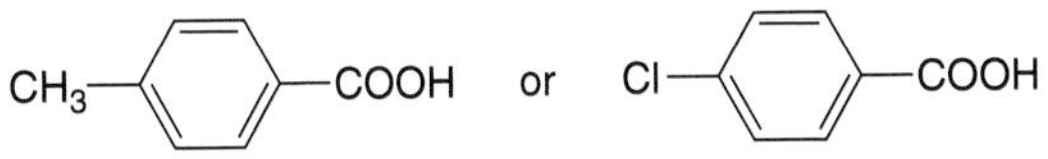

b. $ClCH_2COOH$ or FCH_2COOH

d. $NCCH_2COOH$ or CH_3COOH

19.38 Rank the compounds in each group in order of increasing acidity.

a. 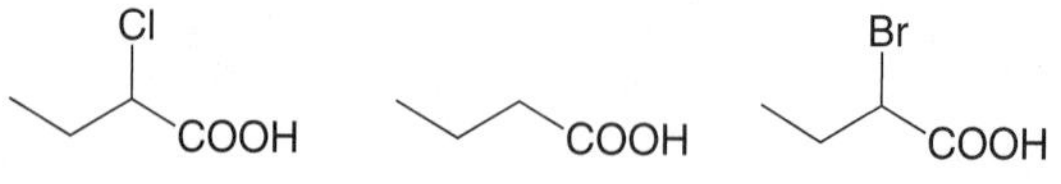

b. 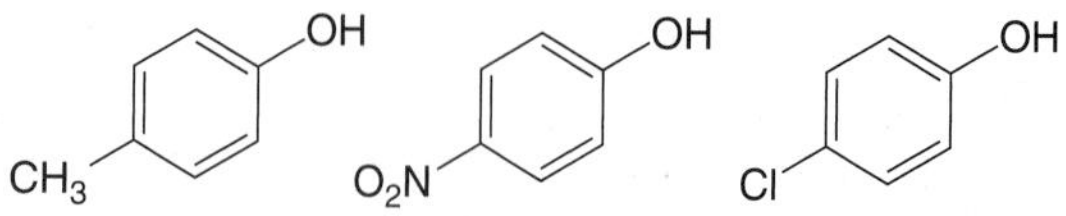

19.39 Rank the compounds in each group in order of increasing basicity.

a. $BrCH_2COO^-$ $(CH_3)_3CCOO^-$ $BrCH_2CH_2COO^-$

b. $C_6H_5NH^-$ $C_6H_5O^-$ $C_6H_5CH_2^-$

c. 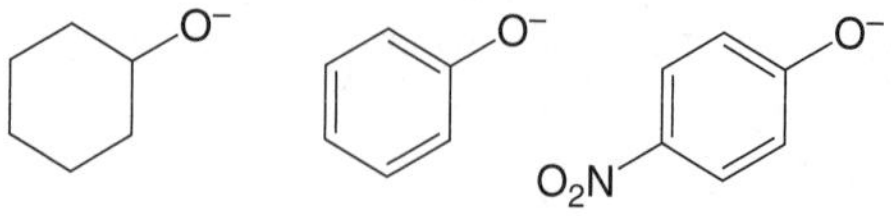

19.40 Match the pK_a values to the appropriate structure. pK_a values: 0.28, 1.24, 2.66, 2.86, and 3.12. Compounds: (a) FCH_2COOH; (b) CF_3COOH; (c) $F_2CHCOOH$; (d) ICH_2COOH; (e) $BrCH_2COOH$.

19.41 Although codeine occurs in low concentration in the opium poppy, most of the codeine used in medicine is prepared from morphine (the principal component of opium) by the following reaction. Explain why selective methylation occurs at only one OH in morphine to give codeine. Codeine is a less potent and less addictive analgesic than morphine.

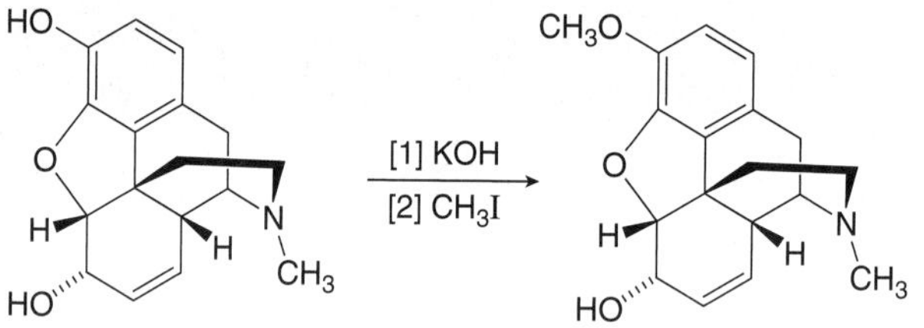

morphine codeine

19.42 Which carboxylic acid has the lower pK_a, pyruvic acid (CH_3COCO_2H) or acetoacetic acid ($CH_3COCH_2CO_2H$)? Explain your choice.

19.43 Explain each statement.

a. The pK_a of *p*-nitrophenol is lower than the pK_a of phenol (7.2 vs. 10).

b. The pK_a of *p*-nitrophenol is lower than the pK_a of *m*-nitrophenol (7.2 vs. 8.3).

19.44 Explain the following statement. Although 2-methoxyacetic acid (CH_3OCH_2COOH) is a stronger acid than acetic acid (CH_3COOH), *p*-methoxybenzoic acid ($CH_3OC_6H_4COOH$) is a weaker acid than benzoic acid (C_6H_5COOH).

19.45 The pK_a of *p*-methylthiophenol ($CH_3SC_6H_4OH$) is 9.53. Is *p*-methylthiophenol more or less reactive in electrophilic aromatic substitution than phenol?

19.46 Explain why the pK_a of compound **A** is lower than the pK_a's of both compounds **B** and **C**.

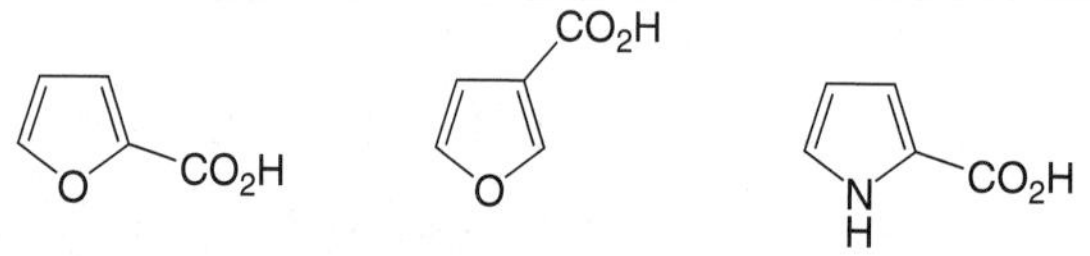

A	**B**	**C**
pK_a = 3.2	pK_a = 3.9	pK_a = 4.4

19.47 Rank the following compounds in order of increasing acidity and explain in detail your choice of order.

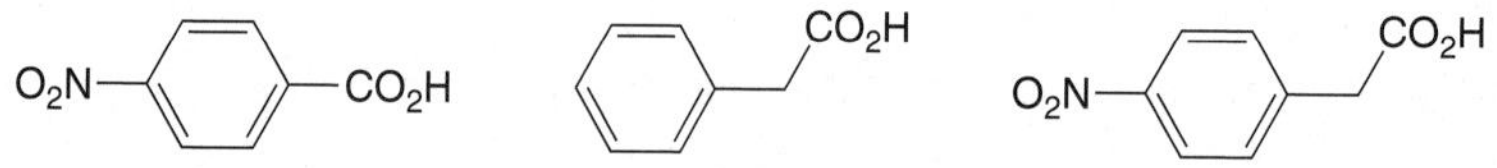

C **D** **E**

19.48 Explain the following result. Acetic acid (CH_3COOH), labeled at its OH oxygen with the uncommon ^{18}O isotope, was treated with aqueous base, and then the solution was acidified. Two products having the ^{18}O label at different locations were formed.

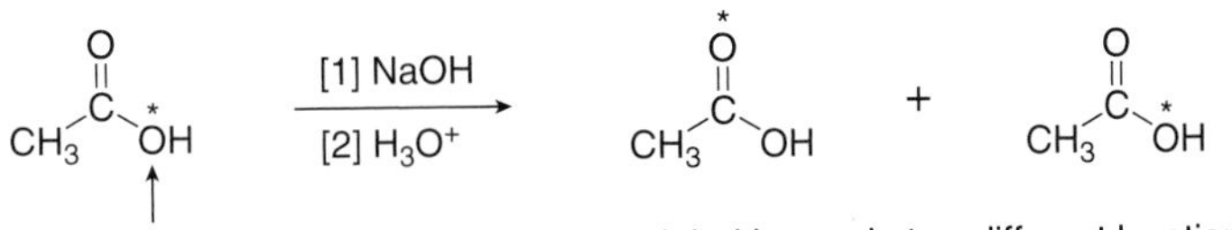

labeled O atom

The label is now in two different locations.

19.49 Draw all resonance structures of the conjugate bases formed by removal of the labeled protons (H_a, H_b, and H_c) in 1,3-cyclohexanedione and acetanilide. For each compound, rank these protons in order of increasing acidity and explain the order you chose.

a. 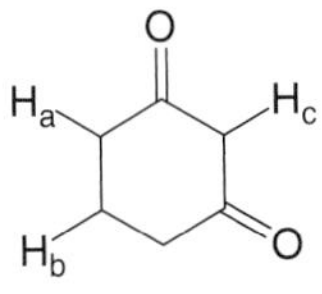

1,3-cyclohexanedione

b. 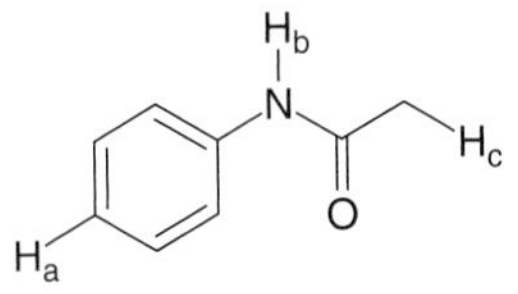

acetanilide

19.50 As we will see in Chapter 23, C–H bonds are sometimes more acidic than O–H bonds. Explain why the pK_a of $CH_2(CHO)_2$ is lower than the pK_a of $HO(CH_2)_3OH$ (9 vs. 16).

19.51 Identify **X** in the following equation, and explain how hexanoic acid, the chapter-opening molecule, is formed by this stepwise reaction sequence.

$$CH_3COOH \xrightarrow[\text{strong base (2 equiv)}]{} \mathbf{X} \xrightarrow[\text{[2] } H_3O^+]{\text{[1] } CH_3CH_2CH_2CH_2Br} CH_3CH_2CH_2CH_2CH_2COOH$$

hexanoic acid

19.52 The pK_a of acetamide (CH_3CONH_2) is 16. Draw the structure for its conjugate base and explain why acetamide is less acidic than CH_3COOH.

Extraction

19.53 Write out the steps needed to separate hydrocarbon **A** and carboxylic acid **B** by using an extraction procedure.

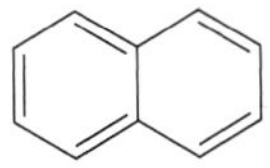

A

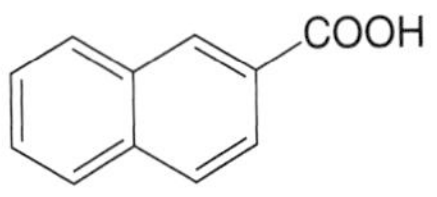

B

19.54 Because phenol (C_6H_5OH) is less acidic than a carboxylic acid, it can be deprotonated by NaOH but not by the weaker base $NaHCO_3$. Using this information, write out an extraction sequence that can be used to separate C_6H_5OH from cyclohexanol. Show what compound is present in each layer at each stage of the process, and if it is present in its neutral or ionic form.

19.55 Can octane and 1-octanol be separated using an aqueous extraction procedure? Explain why or why not.

Spectroscopy

19.56 Identify each compound from its spectral data.

a. Molecular formula: $C_3H_5ClO_2$
IR: 3500–2500 cm^{-1}, 1714 cm^{-1}
^1H NMR data: 2.87 (triplet, 2 H), 3.76 (triplet, 2 H), and 11.8 (singlet, 1 H) ppm

b. Molecular formula: $C_8H_8O_3$
IR: 3500–2500 cm^{-1}, 1688 cm^{-1}
^1H NMR data: 3.8 (singlet, 3 H), 7.0 (doublet, 2 H), 7.9 (doublet, 2 H), and 12.7 (singlet, 1 H) ppm

c. Molecular formula: $C_8H_8O_3$
IR: 3500–2500 cm^{-1}, 1710 cm^{-1}
^1H NMR data: 4.7 (singlet, 2 H), 6.9–7.3 (multiplet, 5 H), and 11.3 (singlet, 1 H) ppm

19.57 Use the ^{1}H NMR and IR spectra given below to identify the structures of two isomers (**A** and **B**) having molecular formula $C_4H_8O_2$.

Compound **A:**

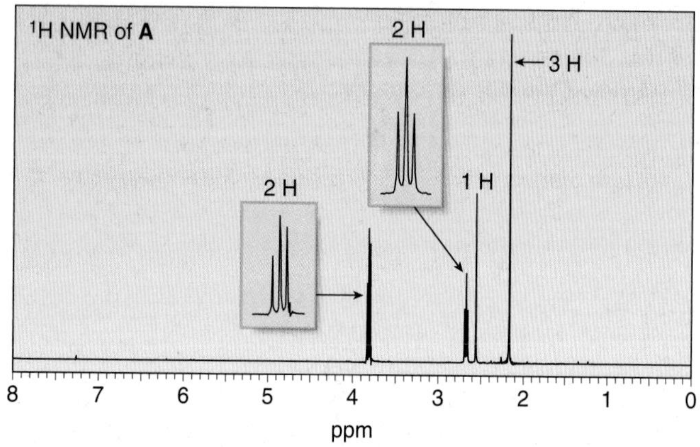

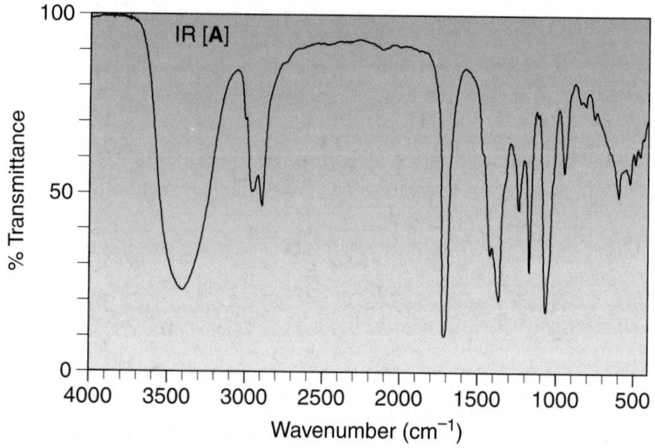

Compound **B:**

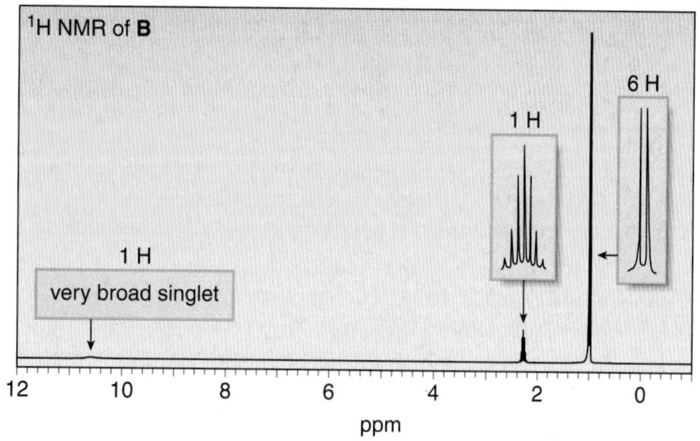

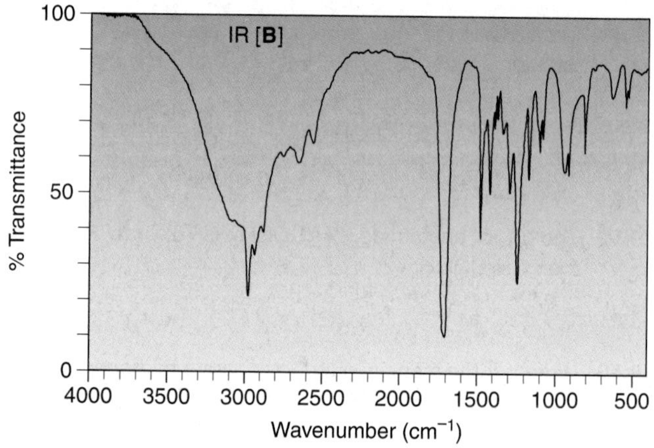

19.58 An unknown compound **C** (molecular formula $C_4H_8O_3$) exhibits IR absorptions at 3600–2500 and 1734 cm^{-1}, as well as the following ^{1}H NMR spectrum. What is the structure of **C**?

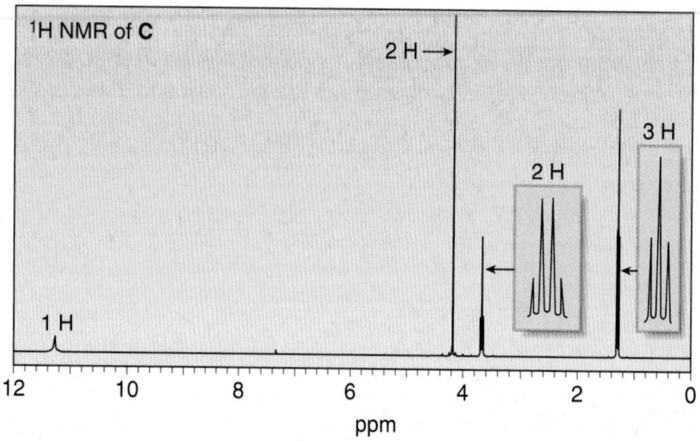

19.59 Propose a structure for **D** (molecular formula $C_9H_9ClO_2$) consistent with the given spectroscopic data.

^{13}C NMR signals at 30, 36, 128, 130, 133, 139, and 179 ppm

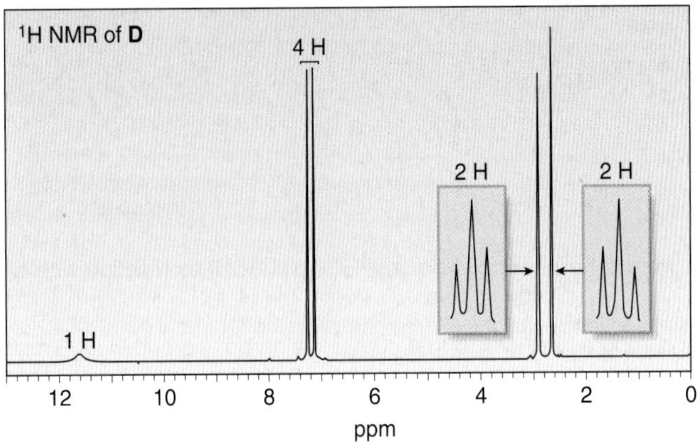

19.60 A monomer needed to synthesize polyethylene terephthalate (PET), a polymer used to make plastic sheeting and soft drink bottles (Section 22.16), shows a strong absorption in its IR spectrum at 1692 cm^{-1} and two singlets in its ^1H NMR spectrum at 8.2 and 10.0 ppm. What is the structure of this monomer (molecular formula $C_8H_6O_4$)?

19.61 Match the ^{13}C NMR data to the appropriate structure.

Spectrum [1]: signals at 14, 22, 27, 34, 181 ppm

Spectrum [2]: signals at 27, 39, 186 ppm

Spectrum [3]: signals at 22, 26, 43, 180 ppm

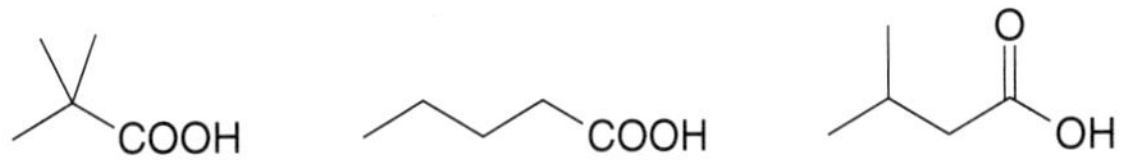

A **B** **C**

19.62 γ-Butyrolactone ($C_4H_6O_2$, GBL) is a biologically inactive compound that is converted to the biologically active recreational drug GHB (Section 19.5) by a lactonase enzyme in the body. Since γ-butyrolactone is more fat soluble than GHB, it is more readily absorbed by tissues and thus produces a faster onset of physiological symptoms. γ-Butyrolactone shows an absorption in its IR spectrum at 1770 cm^{-1} and the following ^1H NMR spectral data: 2.28 (multiplet, 2 H), 2.48 (triplet, 2 H), and 4.35 (triplet, 2 H) ppm. What is the structure of γ-butyrolactone?

Amino Acids

19.63 Threonine is a naturally occurring amino acid that has two stereogenic centers.

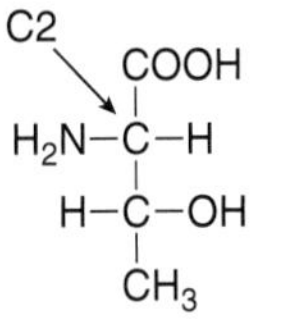

threonine

a. Draw the four possible stereoisomers using wedges and dashes.
b. The naturally occurring amino acid has the 2*S*,3*R* configuration at its two stereogenic centers. Which structure does this correspond to?

19.64 Proline is an unusual amino acid because its N atom on the α carbon is part of a five-membered ring.

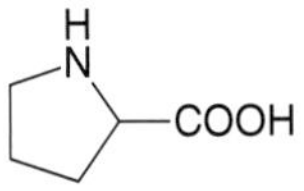

proline

a. Draw both enantiomers of proline.
b. Draw proline in its zwitterionic form.

19.65 For each amino acid [RCH(NH_2)COOH], draw its neutral, positively charged, and negatively charged forms. Which form predominates at pH = 1, 6, and 11? What is the structure of each amino acid at its isoelectric point?

a. methionine (R = $CH_2CH_2SCH_3$)
b. serine (R = CH_2OH)

19.66 Calculate the isoelectric point for each amino acid.

a. cysteine: pK_a (COOH) = 2.05; pK_a (α-NH_3^+) = 10.25
b. methionine: pK_a (COOH) = 2.28; pK_a (α-NH_3^+) = 9.21

19.67 Lysine and tryptophan are two amino acids that contain an additional N atom in the R group bonded to the α carbon. While lysine is classified as a basic amino acid because it contains an additional basic N atom, tryptophan is classified as a neutral amino acid. Explain why this difference in classification occurs.

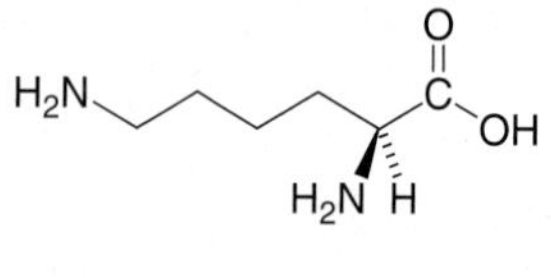

lysine

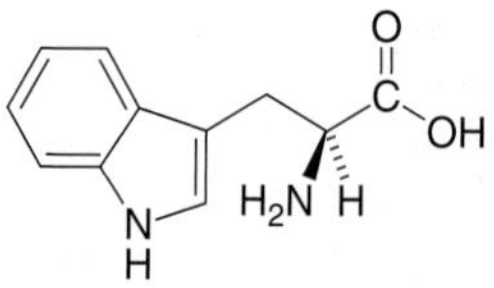

tryptophan

19.68 Amino acids can be prepared from α-halo carboxylic acids [RCH(X)COOH] by reaction with excess NH_3. Why is excess NH_3 needed for this reaction?

19.69 Glutamic acid is a naturally occurring α-amino acid that contains a carboxy group in its R group side chain (Table 19.4). (Glutamic acid is drawn in its neutral form with no charged atoms, a form that does not actually exist at any pH.)

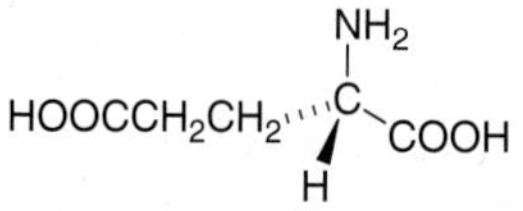

glutamic acid

a. What form of glutamic acid exists at pH = 1?
b. If the pH is gradually increased, what form of glutamic acid exists after one equivalent of base is added? After two equivalents? After three equivalents?
c. Propose a structure of monosodium glutamate, the common flavor enhancer known as MSG.

Challenge Problems

19.70 Explain why using one or two equivalents of NaH results in different products in the following reactions.

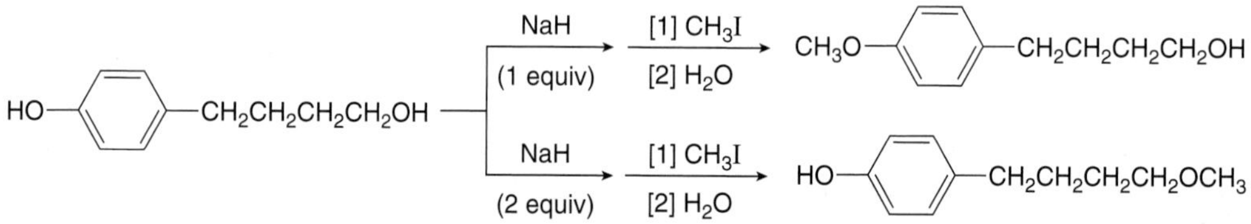

19.71 Although *p*-hydroxybenzoic acid is less acidic than benzoic acid, *o*-hydroxybenzoic acid is slightly more acidic than benzoic acid. Explain this result.

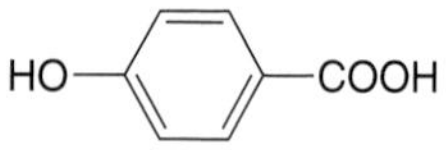

p-hydroxybenzoic acid

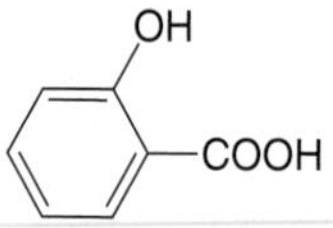

o-hydroxybenzoic acid

19.72 2-Hydroxybutanedioic acid occurs naturally in apples and other fruits. Rank the labeled protons (H_a–H_e) in order of increasing acidity and explain in detail the order you chose.

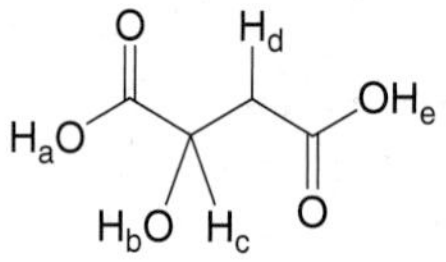

2-hydroxybutanedioic acid

19.73 Although it was initially sold as a rat poison, warfarin is an effective anticoagulant used to prevent blood clots. Label the most acidic proton in warfarin, and explain why its pK_a is comparable to the pK_a of a carboxylic acid.

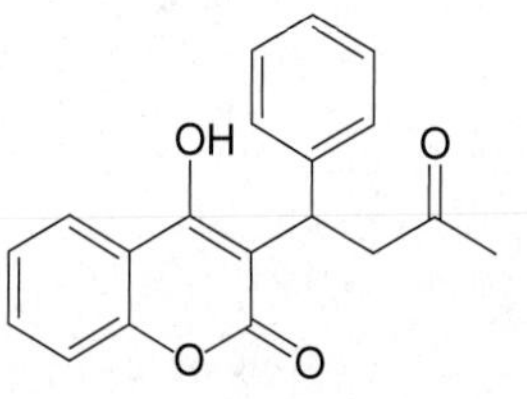

warfarin

Introduction to Carbonyl Chemistry; Organometallic Reagents; Oxidation and Reduction

20

20.1 Introduction
20.2 General reactions of carbonyl compounds
20.3 A preview of oxidation and reduction
20.4 Reduction of aldehydes and ketones
20.5 The stereochemistry of carbonyl reduction
20.6 Enantioselective carbonyl reductions
20.7 Reduction of carboxylic acids and their derivatives
20.8 Oxidation of aldehydes
20.9 Organometallic reagents
20.10 Reaction of organometallic reagents with aldehydes and ketones
20.11 Retrosynthetic analysis of Grignard products
20.12 Protecting groups
20.13 Reaction of organometallic reagents with carboxylic acid derivatives
20.14 Reaction of organometallic reagents with other compounds
20.15 α,β-Unsaturated carbonyl compounds
20.16 Summary—The reactions of organometallic reagents
20.17 Synthesis

Ciguatoxin CTX3C is a potent neurotoxin found in more than 400 species of warm-water fish. Thousands of people contract ciguatera seafood poisoning each year from ingesting tropical reef fish containing this neurotoxin. Interest in providing a practical supply of ciguatoxin CTX3C for biological testing led to its laboratory synthesis in 2001. One step in the multistep synthesis involved a selective reduction, one of the many reactions presented in Chapter 20.

Chapters 20 through 24 of this text discuss carbonyl compounds—aldehydes, ketones, acid halides, esters, amides, and carboxylic acids. **The carbonyl group is perhaps the most important functional group in organic chemistry,** because its electron-deficient carbon and easily broken π bond make it susceptible to a wide variety of useful reactions.

We begin by examining the similarities and differences between two broad classes of carbonyl compounds. We will then spend the remainder of Chapter 20 on reactions that are especially important in organic synthesis. Chapters 21 and 22 present specific reactions that occur at the carbonyl carbon, and Chapters 23 and 24 concentrate on reactions occurring at the α carbon to the carbonyl group.

Although Chapter 20 is "jam-packed" with reactions, most of them follow one of two general pathways, so they can be classified in a well-organized fashion, provided you remember a few basic principles. Keep in mind the following fundamental themes about reactions:

- Nucleophiles attack electrophiles.
- π Bonds are easily broken.
- Bonds to good leaving groups are easily cleaved heterolytically.

20.1 Introduction

Two broad classes of compounds contain a ***carbonyl group:***

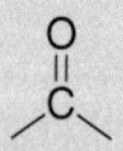

carbonyl group

[1] Compounds that have only carbon and hydrogen atoms bonded to the carbonyl group

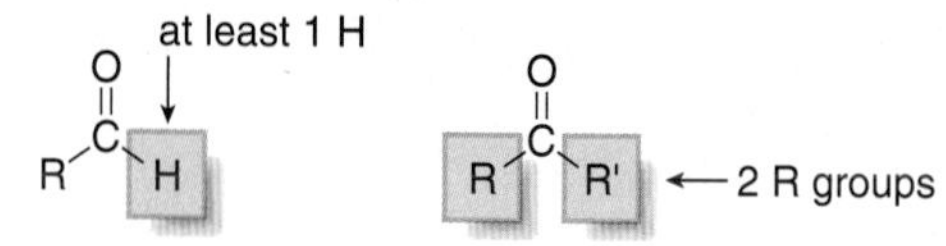

aldehyde ketone

- An **aldehyde** has at least one H atom bonded to the carbonyl group.
- A **ketone** has two alkyl or aryl groups bonded to the carbonyl group.

[2] Compounds that contain an electronegative atom bonded to the carbonyl group

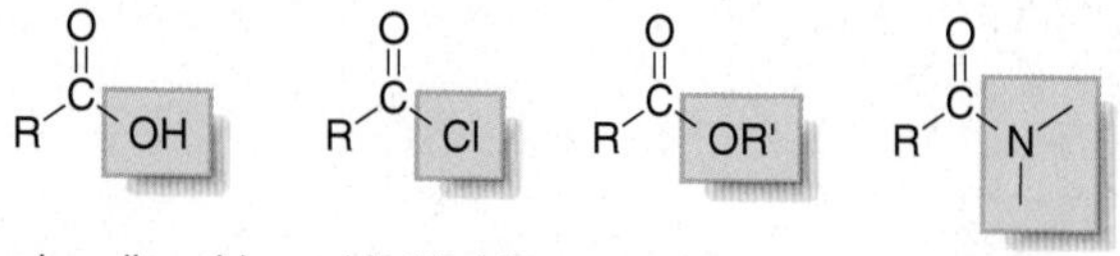

carboxylic acid acid chloride ester amide

These include **carboxylic acids, acid chlorides, esters,** and **amides,** as well as other similar compounds discussed in Chapter 22. Each of these compounds contains an electronegative atom (Cl, O, or N) capable of acting as a **leaving group.** Acid chlorides, esters, and amides are often called **carboxylic acid derivatives,** because they can be synthesized from carboxylic acids (Chapter 22). Since each compound contains an acyl group (RCO−), they are also called **acyl derivatives.**

- The presence or absence of a leaving group on the carbonyl carbon determines the type of reactions these compounds undergo (Section 20.2).

The carbonyl carbon atom is sp^2 hybridized and trigonal planar, and all bond angles are ~120°. The double bond of a carbonyl group consists of one σ bond and one π bond. The π bond is

Figure 20.1
Electrostatic potential map of formaldehyde, $CH_2=O$

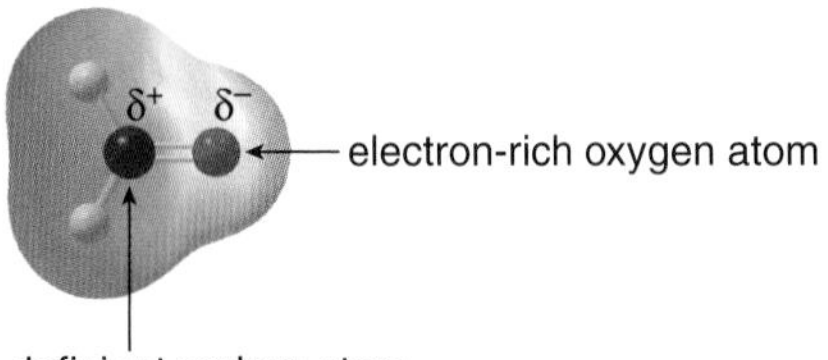

- An electrostatic potential map shows the electron-deficient carbon and the electron-rich oxygen atom of the carbonyl group.

The aldehyde α-sinensal (Problem 20.1) is the major compound responsible for the orange-like odor of mandarin oil, obtained from the mandarin tree in southern China.

formed by the overlap of two *p* orbitals, and extends above and below the plane. In these features the carbonyl group resembles the trigonal planar, sp^2 hybridized carbons of a C−C double bond.

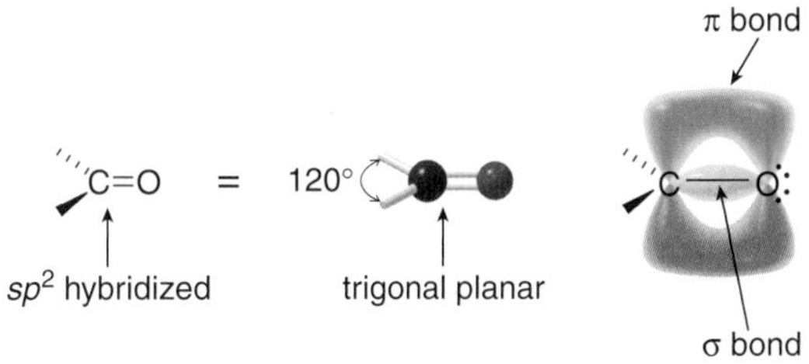

In one important way, though, a C=O and C=C are very different. **The electronegative oxygen atom in the carbonyl group means that the bond is polarized, making the carbonyl carbon electron deficient.** Using a resonance description, the carbonyl group is represented by two resonance structures, with a charge-separated resonance structure a minor contributor to the hybrid. An electrostatic potential plot for formaldehyde, the simplest aldehyde, is shown in Figure 20.1. It clearly indicates the polarized carbonyl group.

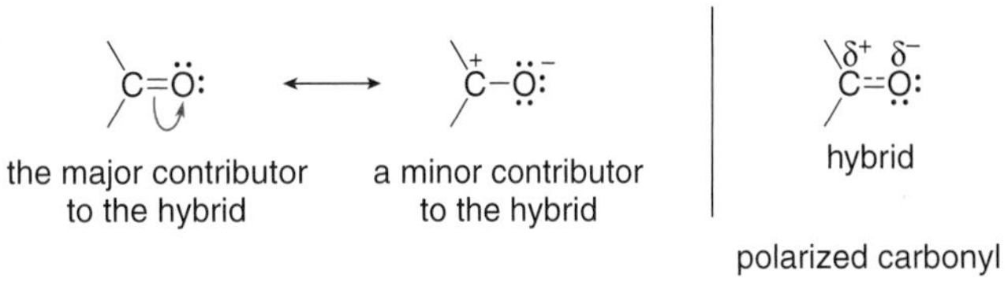

Problem 20.1

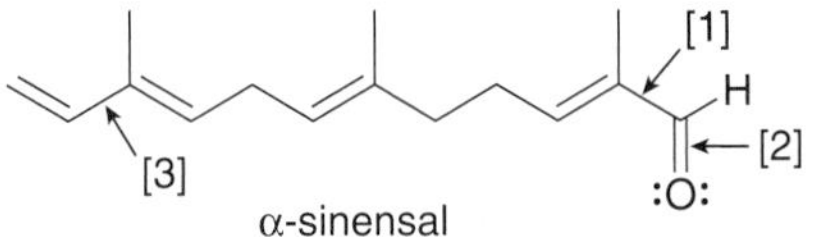

a. What orbitals are used to form the indicated bonds in α-sinensal?
b. In what type of orbitals do the lone pairs on O reside?

20.2 General Reactions of Carbonyl Compounds

With what types of reagents should a carbonyl group react? The electronegative oxygen makes the carbonyl carbon electrophilic, and because it is trigonal planar, a carbonyl carbon is uncrowded. Moreover, a carbonyl group has an easily broken π bond.

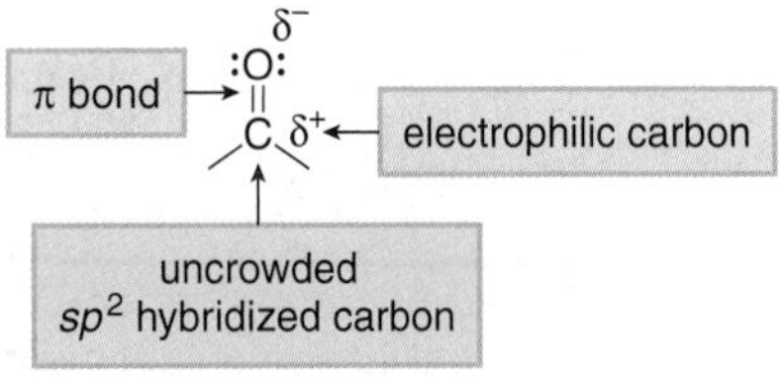

As a result, **carbonyl compounds react with nucleophiles.** The outcome of nucleophilic attack, however, depends on the identity of the carbonyl starting material.

- **Aldehydes and ketones undergo nucleophilic addition.**

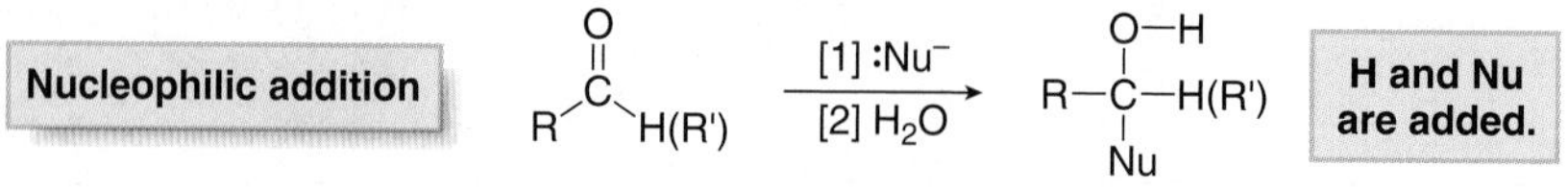

- **Carbonyl compounds that contain leaving groups undergo nucleophilic substitution.**

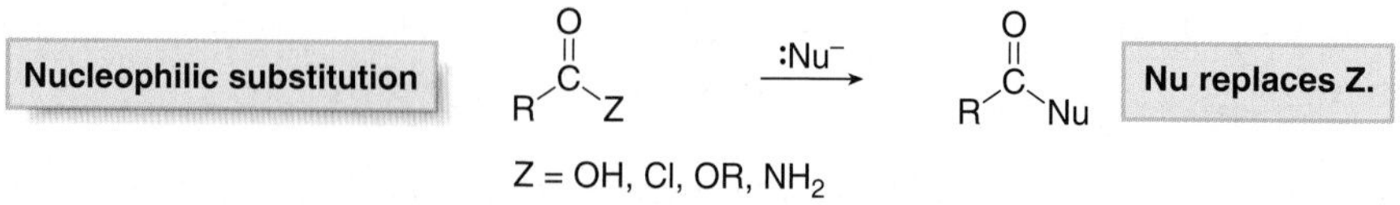

Let's examine each of these general reactions individually.

20.2A Nucleophilic Addition to Aldehydes and Ketones

Aldehydes and ketones react with nucleophiles to form addition products by the two-step process shown in Mechanism 20.1: **nucleophilic attack** followed by **protonation.**

Mechanism 20.1 Nucleophilic Addition—A Two-Step Process

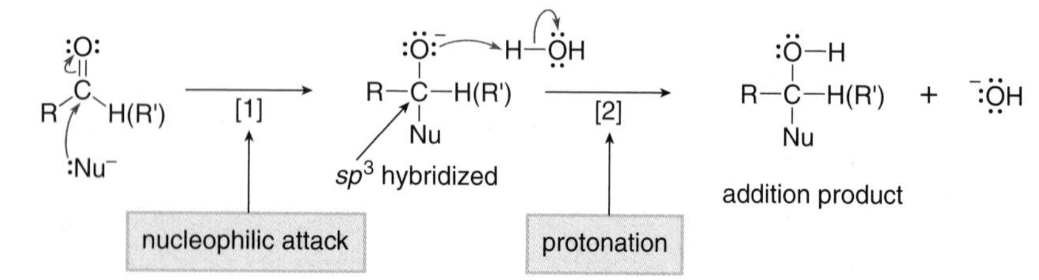

- In Step [1], **the nucleophile (:Nu⁻) attacks the electrophilic carbonyl.** As the new bond to the nucleophile forms, the π bond is broken, moving an electron pair out on the oxygen atom. This forms an sp^3 hybridized intermediate.
- In Step [2], **protonation of the negatively charged oxygen atom by H_2O** (or another proton source) forms the addition product.

More examples of nucleophilic addition to aldehydes and ketones are discussed in Chapter 21.

The net result is that the π bond is broken, two new σ bonds are formed, and the elements of H and Nu are added across the π bond. Nucleophilic addition with two different nucleophiles—**hydride (H:⁻)** and **carbanions (R:⁻)**—is discussed in Chapter 20.

Aldehydes are more reactive than ketones towards nucleophilic attack for both steric and electronic reasons.

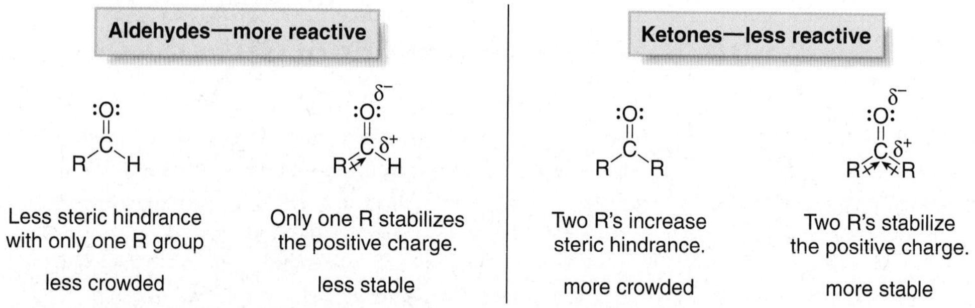

- **The two R groups bonded to the ketone carbonyl group make it more crowded, so nucleophilic attack is more difficult.**
- **The two electron-donor R groups stabilize the partial charge on the carbonyl carbon of a ketone, making it more stable and less reactive.**

20.2B Nucleophilic Substitution of RCOZ (Z = Leaving Group)

Carbonyl compounds with leaving groups react with nucleophiles to form substitution products by the two-step process shown in Mechanism 20.2: **nucleophilic attack,** followed by **loss of the leaving group.**

Mechanism 20.2 Nucleophilic Substitution—A Two-Step Process

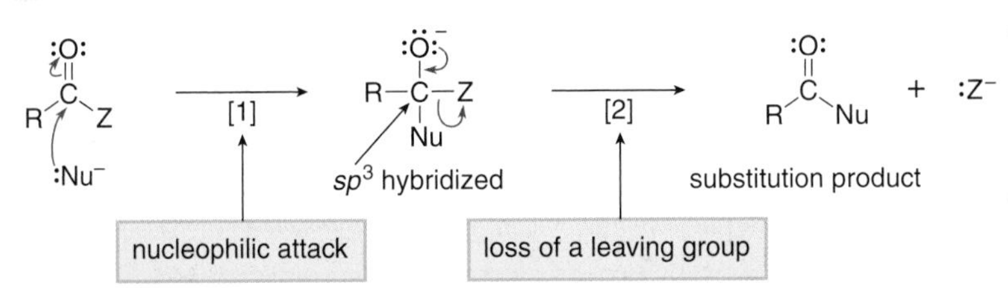

[Z = OH, Cl, OR, NH_2]

- In Step [1], **the nucleophile (:Nu⁻) attacks the electrophilic carbonyl,** forming an sp^3 hybridized intermediate. This step is identical to nucleophilic addition.
- Step [2] is different. Because the intermediate contains an electronegative atom Z, **Z can act as a leaving group.** To do so, an electron pair on O re-forms the π bond, and Z leaves with the electron pair in the C–Z bond.

The net result is that Nu replaces Z—a nucleophilic substitution reaction. This reaction is often called **nucleophilic *acyl* substitution** to distinguish it from the nucleophilic substitution reactions at sp^3 hybridized carbons discussed in Chapter 7. Nucleophilic substitution with two different nucleophiles—**hydride (H:⁻)** and **carbanions (R:⁻)**—is discussed in Chapter 20. Other nucleophiles are examined in Chapter 22.

Carboxylic acid derivatives differ greatly in their reactivity towards nucleophiles. The order in which they react parallels the leaving group ability of the group Z bonded to the carbonyl carbon.

Recall from Section 7.7 that the weaker the base, the better the leaving group.

- **The better the leaving group Z, the more reactive RCOZ is in nucleophilic acyl substitution.**

Thus, the following trends result:

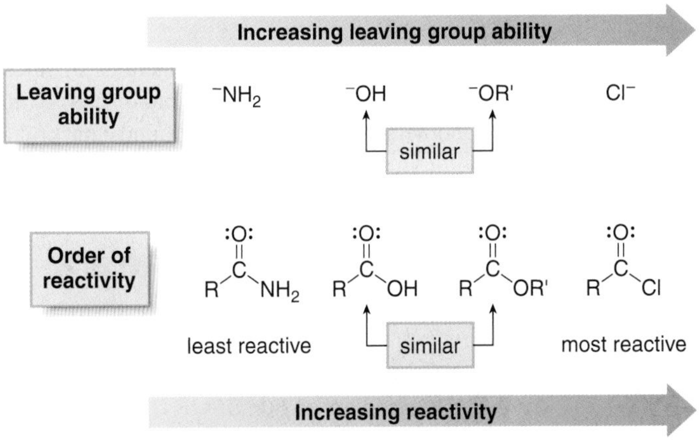

- **Acid chlorides (RCOCl), which have the best leaving group (Cl⁻), are the most reactive carboxylic acid derivatives, and amides ($RCONH_2$), which have the worst leaving group (⁻NH_2), are the least reactive.**
- **Carboxylic acids (RCOOH) and esters (RCOOR'), which have leaving groups of similar basicity (⁻OH and ⁻OR'), fall in the middle.**

Nucleophilic addition and nucleophilic acyl substitution involve the *same* first step—**nucleophilic attack on the electrophilic carbonyl group** to form a tetrahedral intermediate. The difference between them is what then happens to this intermediate. Aldehydes and ketones cannot undergo substitution because they have no leaving group bonded to the newly formed sp^3 hybridized carbon. Nucleophilic substitution with an aldehyde, for example, would form $H:^-$, an extremely strong base and therefore a very poor (and highly unlikely) leaving group.

An aldehyde does not undergo nucleophilic substitution....

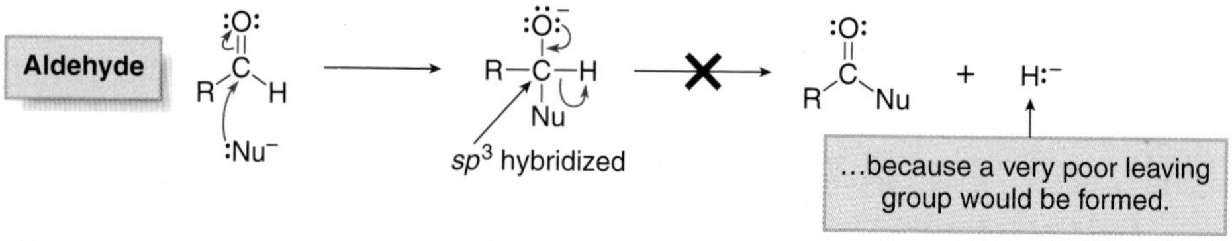

Problem 20.2 Which carbonyl groups in the anticancer drug taxol (Section 5.5) will undergo nucleophilic addition and which will undergo nucleophilic substitution?

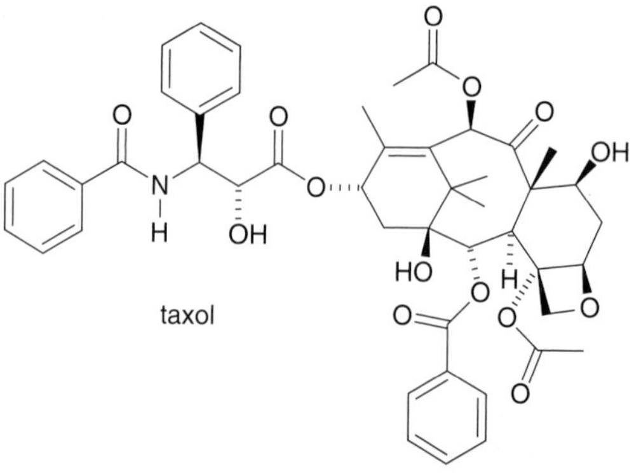

taxol

Problem 20.3 Which compound in each pair is more reactive towards nucleophilic attack?

a. $CH_3CH_2CH_2CHO$ or $CH_3CH_2CH_2COCH_3$
b. $CH_3CH_2COCH_3$ or $CH_3CH(CH_3)COCH_2CH_3$
c. CH_3CH_2COCl or CH_3COOCH_3
d. CH_3COOCH_3 or $CH_3CONHCH_3$

To show how these general principles of nucleophilic substitution and addition apply to carbonyl compounds, we are going to discuss oxidation and reduction reactions, and reactions with organometallic reagents—compounds that contain carbon–metal bonds. We begin with reduction to build on what you learned previously in Chapter 12.

20.3 A Preview of Oxidation and Reduction

Recall the definitions of oxidation and reduction presented in Section 12.1:

- **Oxidation results in an increase in the number of C–Z bonds (usually C–O bonds) or a decrease in the number of C–H bonds.**
- **Reduction results in a decrease in the number of C–Z bonds (usually C–O bonds) or an increase in the number of C–H bonds.**

Carbonyl compounds are either reactants or products in many of these reactions, as illustrated in the accompanying diagram. For example, because aldehydes fall in the middle of this scheme, they can be both oxidized and reduced. Carboxylic acids and their derivatives (RCOZ), on the other hand, are already highly oxidized, so their only useful reaction is reduction.

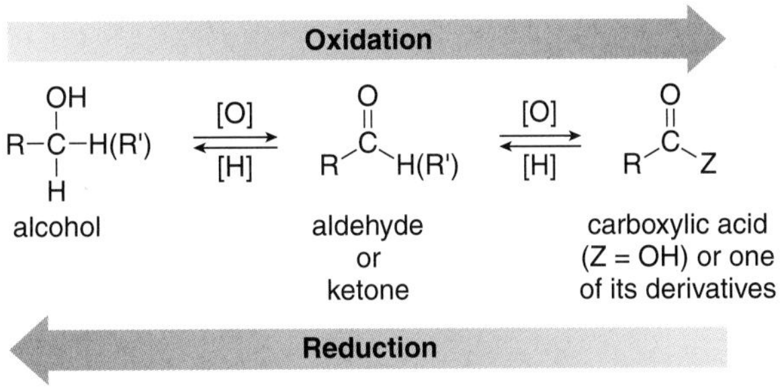

The three most useful oxidation and reduction reactions of carbonyl starting materials can be summarized as follows:

[1] Reduction of aldehydes and ketones to alcohols (Sections 20.4–20.6)

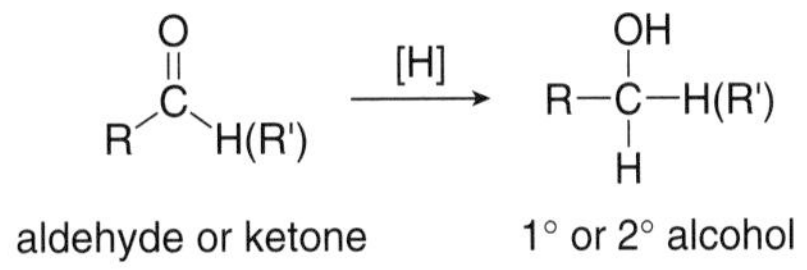

Aldehydes and ketones are reduced to 1° and 2° alcohols, respectively.

[2] Reduction of carboxylic acid derivatives (Section 20.7)

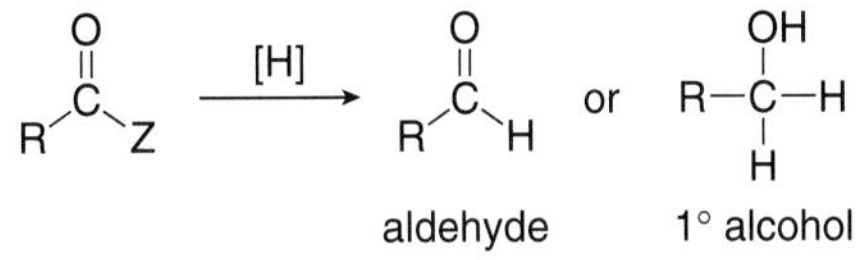

The reduction of carboxylic acids and their derivatives gives a variety of products, depending on the identity of Z and the nature of the reducing agent. The usual products are aldehydes or 1° alcohols.

[3] Oxidation of aldehydes to carboxylic acids (Section 20.8)

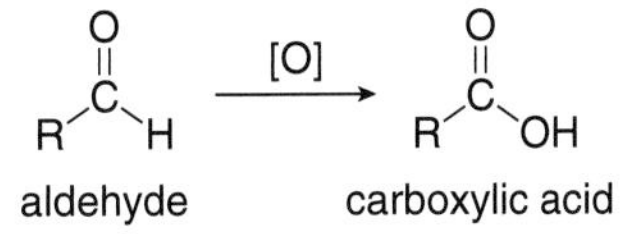

The most useful oxidation reaction of carbonyl compounds is the oxidation of aldehydes to carboxylic acids.

We begin with reduction, because the mechanisms of reduction reactions follow directly from the general mechanisms for nucleophilic addition and substitution.

20.4 Reduction of Aldehydes and Ketones

$LiAlH_4$ and $NaBH_4$ serve as a source of H:$^-$, but there are no free H:$^-$ ions present in reactions with these reagents.

The most useful reagents for reducing aldehydes and ketones are the metal hydride reagents (Section 12.2). The two most common metal hydride reagents are **sodium borohydride ($NaBH_4$)** and **lithium aluminum hydride ($LiAlH_4$).** These reagents contain a polar metal–hydrogen bond that serves as a source of the nucleophile hydride, **H:$^-$.** $LiAlH_4$ is a stronger reducing agent than $NaBH_4$, because the Al–H bond is more polar than the B–H bond.

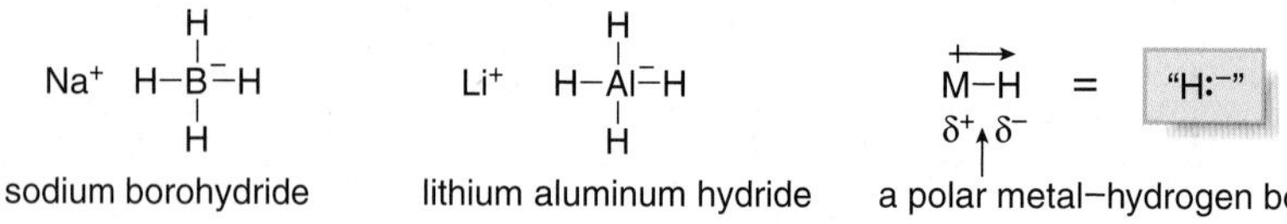

sodium borohydride lithium aluminum hydride a polar metal–hydrogen bond

20.4A Reduction with Metal Hydride Reagents

Treating an aldehyde or a ketone with $NaBH_4$ or $LiAlH_4$, followed by water or some other proton source, affords an **alcohol.** This is an addition reaction because the elements of H_2 are added across the π bond, but it is also a reduction because the product alcohol has fewer C–O bonds than the starting carbonyl compound.

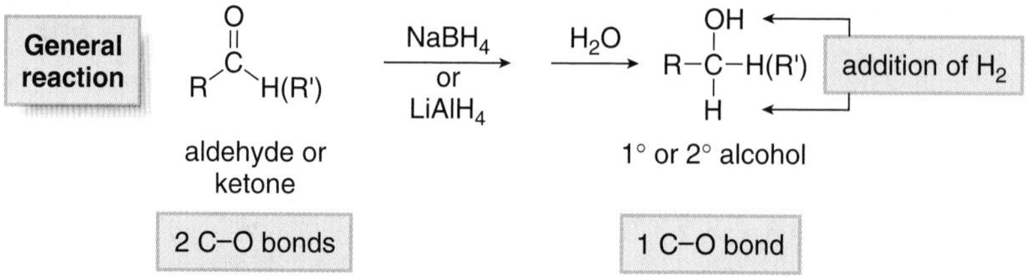

$LiAlH_4$ reductions must be carried out under anhydrous conditions, because water reacts violently with the reagent. Water is added to the reaction mixture (to serve as a proton source) *after* the reduction with $LiAlH_4$ is complete.

The product of this reduction reaction is a **1° alcohol** when the starting carbonyl compound is an aldehyde, and a **2° alcohol** when it is a ketone.

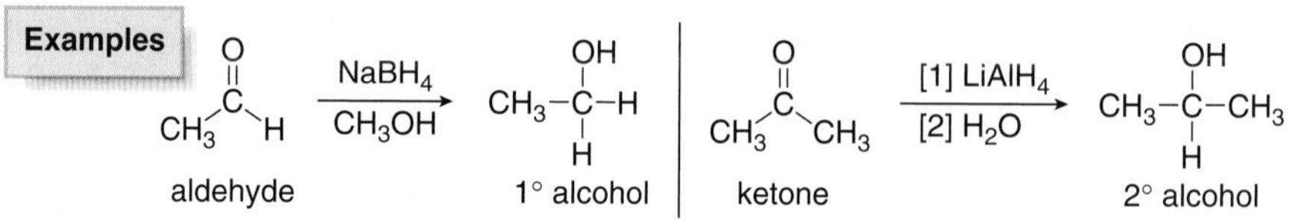

$NaBH_4$ selectively reduces aldehydes and ketones in the presence of most other functional groups. Reductions with $NaBH_4$ are typically carried out in CH_3OH as solvent. $LiAlH_4$ reduces aldehydes and ketones and many other functional groups as well (Sections 12.6 and 20.7).

Problem 20.4 What alcohol is formed when each compound is treated with $NaBH_4$ in CH_3OH?

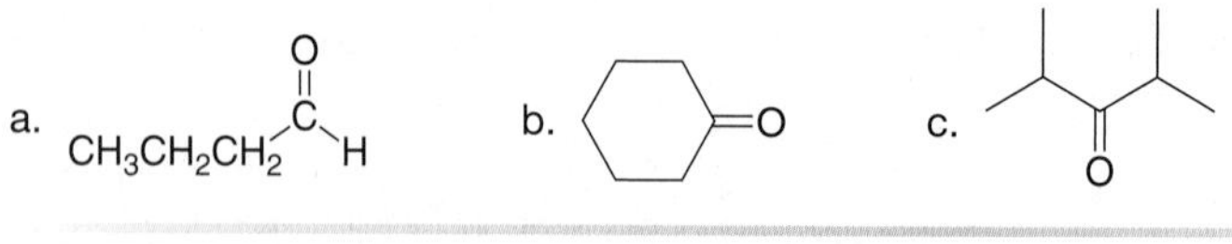

Problem 20.5 What aldehyde or ketone is needed to prepare each alcohol by metal hydride reduction?

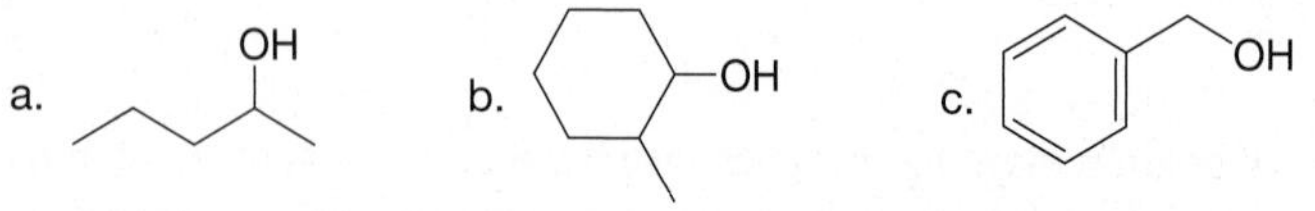

Problem 20.6 Why can't 1-methylcyclohexanol be prepared from a carbonyl compound by reduction?

20.4B The Mechanism of Hydride Reduction

Hydride reduction of aldehydes and ketones occurs via the general mechanism of nucleophilic addition—that is, **nucleophilic attack** followed by **protonation.** Mechanism 20.3 is shown using $LiAlH_4$, but an analogous mechanism can be written for $NaBH_4$.

Mechanism 20.3 $LiAlH_4$ Reduction of RCHO and $R_2C{=}O$

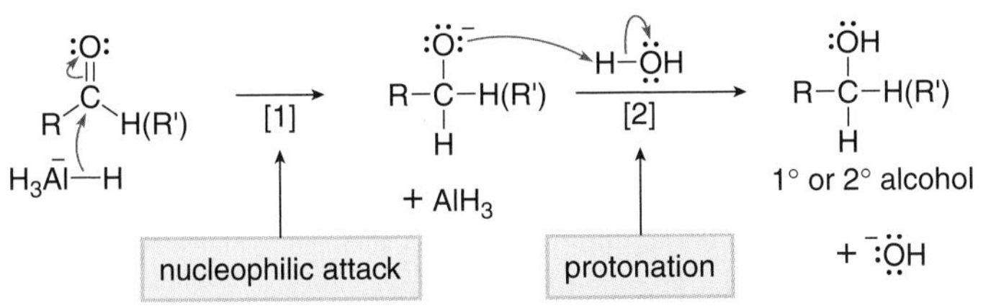

- In Step [1], **the nucleophile (AlH_4^-) donates H:$^-$ to the carbonyl group,** cleaving the π bond, and moving an electron pair onto oxygen. This forms a new C–H bond.
- In Step [2], **the alkoxide is protonated by H_2O (or CH_3OH)** to form the alcohol reduction product. This acid–base reaction forms a new O–H bond.

- **The net result of adding H:$^-$ (from $NaBH_4$ or $LiAlH_4$) and H^+ (from H_2O) is the addition of the elements of H_2 to the carbonyl π bond.**

20.4C Catalytic Hydrogenation of Aldehydes and Ketones

Catalytic hydrogenation also reduces aldehydes and ketones to 1° and 2° alcohols, respectively, using H_2 and Pd-C (or another metal catalyst). H_2 adds to the C=O in much the same way that it adds to the C=C of an alkene (Section 12.3). The metal catalyst (Pd-C) provides a surface that binds the carbonyl starting material and H_2, and two H atoms are sequentially transferred with cleavage of the π bond.

Examples

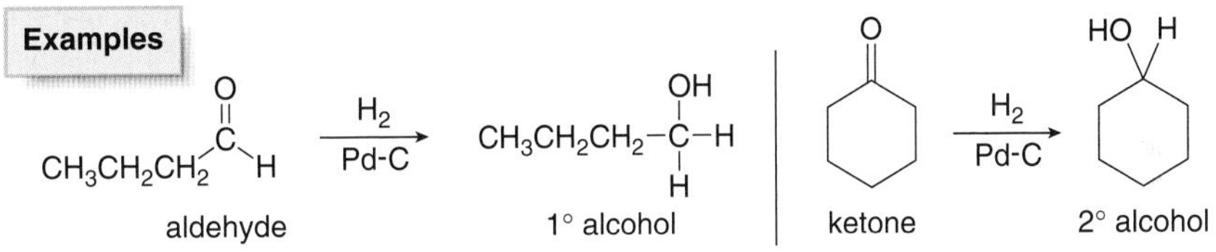

When a compound contains both a carbonyl group and a carbon–carbon double bond, selective reduction of one functional group can be achieved by proper choice of reagent.

- **A C=C is reduced faster than a C=O with H_2 (Pd-C).**
- **A C=O is readily reduced with $NaBH_4$ and $LiAlH_4$, but a C=C is inert.**

Thus, 2-cyclohexenone, a compound that contains both a carbon–carbon double bond and a carbonyl group, can be reduced to three different compounds—an allylic alcohol, a carbonyl compound, or an alcohol—depending on the reagent.

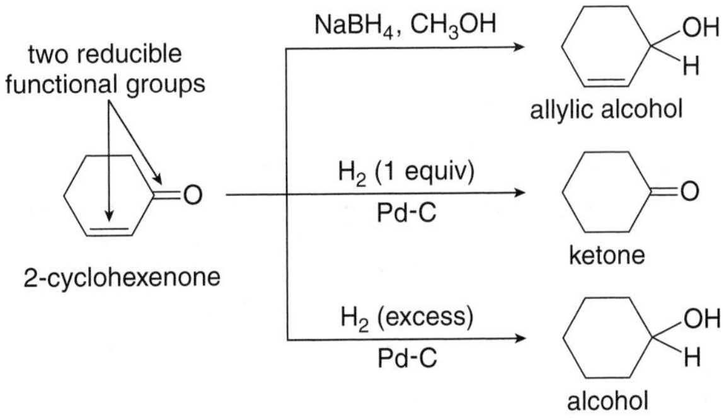

- $NaBH_4$ reduces the C=O selectively to form an allylic alcohol.
- One equivalent of H_2 reduces the C=C selectively to form a ketone.
- Excess H_2 reduces both π bonds to form an alcohol.

Problem 20.7 Draw the products formed when $CH_3COCH_2CH_2CH{=}CH_2$ is treated with each reagent: (a) $LiAlH_4$, then H_2O; (b) $NaBH_4$ in CH_3OH; (c) H_2 (1 equiv), Pd-C; (d) H_2 (excess), Pd-C; (e) $NaBH_4$ (excess) in CH_3OH; (f) $NaBD_4$ in CH_3OH.

The reduction of aldehydes and ketones is a common reaction used in the synthesis of many useful natural products. Two examples are shown in Figure 20.2.

Figure 20.2 $NaBH_4$ reductions used in organic synthesis

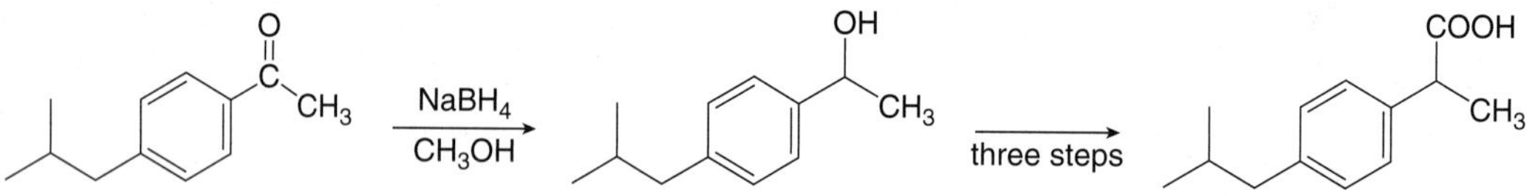

ibuprofen

(anti-inflammatory agent in Motrin and Advil)

The male musk deer, a small antlerless deer found in the mountain regions of China and Tibet, has long been hunted for its musk, a strongly scented liquid used in early medicine and later in perfumery.

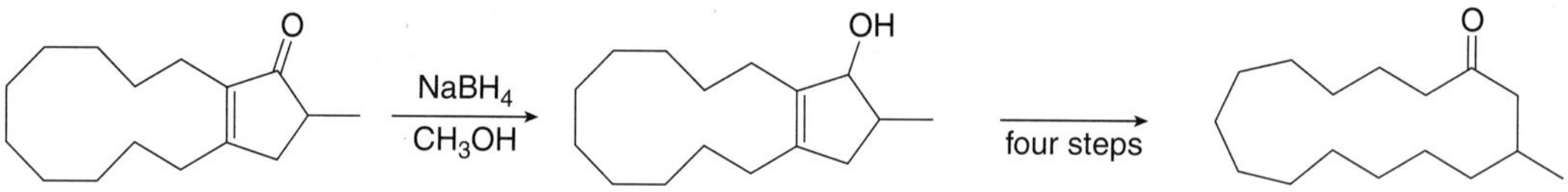

muscone

odor of musk (perfume component)

- **Muscone** is the major compound in musk, one of the oldest known ingredients in perfumes. Musk was originally isolated from the male musk deer, but it can now be prepared synthetically in the laboratory in a variety of ways.

20.5 The Stereochemistry of Carbonyl Reduction

Recall from Section 9.15 that an achiral starting material gives a racemic mixture when a new stereogenic center is formed.

The stereochemistry of carbonyl reduction follows the same principles we have previously learned. Reduction converts a **planar sp^2 hybridized carbonyl carbon to a tetrahedral sp^3 hybridized carbon.** What happens when a new stereogenic center is formed in this process? With an achiral reagent like $NaBH_4$ or $LiAlH_4$, a racemic product is obtained. For example, $NaBH_4$ in CH_3OH solution reduces 2-butanone, an achiral ketone, to 2-butanol, an alcohol that contains a new stereogenic center. Both enantiomers of 2-butanol are formed in equal amounts.

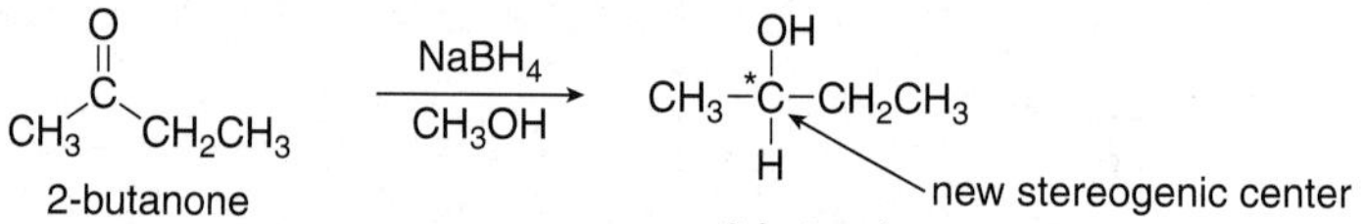

2-butanone

achiral starting material

2-butanol

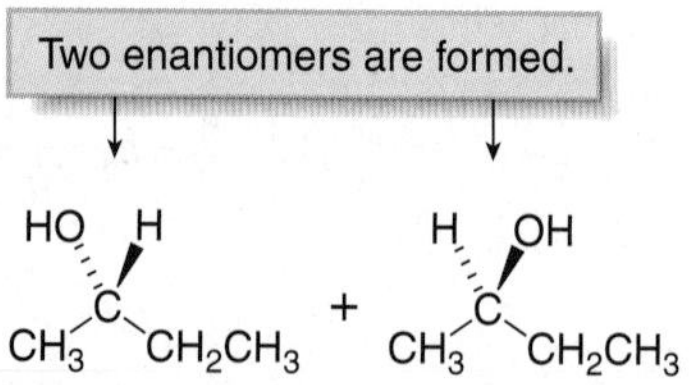

(2S)-2-butanol (2R)-2-butanol

Why is a racemic mixture formed? Because the carbonyl carbon is sp^2 hybridized and planar, hydride can approach the double bond with equal probability from both sides of the plane, forming two alkoxides, which are **enantiomers** of each other. Protonation of the alkoxides gives an equal amount of two alcohols, which are also **enantiomers.**

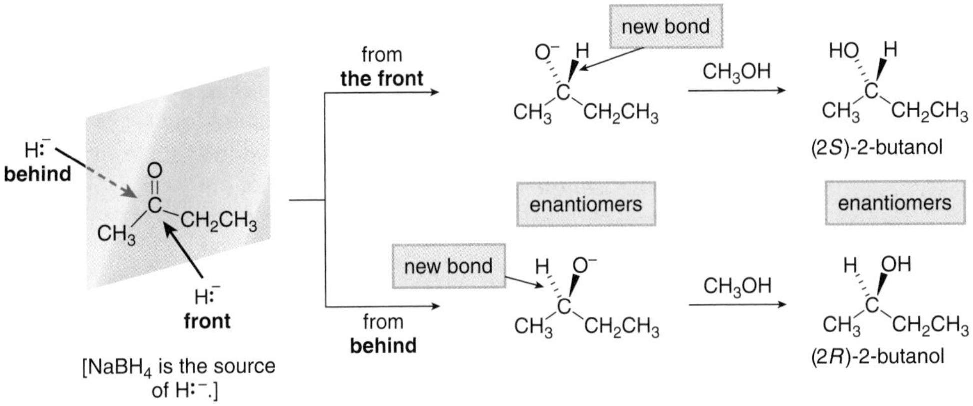

- **Conclusion: Hydride reduction of an achiral ketone with $LiAlH_4$ or $NaBH_4$ gives a racemic mixture of two alcohols when a new stereogenic center is formed.**

Problem 20.8 Draw the products formed (including stereoisomers) when each compound is reduced with $NaBH_4$ in CH_3OH.

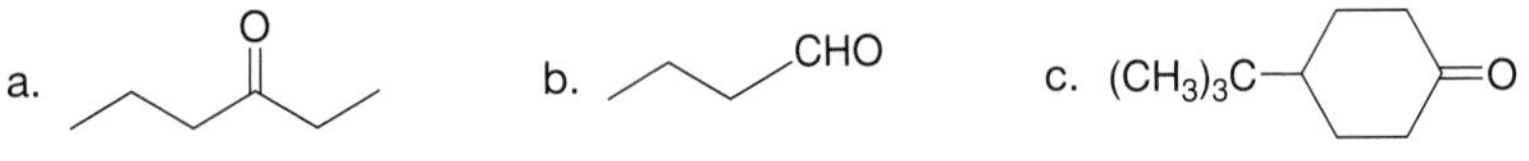

20.6 Enantioselective Carbonyl Reductions

20.6A CBS Reagents

One enantiomer can be formed selectively from the reduction of a carbonyl group, provided a **chiral reducing agent** is used. This strategy is identical to that employed in the Sharpless asymmetric epoxidation reaction (Section 12.15). A reduction that forms one enantiomer predominantly or exclusively is an **enantioselective** or **asymmetric reduction.**

Many different chiral reducing agents have now been prepared for this purpose. One such reagent, formed by reacting borane (**BH_3**) with a heterocycle called an **oxazaborolidine,** has one stereogenic center (and thus two enantiomers).

(*S*)-2-methyl-**CBS**-oxazaborolidine

(*S*)-CBS reagent

(*R*)-2-methyl-**CBS**-oxazaborolidine

(*R*)-CBS reagent

These reagents are called the **(*S*)-CBS reagent** and the **(*R*)-CBS reagent,** named for *C*orey, *B*akshi, and *S*hibata, the chemists who developed these versatile reagents. One B–H bond of BH_3 serves as the source of hydride in this reduction. The stereochemistry of the new stereogenic center in the product is often predictable. For ketones having the general structure C_6H_5COR, draw the starting material with the aryl group on the left side of the carbonyl, as shown with acetophenone. Then, to draw the product, keep in mind:

- **The (*S*)-CBS reagent delivers hydride (H:⁻) from the front side of the C=O. This generally affords the *R* alcohol as the major product.**
- **The (*R*)-CBS reagent delivers hydride (H:⁻) from the back side of the C=O. This generally affords the *S* alcohol as the major product.**

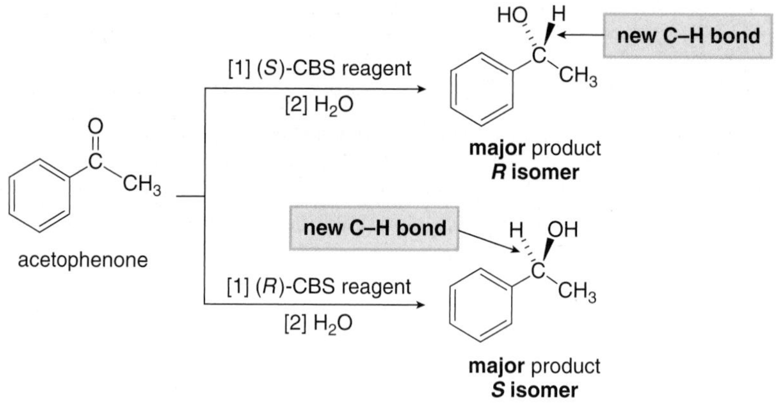

These reagents are highly enantioselective. Treatment of propiophenone with the (*S*)-CBS reagent forms the ***R*** alcohol in 97% enantiomeric excess (*ee*). Enantioselective reductions are key steps in the synthesis of several widely used drugs, including salmeterol, a long-acting bronchodilator shown in Figure 20.3. This new technology provides access to single enantiomers of biologically active compounds, often previously available only as a racemic mixture.

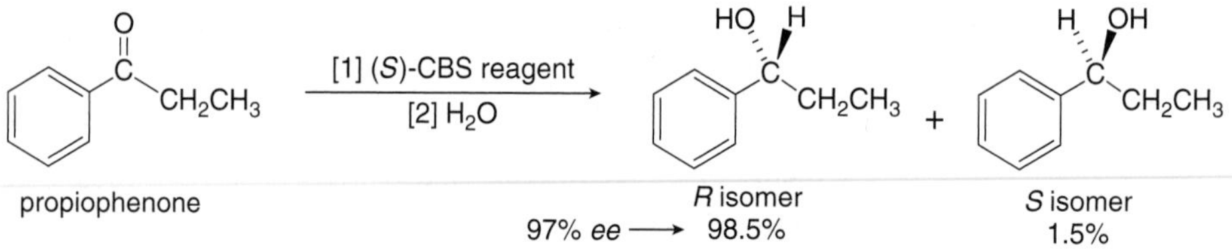

Figure 20.3 Enantioselective reduction—A key step in the synthesis of salmeterol

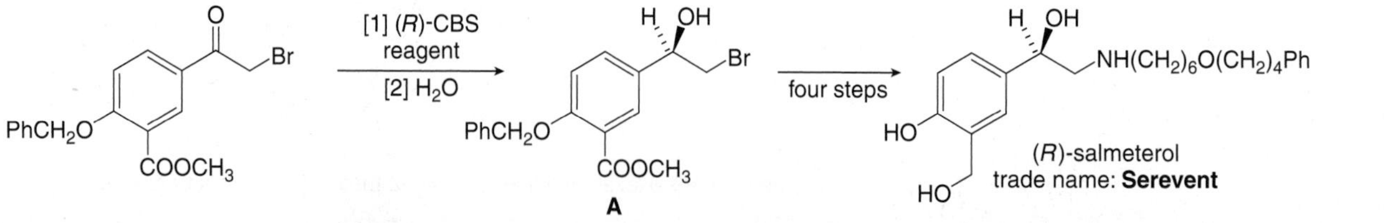

- (*R*)-Salmeterol is a long-acting bronchodilator used for the treatment of asthma.
- In this example, the (*R*)-CBS reagent adds the new H atom from behind, the same result observed with acetophenone and propiophenone. In this case, however, alcohol **A** has the *R* configuration using the rules for assigning priority in Chapter 5.

VYTORIN 10/20
(ezetimibe/simvastatin)

Ezetimibe is sold as a single medication under the trade name of Zetia, or in combination with simvastatin, another cholesterol-lowering medication, and marketed as Vytorin. These drugs are prescribed for individuals who cannot tolerate or derive no benefit from other cholesterol-lowering medications (see Figure 30.12).

Problem 20.9 What carbonyl compound and CBS reagent are needed to prepare **X,** an intermediate in the synthesis of ezetimibe (trade name Zetia), a drug that lowers cholesterol levels by inhibiting its absorption in the intestines.

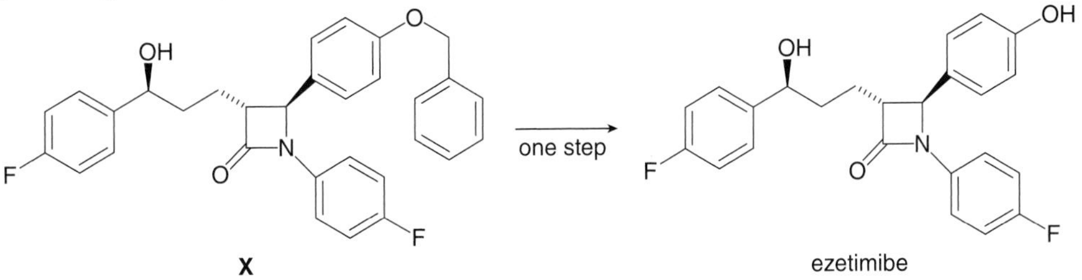
one step

X ezetimibe

20.6B Enantioselective Biological Reduction

Although laboratory reduction reactions often do not proceed with 100% enantioselectivity, biological reductions that occur in cells *always* proceed with complete selectivity, forming a single enantiomer. $NaBH_4$ or chiral boranes are not the reducing agents for these processes. In cells, the reducing agent is **NADH.**

the **reactive** part

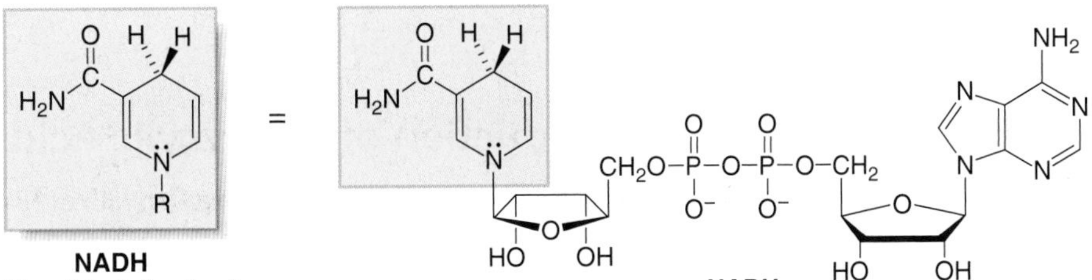

NADH
(abbreviated structure)

NADH
nicotinamide adenine dinucleotide
(reduced form)

NADH is a **coenzyme,** an organic molecule that can function only in the presence of an enzyme. The active site of the enzyme binds both the carbonyl substrate and NADH, keeping them in close proximity. **NADH then donates H:$^-$** in much the same way as a metal hydride reagent; that is, reduction consists of nucleophilic attack followed by protonation.

- In Step [1], **NADH donates H:$^-$ to the carbonyl group** to form an alkoxide. In the process, NADH is converted to NAD^+.
- In Step [2], the alkoxide is protonated by the aqueous medium.

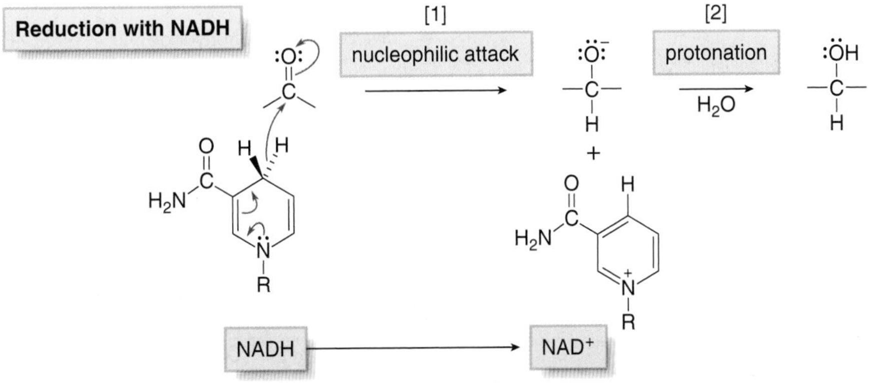
Reduction with NADH
[1]
nucleophilic attack
[2]
protonation
H2O
NADH
NAD+

Pyruvic acid is formed during the metabolism of glucose. During periods of strenuous exercise, when there is insufficient oxygen to metabolize pyruvic acid to CO_2, pyruvic acid is reduced to lactic acid. The tired feeling of sore muscles is a result of lactic acid accumulation.

This reaction is completely enantioselective. For example, reduction of pyruvic acid with NADH catalyzed by lactate dehydrogenase affords a single enantiomer of lactic acid with the *S* configuration. NADH reduces a variety of different carbonyl compounds in biological systems. The configuration of the product (*R* or *S*) depends on the enzyme used to catalyze the process.

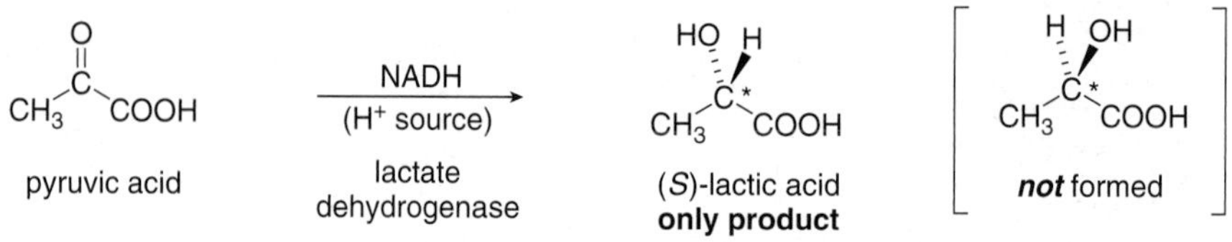

[* denotes a new stereogenic center]

Niacin can be obtained from foods such as soybeans, which contain it naturally, and from breakfast cereals, which are fortified with it to help people consume their recommended daily allowance of this B vitamin.

NAD$^+$, the oxidized form of NADH, is a biological oxidizing agent capable of oxidizing alcohols to carbonyl compounds (it forms NADH in the process). NAD$^+$ is synthesized from the vitamin niacin, which can be obtained from soybeans among other dietary sources.

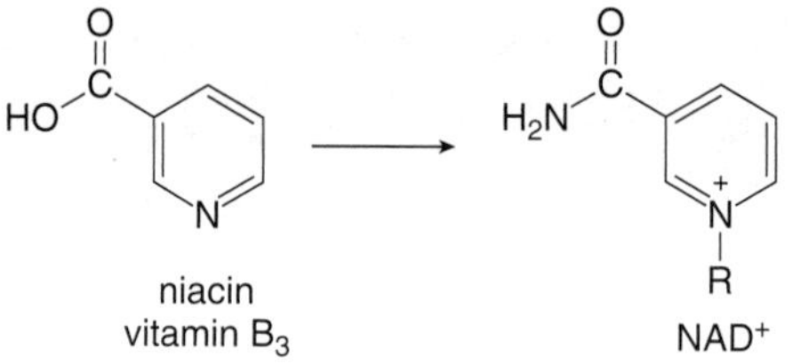

20.7 Reduction of Carboxylic Acids and Their Derivatives

The reduction of carboxylic acids and their derivatives (RCOZ) is complicated because the products obtained depend on the identity of both the leaving group (Z) and the reducing agent. Metal hydride reagents are the most useful reducing reagents. **Lithium aluminum hydride is a strong reducing agent that reacts with *all* carboxylic acid derivatives.** Two other related but more selective reducing agents are also used.

[1] **Diisobutylaluminum hydride, $[(CH_3)_2CHCH_2]_2AlH$,** abbreviated as **DIBAL-H,** has two bulky isobutyl groups, which make this reagent less reactive than $LiAlH_4$. The single H atom is donated as $H:^-$ in hydride reductions.

[2] **Lithium tri-*tert*-butoxyaluminum hydride, $LiAlH[OC(CH_3)_3]_3$,** has three electronegative oxygen atoms bonded to aluminum, which make this reagent less nucleophilic than $LiAlH_4$.

$LiAlH_4$ is a strong, nonselective reducing agent. DIBAL-H and $LiAlH[OC(CH_3)_3]_3$ are milder, more selective reducing agents.

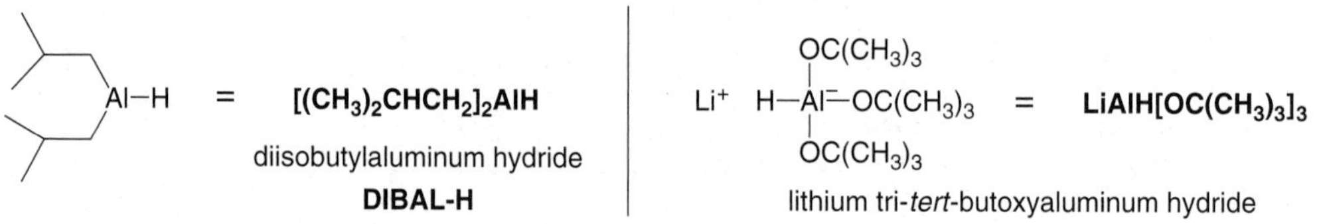

20.7A Reduction of Acid Chlorides and Esters

Acid chlorides and esters can be reduced to either aldehydes or alcohols, depending on the reagent.

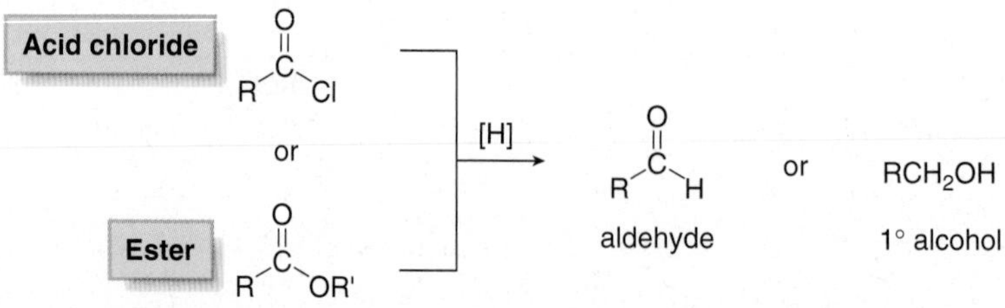

- **$LiAlH_4$ converts RCOCl and RCOOR' to alcohols.**
- **A milder reducing agent (DIBAL-H or $LiAlH[OC(CH_3)_3]_3$) converts RCOCl or RCOOR' to RCHO at low temperatures.**

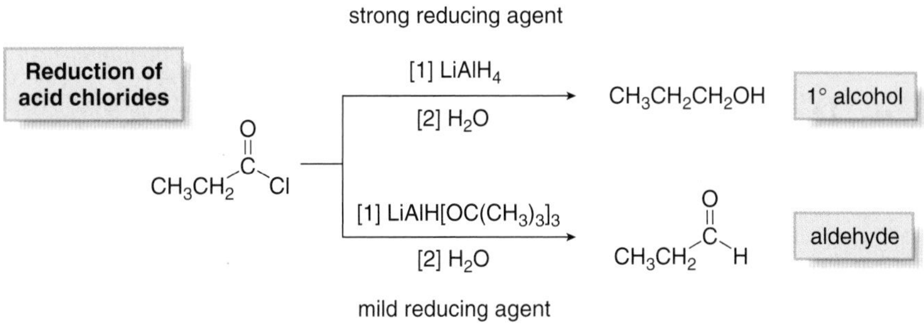

In the reduction of an acid chloride, Cl^- comes off as the leaving group.

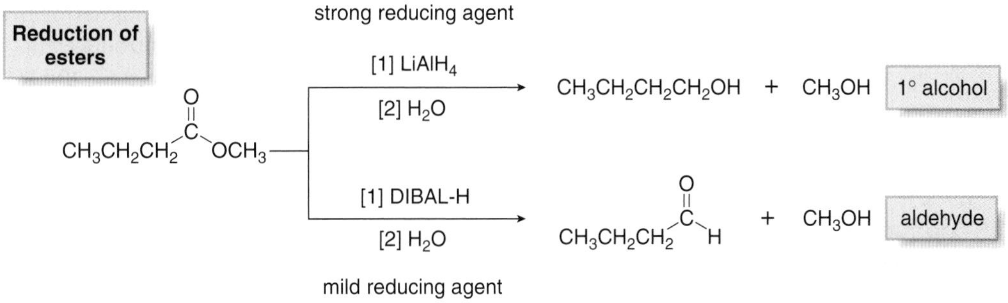

In the reduction of the ester, CH_3O^- comes off as the leaving group, which is then protonated by H_2O to form CH_3OH.

Mechanism 20.4 illustrates why two different products are possible. It can be conceptually divided into two parts: **nucleophilic substitution** to form an aldehyde, followed by **nucleophilic addition** to the aldehyde to form an alcohol. A general mechanism is drawn using $LiAlH_4$ as reducing agent.

Mechanism 20.4 Reduction of RCOCl and RCOOR' with a Metal Hydride Reagent

Part [1] Nucleophilic substitution forms an aldehyde.

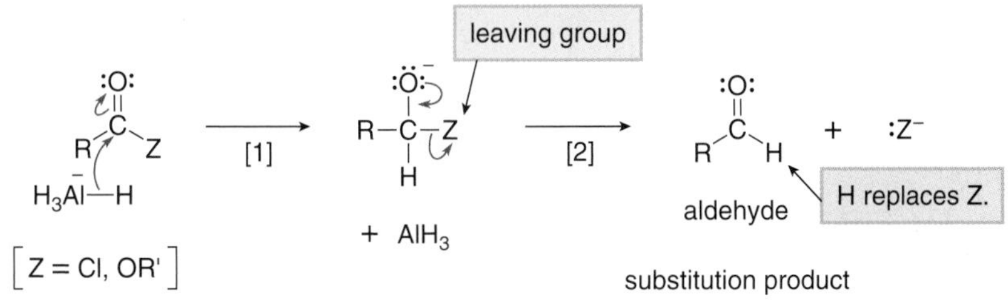

- **Nucleophilic attack of H:$^-$** (from $LiAlH_4$) in Step [1] forms a tetrahedral intermediate with a leaving group Z.
- In Step [2], the π bond is re-formed and **Z^- comes off.** The overall result of the addition of H:$^-$ and elimination of Z^- is the substitution of H for Z.

Part [2] Nucleophilic addition forms a 1° alcohol.

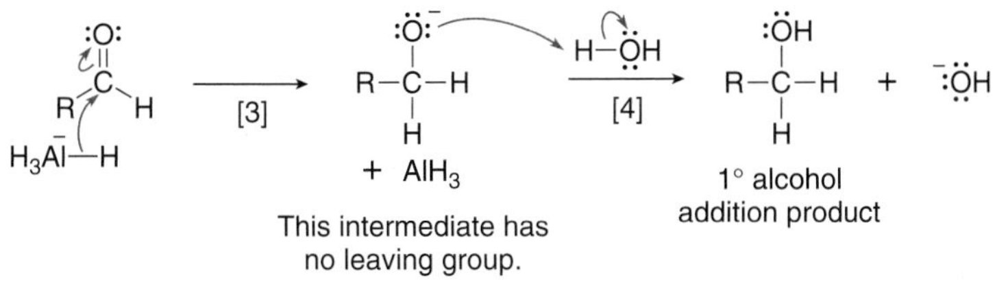

- **Nucleophilic attack of H:$^-$** (from $LiAlH_4$) in Step [3] forms an alkoxide.
- **Protonation of the alkoxide** by H_2O in Step [4] forms the alcohol reduction product. The overall result of Steps [3] and [4] is addition of H_2.

With less nucleophilic reducing agents such as DIBAL-H and $LiAlH[OC(CH_3)_3]_3$, the process stops after reaction with one equivalent of $H:^-$ and the aldehyde is formed as product. With a stronger reducing agent like $LiAlH_4$, two equivalents of $H:^-$ are added and an alcohol is formed.

Problem 20.10 Draw a stepwise mechanism for the following reaction.

$$CH_3COCl \xrightarrow[\text{[2] } H_2O]{\text{[1] } LiAlH_4} CH_3CH_2OH$$

Problem 20.11 Draw the structure of both an acid chloride and an ester that can be used to prepare each compound by reduction.

a. 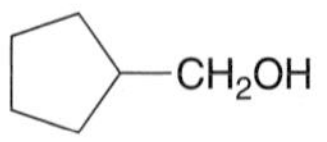

b. 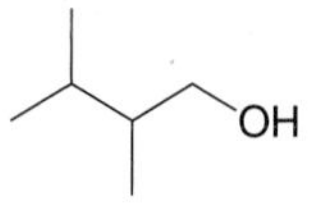

c. 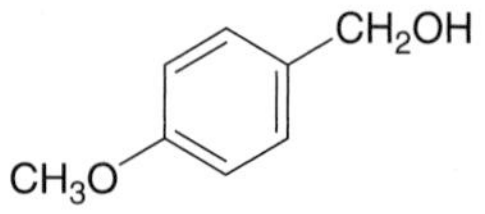

Selective reductions are routinely used in the synthesis of highly complex natural products such as **ciguatoxin CTX3C,** a potent neurotoxin introduced in the chapter opener. One reaction in a synthesis of ciguatoxin CTX3C involved the reduction of an ester to an aldehyde using DIBAL-H, as shown in Figure 20.4.

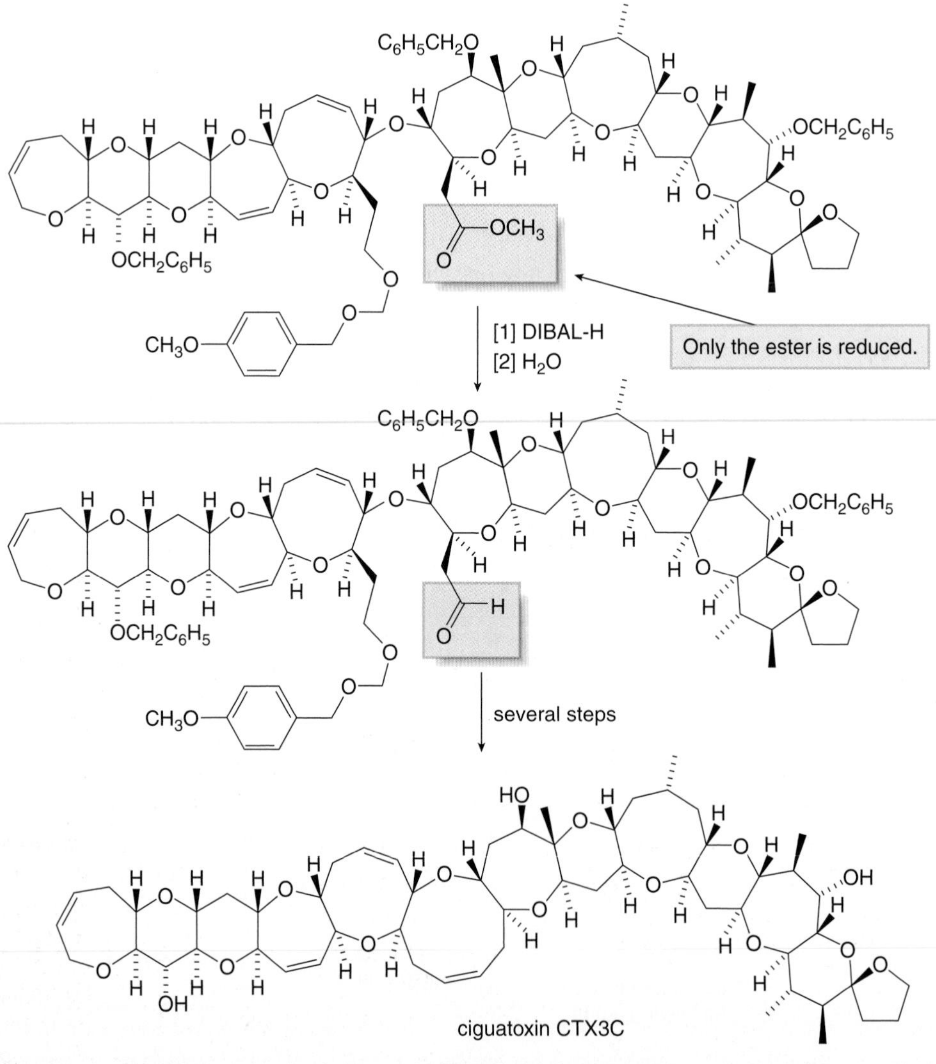

Figure 20.4 The DIBAL-H reduction of an ester to an aldehyde in the synthesis of the marine neurotoxin ciguatoxin CTX3C

- One step in a lengthy synthesis of ciguatoxin CTX3C involved selective reduction of an ester to an aldehyde using DIBAL-H.

20.7B Reduction of Carboxylic Acids and Amides

Carboxylic acids are reduced to alcohols with $LiAlH_4$. $LiAlH_4$ is too strong a reducing agent to stop the reaction at the aldehyde stage, but milder reagents are not strong enough to initiate the reaction in the first place, so this is the only useful reduction reaction of carboxylic acids.

Reduction of a carboxylic acid

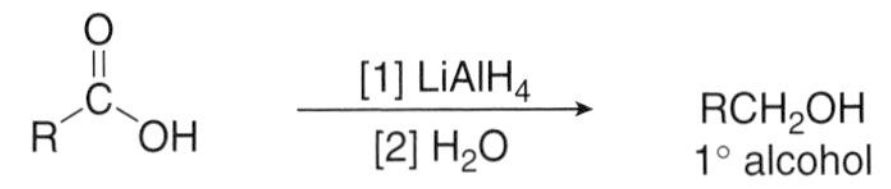
[1] LiAlH4
[2] H2O
RCH2OH
1° alcohol

Example

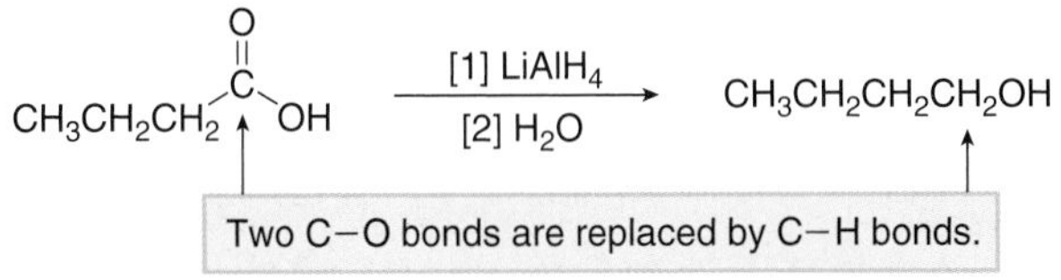
CH3CH2CH2
OH
[1] LiAlH4
[2] H2O
CH3CH2CH2CH2OH
Two C–O bonds are replaced by C–H bonds.

Unlike the $LiAlH_4$ reduction of all other carboxylic acid derivatives, which affords alcohols, the **$LiAlH_4$ reduction of amides forms amines.**

Reduction of an amide

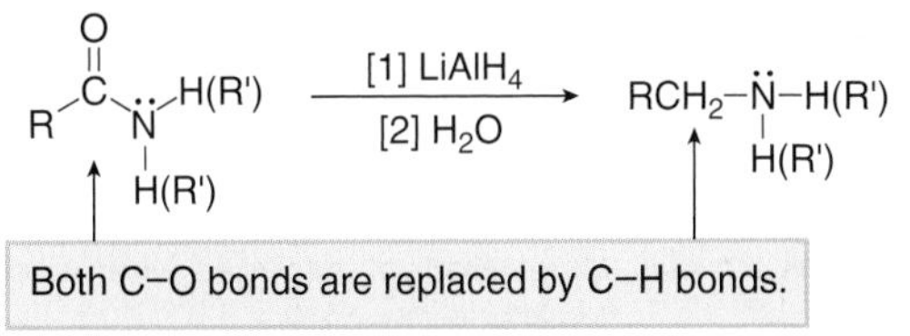
H(R')
H(R')
[1] LiAlH4
[2] H2O
RCH2–N–H(R')
H(R')
Both C–O bonds are replaced by C–H bonds.

amine

Both C–O bonds are reduced to C–H bonds by $LiAlH_4$, and any H atom or R group bonded to the amide nitrogen atom remains bonded to it in the product. Because $^-NH_2$ (or ^-NHR or $^-NR_2$) is a poorer leaving group than Cl^- or ^-OR, $^-NH_2$ is never lost during reduction, and therefore it forms an amine in the final product.

Examples

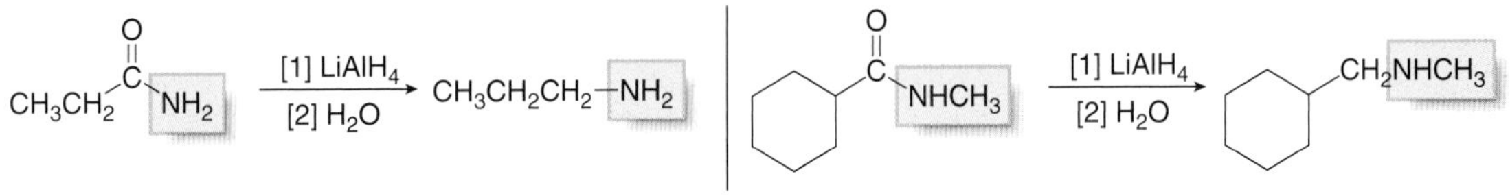
CH3CH2
NH2
[1] LiAlH4
[2] H2O
CH3CH2CH2–NH2
NHCH3
[1] LiAlH4
[2] H2O
CH2NHCH3

Imines and related compounds are discussed in Chapter 21.

The mechanism, illustrated in Mechanism 20.5 with $RCONH_2$ as starting material, is somewhat different than the previous reductions of carboxylic acid derivatives. Amide reduction proceeds with formation of an intermediate ***imine*, a compound containing a C–N double bond,** which is then further reduced to an amine.

Mechanism 20.5 Reduction of an Amide to an Amine with $LiAlH_4$

Part [1] Reduction of an amide to an imine

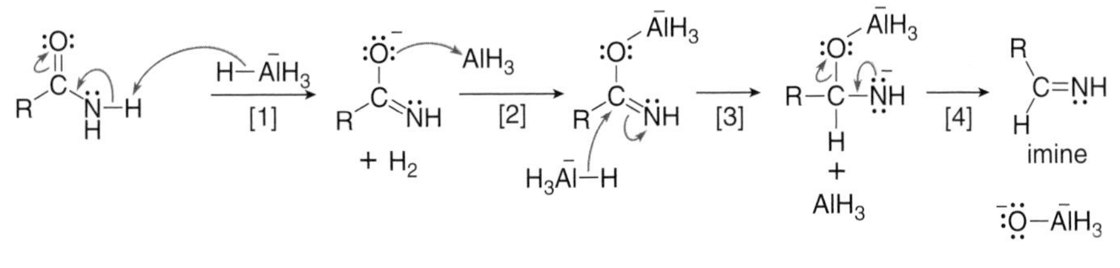
H–AlH3
[1]
+ H2
[2]
H3Al–H
[3]
+
AlH3
[4]
imine
:Ö–AlH3

- In Part [1], the amide is converted to an **imine** by proton transfer, nucleophilic attack of $H:^-$, and loss of $(AlH_3O)^{2-}$.
- The polarized C=N of an imine makes it susceptible to nucleophilic attack.

Part [2] Reduction of an imine to an amine

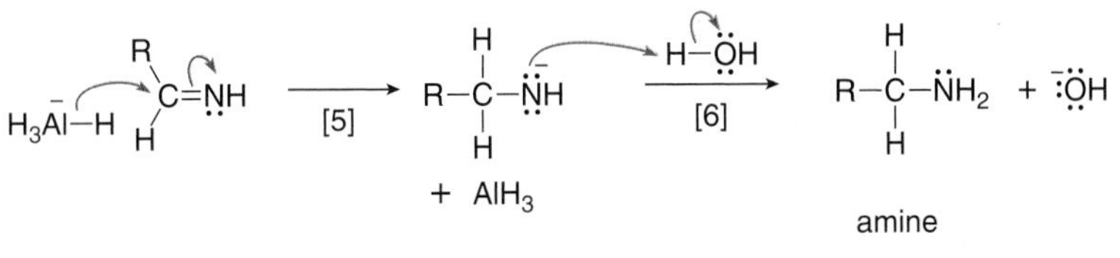
H3Al–H
[5]
+ AlH3
H–ÖH
[6]
R–C–NH2
amine

- **Nucleophilic attack of $H:^-$** (from $LiAlH_4$) in Step [5], followed by protonation forms the **amine.** The overall result of Steps [5] and [6] is addition of H_2 to the intermediate imine.

Problem 20.12 Draw the products formed from $LiAlH_4$ reduction of each compound.

a. 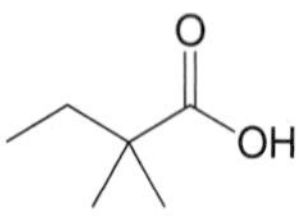
b. 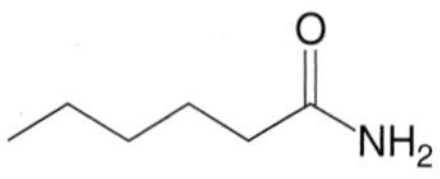
c. 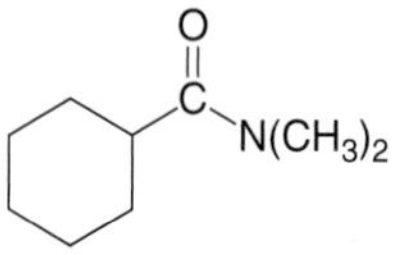
d. 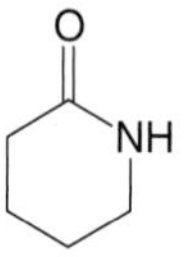

Problem 20.13 What amide(s) will form each of the following amines on treatment with $LiAlH_4$?

a. 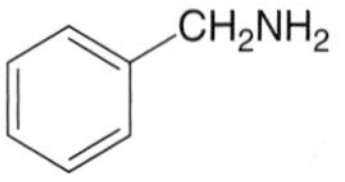
b. 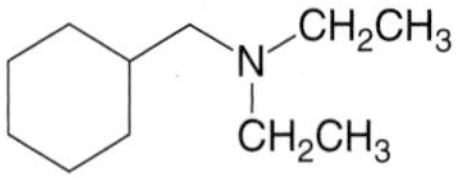
c. $CH_3CH_2NHC(CH_3)_3$

20.7C A Summary of the Reagents for Reduction

The many available metal hydride reagents reduce a wide variety of functional groups. Keep in mind that $LiAlH_4$ is such a strong reducing agent that it *nonselectively* reduces most polar functional groups. All other metal hydride reagents are more selective, and each has its particular reactions that best utilize its reduced reactivity. The reagents and their uses are summarized in Table 20.1.

Problem 20.14 What product is formed when each compound is treated with either $LiAlH_4$ (followed by H_2O), or $NaBH_4$ in CH_3OH?

a. 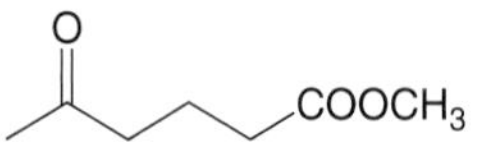
b. 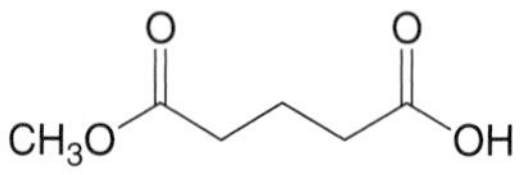
c. 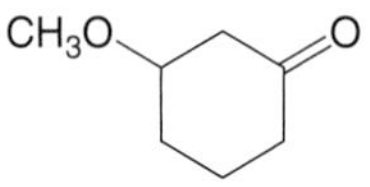

Problem 20.15 What product is formed when $(CH_3)_2C{=}CHCH_2COCH_2CH_2CO_2CH_2CH_3$ is treated with each reagent: (a) H_2 (1 equiv), Pd-C; (b) H_2 (2 equiv), Pd-C; (c) $LiAlH_4$, followed by H_2O; (d) $NaBH_4$, CH_3OH?

Table 20.1 A Summary of Metal Hydride Reducing Agents

	Reagent	Starting material	→	Product
Strong reagent	$LiAlH_4$	RCHO	→	RCH_2OH
		R_2CO	→	R_2CHOH
		RCOOH	→	RCH_2OH
		RCOOR'	→	RCH_2OH
		RCOCl	→	RCH_2OH
		$RCONH_2$	→	RCH_2NH_2
Milder reagents	$NaBH_4$	RCHO	→	RCH_2OH
		R_2CO	→	R_2CHOH
	$LiAlH[OC(CH_3)_3]_3$	RCOCl	→	RCHO
	DIBAL-H	RCOOR'	→	RCHO

20.8 Oxidation of Aldehydes

The most common oxidation reaction of carbonyl compounds is the oxidation of **aldehydes to carboxylic acids.** A variety of oxidizing agents can be used, including CrO_3, $Na_2Cr_2O_7$, $K_2Cr_2O_7$, and $KMnO_4$. Cr^{6+} reagents are also used to oxidize 1° and 2° alcohols, as discussed in Section 12.12. Because ketones have no H on the carbonyl carbon, they do not undergo this oxidation reaction.

Aldehydes give a positive Tollens test; that is, they react with Ag^+ to form RCOOH and Ag. When the reaction is carried out in a glass flask, a silver mirror is formed on its walls. Other functional groups give a negative Tollens test, because no silver mirror forms.

Aldehydes are oxidized selectively in the presence of other functional groups using **silver(I) oxide in aqueous ammonium hydroxide (Ag_2O in NH_4OH).** This is called **Tollens reagent.** Oxidation with Tollens reagent provides a distinct color change, because the Ag^+ reagent is reduced to silver metal (Ag), which precipitates out of solution.

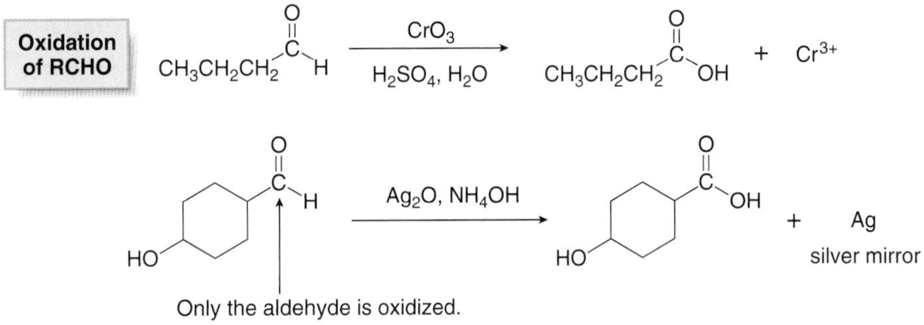
Oxidation of RCHO
CH3CH2CH2CHO
CrO3
H2SO4, H2O
CH3CH2CH2COOH
+ Cr3+
Ag2O, NH4OH
HO
+ Ag
silver mirror
Only the aldehyde is oxidized.

Problem 20.16 What product is formed when each compound is treated with either Ag_2O, NH_4OH or $Na_2Cr_2O_7$, H_2SO_4, H_2O: (a) $C_6H_5CH_2OH$; (b) $CH_3CH(OH)CH_2CH_2CH_2CHO$?

Problem 20.17 Review the oxidation reactions using Cr^{6+} reagents in Section 12.12. Then, draw the product formed when compound **B** is treated with each reagent.

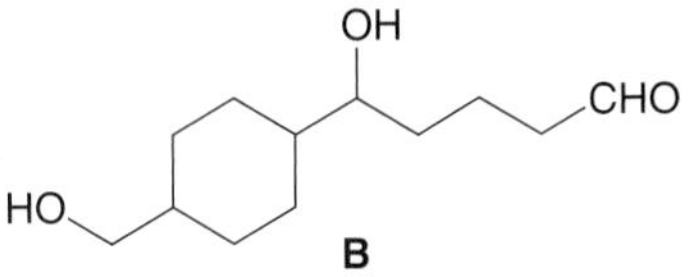
OH
CHO
HO

B

a. $NaBH_4$, CH_3OH
b. [1] $LiAlH_4$; [2] H_2O
c. PCC
d. Ag_2O, NH_4OH
e. CrO_3, H_2SO_4, H_2O

20.9 Organometallic Reagents

We will now discuss the reactions of carbonyl compounds with organometallic reagents, another class of nucleophiles.

- ***Organometallic reagents*** **contain a carbon atom bonded to a metal.**

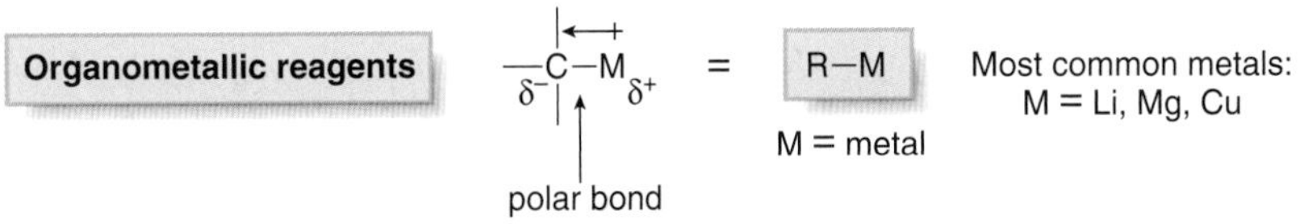
Organometallic reagents
—C—M
δ−
δ+
polar bond
=
R—M
M = metal
Most common metals:
M = Li, Mg, Cu

Lithium, magnesium, and copper are the most commonly used metals in organometallic reagents, but others (such as Sn, Si, Tl, Al, Ti, and Hg) are known. General structures of the three common organometallic reagents are shown. R can be alkyl, aryl, allyl, benzyl, sp^2 hybridized, and with

M = Li or Mg, *sp* hybridized. Because metals are *more electropositive* (less electronegative) than carbon, they donate electron density towards carbon, so that **carbon bears a partial negative charge.**

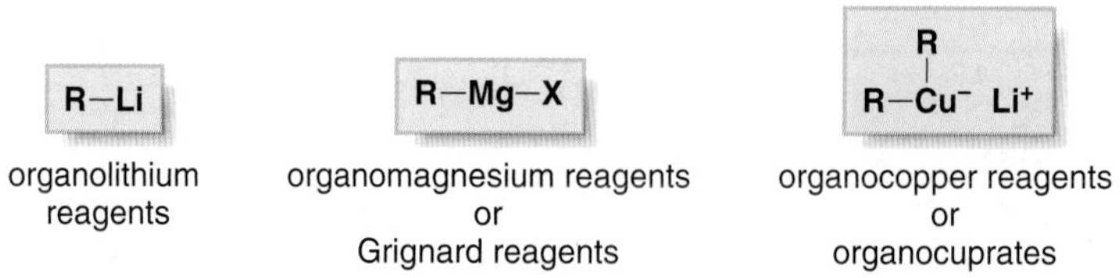

- **The more polar the carbon–metal bond, the more reactive the organometallic reagent.**

Because both Li and Mg are very electropositive metals, **organolithium (RLi)** and **organomagnesium reagents (RMgX)** contain very polar carbon–metal bonds and are therefore very reactive reagents. Organomagnesium reagents are called **Grignard reagents,** after Victor Grignard, who received the Nobel Prize in Chemistry in 1912 for his work with them.

Electronegativity values for carbon and the common metals in R–M reagents are C (2.5), Li (1.0), Mg (1.3), and Cu (1.8).

Organocopper reagents (R_2CuLi), also called **organocuprates,** have a less polar carbon–metal bond and are therefore less reactive. Although organocuprates contain two alkyl groups bonded to copper, only one R group is utilized in a reaction.

Regardless of the metal, organometallic reagents are useful synthetically because they react as if they were free carbanions; that is, carbon bears a partial *negative* charge, so the **reagents react as bases and nucleophiles.**

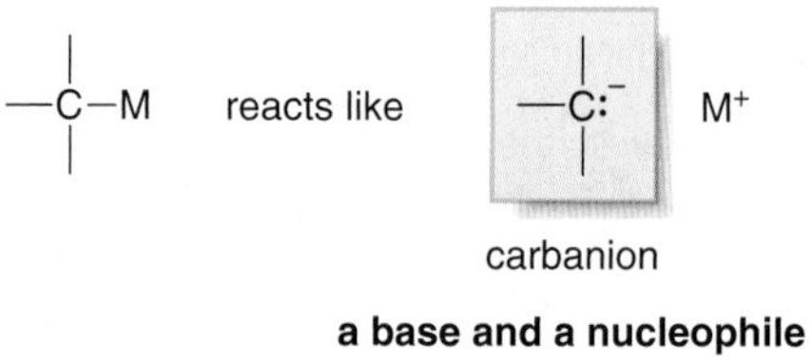

20.9A Preparation of Organometallic Reagents

Organolithium and Grignard reagents are typically prepared by reaction of an organic halide with the corresponding metal, as shown in the accompanying equations.

	Organolithium reagents	Grignard reagents
General reaction	R—X + 2 Li ⟶ R—Li + LiX	R—X + Mg $\xrightarrow{(CH_3CH_2)_2O}$ R—Mg—X
Example	CH_3—Br + 2 Li ⟶ CH_3—Li + LiBr methyllithium	CH_3—Br + Mg $\xrightarrow{(CH_3CH_2)_2O}$ CH_3—Mg—Br methylmagnesium bromide

With lithium, the halogen and metal exchange to form the organolithium reagent. With magnesium, the metal inserts in the carbon–halogen bond, forming the Grignard reagent. Grignard reagents are usually prepared in diethyl ether ($CH_3CH_2OCH_2CH_3$) as solvent. It is thought that two ether oxygen atoms complex with the magnesium atom, stabilizing the reagent.

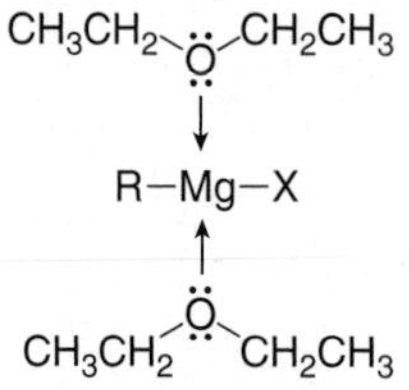

Two molecules of diethyl ether complex with the Mg atom of the Grignard reagent.

Organocuprates are prepared from organolithium reagents by reaction with a Cu^+ salt, often CuI.

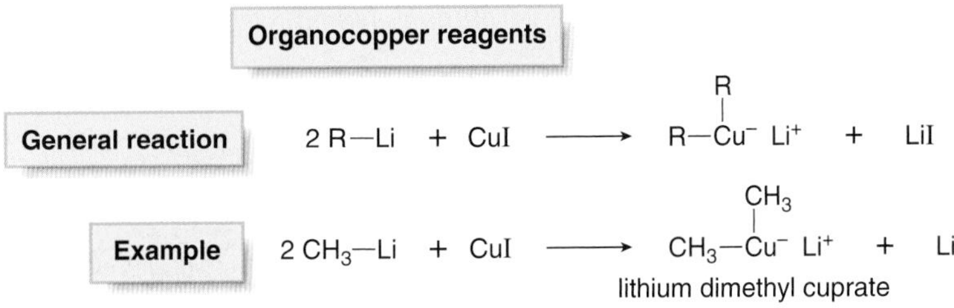
Organocopper reagents
General reaction
2 R—Li + CuI → R—Cu⁻(R) Li⁺ + LiI
Example
2 CH3—Li + CuI → CH3—Cu⁻(CH3) Li⁺ + LiI
lithium dimethyl cuprate

Problem 20.18 Write the step(s) needed to convert CH_3CH_2Br to each reagent: (a) CH_3CH_2Li; (b) CH_3CH_2MgBr; (c) $(CH_3CH_2)_2CuLi$.

20.9B Acetylide Anions

The **acetylide anions** discussed in Chapter 11 are another example of organometallic compounds. These reagents are prepared by an acid–base reaction of an alkyne with a base such as $NaNH_2$ or NaH. We can think of these compounds as **organosodium** reagents. Because sodium is even more electropositive (less electronegative) than lithium, the C–Na bond of these organosodium compounds is best described as **ionic,** rather than polar covalent.

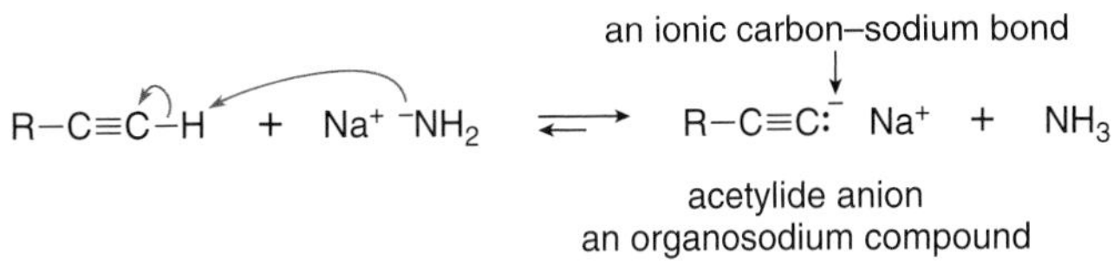
an ionic carbon–sodium bond
R—C≡C—H + Na⁺ ⁻NH2 ⇌ R—C≡C:⁻ Na⁺ + NH3
acetylide anion
an organosodium compound

An acid–base reaction can also be used to prepare *sp* hybridized organolithium compounds. Treatment of a terminal alkyne with CH_3Li affords a lithium acetylide. Equilibrium favors the products because the *sp* hybridized C–H bond of the terminal alkyne is more acidic than the sp^3 hybridized conjugate acid, CH_4, that is formed.

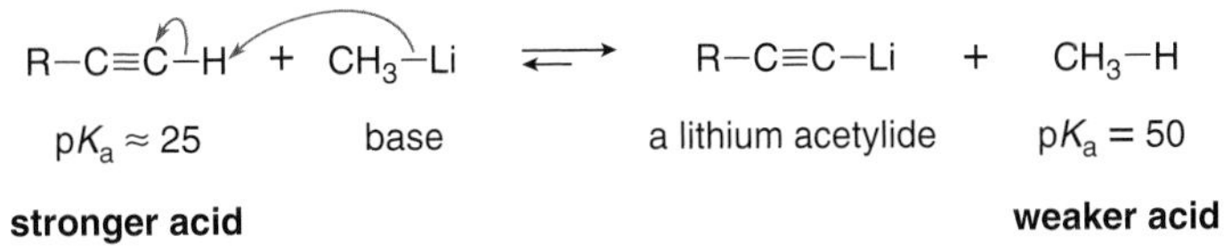
R—C≡C—H + CH3—Li ⇌ R—C≡C—Li + CH3—H
pKa ≈ 25
base
a lithium acetylide
pKa = 50
stronger acid
weaker acid

Problem 20.19 1-Octyne ($HC{\equiv}CCH_2CH_2CH_2CH_2CH_2CH_3$) reacts rapidly with NaH, forming a gas that bubbles out of the reaction mixture, as one product. 1-Octyne also reacts rapidly with CH_3MgBr, and a different gas is produced. Write balanced equations for both reactions and identify the gases formed.

20.9C Reaction as a Base

- **Organometallic reagents are strong bases that readily abstract a proton from water to form hydrocarbons.**

The electron pair in the carbon–metal bond is used to form a new bond to the proton. Equilibrium favors the products of this acid–base reaction because H_2O is a much stronger acid than the alkane product.

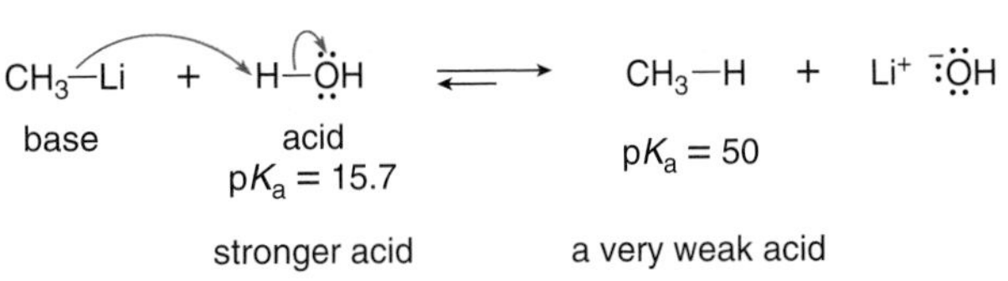
CH3—Li + H—ÖH ⇌ CH3—H + Li⁺ ⁻:ÖH
base
acid
pKa = 15.7
pKa = 50
stronger acid
a very weak acid

Similar reactions occur for the same reason with the O–H proton in alcohols and carboxylic acids, and the N–H protons of amines.

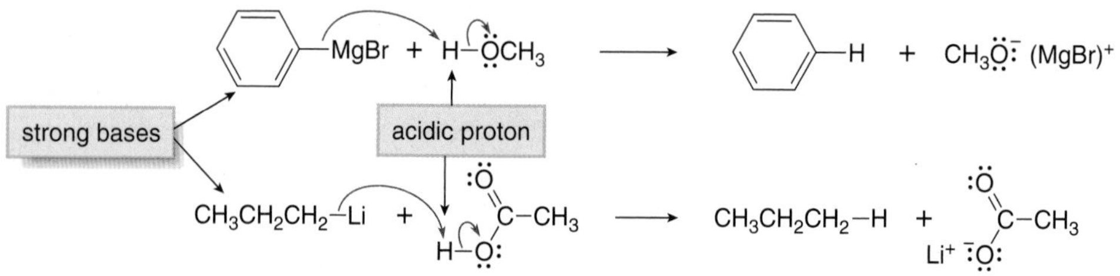

Because organolithium and Grignard reagents are themselves prepared from alkyl halides, a two-step method converts an alkyl halide into an alkane (or another hydrocarbon).

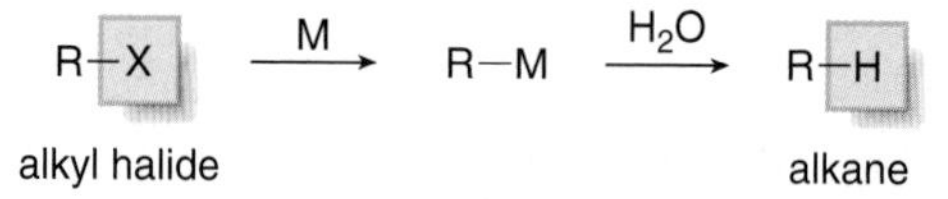

Problem 20.20 Draw the product formed when each organometallic reagent is treated with H_2O.

a. 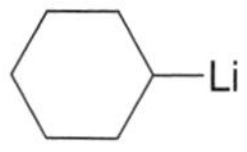 b. $(CH_3)_3CMgBr$ c. 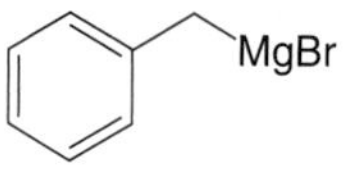 d. $CH_3CH_2C{\equiv}C{-}Li$

20.9D Reaction as a Nucleophile

Organometallic reagents are also strong nucleophiles that react with electrophilic carbon atoms to form new carbon–carbon bonds. These reactions are very valuable in forming the carbon skeletons of complex organic molecules. The following reactions of organometallic reagents are examined in Sections 20.10, 20.13, and 20.14:

[1] Reaction of R–M with aldehydes and ketones to afford alcohols (Section 20.10)

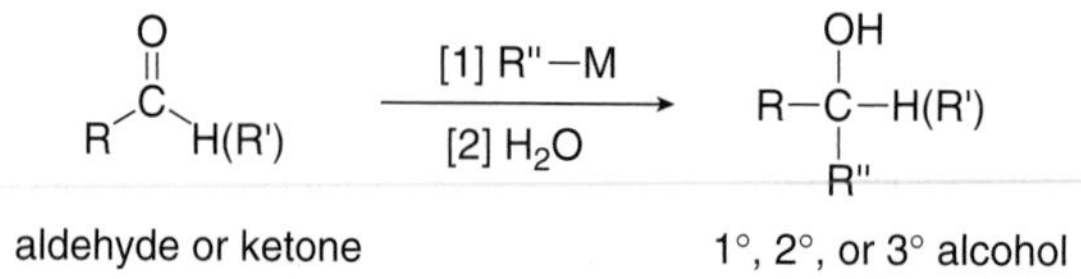

Aldehydes and ketones are converted to 1°, 2°, or 3° alcohols with R"Li or R"MgX.

[2] Reaction of R–M with carboxylic acid derivatives (Section 20.13)

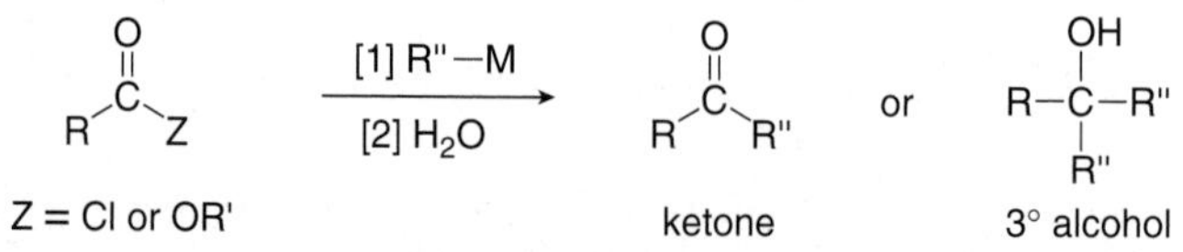

Acid chlorides and esters can be converted to ketones or 3° alcohols with organometallic reagents. The identity of the product depends on the identity of R"–M and the leaving group Z.

[3] **Reaction of R–M with other electrophilic functional groups (Section 20.14)**

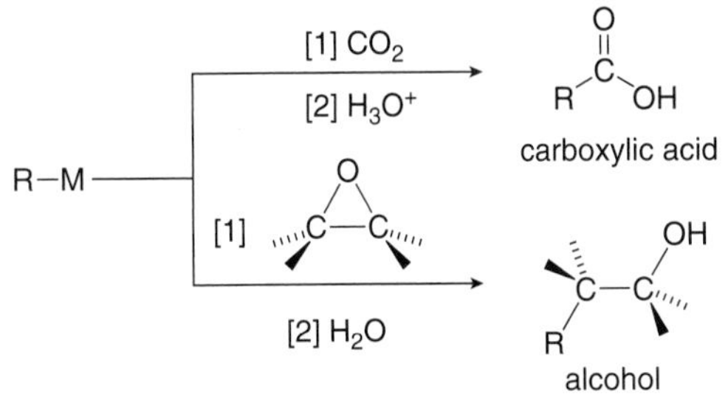

Organometallic reagents also react with CO_2 to form carboxylic acids and with epoxides to form alcohols.

20.10 Reaction of Organometallic Reagents with Aldehydes and Ketones

Treatment of an aldehyde or ketone with either an organolithium or Grignard reagent followed by water forms an alcohol with a new carbon–carbon bond. This reaction is an **addition reaction** because the elements of R'' and H are added across the π bond.

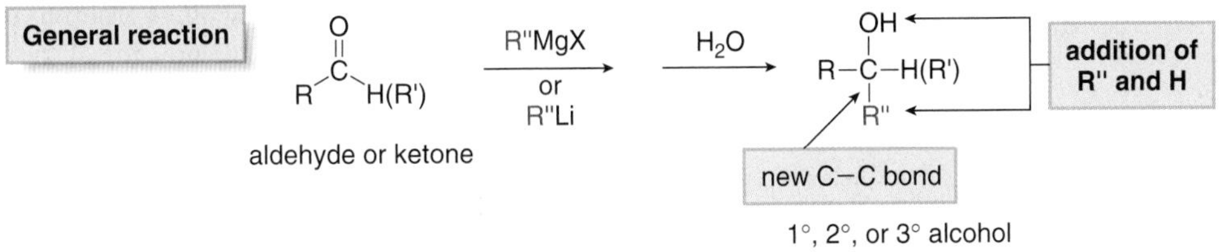

20.10A General Features

This reaction follows the general mechanism for nucleophilic addition (Section 20.2A)—that is, **nucleophilic attack** by a carbanion followed by **protonation.** Mechanism 20.6 is shown using R''MgX, but the same steps occur with organolithium reagents and acetylide anions.

Mechanism 20.6 Nucleophilic Addition of R''MgX to RCHO and $R_2C{=}O$

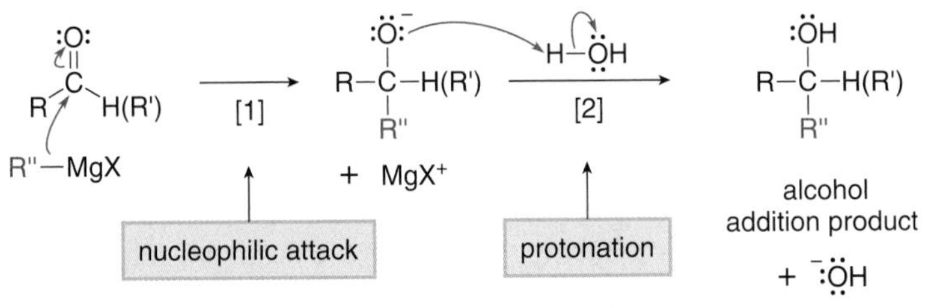

- In Step [1], the **nucleophile $(R'')^-$ attacks the carbonyl carbon** and the π bond cleaves, forming an alkoxide. **This step forms a new carbon–carbon bond.**
- In Step [2], **protonation of the alkoxide by H_2O** forms the alcohol addition product. This acid–base reaction forms a new O–H bond.
- The overall result is addition of $(R'')^-$ (from R''MgX) and H^+ (from H_2O) to the carbonyl group.

This reaction is used to prepare 1°, 2°, and 3° alcohols, depending on the number of alkyl groups bonded to the carbonyl carbon of the aldehyde or ketone.

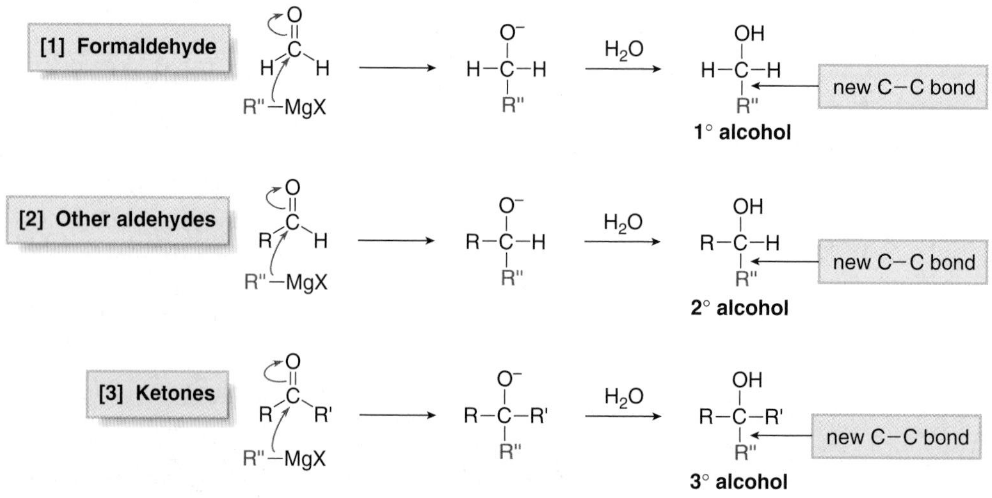
[1] Formaldehyde
H_2O
new C–C bond
1° alcohol
[2] Other aldehydes
H_2O
new C–C bond
2° alcohol
[3] Ketones
H_2O
new C–C bond
3° alcohol

[1] Addition of R"MgX to formaldehyde (CH_2=O) forms a 1° alcohol.
[2] Addition of R"MgX to all other aldehydes forms a 2° alcohol.
[3] Addition of R"MgX to ketones forms a 3° alcohol.

Each reaction results in addition of one new alkyl group to the carbonyl carbon, and forms one new carbon–carbon bond. The reaction is general for all organolithium and Grignard reagents, and works for acetylide anions as well, as illustrated in Equations [1]–[3].

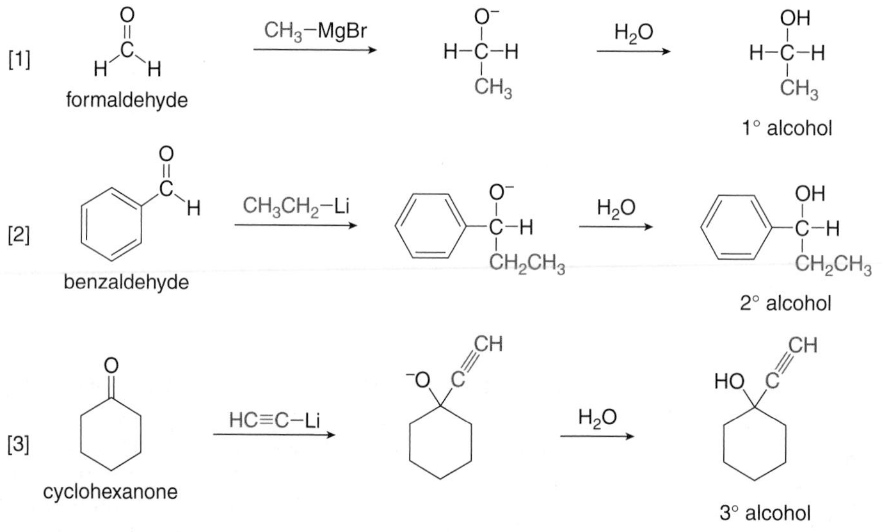
[1]
formaldehyde
CH_3–MgBr
H_2O
1° alcohol
[2]
benzaldehyde
CH_3CH_2–Li
H_2O
2° alcohol
[3]
cyclohexanone
HC≡C–Li
H_2O
3° alcohol

Because organometallic reagents are strong bases that rapidly react with H_2O (Section 20.9C), the addition of the new alkyl group must be carried out under anhydrous conditions to prevent traces of water from reacting with the reagent, thus reducing the yield of the desired alcohol. Water is added after the addition to protonate the alkoxide.

Problem 20.21 Draw the product of each reaction.

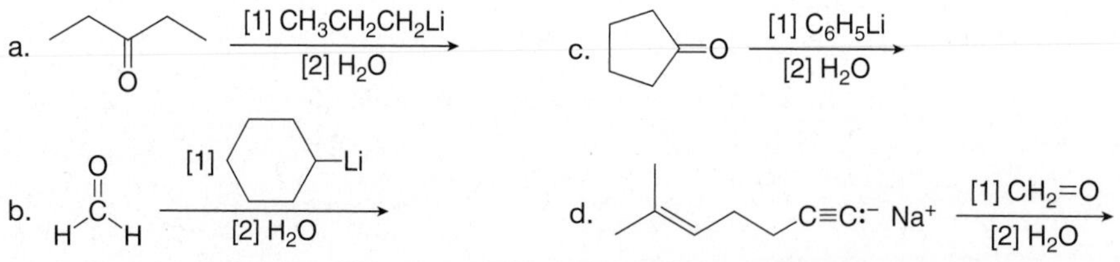
a.
[1] $CH_3CH_2CH_2Li$
[2] H_2O
b.
[1]
[2] H_2O
c.
[1] C_6H_5Li
[2] H_2O
d.
[1] CH_2=O
[2] H_2O

20.10B Stereochemistry

Like reduction, addition of organometallic reagents converts an sp^2 hybridized carbonyl carbon to a tetrahedral sp^3 hybridized carbon. Addition of R–M always occurs from both sides of the trigonal planar carbonyl group. **When a new stereogenic center is formed from an achiral starting material, an equal mixture of enantiomers results,** as shown in Sample Problem 20.1.

Sample Problem 20.1 Draw all stereoisomers formed in the following reaction.

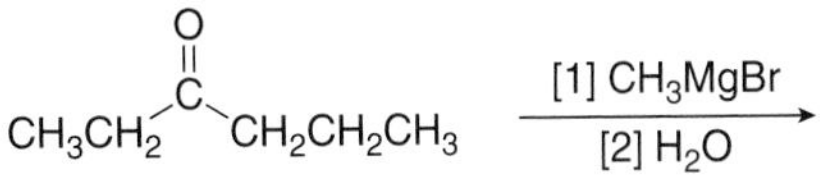

Solution

The Grignard reagent adds from both sides of the trigonal planar carbonyl group, forming two alkoxides, each containing a new stereogenic center. Protonation with water yields **an equal amount of two enantiomers—a racemic mixture.**

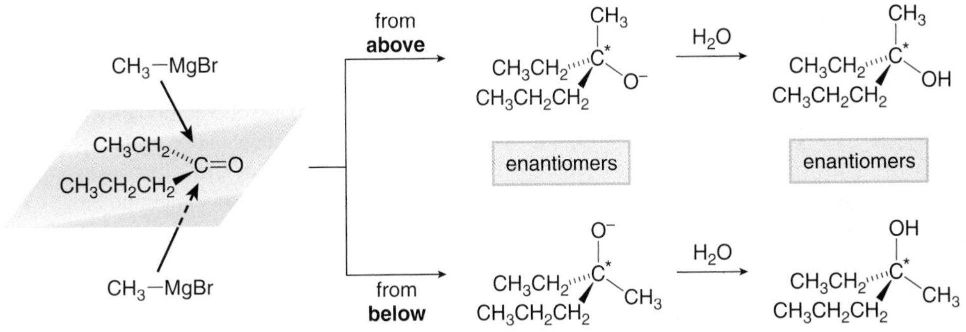

[* denotes a stereogenic center]

Problem 20.22 Draw the products (including stereochemistry) of the following reactions.

a. 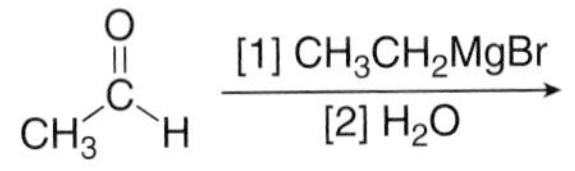

b. 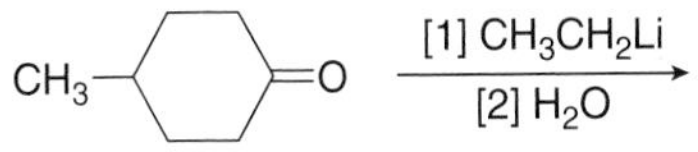

20.10C Applications in Synthesis

Many syntheses of useful compounds utilize the nucleophilic addition of a Grignard or organolithium reagent to form carbon–carbon bonds. For example, a key step in the synthesis of ethynylestradiol (Section 11.4), an oral contraceptive component, is the addition of lithium acetylide to a ketone, as shown in Figure 20.5.

Figure. 20.5 The synthesis of ethynylestradiol

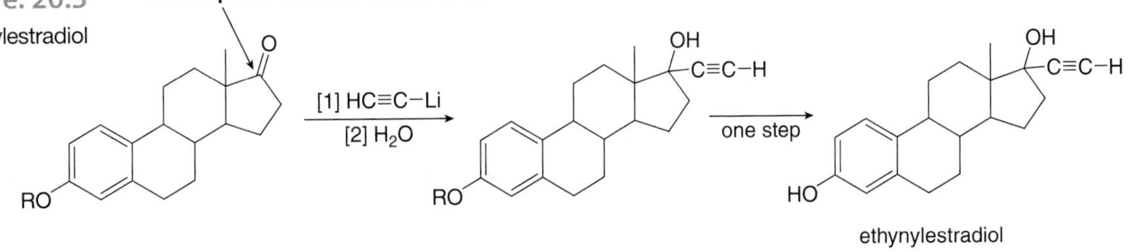

ethynylestradiol

The synthesis of C_{18} juvenile hormone, a member of a group of structurally related molecules that regulate the complex life cycle of an insect, is another example. The last steps of the synthesis are outlined in Figure 20.6.

Figure 20.6
C_{18} juvenile hormone

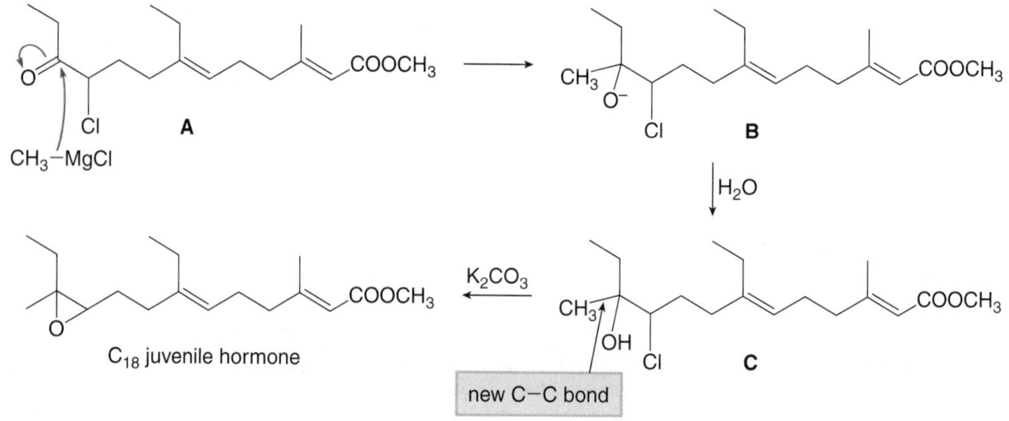

- Addition of CH_3MgCl to ketone **A** gives an alkoxide, **B,** which is protonated with H_2O to form 3° alcohol **C.** Although the ester group ($-COOCH_3$) can also react with the Grignard reagent (Section 20.13), it is less reactive than the ketone carbonyl. Thus, with control of reaction conditions, nucleophilic addition occurs selectively at the ketone.
- Treatment of halohydrin **C** with K_2CO_3 forms the C_{18} juvenile hormone in one step. Conversion of a halohydrin to an epoxide was discussed in Section 9.6.

Juvenile hormones regulate the life cycle of the cecropia moth.

Juvenile hormones maintain the juvenile stage of an insect until it is ready for adulthood. This property has been exploited to control mosquitoes and other insects infecting livestock and crops. Although juvenile hormone itself is too unstable in light and too expensive to synthesize for use in controlling insect populations, related compounds, called **juvenile hormone *mimics,*** have been used effectively. Application of these synthetic hormones to an egg or larva of an insect prevents maturation. With no sexually mature adults to propagate the next generation, the insect population is reduced. The best known example of a synthetic juvenile hormone is called **methoprene,** sold under such trade names as Altocid, Precor, and Diacon. Methoprene is used in cattle salt blocks to control hornflies, in stored tobacco to control pests, and on dogs and cats to control fleas.

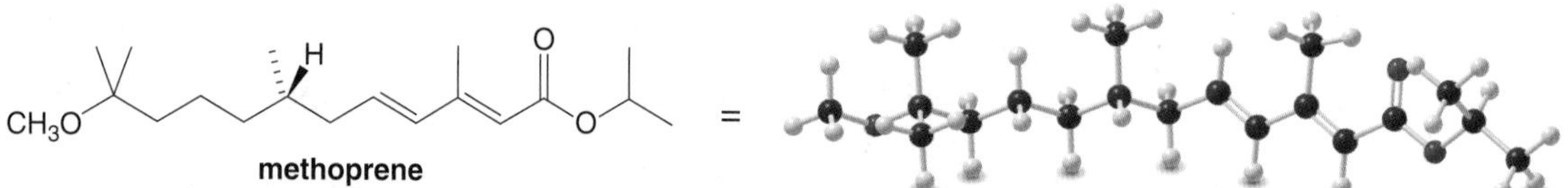

methoprene
juvenile hormone mimic

20.11 Retrosynthetic Analysis of Grignard Products

To use the Grignard addition in synthesis, you must be able to determine what carbonyl and Grignard components are needed to prepare a given compound—that is, **you must work backwards, in the retrosynthetic direction.** This involves a two-step process:

Step [1] **Find the carbon bonded to the OH group in the product.**

Step [2] **Break the molecule into two components: One alkyl group bonded to the carbon with the OH group comes from the organometallic reagent. The rest of the molecule comes from the carbonyl component.**

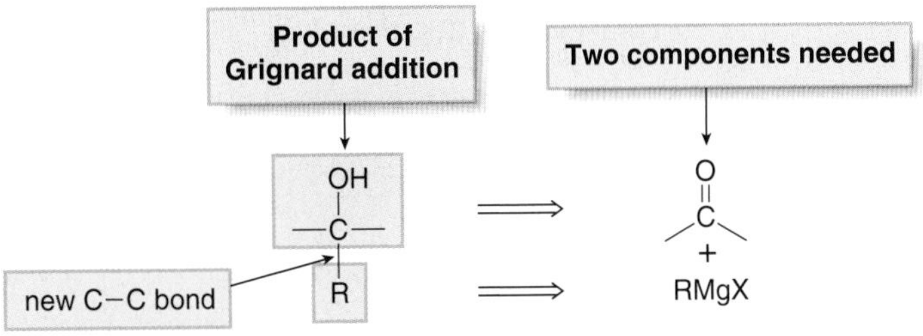
Product of Grignard addition
Two components needed
OH
C
R
new C–C bond
O
C
+
RMgX

For example, to synthesize 3-pentanol [$(CH_3CH_2)_2CHOH$] by a Grignard reaction, locate the carbon bonded to the OH group, and then break the molecule into two components at this carbon. Thus, retrosynthetic analysis shows that one of the ethyl groups on this carbon comes from a Grignard reagent (CH_3CH_2MgX), and the rest of the molecule comes from the carbonyl component, a three-carbon aldehyde.

Retrosynthetic analysis for preparing 3-pentanol

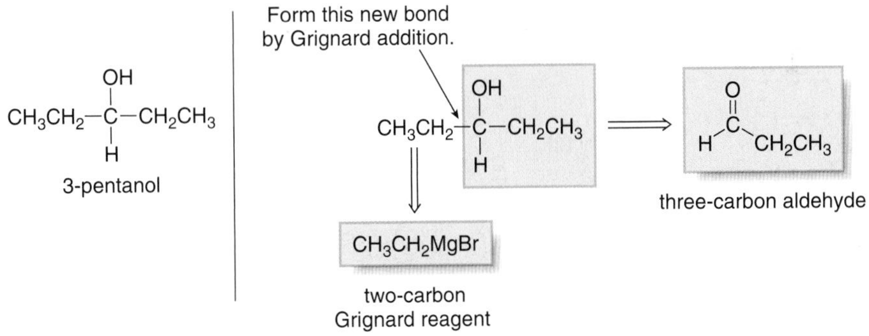
OH
CH3CH2–C–CH2CH3
H
3-pentanol
Form this new bond by Grignard addition.
OH
CH3CH2–C–CH2CH3
H
O
C
H CH2CH3
three-carbon aldehyde
CH3CH2MgBr
two-carbon Grignard reagent

Then, writing the reaction in the synthetic direction—that is, from starting material to product—shows whether the analysis is correct. In this example, a three-carbon aldehyde reacts with CH_3CH_2MgBr to form an alkoxide, which can then be protonated by H_2O to form 3-pentanol, the desired alcohol.

In the synthetic direction:

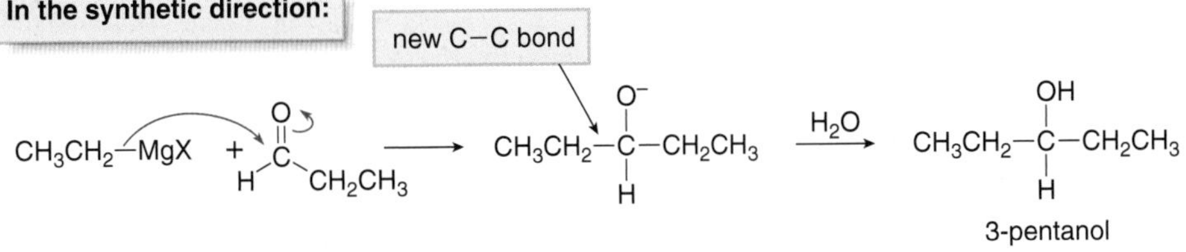
new C–C bond
CH3CH2–MgX
+
O
C
H CH2CH3
O–
CH3CH2–C–CH2CH3
H
H2O
OH
CH3CH2–C–CH2CH3
H
3-pentanol

There is often more than one way to synthesize a 2° alcohol by Grignard addition, as shown in Sample Problem 20.2.

Sample Problem 20.2 Show two different methods to synthesize 2-butanol using a Grignard reaction.

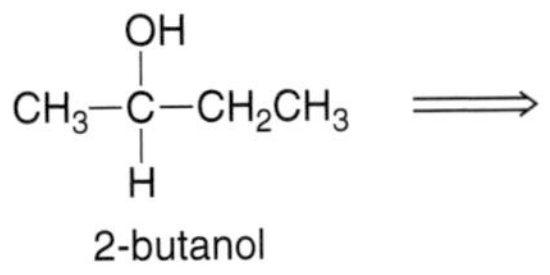
OH
CH3–C–CH2CH3
H
2-butanol

Solution

Because 2-butanol has two different alkyl groups bonded to the carbon bearing the OH group, there are two different ways to form a new carbon–carbon bond by Grignard addition.

Possibility [1] Use CH_3MgX and a three-carbon aldehyde.

Form this new C–C bond.

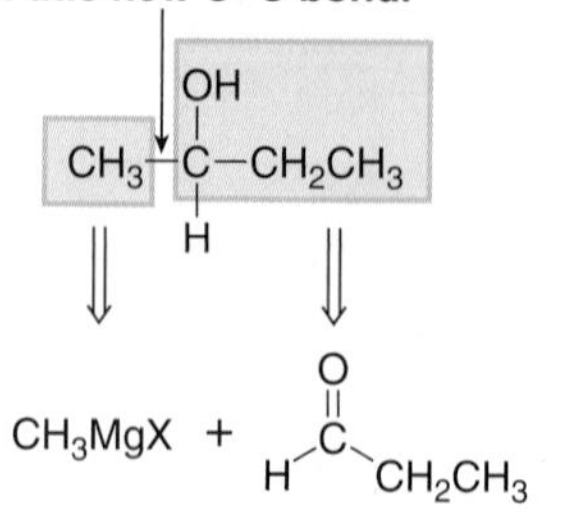

Possibility [2] Use CH_3CH_2MgX and a two-carbon aldehyde.

Form this new C–C bond.

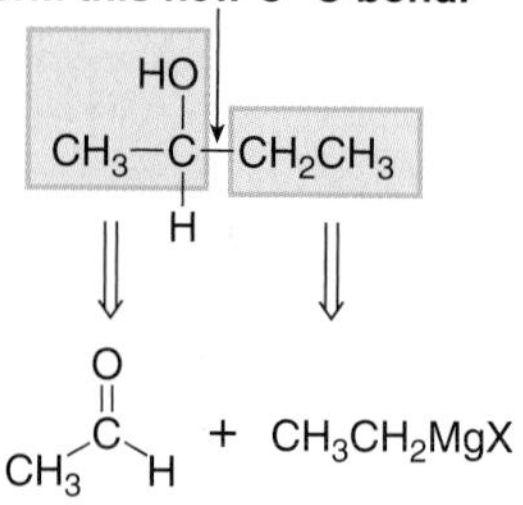

Both methods give the desired product, 2-butanol, as can be seen by writing the reactions from starting material to product.

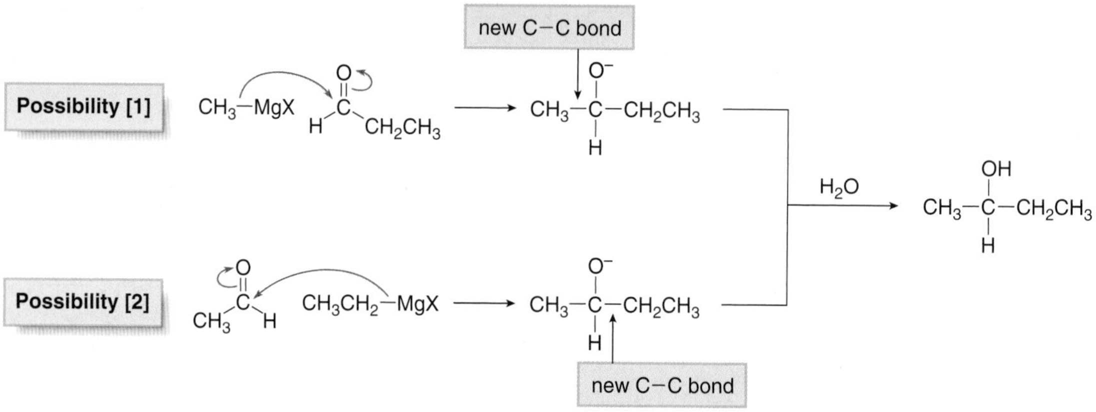

Problem 20.23 What Grignard reagent and carbonyl compound are needed to prepare each alcohol? As shown in part (d), 3° alcohols with three different R groups on the carbon bonded to the OH group can be prepared by three different Grignard reactions.

a. 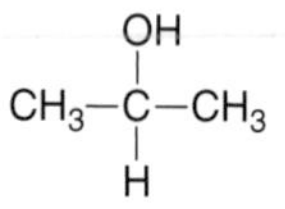
b. 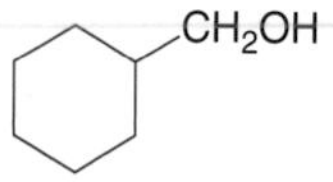
c. 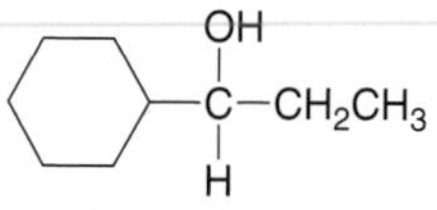
(two methods)
d. 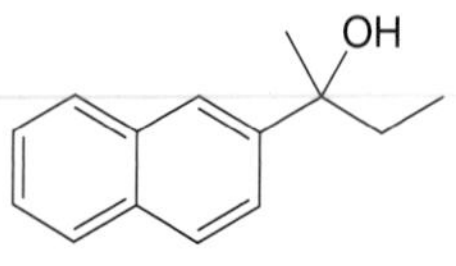
(three methods)

Problem 20.24 Linalool and lavandulol are two of the major components of lavender oil. (a) What organolithium reagent and carbonyl compound can be used to make each alcohol? (b) How might lavandulol be formed by reduction of a carbonyl compound? (c) Why can't linalool be prepared by a similar pathway?

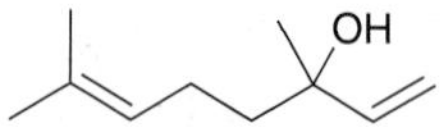
linalool
(three methods)

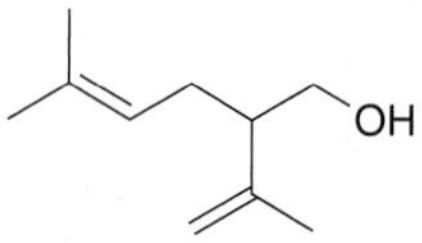
lavandulol

Linalool and lavandulol (Problem 20.24) are two of the over 300 compounds that determine the characteristic fragrance of lavender.

Problem 20.25 What Grignard reagent and carbonyl compound can be used to prepare the antidepressant venlafaxine (trade name Effexor)?

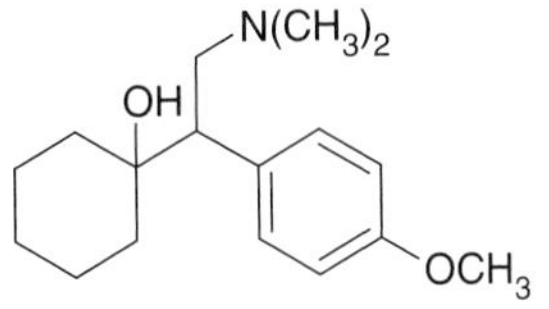

venlafaxine

20.12 Protecting Groups

Although the addition of organometallic reagents to carbonyls is a very versatile reaction, it cannot be used with molecules that contain both a carbonyl group and N–H or O–H bonds.

- **Carbonyl compounds that also contain N–H or O–H bonds undergo an acid–base reaction with organometallic reagents, not nucleophilic addition.**

Rapid acid–base reactions occur between organometallic reagents and all of the following functional groups: ROH, RCOOH, RNH_2, R_2NH, $RCONH_2$, RCONHR, and RSH.

Suppose, for example, that you wanted to add methylmagnesium chloride (CH_3MgCl) to the carbonyl group of 5-hydroxy-2-pentanone to form a diol. Nucleophilic addition will *not* occur with this substrate. Instead, **because Grignard reagents are strong bases and proton transfer reactions are fast, CH_3MgCl removes the O–H proton before nucleophilic addition takes place.** The stronger acid and base react to form the weaker conjugate acid and conjugate base, as we learned in Section 20.9C.

CH_3MgCl does *not* add to the carbonyl group.

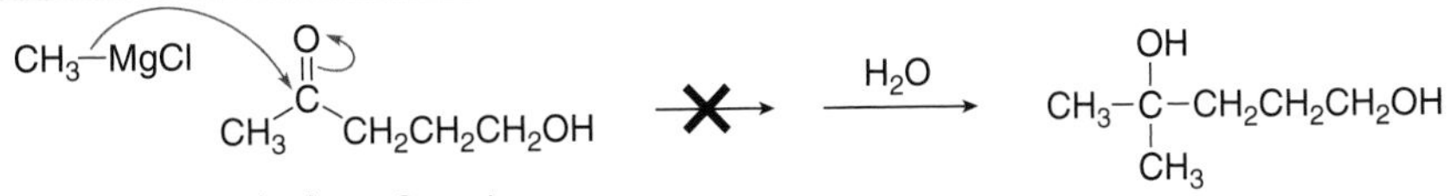

5-hydroxy-2-pentanone

4-methyl-1,4-pentanediol

product of **nucleophilic addition**

CH_3MgCl acts like a base, *not* a nucleophile.

stronger acid — base — product of **proton transfer** — weaker acid

Solving this problem requires a three-step strategy:

Step [1] Convert the OH group into another functional group that does not interfere with the desired reaction. This new blocking group is called a protecting group, and the reaction that creates it is called ***protection.***

Step [2] Carry out the desired reaction.

Step [3] Remove the protecting group. This reaction is called ***deprotection.***

Application of the general strategy to the Grignard addition of CH_3MgCl to 5-hydroxy-2-pentanone is illustrated in Figure 20.7.

Figure 20.7
General strategy for using a protecting group

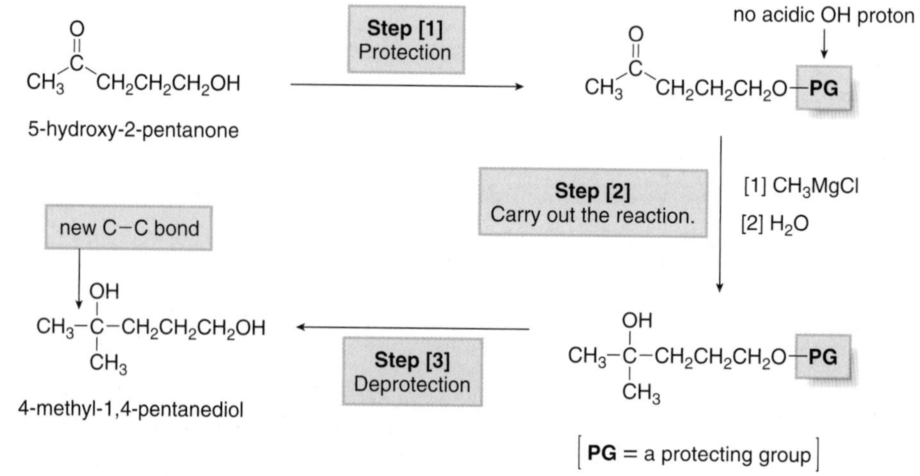

- In Step [1], the OH proton in 5-hydroxy-2-pentanone is replaced with a protecting group, written as **PG.** Because the product of Step [1] no longer has an OH proton, it can now undergo nucleophilic addition.
- In Step [2], CH_3MgCl adds to the carbonyl group to yield a 3° alcohol after protonation with water.
- Removal of the protecting group in Step [3] forms the desired product, 4-methyl-1,4-pentanediol.

A common OH protecting group is a **silyl ether.** A silyl ether has a new O–Si bond in place of the O–H bond of the alcohol. The most widely used silyl ether protecting group is the ***tert*-butyldimethylsilyl ether.**

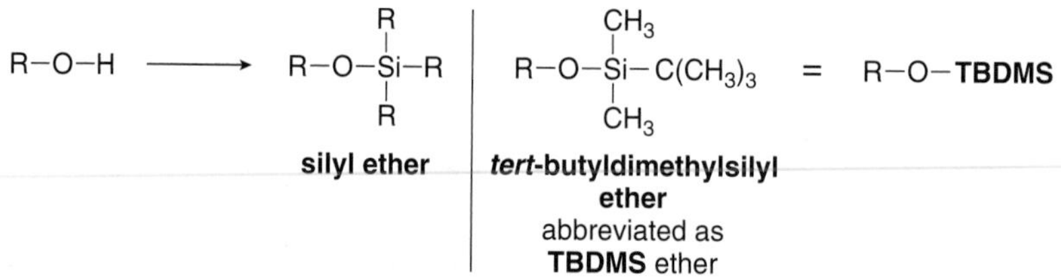

tert-Butyldimethylsilyl ethers are prepared from alcohols by reaction with *tert*-butyldimethylsilyl chloride and an amine base, usually imidazole.

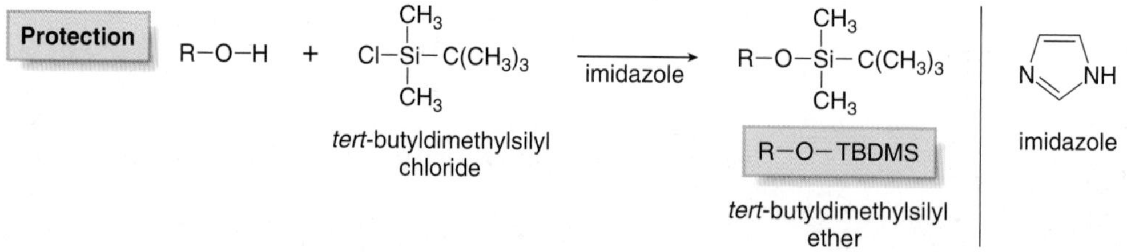

The silyl ether is typically removed with a fluoride salt, usually **tetrabutylammonium fluoride** $(CH_3CH_2CH_2CH_2)_4N^+ F^-$.

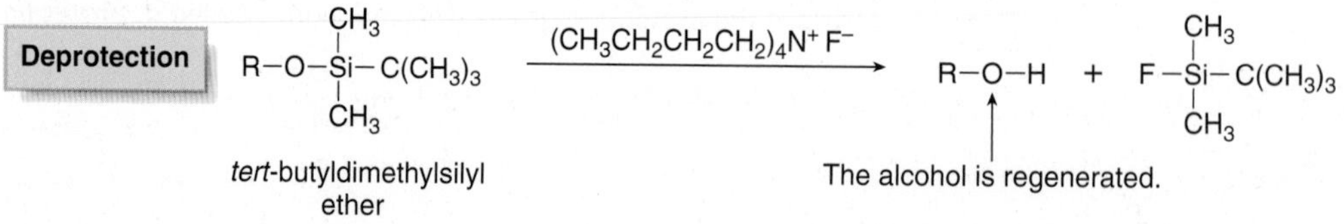

The use of a *tert*-butyldimethylsilyl ether as a protecting group makes possible the synthesis of 4-methyl-1,4-pentanediol by a three-step sequence.

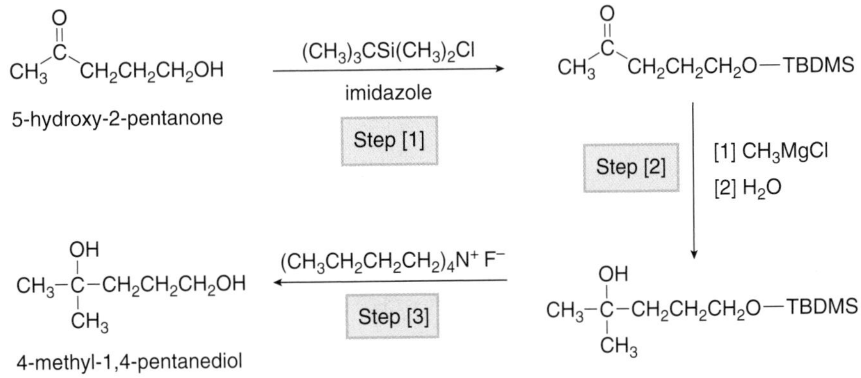

- **Step [1] Protect the OH group** as a *tert*-butyldimethylsilyl ether by reaction with *tert*-butyldimethylsilyl chloride and imidazole.
- **Step [2] Carry out nucleophilic addition** by using CH_3MgCl, followed by protonation.
- **Step [3] Remove the protecting group** with tetrabutylammonium fluoride to form the desired addition product.

Protecting groups block interfering functional groups, and in this way, a wider variety of reactions can take place with a particular substrate. For more on protecting groups, see the discussion of acetals in Section 21.15.

Problem 20.26 Using protecting groups, show how estrone can be converted to ethynylestradiol, a widely used oral contraceptive.

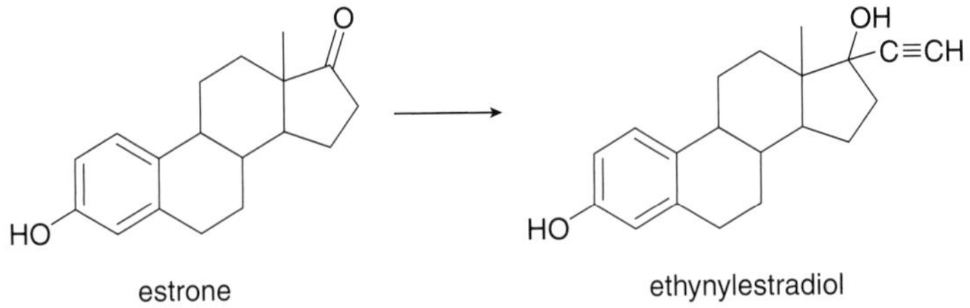

20.13 Reaction of Organometallic Reagents with Carboxylic Acid Derivatives

Organometallic reagents react with carboxylic acid derivatives (RCOZ) to form two different products, depending on the identity of both the leaving group Z and the reagent R−M. The most useful reactions are carried out with esters and acid chlorides, forming either **ketones** or **3° alcohols.**

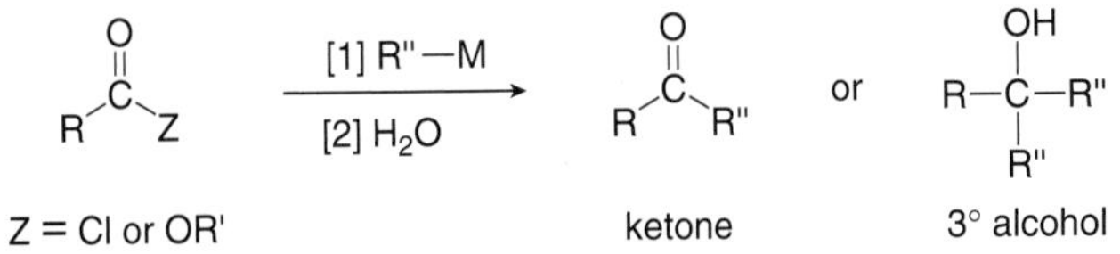

- **Keep in mind that RLi and RMgX are very reactive reagents, whereas R_2CuLi is much less reactive. This reactivity difference makes selective reactions possible.**

20.13A Reaction of RLi and RMgX with Esters and Acid Chlorides

Both esters and acid chlorides form 3° alcohols when treated with two equivalents of either Grignard or organolithium reagents. Two new carbon–carbon bonds are formed in the product.

General reaction

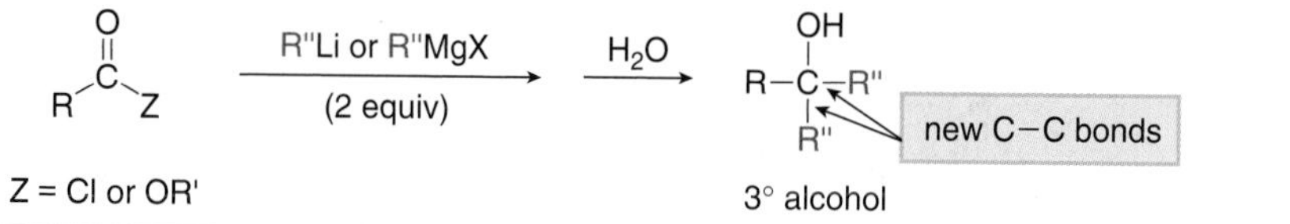

Examples

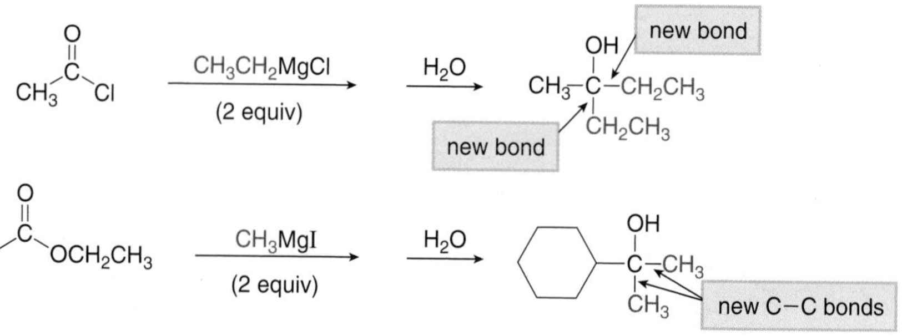

Problem 20.27 Draw the product formed when each compound is treated with two equivalents of $CH_3CH_2CH_2CH_2MgBr$ followed by H_2O.

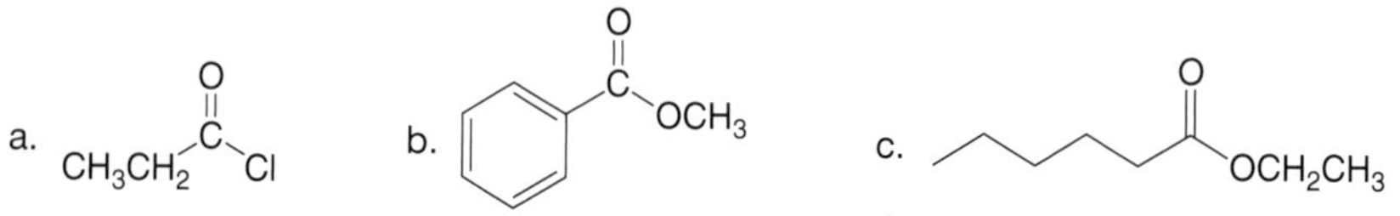

The mechanism for this addition reaction resembles the mechanism for the metal hydride reduction of acid chlorides and esters discussed in Section 20.7A. The mechanism is conceptually divided into two parts: **nucleophilic substitution** to form a ketone, followed by **nucleophilic addition** to form a 3° alcohol, as shown in Mechanism 20.7.

Mechanism 20.7 Reaction of R"MgX or R"Li with RCOCl and RCOOR'

Part [1] Nucleophilic substitution forms a ketone.

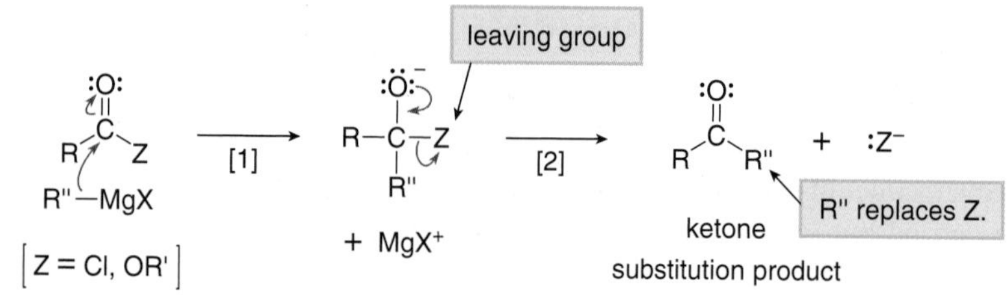

- **Nucleophilic attack of (R")⁻** (from R"MgX) in Step [1] forms a tetrahedral intermediate with a leaving group Z.
- In Step [2], the π bond is re-formed and **Z⁻ comes off.** The overall result of the addition of (R")⁻ and elimination of Z⁻ is the substitution of R" for Z.
- Because the product of Part [1] is a ketone, it can react with a second equivalent of R"MgX to form an alcohol by nucleophilic addition in Part [2].

Part [2] Nucleophilic addition forms a 3° alcohol.

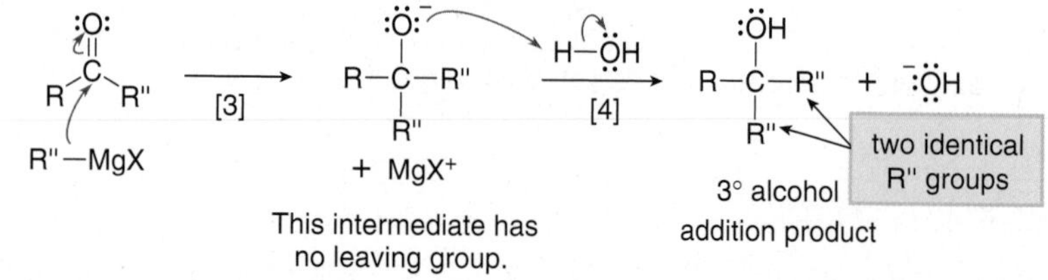

- **Nucleophilic attack of (R")⁻** (from R"MgX) in Step [3] forms an alkoxide.
- **Protonation of the alkoxide** by H_2O in Step [4] forms a 3° alcohol.

Organolithium and Grignard reagents always afford 3° alcohols when they react with esters and acid chlorides. As soon as the ketone forms by addition of one equivalent of reagent to RCOZ (Part [1] of the mechanism), it reacts with a second equivalent of reagent to form the 3° alcohol.

This reaction is more limited than the Grignard addition to aldehydes and ketones, because only 3° alcohols having two identical alkyl groups can be prepared. Nonetheless, it is still a valuable reaction because it forms two new carbon–carbon bonds.

Sample Problem 20.3 What ester and Grignard reagent are needed to prepare the following alcohol?

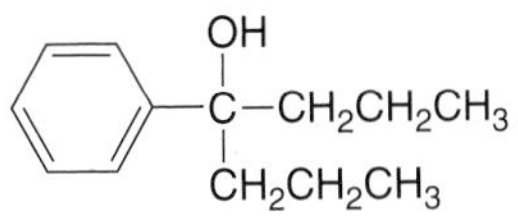
OH
C–CH2CH2CH3
CH2CH2CH3

Solution

A 3° alcohol formed from an ester and Grignard reagent must have **two identical R groups,** and these R groups come from RMgX. The remainder of the molecule comes from the ester.

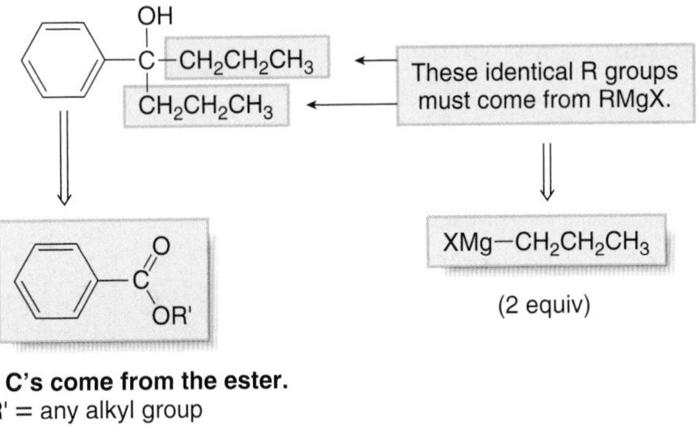
OH
C–CH2CH2CH3
CH2CH2CH3
These identical R groups must come from RMgX.
O
C
OR'
XMg–CH2CH2CH3
(2 equiv)
All other C's come from the ester.
R' = any alkyl group

Checking in the synthetic direction:

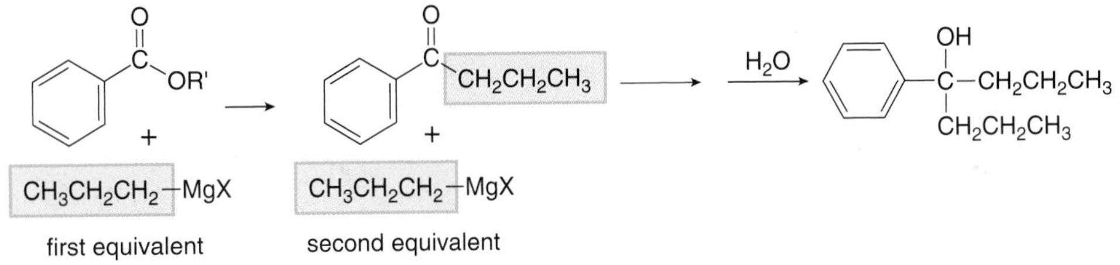
O
C
OR'
+
CH3CH2CH2–MgX
first equivalent
O
C
CH2CH2CH3
+
CH3CH2CH2–MgX
second equivalent
H2O
OH
C–CH2CH2CH3
CH2CH2CH3

Problem 20.28 What ester and Grignard reagent are needed to prepare each alcohol?

a. 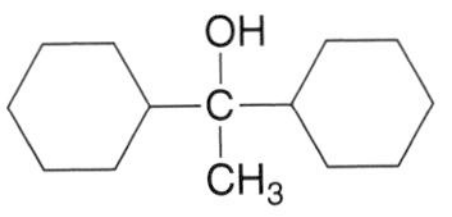
OH
C
CH3

b. $(CH_3CH_2CH_2)_3COH$

c. 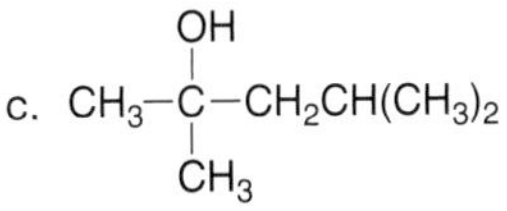
OH
CH3–C–CH2CH(CH3)2
CH3

20.13B Reaction of R_2CuLi with Acid Chlorides

To form a ketone from a carboxylic acid derivative, a less reactive organometallic reagent—namely an **organocuprate**—is needed. **Acid chlorides, which have the best leaving group (Cl^-) of the carboxylic acid derivatives, react with R'_2CuLi, to give a ketone as product.** Esters, which contain a poorer leaving group (^-OR), do not react with R'_2CuLi.

General reaction

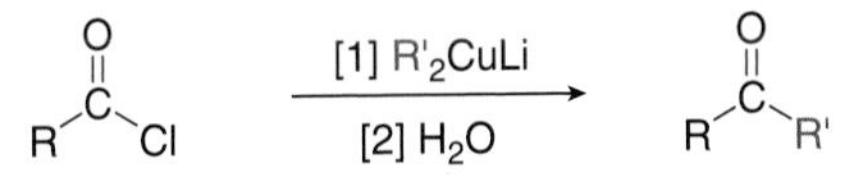
O
C
R Cl
[1] R'2CuLi
[2] H2O
O
C
R R'

Example

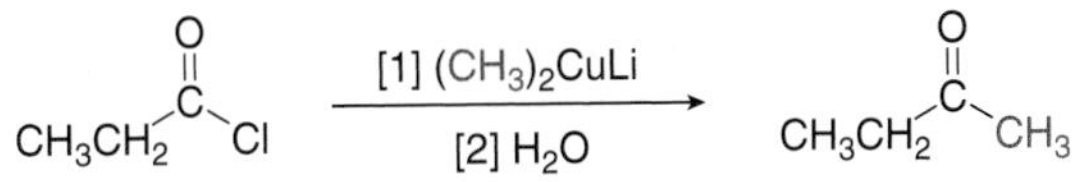
O
C
CH3CH2 Cl
[1] (CH3)2CuLi
[2] H2O
O
C
CH3CH2 CH3

This reaction results in nucleophilic substitution of an alkyl group R' for the leaving group Cl, forming one new carbon–carbon bond.

Problem 20.29 What organocuprate reagent is needed to convert CH_3CH_2COCl to each ketone?

a. 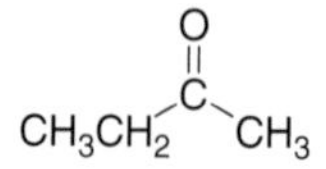

b. 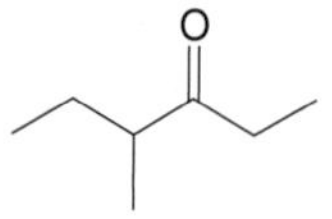

c. 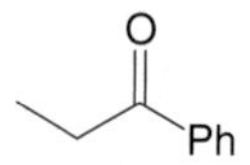

Problem 20.30 What reagent is needed to convert $(CH_3)_2CHCH_2COCl$ into each compound?

a. $(CH_3)_2CHCH_2CHO$

b. 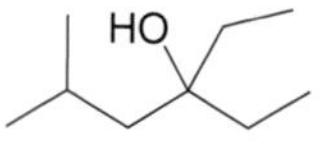

c. 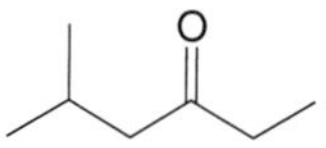

d. $(CH_3)_2CHCH_2CH_2OH$

A ketone with two different R groups bonded to the carbonyl carbon can be made by two different methods, as illustrated in Sample Problem 20.4.

Sample Problem 20.4 Show two different ways to prepare 2-pentanone from an acid chloride and an organocuprate reagent.

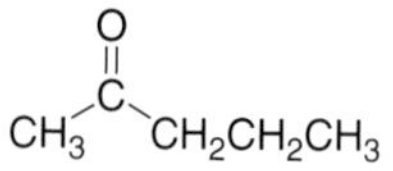

2-pentanone

Solution

In each case, one alkyl group comes from the organocuprate and one comes from the acid chloride.

Possibility [1] Use $(CH_3)_2CuLi$ and a four-carbon acid chloride.

Form this new C–C bond.

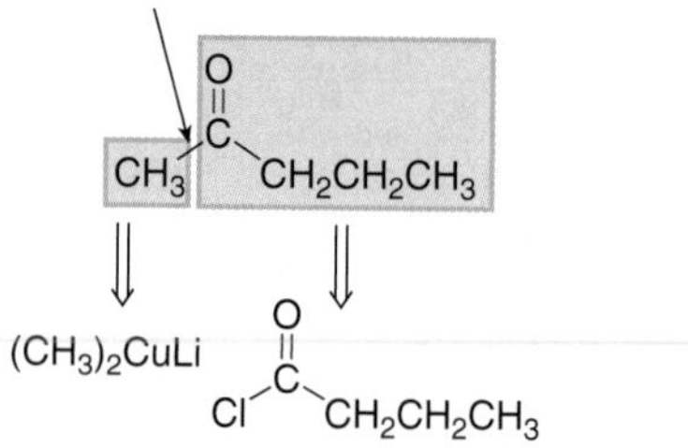

Possibility [2] Use $(CH_3CH_2CH_2)_2CuLi$ and a two-carbon acid chloride.

Form this new C–C bond.

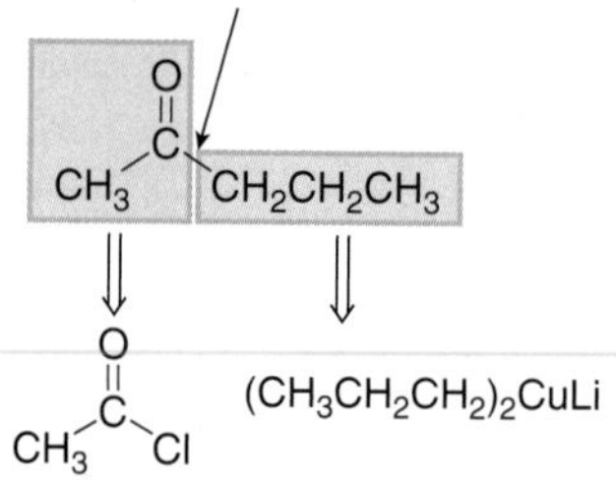

Problem 20.31 Draw two different ways to prepare each ketone from an acid chloride and an organocuprate reagent: (a) $C_6H_5COCH_3$; (b) $(CH_3)_2CHCOC(CH_3)_3$.

20.14 Reaction of Organometallic Reagents with Other Compounds

Because organometallic reagents are strong nucleophiles, they react with many other electrophiles in addition to carbonyl groups. Because these reactions always lead to the formation of new carbon–carbon bonds, they are also valuable in organic synthesis. In Section 20.14, we examine the reactions of organometallic reagents with **carbon dioxide** and **epoxides.**

20.14A Reaction of Grignard Reagents with Carbon Dioxide

Grignard reagents react with CO_2 to give carboxylic acids after protonation with aqueous acid. This reaction, called **carboxylation,** forms a carboxylic acid with one more carbon atom than the Grignard reagent from which it is prepared.

General reaction

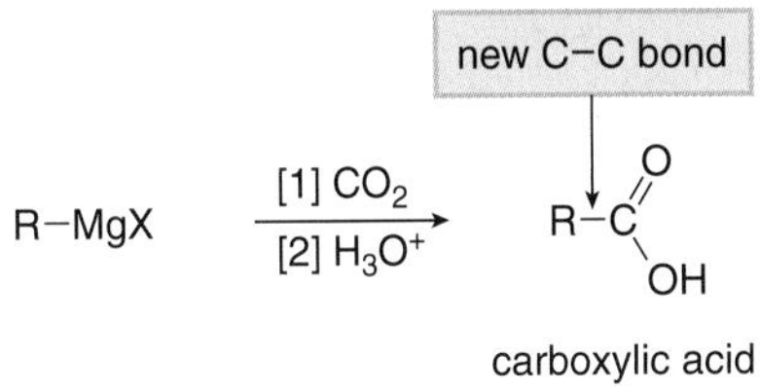

Because Grignard reagents are made from alkyl or aryl halides, an organic halide can be converted to a carboxylic acid having one more carbon atom by a two-step reaction sequence: **formation of a Grignard reagent,** followed by **reaction with CO_2.**

Example

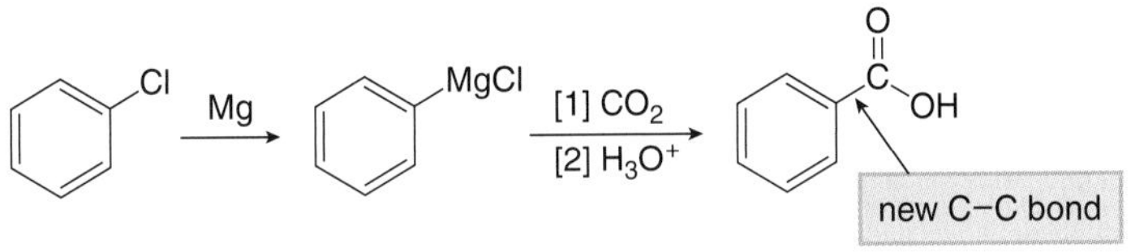

The mechanism resembles earlier reactions of nucleophilic Grignard reagents with carbonyl groups, as shown in Mechanism 20.8.

Mechanism 20.8 Carboxylation—Reaction of RMgX with CO_2

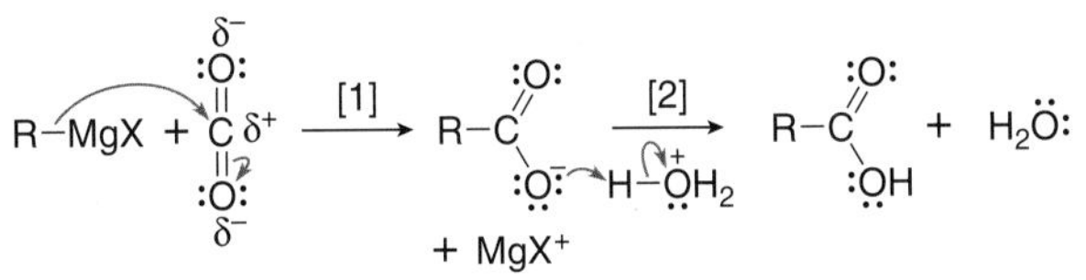

- In Step [1], the nucleophilic Grignard reagent attacks the electrophilic carbon atom of CO_2, cleaving a π bond and forming a new carbon–carbon bond.
- The carboxylate anion is protonated with aqueous acid in Step [2] to form the carboxylic acid.

Problem 20.32 What carboxylic acid is formed from each alkyl halide on treatment with [1] Mg; [2] CO_2; [3] H_3O^+?

a. 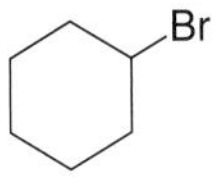

b. 

c. 

20.14B Reaction of Organometallic Reagents with Epoxides

Like other strong nucleophiles, **organometallic reagents**—RLi, RMgX, and R_2CuLi—**open epoxide rings to form alcohols.**

General reaction

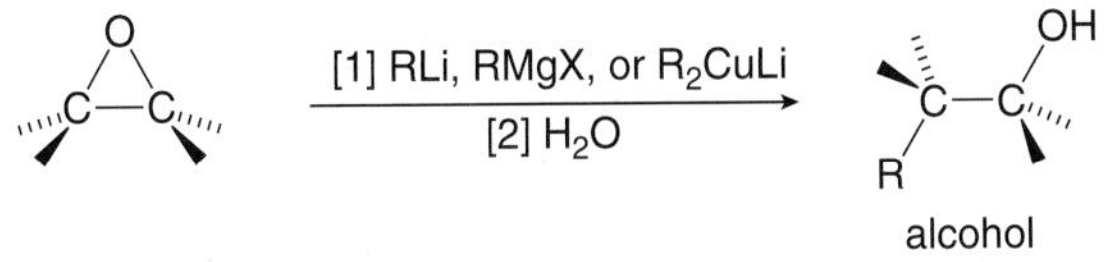

Example

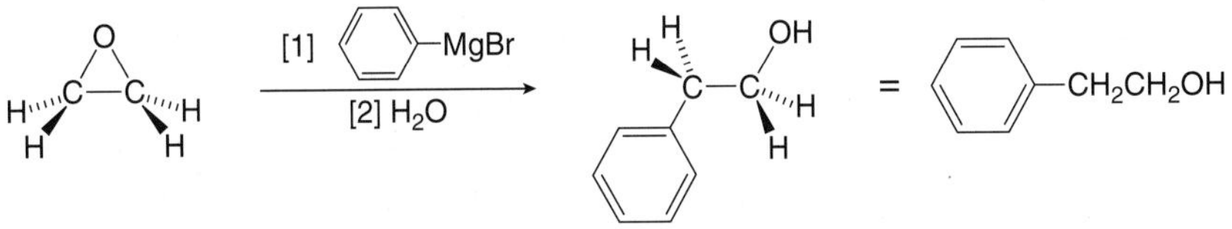

The opening of epoxide rings with negatively charged nucleophiles was discussed in Section 9.15A.

The reaction follows the same two-step process as the opening of epoxide rings with other negatively charged nucleophiles—that is, **nucleophilic attack from the back side of the epoxide ring, followed by protonation of the resulting alkoxide.** In unsymmetrical epoxides, nucleophilic attack occurs at the less substituted carbon atom.

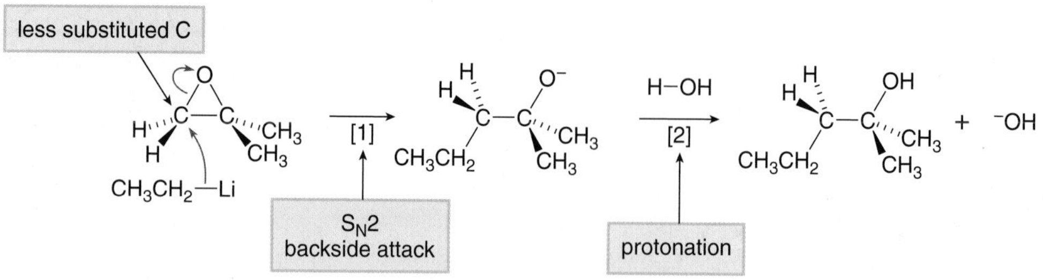

less substituted C
[1]
S_N2 backside attack
H–OH
[2]
protonation
+ ⁻OH

Problem 20.33 What epoxide is needed to convert CH_3CH_2MgBr to each of the following alcohols, after quenching with water?

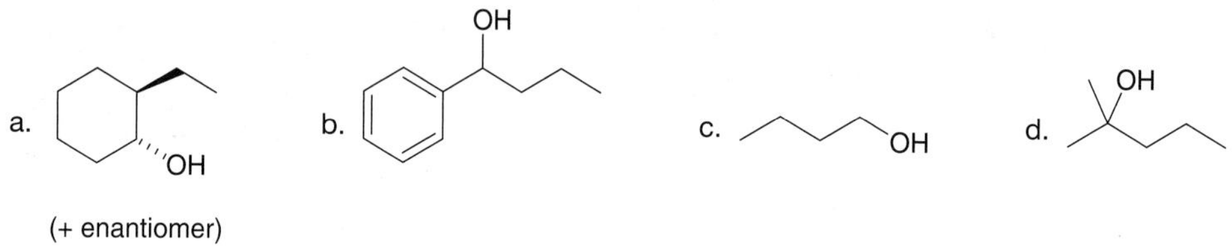

a.
(+ enantiomer)
b.
c.
d.

20.15 α,β-Unsaturated Carbonyl Compounds

α,β-Unsaturated carbonyl compounds are conjugated molecules containing a carbonyl group and a carbon–carbon double bond, separated by a single σ bond.

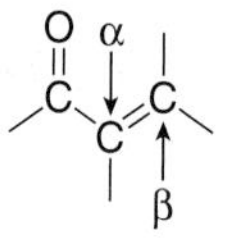

α,β-unsaturated carbonyl compound

Both functional groups of α,β-unsaturated carbonyl compounds have π bonds, but individually, they react with very different kinds of reagents. Carbon–carbon double bonds react with electrophiles (Chapter 10) and carbonyl groups react with nucleophiles (Section 20.2). What happens, then, when these two functional groups having opposite reactivity are in close proximity?

Because the two π bonds are conjugated, the electron density in an α,β-unsaturated carbonyl compound is delocalized over four atoms. Three resonance structures show that the carbonyl carbon and the β carbon bear a partial positive charge. This means that **α,β-unsaturated carbonyl compounds can react with nucleophiles at two different sites.**

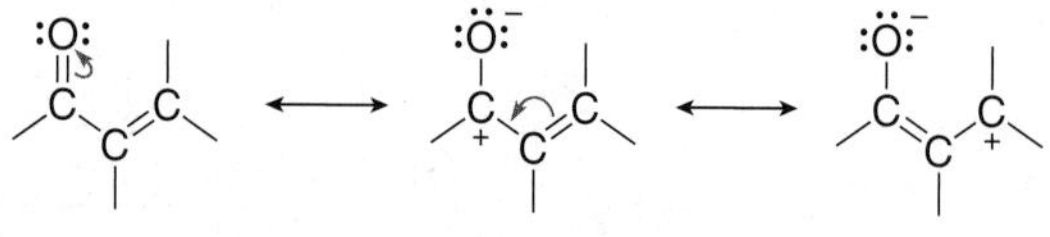

three resonance structures for an α,β-unsaturated carbonyl compound

The hybrid

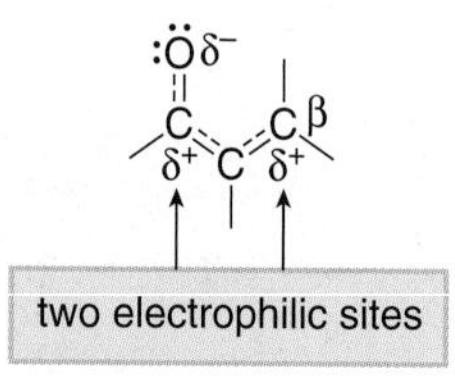

two electrophilic sites

- **Addition of a nucleophile to the carbonyl carbon, called 1,2-addition, adds the elements of H and Nu across the C = O, forming an allylic alcohol.**

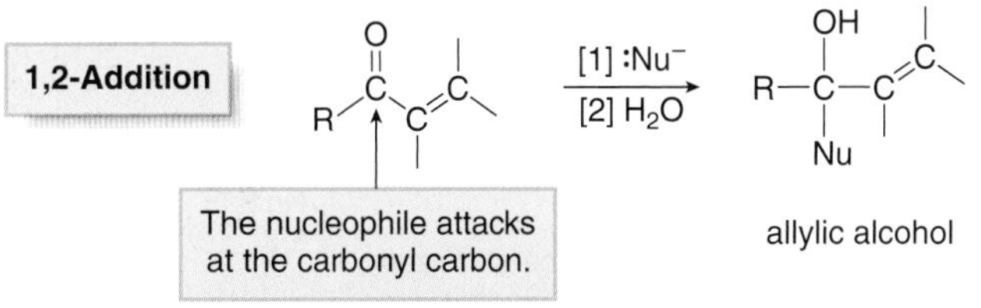

- **Addition of a nucleophile to the β carbon, called 1,4-addition or conjugate addition, forms a carbonyl compound.**

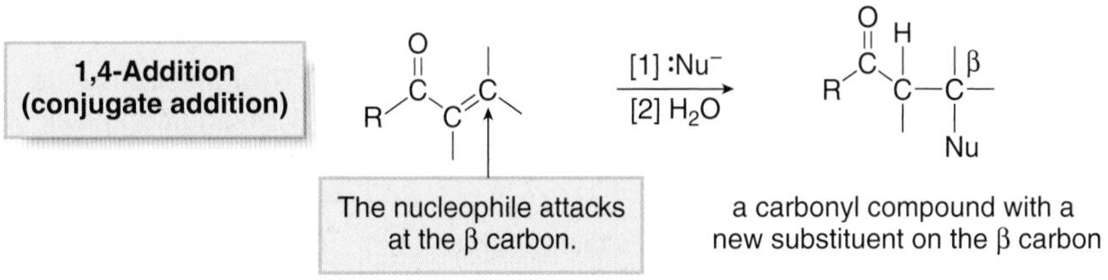

Both 1,2- and 1,4-addition result in nucleophilic addition of the elements of H and Nu.

20.15A The Mechanisms for 1,2-Addition and 1,4-Addition

The steps for the mechanism of 1,2-addition are exactly the same as those for the nucleophilic addition to an aldehyde or ketone—that is, **nucleophilic attack,** followed by **protonation** (Section 20.2A), as shown in Mechanism 20.9.

Mechanism 20.9 1,2-Addition to an α,β-Unsaturated Carbonyl Compound

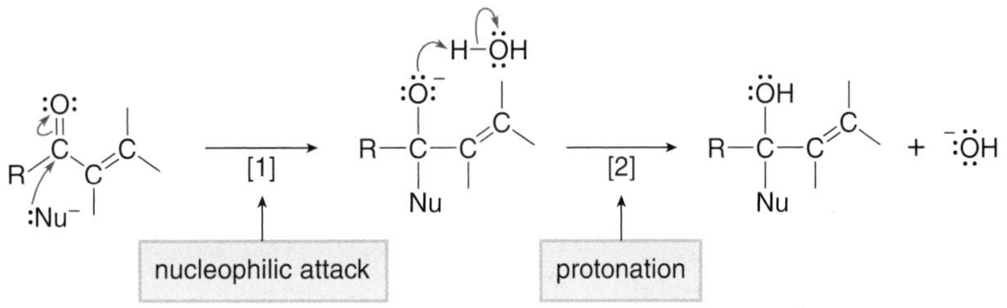

The mechanism for 1,4-addition also begins with nucleophilic attack, and then protonation and tautomerization add the elements of H and Nu to the α and β carbons of the carbonyl compound, as shown in Mechanism 20.10.

Mechanism 20.10 1,4-Addition to an α,β-Unsaturated Carbonyl Compound

Part [1] Nucleophilic attack at the β carbon

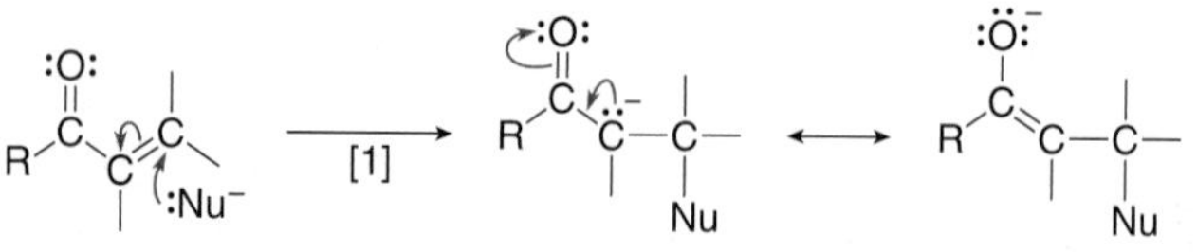

a resonance-stabilized enolate anion

- In Part [1], nucleophilic attack at the β carbon forms a resonance-stabilized anion called an **enolate.** Either resonance structure can be used to continue the mechanism in Part [2].

Part [2] Protonation and tautomerization

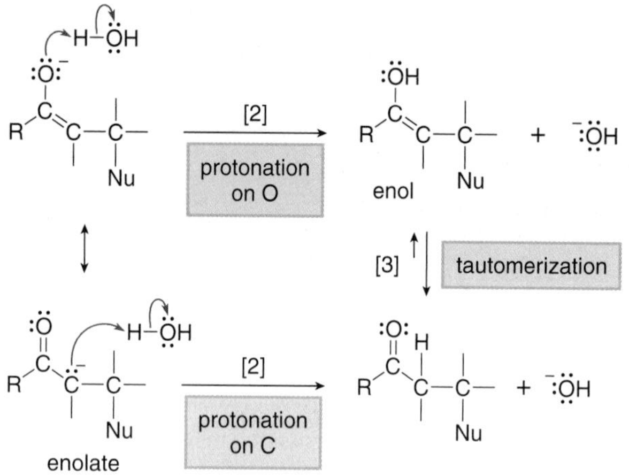

- Protonation on the carbon end of the enolate forms the 1,4-addition product directly.
- Protonation of the oxygen end of the enolate forms an **enol.** Recall from Section 11.9 that enols are unstable and tautomerize (by a two-step process) to carbonyl compounds. Tautomerization forms the same 1,4-addition product that results from protonation on carbon.

20.15B Reaction of α,β-Unsaturated Carbonyl Compounds with Organometallic Reagents

The identity of the metal in an organometallic reagent determines whether it reacts with an α,β-unsaturated aldehyde or ketone by 1,2-addition or 1,4-addition.

Why is conjugate addition also called 1,4-addition? If the atoms of the enol are numbered beginning with the O atom, then the elements of H and Nu are bonded to atoms "1" and "4," respectively.

The enol has H and Nu added to atoms 1 and 4.

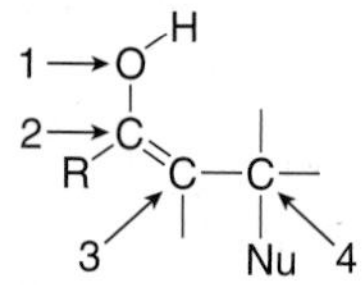

- **Organolithium and Grignard reagents form 1,2-addition products.**

1,2-Addition—General reaction

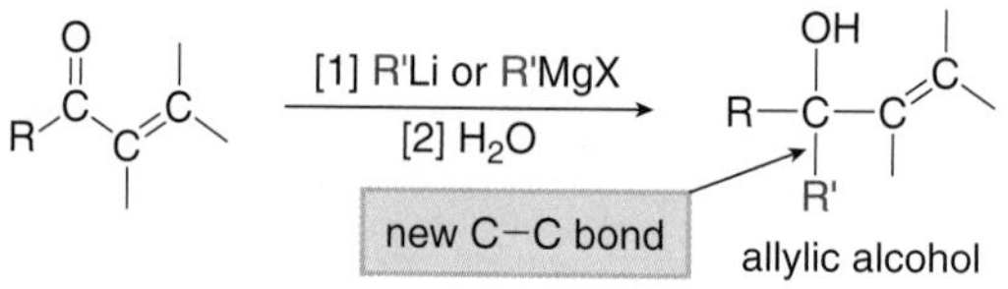

Example

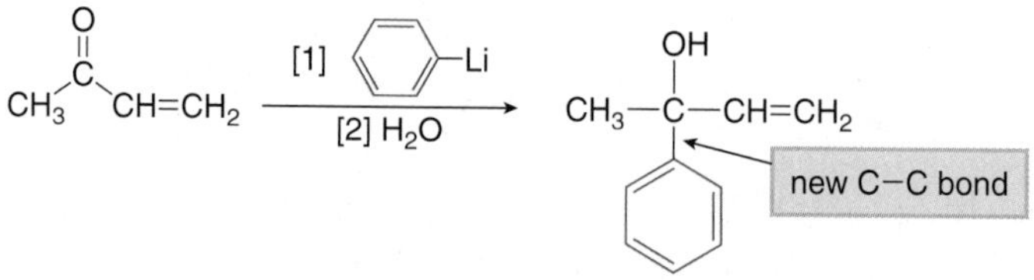

- **Organocuprate reagents form 1,4-addition products.**

1,4-Addition—General reaction

Example

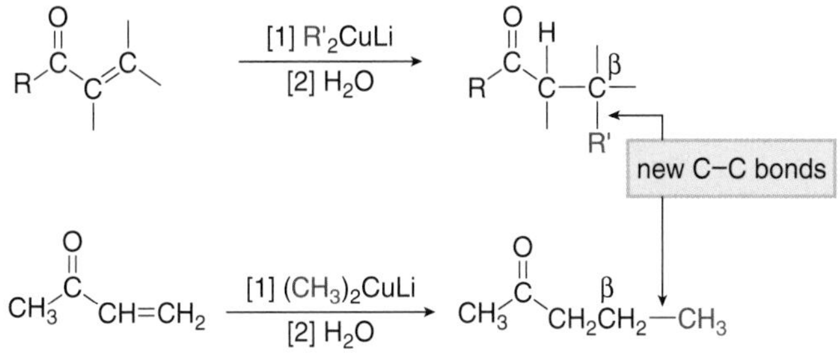
[1] R'$_2$CuLi
[2] H$_2$O
new C–C bonds
[1] (CH$_3$)$_2$CuLi
[2] H$_2$O

Sample Problem 20.5 Draw the products of each reaction.

a. 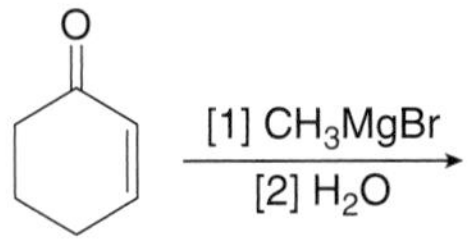
[1] CH$_3$MgBr
[2] H$_2$O

b. 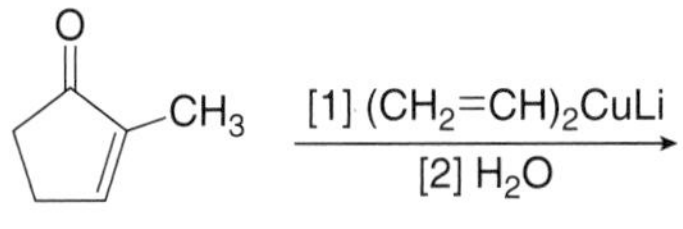
[1] (CH$_2$=CH)$_2$CuLi
[2] H$_2$O

Solution

The characteristic reaction of α,β-unsaturated carbonyl compounds is nucleophilic addition. The reagent determines the mode of addition (1,2- or 1,4-).

a. **Grignard reagents undergo 1,2-addition.** CH_3MgBr adds a new CH_3 group at the carbonyl carbon.

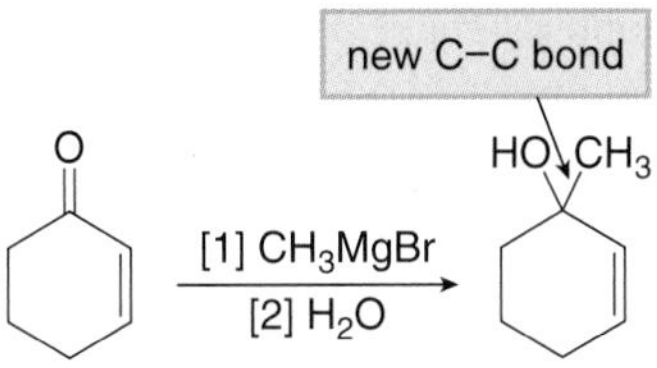
new C–C bond
[1] CH$_3$MgBr
[2] H$_2$O

b. **Organocuprate reagents undergo 1,4-addition.** The cuprate reagent adds a new vinyl group ($CH_2{=}CH$) at the β carbon.

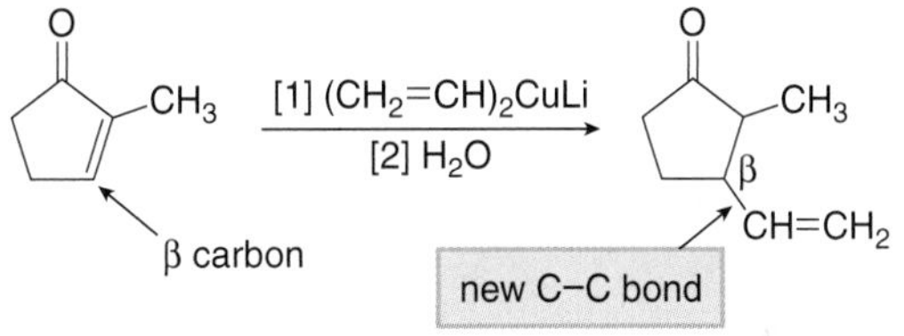
β carbon
[1] (CH$_2$=CH)$_2$CuLi
[2] H$_2$O
new C–C bond

Problem 20.34 Draw the product when each compound is treated with either $(CH_3)_2CuLi$, followed by H_2O, or $HC{\equiv}CLi$, followed by H_2O.

a. 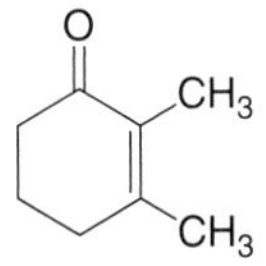

b. 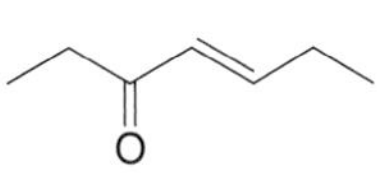

c. 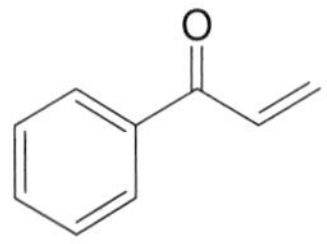

20.16 Summary—The Reactions of Organometallic Reagents

We have now seen many different reactions of organometallic reagents with a variety of functional groups, and you may have some difficulty keeping them all straight. Rather than memorizing them all, keep in mind the following three concepts:

[1] **Organometallic reagents (R – M) attack electrophilic carbon atoms, especially the carbonyl carbon.**

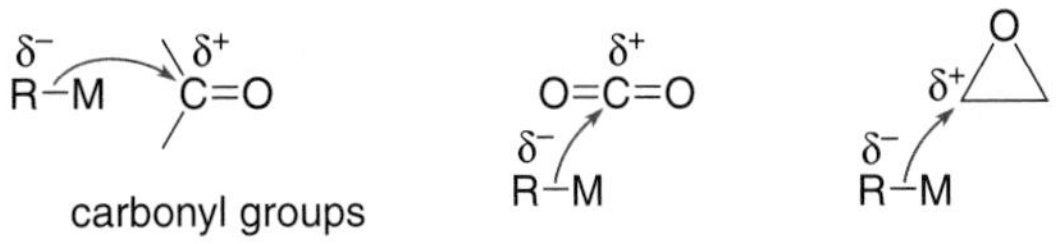

carbonyl groups　　carbon dioxide　　epoxides

[2] After an organometallic reagent adds to a carbonyl group, the fate of the intermediate depends on the presence or absence of a leaving group.

- Without a leaving group, the characteristic reaction is *nucleophilic addition.*
- With a leaving group, it is *nucleophilic substitution.*

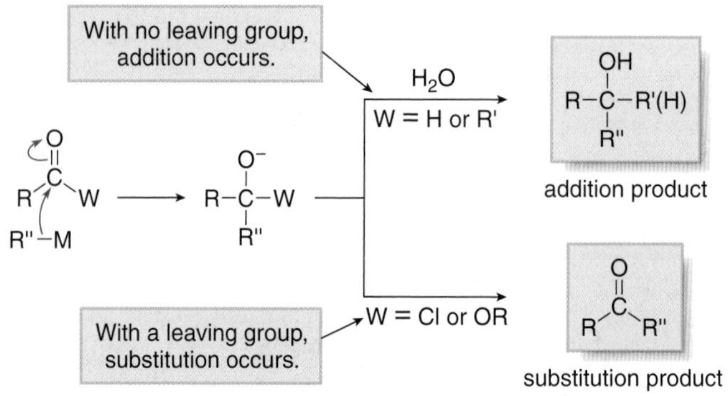

[3] The polarity of the R – M bond determines the reactivity of the reagents.

- RLi and RMgX are very reactive reagents.
- R_2CuLi is much less reactive.

20.17 Synthesis

The reactions learned in Chapter 20 have proven extremely useful in organic synthesis. Oxidation and reduction reactions interconvert two functional groups that differ in oxidation state. Organometallic reagents form new carbon–carbon bonds.

Synthesis is perhaps the most difficult aspect of organic chemistry. It requires you to remember both the new reactions you've just learned, and the ones you've encountered in previous chapters. In a successful synthesis, you must also put these reactions in a logical order. Don't be discouraged. Learn the basic reactions and then practice them over and over again with synthesis problems.

In Sample Problems 20.6–20.8 that follow, keep in mind that the products formed by the reactions of Chapter 20 can themselves be transformed into many other functional groups. For example, 2-hexanol, the product of Grignard addition of butylmagnesium chloride to acetaldehyde, can be transformed into a variety of other compounds, as shown in Figure 20.8.

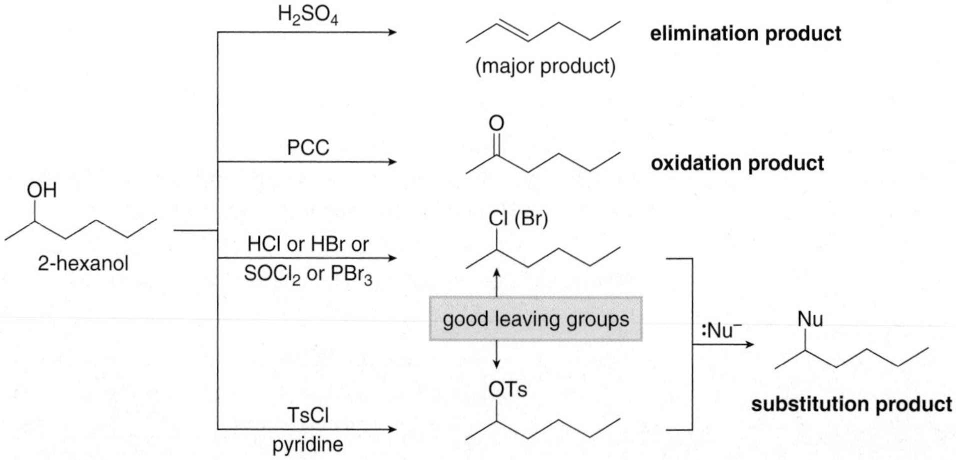

Figure 20.8
Conversion of 2-hexanol into other compounds

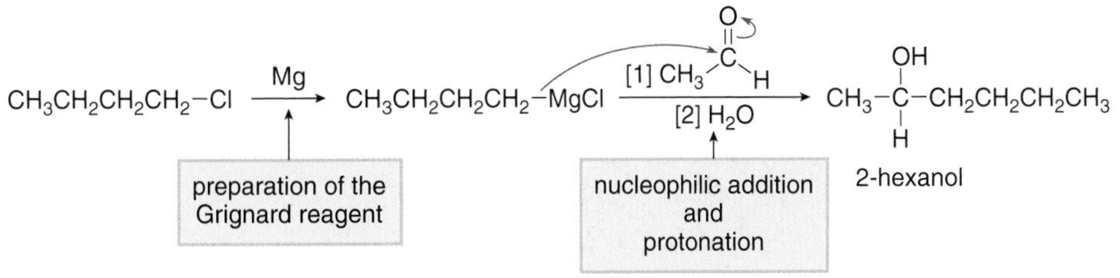

preparation of the Grignard reagent
nucleophilic addition and protonation
2-hexanol

Before proceeding with Sample Problems 20.6–20.8, you should review the stepwise strategy for designing a synthesis found in Section 11.12.

Sample Problem 20.6 Synthesize 1-methylcyclohexene from cyclohexanone and any organic alcohol.

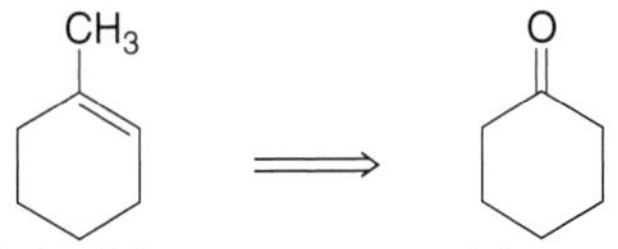

1-methylcyclohexene cyclohexanone

Retrosynthetic Analysis

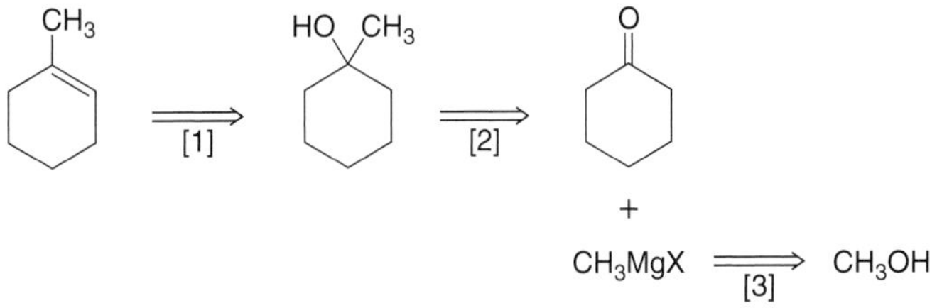

Thinking backwards:

- [1] Form the double bond by dehydration of an alcohol.
- [2] Make the 3° alcohol by Grignard addition of CH_3MgX.
- [3] Prepare the Grignard reagent stepwise from an alcohol.

Synthesis

Four steps are needed:

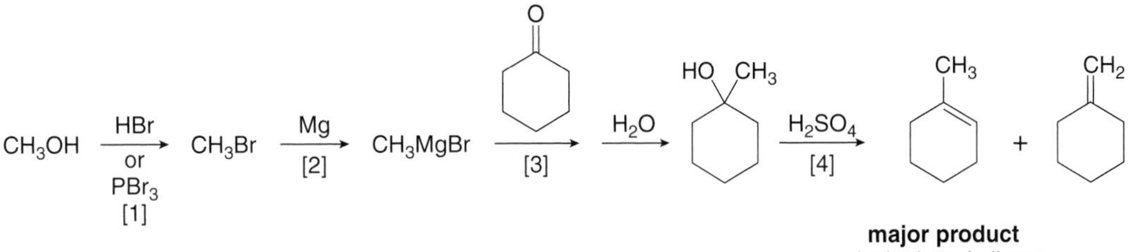

major product
trisubstituted alkene

- Conversion of CH_3OH to the Grignard reagent CH_3MgBr requires two steps: formation of an alkyl halide (Step [1]), followed by reaction with Mg (Step [2]).
- Addition of CH_3MgBr to cyclohexanone followed by protonation forms an alcohol in Step [3].
- Acid-catalyzed elimination of water in Step [4] forms a mixture of alkenes, with the desired trisubstituted alkene as the major product.

Sample Problem 20.7 Synthesize 2,4-dimethyl-3-hexanone from four-carbon alcohols.

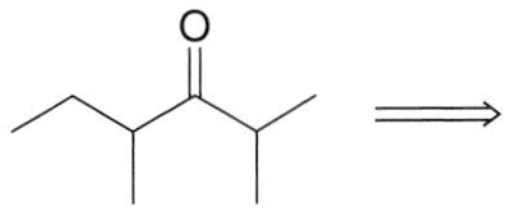

alcohols containing 4 C's

2,4-dimethyl-3-hexanone

Retrosynthetic Analysis

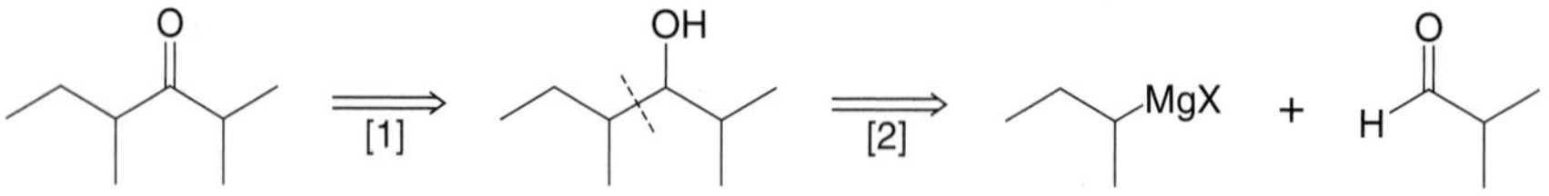

Synthesize each of these components.

Thinking backwards:

- [1] Form the ketone by oxidation of a 2° alcohol.
- [2] Make the 2° alcohol by Grignard addition to an aldehyde. Both of these compounds have 4 C's, and each must be synthesized from an alcohol.

Synthesis

First, make both components needed for the Grignard reaction.

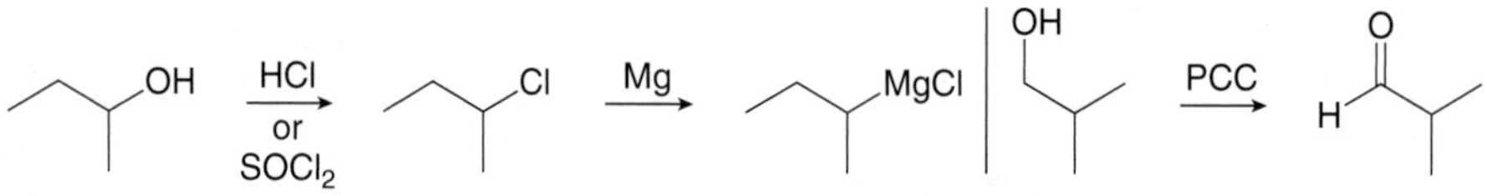

Then, complete the synthesis with Grignard addition, followed by oxidation of the alcohol to the ketone.

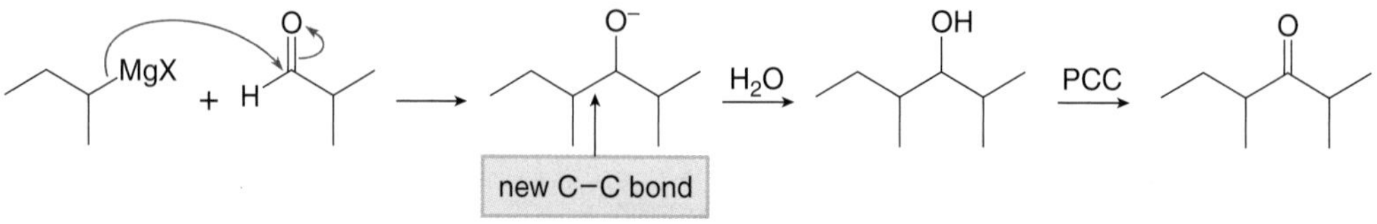

Sample Problem 20.8 Synthesize isopropylcyclopentane from alcohols having ≤ 5 C's.

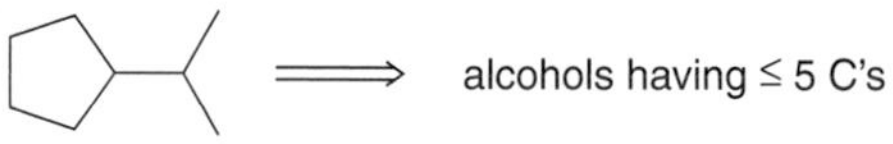

isopropylcyclopentane

Retrosynthetic Analysis

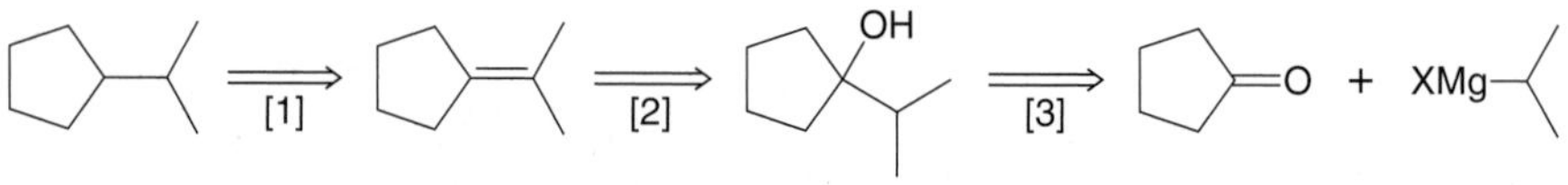

Thinking backwards:

- [1] Form the alkane by hydrogenation of an alkene.
- [2] Introduce the double bond by dehydration of an alcohol.
- [3] Form the 3° alcohol by Grignard addition to a ketone. Both components of the Grignard reaction must then be synthesized.

Synthesis

First make both components needed for the Grignard reaction.

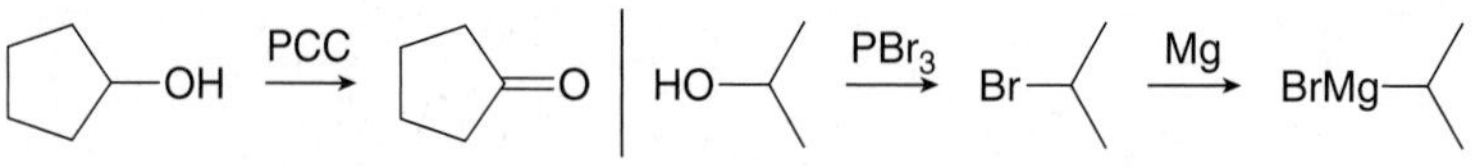

Complete the synthesis with Grignard addition, dehydration, and hydrogenation.

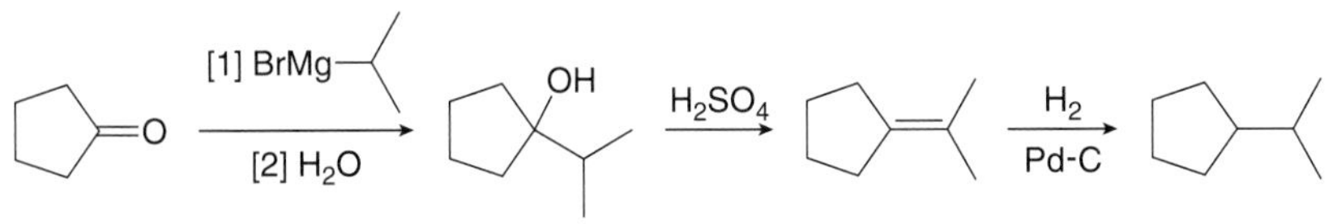

major product
tetrasubstituted
double bond

Problem 20.35 Synthesize each compound from cyclohexanol, ethanol, and any other needed reagents.

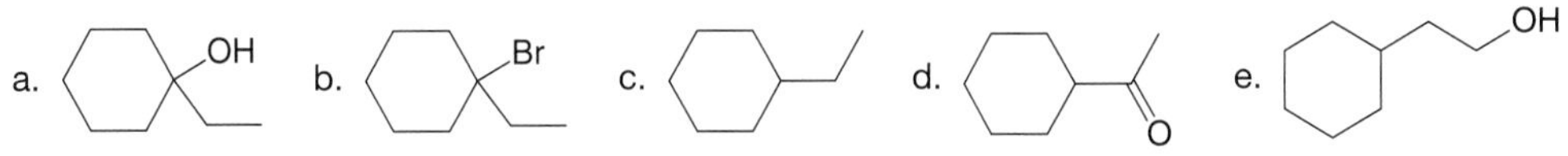

KEY CONCEPTS

Introduction to Carbonyl Chemistry; Organometallic Reagents; Oxidation and Reduction

Reduction Reactions

[1] Reduction of aldehydes and ketones to 1° and 2° alcohols (20.4)

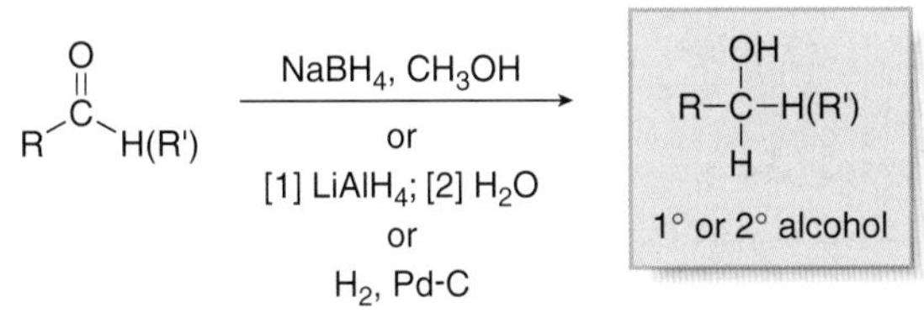

---

[2] Reduction of α,β-unsaturated aldehydes and ketones (20.4C)

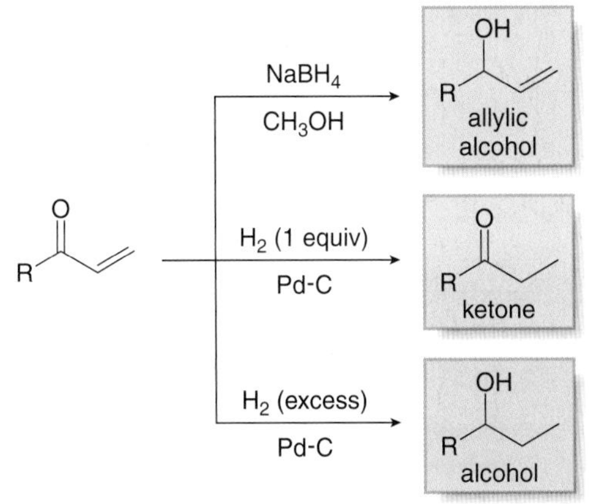

- reduction of the C=O only
- reduction of the C=C only
- reduction of both π bonds

---

[3] Enantioselective ketone reduction (20.6)

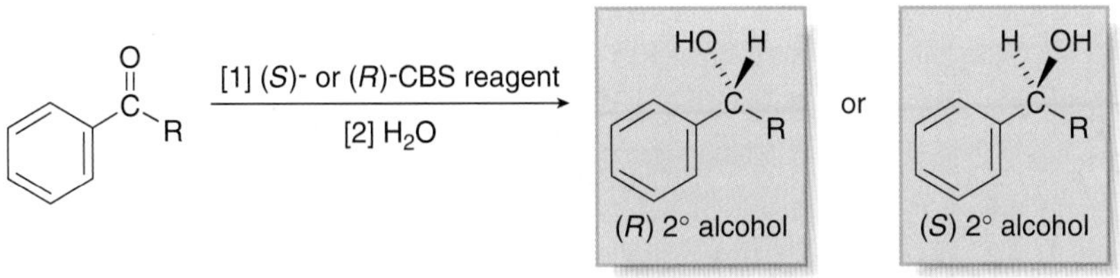

- A single enantiomer is formed.

[4] Reduction of acid chlorides (20.7A)

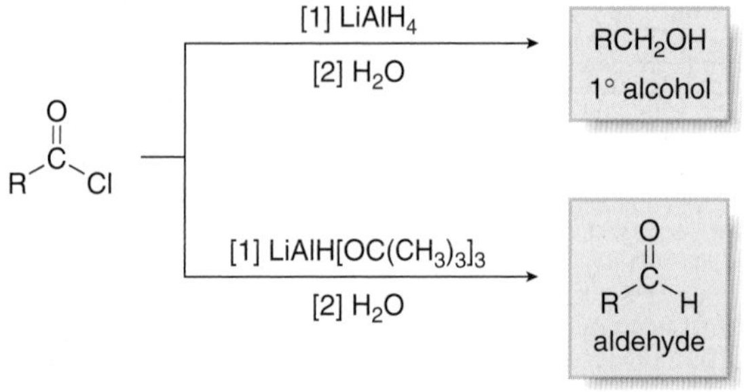

- $LiAlH_4$, a strong reducing agent, reduces an acid chloride to an alcohol.
- With $LiAlH[OC(CH_3)_3]_3$, a milder reducing agent, reduction stops at the aldehyde stage.

[5] Reduction of esters (20.7A)

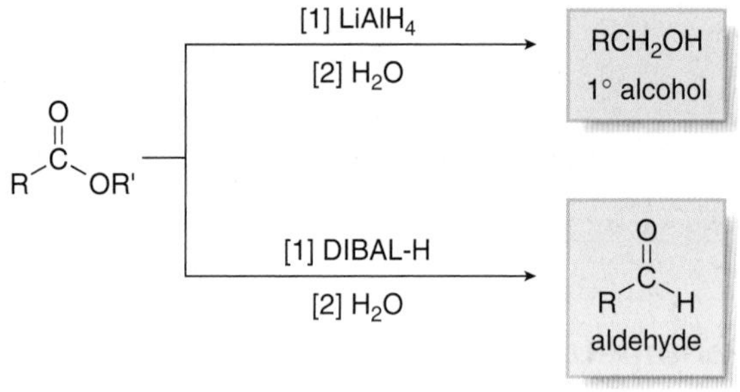

- $LiAlH_4$, a strong reducing agent, reduces an ester to an alcohol.
- With DIBAL-H, a milder reducing agent, reduction stops at the aldehyde stage.

[6] Reduction of carboxylic acids to 1° alcohols (20.7B)

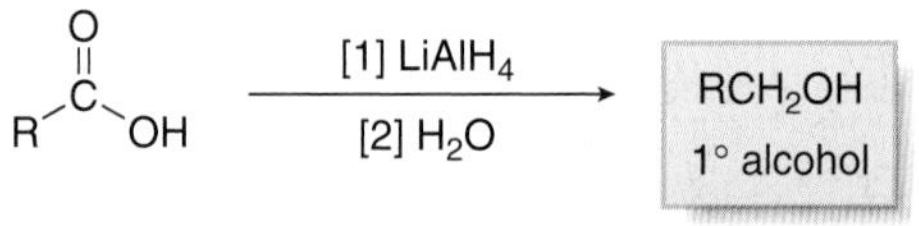

[7] Reduction of amides to amines (20.7B)

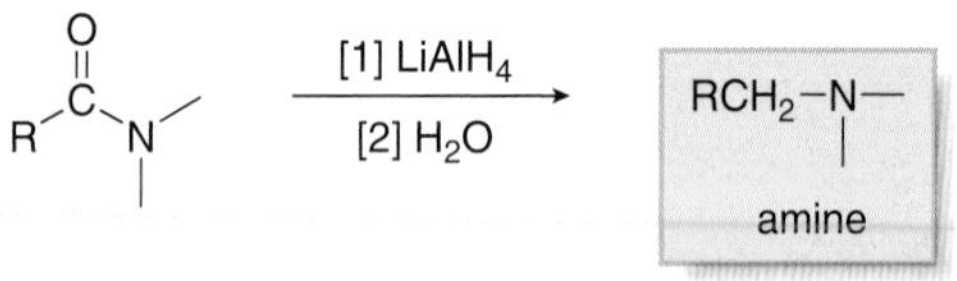

Oxidation Reactions

Oxidation of aldehydes to carboxylic acids (20.8)

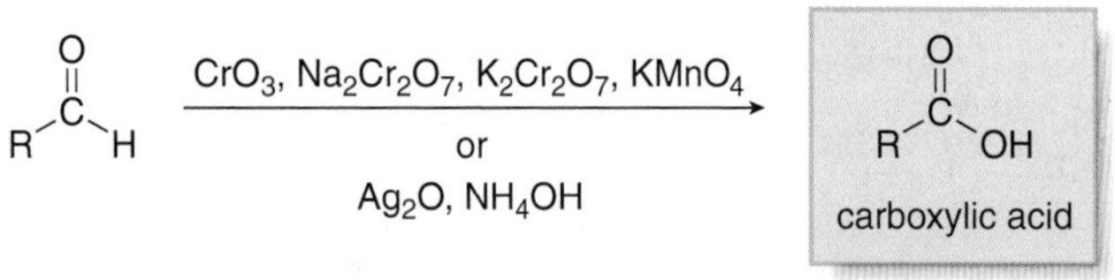

- All Cr^{6+} reagents except PCC oxidize RCHO to RCOOH.
- Tollens reagent (Ag_2O + NH_4OH) oxidizes RCHO only. Primary (1°) and 2° alcohols do not react with Tollens reagent.

Preparation of Organometallic Reagents (20.9)

[1] Organolithium reagents: $R{-}X + 2\,Li \longrightarrow R{-}Li + LiX$

[2] Grignard reagents: $R{-}X + Mg \xrightarrow[(CH_3CH_2)_2O]{} R{-}Mg{-}X$

[3] Organocuprate reagents:

$$R{-}X \;+\; 2\,Li \longrightarrow R{-}Li \;+\; LiX$$

$$2\,R{-}Li \;+\; CuI \longrightarrow \boxed{R_2Cu^-\ Li^+} \;+\; LiI$$

[4] Lithium and sodium acetylides:

$$R{-}C{\equiv}C{-}H \xrightarrow{Na^+\ {}^-NH_2} \boxed{R{-}C{\equiv}C^-\ Na^+} \;+\; NH_3$$

a sodium acetylide

$$R{-}C{\equiv}C{-}H \xrightarrow{R'{-}Li} \boxed{R{-}C{\equiv}C{-}Li} \;+\; R'{-}H$$

a lithium acetylide

Reactions with Organometallic Reagents

[1] Reaction as a base (20.9C)

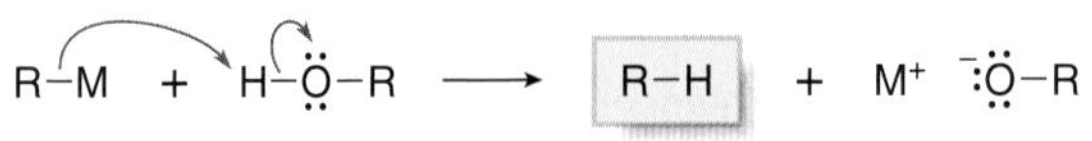

- RM = RLi, RMgX, R_2CuLi
- This acid–base reaction occurs with H_2O, ROH, RNH_2, R_2NH, RSH, RCOOH, $RCONH_2$, and RCONHR.

[2] Reaction with aldehydes and ketones to form 1°, 2°, and 3° alcohols (20.10)

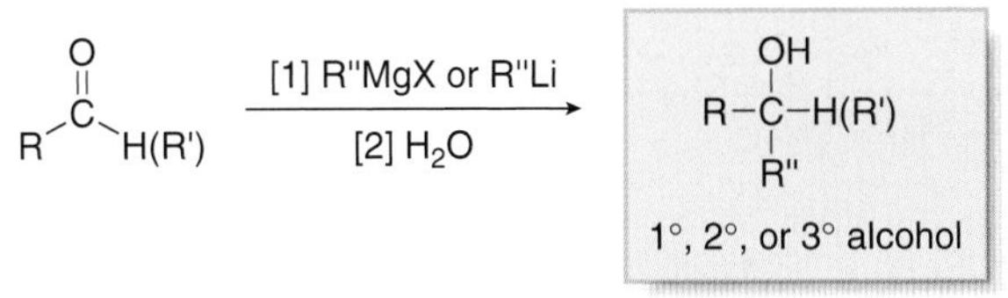

[3] Reaction with esters to form 3° alcohols (20.13A)

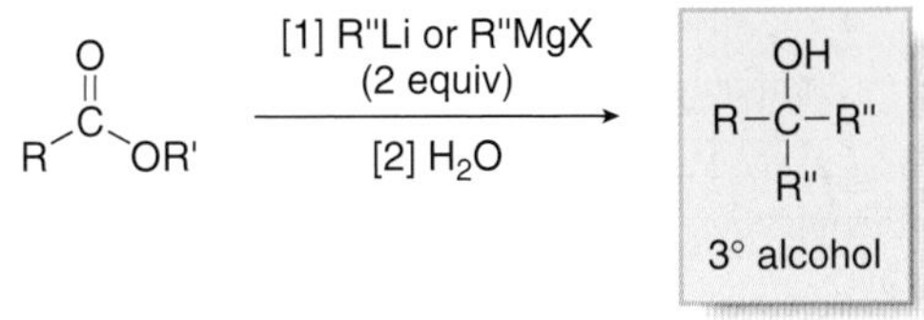

[4] Reaction with acid chlorides (20.13B)

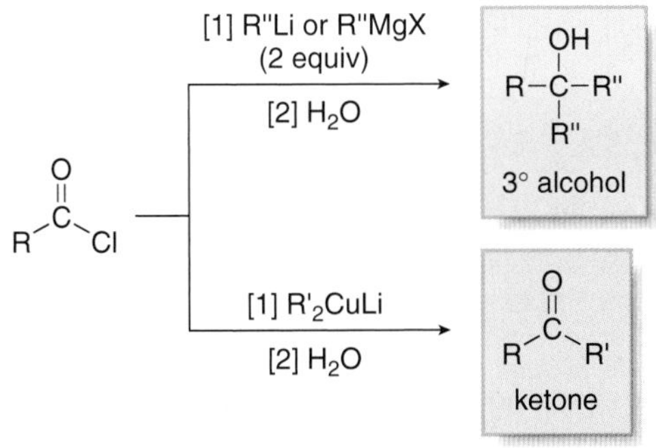

- More reactive organometallic reagents—R"Li and R"MgX—add two equivalents of R" to an acid chloride to form a 3° alcohol with two identical R" groups.
- Less reactive organometallic reagents—R'_2CuLi—add only one equivalent of R' to an acid chloride to form a ketone.

[5] Reaction with carbon dioxide—Carboxylation (20.14A)

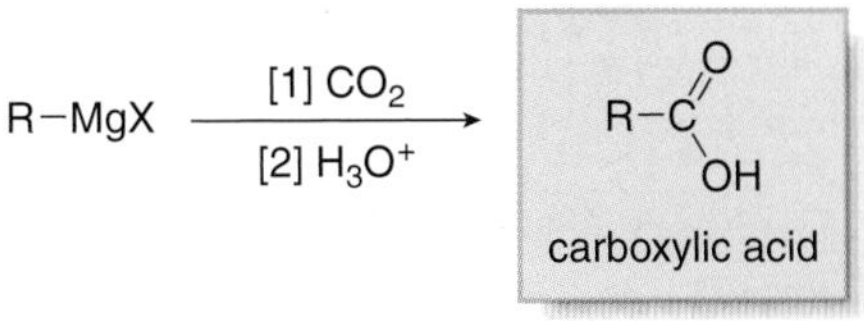

[6] Reaction with epoxides (20.14B)

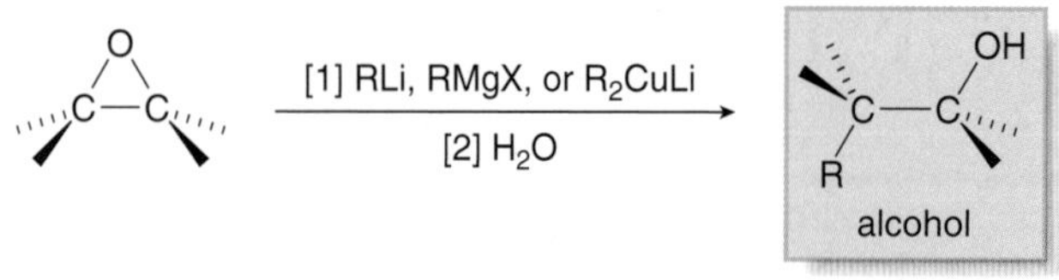

[7] Reaction with α,β-unsaturated aldehydes and ketones (20.15B)

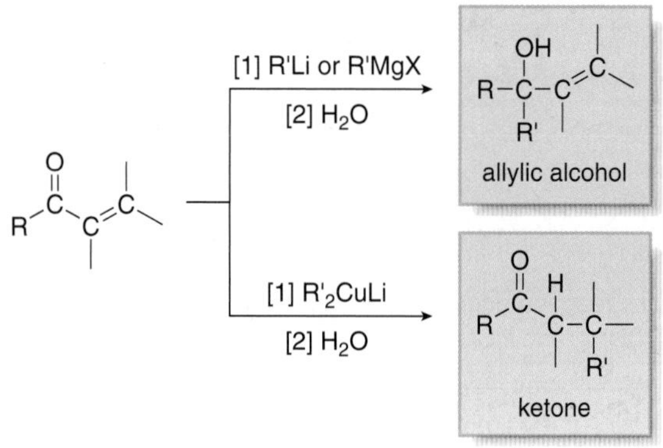

- More reactive organometallic reagents—R'Li and R'MgX—react with α,β-unsaturated carbonyls by 1,2-addition.
- Less reactive organometallic reagents—R'_2CuLi—react with α,β-unsaturated carbonyls by 1,4-addition.

Protecting Groups (20.12)

[1] Protecting an alcohol as a *tert*-butyldimethylsilyl ether

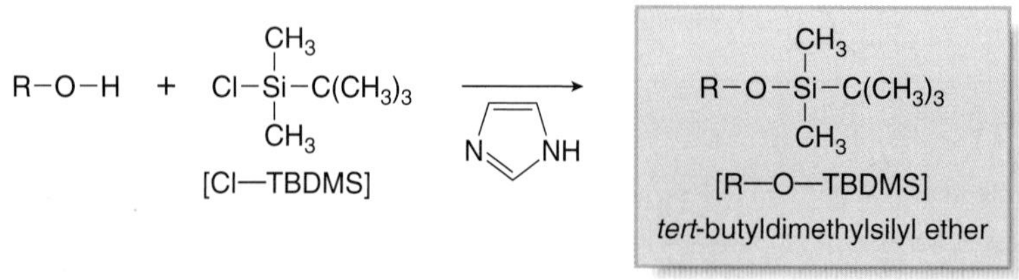

[2] Deprotecting a *tert*-butyldimethylsilyl ether to re-form an alcohol

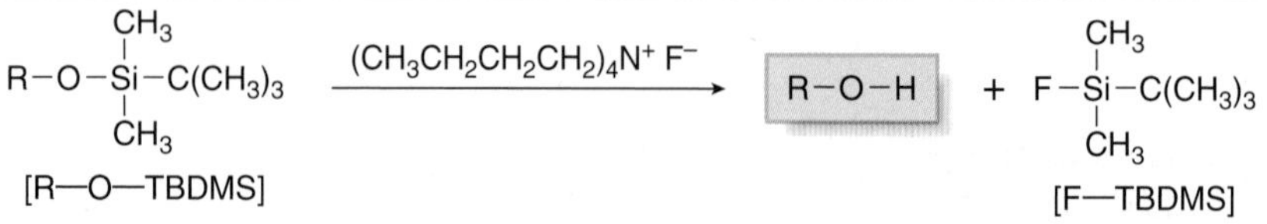

PROBLEMS

Problems Using Three-Dimensional Models

20.36 Draw the products formed when **A** or **B** is treated with each reagent. In some cases, no reaction occurs.

a. $NaBH_4$, CH_3OH
b. [1] $LiAlH_4$; [2] H_2O
c. [1] CH_3MgBr (excess); [2] H_2O
d. [1] C_6H_5Li (excess); [2] H_2O
e. $Na_2Cr_2O_7$, H_2SO_4, H_2O

20.37 Devise a synthesis of each alcohol from organic alcohols having one or two carbons and any required reagents.

a. 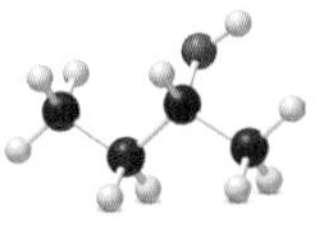 (+ enantiomer)

b. 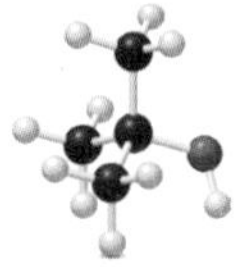

c. 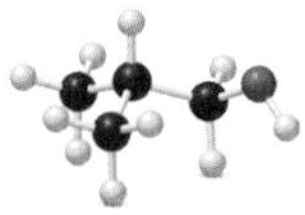

d. 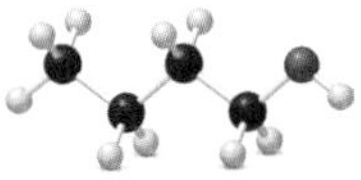

Reactions and Reagents

20.38 Draw the product formed when pentanal ($CH_3CH_2CH_2CH_2CHO$) is treated with each reagent. With some reagents, no reaction occurs.

a. $NaBH_4$, CH_3OH
b. [1] $LiAlH_4$; [2] H_2O
c. H_2, Pd-C
d. PCC
e. $Na_2Cr_2O_7$, H_2SO_4, H_2O
f. Ag_2O, NH_4OH
g. [1] CH_3MgBr; [2] H_2O
h. [1] C_6H_5Li; [2] H_2O
i. [1] $(CH_3)_2CuLi$; [2] H_2O
j. [1] $HC\equiv CNa$; [2] H_2O
k. [1] $CH_3C\equiv CLi$; [2] H_2O
l. The product in (a), then TBDMS–Cl, imidazole

20.39 Draw the product formed when 1-bromobutane is treated with each reagent.

a. Li (2 equiv)
b. Mg in $(CH_3CH_2)_2O$ solvent
c. Li (2 equiv), then CuI (0.5 equiv)
d. The answer in (a), then H_2O
e. The answer in (b), then D_2O
f. The answer in (a), then $CH_3C\equiv CH$

20.40 Draw the product formed when $CH_3CH_2CH_2MgBr$ is treated with each compound.

a. $CH_2{=}O$, then H_2O
b. 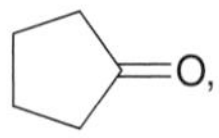, then H_2O
c. CH_3CH_2COCl, then H_2O
d. $CH_3CH_2COOCH_3$, then H_2O
e. CH_3COOH
f. $HC\equiv CH$
g. CO_2, then H_3O^+
h. 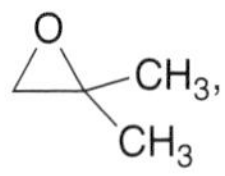, then H_2O
i. D_2O
j. 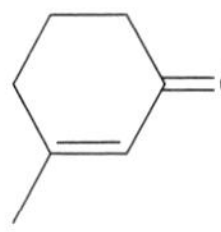, then H_2O

20.41 Draw the product formed when $(CH_3CH_2CH_2CH_2)_2CuLi$ is treated with each compound. In some cases, no reaction occurs.

a. 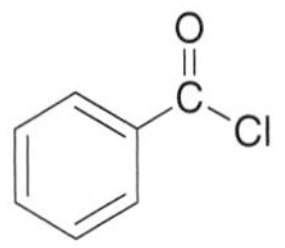
b. 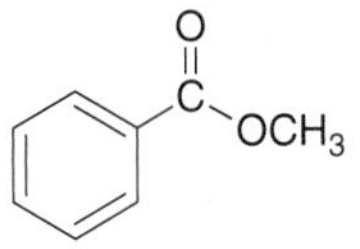
c. 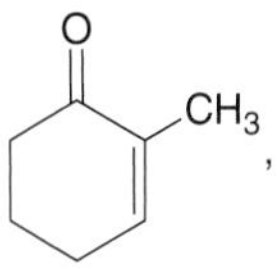, then H_2O
d. 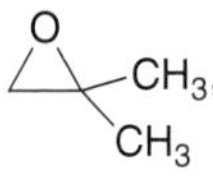, then H_2O

20.42 The stereochemistry of the products of reduction depends on the reagent used, as you learned in Sections 20.5 and 20.6. With this in mind, how would you convert 3,3-dimethyl-2-butanone [$CH_3COC(CH_3)_3$] to: (a) racemic 3,3-dimethyl-2-butanol [$CH_3CH(OH)C(CH_3)_3$]; (b) only (2*R*)-3,3-dimethyl-2-butanol; (c) only (2*S*)-3,3-dimethyl-2-butanol?

20.43 Draw the product formed when the α,β-unsaturated ketone **A** is treated with each reagent.

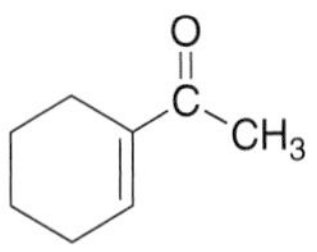

A

a. $NaBH_4$, CH_3OH
b. H_2 (1 equiv), Pd-C
c. H_2 (excess), Pd-C
d. [1] CH_3Li; [2] H_2O
e. [1] CH_3CH_2MgBr; [2] H_2O
f. [1] $(CH_2{=}CH)_2CuLi$; [2] H_2O

20.44 What reagent is needed to convert $(CH_3)_2CHCH_2CH_2COCl$ to each compound?

a. $(CH_3)_2CHCH_2CH_2CHO$
b. $(CH_3)_2CHCH_2CH_2COCH{=}CH_2$
c. $(CH_3)_2CHCH_2CH_2C(OH)(C_6H_5)_2$
d. $(CH_3)_2CHCH_2CH_2CH_2OH$

20.45 What reagent is needed to convert $CH_3CH_2COOCH_2CH_2CH_3$ to each compound?

a. $CH_3CH_2CH_2OH$
b. $CH_3CH_2C(OH)(CH_2CH_2CH_3)_2$
c. CH_3CH_2CHO

20.46 Draw the products of each reduction reaction.

a. 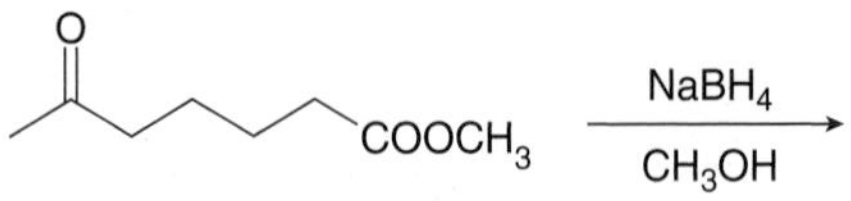

c. 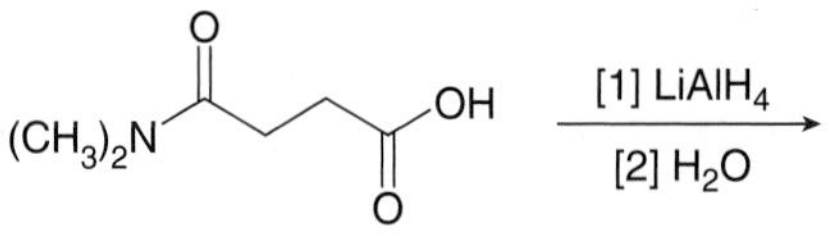

b. 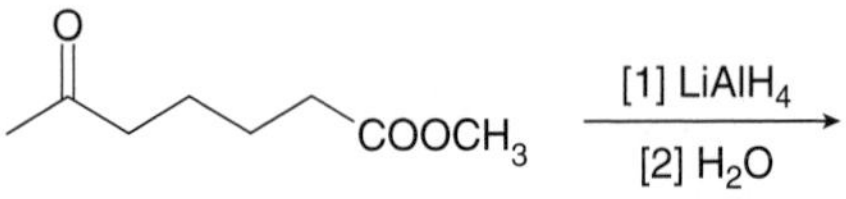

d. 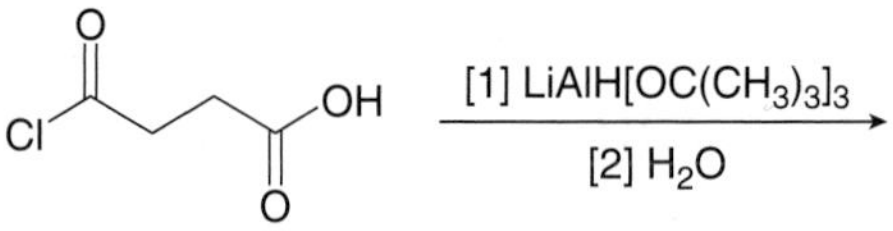

20.47 Draw the products of the following reactions with organometallic reagents.

a. 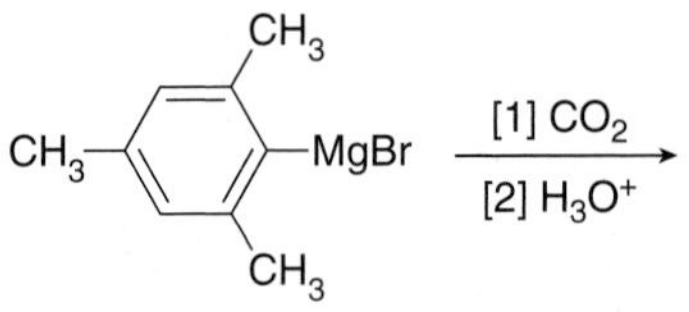

e. 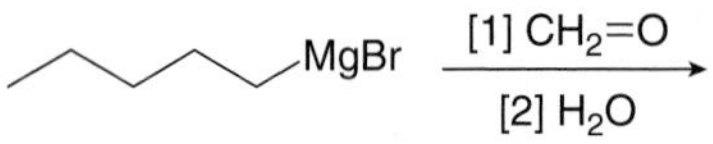

b. 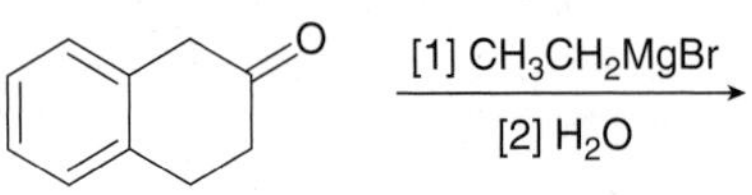

f. 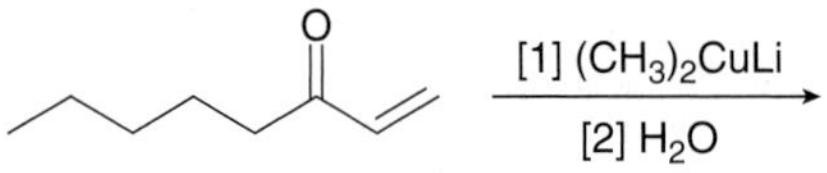

c. 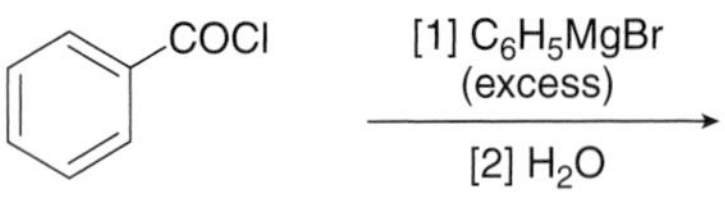

g. 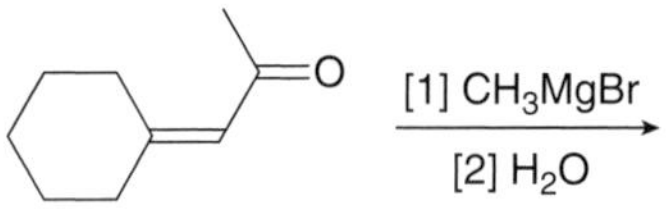

d. 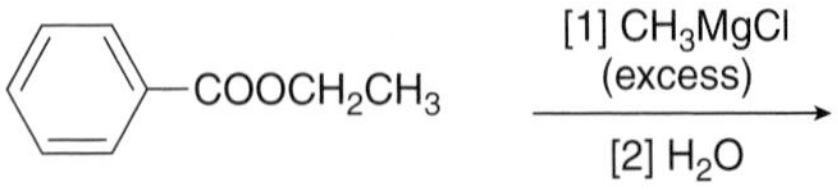

h. 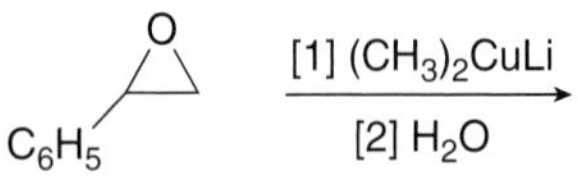

20.48 Draw all stereoisomers formed in each reaction.

a. 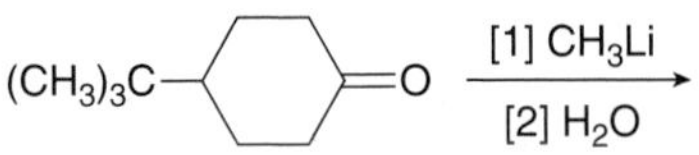

d. 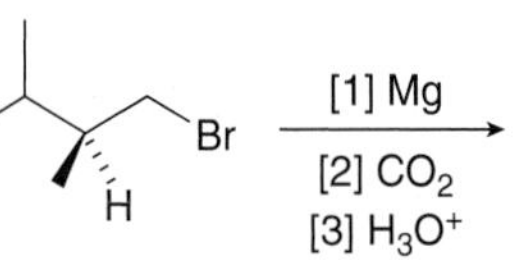

b. 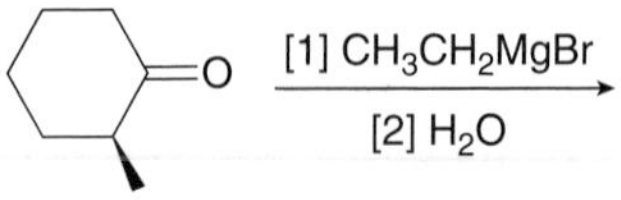

e. 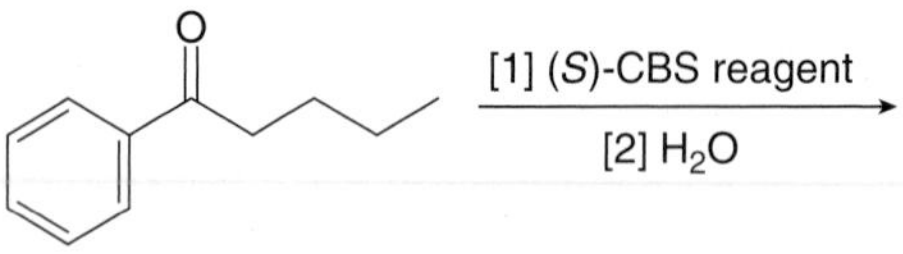

c. 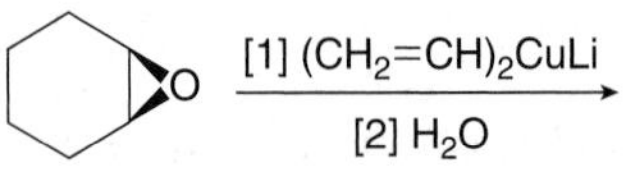

f. 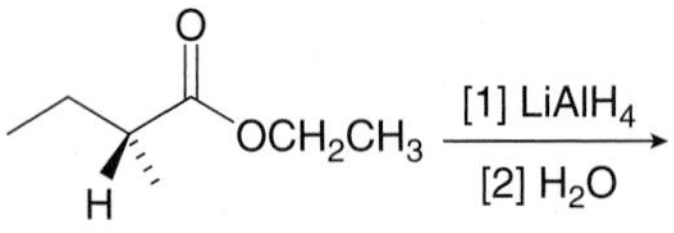

20.49 Which carbon is most electrophilic in **Y?** Explain your choice.

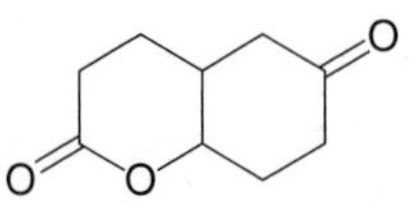

Y

20.50 Treatment of ketone **A** with ethynyllithium (HC≡CLi) followed by D_3O^+ afforded a compound **B** of molecular formula $C_{12}H_{13}DO_3$, which gave an IR absorption at approximately 1715 cm^{-1}. What is the structure of **B** and how is it formed?

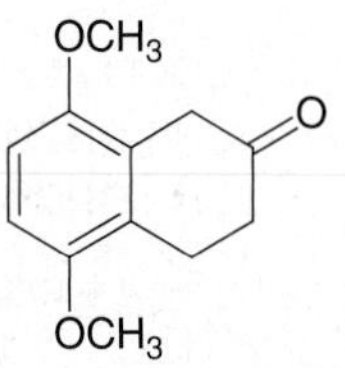

A

20.51 Explain why metal hydride reduction gives an endo alcohol as the major product in one reaction and an exo alcohol as the major product in the other reaction.

endo OH group

exo OH group

20.52 A student tried to carry out the following reaction sequence, but none of diol **A** was formed. Explain what was wrong with this plan, and design a successful stepwise synthesis of **A.**

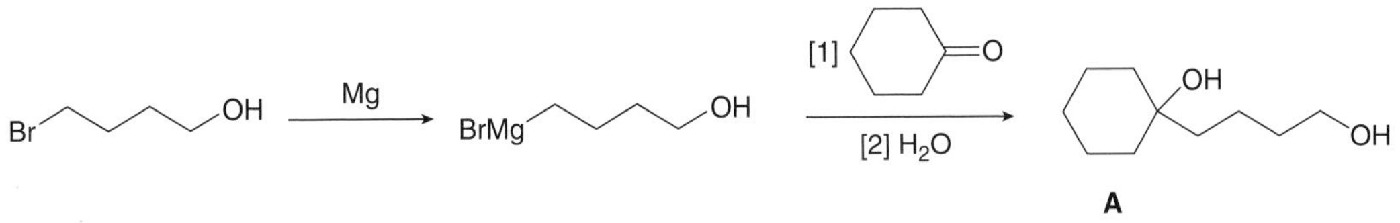

20.53 Identify the lettered compounds in the following reaction scheme. Compounds **F, G,** and **K** are isomers of molecular formula $C_{13}H_{18}O$. How could ^1H NMR spectroscopy distinguish these three compounds from each other?

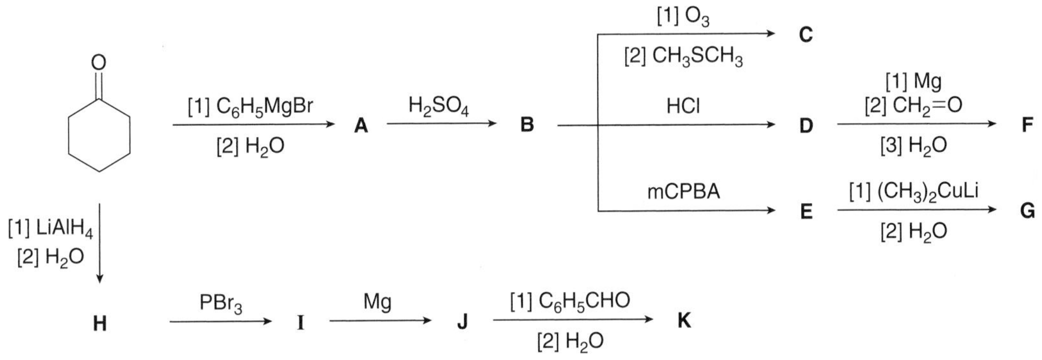

20.54 Fill in the lettered products (**A**–**D**) in the synthesis of (*R*)-isoproterenol, a drug that increases heart rate and dilates lung passages.

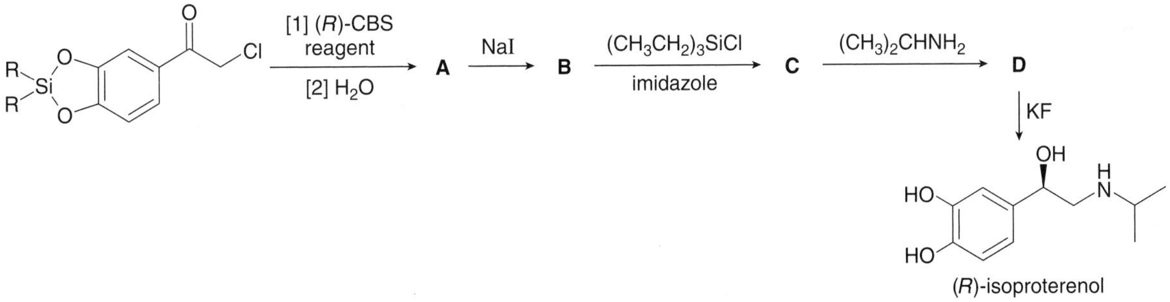

(*R*)-isoproterenol
trade name: Isuprel

Mechanism

20.55 Draw a stepwise mechanism for each reaction.

a. 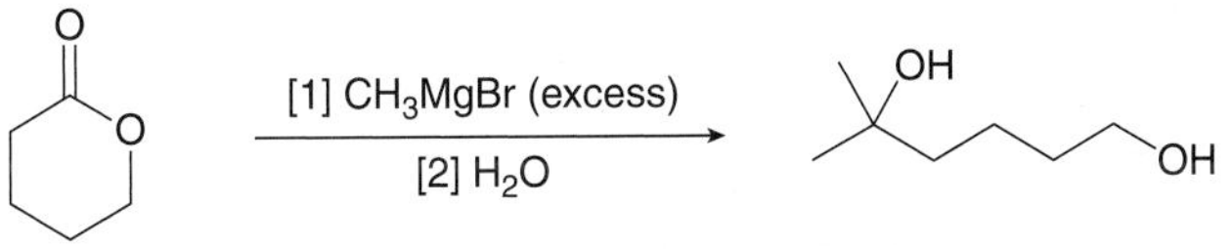

b. 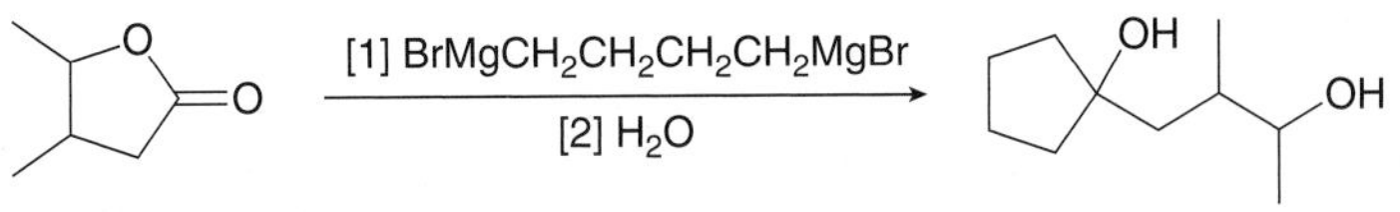

20.56 Tertiary alcohols can be formed by the reaction of dimethyl carbonate [$(CH_3O)_2C=O$] with excess Grignard reagent. Draw a stepwise mechanism for the following transformation.

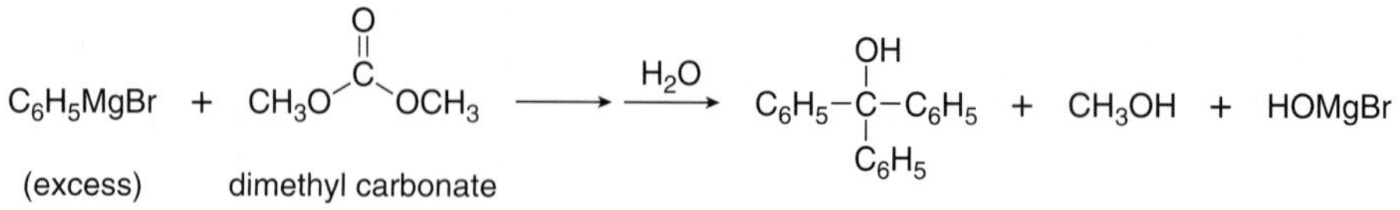
C6H5MgBr
CH3O
OCH3
H2O
C6H5–C–C6H5
CH3OH
HOMgBr

(excess) dimethyl carbonate

20.57 Draw a stepwise mechanism for the following reduction.

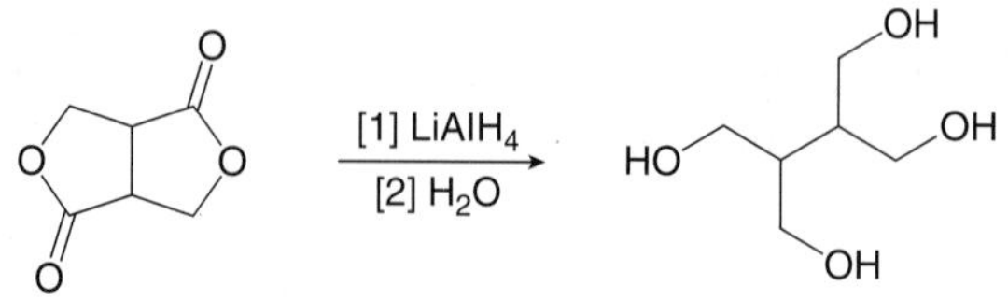
[1] LiAlH4
[2] H2O
HO
OH

Synthesis

20.58 What Grignard reagent and aldehyde (or ketone) are needed to prepare each alcohol? Show all possible routes.

a. 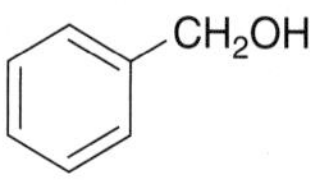
CH2OH

b. 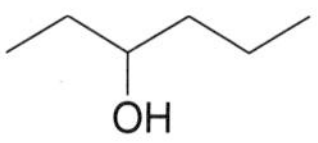
OH

c. $(C_6H_5)_3COH$

d. 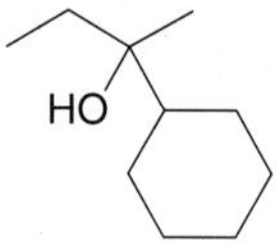
HO

e. 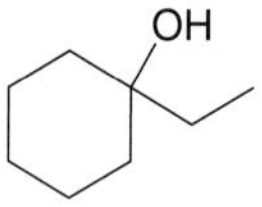
OH

20.59 Procyclidine is a drug that has been used to treat the uncontrolled body movements associated with Parkinson's disease. Draw three different methods to prepare procyclidine using a Grignard reagent.

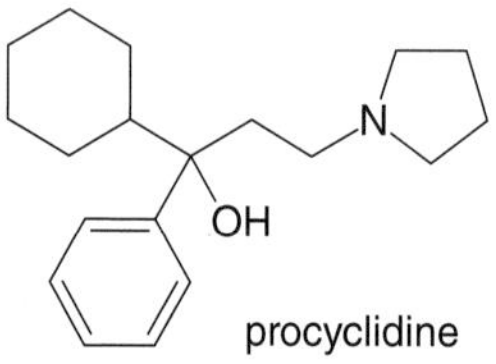
N
OH

procyclidine

20.60 What ester and Grignard reagent are needed to synthesize each alcohol?

a. 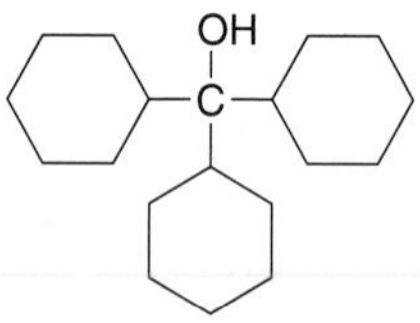
OH
C

b. 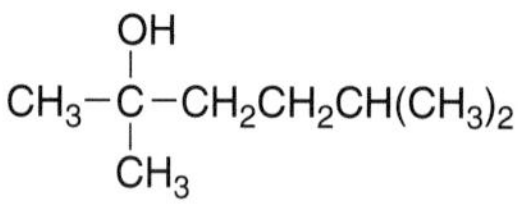
OH
CH3–C–CH2CH2CH(CH3)2
CH3

c. $(CH_3CH_2CH_2CH_2)_2C(OH)CH_3$

20.61 What organolithium reagent and carbonyl compound can be used to prepare each of the following compounds? You may use aldehydes, ketones, or esters as carbonyl starting materials.

a. 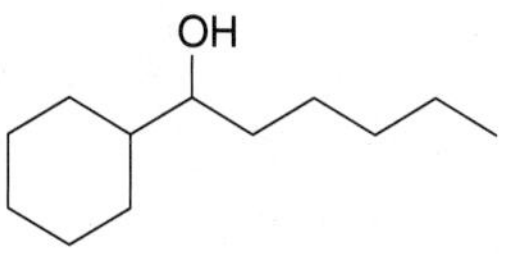
OH

(two ways)

b. 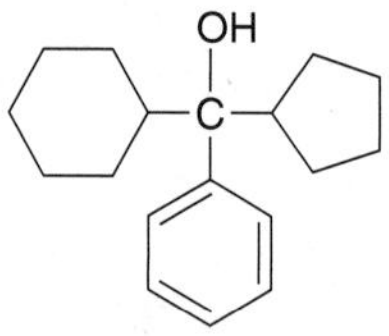
OH
C

(three ways)

c. 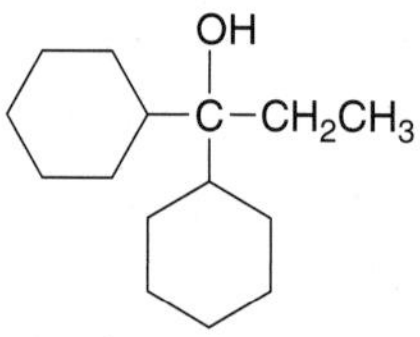
OH
C–CH2CH3

(three ways)

20.62 What epoxide and organometallic reagent are needed to synthesize each alcohol?

a. 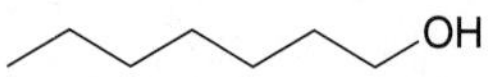
OH

b. 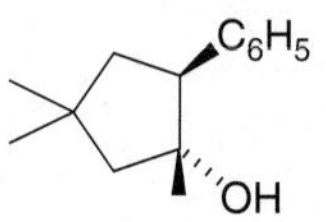
C6H5
OH

c. 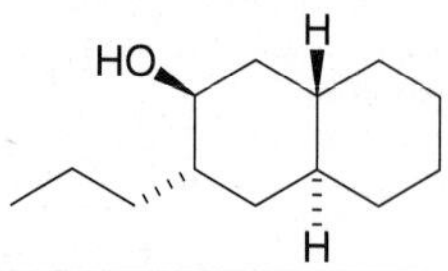
HO
H
H

20.63 Propose at least three methods to convert $C_6H_5CH_2CH_2Br$ to $C_6H_5CH_2CH_3$.

20.64 Propose two different methods to synthesize 1-octen-3-ol [$CH_3(CH_2)_4CH(OH)CH=CH_2$] using a Grignard reagent and a carbonyl compound. 1-Octen-3-ol is commonly called matsutake alcohol because it was first isolated from the Japanese matsutake mushroom.

20.65 Synthesize each compound from cyclohexanol using any other organic or inorganic compounds.

a. 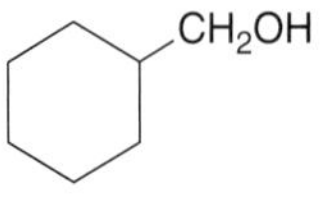

b. 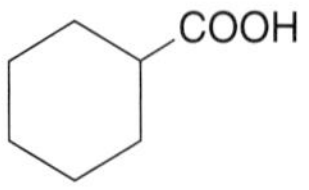

c. 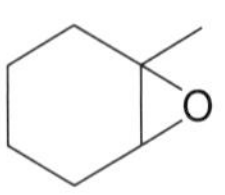

d. 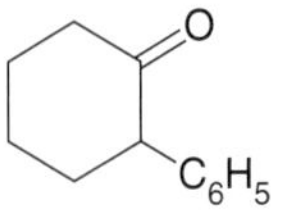

e. 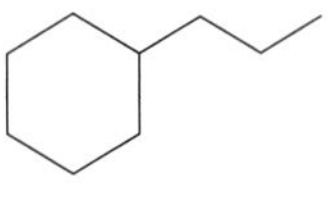

f. 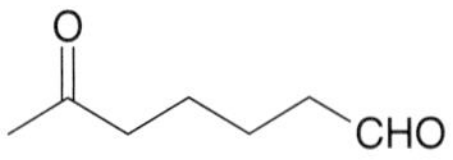

g. 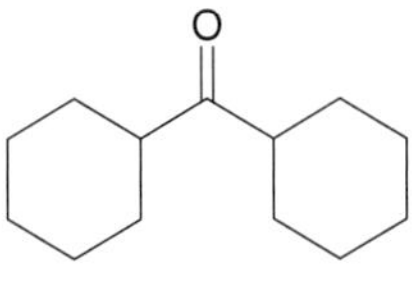

(Each cyclohexane ring must come from cyclohexanol.)

h. 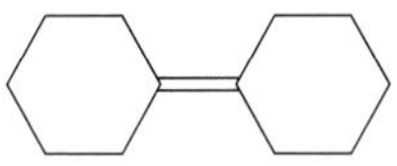

(Each cyclohexane ring must come from cyclohexanol.)

20.66 Convert 2-propanol [$(CH_3)_2CHOH$] into each compound. You may use any other organic or inorganic compounds.

a. $(CH_3)_2CHCH(OH)CH_3$ b. $(CH_3)_2CHCH_2CH_2OH$ c. 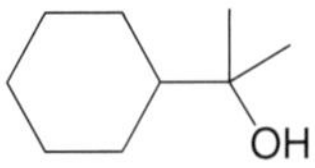

d. 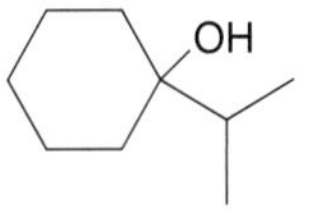

e. 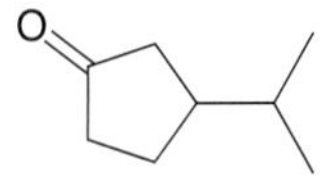

20.67 Devise a synthesis of mestranol, a synthetic estrogen used in oral contraceptives, from the female sex hormone estradiol. You may use any needed organic compounds or inorganic reagents.

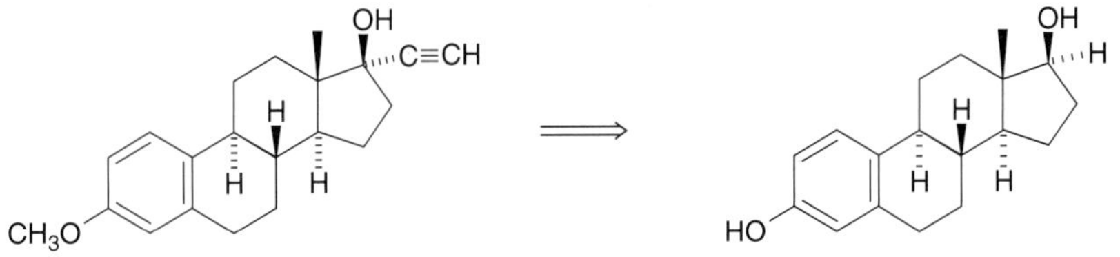

mestranol estradiol

20.68 Devise three different methods to prepare each compound from benzene: (a) $C_6H_5CH_2CH_2OH$ (2-phenylethanol); (b) $C_6H_5COCH_3$ (acetophenone). You may also use organic compounds that have one or two carbons, and any required inorganic reagents. At least two of the three methods must use a reaction of the organometallic reagents described in this chapter.

20.69 Convert benzene into each compound. You may also use any inorganic reagents and organic alcohols having three carbons or fewer. One step of the synthesis must use a Grignard reagent.

a. 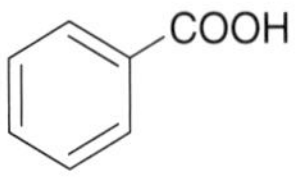

b. 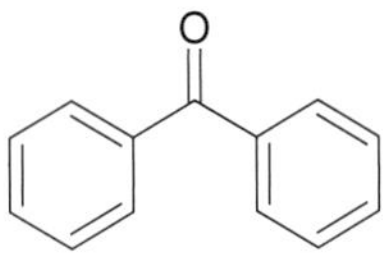

c. 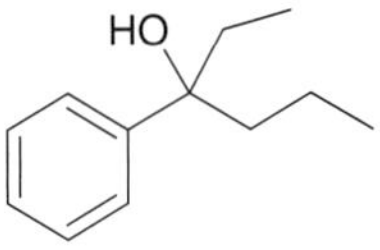

d. 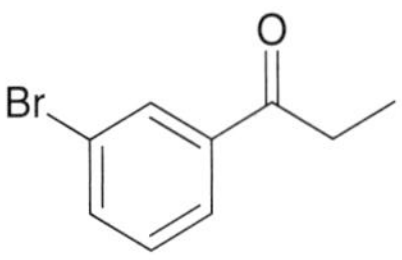

20.70 Design a synthesis of each compound from alcohols having four carbons or fewer as the only organic starting materials. You may use any other inorganic reagents you choose.

a. 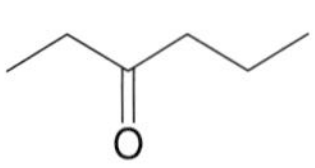

b. 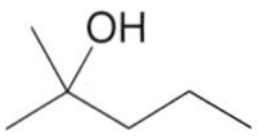

c. 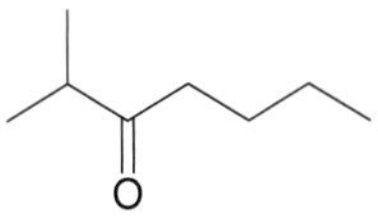

d. 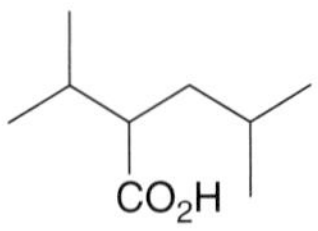

e. 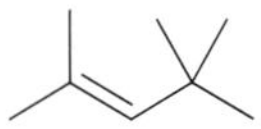

20.71 Synthesize each compound from the given starting material. You may use any other required inorganic reagents.

a. 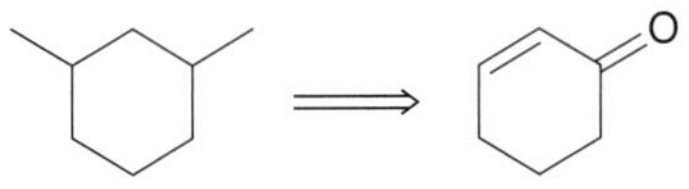

+ organic halides

b. 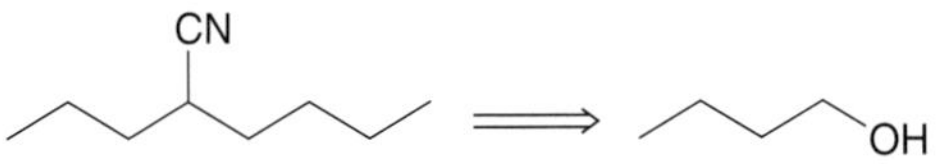

(the only organic starting material)

c. 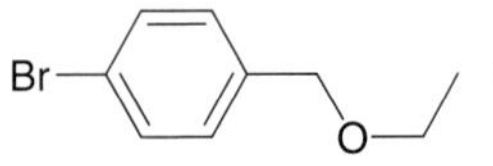

⟹ $C_6H_5CO_2CH_3$

+ organic halides

d. $(CH_3)_2CHCH_2CH_2CH_2OH \Longrightarrow (CH_3)_2C{=}CH_2$

e. $CH_3CH(OH)C{\equiv}CCH_2CH_2OH \Longrightarrow HC{\equiv}CH$
+
compounds having ≤ 2 C's

Spectroscopy

20.72 An unknown compound **A** (molecular formula $C_7H_{14}O$) was treated with $NaBH_4$ in CH_3OH to form compound **B** (molecular formula $C_7H_{16}O$). Compound **A** has a strong absorption in its IR spectrum at 1716 cm^{-1}. Compound **B** has a strong absorption in its IR spectrum at 3600–3200 cm^{-1}. The ^1H NMR spectra of **A** and **B** are given. What are the structures of **A** and **B?**

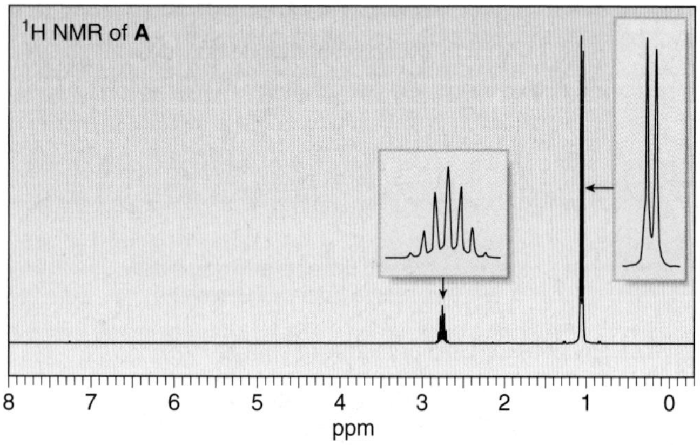

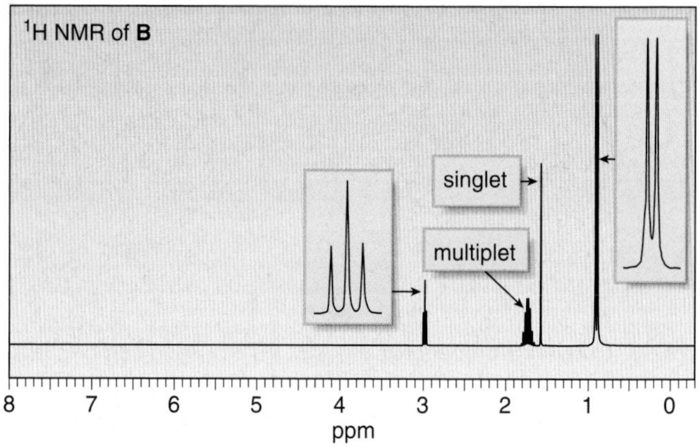

20.73 Treatment of compound **C** (molecular formula C_4H_8O) with C_6H_5MgBr, followed by H_2O, affords compound **D** (molecular formula $C_{10}H_{14}O$). Compound **D** has a strong peak in its IR spectrum at 3600–3200 cm^{-1}. The ^1H NMR spectral data of **C** and **D** are given. What are the structures of **C** and **D?**

Compound **C** signals at 1.3 (singlet, 6 H) and 2.4 (singlet, 2 H) ppm

Compound **D** signals at 1.2 (singlet, 6 H), 1.6 (singlet, 1 H), 2.7 (singlet, 2 H), and 7.2 (multiplet, 5 H) ppm

20.74 Treatment of compound **E** (molecular formula $C_4H_8O_2$) with excess CH_3CH_2MgBr yields compound **F** (molecular formula $C_6H_{14}O$) after protonation with H_2O. **E** shows a strong absorption in its IR spectrum at 1743 cm^{-1}. **F** shows a strong IR absorption at 3600–3200 cm^{-1}. The ^1H NMR spectral data of **E** and **F** are given. What are the structures of **E** and **F?**

Compound **E** signals at 1.2 (triplet, 3 H), 2.0 (singlet, 3 H), and 4.1 (quartet, 2 H) ppm

Compound **F** signals at 0.9 (triplet, 6 H), 1.1 (singlet, 3 H), 1.5 (quartet, 4 H), and 1.55 (singlet, 1 H) ppm

20.75 Reaction of butanenitrile ($CH_3CH_2CH_2CN$) with methylmagnesium bromide (CH_3MgBr), followed by treatment with aqueous acid, forms compound **G. G** has a molecular ion in its mass spectrum at *m/z* = 86 and a base peak at *m/z* = 43. **G** exhibits a strong absorption in its IR spectrum at 1721 cm^{-1} and has the ^1H NMR spectrum given below. What is the structure of **G?** We will learn about the details of this reaction in Chapter 22.

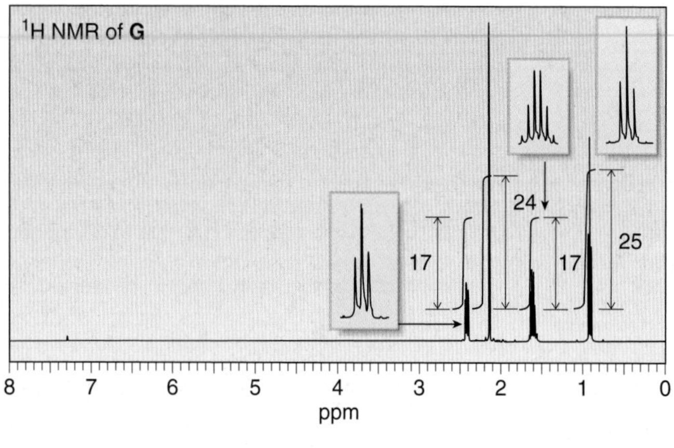

20.76 Treatment of isobutene [$(CH_3)_2C{=}CH_2$] with $(CH_3)_3CLi$ forms a carbanion that reacts with $CH_2{=}O$ to form **H** after water is added to the reaction mixture. **H** has a molecular ion in its mass spectrum at m/z = 86, and shows fragments at 71 and 68. **H** exhibits absorptions in its IR spectrum at 3600–3200 and 1651 cm^{-1}, and has the ^1H NMR spectrum given below. What is the structure of **H?**

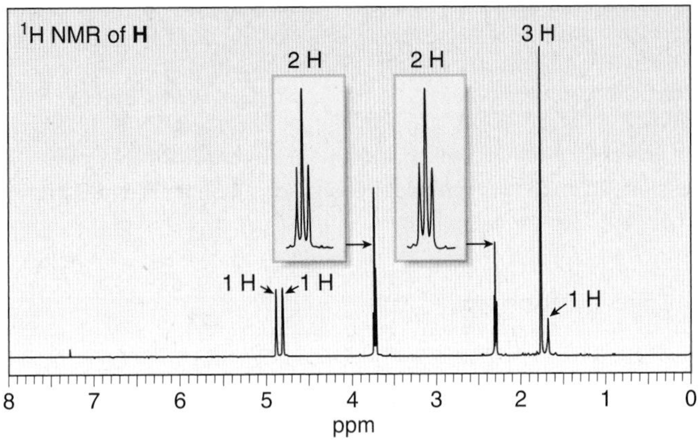

20.77 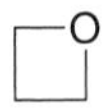 oxetane

Reaction of oxetane with CH_3MgBr followed by H_2O forms a compound that shows a strong absorption in its IR spectrum at 3600–3200 cm^{-1} and the following ^1H NMR data: 0.94 (triplet, 3 H), 1.39 (multiplet, 2 H), 1.53 (multiplet, 2 H), 2.24 (singlet, 1 H), and 3.63 (triplet, 2 H) ppm. Draw the structure of the product and write a mechanism that illustrates its formation.

Challenge Problems

20.78 Design a synthesis of (*R*)-salmeterol (Figure 20.3) from the following starting materials.

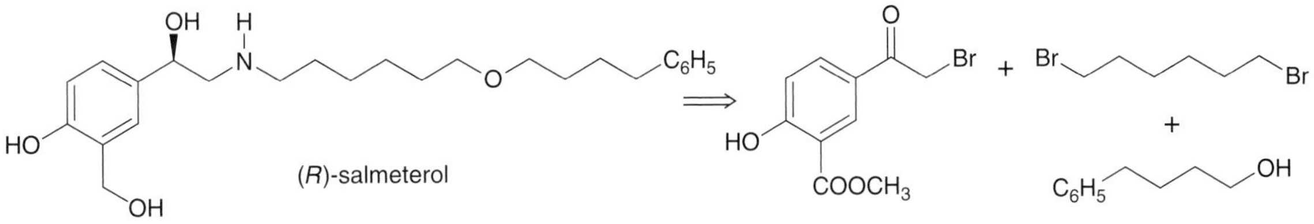

20.79 Lithium tri-*sec*-butylborohydride, also known as L-selectride, is a metal hydride reagent that contains three *sec*-butyl groups bonded to boron. When this reagent is used to reduce cyclic ketones, one stereoisomer often predominates as product. Explain why the reduction of 4-*tert*-butylcyclohexanone with L-selectride forms the cis alcohol as the major product.

$LiBH[CH(CH_3)CH_2CH_3]_3$

lithium tri-*sec*-butylborohydride
L-selectride

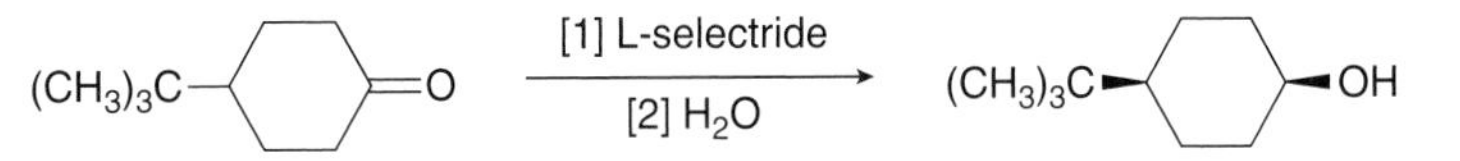

4-*tert*-butylcyclohexanone

cis-4-*tert*-butylcyclohexanol

20.80 Explain why the β carbon of an α,β-unsaturated carbonyl compound absorbs farther downfield in the ^{13}C NMR spectrum than the α carbon, even though the α carbon is closer to the electron-withdrawing carbonyl group. For example, the β carbon of mesityl oxide absorbs at 150.5 ppm, while the α carbon absorbs at 122.5 ppm.

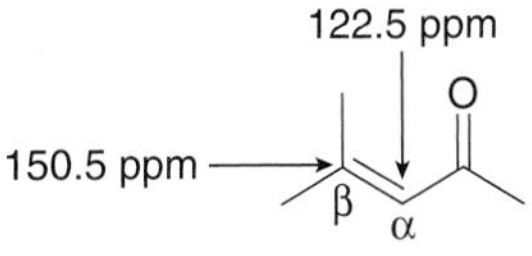

mesityl oxide

20.81 Identify **X** and **Y,** two of the intermediates in a synthesis of the antidepressant venlafaxine (trade name Effexor), in the following reaction scheme. Write a mechanism for the formation of **X** from **W.**

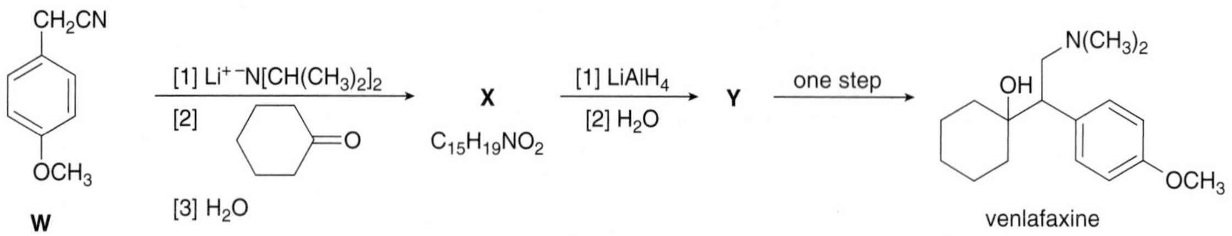
CH2CN
OCH3
W
[1] Li+ −N[CH(CH3)2]2
[2]
O
[3] H2O
X
C15H19NO2
[1] LiAlH4
[2] H2O
Y
one step
N(CH3)2
OH
OCH3
venlafaxine

20.82 Reaction of benzylmagnesium chloride with formaldehyde yields alcohols **N** and **P** after protonation. Draw a stepwise mechanism that shows how both products are formed.

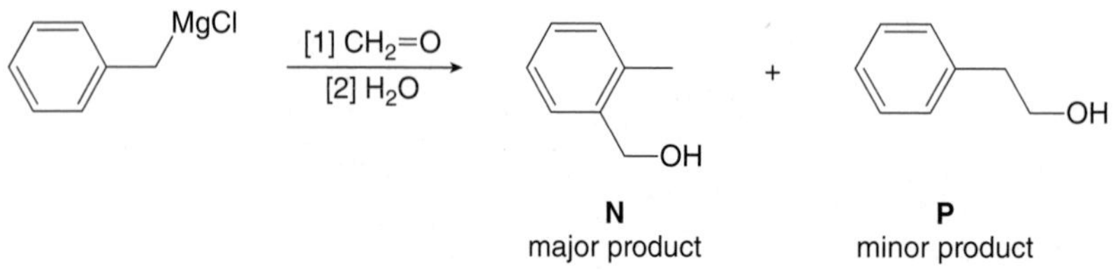
MgCl
[1] CH2=O
[2] H2O
OH
+
OH
N
major product
P
minor product

20.83 Draw a stepwise mechanism for the following reaction. (Hint: Conjugate addition can occur with heteroatoms as well as carbon nucleophiles.)

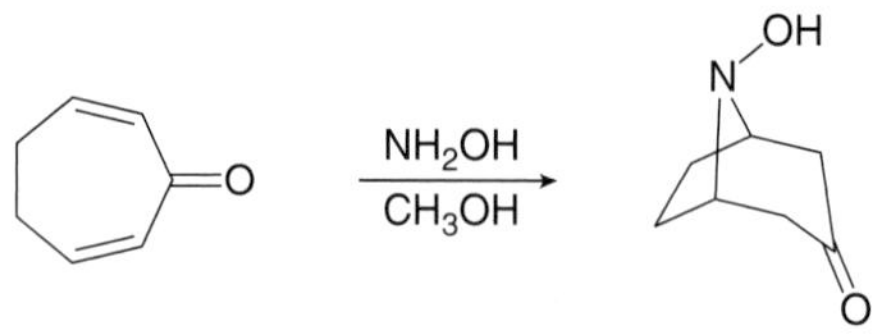
O
NH2OH
CH3OH
OH
N
O

20.84 Draw a stepwise mechanism for the following reaction of a Grignard reagent with a cyclic amide.

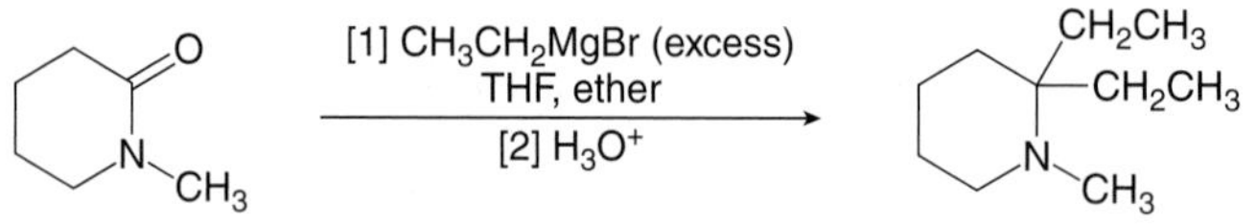
O
N
CH3
[1] CH3CH2MgBr (excess)
THF, ether
[2] H3O+
CH2CH3
CH2CH3
N
CH3

Aldehydes and Ketones—Nucleophilic Addition

21

21.1 Introduction
21.2 Nomenclature
21.3 Physical properties
21.4 Spectroscopic properties
21.5 Interesting aldehydes and ketones
21.6 Preparation of aldehydes and ketones
21.7 Reactions of aldehydes and ketones—General considerations
21.8 Nucleophilic addition of H^- and R^-—A review
21.9 Nucleophilic addition of ^-CN
21.10 The Wittig reaction
21.11 Addition of 1° amines
21.12 Addition of 2° amines
21.13 Addition of H_2O—Hydration
21.14 Addition of alcohols—Acetal formation
21.15 Acetals as protecting groups
21.16 Cyclic hemiacetals
21.17 An introduction to carbohydrates

The natural product **digoxin** has been prescribed since the 1960s for patients with congestive heart failure, a condition that results when fluid builds up in the body because the heart's pumping action is weak. Unlike many commercial medications that are synthesized from simple precursors, digoxin is still obtained by extraction of the leaves of the woolly foxglove plant, which is grown in the Netherlands and shipped to the United States for processing. One thousand kilograms of dried leaves yield one kilogram of digoxin, sold under the trade name of Lanoxin. Digoxin contains three acetal units, which are formed by addition reactions to carbonyl groups. In Chapter 21, we learn about nucleophilic addition, the characteristic reaction of aldehydes and ketones.

In Chapter 21 we continue the study of carbonyl compounds with a detailed look at **aldehydes** and **ketones.** We will first learn about the nomenclature, physical properties, and spectroscopic absorptions that characterize aldehydes and ketones. The remainder of Chapter 21 is devoted to **nucleophilic addition** reactions. Although we have already learned two examples of this reaction in Chapter 20, nucleophilic addition to aldehydes and ketones is a general reaction that occurs with many nucleophiles, forming a wide variety of products.

Every new reaction in Chapter 21 involves nucleophilic addition, so the challenge lies in learning the specific reagents and mechanisms that characterize each reaction.

21.1 Introduction

An aldehyde is often written as **RCHO.** Remember that the **H atom is bonded to the carbon atom,** *not* the oxygen. Likewise, a ketone is written as **RCOR,** or if both alkyl groups are the same, **R_2CO.** Each structure must contain a C=O for every atom to have an octet.

As we learned in Chapter 20, **aldehydes and ketones contain a carbonyl group.** An aldehyde contains at least one H atom bonded to the carbonyl carbon, whereas a ketone has two alkyl or aryl groups bonded to it.

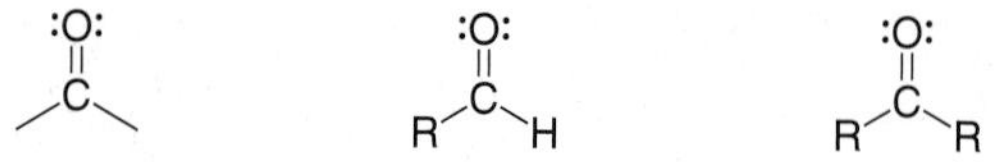

carbonyl group **aldehyde** **ketone**

Two structural features determine the chemistry and properties of aldehydes and ketones.

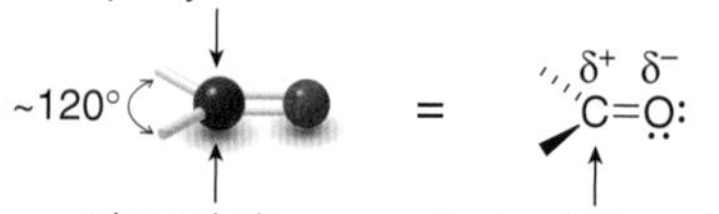

- The carbonyl group is *sp*^{2} hybridized and trigonal planar, making it relatively uncrowded.
- The electronegative oxygen atom polarizes the carbonyl group, making the carbonyl carbon electrophilic.

As a result, **aldehydes and ketones react with nucleophiles.** The relative reactivity of the carbonyl group is determined by the number of R groups bonded to it. **As the number of R groups around the carbonyl carbon increases, the reactivity of the carbonyl compound decreases,** resulting in the following order of reactivity:

Increasing the number of alkyl groups on the carbonyl carbon decreases reactivity for both steric and electronic reasons, as discussed in Section 20.2B.

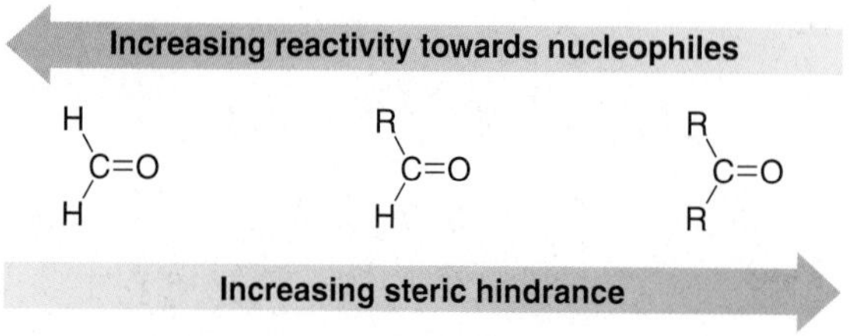

Problem 21.1 Rank the following compounds in order of increasing reactivity towards nucleophilic attack.

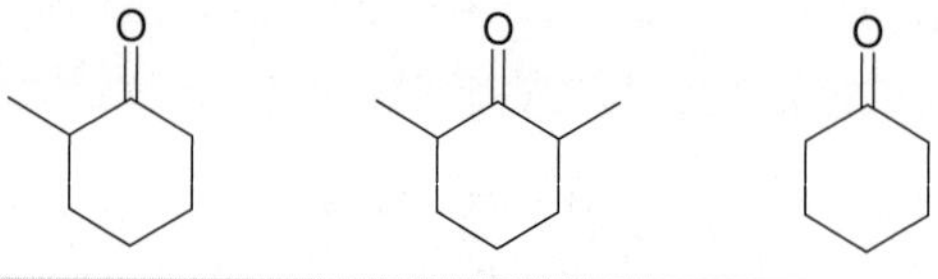

Problem 21.2 Explain why benzaldehyde is less reactive than cyclohexanecarbaldehyde towards nucleophilic attack.

benzaldehyde cyclohexanecarbaldehyde

21.2 Nomenclature

Both IUPAC and common names are used for aldehydes and ketones.

21.2A Naming Aldehydes in the IUPAC System

In IUPAC nomenclature, aldehydes are identified by a suffix added to the parent name of the longest chain. Two different suffixes are used, depending on whether the CHO group is bonded to a chain or a ring.

To name an aldehyde using the IUPAC system:

[1] If the CHO is bonded to a chain of carbons, find the longest chain containing the CHO group, and change the ***-e*** ending of the parent alkane to the suffix ***-al.*** If the CHO group is bonded to a ring, name the ring and add the suffix ***-carbaldehyde.***

[2] Number the chain or ring to put the CHO group at C1, but omit this number from the name. Apply all of the other usual rules of nomenclature.

Sample Problem 21.1 Give the IUPAC name for each compound.

a. 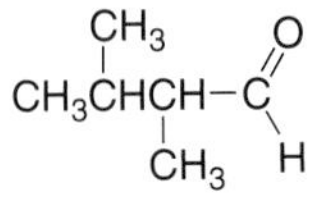
CH3
O
CH3CHCH–C
CH3
H

b. 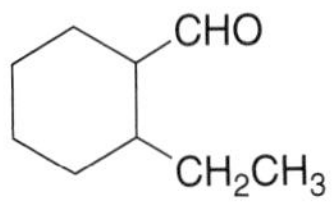
CHO
CH2CH3

Solution

a. [1] Find and name the longest chain containing the CHO:

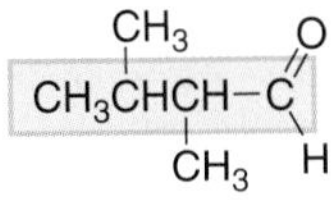
CH3
O
CH3CHCH–C
CH3
H

butane ⟶ butan*al*
(4 C's)

[2] Number and name substituents:

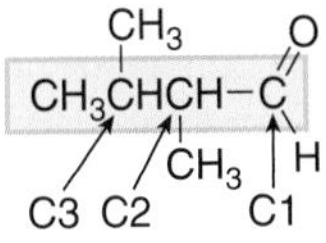
CH3
O
CH3CHCH–C
CH3
H
C3 C2
C1

Answer: 2,3-dimethylbutanal

b. [1] Find and name the ring bonded to the CHO group:

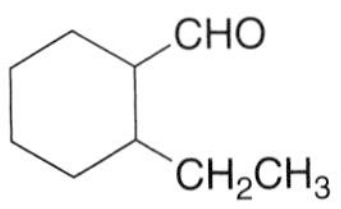
CHO
CH2CH3

cyclohexane + carbaldehyde
(6 C's)

[2] Number and name substituents:

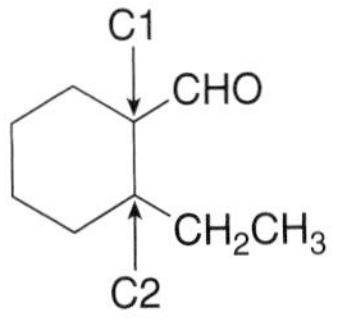
C1
CHO
CH2CH3
C2

Answer:
2-ethylcyclohexanecarbaldehyde

Problem 21.3 Give the IUPAC name for each aldehyde.

a. $(CH_3)_3CC(CH_3)_2CH_2CHO$

b. 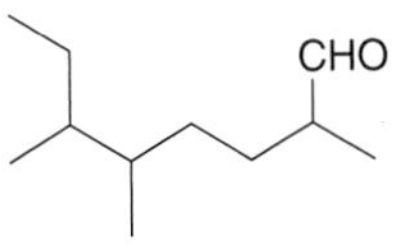
CHO

c. 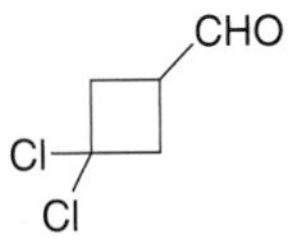
CHO
Cl
Cl

Problem 21.4 Give the structure corresponding to each IUPAC name.

a. 2-isobutyl-3-isopropylhexanal
b. *trans*-3-methylcyclopentanecarbaldehyde
c. 1-methylcyclopropanecarbaldehyde
d. 3,6-diethylnonanal

21.2B Common Names for Aldehydes

Like carboxylic acids, many simple aldehydes have common names that are widely used.

- **A common name for an aldehyde is formed by taking the common parent name and adding the suffix *-aldehyde.***

The common parent names are similar to those used for carboxylic acids, listed in Table 19.1. The common names **formaldehyde, acetaldehyde,** and **benzaldehyde** are virtually always used instead of their IUPAC names.

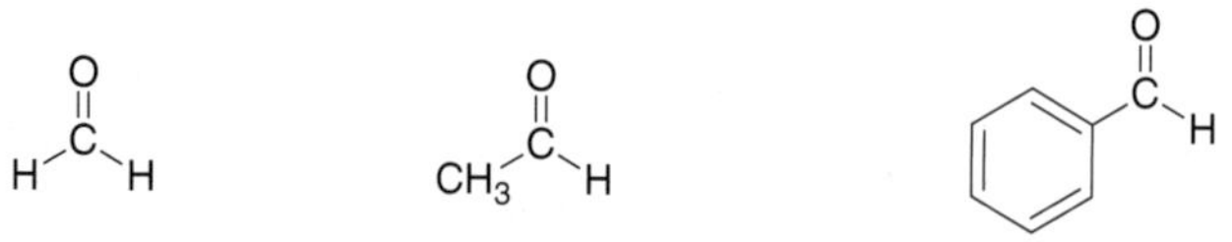

formaldehyde (methanal) | acetaldehyde (ethanal) | benzaldehyde (benzenecarbaldehyde)

(IUPAC names are in parentheses.)

Greek letters are used to designate the location of substituents in common names. **The carbon adjacent to the CHO group is the α carbon,** and so forth down the chain.

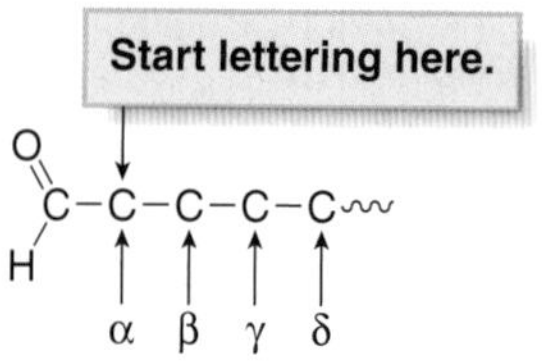
Start lettering here.
α β γ δ

Figure 21.1 gives the common and IUPAC names for three aldehydes.

Figure 21.1 Three examples of aldehyde nomenclature

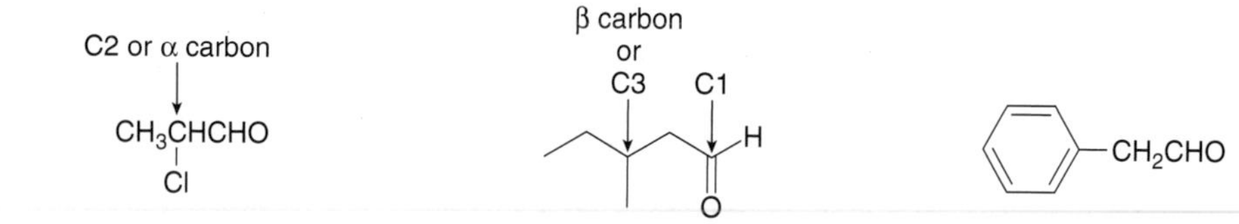
C2 or α carbon
β carbon or C3
C1

2-chloropropanal (α-chloropropionaldehyde) | 3-methylpentanal (β-methylvaleraldehyde) | phenylethanal (phenylacetaldehyde)

(Common names are in parentheses.)

21.2C Naming Ketones in the IUPAC System

- **In the IUPAC system all ketones are identified by the suffix *-one.***

To name an acyclic ketone using IUPAC rules:

[1] Find the longest chain containing the carbonyl group, and change the ***-e*** ending of the parent alkane to the suffix ***-one.***

[2] Number the carbon chain to give the carbonyl carbon the lower number. Apply all of the other usual rules of nomenclature.

With cyclic ketones, numbering always begins at the carbonyl carbon, but the "1" is usually omitted from the name. The ring is then numbered clockwise or counterclockwise to give the first substituent the lower number.

Sample Problem 21.2 Give the IUPAC name for each ketone.

a. 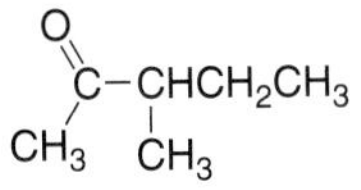 b. 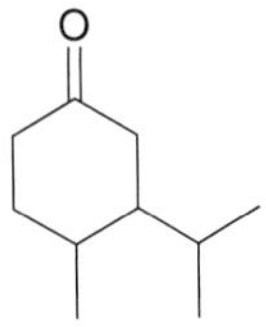

Solution

a. [1] Find and name the longest chain containing the carbonyl group:

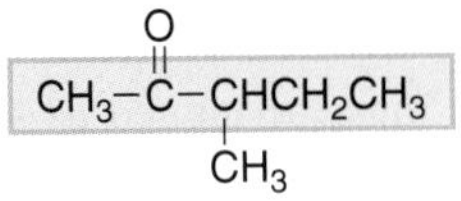

pentane ⟶ pentan*one*
(5 C's)

[2] Number and name substituents:

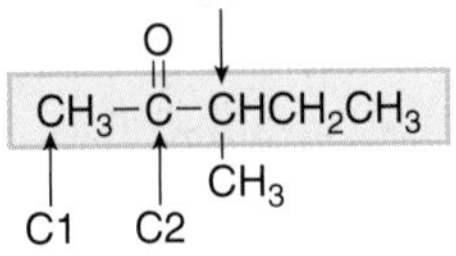
C3
C1
C2

Answer: 3-methyl-2-pentanone

b. [1] Name the ring:

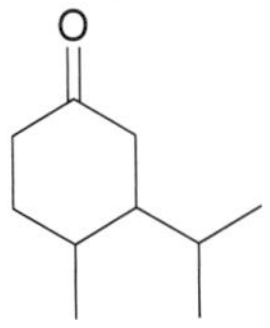

cyclohexane ⟶ cyclohexan*one*
(6 C's)

[2] Number and name substituents:

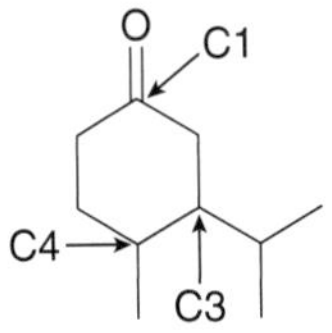
C1
C4
C3

Answer:
3-isopropyl-4-methylcyclohexanone

Problem 21.5 Give the IUPAC name for each ketone.

a. 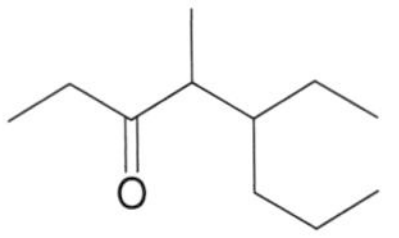 b. 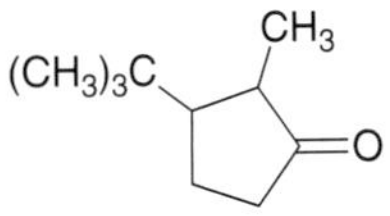 c. $(CH_3)_3CCOC(CH_3)_3$

21.2D Common Names for Ketones

Most common names for ketones are formed by **naming both alkyl groups** on the carbonyl carbon, **arranging them alphabetically,** and adding the word ***ketone.*** Using this method, the common name for 2-butanone becomes ethyl methyl ketone.

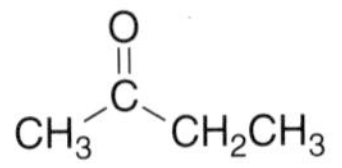

IUPAC name: **2-butanone**

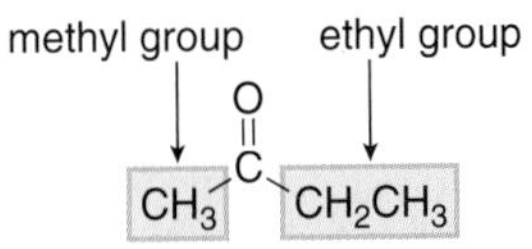
methyl group
ethyl group

Common name: **ethyl methyl ketone**

Three widely used common names for some simple ketones do not follow this convention:

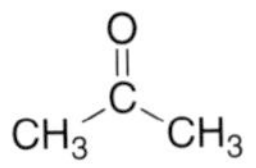

acetone

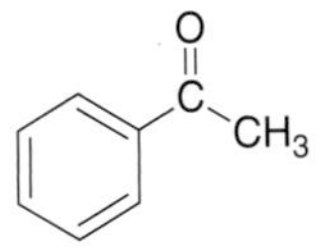

acetophenone

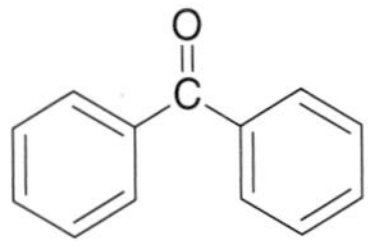

benzophenone

Figure 21.2 gives acceptable names for two ketones.

Figure 21.2 Two examples of ketone nomenclature

IUPAC name: 2-methyl-3-pentanone
Common name: ethyl isopropyl ketone

m-bromoacetophenone
or
3-bromoacetophenone

21.2E Additional Nomenclature Facts

Do not confuse a **benzyl** group with a **benzoyl** group.

Sometimes acyl groups (RCO–) must be named as substituents. To name an acyl group, take either the IUPAC or common parent name and add the suffix ***-yl*** or ***-oyl.*** The three most common acyl groups are drawn below.

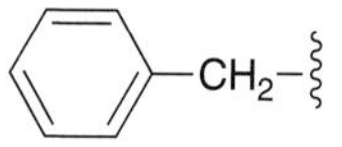

benz*yl* group

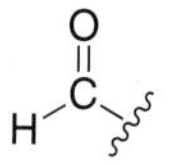

formyl group

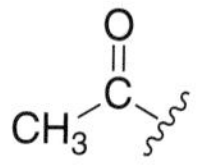

acetyl group

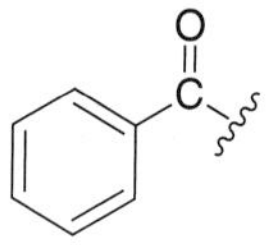

benzoyl group

Compounds containing both a C–C double bond and an aldehyde are named as **enals,** and compounds that contain both a C–C double bond and a ketone are named as **enones.** The chain is numbered to give the carbonyl group the lower number.

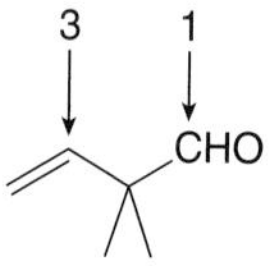

2,2-dimethyl-3-butenal

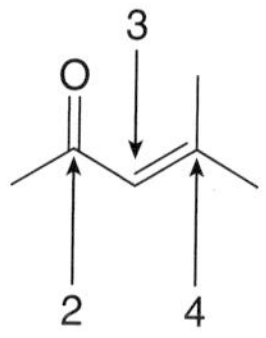

4-methyl-3-penten-2-one

Problem 21.6 Give the structure corresponding to each name: (a) *sec*-butyl ethyl ketone; (b) methyl vinyl ketone; (c) *p*-ethylacetophenone; (d) 3-benzoyl-2-benzylcyclopentanone; (e) 6,6-dimethyl-2-cyclohexenone; (f) 3-ethyl-5-hexenal.

Problem 21.7 Give the IUPAC name (including any *E,Z* designation) for each unsaturated aldehyde. Neral is obtained from lemon grass, and the unmistakable odor of a freshly cut cucumber is due largely to cucumber aldehyde.

a. 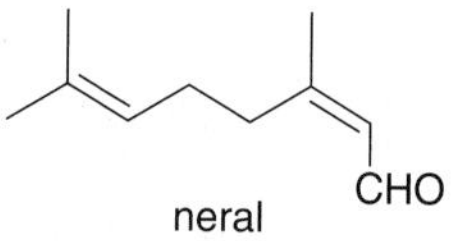

neral

b. 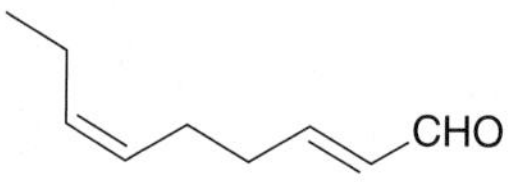

cucumber aldehyde

21.3 Physical Properties

Aldehydes and ketones exhibit dipole–dipole interactions because of their polar carbonyl group. Because they have no O–H bond, two molecules of RCHO or RCOR are incapable of intermolecular hydrogen bonding, making them less polar than alcohols and carboxylic acids. How these intermolecular forces affect the physical properties of aldehydes and ketones is summarized in Table 21.1.

Problem 21.8 The boiling point of 2-butanone (80 °C) is significantly higher than the boiling point of diethyl ether (35 °C), even though both compounds exhibit dipole–dipole interactions and have comparable molecular weights. Offer an explanation.

Table 21.1 Physical Properties of Aldehydes and Ketones

Property	Observation
Boiling point and melting point	• For compounds of comparable molecular weight, bp's and mp's follow the usual trend: The stronger the intermolecular forces, the higher the bp or mp. $CH_3CH_2CH_2CH_2CH_3$: VDW, MW = 72, bp 36 °C $CH_3CH_2CH_2CHO$: VDW, DD, MW = 72, bp 76 °C $CH_3CH_2COCH_3$: VDW, DD, MW = 72, bp 80 °C $CH_3CH_2CH_2CH_2OH$: VDW, DD, HB, MW = 74, bp 118 °C **Increasing strength of intermolecular forces** **Increasing boiling point**
Solubility	• RCHO and RCOR are soluble in organic solvents regardless of size. • RCHO and RCOR having ≤ 5 C's are H_2O soluble because they can hydrogen bond with H_2O (Section 3.4C). • RCHO and RCOR having > 5 C's are H_2O insoluble because the nonpolar alkyl portion is too large to dissolve in the polar H_2O solvent.

Key: VDW = van der Waals, DD = dipole–dipole, HB = hydrogen bonding, MW = molecular weight

21.4 Spectroscopic Properties

The presence of the carbonyl group in aldehydes and ketones gives them characteristic absorptions in their IR and NMR spectra.

21.4A IR Spectra

Aldehydes and ketones exhibit the following characteristic IR absorptions:

- Like all carbonyl compounds, **aldehydes and ketones give a strong peak at ~1700 cm^{-1} due to the C=O.**
- **The *sp*^{2} hybridized C–H bond of an aldehyde shows one or two peaks at ~2700–2830 cm^{-1}.**

The IR spectrum of propanal in Figure 21.3 illustrates these characteristic peaks.

Figure 21.3
The IR spectrum of propanal, CH_3CH_2CHO

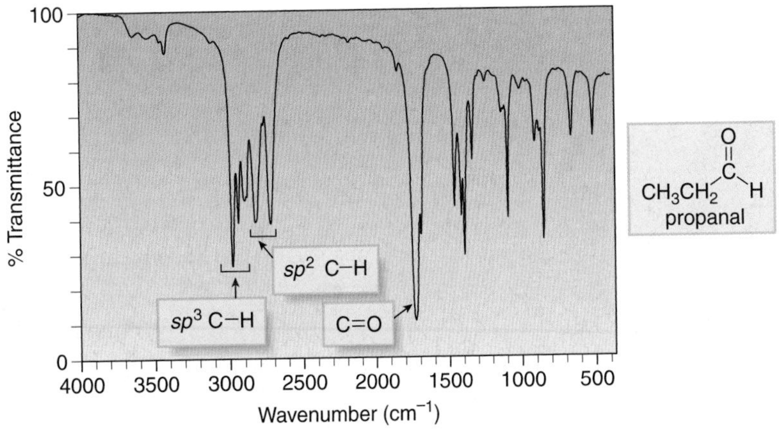

- A strong C=O occurs at 1739 cm^{-1}.
- The *sp*^{2} C–H of the CHO appears as two peaks at 2813 and 2716 cm^{-1}.

The exact position of the carbonyl absorption often provides additional information about a compound. For example, most aldehydes have a C=O peak around **1730 cm^{-1}**, whereas for ketones, it is typically around **1715 cm^{-1}**. Two other structural features—**ring size** (for cyclic ketones) and **conjugation**—affect the location of the carbonyl absorption in a predictable manner.

[1] The carbonyl absorption of cyclic ketones shifts to higher wavenumber as the size of the ring decreases and the ring strain increases.

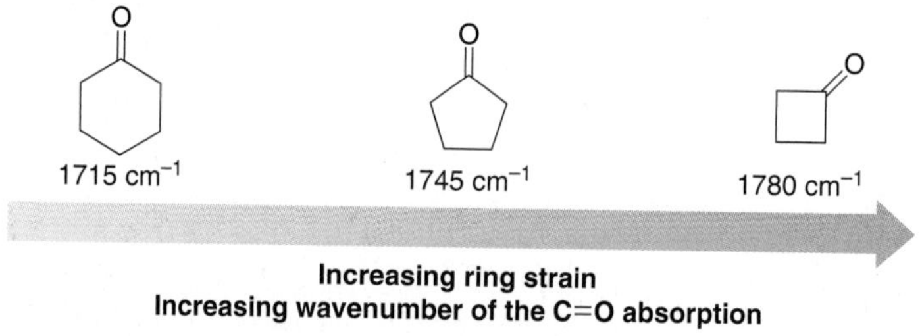
O
O
O
1715 cm^{-1}
1745 cm^{-1}
1780 cm^{-1}
Increasing ring strain
Increasing wavenumber of the C=O absorption

[2] Conjugation of the carbonyl group with a C=C or a benzene ring shifts the absorption to lower wavenumber by ~30 cm^{-1}.

The effect of conjugation on the frequency of the C=O absorption is explained by **resonance.** An α,β-unsaturated carbonyl compound can be written as three resonance structures, two of which place a single bond between the carbon and oxygen atoms of the carbonyl group. Thus, the π bond of the carbonyl group is delocalized, giving the conjugated carbonyl group some single bond character, and making it somewhat **weaker** than an unconjugated C=O. **Weaker bonds absorb at lower frequency (lower wavenumber) in an IR spectrum.**

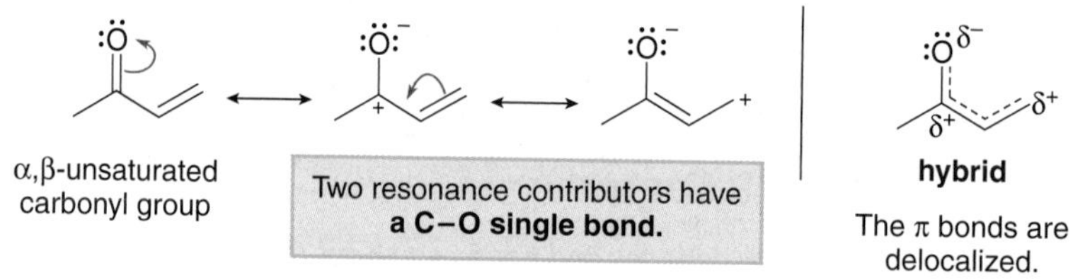
α,β-unsaturated
carbonyl group
Two resonance contributors have
a C–O single bond.
hybrid
The π bonds are
delocalized.

Figure 21.4 illustrates the effects of conjugation on the location of the carbonyl absorption in some representative compounds.

Figure 21.4
The effect of conjugation on the carbonyl absorption in an IR spectrum

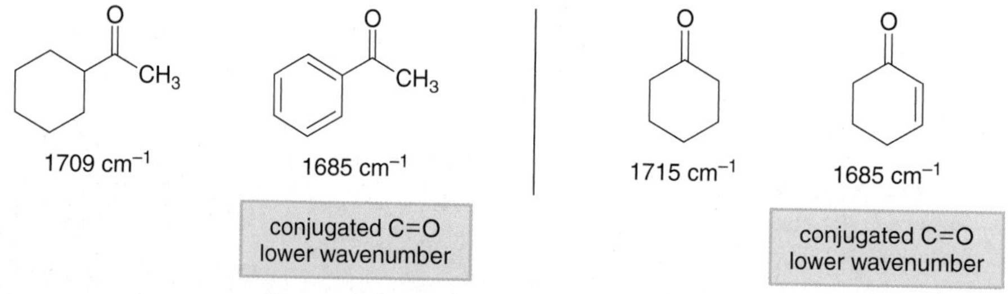
CH3
CH3
1709 cm^{-1}
1685 cm^{-1}
1715 cm^{-1}
1685 cm^{-1}
conjugated C=O
lower wavenumber
conjugated C=O
lower wavenumber

Problem 21.9 Which carbonyl group in each pair absorbs at a higher frequency?

a. 
CHO
or
CHO

b. 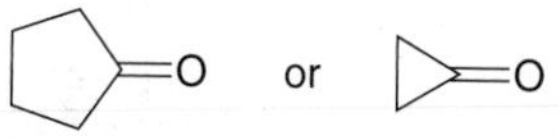
O
or
O

21.4B NMR Spectra

Aldehydes and ketones exhibit the following characteristic ^1H and ^{13}C NMR absorptions:

- **The sp^2 hybridized C–H proton of an aldehyde is highly deshielded and absorbs far downfield at 9–10 ppm.** Splitting occurs with protons on the α carbon, but the coupling constant is often very small (J = 1–3 Hz).
- **Protons on the α carbon to the carbonyl group absorb at 2–2.5 ppm.** Methyl ketones, for example, give a characteristic singlet at ~2.1 ppm.
- In a ^{13}C NMR spectrum, **the carbonyl carbon is highly deshielded, appearing in the 190–215 ppm region.**

The ^1H and ^{13}C NMR spectra of propanal are illustrated in Figure 21.5.

Figure 21.5
The ^1H and ^{13}C NMR spectra of propanal, CH_3CH_2CHO

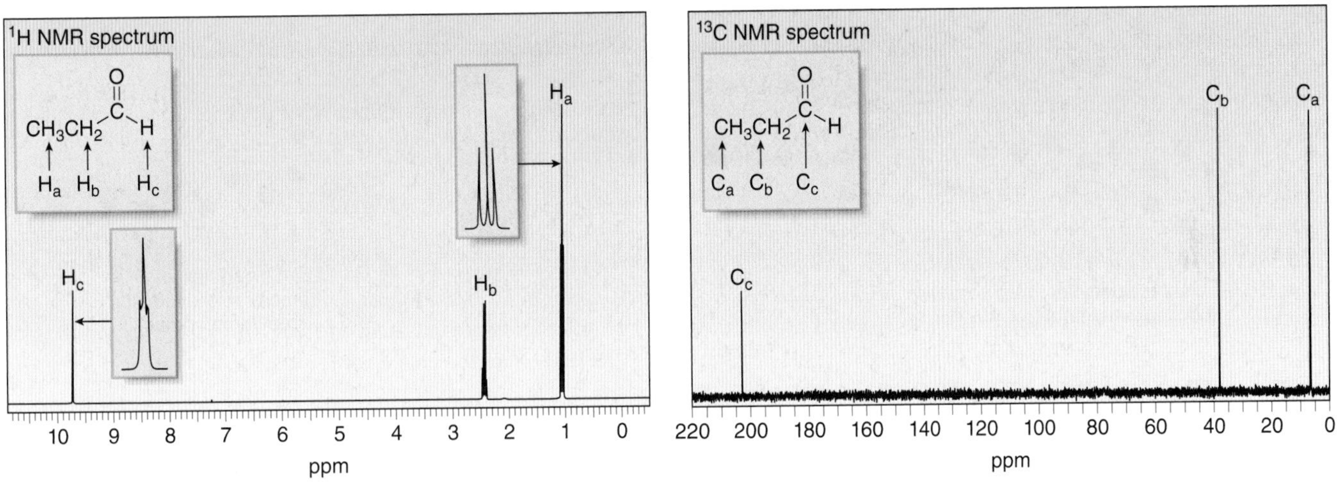

- **^{1}H NMR:** There are three signals due to the three different kinds of hydrogens, labeled H_a, H_b, and H_c. The deshielded CHO proton occurs downfield at 9.8 ppm. The H_c signal is split into a triplet by the adjacent CH_2 group, but the coupling constant is small.
- **^{13}C NMR:** There are three signals due to the three different kinds of carbons, labeled C_a, C_b, and C_c. The deshielded carbonyl carbon absorbs downfield at 203 ppm.

Problem 21.10 Draw the structure of all constitutional isomers that contain a ketone and have molecular formula $C_5H_{10}O$. Give the IUPAC name for each isomer and state how ^{13}C NMR spectroscopy could be used to distinguish these isomers.

21.5 Interesting Aldehydes and Ketones

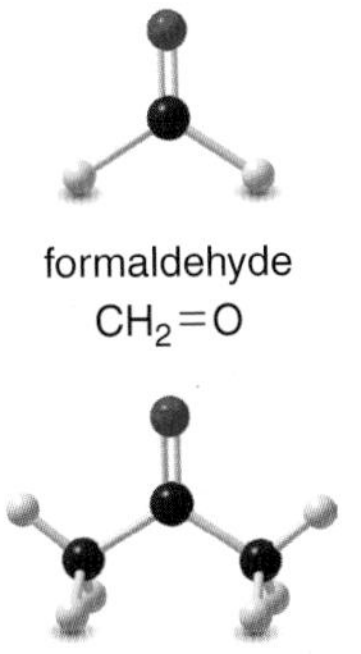

formaldehyde
$CH_2{=}O$

acetone
$(CH_3)_2C{=}O$

Because it is a starting material for the synthesis of many resins and plastics, billions of pounds of **formaldehyde** are produced annually in the United States by the oxidation of methanol (CH_3OH). Formaldehyde is also sold as a 37% aqueous solution called **formalin,** which has been used as a disinfectant, antiseptic, and preservative for biological specimens. Formaldehyde, a product of the incomplete combustion of coal and other fossil fuels, is partly responsible for the irritation caused by smoggy air.

Acetone is an industrial solvent and a starting material in the synthesis of some organic polymers. Acetone is produced in vivo during the breakdown of fatty acids. In diabetes, a common endocrine disease in which normal metabolic processes are altered because of the inadequate secretion of insulin, individuals often have unusually high levels of acetone in their bloodstreams. The characteristic odor of acetone can be detected on the breath of diabetic patients when their disease is poorly controlled.

Many aldehydes with characteristic odors occur in nature, as shown in Figure 21.6.

Figure 21.6 Some naturally occurring aldehydes with strong odors

vanillin
(flavoring agent from vanilla beans)
citronellal
(lemony odor, isolated from lemon grass)
cinnamaldehyde
(odor of cinnamon)
geranial
(lemony odor, isolated from lemon grass)

Many steroid hormones contain a carbonyl along with other functional groups. **Cortisone** and **prednisone** are two anti-inflammatory steroids with closely related structures. Cortisone is secreted by the body's adrenal gland, whereas prednisone is a synthetic analogue used in the treatment of inflammatory diseases such as arthritis and asthma.

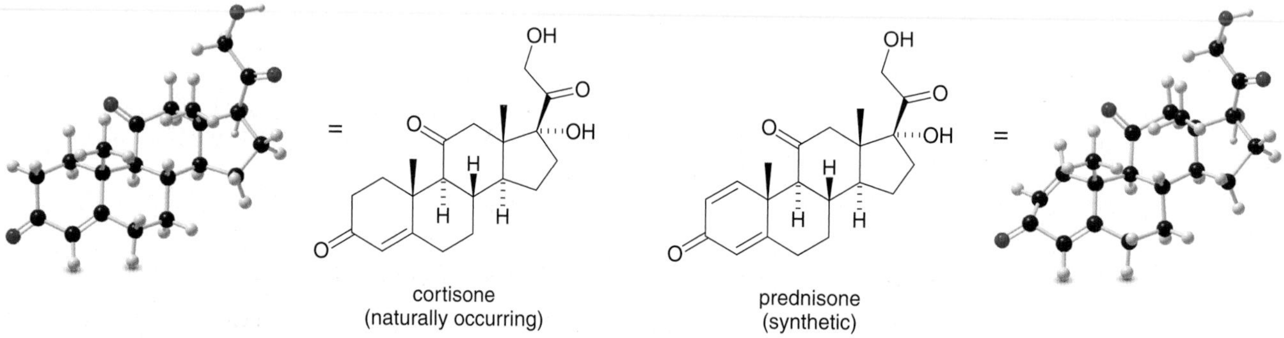
OH
O
OH
H
H
H
O
O
cortisone
(naturally occurring)
prednisone
(synthetic)

21.6 Preparation of Aldehydes and Ketones

Aldehydes and ketones can be prepared by a variety of methods. Because these reactions are needed for many multistep syntheses, Section 21.6 briefly summarizes earlier reactions that synthesize an aldehyde or ketone.

21.6A Common Methods to Synthesize Aldehydes

Aldehydes are prepared from 1° alcohols, esters, acid chlorides, and alkynes.

- **By oxidation of 1° alcohols with PCC**

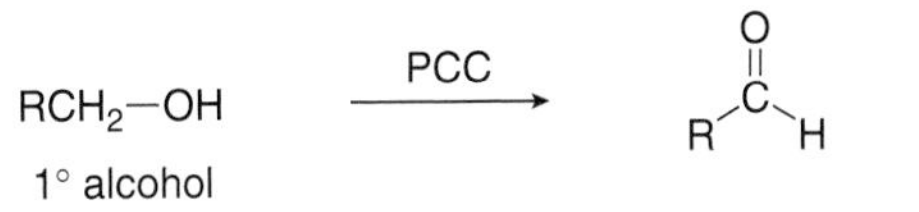

RCH_2-OH
1° alcohol
PCC

(Section 12.12B)

- **By reduction of esters and acid chlorides**

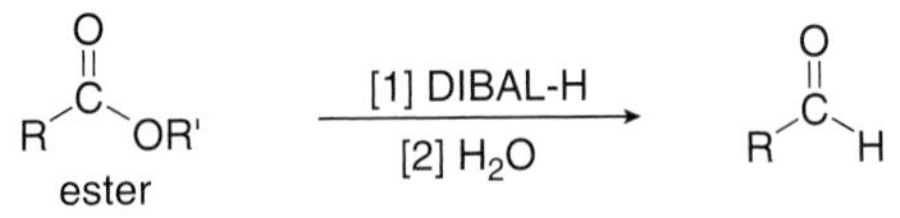

ester
[1] DIBAL-H
[2] H_2O

(Section 20.7A)

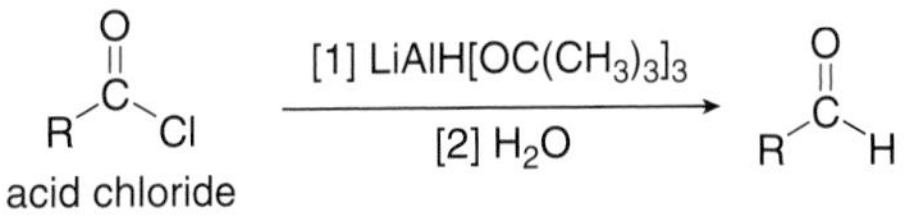

acid chloride
[1] $LiAlH[OC(CH_3)_3]_3$
[2] H_2O

- **By hydroboration–oxidation of an alkyne**

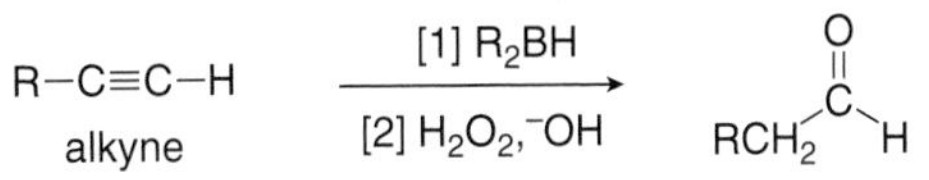

R−C≡C−H
alkyne
[1] R_2BH
[2] H_2O_2, ^-OH

(Section 11.10)

21.6B Common Methods to Synthesize Ketones

Ketones are prepared from 2° alcohols, acid chlorides, and alkynes.

- **By oxidation of 2° alcohols with Cr^{6+} reagents**

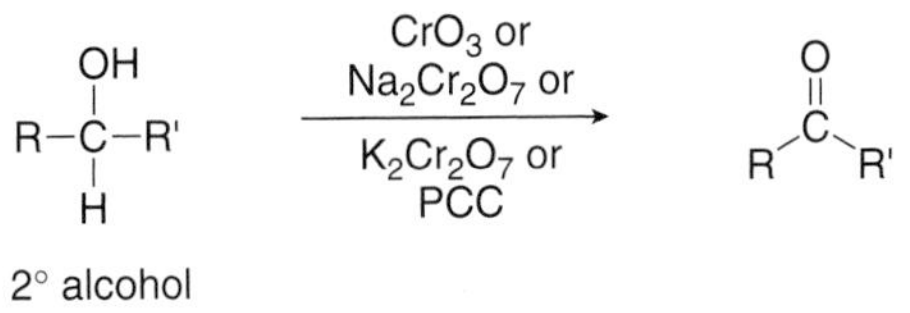

2° alcohol
CrO_3 or
$Na_2Cr_2O_7$ or
$K_2Cr_2O_7$ or
PCC

(Section 12.12A)

- **By reaction of acid chlorides with organocuprates**

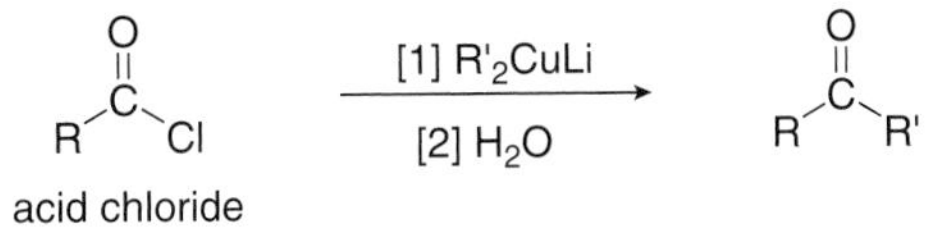

acid chloride
[1] R'_2CuLi
[2] H_2O

(Section 20.13)

- **By Friedel–Crafts acylation**

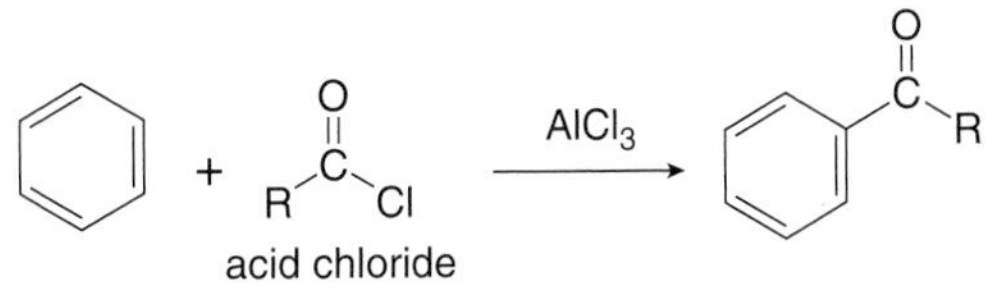

acid chloride
$AlCl_3$

(Section 18.5)

- **By hydration of an alkyne**

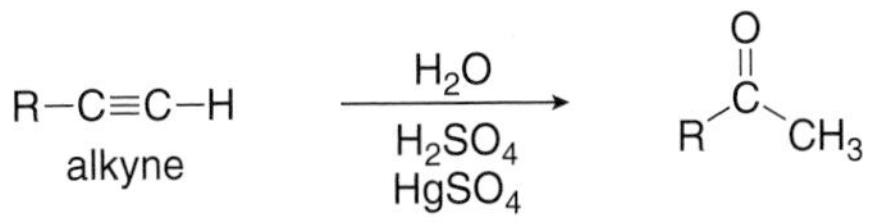

R−C≡C−H
alkyne
H_2O
H_2SO_4
$HgSO_4$

(Section 11.9)

Aldehydes and ketones are also both obtained as products of the oxidative cleavage of alkenes (Section 12.10).

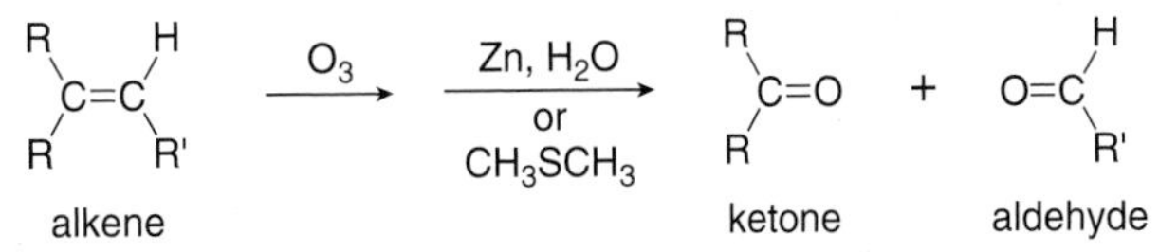

alkene
O_3
Zn, H_2O
or
CH_3SCH_3
ketone
aldehyde

Problem 21.11 What reagents are needed to convert each compound into butanal ($CH_3CH_2CH_2CHO$): (a) $CH_3CH_2CH_2COOCH_3$; (b) $CH_3CH_2CH_2CH_2OH$; (c) $HC{\equiv}CCH_2CH_3$; (d) $CH_3CH_2CH_2CH{=}CHCH_2CH_2CH_3$?

Problem 21.12 What reagents are needed to convert each compound into acetophenone ($C_6H_5COCH_3$): (a) benzene; (b) C_6H_5COCl; (c) $C_6H_5C{\equiv}CH$?

Problem 21.13 What alkene would yield 2,2-dimethoxy-1,3-cyclopentanedicarbaldehyde on treatment with O_3 followed by $(CH_3)_2S$?

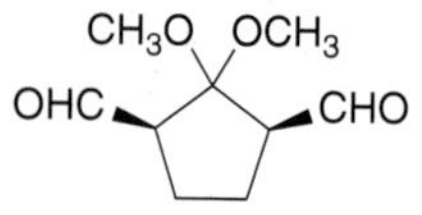

2,2-dimethoxy-1,3-cyclopentanedicarbaldehyde

21.7 Reactions of Aldehydes and Ketones—General Considerations

Let's begin our discussion of carbonyl reactions by looking at the two general kinds of reactions that aldehydes and ketones undergo.

[1] Reaction at the carbonyl carbon

Recall from Chapter 20 that the uncrowded, electrophilic carbonyl carbon makes aldehydes and ketones susceptible to **nucleophilic addition** reactions.

General reaction—Nucleophilic addition

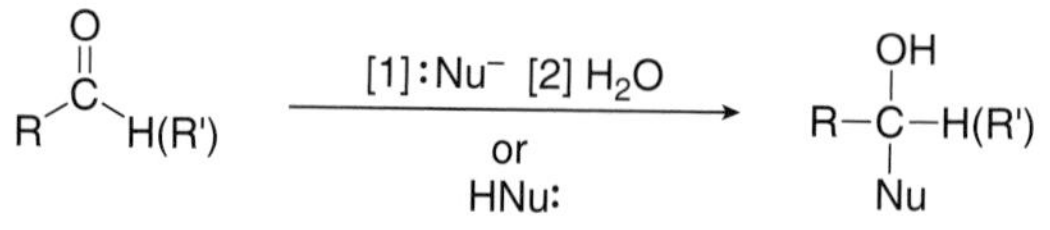

H and Nu are added.

The elements of H and Nu are added to the carbonyl group. In Chapter 20 you learned about this reaction with hydride ($H:^-$) and carbanions ($R:^-$) as nucleophiles. In Chapter 21, we will discuss similar reactions with other nucleophiles.

[2] Reaction at the α carbon

A second general reaction of aldehydes and ketones involves reaction at the **α carbon.** A C–H bond on the α carbon to a carbonyl group is more acidic than many other C–H bonds, because reaction with base forms a resonance-stabilized enolate anion.

- **Enolates are nucleophiles, and so they react with electrophiles to form new bonds on the α carbon.**

General reaction at the α carbon

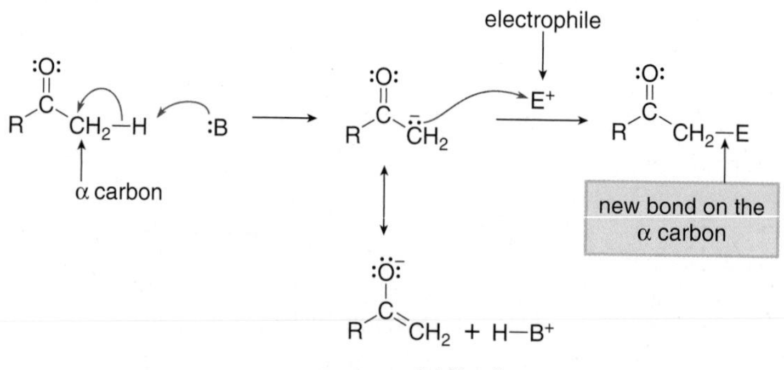

Chapters 23 and 24 are devoted to reactions at the α carbon to a carbonyl group.

- **Aldehydes and ketones react with nucleophiles at the carbonyl carbon.**
- **Aldehydes and ketones form enolates that react with electrophiles at the α carbon.**

21.7A The General Mechanism of Nucleophilic Addition

Two general mechanisms are usually drawn for nucleophilic addition, depending on the nucleophile (negatively charged versus neutral) and the presence or absence of an acid catalyst. With negatively charged nucleophiles, nucleophilic addition follows the two-step process first discussed in Chapter 20—**nucleophilic attack** followed by **protonation,** as shown in Mechanism 21.1.

Mechanism 21.1 General Mechanism—Nucleophilic Addition

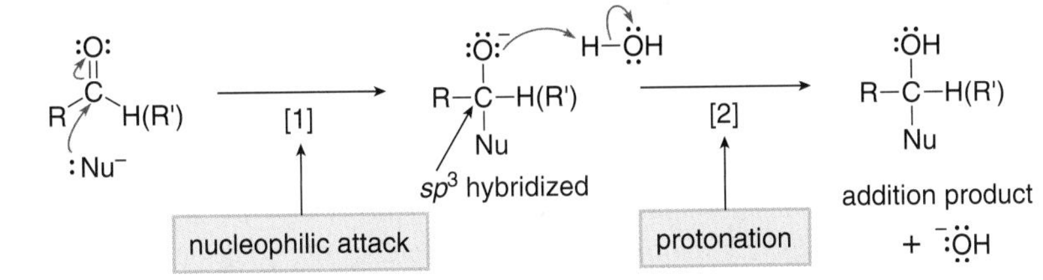

- In Step [1], **the nucleophile attacks the carbonyl group,** cleaving the π bond and moving an electron pair onto oxygen. This forms an *sp*^{3} hybridized intermediate with a new C–Nu bond.
- In Step [2], **protonation of the negatively charged O atom by H_2O** forms the addition product.

In this mechanism **nucleophilic attack *precedes* protonation.** This process occurs with strong neutral or negatively charged nucleophiles.

With some neutral nucleophiles, however, nucleophilic addition does not occur unless an acid catalyst is added. The general mechanism for this reaction consists of three steps (not two), but the same product results because H and Nu add across the carbonyl π bond. In this mechanism, **protonation *precedes* nucleophilic attack.** Mechanism 21.2 is shown with the neutral nucleophile H–Nu: and a general acid H–A.

Mechanism 21.2 General Mechanism—Acid-Catalyzed Nucleophilic Addition

Step [1] Protonation of the carbonyl group

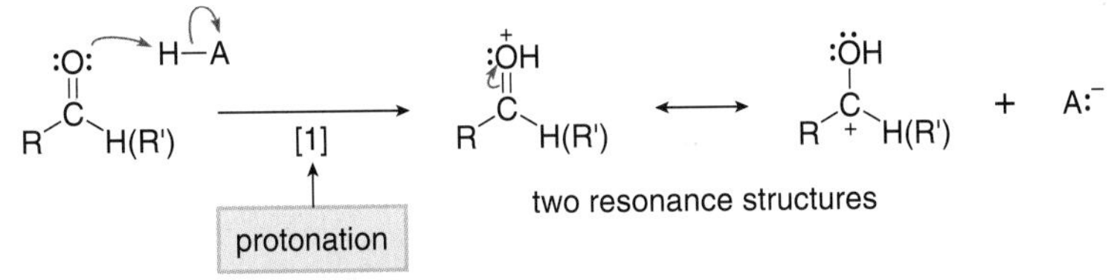

- Protonation of the carbonyl oxygen forms a resonance-stabilized cation that bears a full positive charge.

Steps [2]–[3] Nucleophilic attack and deprotonation

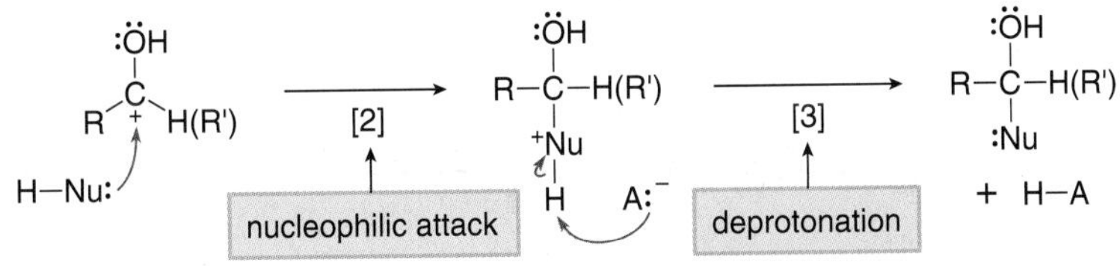

- In Step [2], the nucleophile attacks, and then deprotonation forms the neutral addition product in Step [3].
- The overall result is the addition of H and Nu to the carbonyl group.

The effect of protonation is to convert a neutral carbonyl group to one having a net positive charge. **This protonated carbonyl group is much more electrophilic,** and much more susceptible to attack by a nucleophile. This step is unnecessary with strong nucleophiles like hydride ($H:^-$) that were used in Chapter 20. With weaker nucleophiles, however, nucleophilic attack does not occur unless the carbonyl group is first protonated.

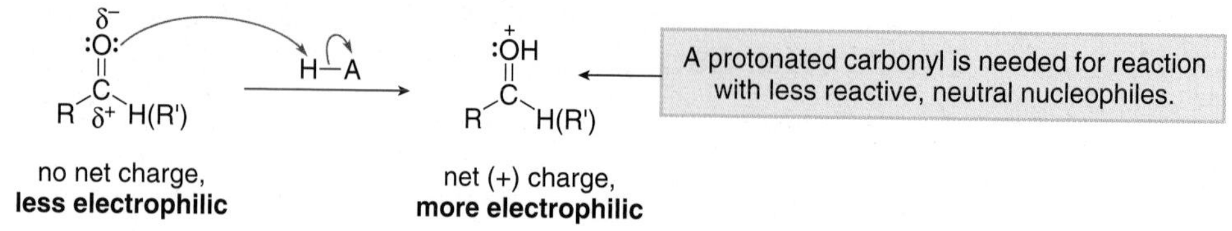

This step is a specific example of a general phenomenon.

- **Any reaction involving a carbonyl group and a strong acid begins with the same first step—protonation of the carbonyl oxygen.**

21.7B The Nucleophile

What nucleophiles add to carbonyl groups? This cannot be predicted solely on the trends in nucleophilicity learned in Chapter 7. Only *some* of the nucleophiles that react well in nucleophilic substitution at sp^3 hybridized carbons give reasonable yields of nucleophilic addition products.

Cl^-, Br^-, and I^- are good nucleophiles in substitution reactions at sp^3 hybridized carbons, but they are ineffective nucleophiles in addition. Addition of Cl^- to a carbonyl group, for example, would cleave the C–O π bond, forming an alkoxide. Because Cl^- is a much weaker base than the alkoxide formed, equilibrium favors the starting materials (the weaker base, Cl^-), *not* the addition product.

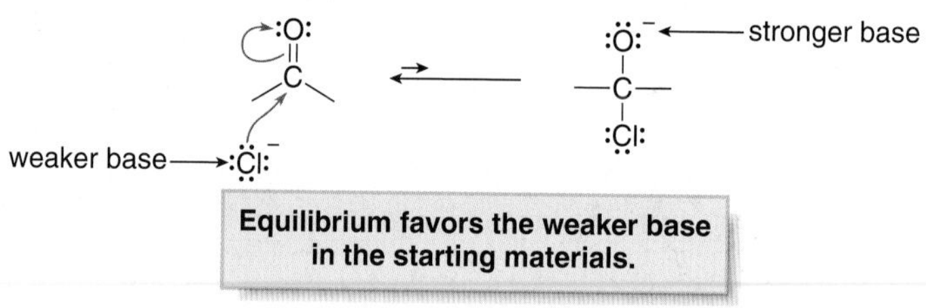

The situation is further complicated because some of the initial nucleophilic addition adducts are unstable and undergo elimination to form a stable product. For example, amines (RNH_2) add to carbonyl groups in the presence of mild acid to form unstable **carbinolamines,** which readily lose water to form **imines.** This addition–elimination sequence replaces a C=O by a C=N. The details of this process are discussed in Section 21.11.

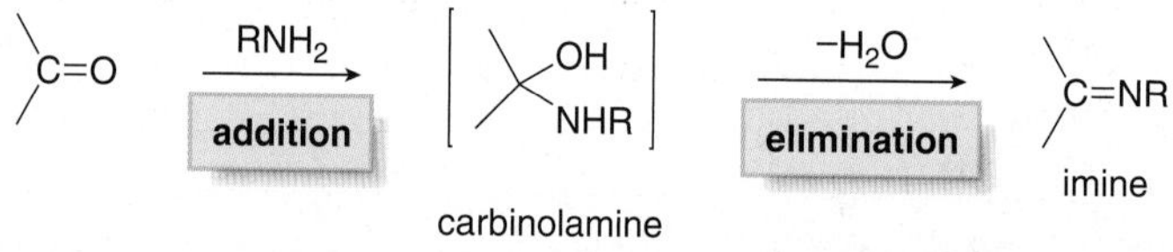

Figure 21.7 lists nucleophiles that add to a carbonyl group, as well as the products obtained from nucleophilic addition using cyclohexanone as a representative ketone. These reactions are discussed in the remaining sections of Chapter 21. In cases in which the initial addition adduct is unstable, it is enclosed within brackets, followed by the final product.

Figure 21.7
Specific examples of nucleophilic addition

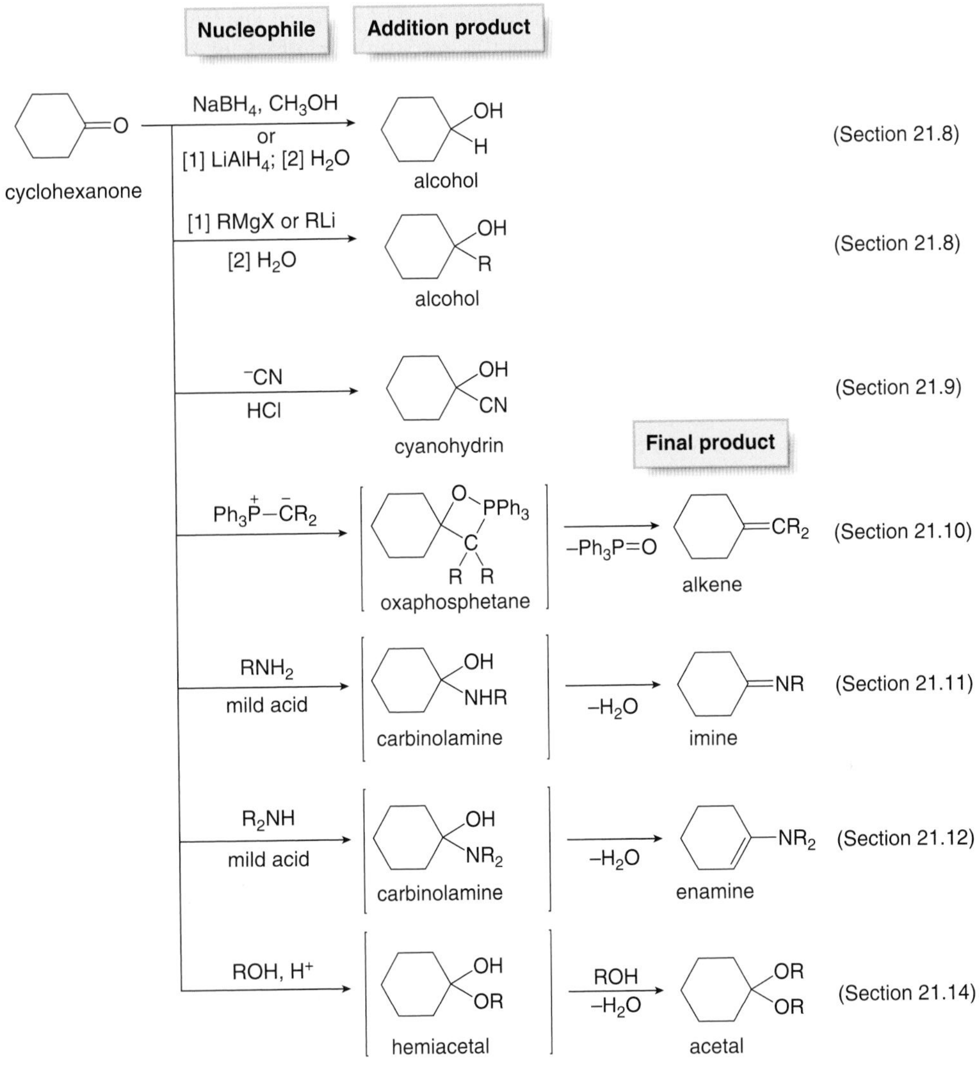

21.8 Nucleophilic Addition of H⁻ and R⁻—A Review

We begin our study of nucleophilic additions to aldehydes and ketones by briefly reviewing nucleophilic addition of hydride and carbanions, two reactions examined in Sections 20.4 and 20.10, respectively.

Treatment of an aldehyde or ketone with either $NaBH_4$ or $LiAlH_4$ followed by protonation forms a 1° or 2° alcohol. $NaBH_4$ and $LiAlH_4$ serve as a source of **hydride, H:⁻—the nucleophile**—and the reaction results in addition of the elements of H_2 across the C–O π bond. Addition of H_2 reduces the carbonyl group to an alcohol.

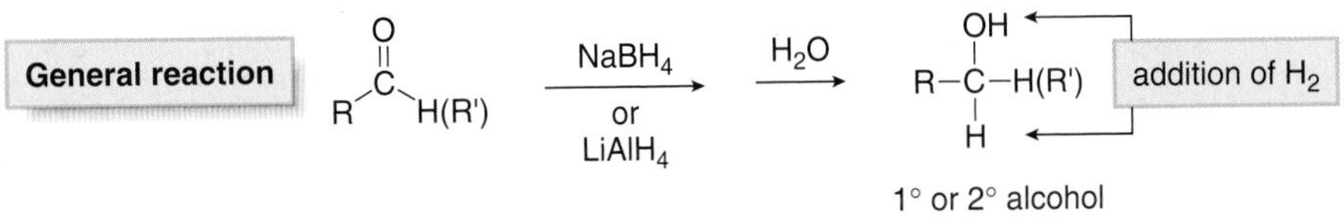

Hydride reduction of aldehydes and ketones occurs via the two-step mechanism of nucleophilic addition—that is, **nucleophilic attack of H:$^-$ followed by protonation**—shown previously in Section 20.4B.

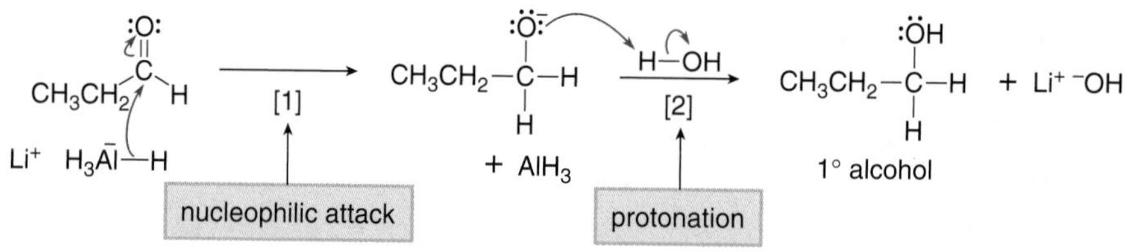

Treatment of an aldehyde or ketone with either an organolithium (R"Li) or Grignard reagent (R"MgX) followed by water forms a 1°, 2°, or 3° alcohol containing a new carbon–carbon bond. R"Li and R"MgX serve as a source of a **carbanion (R")$^-$—the nucleophile**—and the reaction results in addition of the elements of R" and H across the C–O π bond.

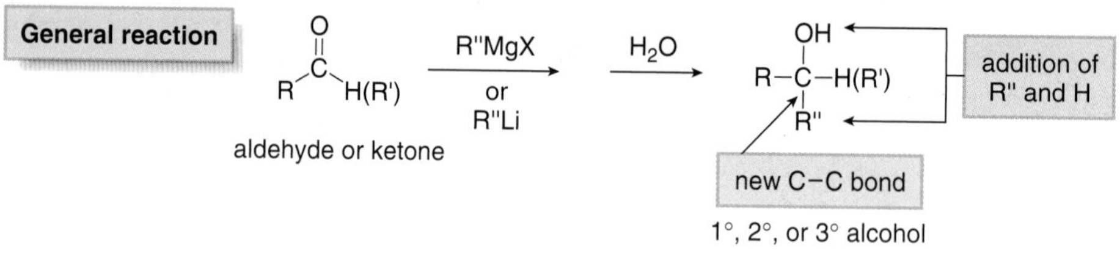

The stereochemistry of hydride reduction and Grignard addition was discussed previously in Sections 20.5 and 20.10B, respectively.

The nucleophilic addition of carbanions to aldehydes and ketones occurs via the two-step mechanism of nucleophilic addition—that is, **nucleophilic attack of (R")$^-$ followed by protonation**—shown previously in Section 20.10.

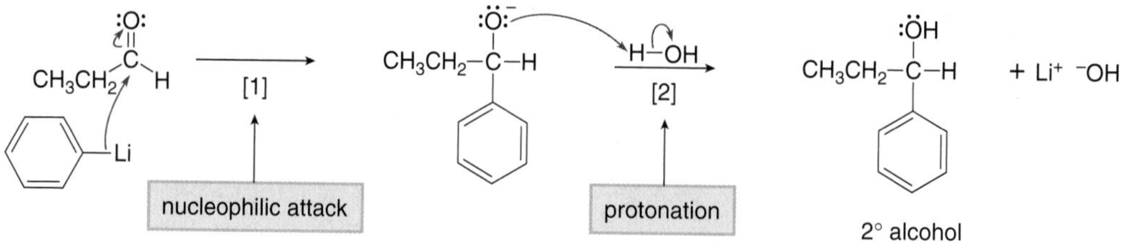

In both reactions, the nucleophile—either hydride or a carbanion—attacks the trigonal planar sp^2 hybridized carbonyl from both sides, so that when a new stereogenic center is formed, a mixture of stereoisomers results, as shown in Sample Problem 21.3.

Sample Problem 21.3 Draw the products (including the stereochemistry) formed in the following reaction.

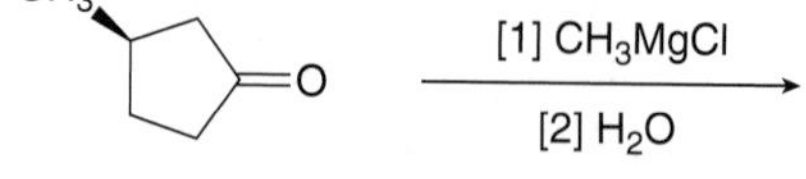

(3*R*)-3-methylcyclopentanone

Solution

The Grignard reagent adds CH_3^- from both sides of the trigonal planar carbonyl group, yielding a mixture of 3° alcohols after protonation with water. In this example, the starting ketone and both alcohol products are chiral. The two products, which contain two stereogenic centers, are stereoisomers but not mirror images—that is, they are **diastereomers.**

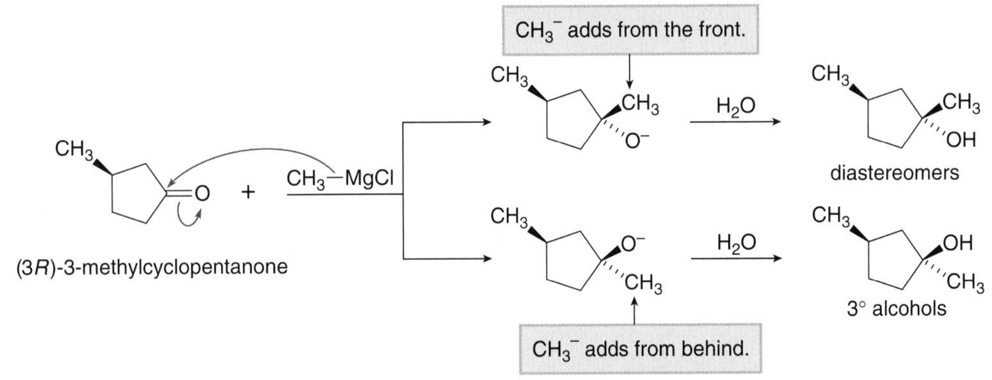

Problem 21.14 Draw the products of each reaction. Include all stereoisomers formed.

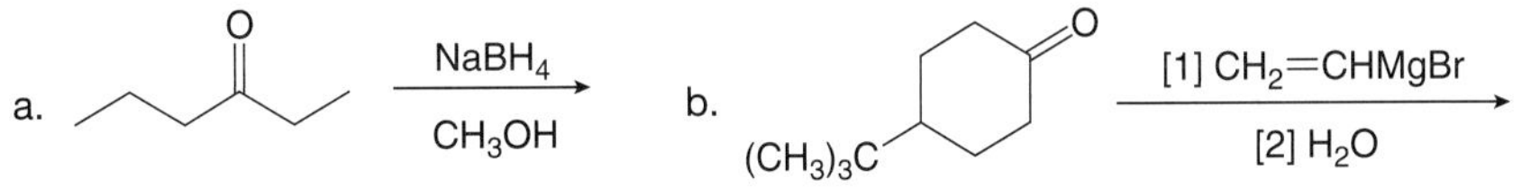

21.9 Nucleophilic Addition of ^{-}CN

Treatment of an aldehyde or ketone with NaCN and a strong acid such as HCl adds the elements of HCN across the carbon–oxygen π bond, forming a **cyanohydrin.**

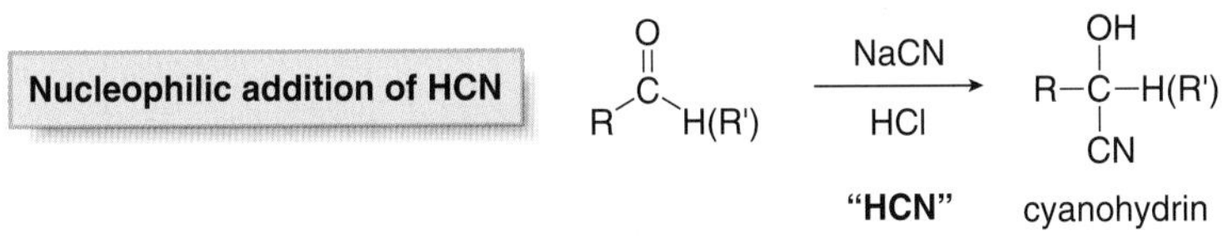

This reaction adds one carbon to the aldehyde or ketone, forming a new carbon–carbon bond.

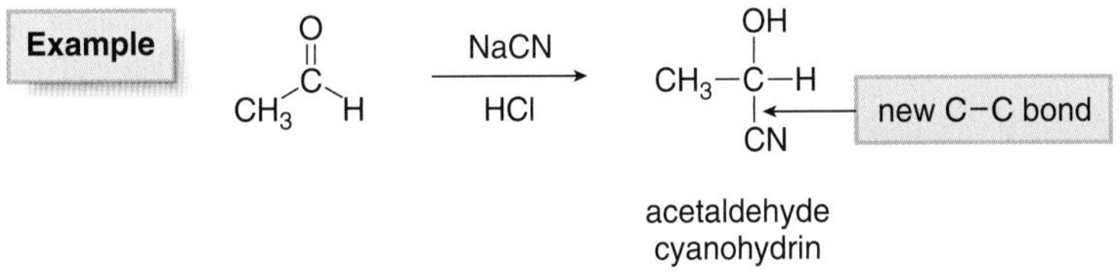

21.9A The Mechanism

The mechanism of cyanohydrin formation involves the usual two steps of nucleophilic addition: **nucleophilic attack followed by protonation** as shown in Mechanism 21.3.

Mechanism 21.3 Nucleophilic Addition of $^{-}$CN—Cyanohydrin Formation

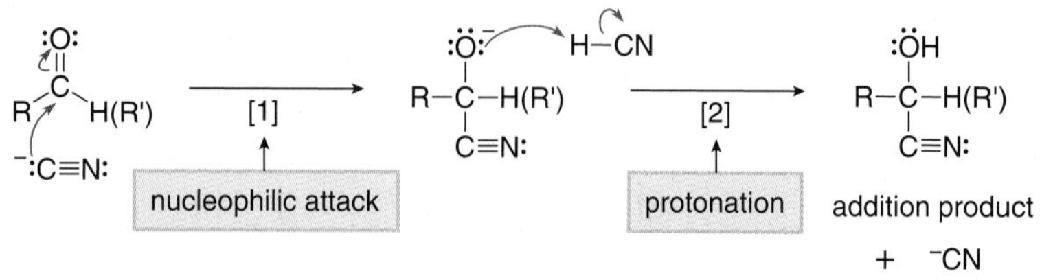

- In Step [1], **nucleophilic attack of $^{-}$CN** forms a new carbon–carbon bond with cleavage of the C–O π bond.
- In Step [2], **protonation of the negatively charged O atom by HCN** forms the addition product. The hydrogen cyanide (HCN) used in this step is formed by the acid–base reaction of cyanide ($^{-}$CN) with the strong acid, HCl.

This reaction does not occur with HCN alone. The **cyanide anion** makes addition possible because it is a strong nucleophile that attacks the carbonyl group.

Cyanohydrins can be reconverted to carbonyl compounds by treatment with base. This process is just the reverse of the addition of HCN: **deprotonation followed by elimination of $^{-}$CN.**

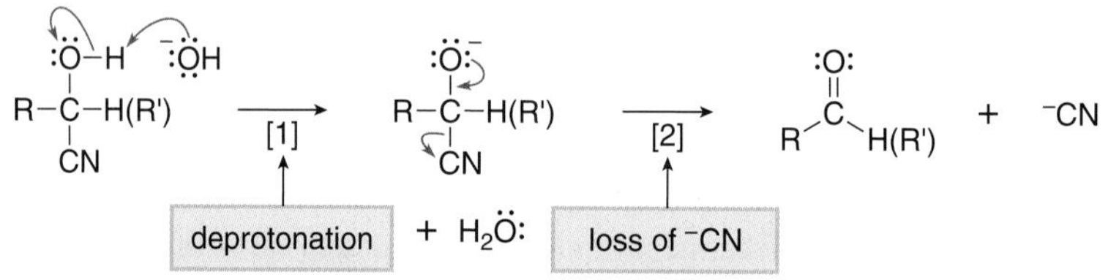

Note the difference between two similar terms. **Hydration** results in *adding* water to a compound. **Hydrolysis** results in *cleaving bonds* with water.

The cyano group (CN) of a cyanohydrin is readily hydrolyzed to a carboxy group (COOH) by heating with aqueous acid or base. Hydrolysis replaces the three C–N bonds by three C–O bonds.

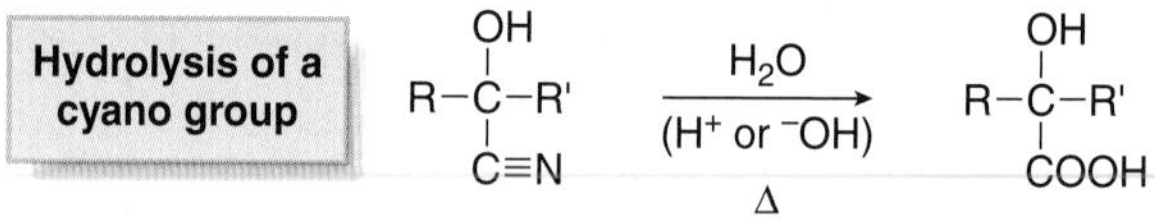

Problem 21.15 Draw the products of each reaction.

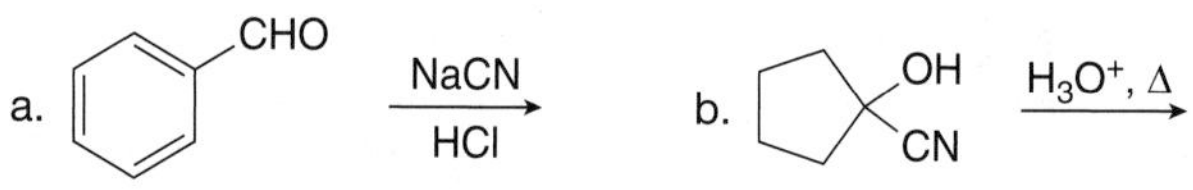

21.9B Application: Naturally Occurring Cyanohydrin Derivatives

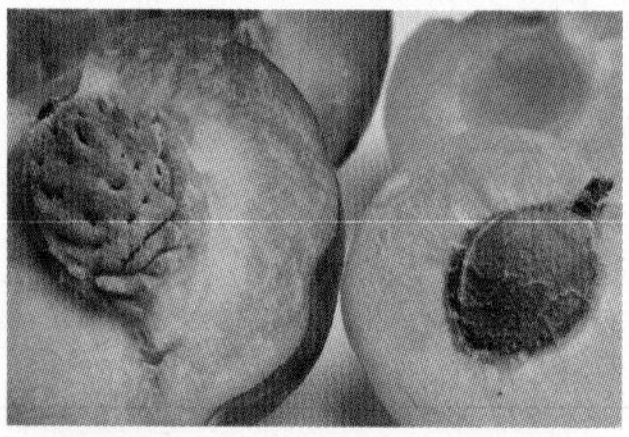

Peach and apricot pits are a natural source of the cyanohydrin derivative amygdalin.

Although the cyanohydrin is an uncommon functional group, **linamarin** and **amygdalin** are two naturally occurring cyanohydrin derivatives. Both contain a carbon atom bonded to both an oxygen atom and a cyano group, analogous to a cyanohydrin.

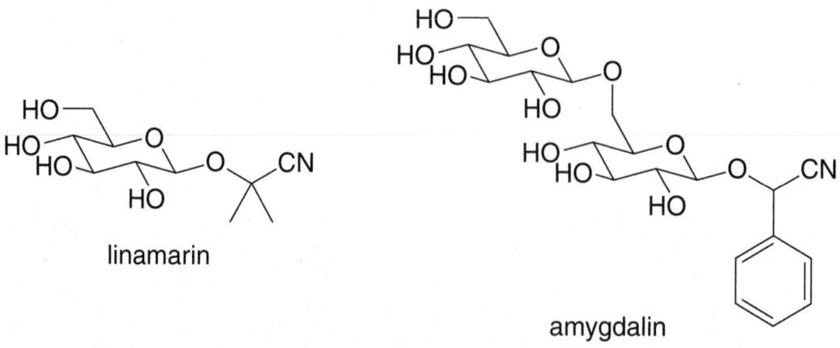

Cassava is a widely grown root crop, first introduced to Africa by Portuguese traders from Brazil in the sixteenth century. The peeled root is eaten after boiling or roasting. If the root is eaten without processing, illness and even death can result from high levels of HCN.

Linamarin is isolated from cassava, a woody shrub grown as a root crop in the humid tropical regions of South America and Africa. **Amygdalin** is present in the seeds and pits of apricots, peaches, and wild cherries. Amygdalin, sometimes called **laetrile,** was once touted as an anticancer drug, and is still available in some countries for this purpose, although its effectiveness is unproven.

Both linamarin and amygdalin are toxic compounds because they are metabolized to cyanohydrins, which are hydrolyzed to carbonyl compounds and toxic HCN gas, a cellular poison with a characteristic almond odor. This second step is merely the reconversion of a cyanohydrin to a carbonyl compound, a process that occurs with base in reactions run in the laboratory (Section 21.9A). If cassava root is processed with care, linamarin is enzymatically metabolized by this reaction sequence and the toxic HCN is released before the root is ingested, making it safe to eat.

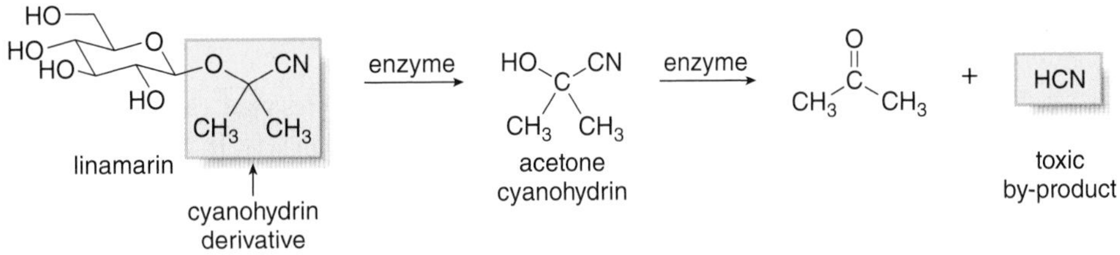

Problem 21.16 What cyanohydrin and carbonyl compound are formed when amygdalin is metabolized in a similar manner to linamarin?

21.10 The Wittig Reaction

The additions of H^-, R^-, and ^-CN all involve the same two steps—nucleophilic attack followed by protonation. Other examples of nucleophilic addition in Chapter 21 are somewhat different. Although they still involve attack of a nucleophile, the initial addition adduct is converted to another product by one or more reactions.

The first reaction in this category is the **Wittig reaction,** named for German chemist Georg Wittig, who was awarded the Nobel Prize in Chemistry in 1979 for its discovery. The Wittig reaction uses a carbon nucleophile, the **Wittig reagent,** to form **alkenes.** When a carbonyl compound is treated with a Wittig reagent, the carbonyl oxygen atom is replaced by the negatively charged alkyl group bonded to the phosphorus—that is, **the C=O is converted to a C=C.**

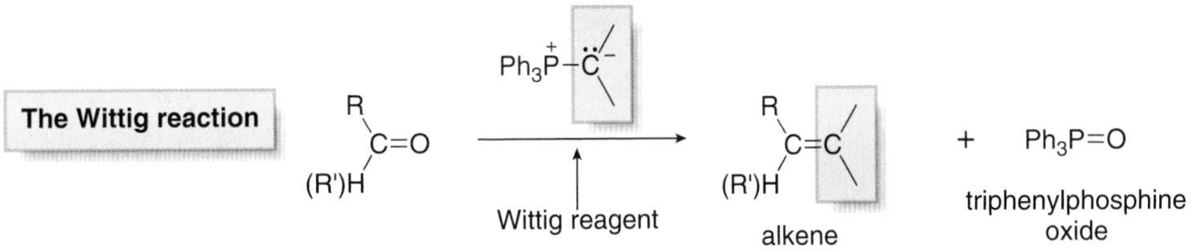

- **A Wittig reaction forms two new carbon–carbon bonds—one new σ bond and one new π bond—as well as a phosphorus by-product, $Ph_3P=O$ (triphenylphosphine oxide).**

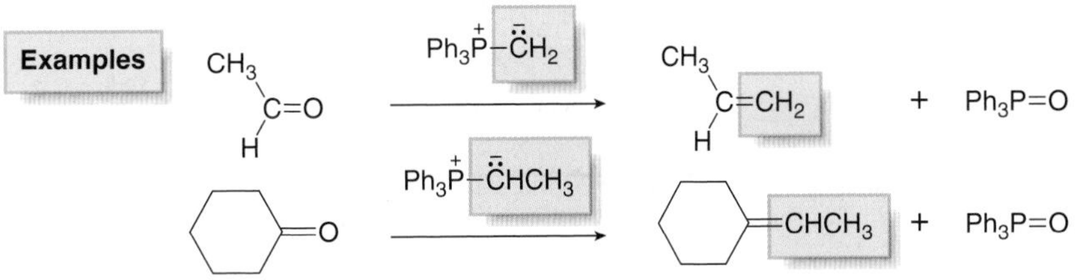

21.10A The Wittig Reagent

A **Wittig reagent** is an **organophosphorus reagent**—a reagent that contains a carbon–phosphorus bond. A typical Wittig reagent has a phosphorus atom bonded to three phenyl groups, plus another alkyl group that bears a negative charge.

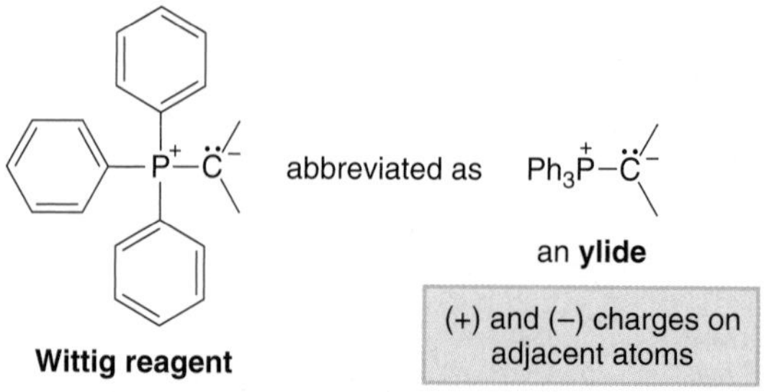
abbreviated as
an ylide
(+) and (–) charges on adjacent atoms
Wittig reagent

Phosphorus ylides are also called **phosphoranes.**

A Wittig reagent is an ***ylide*****, a species that contains two oppositely charged atoms bonded to each other, and both atoms have octets.** In a Wittig reagent, a negatively charged carbon atom is bonded to a positively charged phosphorus atom.

Because phosphorus is a third-row element, it can be surrounded by more than eight electrons. As a result, a second resonance structure can be drawn that places a double bond between carbon and phosphorus. Regardless of which resonance structure is drawn, a **Wittig reagent has no net charge.** In one resonance structure, though, the carbon atom bears a net negative charge, so it is nucleophilic.

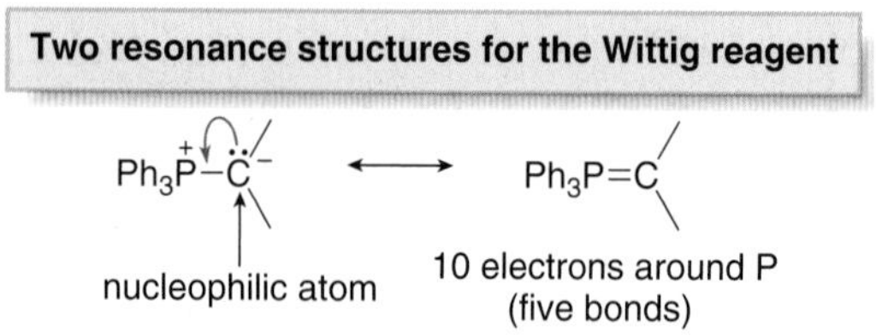
Two resonance structures for the Wittig reagent
nucleophilic atom
10 electrons around P (five bonds)

Wittig reagents are synthesized by a two-step procedure.

Step [1] S_N2 reaction of triphenylphosphine with an alkyl halide forms a phosphonium salt.

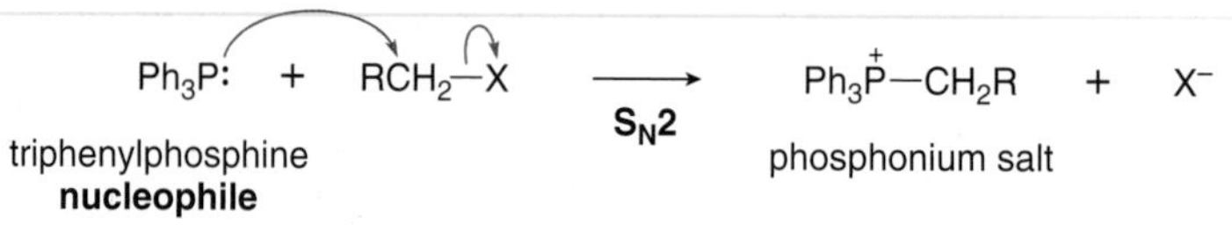
triphenylphosphine
nucleophile
phosphonium salt

Because phosphorus is located below nitrogen in the periodic table, a neutral phosphorus atom with three bonds also has a lone pair of electrons.

Triphenylphosphine (Ph_3P:), which contains a lone pair of electrons on P, is the nucleophile. Because the reaction follows an S_N2 mechanism, it works best with unhindered CH_3X and 1° alkyl halides (RCH_2X). Secondary alkyl halides (R_2CHX) can also be used, although yields are often lower.

Step [2] Deprotonation of the phosphonium salt with a strong base (:B) forms the ylide.

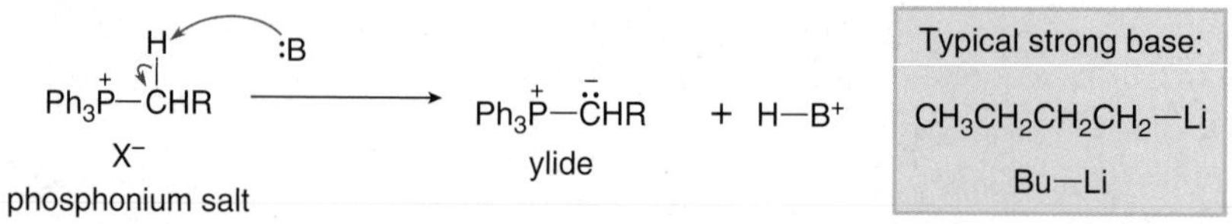
phosphonium salt
ylide
Typical strong base:
CH3CH2CH2CH2—Li
Bu—Li

Because removal of a proton from a carbon bonded to phosphorus generates a resonance-stabilized carbanion (the ylide), this proton is somewhat more acidic than other protons on an

Section 20.9C discussed the reaction of organometallic reagents as strong bases.

alkyl group in the phosphonium salt. Very strong bases are still needed, though, to favor the products of this acid–base reaction. Common bases used for this reaction are the organolithium reagents such as butyllithium, $CH_3CH_2CH_2CH_2Li$, abbreviated as BuLi.

To synthesize the Wittig reagent, $Ph_3P{=}CH_2$, use these two steps:

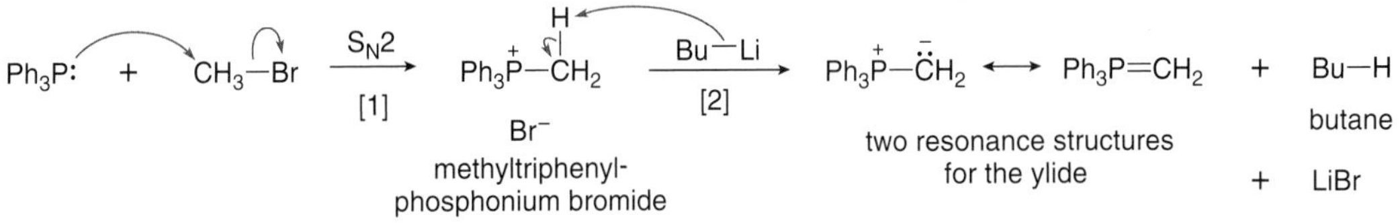

- **Step [1]** Form the phosphonium salt by S_N2 reaction of Ph_3P: and CH_3Br.
- **Step [2]** Form the ylide by removal of a proton using BuLi as a strong base.

Problem 21.17 Draw the products of the following Wittig reactions.

a. $(CH_3)_2C{=}O + Ph_3P{=}CH_2 \longrightarrow$

b. 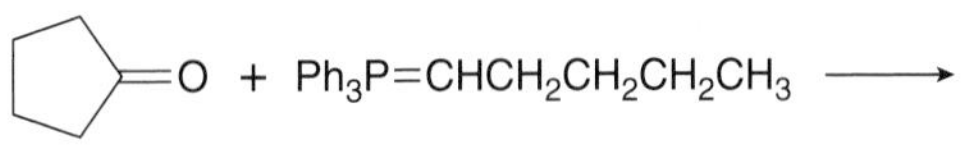

Problem 21.18 Outline a synthesis of each Wittig reagent from Ph_3P and an alkyl halide.

a. $Ph_3P{=}CHCH_3$ b. $Ph_3P{=}C(CH_3)_2$ c. $Ph_3P{=}CHC_6H_5$

21.10B Mechanism of the Wittig Reaction

The currently accepted mechanism of the Wittig reaction involves two steps. Like other nucleophiles, the Wittig reagent attacks an electrophilic carbonyl carbon, but then the initial addition adduct undergoes elimination to form an alkene. Mechanism 21.4 is drawn using $Ph_3P{=}CH_2$.

Mechanism 21.4 The Wittig Reaction

Step [1] Nucleophilic addition forms a four-membered ring.

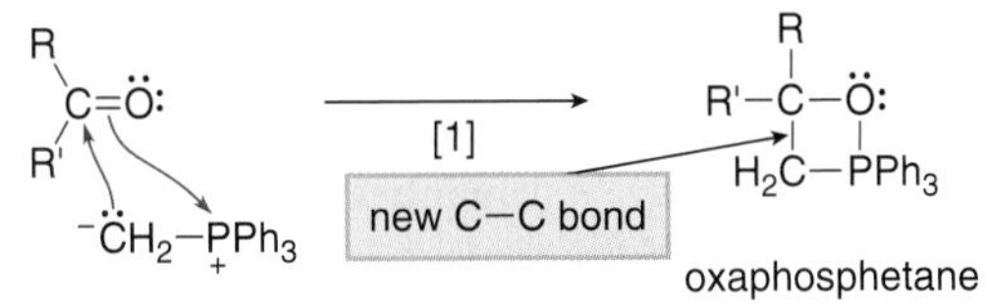

- Step [1] forms two bonds and generates a four-membered ring. The negatively charged carbon atom of the ylide attacks the carbonyl carbon to form a new carbon–carbon σ bond, while the carbonyl O atom attacks the positively charged P atom.
- This process generates an **oxaphosphetane,** a four-membered ring containing a strong P–O bond.

Step [2] Elimination of $Ph_3P{=}O$ forms the alkene.

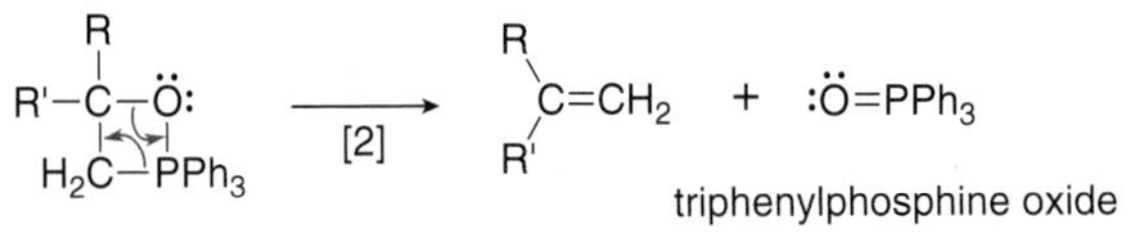

- In Step [2], **$Ph_3P{=}O$ (triphenylphosphine oxide) is eliminated,** forming two new π bonds. The formation of the very strong P–O double bond provides the driving force for the Wittig reaction.

One limitation of the Wittig reaction is that a mixture of alkene stereoisomers sometimes forms. For example, reaction of propanal (CH_3CH_2CHO) with a Wittig reagent forms the mixture of *E* and *Z* isomers shown.

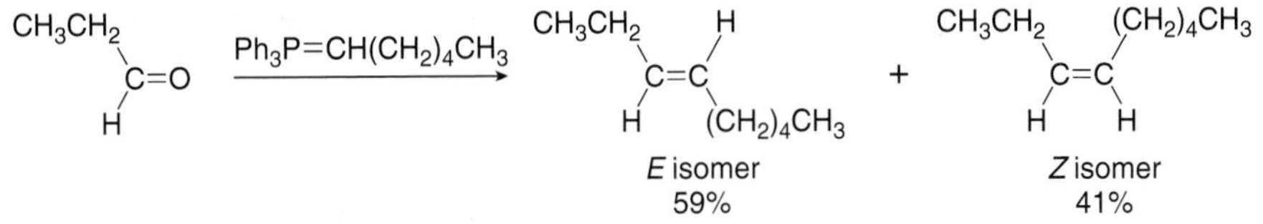

Figure 21.8
A Wittig reaction used to synthesize β-carotene

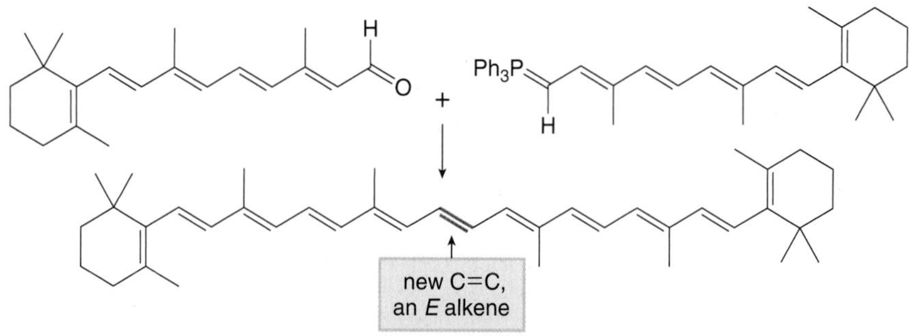

β-carotene
orange pigment found in carrots
(vitamin A precursor)

- The more stable *E* alkene is the major product in this Wittig reaction.

Because the Wittig reaction forms two carbon–carbon bonds in a single reaction, it has been used to synthesize many natural products, including β-carotene, shown in Figure 21.8.

Problem 21.19 Draw the products (including stereoisomers) formed when benzaldehyde (C_6H_5CHO) is treated with each Wittig reagent: (a) $Ph_3P=CHCH_2CH_3$; (b) $Ph_3P=CHC_6H_5$; (c) $Ph_3P=CHCOOCH_3$.

Problem 21.20 Wittig reaction of aldehyde **A** with $Ph_3P=CHCO_2CH_2CH_3$ forms **B,** an intermediate in the synthesis of amphikuemin, a compound involved in the intricate symbiosis between the sea anemone and anemonefish mentioned in the Prologue. Treatment of **B** with one equivalent of H_2 in the presence of a Pd catalyst yields **C.** What is the structure of **C?**

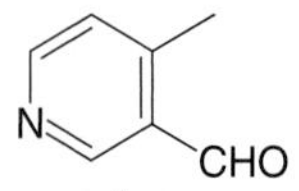

A

21.10C Retrosynthetic Analysis

To use the Wittig reaction in synthesis, you must be able to determine what carbonyl compound and Wittig reagent are needed to prepare a given compound—that is, **you must work backwards, in the retrosynthetic direction.** There can be two different Wittig routes to a given alkene, but one is often preferred on steric grounds.

How To Determine the Starting Materials for a Wittig Reaction Using Retrosynthetic Analysis

Example What starting materials are needed to synthesize alkene X by a Wittig reaction?

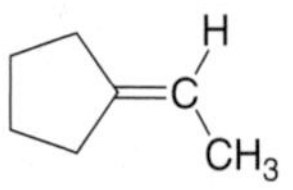

X

Step [1] Cleave the carbon–carbon double bond into two components.

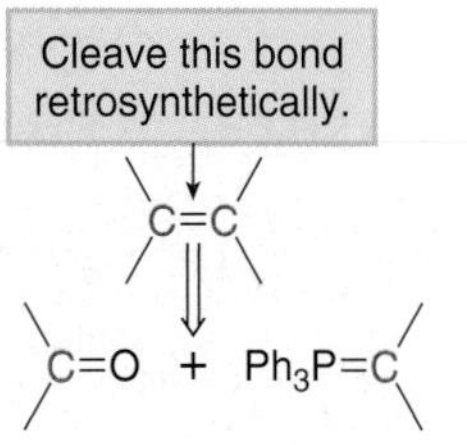

- Part of the molecule becomes the carbonyl component and the other part becomes the Wittig reagent.

How To, continued . . .

There are usually two routes to a given alkene using a Wittig reaction:

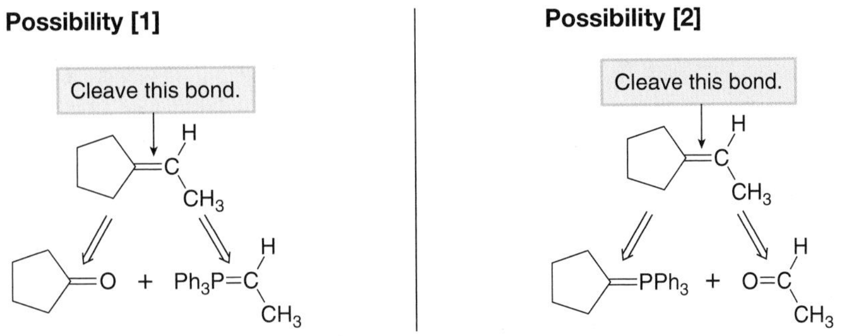

Step [2] **Compare the Wittig reagents. The preferred pathway uses a Wittig reagent derived from an unhindered alkyl halide—CH_3X or RCH_2X.**

Determine what alkyl halide is needed to prepare each Wittig reagent:

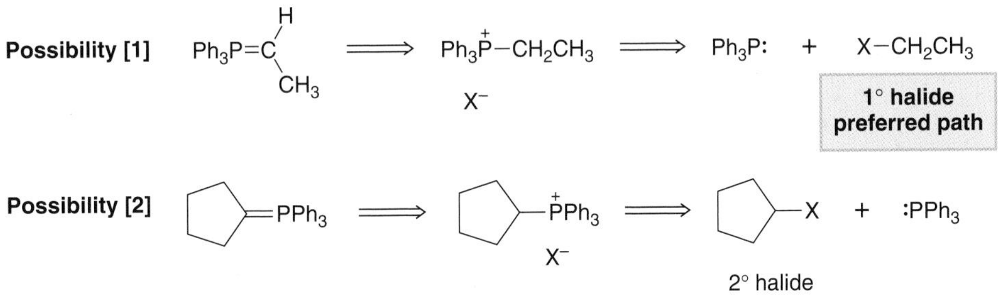

Because the synthesis of the Wittig reagent begins with an S_N2 reaction, **the preferred pathway begins with an unhindered methyl halide or 1° alkyl halide.** In this example, retrosynthetic analysis of both Wittig reagents indicates that only one of them ($Ph_3P=CHCH_3$) can be synthesized from a 1° alkyl halide, making Possibility [1] the preferred pathway.

Problem 21.21 What starting materials are needed to prepare each alkene by a Wittig reaction? When there are two possible routes, indicate which route, if any, is preferred: (a) $(CH_3)_2C=CHCH_2CH_3$; (b) $CH_3CH_2CH=CHCH_2CH_3$; (c) $C_6H_5CH=CHCH_3$.

21.10D Comparing Methods of Alkene Synthesis

An advantage in using the Wittig reaction over other elimination methods to synthesize alkenes is that **you always know the location of the double bond.** Whereas other methods of alkene synthesis often give a mixture of constitutional isomers, the Wittig reaction always gives a single constitutional isomer.

For example, two methods can be used to convert cyclohexanone into alkene **B** (methylenecyclohexane): a two-step method consisting of Grignard addition followed by dehydration, or a one-step Wittig reaction.

cyclohexanone **B**

Recall from Section 9.8 that the major product formed in acid-catalyzed dehydration of an alcohol is the more substituted alkene.

In a two-step method, treatment of cyclohexanone with CH_3MgBr forms a 3° alcohol after protonation. Dehydration of the alcohol with H_2SO_4 forms a mixture of alkenes, in which the desired disubstituted alkene is the minor product.

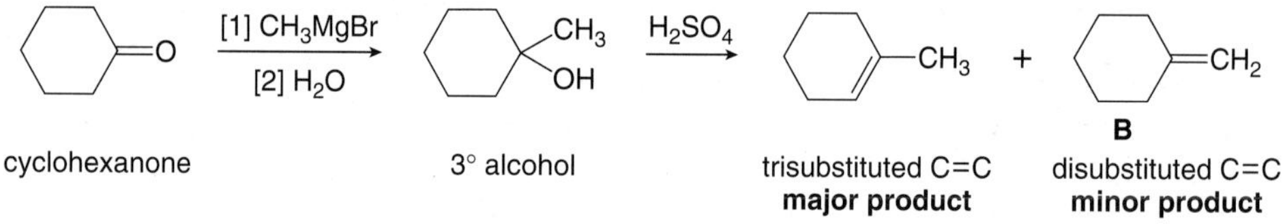
[1] CH_3MgBr
[2] H_2O
CH_3
OH
H_2SO_4
CH_3
+
CH_2
B
cyclohexanone
3° alcohol
trisubstituted C=C
major product
disubstituted C=C
minor product

By contrast, reaction of cyclohexanone with $Ph_3P{=}CH_2$ affords the desired alkene as the only product. The newly formed double bond always joins the carbonyl carbon with the negatively charged carbon of the Wittig reagent. In other words, **the position of the double bond is always unambiguous in the Wittig reaction.** This makes the Wittig reaction an especially attractive method for preparing many alkenes.

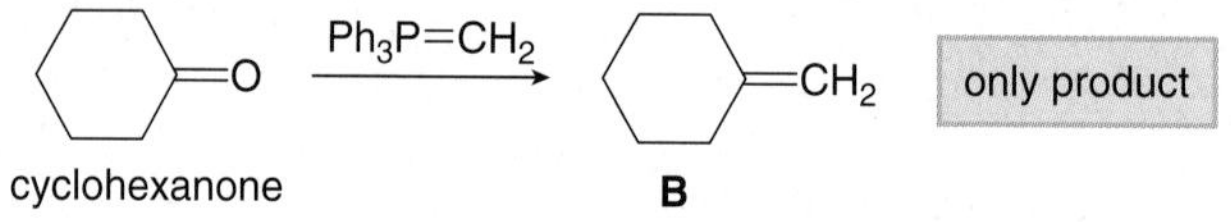
$Ph_3P{=}CH_2$
CH_2
only product
cyclohexanone
B

Problem 21.22 Show two methods to synthesize each alkene: a one-step method using a Wittig reagent, and a two-step method that forms a carbon–carbon bond with an organometallic reagent in one of the steps.

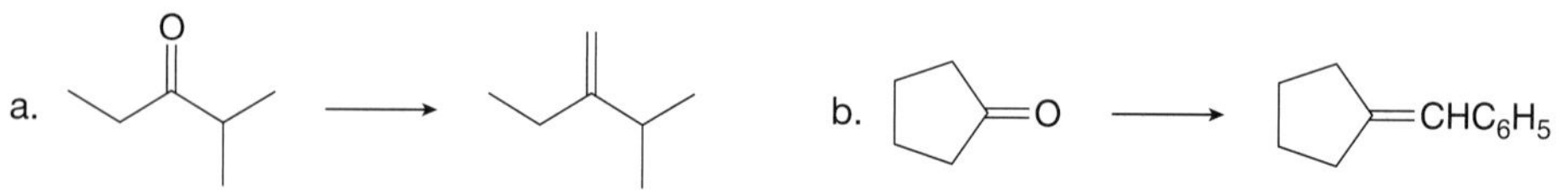
a.
b.
CHC_6H_5

21.11 Addition of 1° Amines

We now move on to the reaction of aldehydes and ketones with nitrogen and oxygen heteroatoms. **Amines, for example, are organic nitrogen compounds that contain a nonbonded electron pair on the N atom.** Amines are classified as 1°, 2°, or 3° by the number of alkyl groups bonded to the *nitrogen* atom.

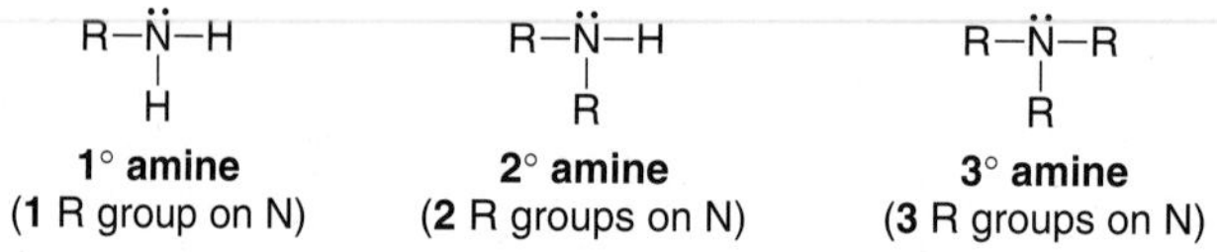
1° amine
(1 R group on N)
2° amine
(2 R groups on N)
3° amine
(3 R groups on N)

Both 1° and 2° amines react with aldehydes and ketones. We begin by examining the reaction of aldehydes and ketones with 1° amines.

21.11A Formation of Imines

Treatment of an aldehyde or ketone with a 1° amine affords an **imine** (also called a **Schiff base**). Nucleophilic attack of the 1° amine on the carbonyl group forms an unstable **carbinolamine,** which loses water to form an imine. The overall reaction results in **replacement of C=O by C=NR.**

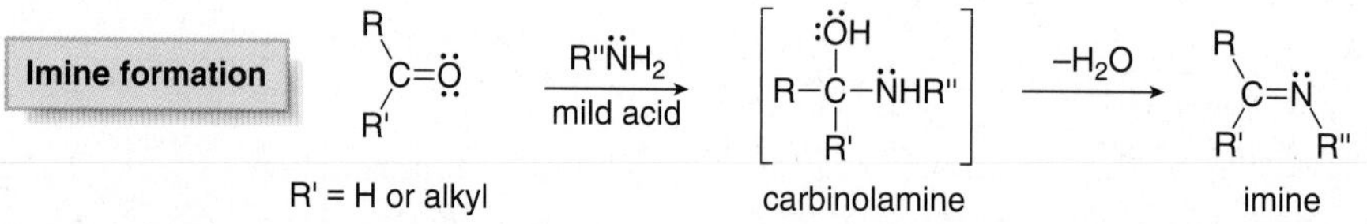
Imine formation
R"NH_2
mild acid
$-H_2O$
R' = H or alkyl
carbinolamine
imine

Because the N atom of an imine is surrounded by three groups (two atoms and a lone pair), it is sp^2 hybridized, making the C–N–R" bond angle ~120° (*not* 180°). Imine formation is fastest when the reaction medium is weakly acidic.

Examples

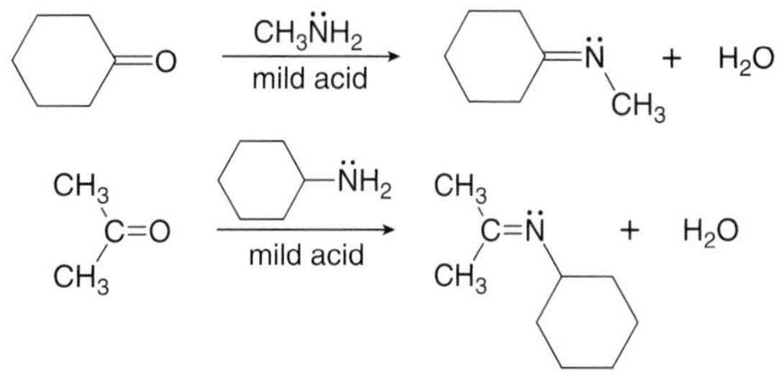

The mechanism of imine formation (Mechanism 21.5) can be divided into two distinct parts: **nucleophilic addition of the 1° amine, followed by elimination of H_2O.** Each step involves a reversible equilibrium, so that the reaction is driven to completion by removing H_2O.

Mechanism 21.5 Imine Formation from an Aldehyde or Ketone

Part [1] Nucleophilic addition forms a carbinolamine.

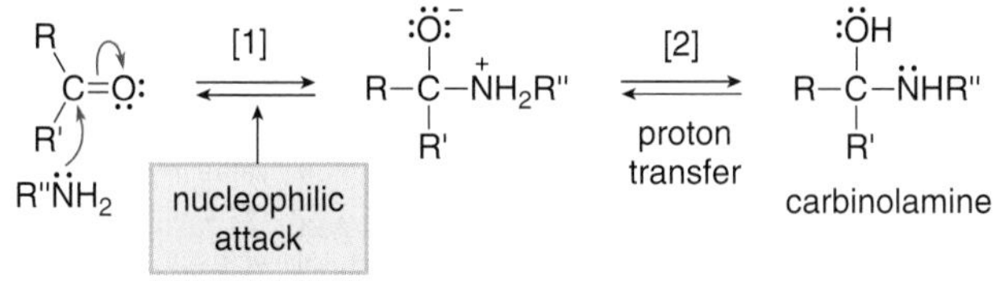

- **Nucleophilic attack** of the amine followed by proton transfer forms the unstable carbinolamine (Steps [1]–[2]). These steps result in the addition of H and NHR" to the carbonyl group.

Part [2] Elimination of H_2O forms an imine.

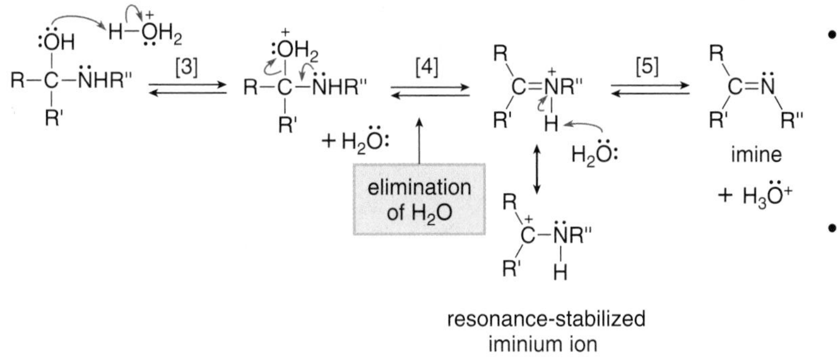

- Elimination of H_2O forms the imine in three steps. Protonation of the OH group in Step [3] forms a good leaving group, leading to **loss of water** in Step [4], giving a resonance-stabilized **iminium ion.** Loss of a proton forms the imine in Step [5].
- Except for Steps [1] (nucleophilic addition) and [4] (H_2O elimination), all other steps in the mechanism are acid–base reactions—that is, moving a proton from one atom to another.

Imine formation is most rapid at pH 4–5. Mild acid is needed for protonation of the hydroxy group in Step [3] to form a **good leaving group.** Under strongly acidic conditions, the reaction rate decreases because the amine nucleophile is protonated. With no free electron pair, it is no longer a nucleophile, and so nucleophilic addition cannot occur.

Protonation makes a good leaving group...but at low pH, the basic amine is protonated.

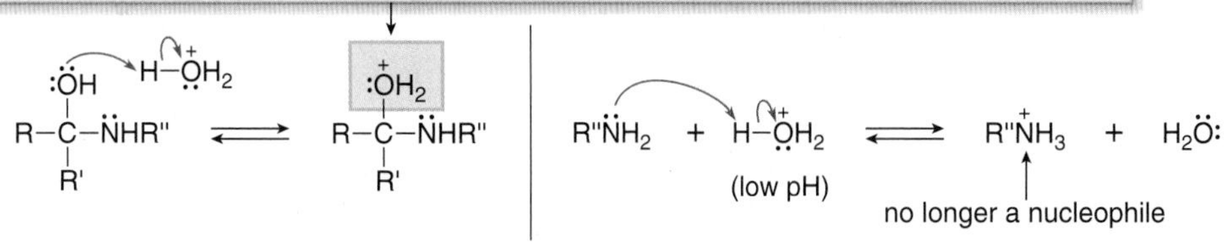

Problem 21.23 Draw the product formed when $CH_3CH_2CH_2CH_2NH_2$ reacts with each carbonyl compound in the presence of mild acid.

a. 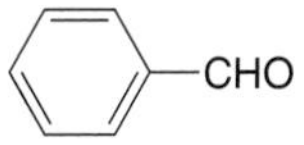

b. 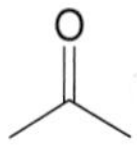

c. 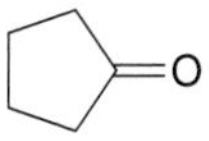

Problem 21.24 What 1° amine and carbonyl compound are needed to prepare each imine?

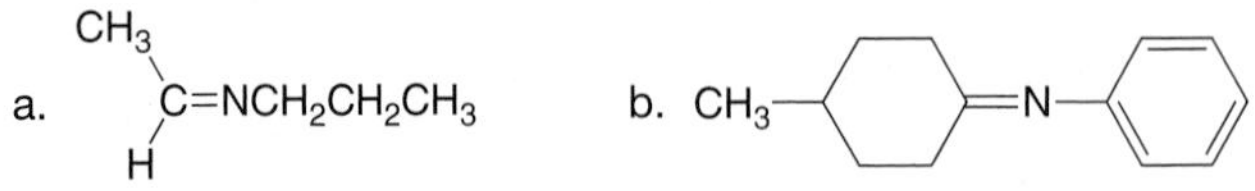

21.11B Application: Retinal, Rhodopsin, and the Chemistry of Vision

Many imines play vital roles in biological systems. A key molecule in the chemistry of vision is the highly conjugated imine **rhodopsin,** which is synthesized in the rod cells of the eye from **11-*cis*-retinal** and a 1° amine in the protein **opsin.**

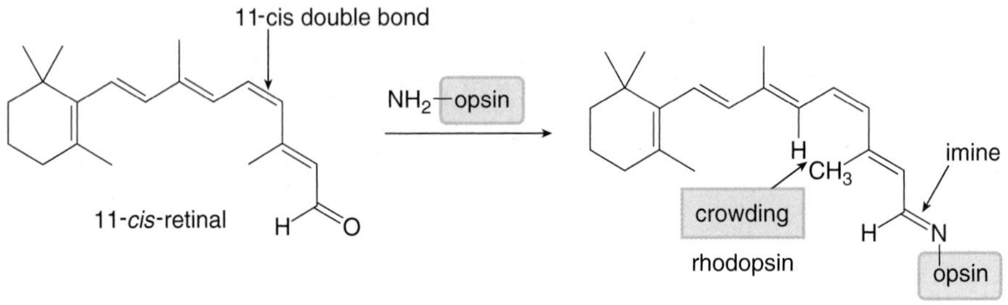

The central role of rhodopsin in the visual process was delineated by Nobel Laureate George Wald of Harvard University.

The complex process of vision centers around this imine derived from retinal (Figure 21.9). The 11-cis double bond in rhodopsin creates crowding in the rather rigid side chain. When light strikes the rod cells of the retina, it is absorbed by the conjugated double bonds of rhodopsin, and the 11-cis double bond is isomerized to the 11-trans arrangement. This isomerization is accompanied by a drastic change in shape in the protein, altering the concentration of Ca^{2+} ions moving across the cell membrane, and sending a nerve impulse to the brain, which is then processed into a visual image.

Figure 21.9 The key reaction in the chemistry of vision

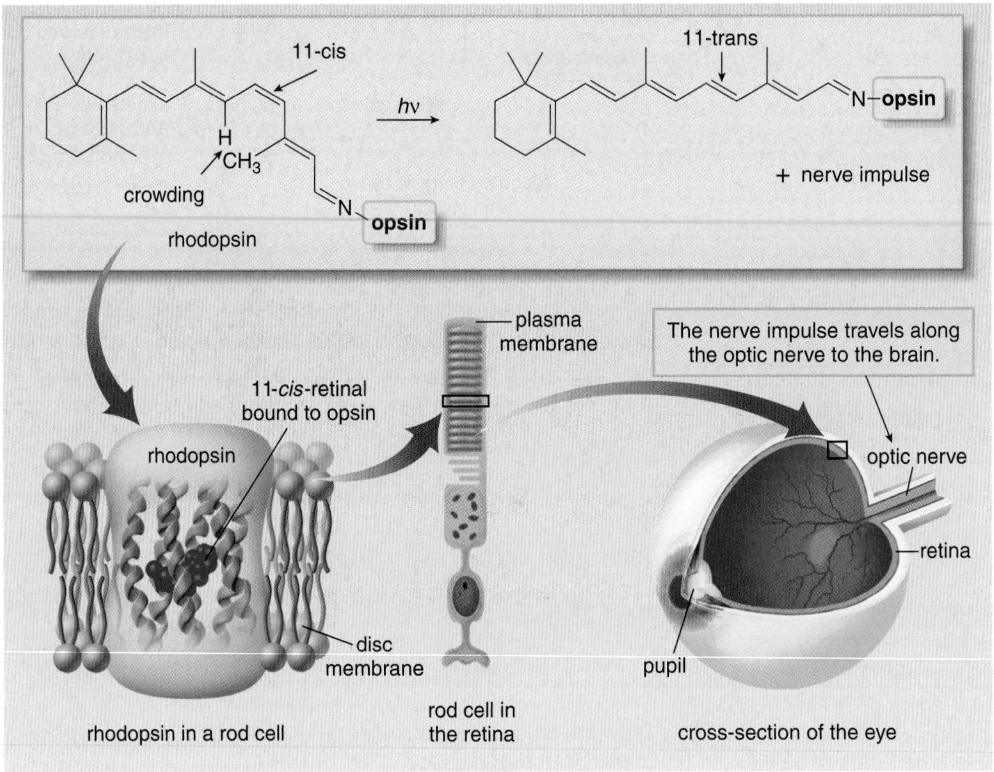

- Rhodopsin is a light-sensitive compound located in the membrane of the rod cells in the retina of the eye. Rhodopsin contains the protein opsin bonded to 11-*cis*-retinal via an imine linkage. When light strikes this molecule, the crowded 11-cis double bond isomerizes to the 11-trans isomer, and a nerve impulse is transmitted to the brain by the optic nerve.

21.12 Addition of 2° Amines

21.12A Formation of Enamines

A 2° amine reacts with an aldehyde or ketone to give an **enamine.** ***Enamines* have a nitrogen atom bonded to a double bond** (alk*ene* + *amine* = *enamine*).

Enamine formation

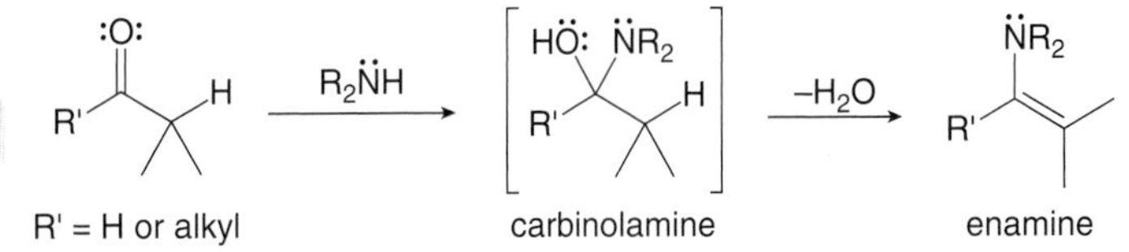

Like imines, enamines are also formed by the addition of a nitrogen nucleophile to a carbonyl group followed by elimination of water. In this case, however, elimination occurs across two adjacent *carbon* atoms to form a new carbon–carbon π bond.

Examples

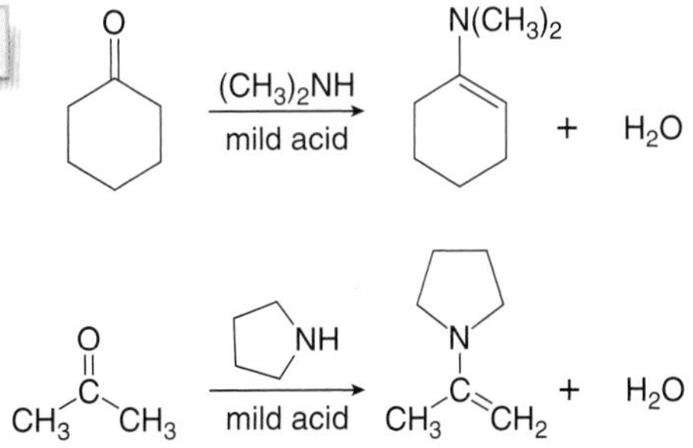

The mechanism for enamine formation (Mechanism 21.6) is identical to the mechanism for imine formation except for the last step, involving formation of the π bond. The mechanism can be divided into two distinct parts: **nucleophilic addition of the 2° amine, followed by elimination of H_2O.** Each step involves a reversible equilibrium once again, so that the reaction is driven to completion by removing H_2O.

Mechanism 21.6 Enamine Formation from an Aldehyde or Ketone

Part [1] Nucleophilic addition forms a carbinolamine.

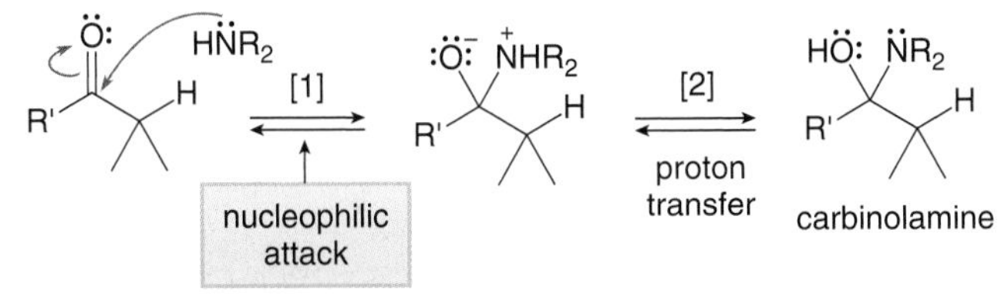

- **Nucleophilic attack** of the amine followed by proton transfer forms the unstable carbinolamine (Steps [1]–[2]).

Part [2] Elimination of H_2O forms an enamine.

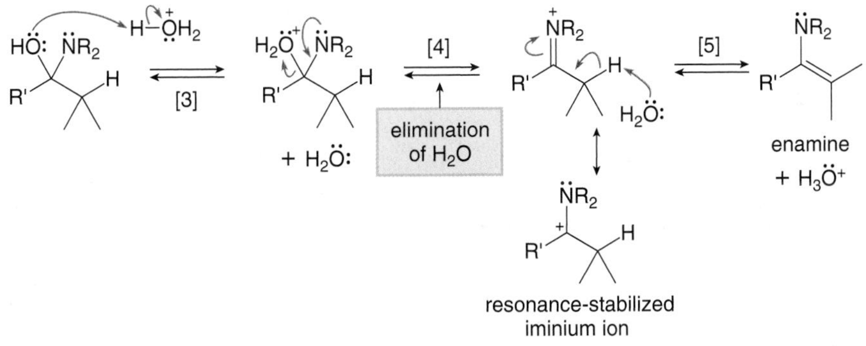

- Protonation of the OH group in Step [3] forms a good leaving group, leading to **loss of water** in Step [4], giving a resonance-stabilized **iminium ion.**
- Removal of a proton from the adjacent C–H bond forms the enamine in Step [5].

Figure 21.10
The formation of imines and enamines compared

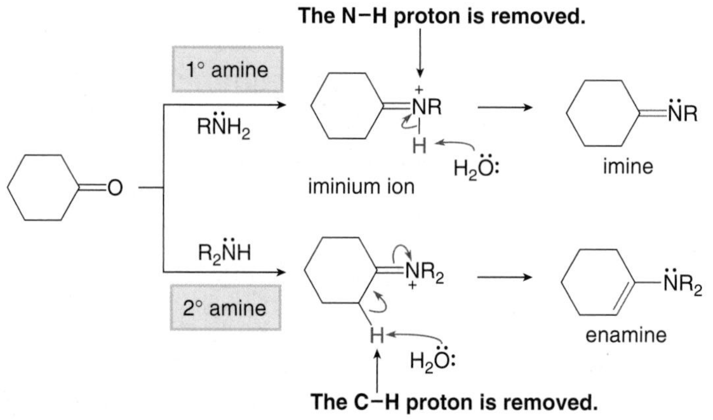

- With a **1° amine,** the intermediate iminium ion still has a proton on the N atom that may be removed to form a C=N.
- With a **2° amine,** the intermediate iminium ion has no proton on the N atom. A proton must be removed from an adjacent C–H bond, and this forms a C=C.

The mechanisms illustrate why **the reaction of 1° amines with carbonyl compounds forms *imines,* but the reaction with 2° amines forms *enamines.*** In Figure 21.10, the last step of both mechanisms is compared using cyclohexanone as starting material. The position of the double bond depends on which proton is removed in the last step. Removal of an N–H proton forms a C=N, whereas removal of a C–H proton forms a C=C.

21.12B Imine and Enamine Hydrolysis

Because imines and enamines are formed by a set of reversible reactions, both can be converted back to carbonyl compounds by hydrolysis with mild acid. The mechanism of these reactions is exactly the *reverse* of the mechanism written for the formation of imines and enamines. In the hydrolysis of enamines, the carbonyl carbon in the product comes from the sp^2 hybridized carbon bonded to the N atom in the starting material.

- **Hydrolysis of imines and enamines forms aldehydes and ketones.**

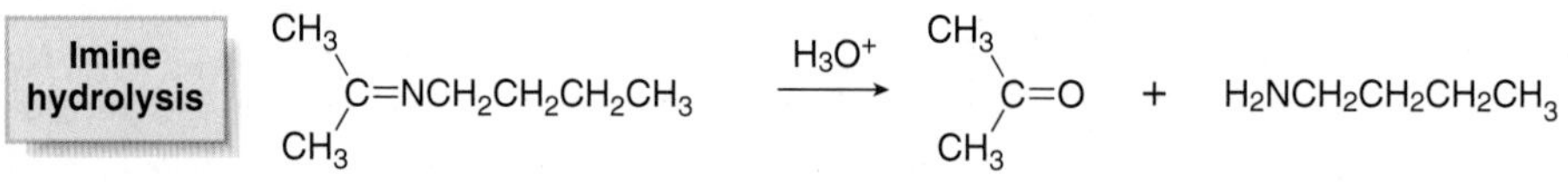

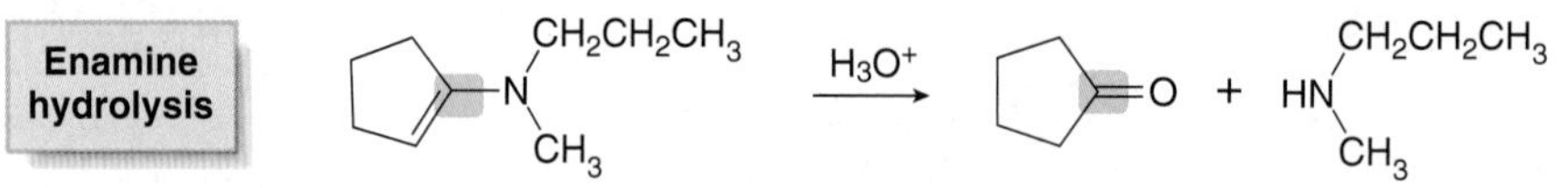

Problem 21.25 What two enamines are formed when 2-methylcyclohexanone is treated with $(CH_3)_2NH$?

Problem 21.26 What carbonyl compound and amine are formed by the hydrolysis of each compound?

a. 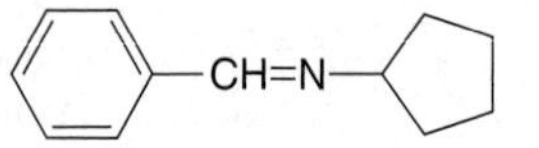

b. 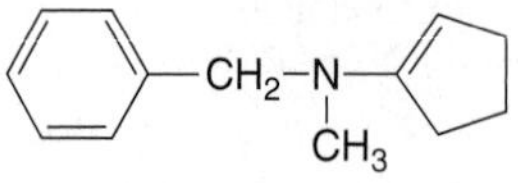

c. $(CH_3)_2NCH{=}C(CH_3)_2$

21.13 Addition of H_2O—Hydration

Treatment of a carbonyl compound with H_2O in the presence of an acid or base catalyst **adds the elements of H and OH across the carbon–oxygen π bond,** forming a ***gem*-diol** or **hydrate.**

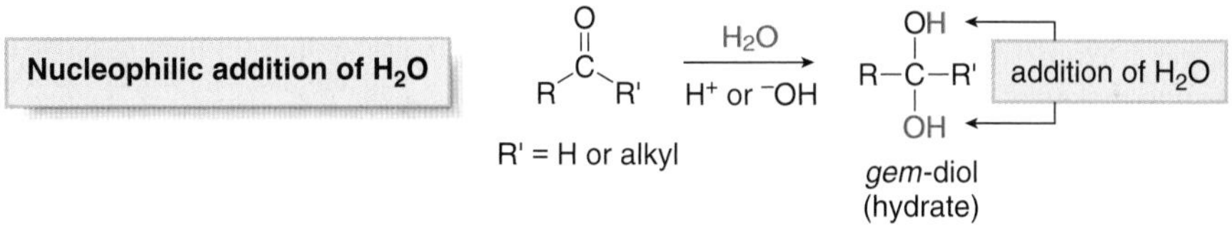

Hydration of a carbonyl group gives a good yield of *gem*-diol only with an unhindered aldehyde like formaldehyde, and with aldehydes containing nearby electron-withdrawing groups.

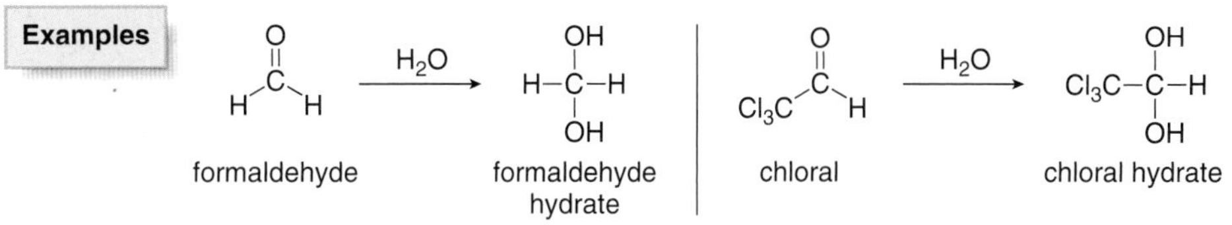

21.13A The Thermodynamics of Hydrate Formation

Whether addition of H_2O to a carbonyl group affords a good yield of the *gem*-diol depends on the relative energies of the starting material and the product. With less stable carbonyl starting materials, equilibrium favors the hydrate product, whereas with more stable carbonyl starting materials, equilibrium favors the carbonyl starting material. Because **alkyl groups stabilize a carbonyl group** (Section 20.2B):

- **Increasing the number of alkyl groups on the carbonyl carbon decreases the amount of hydrate at equilibrium.**

This can be illustrated by comparing the amount of hydrate formed from formaldehyde, acetaldehyde, and acetone.

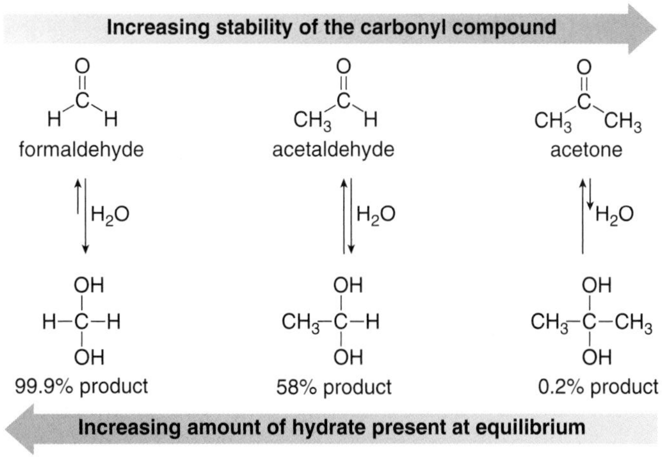

Formaldehyde, the least stable carbonyl compound, forms the largest percentage of hydrate. On the other hand, acetone and other ketones, which have two electron-donor R groups, form < 1% of the hydrate at equilibrium. Other electronic factors come into play as well.

- **Electron-donating groups near the carbonyl carbon stabilize the carbonyl group, decreasing the amount of the hydrate at equilibrium.**
- **Electron-withdrawing groups near the carbonyl carbon destabilize the carbonyl group, increasing the amount of hydrate at equilibrium.**

Chloral hydrate, a sedative sometimes administered to calm a patient prior to a surgical procedure, has also been used for less reputable purposes. Adding it to an alcoholic beverage makes a so-called knock-out drink, causing an individual who drinks it to pass out. Because it is addictive and care must be taken in its administration, it is a controlled substance.

This explains why chloral (trichloroacetaldehyde) forms a large amount of hydrate at equilibrium. Three electron-withdrawing Cl atoms place a partial positive charge on the α carbon to the carbonyl, destabilizing the carbonyl group, and therefore increasing the amount of hydrate at equilibrium.

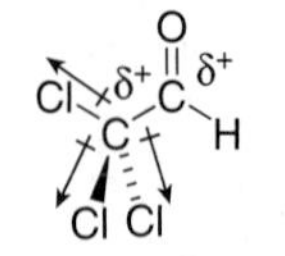

chloral

Having two similar charges (δ^+) on adjacent atoms destabilizes the carbonyl group.

↓

A less stable carbonyl compound means more hydrate at equilibrium.

Problem 21.27 Which compound in each pair forms the higher percentage of *gem*-diol at equilibrium: (a) $CH_3CH_2CH_2CHO$ or $CH_3CH_2COCH_3$; (b) CH_3CF_2CHO or CH_3CH_2CHO?

21.13B The Kinetics of Hydrate Formation

Although H_2O itself adds slowly to a carbonyl group, both acid and base catalyze the addition. In base, the nucleophile is ^-OH, and the mechanism follows the usual two steps for nucleophilic addition: **nucleophilic attack followed by protonation,** as shown in Mechanism 21.7.

Mechanism 21.7 Base-Catalyzed Addition of H_2O to a Carbonyl Group

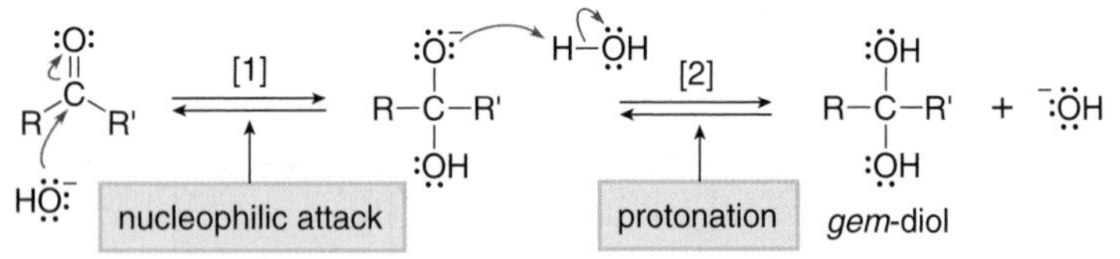

- In Step [1], **the nucleophile ($^-$OH) attacks the carbonyl group,** cleaving the π bond, and moving an electron pair onto oxygen.
- In Step [2], **protonation of the negatively charged O atom by H_2O** forms the *gem*-diol.

The acid-catalyzed addition follows the general mechanism presented in Section 21.7A. For a poorer nucleophile like H_2O to attack a carbonyl group, the **carbonyl must be protonated by acid first; thus, protonation *precedes* nucleophilic attack.** The overall mechanism has three steps, as shown in Mechanism 21.8.

Mechanism 21.8 Acid-Catalyzed Addition of H_2O to a Carbonyl Group

Step [1] Protonation of the carbonyl group

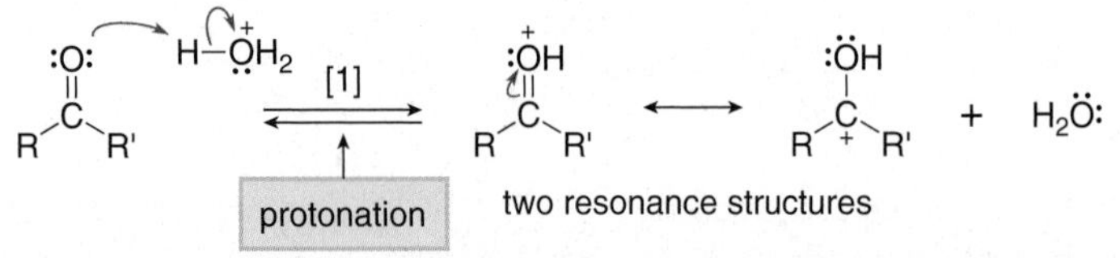

- Protonation of the carbonyl oxygen forms a resonance-stabilized cation that bears a full positive charge.

Steps [2]–[3] Nucleophilic attack and deprotonation

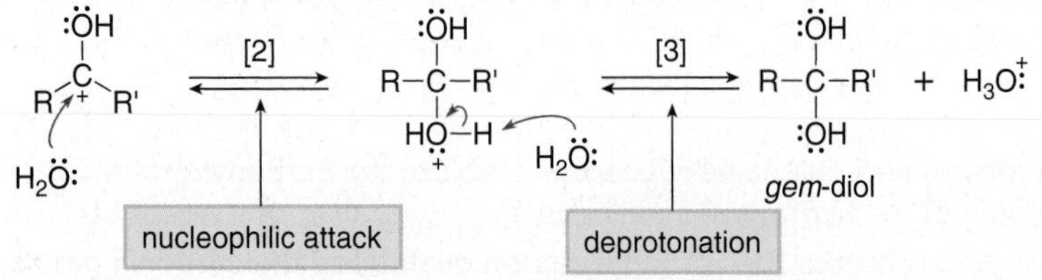

- In Step [2], the nucleophile (H_2O) attacks, and then deprotonation forms the neutral addition product in Step [3].
- The overall result is the addition of H and OH to the carbonyl group and regeneration of the acid catalyst.

Acid and base increase the rate of reaction for different reasons.

- **Base converts H_2O into ^-OH, a *stronger nucleophile.***
- **Acid protonates the carbonyl group, making it *more electrophilic* towards nucleophilic attack.**

These catalysts increase the rate of the reaction, but they do not affect the equilibrium constant. Starting materials that give a low yield of *gem*-diol do so whether or not a catalyst is present. Because these reactions are reversible, the conversion of *gem*-diols to aldehydes and ketones is also catalyzed by acid and base, and the steps of the mechanism are reversed.

Problem 21.28 Draw a stepwise mechanism for the following reaction.

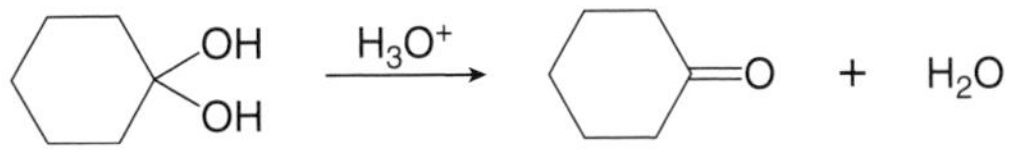

21.14 Addition of Alcohols—Acetal Formation

Aldehydes and ketones react with *two* equivalents of alcohol to form acetals. In an acetal, the carbonyl carbon from the aldehyde or ketone is now singly bonded to two OR" (alkoxy) groups.

Acetal formation

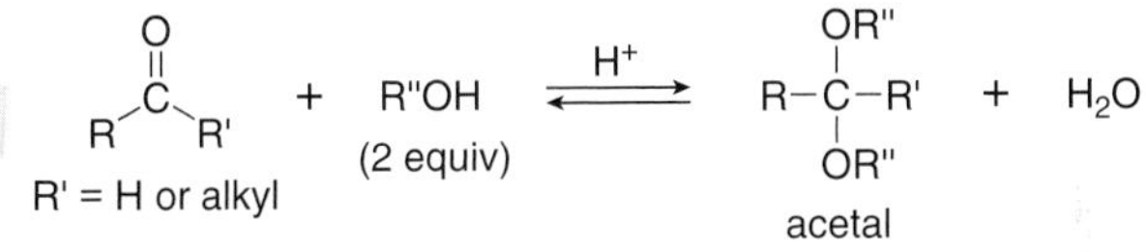

This reaction differs from other additions we have seen thus far, because **two equivalents of alcohol are added to the carbonyl group,** and two new C–O σ bonds are formed. Acetal formation is catalyzed by acids, commonly *p*-toluenesulfonic acid (TsOH).

Example

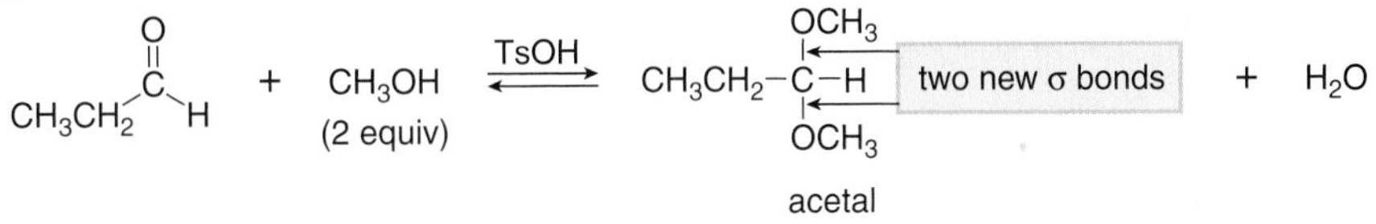

The term *acetal* refers to any compound derived from an aldehyde or ketone, having two OR groups bonded to a single carbon. The term *ketal* is sometimes used when the starting carbonyl compound is a ketone; that is, the carbon bonded to the alkoxy groups is *not* bonded to a H atom and the general structure is $R_2C(OR')_2$. Since ketals are considered a subclass of acetals in the IUPAC system, we will use the single general term *acetal* for any compound having two OR groups on a carbon atom.

When a diol such as ethylene glycol is used in place of two equivalents of ROH, a cyclic acetal is formed. Both oxygen atoms in the cyclic acetal come from the diol.

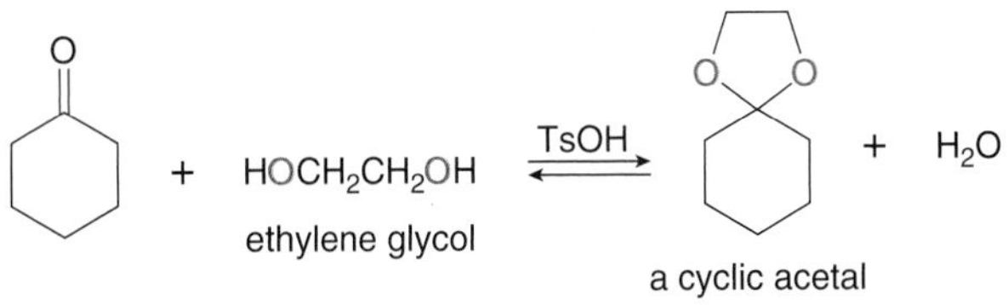

Like *gem*-diol formation, the synthesis of acetals is reversible, and often the equilibrium favors reactants, not products. In acetal synthesis, however, water is formed as a by-product, so the equilibrium can be driven to the right by removing the water as it is formed. This can be done in a variety of ways in the laboratory. A drying agent can be added that reacts with the water, or more commonly, the water can be distilled from the reaction mixture as it is formed by using a Dean–Stark trap, as pictured in Figure 21.11. Driving an equilibrium to the right by removing one of the products is an application of Le Châtelier's principle (see Section 9.8).

Acetals are *not* ethers, even though both functional groups contain a C–O σ bond. Having two C–O σ bonds on the *same* carbon atom makes an acetal very different from an ether.

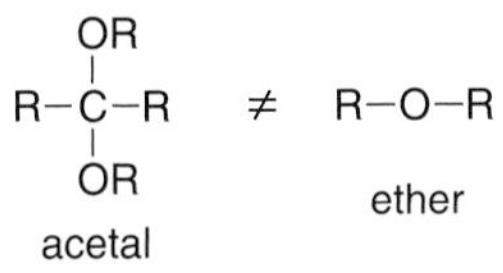

Problem 21.29 Draw the products of each reaction.

a. 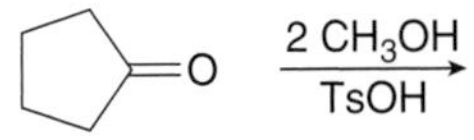

b. 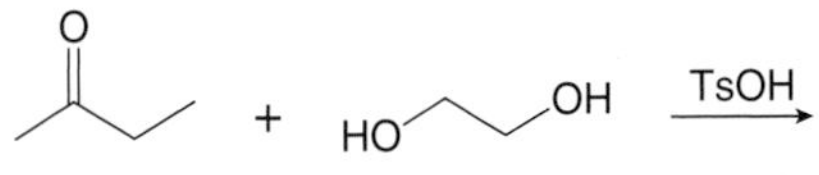

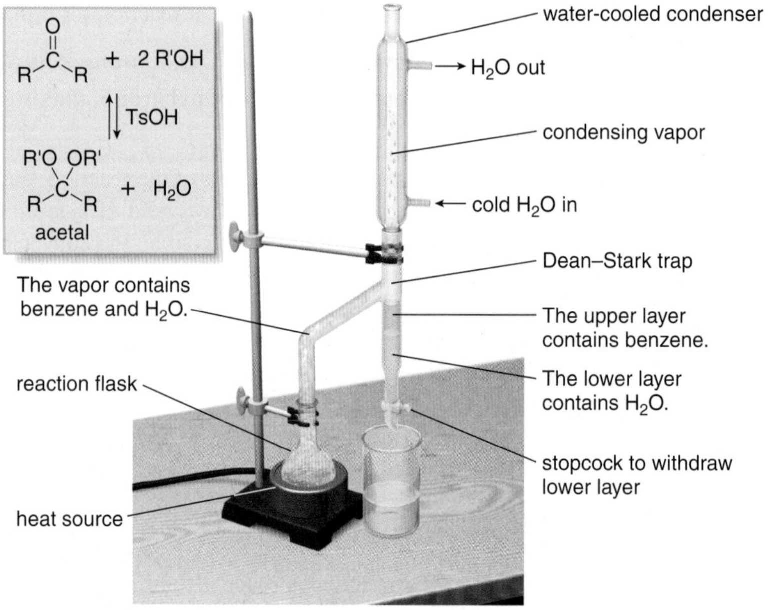

Figure 21.11
A Dean–Stark trap for removing water

- **A Dean–Stark trap is an apparatus used for removing water from a reaction mixture.** To use a Dean–Stark trap to convert a carbonyl compound to an acetal:

  The carbonyl compound, an alcohol, and an acid are dissolved in benzene. As the mixture is heated, the carbonyl compound is converted to the acetal with water as a by-product. Benzene and water co-distill from the reaction mixture. When the hot vapors reach the cold condenser, they condense, forming a liquid that then collects in the glass tube below. Water, the more dense liquid, forms the lower layer, so that as it collects, it can be drained through the stopcock into a flask. In this way, water can be removed from a reaction mixture, driving the equilibrium.

21.14A The Mechanism

The mechanism for acetal formation can be divided into two parts: **the addition of one equivalent of alcohol** to form a **hemiacetal,** followed by the **conversion of the hemiacetal** to the **acetal.** A **hemiacetal** has a carbon atom bonded to one OH group and one OR group.

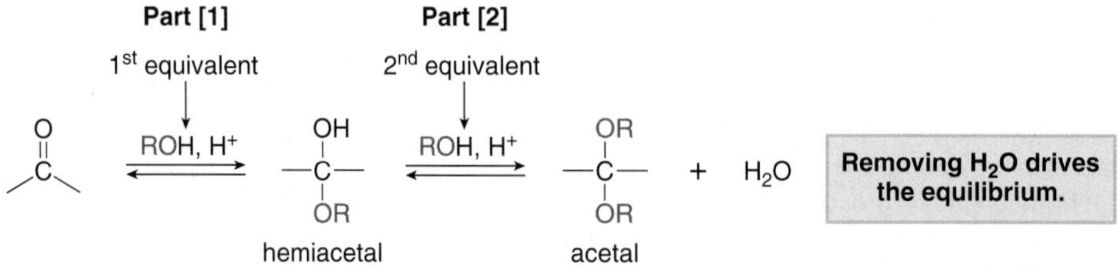

Like *gem*-diols, hemiacetals are often higher in energy than their carbonyl starting materials, making the direction of equilibrium unfavorable for hemiacetal formation. The elimination of H_2O, which can be removed from the reaction mixture to drive the equilibrium to favor product, occurs during the conversion of the hemiacetal to the acetal. This explains why two equivalents of ROH react with a carbonyl compound, forming the acetal as product.

The mechanism is written in two parts (Mechanisms 21.9 and 21.10) with a general acid HA.

Mechanism 21.9 Acetal Formation—Part [1] Formation of a Hemiacetal

Step [1] Protonation of the carbonyl group

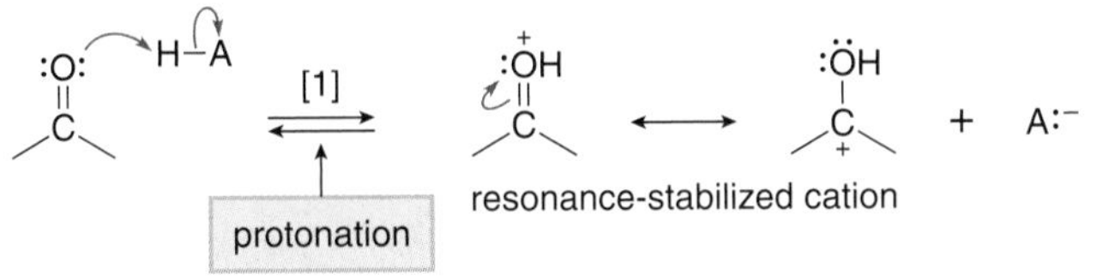

- **Protonation** of the carbonyl oxygen forms a resonance-stabilized cation that bears a full positive charge.

Steps [2]–[3] Nucleophilic attack and deprotonation

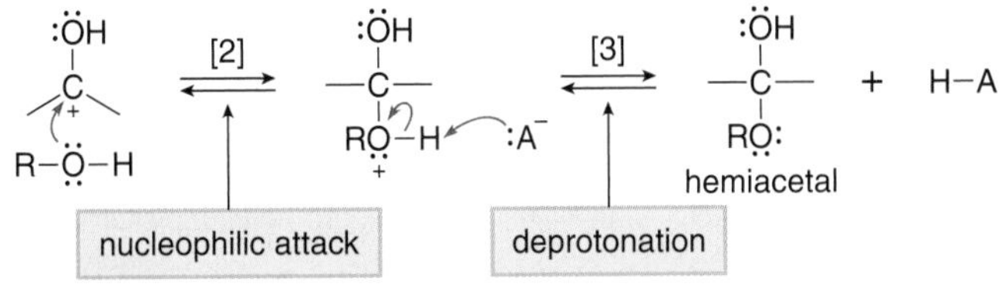

- In Step [2], the **nucleophile (ROH) attacks,** and then deprotonation forms the neutral addition product in Step [3].
- **The overall result is the addition of H and OR to the carbonyl group.**

Formation of the acetal requires a second nucleophilic attack of ROH. For this to occur, however, **H_2O must first come off as a leaving group,** as shown in Mechanism 21.10.

Mechanism 21.10 Acetal Formation—Part [2] Formation of the Acetal

Steps [4]–[5] Elimination of H_2O

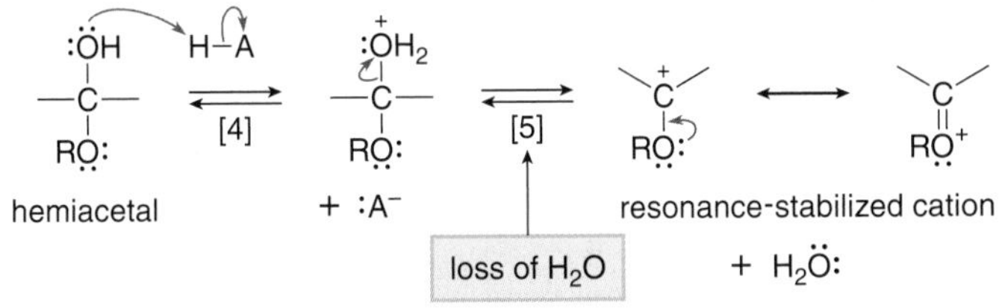

- Protonation of the OH group in the hemiacetal in Step [4] forms a **good leaving group** (H_2O). Loss of H_2O in Step [5] forms a resonance-stabilized cation.

Steps [6]–[7] Nucleophilic attack and deprotonation

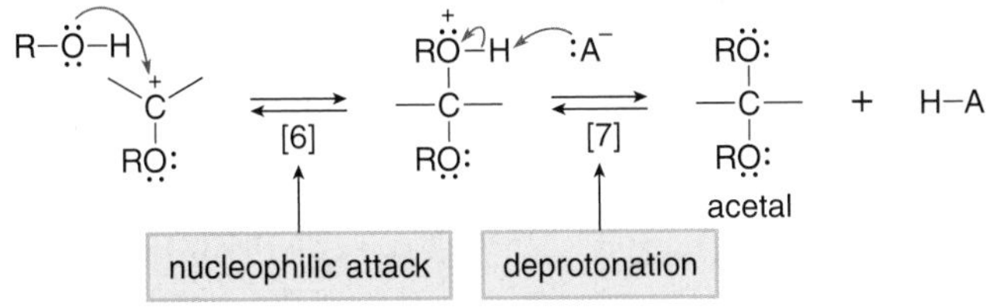

- Nucleophilic attack on the cation in Step [6] followed by loss of a proton forms the acetal.
- **The overall result of Steps [4]–[7] is the addition of a second OR group to the carbonyl group.**

Although this mechanism is lengthy—there are seven steps altogether—there are only three different kinds of reactions: **addition of a nucleophile, elimination of a leaving group, and proton transfer.** Steps [2] and [6] involve nucleophilic attack and Step [5] eliminates H_2O. The other four steps in the mechanism shuffle protons from one oxygen atom to another, to make a better leaving group or a more electrophilic carbonyl group.

Problem 21.30 Label each compound as an acetal, a hemiacetal, or an ether.

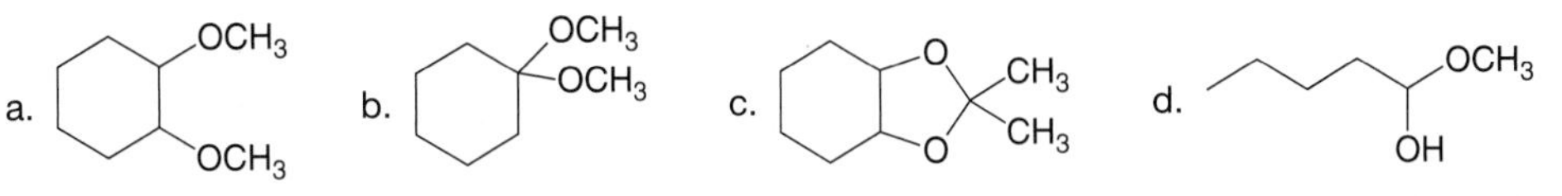

Problem 21.31 Draw a stepwise mechanism for the following reaction.

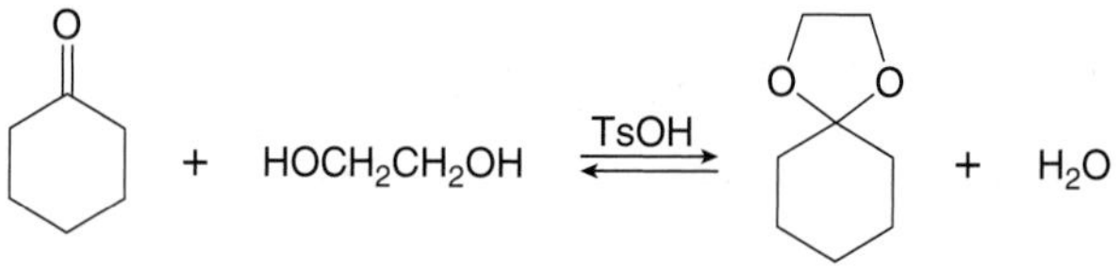

21.14B Hydrolysis of Acetals

Conversion of an aldehyde or ketone to an acetal is a **reversible reaction,** so **an acetal can be hydrolyzed to an aldehyde or ketone by treatment with aqueous acid.** Because this reaction is also an equilibrium process, it is driven to the right by using a large excess of water for hydrolysis.

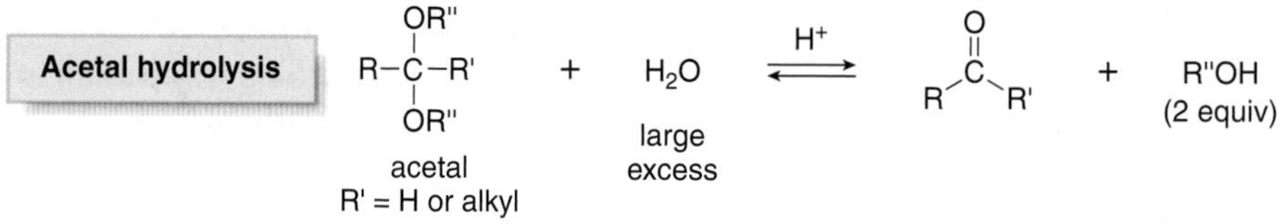

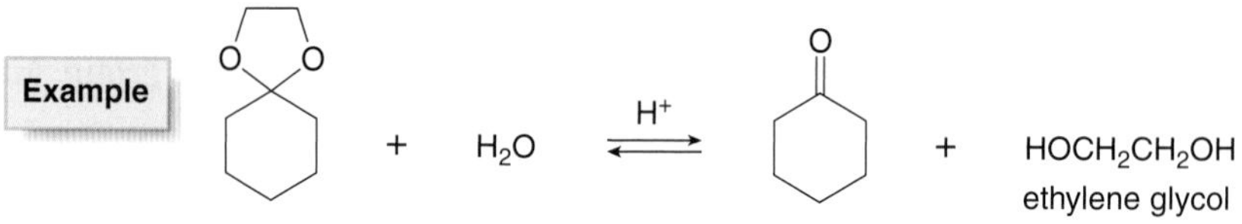

The mechanism for this reaction is the reverse of acetal synthesis, as illustrated in Sample Problem 21.4.

Sample Problem 21.4 Draw a stepwise mechanism for the following reaction.

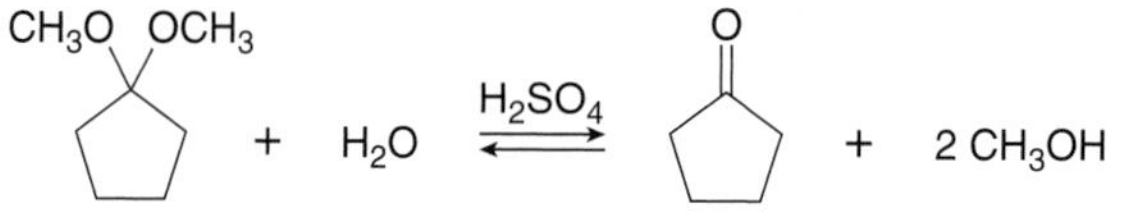

Solution

The mechanism is the reverse of acetal formation and involves two parts—conversion of the acetal to a hemiacetal, followed by conversion of the hemiacetal to the carbonyl compound.

Part [1] Conversion of the acetal to a hemiacetal

To convert this acetal to a hemiacetal, one molecule of CH_3OH must be eliminated and one molecule of H_2O must be added.

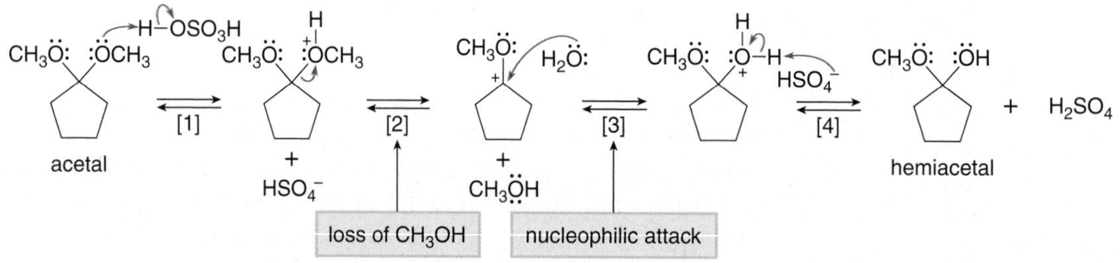

Part [2] Conversion of the hemiacetal to the carbonyl compound

To convert the hemiacetal to a carbonyl compound, one molecule of CH_3OH must be eliminated and the C–O π bond must be formed.

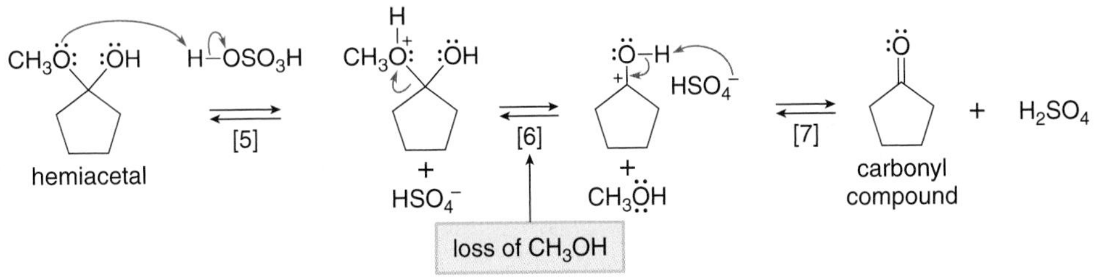

Steps [2] and [6] involve loss of the leaving group (CH_3OH), and Step [3] involves nucleophilic attack of H_2O. The other four steps in the mechanism shuffle protons from one oxygen atom to another. Steps [2] and [6] form resonance-stabilized carbocations, but only one resonance structure is drawn.

Acetal hydrolysis requires a strong acid to make a good leaving group (ROH). In Sample Problem 21.4, H_2SO_4 converts CH_3O^- into CH_3OH, a weak base and neutral leaving group. Acetal hydrolysis does not occur in base.

Problem 21.32 Draw the products of each reaction.

a. 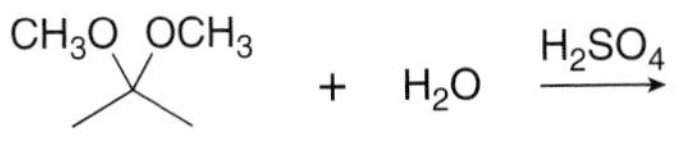

b. 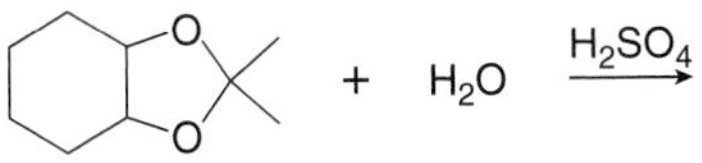

Problem 21.33 Safrole is a naturally occurring acetal isolated from sassafras plants. Once used as a common food additive in root beer and other beverages, it is now banned because it is carcinogenic. What compounds are formed when safrole is hydrolyzed with aqueous acid?

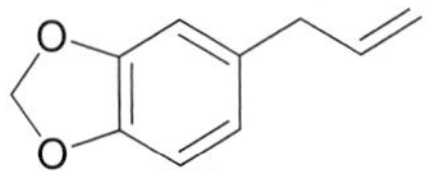

safrole

Sassafras, source of safrole

21.15 Acetals as Protecting Groups

Just as the *tert*-butyldimethylsilyl ethers are used as protecting groups for alcohols (Section 20.12), **acetals are valuable protecting groups for aldehydes and ketones.**

Suppose a starting material **A** contains both a ketone and an ester, and it is necessary to selectively reduce the ester to an alcohol (6-hydroxy-2-hexanone), leaving the ketone untouched. Such a selective reduction is *not* possible in one step. Because ketones are more readily reduced, methyl 5-hydroxyhexanoate is formed instead.

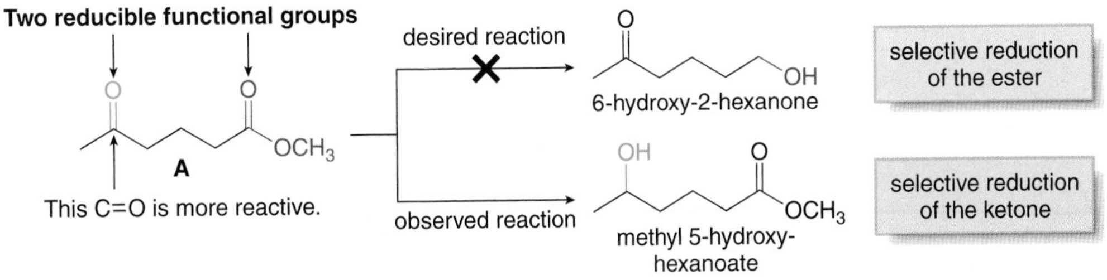

To solve this problem we can use a protecting group to block the more reactive ketone carbonyl group. The overall process requires three steps.

[1] Protect the interfering functional group—the ketone carbonyl.

[2] Carry out the desired reaction—reduction.

[3] Remove the protecting group.

The following three-step sequence using a cyclic acetal leads to the desired product.

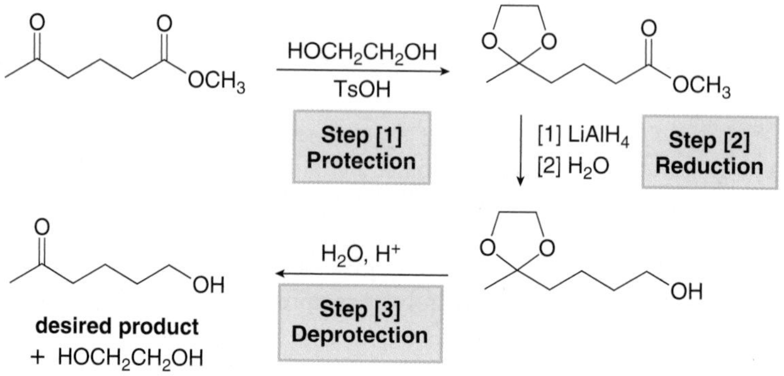

- **Step [1]** The ketone carbonyl is protected as a cyclic acetal by reaction of the starting material with $HOCH_2CH_2OH$ and TsOH.
- **Step [2]** Reduction of the ester is then carried out with $LiAlH_4$, followed by treatment with H_2O.
- **Step [3]** The acetal is then converted back to a ketone carbonyl group with aqueous acid.

Acetals are widely used protecting groups for aldehydes and ketones because they are easy to add and easy to remove, and they are stable to a wide variety of reaction conditions. Acetals do not react with base, oxidizing agents, reducing agents, or nucleophiles. Good protecting groups must survive a variety of reaction conditions that take place at other sites in a molecule, but they must also be selectively removed under mild conditions when needed.

Problem 21.34 How would you use a protecting group to carry out the following transformation?

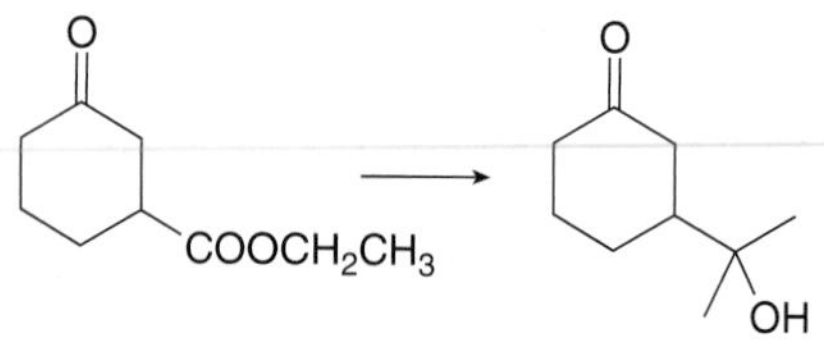

21.16 Cyclic Hemiacetals

Cyclic hemiacetals are also called **lactols.**

Although acyclic hemiacetals are generally unstable and therefore not present in appreciable amounts at equilibrium, **cyclic hemiacetals containing five- and six-membered rings are stable compounds** that are readily isolated.

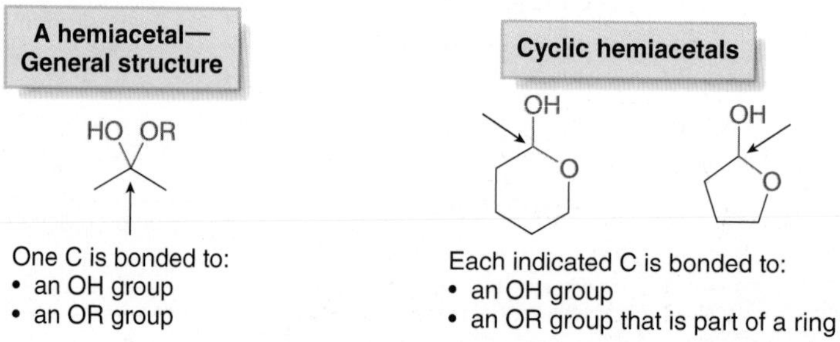

21.16A Forming Cyclic Hemiacetals

All hemiacetals are formed by nucleophilic addition of a hydroxy group to a carbonyl group. In the same way, cyclic hemiacetals are formed by **intramolecular cyclization of hydroxy aldehydes.**

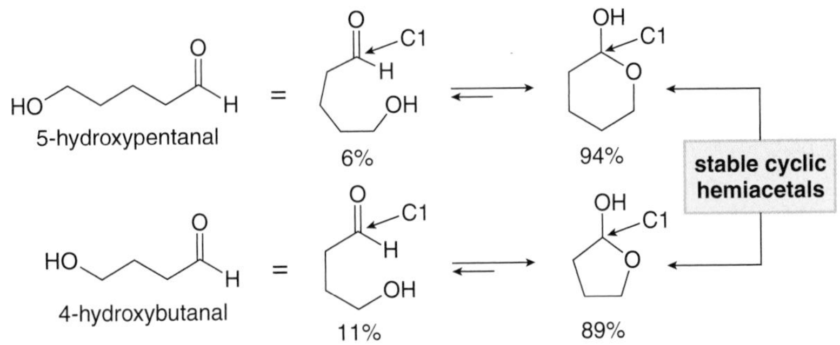

[Equilibrium proportions of each compound are given.]

Such intramolecular reactions to form five- and six-membered rings are faster than the corresponding intermolecular reactions. The two reacting functional groups, in this case OH and C=O, are held in close proximity, increasing the probability of reaction.

Problem 21.35 What lactol (cyclic hemiacetal) is formed from intramolecular cyclization of each hydroxy aldehyde?

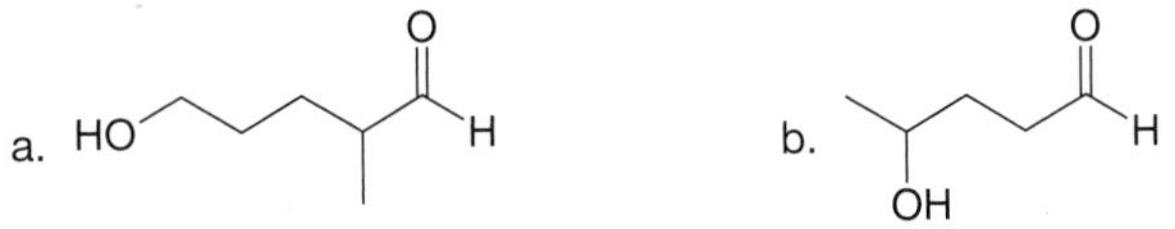

Hemiacetal formation is catalyzed by both acid and base. The acid-catalyzed mechanism is identical to Mechanism 21.9, except that the reaction occurs in an **intramolecular** fashion, as shown for the acid-catalyzed cyclization of 5-hydroxypentanal to form a six-membered cyclic hemiacetal in Mechanism 21.11.

Mechanism 21.11 Acid-Catalyzed Cyclic Hemiacetal Formation

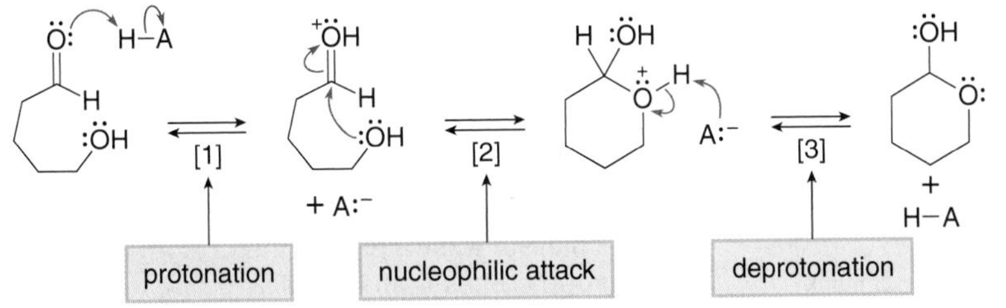

- Protonation of the carbonyl oxygen in Step [1] followed by **intramolecular nucleophilic attack** in Step [2] forms the six-membered ring.
- Deprotonation in Step [3] forms the neutral cyclic hemiacetal.

Intramolecular cyclization of a hydroxy aldehyde forms a **hemiacetal with a new stereogenic center, so that an equal amount of two enantiomers** results.

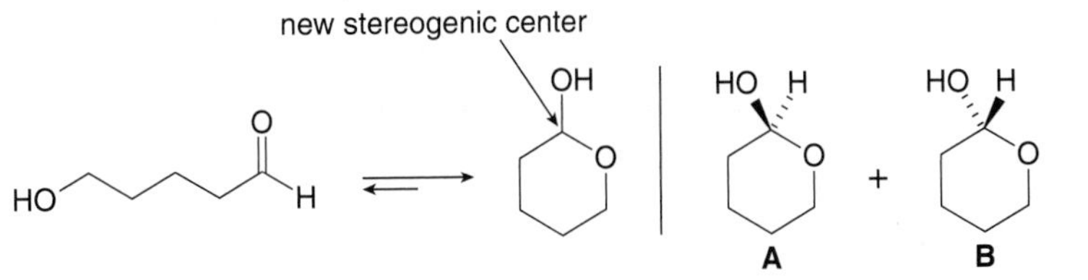

Two enantiomers are formed.

Re-drawing the starting material and products in a three-dimensional representation results in the following:

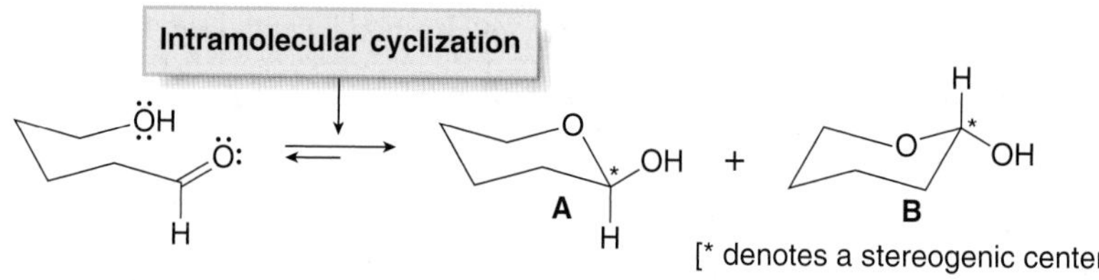

[* denotes a stereogenic center.]

21.16B The Conversion of Hemiacetals to Acetals

Cyclic hemiacetals can be converted to acetals by treatment with an alcohol and acid. This reaction converts the OH group that is part of the hemiacetal to an OR group.

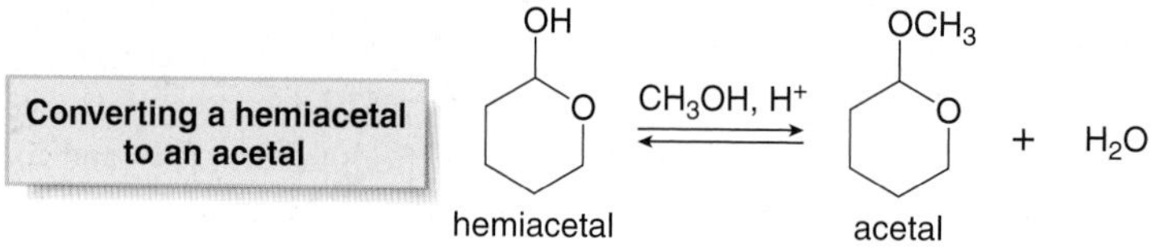

Mechanism 21.12, which is similar to Mechanism 21.10, illustrates the conversion of an acyclic hemiacetal to an acetal.

Mechanism 21.12 A Cyclic Acetal from a Cyclic Hemiacetal

Steps [1]–[2] Protonation and loss of the leaving group

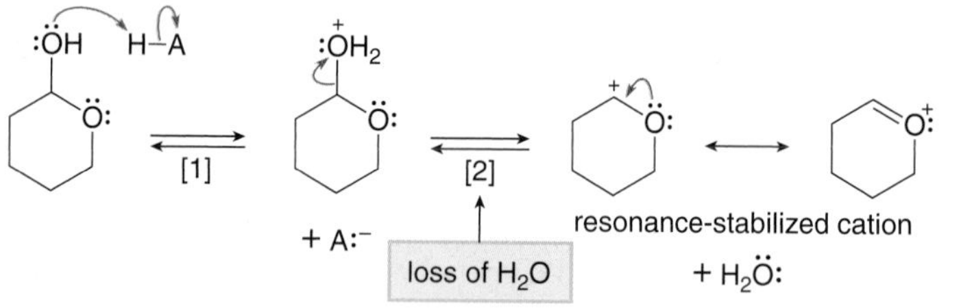

- Protonation of the OH group followed by **loss of H_2O** forms a resonance-stabilized cation (Steps [1] and [2]).

Steps [3]–[4] Nucleophilic attack and deprotonation

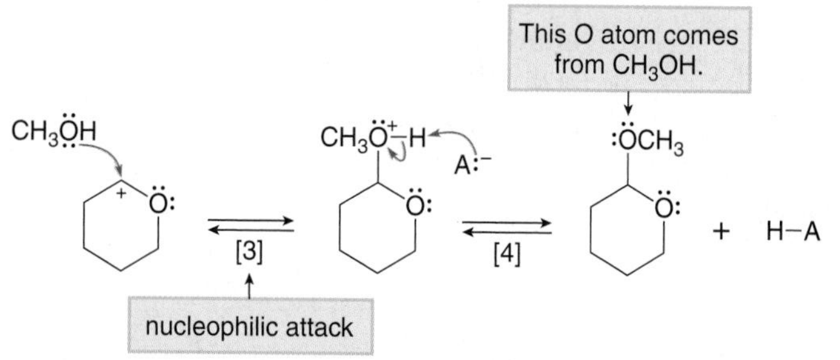

- **Nucleophilic attack of CH_3OH** followed by deprotonation forms the acetal (Steps [3] and [4]). The mechanism illustrates that the O atom in the OCH_3 group comes from CH_3OH.

The overall result of this reaction is the **replacement of the hemiacetal OH group by an OCH_3 group.** This substitution reaction readily occurs because the carbocation formed in Step [2] is stabilized by resonance. This fact makes the OH group of a hemiacetal different from the hydroxy group in other alcohols.

Thus, when a compound that contains both an alcohol OH group and a hemiacetal OH group is treated with an alcohol and acid, only the hemiacetal OH group reacts to form an acetal. The alcohol OH group does *not* react.

The conversion of cyclic hemiacetals to acetals is an important reaction in carbohydrate chemistry, as discussed in Chapter 28.

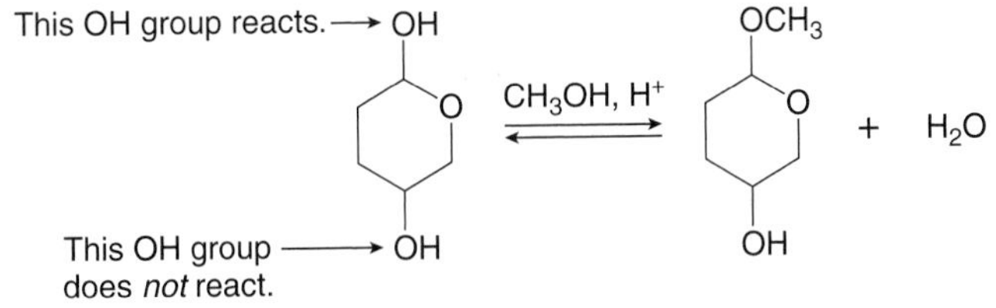
This OH group reacts.
OH
CH_3OH, H^+
OCH_3
+ H_2O
This OH group does *not* react.
OH
OH

Problem 21.36 Two naturally occurring compounds that contain stable cyclic hemiacetals and acetals are monensin and digoxin, the chapter-opening molecule. Monensin, a polyether antibiotic produced by *Streptomyces cinamonensis,* is used as an additive in cattle feed. Digoxin is a widely prescribed cardiac drug used to increase the force of heart contractions. Label each acetal, hemiacetal, and ether in both compounds.

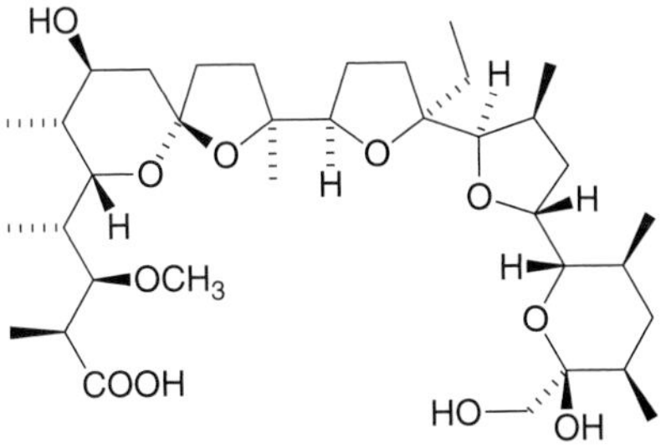

monensin

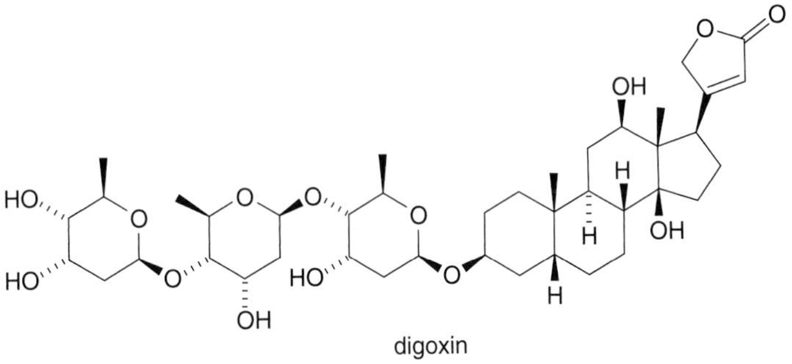

digoxin

Problem 21.37 Draw the products of each reaction.

a. 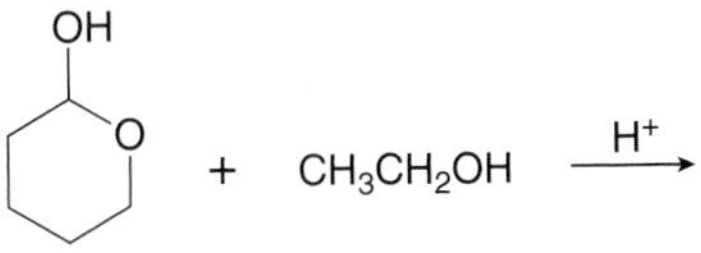
CH_3CH_2OH
H^+

b. 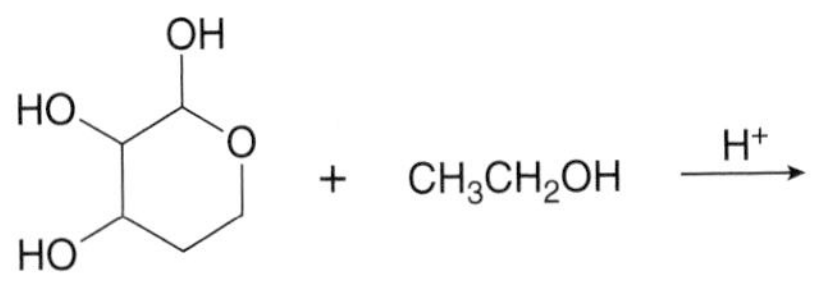
CH_3CH_2OH
H^+

21.17 An Introduction to Carbohydrates

Carbohydrates, commonly referred to as sugars and starches, are polyhydroxy aldehydes and ketones, or compounds that can be hydrolyzed to them. Along with proteins, fatty acids, and nucleotides, they form one of the four main groups of biomolecules responsible for the structure and function of all living cells.

Many carbohydrates contain cyclic acetals or hemiacetals. Examples include **glucose,** the most common simple sugar, and **lactose,** the principal carbohydrate in milk.

Glucose is the carbohydrate that is transported in the blood to individual cells. The hormone insulin regulates the level of glucose in the blood. Diabetes is a common disease that results from a deficiency of insulin, resulting in increased glucose levels in the blood and other metabolic abnormalities. Insulin injections control glucose levels.

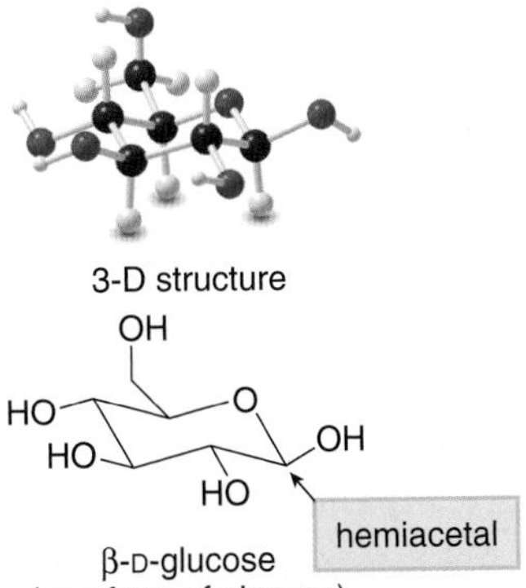
3-D structure
hemiacetal

β-D-glucose
(one form of glucose)

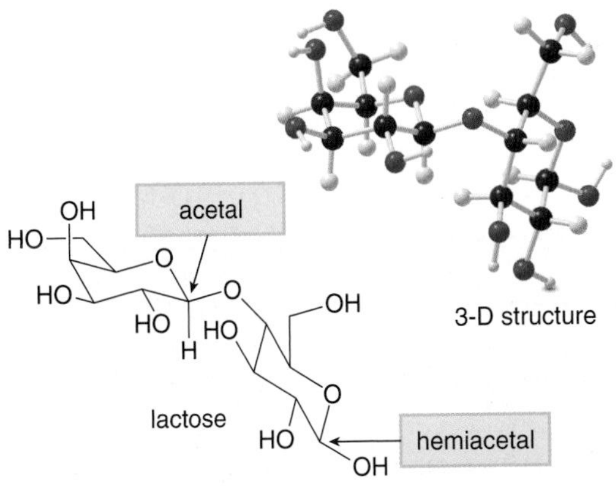
acetal
lactose
hemiacetal
3-D structure

Hemiacetals in sugars are formed in the same way that other hemiacetals are formed—that is, by **cyclization of hydroxy aldehydes.** Thus, the hemiacetal of glucose is formed by cyclization of an acyclic *poly*hydroxy aldehyde **A,** as shown in the accompanying equation. This process illustrates two important features.

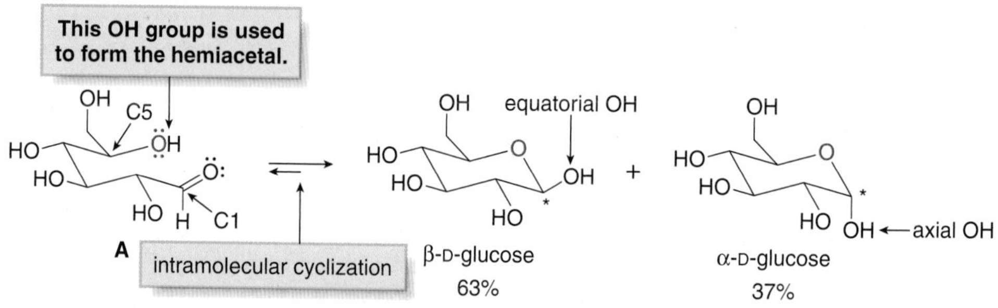

[* denotes a new stereogenic center.]

- When the OH group on C5 is the nucleophile, **cyclization yields a six-membered ring,** and this ring size is preferred.
- **Cyclization forms a new stereogenic center,** exactly analogous to the cyclization of the simpler hydroxy aldehyde (5-hydroxypentanal) in Section 21.16A. **The new OH group of the hemiacetal can occupy either the equatorial or axial position.**

For glucose, this results in two cyclic forms, called **β-D-glucose** (having an equatorial OH group) and **α-D-glucose** (having an axial OH group). Because β-D-glucose has the new OH group in the more roomy equatorial position, this cyclic form of glucose is the major product. At equilibrium, only a trace of the acyclic hydroxy aldehyde **A** is present.

Many more details on this process and other aspects of carbohydrate chemistry are presented in Chapter 28.

Problem 21.38

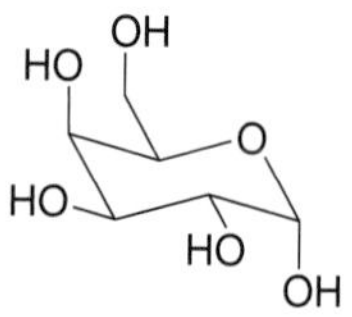

α-D-galactose

a. How many stereogenic centers are present in α-D-galactose?
b. Label the hemiacetal carbon in α-D-galactose.
c. Draw the structure of β-D-galactose.
d. Draw the structure of the polyhydroxy aldehyde that cyclizes to α- and β-D-galactose.
e. From what you learned in Section 21.16B, what product(s) is (are) formed when α-D-galactose is treated with CH_3OH and an acid catalyst?

KEY CONCEPTS

Aldehydes and Ketones—Nucleophilic Addition

General Facts

- Aldehydes and ketones contain a carbonyl group bonded to only H atoms or R groups. The carbonyl carbon is sp^2 hybridized and trigonal planar (21.1).
- Aldehydes are identified by the suffix *-al,* whereas ketones are identified by the suffix *-one* (21.2).
- Aldehydes and ketones are polar compounds that exhibit dipole–dipole interactions (21.3).

Summary of Spectroscopic Absorptions of RCHO and R_2CO (21.4)

IR absorptions	C=O	~1715 cm^{-1} for ketones (increasing frequency with decreasing ring size) ~1730 cm^{-1} for aldehydes • For both RCHO and R_2CO, the frequency decreases with conjugation.
	C_{sp^2}–H of CHO	~2700–2830 cm^{-1} (one or two peaks)
^{1}H NMR absorptions	CHO	9–10 ppm (highly deshielded proton)
	C–H α to C=O	2–2.5 ppm (somewhat deshielded C_{sp^3}–H)
^{13}C NMR absorption	C=O	190–215 ppm

Nucleophilic Addition Reactions

[1] Addition of hydride (H^-) (21.8)

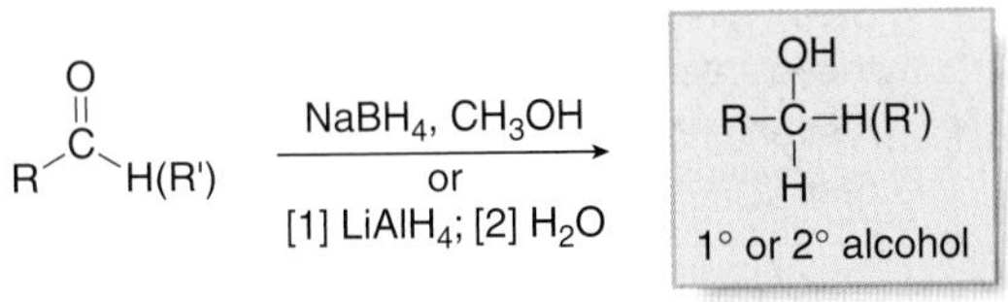

- The mechanism has two steps.
- $H:^-$ adds to the planar C=O from both sides.

[2] Addition of organometallic reagents (R^-) (21.8)

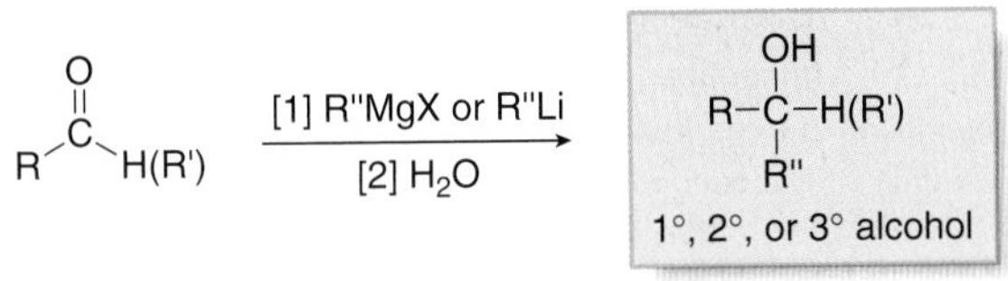

- The mechanism has two steps.
- $(R")^-$ adds to the planar C=O from both sides.

[3] Addition of cyanide (^-CN) (21.9)

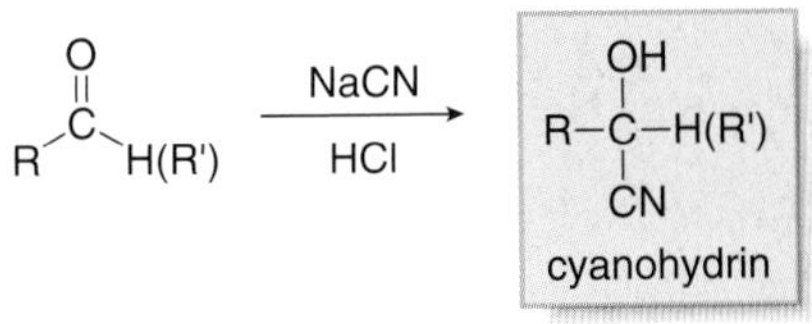

- The mechanism has two steps.
- ^-CN adds to the planar C=O from both sides.

[4] Wittig reaction (21.10)

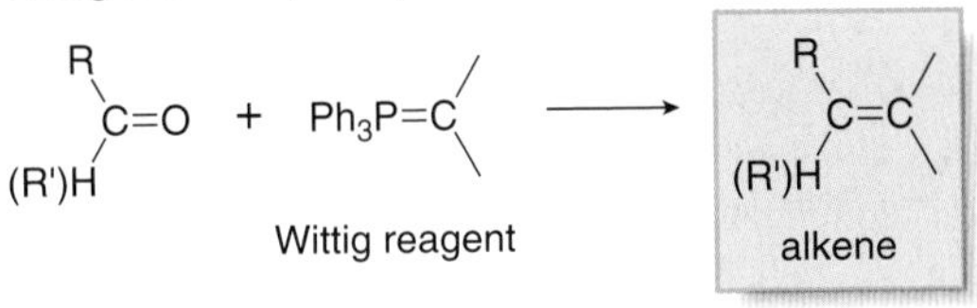

- The reaction forms a new C–C σ bond and a new C–C π bond.
- $Ph_3P=O$ is formed as by-product.

[5] Addition of 1° amines (21.11)

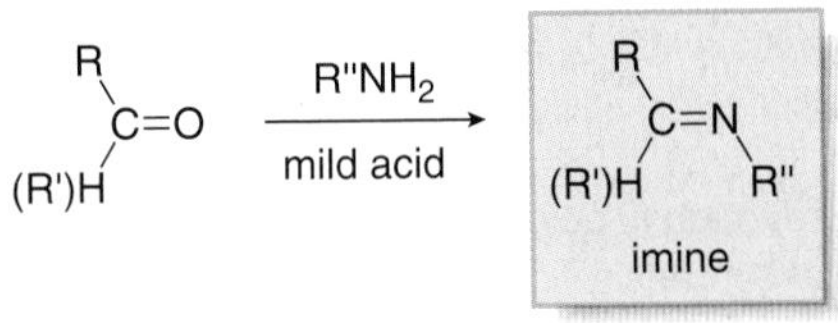

- The reaction is fastest at pH 4–5.
- The intermediate carbinolamine is unstable, and loses H_2O to form the C=N.

[6] Addition of 2° amines (21.12)

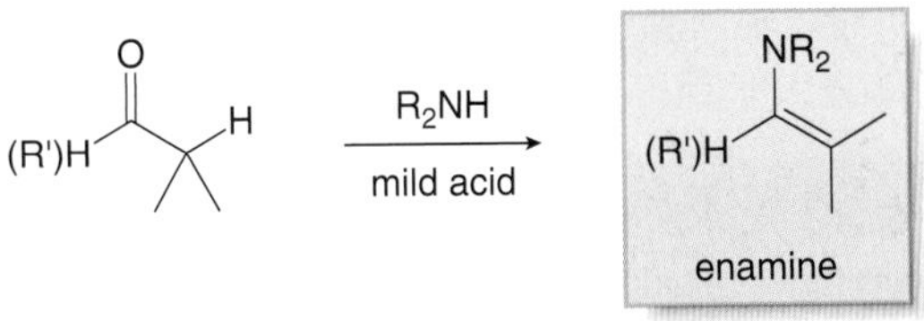

- The reaction is fastest at pH 4–5.
- The intermediate carbinolamine is unstable, and loses H_2O to form the C=C.

[7] Addition of H_2O—Hydration (21.13)

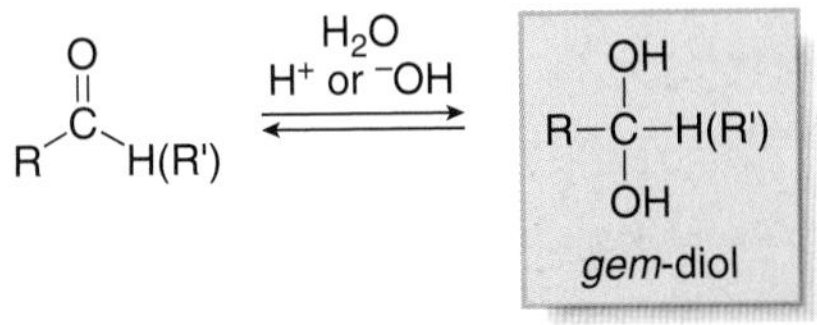

- The reaction is reversible. Equilibrium favors the product only with less stable carbonyl compounds (e.g., H_2CO and Cl_3CCHO).
- The reaction is catalyzed by either H^+ or ^-OH.

[8] Addition of alcohols (21.14)

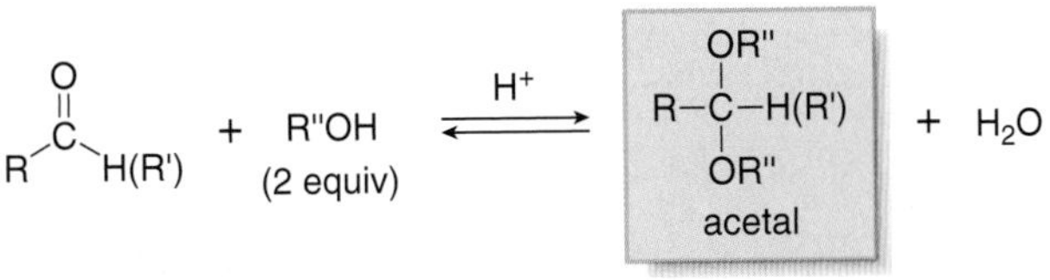

- The reaction is reversible.
- The reaction is catalyzed by acid.
- Removal of H_2O drives the equilibrium to favor the products.

Other Reactions

[1] Synthesis of Wittig reagents (21.10A)

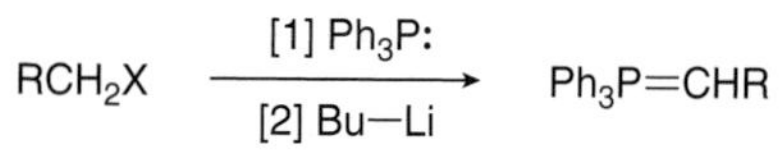

- Step [1] is best with CH_3X and RCH_2X because the reaction follows an S_N2 mechanism.
- A strong base is needed for proton removal in Step [2].

[2] Conversion of cyanohydrins to aldehydes and ketones (21.9)

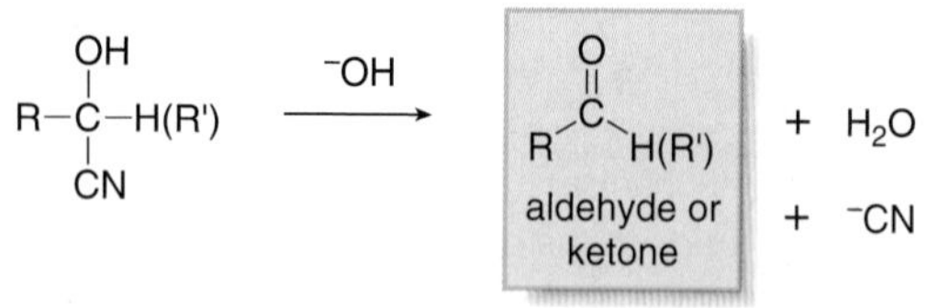

- This reaction is the reverse of cyanohydrin formation.

[3] Hydrolysis of nitriles (21.9)

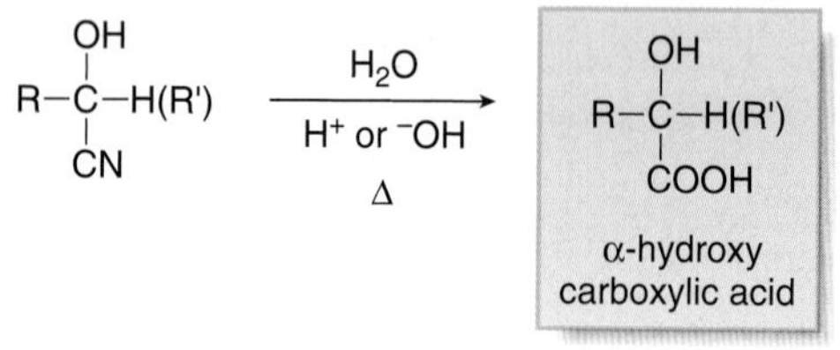

[4] Hydrolysis of imines and enamines (21.12)

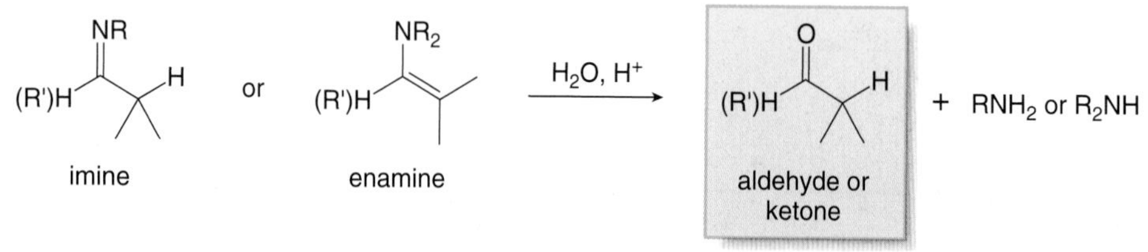

[5] Hydrolysis of acetals (21.14)

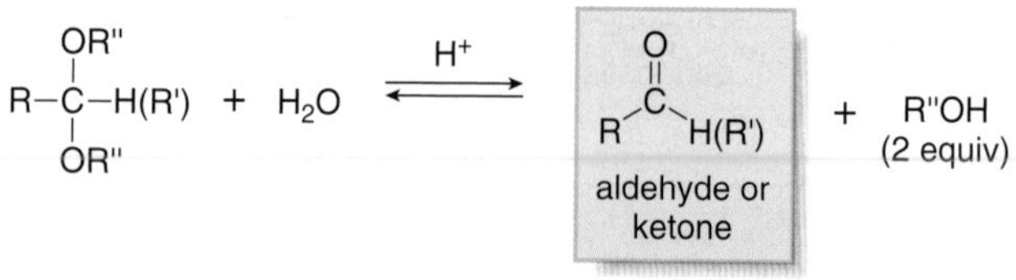

- The reaction is acid catalyzed and is the reverse of acetal synthesis.
- A large excess of H_2O drives the equilibrium to favor the products.

PROBLEMS

Problems Using Three-Dimensional Models

21.39 (a) Give the IUPAC name for **A** and **B.** (b) Draw the product formed when **A** or **B** is treated with each reagent: [1] $NaBH_4$, CH_3OH; [2] CH_3MgBr, then H_2O; [3] $Ph_3P{=}CHOCH_3$; [4] $CH_3CH_2CH_2NH_2$, mild acid; [5] $HOCH_2CH_2CH_2OH$, H^+.

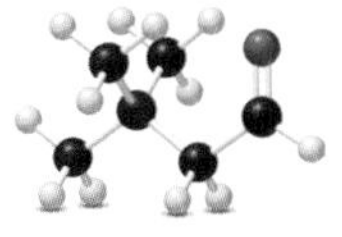

A

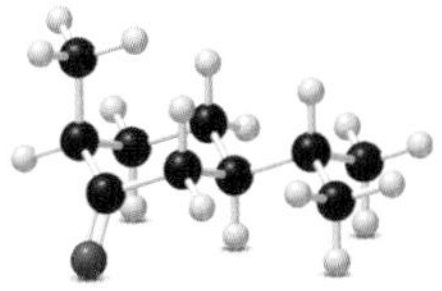

B

21.40 Rank the following compounds in order of increasing reactivity in nucleophilic addition.

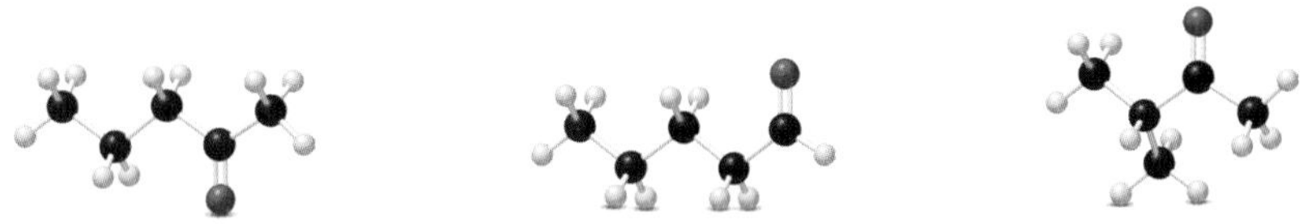

21.41 What carbonyl compound and diol are needed to prepare each compound?

a. 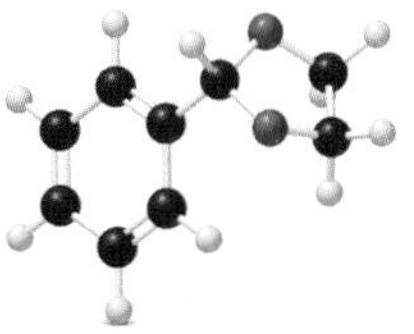

b. 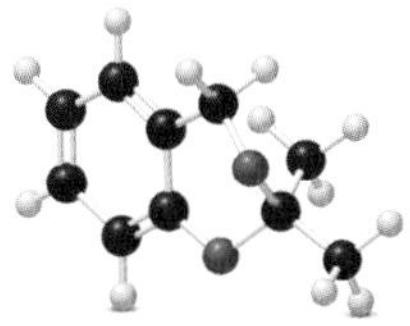

Nomenclature

21.42 Give the IUPAC name for each compound.

a. 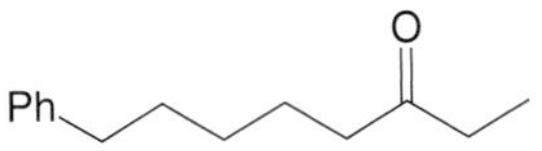

b. 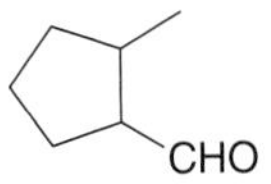

c. 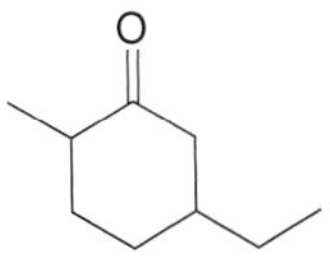

d. 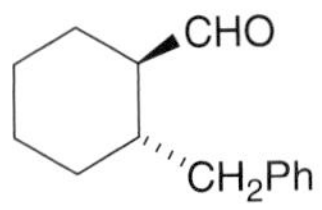

e. 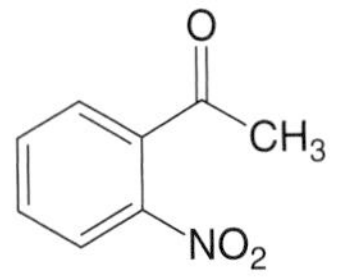

f. 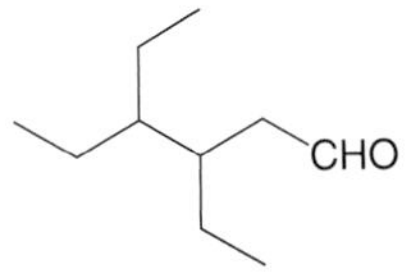

g. 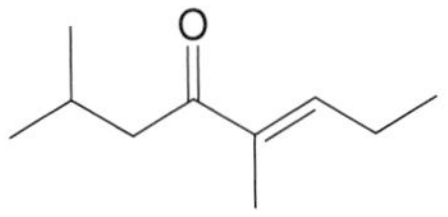

h. 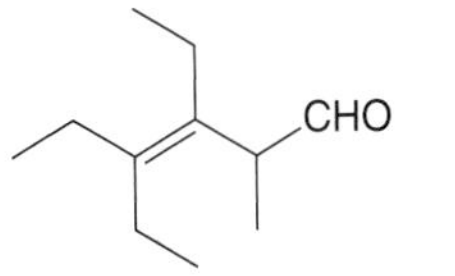

21.43 Give the structure corresponding to each name.

a. 2-methyl-3-phenylbutanal
b. dipropyl ketone
c. 3,3-dimethylcyclohexanecarbaldehyde
d. α-methoxypropionaldehyde
e. 3-benzoylcyclopentanone
f. 2-formylcyclopentanone
g. (3*R*)-3-methyl-2-heptanone
h. *m*-acetylbenzaldehyde
i. 2-*sec*-butyl-3-cyclopentenone
j. 5,6-dimethyl-1-cyclohexenecarbaldehyde

21.44 Including stereoisomers, draw the 11 aldehydes with molecular formula $C_6H_{12}O$, and give the IUPAC name (with any needed *R,S* designation) for each compound.

Reactions

21.45 Draw the product formed when phenylacetaldehyde ($C_6H_5CH_2CHO$) is treated with each reagent. Phenylacetaldehyde is partly responsible for the fragrance of the flowers of the plumeria tree, which is native to the tropical and subtropical Americas.

a. $NaBH_4$, CH_3OH
b. [1] $LiAlH_4$; [2] H_2O
c. [1] CH_3MgBr; [2] H_2O
d. NaCN, HCl
e. $Ph_3P{=}CHCH_3$
f. $(CH_3)_2CHNH_2$, mild acid
g. $(CH_3CH_2)_2NH$, mild acid
h. CH_3CH_2OH (excess), H^+
i. 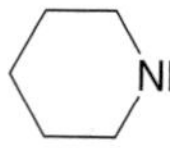 NH, mild acid
j. $HOCH_2CH_2OH$, H^+

21.46 Draw the products formed in each reaction sequence.

a. CH_3CH_2Cl → [1] Ph_3P; [2] BuLi; [3] $(CH_3)_2C{=}O$

b. $C_6H_5CH_2Br$ → [1] Ph_3P; [2] BuLi; [3] $C_6H_5CH_2CH_2CHO$

c. 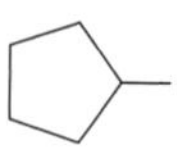 $–CH_2Cl$ → [1] Ph_3P; [2] BuLi; [3] $CH_3CH_2CH_2CHO$

21.47 What alkyl halide is needed to prepare each Wittig reagent?

a. $Ph_3P{=}CHCH_2CH_2CH_3$
b. $Ph_3P{=}C(CH_2CH_2CH_3)_2$
c. $Ph_3P{=}CHCH{=}CH_2$

21.48 Draw the products of each reaction.

a.
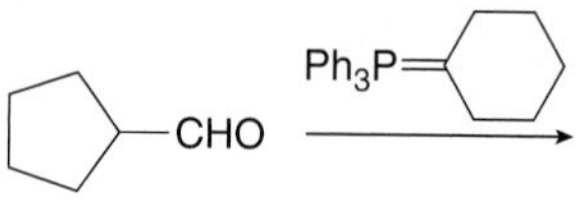

b.
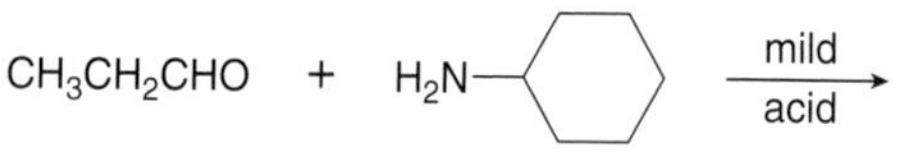

c.
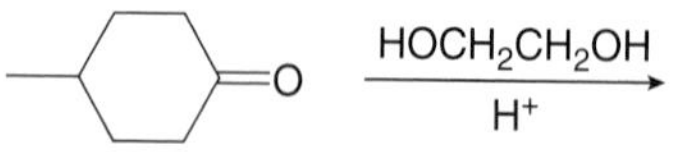

d.
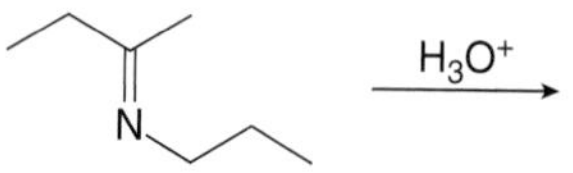

e.
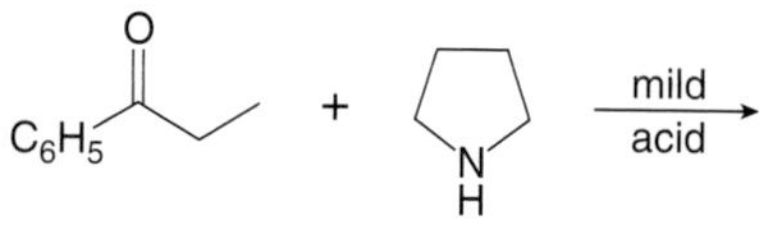

f.
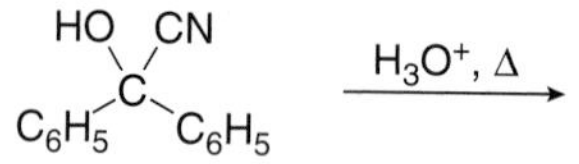

g.
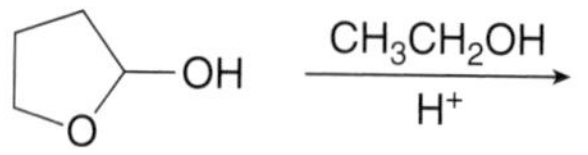

h.
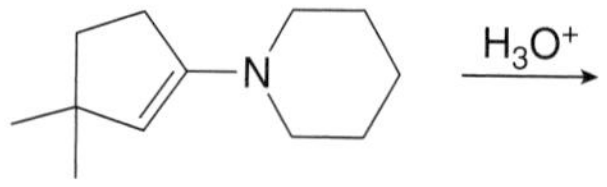

i.
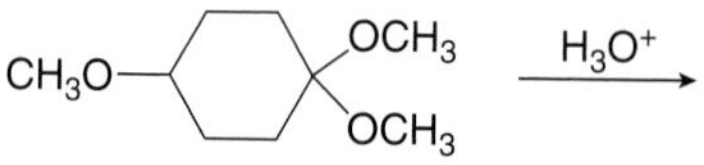

j.
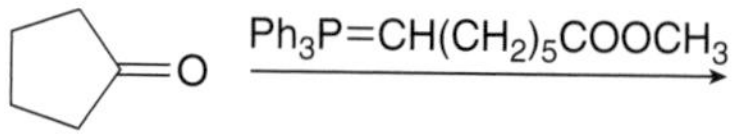

21.49 What carbonyl compound and alcohol are formed by hydrolysis of each acetal?

a.
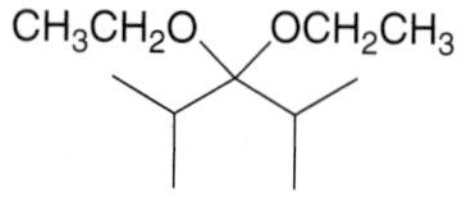

b.
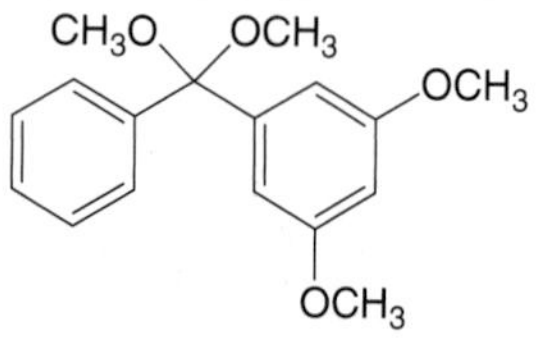

c.
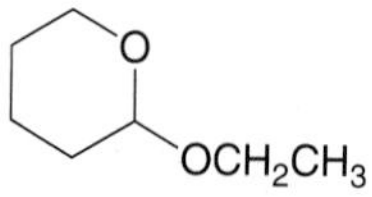

21.50 Identify the lettered intermediates in the following reaction sequence. When a mixture of ortho and para products results in electrophilic aromatic substitution, consider the para product only. The ^1H NMR spectrum of **G** shows two singlets at 2.6 and 8.18 ppm.

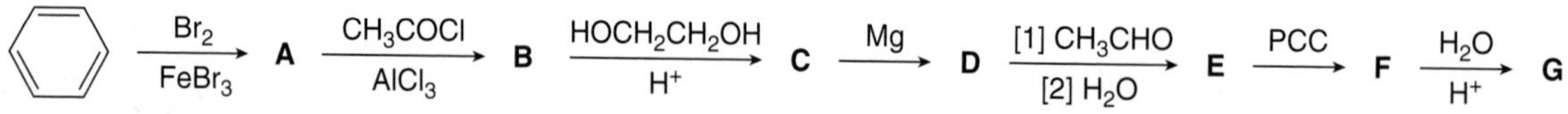

21.51 Draw all stereoisomers formed in each reaction.

a. $CH_3CH_2CH_2CHO$ → $Ph_3P{=}CHCH_2CH_2CH_3$

b.
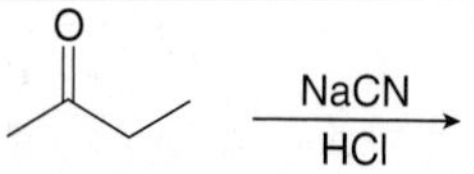

c.
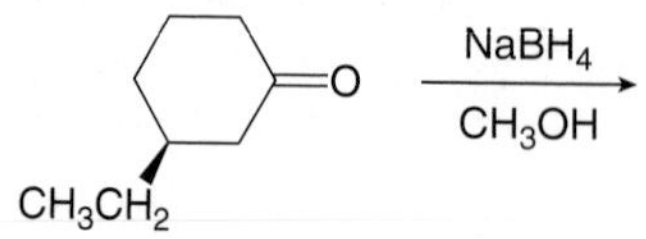

d.
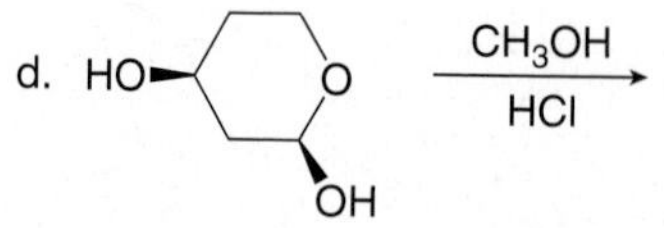

21.52 Hydroxy aldehydes **A** and **B** readily cyclize to form hemiacetals. Draw the stereoisomers formed in this reaction from both **A** and **B.** Explain why this process gives an optically inactive product mixture from **A,** and an optically active product mixture from **B.**

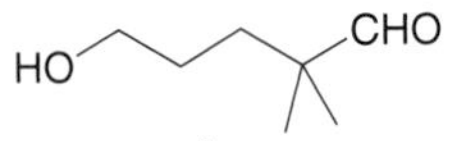
A

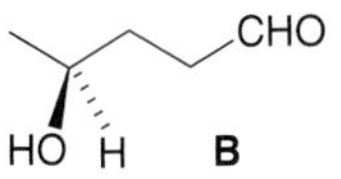
B

21.53 Etoposide, sold as a phosphate derivative with the trade name of Etopophos, is used for the treatment of lung cancer, testicular cancer, and lymphomas. (a) Locate the acetals in etoposide. (b) What products are formed when all of the acetals are hydrolyzed with aqueous acid?

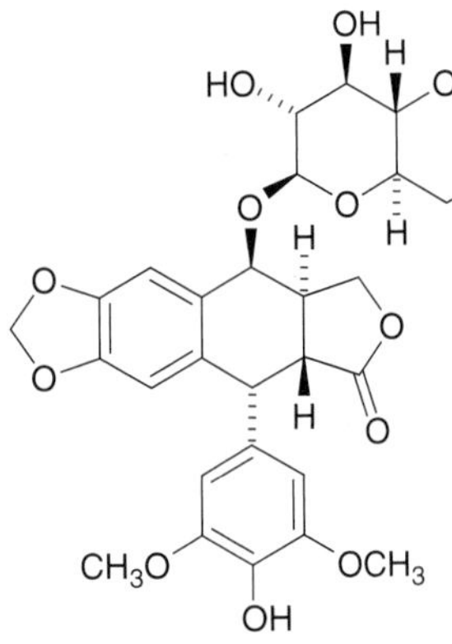
etoposide

Properties of Aldehydes and Ketones

21.54 Rank the following compounds in order of increasing reactivity in nucleophilic addition.

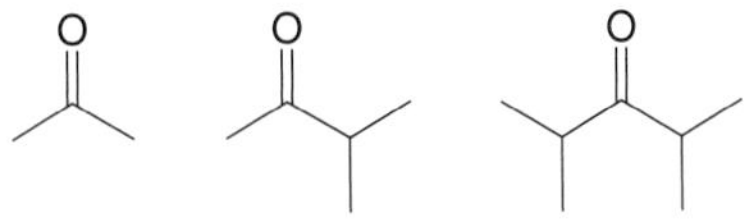

21.55 Which compound forms the higher concentration of hydrate at equilibrium, $PhCOCHO$ or $PhCH_2CHO$? Explain your reasoning.

21.56 Consider the para-substituted aromatic ketones, $NO_2C_6H_4COCH_3$ (*p*-nitroacetophenone) and $CH_3OC_6H_4COCH_3$ (*p*-methoxyacetophenone).

a. Which carbonyl compound is more stable?

b. Which compound forms the higher percentage of hydrate at equilibrium?

c. Which compound exhibits a carbonyl absorption at higher wavenumber in its IR spectrum? Explain your reasoning in each part.

Synthesis

21.57 What Wittig reagent and carbonyl compound are needed to prepare each alkene? When two routes are possible, indicate which route, if any, is preferred.

a. $(CH_3CH_2)_2C{=}CHCH_2CH_2CH_3$

b. 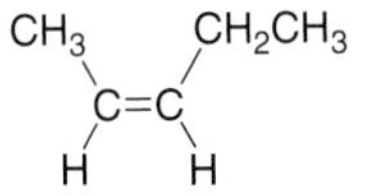

c. 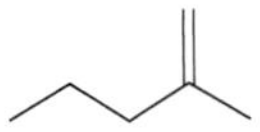

d. 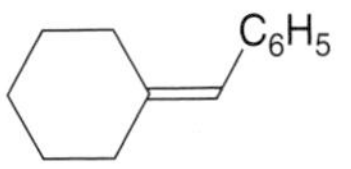

21.58 What carbonyl compound and amine or alcohol are needed to prepare each product?

a. 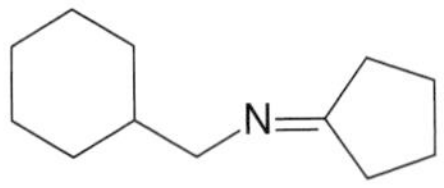

b. 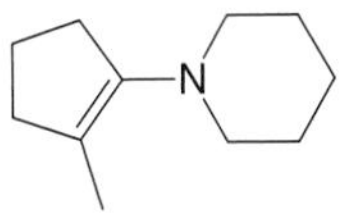

c. 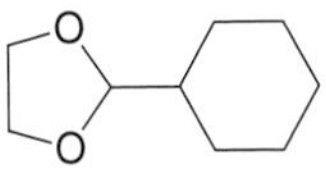

d. 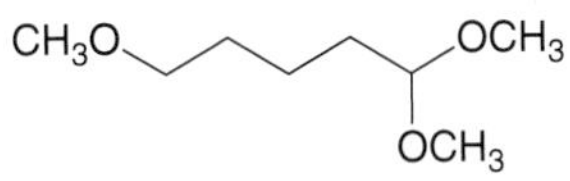

21.59 What reagents are needed to convert each compound to benzaldehyde (C_6H_5CHO)? More than one step may be required.

a. $C_6H_5CH_2OH$

b. C_6H_5COCl

c. $C_6H_5COOCH_3$

d. C_6H_5COOH

e. $C_6H_5CH_3$

f. $C_6H_5CH{=}CH_2$

g. $C_6H_5CH{=}NCH_2CH_2CH_3$

h. $C_6H_5CH(OCH_2CH_3)_2$

21.60 What reagents are needed to convert each compound to 2-butanone ($CH_3COCH_2CH_3$)?

a. 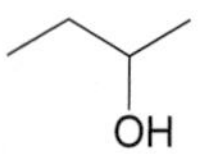 b. 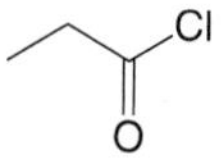 c. CH_3COCl d. $CH_3CH_2C{\equiv}CH$ e. $CH_3C{\equiv}CCH_3$

21.61 Show two different methods to carry out each transformation: a one-step method using a Wittig reagent, and a two-step method using a Grignard reagent. Which route, if any, is preferred for each compound?

a. 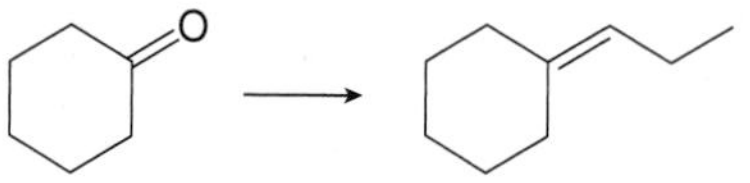

b. 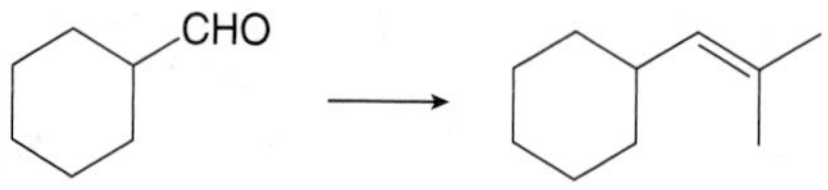

21.62 Devise a synthesis of each alkene using a Wittig reaction to form the double bond. You may use benzene and organic alcohols having four or fewer carbons as starting materials and any required reagents.

a. $CH_3CH_2CH_2CH{=}CHCH_3$ b. $C_6H_5CH{=}CHCH_2CH_2CH_3$ c. $(CH_3)_2C{=}CHCH(CH_3)_2$

21.63 Devise a synthesis of each compound from cyclohexene and organic alcohols. You may use any other required organic or inorganic reagents.

a. 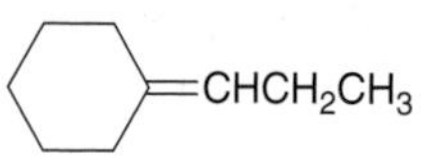

b. 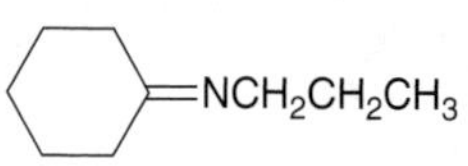

c. 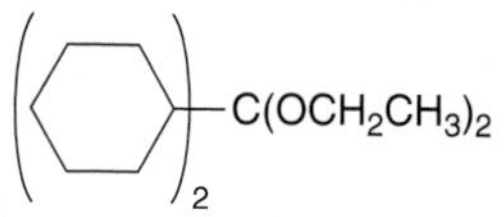

d. 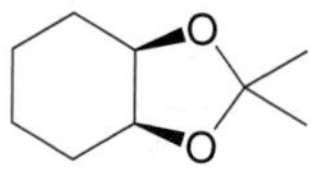

21.64 Devise a synthesis of each compound from the given starting materials. You may also use organic alcohols having four or fewer carbons, and any organic or inorganic reagents.

a. 

b. 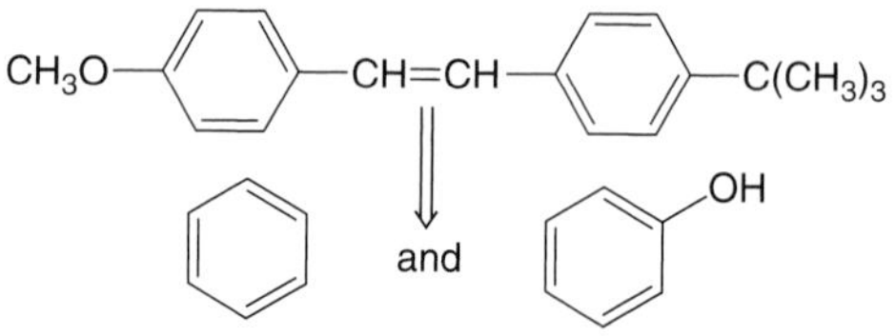

21.65 Devise a synthesis of each compound from 5-hydroxy-2-pentanone ($CH_3COCH_2CH_2CH_2OH$) as starting material. You may also use alcohols having three or fewer carbons and any required organic or inorganic reagents.

a. 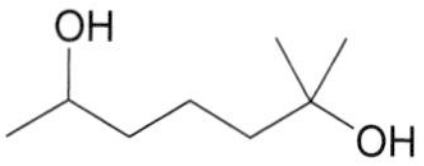

b. 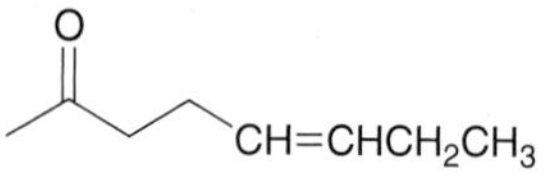

(*E/Z* mixture)

21.66 Devise a synthesis of each compound from ethanol (CH_3CH_2OH) as the only source of carbon atoms. You may use any other organic or inorganic reagents you choose.

a. 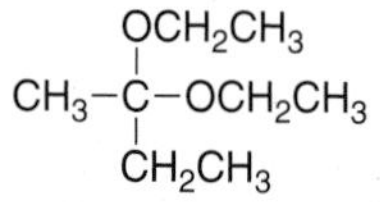

b. 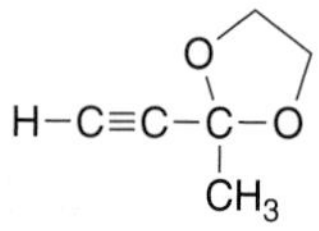

21.67 Albuterol is a bronchodilator used to treat the symptoms of asthma. Devise a synthesis of albuterol from **X** using any required organic compounds or inorganic reagents.

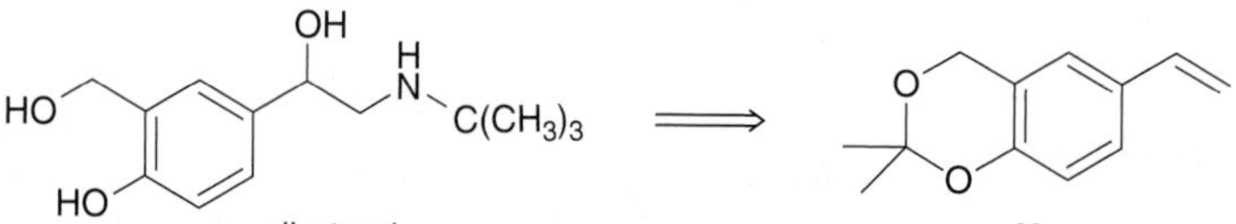

albuterol **X**

Protecting Groups

21.68 Design a stepwise synthesis to convert cyclopentanone and 4-bromobutanal to hydroxy aldehyde **A**.

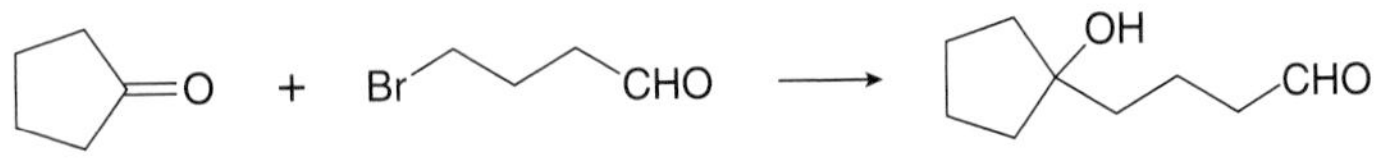

cyclopentanone 4-bromobutanal **A**

21.69 Besides the *tert*-butyldimethylsilyl ethers introduced in Chapter 20, there are many other widely used alcohol protecting groups. For example, an alcohol such as cyclohexanol can be converted to a **meth**oxy **m**ethyl ether (a MOM protecting group) by treatment with base and chloromethyl methyl ether, $ClCH_2OCH_3$. The protecting group can be removed by treatment with aqueous acid.

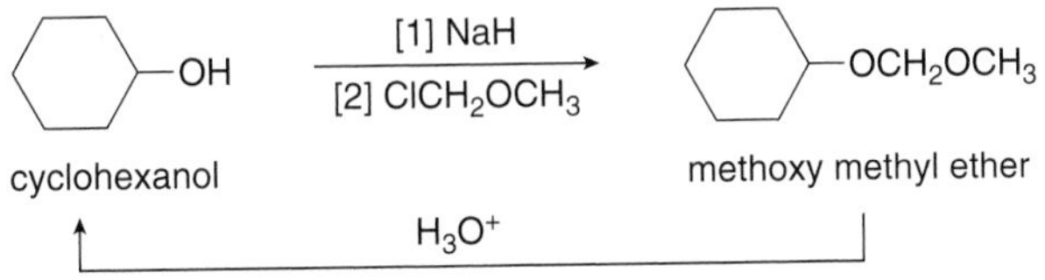

a. Write a stepwise mechanism for the formation of a MOM ether from cyclohexanol.
b. What functional group comprises a MOM ether?
c. Besides cyclohexanol, what other products are formed by aqueous hydrolysis of the MOM ether? Draw a stepwise mechanism that accounts for formation of each product.

Mechanism

21.70 Draw a stepwise mechanism for the following reaction.

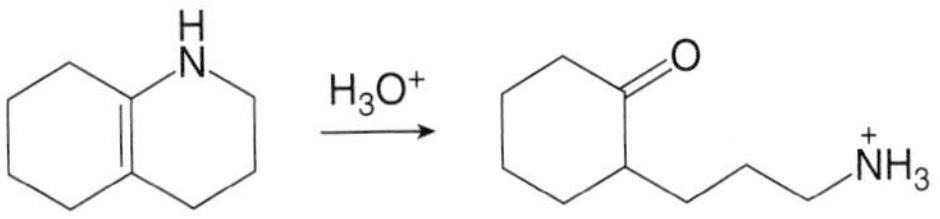

21.71 Draw a stepwise mechanism for the following reaction, a key step in the synthesis of the anti-inflammatory drug celecoxib (trade name Celebrex, Section 30.6).

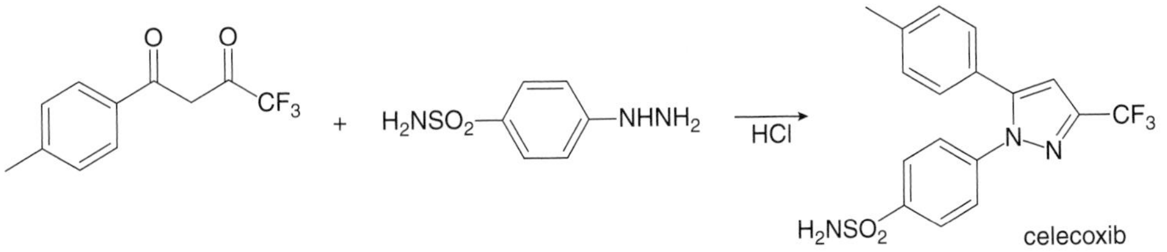

21.72 Treatment of $(HOCH_2CH_2CH_2CH_2)_2CO$ with acid forms a product of molecular formula $C_9H_{16}O_2$ and a molecule of water. Draw the structure of the product and explain how it is formed.

21.73 Draw a stepwise mechanism for each reaction.

a. 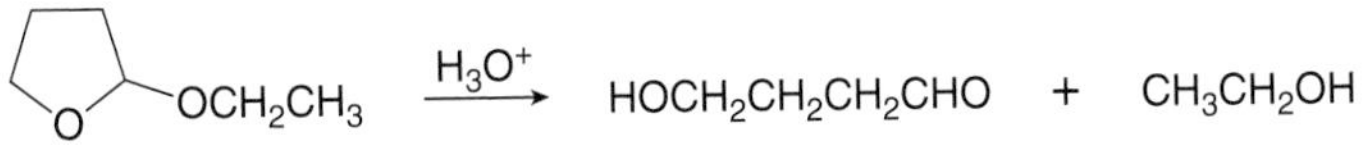

b. 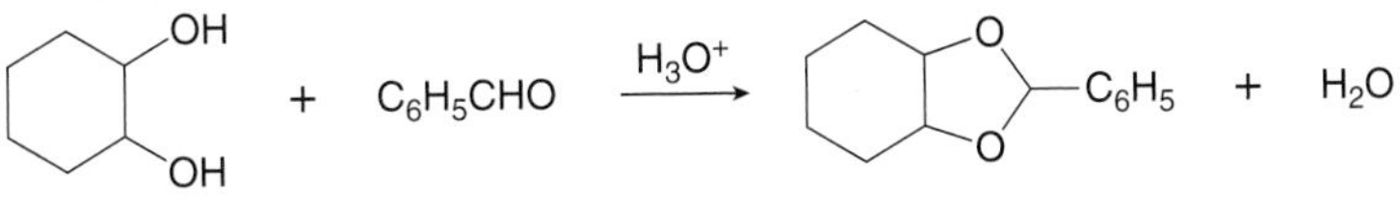

21.74 Draw a stepwise mechanism for the following reaction that converts a dicarbonyl compound to a furan.

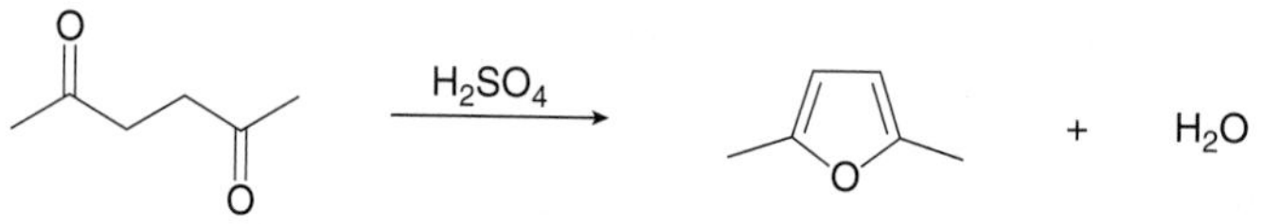

21.75 Draw a stepwise mechanism for the following reaction, a key step in the synthesis of ticlopidine, a drug that inhibits platelet aggregation. Ticlopidine has been used to reduce the risk of stroke in patients who cannot tolerate aspirin.

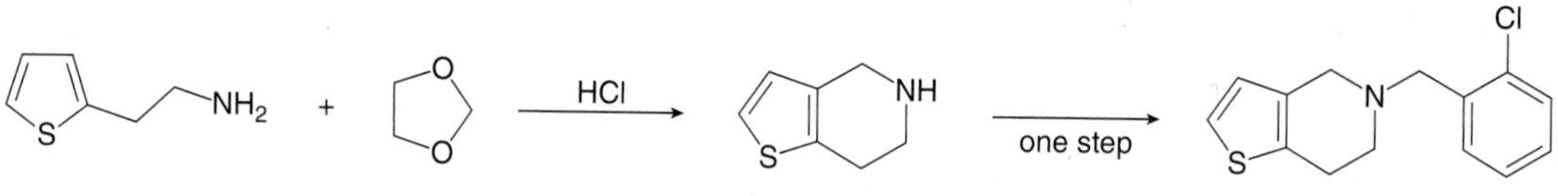

ticlopidine

21.76 Salsolinol is a naturally occurring compound found in bananas, chocolate, and several foods derived from plant sources. Salsolinol is also formed in the body when acetaldehyde, an oxidation product of the ethanol ingested in an alcoholic beverage, reacts with dopamine, a neurotransmitter. Draw a stepwise mechanism for the formation of salsolinol in the following reaction.

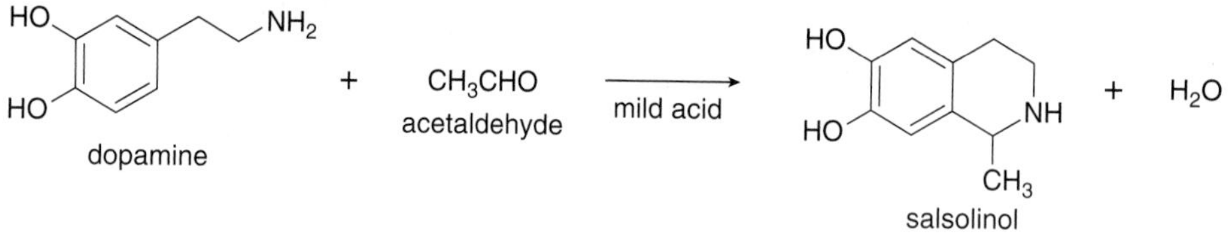

21.77 Sulfur ylides, like Wittig reagents, are useful intermediates in organic synthesis. Sulfur ylides are formed by the treatment of sulfonium salts with butyllithium. They react with carbonyl compounds to form epoxides. Draw the mechanism for formation of epoxide **X** from cyclohexanone using a sulfur ylide.

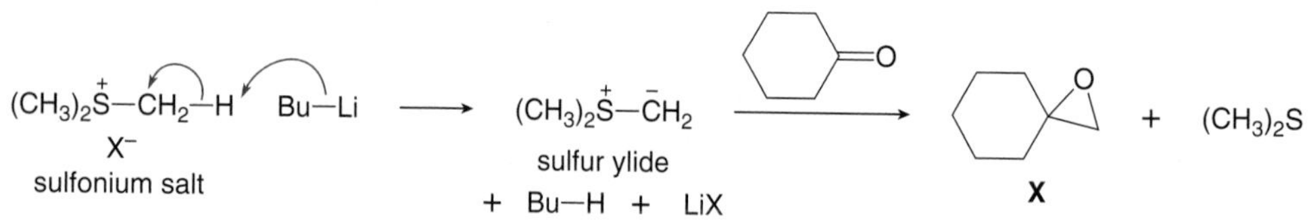

21.78 (a) Explain how $NaBH_4$ in CH_3OH can reduce hemiacetal **A** to 1,4-butanediol ($HOCH_2CH_2CH_2CH_2OH$). (b) What product is formed when **A** is treated with $Ph_3P{=}CHCH_2CH(CH_3)_2$? (c) The drug isotretinoin is formed by reaction of **X** and **Y.** What is the structure of isotretinoin? Although isotretinoin (trade name Accutane or Roaccutane) is used for the treatment of severe acne, it is dispensed under strict controls because it also causes birth defects.

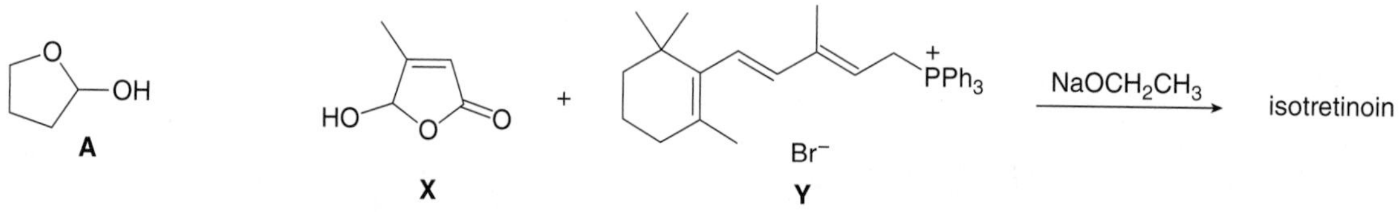

21.79 Reaction of 5,5-dimethoxy-2-pentanone with methylmagnesium iodide followed by treatment with aqueous acid forms cyclic hemiacetal **Y.** Draw a stepwise mechanism that illustrates how **Y** is formed.

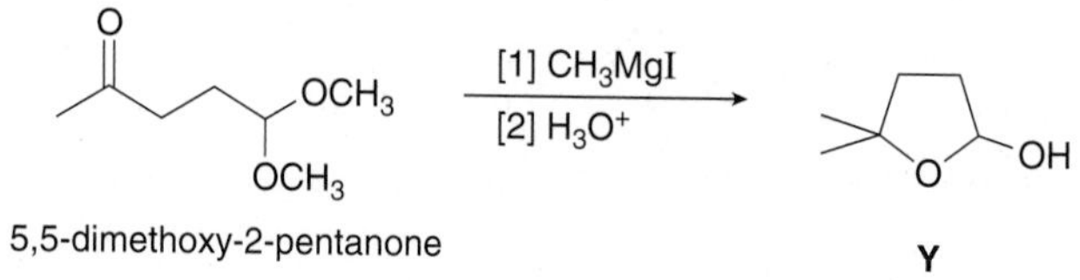

Spectroscopy

21.80 Although the carbonyl absorption of cyclic ketones generally shifts to higher wavenumber with decreasing ring size, the C=O of cyclopropenone absorbs at lower wavenumber in its IR spectrum than the C=O of cyclohexenone. Explain this observation by using the principles of aromaticity learned in Chapter 17.

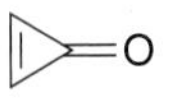

cyclopropenone ($1640\ cm^{-1}$)

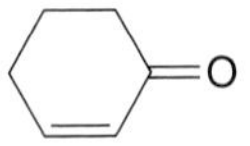

2-cyclohexenone ($1685\ cm^{-1}$)

21.81 Use the ^1H NMR and IR data to determine the structure of each compound.

Compound **A**
- Molecular formula: $C_5H_{10}O$
- IR absorptions at: 1728, 2791, and 2700 cm^{-1}
- ^1H NMR data: 1.08 (singlet, 9 H) and 9.48 (singlet, 1 H) ppm

Compound **B**
- Molecular formula: $C_5H_{10}O$
- IR absorption at: 1718 cm^{-1}
- ^1H NMR data: 1.10 (doublet, 6 H), 2.14 (singlet, 3 H), and 2.58 (septet, 1 H) ppm

Compound **C**
- Molecular formula: $C_{10}H_{12}O$
- IR absorption at: 1686 cm^{-1}
- ^1H NMR data: 1.21 (triplet, 3 H), 2.39 (singlet, 3 H), 2.95 (quartet, 2 H), 7.24 (doublet, 2 H), and 7.85 (doublet, 2 H) ppm

Compound **D**
- Molecular formula: $C_{10}H_{12}O$
- IR absorption at: 1719 cm^{-1}
- ^1H NMR data: 1.02 (triplet, 3 H), 2.45 (quartet, 2 H), 3.67 (singlet, 2 H), and 7.06–7.48 (multiplet, 5 H) ppm

21.82 A solution of acetone [$(CH_3)_2C=O$] in ethanol (CH_3CH_2OH) in the presence of a trace of acid was allowed to stand for several days, and a new compound of molecular formula $C_7H_{16}O_2$ was formed. The IR spectrum showed only one major peak in the functional group region around 3000 cm^{-1}, and the ^1H NMR spectrum is given here. What is the structure of the product?

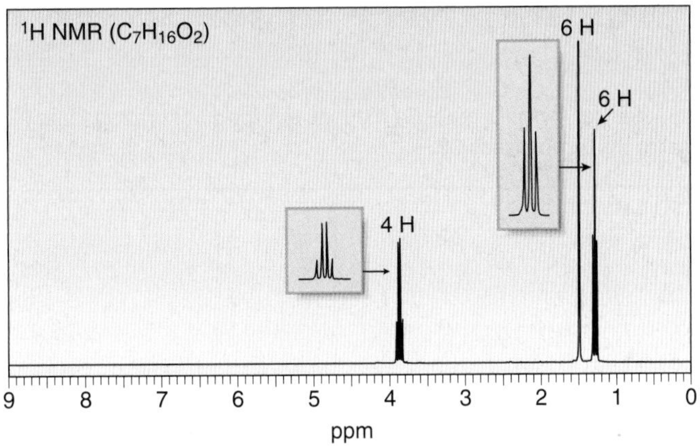

21.83 Compounds **A** and **B** have molecular formula $C_9H_{10}O$. Identify their structures from the ^1H NMR and IR spectra given.

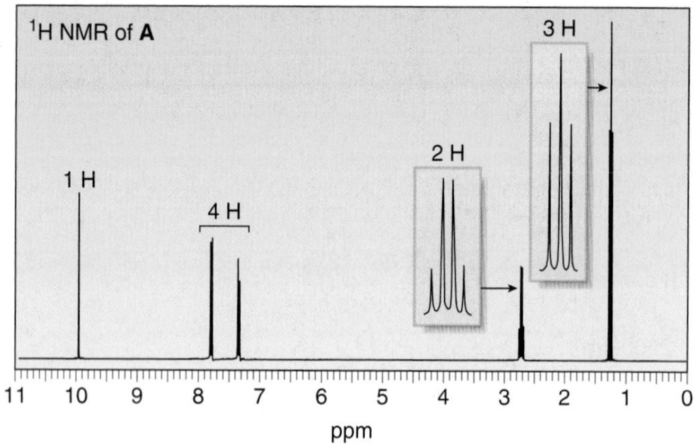

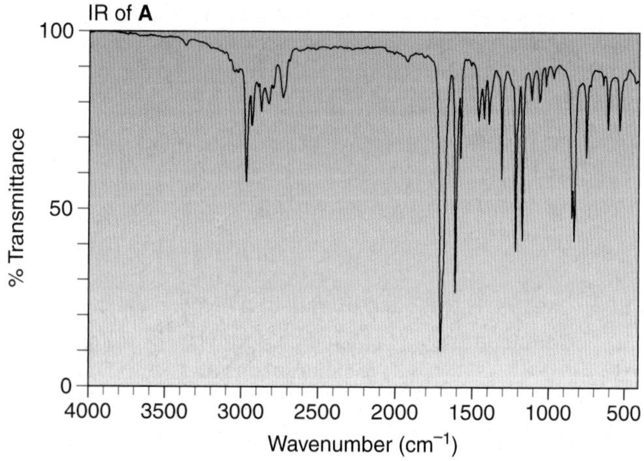

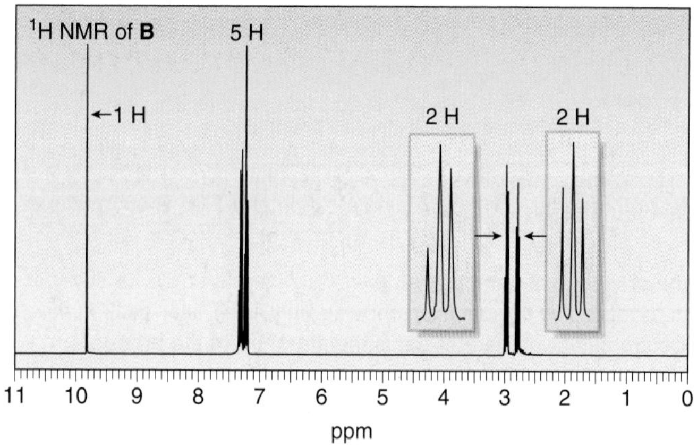

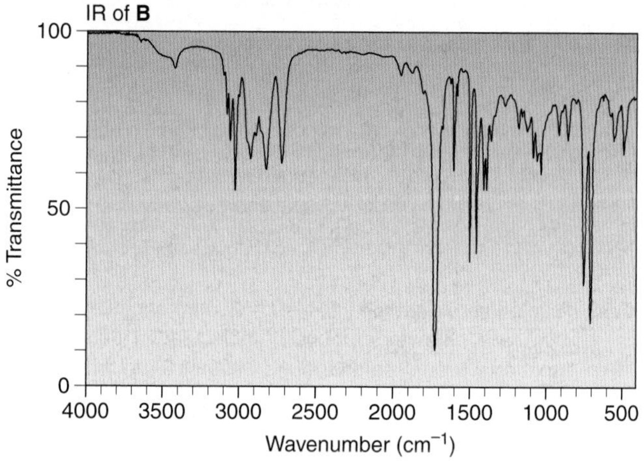

21.84 An unknown compound **C** of molecular formula $C_6H_{12}O_3$ exhibits a strong absorption in its IR spectrum at 1718 cm^{-1} and the given ^1H NMR spectrum. What is the structure of **C?**

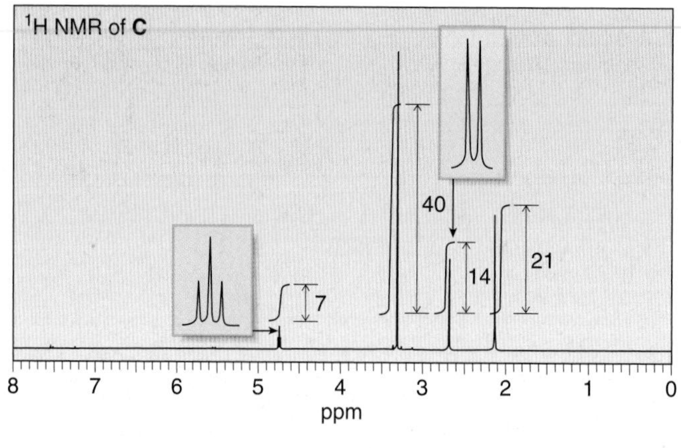

21.85 An unknown compound **D** exhibits a strong absorption in its IR spectrum at 1692 cm^{-1}. The mass spectrum of **D** shows a molecular ion at $m/z = 150$ and a base peak at 121. The ^1H NMR spectrum of **D** is shown below. What is the structure of **D?**

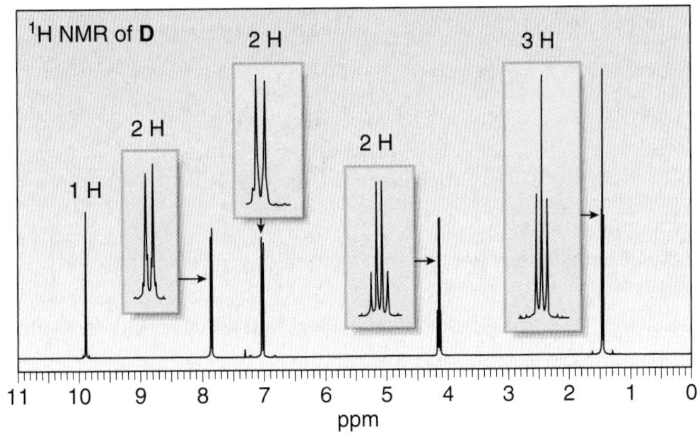

Carbohydrates

21.86 Draw the structure of the acyclic polyhydroxy aldehyde that cyclizes to each hemiacetal.

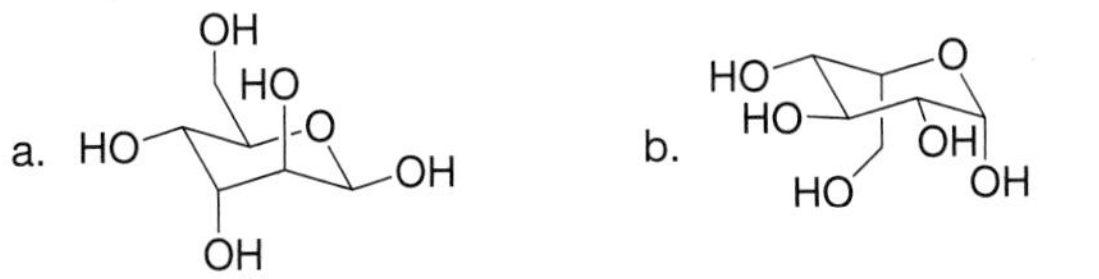

21.87 β-D-Glucose, a hemiacetal, can be converted to a mixture of acetals on treatment with CH_3OH in the presence of acid. Draw a stepwise mechanism for this reaction. Explain why two acetals are formed from a single starting material.

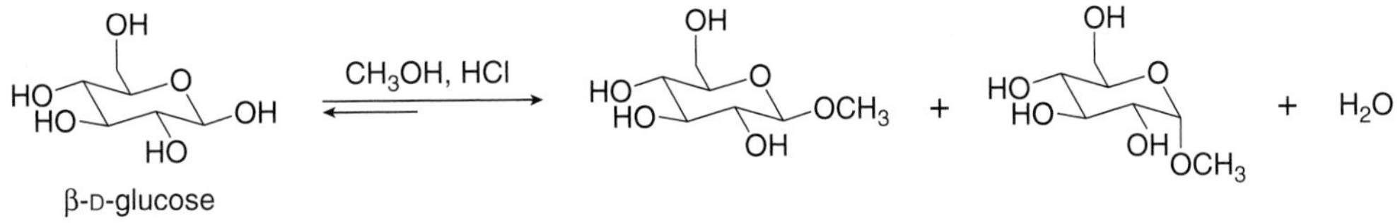

Challenge Problems

21.88 Draw a stepwise mechanism for the following reaction.

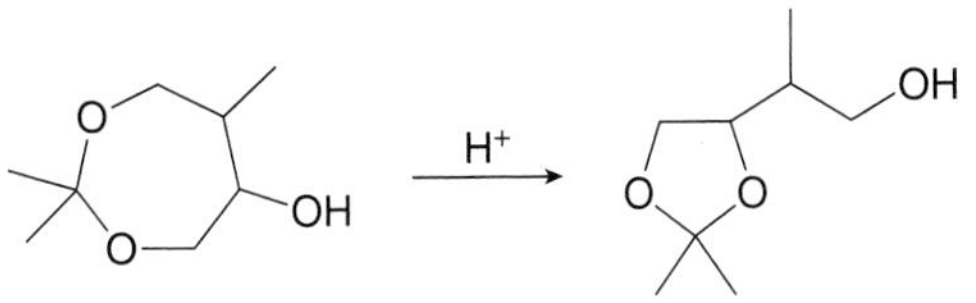

21.89 Brevicomin, the aggregation pheromone of the western pine bark beetle, contains a bicyclic bridged ring system and is prepared by the acid-catalyzed cyclization of 6,7-dihydroxy-2-nonanone.

a. Suggest a structure for brevicomin.

b. Devise a synthesis of 6,7-dihydroxy-2-nonanone from 6-bromo-2-hexanone. You may also use three-carbon alcohols and any required organic or inorganic reagents.

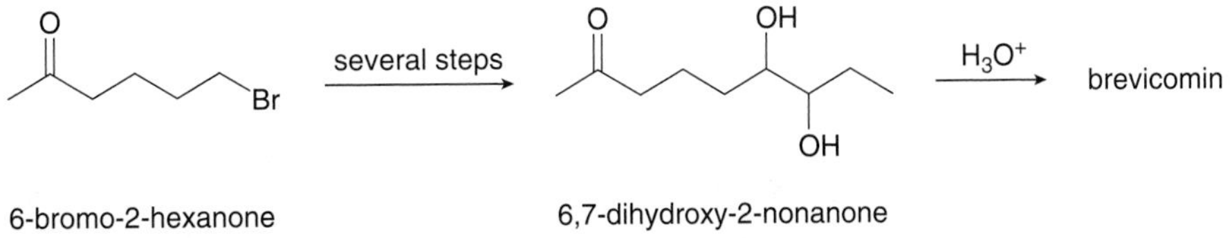

21.90 Maltose is a carbohydrate present in malt, the liquid obtained from barley and other grains. Although maltose has numerous functional groups, its reactions are explained by the same principles we have already encountered.

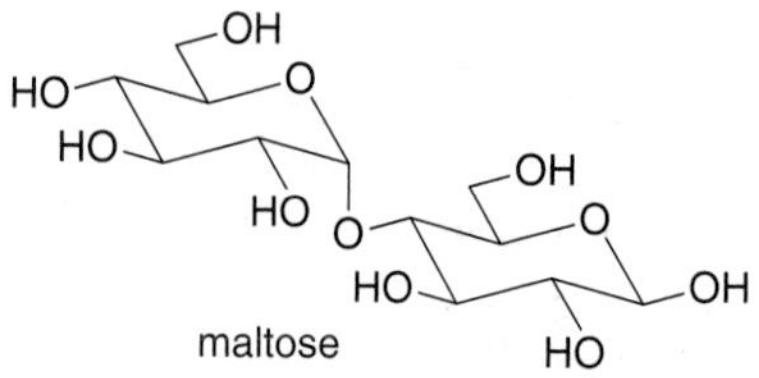

a. Label the acetal and hemiacetal carbons.
b. What products are formed when maltose is treated with each of the following reagents: [1] H_3O^+; [2] CH_3OH and HCl; [3] excess NaH, then excess CH_3I?
c. Draw the products formed when the compound formed in Reaction [3] of part (b) is treated with aqueous acid.

The reactions in parts (b) and (c) are used to determine structural features of carbohydrates like maltose. We will learn much more about maltose and similar carbohydrates in Chapter 28.

21.91 Identify **R** and **S** in the following reaction sequence, and draw a mechanism for the conversion of **R** to **S** (molecular formula $C_6H_{10}O_3$). **S** was used in the synthesis of darunavir (trade name Prezista), used to treat HIV.

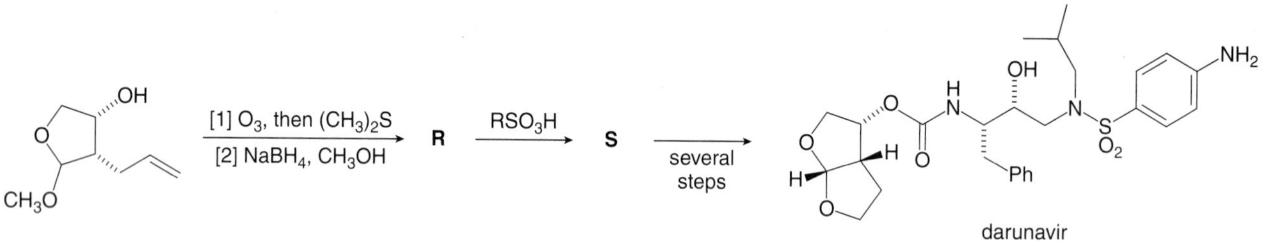

21.92 Draw a stepwise mechanism for the following reaction, a key step in the synthesis of conivaptan (trade name Vaprisol), a drug used in the treatment of low sodium levels.

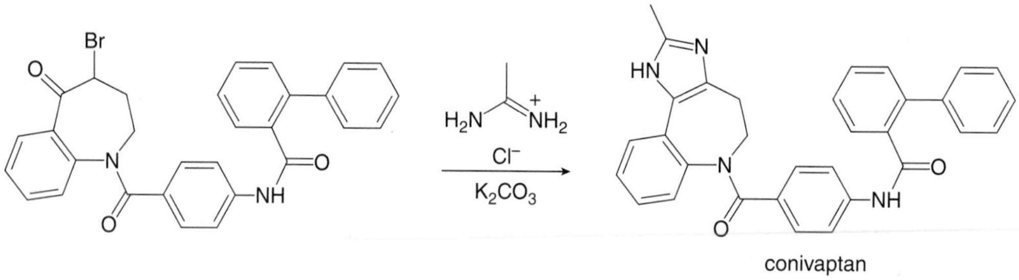

Carboxylic Acids and Their Derivatives—Nucleophilic Acyl Substitution

22

22.1 Introduction
22.2 Structure and bonding
22.3 Nomenclature
22.4 Physical properties
22.5 Spectroscopic properties
22.6 Interesting esters and amides
22.7 Introduction to nucleophilic acyl substitution
22.8 Reactions of acid chlorides
22.9 Reactions of anhydrides
22.10 Reactions of carboxylic acids
22.11 Reactions of esters
22.12 Application: Lipid hydrolysis
22.13 Reactions of amides
22.14 Application: The mechanism of action of β-lactam antibiotics
22.15 Summary of nucleophilic acyl substitution reactions
22.16 Natural and synthetic fibers
22.17 Biological acylation reactions
22.18 Nitriles

Ginkgolide B, a major constituent of the extracts of the ginkgo tree *Ginkgo biloba,* is a complex molecule whose structure was determined in 1967. Although its compact, rigid ring system of 20 carbons made it a challenging molecule to prepare in the laboratory, Nobel Laureate E. J. Corey and co-workers reported its synthesis in 1988. Ginkgo extracts are widely used herbal supplements, taken to enhance memory and treat dementia. Recent findings of the National Institutes of Health, however, have cast doubt on their efficacy in providing long-term improvement in cognitive function. In Chapter 22 we learn about the reactions of esters, three of the many functional groups in ginkgolide B.

Chapter 22 continues the study of carbonyl compounds with a detailed look at **nucleophilic acyl substitution,** a key reaction of carboxylic acids and their derivatives. Substitution at sp^2 hybridized carbon atoms was introduced in Chapter 20 with reactions involving carbon and hydrogen nucleophiles. In Chapter 22, we learn that nucleophilic acyl substitution is a general reaction that occurs with a variety of heteroatomic nucleophiles. This reaction allows the conversion of one carboxylic acid derivative into another. ***Every*** **reaction in Chapter 22 that begins with a carbonyl compound involves nucleophilic substitution.** Chapter 22 also discusses the properties and chemical reactions of **nitriles,** compounds that contain a carbon–nitrogen triple bond. Nitriles are in the same carbon oxidation state as carboxylic acids, and they undergo reactions that form related products.

22.1 Introduction

Chapter 22 focuses on carbonyl compounds that contain an **acyl group bonded to an electronegative atom.** These include the **carboxylic acids,** as well as carboxylic acid derivatives that can be prepared from them: **acid chlorides, anhydrides, esters, and amides.**

General structure

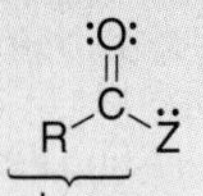

acyl group

Z = electronegative atom

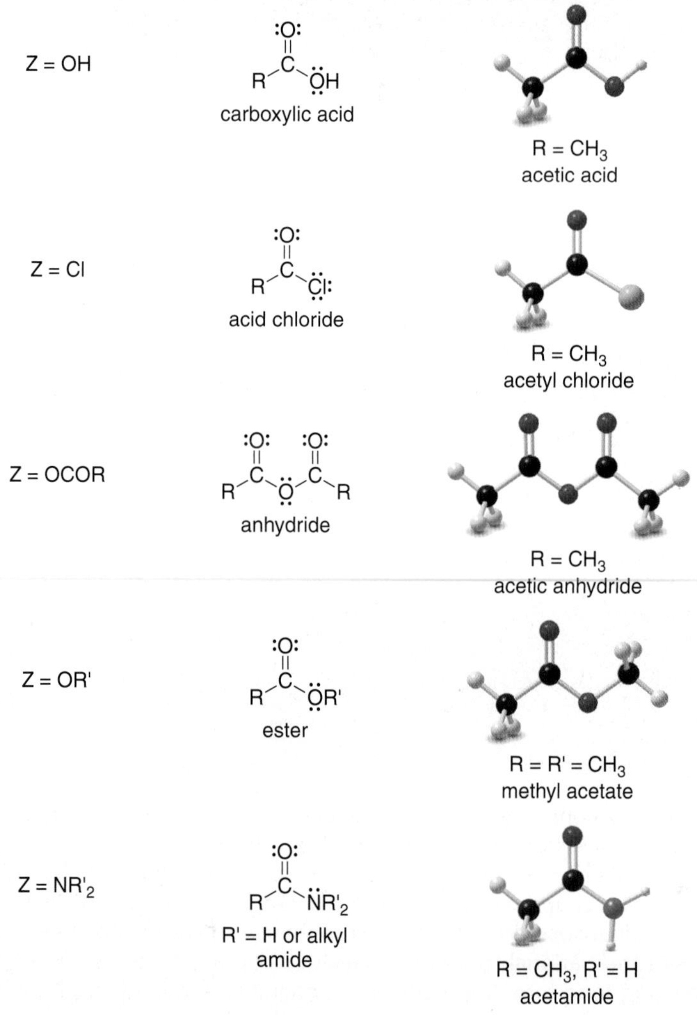

Anhydrides contain two carbonyl groups joined by a single oxygen atom. **Symmetrical anhydrides** have two identical alkyl groups bonded to the carbonyl carbons, and **mixed anhydrides** have two different alkyl groups. **Cyclic anhydrides** are also known.

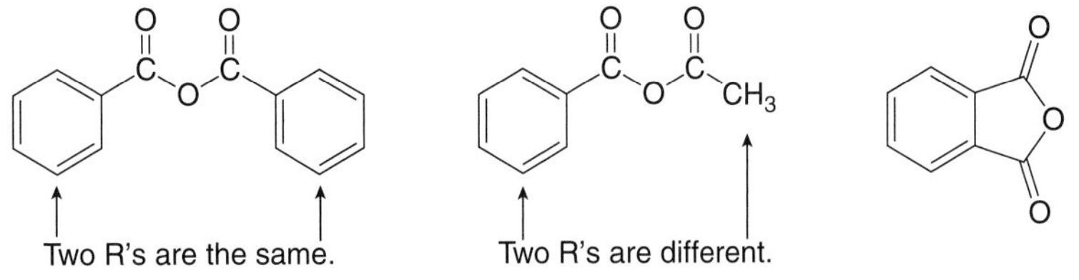
Two R's are the same.
Two R's are different.

symmetrical anhydride mixed anhydride cyclic anhydride

Amides are classified as **1°, 2°,** or **3°** depending on the number of carbon atoms bonded directly to the *nitrogen* atom.

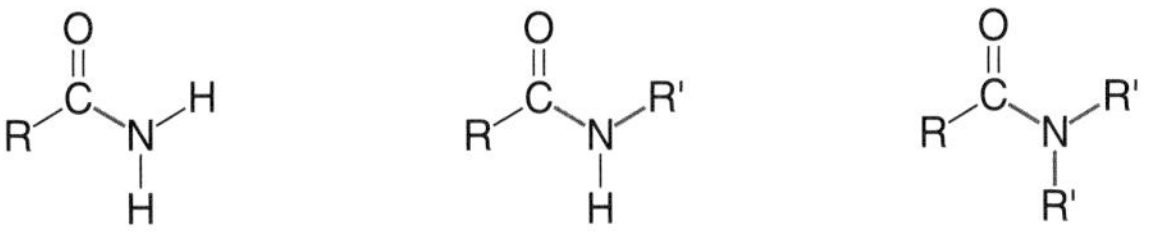

1° amide
1 C–N bond

2° amide
2 C–N bonds

3° amide
3 C–N bonds

Cyclic esters and amides are called **lactones** and **lactams,** respectively. The ring size of the heterocycle is indicated by a Greek letter. An amide in a four-membered ring is called a **β-lactam,** because the β carbon to the carbonyl is bonded to the heteroatom. An ester in a five-membered ring is called a **γ-lactone.**

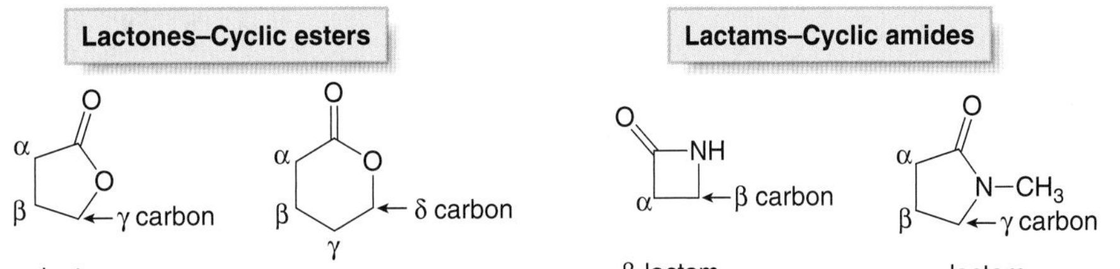
Lactones–Cyclic esters
Lactams–Cyclic amides
γ carbon
δ carbon
β carbon
γ carbon

γ-lactone δ-lactone β-lactam γ-lactam

Nucleophilic acyl substitution was first discussed in Chapter 20 with R⁻ and H⁻ as the nucleophiles. This substitution reaction is general for a variety of nucleophiles, making it possible to form many different substitution products, as discussed in Sections 22.8–22.13.

All of these compounds contain an acyl group bonded to an electronegative atom Z that can serve as a **leaving group.** As a result, these compounds undergo **nucleophilic acyl substitution.** Recall from Chapters 20 and 21 that aldehydes and ketones do *not* undergo nucleophilic substitution because they have no leaving group on the carbonyl carbon.

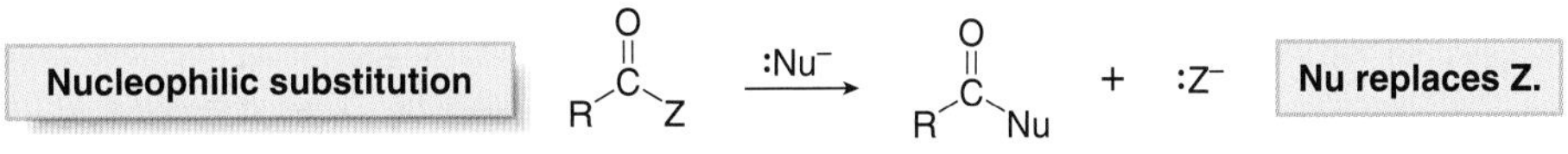
Nucleophilic substitution
:Nu⁻
+ :Z⁻
Nu replaces Z.

Z = OH, Cl, OCOR, OR', NR'$_2$

***Nitriles* are compounds that contain a cyano group, C≡N, bonded to an alkyl group.** Nitriles have no carbonyl group, so they are structurally distinct from carboxylic acids and their derivatives. The carbon atom of the cyano group, however, has the same oxidation state as the carbonyl carbon of carboxylic acid derivatives, so there are certain parallels in their chemistry.

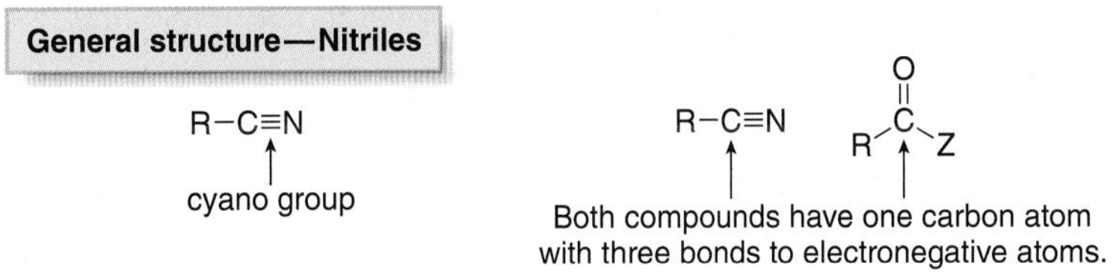
General structure—Nitriles
R–C≡N
cyano group
Both compounds have one carbon atom with three bonds to electronegative atoms.

Problem 22.1 Oxytocin, sold under the trade name Pitocin, is a naturally occurring hormone used to stimulate uterine contractions and induce labor. Classify each amide in oxytocin as 1°, 2°, or 3°.

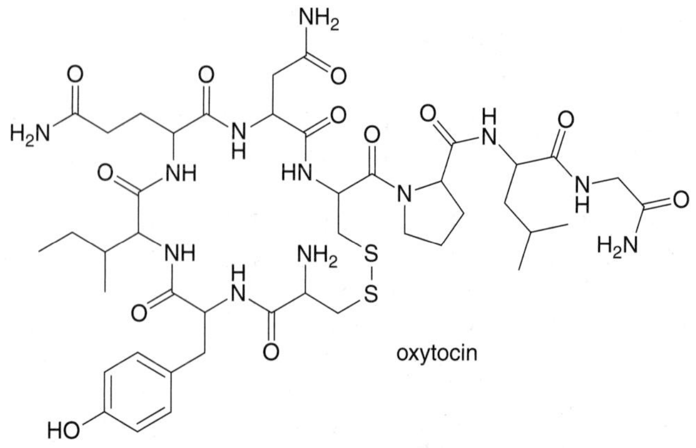

oxytocin

22.2 Structure and Bonding

The two most important features of any carbonyl group, regardless of the other groups bonded to it, are the following:

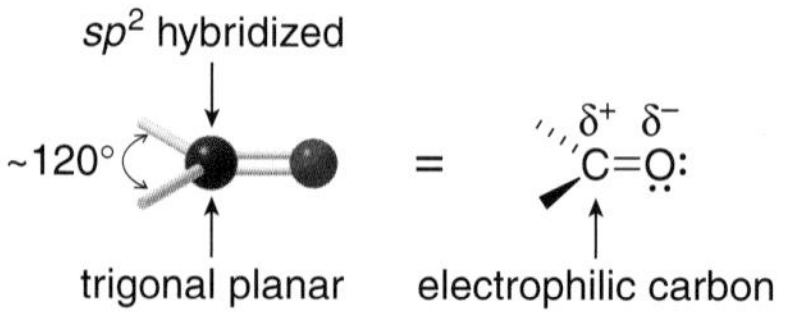

- **The carbonyl carbon is *sp*² hybridized and trigonal planar, making it relatively uncrowded.**
- **The electronegative oxygen atom polarizes the carbonyl group, making the carbonyl carbon electrophilic.**

Because carboxylic acid derivatives (RCOZ) all contain an atom Z with a nonbonded electron pair, three resonance structures can be drawn for RCOZ, compared to just two for aldehydes and ketones (Section 20.1). These three resonance structures stabilize RCOZ by delocalizing electron density. In fact, the more resonance structures **2** and **3** contribute to the resonance hybrid, the more stable RCOZ is.

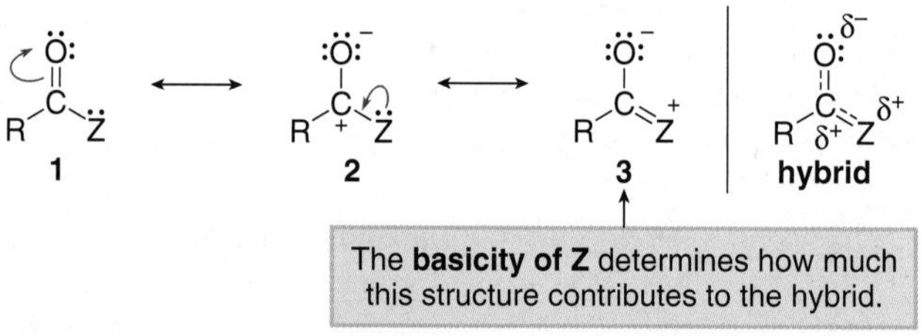

- **The more basic Z is, the more it donates its electron pair, and the more resonance structure 3 contributes to the hybrid.**

To determine the relative basicity of the leaving group Z, we compare the pK_a values of the conjugate acids HZ, given in Table 22.1. The following order of basicity results:

Trends in basicity

Cl^-	$RCOO^-$	^-OH		$^-OR'$	$^-NR'_2$
weakest base			similar (^-OH ~ $^-OR'$)		strongest base

Increasing basicity →

Table 22.1 pK_a Values of the Conjugate Acids (HZ) for Common Z Groups of Acyl Compounds (RCOZ)

Structure	Leaving group (Z^-)	Conjugate acid (HZ)	pK_a
RCOCl acid chloride	Cl^-	HCl	–7
$(RCO)_2O$ anhydride	$RCOO^-$	RCOOH	3–5
RCOOH carboxylic acid	^-OH	H_2O	15.7
RCOOR' ester	$^-OR'$	R'OH	15.5–18
$RCONR'_2$ amide	$^-NR'_2$	R'_2NH	38–40

Increasing basicity of Z (down); Increasing acidity of HZ (up)

Because the basicity of Z determines the relative stability of the carboxylic acid derivatives, the following **order of stability** results:

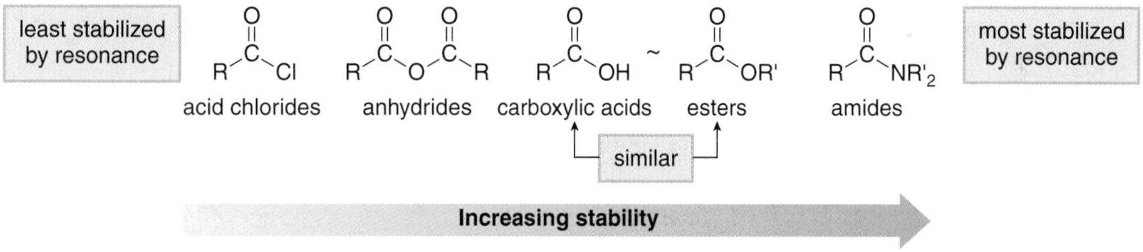

Thus, an acid chloride is the least stable carboxylic acid derivative because Cl^- is the weakest base. An amide is the most stable carboxylic acid derivative because $^-NR'_2$ is the strongest base.

- **In summary: As the basicity of Z increases, the stability of RCOZ increases because of added resonance stabilization.**

Problem 22.2 Draw the three possible resonance structures for an acid bromide, RCOBr. Then, using the pK_a values in Appendix A, decide if RCOBr is more or less stabilized by resonance than a carboxylic acid (RCOOH).

Problem 22.3 How do the following experimental results support the resonance description of the relative stability of acid chlorides compared to amides? The C – Cl bond lengths in CH_3Cl and CH_3COCl are identical (178 pm), but the C – N bond in $HCONH_2$ is shorter than the C – N bond in CH_3NH_2 (135 pm versus 147 pm).

The structure and bonding in nitriles is very different from the carboxylic acid derivatives, and resembles the carbon–carbon triple bond of alkynes.

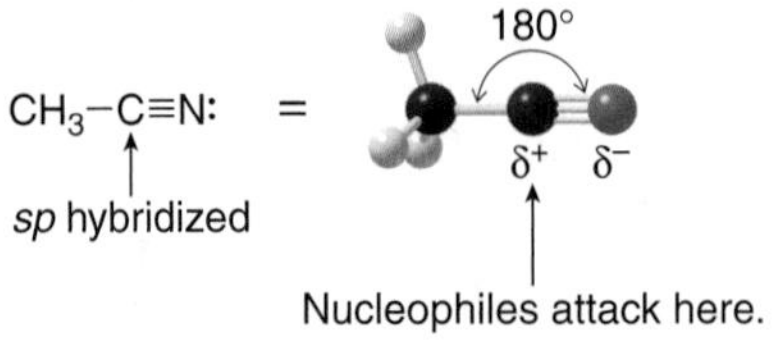

- **The carbon atom of the C ≡ N group is *sp* hybridized, making it linear with a bond angle of 180°.**
- **The triple bond consists of one σ and two π bonds.**

Like the carboxylic acid derivatives, **nitriles contain an electrophilic carbon atom,** making them susceptible to nucleophilic attack.

22.3 Nomenclature

The names of carboxylic acid derivatives are formed from the names of the parent carboxylic acids discussed in Section 19.2. Keep in mind that the common names **formic acid, acetic acid,** and **benzoic acid** are virtually always used for the parent acid, so these common parent names are used for their derivatives as well.

22.3A Naming an Acid Chloride—RCOCl

Acid chlorides are named by naming the acyl group and adding the word ***chloride.*** Two different methods are used.

[1] For acyclic acid chlorides: Change the suffix *-ic acid* of the parent carboxylic acid to the suffix *-yl chloride*; or

[2] When the –COCl group is bonded to a ring: Change the suffix *-carboxylic acid* to *-carbonyl chloride*.

Naming acid chlorides

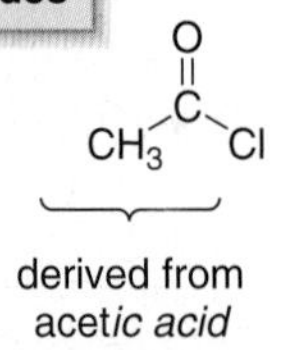

acetyl chloride

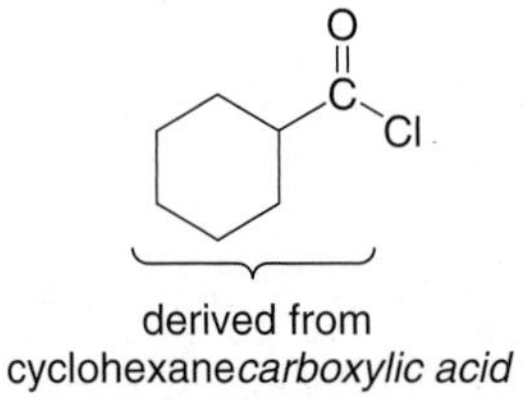

cyclohexanecarbonyl chloride

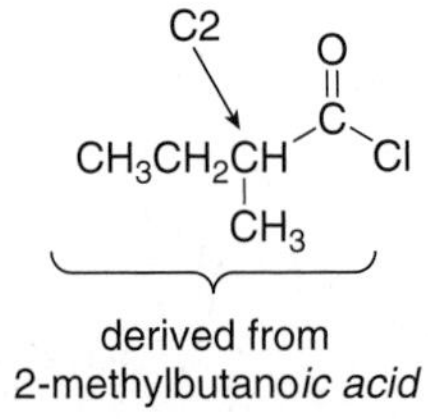

2-methylbutanoyl chloride

22.3B Naming an Anhydride

The word *anhydride* means "without water." Removing one molecule of water from two molecules of carboxylic acid forms an anhydride.

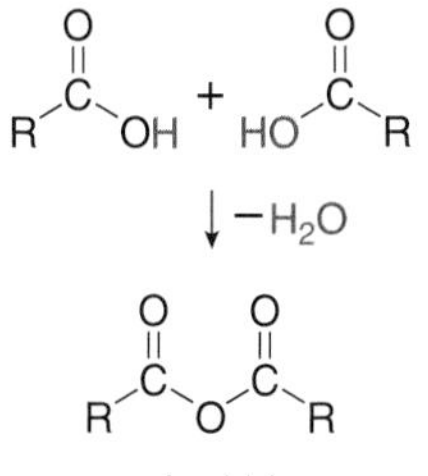

anhydride

Symmetrical anhydrides are named by changing the ***acid*** ending of the parent carboxylic acid to the word ***anhydride.*** **Mixed anhydrides,** which are derived from two different carboxylic acids, are named by alphabetizing the names for both acids and replacing the word ***acid*** by the word ***anhydride.***

Symmetrical anhydride

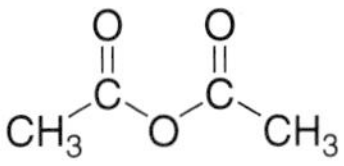

derived from acetic acid

acetic anhydride

Mixed anhydride

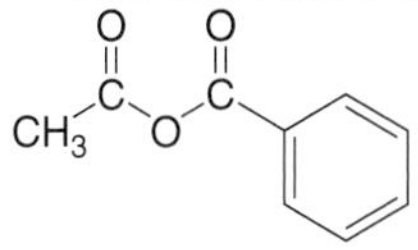

derived from acetic acid and benzoic acid

acetic benzoic anhydride

22.3C Naming an Ester—RCOOR'

Esters are often written as RCOOR', where the alkyl group (R') is written *last.* When an ester is named, however, the R' group appears *first* in the name.

An ester has two parts to its structure, each of which must be named: an **acyl group (RCO−)** and an **alkyl group** (designated as **R'**) bonded to an oxygen atom.

- **In the IUPAC system, esters are identified by the suffix *-ate.***

How To Name an Ester (RCO_2R') Using the IUPAC System

Example Give a systematic name for each ester:

a. 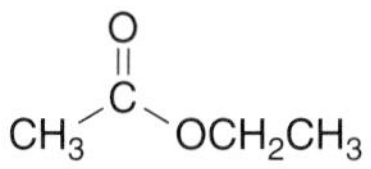

b. 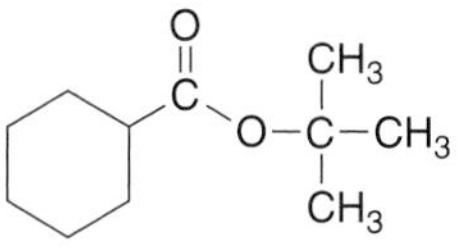

Step [1] Name the R' group bonded to the oxygen atom as an alkyl group.

- The name of the alkyl group, ending in the suffix *-yl,* becomes the *first* part of the ester name.

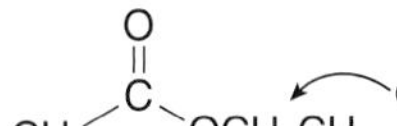

ethyl group

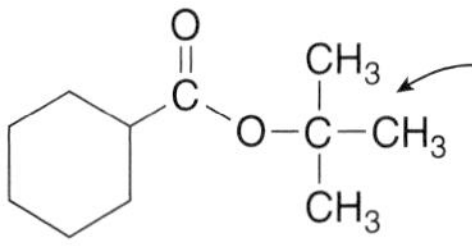

tert-butyl group

Step [2] Name the acyl group (RCO−) by changing the *-ic acid* ending of the parent carboxylic acid to the suffix *-ate.*

- The name of the acyl group becomes the *second* part of the name.

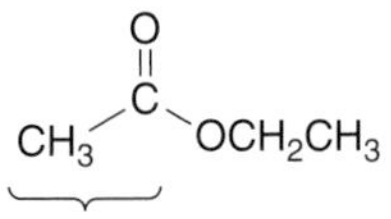

derived from acet*ic acid* ---→ acet*ate*

Answer: ethyl acetate

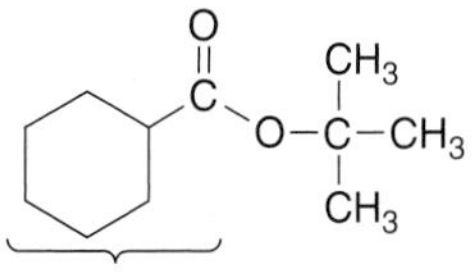

derived from cyclohexanecarboxyl*ic acid* ---→ cyclohexanecarboxyl*ate*

Answer: *tert*-butyl cyclohexanecarboxylate

22.3D Naming an Amide

All 1° amides are named by replacing the ***-ic acid, -oic acid,*** or ***-ylic acid*** ending with the suffix **amide.**

Naming 1° amides

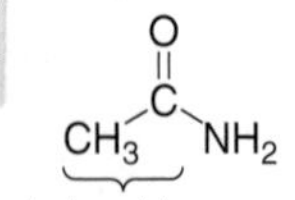
derived from acetic *acid*

acetamide

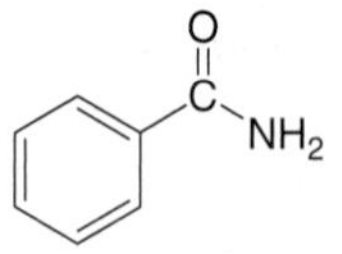
derived from benzoic *acid*

benzamide

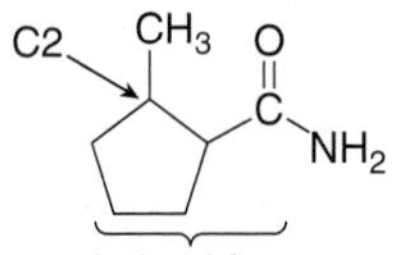
derived from 2-methylcyclopentanecarbox*ylic acid*

2-methylcyclopentanecarboxamide

A 2° or 3° amide has two parts to its structure: an **acyl group** that contains the carbonyl group **(RCO–)** and one or two **alkyl groups** bonded to the nitrogen atom.

How To Name a 2° or 3° Amide

Example Give a systematic name for each amide:

a. 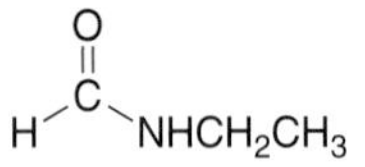

b. 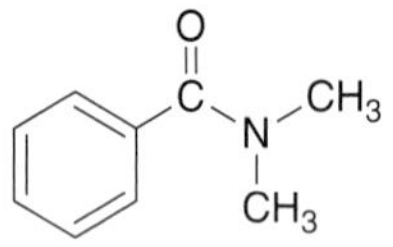

Step [1] **Name the alkyl group (or groups) bonded to the N atom of the amide. Use the prefix "*N*-" preceding the name of each alkyl group.**

- The names of the alkyl groups form the first part of each amide name.
- For 3° amides, use the prefix **di-** if the two alkyl groups on N are the same. If the two alkyl groups are different, **alphabetize** their names. One "***N*-**" is needed for each alkyl group, even if both R groups are identical.

a. 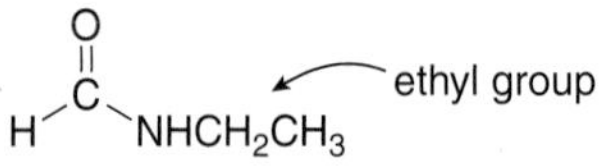

- The compound is a 2° amide with one ethyl group → *N*-ethyl.

b. 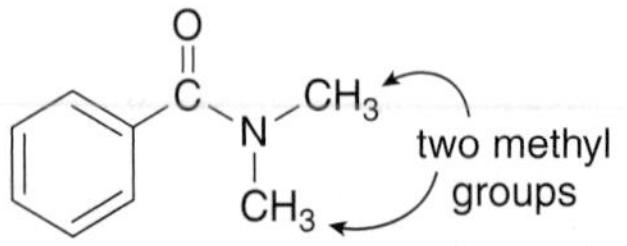

- The compound is a 3° amide with two methyl groups.
- Use the prefix di- and two "*N*-" to begin the name → *N,N*-dimethyl.

Step [2] **Name the acyl group (RCO–) with the suffix *-amide.***

a. 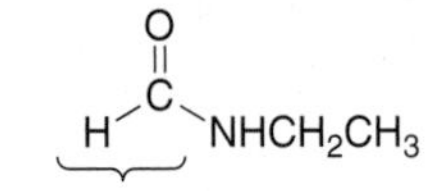
derived from form*ic acid* -----> form*amide*

- Change the *-ic acid* or *-oic acid* suffix of the parent carboxylic acid to the suffix *-amide.*
- Put the two parts of the name together.
- **Answer: *N*-ethylformamide**

b. 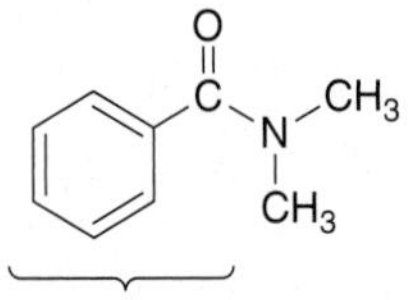
derived from benz*oic acid* ---> benz*amide*

- Change benz*oic acid* to benz*amide.*
- Put the two parts of the name together.
- **Answer: *N,N*-dimethylbenzamide**

22.3E Naming a Nitrile

In contrast to the carboxylic acid derivatives, **nitriles are named as alkane derivatives.** To name a nitrile using IUPAC rules:

- **Find the longest chain that contains the CN and add the word *nitrile* to the name of the parent alkane. Number the chain to put CN at C1, but omit this number from the name.**

In naming a nitrile, the CN carbon is one carbon atom of the longest chain. **CH_3CH_2CN is propanenitrile, *not* ethanenitrile.**

Common names for nitriles are derived from the names of the carboxylic acid having the same number of carbon atoms by replacing the ***-ic acid*** ending of the carboxylic acid by the suffix ***-onitrile.***

When CN is named as a substituent, it is called a ***cyano*** group. Figure 22.1 illustrates features of nitrile nomenclature.

Table 22.2 summarizes the most important points about the nomenclature of carboxylic acid derivatives.

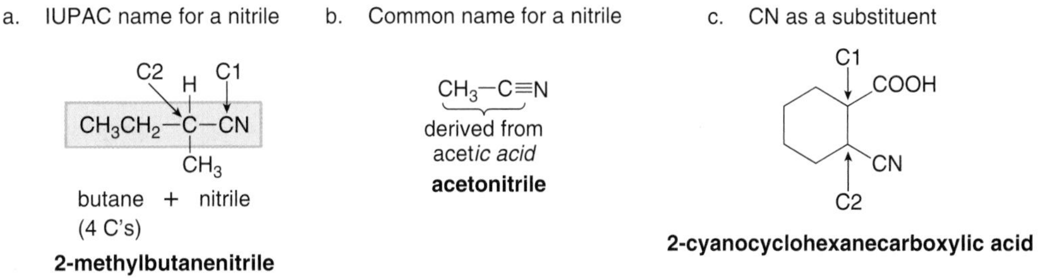
a. IUPAC name for a nitrile
C2
H
C1
CH3CH2–C–CN
CH3
butane + nitrile
(4 C's)
2-methylbutanenitrile
b. Common name for a nitrile
CH3–C≡N
derived from
acetic acid
acetonitrile
c. CN as a substituent
C1
COOH
CN
C2
2-cyanocyclohexanecarboxylic acid

Figure 22.1 Summary of nitrile nomenclature

Table 22.2 Summary: Nomenclature of Carboxylic Acid Derivatives and Nitriles

Compound	Name ending	Example	Name
acid chloride	**-yl chloride** or **-carbonyl chloride**	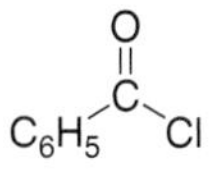	benzoyl chloride
anhydride	**anhydride**	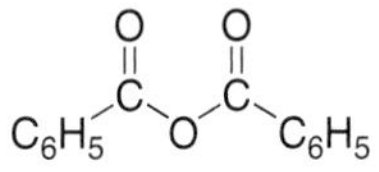	benzoic anhydride
ester	**-ate**	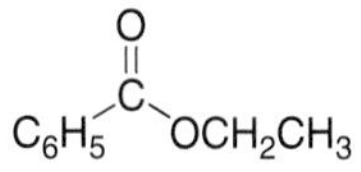	ethyl benzoate
amide	**-amide**	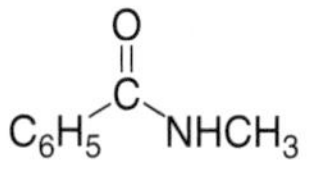	*N*-methylbenzamide
nitrile	**-nitrile** or **-onitrile**	$C_6H_5{-}C{\equiv}N$	benzonitrile

Sample Problem 22.1 Give the IUPAC name for each compound.

a. 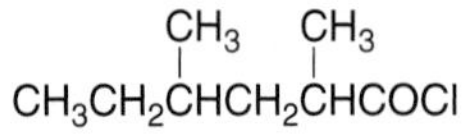

b. 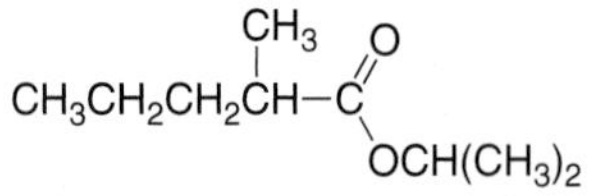

Solution

a. The functional group is an acid chloride bonded to a chain of atoms, so the name ends in ***-yl chloride.***

[1] Find and name the longest chain containing the COCl:

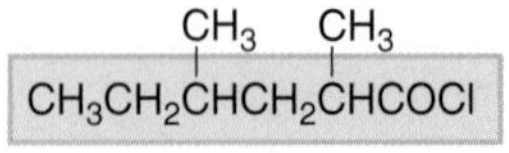

hexano*ic acid* → **hexano*yl chloride***
(6 C's)

[2] Number and name the substituents:

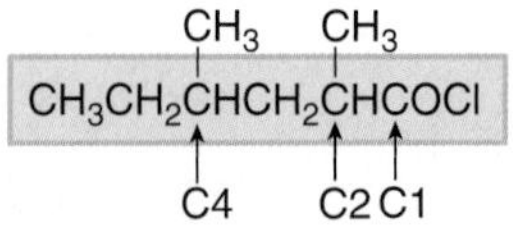

Answer:
2,4-dimethylhexanoyl chloride

b. The functional group is an ester, so the name ends in ***-ate.***

[1] Find and name the longest chain containing the carbonyl group:

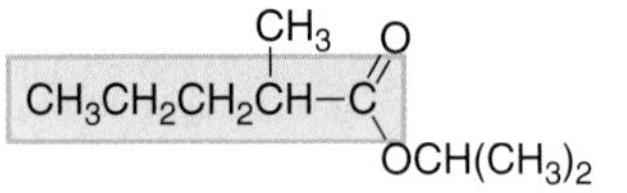

pentano*ic acid* → **pentano*ate***
(5 C's)

[2] Number and name the substituents:

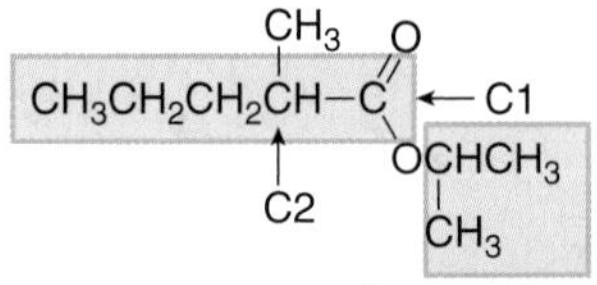

isopropyl group

Answer: isopropyl 2-methylpentanoate

The name of the alkyl group on the O atom goes **first** in the name.

Problem 22.4 Give an IUPAC or common name for each compound.

a. $(CH_3CH_2)_2CHCOCl$
b. $C_6H_5COOCH_3$
c. $CH_3CH_2CON(CH_3)CH_2CH_3$
d. 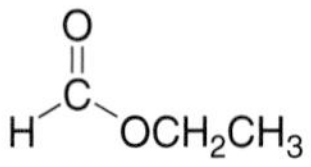
e. 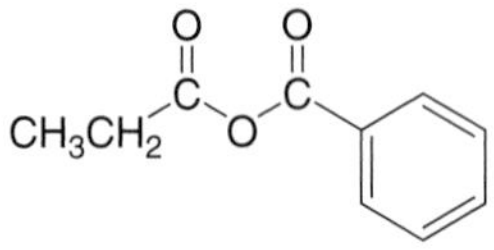
f. 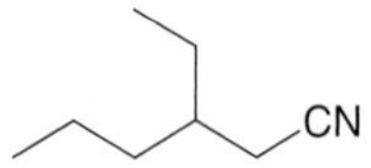

Problem 22.5 Draw the structure corresponding to each name.

a. 5-methylheptanoyl chloride
b. isopropyl propanoate
c. acetic formic anhydride
d. *N*-isobutyl-*N*-methylbutanamide
e. 3-methylpentanenitrile
f. *o*-cyanobenzoic acid
g. *sec*-butyl 2-methylhexanoate
h. *N*-ethylhexanamide

22.4 Physical Properties

Because all carbonyl compounds have a polar carbonyl group, they exhibit **dipole–dipole interactions.** Nitriles also have dipole–dipole interactions because they have a polar C≡N group. Because they contain one or two N–H bonds, 1° and 2° amides are capable of intermolecular hydrogen bonding. The N–H bond of one amide intermolecularly hydrogen bonds to the C=O of another amide, as shown using two acetamide molecules (CH_3CONH_2) in Figure 22.2.

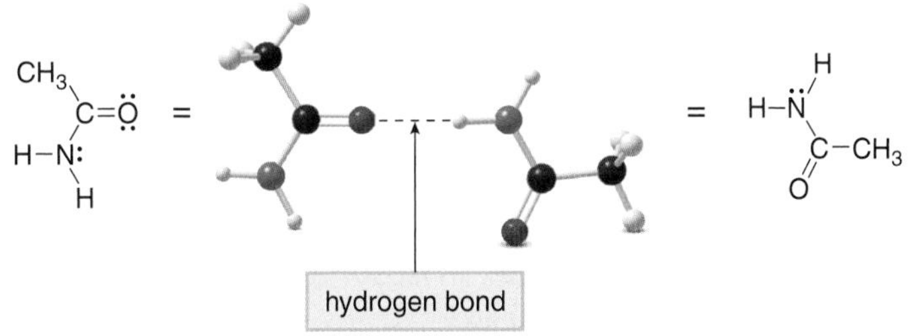

Figure 22.2 Intermolecular hydrogen bonding between two CH_3CONH_2 molecules

Table 22.3 Physical Properties of Carboxylic Acid Derivatives

Property	Observation
Boiling point and melting point	• Primary (1°) and 2° amides have *higher* boiling points and melting points than compounds of comparable molecular weight. • The boiling points and melting points of other carboxylic acid derivatives are similar to those of other polar compounds of comparable size and shape.  MW = 78.5, bp 52 °C ~ MW = 74, bp 58 °C ~ MW = 72, bp 80 °C < MW = 73, bp 213 °C similar boiling points — higher boiling point, 1° amide
Solubility	• Carboxylic acid derivatives are soluble in organic solvents regardless of size. • Most carboxylic acid derivatives having ≤ 5 C's are H_2O soluble because they can hydrogen bond with H_2O (Section 3.4C). • Carboxylic acid derivatives having > 5 C's are H_2O insoluble because the nonpolar alkyl portion is too large to dissolve in the polar H_2O solvent.

Key: MW = molecular weight

How these factors affect the physical properties of carboxylic acid derivatives is summarized in Table 22.3.

Problem 22.6 Explain why the boiling point of CH_3CONH_2 (221 °C) is significantly higher than the boiling point of $CH_3CON(CH_3)_2$ (166 °C), even though the latter compound has a higher molecular weight and more surface area.

22.5 Spectroscopic Properties

22.5A IR Spectra

The most prominent IR absorptions for carboxylic acid derivatives and nitriles are as follows:

[1] Like all carbonyl compounds, carboxylic acid derivatives have a **strong C=O absorption between 1600 and 1850 cm^{-1}.**

[2] **Primary (1°) and 2° amides** have two additional absorptions due to the N–H bonds:
- one or two N–H stretching peaks at **3200–3400 cm^{-1}**
- an N–H bending absorption at **~1640 cm^{-1}**

[3] **Nitriles** have an absorption at **2250 cm^{-1} for the C≡N.**

The exact location of the carbonyl absorption varies with the identity of Z in the carbonyl compound RCOZ. As detailed in Section 22.2, as the basicity of Z increases, resonance stabilization of RCOZ increases, resulting in the following trend:

- **As the carbonyl π bond becomes more delocalized, the C=O absorption shifts to lower frequency.**

Thus, the carbonyl group of an acid chloride and anhydride, which are least stabilized by resonance, absorb at higher frequency than the carbonyl group of an amide, which is more stabilized by resonance. Table 22.4 lists specific values for the carbonyl absorptions of the carboxylic acid derivatives.

Table 22.4 IR Absorptions for the Carbonyl Group of Carboxylic Acid Derivatives

Compound type	Structure (RCOZ)	Carbonyl absorption ($\tilde{\nu}$)
acid chloride	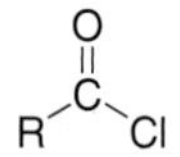	~1800
anhydride	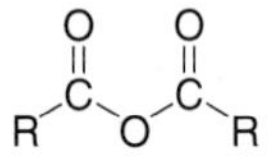	1820 and 1760 (2 peaks)
ester	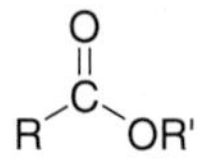	1735–1745
amide	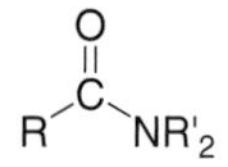 R' = H or alkyl	1630–1680

Increasing basicity of Z (arrow pointing down, acid chloride to amide); Increasing $\tilde{\nu}$ of absorption (arrow pointing up, amide to acid chloride)

The effects of conjugation and ring size on the location of a carbonyl absorption were first discussed in Section 21.4A.

Conjugation and ring size affect the location of these carbonyl absorptions.

- **Conjugation shifts a carbonyl absorption to lower frequencies.**
- **For cyclic carboxylic acid derivatives, decreasing ring size shifts a carbonyl absorption to higher frequencies.**

Problem 22.7 How would the compounds in each pair differ in their IR spectra?

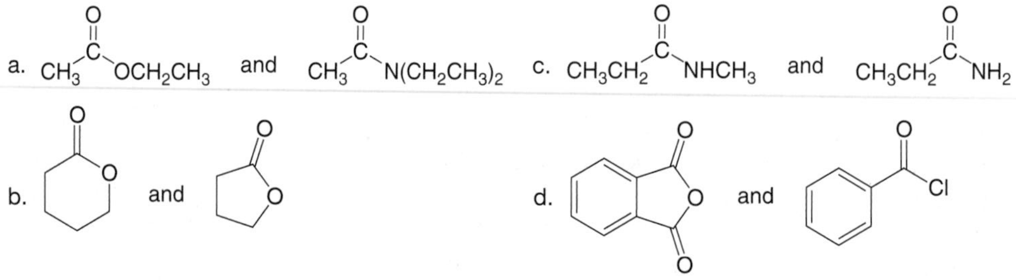

22.5B NMR Spectra

Carboxylic acid derivatives have two characteristic ^{1}H NMR absorptions.

[1] **Protons on the α carbon to the carbonyl absorb at 2–2.5 ppm.**

[2] **The N–H protons of 1° and 2° amides absorb at 7.5–8.5 ppm.**

In their ^{13}C NMR spectra, carboxylic acid derivatives give a highly deshielded peak at 160–180 ppm due to the carbonyl carbon. This is somewhat upfield from the carbonyl absorption of aldehydes and ketones, which occurs at 190–215 ppm.

Nitriles give a peak at 115–120 ppm in their ^{13}C NMR spectrum due to the *sp* hybridized carbon. This is farther downfield than the signal due to the *sp* hybridized carbon of an alkyne, which occurs at 65–100 ppm.

Problem 22.8 Deduce the structures of compounds **A** and **B**, two of the major components of jasmine oil, from the given data.

Compound **A:** $C_9H_{10}O_2$; IR absorptions at 3091–2895 and 1743 cm^{-1}; ^1H NMR signals at 2.06 (singlet, 3 H), 5.08 (singlet, 2 H), and 7.33 (broad singlet, 5 H) ppm.
Compound **B:** $C_{14}H_{12}O_2$; IR absorptions at 3091–2953 and 1718 cm^{-1}; ^1H NMR signals at 5.35 (singlet, 2 H) and 7.26–8.15 (multiplets, 10 H) ppm.

22.6 Interesting Esters and Amides

22.6A Esters

The characteristic odor of many fruits is due to low molecular weight esters.

The coca plant, *Erythroxylon coca,* is the source of the addictive drug cocaine.

Many low molecular weight esters have pleasant and very characteristic odors.

$CH_3COOCH_2CH_2CH(CH_3)_2$

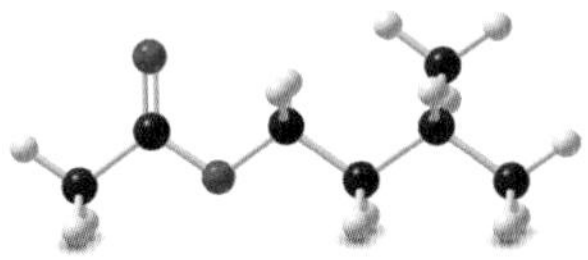

isoamyl acetate
odor of banana

$CH_3CH_2CH_2COOCH_2CH_3$

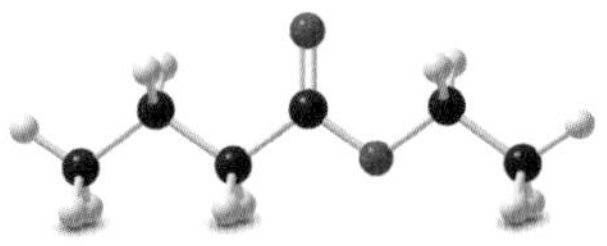

ethyl butanoate
odor of mango

$CH_3CH_2CH(CH_3)CO_2CH_3$

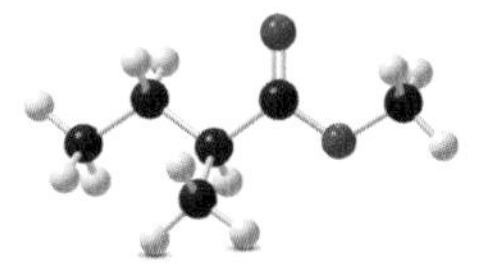

methyl 2-methylbutanoate
odor of pineapple

Several esters, including vitamin C and cocaine, have important biological activities.

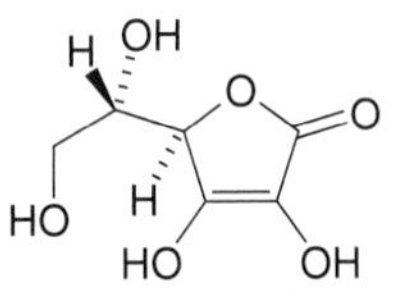

vitamin C

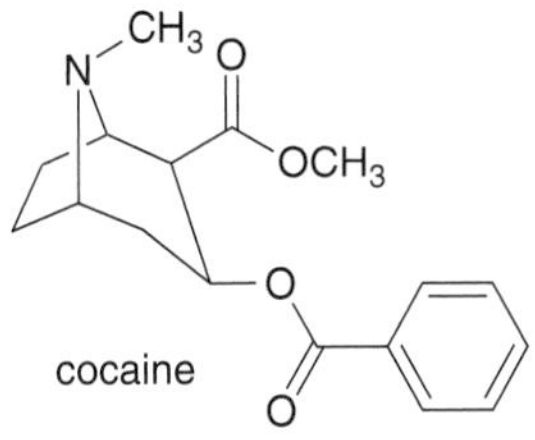

cocaine

- **Vitamin C** (or **ascorbic acid**) is a water-soluble vitamin containing a five-membered lactone that we first discussed in Section 3.5B. Although vitamin C is synthesized in plants, humans do not have the necessary enzymes to make it, and so they must obtain it from their diet.
- **Cocaine** is an addictive stimulant obtained from the leaves of the coca plant. Chewing coca leaves for pleasure has been practiced by the indigenous peoples of South America for over a thousand years, and coca leaves were a very minor ingredient in Coca-Cola for the first 20 years of its production. Cocaine is a widely abused recreational drug, and the possession and use of cocaine is currently illegal in most countries.

22.6B Amides

An important group of naturally occurring amides consists of ***proteins,* polymers of amino acids joined together by amide linkages.** Proteins differ in the length of the polymer chain, as well as in the identity of the R groups bonded to it. The word *protein* is usually reserved for high molecular weight polymers composed of 40 or more amino acid units, while the designation *peptide* is given to polymers of lower molecular weight.

Portion of a protein molecule

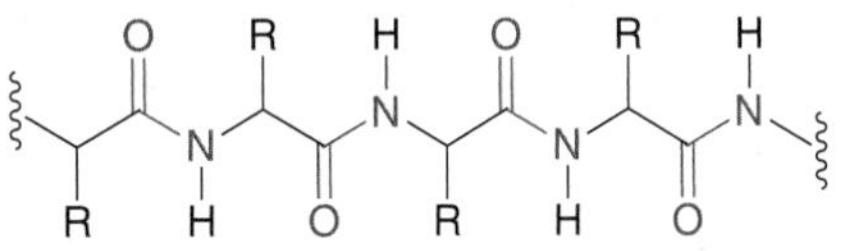

The R groups come from amino acids joined together to form the protein.

[Amide bonds are shown in red.]

Peptides and proteins are discussed in detail in Chapter 29.

Proteins and peptides have diverse functions in the cell. They form the structural components of muscle, connective tissue, hair, and nails. They catalyze reactions and transport ions and molecules across cell membranes. **Met-enkephalin,** for example, a peptide with four amide bonds found predominately in nerve tissue cells, relieves pain and acts as an opiate by producing morphine-like effects.

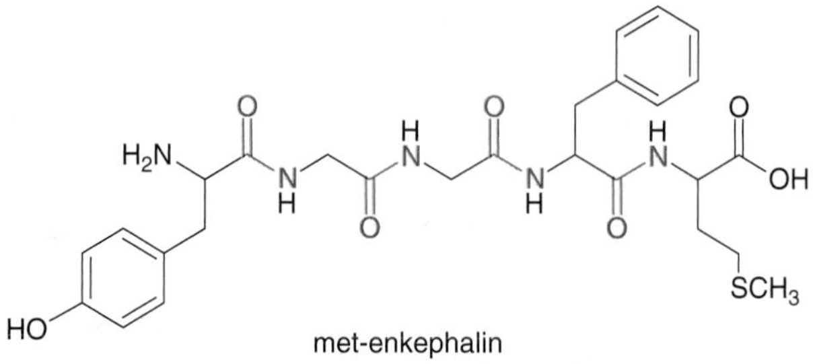

met-enkephalin
[The four amide bonds are shown in red.]

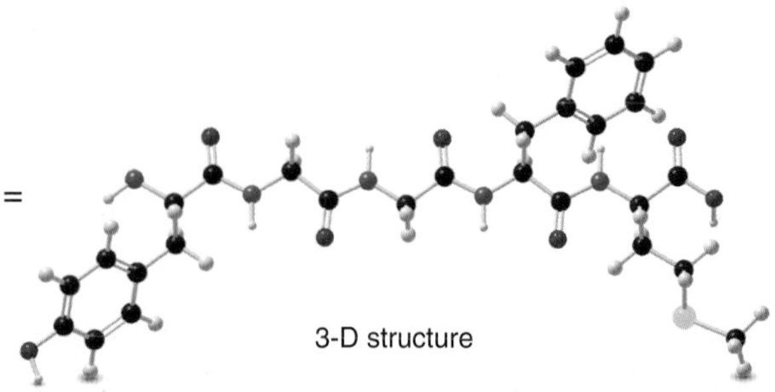

3-D structure

Several useful drugs are amides. For example, **Gleevec** (generic name: imatinib mesylate), an amide sold as a salt with methanesulfonic acid (CH_3SO_3H), is an anticancer drug used for the treatment of chronic myeloid leukemia as well as certain gastrointestinal tumors. Gleevec represents a new approach to cancer chemotherapy, which targets a single molecule to disable the molecular mechanism responsible for a specific type of cancer.

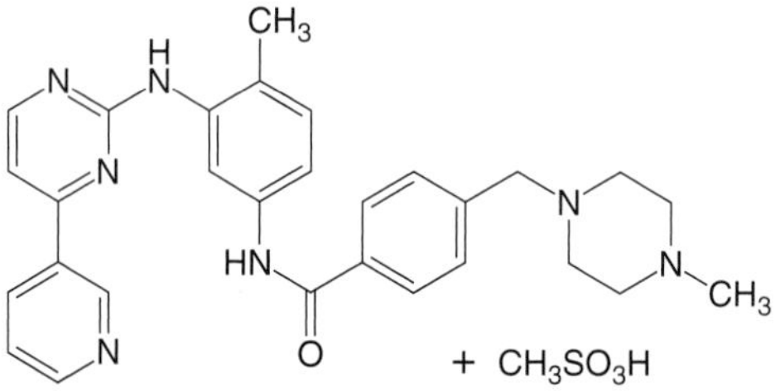

Trade name: Gleevec
Generic name: imatinib mesylate

Penicillins are a group of structurally related antibiotics, known since the pioneering work of Sir Alexander Fleming led to the discovery of penicillin G in the 1920s. All penicillins contain a strained β-lactam fused to a five-membered ring, as well as a second amide located α to the β-lactam carbonyl group. Particular penicillins differ in the identity of the R group in the amide side chain.

General structure—Penicillin

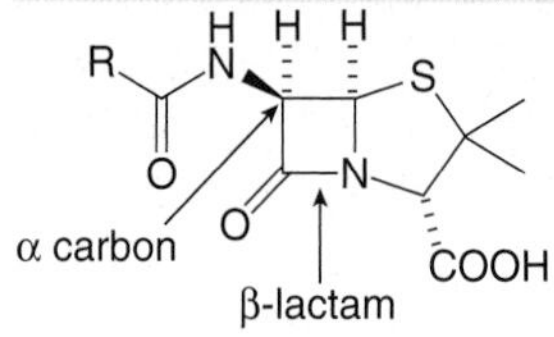

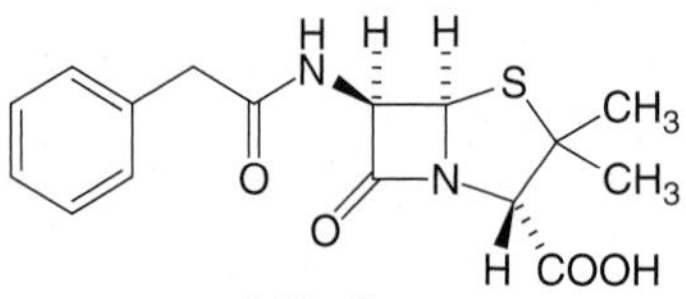

penicillin G

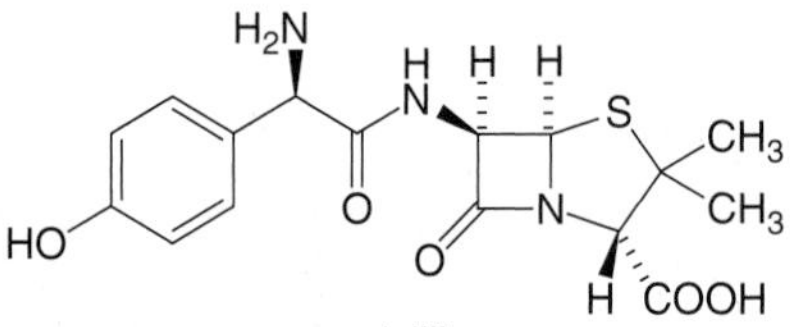

amoxicillin

Cephalosporins represent a second group of β-lactam antibiotics that contain a four-membered ring fused to a six-membered ring. Cephalosporins are generally active against a broader range of bacteria than penicillins.

General structure—Cephalosporin

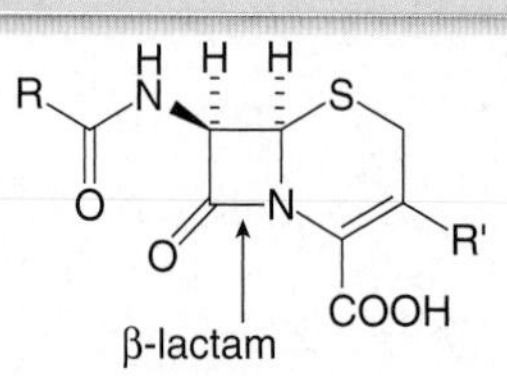

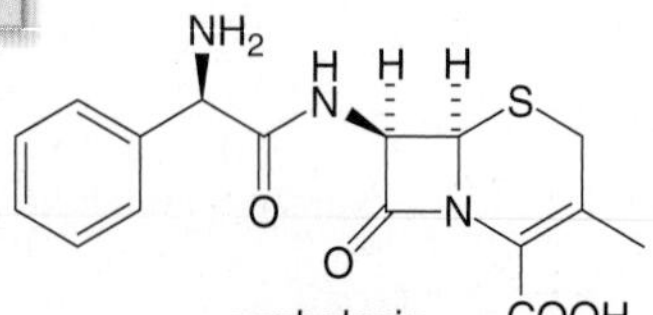

cephalexin
Trade name: Keflex

22.7 Introduction to Nucleophilic Acyl Substitution

The characteristic reaction of carboxylic acid derivatives is *nucleophilic acyl substitution.* This is a general reaction that occurs with both negatively charged nucleophiles ($Nu:^-$) and neutral nucleophiles (HNu:).

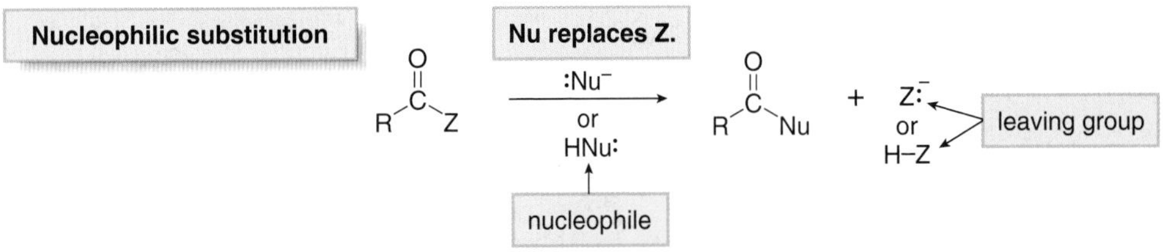

- **Carboxylic acid derivatives (RCOZ) react with nucleophiles because they contain an electrophilic, unhindered carbonyl carbon.**
- **Substitution occurs, *not* addition, because carboxylic acid derivatives (RCOZ) have a leaving group Z on the carbonyl carbon.**

22.7A The Mechanism

The mechanism for nucleophilic acyl substitution was first presented in Section 20.2.

The general mechanism for nucleophilic acyl substitution is a two-step process: **nucleophilic attack** followed by **loss of the leaving group,** as shown in Mechanism 22.1.

Mechanism 22.1 General Mechanism—Nucleophilic Acyl Substitution

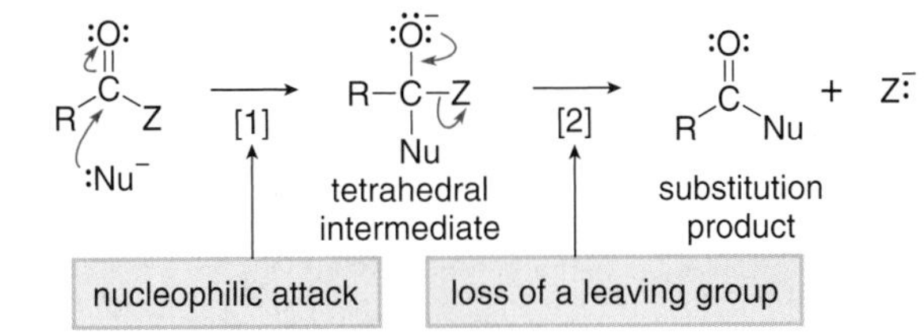

[Z = Cl, OCOR, OH, OR', NR'_2]

- In Step [1], **the nucleophile attacks the carbonyl group,** cleaving the π bond, and forming a tetrahedral intermediate with a new C – Nu bond.
- In Step [2], **elimination of the leaving group** forms the substitution product.

The overall result of addition of a nucleophile and elimination of a leaving group is substitution of the nucleophile for the leaving group. Recall from Chapter 20 that nucleophilic substitution occurs with carbanions (R^-) and hydride (H^-) as nucleophiles. A variety of oxygen and nitrogen nucleophiles also participate in this reaction.

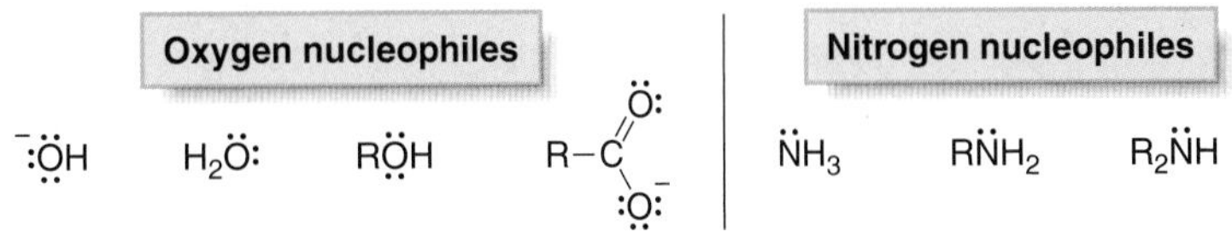

Nucleophilic acyl substitution using heteroatomic nucleophiles results in the conversion of one carboxylic acid derivative into another, as shown in two examples.

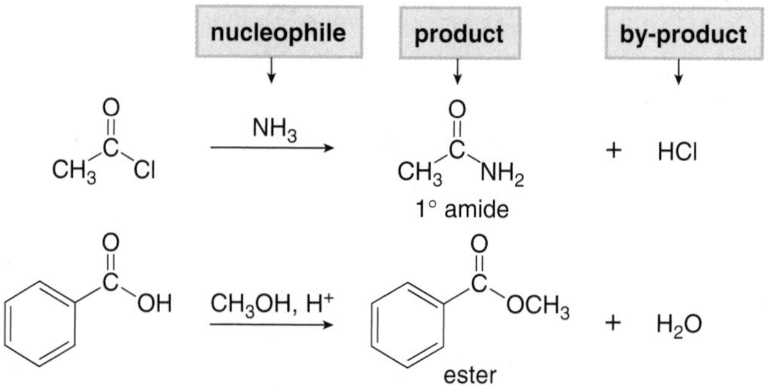

Each reaction results in the replacement of the leaving group by the nucleophile, regardless of the identity of or charge on the nucleophile. To draw any nucleophilic acyl substitution product:

- **Find the *sp*^{2} hybridized carbon with the leaving group.**
- **Identify the nucleophile.**
- **Substitute the nucleophile for the leaving group. With a neutral nucleophile a proton must be lost to obtain a neutral substitution product.**

22.7B Relative Reactivity of Carboxylic Acids and Their Derivatives

As discussed in Section 20.2B, carboxylic acids and their derivatives differ greatly in reactivity toward nucleophiles. The order of reactivity parallels the leaving group ability of the group Z.

- **The better the leaving group, the more reactive RCOZ is in nucleophilic acyl substitution.**

Recall that the **best leaving group is the weakest base.** The relative basicity of the common leaving groups, Z, is given in Table 22.1.

Thus, the following trends result:

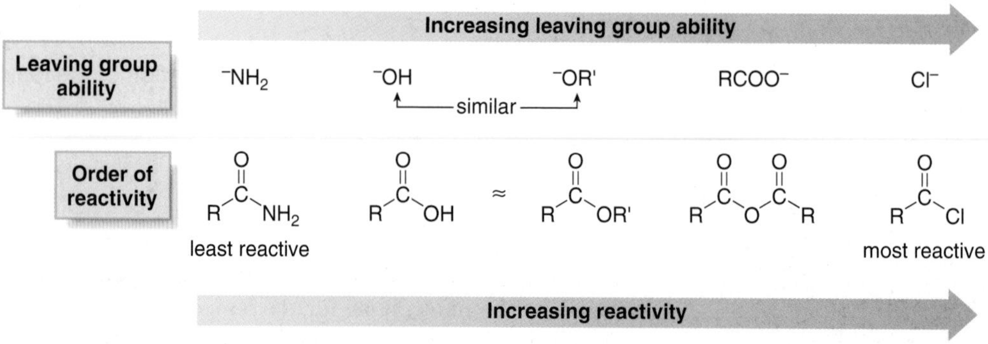

Based on this order of reactivity, **more reactive acyl compounds (acid chlorides and anhydrides) can be converted to less reactive ones (carboxylic acids, esters, and amides). The reverse is not usually true.**

To see why this is so, recall that nucleophilic addition to a carbonyl group forms a tetrahedral intermediate with two possible leaving groups, Z^- or $:Nu^-$. The group that is subsequently eliminated is the *better* of the two leaving groups. For a reaction to form a substitution product, therefore, Z^- must be the better leaving group, making the starting material RCOZ a more reactive acyl compound.

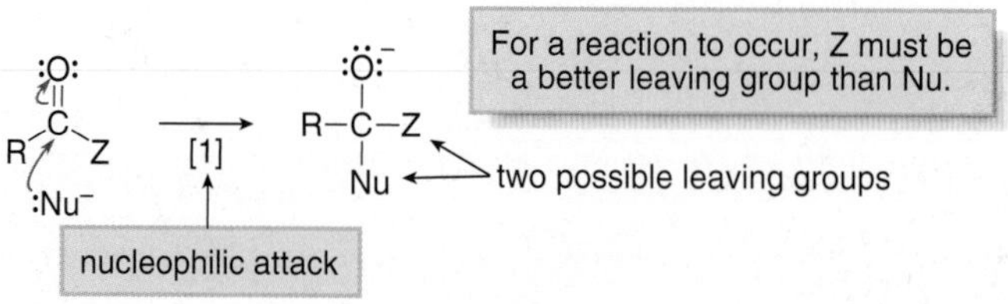

To evaluate whether a nucleophilic substitution reaction will occur, **compare the leaving group ability of the incoming nucleophile and the departing leaving group,** as shown in Sample Problem 22.2.

Sample Problem 22.2 Determine whether each nucleophilic acyl substitution is likely to occur.

a. 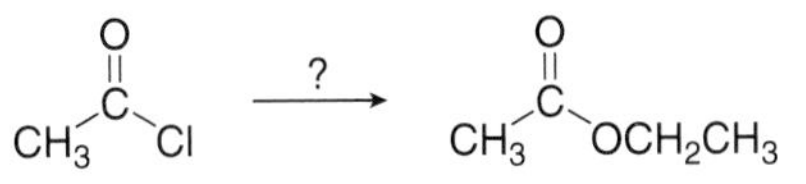

b. 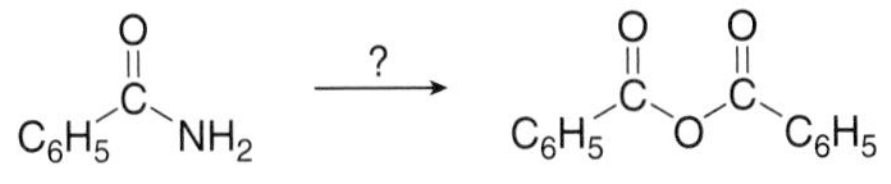

Solution

a. Conversion of CH_3COCl to $CH_3COOCH_2CH_3$ requires the substitution of Cl^- by $^-OCH_2CH_3$. Because Cl^- is a weaker base and therefore a better leaving group than $^-OCH_2CH_3$, **this reaction occurs.**

b. Conversion of $C_6H_5CONH_2$ to $(C_6H_5CO)_2O$ requires the substitution of $^-NH_2$ by $^-OCOC_6H_5$. Because $^-NH_2$ is a stronger base and therefore a poorer leaving group than $^-OCOC_6H_5$, **this reaction does *not* occur.**

Problem 22.9 Without reading ahead in Chapter 22, state whether it should be possible to carry out each of the following nucleophilic substitution reactions.

a. $CH_3COCl \longrightarrow CH_3COOH$

b. $CH_3CONHCH_3 \longrightarrow CH_3COOCH_3$

c. $CH_3COOCH_3 \longrightarrow CH_3COCl$

d. $(CH_3CO)_2O \longrightarrow CH_3CONH_2$

To summarize:

- **Nucleophilic substitution occurs when the leaving group Z^- is a weaker base and therefore better leaving group than the attacking nucleophile $:Nu^-$.**
- **More reactive acyl compounds can be converted to less reactive acyl compounds by nucleophilic substitution.**

Learn the order of reactivity of carboxylic acid derivatives. Keeping this in mind allows you to organize a very large number of reactions.

Problem 22.10 Rank the compounds in each group in order of increasing reactivity in nucleophilic acyl substitution.

a. $C_6H_5COOCH_3$, C_6H_5COCl, $C_6H_5CONH_2$

b. CH_3CH_2COOH, $(CH_3CH_2CO)_2O$, $CH_3CH_2CONHCH_3$

Problem 22.11 Explain why trichloroacetic anhydride [$(Cl_3CCO)_2O$] is more reactive than acetic anhydride [$(CH_3CO)_2O$] in nucleophilic acyl substitution reactions.

22.7C A Preview of Specific Reactions

Sections 22.8–22.14 are devoted to specific examples of nucleophilic acyl substitution using heteroatoms as nucleophiles. There are a great many reactions, and it is easy to confuse them unless you learn the general order of reactivity of carboxylic acid derivatives. **Keep in mind that every reaction that begins with an acyl starting material involves nucleophilic substitution.**

In this text, all of the nucleophilic substitution reactions are grouped according to the carboxylic acid derivative used as a starting material. We begin with the reactions of acid chlorides, the most reactive acyl compounds, then proceed to less and less reactive carboxylic acid derivatives, ending with amides. Acid chlorides undergo many reactions, because they have the best leaving group of all acyl compounds, whereas amides undergo only one reaction, which must be carried out under harsh reaction conditions, because amides have a poor leaving group.

In general, we will examine nucleophilic acyl substitution with four different nucleophiles, as shown in the following equations.

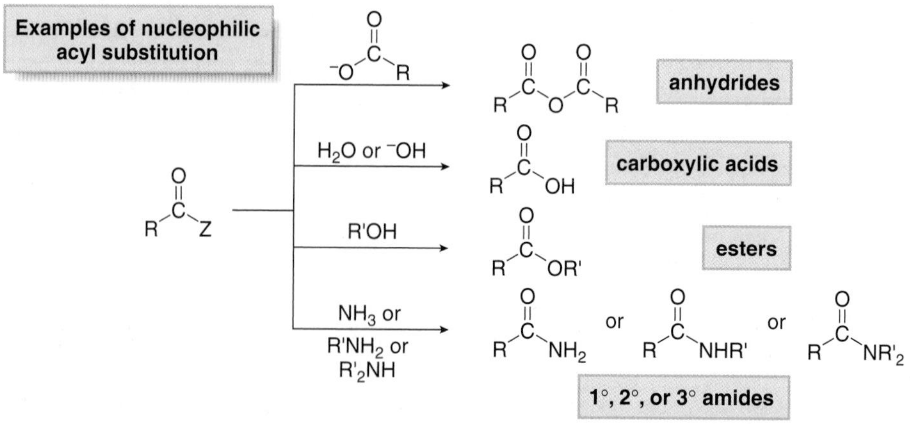

These reactions are used to make anhydrides, carboxylic acids, esters, and amides, but not acid chlorides, from other acyl compounds. Acid chlorides are the most reactive acyl compounds (they have the best leaving group), so they are not easily formed as a product of nucleophilic substitution reactions. They can only be prepared from carboxylic acids using special reagents, as discussed in Section 22.10A.

22.8 Reactions of Acid Chlorides

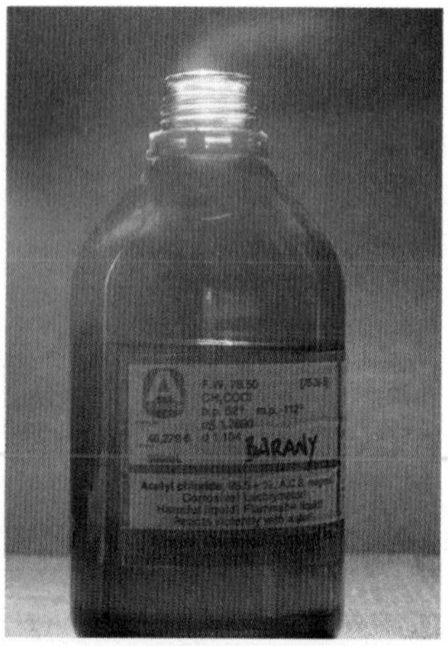

The reaction of acid chlorides with water is rapid. Exposure of an acid chloride to moist air on a humid day leads to some hydrolysis, giving the acid chloride a very acrid odor, due to the HCl formed as a by-product.

Acid chlorides readily react with nucleophiles to form nucleophilic substitution products, with HCl usually formed as a reaction by-product. A weak base like pyridine is added to the reaction mixture to remove this strong acid, forming an ammonium salt.

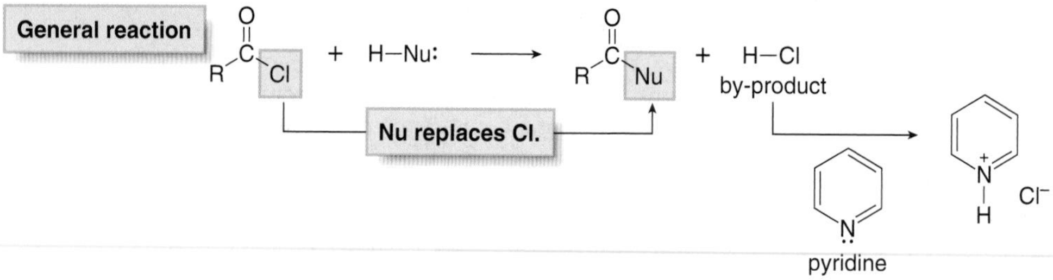

Acid chlorides react with oxygen nucleophiles to form anhydrides, carboxylic acids, and esters.

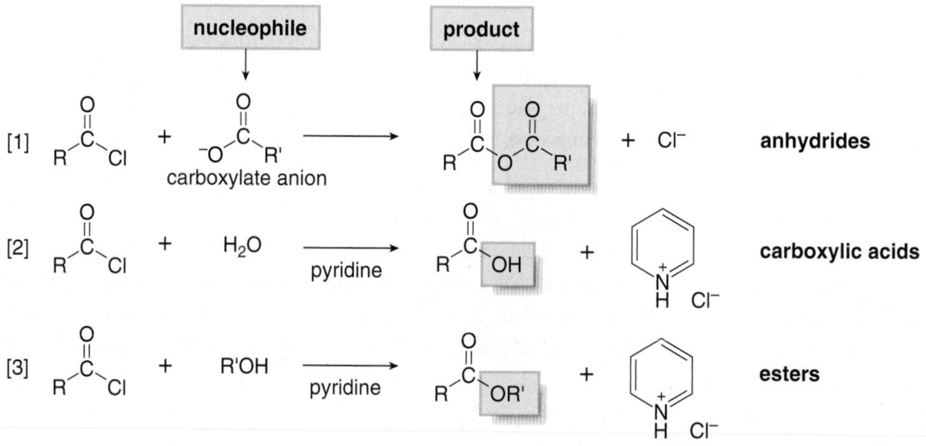

Acid chlorides also react with ammonia and 1° and 2° amines to form 1°, 2°, and 3° amides, respectively. Two equivalents of NH_3 or amine are used. One equivalent acts as a nucleophile to replace Cl and form the substitution product, while the second equivalent reacts as a base with the HCl by-product to form an ammonium salt.

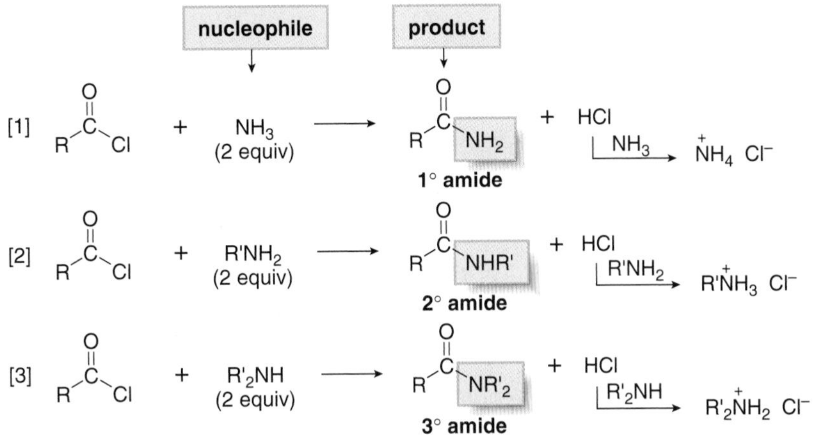

Insect repellents containing DEET have become particularly popular because of the recent spread of many insect-borne diseases such as West Nile virus and Lyme disease. DEET does not kill insects—it repels them. It is thought that DEET somehow confuses insects so that they can no longer sense the warm moist air that surrounds a human body.

As an example, reaction of an acid chloride with diethylamine forms the 3° amide *N,N*-diethyl-*m*-toluamide, popularly known as **DEET.** DEET, the active ingredient in the most widely used insect repellents, is effective against mosquitoes, fleas, and ticks.

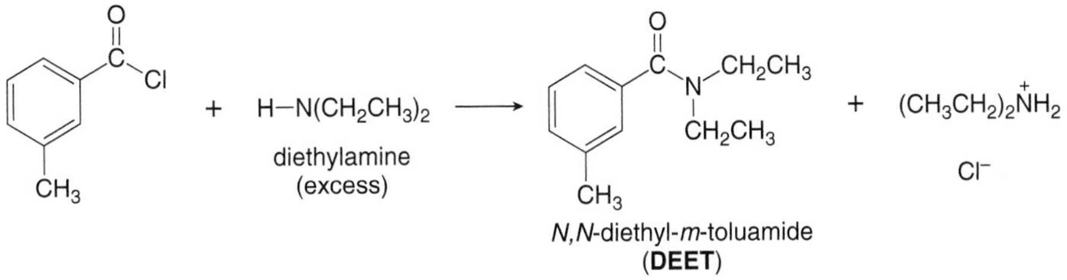

Problem 22.12 Draw the products formed when benzoyl chloride (C_6H_5COCl) is treated with each nucleophile: (a) H_2O, pyridine; (b) CH_3COO^-; (c) NH_3 (excess); (d) $(CH_3)_2NH$ (excess).

With a carboxylate nucleophile the mechanism follows the general, two-step mechanism discussed in Section 22.7: **nucleophilic attack followed by loss of the leaving group,** as shown in Mechanism 22.2.

Mechanism 22.2 Conversion of Acid Chlorides to Anhydrides

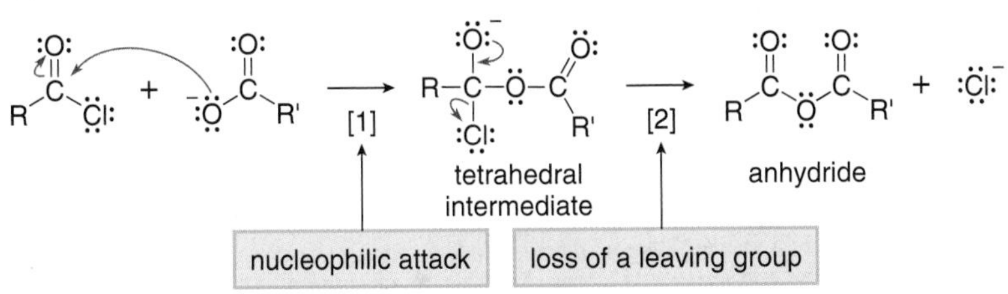

- In Step [1], **nucleophilic addition of R'COO⁻** forms a tetrahedral intermediate.
- In Step [2], **elimination of the leaving group (Cl⁻)** forms the substitution product, an **anhydride.**

Nucleophilic substitution with the neutral nucleophiles (H_2O, R'OH, NH_3, and so forth) requires an additional step for proton transfer. For example, the reaction of an acid chloride with H_2O as nucleophile converts an acid chloride to a carboxylic acid in three steps (Mechanism 22.3).

Mechanism 22.3 Conversion of Acid Chlorides to Carboxylic Acids

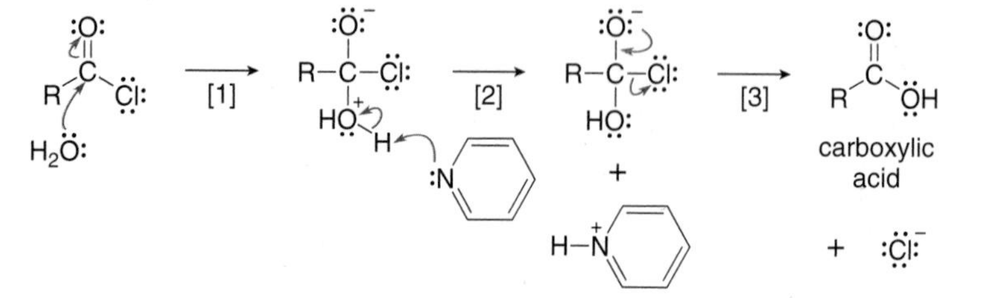

- In Step [1], **nucleophilic attack by H_2O** forms a tetrahedral intermediate.
- Removal of a proton followed by **elimination of the leaving group, Cl^-** (Steps [2]–[3]), forms the substitution product, a **carboxylic acid.**

The exact same three-step process can be written for any neutral nucleophile that reacts with acid chlorides.

Problem 22.13 Draw a stepwise mechanism for the formation of **A** from an alcohol and acid chloride. **A** was converted in one step to blattellaquinone, the sex pheromone of the female German cockroach *Blattella germanica*.

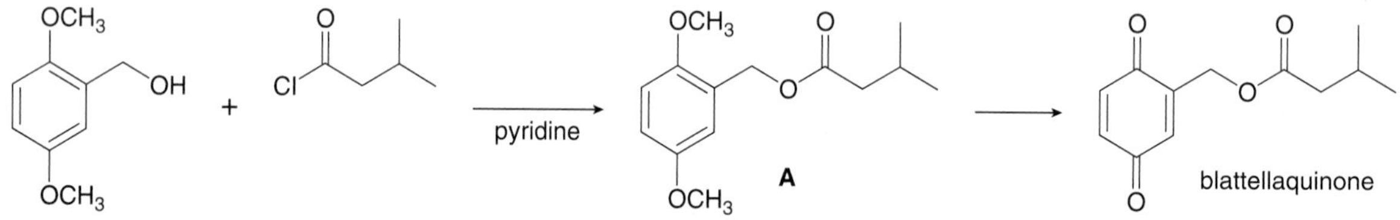

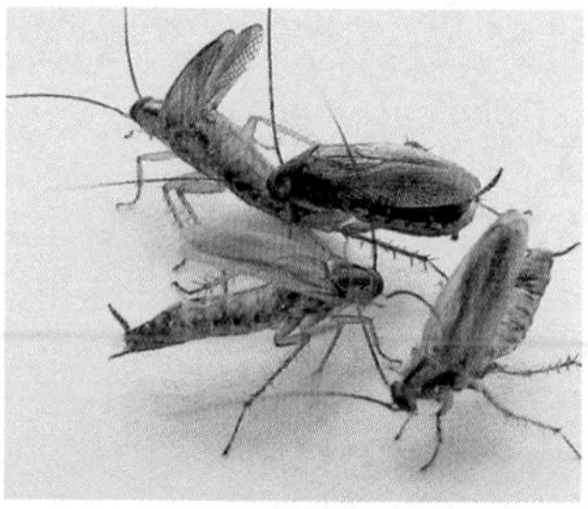

A short laboratory synthesis of blattellaquinone (Problem 22.13), the sex pheromone of the female German cockroach, opens new possibilities for cockroach population control using pheromone-baited traps.

Nucleophilic substitution occurs only when the leaving group is a weaker base and therefore a better leaving group than the attacking nucleophile.

22.9 Reactions of Anhydrides

Although somewhat less reactive than acid chlorides, anhydrides nonetheless readily react with most nucleophiles to form substitution products. Nucleophilic substitution reactions of anhydrides are no different than the reactions of other carboxylic acid derivatives, even though anhydrides contain two carbonyl groups. **Nucleophilic attack occurs at one carbonyl group, while the second carbonyl becomes part of the leaving group.**

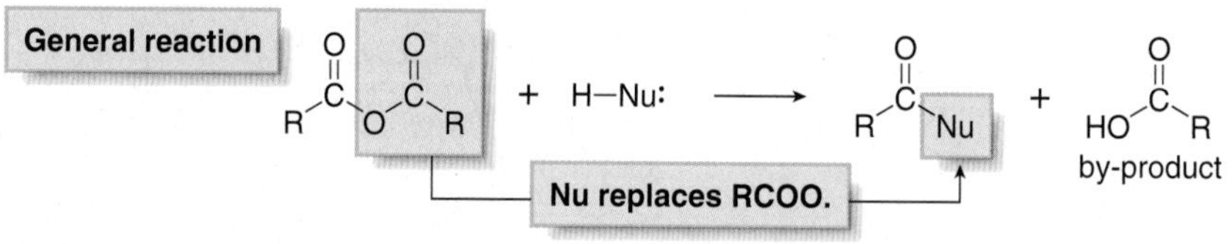

Anhydrides can't be used to make acid chlorides, because $RCOO^-$ is a stronger base and therefore a poorer leaving group than Cl^-. Anhydrides can be used to make all other acyl derivatives, however. Reaction with water and alcohols yields **carboxylic acids** and **esters,** respectively. Reaction with two equivalents of NH_3 or amines forms **1°, 2°,** and **3° amides.** A molecule of carboxylic acid (or a carboxylate salt) is always formed as a by-product.

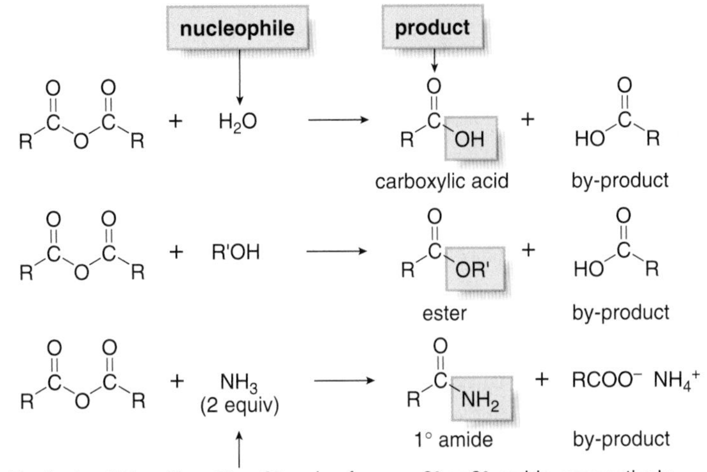

Replacing NH_3 with a 1° or 2° amine forms a 2° or 3° amide, respectively.

Problem 22.14 Draw the products formed when benzoic anhydride $[(C_6H_5CO)_2O]$ is treated with each nucleophile: (a) H_2O; (b) CH_3OH; (c) NH_3 (excess); (d) $(CH_3)_2NH$ (excess).

The conversion of an anhydride to an amide illustrates the mechanism of nucleophilic acyl substitution with an anhydride as starting material (Mechanism 22.4). Besides the usual steps of **nucleophilic addition** and **elimination of the leaving group,** an additional proton transfer is needed.

Mechanism 22.4 Conversion of an Anhydride to an Amide

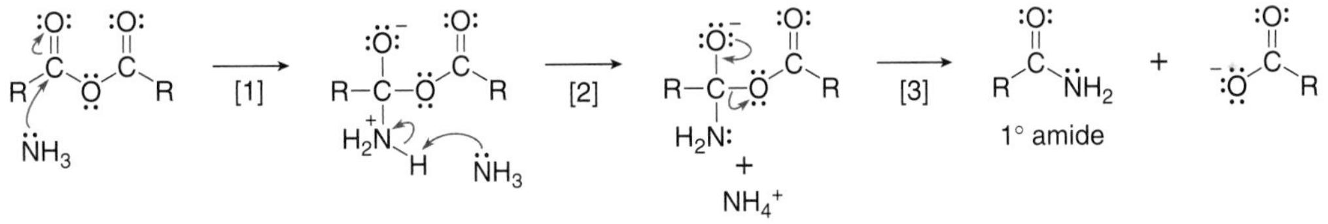

- In Step [1], **nucleophilic attack by NH_3** forms a tetrahedral intermediate.
- Removal of a proton followed by **elimination of the leaving group, $RCOO^-$** (Steps [2]–[3]), forms the substitution product, a **1° amide.**

Acetaminophen reduces pain and fever, but it is not anti-inflammatory, so it is ineffective in treating conditions like arthritis, which have a significant inflammatory component. In large doses, acetaminophen causes liver damage, so dosage recommendations must be carefully followed.

Anhydrides react with alcohols and amines with ease, so they are often used in the laboratory to prepare esters and amides. For example, acetic anhydride is used to prepare two analgesics, **acetylsalicylic acid** (aspirin) and **acetaminophen** (the active ingredient in Tylenol).

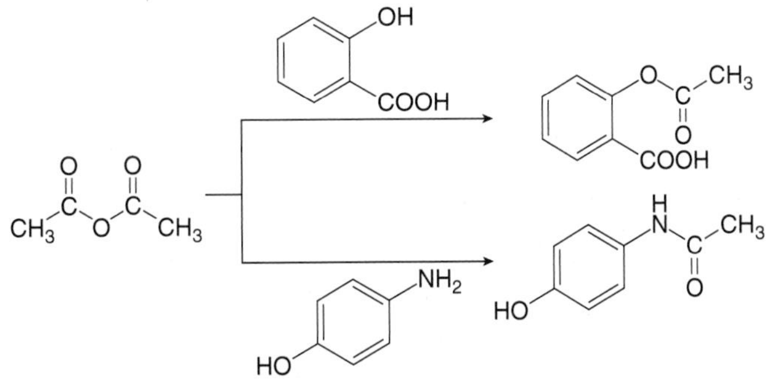

acetylsalicylic acid (aspirin)

acetaminophen (active ingredient in Tylenol)

These are called **acetylation** reactions because they result in the transfer of an acetyl group, CH_3CO-, from one heteroatom to another.

Heroin is prepared by the acetylation of morphine, an analgesic compound isolated from the opium poppy. Both OH groups of morphine are readily acetylated with acetic anhydride to form the diester present in heroin.

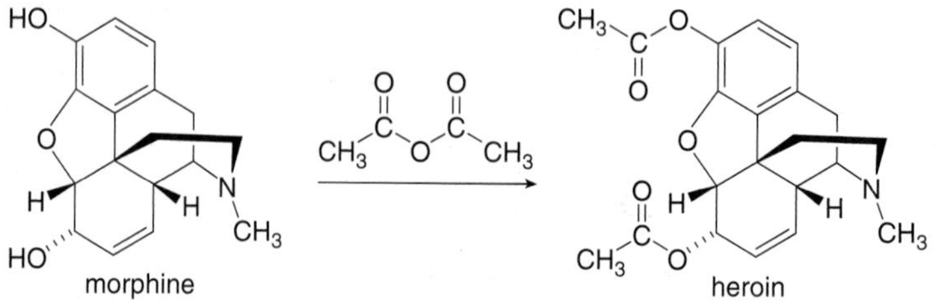

22.10 Reactions of Carboxylic Acids

Carboxylic acids are strong organic acids. Because acid–base reactions proceed rapidly, any nucleophile that is also a strong base will react with a carboxylic acid by removing a proton ***first,*** before any nucleophilic substitution reaction can take place.

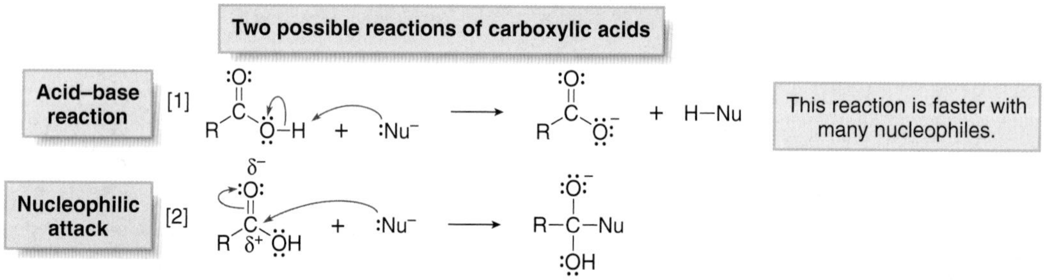

An acid–base reaction (Reaction [1]) occurs with ^-OH, NH_3, and amines, all common nucleophiles used in nucleophilic acyl substitution reactions. Nonetheless, carboxylic acids can be converted to a variety of other acyl derivatives using special reagents, with acid catalysis, or sometimes, by using rather forcing reaction conditions. These reactions are summarized in Figure 22.3 and detailed in Sections 22.10A–22.10D.

Figure 22.3
Nucleophilic acyl substitution reactions of carboxylic acids

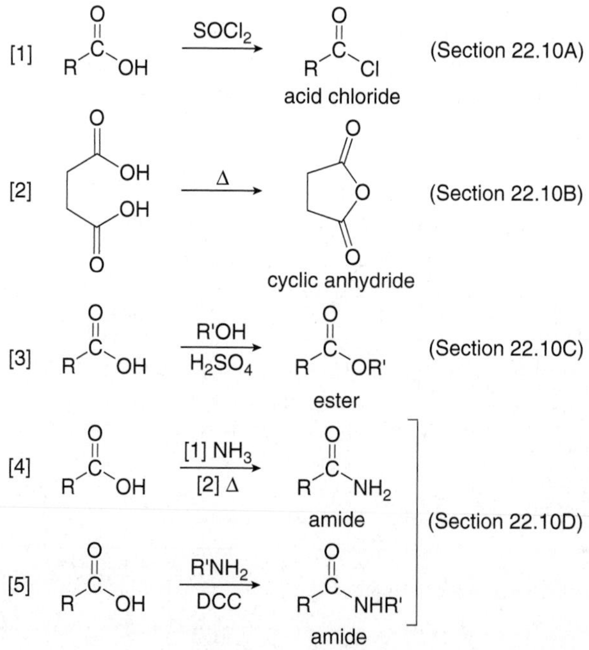

22.10A Conversion of RCOOH to RCOCl

Carboxylic acids can't be converted to acid chlorides by using Cl^- as a nucleophile, because the attacking nucleophile Cl^- is a weaker base than the departing leaving group, ^-OH. But carboxylic acids *can* be converted to acid chlorides using thionyl chloride, **$SOCl_2$,** a reagent that was introduced in Section 9.12 to convert alcohols to alkyl chlorides.

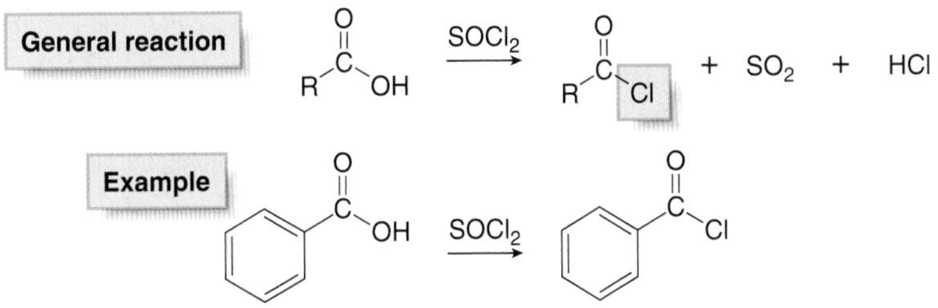

This reaction converts a less reactive acyl derivative (a carboxylic acid) into a more reactive one (an acid chloride). This is possible because thionyl chloride converts the OH group of the acid into a better leaving group, and because it provides the nucleophile (Cl^-) to displace the leaving group. The steps in the process are illustrated in Mechanism 22.5.

Mechanism 22.5 Conversion of Carboxylic Acids to Acid Chlorides

Steps [1] and [2] Conversion of the OH group into a good leaving group

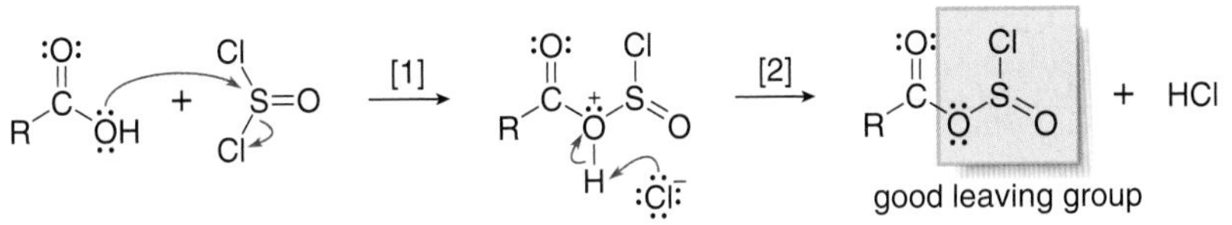

- Reaction of the OH group with $SOCl_2$ forms an intermediate that loses a proton in Step [2]. This two-step process converts the OH group into OSOCl, a **good leaving group.**

Steps [3] and [4] Substitution of the leaving group by Cl

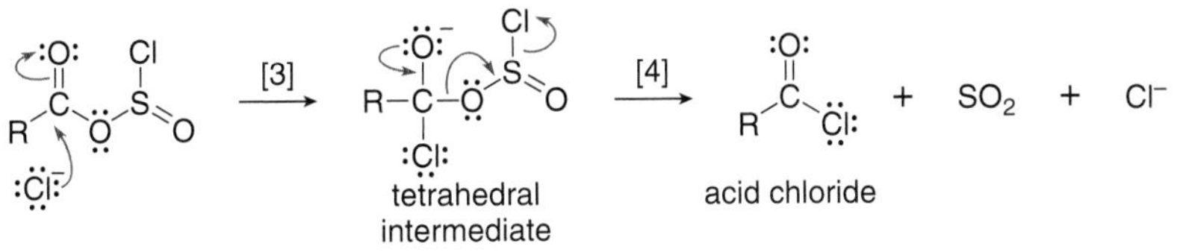

- **Nucleophilic attack by Cl^- and loss of the leaving group** (SO_2 + Cl^-) forms the acid chloride.

Problem 22.15 Draw the products of each reaction.

a. 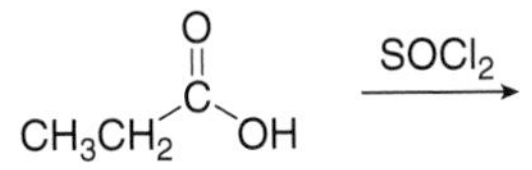

b. 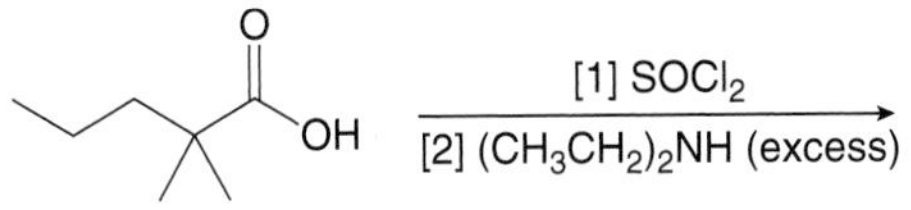

22.10B Conversion of RCOOH to $(RCO)_2O$

Carboxylic acids cannot be readily converted to anhydrides, but dicarboxylic acids can be converted to cyclic anhydrides by heating to high temperatures. This is a **dehydration** reaction because a water molecule is lost from the diacid.

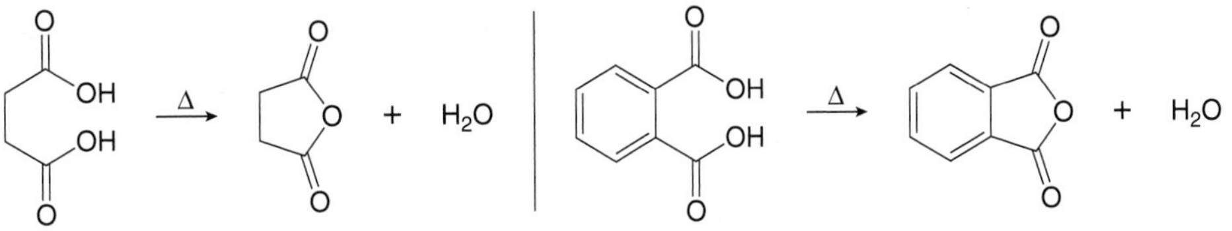

22.10C Conversion of RCOOH to RCOOR'

Treatment of a carboxylic acid with an alcohol in the presence of an acid catalyst forms an ester. This reaction is called a **Fischer esterification.**

Fischer esterification

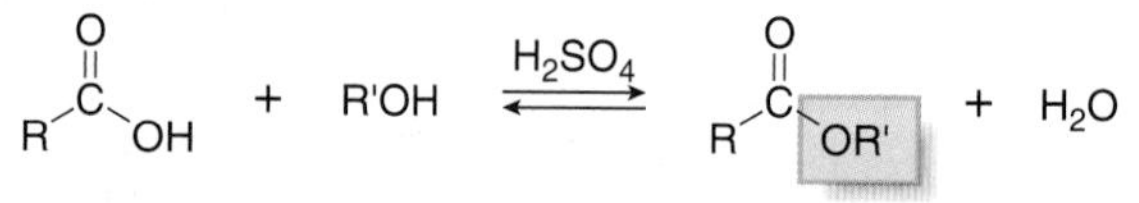

R'OH
H_2SO_4
OR'
H_2O

This reaction is an equilibrium. According to Le Châtelier's principle, it is driven to the right by using excess alcohol or by removing the water as it is formed.

Ethyl acetate is a common organic solvent with a characteristic odor. It is used in nail polish remover and model airplane glue.

Examples

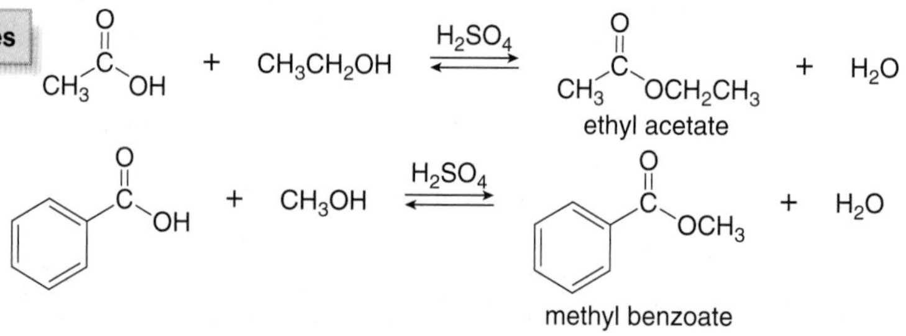

CH_3CH_2OH
H_2SO_4
ethyl acetate
CH_3OH
methyl benzoate

The mechanism for the Fischer esterification involves the usual two steps of nucleophilic acyl substitution—that is, **addition of a nucleophile followed by elimination of a leaving group.** Because the reaction is acid catalyzed, however, there are additional protonation and deprotonation steps. As always, though, the first step of any mechanism with an oxygen-containing starting material and an acid is to **protonate an oxygen atom** as shown with a general acid HA in Mechanism 22.6.

Mechanism 22.6 Fischer Esterification—Acid-Catalyzed Conversion of Carboxylic Acids to Esters

Part [1] Addition of the nucleophile R'OH

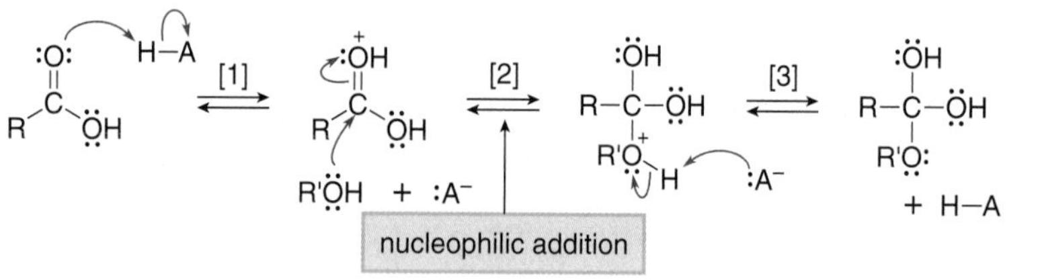

[1]
[2]
[3]
nucleophilic addition

- **Protonation** in Step [1] makes the carbonyl group more electrophilic.
- **Nucleophilic addition of R'OH** forms a tetrahedral intermediate, and loss of a proton forms the neutral addition product (Steps [2]–[3]).

Part [2] Elimination of the leaving group H_2O

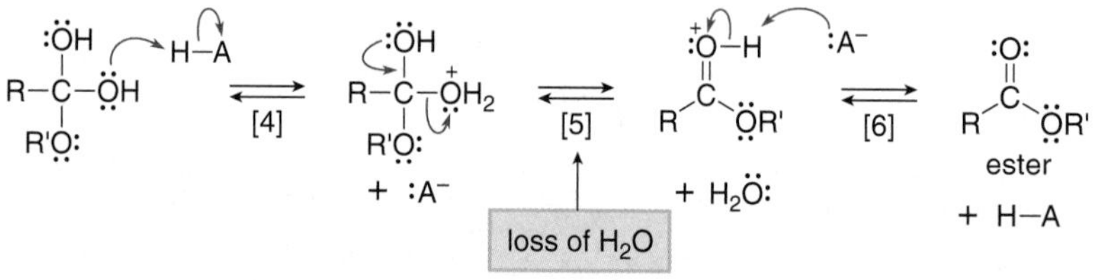

[4]
[5]
[6]
ester
loss of H_2O

- Protonation of an OH group in Step [4] forms a good leaving group that is **eliminated in Step [5].**
- Loss of a proton in Step [6] forms the ester.
- Only one resonance structure is drawn for the resonance-stabilized cations formed in Steps [1] and [5].

Esterification of a carboxylic acid occurs in the presence of acid but not in the presence of base. Base removes a proton from the carboxylic acid, forming a carboxylate anion, which does not react with an electron-rich nucleophile.

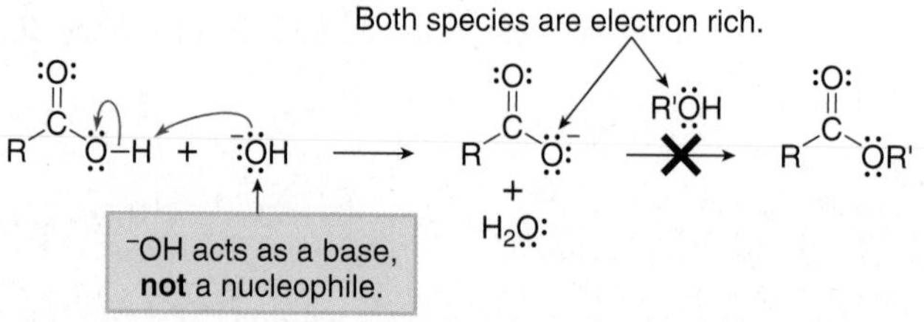

Both species are electron rich.
⁻OH acts as a base, **not** a nucleophile.

Intramolecular esterification of γ- and δ-hydroxy carboxylic acids forms five- and six-membered lactones.

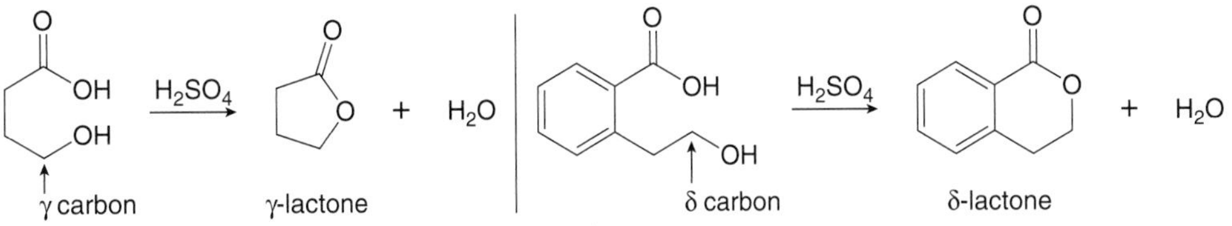

Problem 22.16 Draw the products of each reaction.

a. 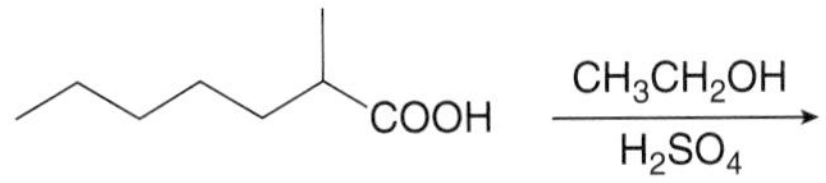

c. 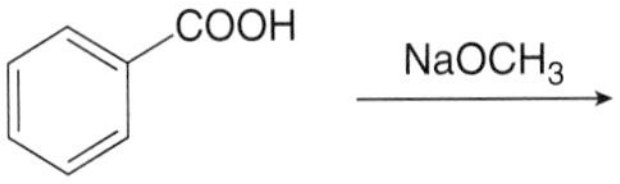

b. 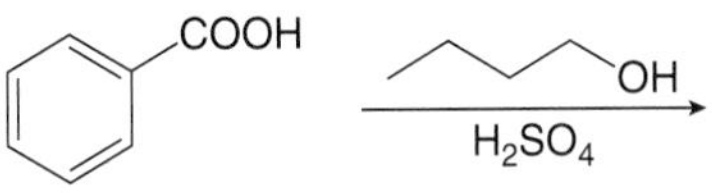

d. 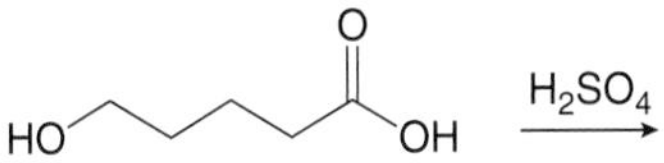

Problem 22.17 Draw the products formed when benzoic acid (C_6H_5COOH) is treated with CH_3OH having its O atom labeled with ^{18}O ($CH_3{}^{18}OH$). Indicate where the labeled oxygen atom resides in the products.

Problem 22.18 Draw a stepwise mechanism for the following reaction.

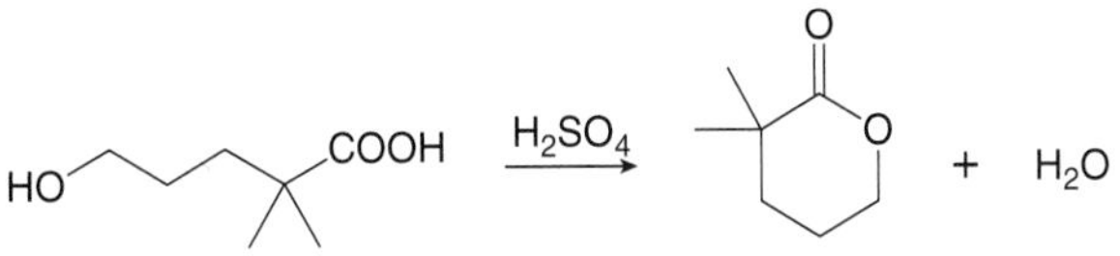

22.10D Conversion of RCOOH to RCONR'$_2$

The direct conversion of a carboxylic acid to an amide with NH_3 or an amine is very difficult, even though a more reactive acyl compound is being transformed into a less reactive one. The problem is that carboxylic acids are strong organic acids and NH_3 and amines are bases, so they undergo an **acid–base reaction to form an ammonium salt** before any nucleophilic substitution occurs.

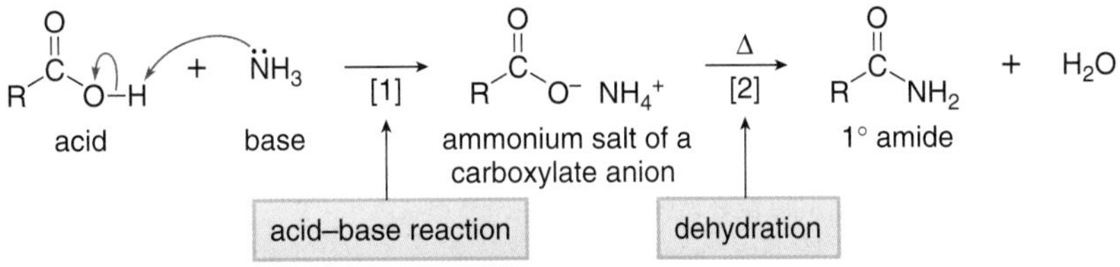

Heating at high temperature (>100 °C) dehydrates the resulting ammonium salt of the carboxylate anion to form an amide, though the yield can be low.

Amides are much more easily prepared from acid chlorides and anhydrides, as discussed in Sections 22.8 and 22.9.

Therefore, the overall conversion of RCOOH to $RCONH_2$ requires two steps:

[1] **Acid–base reaction of RCOOH with NH_3 to form an ammonium salt**
[2] **Dehydration at high temperature (>100 °C)**

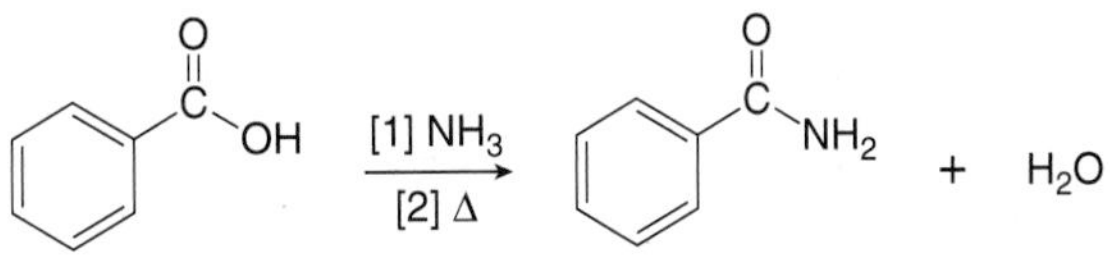

A carboxylic acid and an amine readily react to form an amide in the presence of an additional reagent, **dicyclohexylcarbodiimide (DCC),** which is converted to the by-product dicyclohexylurea in the course of the reaction.

Amide formation using DCC

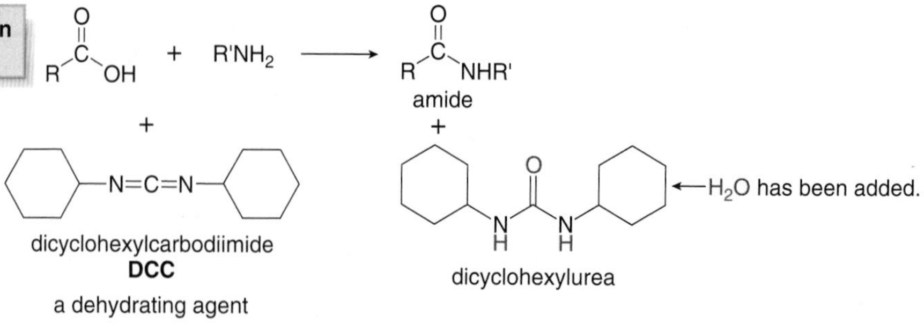

DCC is a dehydrating agent. The dicyclohexylurea by-product is formed by adding the elements of H_2O to DCC. DCC promotes amide formation by converting the carboxy OH group into a better leaving group.

Example

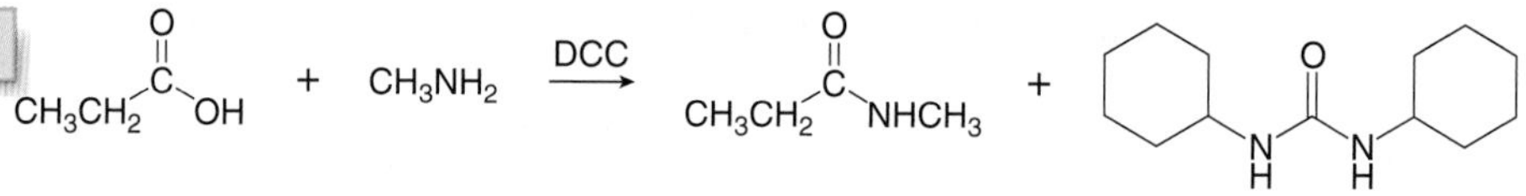

The mechanism consists of two parts: [1] conversion of the OH group into a better leaving group, followed by [2] **addition of the nucleophile and loss of the leaving group** to form the product of nucleophilic acyl substitution (Mechanism 22.7).

Mechanism 22.7 Conversion of Carboxylic Acids to Amides with DCC

Part [1] Conversion of OH into a better leaving group

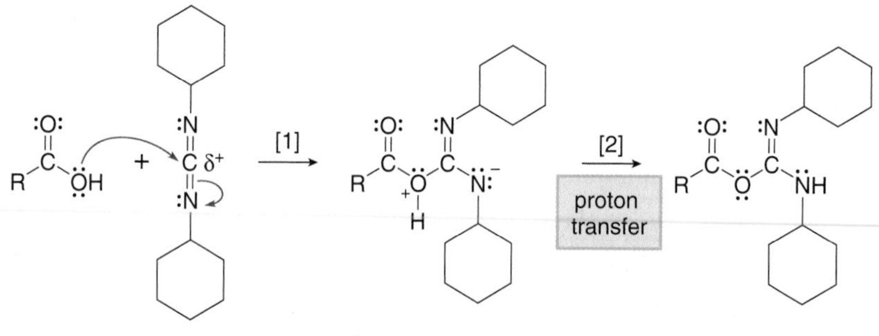

- The first part of the mechanism consists of two steps that convert the carboxy OH group into a **better leaving group.**
- This process *activates* the carboxy group towards nucleophilic attack in Part [2].

Part [2] Addition of the nucleophile and loss of the leaving group

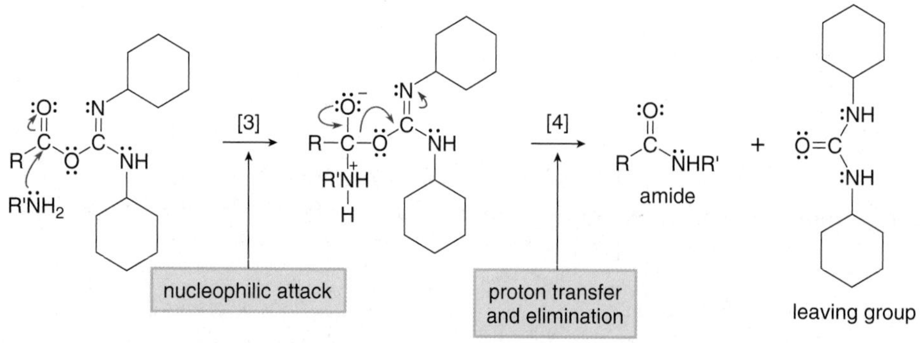

- In Steps [3] and [4], **nucleophilic attack of the amine** on the activated carboxy group, followed by **elimination of dicyclohexylurea** as the leaving group, forms the amide.

The reaction of an acid and an amine with DCC is often used in the laboratory to form the amide bond in peptides, as is discussed in Chapter 29.

Problem 22.19 What product is formed when acetic acid is treated with each reagent: (a) CH_3NH_2; (b) CH_3NH_2, then heat; (c) CH_3NH_2 + DCC?

22.11 Reactions of Esters

Esters can be converted into carboxylic acids and amides.

- **Esters are hydrolyzed with water in the presence of either acid or base to form carboxylic acids or carboxylate anions.**

Ester hydrolysis

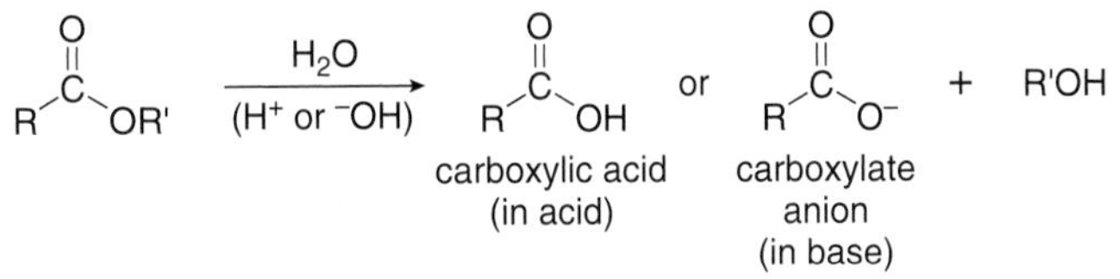

- **Esters react with NH_3 and amines to form 1°, 2°, or 3° amides.**

Reaction with nitrogen nucleophiles

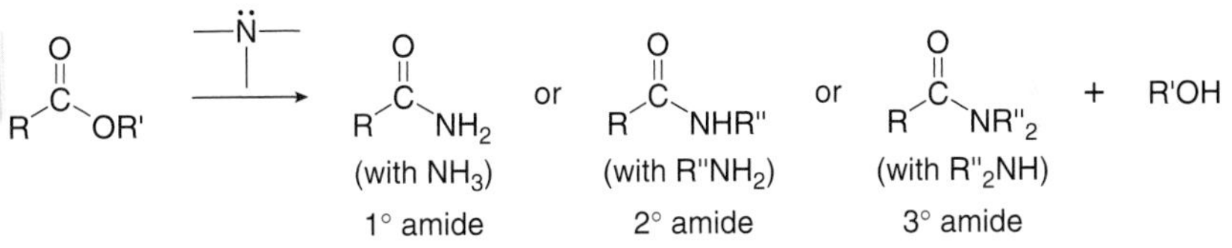

22.11A Ester Hydrolysis in Aqueous Acid

The first step in acid-catalyzed ester hydrolysis is **protonation on oxygen,** the same first step of any mechanism involving an oxygen-containing starting material and an acid.

The hydrolysis of esters in aqueous acid is a reversible equilibrium reaction that is driven to the right by using a large excess of water.

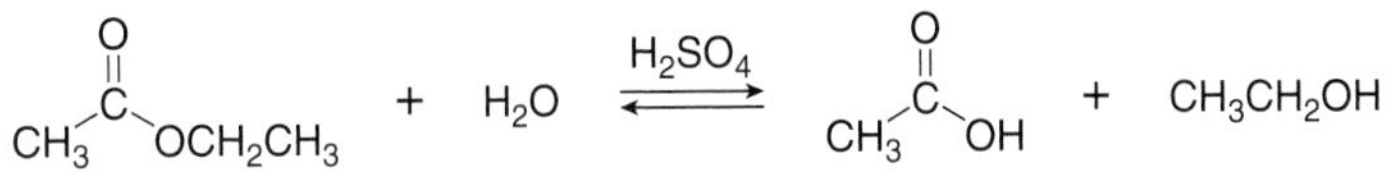

The mechanism of ester hydrolysis in acid (shown in Mechanism 22.8) is the reverse of the mechanism of ester synthesis from carboxylic acids (Mechanism 22.6). Thus, the mechanism consists of the addition of the nucleophile and the elimination of the leaving group, the two steps common to all nucleophilic acyl substitutions, as well as several proton transfers, because the reaction is acid-catalyzed.

Mechanism 22.8 Acid-Catalyzed Hydrolysis of an Ester to a Carboxylic Acid

Part [1] Addition of the nucleophile H_2O

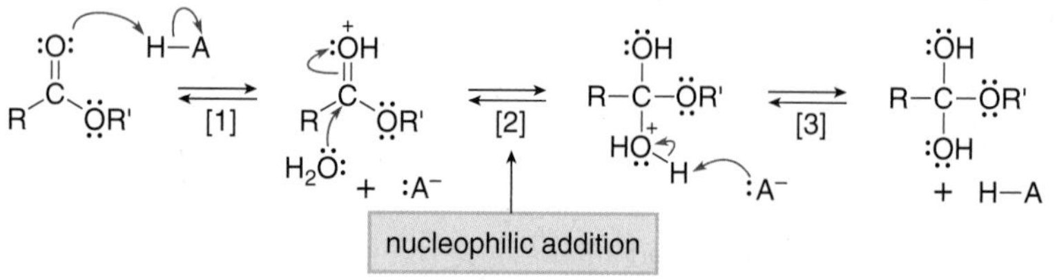

- **Protonation** in Step [1] makes the carbonyl group more electrophilic.
- **Nucleophilic addition of H_2O** forms a tetrahedral intermediate, and loss of a proton forms the neutral addition product (Steps [2]–[3]).

Part [2] Elimination of the leaving group R'OH

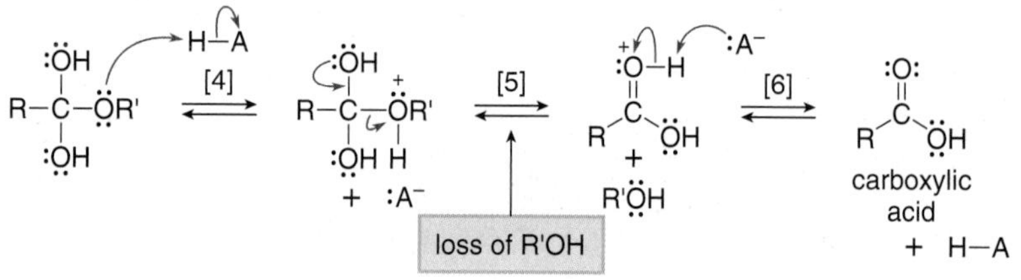

- Protonation of the OR' group in Step [4] forms a **good leaving group (R'OH) that is eliminated** in Step [5].
- Loss of a proton in Step [6] forms the carboxylic acid.

22.11B Ester Hydrolysis in Aqueous Base

The word **saponification** comes from the Latin *sapo* meaning **soap.** Soap is prepared by hydrolyzing esters in fats with aqueous base, as explained in Section 22.12B.

Esters are hydrolyzed in aqueous base to form carboxylate anions. Basic hydrolysis of an ester is called **saponification.**

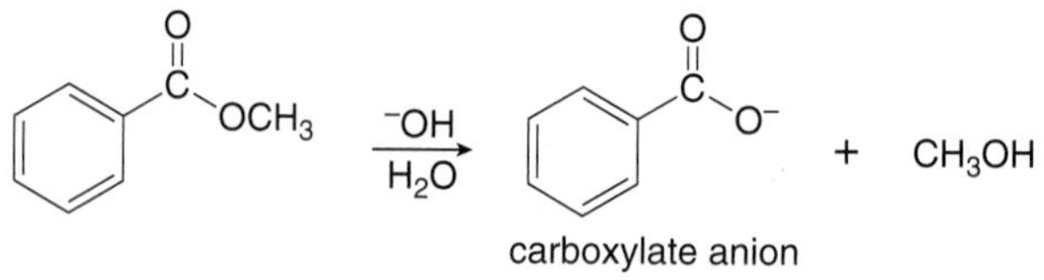

The mechanism for this reaction has the usual two steps of the general mechanism for nucleophilic acyl substitution presented in Section 22.7—**addition of the nucleophile** followed by **loss of a leaving group**—plus an additional step involving proton transfer (Mechanism 22.9).

Mechanism 22.9 Base-Promoted Hydrolysis of an Ester to a Carboxylic Acid

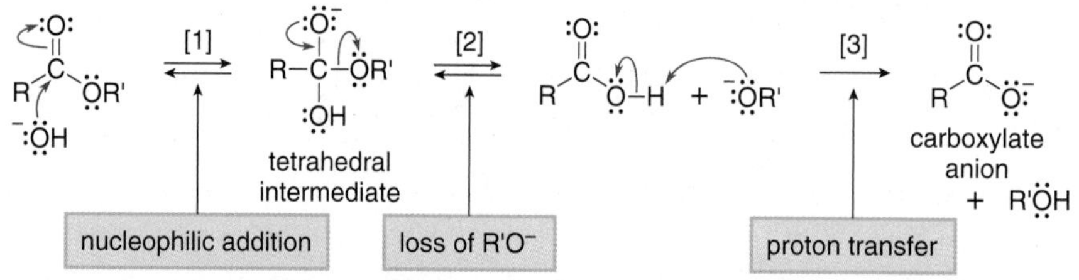

- Steps [1] and [2] result in **addition of the nucleophile, ⁻OH**, followed by **elimination of the leaving group, ⁻OR'.** These two steps, which form the carboxylic acid, are reversible, because the stability of the reactants and products is comparable.
- Next, the carboxylic acid is a strong organic acid and the leaving group (⁻OR') is a strong base, so an **acid–base reaction** occurs in Step [3] to form the carboxylate anion.

The carboxylate anion is resonance stabilized, and this drives the equilibrium in its favor. Once the reaction is complete and the carboxylate anion is formed, it can be protonated with strong acid to form the neutral carboxylic acid.

Hydrolysis is base promoted, *not* base catalyzed, because the base (^-OH) is the nucleophile that adds to the ester and forms part of the product. It participates in the reaction and is not regenerated later.

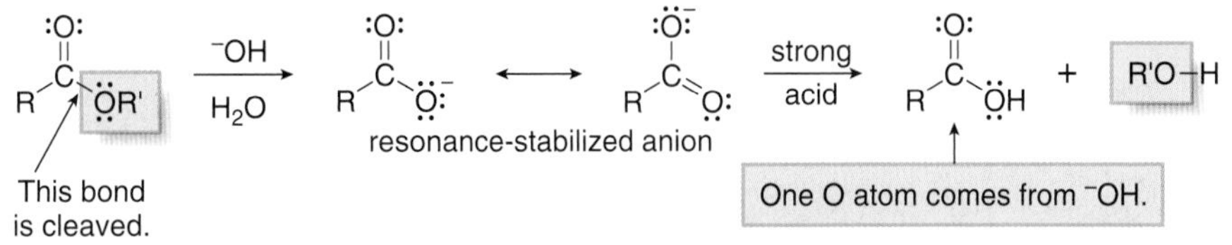

Where do the oxygen atoms in the product come from? The C–OR' bond in the ester is cleaved, so the OR' group becomes the alcohol by-product (R'OH) and one of the oxygens in the carboxylate anion product comes from ^-OH (the nucleophile).

Problem 22.20 Sunscreens that contain esters can slowly degrade over time because the ester can be hydrolyzed. Draw the products formed when each commercial sunscreen undergoes hydrolysis with [1] H_3O^+ or [2] H_2O, ^-OH.

a. 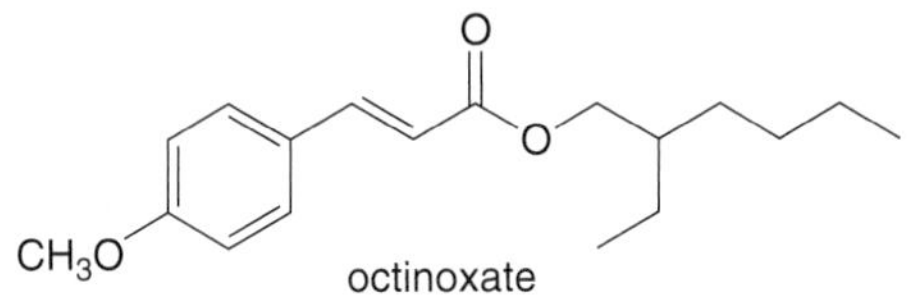

octinoxate

b. 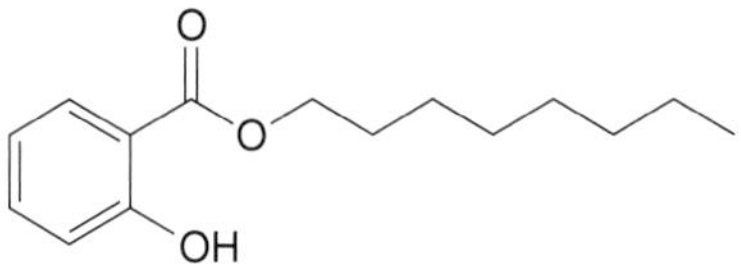

octyl salicylate

Problem 22.21 What product is formed when the esters in ginkgolide B, the chapter-opening molecule, are hydrolyzed in aqueous acid? Indicate the stereochemistry of all stereogenic centers.

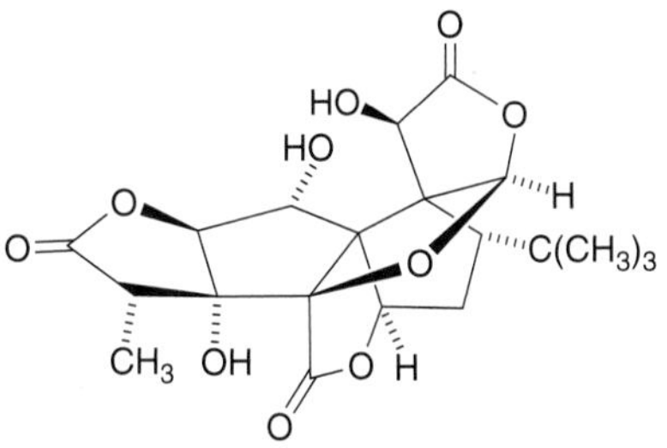

ginkgolide B

22.12 Application: Lipid Hydrolysis

22.12A Olestra—A Synthetic Fat

The most prevalent naturally occurring esters are the **triacylglycerols,** which were first discussed in Section 10.6. **Triacylglycerols are the lipids that comprise animal fats and vegetable oils.**

- **Each triacylglycerol is a triester, containing three long hydrocarbon side chains.**
- **Unsaturated triacylglycerols have one or more double bonds in their long hydrocarbon chains, whereas saturated triacylglycerols have none.**

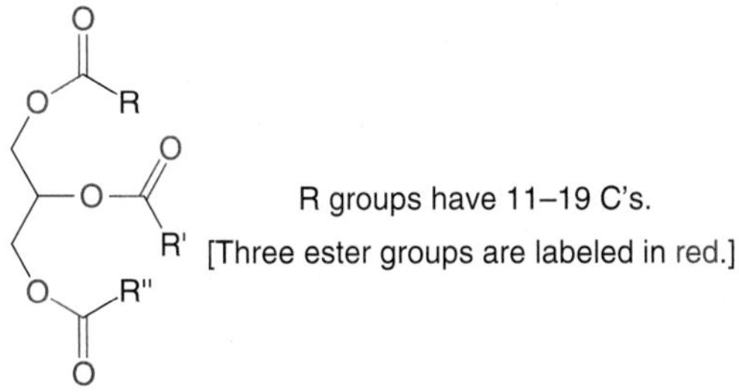

triacylglycerol
the most common type of lipid

Figure 22.4
The three-dimensional structure of a saturated triacylglycerol

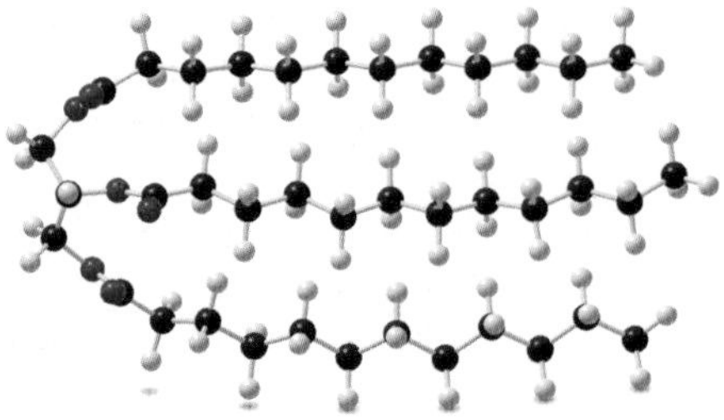

- This triacylglycerol has no double bonds in the three R groups (each with 11 C's) bonded to the ester carbonyls, making it a saturated fat.

Figure 22.4 contains a ball-and-stick model of a saturated fat.

Animals store energy in the form of triacylglycerols, kept in a layer of fat cells below the surface of the skin. This fat serves to insulate the organism, as well as provide energy for its metabolic needs for long periods. The first step in the metabolism of a triacylglycerol is hydrolysis of the ester bonds to form glycerol and three fatty acids. **This reaction is simply ester hydrolysis.** In cells, this reaction is carried out with enzymes called **lipases.**

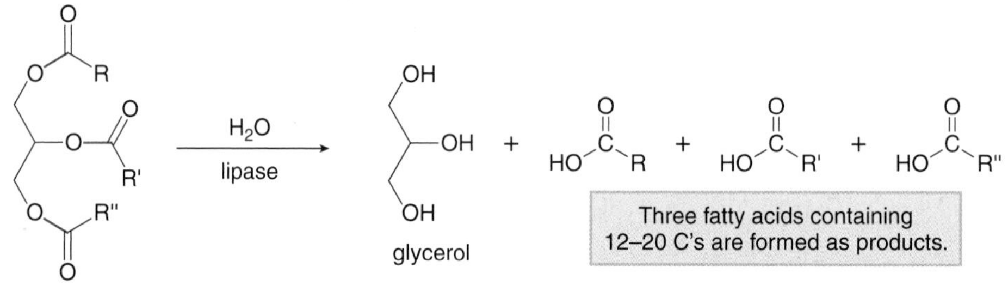

H_2O
lipase
glycerol
Three fatty acids containing 12–20 C's are formed as products.

triacylglycerol

[The three bonds drawn in red are cleaved in hydrolysis.]

The fatty acids produced on hydrolysis are then oxidized in a stepwise fashion, ultimately yielding CO_2 and H_2O, as well as a great deal of energy. Oxidation of fatty acids yields twice as much energy per gram as oxidation of an equivalent weight of carbohydrate.

Diets high in fat content lead to a large amount of stored fat, ultimately causing an individual to be overweight. One recent attempt to reduce calories in common snack foods has been to substitute "fake fats" such as **olestra** (trade name: **Olean**) for triacylglycerols.

sour cream & onion
50% Fewer CALORIES
Artificially Flavored
MADE WITH OLESTRA

Some snack foods contain the "fake fat" olestra, giving them fewer calories for the calorie-conscious consumer.

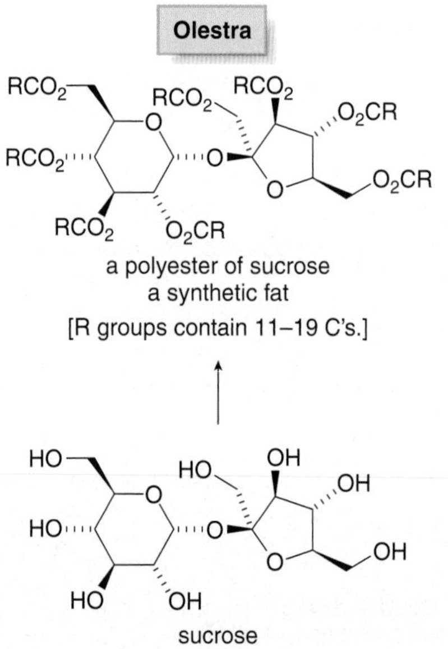

Olestra
a polyester of sucrose
a synthetic fat
[R groups contain 11–19 C's.]
sucrose

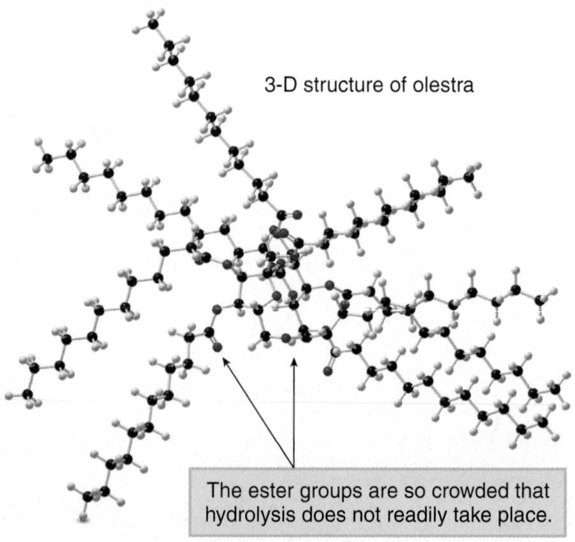

3-D structure of olestra
The ester groups are so crowded that hydrolysis does not readily take place.

Olestra is a polyester formed from long-chain fatty acids and sucrose, the sweet-tasting carbohydrate in table sugar. Naturally occurring triacylglycerols are also polyesters formed from long-chain fatty acids, but olestra has so many ester units clustered together in close proximity that they are too hindered to be hydrolyzed. As a result, olestra is not metabolized. Instead, it passes through the body unchanged, providing no calories to the consumer.

Thus, olestra's many C–C and C–H bonds make it similar in solubility to naturally occurring triacylglycerols, but its three-dimensional structure makes it inert to hydrolysis because of steric hindrance.

Problem 22.22 How would you synthesize olestra from sucrose?

22.12B The Synthesis of Soap

Soap has been previously discussed in Section 3.6.

All soaps are salts of fatty acids. The main difference between soaps is the addition of other ingredients that do not alter their cleaning properties: dyes for color, scents for a pleasing odor, and oils for lubrication. Soaps that float are aerated so that they are less dense than water.

Soap is prepared by the basic hydrolysis or saponification of a triacylglycerol. Heating an animal fat or vegetable oil with aqueous base hydrolyzes the three esters to form glycerol and sodium salts of three fatty acids. These carboxylate salts are **soaps,** which clean away dirt because of their two structurally different regions. The nonpolar tail dissolves grease and oil and the polar head makes it soluble in water (Figure 3.6). Most triacylglycerols have two or three different R groups in their hydrocarbon chains, so soaps are usually mixtures of two or three different carboxylate salts.

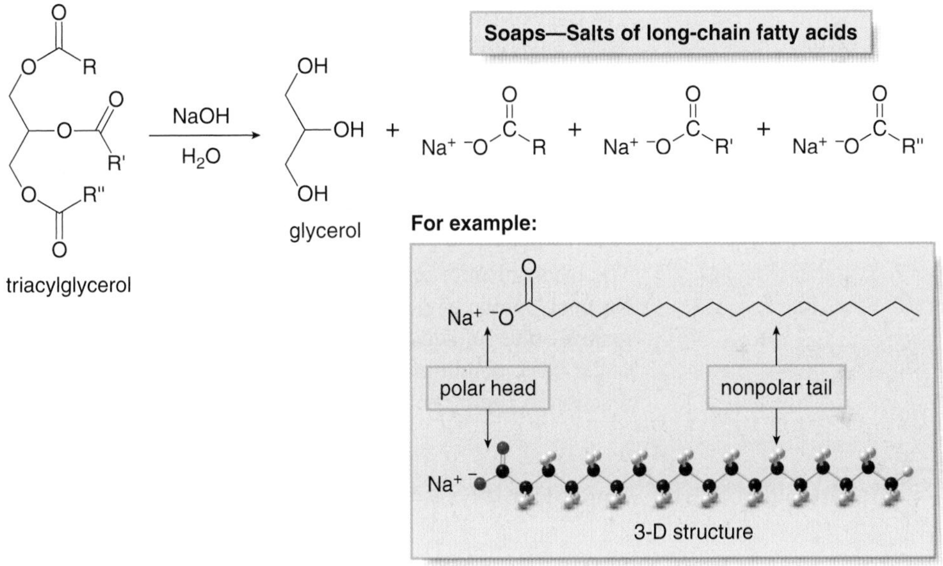

Soaps are typically made from lard (from hogs), tallow (from cattle or sheep), coconut oil, or palm oil. All soaps work in the same way, but have somewhat different properties depending on the lipid source. The length of the carbon chain in the fatty acids and the number of degrees of unsaturation affect the properties of the soap to some extent.

Problem 22.23 What is the composition of the soap prepared by hydrolysis of this triacylglycerol?

$$CH_2OCO(CH_2)_{15}CH_3$$
$$CHOCO(CH_2)_{15}CH_3$$
$$CH_2OCO(CH_2)_7CH{=}CH(CH_2)_7CH_3$$
cis

22.13 Reactions of Amides

Because amides have the poorest leaving group of all the carboxylic acid derivatives, they are the least reactive. Under strenuous reaction conditions, **amides are hydrolyzed in acid or base to form carboxylic acids or carboxylate anions.**

Amide hydrolysis

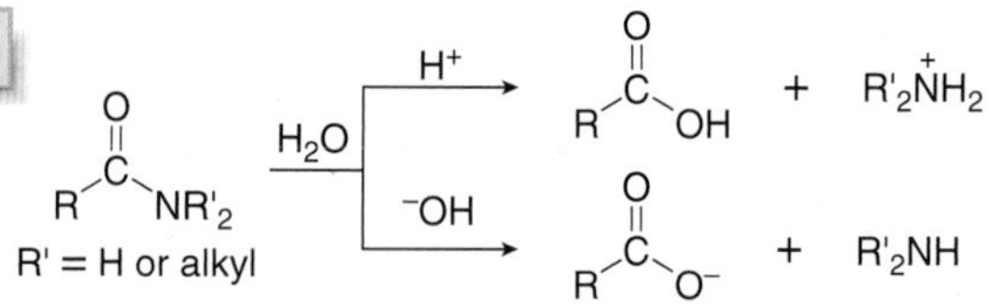

In acid, the amine by-product is protonated as an ammonium ion, whereas in base, a neutral amine is formed.

Examples

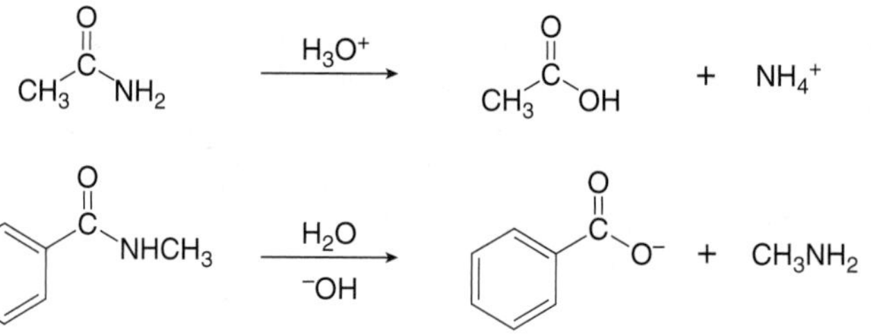

The relative lack of reactivity of the amide bond is notable in proteins, which are polymers of amino acids connected by amide linkages (Section 22.6B). Proteins are stable in aqueous solution in the absence of acid or base, so they can perform their various functions in the aqueous cellular environment without breaking down. The hydrolysis of the amide bonds in proteins requires a variety of specific enzymes.

The mechanism of amide hydrolysis in acid is exactly the same as the mechanism of ester hydrolysis in acid (Section 22.11A) except that the leaving group is different.

The mechanism of amide hydrolysis in base has the usual two steps of the general mechanism for nucleophilic acyl substitution—**addition of the nucleophile** followed by **loss of a leaving group**—plus an additional proton transfer. The initially formed carboxylic acid reacts further under basic conditions to form the resonance-stabilized carboxylate anion, and this drives the reaction to completion. Mechanism 22.10 is written for a 1° amide.

Mechanism 22.10 Amide Hydrolysis in Base

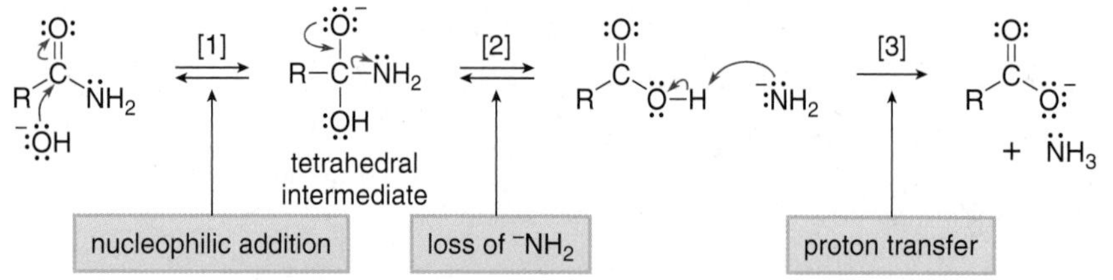

- Steps [1] and [2] result **in addition of the nucleophile, ^-OH, followed by elimination of the leaving group, $^-NH_2$.**
- Because the carboxylic acid is a strong organic acid and the leaving group ($^-NH_2$) is a strong base, an **acid–base reaction** occurs in Step [3] to form the carboxylate anion.

Step [2] of Mechanism 22.10 deserves additional comment. For amide hydrolysis to occur, the tetrahedral intermediate must lose $^-NH_2$, a stronger base and therefore poorer leaving group than ^-OH (Step [2]). This means that loss of $^-NH_2$ does not often happen. Instead, ^-OH is lost as the leaving group most of the time, and the starting material is regenerated. But, when $^-NH_2$ is occasionally eliminated, the carboxylic acid product is converted to a lower energy carboxylate anion in Step [3], and this drives the equilibrium to favor its formation.

Problem 22.24 Draw a stepwise mechanism for the following reaction.

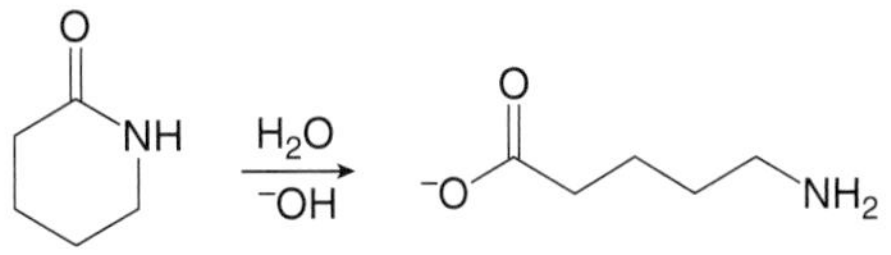

NH
H_2O
^-OH
^-O
NH_2

Problem 22.25 With reference to the structures of acetylsalicylic acid (aspirin, Chapter 2 opening molecule) and acetaminophen (the active ingredient in Tylenol), explain each statement: (a) Acetaminophen tablets can be stored in the medicine cabinet for years, but aspirin slowly decomposes over time; (b) Children's Tylenol can be sold as a liquid (acetaminophen dissolved in water), but aspirin cannot.

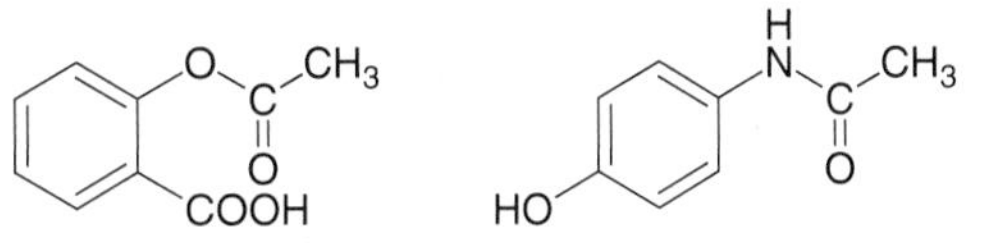

CH_3
COOH
HO

acetylsalicylic acid acetaminophen

22.14 Application: The Mechanism of Action of β-Lactam Antibiotics

Penicillin and related β-lactams kill bacteria by a nucleophilic acyl substitution reaction. All penicillins have an unreactive amide side chain and a very reactive amide that is part of a β-lactam. The β-lactam is more reactive than other amides because it is part of a strained, four-membered ring that is readily opened with nucleophiles.

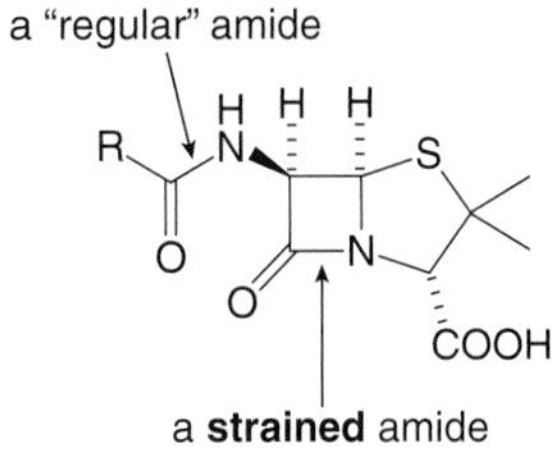

a "regular" amide
COOH
a **strained** amide

penicillin

Unlike mammalian cells, bacterial cells are surrounded by a fairly rigid cell wall, which allows the bacterium to live in many different environments. This protective cell wall is composed of carbohydrates linked together by peptide chains containing amide linkages, formed using the enzyme **glycopeptide transpeptidase.**

Penicillin interferes with the synthesis of the bacterial cell wall. A nucleophilic OH group of the glycopeptide transpeptidase enzyme cleaves the β-lactam ring of penicillin by a nucleophilic acyl substitution reaction. The opened ring of the penicillin molecule remains covalently bonded to the enzyme, thus deactivating the enzyme, halting cell wall construction, and killing the bacterium. Penicillin has no effect on mammalian cells because they are surrounded by a flexible membrane composed of a lipid bilayer (Chapter 3) and not a cell wall.

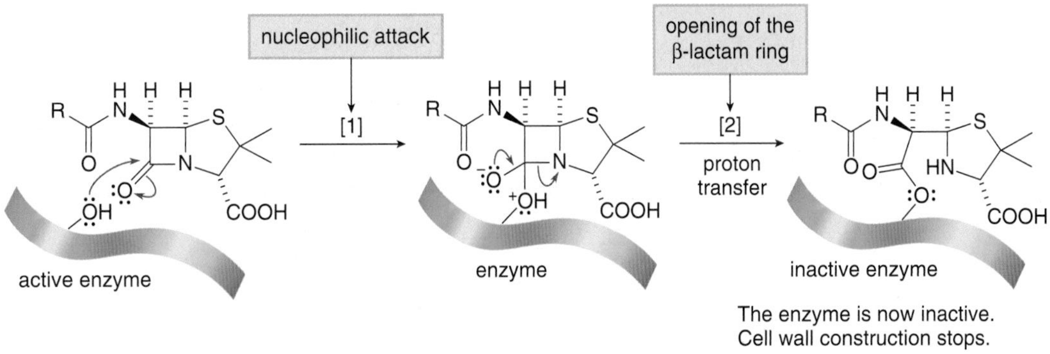

nucleophilic attack
opening of the β-lactam ring
[1]
[2]
proton transfer
COOH
active enzyme
enzyme
inactive enzyme
The enzyme is now inactive.
Cell wall construction stops.

Thus, penicillin and other β-lactam antibiotics are biologically active precisely because they undergo a nucleophilic acyl substitution reaction with an important bacterial enzyme.

Problem 22.26 Some penicillins cannot be administered orally because their β-lactam is rapidly hydrolyzed by the acidic environment of the stomach. What product is formed in the following hydrolysis reaction?

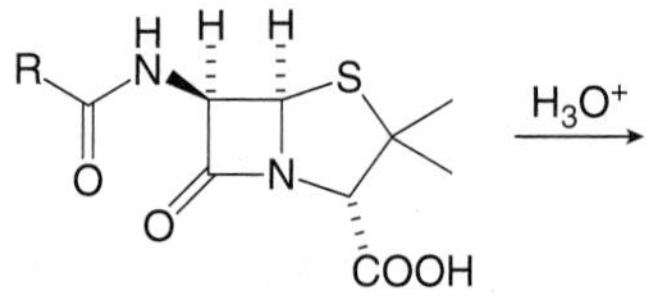

22.15 Summary of Nucleophilic Acyl Substitution Reactions

To help you organize and remember all of the nucleophilic acyl substitution reactions that can occur at a carbonyl carbon, keep in mind the following two principles:

- **The better the leaving group, the more reactive the carboxylic acid derivative.**
- **More reactive acyl compounds can always be converted to less reactive ones. The reverse is not usually true.**

This results in the following order of reactivity:

$RCONR'_2$ $RCOOH \approx RCOOR'$ $(RCO)_2O$ $RCOCl$

Increasing reactivity →

Table 22.5 summarizes the specific nucleophilic acyl substitution reactions. Use it as a quick reference to remind you which products can be formed from a given starting material.

Table 22.5 Summary of the Nucleophilic Substitution Reactions of Carboxylic Acids and Their Derivatives

Starting material		Product: RCOCl	$(RCO)_2O$	RCOOH	RCOOR'	$RCONR'_2$
[1] RCOCl	→	–	✓	✓	✓	✓
[2] $(RCO)_2O$	→	✗	–	✓	✓	✓
[3] RCOOH	→	✓	✓	–	✓	✓
[4] RCOOR'	→	✗	✗	✓	–	✓
[5] $RCONR'_2$	→	✗	✗	✓	✗	–

Table key: ✓ = A reaction occurs.
✗ = No reaction occurs.

22.16 Natural and Synthetic Fibers

All natural and synthetic fibers are high molecular weight polymers. Natural fibers are obtained from either plant or animal sources, and this determines the fundamental nature of their chemical structure. Fibers like **wool and silk obtained from animals are proteins,** and so they are formed from amino acids joined together by many amide linkages. **Cotton and linen,** on the other hand, are derived from plants and so they are **carbohydrates having the general structure of cellulose,** formed from glucose monomers. General structures for these polymers are shown in Figure 22.5.

Figure 22.5
The general structure of the common natural fibers

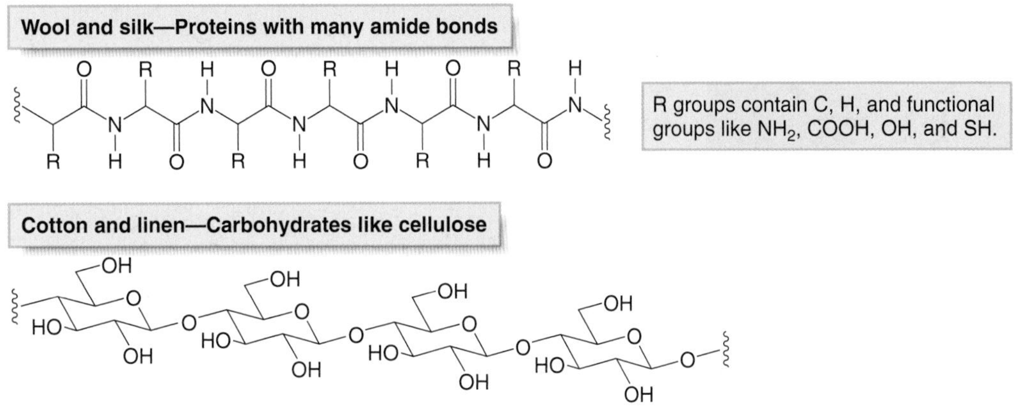

An important practical application of organic chemistry has been the synthesis of synthetic fibers, many of which have properties that are different from and sometimes superior to their naturally occurring counterparts. The two most common classes of synthetic polymers are based on polyamides and polyesters.

22.16A Nylon—A Polyamide

DuPont built the first commercial nylon plant in 1938. Although it was initially used by the military to make parachutes, nylon quickly replaced silk in many common clothing articles after World War II.

The search for a synthetic fiber led to the discovery of **nylon,** a **polyamide** that is strong and durable and resembles the silk produced by silkworms. There are several different kinds of nylon, but the most well known is called nylon 6,6.

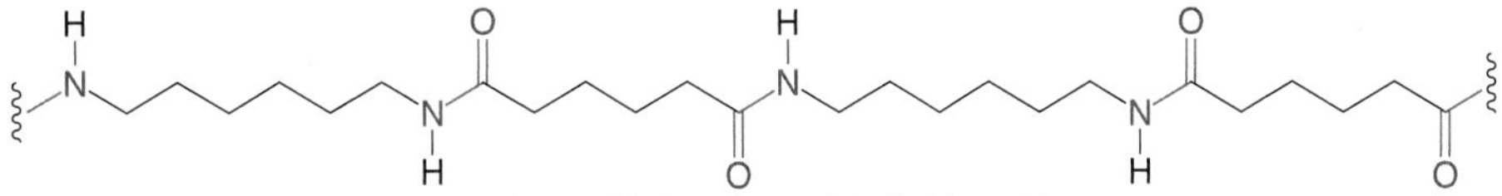

[The amide bonds are labeled in red.]

nylon 6,6

Nylon 6,6 can be synthesized from two six-carbon monomers (hence its name)—adipoyl chloride **($ClOCCH_2CH_2CH_2CH_2COCl$)** and hexamethylenediamine **($H_2NCH_2CH_2CH_2CH_2CH_2CH_2NH_2$).** This diacid chloride and diamine react together to form new amide bonds, yielding the polymer. Nylon is called a **condensation polymer** because a small molecule, in this case HCl, is eliminated during its synthesis.

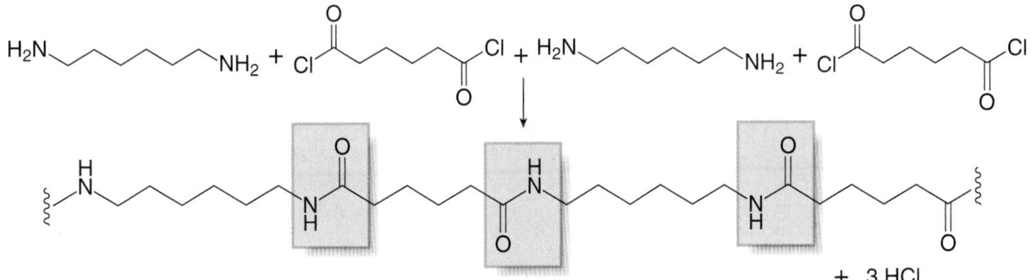

nylon 6,6

Three new amide bonds are shown.

Problem 22.27 What two monomers are needed to prepare nylon 6,10?

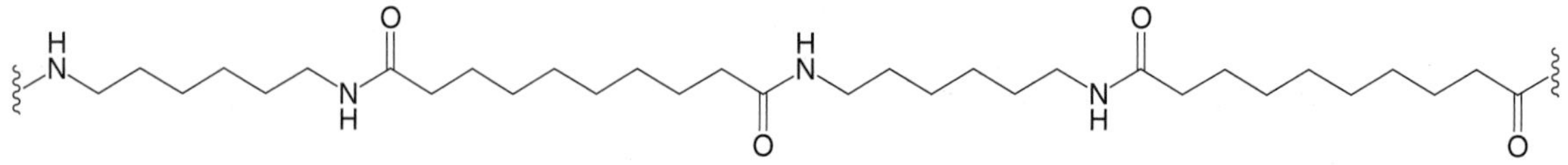

nylon 6,10

22.16B Polyesters

Bottles...

As we will learn in Section 31.9, PET is more easily recycled than other common polymers. For example, recycled PET is used to make reusable shopping bags.

Polyesters constitute a second major class of condensation polymers. The most common polyester is polyethylene terephthalate **(PET),** which is sold under a variety of trade names (Dacron, Terylene, and Mylar) depending on its use.

Polyethylene terephthalate
PET
(Dacron, Terylene, and Mylar)

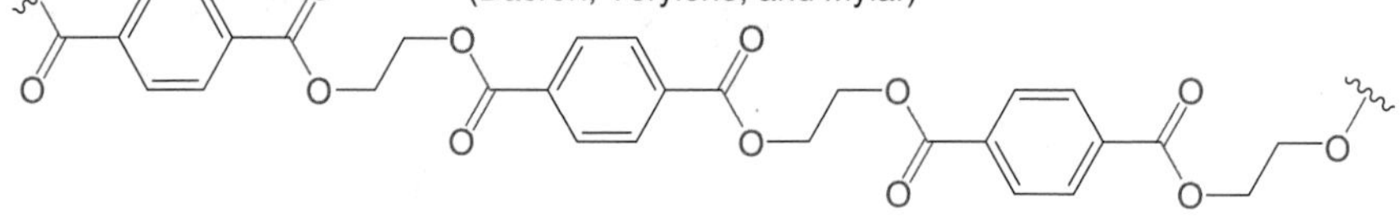

Ester bonds (in red) join the carbon skeleton together.

One method of synthesizing a polyester is by acid-catalyzed esterification of a diacid with a diol (Fischer esterification).

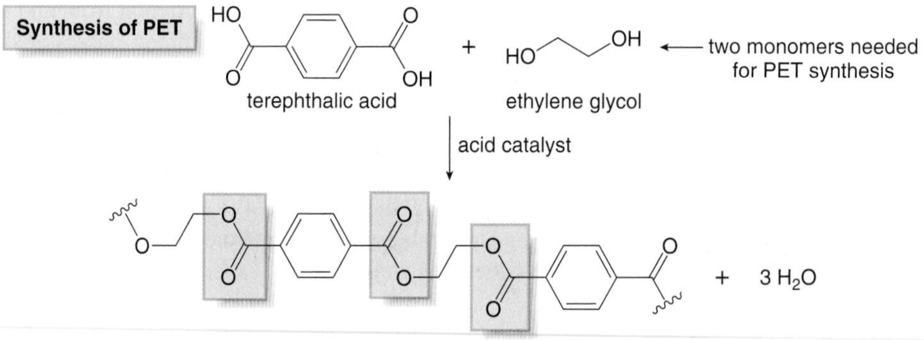
Synthesis of PET
terephthalic acid
ethylene glycol
two monomers needed for PET synthesis
acid catalyst
+ 3 H2O

Three new ester bonds are shown.

Because these polymers are easily and cheaply prepared and form strong and chemically stable materials, they have been used in clothing, films, tires, and many other products.

Problem 22.28 Draw the structure of Kodel, a polyester formed from 1,4-dihydroxymethylcyclohexane and terephthalic acid. Explain why fabrics made from Kodel are stiff and crease resistant.

1,4-dihydroxymethylcyclohexane terephthalic acid

Problem 22.29 Poly(lactic acid) (PLA) has received much recent attention because the lactic acid monomer [$CH_3CH(OH)COOH$] from which it is made can be obtained from carbohydrates rather than petroleum. This makes PLA a more "environmentally friendly" polyester. (A more in-depth discussion of green polymer synthesis is presented in Section 31.8.) Draw the structure of PLA.

22.17 Biological Acylation Reactions

Nucleophilic acyl substitution is a common reaction in biological systems. These acylation reactions are called **acyl transfer reactions** because they result in the transfer of an acyl group from one atom to another (from Z to Nu in this case).

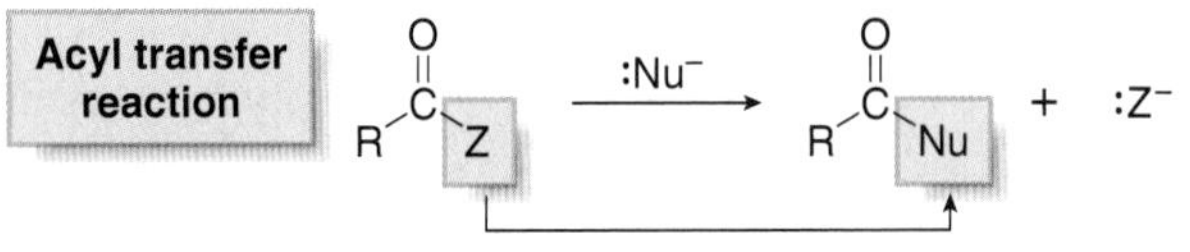

The acyl group is transferred from Z to Nu.

In cells, such acylations occur with the sulfur analogue of an ester, called a **thioester,** having the general structure **RCOSR'.** The most common thioester is called **acetyl coenzyme A,** often referred to merely as **acetyl CoA.**

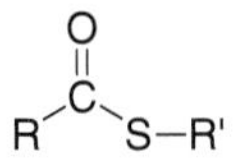

thioester

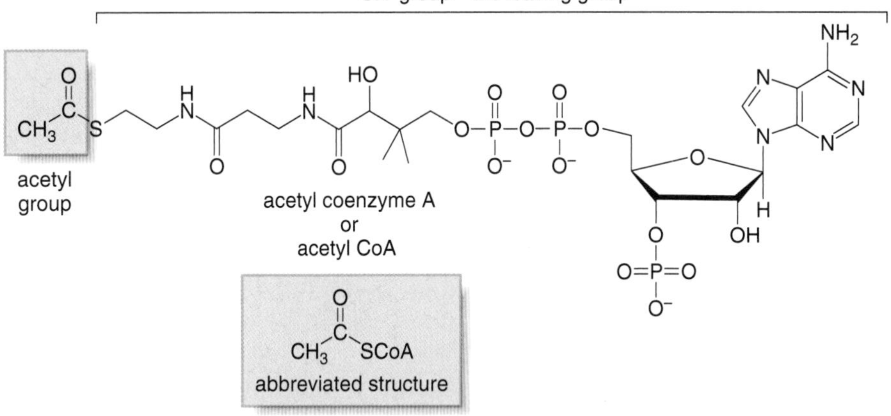

- **A thioester (RCOSR') has a good leaving group (⁻SR'), so, like other acyl compounds, it undergoes substitution reactions with other nucleophiles.**

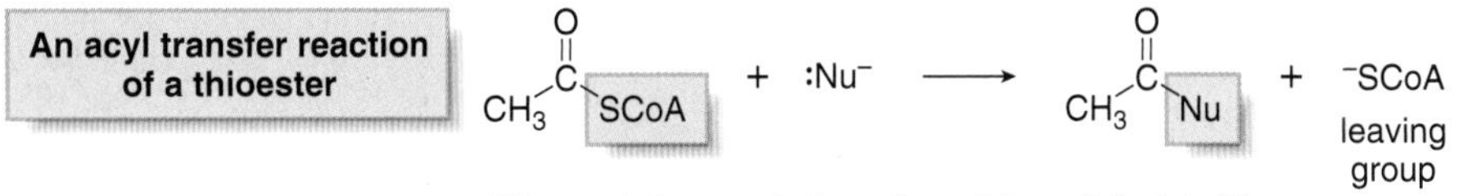

The acetyl group is transferred from SCoA to Nu.

For example, acetyl CoA undergoes enzyme-catalyzed nucleophilic acyl substitution with choline, forming acetylcholine, a charged compound that transmits nerve impulses between nerve cells.

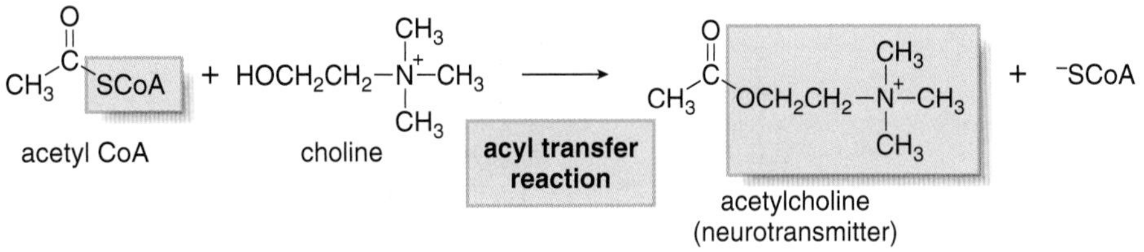

Many other acyl transfer reactions are important cellular processes. Thioesters of fatty acids react with cholesterol, forming **cholesteryl esters** in an enzyme-catalyzed reaction (Figure 22.6). These esters are the principal form in which cholesterol is stored and transported in the body. Because cholesterol is a lipid, insoluble in the aqueous environment of the blood, it travels through the bloodstream in particles that also contain proteins and phospholipids. These particles are classified by their density.

- **LDL particles** (low density lipoproteins) transport cholesterol from the liver to the tissues.
- **HDL particles** (high density lipoproteins) transport cholesterol from the tissues back to the liver, where it is metabolized or converted to other steroids.

Atherosclerosis is a disease that results from the buildup of fatty deposits on the walls of arteries, forming deposits called **plaque.** Plaque is composed largely of the cholesterol (esterified as an ester) of LDL particles. LDL is often referred to as "bad cholesterol" for this reason. In contrast, HDL particles are called "good cholesterol" because they reduce the amount of cholesterol in the bloodstream by transporting it back to the liver.

Figure 22.6
Cholesteryl esters and lipoprotein particles

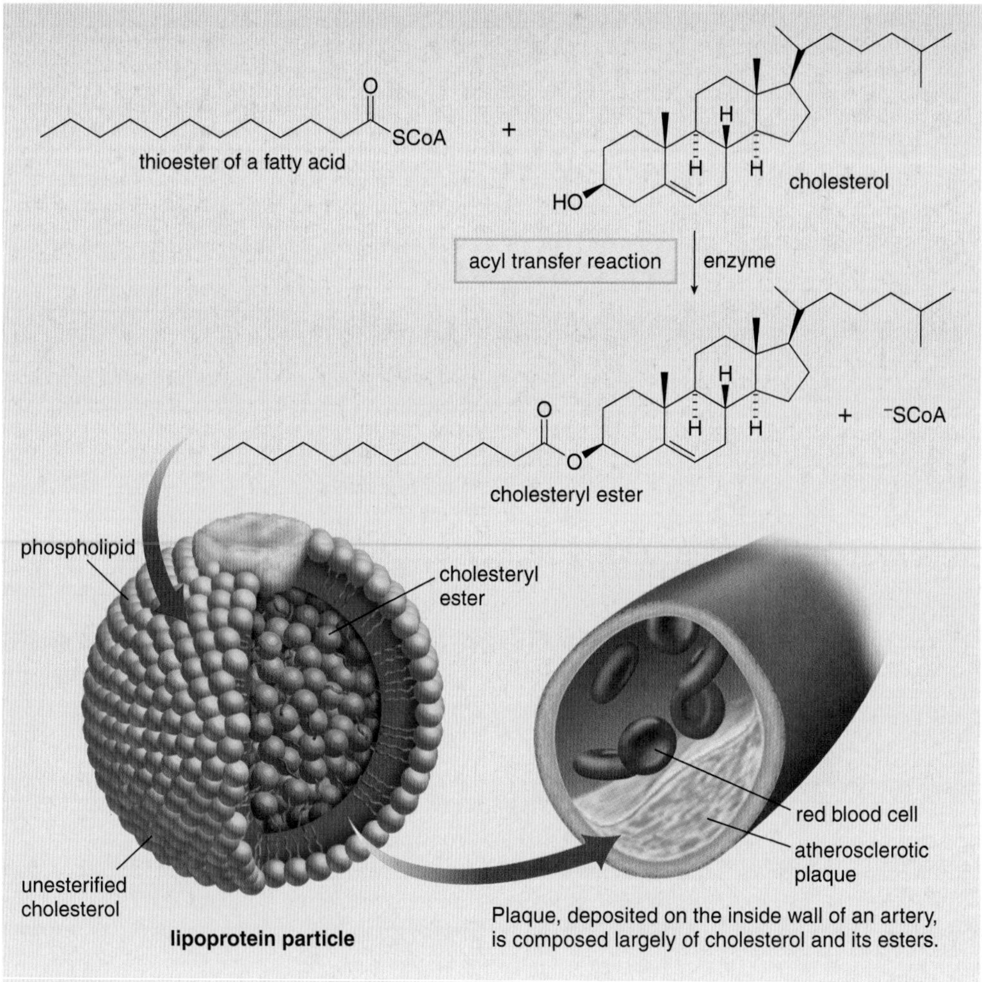
O
SCoA
thioester of a fatty acid
+
HO
H
H
H
cholesterol
acyl transfer reaction
enzyme
O
O
H
H
H
+ ⁻SCoA
cholesteryl ester
phospholipid
cholesteryl ester
unesterified cholesterol
lipoprotein particle
red blood cell
atherosclerotic plaque
Plaque, deposited on the inside wall of an artery, is composed largely of cholesterol and its esters.

Problem 22.30 Glucosamine is a dietary supplement available in many over-the-counter treatments for osteoarthritis. Reaction of acetyl CoA with glucosamine forms NAG, *N*-acetylglucosamine, the monomer used to form chitin, the carbohydrate that forms the rigid shells of lobsters and crabs. What is the structure of NAG?

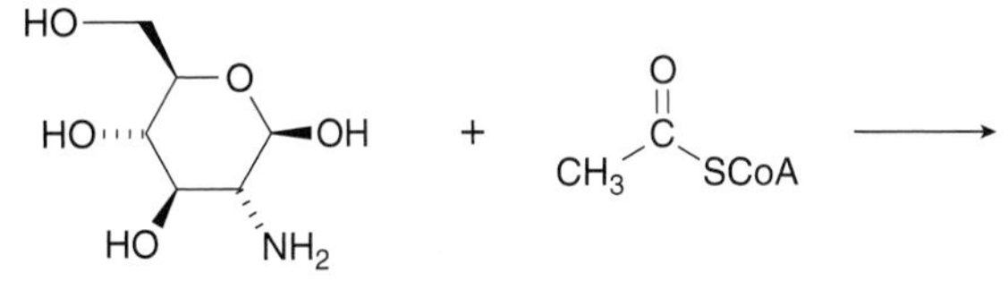
HO
O
HO
OH
HO
NH2
+
O
C
CH3
SCoA

glucosamine

22.18 Nitriles

We end Chapter 22 with the chemistry of **nitriles (RC≡N).** Nitriles have a carbon atom in the same oxidation state as in the acyl compounds that are the principal focus of Chapter 22. Moreover, the chemical reactions of nitriles illustrate some of the concepts first discussed earlier in Chapter 22 and in Chapters 20 and 21.

In addition to the cyanohydrins discussed in Section 21.9, two useful biologically active nitriles are **letrozole** and **anastrozole,** new drugs that reduce the recurrence of breast cancer in women whose tumors are estrogen positive.

Letrozole and anastrozole are called **aromatase inhibitors** because they block the activity of the aromatase enzyme, which is responsible for estrogen synthesis. This inhibits tumor growth in those forms of breast cancer that are stimulated by estrogen.

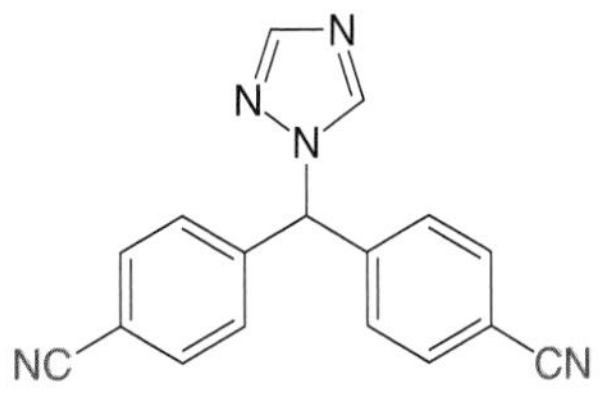
N
N
N
NC
CN

Generic name: letrozole
Trade name: Femara

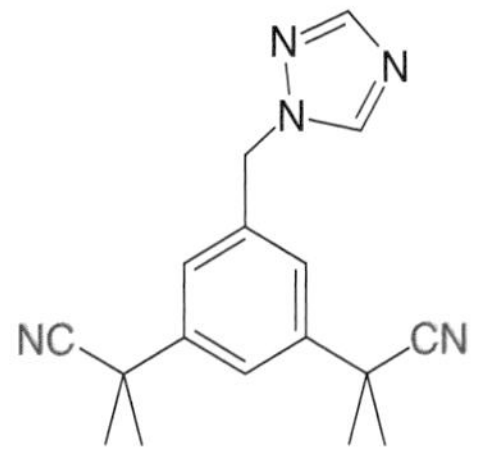
N
N
N
NC
CN

Generic name: anastrozole
Trade name: Arimidex

Nitriles are readily prepared by S_N2 substitution reactions of unhindered methyl and 1° alkyl halides with $^-$CN. This reaction adds one carbon to the alkyl halide and **forms a new carbon–carbon bond.**

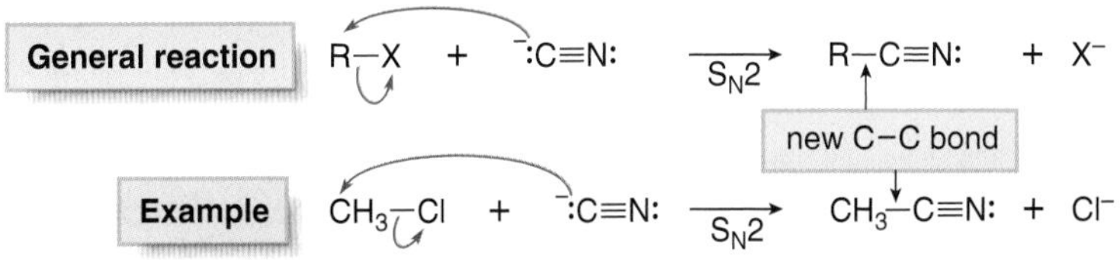
General reaction
R–X + ⁻:C≡N:
SN2
R–C≡N: + X⁻
new C–C bond
Example
CH3–Cl + ⁻:C≡N:
SN2
CH3–C≡N: + Cl⁻

Because nitriles have no leaving group, they do not undergo nucleophilic substitution reactions like carboxylic acid derivatives. Because the cyano group contains an electrophilic carbon atom that is part of a multiple bond, a nitrile reacts with nucleophiles by a **nucleophilic addition reaction.** The nature of the nucleophile determines the structure of the product.

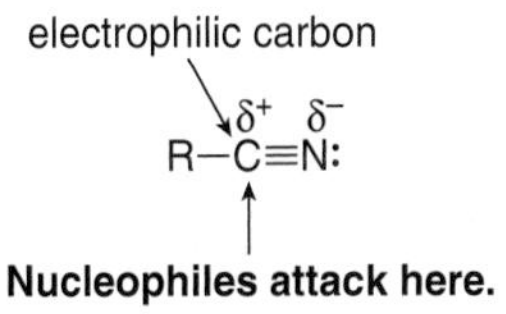
electrophilic carbon
δ+ δ−
R–C≡N:
Nucleophiles attack here.

The reactions of nitriles with water, hydride, and organometallic reagents as nucleophiles are as follows:

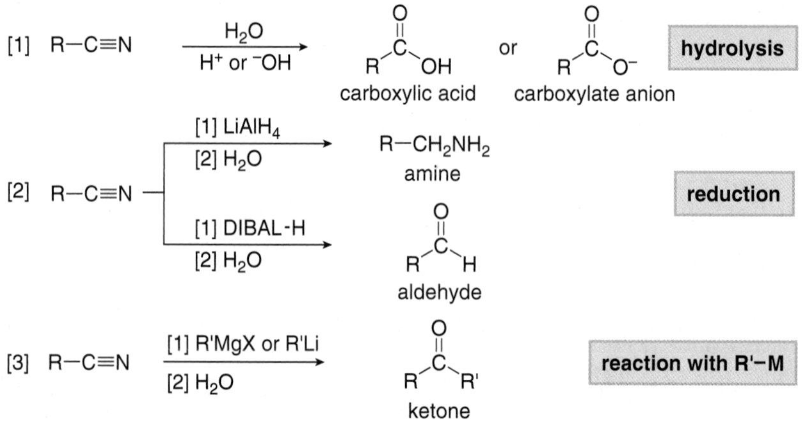
[1] R−C≡N
H2O
H+ or −OH
carboxylic acid
or
carboxylate anion
hydrolysis
[2] R−C≡N
[1] LiAlH4
[2] H2O
R−CH2NH2
amine
[1] DIBAL-H
[2] H2O
aldehyde
reduction
[3] R−C≡N
[1] R'MgX or R'Li
[2] H2O
ketone
reaction with R'−M

22.18A Hydrolysis of Nitriles

Nitriles are hydrolyzed with water in the presence of acid or base to yield **carboxylic acids** or **carboxylate anions.** In this reaction, the three C−N bonds are replaced by three C−O bonds.

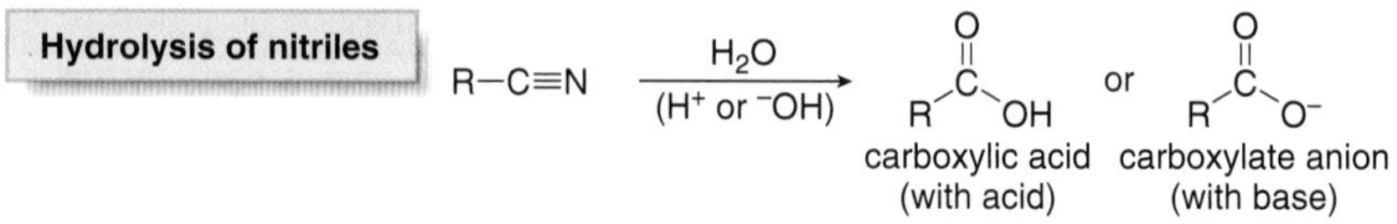
Hydrolysis of nitriles
R−C≡N
H2O
(H+ or −OH)
carboxylic acid
(with acid)
or
carboxylate anion
(with base)

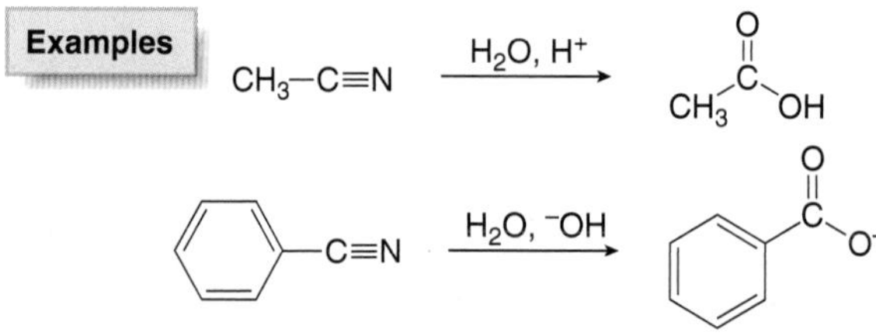
Examples
CH3−C≡N
H2O, H+
H2O, −OH

The mechanism of this reaction involves the formation of an amide tautomer. Two tautomers can be drawn for any carbonyl compound, and those for a 1° amide are as follows:

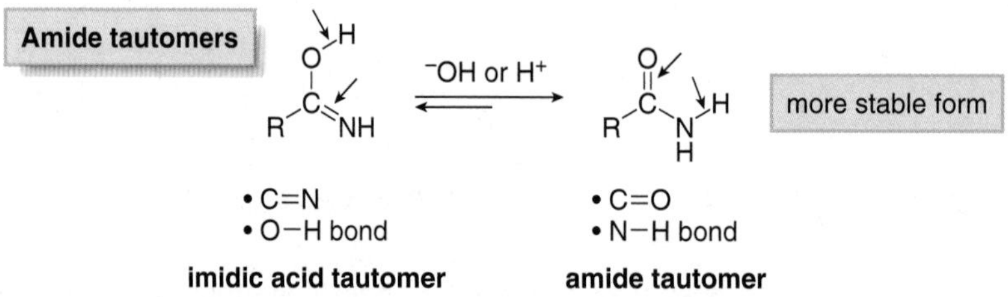
Amide tautomers
−OH or H+
more stable form
• C=N
• O−H bond
imidic acid tautomer
• C=O
• N−H bond
amide tautomer

Recall from Chapter 11 that tautomers are constitutional isomers that differ in the location of a double bond and a proton.

- **The amide form is the more stable tautomer, having a C=O and an N−H bond.**
- **The imidic acid tautomer is the less stable form, having a C=N and an O−H bond.**

Recall from Chapter 11 that the keto and enol tautomers of a carbonyl compound are in equilibrium, but the keto form is lower in energy, so it is highly favored in most cases.

The imidic acid and amide tautomers are interconverted by treating with acid or base, analogous to the keto–enol tautomers of other carbonyl compounds. In fact, the two amide tautomers are exactly the same as keto–enol tautomers except that a nitrogen atom replaces a carbon atom bonded to the carbonyl group.

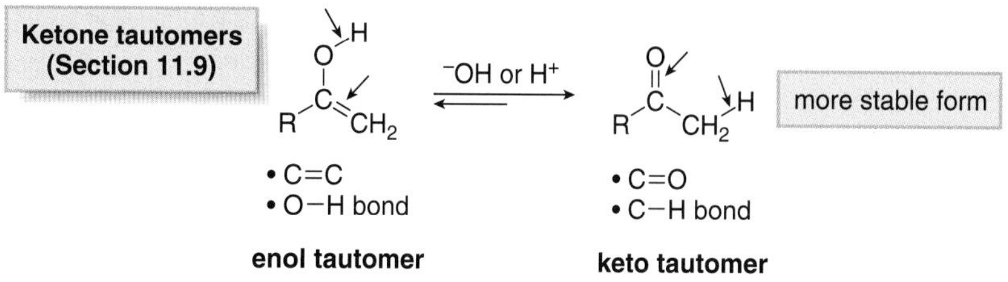

The mechanism of nitrile hydrolysis in both acid and base consists of three parts: [1] **nucleophilic addition** of H_2O or ^-OH to form the imidic acid tautomer; [2] **tautomerization** to form the amide, and [3] **hydrolysis of the amide** to form RCOOH or $RCOO^-$. The mechanism is shown for the basic hydrolysis of RCN to $RCOO^-$ (Mechanism 22.11).

Mechanism 22.11 Hydrolysis of a Nitrile in Base

Part [1] Addition of the nucleophile (^-OH) to form an imidic acid

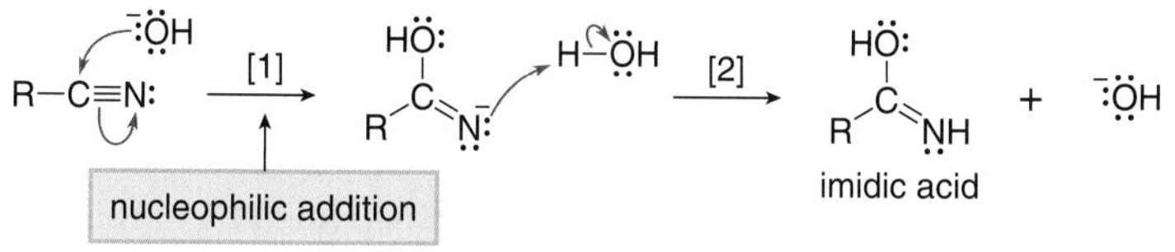

- **Nucleophilic attack of $^-$OH** followed by protonation forms an imidic acid.

Part [2] Tautomerization of the imidic acid to an amide

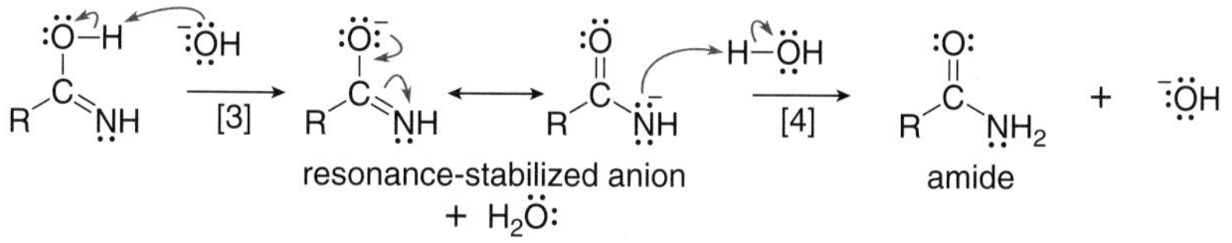

- Tautomerization occurs by a two-step sequence—**deprotonation followed by protonation.**

Part [3] Hydrolysis of the 1° amide to a carboxylate anion

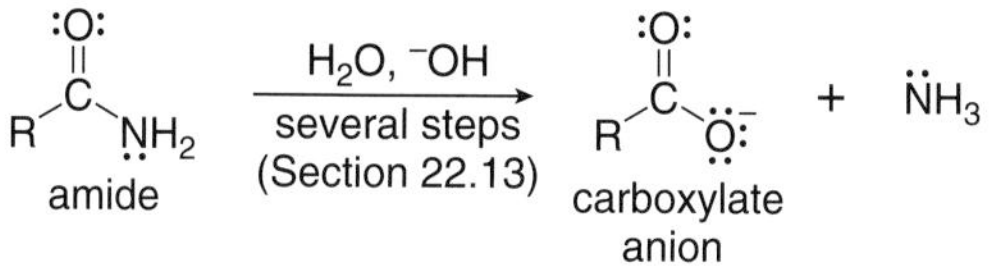

- Conversion of the amide to the carboxylate anion occurs by the multistep sequence detailed in Section 22.13.

Problem 22.31 Draw the products of each reaction.

a. $CH_3CH_2CH_2{-}Br \xrightarrow{NaCN}$

b. 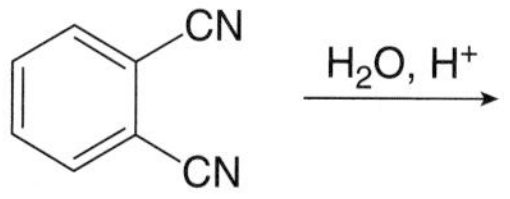

c. 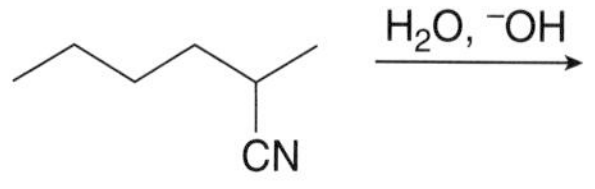

Problem 22.32 Draw a tautomer of each compound.

a. 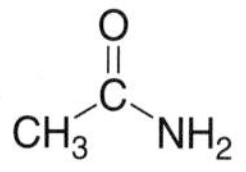

b. 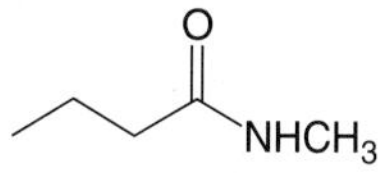

c. 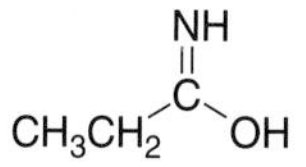

22.18B Reduction of Nitriles

Nitriles are reduced with metal hydride reagents to form either 1° amines or aldehydes, depending on the reducing agent.

- **Treatment of a nitrile with $LiAlH_4$ followed by H_2O adds two equivalents of H_2 across the triple bond, forming a 1° amine.**

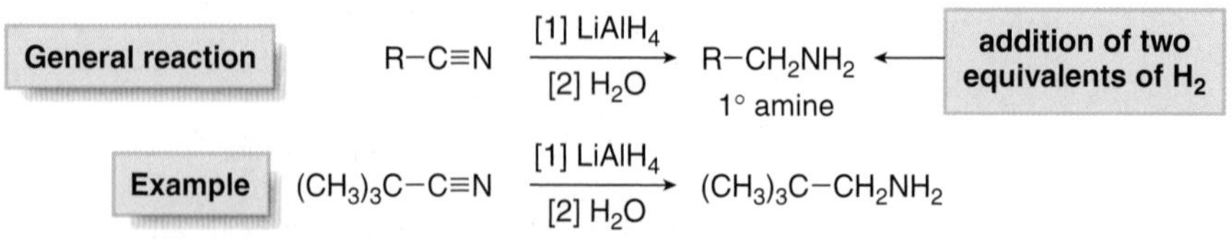
General reaction
R−C≡N
[1] LiAlH4
[2] H2O
R−CH2NH2
1° amine
addition of two equivalents of H2
Example
(CH3)3C−C≡N
[1] LiAlH4
[2] H2O
(CH3)3C−CH2NH2

- **Treatment of a nitrile with a milder reducing agent such as DIBAL-H followed by H_2O forms an aldehyde.**

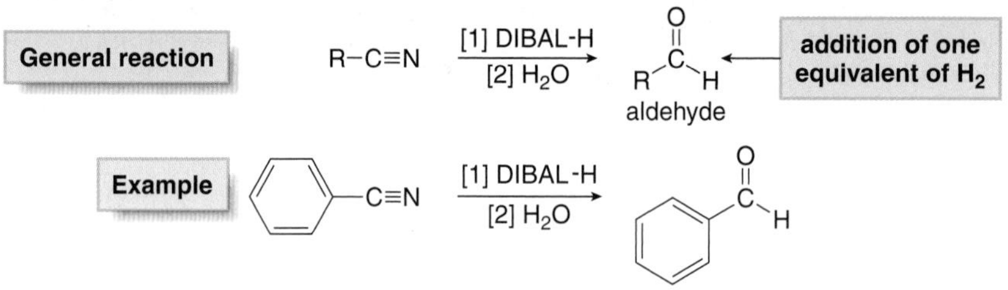
General reaction
R−C≡N
[1] DIBAL-H
[2] H2O
aldehyde
addition of one equivalent of H2
Example
C≡N
[1] DIBAL-H
[2] H2O

The mechanism of both reactions involves **nucleophilic addition of hydride (H^-) to the polarized C−N triple bond.** Mechanism 22.12 illustrates that reduction of a nitrile to an amine requires addition of two equivalents of $H:^-$ from $LiAlH_4$. It is likely that intermediate nitrogen anions complex with AlH_3 (formed in situ) to facilitate the addition. Protonation of the dianion in Step [4] forms the amine.

Mechanism 22.12 Reduction of a Nitrile with $LiAlH_4$

Part [1] Addition of one equivalent of hydride

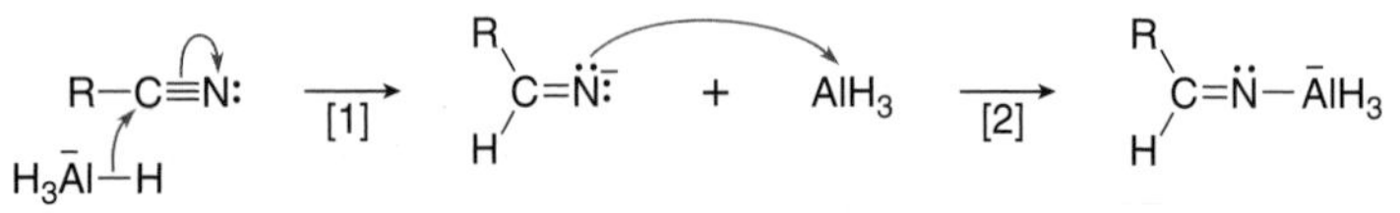

- Addition of one equivalent of $H:^-$ from $LiAlH_4$ forms an intermediate that complexes with the AlH_3 also formed during addition (Steps [1]–[2]).

Part [2] Addition of a second equivalent of hydride

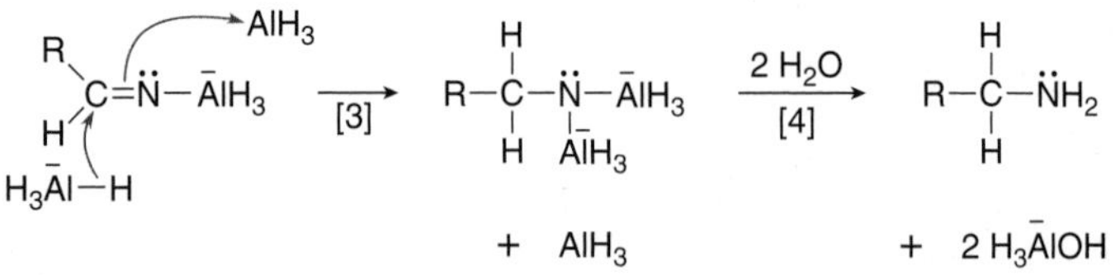

- Addition of a second equivalent of $H:^-$ and complexation with AlH_3 yield a dianion with two new C−H bonds.
- Hydrolysis with water forms the 1° amine in Step [4].

With **DIBAL-H,** nucleophilic addition of one equivalent of hydride forms an anion (Step [1]), which is protonated with water to generate an **imine,** as shown in Mechanism 22.13. As described in Section 21.12, imines are hydrolyzed in water to form aldehydes. Mechanism 22.13 is written without complexation of aluminum with the anion formed in Step [1], to emphasize the identity of intermediates formed during reduction.

Mechanism 22.13 Reduction of a Nitrile with DIBAL-H

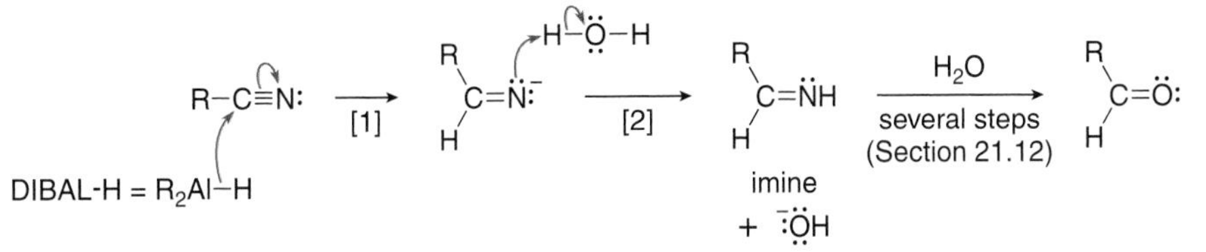
R−C≡N:
DIBAL-H = R_2Al−H
[1]
[2]
imine
H_2O
several steps
(Section 21.12)

Problem 22.33 Draw the product of each reaction.

a. $CH_3CH_2-Br \xrightarrow[\text{[2] } LiAlH_4 \text{ [3] } H_2O]{\text{[1] NaCN}}$ b. $CH_3CH_2CH_2-CN \xrightarrow[\text{[2] } H_2O]{\text{[1] DIBAL-H}}$

22.18C Addition of Grignard and Organolithium Reagents to Nitriles

Both Grignard and organolithium reagents react with nitriles to form ketones with a new carbon–carbon bond.

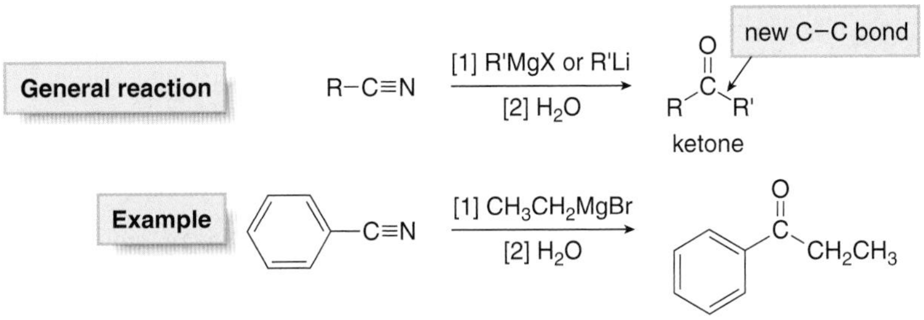
General reaction
R−C≡N
[1] R'MgX or R'Li
[2] H_2O
new C−C bond
ketone
Example
[1] CH_3CH_2MgBr
[2] H_2O

The reaction occurs by nucleophilic addition of the organometallic reagent to the polarized C−N triple bond to form an anion (Step [1]), which is protonated with water to form an **imine.** Water then hydrolyzes the imine, replacing the C=N by C=O as described in Section 21.12. The final product is a ketone with a new carbon–carbon bond (Mechanism 22.14).

Mechanism 22.14 Addition of Grignard and Organolithium Reagents (R−M) to Nitriles

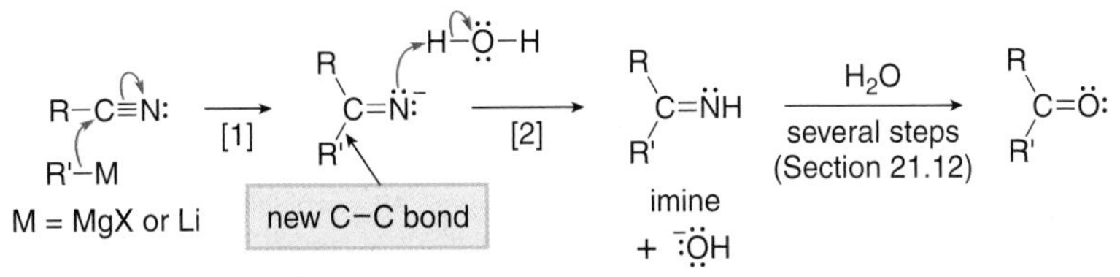
M = MgX or Li
[1]
new C−C bond
[2]
imine
H_2O
several steps
(Section 21.12)

Problem 22.34 Draw the products of each reaction.

a. 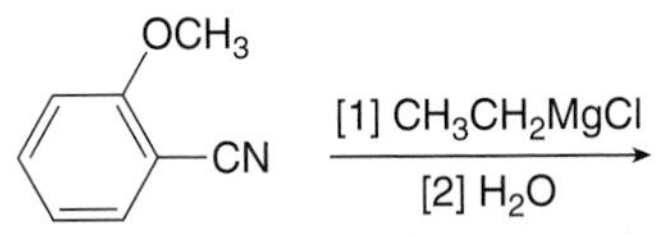
OCH_3
CN
[1] CH_3CH_2MgCl
[2] H_2O

b. 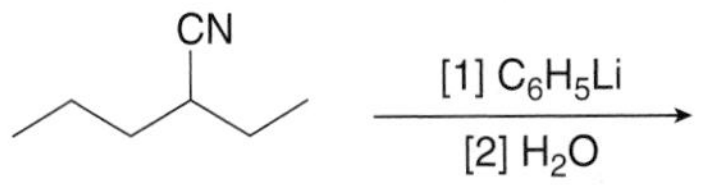
CN
[1] C_6H_5Li
[2] H_2O

Problem 22.35 What reagents are needed to convert phenylacetonitrile ($C_6H_5CH_2CN$) to each compound: (a) $C_6H_5CH_2COCH_3$; (b) $C_6H_5CH_2COC(CH_3)_3$; (c) $C_6H_5CH_2CHO$; (d) $C_6H_5CH_2COOH$?

Problem 22.36 Outline two different ways that 2-butanone can be prepared from a nitrile and a Grignard reagent.

KEY CONCEPTS

Carboxylic Acids and Their Derivatives—Nucleophilic Acyl Substitution

Summary of Spectroscopic Absorptions of RCOZ (22.5)

IR absorptions

- All RCOZ compounds have a C = O absorption in the region 1600–1850 cm^{-1}.
  - RCOCl: 1800 cm^{-1}
  - $(RCO)_2O$: 1820 and 1760 cm^{-1} (two peaks)
  - RCOOR': 1735–1745 cm^{-1}
  - $RCONR'_2$: 1630–1680 cm^{-1}
- Additional amide absorptions occur at 3200–3400 cm^{-1} (N – H stretch) and 1640 cm^{-1} (N – H bending).
- Decreasing the ring size of a cyclic lactone, lactam, or anhydride increases the frequency of the C = O absorption.
- Conjugation shifts the C = O to lower wavenumber.

^{1}H NMR absorptions

- C – H α to the C = O absorbs at 2–2.5 ppm.
- N – H of an amide absorbs at 7.5–8.5 ppm.

^{13}C NMR absorption

- C = O absorbs at 160–180 ppm.

Summary of Spectroscopic Absorptions of RCN (22.5)

IR absorption

- C ≡ N absorbs at ~2250 cm^{-1}.

^{13}C NMR absorption

- C ≡ N absorbs at 115–120 ppm.

Summary: The Relationship between the Basicity of Z^- and the Properties of RCOZ

- **Increasing basicity of the leaving group** (22.2)
- **Increasing resonance stabilization** (22.2)

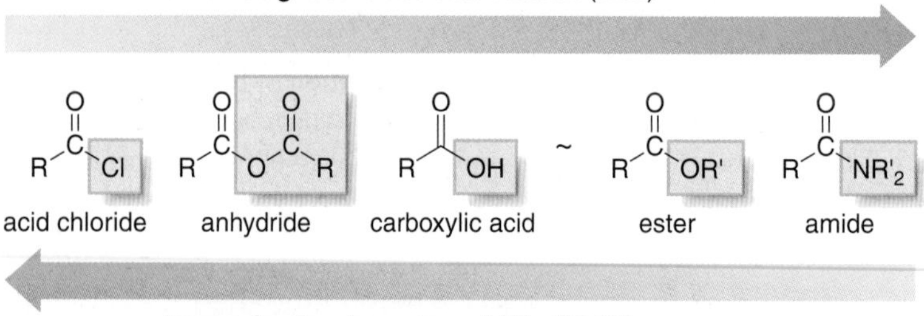

acid chloride · anhydride · carboxylic acid · ester · amide

- **Increasing leaving group ability** (22.7B)
- **Increasing reactivity** (22.7B)
- **Increasing frequency of the C=O absorption in the IR** (22.5)

General Features of Nucleophilic Acyl Substitution

- The characteristic reaction of compounds having the general structure RCOZ is nucleophilic acyl substitution (22.1).
- The mechanism consists of two steps (22.7A):
  [1] Addition of a nucleophile to form a tetrahedral intermediate
  [2] Elimination of a leaving group
- More reactive acyl compounds can be used to prepare less reactive acyl compounds. The reverse is not necessarily true (22.7B).

Nucleophilic Acyl Substitution Reactions

[1] Reactions that produce acid chlorides (RCOCl)

From RCOOH (22.10A):

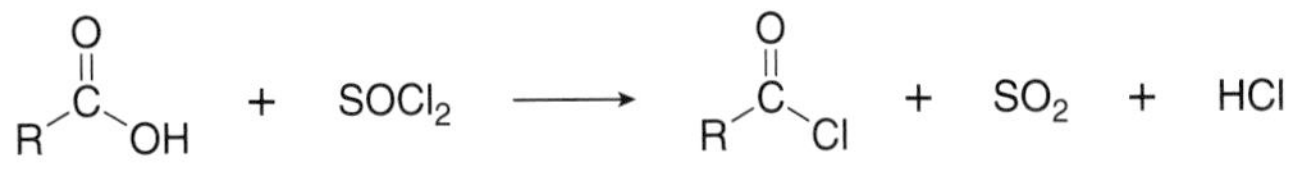
SOCl2
SO2
HCl

[2] Reactions that produce anhydrides [(RCO)$_2$O]

a. From RCOCl (22.8):

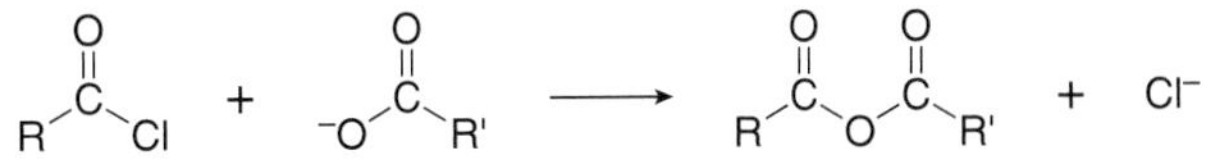
Cl⁻

b. From dicarboxylic acids (22.10B):

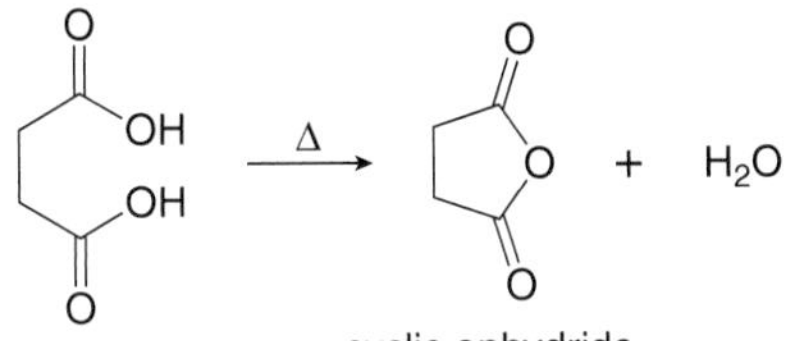
Δ
H2O

cyclic anhydride

[3] Reactions that produce carboxylic acids (RCOOH)

a. From RCOCl (22.8):

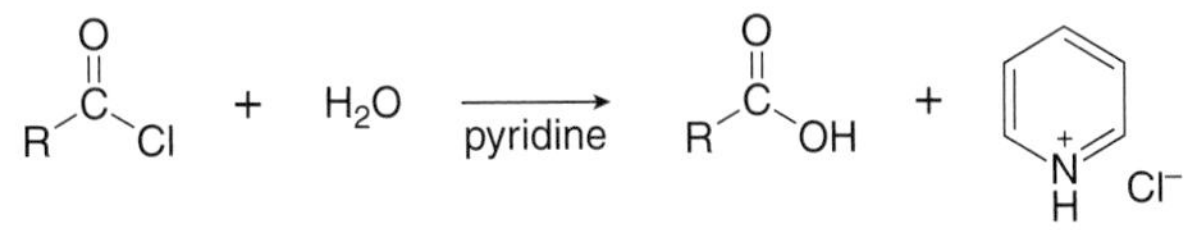
H2O
pyridine

b. From (RCO)$_2$O (22.9):

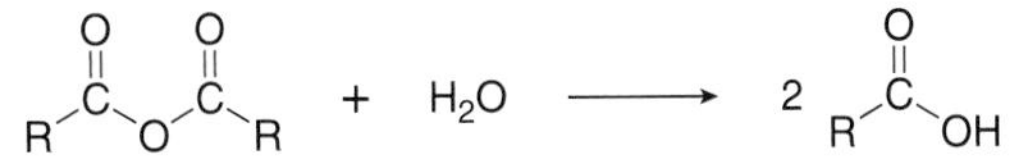
H2O

c. From RCOOR' (22.11):

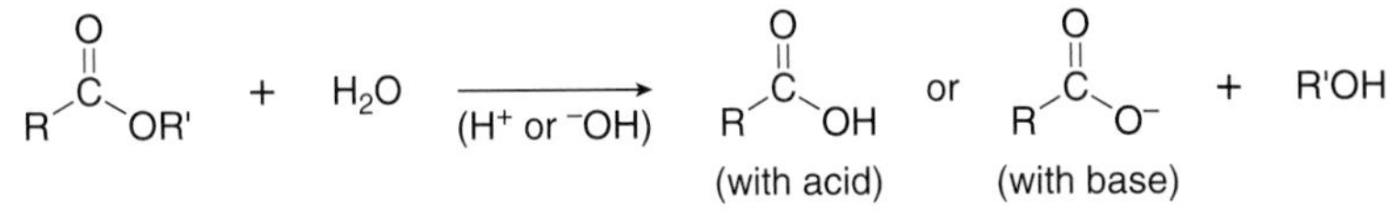
H2O
(H⁺ or ⁻OH)
or
R'OH
(with acid)
(with base)

d. From RCONR'$_2$ (R' = H or alkyl, 22.13):

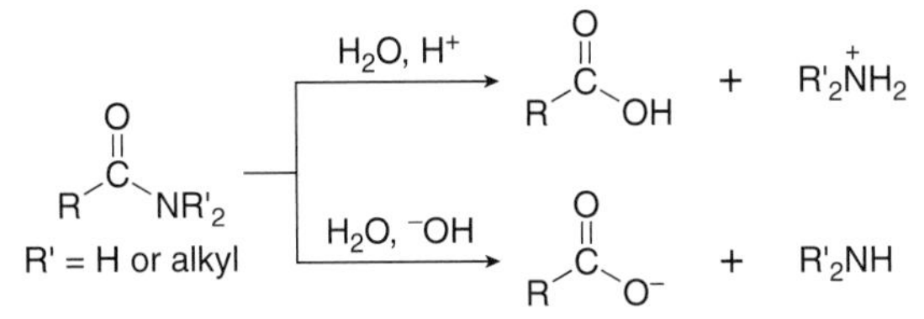
R' = H or alkyl
H2O, H⁺
H2O, ⁻OH
R'2NH2
R'2NH

[4] Reactions that produce esters (RCOOR')

a. From RCOCl (22.8):

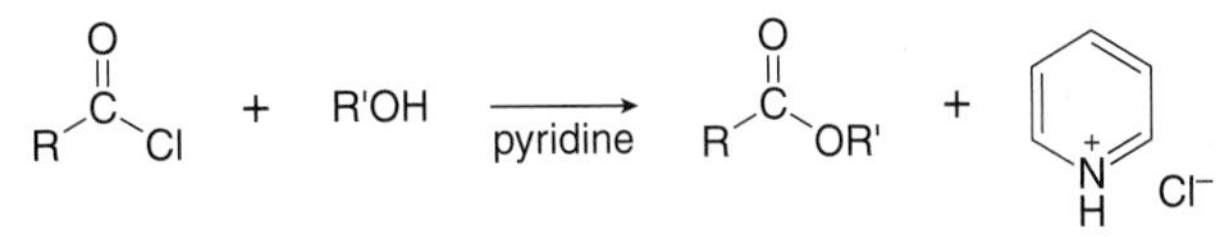
R'OH
pyridine

b. From (RCO)$_2$O (22.9):

R'OH
RCOOH

c. From RCOOH (22.10C):

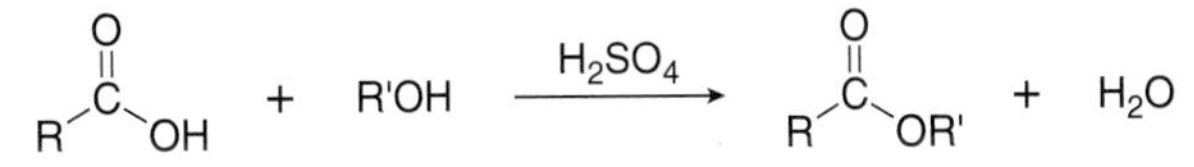
R'OH
H2SO4
H2O

[5] Reactions that produce amides ($RCONH_2$) [The reactions are written with NH_3 as nucleophile to form $RCONH_2$. Similar reactions occur with $R'NH_2$ to form RCONHR', and with R'_2NH to form $RCONR'_2$.]

a. From RCOCl (22.8):

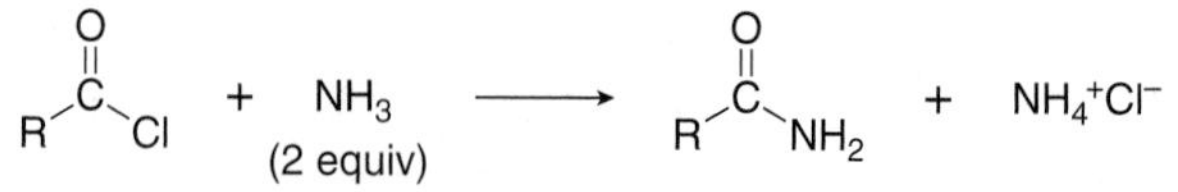

b. From $(RCO)_2O$ (22.9):

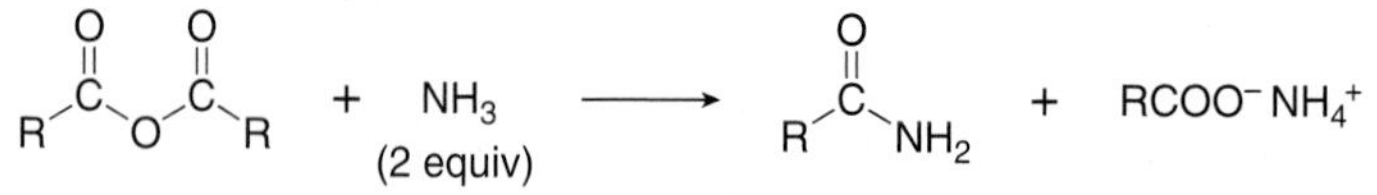

c. From RCOOH (22.10D):

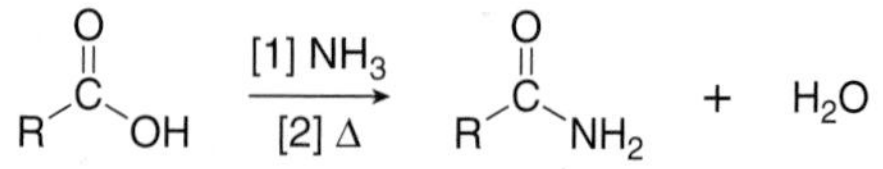

d. From RCOOR' (22.11):

Nitrile Synthesis (22.18)

Nitriles are prepared by S_N2 substitution using unhindered alkyl halides as starting materials.

$$\underset{R = CH_3,\ 1°}{R{-}X} + {}^{-}CN \xrightarrow[S_N2]{} R{-}C{\equiv}N + X^{-}$$

Reactions of Nitriles

[1] Hydrolysis (22.18A)

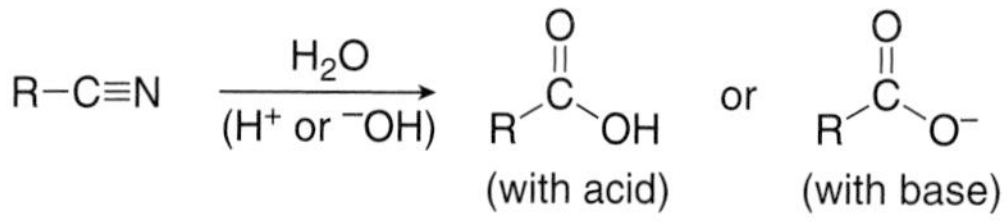

[2] Reduction (22.18B)

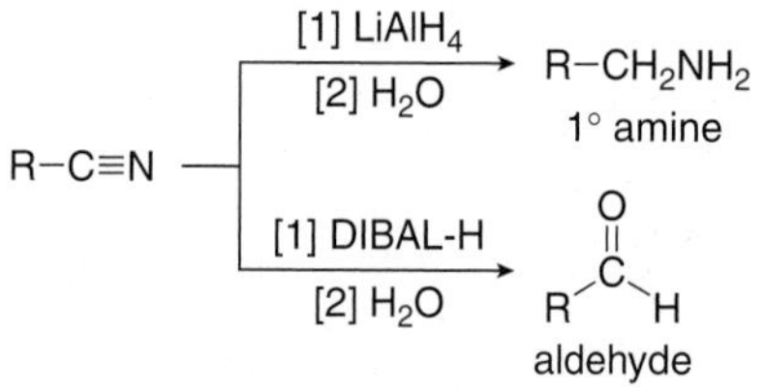

[3] Reaction with organometallic reagents (22.18C)

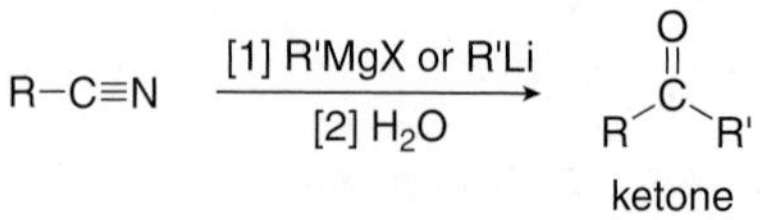

PROBLEMS

Problems Using Three-Dimensional Models

22.37 Rank the following compounds in order of increasing reactivity in nucleophilic acyl substitution.

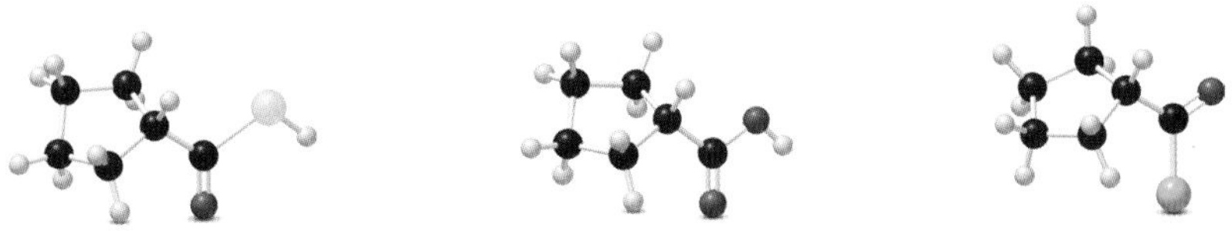

22.38 (a) Give an acceptable name for each compound. (b) Draw the organic products formed when **A** or **B** is treated with each reagent: [1] H_3O^+; [2] ^-OH, H_2O; [3] $CH_3CH_2CH_2MgBr$ (excess), then H_2O; [4] $LiAlH_4$, then H_2O.

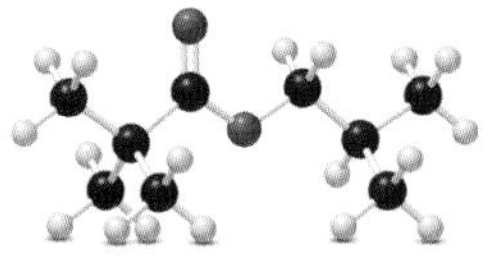

A

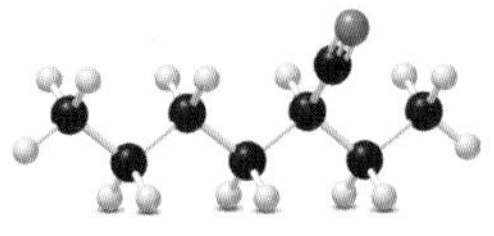

B

22.39 Which ester, **C** or **D,** is more reactive in nucleophilic acyl substitution? Explain your reasoning.

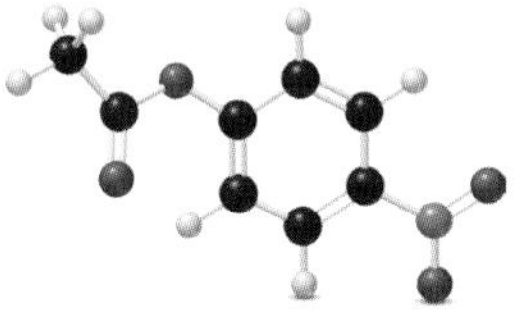

C

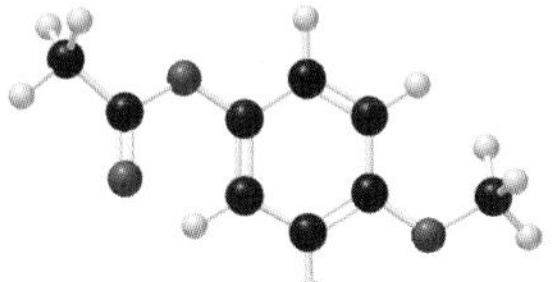

D

Nomenclature

22.40 Give the IUPAC or common name for each compound.

a. $(CH_3)_3CCOCl$

b. 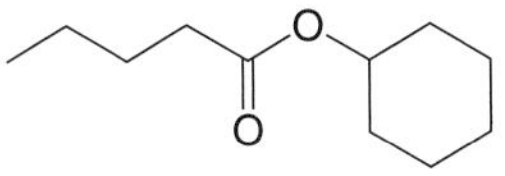

c. 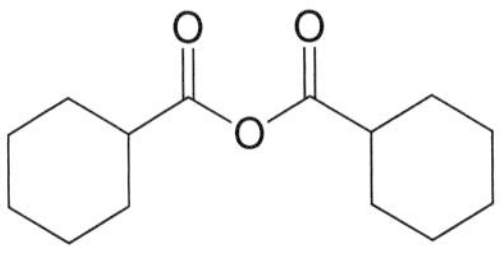

d. $C_6H_5CH_2COOC_6H_5$

e. 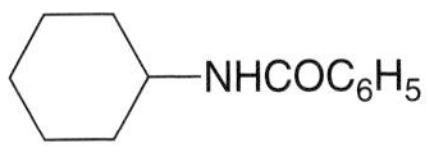

f. 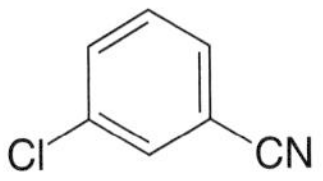

g. $C_6H_5CH_2CH_2COCl$

h. 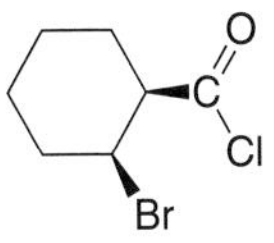

i. 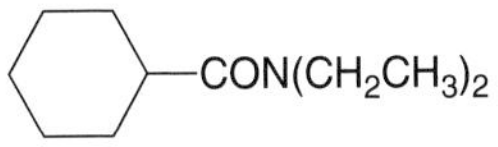

j. 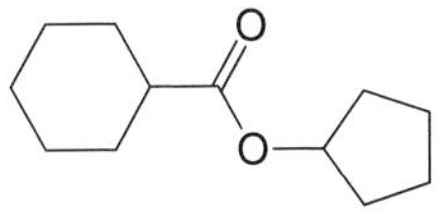

22.41 Give the structure corresponding to each name.

a. propanoic anhydride
b. α-chlorobutyryl chloride
c. cyclohexyl propanoate
d. cyclohexanecarboxamide
e. isopropyl formate
f. *N*-cyclopentylpentanamide
g. 4-methylheptanenitrile
h. vinyl acetate
i. benzoic propanoic anhydride
j. 3-methylhexanoyl chloride
k. octyl butanoate
l. *N,N*-dibenzylformamide

Properties of Carboxylic Acid Derivatives

22.42 Rank the compounds in each group in order of increasing reactivity in nucleophilic acyl substitution.

a. $CH_3CH_2CH_2CONH_2$, $CH_3CH_2CH_2COCl$, $CH_3CH_2CH_2COOCH_2CH_2CH_3$
b. $(CH_3CH_2CO)_2O$, $(CF_3CO)_2O$, $CH_3CH_2CO_2CH_2CH_2CH_3$

22.43 Explain why imidazolides are much more reactive than other amides in nucleophilic acyl substitution.

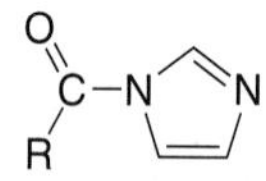

imidazolide

22.44 Explain why CH_3CONH_2 is a stronger acid and a weaker base than $CH_3CH_2NH_2$.

Reactions

22.45 Draw the product formed when pentanoyl chloride ($CH_3CH_2CH_2CH_2COCl$) is treated with each reagent.

a. H_2O, pyridine
b. CH_3CH_2OH, pyridine
c. CH_3COO^-
d. NH_3 (excess)
e. $(CH_3CH_2)_2NH$ (excess)
f. $C_6H_5NH_2$ (excess)

22.46 Draw the product formed when pentanoic anhydride [$(CH_3CH_2CH_2CH_2CO)_2O$] is treated with each reagent. With some reagents, no reaction occurs.

a. $SOCl_2$
b. H_2O
c. CH_3OH
d. NaCl
e. $(CH_3CH_2)_2NH$ (excess)
f. $CH_3CH_2NH_2$ (excess)

22.47 Draw the product formed when phenylacetic acid ($C_6H_5CH_2COOH$) is treated with each reagent. With some reagents, no reaction occurs.

a. $NaHCO_3$
b. NaOH
c. $SOCl_2$
d. NaCl
e. NH_3 (1 equiv)
f. NH_3, Δ
g. CH_3OH, H_2SO_4
h. CH_3OH, ^-OH
i. [1] NaOH; [2] CH_3COCl
j. CH_3NH_2, DCC
k. [1] $SOCl_2$; [2] $CH_3CH_2CH_2NH_2$ (excess)
l. [1] $SOCl_2$; [2] $(CH_3)_2CHOH$

22.48 Draw the product formed when ethyl butanoate ($CH_3CH_2CH_2COOCH_2CH_3$) is treated with each reagent. With some reagents, no reaction occurs.

a. $SOCl_2$ b. H_3O^+ c. H_2O, ^-OH d. NH_3 e. $CH_3CH_2NH_2$

22.49 Draw the product formed when phenylacetamide ($C_6H_5CH_2CONH_2$) is treated with each reagent.

a. H_3O^+ b. H_2O, ^-OH

22.50 Draw the product formed when phenylacetonitrile ($C_6H_5CH_2CN$) is treated with each reagent.

a. H_3O^+
b. H_2O, ^-OH
c. [1] CH_3MgBr; [2] H_2O
d. [1] CH_3CH_2Li; [2] H_2O
e. [1] DIBAL-H; [2] H_2O
f. [1] $LiAlH_4$; [2] H_2O

22.51 Draw the organic products formed in each reaction.

a. 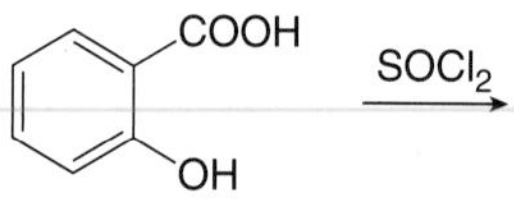

b. C_6H_5COCl + 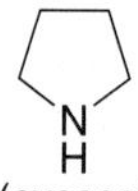 ⟶

(excess)

c. $C_6H_5CN \xrightarrow[\text{[2] } H_2O]{\text{[1] } CH_3CH_2CH_2MgBr}$

d. $(CH_3)_2CHCOOH + CH_3CH_2CH(CH_3)OH \xrightarrow{H_2SO_4}$

e. 

f. 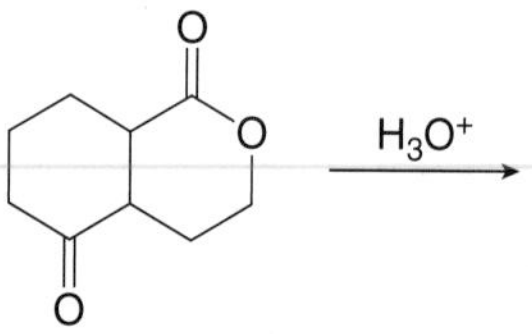

g. $CH_3CH_2CH_2CH_2Br \xrightarrow[\text{[2] } H_2O,\ ^-OH]{\text{[1] NaCN}}$

h. $C_6H_5CH_2COOH$ → [1] $SOCl_2$; [2] $CH_3CH_2CH_2CH_2NH_2$; [3] $LiAlH_4$; [4] H_2O

i. 

j. $(CH_3CO)_2O$ + 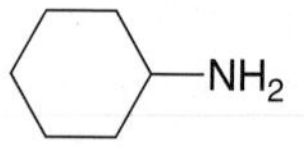 ⟶

(excess)

22.52 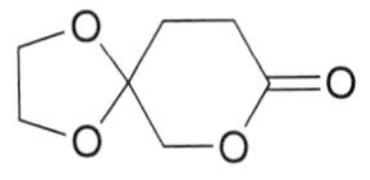

X

What products are formed when **X,** which contains both a lactone and an acetal, is treated with each reagent: (a) H_3O^+; (b) NaOH, H_2O?

22.53 Identify compounds **A–M** in the following reaction sequence.

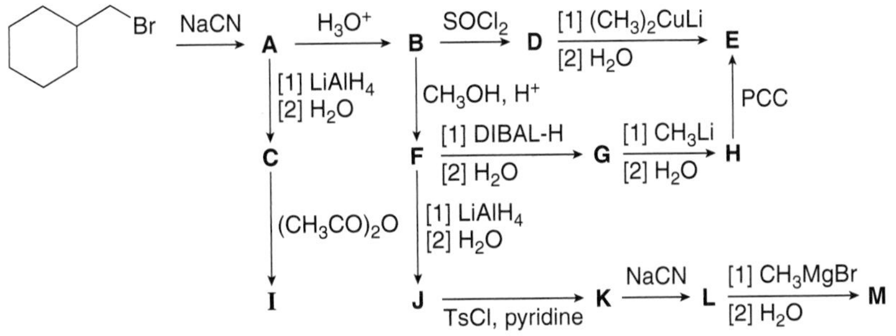

22.54 Draw the products of each reaction and indicate the stereochemistry at any stereogenic centers.

a. 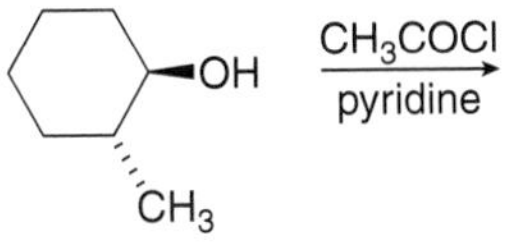

c. 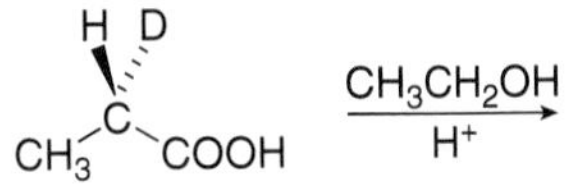

b. 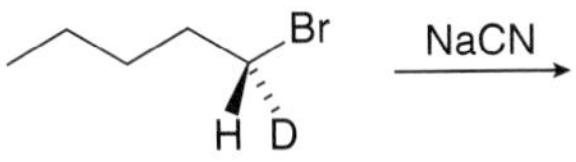

d. 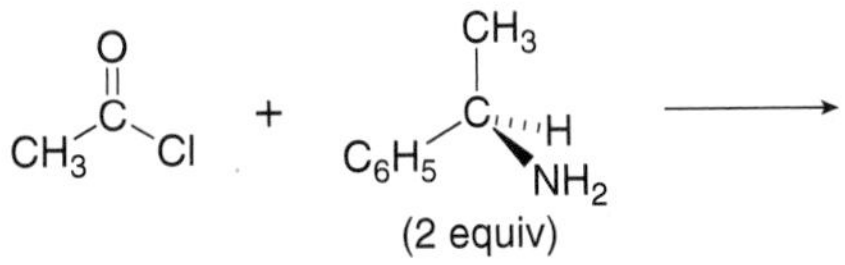

22.55 What products are formed when all of the amide and ester bonds are hydrolyzed in each of the following compounds? **Tamiflu** [part (a)] is the trade name of the antiviral agent oseltamivir, thought to be the most effective agent in treating influenza. Governments are stockpiling the drug in the event of an influenza pandemic. **Aspartame** [part (b)] is the artificial sweetener used in Equal and many diet beverages. One of the products of this hydrolysis reaction is the amino acid phenylalanine. Infants afflicted with phenylketonuria cannot metabolize this amino acid, so it accumulates, causing mental retardation. When the affliction is identified early, a diet limiting the consumption of phenylalanine (and compounds like aspartame that are converted to it) can make a normal life possible.

a. 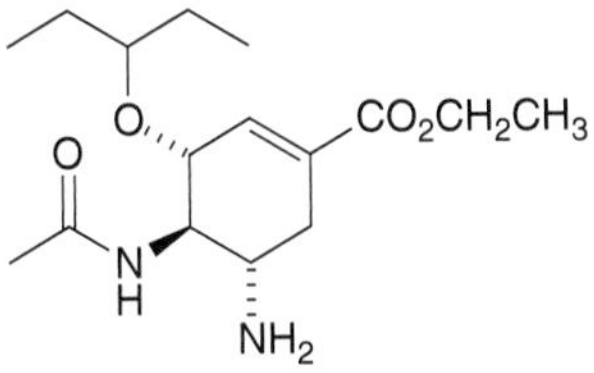

oseltamivir

b. 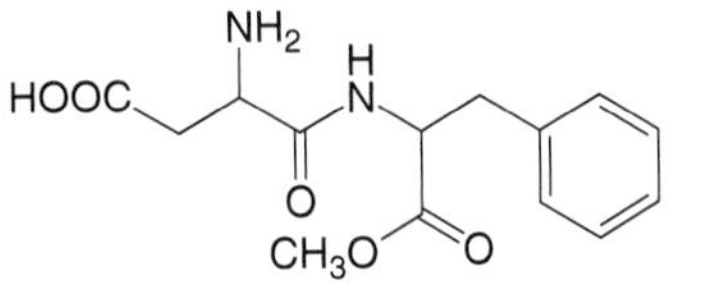

aspartame

22.56 Identify **F** in the following reaction sequence. **F** was converted in several steps to the antidepressant paroxetine (trade name Paxil; see also Problem 9.11).

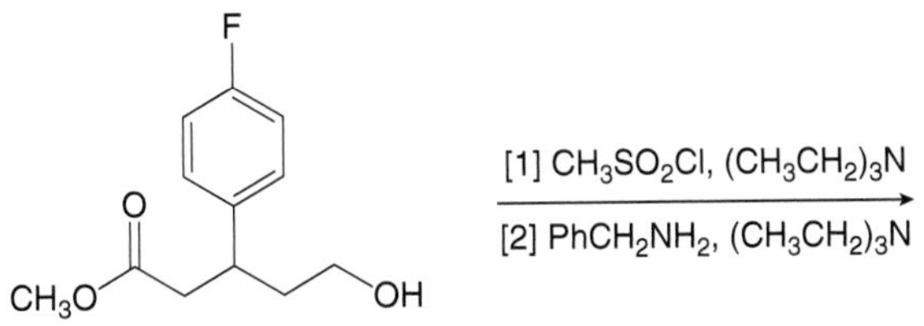

F

$C_{18}H_{18}FNO$

Mechanism

22.57 Draw a stepwise mechanism for each reaction.

a. 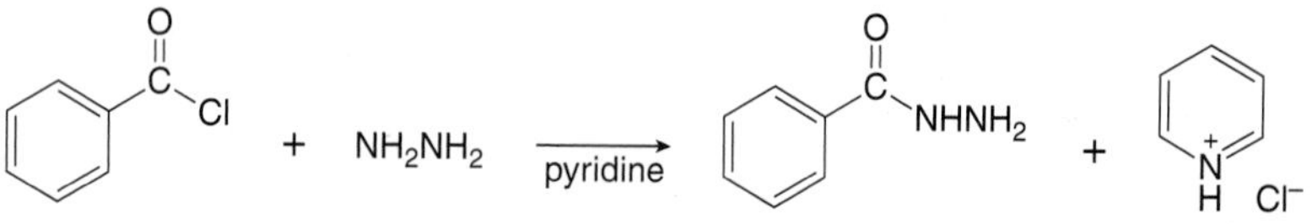

b. 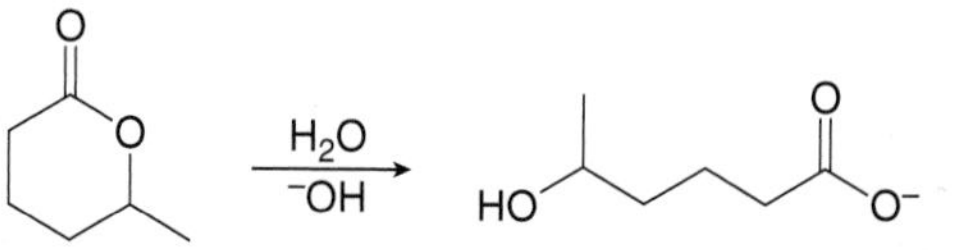

22.58 When acetic acid (CH_3COOH) is treated with a trace of acid in water labeled with ^{18}O, the label gradually appears in both oxygen atoms of the carboxylic acid. Draw a mechanism that explains this phenomenon.

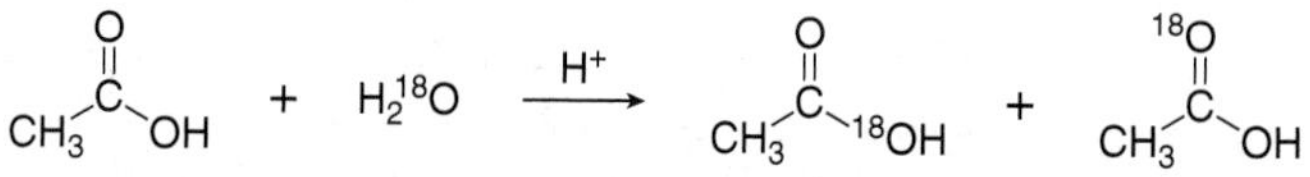

22.59 Although γ-butyrolactone (Problem 19.62) is a biologically inactive compound, it is converted in the body to 4-hydroxybutanoic acid (GHB), an addictive and intoxicating recreational drug (Section 19.5). Draw a stepwise mechanism for this conversion in the presence of acid.

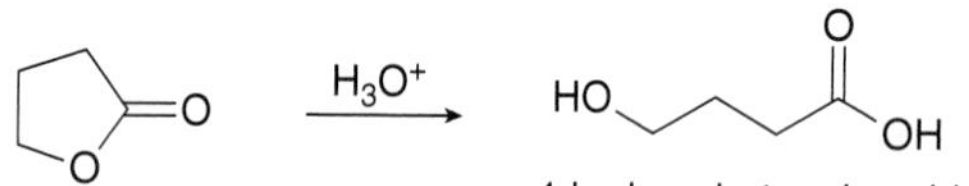

γ-butyrolactone

4-hydroxybutanoic acid
GHB

22.60 Aspirin is an anti-inflammatory agent because it inhibits the conversion of arachidonic acid to prostaglandins by the transfer of its acetyl group (CH_3CO-) to an OH group at the active site of an enzyme (Section 19.6). This reaction, called transesterification, results in the conversion of one ester to another by a nucleophilic acyl substitution reaction. Draw a stepwise mechanism for the given transesterification.

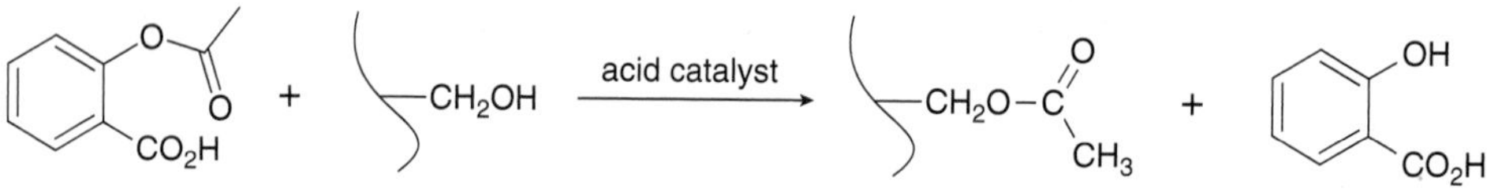

aspirin — enzyme — inactive enzyme — salicylic acid

22.61 Draw a stepwise mechanism for the following reaction, one step in the synthesis of the cholesterol-lowering drug ezetimibe (Section 20.6).

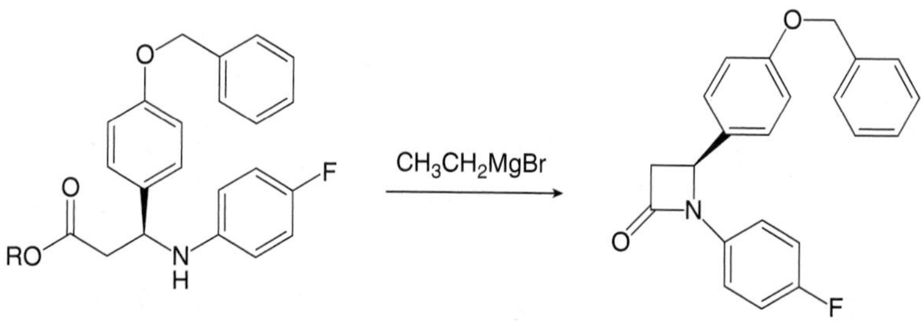

22.62 Draw a stepwise mechanism for the conversion of lactone **C** to carboxylic acid **D.** **C** is a key intermediate in the synthesis of prostaglandins (Section 19.6) by Nobel Laureate E. J. Corey and co-workers at Harvard University.

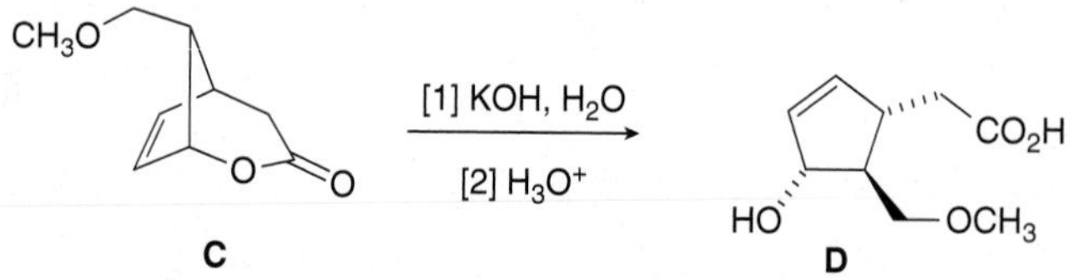

C **D**

22.63 Draw a stepwise mechanism for the conversion of lactone **A** to ester **B** using HCl in ethanol. **B** is converted in one step to ethyl chrysanthemate, a useful intermediate in the synthesis of a variety of pyrethrins, naturally occurring insecticides with three-membered rings that are isolated from chrysanthemums (Section 26.4).

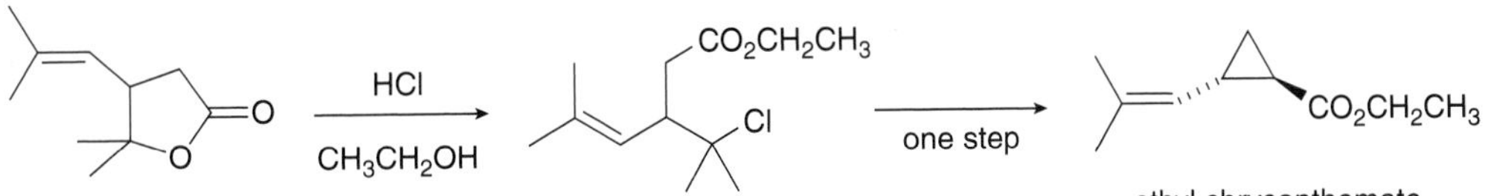

A **B** ethyl chrysanthemate

22.64 Draw a stepwise mechanism for the following reaction.

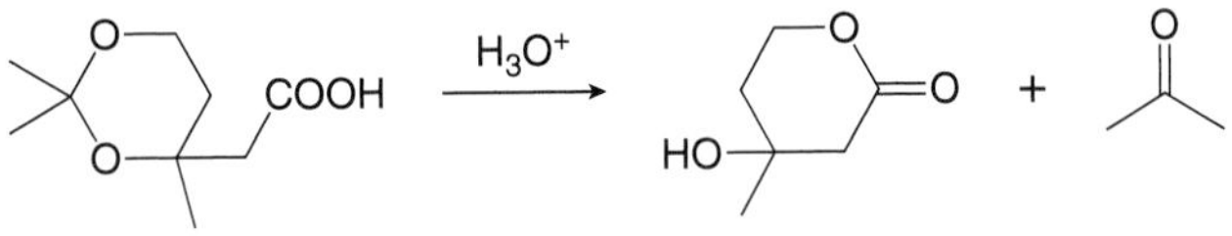

22.65 Acid-catalyzed hydrolysis of $HOCH_2CH_2C(CH_3)_2CN$ forms compound **A** ($C_6H_{10}O_2$). **A** shows a strong peak in its IR spectrum at 1770 cm^{-1} and the following signals in its ^{1}H NMR spectrum: 1.27 (singlet, 6 H), 2.12 (triplet, 2 H), and 4.26 (triplet, 2 H) ppm. Draw the structure for **A** and give a stepwise mechanism that accounts for its formation.

Synthesis

22.66 What carboxylic acid and alcohol are needed to prepare each ester by Fischer esterification?

a. $(CH_3)_3CCO_2CH_2CH_3$

b. 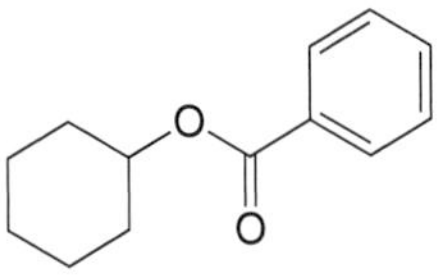

c. 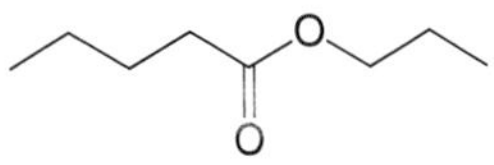

d. 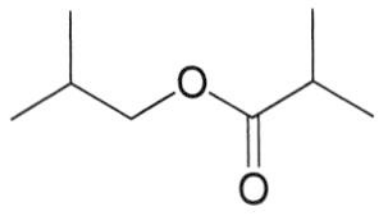

22.67 Devise a synthesis of each compound using 1-bromobutane ($CH_3CH_2CH_2CH_2Br$) as the only organic starting material. You may use any other inorganic reagents.

a. 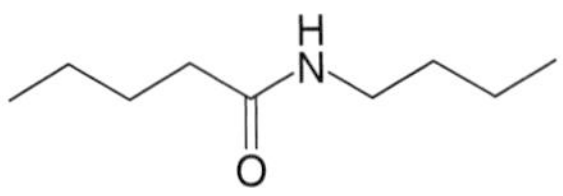

b. 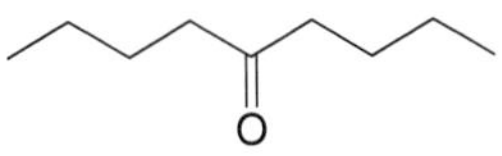

c. 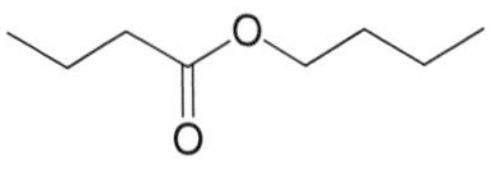

d. 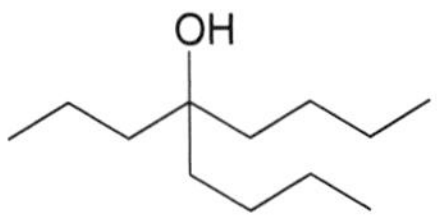

22.68 Convert 1-bromohexane ($CH_3CH_2CH_2CH_2CH_2CH_2Br$) into each compound. More than one step is required. You may use any other organic or inorganic reagents.

a. $CH_3CH_2CH_2CH_2CH_2CH_2COCl$
b. $CH_3CH_2CH_2CH_2CH_2CH_2CO_2CH_2CH_3$
c. $CH_3CH_2CH_2CH_2CH_2CH_2COCH_3$
d. $CH_3CH_2CH_2CH_2CH_2CH_2CH_2NHCOCH_3$

22.69 Two methods convert an alkyl halide into a carboxylic acid having one more carbon atom.

[1] R–X + $^-$CN ⟶ R–CN + X$^-$ $\xrightarrow{H_3O^+}$ R–COOH (Section 22.18)

new C–C bond

[2] R–X + Mg ⟶ R–MgX $\xrightarrow[\text{[2] } H_3O^+]{\text{[1] } CO_2}$ R–COOH (Section 20.14)

Depending on the structure of the alkyl halide, one or both of these methods may be employed. For each alkyl halide, write out a stepwise sequence that converts it to a carboxylic acid with one more carbon atom. If both methods work, draw both routes. If one method cannot be used, state why it can't.

a. CH_3Cl

b. 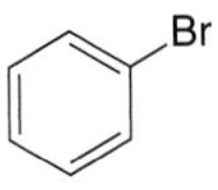

c. $(CH_3)_3CCl$

d. $HOCH_2CH_2CH_2CH_2Br$

22.70 Devise a synthesis of benzocaine, ethyl *p*-aminobenzoate ($H_2NC_6H_4CO_2CH_2CH_3$), from benzene, organic alcohols, and any needed organic or inorganic reagents. Benzocaine is the active ingredient in the topical anesthetic Orajel (Section 18.15C).

22.71 Devise a synthesis of melatonin, the mammalian hormone involved in regulating the sleep–wake cycle, from the neurotransmitter serotonin, alcohols, and any needed organic and inorganic reagents.

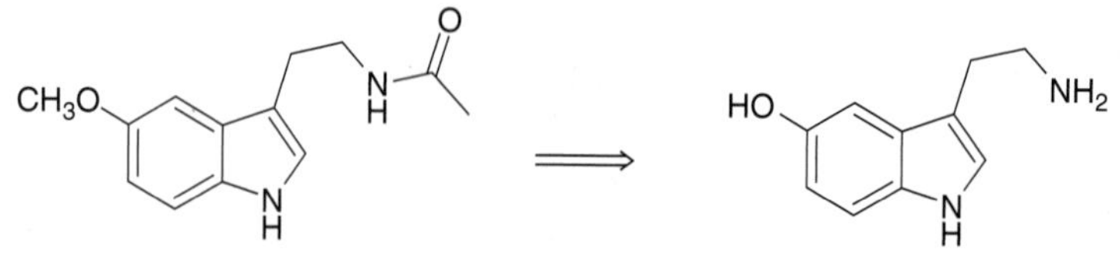

melatonin serotonin

22.72 Devise a synthesis of each analgesic compound from phenol (C_6H_5OH) and any other organic or inorganic reagents.

a. 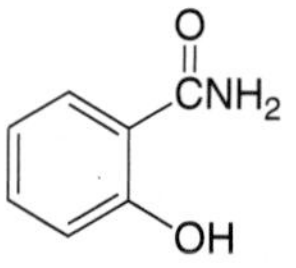
salicylamide

b. 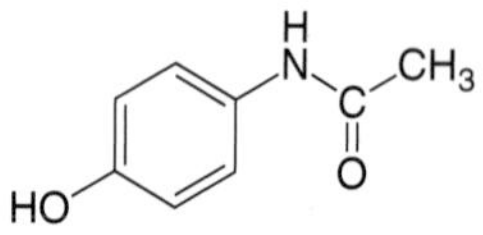
acetaminophen

c. 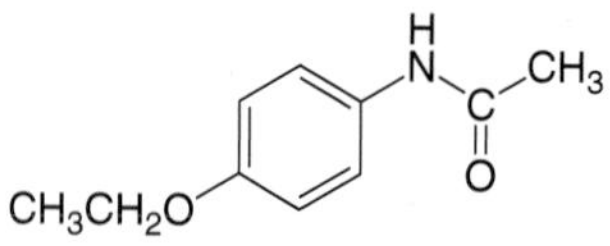
p-acetophenetidin

22.73 Devise a synthesis of each compound from benzene and organic alcohols containing four or fewer carbons. You may also use any required organic or inorganic reagents.

a. 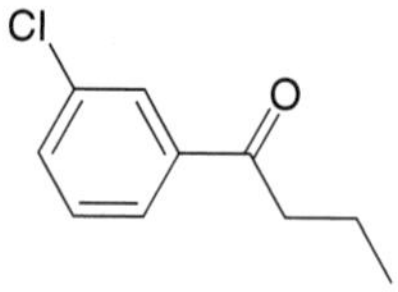

b. 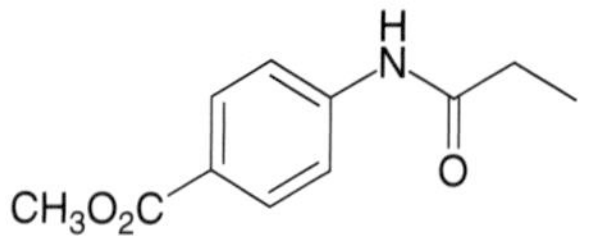

c. 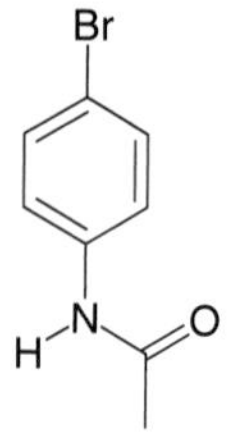

d. 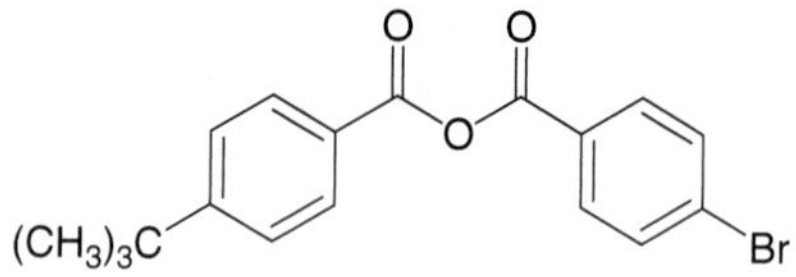

22.74 Devise a synthesis of each ester from benzene, organic alcohols, and any other needed inorganic reagents.

a. 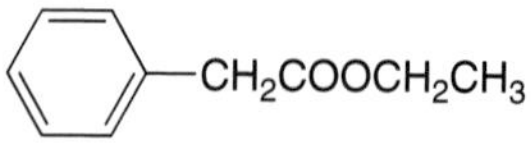
ethyl phenylacetate
(odor of honey)

b. 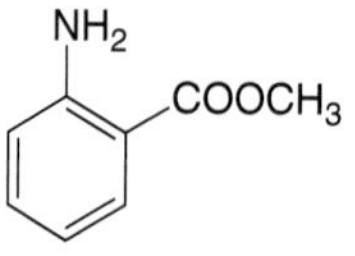
methyl anthranilate
(odor of grape)

c. 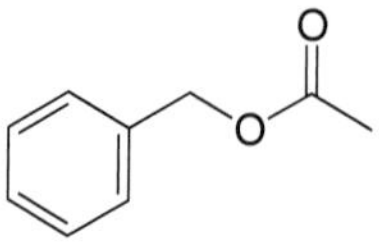
benzyl acetate
(odor of peach)

22.75 Devise a synthesis of each labeled compound using $H_2{}^{18}O$ and $CH_3{}^{13}CH_2OH$ as the only sources of labeled starting materials. You may use any other unlabeled organic compounds and inorganic reagents.

a. 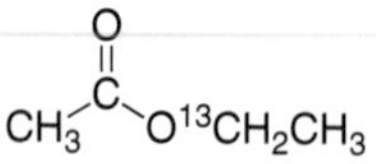

b. 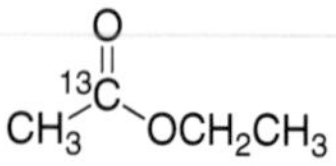

c. 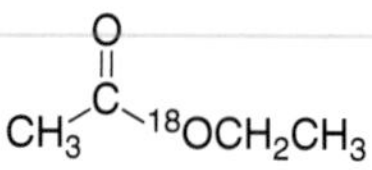

d. 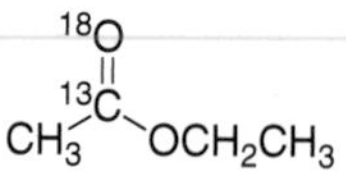

Polymers

22.76 What polyester or polyamide can be prepared from each pair of monomers?

a. 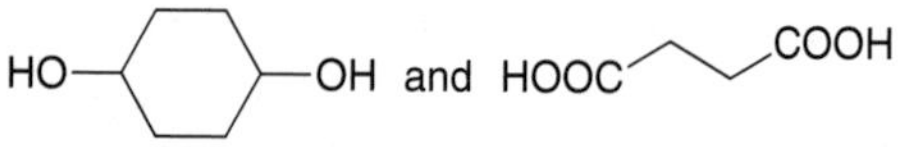

b. 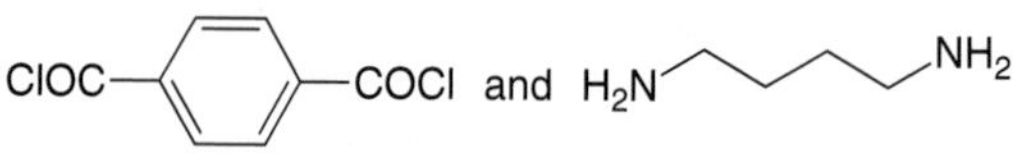

22.77 What two monomers are needed to prepare each polymer?

a. 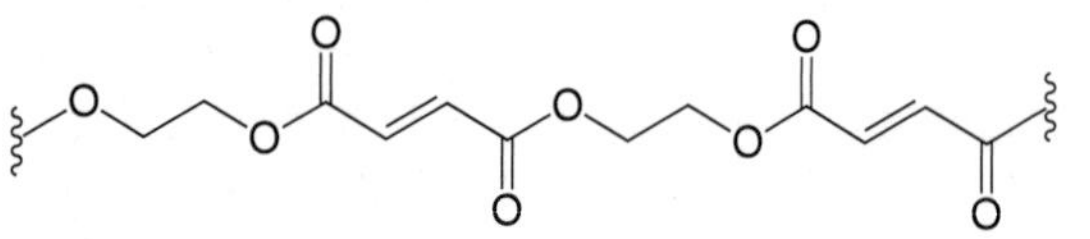

b. 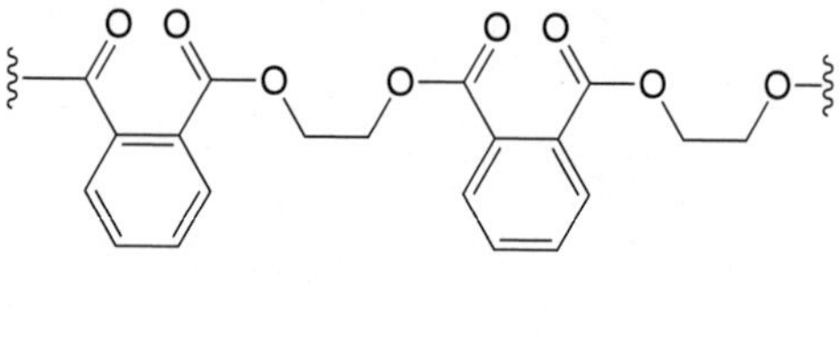

General Problem

22.78 Taxotere is the trade name for the synthetic anticancer drug docetaxel, whose structure closely resembles the naturally occurring compound taxol, which is isolated from the Pacific yew tree (Section 5.5).

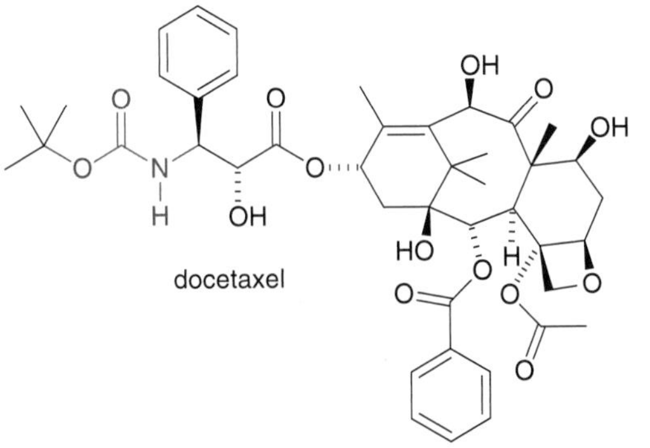

docetaxel

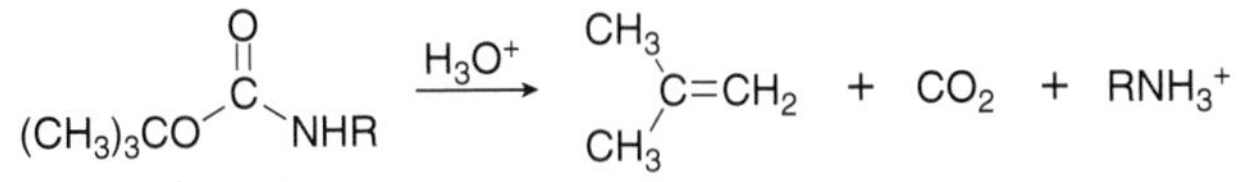

carbamate

a. Taxol's limited water solubility led to an extensive search for related compounds with increased water solubility. What structural features give docetaxel a better water solubility profile?

b. Docetaxel contains a carbamate (labeled in red), a functional group with a carbonyl group bonded to a nitrogen and oxygen atom. Draw three more resonance structures for a carbamate (in addition to the Lewis structure with all neutral atoms given). Rank all four resonance structures in order of increasing stability.

c. A carbamate with a *tert*-butoxy group [$(CH_3)_3CO-$] is hydrolyzed according to the given equation. Draw a stepwise mechanism for the hydrolysis of a carbamate to the three products shown.

d. Assuming that all ester and carbamate bonds are cleaved, draw all products formed when docetaxel is hydrolyzed with aqueous acid.

Spectroscopy

22.79 How can IR spectroscopy be used to distinguish between each pair of isomers?

a. 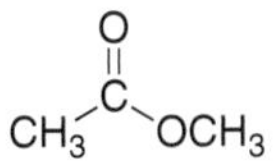 and 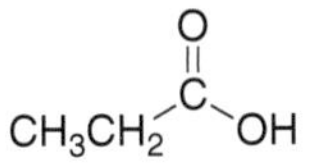

c. 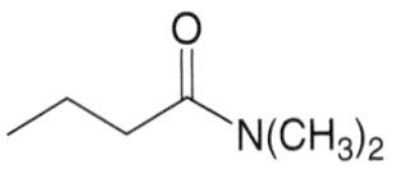 and 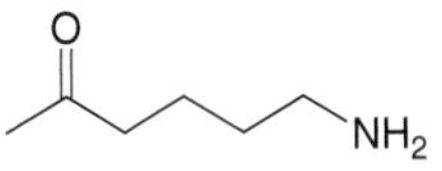

b. 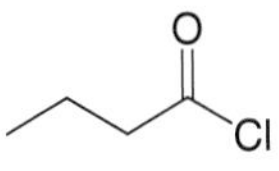 and 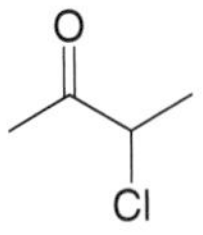

d. 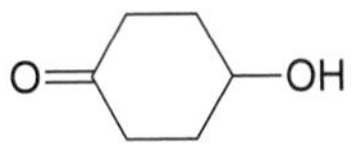 and 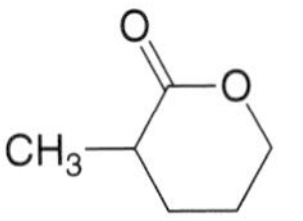

22.80 Rank the compounds in each group in order of increasing frequency of the C=O absorption in their IR spectra.

a. 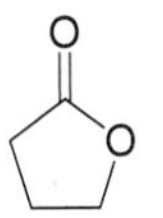 $CH_3CH_2COOCH_2CH_3$ $C_6H_5COOCH_2CH_3$

b. CH_3COCl CH_3CONH_2 CH_3COOCH_3

22.81 Identify the structures of each compound from the given data.

a. Molecular formula: $C_6H_{12}O_2$
IR absorption: 1738 cm^{-1}
^1H NMR: 1.12 (triplet, 3 H), 1.23 (doublet, 6 H), 2.28 (quartet, 2 H), and 5.00 (septet, 1 H) ppm

b. Molecular formula: C_4H_7N
IR absorption: 2250 cm^{-1}
^1H NMR: 1.08 (triplet, 3 H), 1.70 (multiplet, 2 H), and 2.34 (triplet, 2 H) ppm

c. Molecular formula: C_8H_9NO
IR absorptions: 3328 and 1639 cm^{-1}
^1H NMR: 2.95 (singlet, 3 H), 6.95 (singlet, 1 H), and 7.3–7.7 (multiplet, 5 H) ppm

d. Molecular formula C_4H_7ClO
IR absorption: $1802\ cm^{-1}$
^1H NMR: 0.95 (triplet, 3 H), 1.07 (multiplet, 2 H), and 2.90 (triplet, 2 H) ppm

e. Molecular formula $C_5H_{10}O_2$
IR absorption: $1750\ cm^{-1}$
^1H NMR: 1.20 (doublet, 6 H), 2.00 (singlet, 3 H), and 4.95 (septet, 1 H) ppm

f. Molecular formula $C_{10}H_{12}O_2$
IR absorption: $1740\ cm^{-1}$
^1H NMR: 1.2 (triplet, 3 H), 2.4 (quartet, 2 H), 5.1 (singlet, 2 H), and 7.1–7.5 (multiplet, 5 H) ppm

g. Molecular formula $C_8H_{14}O_3$
IR absorptions: 1810 and $1770\ cm^{-1}$
^1H NMR: 1.25 (doublet, 12 H) and 2.65 (septet, 2 H) ppm

22.82 Identify the structures of **A** and **B,** isomers of molecular formula $C_{10}H_{12}O_2$, from their IR data and ^1H NMR spectra.

a. IR absorption for **A** at $1718\ cm^{-1}$

b. IR absorption for **B** at $1740\ cm^{-1}$

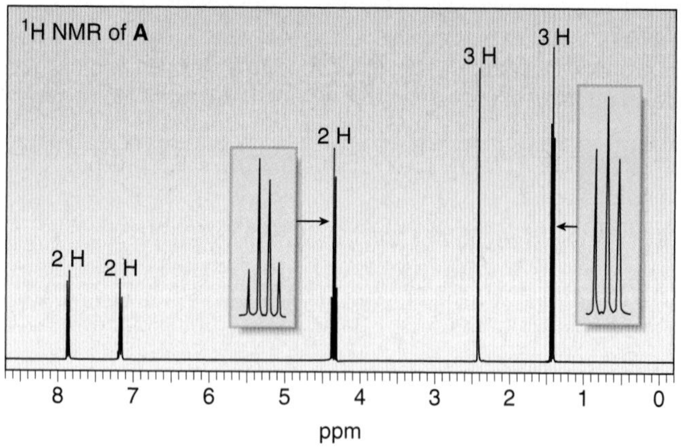

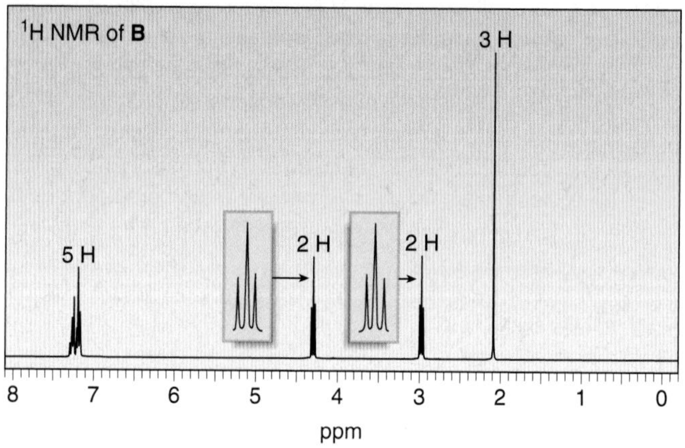

22.83 Phenacetin is an analgesic compound having molecular formula $C_{10}H_{13}NO_2$. Once a common component in over-the-counter pain relievers such as APC (**a**spirin, **p**henacetin, **c**affeine), phenacetin is no longer used because of its liver toxicity. Deduce the structure of phenacetin from its ^1H NMR and IR spectra.

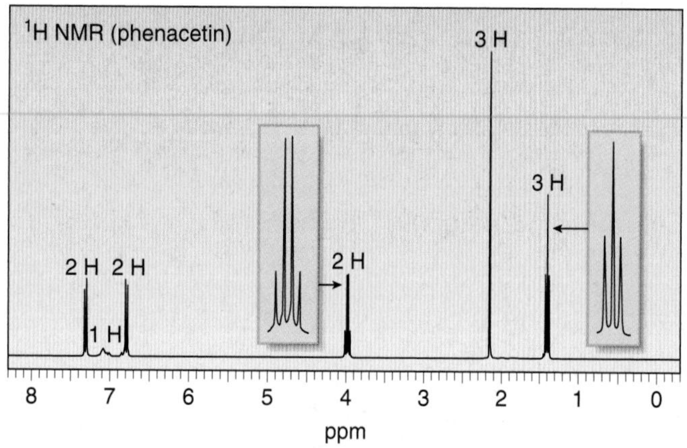

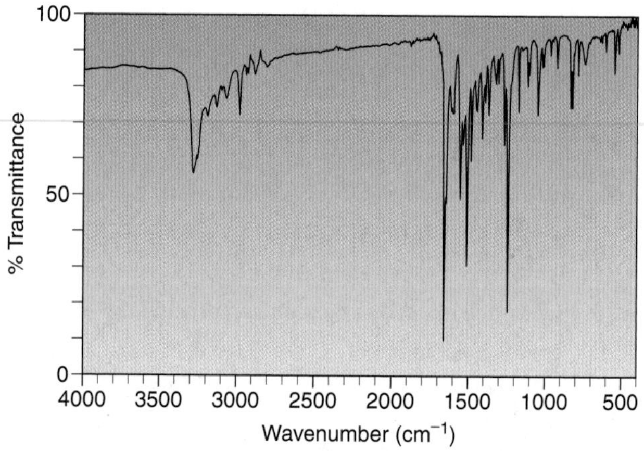

22.84 Identify the structure of compound **C** (molecular formula $C_{11}H_{15}NO_2$), which has an IR absorption at 1699 cm^{-1} and the ^1H NMR spectrum shown below.

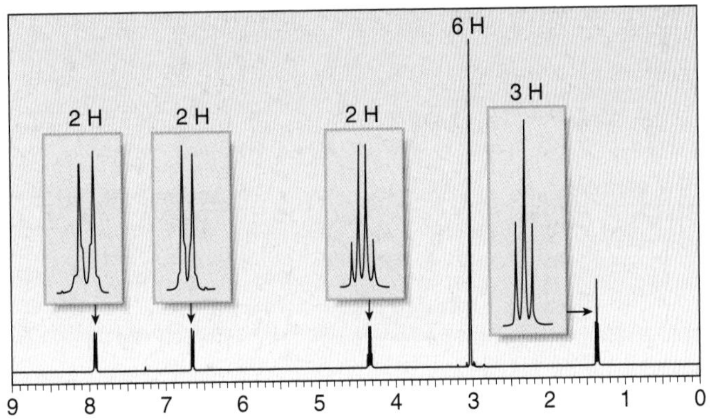

22.85 Identify the structures of **D** and **E,** isomers of molecular formula $C_6H_{12}O_2$, from their IR and ^1H NMR data. Signals at 1.35 and 1.60 ppm in the ^1H NMR spectrum of **D** and 1.90 ppm in the ^1H NMR spectrum of **E** are multiplets.

a. IR absorption for **D** at 1743 cm^{-1}

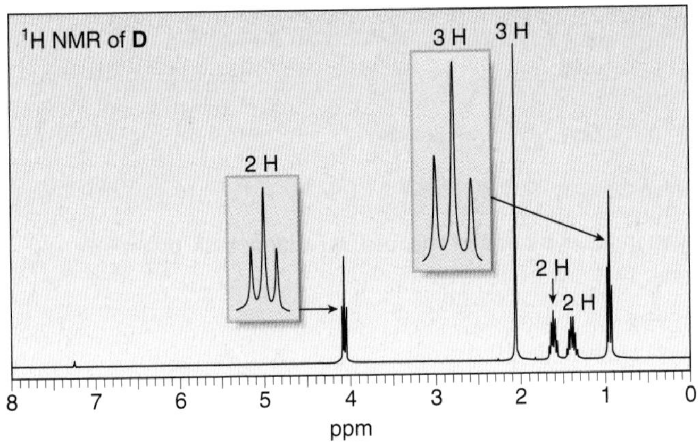

b. IR absorption for **E** at 1746 cm^{-1}

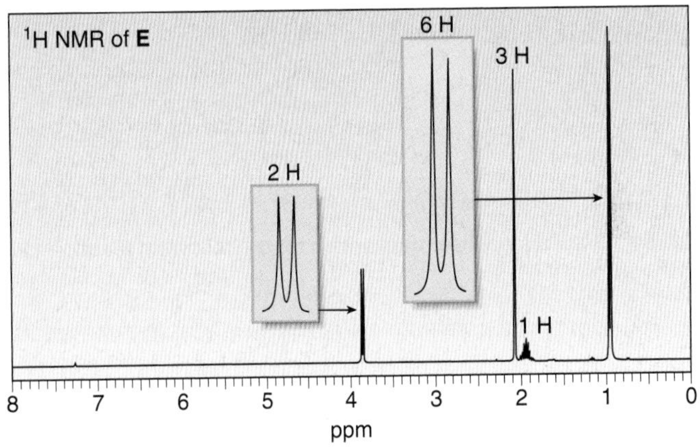

Challenge Problems

22.86 With reference to amides **A** and **B,** the carbonyl of one amide absorbs at a much higher wavenumber in its IR spectrum than the carbonyl of the other amide. Which absorbs at higher wavenumber and why?

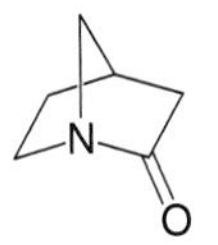

A

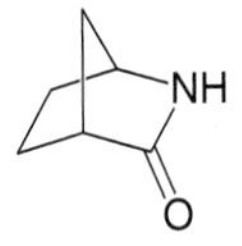

B

22.87 The ^1H NMR spectrum of 2-chloroacetamide ($ClCH_2CONH_2$) shows three signals at 4.02, 7.35, and 7.60 ppm. What protons give rise to each signal? Explain why three signals are observed.

22.88 Compelling evidence for the existence of a tetrahedral intermediate in nucleophilic acyl substitution was obtained in a series of elegant experiments carried out by Myron Bender in 1951. The key experiment was the reaction of aqueous ^-OH with ethyl benzoate ($C_6H_5COOCH_2CH_3$) labeled at the carbonyl oxygen with ^{18}O. Bender did not allow the hydrolysis to go to completion, and then examined the presence of a label in the *recovered starting material.* He found that some of the recovered ethyl benzoate no longer contained a label at the carbonyl oxygen. With reference to the accepted mechanism of nucleophilic acyl substitution, explain how this provides evidence for a tetrahedral intermediate.

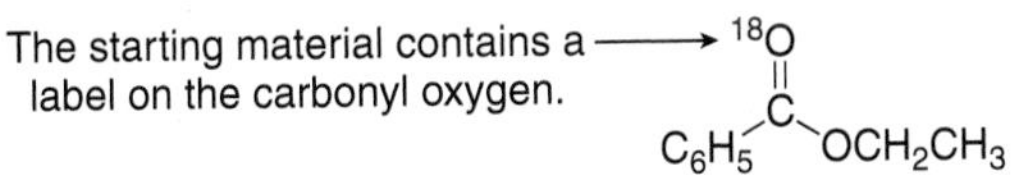

ethyl benzoate

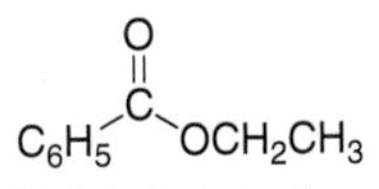

Unlabeled starting material was recovered.

22.89 Draw a stepwise mechanism for the following reactions, two steps in R. B. Woodward's classic synthesis of reserpine in 1958. Reserpine, which is isolated from the extracts of the Indian snakeroot *Rauwolfia serpentina Benth,* was used at one time to manage mild hypertension associated with anxiety.

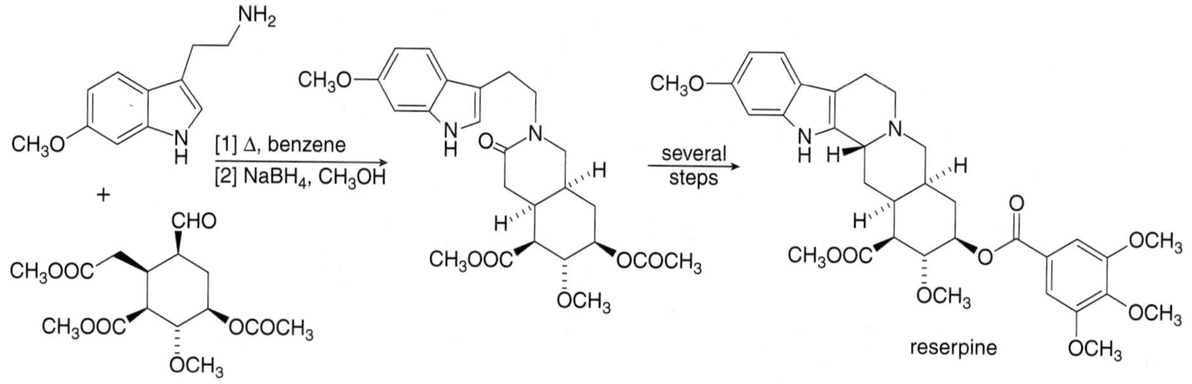

22.90 Draw a stepwise mechanism for the following reaction, the last step in a five-step industrial synthesis of vitamin C that begins with the simple carbohydrate glucose.

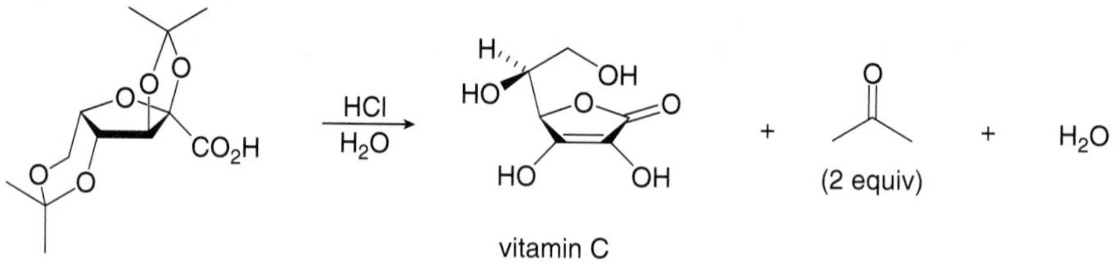

vitamin C

22.91 Draw a stepwise mechanism for the following reaction, a key step in the synthesis of linezolid, an antibacterial agent.

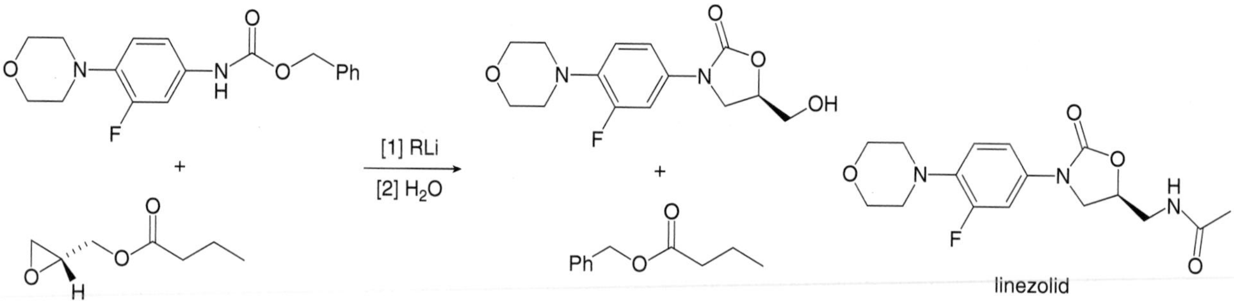

linezolid

Substitution Reactions of Carbonyl Compounds at the α Carbon

23

23.1 Introduction
23.2 Enols
23.3 Enolates
23.4 Enolates of unsymmetrical carbonyl compounds
23.5 Racemization at the α carbon
23.6 A preview of reactions at the α carbon
23.7 Halogenation at the α carbon
23.8 Direct enolate alkylation
23.9 Malonic ester synthesis
23.10 Acetoacetic ester synthesis

Tamoxifen is a potent anticancer drug used widely in the treatment of breast cancer. Tamoxifen binds to estrogen receptors, and in this way inhibits the growth of breast cancers that are estrogen dependent. One method to synthesize tamoxifen forms a new carbon–carbon bond on the α carbon to a carbonyl group using an intermediate enolate. In Chapter 23 we learn about these and other carbon–carbon bond-forming reactions that occur at the α carbon.

Chapters 23 and 24 focus on reactions that occur at the α carbon to a carbonyl group. These reactions are different from the reactions of Chapters 20–22, all of which involved nucleophilic attack at the electrophilic carbonyl carbon. In reactions at the α carbon, the carbonyl compound serves as a *nucleophile* that reacts with a carbon or halogen electrophile to form a new bond to the α carbon.

Chapter 23 concentrates on **substitution reactions at the α carbon,** whereas Chapter 24 concentrates on reactions between two carbonyl compounds, one of which serves as the nucleophile and one of which is the electrophile. Many of the reactions in Chapter 23 form new carbon–carbon bonds, thus adding to your repertoire of reactions that can be used to synthesize more complex organic molecules from simple precursors. As you will see, the reactions introduced in Chapter 23 have been used to prepare a wide variety of interesting and useful compounds.

23.1 Introduction

Up to now, the discussion of carbonyl compounds has centered on their reactions with nucleophiles at the electrophilic carbonyl carbon. **Two general reactions are observed,** depending on the structure of the carbonyl starting material.

- ***Nucleophilic addition*** **occurs when there is no electronegative atom Z on the carbonyl carbon (as with aldehydes and ketones).**

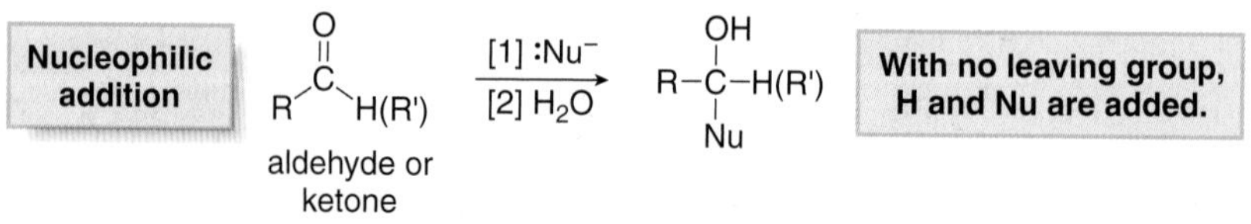

- ***Nucleophilic acyl substitution*** **occurs when there is an electronegative atom Z on the carbonyl carbon (as with carboxylic acids and their derivatives).**

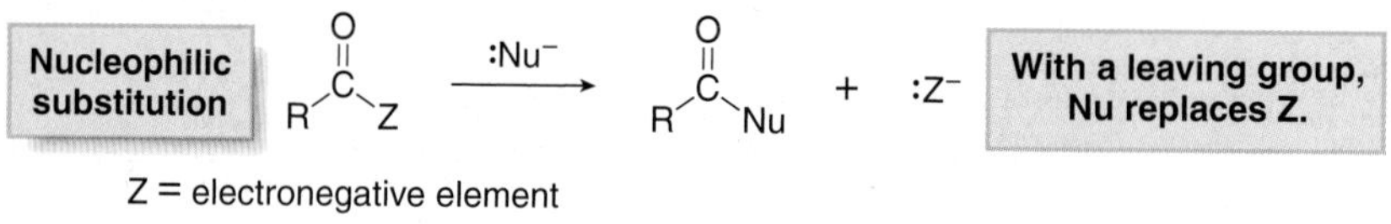

Reactions can also occur at the α carbon to the carbonyl group. These reactions proceed by way of **enols** or **enolates,** two electron-rich intermediates that react with electrophiles, forming a new bond on the α carbon. This reaction results in the **substitution of the electrophile E for hydrogen.**

Hydrogen atoms on the α carbon are called α **hydrogens.**

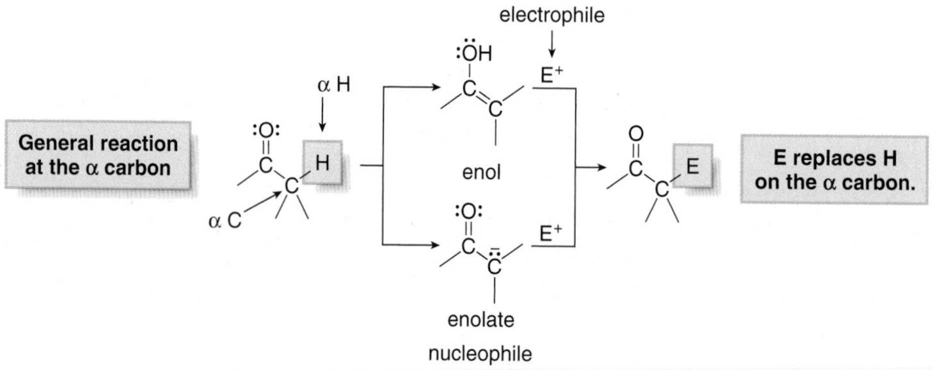

23.2 Enols

Recall from Chapter 11 that **enol and keto forms are tautomers of the carbonyl group that differ in the position of a double bond and a proton.** These constitutional isomers are in equilibrium with each other.

Two tautomers of a carbonyl group

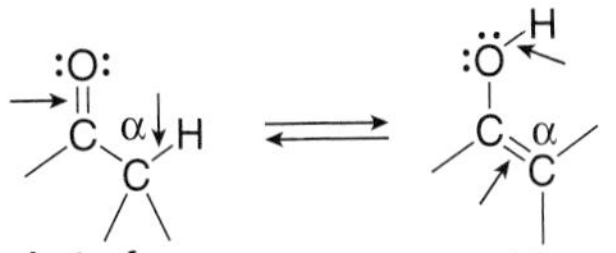

keto form enol form

- **A keto tautomer has a C=O and an additional C–H bond.**
- **An enol tautomer has an O–H group bonded to a C=C.**

Equilibrium favors the keto form for most carbonyl compounds largely because a C=O is much stronger than a C=C. For simple carbonyl compounds, < 1% of the enol is present at equilibrium. With unsymmetrical ketones, moreover, two different enols are possible, yet they still total < 1%.

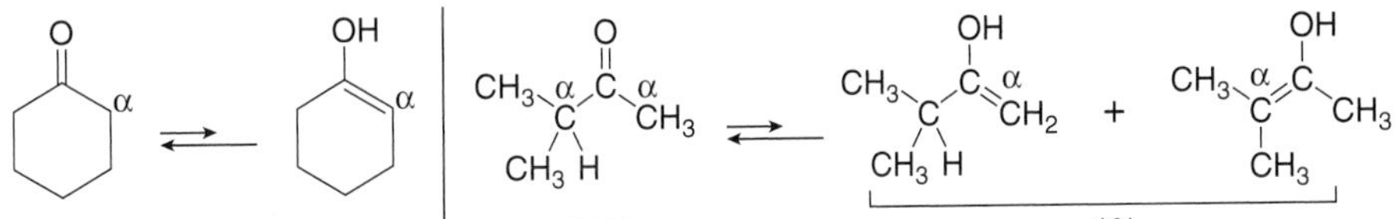

> 99% < 1% > 99% < 1%

With compounds containing two carbonyl groups separated by a single carbon (called β-dicarbonyl compounds or 1,3-dicarbonyl compounds), however, the concentration of the enol form sometimes exceeds the concentration of the keto form.

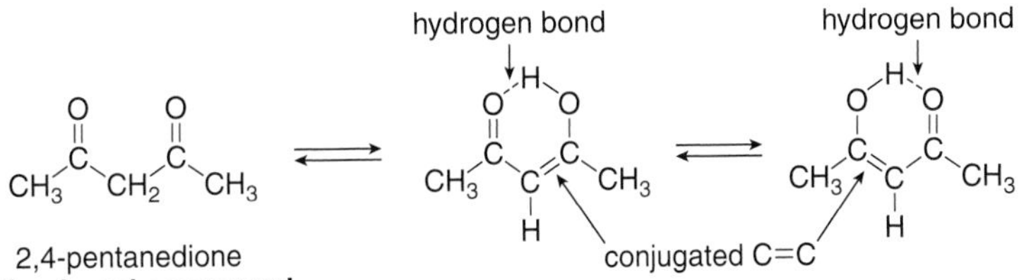

2,4-pentanedione
β-dicarbonyl compound
24% keto tautomer

76% enol tautomers

Two factors stabilize the enol of β-dicarbonyl compounds: **conjugation** and **intramolecular hydrogen bonding.** The C=C of the enol is conjugated with the carbonyl group, allowing delocalization of the electron density in the π bonds. Moreover, the OH of the enol can hydrogen bond to the oxygen of the nearby carbonyl group. Such intramolecular hydrogen bonds are especially stabilizing when they form a six-membered ring, as in this case.

Sample Problem 23.1 Convert each compound to its enol or keto tautomer.

a. 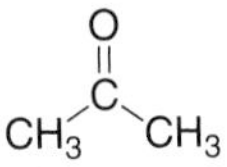

b. 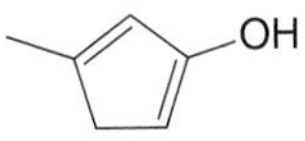

Solution

a. To convert a carbonyl compound to its enol tautomer, draw a double bond between the carbonyl carbon and the α carbon, and change the C=O to C–OH. In this case, both α carbons are identical, so only one enol is possible.

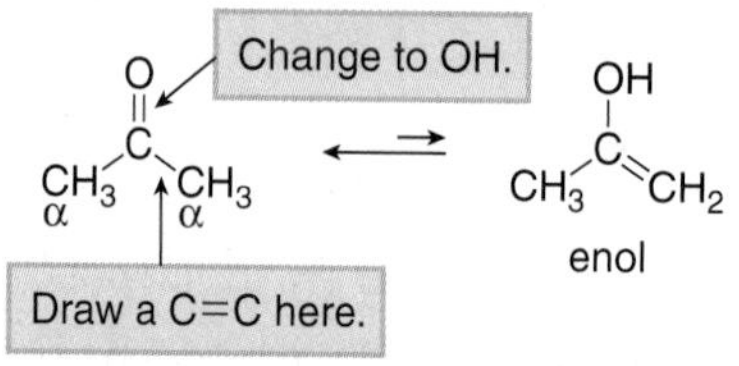
Change to OH.
Draw a C=C here.
enol

b. To convert an enol to its keto tautomer, change the C–OH to C=O and add a proton to the other end of the C=C.

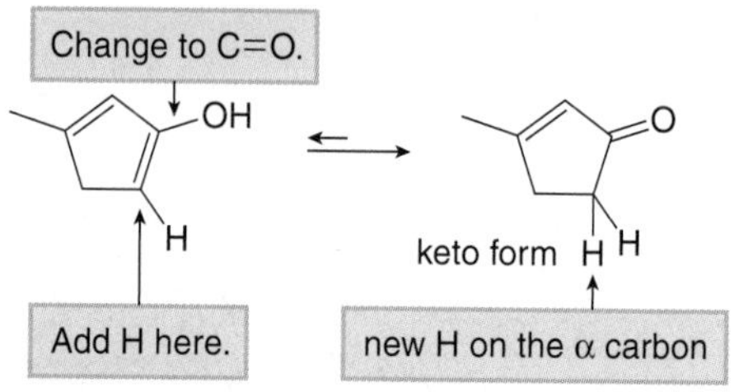
Change to C=O.
Add H here.
keto form
new H on the α carbon

Problem 23.1 Draw the enol or keto tautomer(s) of each compound.

a. 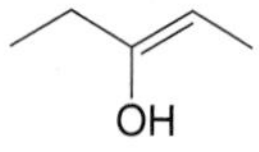

b. $C_6H_5CH_2CHO$

c. 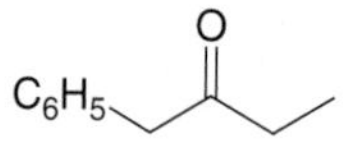

d. 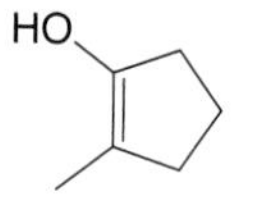

e. $C_6H_5CH_2CH_2CO_2CH_2CH_3$

f. 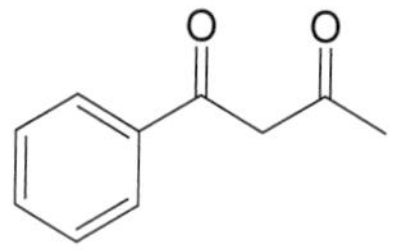

[Draw mono enol tautomers only.]

23.2A The Mechanism of Tautomerization

Tautomerization, the process of converting one tautomer into another, is catalyzed by both acid and base. Tautomerization always requires two steps (**protonation** and **deprotonation**), but the order of these steps depends on whether the reaction takes place in acid or base. In Mechanisms 23.1 and 23.2 for tautomerization, the keto form is converted to the enol form. All of the steps are reversible, though, so they equally apply to the conversion of the enol form to the keto form.

Mechanism 23.1 Tautomerization in Acid

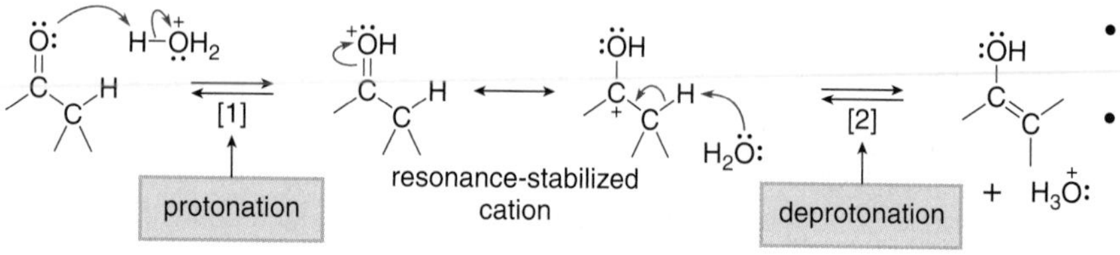
[1]
protonation
resonance-stabilized cation
[2]
deprotonation

- With acid, **protonation *precedes* deprotonation.**
- **Protonation** of the carbonyl oxygen forms a resonance-stabilized cation in Step [1], and deprotonation in Step [2] forms the enol. The net result of these two steps is the movement of a double bond and a proton.

Mechanism 23.2 Tautomerization in Base

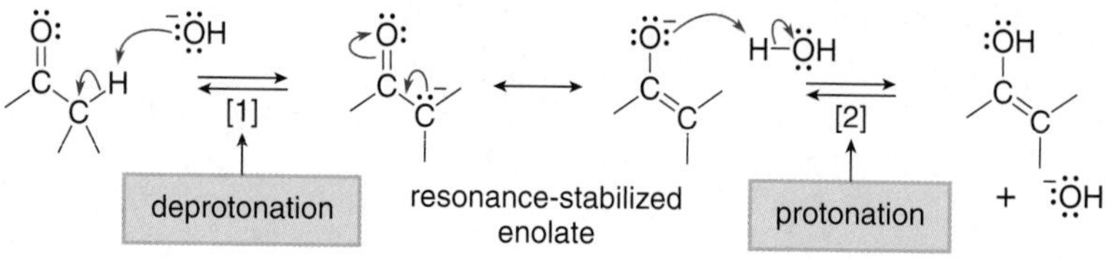
[1]
deprotonation
resonance-stabilized enolate
[2]
protonation

- With base, **deprotonation *precedes* protonation.**
- **Removal of a proton from the α carbon** forms a resonance-stabilized enolate in Step [1].
- **Protonation** of the enolate with H_2O forms the enol in Step [2].

Problem 23.2 Draw a stepwise mechanism for the following reaction.

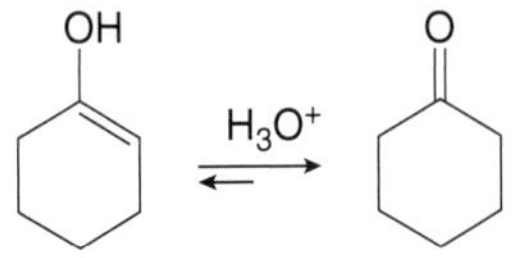

23.2B How Enols React

Like other compounds with carbon–carbon double bonds, **enols are electron rich, so they react as nucleophiles.** Enols are even more electron rich than alkenes, though, because the OH group has a powerful electron-donating resonance effect. A second resonance structure can be drawn for the enol that places a negative charge on one of the carbon atoms. As a result, this carbon atom is especially nucleophilic, and it can react with an electrophile E^+ to form a new bond to carbon. Loss of a proton then forms a neutral product.

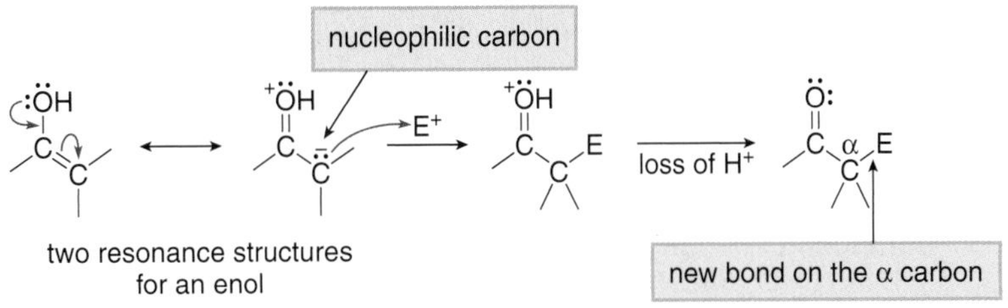

- **Reaction of an enol with an electrophile E^+ forms a new C – E bond on the α carbon. The net result is substitution of H by E on the α carbon.**

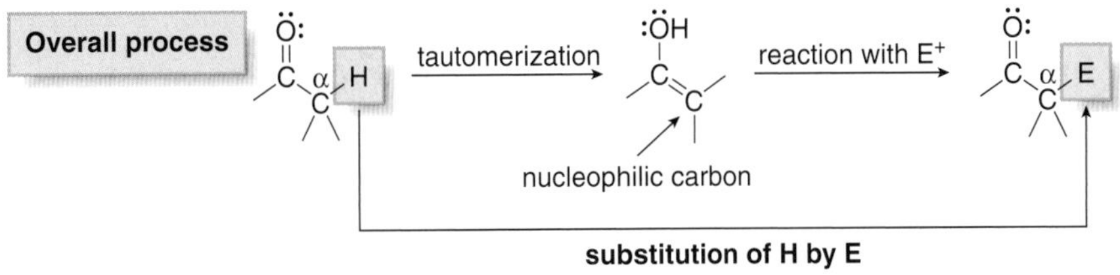

Problem 23.3 When phenylacetaldehyde ($C_6H_5CH_2CHO$) is dissolved in D_2O with added DCl, the hydrogen atoms α to the carbonyl are gradually replaced by deuterium atoms. Write a mechanism for this process that involves enols as intermediates.

23.3 Enolates

Enolates are formed when a base removes a proton on the α carbon to a carbonyl group. A C–H bond on the α carbon is more acidic than many other sp^3 hybridized C–H bonds, because the resulting enolate is resonance stabilized. Moreover, one of the resonance structures is especially stable because it places a negative charge on an electronegative oxygen atom.

Forming enolates from carbonyl compounds was first discussed in Section 21.7.

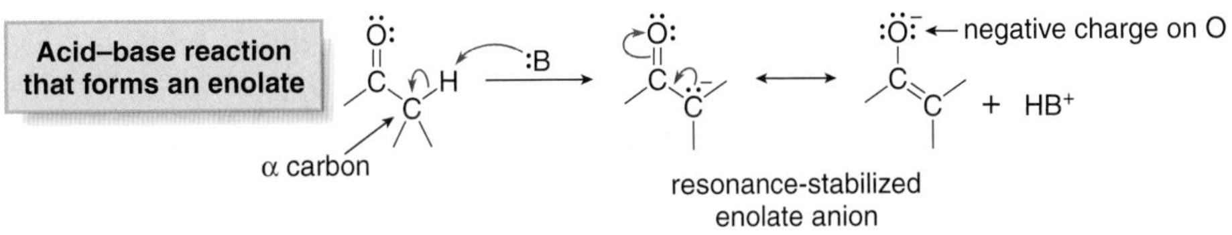

Enolates are always formed by removal of a proton on the **α carbon.**

Examples

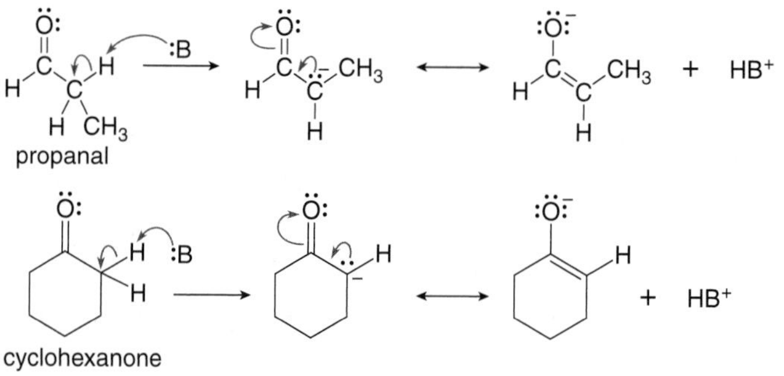

The pK_a of the α hydrogen in an aldehyde or ketone is **~20.** As shown in Table 23.1, this makes it considerably more acidic than the C–H bonds in CH_3CH_3 and $CH_3CH{=}CH_2$. Although C–H bonds α to a carbonyl are more acidic than many other C–H bonds, they are still less acidic than O–H bonds that always place the negative charge of the conjugate base on an electronegative oxygen atom (c.f. CH_3CH_2OH and CH_3COOH in Table 23.1).

Table 23.1 A Comparison of pK_a Values

Compound	pK_a	Conjugate base	Structural features of the conjugate base
CH_3CH_3	50	$CH_3\ddot{C}H_2^-$	• The conjugate base has a (–) charge on C, but is not resonance stabilized.
$CH_2{=}CHCH_3$	43	$CH_2{=}CH{-}\ddot{C}H_2^-$ ⟷ $\ddot{C}H_2^-{-}CH{=}CH_2$	• The conjugate base has a (–) charge on C, and is resonance stabilized.
$(CH_3)_2C{=}O$	19.2	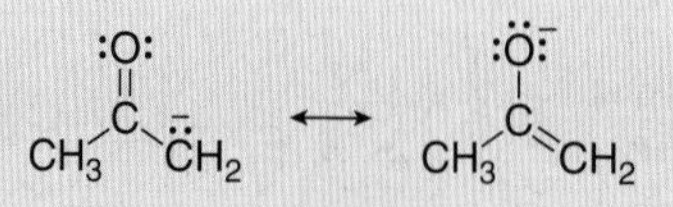	• **The conjugate base has two resonance structures, one of which has a (–) charge on O.**
CH_3CH_2OH	16	$CH_3CH_2\ddot{O}:^-$	• The conjugate base has a (–) charge on O, but is not resonance stabilized.
CH_3CO_2H	4.8	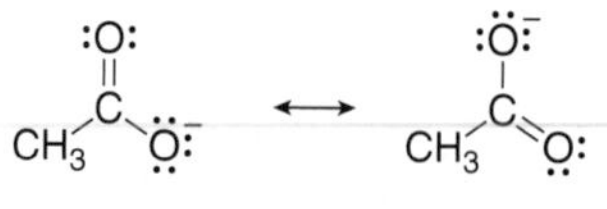	• The conjugate base has two resonance structures, both of which have a (–) charge on O.

Increasing acidity
Increasing stability of the conjugate base

- **Resonance stabilization of the conjugate base increases acidity.**
  - $CH_2{=}CHCH_3$ is more acidic than $CH_3CH_2CH_3$.
  - CH_3COOH is more acidic than CH_3CH_2OH.
- **Placing a negative charge on O in the conjugate base increases acidity.**
  - CH_3CH_2OH is more acidic than $CH_3CH_2CH_3$.
  - CH_3COCH_3 is more acidic than $CH_2{=}CHCH_3$.
  - CH_3COOH (with two O atoms) is more acidic than CH_3COCH_3.

The electrostatic potential plots in Figure 23.1 compare the electron density of the acetone enolate, which is resonance stabilized and delocalized, with that of $(CH_3)_2CHO^-$, an alkoxide that is not resonance stabilized.

Figure 23.1
Electron density in an enolate and an alkoxide

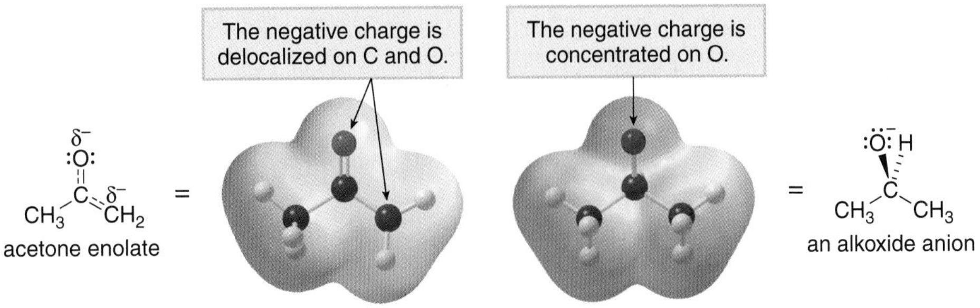

- The acetone enolate is resonance stabilized. The negative charge is delocalized on the oxygen atom (pale red) and the carbon atom (pale green).
- The alkoxide anion is not resonance stabilized. The negative charge is concentrated on the oxygen atom only (deep red).

23.3A Examples of Enolates and Related Anions

In addition to enolates from aldehydes and ketones, **enolates from esters and 3° amides can be formed as well,** although the α hydrogen is somewhat less acidic. **Nitriles** also have acidic protons on the carbon atom adjacent to the cyano group, because the negative charge of the conjugate base is stabilized by delocalization onto an electronegative nitrogen atom.

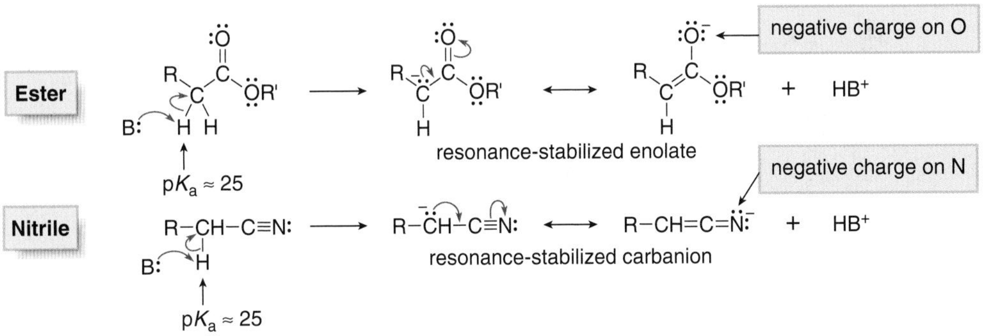

The protons on the carbon between the two carbonyl groups of a β-dicarbonyl compound are especially acidic because resonance delocalizes the negative charge on two different oxygen atoms. Table 23.2 lists pK_a values for β-dicarbonyl compounds as well as other carbonyl compounds and nitriles.

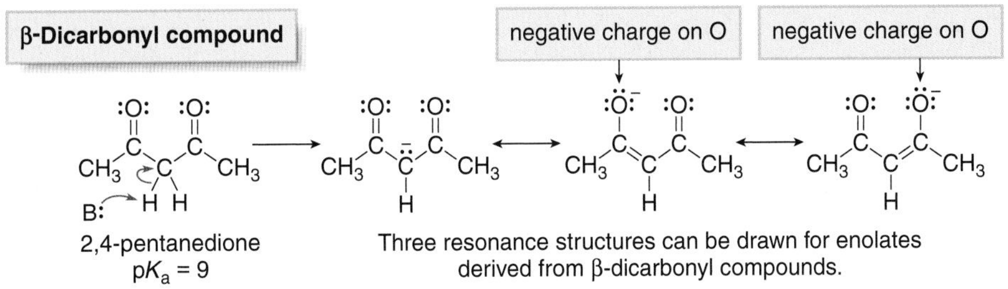

Table 23.2 pK_a Values for Some Carbonyl Compounds and Nitriles

Compound type	Example	pK_a	Compound type	Example	pK_a
[1] Amide	$CH_3C(=O)N(CH_3)_2$	30	[6] 1,3-Diester	$CH_3CH_2OC(=O)CH_2C(=O)OCH_2CH_3$	13.3
[2] Nitrile	$CH_3-C\equiv N$	25	[7] 1,3-Dinitrile	$N\equiv C-CH_2-C\equiv N$	11
[3] Ester	$CH_3C(=O)OCH_2CH_3$	25	[8] β-Keto ester	$CH_3C(=O)CH_2C(=O)OCH_2CH_3$	10.7
[4] Ketone	$CH_3C(=O)CH_3$	19.2	[9] β-Diketone	$CH_3C(=O)CH_2C(=O)CH_3$	9
[5] Aldehyde	$CH_3C(=O)H$	17			

Problem 23.4 Draw additional resonance structures for each anion.

a. $\bar{:}CH(COOCH_2CH_3)_2$

b. 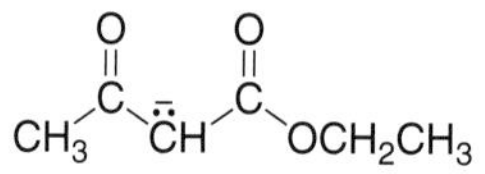

c. 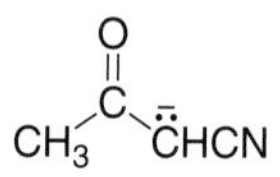

Problem 23.5 Which C–H bonds in the following molecules are acidic because the resulting conjugate base is resonance stabilized?

a. 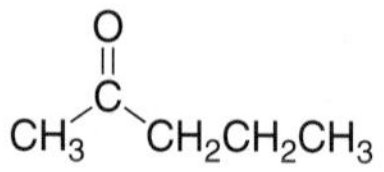

b. $CH_3CH_2CH_2-CN$

c. 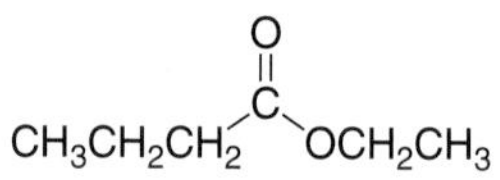

d. 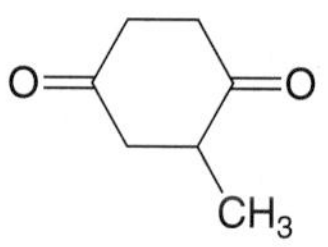

Problem 23.6 Rank the protons in the indicated CH_2 groups in order of increasing acidity, and explain why you chose this order.

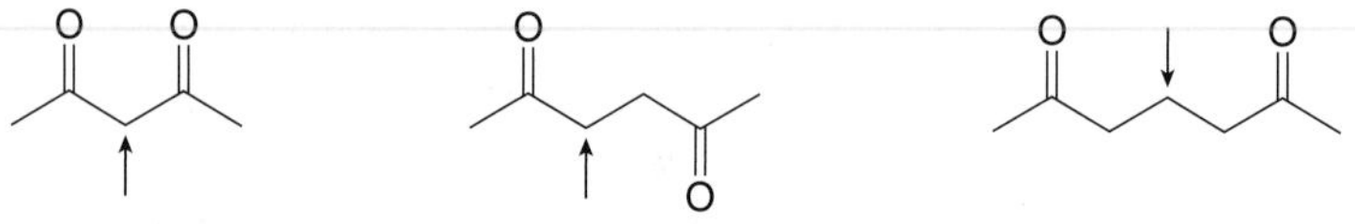

23.3B The Base

The formation of an enolate is an acid–base equilibrium, so the **stronger the base, the more enolate that forms.**

Enolate formation—An acid–base equilibrium

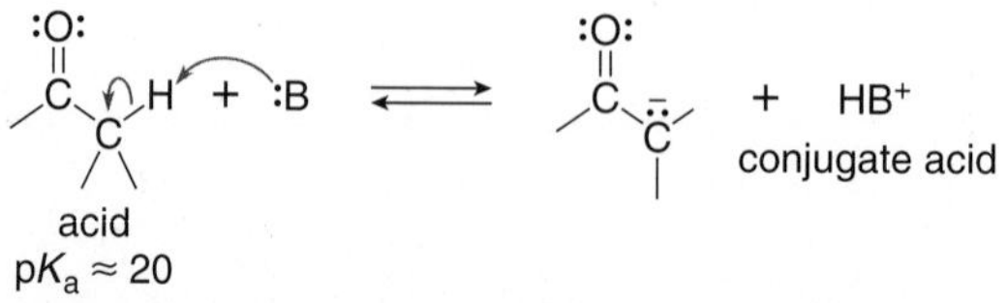

Stronger bases drive the equilibrium to the right.

We have now used the term ***amide*** in two different ways—first as a functional group (e.g., the carboxylic acid derivative $RCONH_2$) and now as a base (e.g., $^-NH_2$, which can be purchased as a sodium or lithium salt, $NaNH_2$ or $LiNH_2$, respectively). In Chapter 23 we will use dialkylamides, $^-NR_2$, in which the two H atoms of $^-NH_2$ have been replaced by R groups.

Enolate formation with LDA is typically carried out at –78 °C, a convenient temperature to maintain in the laboratory because it is the temperature at which dry ice (solid CO_2) sublimes. A low-temperature cooling bath can be made by adding dry ice to acetone until the acetone cools to –78 °C. Immersing a reaction flask in this cooling bath keeps its contents at a constant low temperature.

We can predict the extent of an acid–base reaction by comparing the pK_a of the starting acid (the carbonyl compound in this case) with the pK_a of the conjugate acid formed. **The equilibrium favors the side with the weaker acid (the acid with the higher pK_a value).** The pK_a of many carbonyl compounds is ~20, so a significant amount of enolate will form only if the pK_a of the conjugate acid is > 20.

The common bases used to form enolates are hydroxide (^-OH), various alkoxides (^-OR), hydride (H^-), and dialkylamides ($^-NR_2$). How much enolate is formed using each of these bases is indicated in Table 23.3.

Table 23.3 Enolate Formation with Various Bases: $RCOCH_3$ ($pK_a \approx 20$) + B: → $RCOCH_2^-$ + HB^+

	Base (B:)	Conjugate acid (HB^+)	pK_a of HB^+	% Enolate
[1]	$Na^+ \, ^-OH$	H_2O	15.7	< 1%
[2]	$Na^+ \, ^-OCH_2CH_3$	CH_3CH_2OH	16	< 1%
[3]	$K^+ \, ^-OC(CH_3)_3$	$(CH_3)_3COH$	18	1–10% (depending on the carbonyl compound)
[4]	Na^+H^-	H_2	35	100%
[5]	$Li^+ \, ^-N[CH(CH_3)_2]_2$	$HN[CH(CH_3)_2]_2$	40	100%

When the pK_a of the conjugate acid is < 20, as it is for ^-OH and all ^-OR (entries 1–3), only a small amount of enolate is formed at equilibrium. These bases are more useful in forming enolates when more acidic 1,3-dicarbonyl compounds are used as starting materials. They are also used when both the enolate and the carbonyl starting material are involved in the reaction, as is the case for reactions described in Chapter 24.

To form an enolate in essentially 100% yield, a much stronger base such as lithium diisopropylamide, **$Li^+ \, ^-N[CH(CH_3)_2]_2$**, abbreviated as **LDA,** is used (entry 5). **LDA is a strong nonnucleophilic base.** Like the other nonnucleophilic bases (Sections 7.8B and 8.1), its bulky isopropyl groups make the nitrogen atom too hindered to serve as a nucleophile. It is still able, though, to remove a proton in an acid–base reaction.

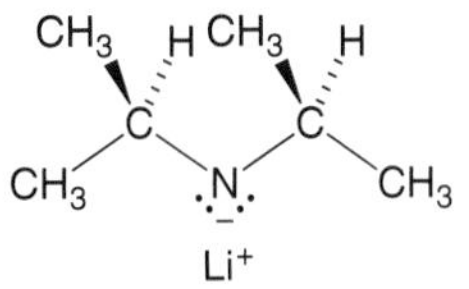
CH3
H
CH3
H
C
C
CH3
N
CH3
Li+

lithium diisopropylamide

LDA

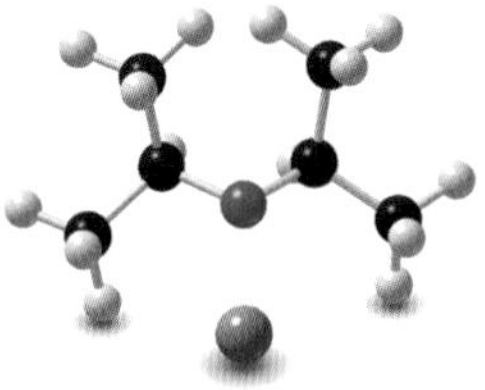

The N atom is too crowded to be a nucleophile.

THF
tetrahydrofuran
a polar aprotic solvent

LDA quickly deprotonates essentially all of the carbonyl starting material, even at –78 °C, to form the enolate product. THF is the typical solvent for these reactions.

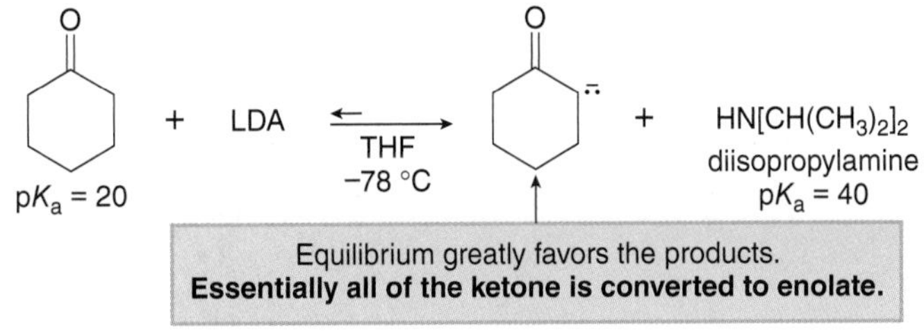
O
+ LDA
THF
–78 °C
O
+ HN[CH(CH3)2]2
diisopropylamine
pKa = 40
pKa = 20
Equilibrium greatly favors the products.
Essentially all of the ketone is converted to enolate.

LDA can be prepared by deprotonating diisopropylamine with an organolithium reagent such as butyllithium, and then used immediately in a reaction.

Preparation of LDA

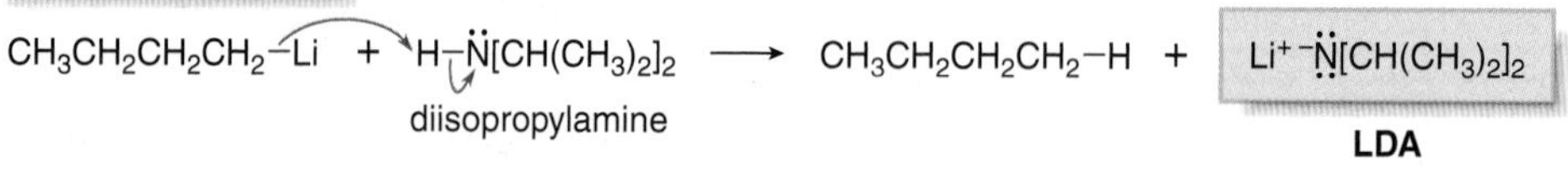
CH3CH2CH2CH2–Li + H–N̈[CH(CH3)2]2 ⟶ CH3CH2CH2CH2–H + Li+ –N̈[CH(CH3)2]2
diisopropylamine
LDA

Problem 23.7 Draw the product formed when each starting material is treated with LDA in THF solution at −78 °C.

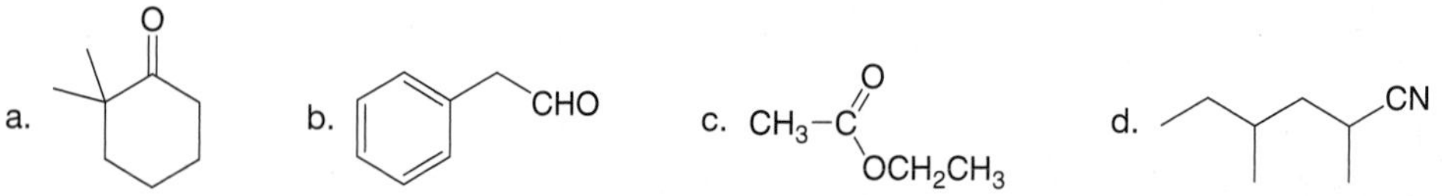
a.
b.
CHO
c.
CH3–C
O
OCH2CH3
d.
CN

Problem 23.8 When ethyl acetoacetate ($CH_3COCH_2CO_2CH_2CH_3$) is treated with one equivalent of CH_3MgBr, a gas is evolved from the reaction mixture, and after adding aqueous acid, ethyl acetoacetate is recovered in high yield. Identify the gas formed and explain why the starting material was recovered in this reaction.

Problem 23.9 As we learned in Chapter 20, organolithium reagents (RLi) are strong bases that readily react with acidic protons. Why aren't organolithium reagents used to generate enolates?

23.3C General Reactions of Enolates

Enolates are nucleophiles, and as such they react with many electrophiles. Because an enolate is resonance stabilized, however, it has two reactive sites—the carbon and oxygen atoms that bear the negative charge. **A nucleophile with two reactive sites is called an *ambident nucleophile.*** In theory, each of these atoms could react with an electrophile to form two different products, one with a new bond to carbon, and one with a new bond to oxygen.

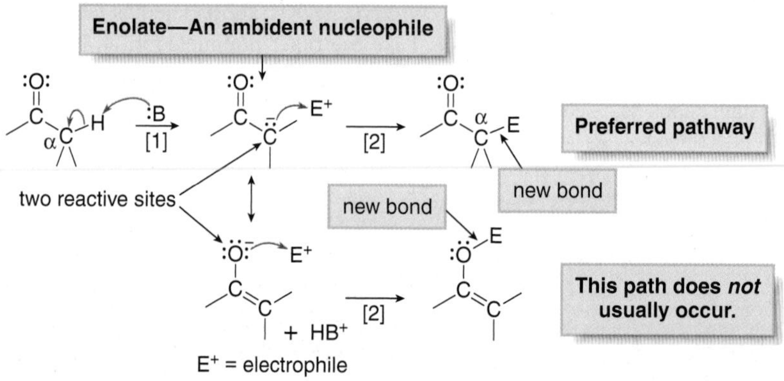
Enolate—An ambident nucleophile
:B
[1]
E+
[2]
Preferred pathway
two reactive sites
new bond
new bond
E+
+ HB+
[2]
This path does not usually occur.
E+ = electrophile

Because enolates usually react at carbon instead of oxygen, the resonance structure that places the negative charge on oxygen will often be omitted in multistep mechanisms.

An enolate usually reacts at the carbon end, however, because this site is more nucleophilic. Thus, **enolates generally react with electrophiles on the α carbon** so that many reactions in Chapter 23 follow a two-step path:

[1] Reaction of a carbonyl compound with base forms an enolate.
[2] Reaction of the enolate with an electrophile forms a new bond on the α carbon.

23.4 Enolates of Unsymmetrical Carbonyl Compounds

What happens when an unsymmetrical carbonyl compound like 2-methylcyclohexanone is treated with base? **Two enolates are possible,** one formed by removal of a 2° hydrogen, and one formed by removal of a 3° hydrogen.

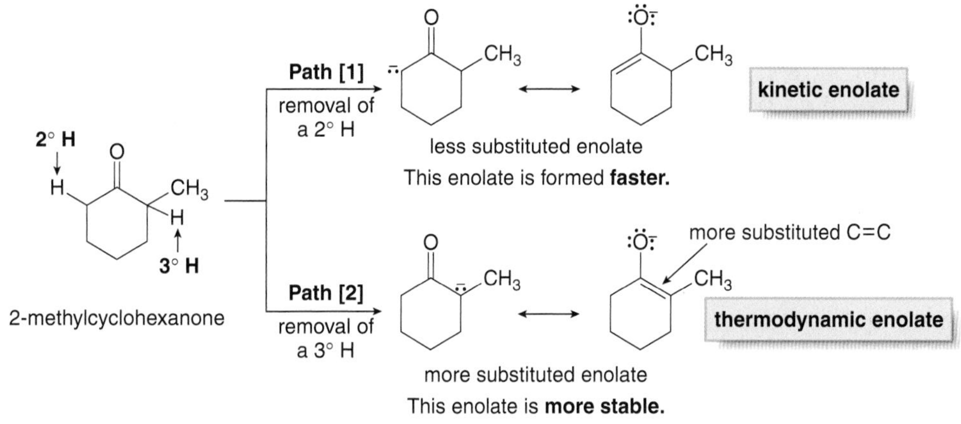

Path [1] occurs *faster* than Path [2] because it results in removal of the less hindered 2° hydrogen, forming an enolate on the less substituted α carbon. Path [2] results in removal of a 3° hydrogen, forming the *more stable* enolate with the more substituted double bond. This enolate predominates at equilibrium.

- **The kinetic enolate is formed faster because it is the less substituted enolate.**
- **The thermodynamic enolate is lower in energy because it is the more substituted enolate.**

It is possible to regioselectively form one or the other enolate by the proper use of reaction conditions, because the base, solvent, and reaction temperature all affect the identity of the enolate formed.

Kinetic Enolates

The kinetic enolate forms faster, so mild reaction conditions favor it over slower processes with higher energies of activation. It is the less stable enolate, so it must not be allowed to equilibrate to the more stable thermodynamic enolate. **The kinetic enolate is favored by:**

[1] **A strong nonnucleophilic base.** A strong base assures that the enolate is formed rapidly. A **bulky base like LDA removes the more accessible proton on the less substituted carbon** much faster than a more hindered proton.

[2] **Polar aprotic solvent.** The solvent must be polar to dissolve the polar starting materials and intermediates. It must be aprotic so that it does not protonate any enolate that is formed. **THF** is both polar and aprotic.

[3] **Low temperature.** The temperature must be low **(–78 °C)** to prevent the kinetic enolate from equilibrating to the thermodynamic enolate.

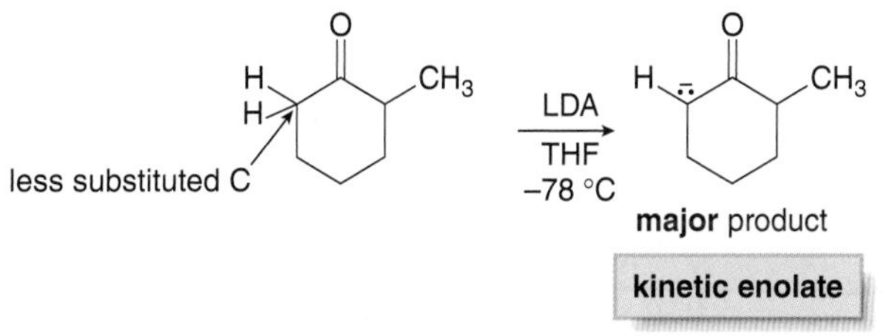

- **A kinetic enolate is formed with a strong, nonnucleophilic base (LDA) in a polar aprotic solvent (THF) at low temperature (–78 °C).**

Thermodynamic Enolates

A thermodynamic enolate is favored by equilibrating conditions. This is often achieved using a **strong base in a protic solvent.** A strong base yields both enolates, but in a protic solvent, enolates can also be protonated to re-form the carbonyl starting material. At equilibrium, the lower energy intermediate always wins out, so that **the more stable, more substituted enolate is present in higher concentration.** Thus, the **thermodynamic enolate is favored by:**

[1] **A strong base. $Na^{+}\,^{-}OCH_2CH_3$, $K^{+}\,^{-}OC(CH_3)_3$,** or other alkoxides are common.
[2] **Protic solvent. CH_3CH_2OH** or other alcohols.
[3] **Room temperature (25 °C).**

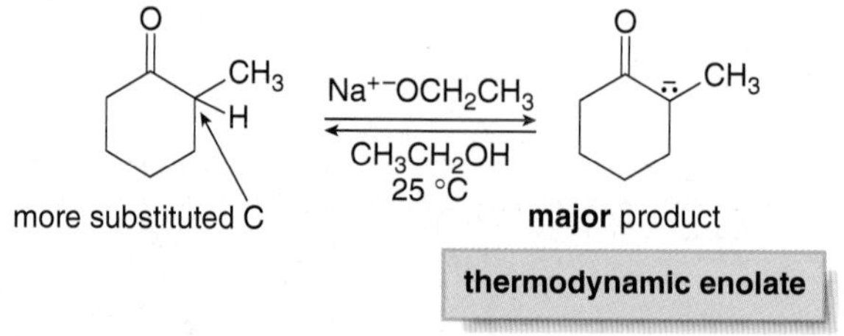

- **A thermodynamic enolate is formed with a strong base (RO⁻) in a polar protic solvent (ROH) at room temperature.**

Sample Problem 23.2 What is the major enolate formed in each reaction?

a. 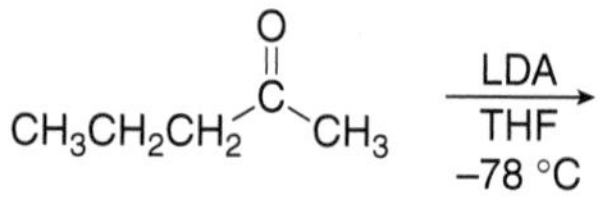

b. 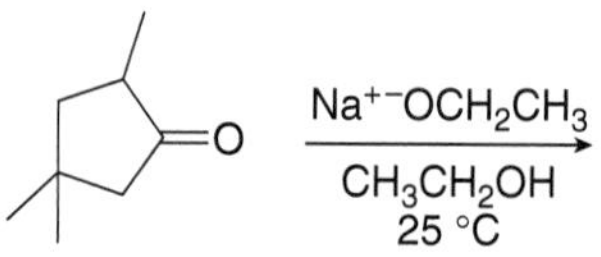

Solution

a. LDA is a strong, nonnucleophilic base that removes a proton on the less substituted α carbon to form the kinetic enolate.

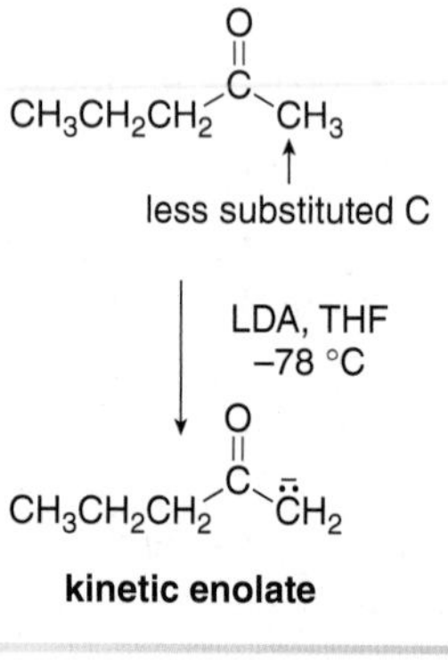

b. $NaOCH_2CH_3$ (a strong base) and CH_3CH_2OH (a protic solvent) favor removal of a proton from the more substituted α carbon to form the thermodynamic enolate.

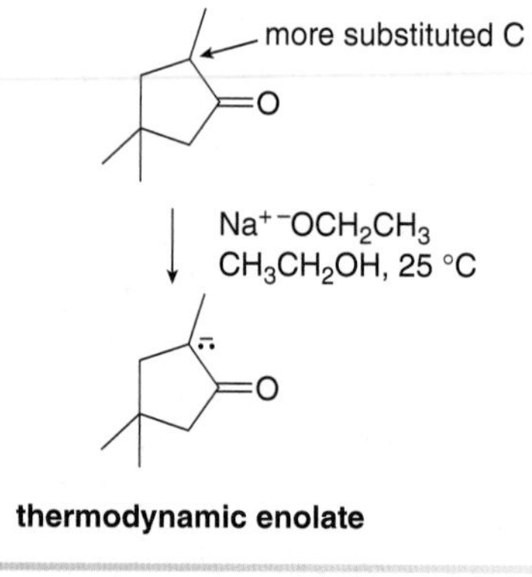

Problem 23.10 What enolate is formed when each ketone is treated with LDA in THF solution? What enolate is formed when these same ketones are treated with $NaOCH_3$ in CH_3OH solution?

a. 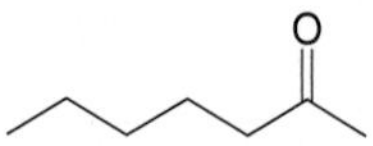

b. 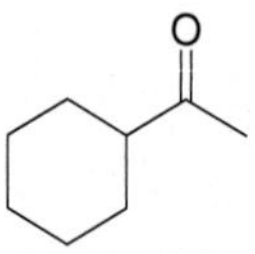

c. 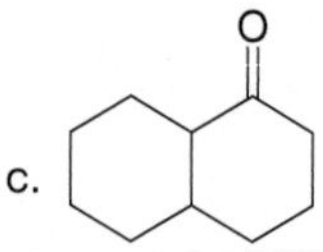

23.5 Racemization at the α Carbon

Recall from Section 16.5 that an enolate can be stabilized by the delocalization of electron density only if it possesses the proper geometry and hybridization.

- **The electron pair on the carbon adjacent to the C=O must occupy a *p* orbital that overlaps with the two other *p* orbitals of the C=O, making an enolate conjugated.**

- **Thus, all three atoms of the enolate are sp^2 hybridized and trigonal planar.**

These bonding features are shown in the acetone enolate in Figure 23.2.

Figure 23.2
The hybridization and geometry of the acetone enolate $(CH_3COCH_2)^-$

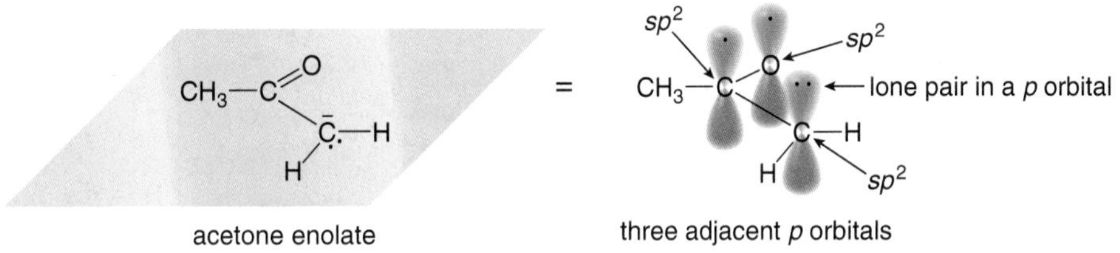

- The O atom and both C's of the enolate are sp^2 hybridized and lie in a plane.
- Each atom has a *p* orbital extending above and below the plane; these orbitals overlap to delocalize electron density.

When the α carbon to the carbonyl is a stereogenic center, treatment with aqueous base leads to **racemization** by a two-step process: **deprotonation to form an enolate and protonation to re-form the carbonyl compound.** For example, chiral ketone **A** reacts with aqueous ^-OH to form an achiral enolate having an sp^2 hybridized α carbon. Because the enolate is planar, it can be protonated with H_2O with equal probability from both directions, yielding a racemic mixture of two ketones.

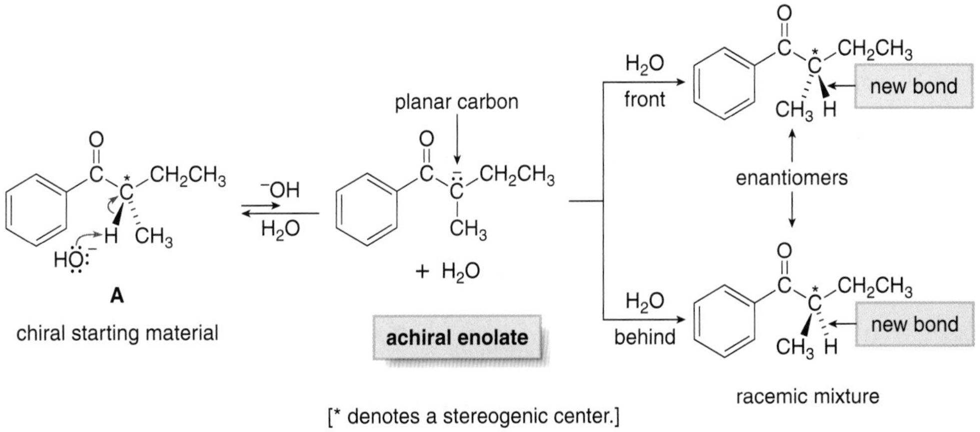

Problem 23.11 Explain each observation: (a) When (2*R*)-2-methylcyclohexanone is treated with NaOH in H_2O, the optically active solution gradually loses optical activity. (b) When (3*R*)-3-methylcyclohexanone is treated with NaOH in H_2O, the solution remains optically active.

23.6 A Preview of Reactions at the α Carbon

Having learned about the synthesis and properties of enolates, we can now turn our attention to their reactions. Like enols, **enolates are nucleophiles,** but because they are negatively charged, enolates are much more nucleophilic than neutral enols. Consequently, they undergo a wider variety of reactions.

Two general types of reactions of enolates—**substitutions** and **reactions with other carbonyl compounds**—will be discussed in the remainder of Chapter 23 and in Chapter 24. Both reactions form new bonds to the carbon α to the carbonyl.

- **Enolates react with electrophiles to afford substitution products.**

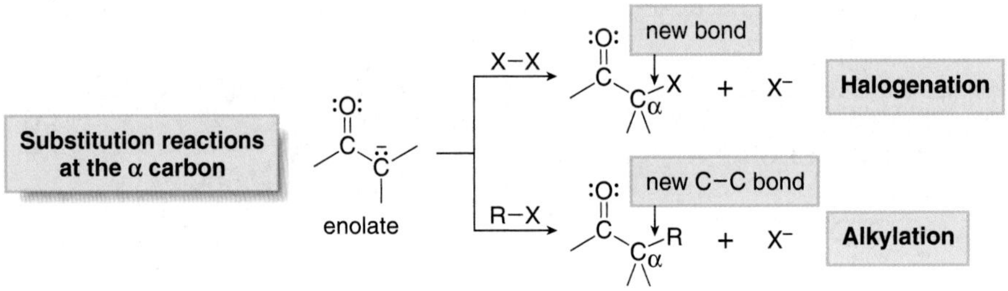

Two different kinds of substitution reactions are examined: **halogenation** with X_2 and **alkylation** with alkyl halides RX. These reactions are detailed in Sections 23.7–23.10.

- **Enolates react with other carbonyl groups at the electrophilic carbonyl carbon.**

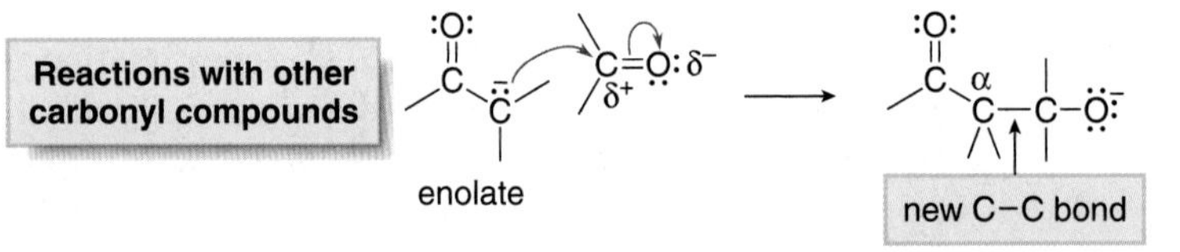

These reactions are more complicated because the initial addition adduct goes on to form different products depending on the structure of the carbonyl group. These reactions form the subject of Chapter 24.

23.7 Halogenation at the α Carbon

The first substitution reaction we examine is **halogenation.** Treatment of a ketone or aldehyde with halogen and either acid or base results in **substitution of X for H on the α carbon,** forming an **α-halo aldehyde or ketone.** Halogenation readily occurs with Cl_2, Br_2, and I_2.

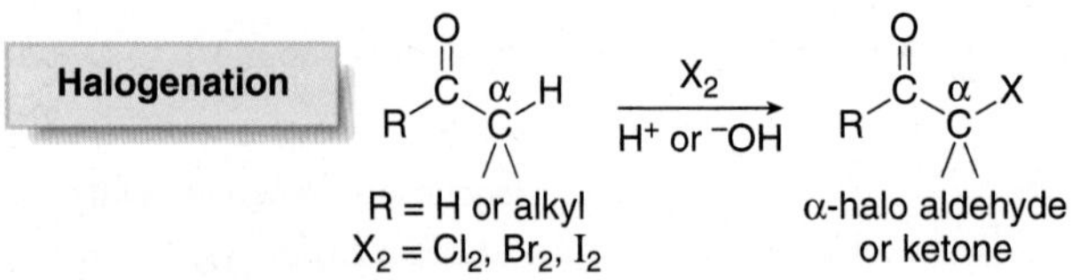

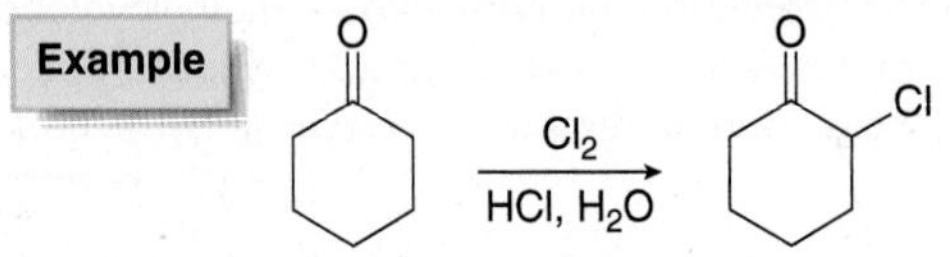

The mechanisms of halogenation in acid and base are somewhat different.

- **Reactions done in acid generally involve *enol* intermediates.**
- **Reactions done in base generally involve *enolate* intermediates.**

23.7A Halogenation in Acid

Halogenation is often carried out by treating a carbonyl compound with a halogen in acetic acid. In this way, acetic acid is both the solvent and the acid catalyst for the reaction.

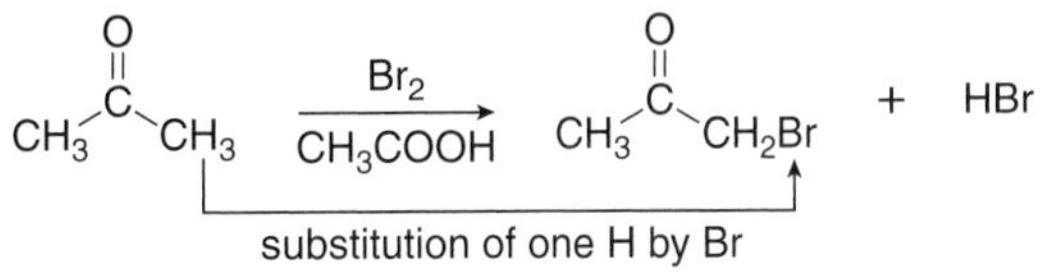

O
CH3 C CH3
Br2
CH3COOH
O
CH3 C CH2Br
+ HBr
substitution of one H by Br

The mechanism of acid-catalyzed halogenation consists of two parts: **tautomerization** of the carbonyl compound to the enol form, and **reaction of the enol with halogen.** Mechanism 23.3 illustrates the reaction of $(CH_3)_2C{=}O$ with Br_2 in CH_3COOH.

Mechanism 23.3 Acid-Catalyzed Halogenation at the α Carbon

Part [1] Tautomerization to the enol

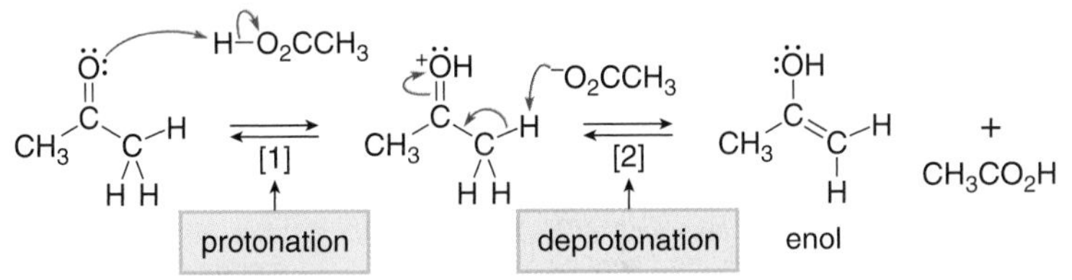

[1]
protonation
[2]
deprotonation
+
CH3CO2H
enol

- In Part [1], the ketone is converted to its enol tautomer by the usual two-step process: **protonation** of the carbonyl oxygen, followed by **deprotonation** of the α carbon atom.

Part [2] Reaction of the enol with halogen

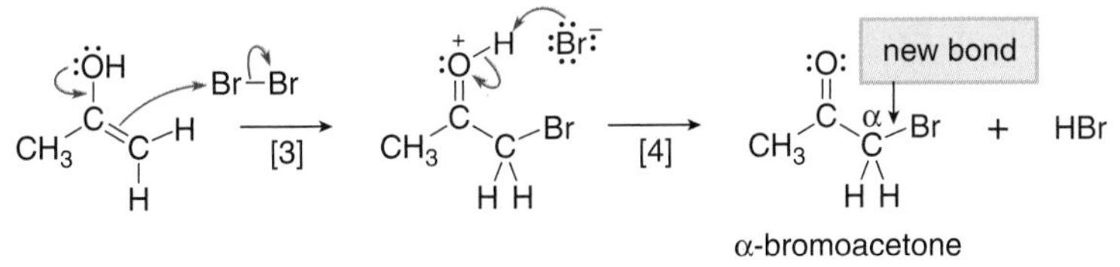

[3]
[4]
new bond
+ HBr
α-bromoacetone

- In Part [2], addition of the halogen to the enol followed by deprotonation forms the neutral substitution product (Steps [3]–[4]). **The overall process results in substitution of H by Br on the α carbon.**

Problem 23.12 Draw the products of each reaction.

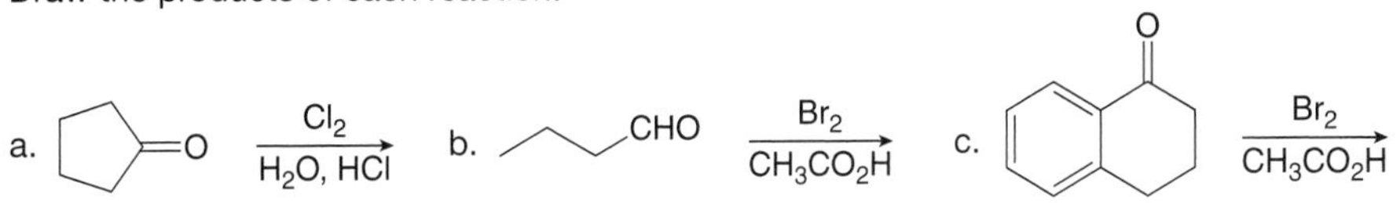

a.
Cl2
H2O, HCl
b.
CHO
Br2
CH3CO2H
c.
Br2
CH3CO2H

23.7B Halogenation in Base

Halogenation in base is much less useful, because it is often difficult to stop the reaction after addition of just one halogen atom to the α carbon. For example, treatment of propiophenone with Br_2 and aqueous ^-OH yields a dibromo ketone.

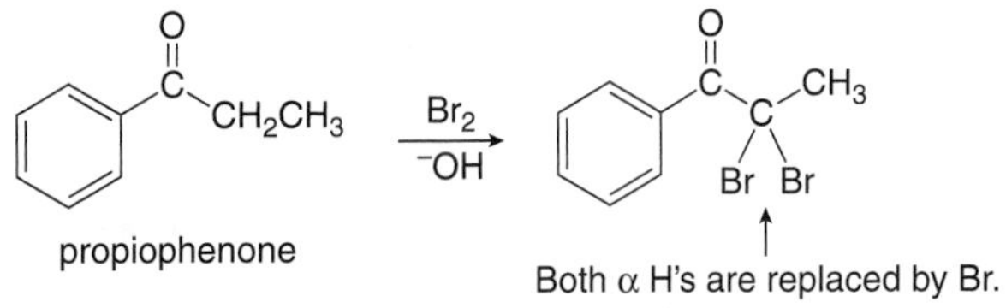

CH2CH3
propiophenone
Br2
−OH
CH3
Br Br
Both α H's are replaced by Br.

Reactions of carbonyl compounds with base invariably involve enolates because the α hydrogens of the carbonyl compound are easily removed.

The mechanism for introduction of each Br atom involves the same two steps: **deprotonation with base followed by reaction with Br_2** to form a new C–Br bond, as shown in Mechanism 23.4.

Mechanism 23.4 Halogenation at the α Carbon in Base

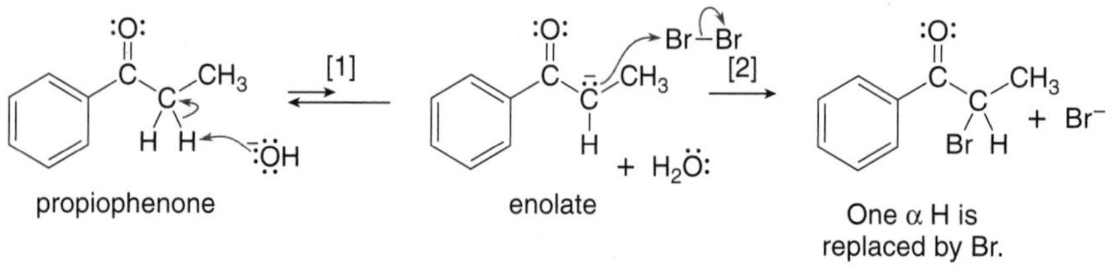

[1]
[2]
+ $H_2\ddot{O}$:
+ Br^-
propiophenone
enolate
One α H is replaced by Br.

- Treatment of the ketone with base forms a nucleophilic enolate in Step [1], which reacts with Br_2 (the electrophile) to form the monosubstitution product—that is, one α H is replaced by one Br on the α carbon.

Only a small amount of the enolate forms at equilibrium using ^-OH as base, but the enolate is such a strong nucleophile that it readily reacts with Br_2, thus driving the equilibrium to the right. Then, the same two steps introduce the second Br atom on the α carbon: **deprotonation** followed by **nucleophilic attack.**

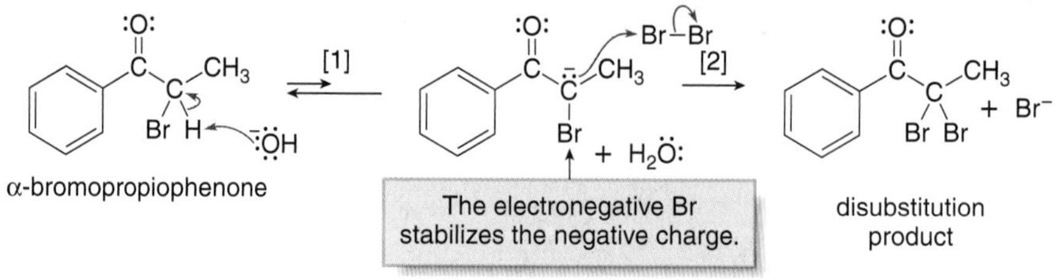

[1]
[2]
α-bromopropiophenone
The electronegative Br stabilizes the negative charge.
disubstitution product

It is difficult to stop this reaction after the addition of one Br atom because the electron-withdrawing inductive effect of Br stabilizes the second enolate. As a result, the α H of α-bromopropiophenone is more acidic than the α H atoms of propiophenone, making it easier to remove with base.

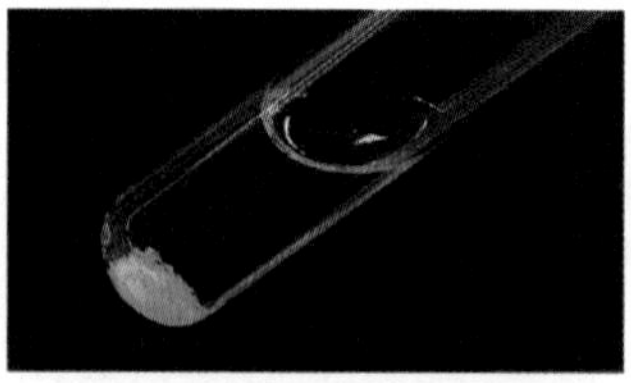

Although all ketones with α hydrogens react with base and I_2, only **methyl** ketones form CHI_3 (iodoform), a pale yellow solid that precipitates from the reaction mixture. This reaction is the basis of the **iodoform test,** once a common chemical method to detect methyl ketones. Methyl ketones give a positive iodoform test (appearance of a yellow solid), whereas other ketones give a negative iodoform test (no change in the reaction mixture).

Halogenation of a methyl ketone with excess halogen, called the **haloform reaction,** results in cleavage of a carbon–carbon σ bond and formation of two products, a carboxylate anion and CHX_3 (commonly called **haloform**).

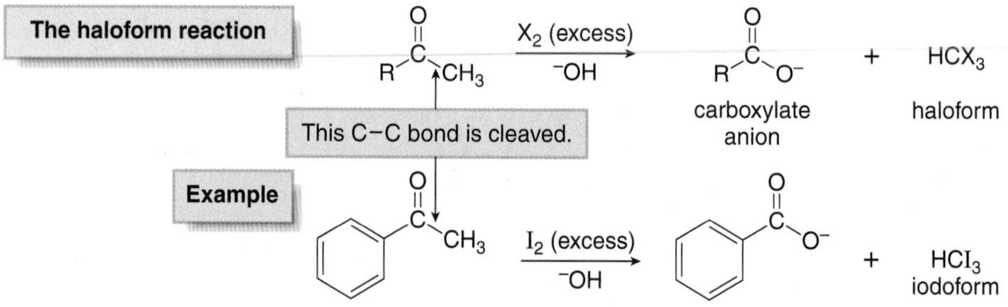

The haloform reaction
X_2 (excess)
^-OH
carboxylate anion
haloform
This C–C bond is cleaved.
Example
I_2 (excess)
^-OH
HCI_3
iodoform

In the haloform reaction, the three H atoms of the CH_3 group are successively replaced by X to form an intermediate that is oxidatively cleaved with base. Mechanism 23.5 is written with I_2 as halogen, forming CHI_3 (iodoform) as product.

Mechanism 23.5 The Haloform Reaction

Part [1] The conversion of CH_3 to CI_3

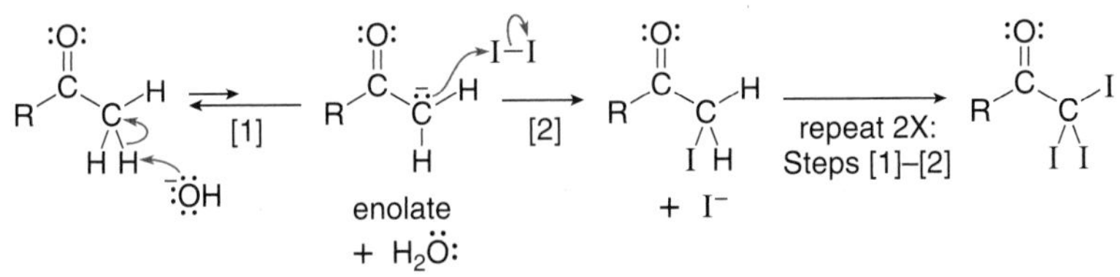

- In Part [1], each of the three hydrogen atoms of the CH_3 group is replaced with iodine via the two-step mechanism previously discussed—that is, deprotonation followed by halogenation to form the substitution product.
- Steps [1] and [2] are then repeated twice more to form the triiodo substitution product.

Part [2] Oxidative cleavage with ^{-}OH

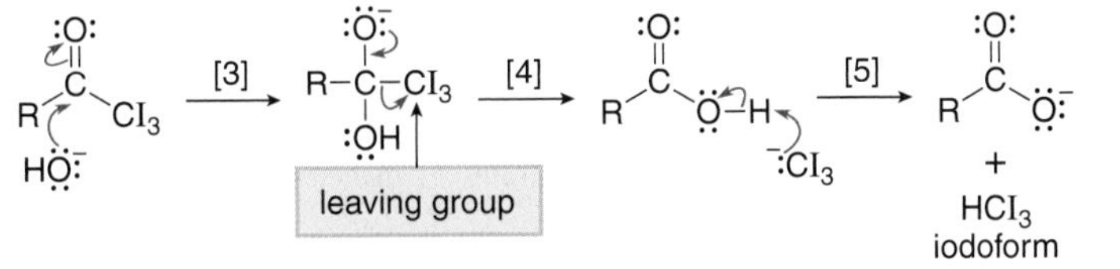

- In Step [3], ^{-}OH adds to the carbonyl group in a typical **nucleophilic addition** reaction of a ketone, but the three I atoms give this ketone a good leaving group, $^{-}CI_3$.
- **Elimination of $^{-}CI_3$ in Step [4] results in cleavage of a carbon–carbon bond,** and then in the last step, proton transfer forms the carboxylate anion and iodoform.

Steps [3] and [4] result in a **nucleophilic *substitution*** reaction of a *ketone.* Because ketones normally undergo **nucleophilic *addition*,** this two-step sequence makes the haloform reaction unique. Substitution occurs because the three electronegative halogen atoms make CX_3 (CI_3 in the example) a good leaving group.

Figure 23.3 summarizes the three possible outcomes of halogenation at the α carbon, depending on the substrate and chosen reaction conditions.

Problem 23.13 Draw the products of each reaction. Assume excess halogen is present.

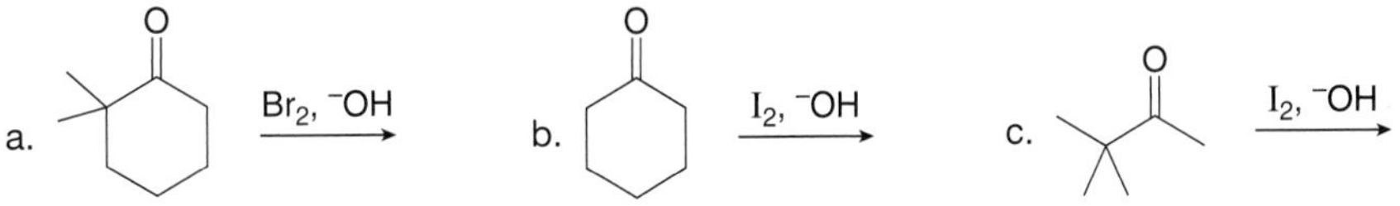

Figure 23.3 Summary: Halogenation reactions at the α carbon to a carbonyl group

[1] Halogenation in acid

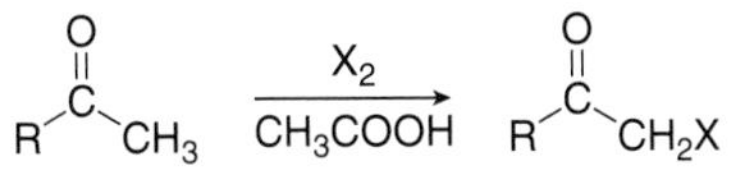

monosubstitution on the α carbon

[2] General halogenation in base

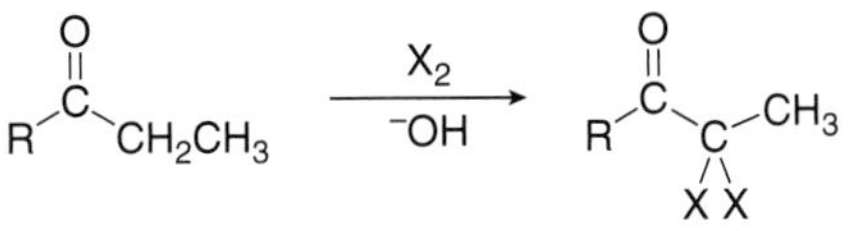

polysubstitution on the α carbon

[3] Halogenation of *methyl* ketones with excess X_2 and base

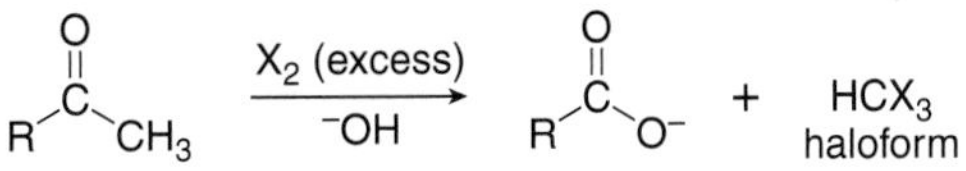

oxidative cleavage

23.7C Reactions of α-Halo Carbonyl Compounds

α-Halo carbonyl compounds undergo two useful reactions—**elimination** with base and **substitution** with nucleophiles.

For example, treatment of 2-bromocyclohexanone with the base Li_2CO_3 in the presence of LiBr in the polar aprotic solvent DMF [$HCON(CH_3)_2$] affords 2-cyclohexenone by elimination of the elements of Br and H from the α and β carbons, respectively. Thus, a two-step method can convert a carbonyl compound such as cyclohexanone into an α,β-unsaturated carbonyl compound such as 2-cyclohexenone.

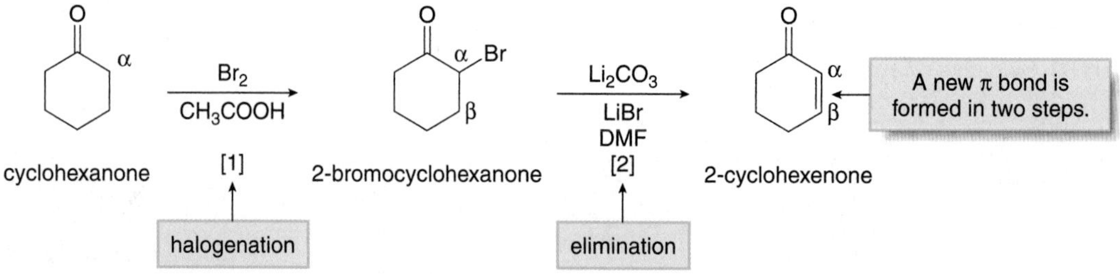

α,β-Unsaturated carbonyl compounds undergo a variety of 1,2- and 1,4-addition reactions as discussed in Section 20.15.

[1] Bromination at the α carbon is accomplished with Br_2 in CH_3COOH.

[2] Elimination of Br and H occurs with Li_2CO_3 and LiBr in DMF.

α-Halo carbonyl compounds also react with nucleophiles by S_N2 reactions. For example, reaction of 2-bromocyclohexanone with CH_3NH_2 affords the substitution product **A.** A related intramolecular nucleophilic substitution of an α-halo ketone was a key step in the synthesis of the antimalarial drug quinine, as shown in Figure 23.4.

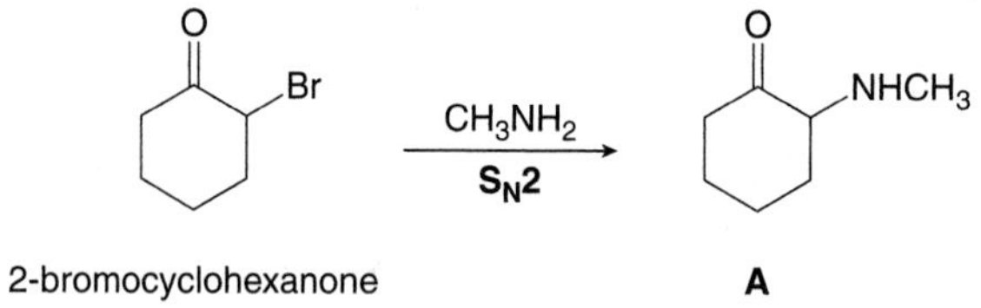

Problem 23.14 Draw the organic products formed when 2-bromo-3-pentanone ($CH_3CH_2COCHBrCH_3$) is treated with each reagent: (a) Li_2CO_3, LiBr, DMF; (b) $CH_3CH_2NH_2$; (c) CH_3SH.

Problem 23.15 Identify the product **M** of the following two-step reaction sequence. **M** was converted to the hallucinogen LSD (Figure 18.4) in several steps.

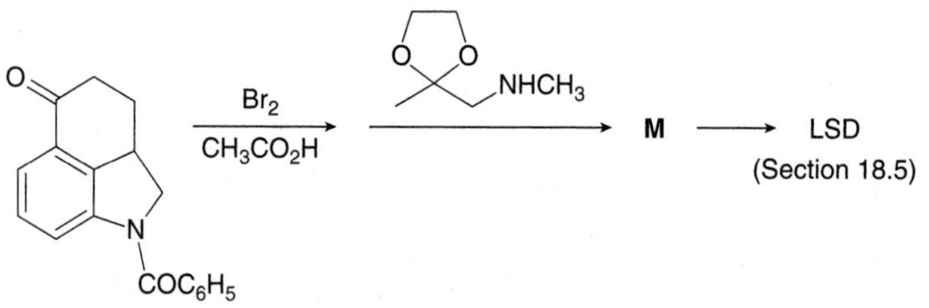

Figure 23.4 Intramolecular nucleophilic substitution in the synthesis of quinine

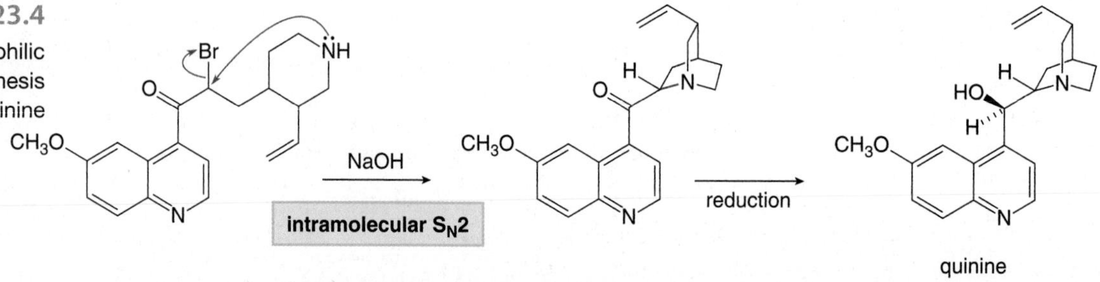

- Intramolecular S_N2 reaction of a nitrogen nucleophile with an α-halo ketone affords a compound that can be converted to quinine in a single step. The new C–N bond on the α carbon is labeled in red.

23.8 Direct Enolate Alkylation

Treatment of an aldehyde or ketone with base and an alkyl halide (RX) results in ***alkylation*—the substitution of R for H on the α carbon atom.** Alkylation forms a new carbon–carbon bond on the α carbon.

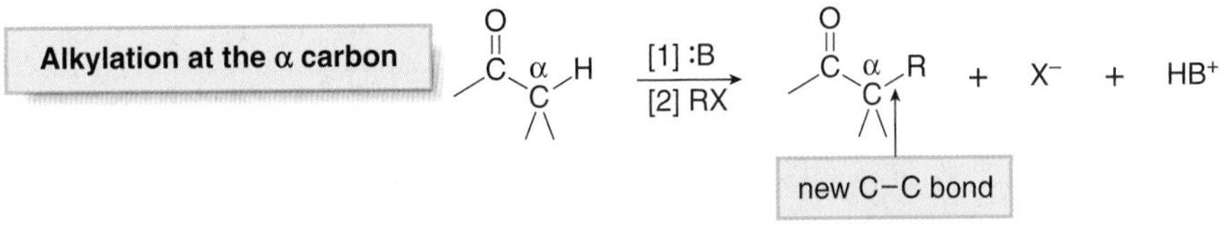

23.8A General Features

We will begin with the most direct method of alkylation, and then (in Sections 23.9 and 23.10) examine two older, multistep methods that are still used today. Direct alkylation is carried out by a two-step process:

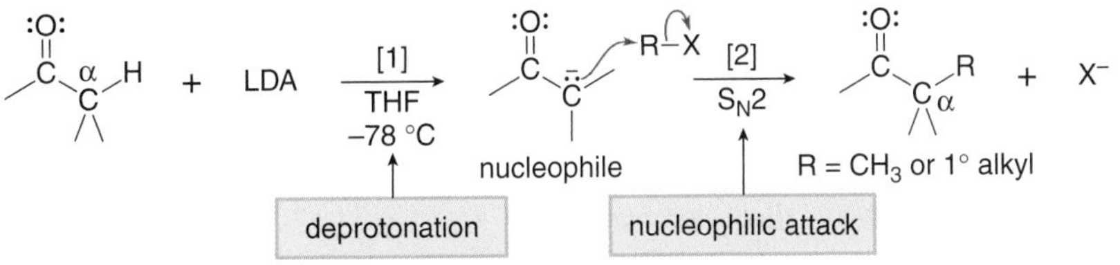

[1] **Deprotonation:** Base removes a proton from the α carbon to generate an enolate. The reaction works best with a strong nonnucleophilic base like LDA in THF solution at low temperature (–78 °C).

[2] **Nucleophilic attack:** The nucleophilic enolate attacks the alkyl halide, displacing the halide (a good leaving group) and forming the alkylation product by an S_N2 reaction.

Because Step [2] is an S_N2 reaction, it works best with unhindered methyl and 1° alkyl halides. Hindered alkyl halides and those with halogens bonded to sp^2 hybridized carbons do not undergo substitution.

R_3CX, $CH_2{=}CHX$, and C_6H_5X do not undergo alkylation reactions with enolates, because they are unreactive in S_N2 reactions.

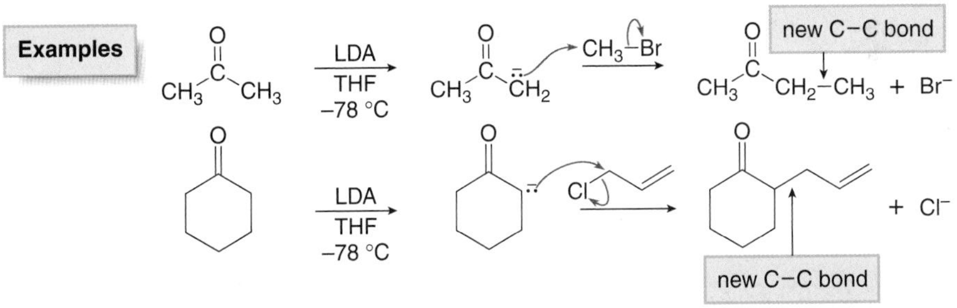

Ester enolates and carbanions derived from nitriles are also alkylated under these conditions.

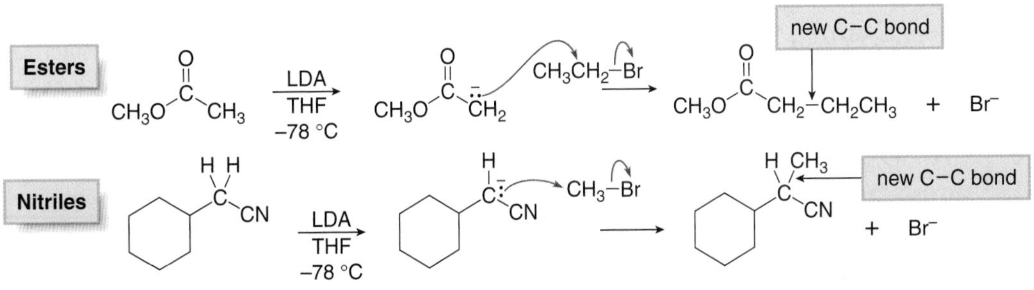

Problem 23.16 What product is formed when each compound is treated first with LDA in THF solution at low temperature, followed by CH_3CH_2I?

a. 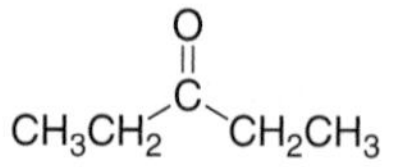
CH3CH2 C CH2CH3
O

b. 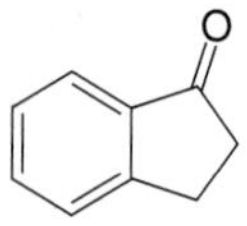

c. 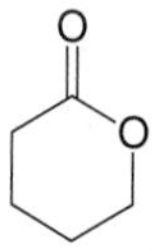

d. 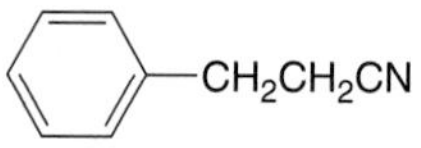
CH2CH2CN

The stereochemistry of enolate alkylation follows the general rule governing the stereochemistry of reactions: **an achiral starting material yields an achiral or racemic product.** For example, when cyclohexanone (an achiral starting material) is converted to 2-ethylcyclohexanone by treatment with base and CH_3CH_2I, a new stereogenic center is introduced, and both enantiomers of the product are formed in equal amounts—that is, a **racemic mixture.**

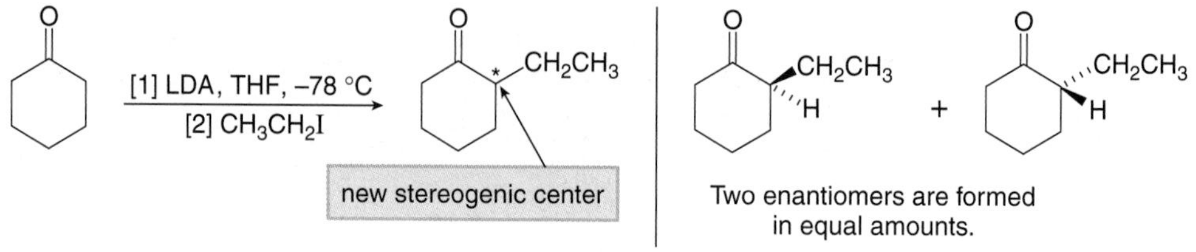
[1] LDA, THF, –78 °C
[2] CH3CH2I
CH2CH3
new stereogenic center
CH2CH3
H
+
CH2CH3
H
Two enantiomers are formed in equal amounts.

Problem 23.17 Draw the products obtained (including stereochemistry) when each compound is treated with LDA, followed by CH_3I.

a. 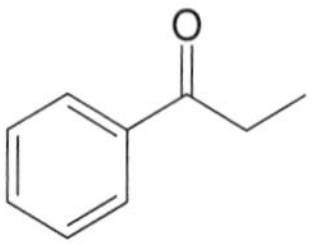

b. 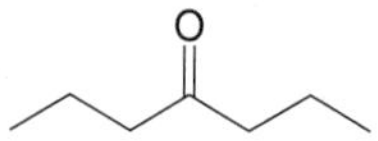

c. 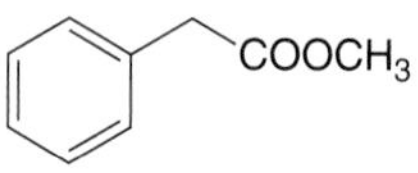
COOCH3

Problem 23.18 The analgesic naproxen can be prepared by a stepwise reaction sequence from ester **A.** Using enolate alkylation in one step, what reagents are needed to convert **A** to naproxen? Write the structure of each intermediate. Explain why a racemic product is formed.

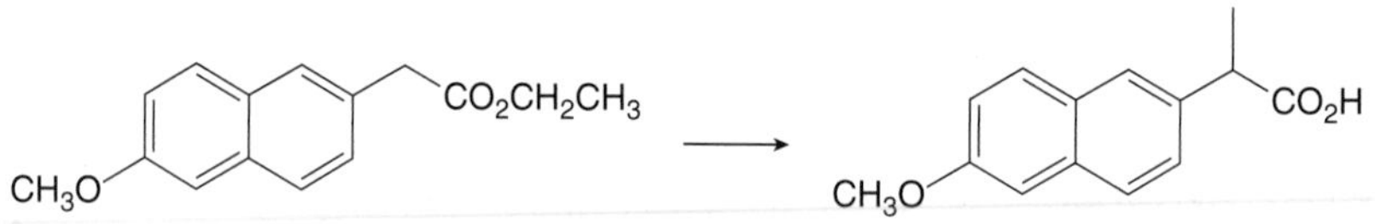
CO2CH2CH3
CH3O
CO2H
CH3O

A naproxen

23.8B Alkylation of Unsymmetrical Ketones

An unsymmetrical ketone can be regioselectively alkylated to yield one major product. The strategy depends on the use of the appropriate base, solvent, and temperature to form the kinetic or thermodynamic enolate (Section 23.4), which is then treated with an alkyl halide to form the alkylation product.

For example, 2-methylcyclohexanone can be converted to either 2,6-dimethylcyclohexanone (**A**) or 2,2-dimethylcyclohexanone (**B**) by proper choice of reaction conditions.

- **Treatment of 2-methylcyclohexanone with LDA in THF solution at –78 °C gives the less substituted kinetic enolate,** which then reacts with CH_3I to form **A.**

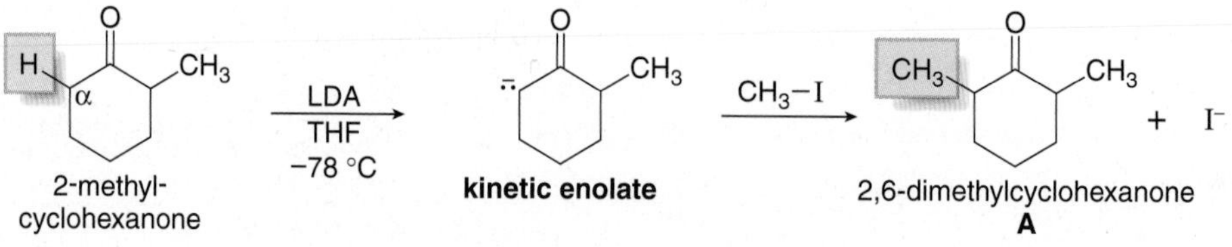
H
α
CH3
2-methyl-
cyclohexanone
LDA
THF
–78 °C
CH3
kinetic enolate
CH3–I
CH3
CH3
+ I⁻
2,6-dimethylcyclohexanone
A

- **Treatment of 2-methylcyclohexanone with $KOC(CH_3)_3$ in $(CH_3)_3COH$ solution at room temperature forms the more substituted thermodynamic enolate,** which then reacts with CH_3I to form **B.**

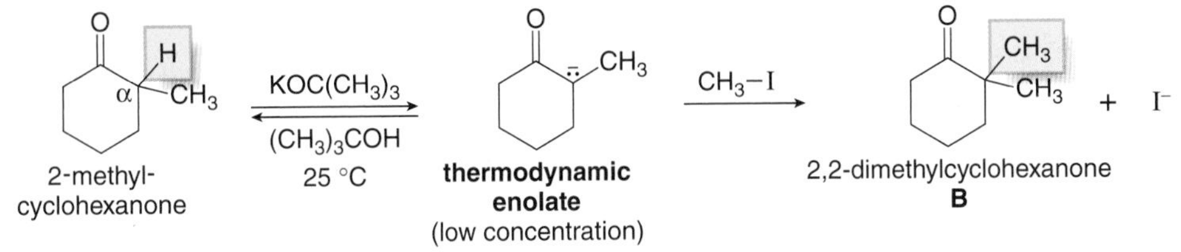

Finally, while enolate alkylation at the less substituted α carbon using LDA is a reliable regioselective reaction, enolate alkylation at the more substituted α carbon with $KOC(CH_3)_3$ may lead to mixtures of products. Regioselectivity depends on the identity of the substrate and the experimental parameters, which sometimes must be carefully monitored to maximize the yield of the desired alkylation product.

Problem 23.19 How can 2-pentanone be converted into each compound?

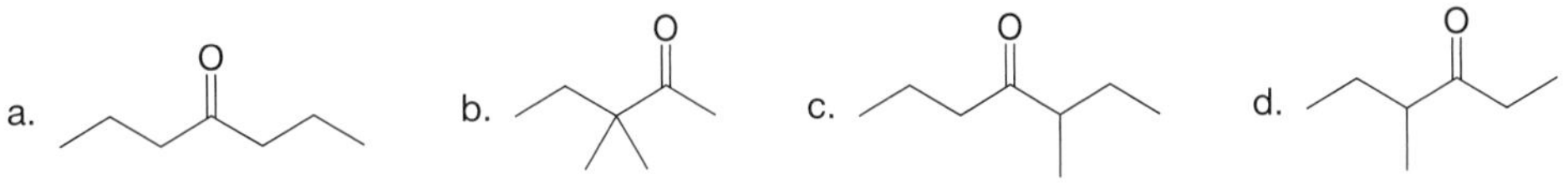

23.8C Application of Enolate Alkylation: Tamoxifen Synthesis

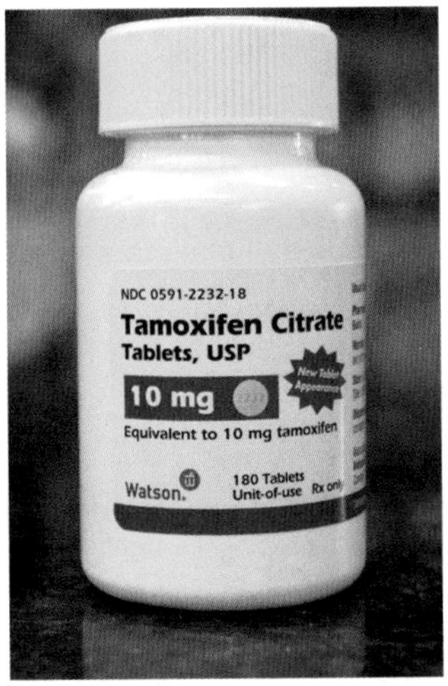

Tamoxifen has been commercially available since the 1970s, sold under the brand name of Nolvadex.

Tamoxifen, the chapter-opening molecule, is a potent anticancer drug that has been used to treat certain forms of breast cancer for many years. One step in the synthesis of tamoxifen involves the treatment of ketone **A** with NaH as base to form an enolate. Alkylation of this enolate with CH_3CH_2I forms **B** in high yield. **B** is converted to tamoxifen in several steps, some of which are reactions you have already learned.

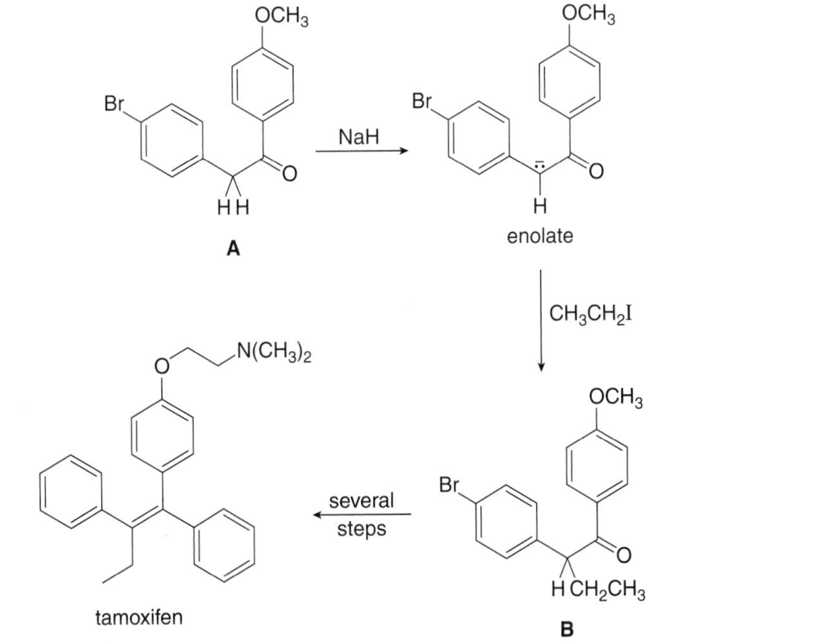

Only the *Z* isomer of the C=C provides beneficial effects.

Problem 23.20 Identify **A, B,** and **C,** intermediates in the synthesis of the five-membered ring called an α-methylene-γ-butyrolactone. This heterocyclic ring system is present in some antitumor agents.

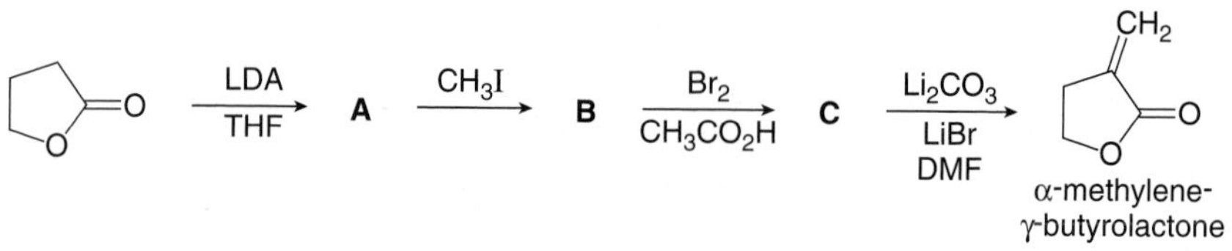
LDA
THF
A
CH_3I
B
Br_2
CH_3CO_2H
C
Li_2CO_3
LiBr
DMF
CH_2
α-methylene-
γ-butyrolactone

23.9 Malonic Ester Synthesis

Besides the direct method of enolate alkylation discussed in Section 23.8, a new alkyl group can also be introduced on the α carbon using the malonic ester synthesis and the acetoacetic ester synthesis.

- **The malonic ester synthesis prepares carboxylic acids** having two general structures:

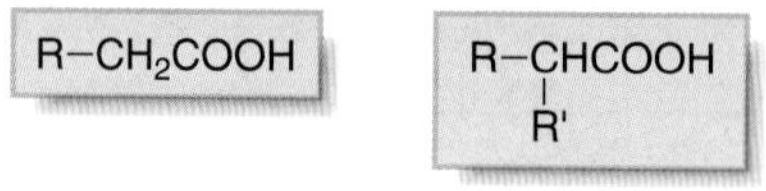
R–CH2COOH
R–CHCOOH
R'

- **The acetoacetic ester synthesis prepares methyl ketones** having two general structures:

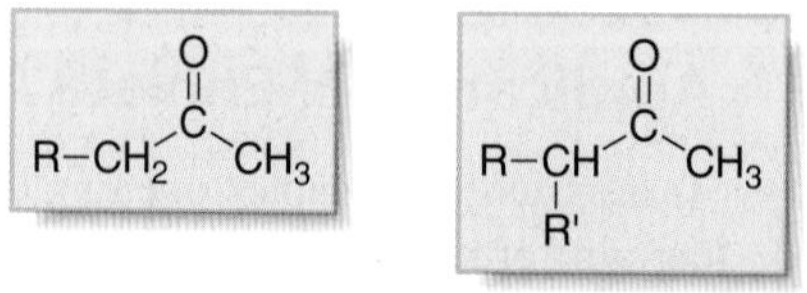
R–CH2
CH3
R–CH
CH3
R'

23.9A Background for the Malonic Ester Synthesis

- **The malonic ester synthesis is a stepwise method for converting diethyl malonate into a carboxylic acid having one or two alkyl groups on the α carbon.**

To simplify the structures, the CH_3CH_2 groups of the esters are abbreviated as Et.

Malonic ester synthesis

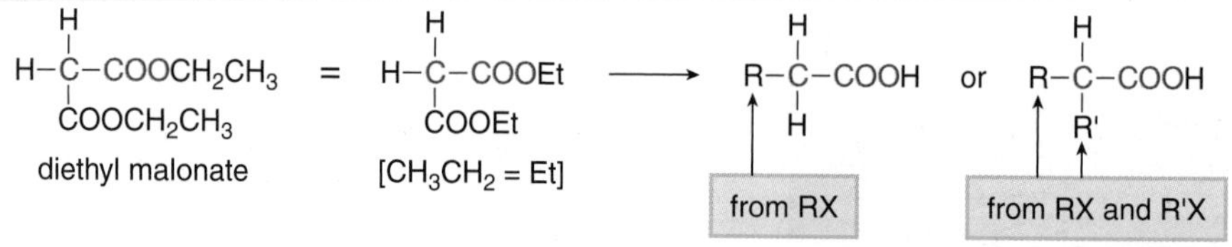
diethyl malonate
[CH3CH2 = Et]
or
from RX
from RX and R'X

Before writing out the steps in the malonic ester synthesis, recall from Section 22.11 that esters are hydrolyzed by aqueous acid. Thus, heating diethyl malonate with acid and water hydrolyzes both esters to carboxy groups, forming a β-diacid (1,3-diacid).

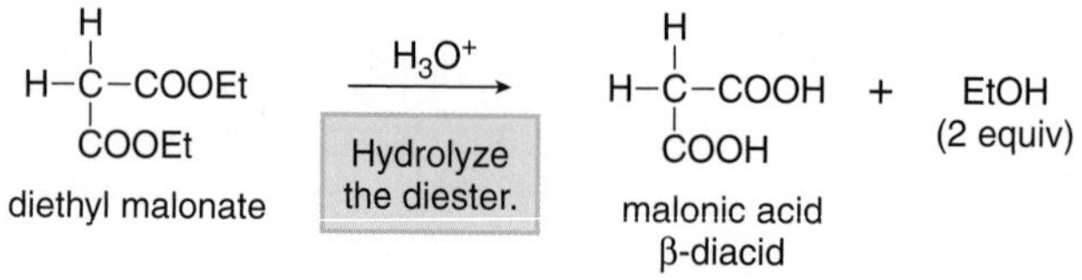
H3O+
Hydrolyze
the diester.
+
EtOH
(2 equiv)
diethyl malonate
malonic acid
β-diacid

The resulting β-diacids are unstable to heat. They **decarboxylate (lose CO_2)**, resulting in cleavage of a carbon–carbon bond and formation of a carboxylic acid. Decarboxylation is not a general reaction of all carboxylic acids. It occurs with β-diacids, however, because CO_2 can be eliminated through a cyclic, six-atom transition state. This forms an enol of a carboxylic acid, which in turn tautomerizes to the more stable keto form.

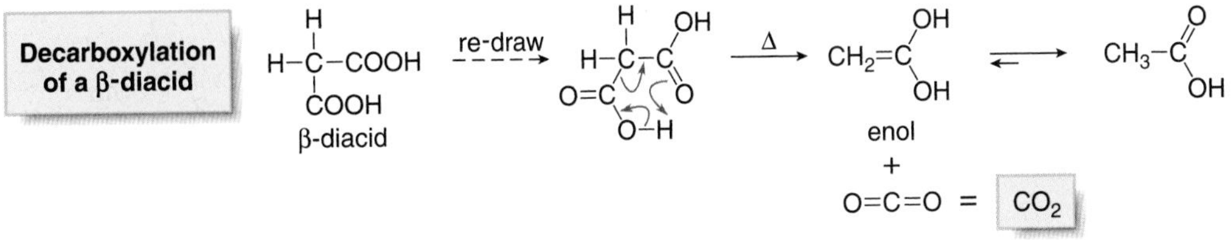

The net result of decarboxylation is cleavage of a carbon–carbon bond on the α carbon, with loss of CO_2.

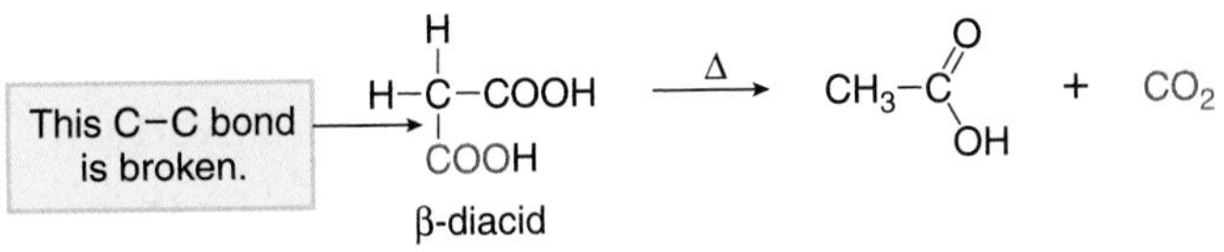

Decarboxylation occurs readily whenever a carboxy group (COOH) is bonded to the α carbon of another carbonyl group. For example, β-keto acids also readily lose CO_2 on heating to form ketones.

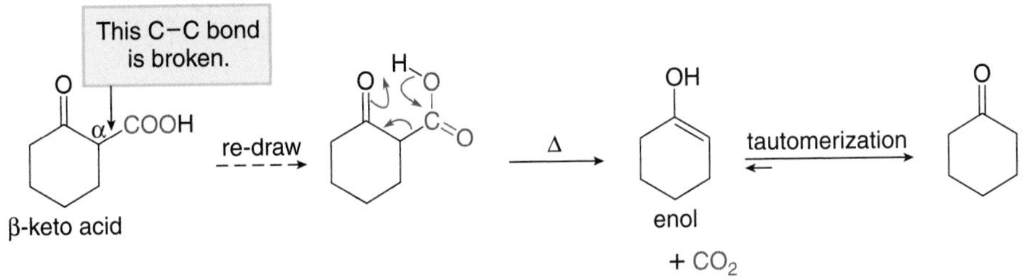

Problem 23.21 Which of the following compounds will readily lose CO_2 when heated?

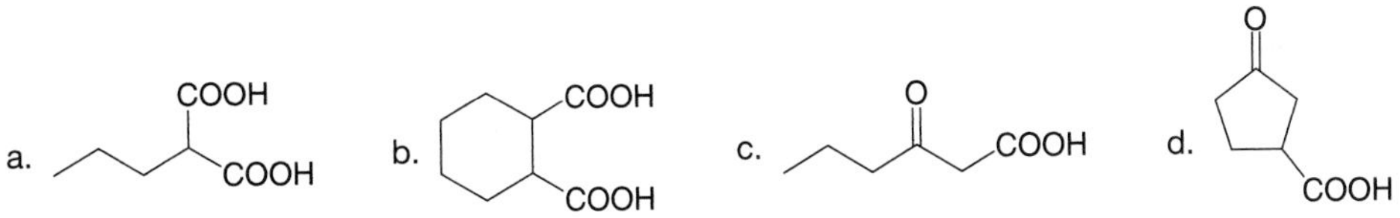

23.9B Steps in the Malonic Ester Synthesis

The malonic ester synthesis converts diethyl malonate to a carboxylic acid in three steps.

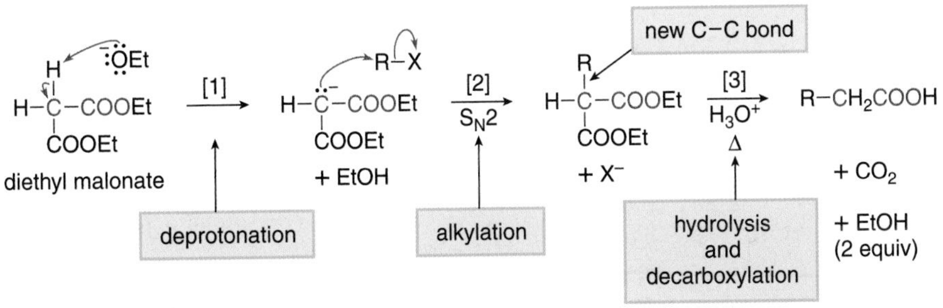

[1] **Deprotonation.** Treatment of diethyl malonate with $^{-}$OEt removes the acidic α proton between the two carbonyl groups. Recall from Section 23.3A that these protons are more acidic than other α protons because three resonance structures can be drawn for the enolate, instead of the usual two. Thus, $^{-}$OEt, rather than the stronger base LDA, can be used for this reaction.

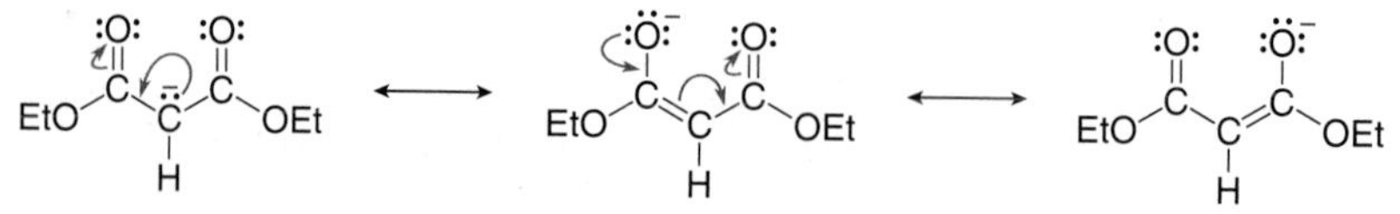

three resonance structures for the conjugate base

[2] **Alkylation.** The nucleophilic enolate reacts with an alkyl halide in an $\mathbf{S_N2}$ reaction to form a substitution product. Because the mechanism is S_N2, the yields are higher when R is CH_3 or a 1° alkyl group.

[3] **Hydrolysis and decarboxylation.** Heating the diester with aqueous acid hydrolyzes the diester to a β-diacid, which loses CO_2 to form a carboxylic acid.

The synthesis of butanoic acid ($CH_3CH_2CH_2COOH$) from diethyl malonate illustrates the basic process:

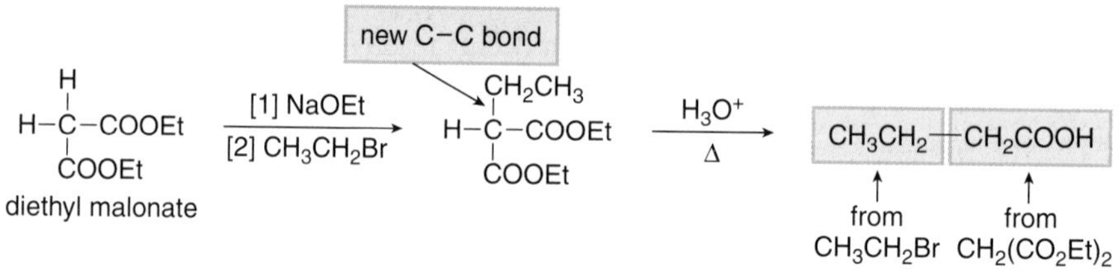

If the first two steps of the reaction sequence are repeated *prior* to hydrolysis and decarboxylation, then a carboxylic acid having *two new alkyl groups* on the α carbon can be synthesized. This is illustrated in the synthesis of 2-benzylbutanoic acid [$CH_3CH_2CH(CH_2C_6H_5)COOH$] from diethyl malonate:

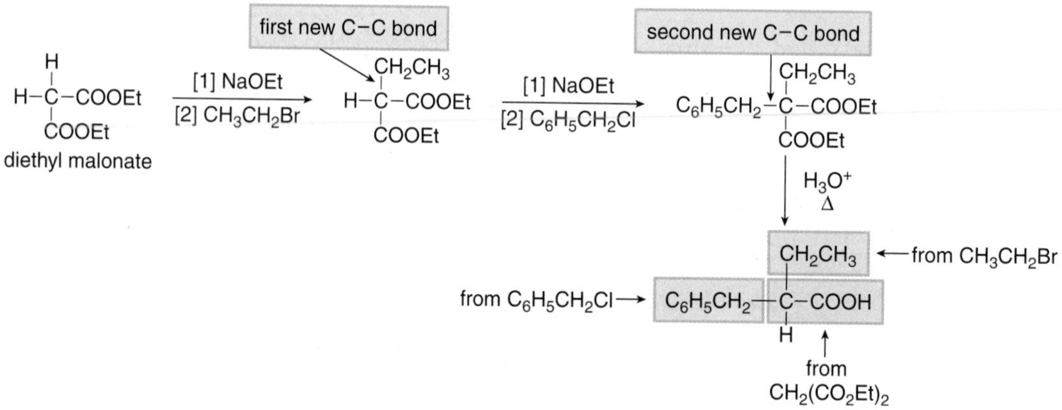

An intramolecular malonic ester synthesis can be used to form rings having three to six atoms, provided the appropriate dihalide is used as starting material. For example, cyclopentanecarboxylic acid can be prepared from diethyl malonate and 1,4-dibromobutane ($BrCH_2CH_2CH_2CH_2Br$) by the following sequence of reactions:

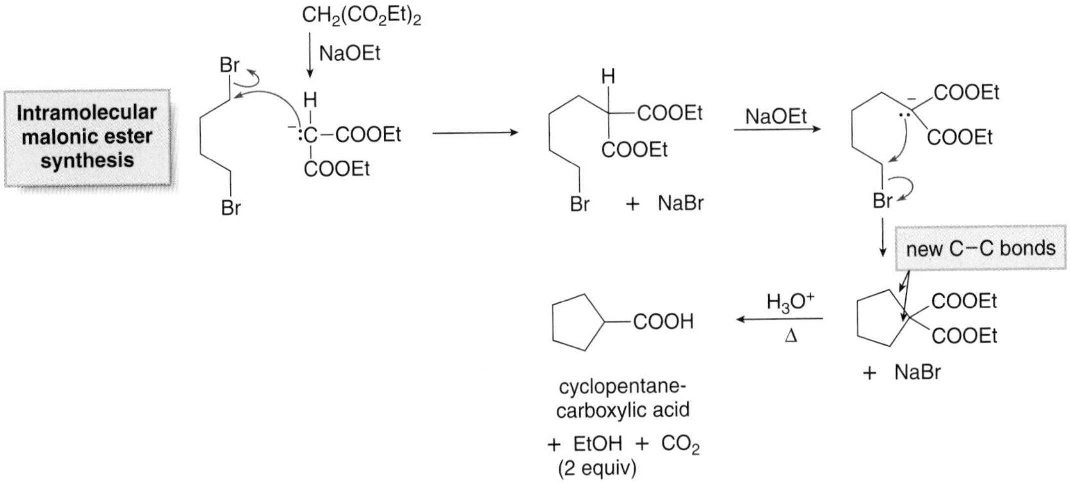

Problem 23.22 Draw the products of each reaction.

a.

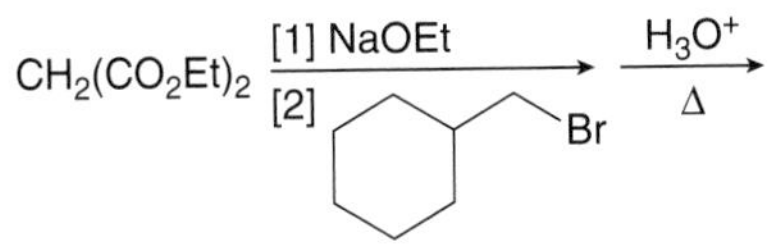

b. $CH_2(CO_2Et)_2 \xrightarrow[\text{[2] } CH_3Br]{\text{[1] NaOEt}} \xrightarrow[\text{[2] } CH_3Br]{\text{[1] NaOEt}} \xrightarrow[\Delta]{H_3O^+}$

Problem 23.23 What cyclic product is formed from each dihalide using the malonic ester synthesis: (a) $ClCH_2CH_2CH_2Cl$; (b) $(BrCH_2CH_2)_2O$?

23.9C Retrosynthetic Analysis

To use the malonic ester synthesis you must be able to determine what starting materials are needed to prepare a given compound—that is, you must **work backwards in the retrosynthetic direction.** This involves a two-step process:

> **[1] Locate the α carbon to the COOH group, and identify all alkyl groups bonded to the α carbon.**
>
> **[2] Break the molecule into two (or three) components: Each alkyl group bonded to the α carbon comes from an alkyl halide. The remainder of the molecule comes from $CH_2(COOEt)_2$.**

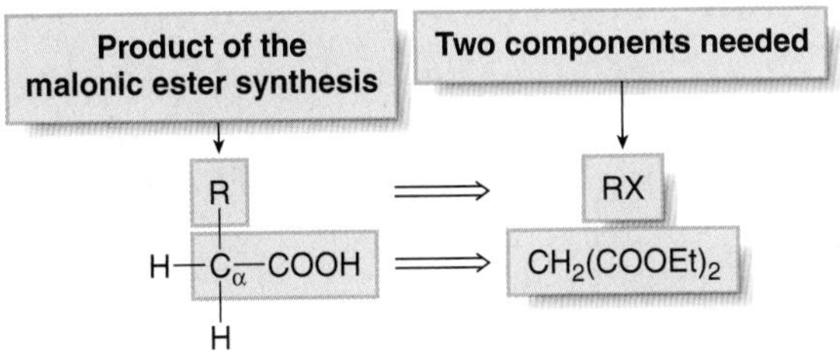

Sample Problem 23.3 What starting materials are needed to prepare 2-methylhexanoic acid [$CH_3CH_2CH_2CH_2CH(CH_3)COOH$] using a malonic ester synthesis?

Solution

The target molecule has two different alkyl groups bonded to the α carbon, so three components are needed for the synthesis:

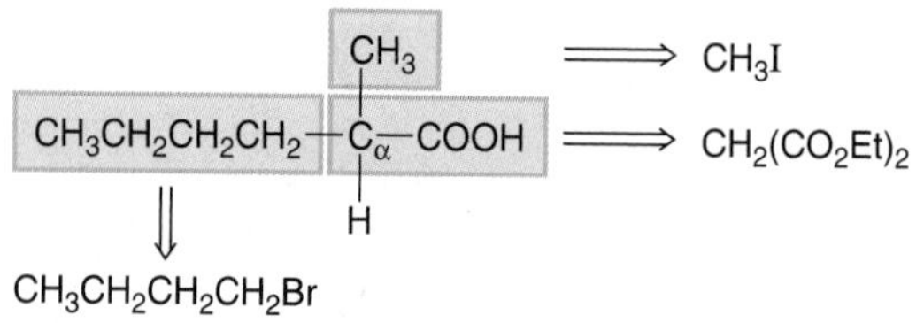

Writing the synthesis in the synthetic direction:

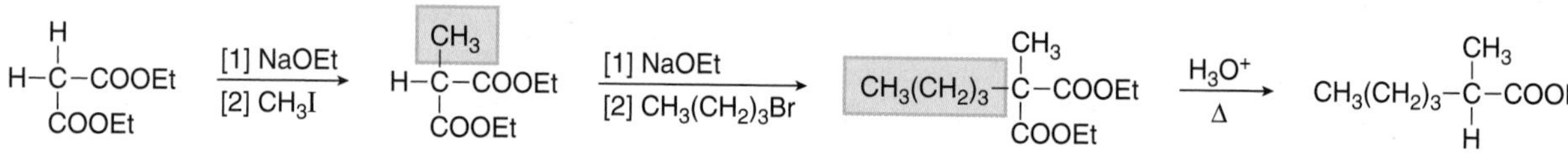

Problem 23.24 What alkyl halides are needed to prepare each carboxylic acid by the malonic ester synthesis?

a. $(CH_3)_2CHCH_2CH_2CH_2CH_2CH_2COOH$ b.

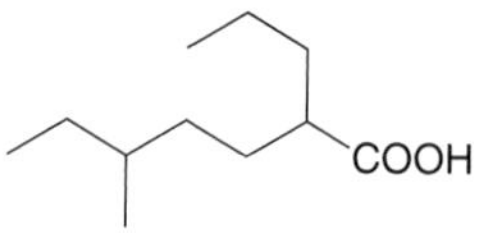

c. $(CH_3CH_2CH_2CH_2)_2CHCOOH$

Problem 23.25 Explain why each of the following carboxylic acids cannot be prepared by a malonic ester synthesis: (a) $(CH_3)_3CCH_2COOH$; (b) $C_6H_5CH_2COOH$; (c) $(CH_3)_3CCOOH$.

23.10 Acetoacetic Ester Synthesis

- **The acetoacetic ester synthesis is a stepwise method for converting ethyl acetoacetate into a ketone having one or two alkyl groups on the α carbon.**

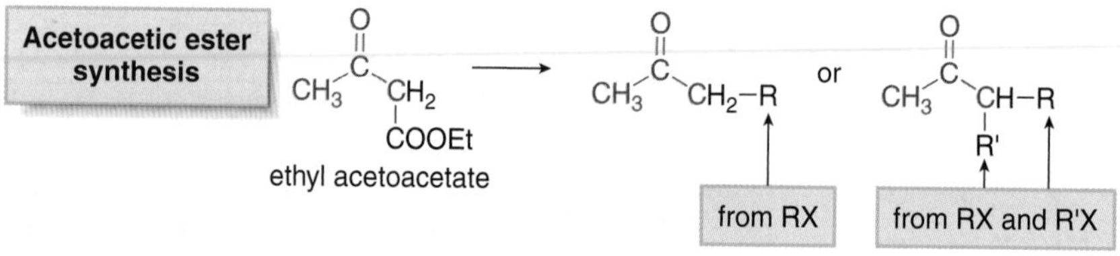

23.10A Steps in the Acetoacetic Ester Synthesis

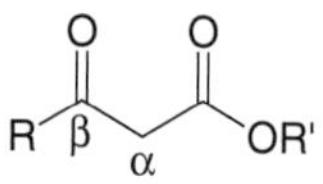

β-keto ester

The steps in the acetoacetic ester synthesis are exactly the same as those in the malonic ester synthesis. Because the starting material, CH_3COCH_2COOEt, is a β-keto ester, the final product is a **ketone,** not a carboxylic acid.

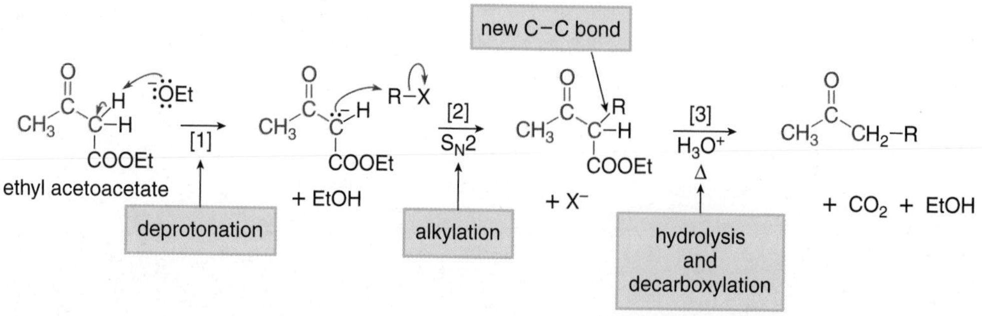

[1] **Deprotonation.** Treatment of ethyl acetoacetate with ^{-}OEt removes the acidic proton between the two carbonyl groups.

[2] **Alkylation.** The nucleophilic enolate reacts with an alkyl halide (RX) in an S_N2 reaction to form a substitution product. Because the mechanism is S_N2, the yields are higher when R is CH_3 or a 1° alkyl group.

[3] **Hydrolysis and decarboxylation.** Heating the β-keto ester with aqueous acid hydrolyzes the ester to a β-keto acid, which loses CO_2 to form a ketone.

If the first two steps of the reaction sequence are repeated *prior* to hydrolysis and decarboxylation, then a ketone having *two new alkyl groups* on the α carbon can be synthesized.

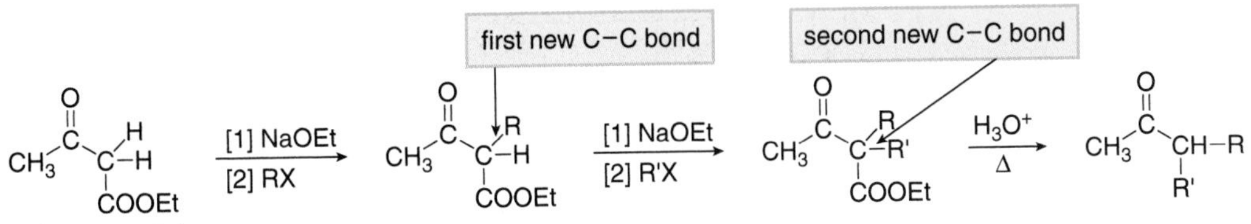
first new C–C bond
second new C–C bond
ethyl acetoacetate
[1] NaOEt
[2] RX
[1] NaOEt
[2] R'X
H3O+
Δ
COOEt

Problem 23.26 What ketones are prepared by the following reactions?

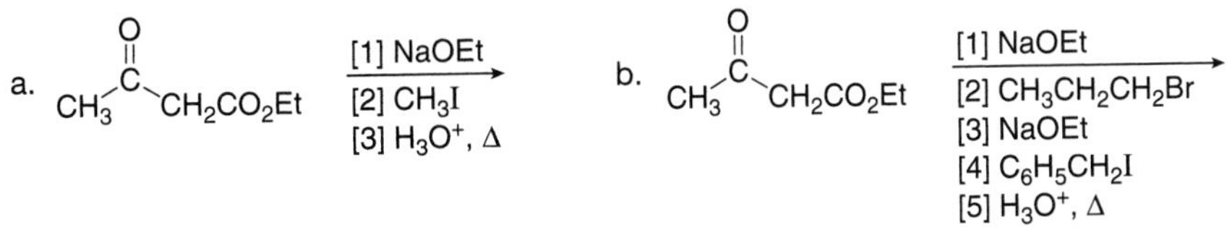
a.
CH3COCH2CO2Et
[1] NaOEt
[2] CH3I
[3] H3O+, Δ
b.
CH3COCH2CO2Et
[1] NaOEt
[2] CH3CH2CH2Br
[3] NaOEt
[4] C6H5CH2I
[5] H3O+, Δ

23.10B Retrosynthetic Analysis

To determine what starting materials are needed to prepare a given ketone using the acetoacetic ester synthesis, you must again work in the **retrosynthetic** direction. This involves a two-step process:

[1] Identify the alkyl groups bonded to the α carbon to the carbonyl group.

[2] Break the molecule into two (or three) components: Each alkyl group bonded to the α carbon comes from an alkyl halide. The remainder of the molecule comes from CH_3COCH_2COOEt.

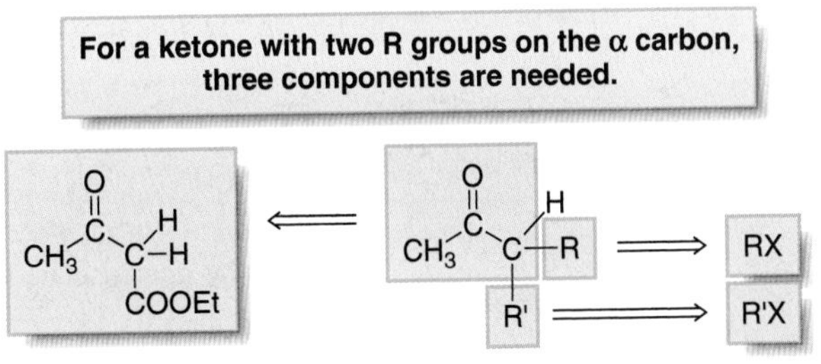
For a ketone with two R groups on the α carbon, three components are needed.
COOEt
RX
R'X

Sample Problem 23.4 What starting materials are needed to synthesize 2-heptanone using the acetoacetic ester synthesis?

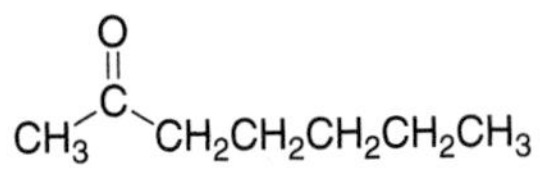
2-heptanone

Solution

2-Heptanone has only one alkyl group bonded to the α carbon, so only one alkyl halide is needed in the acetoacetic ester synthesis.

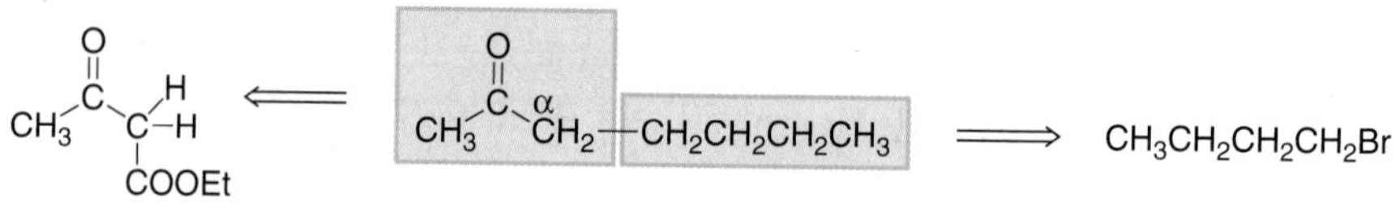
CH3 C(=O) C(H)(H) COOEt
CH3 C(=O) α CH2—CH2CH2CH2CH3
CH3CH2CH2CH2Br

Writing the acetoacetic ester synthesis in the synthetic direction:

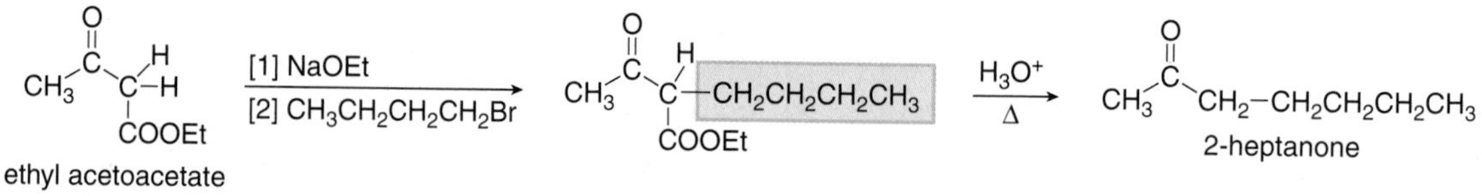
ethyl acetoacetate
[1] NaOEt
[2] CH3CH2CH2CH2Br
COOEt
H3O+
Δ
CH2—CH2CH2CH2CH3
2-heptanone

Problem 23.27 What alkyl halides are needed to prepare each ketone using the acetoacetic ester synthesis?

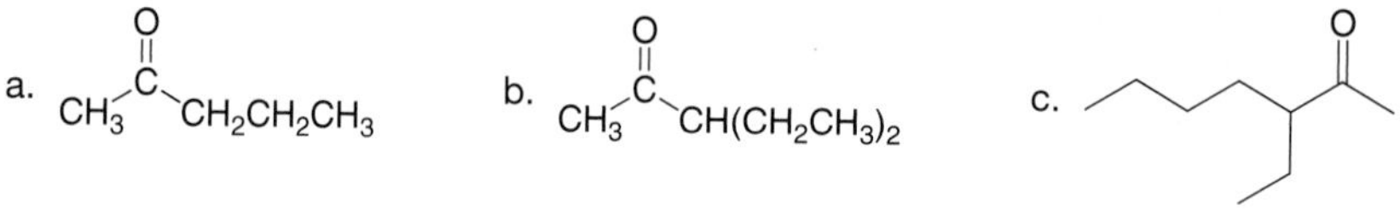
a. CH3 C(=O) CH2CH2CH3
b. CH3 C(=O) CH(CH2CH3)2
c.

Problem 23.28 Treatment of ethyl acetoacetate with NaOEt (2 equiv) and $BrCH_2CH_2Br$ forms compound **X**. This reaction is the first step in the synthesis of illudin-S, an antitumor substance isolated from the jack-o'-lantern, a poisonous, saffron-colored mushroom. What is the structure of **X?**

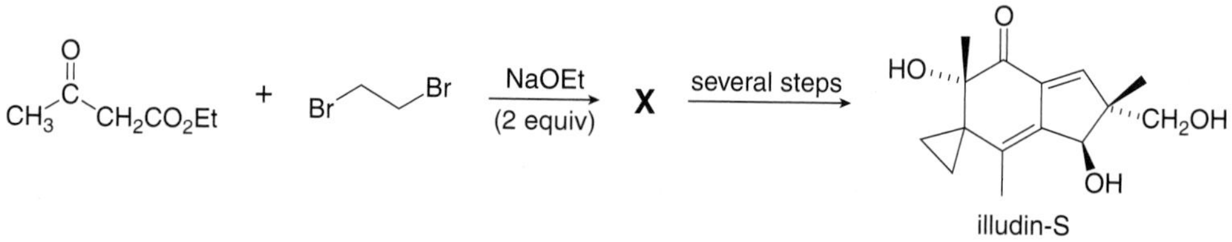
CH3 C(=O) CH2CO2Et
+
Br Br
NaOEt
(2 equiv)
X
several steps
HO
CH2OH
OH
illudin-S

The jack-o'-lantern, source of the antitumor agent illudin-S

The acetoacetic ester synthesis and direct enolate alkylation are two different methods that prepare similar ketones. 2-Butanone, for example, can be synthesized from acetone by direct enolate alkylation with CH_3I (Method [1]), or by alkylation of ethyl acetoacetate followed by hydrolysis and decarboxylation (Method [2]).

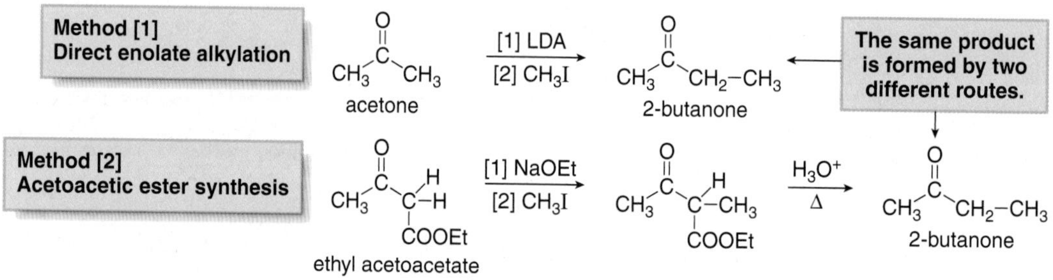
Method [1]
Direct enolate alkylation
acetone
[1] LDA
[2] CH3I
2-butanone
The same product is formed by two different routes.
Method [2]
Acetoacetic ester synthesis
ethyl acetoacetate
[1] NaOEt
[2] CH3I
COOEt
H3O+
Δ
2-butanone

Why would you ever make 2-butanone from ethyl acetoacetate when you could make it in fewer steps from acetone? There are many factors to consider. First of all, synthetic organic chemists like to have a variety of methods to accomplish a single kind of reaction. Sometimes subtle changes in the structure of a starting material make one reaction work better than another.

In the chemical industry, moreover, cost is an important issue. Any reaction needed to make a large quantity of a useful drug or other consumer product must use cheap starting materials. Direct enolate alkylation usually requires a very strong base like LDA to be successful, whereas the acetoacetic ester synthesis utilizes NaOEt. NaOEt can be prepared from cheaper starting materials, and this makes the acetoacetic ester synthesis an attractive method, even though it involves more steps.

Thus, each method has its own advantages and disadvantages, depending on the starting material, the availability of reagents, the cost, and the occurrence of side reactions.

Problem 23.29 Nabumetone is a pain reliever and anti-inflammatory agent sold under the brand name of Relafen.

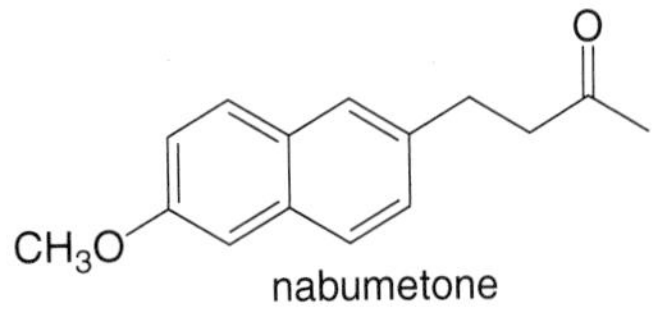
O
CH_3O
nabumetone

a. Write out a synthesis of nabumetone from ethyl acetoacetate.
b. What ketone and alkyl halide are needed to synthesize nabumetone by direct enolate alkylation?

KEY CONCEPTS

Substitution Reactions of Carbonyl Compounds at the α Carbon

Kinetic Versus Thermodynamic Enolates (23.4)

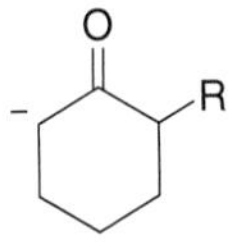
O
R
kinetic enolate

Kinetic enolate
- The less substituted enolate
- Favored by strong base, polar aprotic solvent, low temperature: LDA, THF, –78 °C

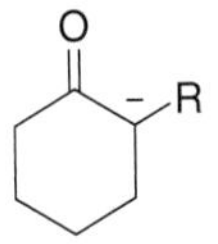
O
R
thermodynamic enolate

Thermodynamic enolate
- The more substituted enolate
- Favored by strong base, protic solvent, higher temperature: $NaOCH_2CH_3$, CH_3CH_2OH, room temperature

Halogenation at the α Carbon

[1] Halogenation in acid (23.7A)

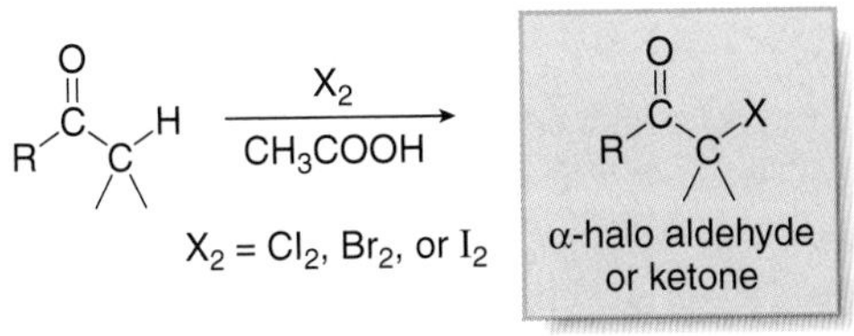
X_2
CH_3COOH
$X_2 = Cl_2, Br_2, \text{or } I_2$
α-halo aldehyde or ketone

- The reaction occurs via enol intermediates.
- Monosubstitution of X for H occurs on the α carbon.

---

[2] Halogenation in base (23.7B)

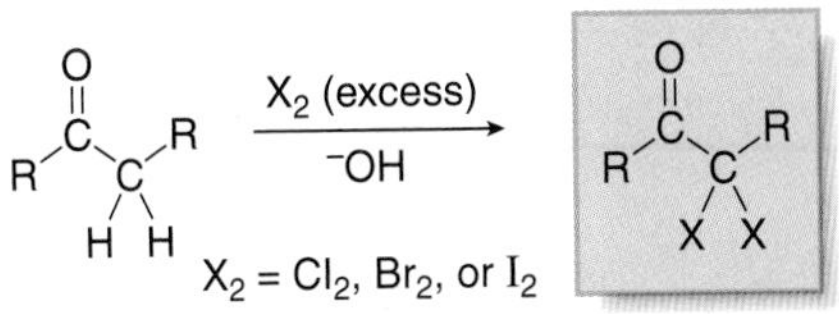
X_2 (excess)
^-OH
$X_2 = Cl_2, Br_2, \text{or } I_2$

- The reaction occurs via enolate intermediates.
- Polysubstitution of X for H occurs on the α carbon.

[3] Halogenation of *methyl* ketones in base—The haloform reaction (23.7B)

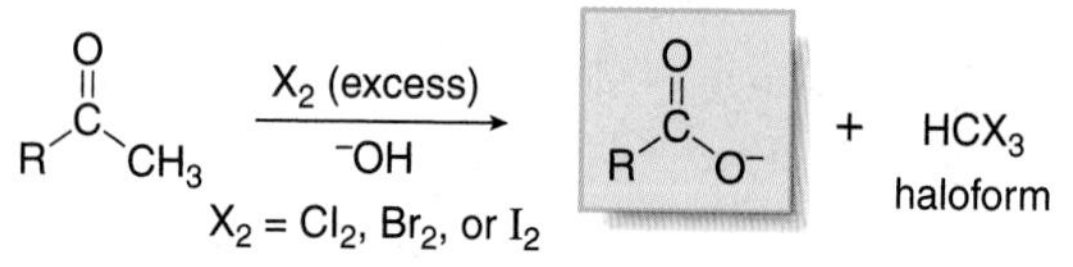

- The reaction occurs with methyl ketones and results in cleavage of a carbon–carbon σ bond.

Reactions of α-Halo Carbonyl Compounds (23.7C)

[1] Elimination to form α,β-unsaturated carbonyl compounds

- Elimination of the elements of Br and H forms a new π bond, giving an α,β-unsaturated carbonyl compound.

[2] Nucleophilic substitution

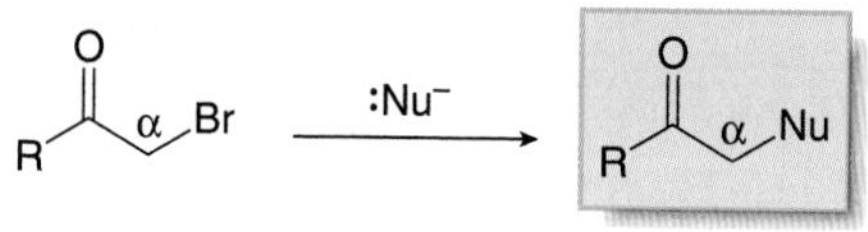

- The reaction follows an S_N2 mechanism, generating an α-substituted carbonyl compound.

Alkylation Reactions at the α Carbon

[1] Direct alkylation at the α carbon (23.8)

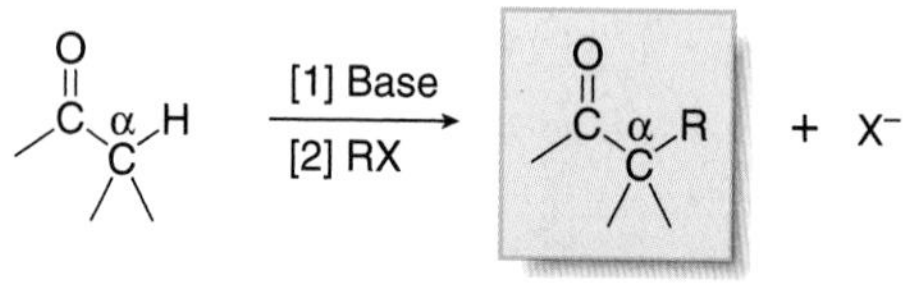

- The reaction forms a new C–C bond to the α carbon.
- LDA is a common base used to form an intermediate enolate.
- The alkylation in Step [2] follows an S_N2 mechanism.

[2] Malonic ester synthesis (23.9)

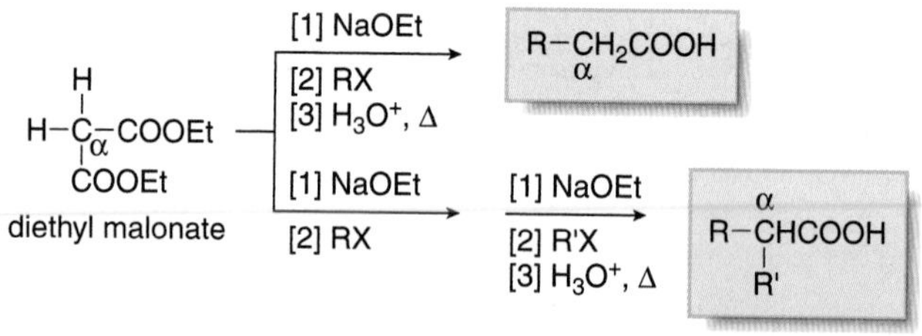

- The reaction is used to prepare carboxylic acids with one or two alkyl groups on the α carbon.
- The alkylation in Step [2] follows an S_N2 mechanism.

[3] Acetoacetic ester synthesis (23.10)

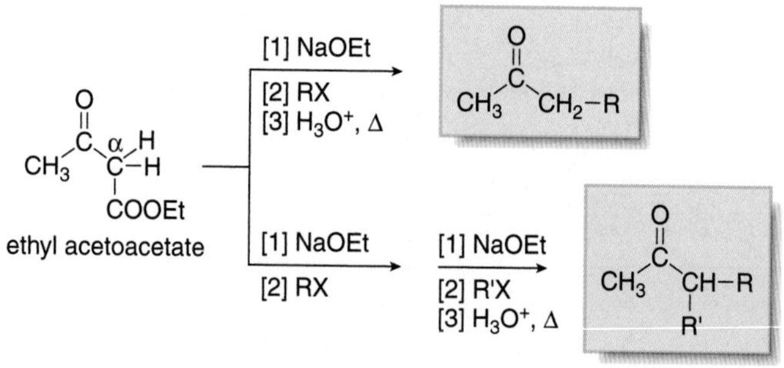

- The reaction is used to prepare ketones with one or two alkyl groups on the α carbon.
- The alkylation in Step [2] follows an S_N2 mechanism.

PROBLEMS

Problems Using Three-Dimensional Models

23.30 Draw enol tautomer(s) for each compound. Ignore stereoisomers.

a. 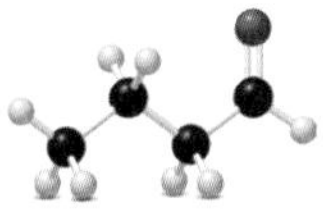

b. 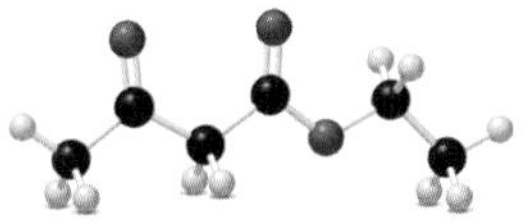

23.31 The cis ketone **A** is isomerized to a trans ketone **B** with aqueous NaOH. A similar isomerization does not occur with ketone **C.** (a) Draw the structure of **B** using a chair cyclohexane. (b) Label the substituents in **C** as cis or trans, and explain the difference in reactivity.

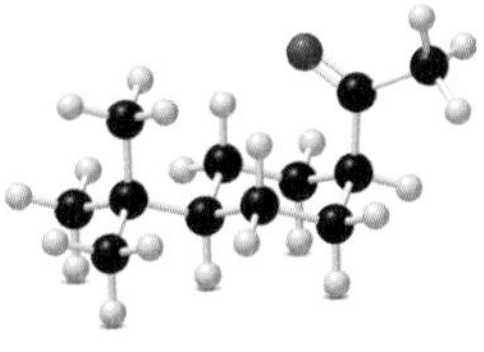

A

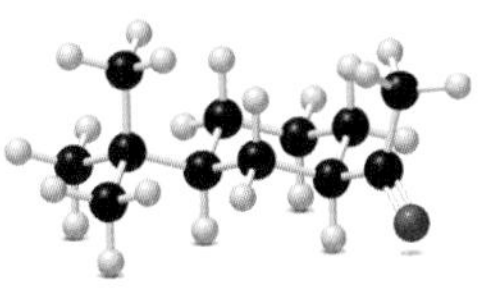

C

Enols, Enolates, and Acidic Protons

23.32 Draw enol tautomer(s) for each compound.

a. 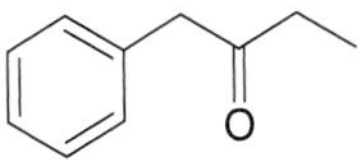

b. $CH_3CH_2CH_2CH_2CO_2CH_2CH_3$

c. 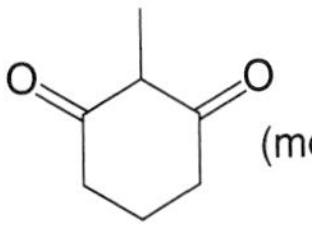 (mono enol form)

d. $CH_3CH_2CHCOOH$ (with CH_3 on the CH)

23.33 Both 2,4-pentanedione and ethyl acetoacetate have two carbonyl groups separated by a single carbon atom. Although an equilibrium mixture of 2,4-pentanedione tautomers contains 76% of the enol forms, an equilibrium mixture of ethyl acetoacetate tautomers contains only 8% of the enol forms. Suggest a reason for this difference.

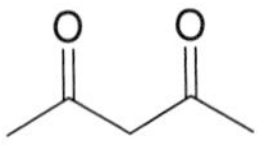

2,4-pentanedione

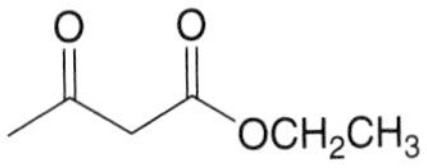

ethyl acetoacetate

23.34 What hydrogen atoms in each compound have a $pK_a \leq 25$?

a. $CH_3CH_2CH_2CO_2CH(CH_3)_2$

b. 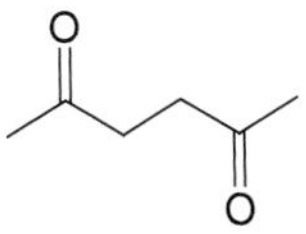

c. 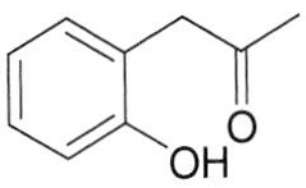

d. 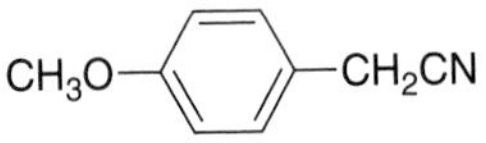

e. 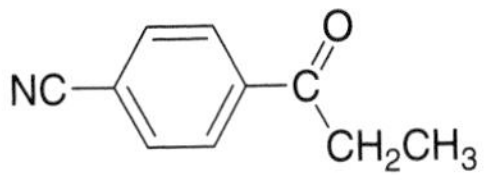

f. 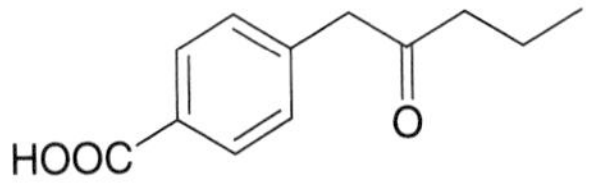

23.35 Rank the labeled protons in each compound in order of increasing acidity.

a. 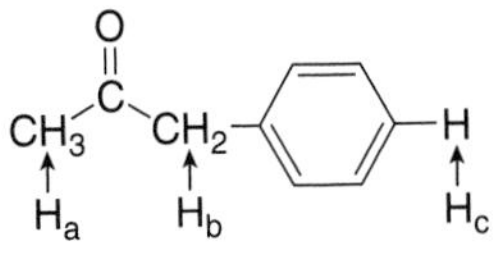

b. 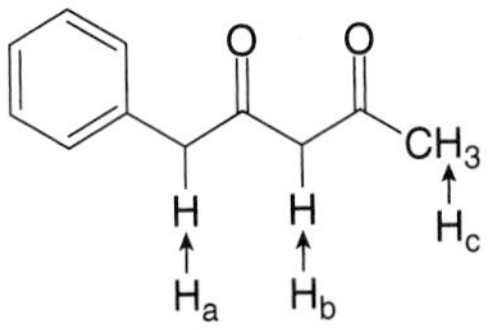

c. 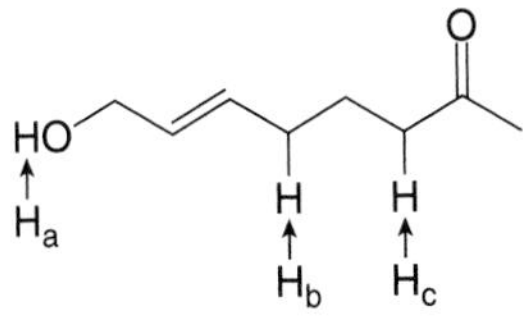

23.36 What is the major enolate (or carbanion) formed when each compound is treated with LDA?

a. 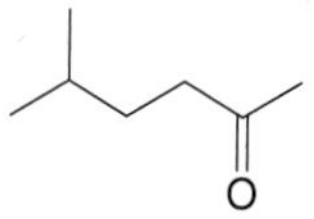

c. 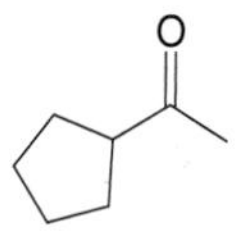

e. 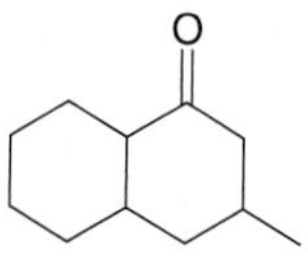

b. 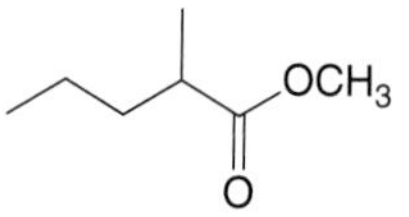
OCH3

d. 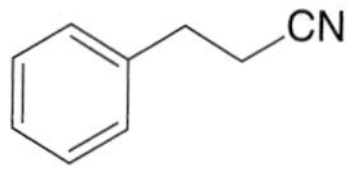
CN

f. 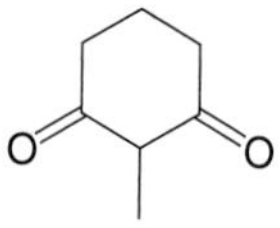

23.37 How could IR spectroscopy be used to detect the presence of enol tautomers?

23.38 Why is the pK_a of the H_a protons in 1-acetylcyclohexene higher than the pK_a of the H_b protons?

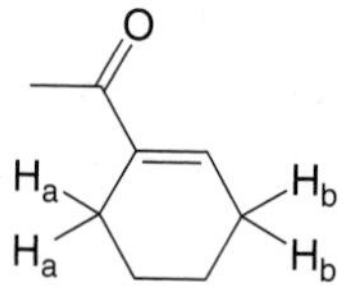
Ha
Ha
Hb
Hb

1-acetylcyclohexene

23.39 Explain why 5,5-dimethyl-1,3-cyclohexanedione exists predominantly in its enol form, but 2,2-dimethyl-1,3-cyclohexanedione does not.

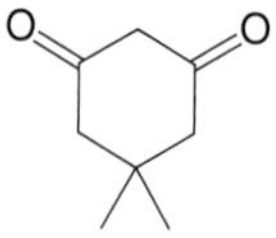

5,5-dimethyl-1,3-cyclohexanedione

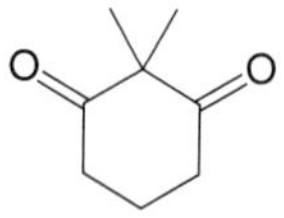

2,2-dimethyl-1,3-cyclohexanedione

23.40 Acyclovir is an effective antiviral agent used to treat the herpes simplex virus. (a) Draw the enol form of acyclovir, and explain why it is aromatic. (b) Why is acyclovir typically drawn in its keto form, despite the fact that its enol is aromatic?

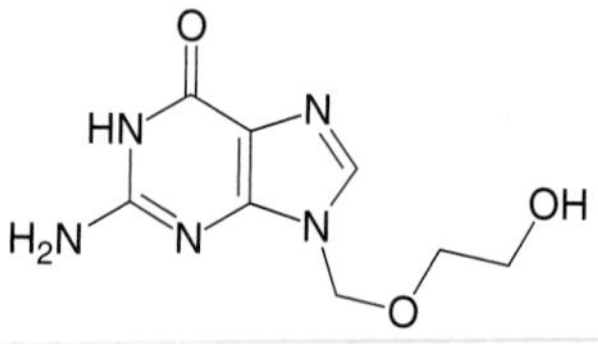
HN
N
N
N
H2N
OH
O

acyclovir

23.41 Explain why the α protons of an ester are less acidic than the α protons of a ketone by ~5 pK_a units.

23.42 Explain why 2,4-pentanedione forms two different alkylation products (**A** or **B**) when the number of equivalents of base is increased from one to two.

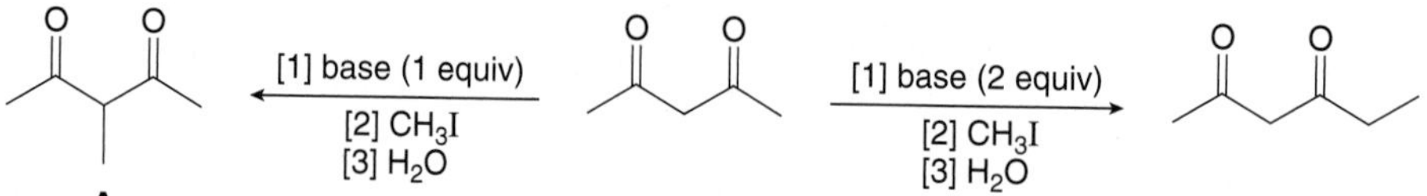
[1] base (1 equiv)
[2] CH3I
[3] H2O
[1] base (2 equiv)
[2] CH3I
[3] H2O

A 2,4-pentanedione **B**

Halogenation

23.43 Acid-catalyzed bromination of 2-pentanone ($CH_3COCH_2CH_2CH_3$) forms two products: $BrCH_2COCH_2CH_2CH_3$ (**A**) and $CH_3COCH(Br)CH_2CH_3$ (**B**). Explain why the major product is **B,** with the Br atom on the more substituted side of the carbonyl group.

23.44 Draw a stepwise mechanism for each reaction.

a. 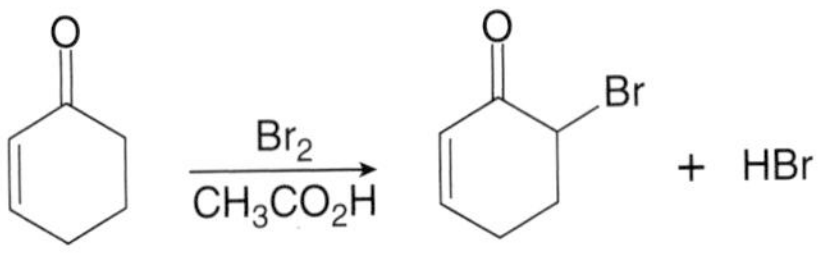
O
Br₂
CH₃CO₂H
O
Br
+ HBr

b. 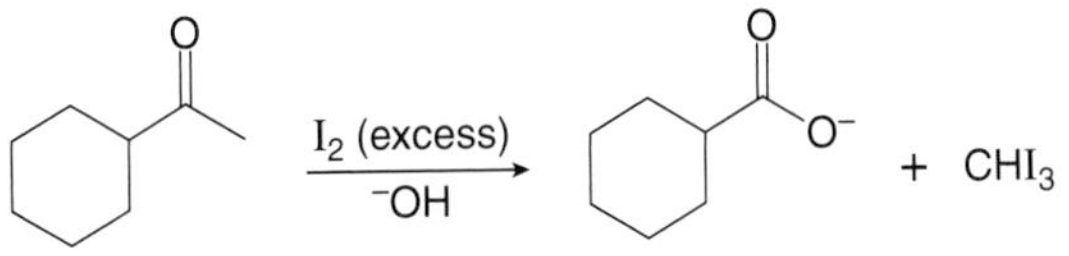
O
I₂ (excess)
⁻OH
O
O⁻
+ CHI₃

Malonic Ester Synthesis

23.45 What alkyl halides are needed to prepare each carboxylic acid using the malonic ester synthesis?

a. $CH_3OCH_2CH_2COOH$

b. 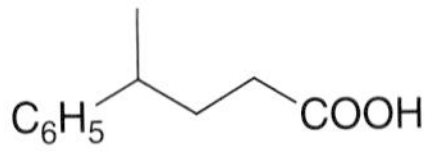
C₆H₅
COOH

c. 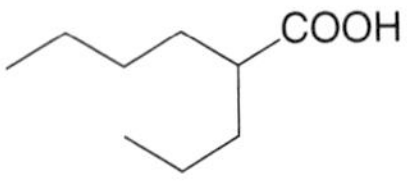
COOH

23.46 Use the malonic ester synthesis to prepare each carboxylic acid.

a. $CH_3CH_2CH_2CH_2CH_2CH_2COOH$

b. 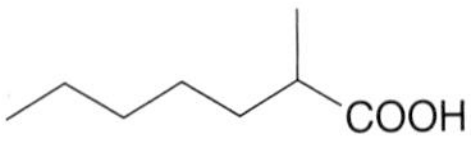
COOH

c. 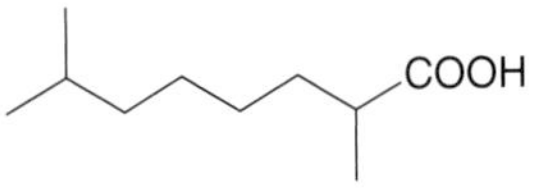
COOH

23.47 Devise a synthesis of valproic acid [$(CH_3CH_2CH_2)_2CHCO_2H$], a medicine used to treat epileptic seizures, using the malonic ester synthesis.

23.48 Synthesize each compound from diethyl malonate. You may use any other organic or inorganic reagents.

a. 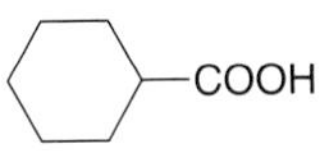
COOH

b. 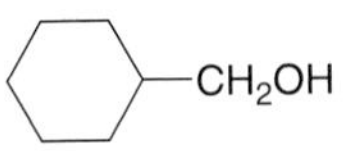
CH₂OH

c. 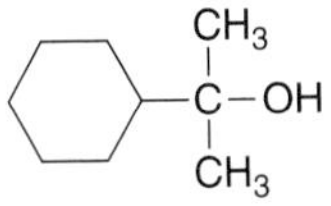
CH₃
C–OH
CH₃

d. 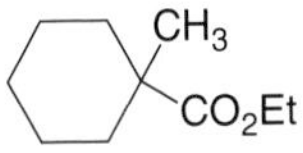
CH₃
CO₂Et

23.49 The enolate derived from diethyl malonate reacts with a variety of electrophiles (not just alkyl halides) to form new carbon–carbon bonds. With this in mind, draw the products formed when $Na^+ \,^-CH(COOEt)_2$ reacts with each electrophile, followed by treatment with H_2O.

a. 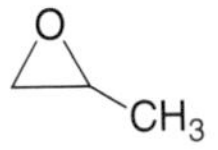
O
CH₃

b. $CH_2{=}O$

c. 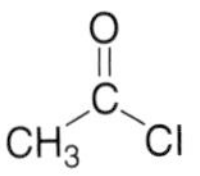
O
C
CH₃
Cl

d. 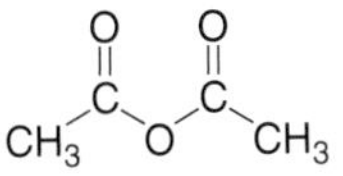
O
O
C
C
CH₃
O
CH₃

Acetoacetic Ester Synthesis

23.50 What alkyl halides are needed to prepare each ketone using the acetoacetic ester synthesis?

a. 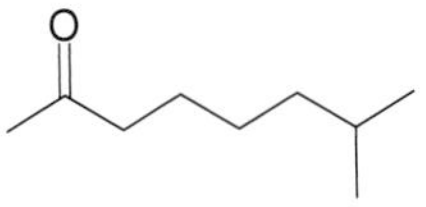
O

b. 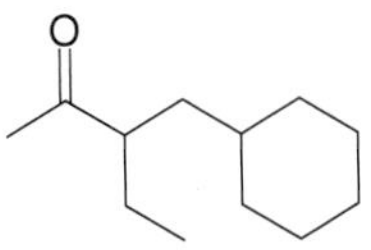
O

c. 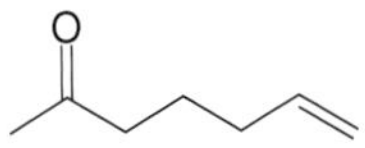
O

d. 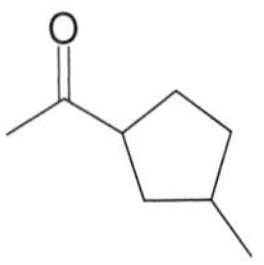
O

23.51 Synthesize each compound from ethyl acetoacetate. You may use any other organic or inorganic reagents.

a. 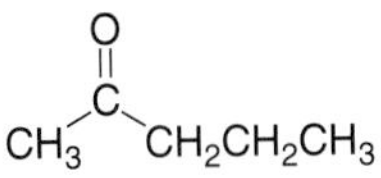
O
C
CH₃
CH₂CH₂CH₃

b. 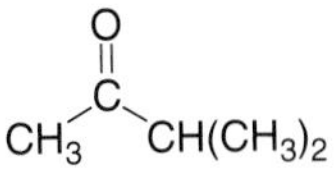
O
C
CH₃
CH(CH₃)₂

c. 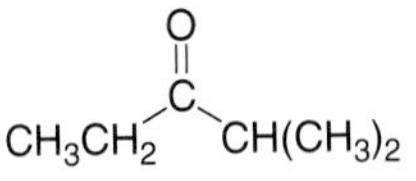
O
C
CH₃CH₂
CH(CH₃)₂

d. 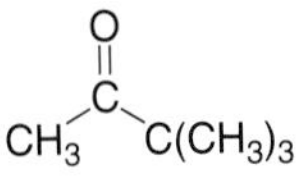
O
C
CH₃
C(CH₃)₃

Reactions

23.52 Draw the organic products formed in each reaction.

a. 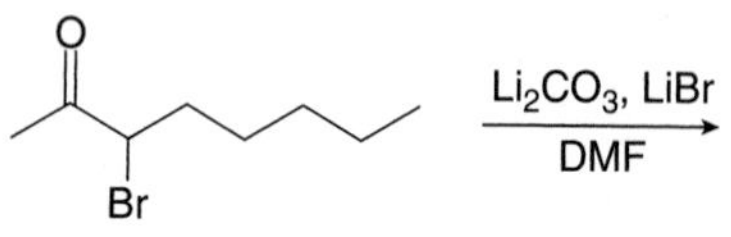
Br
Li₂CO₃, LiBr
DMF

f. 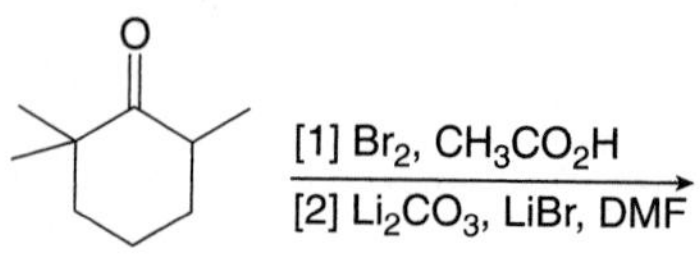
[1] Br₂, CH₃CO₂H
[2] Li₂CO₃, LiBr, DMF

b. 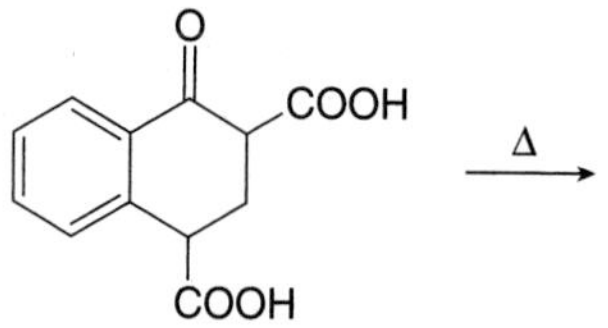
COOH
COOH
Δ

g. 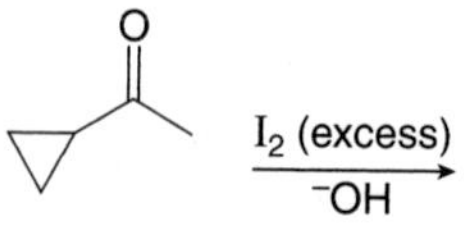
I₂ (excess)
⁻OH

c. $CH_3CH_2CH_2CO_2Et$ $\xrightarrow[\text{[2] } CH_3CH_2I]{\text{[1] LDA}}$

h. 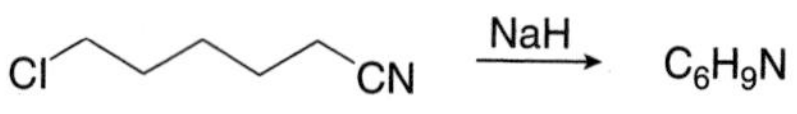
Cl
CN
NaH
C₆H₉N

d. 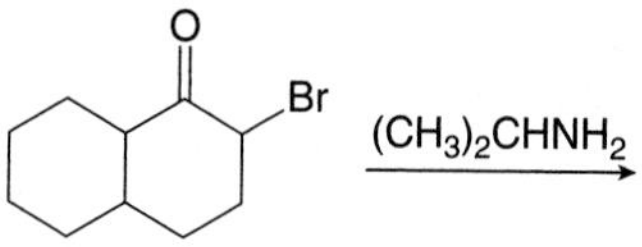
Br
(CH₃)₂CHNH₂

i. 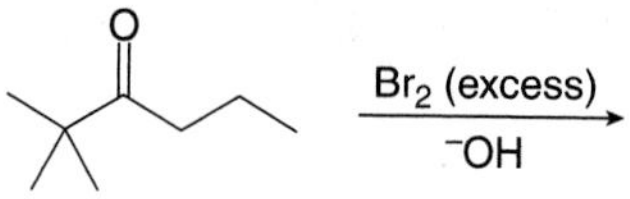
Br₂ (excess)
⁻OH

e. 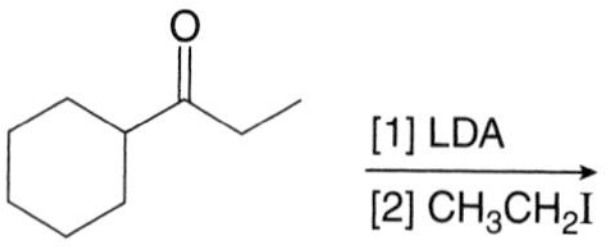
[1] LDA
[2] CH₃CH₂I

j. 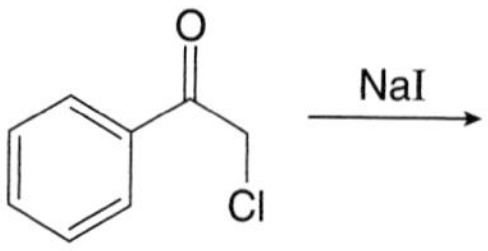
Cl
NaI

23.53 Draw the products formed (including stereoisomers) in each reaction.

a. 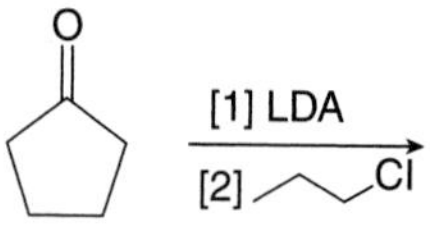
[1] LDA
[2] Cl

b. 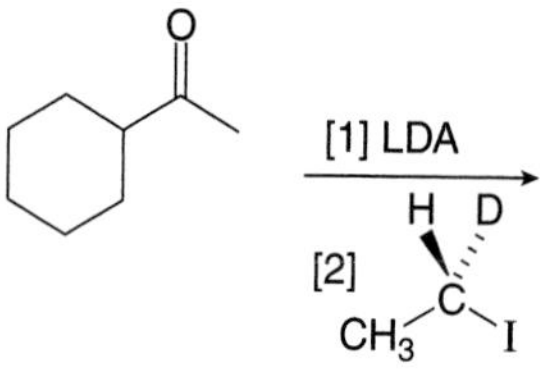
[1] LDA
[2] H D C CH₃ I

c. 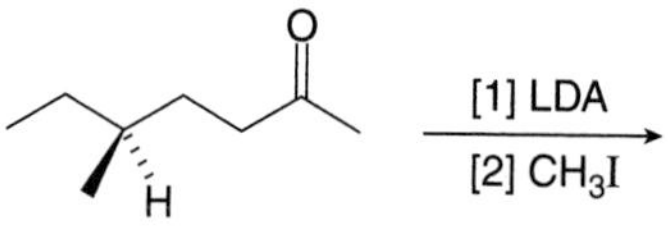
H
[1] LDA
[2] CH₃I

23.54 a. Identify intermediates **A–C** in the following stepwise conversion of *p*-isobutylbenzaldehyde to the analgesic ibuprofen.

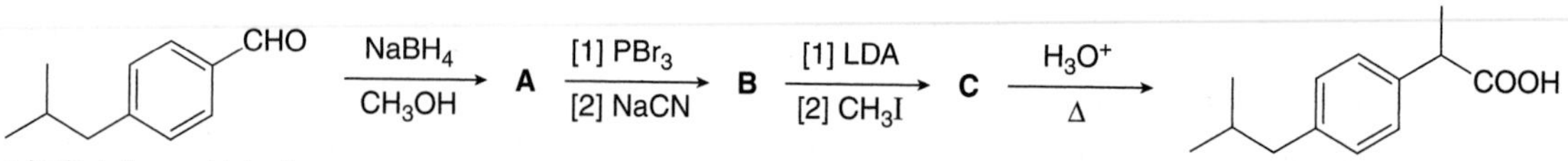
CHO
NaBH₄
CH₃OH
A
[1] PBr₃
[2] NaCN
B
[1] LDA
[2] CH₃I
C
H₃O⁺
Δ
COOH

p-isobutylbenzaldehyde

ibuprofen

b. Direct alkylation of **D** by treatment with one equivalent of LDA and CH_3I does not form ibuprofen. Identify the product of this reaction and explain how it is formed.

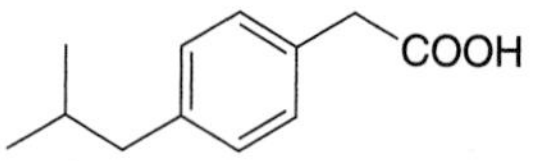
COOH

D

23.55 a. Clopidogrel is the generic name for Plavix, a drug used to prevent the formation of blood clots in patients that have a history of heart attacks or strokes. The racemic drug can be prepared from the racemic α-halo ester by the following reaction. What is the structure of clopidogrel?

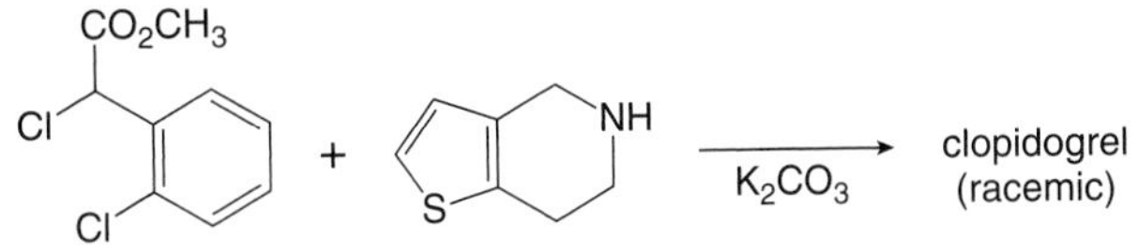

b. A single enantiomer of clopidogrel can be prepared in three steps from the chiral α-hydroxy acid **A.** Identify **B** and **C** in the following reaction sequence, and designate the configuration of the enantiomer formed by this route as *R* or *S*.

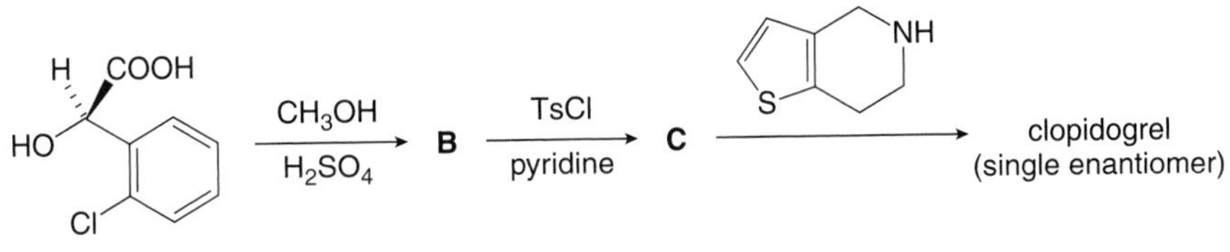

A

23.56 What reaction conditions—base, solvent, and temperature—are needed to convert ketone **A** to either **B** or **C** by an intramolecular alkylation reaction?

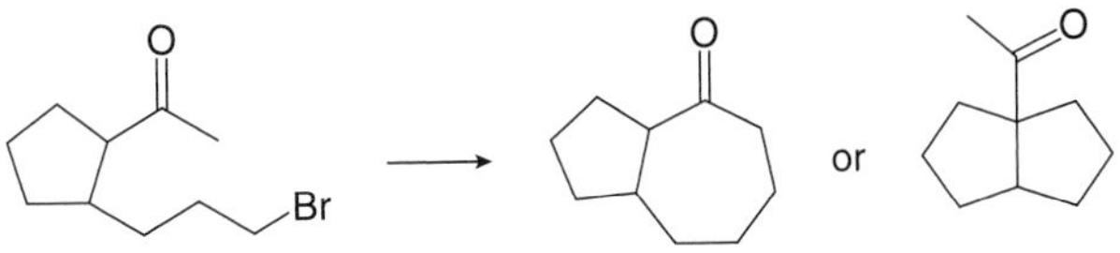

A **B** **C**

23.57 Explain why each of the following reactions will ***not*** proceed as written.

a. 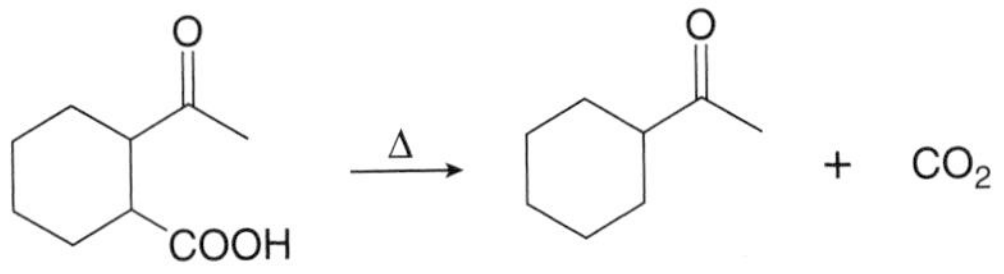

c. 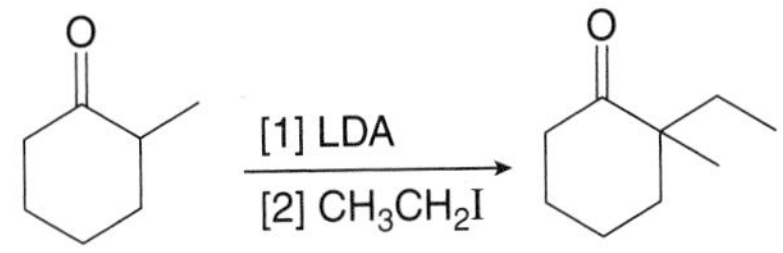

b. $CH_2(CO_2Et)_2 \xrightarrow[\text{[2] }(CH_3CH_2)_3CBr]{\text{[1] NaOEt}} (CH_3CH_2)_3CCH(CO_2Et)_2$

Mechanism

23.58 Although ibuprofen is sold as a racemic mixture, only the *S* enantiomer acts as an analgesic. In the body, however, some of the *R* enantiomer is converted to the *S* isomer by tautomerization to an enol and then protonation to regenerate the carbonyl compound. Write a stepwise mechanism for this isomerization.

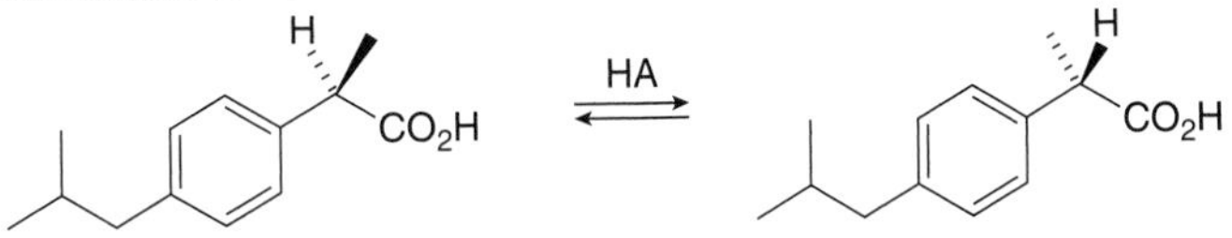

R isomer
inactive enantiomer

S isomer
active enantiomer

23.59 Draw a stepwise mechanism showing how two alkylation products are formed in the following reaction.

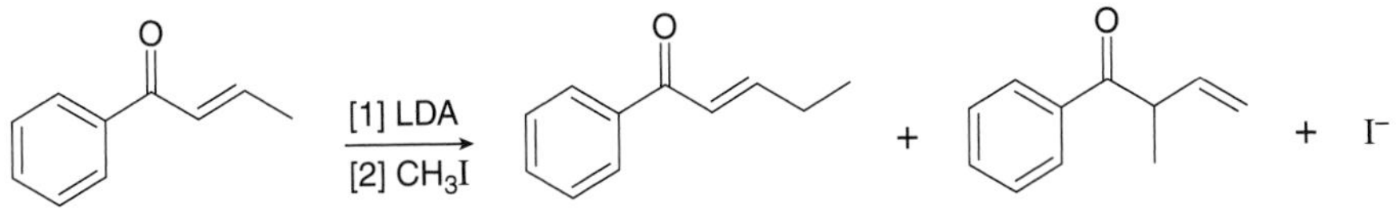

23.60 Draw a stepwise mechanism for the following reaction.

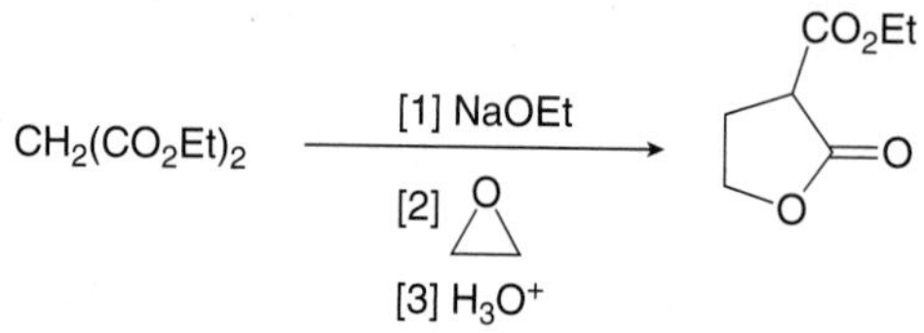
CH2(CO2Et)2
[1] NaOEt
[2]
[3] H3O+
CO2Et
O
O

23.61 Treatment of α,β-unsaturated carbonyl compound **X** with base forms the diastereomer **Y.** Write a stepwise mechanism for this reaction. Explain why one stereogenic center changes configuration but the other does not.

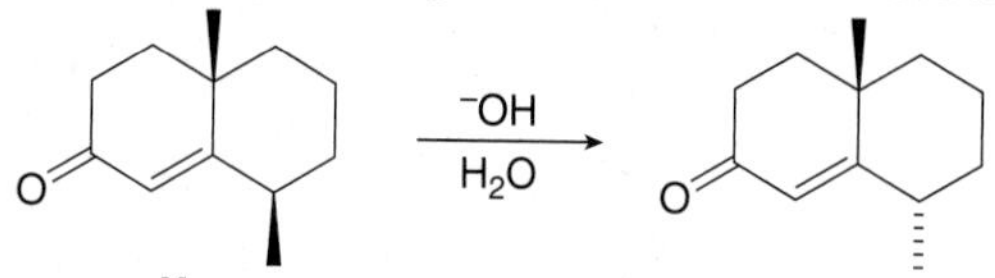
−OH
H2O

X **Y**

23.62 Draw stepwise mechanisms illustrating how each product is formed.

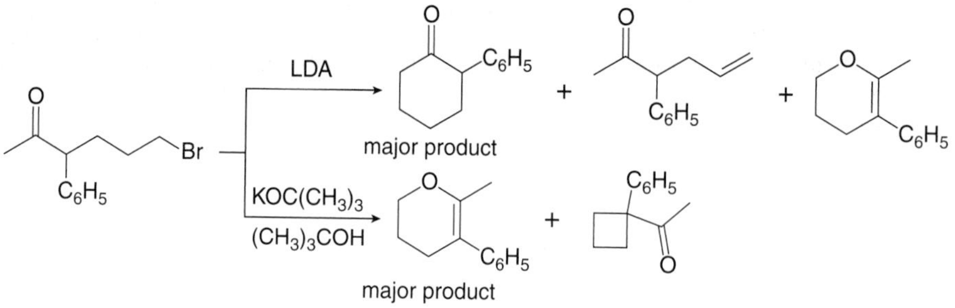
Br
C6H5
LDA
major product
KOC(CH3)3
(CH3)3COH
major product
C6H5

23.63 A key step in the synthesis of β-vetivone, a major constituent of vetiver, a perennial grass found in tropical and subtropical regions of the world, involved the reaction of compound **A** and dihalide **B** with two equivalents of LDA to form **C.** Draw a stepwise mechanism for this reaction. β-Vetivone contains a spiro ring system—that is, two rings that share a single carbon atom.

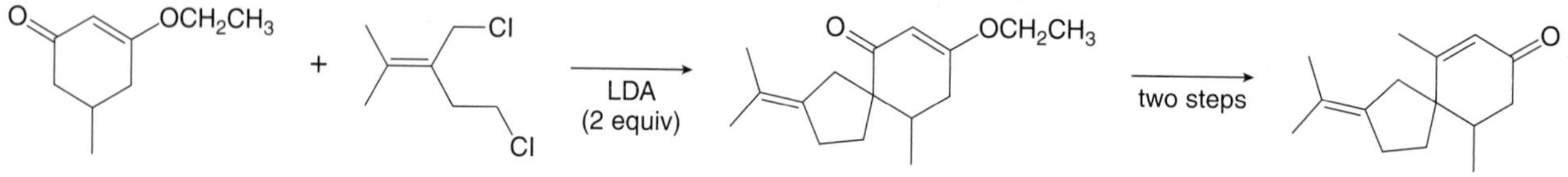
OCH2CH3
Cl
Cl
LDA
(2 equiv)
OCH2CH3
two steps

A **B** **C** β-vetivone

Synthesis

23.64 (a) Draw two different halo ketones that can form **A** by an intramolecular alkylation reaction. (b) How can **A** be synthesized by an acetoacetic ester synthesis?

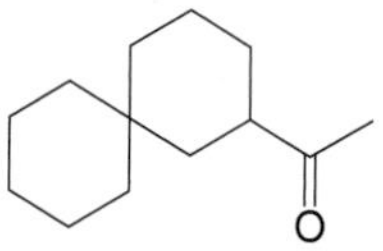

A

23.65 Convert acetophenone ($C_6H_5COCH_3$) into each of the following compounds. You may use any other organic compounds or required inorganic reagents. More than one step may be required.

a. 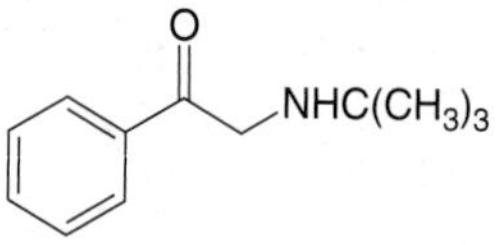
NHC(CH3)3

b. 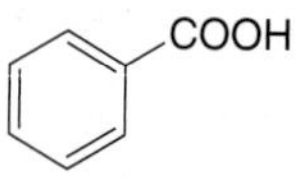
COOH

c. 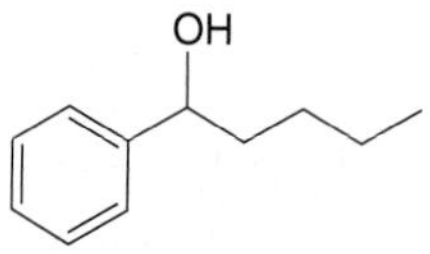
OH

d. 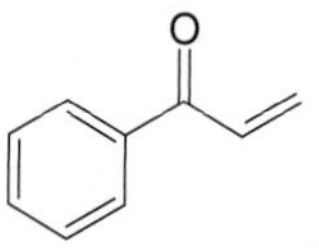

23.66 Synthesize each compound from cyclohexanone and organic halides having ≤ 4 C's. You may use any other inorganic reagents.

a. 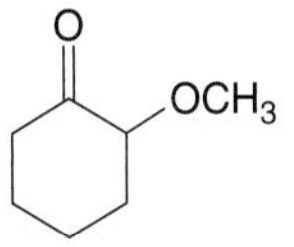
c. 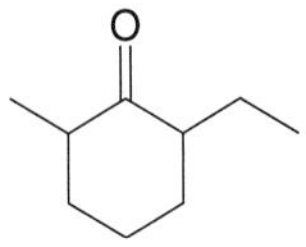
e. 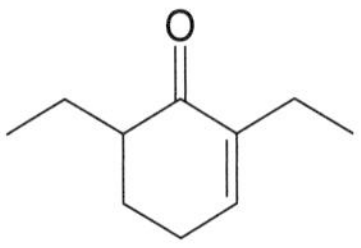
b. 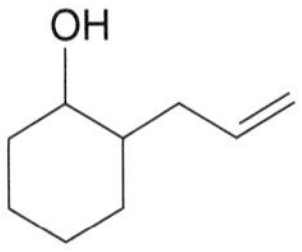
d. 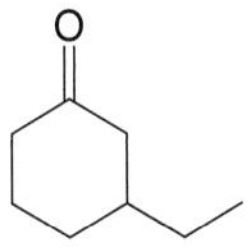
f. 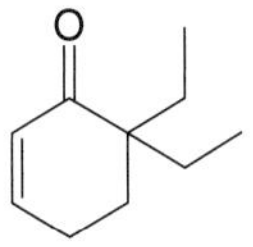

23.67 Bupropion, sold under the trade name of Zyban, is an antidepressant that was approved to aid smoking cessation in 1997. Devise a synthesis of bupropion from benzene, organic compounds that have fewer than five carbons, and any required inorganic reagents.

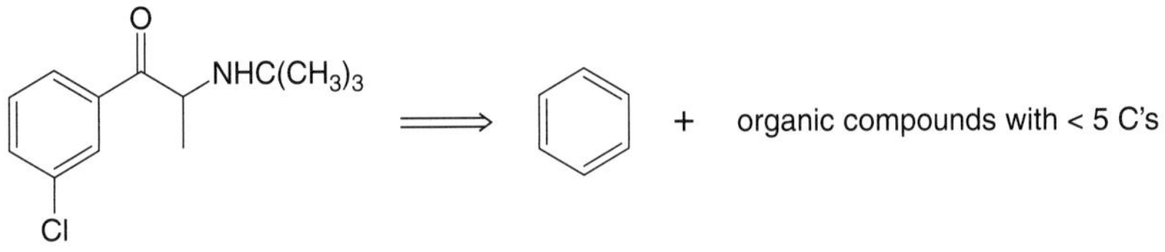

bupropion

23.68 Devise a synthesis of anastrozole, a drug used to reduce the recurrence of breast cancer (Section 22.18), from the given compounds. You may use any other needed organic compounds or inorganic reagents.

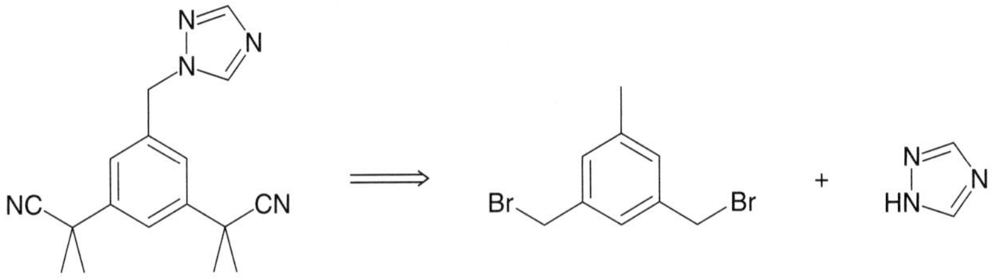

anastrozole

23.69 Synthesize each product from ethyl acetoacetate ($CH_3COCH_2CO_2Et$) and the given starting material. You may also use any other organic compounds or required inorganic reagents.

a. 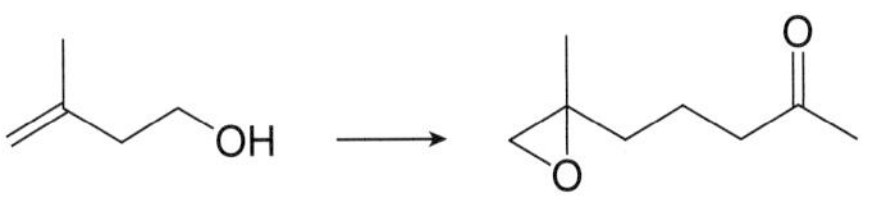
b. $HC{\equiv}CCH_2Br$ 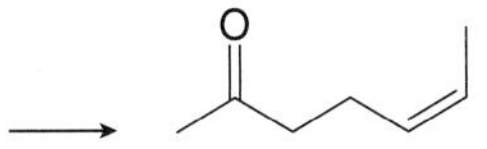

23.70 Synthesize each compound from 3-pentanone [$(CH_3CH_2)_2C{=}O$]. You may also use benzene, organic alcohols having ≤ 3 C's, and any required inorganic reagents.

a. 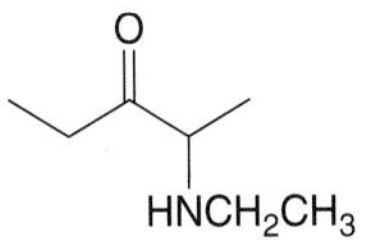
b. 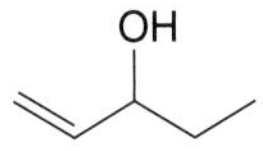
c. 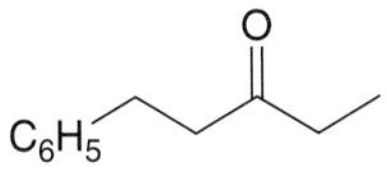
d. 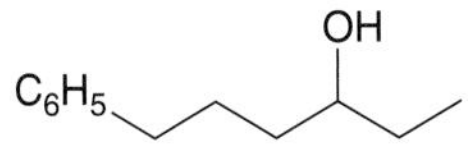

23.71 Treatment of ketone **A** with LDA followed by CH_3CH_2I did not form the desired alkylation product **B.** What product was formed instead? Devise a multistep method to convert **A** to **B,** a synthetic intermediate used to prepare the anticancer drug tamoxifen (Section 23.8C and the chapter-opening molecule).

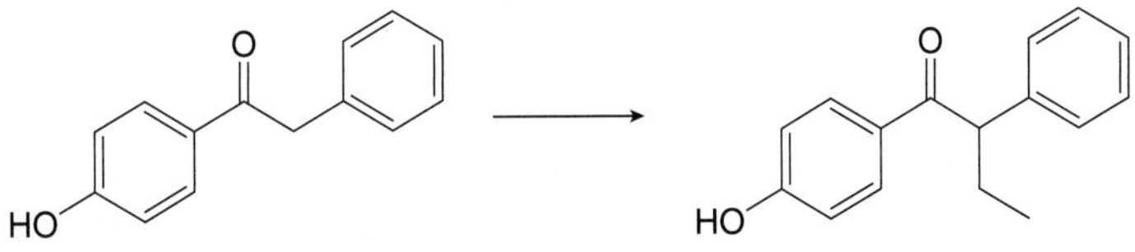

A **B**

23.72 Capsaicin, the spicy component of hot peppers, can be prepared from amine **X** and acid chloride **Y.** Devise a synthesis of **Y** from (4*E*)-6-methyl-4-hepten-1-ol [$(CH_3)_2CHCH{=}CH(CH_2)_3OH$], $CH_2(CO_2Et)_2$, and any required inorganic reagents.

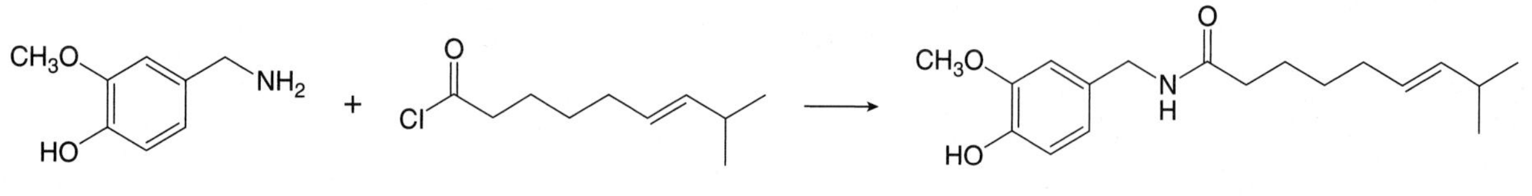
CH3O
HO
NH2
+
O
Cl
N
H
X
Y
capsaicin

Spectroscopy

23.73 Treatment of **W** with CH_3Li, followed by CH_3I, affords compound **Y** ($C_7H_{14}O$) as the major product. **Y** shows a strong absorption in its IR spectrum at 1713 cm^{-1}, and its ^1H NMR spectrum is given below. (a) Propose a structure for **Y.** (b) Draw a stepwise mechanism for the conversion of **W** to **Y.**

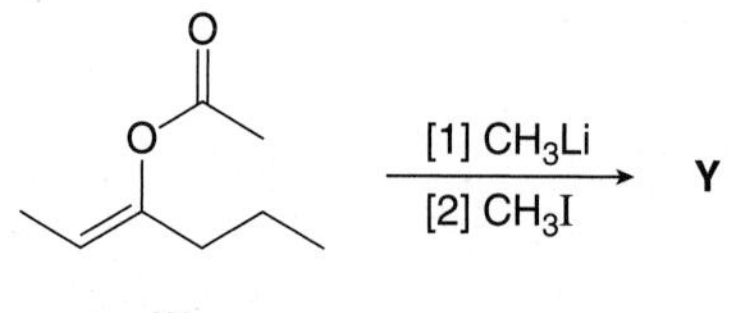
O
[1] CH3Li
[2] CH3I
Y
W

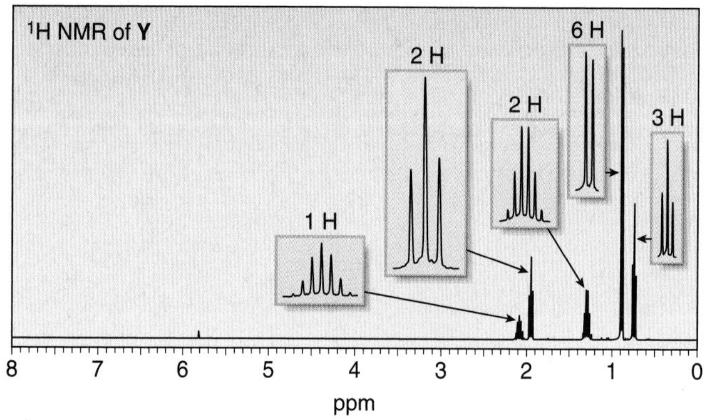
1H NMR of Y
6 H
2 H
2 H
3 H
1 H
8
7
6
5
4
3
2
1
0
ppm

Challenge Problems

23.74 Explain why H_a is much less acidic than H_b. Then draw a mechanism for the following reaction.

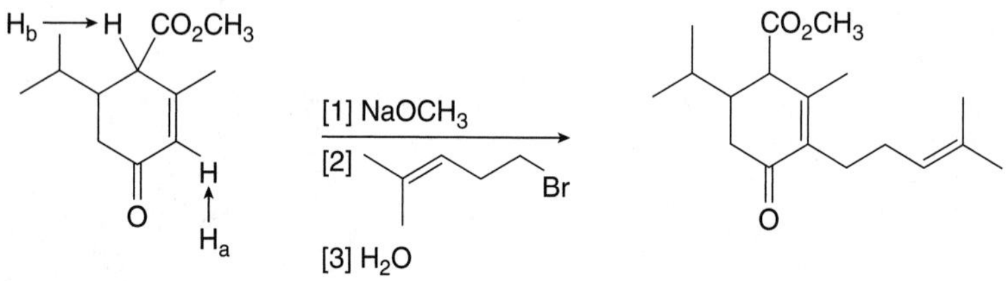
Hb
H
CO2CH3
H
Ha
O
[1] NaOCH3
[2]
Br
[3] H2O
CO2CH3
O

23.75 Devise a stepwise mechanism for the following reaction.

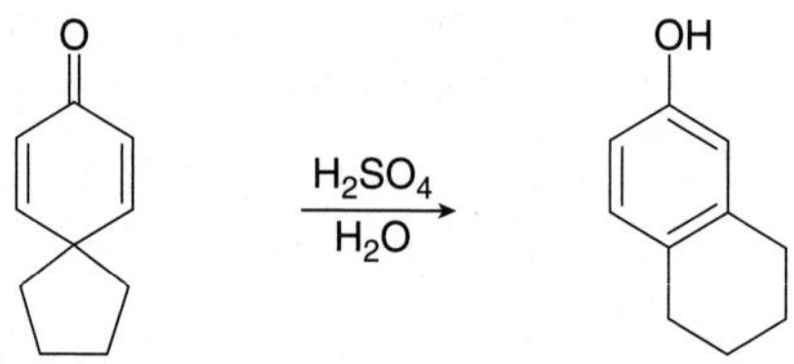
O
H2SO4
H2O
OH

23.76 The last step in the synthesis of β-vetivone (Problem 23.63) involves treatment of **C** with CH_3Li to form an intermediate **X,** which forms β-vetivone with aqueous acid. Identify the structure of **X** and draw a mechanism for converting **X** to β-vetivone.

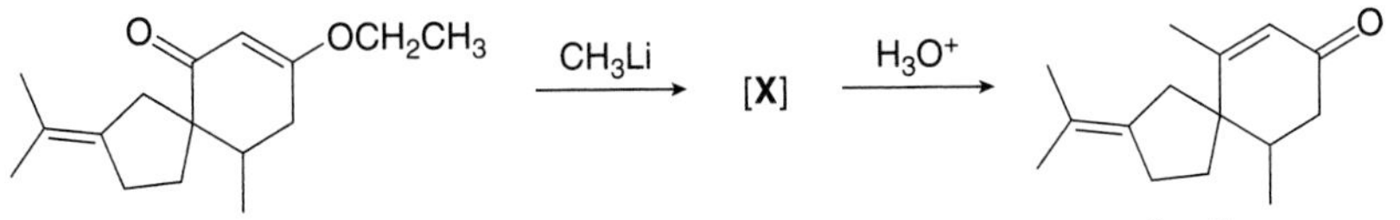

C β-vetivone

23.77 Keeping in mind the mechanism for the dissolving metal reduction of alkynes to trans alkenes in Chapter 12, write a stepwise mechanism for the following reaction, which involves the conversion of an α,β-unsaturated carbonyl compound to a carbonyl compound with a new alkyl group on the α carbon.

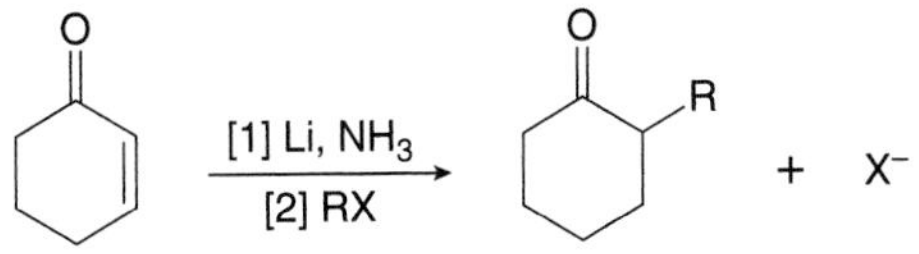

23.78 (–)-Hyoscyamine, an optically active drug used to treat gastrointestinal disorders, is isolated from *Atropa belladonna,* the deadly nightshade plant, by a basic aqueous extraction procedure. If too much base is used during isolation, optically inactive material is isolated. (a) Explain this result by drawing a stepwise mechanism. (b) Explain why littorine, an isomer isolated from the tailflower plant in Australia, can be obtained optically pure regardless of the amount of base used during isolation.

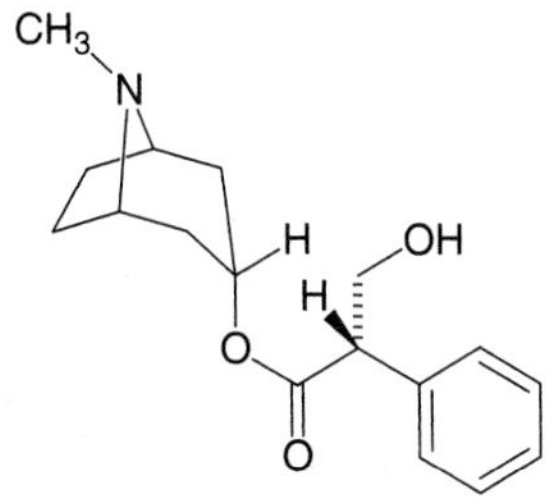

(–)-hyoscyamine

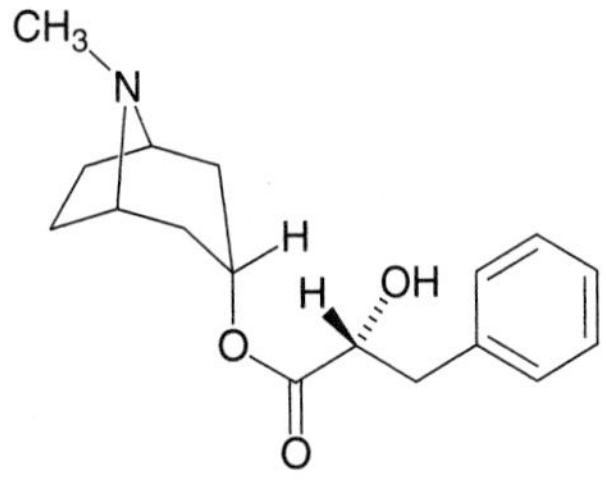

(–)-littorine

24 Carbonyl Condensation Reactions

24.1 The aldol reaction
24.2 Crossed aldol reactions
24.3 Directed aldol reactions
24.4 Intramolecular aldol reactions
24.5 The Claisen reaction
24.6 The crossed Claisen and related reactions
24.7 The Dieckmann reaction
24.8 The Michael reaction
24.9 The Robinson annulation

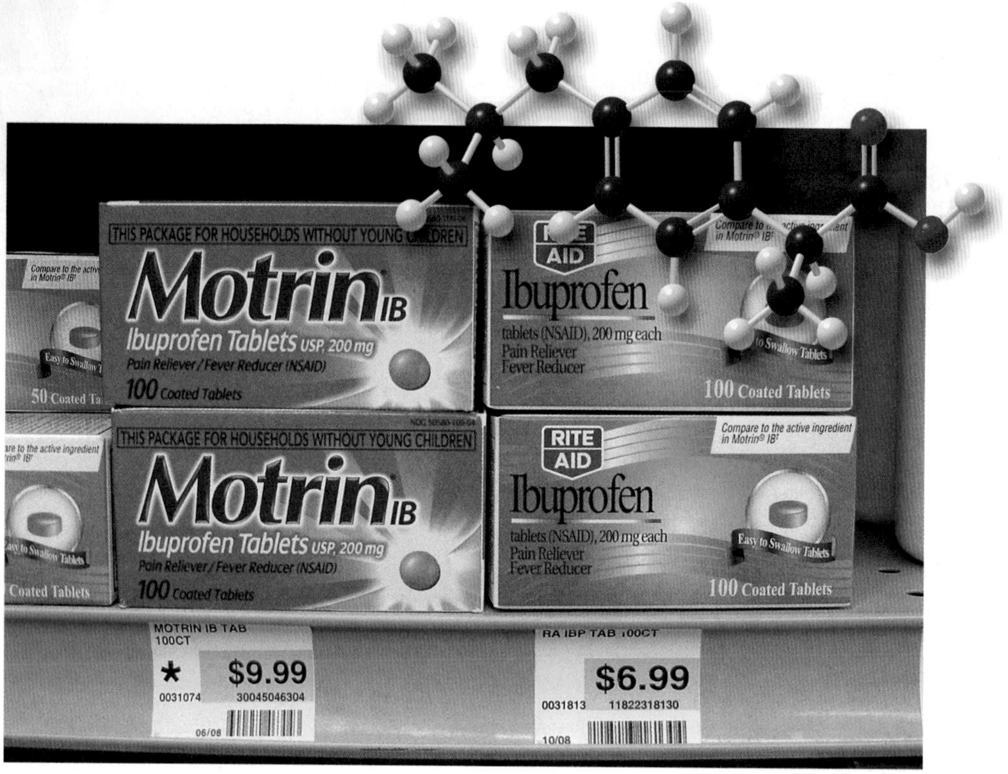

Ibuprofen is the generic name for the pain reliever known by the trade names of Motrin and Advil. Like aspirin, ibuprofen acts as an anti-inflammatory agent by blocking the synthesis of prostaglandins from arachidonic acid. One step in a commercial synthesis of ibuprofen involves the reaction of a nucleophilic enolate with an electrophilic carbonyl group. In Chapter 24, we learn about the carbon–carbon bond-forming reactions of enolates with carbonyl electrophiles.

In Chapter 24, we examine **carbonyl condensations**—that is, reactions between two carbonyl compounds—a second type of reaction that occurs at the α carbon of a carbonyl group. Much of what is presented in Chapter 24 applies principles you have already learned. Many of the reactions may look more complicated than those in previous chapters, but they are fundamentally the same. Nucleophiles attack electrophilic carbonyl groups to form the products of nucleophilic addition or substitution, depending on the structure of the carbonyl starting material.

Every reaction in Chapter 24 forms a new carbon–carbon bond at the α carbon to a carbonyl group, so these reactions are extremely useful in the synthesis of complex natural products.

24.1 The Aldol Reaction

Chapter 24 concentrates on the second general reaction of enolates—**reaction with other carbonyl compounds.** In these reactions, one carbonyl component serves as the nucleophile and one serves as the electrophile, and a new carbon–carbon bond is formed.

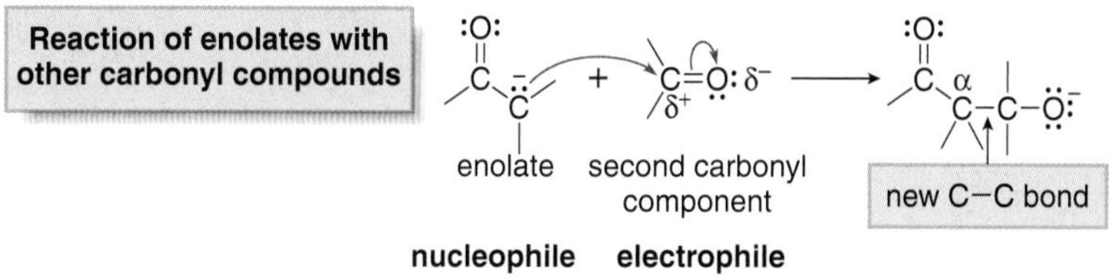

The presence or absence of a leaving group on the electrophilic carbonyl carbon determines the structure of the product. Even though they appear somewhat more complicated, these reactions are often reminiscent of the nucleophilic addition and nucleophilic acyl substitution reactions of Chapters 21 and 22. Four types of reactions are examined:

- **Aldol reaction** (Sections 24.1–24.4)
- **Claisen reaction** (Sections 24.5–24.7)
- **Michael reaction** (Section 24.8)
- **Robinson annulation** (Section 24.9)

24.1A General Features of the Aldol Reaction

In the **aldol reaction,** two molecules of an aldehyde or ketone react with each other in the presence of base to form a **β-hydroxy carbonyl compound.** For example, treatment of acetaldehyde with aqueous ^{-}OH forms 3-hydroxybutanal, a **β-hydroxy aldehyde.**

Many aldol products contain an ***ald***ehyde and an alcoh***ol***—hence the name ***aldol.***

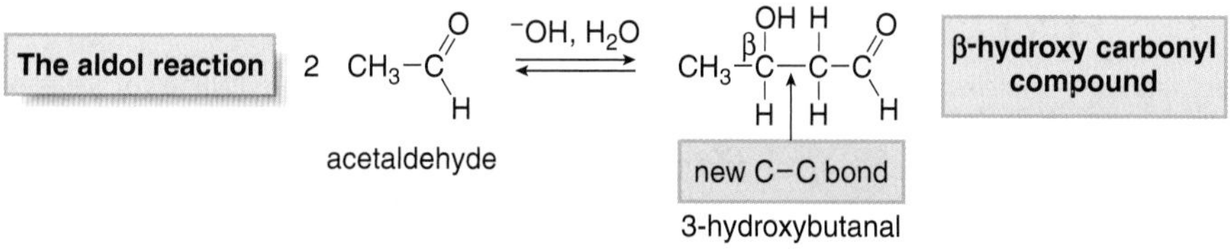

The mechanism of the aldol reaction has **three steps,** as shown in Mechanism 24.1. Carbon–carbon bond formation occurs in Step [2], when the nucleophilic enolate reacts with the electrophilic carbonyl carbon.

Mechanism 24.1 The Aldol Reaction

Step [1] Formation of a nucleophilic enolate

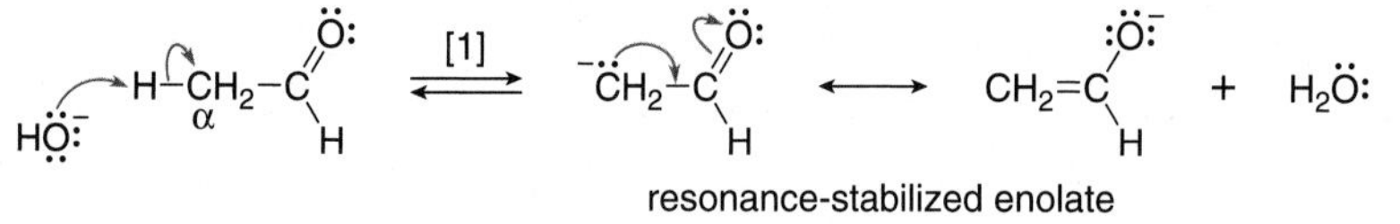

- In Step [1], the base removes a proton from the α carbon to form a **resonance-stabilized enolate.**

Steps [2]–[3] Nucleophilic addition and protonation

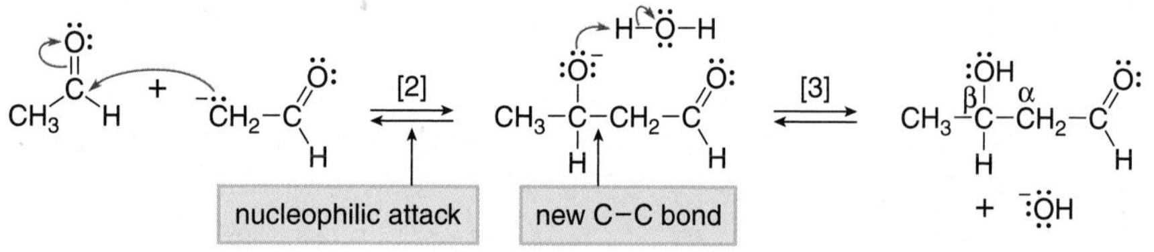

- In Step [2], the nucleophilic enolate attacks the electrophilic carbonyl carbon of another molecule of aldehyde, thus forming a new carbon–carbon bond. **This joins the α carbon of one aldehyde to the carbonyl carbon of a second aldehyde.**
- Protonation of the alkoxide in Step [3] forms the **β-hydroxy aldehyde.**

The aldol reaction is a reversible equilibrium, so the position of the equilibrium depends on the base and the carbonyl compound. **$^{-}$OH is the base** typically used in an aldol reaction. Recall from Section 23.3B that only a small amount of enolate forms with $^{-}$OH. In this case, that's appropriate because the starting aldehyde is needed to react with the enolate in the second step of the mechanism.

Aldol reactions can be carried out with either aldehydes or ketones. With aldehydes, the equilibrium usually favors the products, but with ketones the equilibrium favors the starting materials. There are ways of driving this equilibrium to the right, however, so we will write aldol products whether the substrate is an aldehyde or a ketone.

- **The characteristic reaction of aldehydes and ketones is nucleophilic addition (Section 21.7). An aldol reaction is a nucleophilic addition in which an enolate is the nucleophile. See the comparison in Figure 24.1.**

Figure 24.1
The aldol reaction—An example of nucleophilic addition

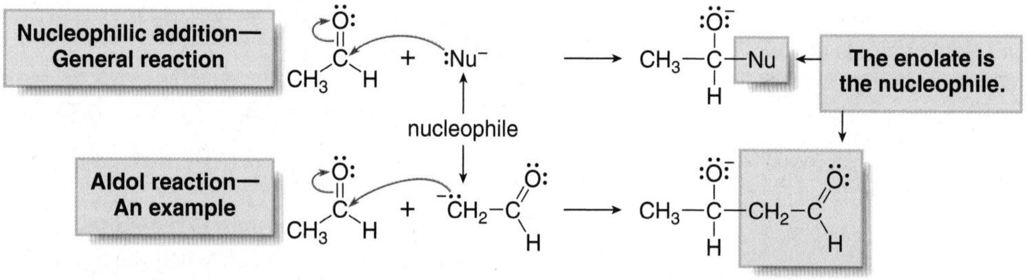

- Aldehydes and ketones react by nucleophilic addition. In an aldol reaction, an enolate is the nucleophile that adds to the carbonyl group.

A **second example of an aldol** reaction is shown with propanal as starting material. The two molecules of the aldehyde that participate in the aldol reaction react in opposite ways.

- **One molecule of propanal becomes an enolate—an electron-rich *nucleophile*.**
- **One molecule of propanal serves as the *electrophile* because its carbonyl carbon is electron deficient.**

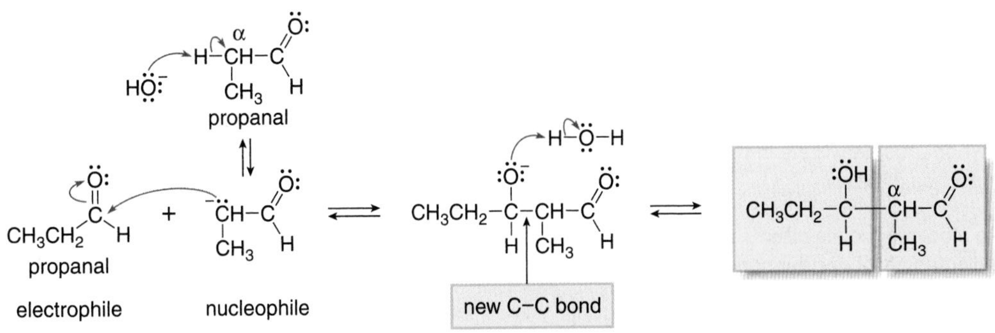

These two examples illustrate the general features of the aldol reaction. **The α carbon of one carbonyl component becomes bonded to the carbonyl carbon of the other component.**

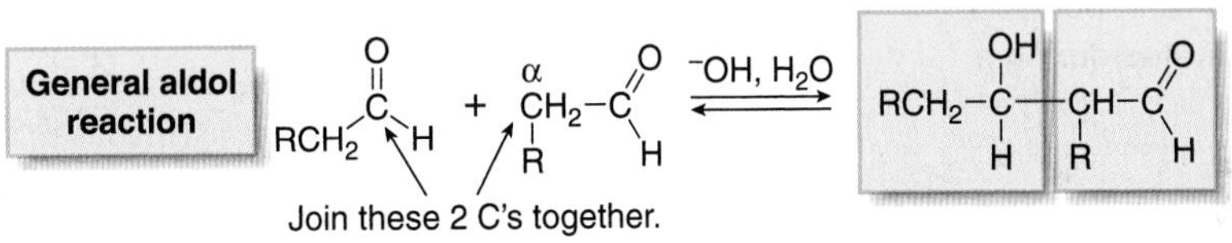

Problem 24.1 Draw the aldol product formed from each compound.

a. 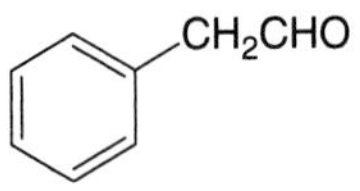

b. $(CH_3)_3CCH_2CHO$

c. 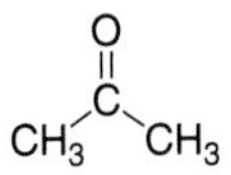

d. 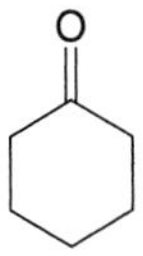

Problem 24.2 Which carbonyl compounds do *not* undergo an aldol reaction when treated with ^{-}OH in H_2O?

a. 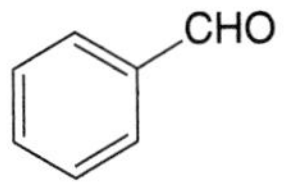

b. 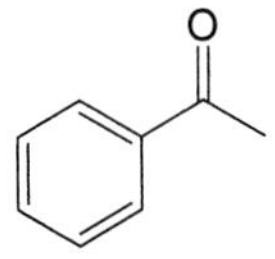

c. 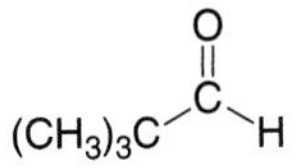

d. 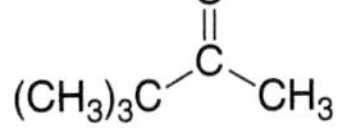

e. 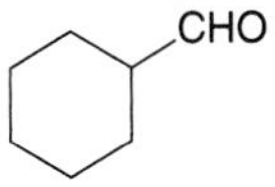

24.1B Dehydration of the Aldol Product

The β-hydroxy carbonyl compounds formed in the aldol reaction dehydrate more readily than other alcohols. In fact, under the basic reaction conditions, the initial aldol product is often not isolated. Instead, **it loses the elements of H_2O from the α and β carbons to form an α,β-unsaturated carbonyl compound.**

All alcohols—including β-hydroxy carbonyl compounds—dehydrate in the presence of acid. Only β-hydroxy carbonyl compounds dehydrate in the presence of base.

An aldol reaction is often called an **aldol condensation,** because the β-hydroxy carbonyl compound that is initially formed loses H_2O by dehydration. **A *condensation reaction* is one in which a small molecule, in this case H_2O, is eliminated during a reaction.**

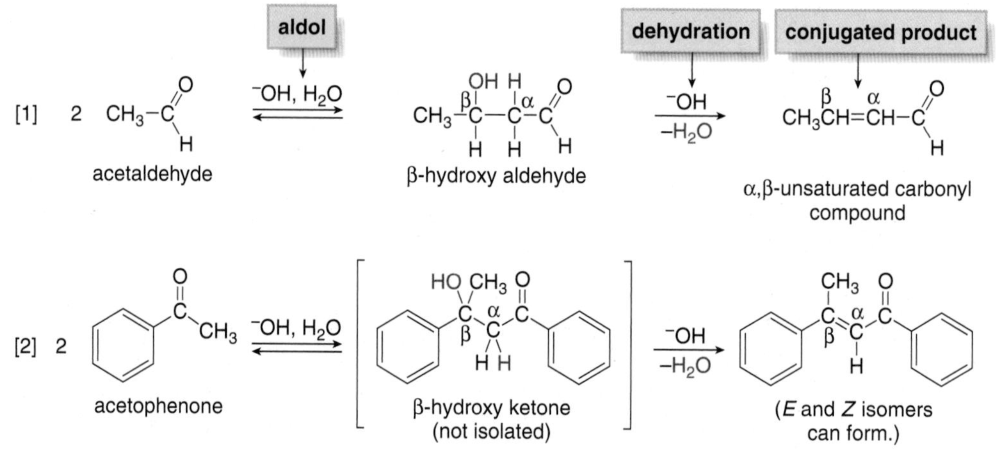

It may or may not be possible to isolate the β-hydroxy carbonyl compound under the conditions of the aldol reaction. When the α,β-unsaturated carbonyl compound is further conjugated with a carbon–carbon double bond or a benzene ring, as in the case of Reaction [2], **elimination of H_2O is spontaneous** and the β-hydroxy carbonyl compound cannot be isolated.

The mechanism of dehydration consists of two steps: **deprotonation followed by loss of ^-OH,** as shown in Mechanism 24.2.

Mechanism 24.2 Dehydration of β-Hydroxy Carbonyl Compounds with Base

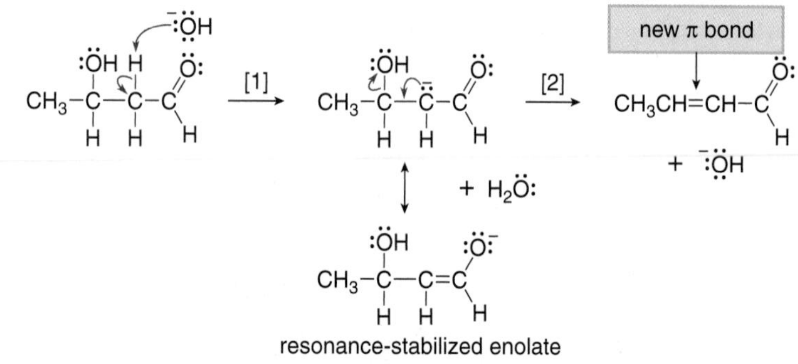

- In Step [1], base removes a proton from the α carbon, thus forming a resonance-stabilized enolate.
- In Step [2], the electron pair of the enolate forms the π bond as ^-OH is eliminated.

Like E1 elimination, E1cB requires two steps. Unlike E1, though, the intermediate in E1cB is a *carbanion,* not a carbocation. E1cB stands for **Elimination, unimolecular, conjugate base.**

This elimination mechanism, called the **E1cB mechanism,** differs from the two more general mechanisms of elimination, E1 and E2, which were discussed in Chapter 8. The E1cB mechanism involves two steps, and proceeds by way of an **anionic** intermediate.

Regular alcohols dehydrate only in the presence of acid but not base, because hydroxide is a poor leaving group. When the hydroxy group is β to a carbonyl group, however, loss of H and OH from the α and β carbons forms a **conjugated double bond,** and the stability of the conjugated system makes up for having such a poor leaving group.

Dehydration of the initial β-hydroxy carbonyl compound drives the equilibrium of an aldol reaction to the right, thus favoring product formation. Once the conjugated α,β-unsaturated carbonyl compound forms, it is *not* re-converted to the β-hydroxy carbonyl compound.

Problem 24.3 What unsaturated carbonyl compound is formed by dehydration of each β-hydroxy carbonyl compound?

a. 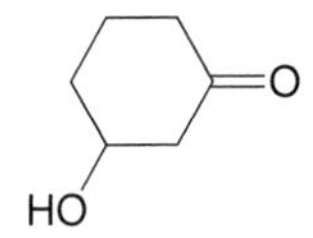

b. 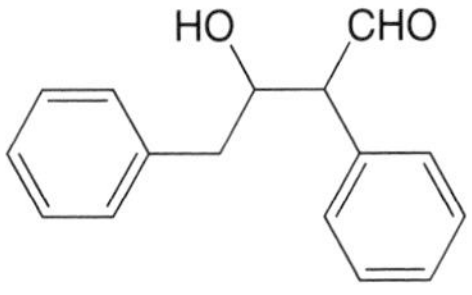

c. 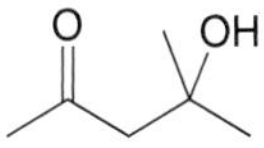

Problem 24.4 Acid-catalyzed dehydration of β-hydroxy carbonyl compounds occurs by the mechanism discussed in Section 9.8. With this in mind, draw a stepwise mechanism for the following reaction.

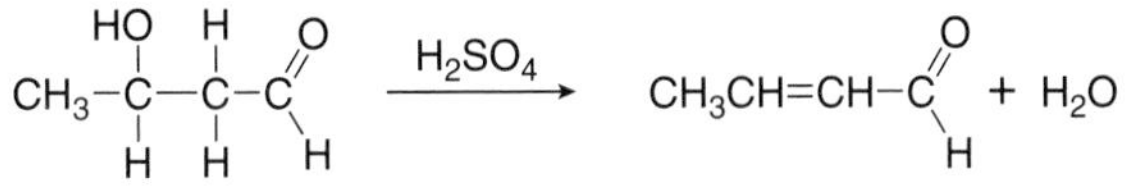

24.1C Retrosynthetic Analysis

To utilize the aldol reaction in synthesis, you must be able to determine which aldehyde or ketone is needed to prepare a particular β-hydroxy carbonyl compound or α,β-unsaturated carbonyl compound—that is, you must be able to **work backwards, in the retrosynthetic direction.**

How To Synthesize a Compound Using the Aldol Reaction

Example What starting material is needed to prepare each compound by an aldol reaction?

a. 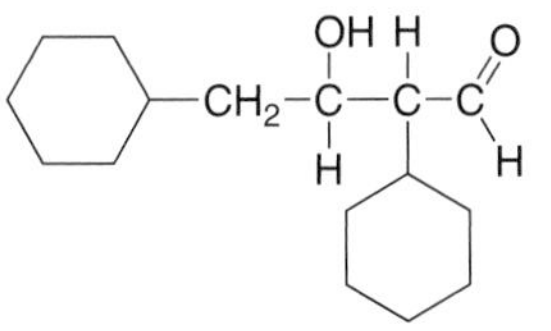

b. 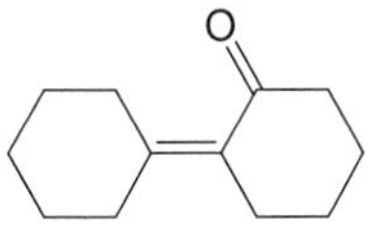

Step [1] Locate the α and β carbons of the carbonyl group.

- When a carbonyl group has two different α carbons, choose the side that contains the OH group (in a β-hydroxy carbonyl compound) or is part of the C=C (in an α,β-unsaturated carbonyl compound).

Step [2] Break the molecule into two components between the α and β carbons.

- The α carbon and all remaining atoms bonded to it belong to one carbonyl component. The β carbon and all remaining atoms bonded to it belong to the other carbonyl component. Both components are identical in all aldols we have thus far examined.

a. 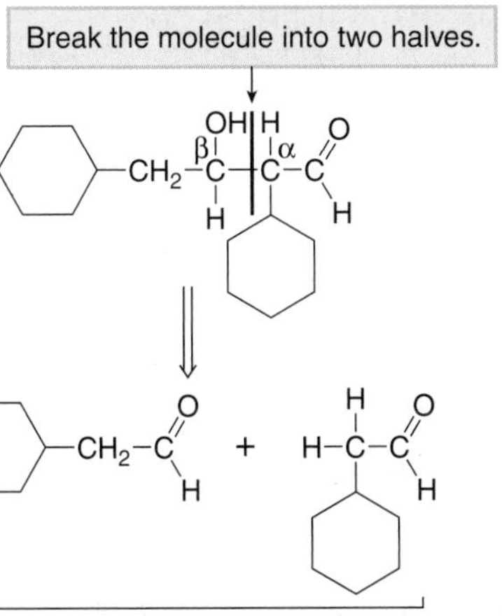

two molecules of the same aldehyde

b. 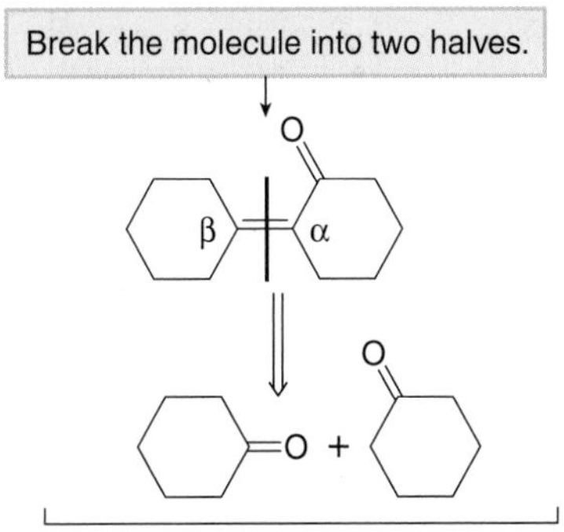

two molecules of cyclohexanone

Problem 24.5 What aldehyde or ketone is needed to prepare each compound by an aldol reaction?

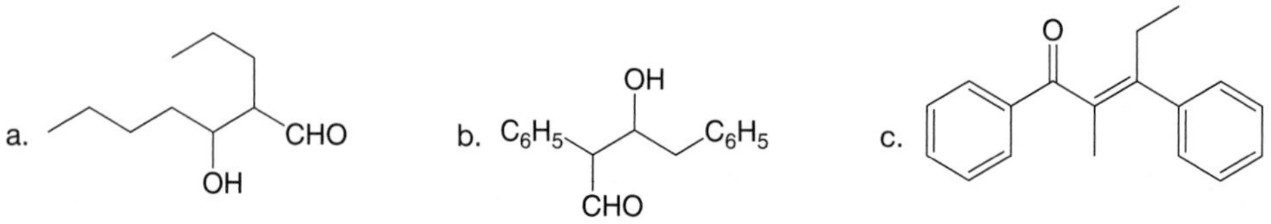

24.2 Crossed Aldol Reactions

In all of the aldol reactions discussed so far, the electrophilic carbonyl and the nucleophilic enolate have originated from the *same* aldehyde or ketone. Sometimes, though, it is possible to carry out an aldol reaction between two *different* carbonyl compounds.

- **An aldol reaction between two different carbonyl compounds is called a *crossed aldol* or *mixed aldol reaction.***

24.2A A Crossed Aldol Reaction with Two Different Aldehydes, Both Having α H Atoms

When two different aldehydes, both having α H atoms, are combined in an aldol reaction, four different β-hydroxy carbonyl compounds are formed. Four products form, not one, because *both* aldehydes can lose an acidic α hydrogen atom and form an enolate in the presence of base. *Both* enolates can then react with *both* carbonyl compounds, as shown for acetaldehyde and propanal in the following reaction scheme.

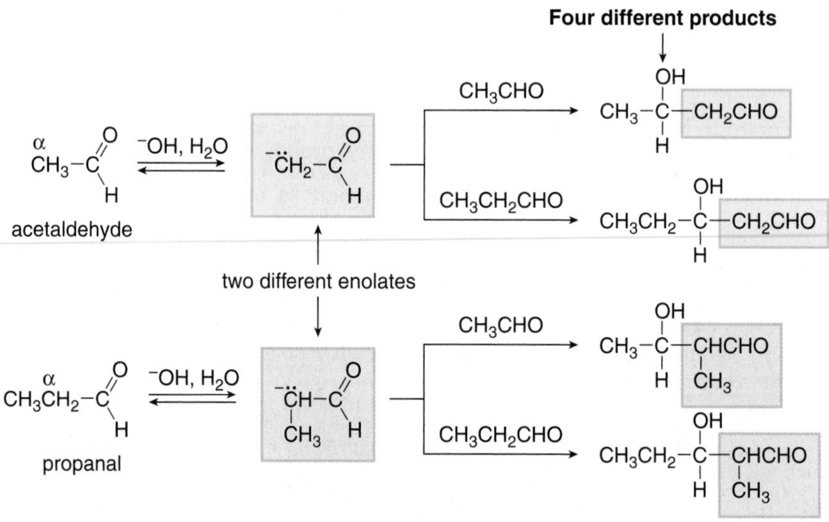

- **Conclusion: When two different aldehydes have α hydrogens, a crossed aldol reaction is *not* synthetically useful.**

24.2B Synthetically Useful Crossed Aldol Reactions

Crossed aldols are synthetically useful in two different situations.

- **A crossed aldol occurs when only one carbonyl component has α H atoms.**

When one carbonyl compound has no α hydrogens, a crossed aldol reaction often leads to one product. Two common carbonyl compounds with no α hydrogens used for this purpose are **formaldehyde ($CH_2=O$)** and **benzaldehyde (C_6H_5CHO).**

For example, reaction of C_6H_5CHO (as the electrophile) with either acetaldehyde (CH_3CHO) or acetone [$(CH_3)_2C=O$] in the presence of base forms a single α,β-unsaturated carbonyl compound after dehydration.

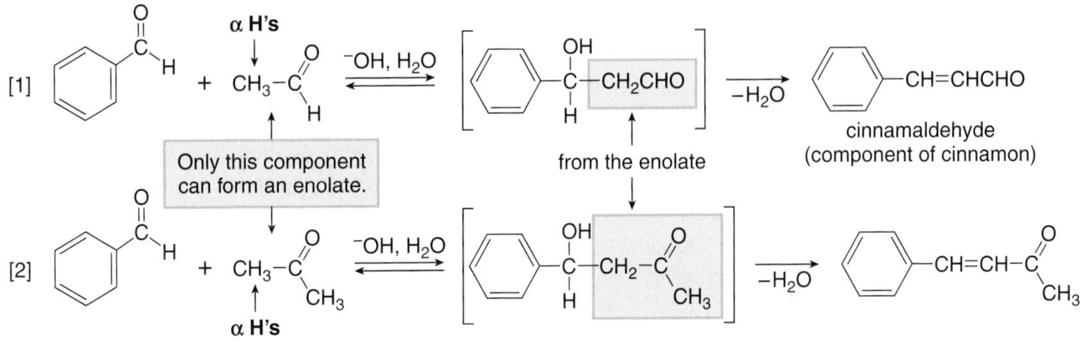

The yield of a single crossed aldol product is increased further if the electrophilic carbonyl component is relatively unhindered (as is the case with most aldehydes), and if it is used in excess.

Problem 24.6 2-Pentylcinnamaldehyde, commonly called flosal, is a perfume ingredient with a jasmine-like odor. Flosal is an α,β-unsaturated aldehyde made by a crossed aldol reaction between benzaldehyde (C_6H_5CHO) and heptanal ($CH_3CH_2CH_2CH_2CH_2CH_2CHO$), followed by dehydration. Draw a stepwise mechanism for the following reaction that prepares flosal.

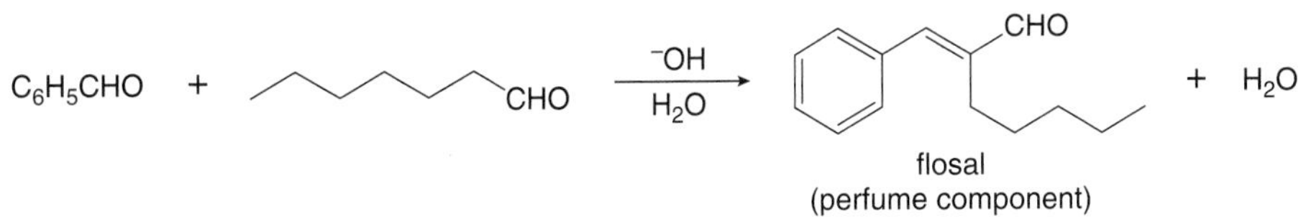

Problem 24.7 Draw the products formed in each crossed aldol reaction.

a. $CH_3CH_2CH_2CHO$ and $CH_2=O$

b. C_6H_5CHO and 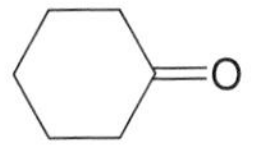

- **A crossed aldol occurs when one carbonyl component has especially acidic α H atoms.**

A useful crossed aldol reaction takes place between an aldehyde or ketone and a β-dicarbonyl (or similar) compound.

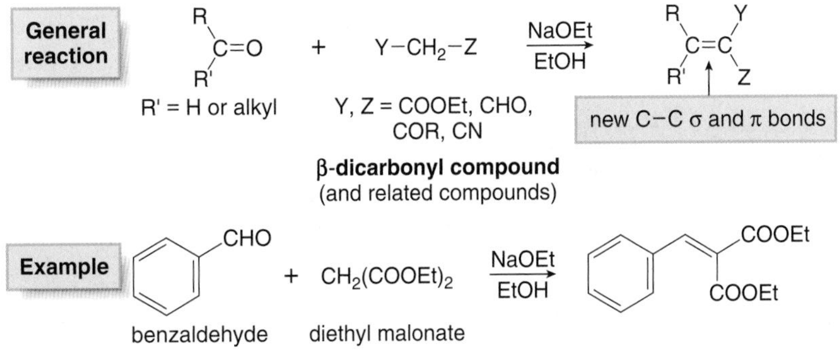

Figure 24.2
Crossed aldol reaction between benzaldehyde and $CH_2(COOEt)_2$

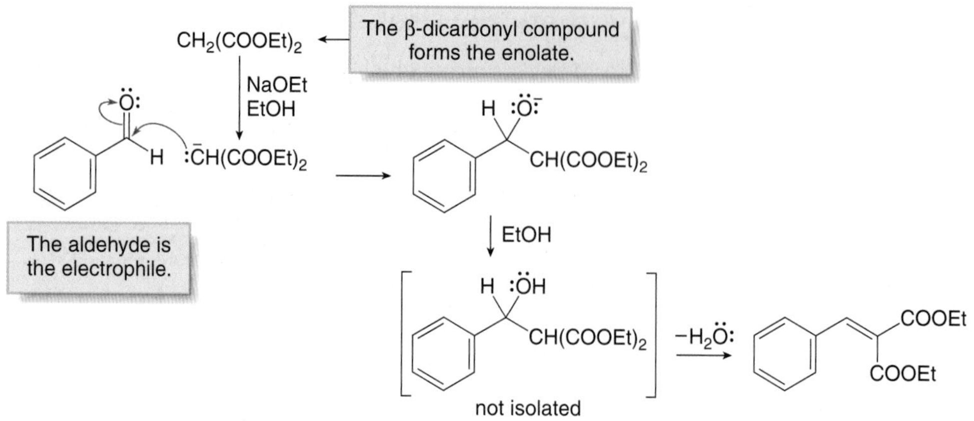

As we learned in Section 23.3, the α hydrogens between two carbonyl groups are especially acidic, and so they are more readily removed than other α H atoms. As a result, **the β-dicarbonyl compound always becomes the enolate component of the aldol reaction.** Figure 24.2 shows the steps for the crossed aldol reaction between diethyl malonate and benzaldehyde. In this type of crossed aldol reaction, the initial β-hydroxy carbonyl compound *always* loses water to form the highly conjugated product.

β-Dicarbonyl compounds are sometimes called **active methylene compounds** because they are more reactive towards base than other carbonyl compounds. **1,3-Dinitriles** and **α-cyano carbonyl compounds** are also active methylene compounds.

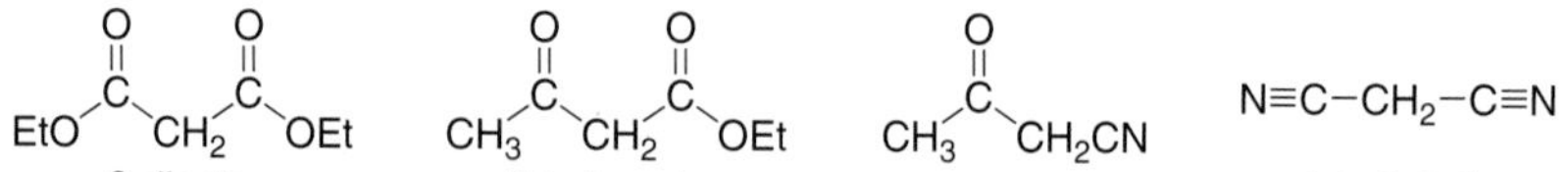

Problem 24.8 Draw the products formed in the crossed aldol reaction of phenylacetaldehyde ($C_6H_5CH_2CHO$) with each compound: (a) $CH_2(COOEt)_2$; (b) $CH_2(COCH_3)_2$; (c) CH_3COCH_2CN.

24.2C Useful Transformations of Aldol Products

The aldol reaction is synthetically useful because it forms new carbon–carbon bonds, generating products with two functional groups. Moreover, the β-hydroxy carbonyl compounds formed in aldol reactions are readily transformed into a variety of other compounds. Figure 24.3 illustrates how the crossed aldol product obtained from cyclohexanone and formaldehyde ($CH_2{=}O$) can be converted to other compounds by reactions learned in earlier chapters.

Problem 24.9 What aldol product is formed when two molecules of butanal react together in the presence of base? What reagents are needed to convert this product to each of the following compounds?

a. 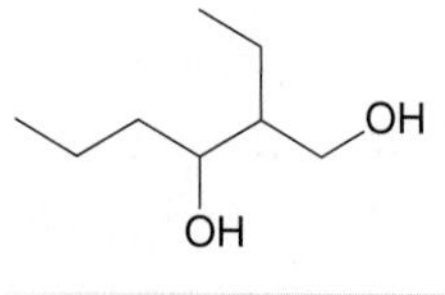

b. 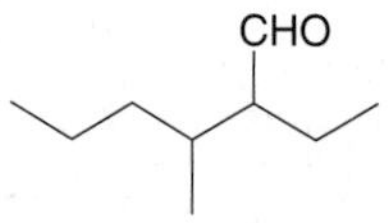

c. $CH_3CH_2CH_2CH{=}C(CH_2CH_3)CH_2OH$
d. $CH_3CH_2CH_2CH{=}C(CH_2CH_3)CH(CH_3)OH$

Figure 24.3
Conversion of a β-hydroxy carbonyl compound into other compounds

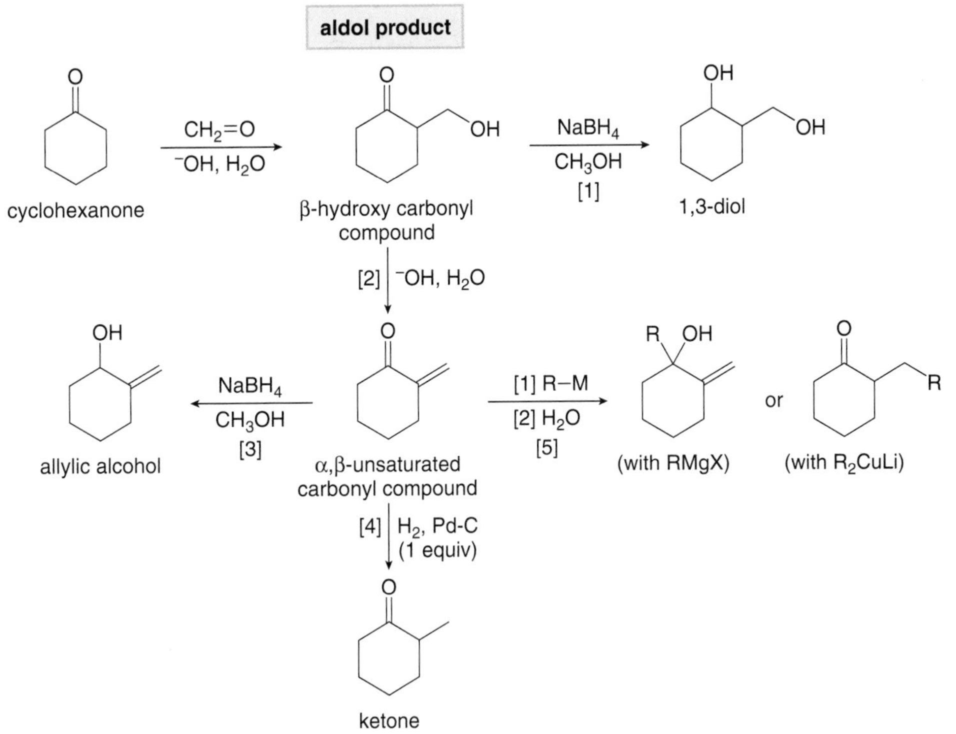

- The β-hydroxy carbonyl compound formed from the crossed aldol reaction can be reduced with $NaBH_4$, CH_3OH (Section 20.4A) to form a 1,3-diol (Reaction [1]) or dehydrated to form an α,β-unsaturated carbonyl compound (Reaction [2]).
- Reduction of the α,β-unsaturated carbonyl compound forms an allylic alcohol with $NaBH_4$ (Reaction [3]), or a ketone with H_2 and Pd-C (Reaction [4]); see Section 20.4C.
- Reaction of the α,β-unsaturated carbonyl compound with an organometallic reagent forms two different products depending on the choice of RM (Reaction [5]); see Section 20.15.

24.3 Directed Aldol Reactions

A **directed aldol reaction** is a variation of the crossed aldol reaction that clearly defines which carbonyl compound becomes the nucleophilic enolate and which reacts at the electrophilic carbonyl carbon. The strategy of a directed aldol reaction is as follows:

[1] Prepare the enolate of one carbonyl component with LDA.

[2] Add the second carbonyl compound (the electrophile) to this enolate.

Because the steps are done sequentially and a strong nonnucleophilic base is used to form the enolate of one carbonyl component only, a variety of carbonyl substrates can be used in the reaction. Both carbonyl components can have α hydrogens because only one enolate is prepared with LDA. Also, when an unsymmetrical ketone is used, LDA selectively forms the **less substituted, kinetic enolate.**

Sample Problem 24.1 illustrates the steps of a directed aldol reaction between a ketone and an aldehyde, both of which have α hydrogens.

Sample Problem 24.1 Draw the product of the following directed aldol reaction.

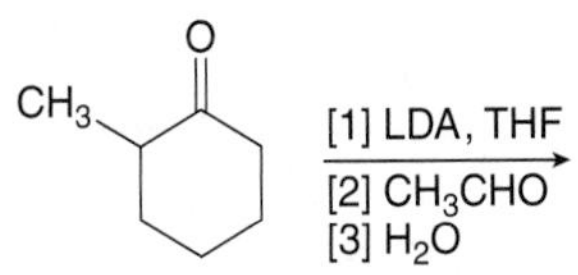

2-methylcyclohexanone

Solution

2-Methylcyclohexanone forms an enolate on the less substituted carbon, which then reacts with the electrophile, CH_3CHO.

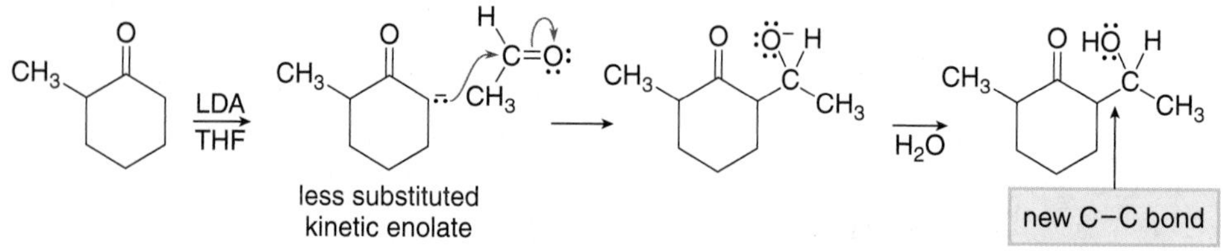

Figure 24.4 illustrates how a directed aldol reaction was used in the synthesis of **periplanone B,** the sex pheromone of the female American cockroach.

Figure 24.4
A directed aldol reaction in the synthesis of periplanone B

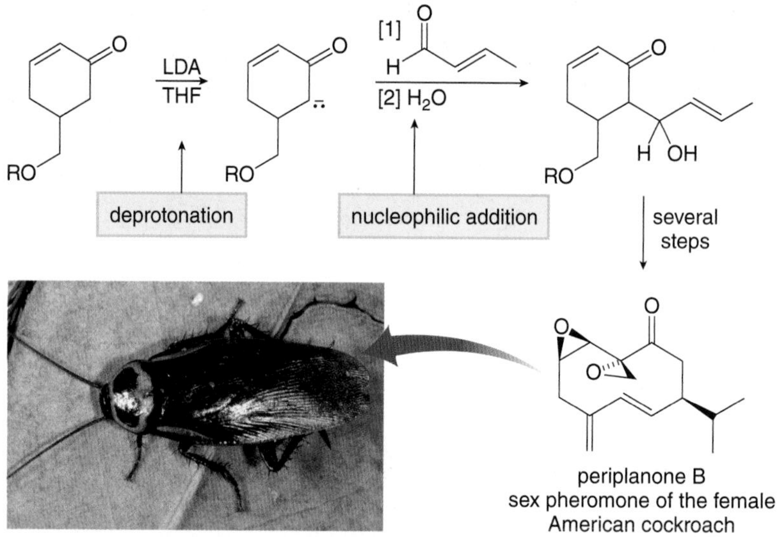

To determine the needed carbonyl components for a directed aldol, follow the same strategy used for a regular aldol reaction in Section 24.1C, as shown in Sample Problem 24.2.

Sample Problem 24.2 What starting materials are needed to prepare *ar*-turmerone using a directed aldol reaction? *ar*-Turmerone is a principal component of the essential oil derived from turmeric root.

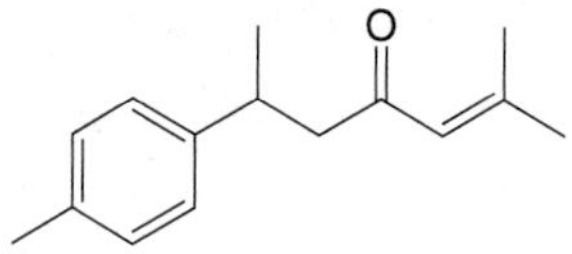

ar-turmerone

The dried and ground root of the turmeric plant, a tropical perennial in the ginger family, is an essential ingredient in curry powder.

Solution

When the desired product is an α,β-unsaturated carbonyl compound, identify the α and β carbons that are part of the C=C, and break the molecule into two components between these carbons.

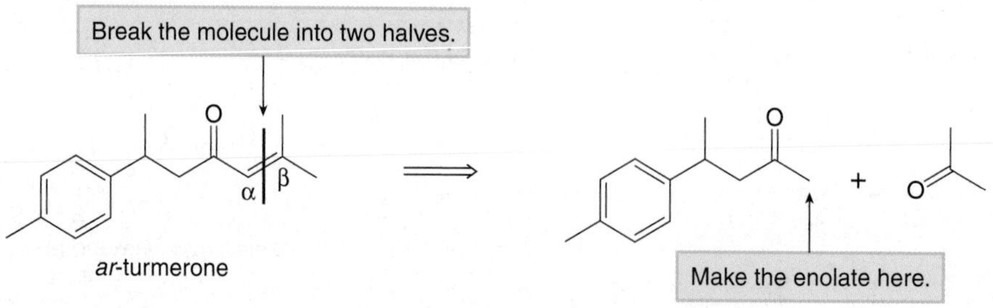

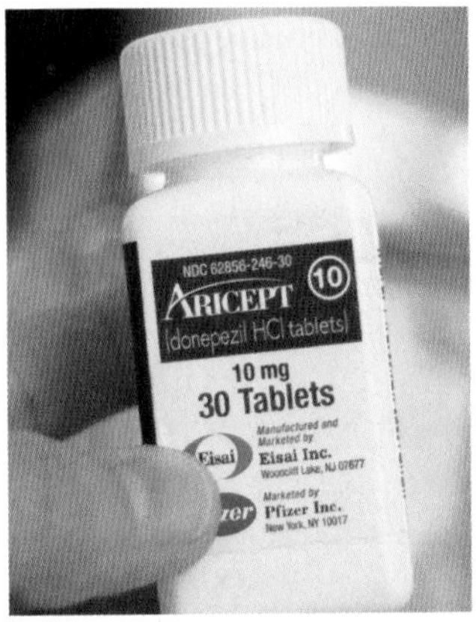

Donepezil (trade name Aricept) is a drug used to improve cognitive function in patients suffering from dementia and Alzheimer's disease.

Problem 24.10 What carbonyl starting materials are needed to prepare each compound using a directed aldol reaction?

a. 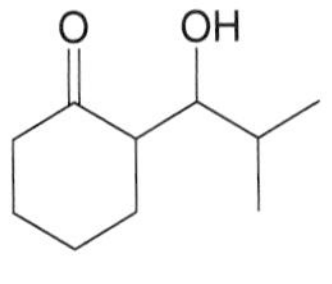

b. 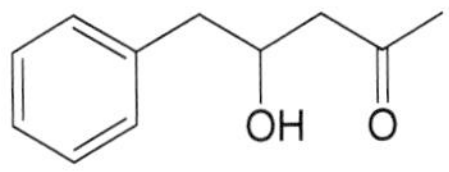

c. 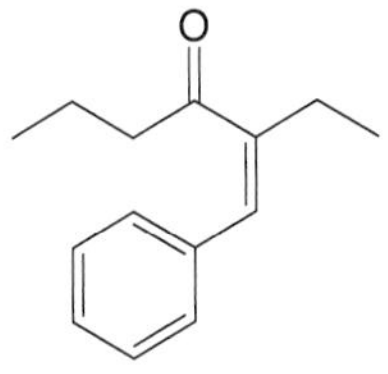

Problem 24.11 A key step in the synthesis of donepezil (trade name Aricept) is a directed aldol reaction that forms α,β-unsaturated carbonyl compound **X**. What carbonyl starting materials are needed to prepare **X** using a directed aldol reaction? What reagents are needed to convert **X** to donepezil?

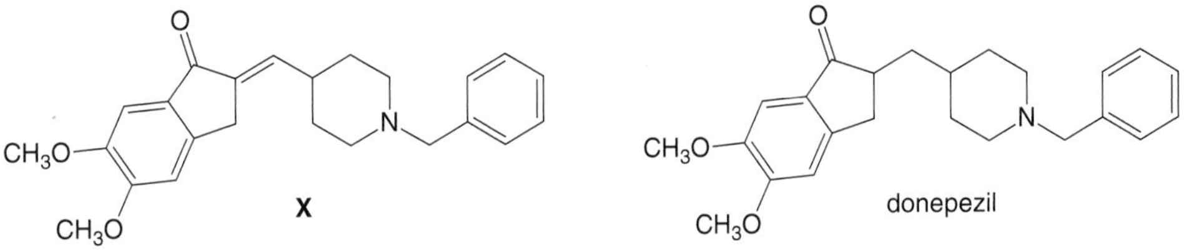

24.4 Intramolecular Aldol Reactions

2,5-Hexanedione is called a **1,4-dicarbonyl compound** to emphasize the relative positions of its carbonyl groups. 1,4-Dicarbonyl compounds are starting materials for synthesizing **five-membered rings.**

Aldol reactions with dicarbonyl compounds can be used to make five- and six-membered rings. The enolate formed from one carbonyl group is the nucleophile, and the carbonyl carbon of the other carbonyl group is the electrophile. For example, treatment of 2,5-hexanedione with base forms a five-membered ring.

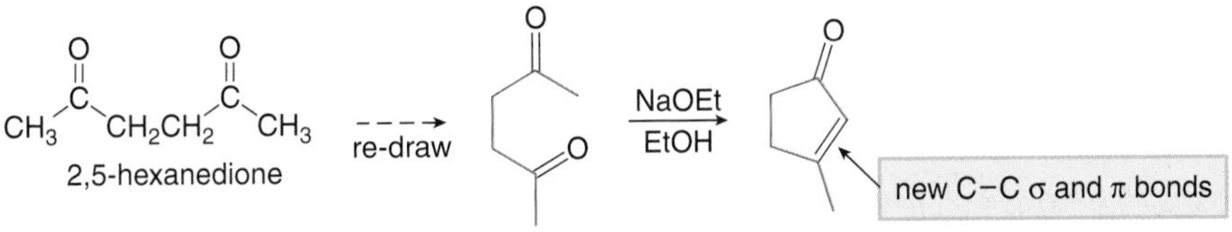

The steps in this process, shown in Mechanism 24.3, are no different from the general mechanisms of the aldol reaction and dehydration described previously in Section 24.1.

Mechanism 24.3 The Intramolecular Aldol Reaction

Step [1] Formation of an enolate

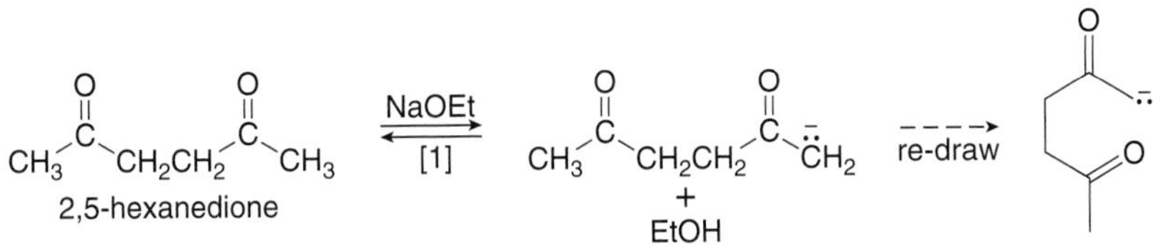

- Deprotonation of the CH_3 group with base forms a nucleophilic enolate, which is re-drawn to more clearly show the intramolecular reaction in Step [2].

Steps [2]–[4] Cyclization and dehydration

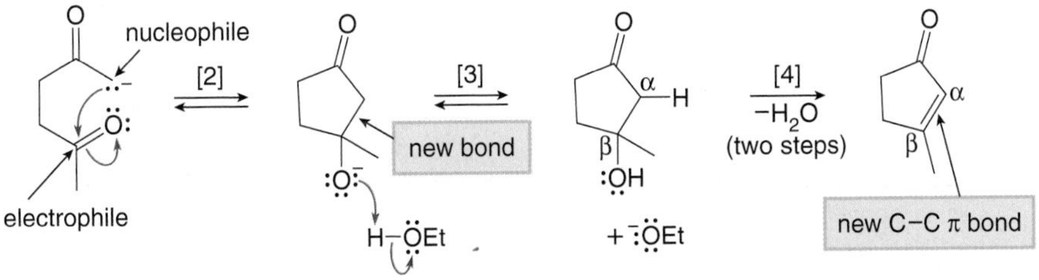

- In Step [2], the nucleophilic enolate attacks the electrophilic carbonyl carbon in the same molecule, forming a new carbon–carbon σ bond. **This generates the five-membered ring.**
- Protonation of the alkoxide in Step [3] and loss of H_2O by the two steps outlined in Mechanism 24.2 form a new C–C π bond.

When 2,5-hexanedione is treated with base in Step [1], two different enolates are possible—enolates **A** and **B,** formed by removal of H_a and H_b, respectively. Although enolate **A** goes on to form the five-membered ring, intramolecular cyclization using enolate **B** would lead to a strained three-membered ring.

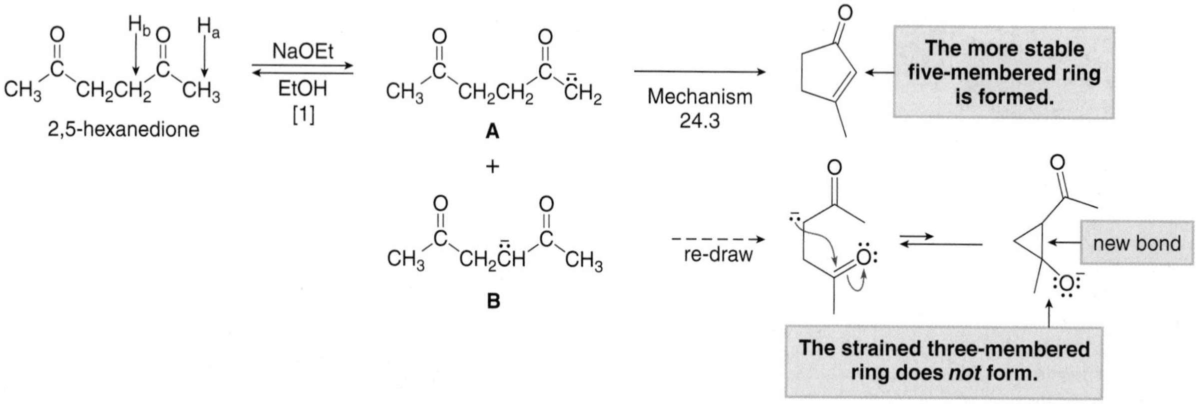

Because the three-membered ring is much higher in energy than the enolate starting material, equilibrium greatly favors the starting materials and the **three-membered ring does not form.** Under the reaction conditions, enolate **B** is re-protonated to form 2,5-hexanedione, because all steps except dehydration are equilibria. **Thus, equilibrium favors formation of the more stable five-membered ring over the much less stable three-membered ring.**

In a similar fashion, six-membered rings can be formed from the intramolecular aldol reaction of **1,5-dicarbonyl compounds.**

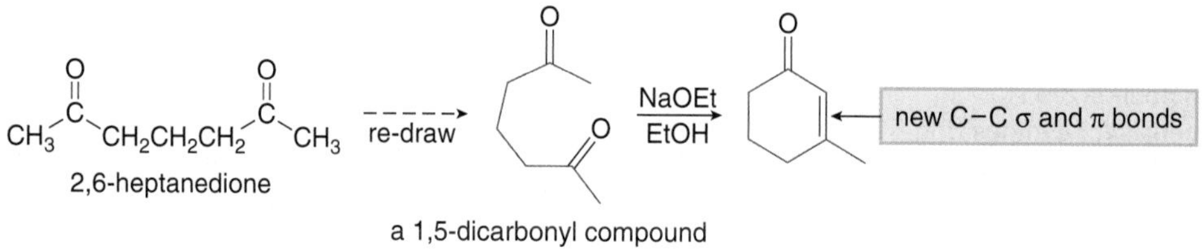

The synthesis of the female sex hormone **progesterone** by W. S. Johnson and co-workers at Stanford University is considered one of the classics in total synthesis. The last six-membered ring needed in the steroid skeleton was prepared by a two-step sequence using an intramolecular aldol reaction, as shown in Figure 24.5.

Problem 24.12 Draw a stepwise mechanism for the conversion of 2,6-heptanedione to 3-methyl-2-cyclohexenone with NaOEt, EtOH.

Figure 24.5 The synthesis of progesterone using an intramolecular aldol reaction

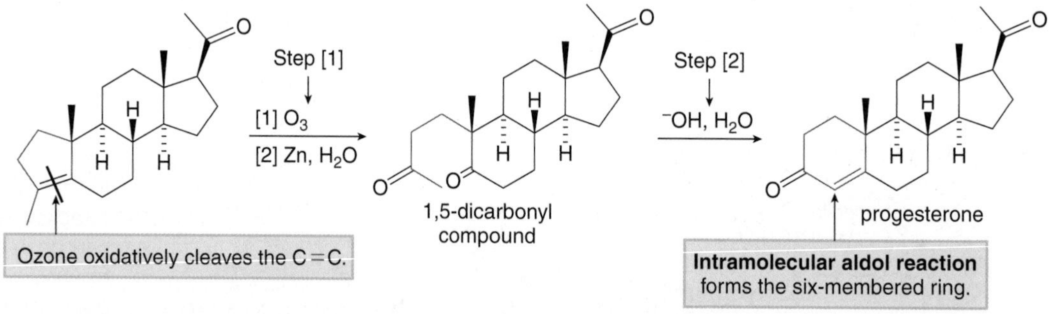

- **Step [1]:** Oxidative cleavage of the alkene with O_3, followed by Zn, H_2O (Section 12.10), gives the 1,5-dicarbonyl compound.
- **Step [2]:** Intramolecular aldol reaction of the 1,5-dicarbonyl compound with dilute ^-OH in H_2O solution forms progesterone.
- **This two-step reaction sequence converts a five-membered ring into a six-membered ring.** Reactions that synthesize larger rings from smaller ones are called **ring expansion reactions.**

Problem 24.13 What cyclic product is formed when each 1,5-dicarbonyl compound is treated with aqueous ^{-}OH?

a. 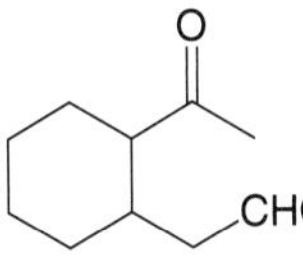

b. 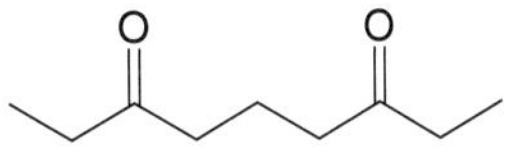

Problem 24.14 Following the two-step reaction sequence depicted in Figure 24.5, write out the steps needed to convert **A** to **B.**

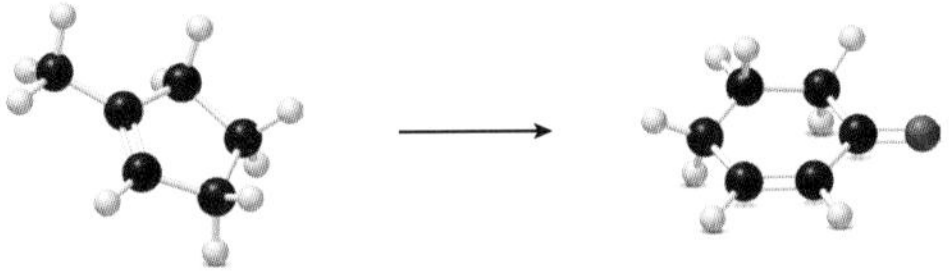

A **B**

24.5 The Claisen Reaction

The **Claisen reaction** is the second general reaction of enolates with other carbonyl compounds. In the Claisen reaction, two molecules of an ester react with each other in the presence of an alkoxide base to form a **β-keto ester.** For example, treatment of ethyl acetate with NaOEt forms ethyl acetoacetate after protonation with aqueous acid.

Unlike the aldol reaction, which is base-catalyzed, a full equivalent of base is needed to deprotonate the β-keto ester formed in Step [3] of the Claisen reaction.

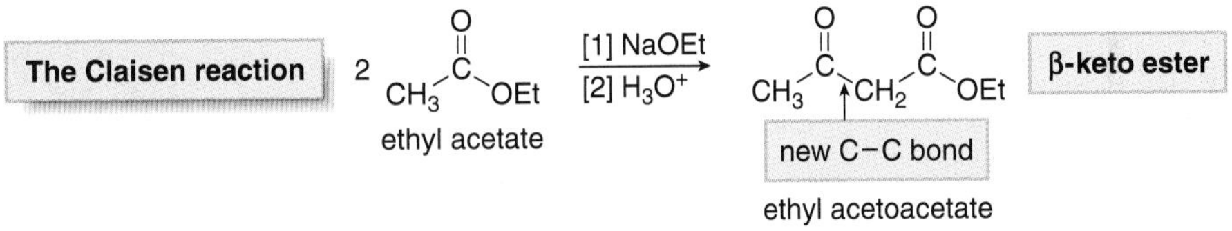

The mechanism for the Claisen reaction (Mechanism 24.4) resembles the mechanism of an aldol reaction in that it involves nucleophilic addition of an enolate to an electrophilic carbonyl group. Because esters have a leaving group on the carbonyl carbon, however, loss of a leaving group occurs to form the product of **substitution, *not* addition.**

Because the generation of a resonance-stabilized enolate from the product β-keto ester drives the Claisen reaction (Step [4] of Mechanism 24.4), **only esters with two or three hydrogens on the α carbon undergo this reaction;** that is, esters must have the general structure CH_3CO_2R' or RCH_2CO_2R'.

- **Keep in mind: The characteristic reaction of esters is nucleophilic substitution. A Claisen reaction is a nucleophilic substitution in which an enolate is the nucleophile.**

Figure 24.6 compares the general reaction for nucleophilic substitution of an ester with the Claisen reaction. Sample Problem 24.3 reinforces the basic features of the Claisen reaction.

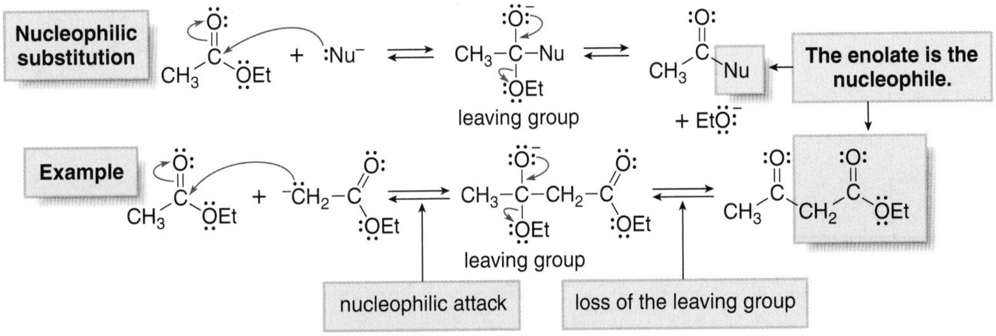

Figure 24.6 The Claisen reaction—An example of nucleophilic substitution

- Esters react by nucleophilic substitution. In a Claisen reaction, an enolate is the nucleophile that adds to the carbonyl group.

Mechanism 24.4 The Claisen Reaction

Step [1] Formation of a nucleophilic enolate

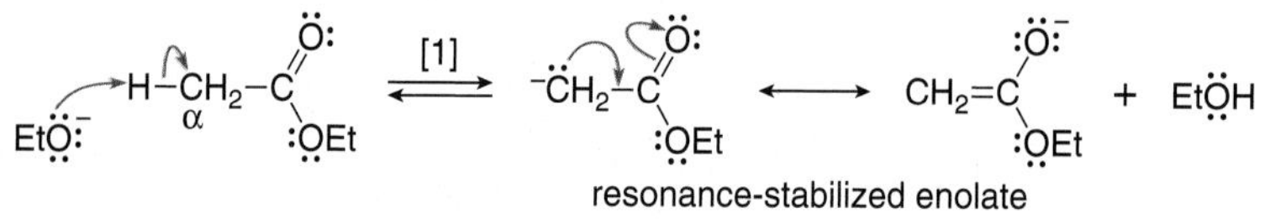
[1]
α
EtÖ:⁻
:ÖEt
resonance-stabilized enolate
+ EtÖH

- In Step [1], the base removes a proton from the α carbon to form a **resonance-stabilized enolate.**

Steps [2]–[3] Nucleophilic addition and loss of the leaving group

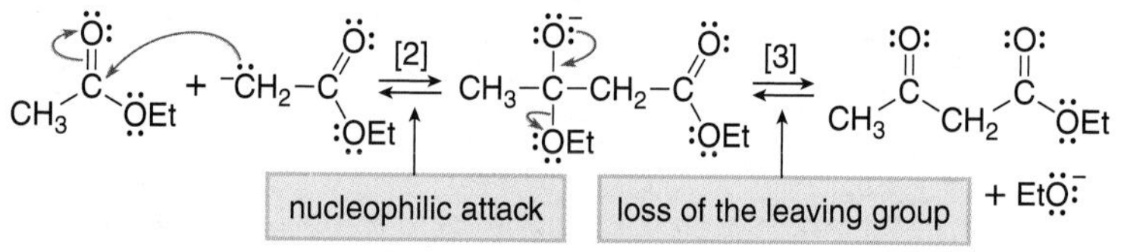
[2]
[3]
nucleophilic attack
loss of the leaving group
+ EtÖ:⁻

- In Step [2], the nucleophilic enolate attacks the electrophilic carbonyl carbon of another molecule of ester, forming a new carbon–carbon bond. **This joins the α carbon of one ester to the carbonyl carbon of a second ester.**
- Elimination of the leaving group, EtO^-, forms a β-keto ester in Step [3]. Steps [1]–[3] are reversible equilibria.

Steps [4]–[5] Deprotonation and protonation

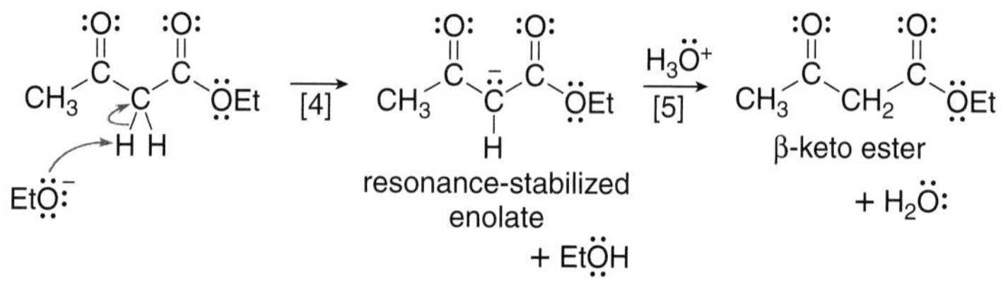
[4]
[5]
H₃Ö⁺
EtÖ:⁻
resonance-stabilized enolate
+ EtÖH
β-keto ester
+ H₂Ö:

- Because the β-keto ester formed in Step [3] has especially acidic protons between its two carbonyl groups, a proton is removed under the basic reaction conditions to form an enolate (Step [4]). **The formation of this resonance-stabilized enolate drives the equilibrium in the Claisen reaction.**
- Protonation of this enolate with strong acid re-forms the neutral β-keto ester to complete the reaction.

Sample Problem 24.3

Draw the product of the following Claisen reaction.

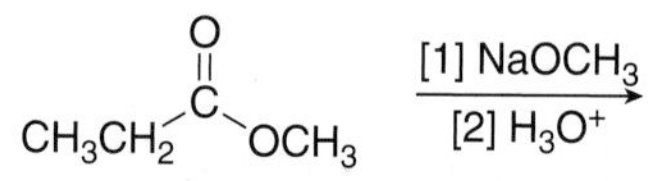
[1] NaOCH₃
[2] H₃O⁺

Solution

To draw the product of any Claisen reaction, form a new carbon–carbon bond between the α carbon of one ester and the carbonyl carbon of another ester, with elimination of the leaving group ($^-OCH_3$ in this case).

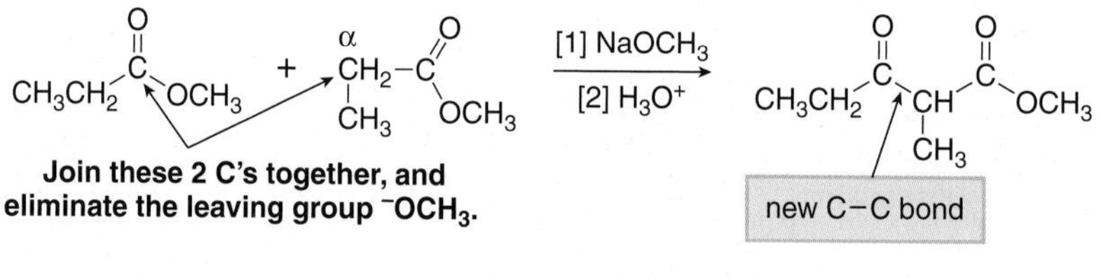
α
[1] NaOCH₃
[2] H₃O⁺
Join these 2 C's together, and eliminate the leaving group ⁻OCH₃.
new C–C bond

Next, write out the steps of the reaction to verify this product.

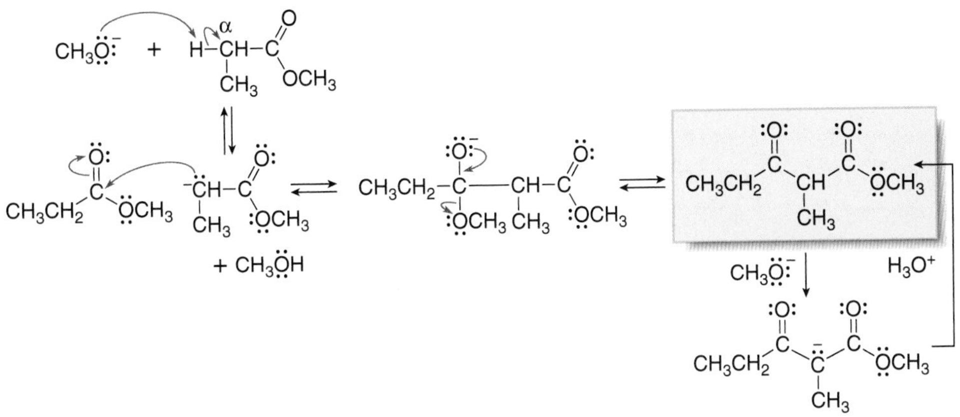

Problem 24.15 What β-keto ester is formed when each ester is used in a Claisen reaction?

24.6 The Crossed Claisen and Related Reactions

Like the aldol reaction, it is sometimes possible to carry out a Claisen reaction with two different carbonyl components as starting materials.

- **A Claisen reaction between two different carbonyl compounds is called a *crossed Claisen reaction.***

24.6A Two Useful Crossed Claisen Reactions

A crossed Claisen reaction is synthetically useful in two different instances.

- **A crossed Claisen occurs between two different esters when only one has α hydrogens.**

When one ester has no α hydrogens, a crossed Claisen reaction often leads to one product. Common esters with no α H atoms include ethyl formate (**HCO_2Et**) and ethyl benzoate (**$C_6H_5CO_2Et$**). For example, the reaction of ethyl benzoate (as the electrophile) with ethyl acetate (which forms the enolate) in the presence of base forms predominately one β-keto ester.

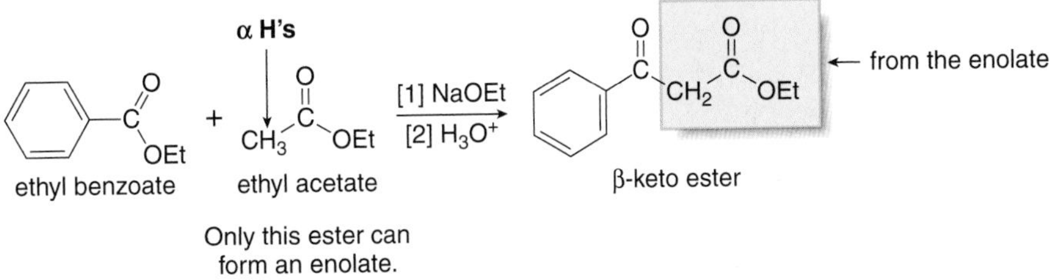

- **A crossed Claisen occurs between a ketone and an ester.**

The reaction of a ketone and an ester in the presence of base also forms the product of a crossed Claisen reaction. The enolate is generally formed from the ketone component, and the reaction works best when the ester has no α hydrogens. The product of this crossed Claisen reaction is a **β-dicarbonyl compound,** but ***not*** a β-keto ester.

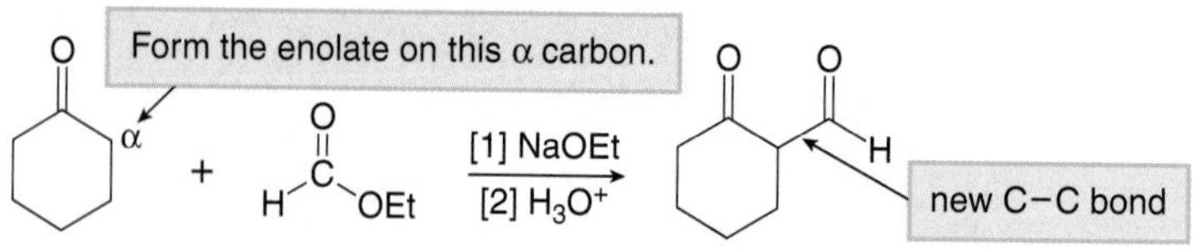

β-dicarbonyl compound

Problem 24.16 What crossed Claisen product is formed from each pair of compounds?

a. CH_3CH_2COOEt and HCO_2Et
b. $CH_3(CH_2)_5CO_2Et$ and HCO_2Et
c. $(CH_3)_2C=O$ and CH_3CO_2Et
d.

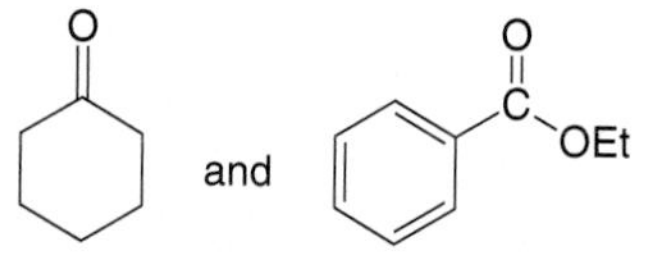

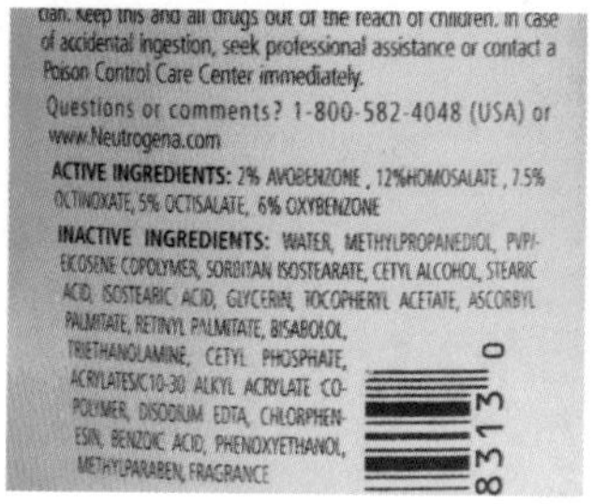

Sunscreen ingredients

Problem 24.17 Avobenzone is a conjugated compound that absorbs ultraviolet light with wavelengths in the 320–400 nm region, so it is a common ingredient in commercial sunscreens. Write out two different crossed Claisen reactions that form avobenzone.

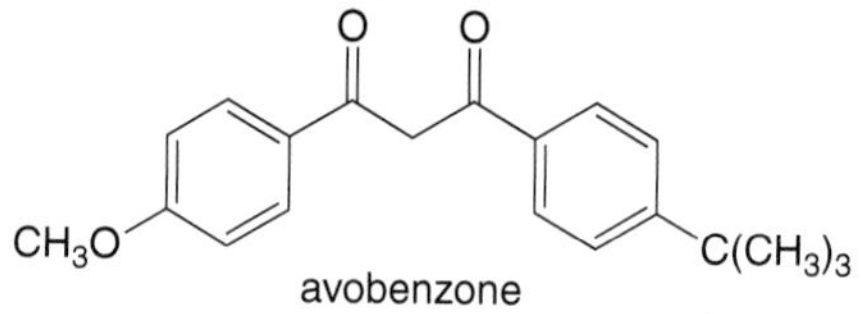

avobenzone

24.6B Other Useful Variations of the Crossed Claisen Reaction

β-Dicarbonyl compounds are also prepared by reacting an enolate with **ethyl chloroformate** and **diethyl carbonate.**

ethyl chloroformate diethyl carbonate

These reactions resemble a Claisen reaction because they involve the same three steps:

[1] Formation of an enolate
[2] Nucleophilic addition to a carbonyl group
[3] Elimination of a leaving group

For example, reaction of an ester enolate with diethyl carbonate yields a β-diester (Reaction [1]), whereas reaction of a ketone enolate with ethyl chloroformate forms a β-keto ester (Reaction [2]).

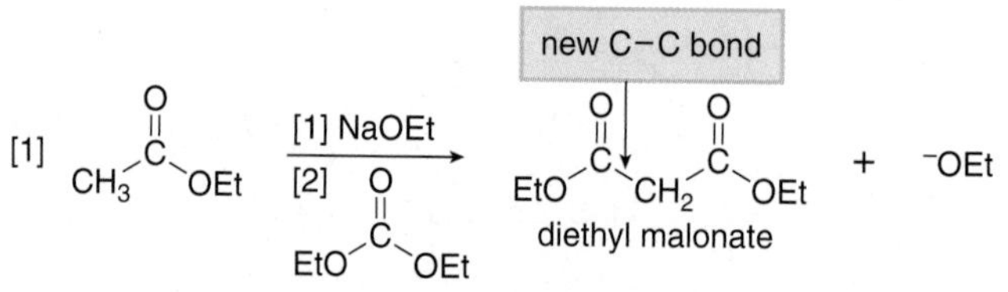

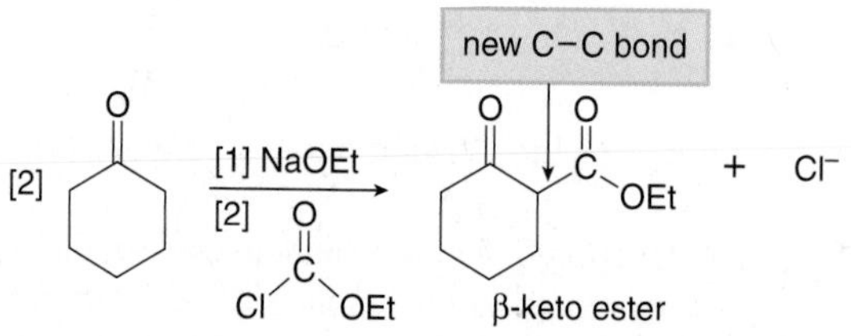

Reaction [2] is noteworthy because it provides easy access to **β-keto esters,** which are useful starting materials in the acetoacetic ester synthesis (Section 23.10). In this reaction, Cl^- is eliminated rather than ^-OEt in Step [3], because Cl^- is a better leaving group, as shown in the following steps.

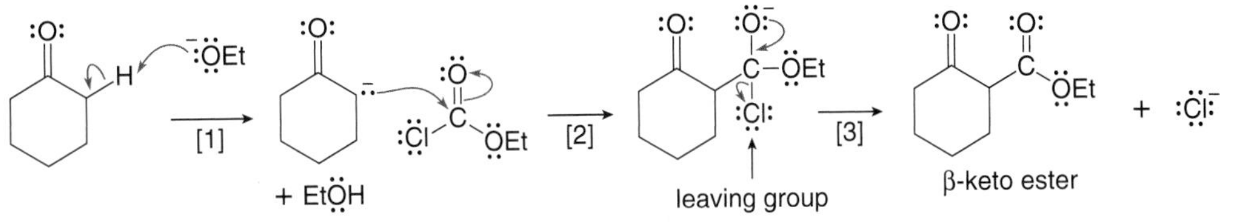

Problem 24.18 Draw the products of each reaction.

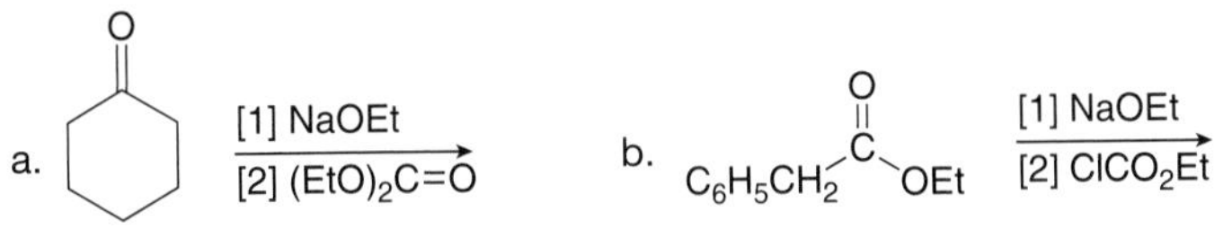

Problem 24.19 Two steps in a synthesis of the analgesic ibuprofen, the chapter-opening molecule, include a carbonyl condensation reaction, followed by an alkylation reaction. Identify intermediates **A** and **B** in the synthesis of ibuprofen.

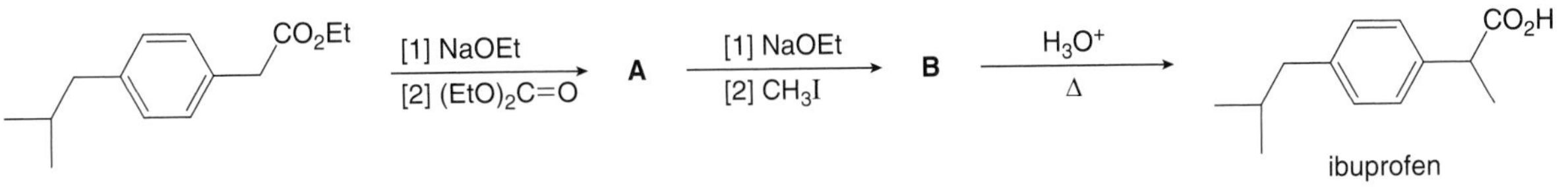

ibuprofen

24.7 The Dieckmann Reaction

Intramolecular Claisen reactions of diesters form five- and six-membered rings. The enolate of one ester is the nucleophile, and the carbonyl carbon of the other is the electrophile. An intramolecular Claisen reaction is called a **Dieckmann reaction.** Two types of diesters give good yields of cyclic products.

- **1,6-Diesters yield five-membered rings by the Dieckmann reaction.**

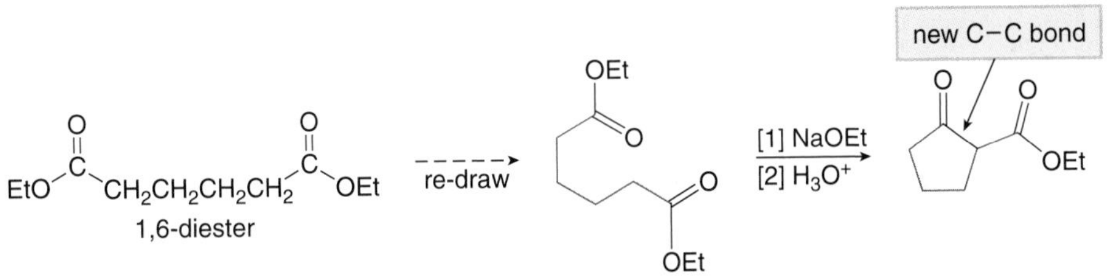

- **1,7-Diesters yield six-membered rings by the Dieckmann reaction.**

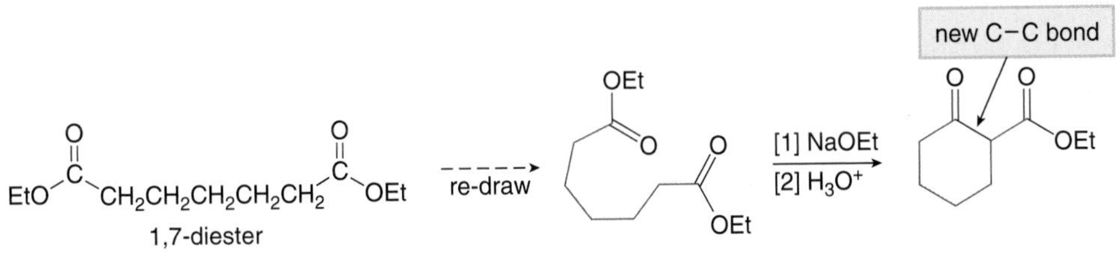

The mechanism of the Dieckmann reaction is exactly the same as the mechanism of an intermolecular Claisen reaction. It is illustrated in Mechanism 24.5 for the formation of a six-membered ring.

Mechanism 24.5 The Dieckmann Reaction

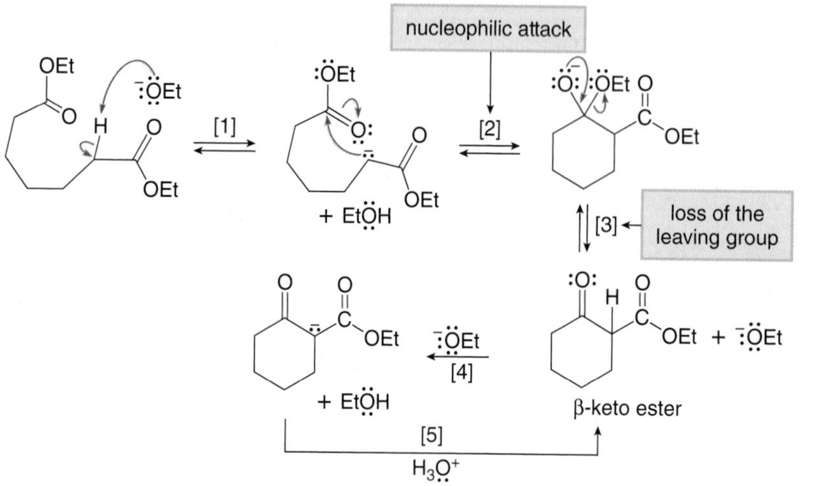

- In Step [1], the base removes a proton to form an enolate, which attacks the carbonyl group of the second ester in Step [2], thus forming a new carbon–carbon bond.
- In Step [3], elimination of ^-OEt forms the β-keto ester.
- To complete the reaction, the proton between the two carbonyl groups is removed with base, and then protonation of the enolate re-forms the β-keto ester (Steps [4] and [5]).

Problem 24.20 What two β-keto esters are formed in the Dieckmann reaction of the following diester?

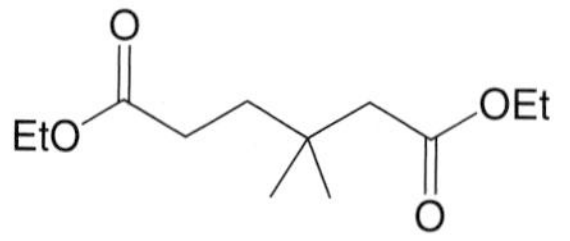

24.8 The Michael Reaction

Like the aldol and Claisen reactions, the **Michael reaction involves two carbonyl components—the enolate of one carbonyl compound and an α,β-unsaturated carbonyl compound.**

Two components of a Michael reaction

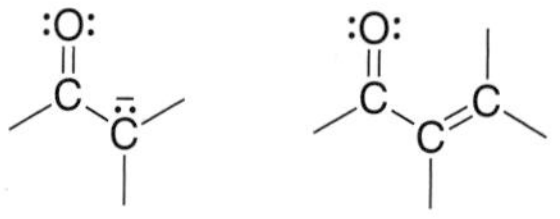

enolate

α,β-unsaturated carbonyl compound

Recall from Section 20.15 that α,β-unsaturated carbonyl compounds are resonance stabilized and have **two electrophilic sites—the carbonyl carbon and the β carbon.**

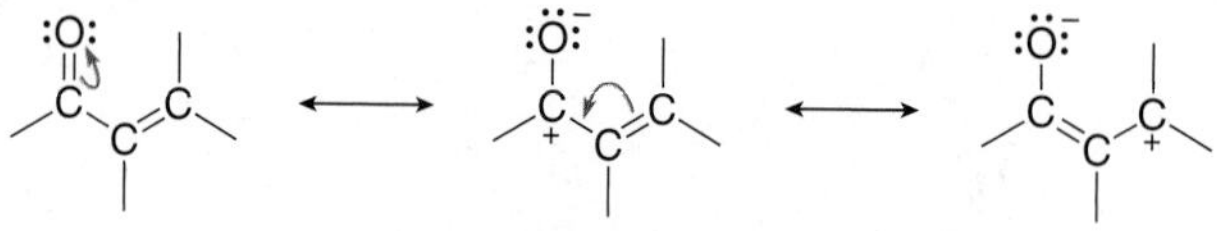

three resonance structures for an α,β-unsaturated carbonyl compound

The hybrid

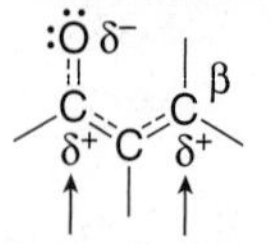

two electrophilic sites

- **The Michael reaction involves the conjugate addition (1,4-addition) of a resonance-stabilized enolate to the β carbon of an α,β-unsaturated carbonyl system.**

All conjugate additions add the **elements of H and Nu across the α and β carbons.** In the Michael reaction, the **nucleophile is an enolate.** Enolates of active methylene compounds are particularly common. The α,β-unsaturated carbonyl component is often called a **Michael acceptor.**

Conjugate addition

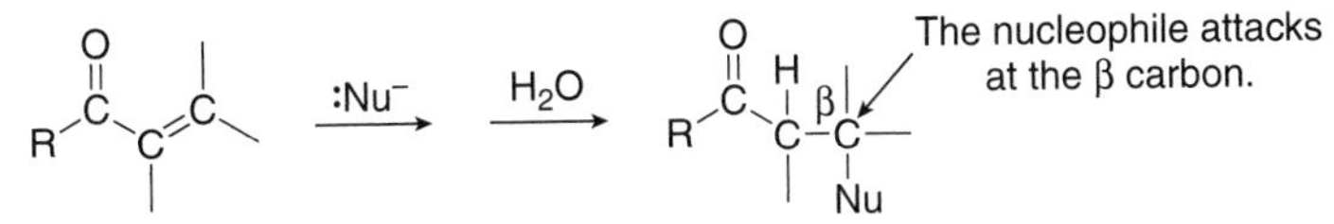
:Nu⁻
H_2O
The nucleophile attacks at the β carbon.
Nu

Michael reaction

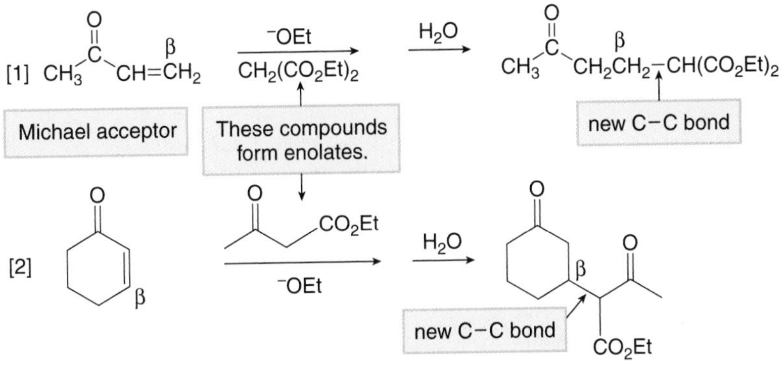
[1] CH_3 CH=CH_2
⁻OEt
$CH_2(CO_2Et)_2$
H_2O
CH_3 CH_2CH_2–$CH(CO_2Et)_2$
new C–C bond
Michael acceptor
These compounds form enolates.
[2]
CO_2Et
⁻OEt
H_2O
new C–C bond
CO_2Et

Problem 24.21 Which of the following compounds can serve as Michael acceptors?

a.
b.
c.
d. CH_3O

The Michael reaction always forms a new carbon–carbon bond on the β carbon of the Michael acceptor. Reaction [2] is used to illustrate the mechanism of the Michael reaction in Mechanism 24.6. The key step is nucleophilic addition of the enolate to the β carbon of the Michael acceptor in Step [2].

Mechanism 24.6 The Michael Reaction

Step [1] Enolate formation

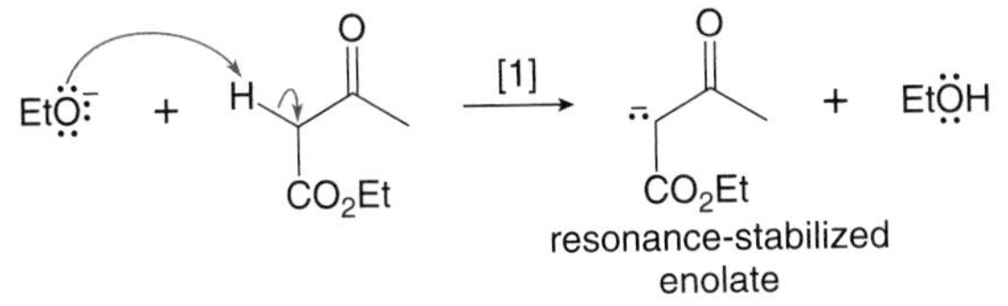
EtÖ:⁻
[1]
EtÖH
CO_2Et
CO_2Et
resonance-stabilized enolate

- Base removes the acidic proton between the two carbonyl groups, **forming the enolate** in Step [1]. Only one of the three resonance structures is drawn.

Steps [2]–[3] Nucleophilic attack at the β carbon and protonation

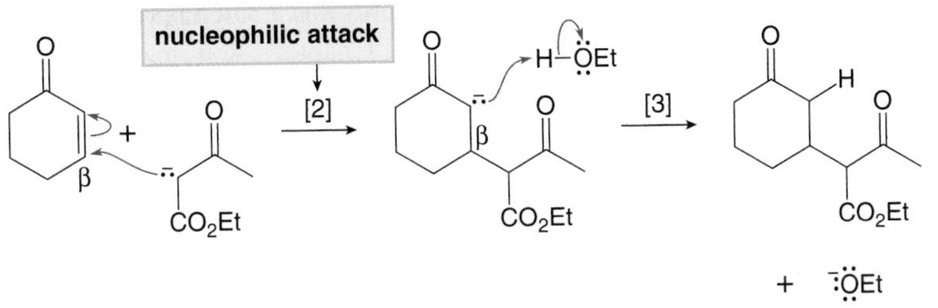
nucleophilic attack
[2]
H–ÖEt
[3]
CO_2Et
CO_2Et
CO_2Et
+ ⁻:ÖEt

- **The nucleophilic enolate adds to the β carbon** of the α,β-unsaturated carbonyl compound, forming a new carbon–carbon bond and a resonance-stabilized enolate.
- Protonation of the enolate forms the 1,4-addition product in Step [3].

Figure 24.7
Using a Michael reaction in the synthesis of the steroid estrone

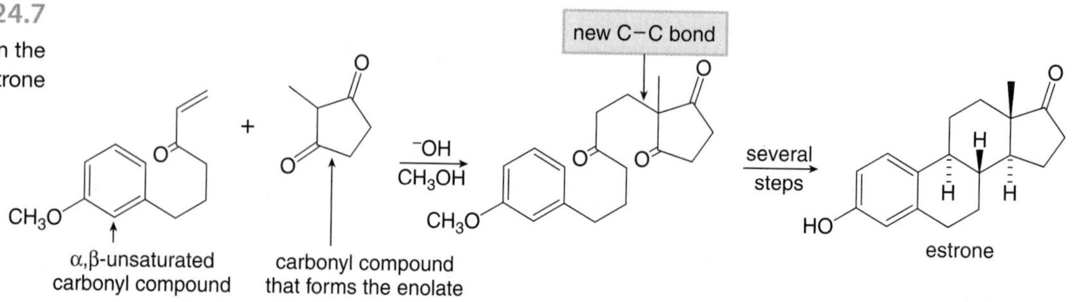
new C–C bond
$^{-}$OH
CH_3OH
several steps
CH_3O
HO
H
α,β-unsaturated carbonyl compound
carbonyl compound that forms the enolate
estrone

When the product of a Michael reaction is also a β-keto ester, it can be hydrolyzed and decarboxylated by heating in aqueous acid, as discussed in Section 23.9. This forms a **1,5-dicarbonyl compound.** Figure 24.7 shows a Michael reaction that was a key step in the synthesis of **estrone,** a female sex hormone.

1,5-Dicarbonyl compounds are starting materials for intramolecular aldol reactions, as described in Section 24.4.

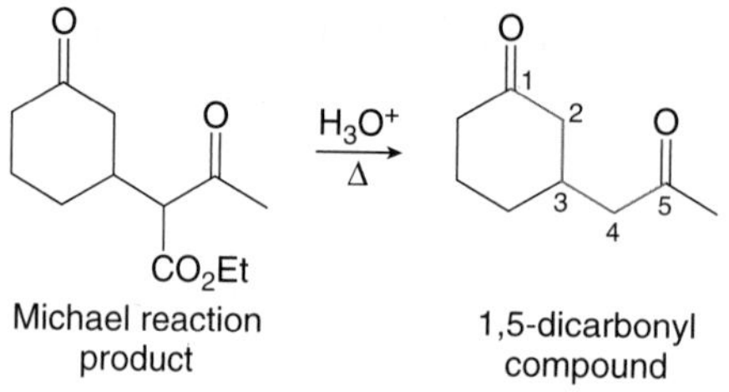
H_3O^+
Δ
CO_2Et
Michael reaction product
1,5-dicarbonyl compound

Problem 24.22 What product is formed when each pair of compounds is treated with NaOEt in ethanol?

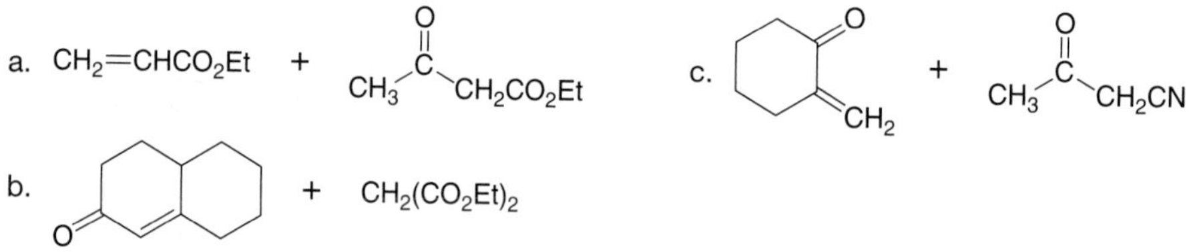
a. $CH_2{=}CHCO_2Et$ + $CH_3COCH_2CO_2Et$
b. + $CH_2(CO_2Et)_2$
c. + CH_3COCH_2CN
CH_2

Problem 24.23 What starting materials are needed to prepare each compound by the Michael reaction?

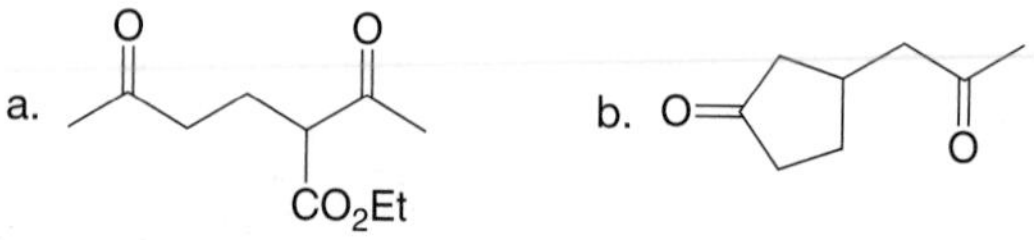
a.
CO_2Et
b.

24.9 The Robinson Annulation

The word **annulation** comes from the Greek word *annulus* for ring. The Robinson annulation is named for English chemist Sir Robert Robinson, who was awarded the 1947 Nobel Prize in Chemistry.

The Robinson annulation is a ring-forming reaction that combines a Michael reaction with an intramolecular aldol reaction. Like the other reactions in Chapter 24, it involves enolates and it forms carbon–carbon bonds. The two starting materials for a Robinson annulation are an α,β-unsaturated carbonyl compound and an enolate.

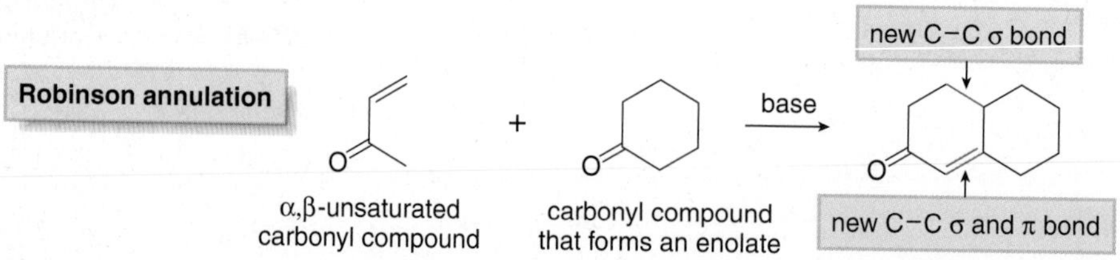
Robinson annulation
base
new C–C σ bond
new C–C σ and π bond
α,β-unsaturated carbonyl compound
carbonyl compound that forms an enolate

The Robinson annulation forms a six-membered ring and three new carbon–carbon bonds—two σ bonds and one π bond. The product contains an α,β-unsaturated ketone in a cyclohexane ring—that is, a **2-cyclohexenone** ring. To generate the enolate component of the Robinson annulation, ^{-}OH in H_2O and ^{-}OEt in EtOH are typically used.

Examples

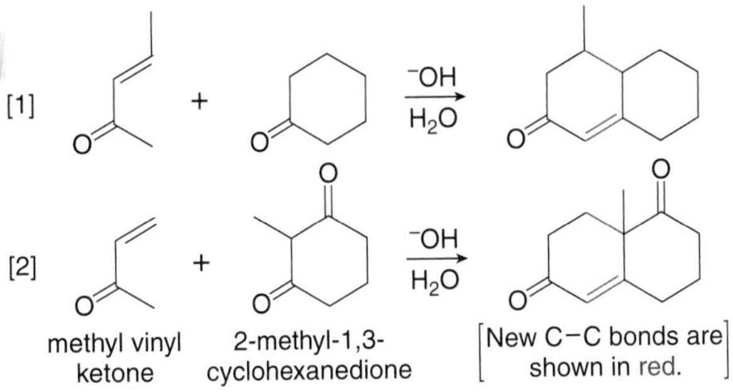

The mechanism of the Robinson annulation consists of two parts: a **Michael addition** to the α,β-unsaturated carbonyl compound to form a 1,5-dicarbonyl compound, followed by an **intramolecular aldol reaction** to form the six-membered ring. The mechanism is written out in two parts (Mechanisms 24.7 and 24.8) for Reaction [2] between methyl vinyl ketone and 2-methyl-1,3-cyclohexanedione.

Mechanism 24.7 The Robinson Annulation—Part [A] Michael Addition to Form a 1,5-Dicarbonyl Compound

Step [1] Enolate formation

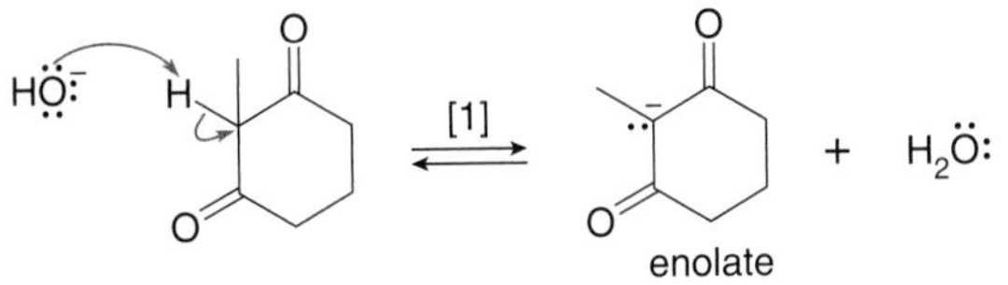

- Base removes the most acidic proton—that is, the proton between the two carbonyl groups—forming the enolate in Step [1]. Only one of the three resonance structures is drawn.

Steps [2]–[3] Nucleophilic attack at the β carbon and protonation

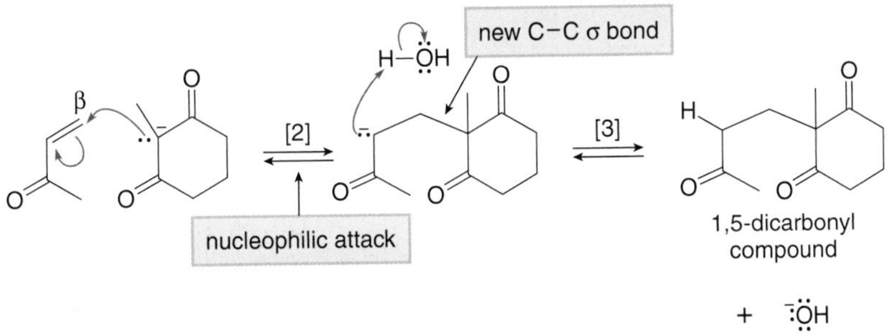

- **Conjugate addition of the enolate to the β carbon** of the α,β-unsaturated carbonyl compound forms a new carbon–carbon bond and a resonance-stabilized enolate.
- Protonation of the enolate forms the 1,5-dicarbonyl compound.

Part [A] illustrates the three-step mechanism for the Michael addition that forms the first carbon–carbon σ bond, generating the 1,5-dicarbonyl compound. The first step always involves removal of the most acidic proton to form an enolate.

In Part [B] of the mechanism, an intramolecular aldol reaction followed by dehydration forms the six-membered ring.

Mechanism 24.8 The Robinson Annulation—Part [B] Intramolecular Aldol Reaction to Form a 2-Cyclohexenone

Steps [4]–[6] Intramolecular aldol reaction to form a β-hydroxy ketone

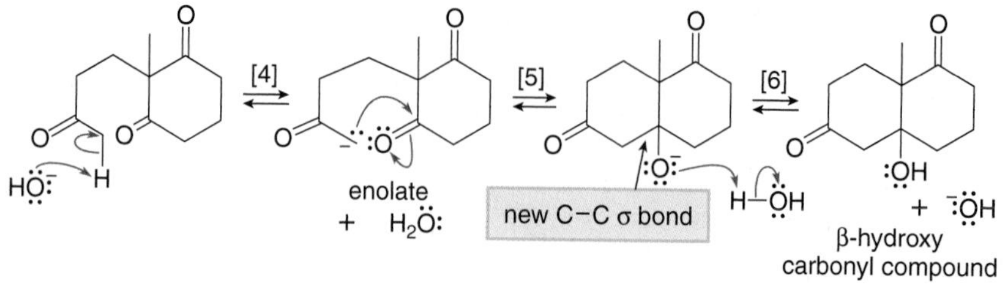

- The **intramolecular aldol reaction** consists of three steps: [4] **enolate formation,** [5] **nucleophilic attack,** and [6] **protonation.** This forms another carbon–carbon σ bond and a β-hydroxy carbonyl compound (compare Section 24.4).

Steps [7]–[8] Dehydration to form the α,β-unsaturated ketone

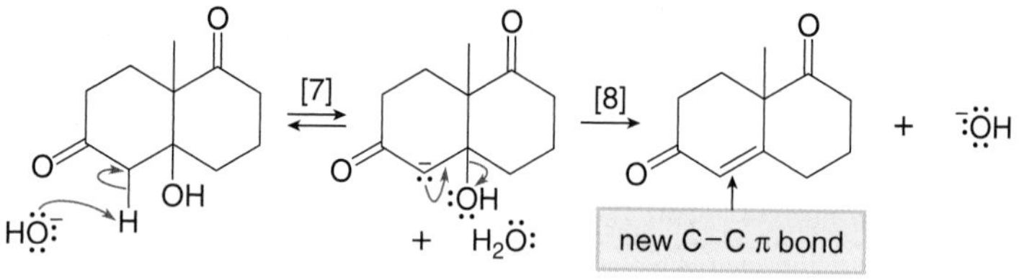

- Dehydration consists of two steps: **deprotonation** and **loss of $^-$OH** (Section 24.1B). This reaction forms the new π bond in the α,β-unsaturated ketone.

All of the parts of this mechanism have been discussed in previous sections of Chapter 24. However, the end result of the Robinson annulation—the formation of a 2-cyclohexenone ring—is new.

To draw the product of Robinson annulation without writing out the mechanism each time, place the α carbon of the compound that becomes the enolate next to the β carbon of the α,β-unsaturated carbonyl compound. Then, join the appropriate carbons together as shown. If you follow this method of drawing the starting materials, the double bond in the product always ends up in the same position in the six-membered ring.

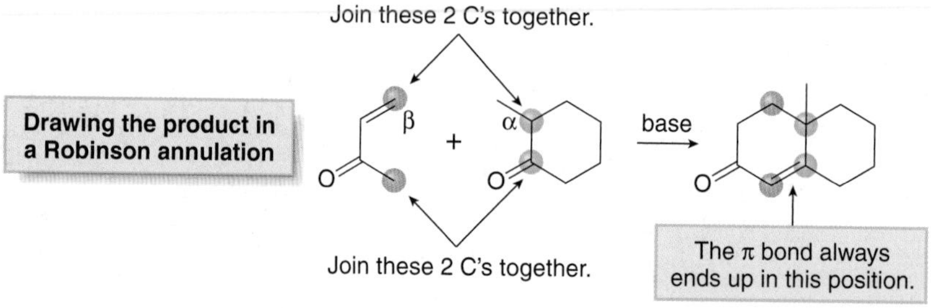

Sample Problem 24.4 Draw the Robinson annulation product formed from the following starting materials.

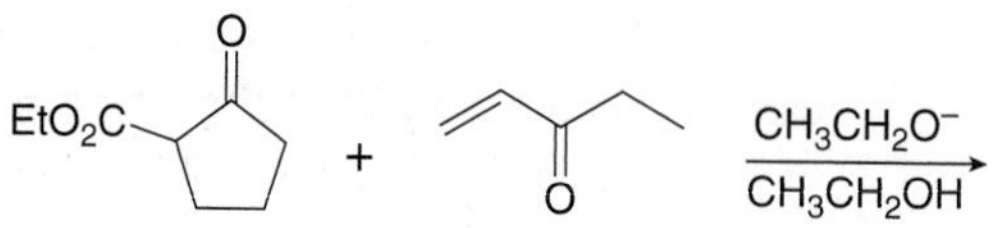

Solution

Arrange the starting materials to put the reactive atoms next to each other. For example:

- Place the α,β-unsaturated carbonyl compound *to the left* of the carbonyl compound.
- Determine which α carbon will become the enolate. The most acidic H is always removed with base first, which in this case is the H on the α carbon between the two carbonyl groups. This α carbon is drawn adjacent to the β carbon of the α,β-unsaturated carbonyl compound.

Then draw the bonds to form the new six-membered ring.

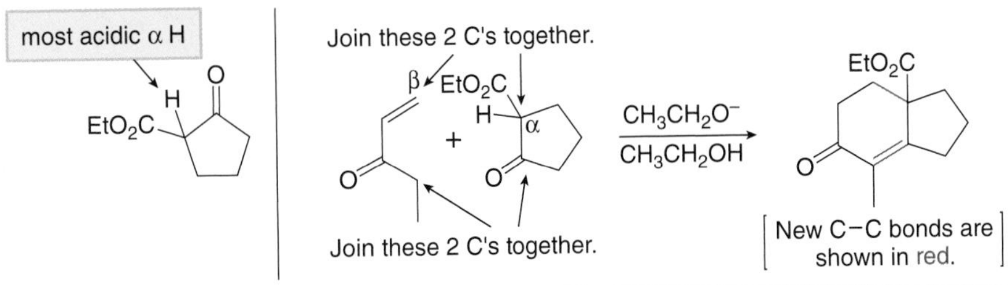
most acidic α H
H
O
EtO2C
Join these 2 C's together.
β
EtO2C
H
α
+
O
O
CH3CH2O−
CH3CH2OH
EtO2C
O
Join these 2 C's together.
New C–C bonds are shown in red.

Problem 24.24 Draw the products when each pair of compounds is treated with $CH_3CH_2O^-$, CH_3CH_2OH in a Robinson annulation reaction.

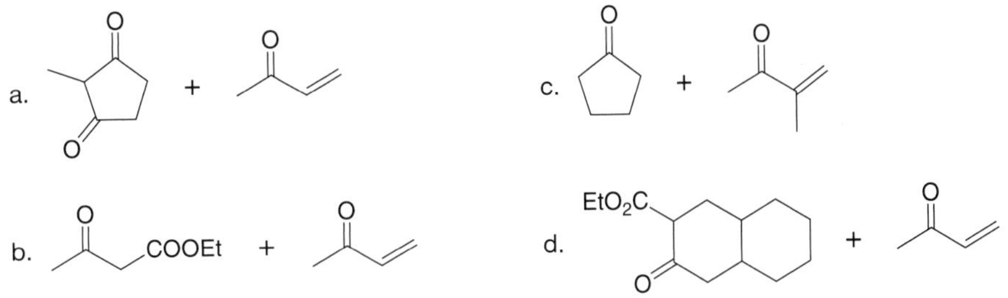
a.
+
b.
COOEt
+
c.
+
d.
EtO2C
+

To use the Robinson annulation in synthesis, you must be able to determine what starting materials are needed to prepare a given compound, by working in the retrosynthetic direction.

How To Synthesize a Compound Using the Robinson Annulation

Example What starting materials are needed to synthesize the following compound using a Robinson annulation?

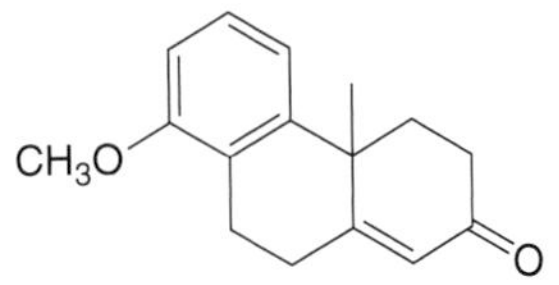
CH3O
O

Step [1] Locate the 2-cyclohexenone ring and re-draw the target molecule if necessary.

- To most easily determine the starting materials, always arrange the α,β-unsaturated carbonyl system in the same location. The target compound may have to be flipped or rotated, and you must be careful not to move any bonds to the wrong location during this process.

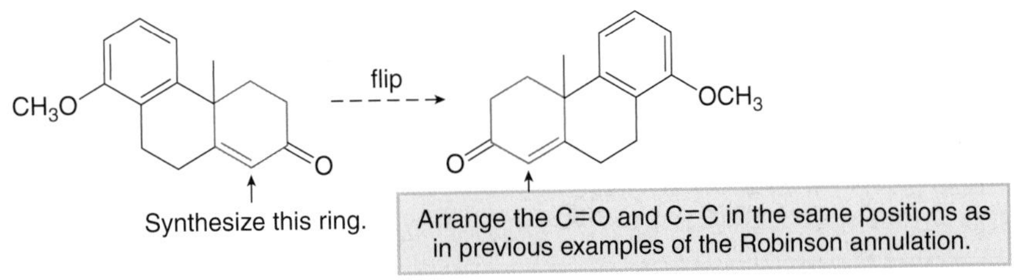
CH3O
O
flip
OCH3
O
Synthesize this ring.
Arrange the C=O and C=C in the same positions as in previous examples of the Robinson annulation.

—Continued

How To, continued . . .

Step [2] **Break the 2-cyclohexenone ring into two components.**

- Break the C=C. One half becomes the carbonyl group of the enolate component.
- Break the bond between the β carbon and the carbon to which it is bonded.

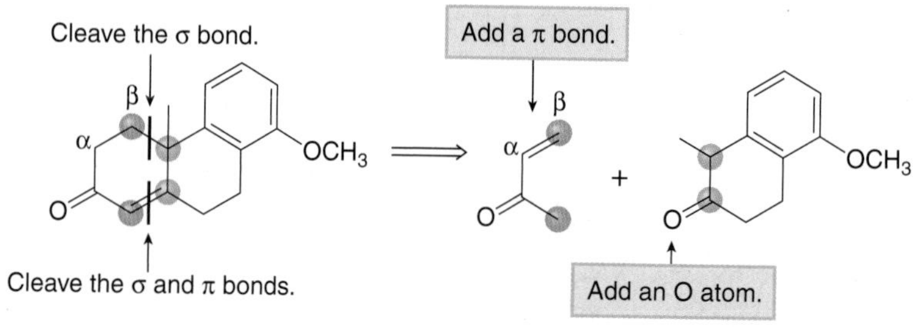

two components needed for the Robinson annulation

Problem 24.25 What starting materials are needed to synthesize each compound by a Robinson annulation?

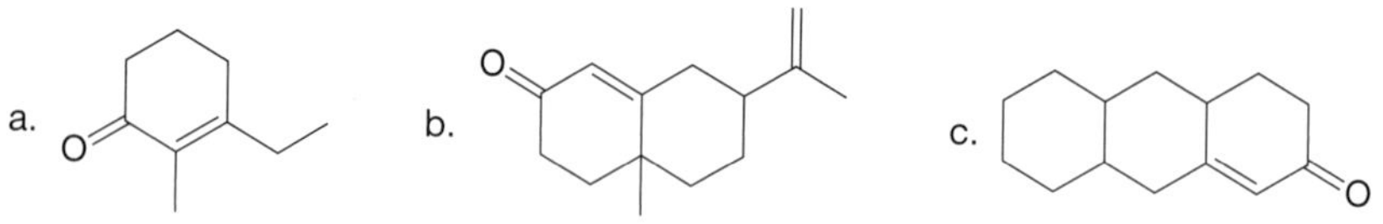

KEY CONCEPTS

Carbonyl Condensation Reactions

The Four Major Carbonyl Condensation Reactions

Reaction type	Reaction [New C–C bonds are shown in red.]
[1] Aldol reaction (24.1)	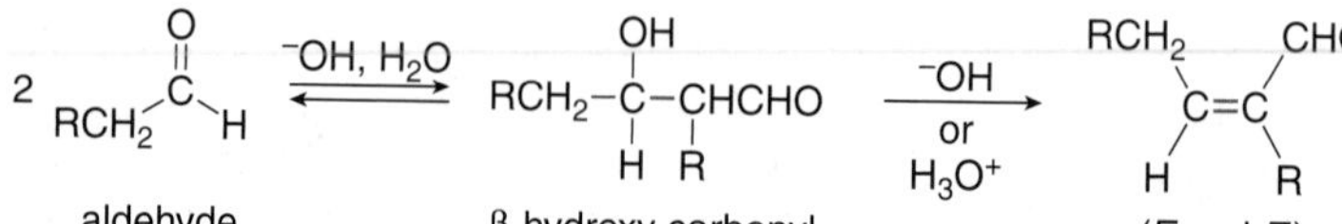 aldehyde (or ketone); β-hydroxy carbonyl compound; (*E* and *Z*) α,β-unsaturated carbonyl compound
[2] Claisen reaction (24.5)	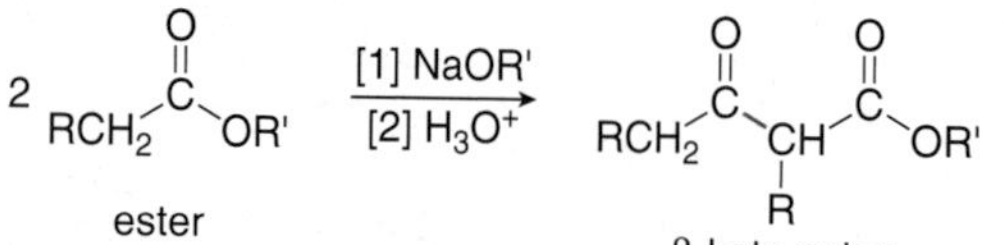 ester; β-keto ester
[3] Michael reaction (24.8)	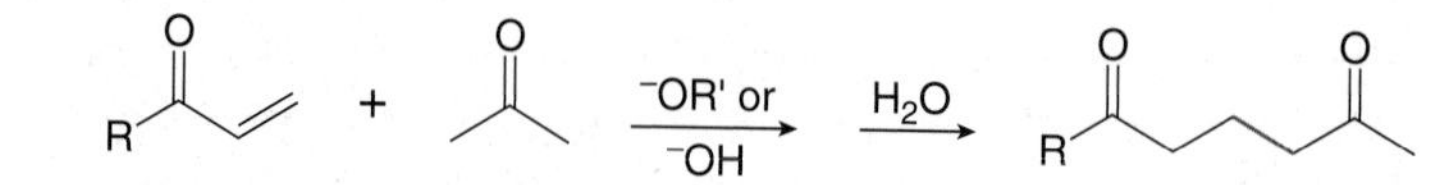 α,β-unsaturated carbonyl compound; carbonyl compound; 1,5-dicarbonyl compound
[4] Robinson annulation (24.9)	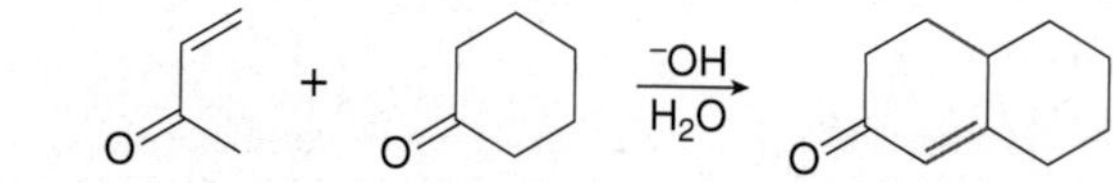 α,β-unsaturated carbonyl compound; carbonyl compound; 2-cyclohexenone

Useful Variations

[New C – C bonds are shown in red.]

[1] Directed aldol reaction (24.3)

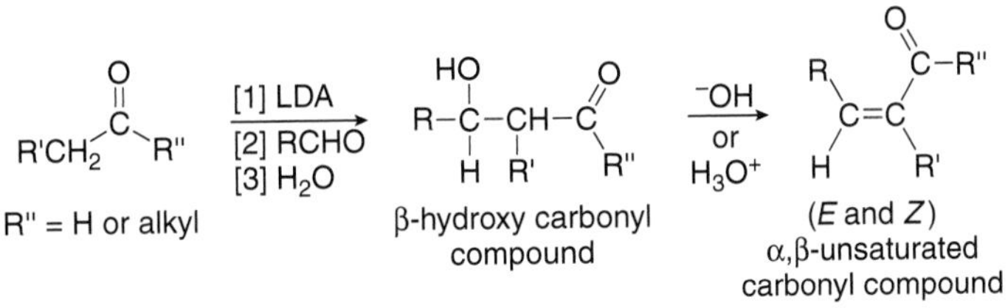
[1] LDA
[2] RCHO
[3] H2O
-OH
or
H3O+
R'' = H or alkyl
β-hydroxy carbonyl compound
(E and Z)
α,β-unsaturated carbonyl compound

[2] Intramolecular aldol reaction (24.4)

a. With 1,4-dicarbonyl compounds:

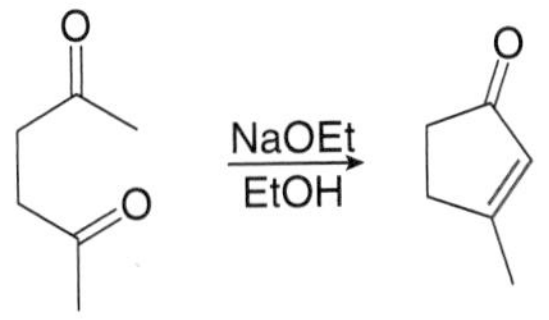
NaOEt
EtOH

b. With 1,5-dicarbonyl compounds:

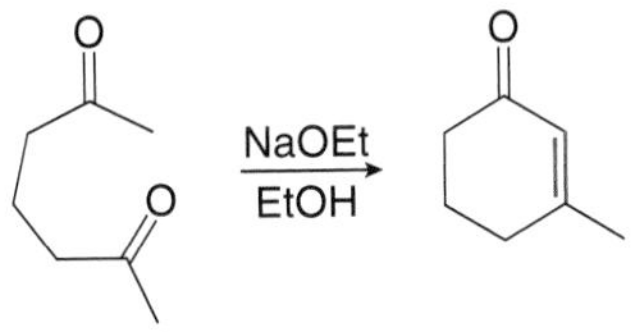
NaOEt
EtOH

[3] Dieckmann reaction (24.7)

a. With 1,6-diesters:

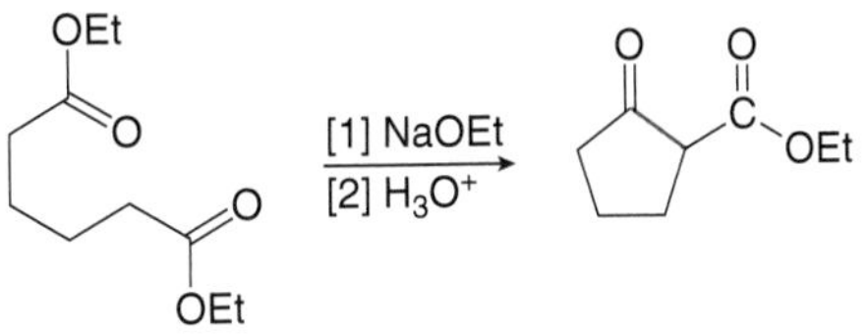
[1] NaOEt
[2] H3O+

b. With 1,7-diesters:

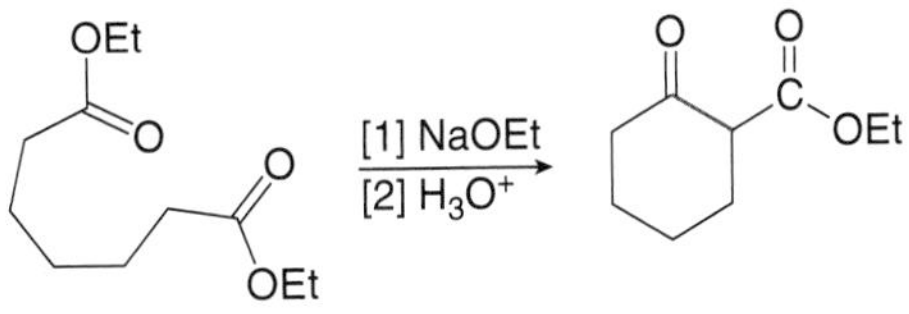
[1] NaOEt
[2] H3O+

PROBLEMS

Problems Using Three-Dimensional Models

24.26 Draw the aldol product formed from each pair of starting materials using ^{-}OH, H_2O.

a. 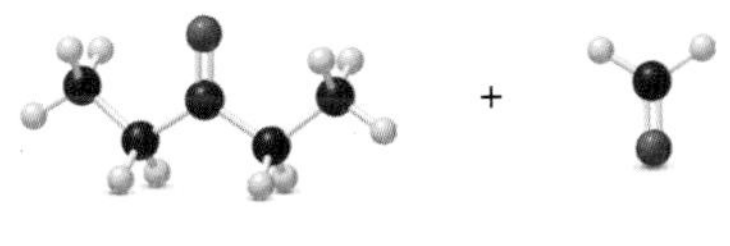

b. 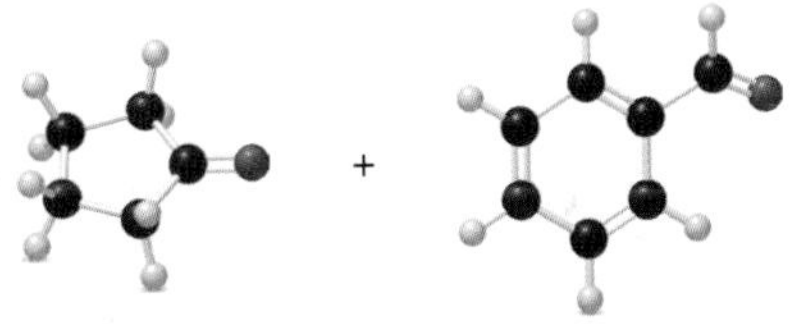

24.27 What steps are needed to convert **A** to **B?**

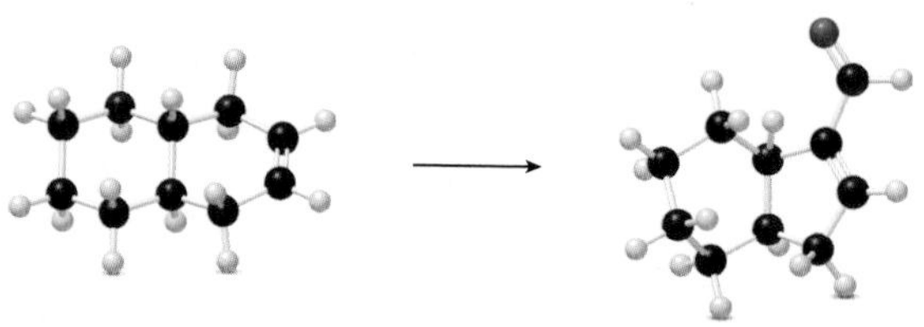

A B

The Aldol Reaction

24.28 Draw the product formed from an aldol reaction with the given starting material(s) using ^{-}OH, H_2O.

a. $(CH_3)_2CHCHO$ only b. $(CH_3)_2CHCHO + CH_2{=}O$ c. $C_6H_5CHO + CH_3CH_2CH_2CHO$ d. $(CH_3CH_2)_2C{=}O$ only

24.29 What four β-hydroxy aldehydes are formed by a crossed aldol reaction of $CH_3CH_2CH_2CHO$ and $C_6H_5CH_2CHO$?

24.30 Draw the product formed in each directed aldol reaction.

a. 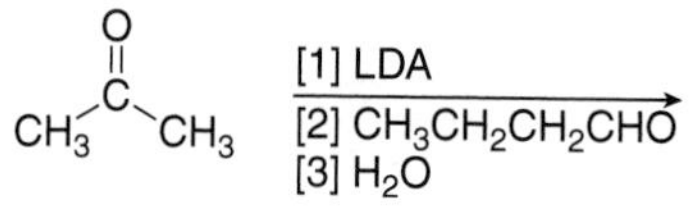
O
C
CH3 CH3
[1] LDA
[2] CH3CH2CH2CHO
[3] H2O

b. 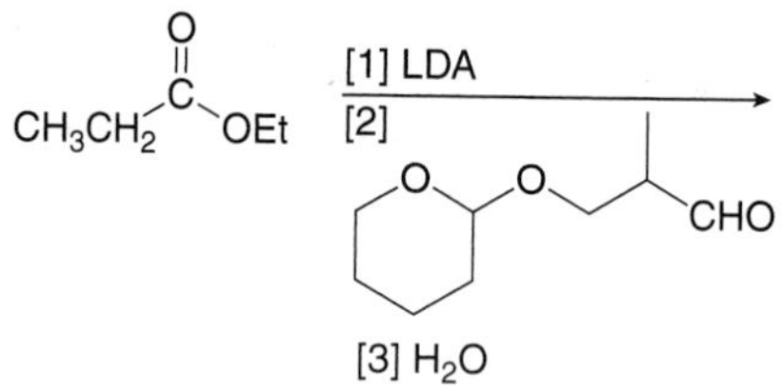
O
C
CH3CH2 OEt
[1] LDA
[2]
O O
CHO
[3] H2O

24.31 Draw the product formed when each dicarbonyl compound undergoes an intramolecular aldol reaction followed by dehydration.

a. 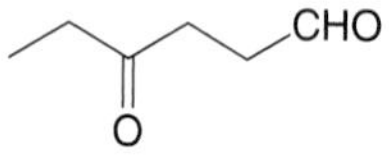
CHO
O

b. OHC  CHO

c. 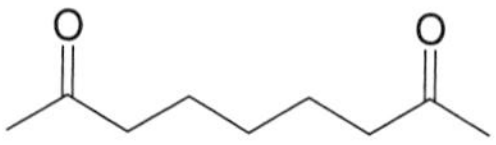
O
O

24.32 What starting materials are needed to synthesize each compound using an aldol or similar reaction?

a. 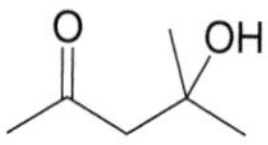
O
OH

b. 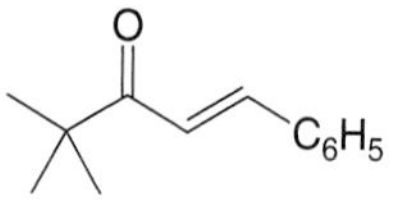
O
C6H5

c. 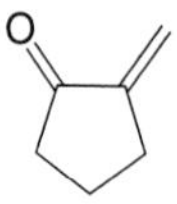
O

d. 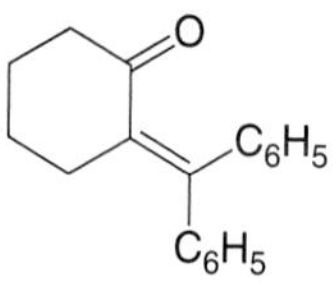
O
C6H5
C6H5

e. 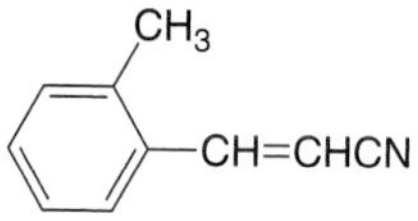
CH3
CH=CHCN

24.33 A published synthesis of the analgesic nabumetone uses a crossed aldol reaction to form **X.** What is the structure of **X? X** is converted to nabumetone in one step by hydrogenation with H_2 and Pd-C. (See Problem 23.29 for another way to make nabumetone.)

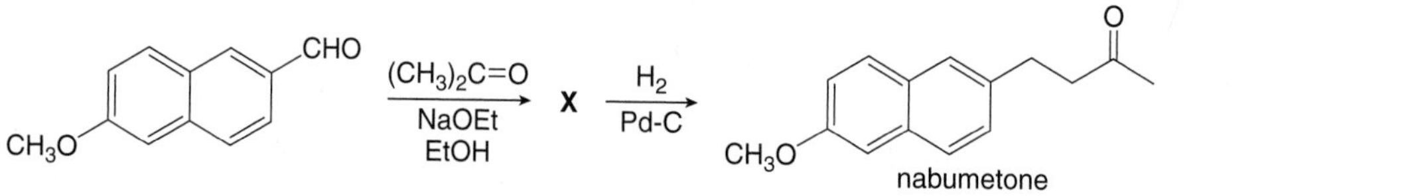
CHO
CH3O
(CH3)2C=O
NaOEt
EtOH
X
H2
Pd-C
O
CH3O

nabumetone

24.34 What product is formed when a solution of **A** and **B** is treated with mild base? This reaction is the first step in the synthesis of rosuvastatin (sold as a calcium salt under the trade name Crestor), a drug used to treat patients with high cholesterol.

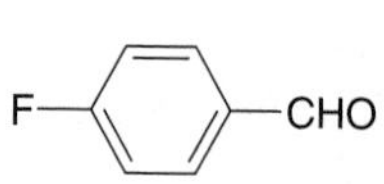
F
CHO

A

+

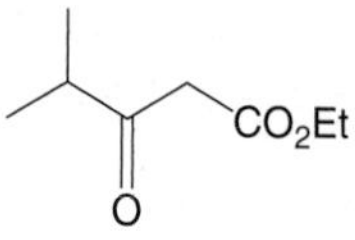
CO2Et
O

B

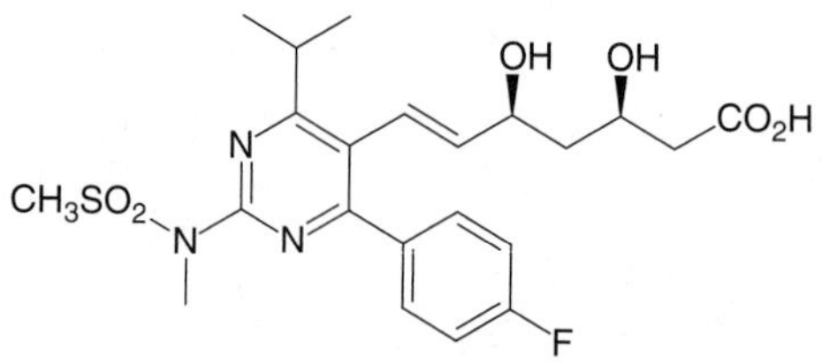
OH OH
CO2H
N
CH3SO2
N
N
F

rosuvastatin

24.35 What dicarbonyl compound is needed to prepare each compound by an intramolecular aldol reaction?

a. 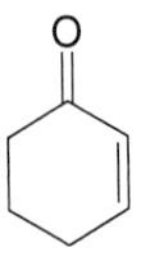 b. 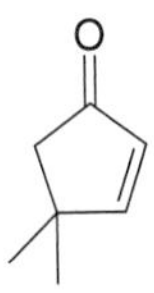 c. 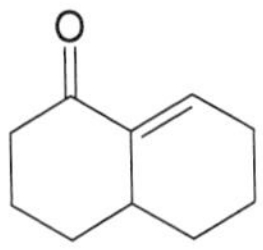 d. 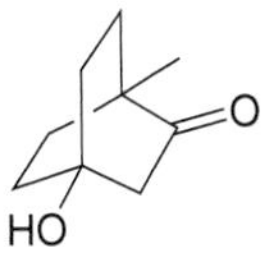
HO

24.36 Identify the structures of **C** and **D** in the following reaction sequence.

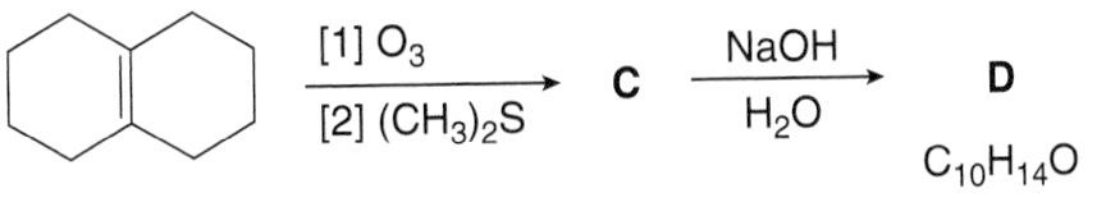
[1] O3
[2] (CH3)2S
C
NaOH
H2O
D
C10H14O

24.37 Explain why ketone **K** undergoes aldol reactions but ketone **J** does not.

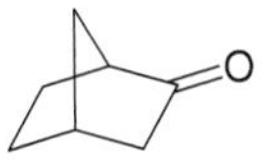
K

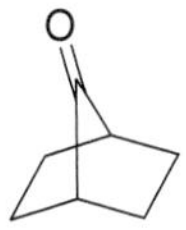
J

The Claisen and Dieckmann Reactions

24.38 Draw the Claisen product formed from each ester.

a. $C_6H_5CH_2CH_2CH_2CO_2Et$
b. $(CH_3)_2CHCH_2CH_2CH_2CO_2Et$
c. 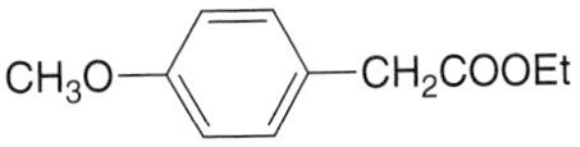
CH3O
CH2COOEt

24.39 What four compounds are formed from the crossed Claisen reaction of $CH_3CH_2CH_2CH_2CO_2Et$ and $CH_3CH_2CO_2Et$?

24.40 Draw the product formed from a Claisen reaction with the given starting materials using ^-OEt, EtOH.

a. $CH_3CH_2CH_2CO_2Et + C_6H_5CO_2Et$
b. $CH_3CH_2CH_2CO_2Et + (CH_3)_2C{=}O$
c. $EtO_2CC(CH_3)_2CH_2CH_2CH_2CO_2Et$
d. $CH_3CH_2CO_2Et + (EtO)_2C{=}O$
e. 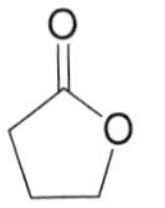 + HCO_2Et
f.  + 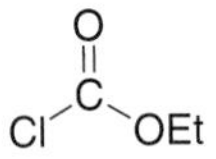
Cl
C
OEt

24.41 What starting materials are needed to synthesize each compound by a crossed Claisen reaction?

a. 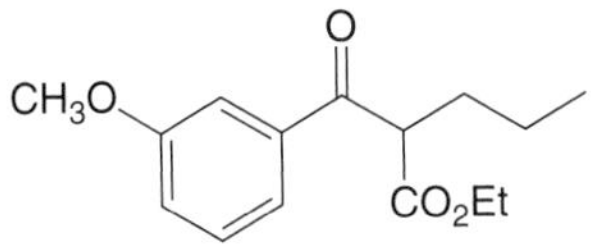
CH3O
CO2Et
b. 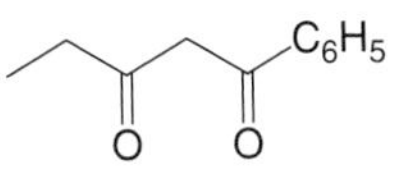
C6H5
c. 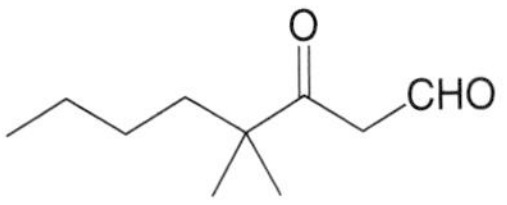
CHO
d. $C_6H_5CH(COOEt)_2$

24.42 Even though **B** contains three ester groups, a single Dieckmann product results when **B** is treated with $NaOCH_3$ in CH_3OH, followed by H_3O^+. Draw the structure and explain why it is the only product formed.

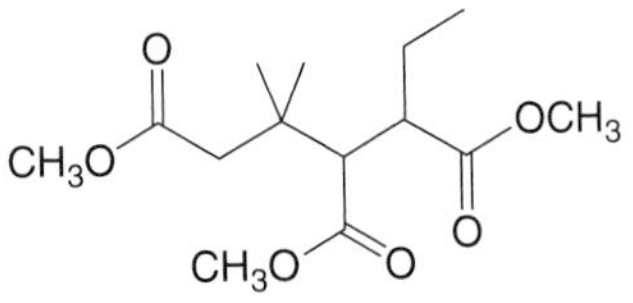
CH3O
OCH3
CH3O
B

Michael Reaction

24.43 Draw the product formed from a Michael reaction with the given starting materials using ^-OEt, EtOH.

a. 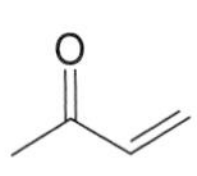 + 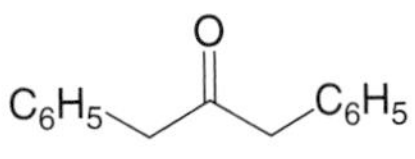
C6H5
C6H5
b. 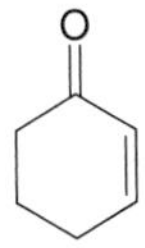 + $CH_2(CN)_2$

24.44 What starting materials are needed to prepare each compound using a Michael reaction?

a. 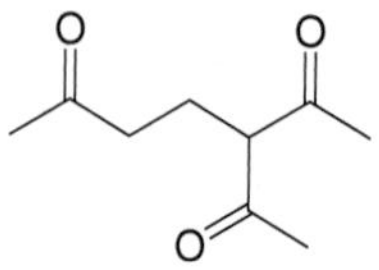

b. 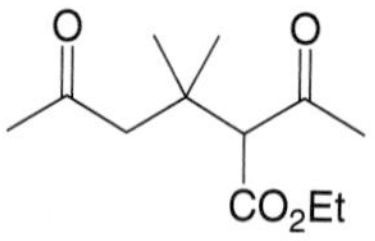

c. 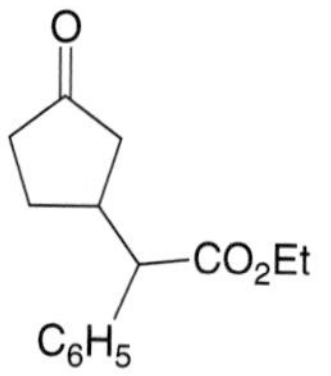

d. 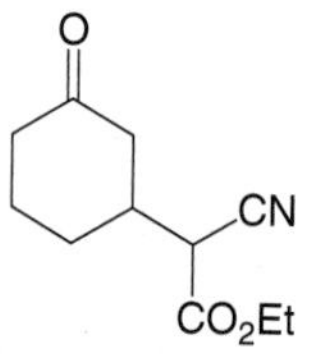

24.45 β-Vetivone is isolated from vetiver, a perennial grass that yields a variety of compounds used in traditional eastern medicine, pest control, and fragrance. In one synthesis, ketone **A** is converted to β-vetivone by a two-step process: Michael reaction, followed by intramolecular aldol reaction. (a) What Michael acceptor is needed for the conjugate addition? (See Problem 23.63 for another method to form the bicyclic ring system of β-vetivone.) (b) Draw a stepwise mechanism for the aldol reaction, which forms the six-membered ring.

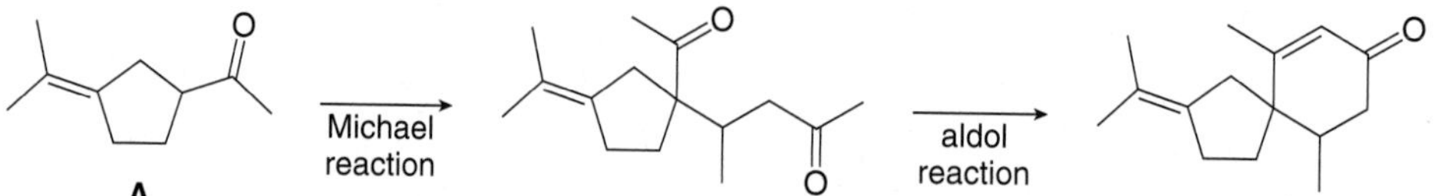

A β-vetivone

Robinson Annulation

24.46 Draw the product of each Robinson annulation from the given starting materials using ^{-}OH in H_2O solution.

a. 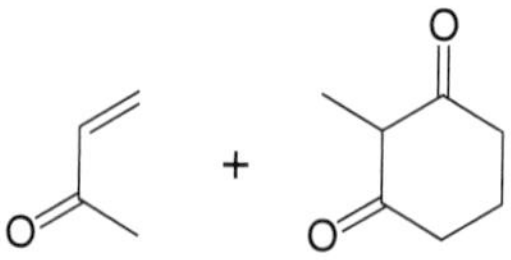

c. 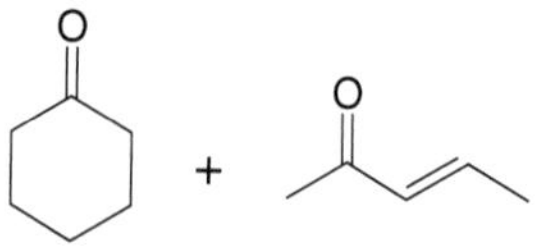

b. 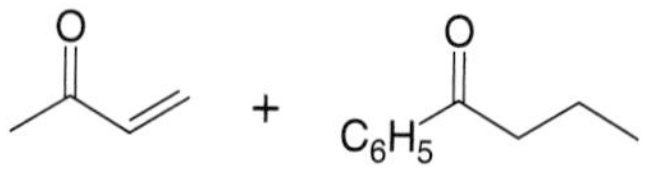

d. 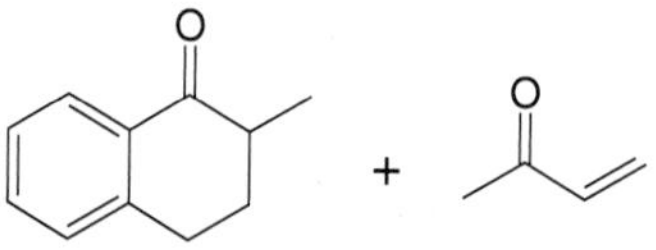

24.47 What starting materials are needed to synthesize each compound using a Robinson annulation?

a. 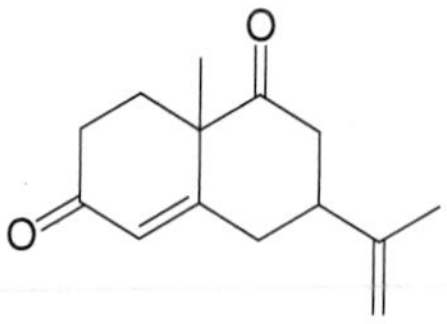

b. 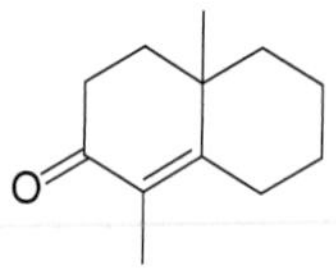

c. 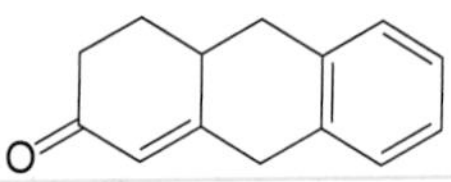

d. 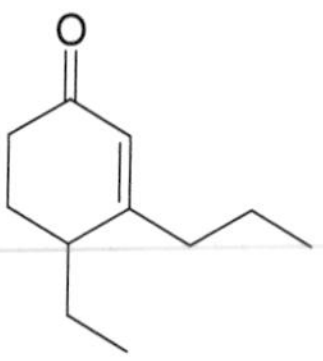

Reactions

24.48 Draw the organic products formed when butanal ($CH_3CH_2CH_2CHO$) is treated with each reagent.

a. ^{-}OH, H_2O
b. ^{-}OH, $CH_2=O$, H_2O
c. [1] LDA; [2] CH_3CHO; [3] H_2O
d. $CH_2(CO_2Et)_2$, NaOEt, EtOH
e. [1] CH_3Li; [2] H_2O
f. $NaBH_4$, CH_3OH
g. H_2, Pd-C
h. $HOCH_2CH_2OH$, TsOH
i. CH_3NH_2, mild acid
j. $(CH_3)_2NH$, mild acid
k. CrO_3, H_2SO_4
l. Br_2, CH_3COOH
m. $Ph_3P=CH_2$
n. NaCN, HCl
o. [1] LDA; [2] CH_3I

24.49 Draw the organic products formed in each reaction.

a. 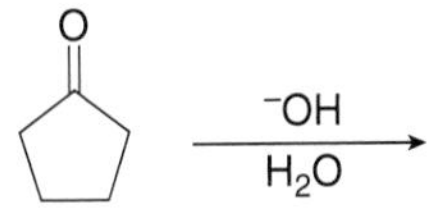

b. 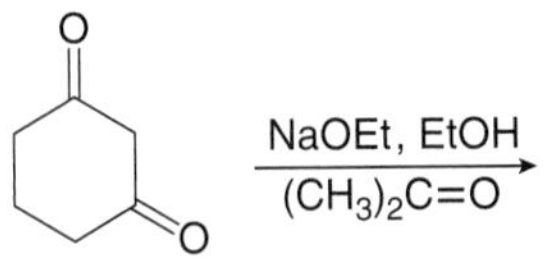

c. 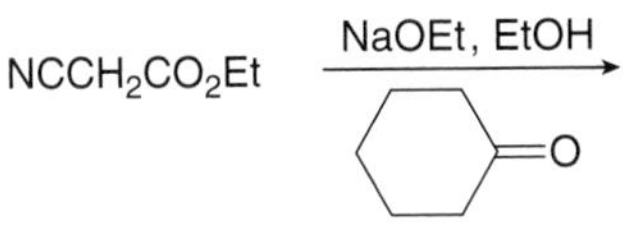

d. 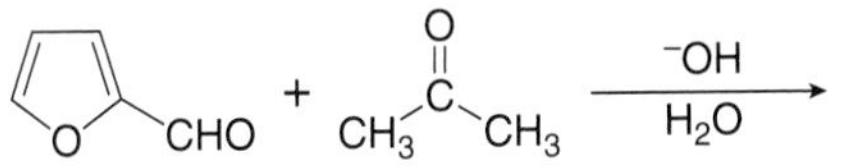

e. 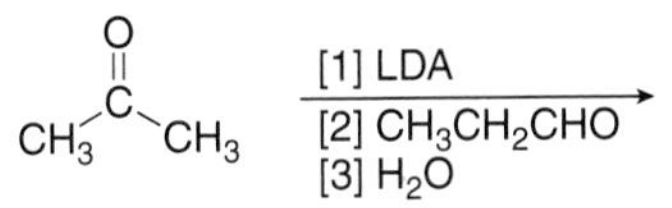

f. 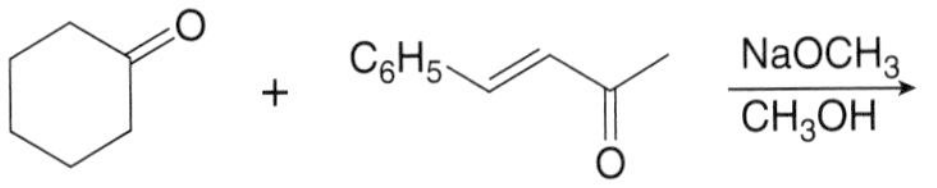

g. 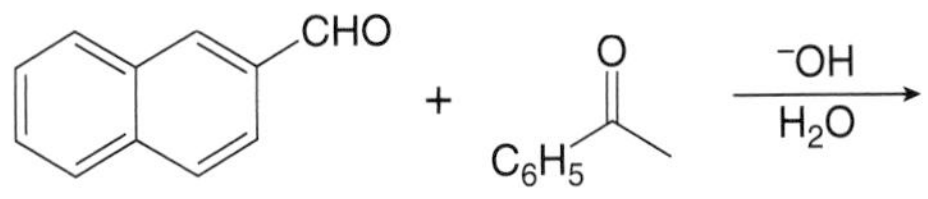

h. 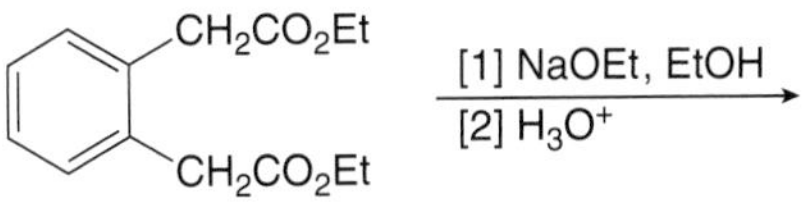

24.50 Fill in the lettered reagents needed for each reaction.

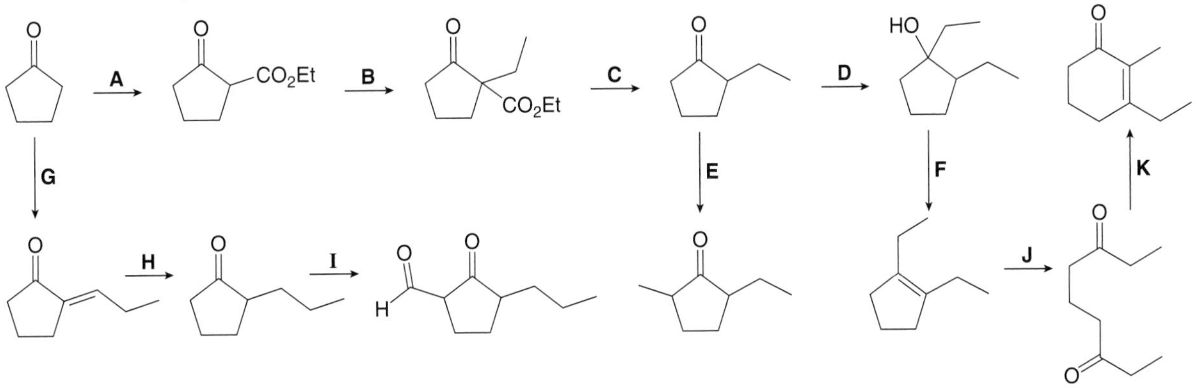

24.51 Identify compounds **A** and **B,** two synthetic intermediates in the 1979 synthesis of the plant growth hormone gibberellic acid by Corey and Smith. Gibberellic acid induces cell division and elongation, thus making plants tall and leaves large.

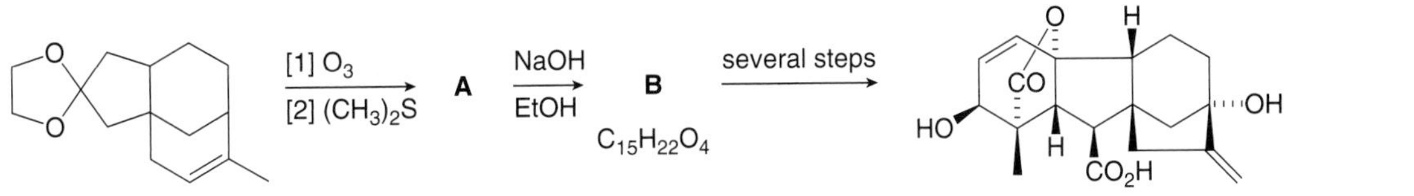

gibberellic acid

Mechanisms

24.52 When acetaldehyde (CH_3CHO) is treated with three equivalents of formaldehyde ($CH_2=O$) in the presence of aqueous Na_2CO_3, $(HOCH_2)_3CCHO$ is formed as product. Draw a stepwise mechanism for this process.

24.53 In theory, the intramolecular aldol reaction of 6-oxoheptanal could yield the three compounds shown. It turns out, though, that 1-acetylcyclopentene is by far the major product. Why are the other two compounds formed in only minor amounts? Draw a stepwise mechanism to show how all three products are formed.

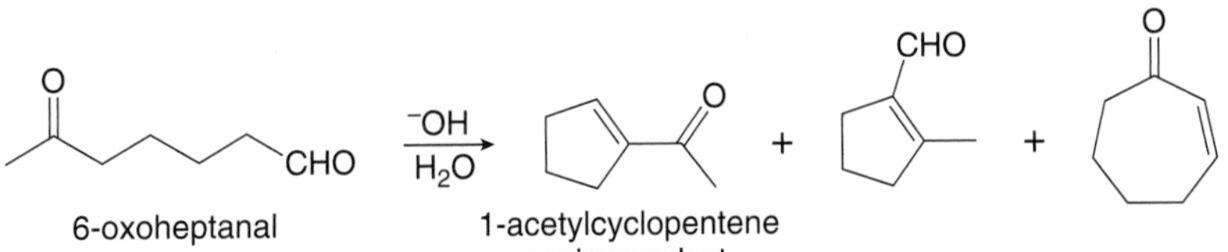

6-oxoheptanal

1-acetylcyclopentene
major product

24.54 Draw a stepwise mechanism for the following cyclization reaction.

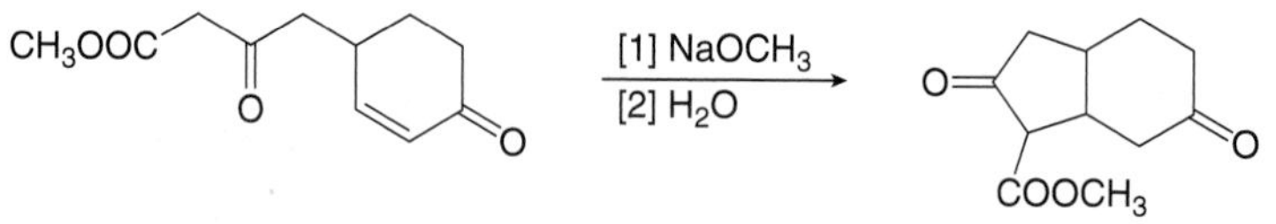

24.55 Draw a stepwise mechanism for the following variation of the aldol reaction, often called a nitro aldol reaction.

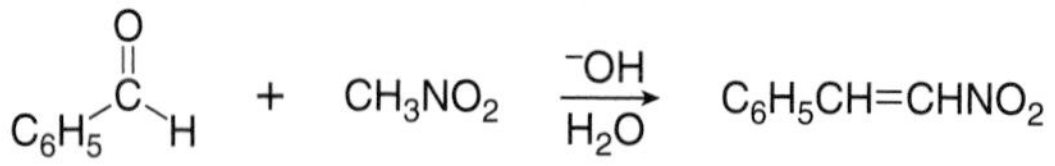

24.56 Draw a stepwise mechanism for the following Robinson annulation. This reaction was a key step in a synthesis of the steroid cortisone by R. B. Woodward and co-workers at Harvard University in 1951.

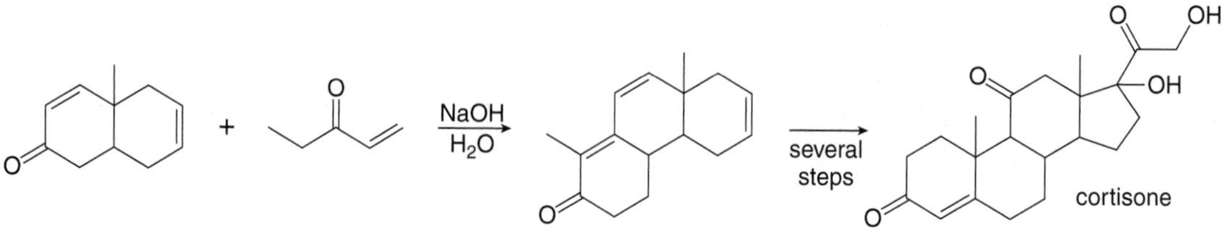

24.57 Reaction of **X** and phenylacetic acid forms an intermediate **Y,** which undergoes an intramolecular reaction to yield rofecoxib. Rofecoxib is a nonsteroidal anti-inflammatory agent once marketed under the trade name Vioxx, now withdrawn from the market because of increased risk of heart attacks from long-term use in some patients. Identify **Y** and draw a stepwise mechanism for its conversion to rofecoxib.

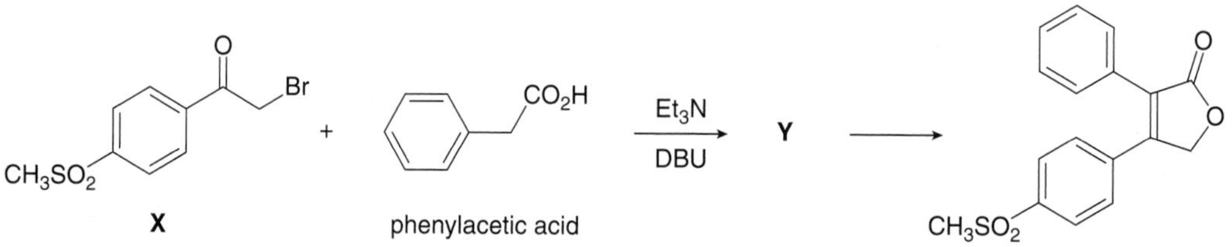

24.58 Green polymer synthesis—the preparation of polymers by environmentally friendly methods using starting materials that are not derived from petroleum—is an active area of research. One example is the polymerization of tulipalin A, a natural product derived from tulips, to afford polytulipalin. Polytulipalin has properties similar to some petroleum-derived polymers, but its availability from a natural source has made it a possible attractive alternative to these polymers. Polymerization occurs in the presence of a strong base (B:), and each new C–C bond in polytulipalin is formed by a Michael reaction. Draw a stepwise mechanism for the formation of one C–C bond in polytulipalin. (See Section 31.8 for other aspects of green polymer chemistry.)

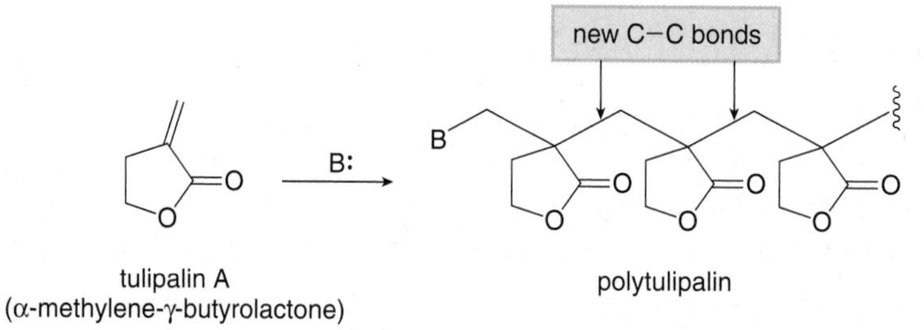

24.59 Coumarin, a naturally occurring compound isolated from lavender, sweet clover, and tonka bean, is made in the laboratory from *o*-hydroxybenzaldehyde by the reaction depicted below. Draw a stepwise mechanism for this reaction. Coumarin derivatives are useful synthetic anticoagulants.

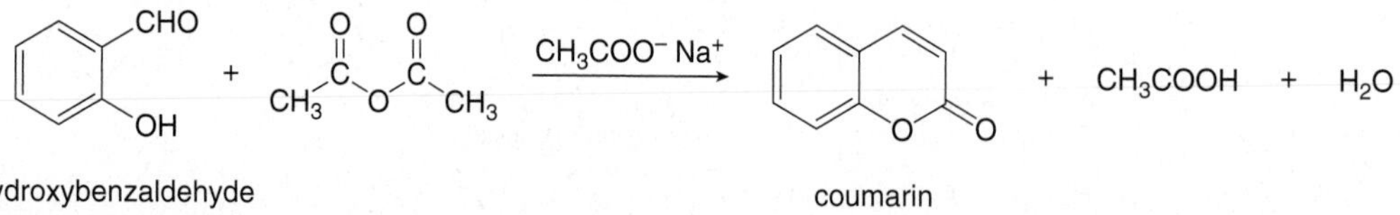

24.60 (a) Draw a stepwise mechanism for the reaction of ethyl 2,4-hexadienoate with diethyl oxalate in the presence of base. (b) How does your mechanism explain why a new carbon–carbon bond forms on C6? (c) Why is this reaction an example of a crossed Claisen reaction?

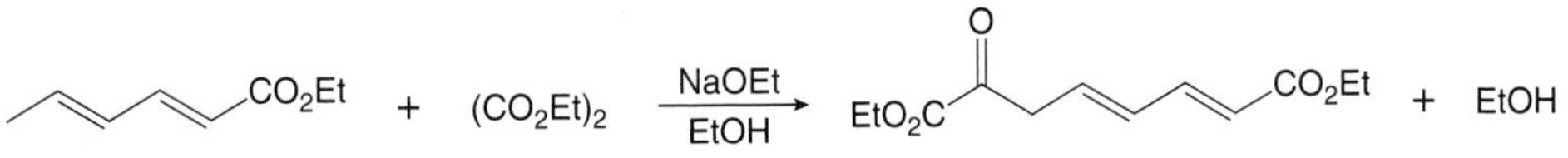

ethyl 2,4-hexadienoate   diethyl oxalate

Synthesis

24.61 Convert acetophenone ($C_6H_5COCH_3$) into each compound by one or more steps. You may use any other organic compounds or required inorganic reagents.

a. 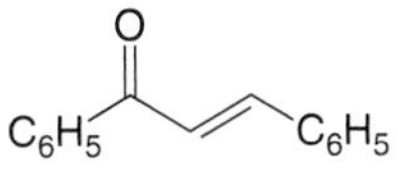

c. 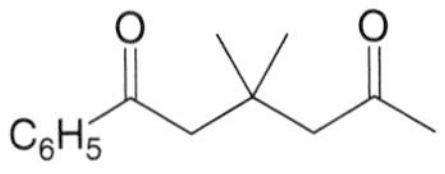

e. 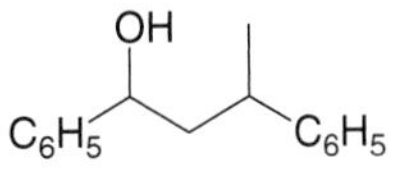

b. 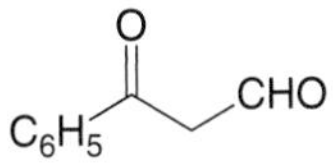

d. 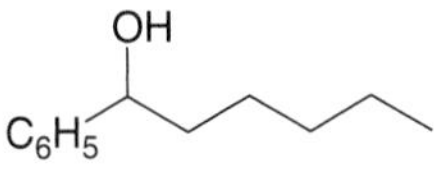

24.62 How would you convert cyclohexanone into each compound using any required inorganic reagents and needed organic compounds?

a. 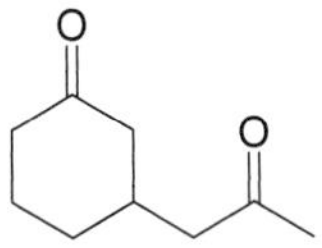

b. 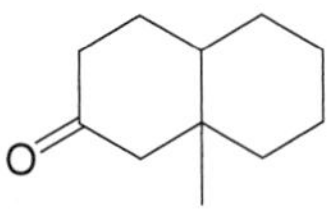

24.63 Devise a synthesis of each compound from cyclopentanone, benzene, and organic alcohols having ≤ 3 C's. You may also use any required organic or inorganic reagents.

a. 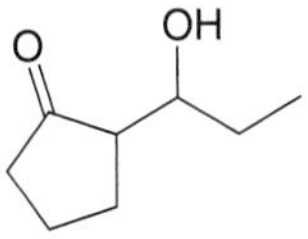

b. 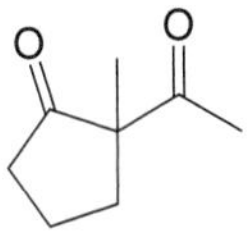

c. 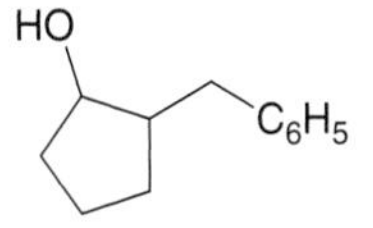

d. 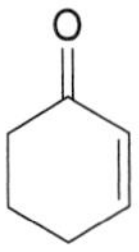

24.64 Devise a synthesis of each compound from $CH_3CH_2CH_2CO_2Et$, benzene, and alcohols having ≤ 2 C's. You may also use any required organic or inorganic reagents.

a. 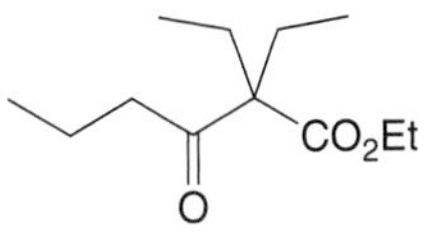

b. 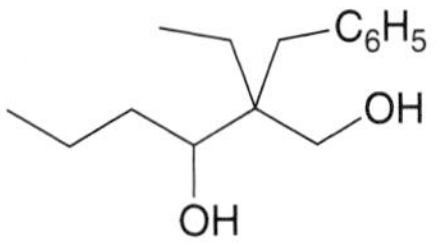

c. 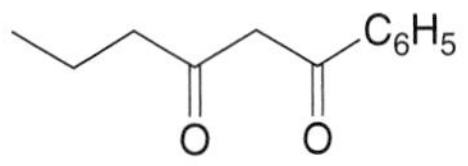

24.65 Devise a synthesis of 2-methylcyclopentanone from cyclohexene. You may also use any required reagents.

24.66 Octinoxate is an unsaturated ester used as an active ingredient in sunscreens. (a) What carbonyl compounds are needed to synthesize this compound using a condensation reaction? (b) Devise a synthesis of octinoxate from the given organic starting materials and any other needed reagents.

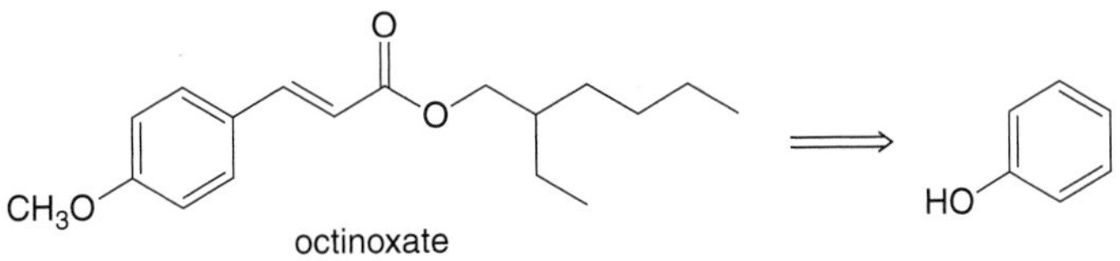

+ alcohols with < 5 C's

octinoxate

General Problems

24.67 Answer the following questions about 2-acetylcyclopentanone.

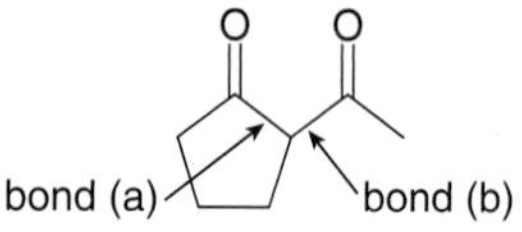

2-acetylcyclopentanone

a. What starting materials are needed to form 2-acetylcyclopentanone by a Claisen reaction that forms bond (a)?

b. What starting materials are needed to form 2-acetylcyclopentanone by a Claisen reaction that forms bond (b)?

c. What product is formed when 2-acetylcyclopentanone is treated with $NaOCH_2CH_3$, followed by CH_3I?

d. Draw the Robinson annulation product(s) formed by reaction of 2-acetylcyclopentanone with methyl vinyl ketone ($CH_2=CHCOCH_3$).

e. Draw the structure of the most stable enol tautomer(s).

24.68 Four steps in the synthesis of helminthosporal, a toxin produced by a wheat plant fungus, are shown below.

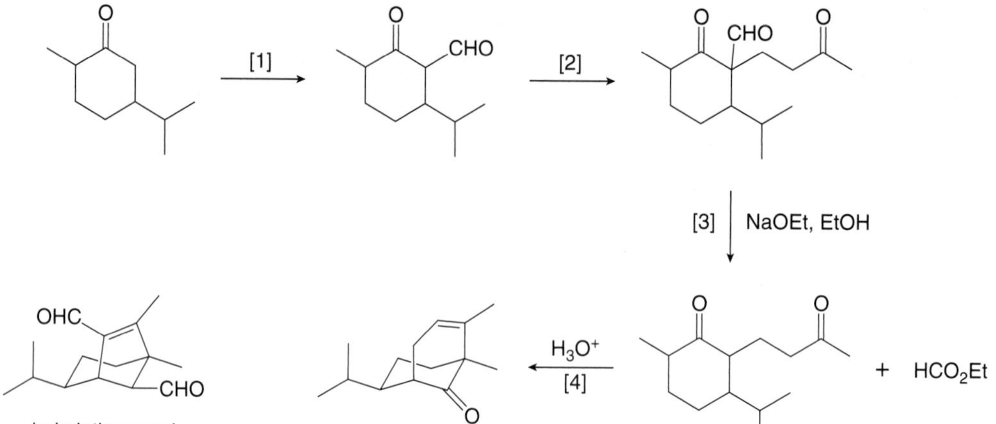

helminthosporal

a. What compounds are needed to carry out Step [1]?

b. What compounds are needed to carry out Step [2]?

c. Write a detailed mechanism for Step [3].

d. Write a detailed mechanism for Step [4]. What is unusual about the product of this reaction?

e. Step [1] adds a formyl group (HCO−) and Step [3] removes it. Why was this apparently unnecessary process done?

Challenge Problems

24.69 Draw a stepwise mechanism for the following reaction, which was used in the synthesis of the ezetimibe (Section 20.6), a drug used to treat patients with high cholesterol.

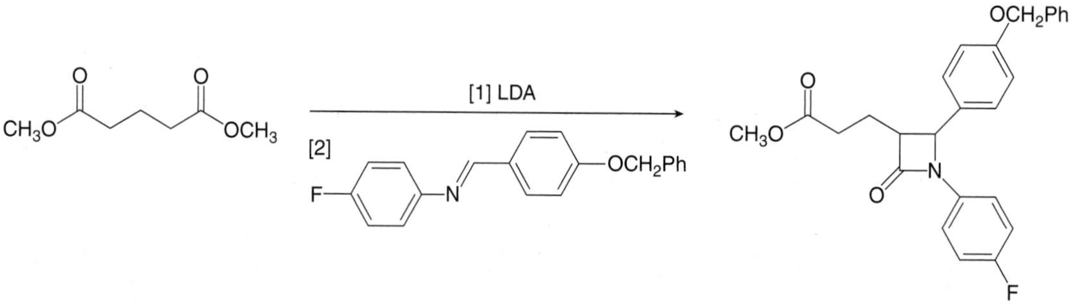

24.70 Propose a stepwise mechanism for the following reaction of a β-keto ester. Suggest a reason why this rearrangement reaction occurs.

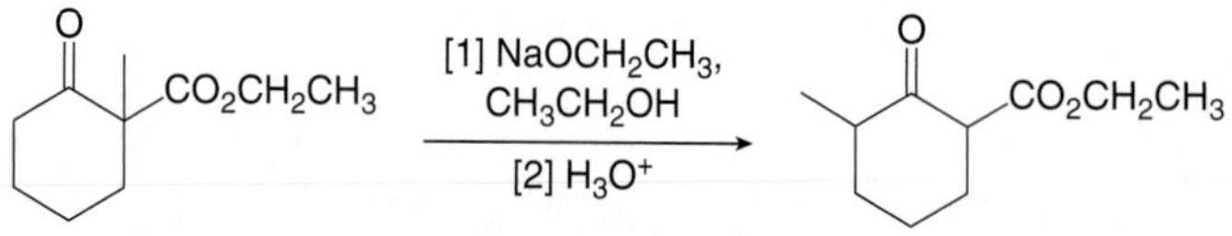

24.71 Isophorone is formed from three molecules of acetone [$(CH_3)_2C=O$] in the presence of base. Draw a mechanism for this process.

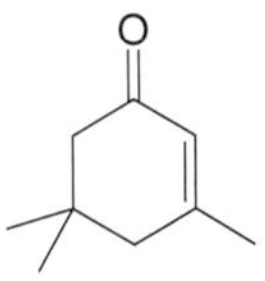

isophorone

24.72 Draw a stepwise mechanism for the following reaction. [*Hint:* Two Michael reactions are needed.]

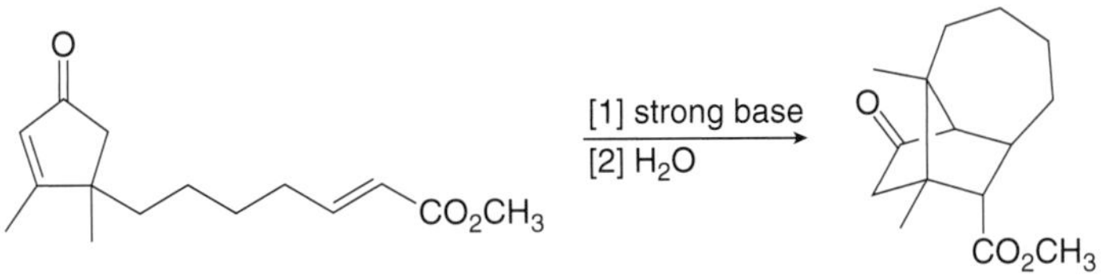

24.73 4-Methylpyridine reacts with benzaldehyde (C_6H_5CHO) in the presence of base to form **A.** (a) Draw a stepwise mechanism for this reaction. (b) Would you expect 2-methylpyridine or 3-methylpyridine to undergo a similar type of condensation reaction? Explain why or why not.

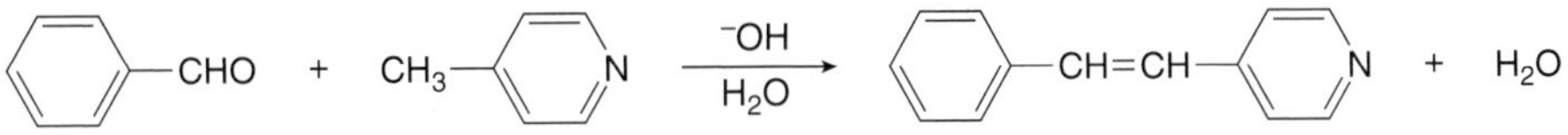

4-methylpyridine

A

24.74 Draw a stepwise mechanism for the following reaction, one step in the synthesis of the cholesterol-lowering drug pitavastatin, marketed in Japan as a calcium salt under the name Livalo.

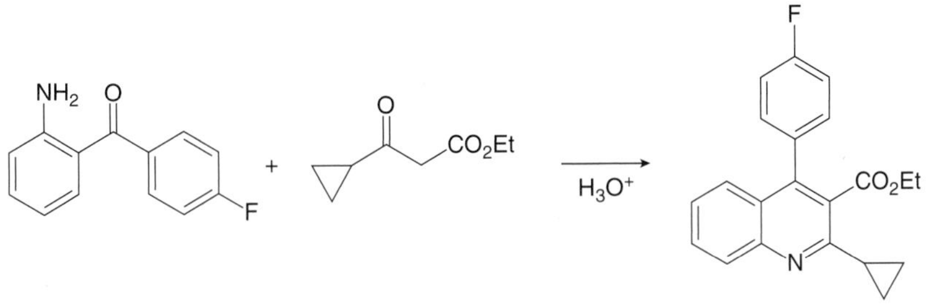

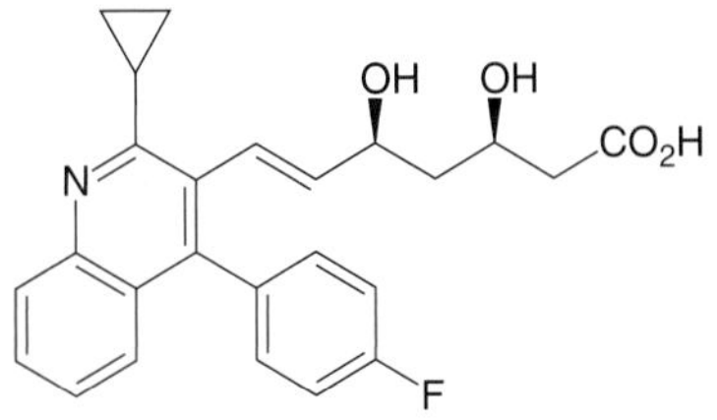

pitavastatin

24.75 Devise a stepwise mechanism for the following reaction, a key step in the synthesis of the antibiotic abyssomicin C. Abyssomicin C was isolated from sediment collected from almost 1000 ft below the surface in the Sea of Japan. [*Hint:* The mechanism begins with a Dieckmann reaction.]

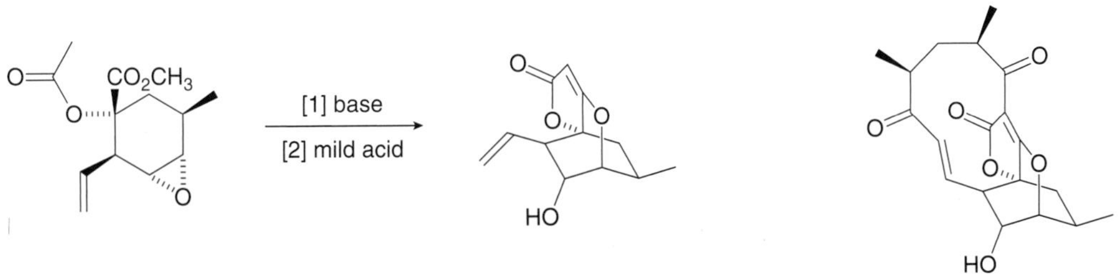

abyssomicin C

25 Amines

25.1 Introduction
25.2 Structure and bonding
25.3 Nomenclature
25.4 Physical properties
25.5 Spectroscopic properties
25.6 Interesting and useful amines
25.7 Preparation of amines
25.8 Reactions of amines—General features
25.9 Amines as bases
25.10 Relative basicity of amines and other compounds
25.11 Amines as nucleophiles
25.12 Hofmann elimination
25.13 Reaction of amines with nitrous acid
25.14 Substitution reactions of aryl diazonium salts
25.15 Coupling reactions of aryl diazonium salts
25.16 Application: Synthetic dyes
25.17 Application: Sulfa drugs

Scopolamine is a complex amine that occurs in angel's trumpets, ornamental plants with large trumpet-shaped flowers native to South America. Transdermal patches that release a minute dose of scopolamine are used to treat the nausea and vomiting associated with motion sickness. Scopolamine is an **alkaloid,** a naturally occurring amine derived from plant sources. In Chapter 25 we learn about the properties and reactions of amines like scopolamine.

We now leave the chemistry of carbonyl compounds to concentrate on **amines,** organic derivatives of ammonia (NH_3), formed by replacing one or more hydrogen atoms by alkyl or aryl groups. **Amines are stronger bases and better nucleophiles than other neutral organic compounds,** so much of Chapter 25 focuses on these properties.

Like that of alcohols, the chemistry of amines does not fit neatly into one reaction class, and this can make learning the reactions of amines challenging. Many interesting natural products and widely used drugs are amines, so you also need to know how to introduce this functional group into organic molecules.

25.1 Introduction

Classifying amines as 1°, 2°, or 3° is reminiscent of classifying amides in Chapter 22, but is *different* from classifying other atoms and functional groups as 1°, 2°, and 3°. Compare, for example, a 2° amine and a 2° alcohol. A 2° amine (R_2NH) has *two* C–N bonds. A 2° alcohol (R_2CHOH), on the other hand, has only *one* C–O bond, but *two* C–C bonds on the carbon bonded to oxygen.

***Amines* are organic nitrogen compounds,** formed by replacing one or more hydrogen atoms of ammonia (NH_3) with alkyl groups. As discussed in Section 21.11, amines are classified as 1°, 2°, or 3° by the number of alkyl groups bonded to the *nitrogen* atom.

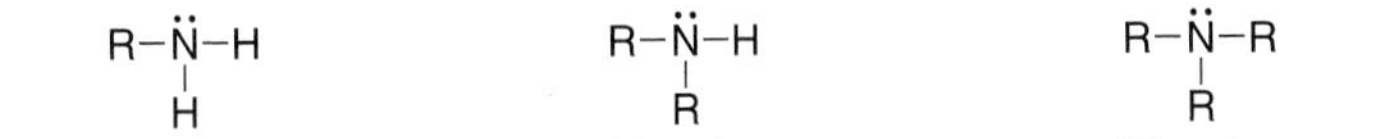

1° amine (1 R group on N) | 2° amine (2 R groups on N) | 3° amine (3 R groups on N)

Like ammonia, **the amine nitrogen atom has a nonbonded electron pair,** making it both a base and a nucleophile. As a result, amines react with electrophiles to form **ammonium salts**—compounds with four bonds to nitrogen.

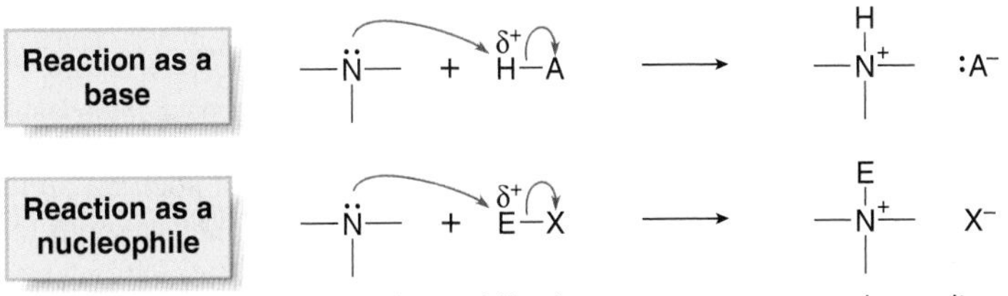

E = an electrophilic site | ammonium salt

- **The chemistry of amines is dominated by the nonbonded electron pair on the nitrogen atom.**

Problem 25.1 Classify each amine in the following compounds as 1°, 2°, or 3°.

a. 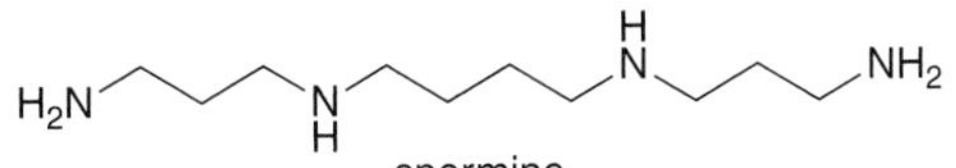

spermine (isolated from semen)

b. 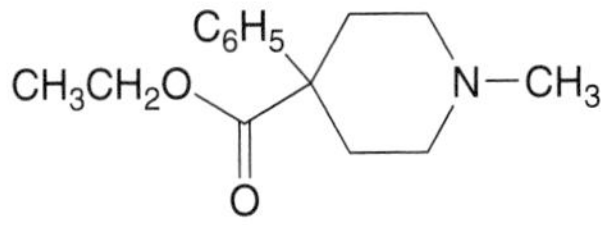

meperidine (a narcotic) Trade name: Demerol

Problem 25.2 Draw the structure of a compound of molecular formula $C_4H_{11}NO$ that fits each description: (a) a compound that contains a 1° amine and a 3° alcohol; (b) a compound that contains a 3° amine and a 1° alcohol.

25.2 Structure and Bonding

An amine nitrogen atom is surrounded by three atoms and one nonbonded electron pair, making the N atom sp^3 hybridized and trigonal pyramidal, with bond angles of approximately 109.5°.

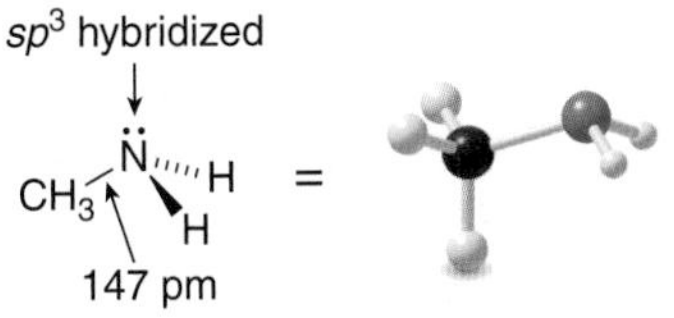

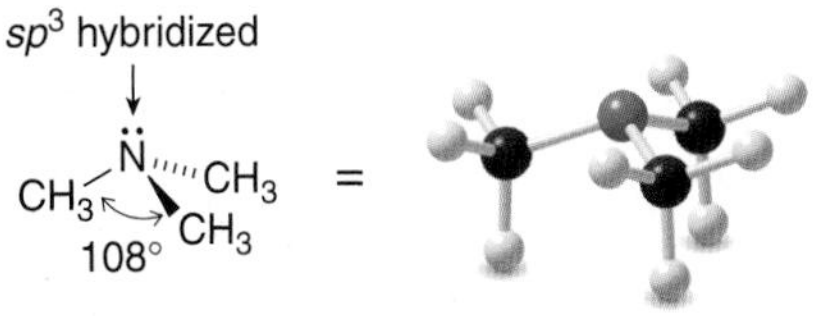

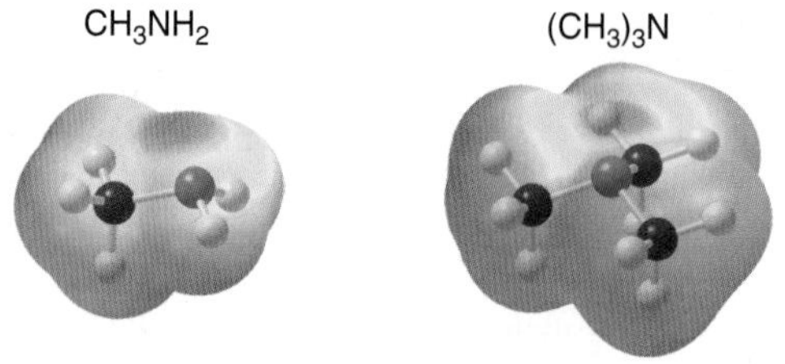

Figure 25.1
Electrostatic potential plots of CH_3NH_2 and $(CH_3)_3N$

- Both amines clearly show the electron-rich region (in red) at the N atom.

Because nitrogen is much more electronegative than carbon or hydrogen, **the C−N and N−H bonds are all polar,** with the N atom electron rich and the C and H atoms electron poor. The electrostatic potential maps in Figure 25.1 show the polar C−N and N−H bonds in CH_3NH_2 (methylamine) and $(CH_3)_3N$ (trimethylamine).

An amine nitrogen atom bonded to an electron pair and three different alkyl groups is technically a stereogenic center, so two nonsuperimposable trigonal pyramids can be drawn.

An amine with four different groups around N

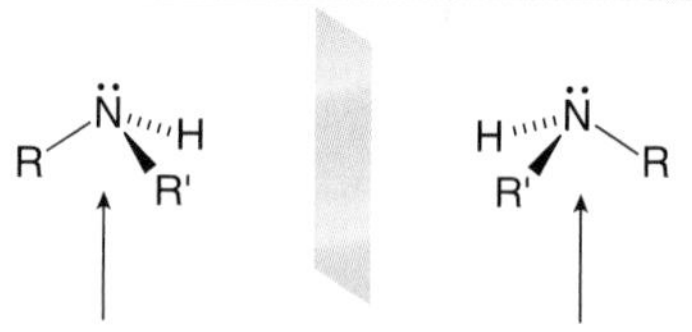

nonsuperimposable mirror images

This does not mean, however, that such an amine exists as two different enantiomers, because one is rapidly converted to the other at room temperature. The amine flips inside out, passing through a trigonal planar (achiral) transition state. **Because the two enantiomers interconvert, we can ignore the chirality of the amine nitrogen.**

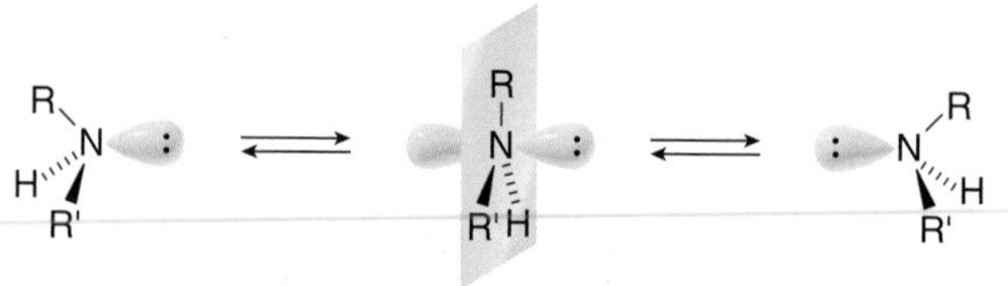

The two mirror images are interconverted.

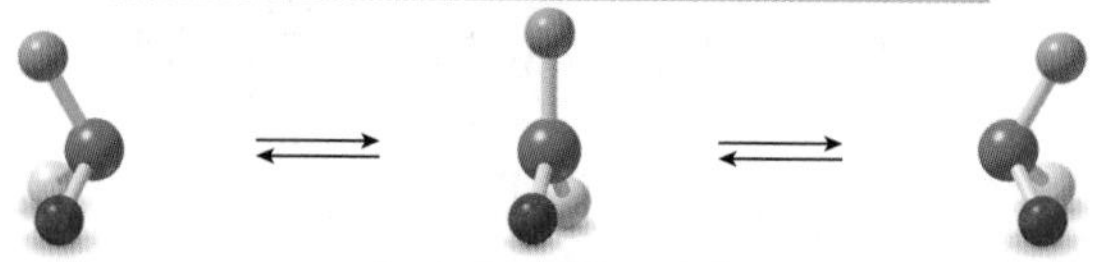

planar transition state

In contrast, the chirality of an ammonium salt with four different groups on N cannot be ignored. Because there is no nonbonded electron pair on the nitrogen atom, interconversion cannot occur, and the N atom is just like a carbon atom with four different groups around it.

Two enantiomers of an ammonium salt

- **The N atom of an ammonium salt is a stereogenic center when N is surrounded by four different groups.**

Problem 25.3 Label the stereogenic centers in each molecule.

a. 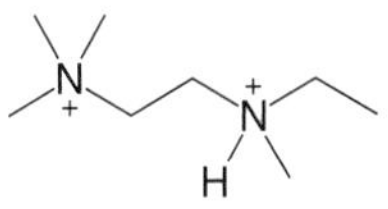

b. 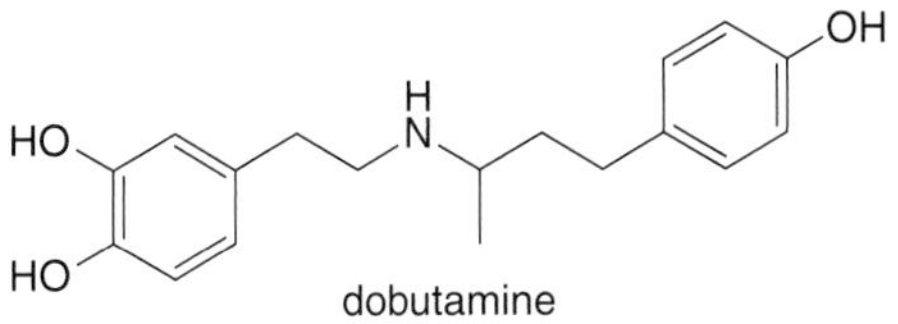

dobutamine
(heart stimulant used in stress tests
to measure cardiac fitness)

25.3 Nomenclature

25.3A Primary Amines

Primary amines are named using either systematic or common names.

- To assign the **systematic name,** find the longest continuous carbon chain bonded to the amine nitrogen, and change the ***-e*** ending of the parent alkane to the suffix ***-amine.*** Then use the usual rules of nomenclature to number the chain and name the substituents.
- To assign a **common name,** name the alkyl group bonded to the nitrogen atom and add the suffix ***-amine,*** forming a single word.

Examples

CH_3NH_2

Systematic name: **methanamine**
Common name: **methylamine**

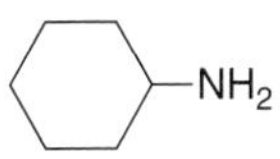

Systematic name: **cyclohexanamine**
Common name: **cyclohexylamine**

25.3B Secondary and Tertiary Amines

Secondary and tertiary amines having identical alkyl groups are named by using the prefix **di-** or **tri-** with the name of the primary amine.

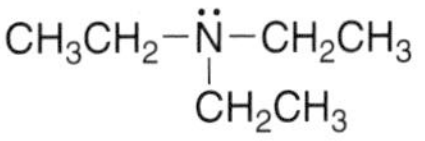

triethylamine

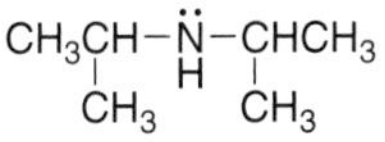

diisopropylamine

Secondary and tertiary amines having more than one kind of alkyl group are named as ***N*-substituted primary amines,** using the following procedure.

How To Name 2° and 3° Amines with Different Alkyl Groups

Example Name the following 2° amine: $(CH_3)_2CHNHCH_3$.

Step [1] Designate the longest alkyl chain (or largest ring) bonded to the N atom as the parent amine and assign a common or systematic name.

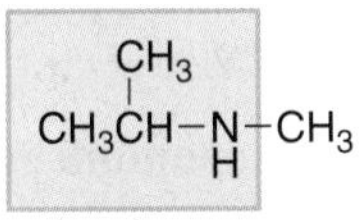

3 C's in the longest chain ----> isopropylamine (common name) or 2-propanamine (systematic name)

Step [2] Name the other groups on the N atom as alkyl groups, alphabetize the names, and put the prefix *N*- before the name.

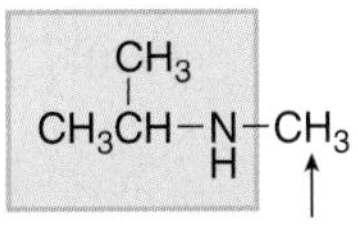

one methyl substituent

Answer: *N*-methylisopropylamine (common name)
or
***N*-methyl-2-propanamine (systematic name)**

Sample Problem 25.1 Name each amine.

a. $CH_3CHCH_2CH_2CH_2NH_2$ (with CH_3 on C2)

b. 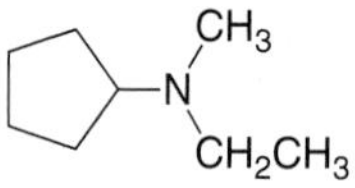

Solution

a. [1] A 1° amine: Find and name the longest chain containing the amine nitrogen.

$CH_3CHCH_2CH_2CH_2NH_2$ (with CH_3 branch)

pentane ---→ **pentan*amine***
(5 C's)

[2] Number and name the substituents:

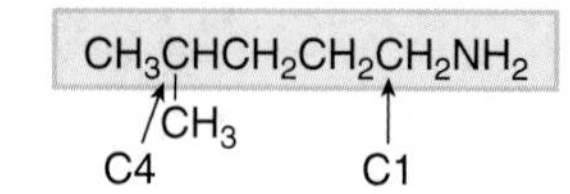

You must use a number to show the location of the NH_2 group.

Answer: 4-methyl-1-pentanamine

b. For a 3° amine, one alkyl group on N is the principal R group and the others are substituents.

[1] Name the ring bonded to the N:

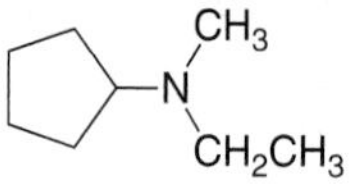

cyclopentanamine
or
cyclopentylamine

[2] Name the substituents:

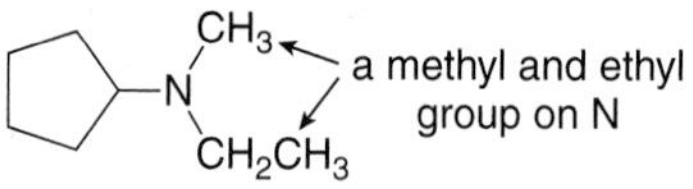

Two N's are needed, one for each alkyl group.

Answer: *N*-ethyl-*N*-methylcyclopentanamine
or
***N*-ethyl-*N*-methylcyclopentylamine**

Problem 25.4 Name each amine.

a. $CH_3CH_2CH(NH_2)CH_3$

b. $(CH_3CH_2CH_2CH_2)_2NH$

c. 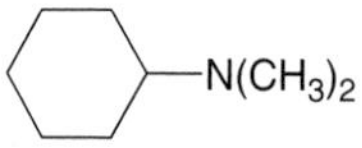

d. 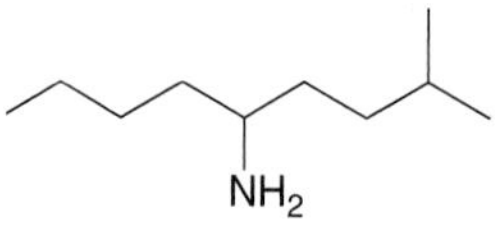

e. 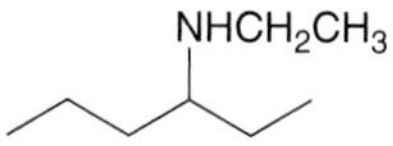

f. 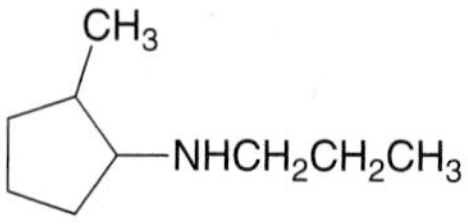

25.3C Aromatic Amines

Aromatic amines are named as derivatives of aniline.

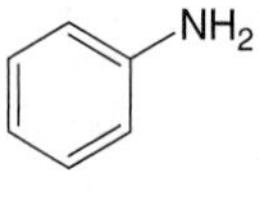

aniline

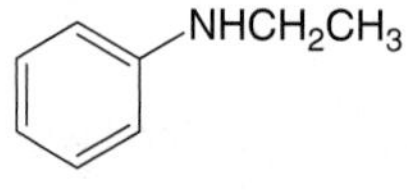

N-ethylaniline

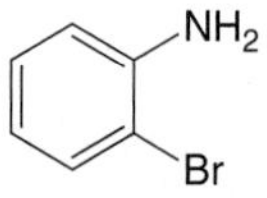

o-bromoaniline

25.3D Miscellaneous Nomenclature Facts

An $\mathbf{NH_2}$ group named as a substituent is called an **amino group.**

There are many different **nitrogen heterocycles,** and each ring type is named differently depending on the number of N atoms in the ring, the ring size, and whether it is aromatic or not. The structures and names of four common nitrogen heterocycles are shown. In numbering these heterocycles, the **N atom is always placed at the "1" position.**

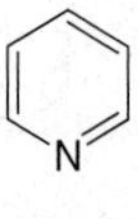

pyridine

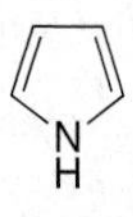

pyrrole

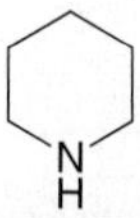

piperidine

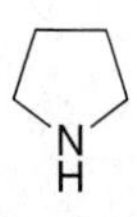

pyrrolidine

Problem 25.5 Draw a structure corresponding to each name.

a. 2,4-dimethyl-3-hexanamine
b. *N*-methylpentylamine
c. *N*-isopropyl-*p*-nitroaniline
d. *N*-methylpiperidine
e. *N,N*-dimethylethylamine
f. 2-aminocyclohexanone
g. *N*-methylaniline
h. *m*-ethylaniline

25.4 Physical Properties

Amines exhibit dipole–dipole interactions because of the polar C–N and N–H bonds. **Primary and secondary amines are also capable of intermolecular hydrogen bonding,** because they contain N–H bonds. Because nitrogen is less electronegative than oxygen, however, intermolecular hydrogen bonds between N and H are *weaker* than those between O and H. How these factors affect the physical properties of amines is summarized in Table 25.1.

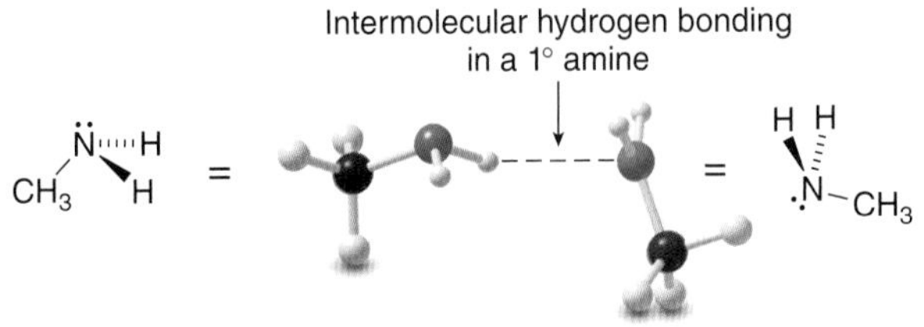

Problem 25.6 Arrange the compounds in order of increasing boiling point.

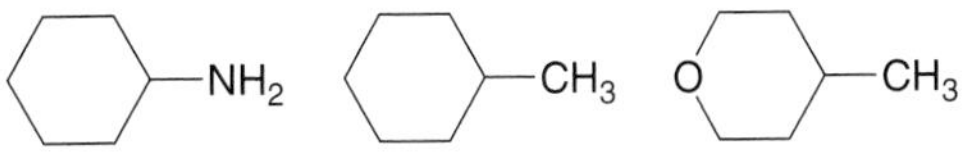

Table 25.1 Physical Properties of Amines

Property	Observation
Boiling point and melting point	• Primary (1°) and 2° amines have higher bp's than similar compounds (like ethers) incapable of hydrogen bonding, but lower bp's than alcohols that have stronger intermolecular hydrogen bonds. $CH_3CH_2OCH_2CH_3$ MW = 74, bp 38 °C; $CH_3CH_2CH_2CH_2NH_2$ MW = 73, bp 78 °C; $CH_3CH_2CH_2CH_2OH$ MW = 74, bp 118 °C **Increasing intermolecular forces** **Increasing boiling point** • Tertiary (3°) amines have lower boiling points than 1° and 2° amines of comparable molecular weight, because they have no N–H bonds and are incapable of hydrogen bonding. 3° amine: $CH_3CH_2N(CH_3)_2$ MW = 73, bp 38 °C, **no N–H bond** $CH_3CH_2{-}NH{-}CH_2CH_3$ ← 2° amine higher bp: MW = 73, bp 56 °C, **N–H bond**
Solubility	• Amines are soluble in organic solvents regardless of size. • All amines having ≤ 5 C's are H_2O soluble because they can hydrogen bond with H_2O (Section 3.4C). • Amines having > 5 C's are H_2O insoluble because the nonpolar alkyl portion is too large to dissolve in the polar H_2O solvent.

MW = molecular weight

25.5 Spectroscopic Properties

Amines exhibit characteristic features in their mass spectra, IR spectra, and ^{1}H and ^{13}C NMR spectra.

25.5A Mass Spectra

Amines differ from compounds that contain only C, H, and O atoms, which always have a molecular ion with an *even* mass in their mass spectra. This is apparent in the mass spectrum of butylamine, which is shown in Figure 25.2.

The general molecular formula for an amine with one N atom is $C_nH_{2n+3}N$.

- **Amines with an odd number of N atoms give an odd molecular ion in their mass spectra.**

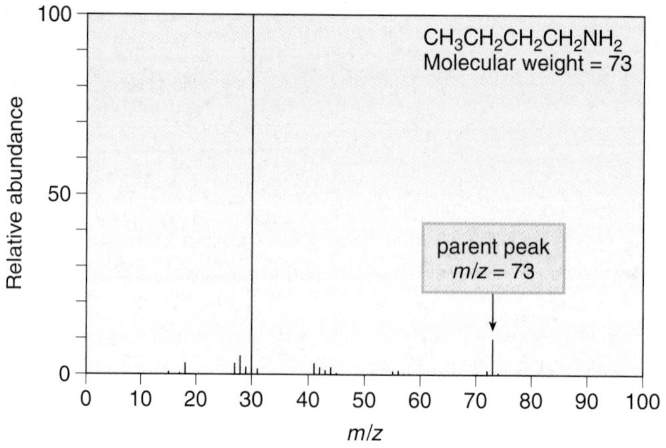

Figure 25.2 Mass spectrum of butylamine

- The molecular ion for $CH_3CH_2CH_2CH_2NH_2$ occurs at $m/z = 73$. This odd mass for a molecular ion is characteristic of an amine with an odd number of N atoms.

25.5B IR Spectra

Amines with N–H bonds show characteristic absorptions in their IR spectra.

- **1° Amines show *two* N–H absorptions at 3300–3500 cm^{-1}.**
- **2° Amines show *one* N–H absorption at 3300–3500 cm^{-1}.**

Because 3° amines have no N–H bonds, they do *not* absorb in this region in their IR spectra. The single bond region (> 2500 cm^{-1}) of the IR spectra for 1°, 2°, and 3° amines illustrates these features in Figure 25.3.

Figure 25.3 The single bond region of the IR spectra for a 1°, 2°, and 3° amine

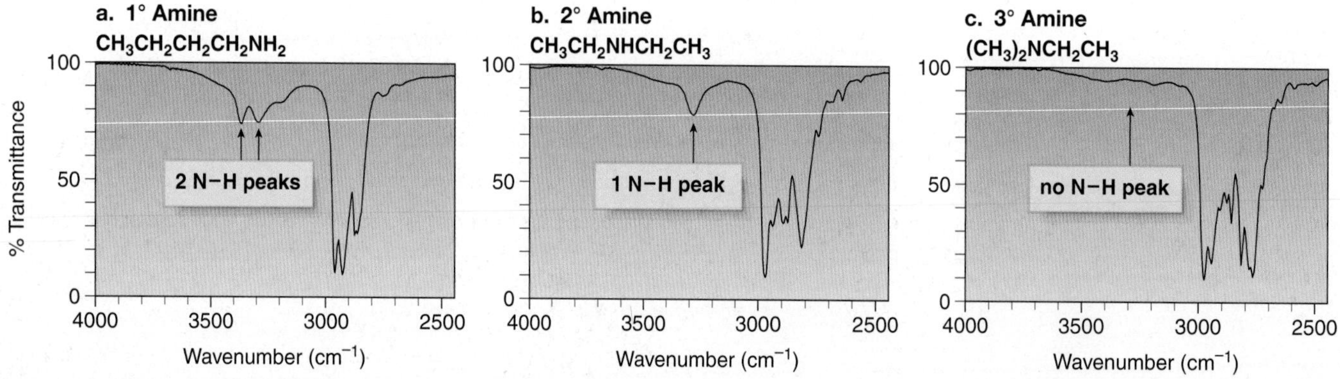

25.5C NMR Spectra

Amines exhibit the following characteristic ^1H NMR and ^{13}C NMR absorptions.

- **The NH signal appears between 0.5 and 5.0 ppm.** The exact location depends on the degree of hydrogen bonding and the concentration of the sample.
- The protons on the carbon bonded to the amine nitrogen are deshielded and typically absorb at **2.3–3.0 ppm.**
- In the **^{13}C NMR** spectrum, the carbon bonded to the N atom is deshielded and typically absorbs at **30–50 ppm.**

Like the OH absorption of an alcohol, the **NH absorption is not split by adjacent protons, nor does it cause splitting of adjacent C–H absorptions in a ^1H NMR spectrum.** The NH peak of an amine is sometimes somewhat broader than other peaks in the spectrum. The ^1H NMR spectrum of *N*-methylaniline is shown in Figure 25.4.

Problem 25.7 What is the structure of an unknown compound with molecular formula $C_6H_{15}N$ that gives the following ^1H NMR absorptions: 0.9 (singlet, 1 H), 1.10 (triplet, 3 H), 1.15 (singlet, 9 H), and 2.6 (quartet, 2 H) ppm?

Figure 25.4 The ^1H NMR spectrum of *N*-methylaniline

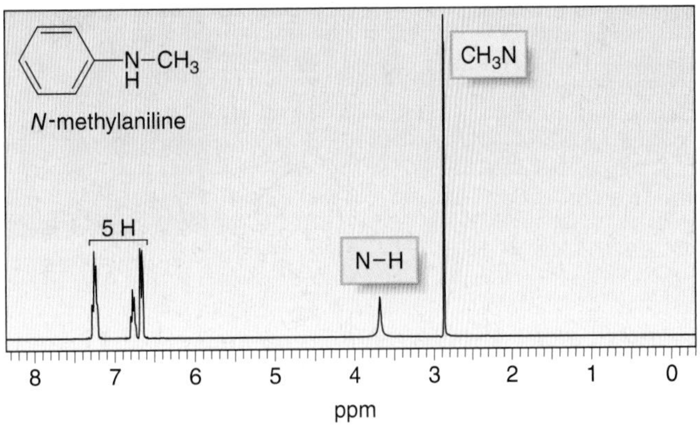

- The CH_3 group appears as a singlet at 2.7 ppm because there is no splitting by the adjacent NH proton.
- The NH proton appears as a broad singlet at 3.6 ppm.
- The five H atoms of the aromatic ring appear as a complex pattern at 6.6–7.2 ppm.

25.6 Interesting and Useful Amines

A great many simple and complex amines occur in nature, and others with biological activity have been synthesized in the lab.

25.6A Simple Amines and Alkaloids

Many low molecular weight amines have *very* foul odors. **Trimethylamine** [$(CH_3)_3N$], formed when enzymes break down certain fish proteins, has the characteristic odor of rotting fish. **Putrescine** ($NH_2CH_2CH_2CH_2CH_2NH_2$) and **cadaverine** ($NH_2CH_2CH_2CH_2CH_2CH_2NH_2$) are both poisonous diamines with putrid odors. They, too, are present in rotting fish, and are partly responsible for the odors of semen, urine, and bad breath.

The word **alkaloid** is derived from the word *alkali,* because aqueous solutions of alkaloids are slightly basic.

Naturally occurring amines derived from plant sources are called **alkaloids.** Alkaloids previously encountered in the text include **quinine** (Problem 17.13), **morphine** (Section 22.9), and **cocaine** (Problem 3.46). Three other common alkaloids are **atropine, nicotine,** and **coniine,** illustrated in Figure 25.5.

Figure 25.5 Three common alkaloids—Atropine, nicotine, and coniine

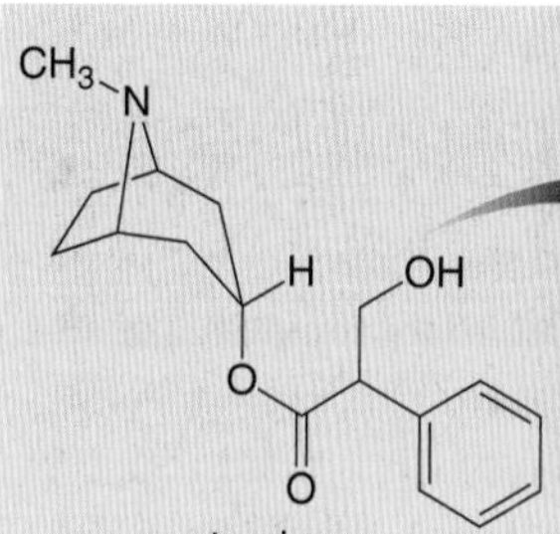
atropine

nightshade

- **Atropine** is an alkaloid isolated from *Atropa belladonna*, the deadly nightshade plant. In the Renaissance, women used the juice of the berries of the nightshade to enlarge the pupils of their eyes for cosmetic reasons. Atropine causes an increase in heart rate, relaxes smooth muscles, and interferes with nerve impulses transmitted by acetylcholine. In higher doses atropine is poisonous, leading to convulsions, coma, and death.

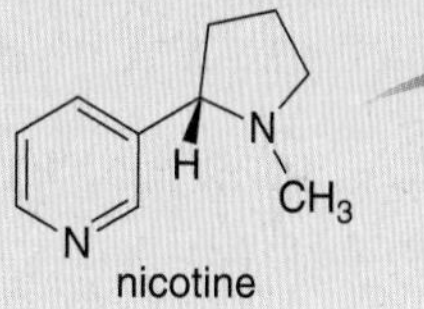
nicotine

tobacco

- **Nicotine** is an addictive and highly toxic compound isolated from tobacco. In small doses it acts as a stimulant, but in large doses it causes depression, nausea, and even death. Nicotine is synthesized in plants as a defense against insect predators, and is used commercially as an insecticide.

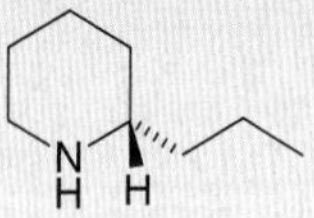
coniine

hemlock

- **Coniine,** a poisonous alkaloid isolated from the seeds, leaves, and roots of hemlock (*Conium maculatum*), has been known since ancient times. Ingestion causes weakness, paralysis, and finally death. The Greek philosopher Socrates was executed by being forced to drink a potion prepared from hemlock in 339 B.C.

25.6B Histamine and Antihistamines

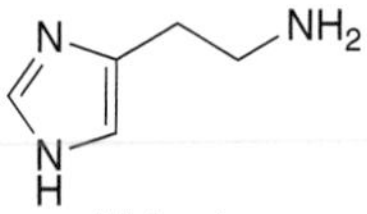
histamine

Histamine, a rather simple triamine first discussed in Section 17.8, is responsible for a wide variety of physiological effects. Histamine is a vasodilator (it dilates capillaries), so it is released at the site of an injury or infection to increase blood flow. It is also responsible for the symptoms of allergies, including a runny nose and watery eyes. In the stomach, histamine stimulates the secretion of acid.

Understanding the central role of histamine in these biochemical processes has helped chemists design drugs to counteract some of its undesirable effects.

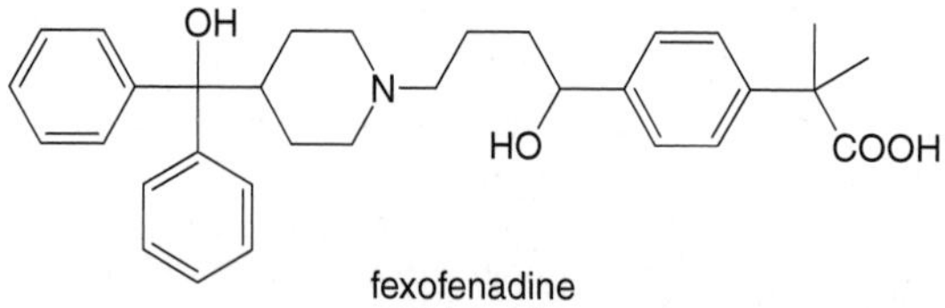
fexofenadine
antihistamine

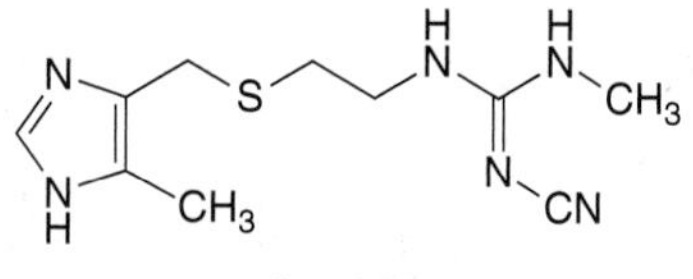
cimetidine
(Tagamet)
antiulcer drug

Antihistamines bind to the same active site of the enzyme that binds histamine in the cell, but they evoke a different response. An antihistamine like **fexofenadine** (trade name Allegra), for example, inhibits vasodilation, so it is used to treat the symptoms of the common cold and allergies. Unlike many antihistamines, fexofenadine does not cause drowsiness because it binds to histamine receptors but does not cross the blood–brain barrier, so it does not affect the central nervous system. **Cimetidine** (trade name Tagamet) is a histamine mimic that blocks the secretion of hydrochloric acid in the stomach, so it is used to treat individuals with ulcers.

25.6C Derivatives of 2-Phenylethylamine

A large number of physiologically active compounds are derived from **2-phenylethylamine, $C_6H_5CH_2CH_2NH_2$.** Some of these compounds are synthesized in cells and needed to maintain healthy mental function. Others are isolated from plant sources or are synthesized in the laboratory and have a profound effect on the brain because they interfere with normal neurochemistry. These compounds include **adrenaline, noradrenaline, methamphetamine,** and **mescaline.** Each contains a benzene ring bonded to a two-carbon unit with a nitrogen atom (shown in red).

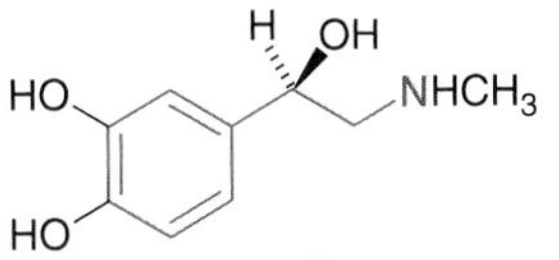

adrenaline
(epinephrine)

a hormone secreted in response to stress
(Figure 7.14)

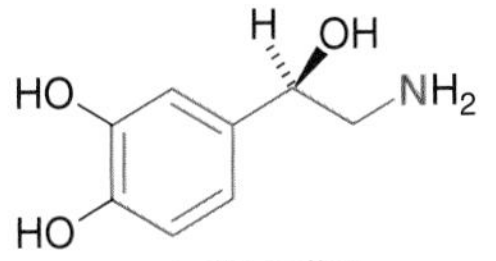

noradrenaline
(norepinephrine)

a neurotransmitter that increases heart rate and dilates air passages

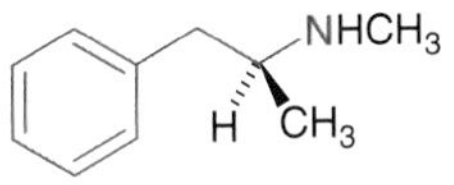

methamphetamine

an addictive stimulant sold as speed, meth, or crystal meth

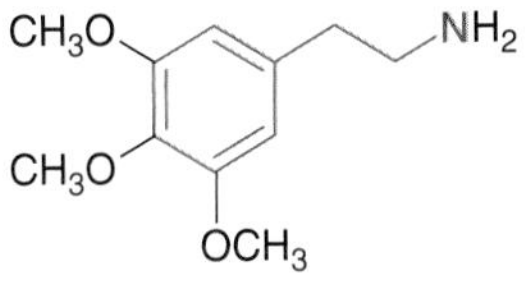

mescaline

a hallucinogen isolated from peyote, a cactus native to the southwestern United States and Mexico

Another example, **dopamine,** is a neurotransmitter, a chemical messenger released by one nerve cell (neuron), which then binds to a receptor in a neighboring target cell (Figure 25.6). Dopamine

Figure 25.6 Dopamine—A neurotransmitter

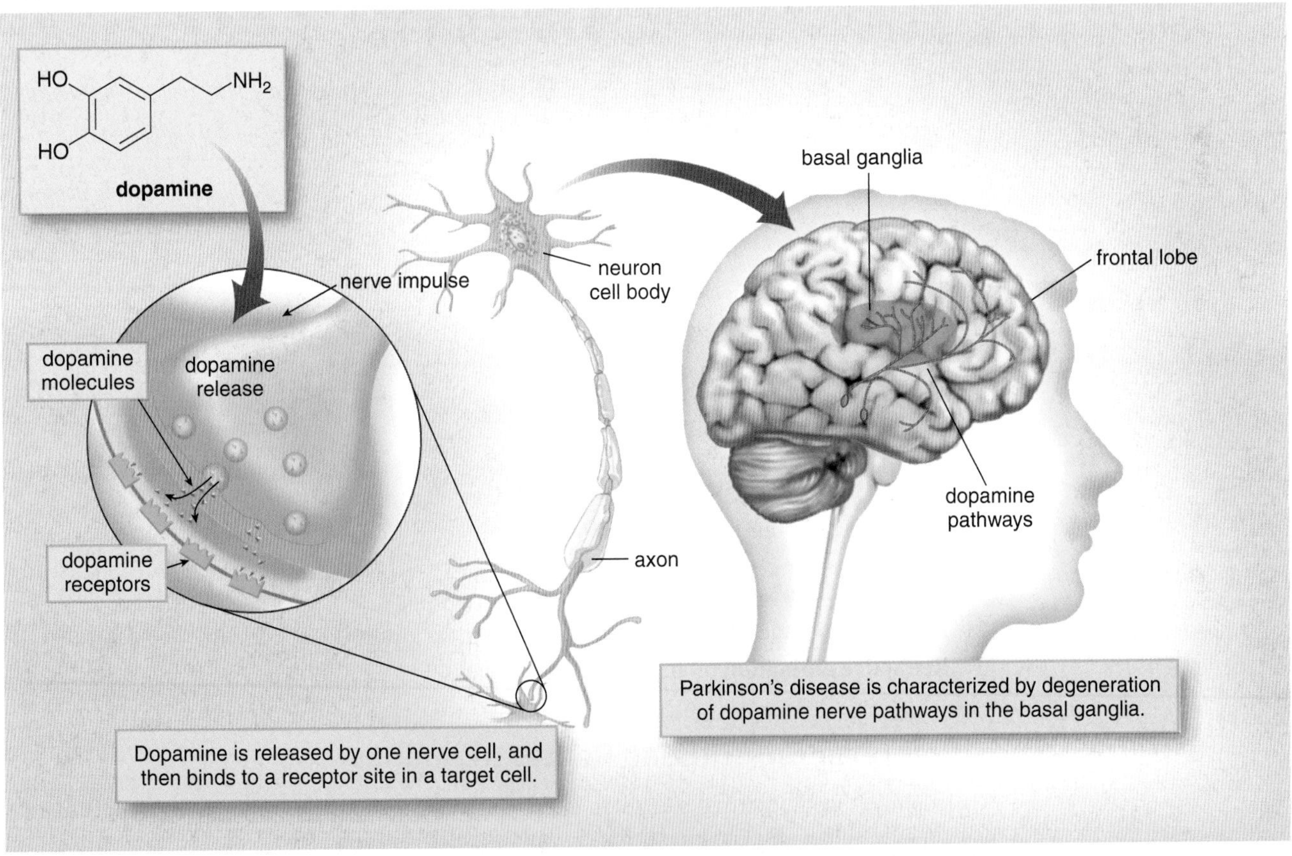
HO
NH2
HO
dopamine
nerve impulse
neuron
cell body
basal ganglia
frontal lobe
dopamine
molecules
dopamine
release
dopamine
receptors
axon
dopamine
pathways
Parkinson's disease is characterized by degeneration of dopamine nerve pathways in the basal ganglia.
Dopamine is released by one nerve cell, and then binds to a receptor site in a target cell.

affects brain processes that control movement and emotions, so proper dopamine levels are necessary to maintain an individual's mental and physical health. For example, when dopamine-producing neurons die, the level of dopamine drops, resulting in the loss of motor control symptomatic of Parkinson's disease.

Serotonin is a neurotransmitter that plays an important role in mood, sleep, perception, and temperature regulation. A deficiency of serotonin causes depression. Understanding the central role of serotonin in determining one's mood has led to the development of a variety of drugs for the treatment of depression. The most widely used antidepressants today are selective serotonin reuptake inhibitors (SSRIs). These drugs act by inhibiting the reuptake of serotonin by the neurons that produce it, thus effectively increasing its concentration. Fluoxetine (trade name Prozac) is a common antidepressant that acts in this way.

Cocaine, amphetamines, and several other addicting drugs increase the level of dopamine in the brain, which results in a pleasurable "high." With time, the brain adapts to increased dopamine levels, so more drug is required for the same sensation.

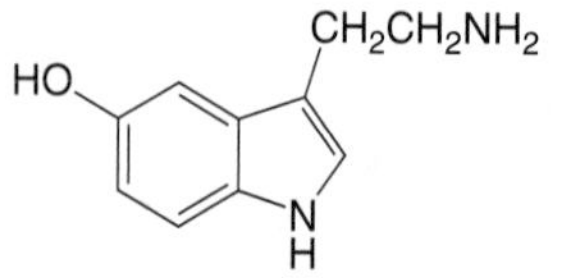

serotonin

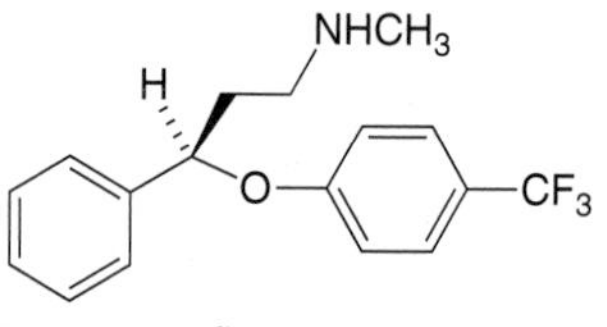

fluoxetine

Bufo toads from the Amazon jungle are the source of the hallucinogen bufotenin.

Drugs that interfere with the metabolism of serotonin have a profound effect on mental state. For example, bufotenin, isolated from *Bufo* toads from the Amazon jungle, and psilocin, isolated from *Psilocybe* mushrooms, are very similar in structure to serotonin and both cause intense hallucinations.

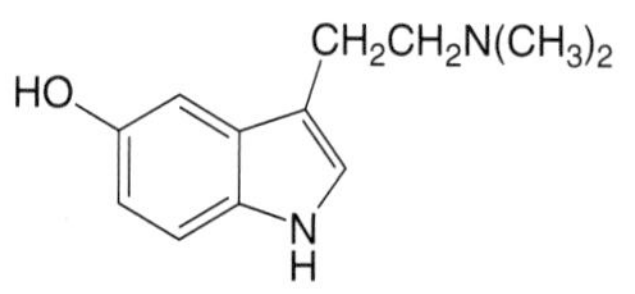

bufotenin

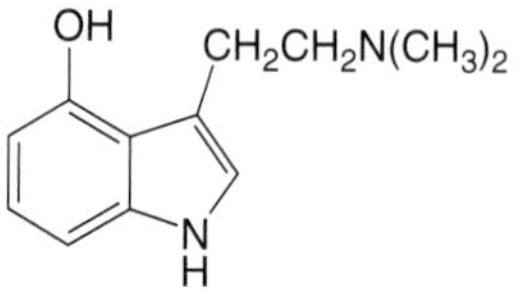

psilocin

Problem 25.8 LSD (a hallucinogen) and codeine (a narcotic) are structurally more complex derivatives of 2-phenylethylamine. Identify the atoms of 2-phenylethylamine in each of the following compounds.

a. 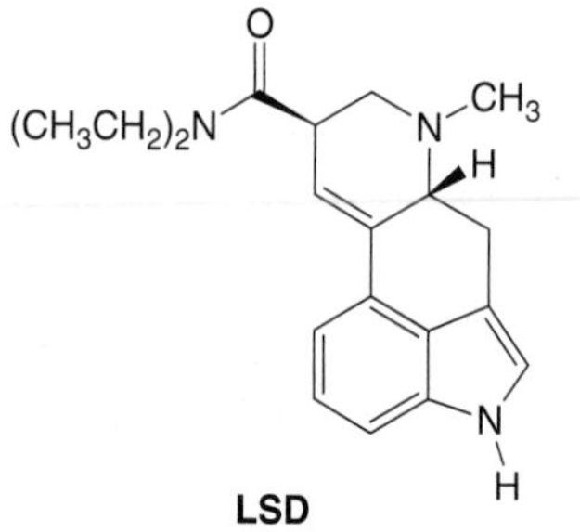

LSD
lysergic acid diethyl amide

b. 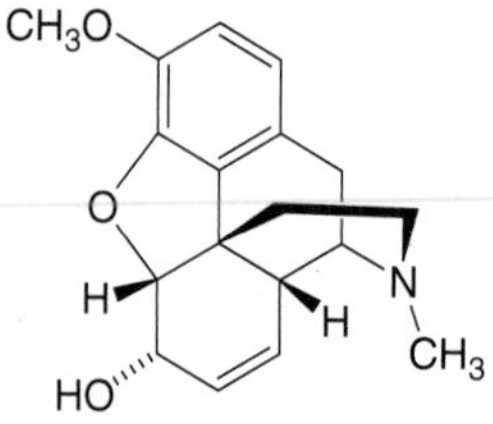

codeine

25.7 Preparation of Amines

In the preparations of a given functional group, many different starting materials form a common product (amines, in this case).

Three types of reactions are used to prepare an amine:

[1] **Nucleophilic substitution** using nitrogen nucleophiles
[2] **Reduction** of other nitrogen-containing functional groups
[3] **Reductive amination** of aldehydes and ketones

25.7A Nucleophilic Substitution Routes to Amines

Nucleophilic substitution is the key step in two different methods for synthesizing amines: direct nucleophilic substitution and the Gabriel synthesis of 1° amines.

Direct Nucleophilic Substitution

Conceptually, the simplest method to synthesize an amine is by **S_N2 reaction of an alkyl halide with NH_3 or an amine.** The method requires two steps:

[1] **Nucleophilic attack** of the nitrogen nucleophile forms an ammonium salt.
[2] **Removal of a proton** on N forms the amine.

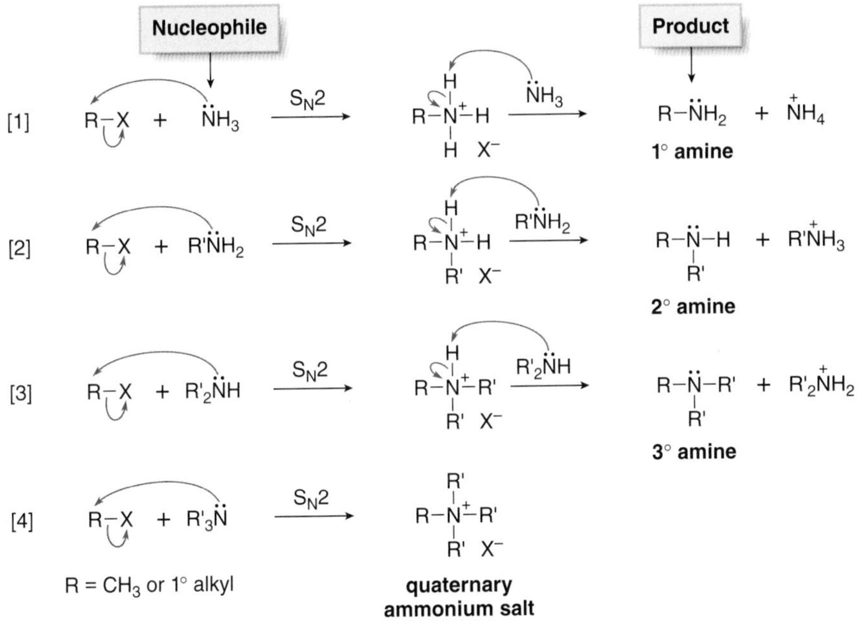

Nucleophile
Product
[1]
[2]
[3]
[4]
S_N2
1° amine
2° amine
3° amine
R = CH_3 or 1° alkyl
quaternary ammonium salt

The identity of the nitrogen nucleophile determines the type of amine or ammonium salt formed as product. One new carbon–nitrogen bond is formed in each reaction. Because the reaction follows an S_N2 mechanism, the alkyl halide must be unhindered—that is, CH_3X or RCH_2X.

Although this process seems straightforward, polyalkylation of the nitrogen nucleophile limits its usefulness. **Any amine formed by nucleophilic substitution still has a nonbonded electron pair, making it a nucleophile as well.** It will react with remaining alkyl halide to form a more substituted amine. Because of this, a mixture of 1°, 2°, and 3° amines often results. Only the final product—called a **quaternary ammonium salt** because it has four alkyl groups on N—cannot react further, and so the reaction stops.

As a result, this reaction is most useful for preparing 1° amines by using a very large excess of NH_3 (a relatively inexpensive starting material) and for preparing quaternary ammonium salts by alkylating any nitrogen nucleophile with one or more equivalents of alkyl halide.

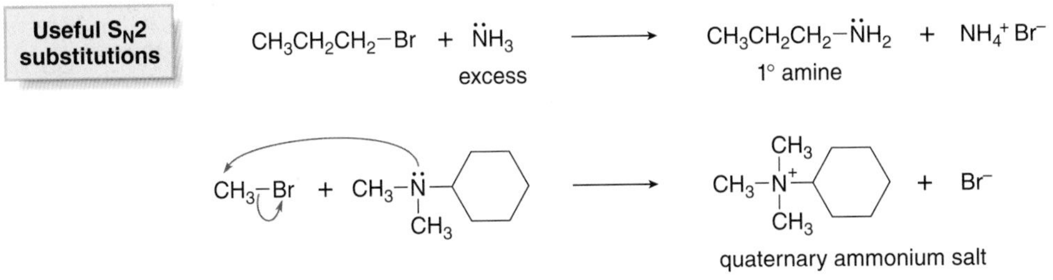

Useful S_N2 substitutions
$CH_3CH_2CH_2$–Br + NH_3
excess
$CH_3CH_2CH_2$–NH_2 + NH_4^+ Br^-
1° amine
+ Br^-
quaternary ammonium salt

Problem 25.9 Draw the product of each reaction.

a. 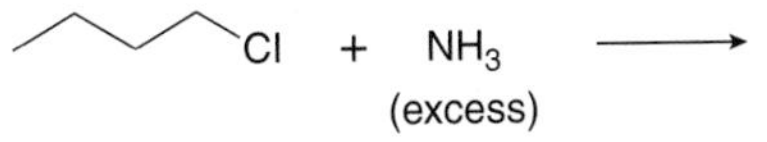

Cl
+ NH_3
(excess)

b. 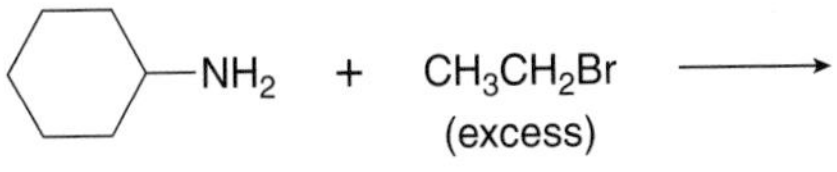

–NH_2
+ CH_3CH_2Br
(excess)

The Gabriel Synthesis of 1° Amines

To avoid polyalkylation, a nitrogen nucleophile can be used that reacts in a single nucleophilic substitution reaction—that is, the reaction forms a product that does not contain a nucleophilic nitrogen atom capable of reacting further.

The **Gabriel synthesis** consists of two steps and uses a resonance-stabilized nitrogen nucleophile to synthesize 1° amines via nucleophilic substitution. The Gabriel synthesis begins with **phthalimide,** one of a group of compounds called **imides.** The **N–H bond of an imide is especially acidic** because the resulting anion is resonance stabilized by the two flanking carbonyl groups.

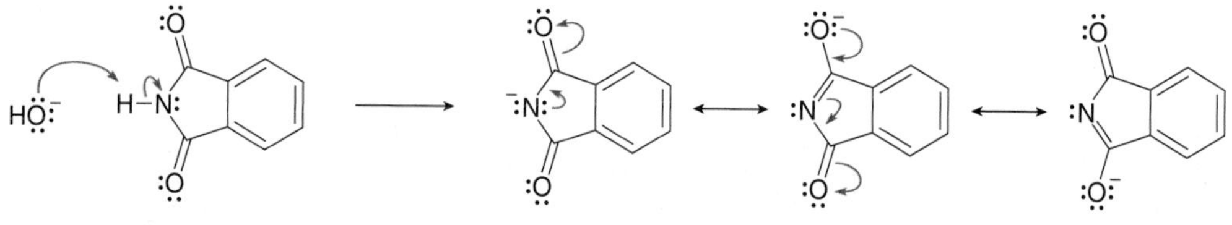

phthalimide
$pK_a = 10$

resonance-stabilized anion

An acid–base reaction forms a nucleophilic anion that can react with an unhindered alkyl halide—that is, CH_3X or RCH_2X—in an S_N2 reaction to form a substitution product. This alkylated imide is then hydrolyzed with aqueous base to give a 1° amine and a dicarboxylate. This reaction is similar to the hydrolysis of amides to afford carboxylate anions and amines, as discussed in Section 22.13. The overall result of this two-step sequence is **nucleophilic substitution of X by NH_2,** so the Gabriel synthesis can be used to prepare 1° amines only.

Steps in the Gabriel synthesis

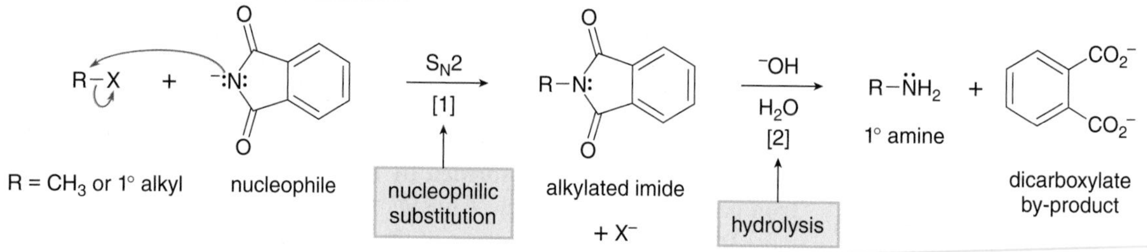
R = CH3 or 1° alkyl
nucleophile
SN2
[1]
nucleophilic substitution
alkylated imide
+ X−
−OH
H2O
[2]
hydrolysis
1° amine
dicarboxylate by-product

- **The Gabriel synthesis converts an alkyl halide into a 1° amine by a two-step process: nucleophilic substitution followed by hydrolysis.**

Example

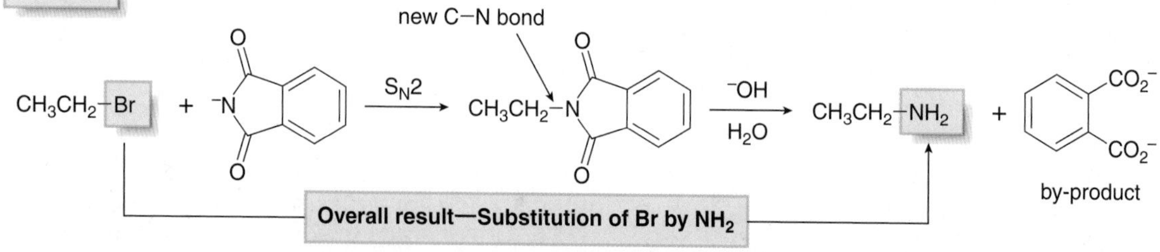
new C–N bond
CH3CH2–Br
SN2
CH3CH2–N
−OH
H2O
CH3CH2–NH2
by-product
Overall result—Substitution of Br by NH2

Problem 25.10 What alkyl halide is needed to prepare each 1° amine by a Gabriel synthesis?

a. 
NH2

b. $(CH_3)_2CHCH_2CH_2NH_2$

c. 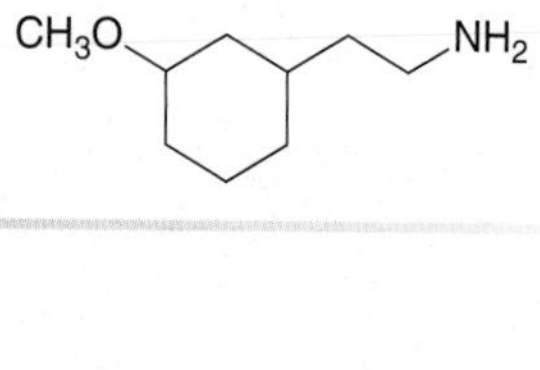
CH3O
NH2

Problem 25.11 Which amines cannot be prepared by a Gabriel synthesis? Explain your choices.

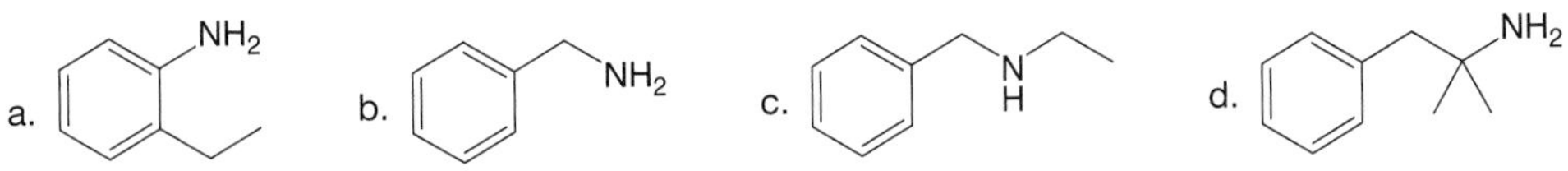
a.
NH_2
b.
NH_2
c.
N
H
d.
NH_2

25.7B Reduction of Other Functional Groups That Contain Nitrogen

Amines can be prepared by reduction of nitro compounds, nitriles, and amides. Because the details of these reactions have been discussed previously, they are presented here in summary form only.

[1] From nitro compounds (Section 18.15C)

Nitro groups are reduced to 1° amines using a variety of reducing agents.

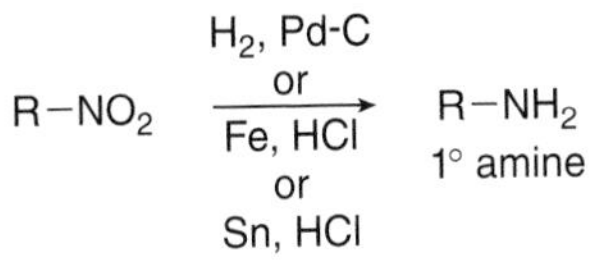
$R-NO_2$
H_2, Pd-C
or
Fe, HCl
or
Sn, HCl
$R-NH_2$
1° amine

[2] From nitriles (Section 22.18B)

Nitriles are reduced to 1° amines with $LiAlH_4$.

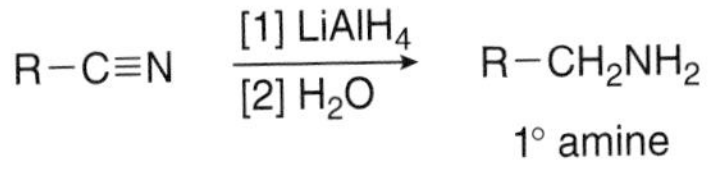
R−C≡N
[1] $LiAlH_4$
[2] H_2O
$R-CH_2NH_2$
1° amine

Because a cyano group is readily introduced by S_N2 substitution of alkyl halides with ^-CN, this provides **a two-step method to convert an alkyl halide to a 1° amine with one more carbon atom.** The conversion of CH_3Br to $CH_3CH_2NH_2$ illustrates this two-step sequence.

Example

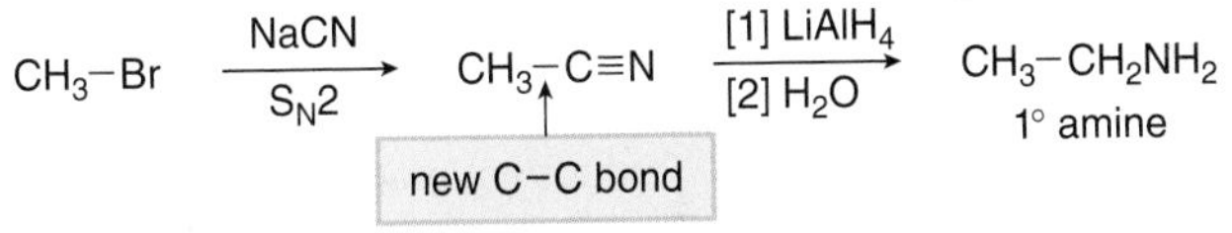
CH_3-Br
NaCN
S_N2
$CH_3-C≡N$
new C−C bond
[1] $LiAlH_4$
[2] H_2O
$CH_3-CH_2NH_2$
1° amine

[3] From amides (Section 20.7B)

Primary (1°), 2°, and 3° amides are reduced to 1°, 2°, and 3° amines, respectively, by using $LiAlH_4$.

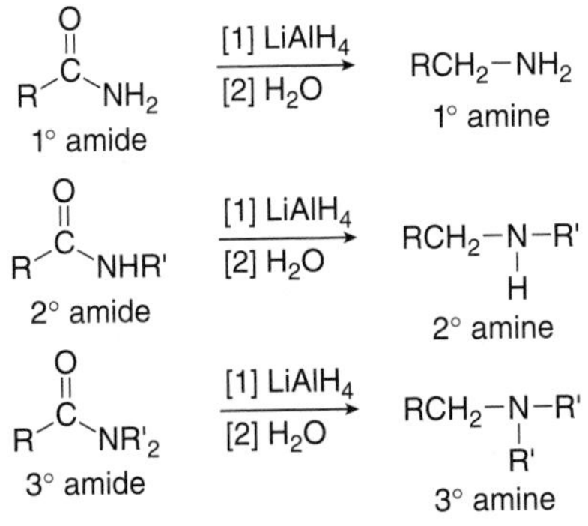
1° amide
[1] $LiAlH_4$
[2] H_2O
RCH_2-NH_2
1° amine
NHR'
2° amide
RCH_2-N-R'
H
2° amine
NR'_2
3° amide
R'
3° amine

Problem 25.12 What nitro compound, nitrile, and amide are reduced to each compound?

a. $CH_3CHCH_2NH_2$ (with CH_3 on the second carbon)

b. 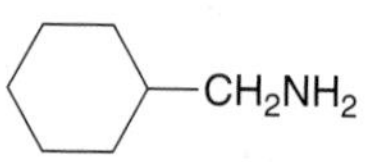
CH2NH2

c. 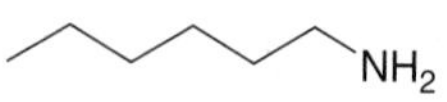
NH2

Problem 25.13 What amine is formed by reduction of each amide?

a. 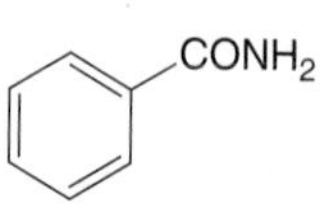
CONH2

b. 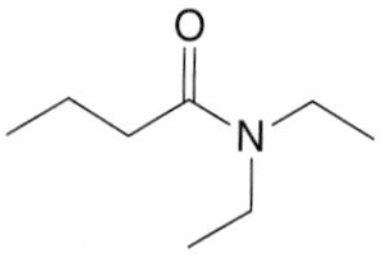
O
N

c. 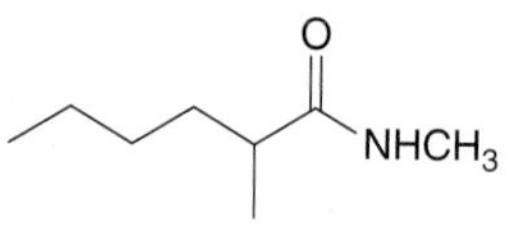
O
NHCH3

Problem 25.14 Which amines cannot be prepared by reduction of an amide?

a. 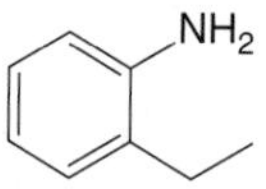
NH2

b. 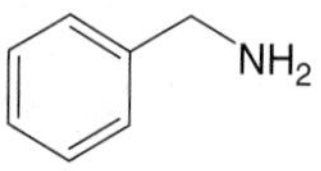
NH2

c. 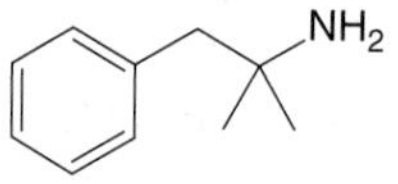
NH2

d. 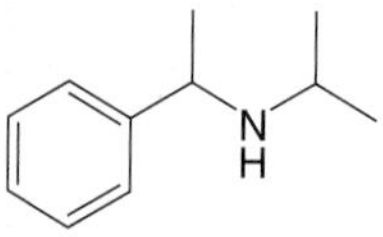
N
H

25.7C Reductive Amination of Aldehydes and Ketones

Reductive amination is a two-step method that converts aldehydes and ketones into 1°, 2°, and 3° amines. Let's first examine this method using NH_3 to prepare 1° amines. There are two distinct parts in reductive amination:

[1] **Nucleophilic attack of NH_3 on the carbonyl group forms an imine** (Section 21.11A), which is not isolated; then,

[2] **Reduction of the imine forms an amine** (Section 20.7B).

Reductive amination—A two-step process

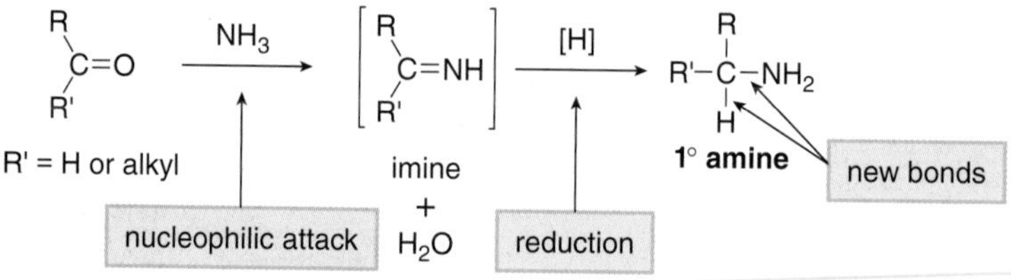
R
C=O
R'
R' = H or alkyl
NH3
nucleophilic attack
R
C=NH
R'
imine
+
H2O
[H]
reduction
R
R'–C–NH2
H
1° amine
new bonds

- **Reductive amination replaces a C=O by a C–H and C–N bond.**

The most effective reducing agent for this reaction is sodium cyanoborohydride ($NaBH_3CN$). This hydride reagent is a derivative of sodium borohydride ($NaBH_4$), formed by replacing one H atom by CN.

$NaBH_3CN$
sodium cyanoborohydride

Reductive amination combines two reactions we have already learned in a different way. Two examples are shown. The second reaction is noteworthy because the product is **amphetamine,** a potent central nervous system stimulant.

Examples

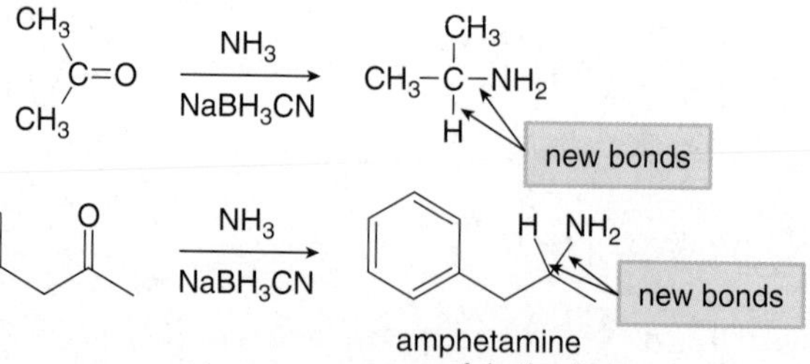
CH3
C=O
CH3
NH3
NaBH3CN
CH3
CH3–C–NH2
H
new bonds
O
NH3
NaBH3CN
H NH2
new bonds

amphetamine
a powerful stimulant

With a 1° or 2° amine as starting material, reductive amination is used to prepare 2° and 3° amines, respectively. Note the result: Reductive amination uses an aldehyde or ketone to replace one H atom on a nitrogen atom by an alkyl group, making a more substituted amine.

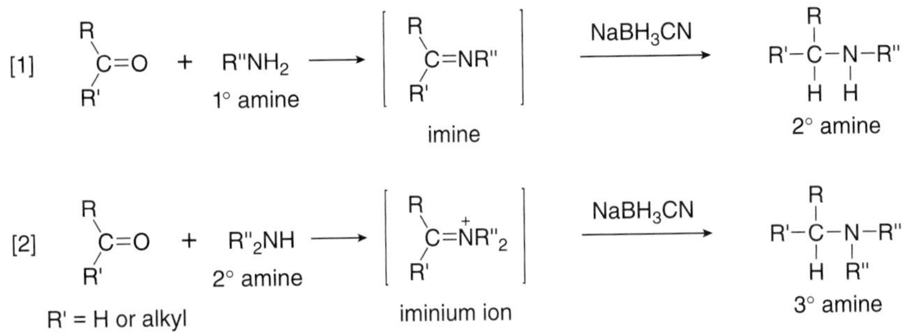
[1]
1° amine
imine
$NaBH_3CN$
2° amine
[2]
2° amine
iminium ion
$NaBH_3CN$
3° amine
R' = H or alkyl

The synthesis of methamphetamine (Section 25.6C) by reductive amination is illustrated in Figure 25.7.

Problem 25.15 Draw the product of each reaction.

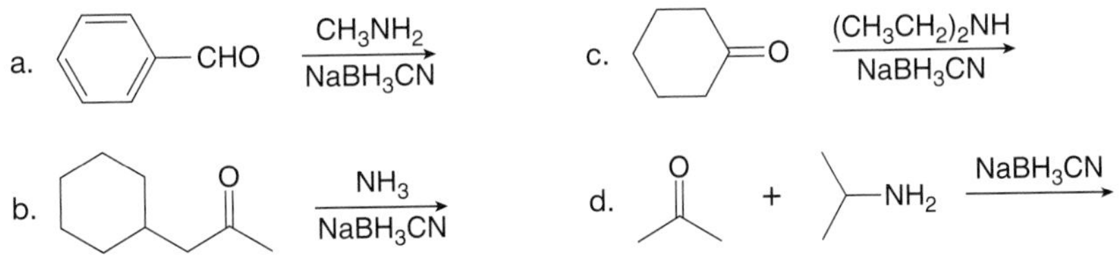
a.
CHO
CH_3NH_2
$NaBH_3CN$
b.
NH_3
$NaBH_3CN$
c.
$(CH_3CH_2)_2NH$
$NaBH_3CN$
d.
NH_2
$NaBH_3CN$

Problem 25.16 Enalapril, a drug used to treat hypertension, is prepared from compounds **D** and **E** by reductive amination. What is the structure of enalapril?

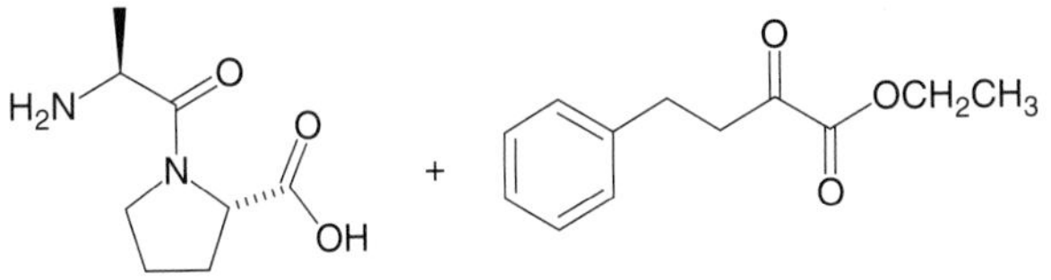
H_2N
OH
OCH_2CH_3

D **E**

Figure 25.7 Synthesis of methamphetamine by reductive amination

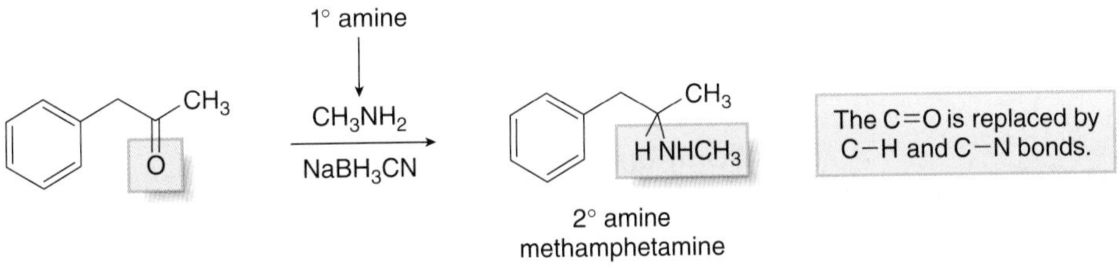
1° amine
CH_3
CH_3NH_2
$NaBH_3CN$
CH_3
H $NHCH_3$
The C=O is replaced by C–H and C–N bonds.
2° amine
methamphetamine

- In reductive amination, one of the H atoms bonded to N is replaced by an alkyl group. As a result, a 1° amine is converted to a 2° amine and a 2° amine is converted to a 3° amine. In this reaction, CH_3NH_2 (a 1° amine) is converted to methamphetamine (a 2° amine).

To use reductive amination in synthesis, you must be able to determine what aldehyde or ketone and nitrogen compound are needed to prepare a given amine—that is, you must work backwards in the retrosynthetic direction. Keep in mind the following two points:

- **One alkyl group on N comes from the carbonyl compound.**
- **The remainder of the molecule comes from NH_3 or an amine.**

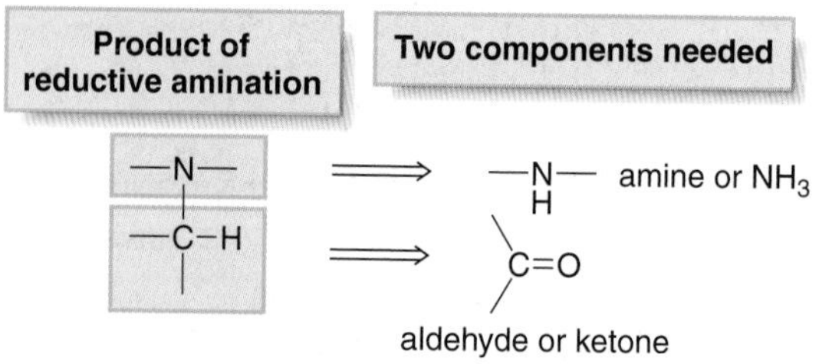
Product of reductive amination
Two components needed
amine or NH3
aldehyde or ketone

For example, 2-phenylethylamine is a 1° amine, so it has only one alkyl group bonded to N. This alkyl group must come from the carbonyl compound, and the rest of the molecule then comes from the nitrogen component. **For a 1° amine, the nitrogen component must be NH_3.**

Retrosynthetic analysis for preparing 2-phenylethylamine:

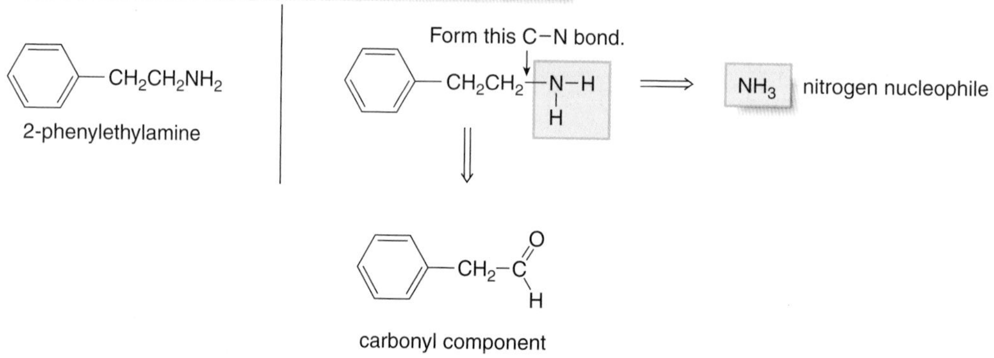
CH2CH2NH2
2-phenylethylamine
Form this C–N bond.
CH2CH2–N–H
NH3
nitrogen nucleophile
CH2–C
carbonyl component

There is usually more than one way to use reductive amination to synthesize 2° and 3° amines, as shown in Sample Problem 25.2 for a 2° amine.

Sample Problem 25.2 What aldehyde or ketone and nitrogen component are needed to synthesize *N*-ethylcyclohexanamine by a reductive amination reaction?

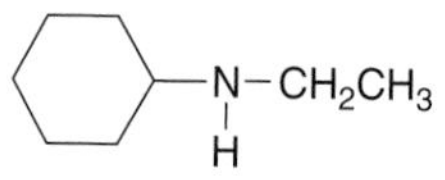

N-ethylcyclohexanamine

Solution

Because *N*-ethylcyclohexanamine has two different alkyl groups bonded to the N atom, either R group can come from the carbonyl component and there are two different ways to form a C–N bond by reductive amination.

Possibility [1] Use $CH_3CH_2NH_2$ and cyclohexanone.

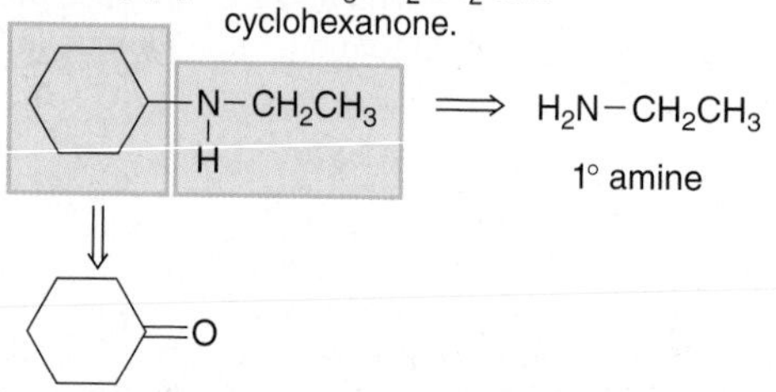
N–CH2CH3
H2N–CH2CH3
1° amine

Possibility [2] Use cyclohexylamine and an aldehyde.

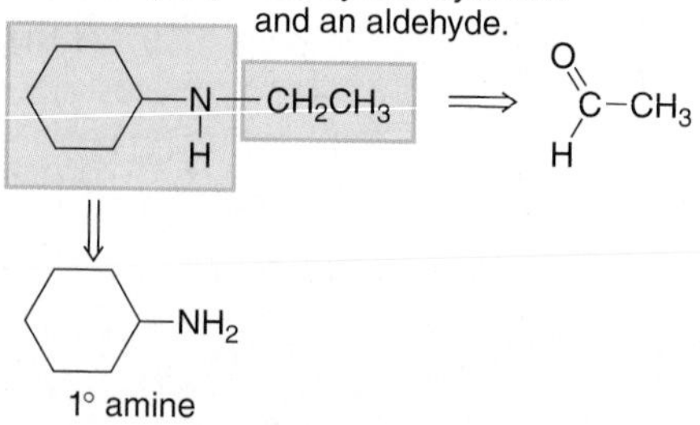
N–CH2CH3
C–CH3
NH2
1° amine

Because reductive amination adds one R group to a nitrogen atom, both routes to form the 2° amine begin with a 1° amine.

Problem 25.17 What starting materials are needed to prepare each drug using reductive amination? Give all possible pairs of compounds when more than one route is possible.

a. 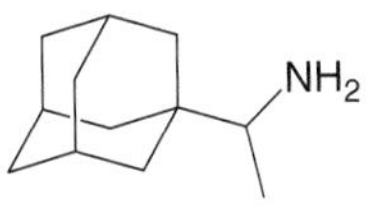
NH2

rimantadine
antiviral used to treat influenza

b. 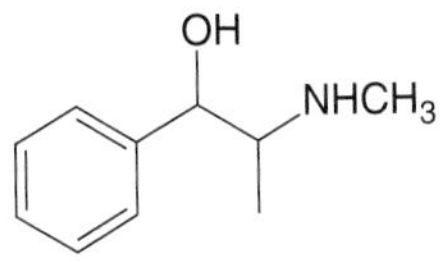
OH
NHCH3

pseudoephedrine
nasal decongestant

Problem 25.18 (a) Explain why phentermine [$PhCH_2C(CH_3)_2NH_2$] can't be made by a reductive amination reaction.
(b) Give a systematic name for phentermine, one of the components of the banned diet drug fen–phen.

25.8 Reactions of Amines—General Features

- **The chemistry of amines is dominated by the lone pair of electrons on nitrogen.**

Only three elements in the second row of the periodic table have nonbonded electron pairs in neutral organic compounds: nitrogen, oxygen, and fluorine. Because basicity and nucleophilicity decrease across the row, **nitrogen is the most basic and most nucleophilic** of these elements.

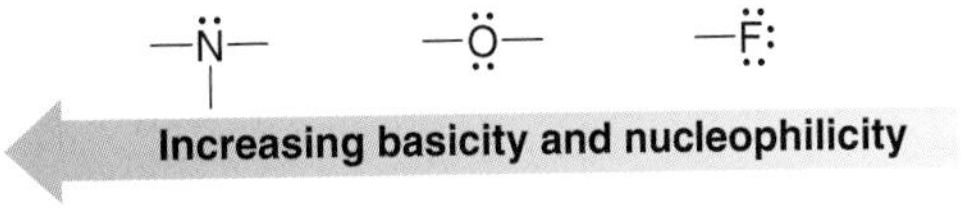
Increasing basicity and nucleophilicity

- **Amines are stronger bases and nucleophiles than other neutral organic compounds.**

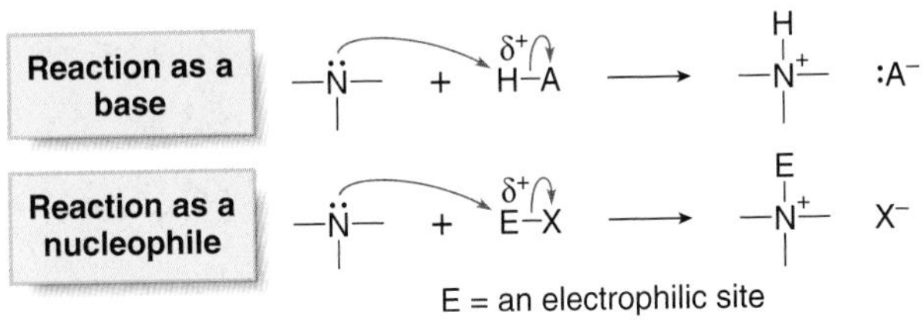
Reaction as a base
Reaction as a nucleophile
δ+
H–A
:A⁻
E–X
X⁻

E = an electrophilic site

- **Amines react as bases with compounds that contain acidic protons.**
- **Amines react as nucleophiles with compounds that contain electrophilic carbons.**

25.9 Amines as Bases

Amines react as bases with a variety of organic and inorganic acids.

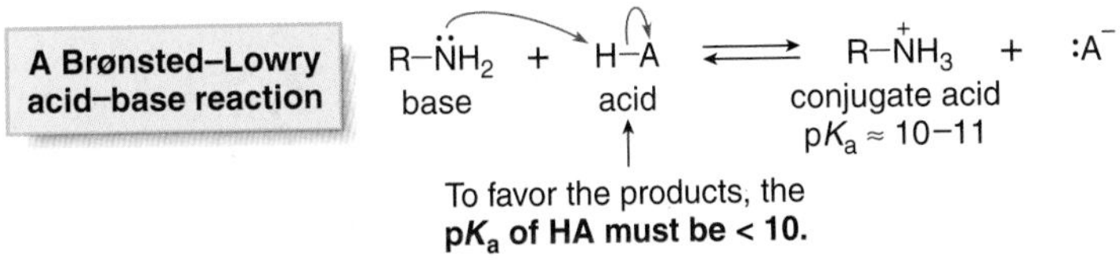
A Brønsted–Lowry acid–base reaction
R–NH2 + H–A ⇌ R–NH3 + :A⁻
base
acid
conjugate acid
pKa ≈ 10–11
To favor the products, the
pKa of HA must be < 10.

What acids can be used to protonate an amine? Equilibrium favors the products of an acid–base reaction when the weaker acid and base are formed. Because the pK_a of many protonated amines is 10–11, the pK_a of the starting acid must be **less than 10** for equilibrium to favor the products. Amines are thus readily protonated by strong inorganic acids like HCl and H_2SO_4, and by carboxylic acids as well.

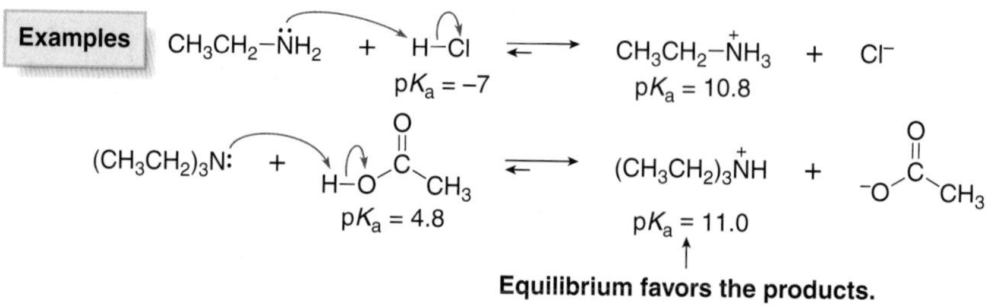

The principles used in an extraction procedure were detailed in Section 19.12.

Because amines are protonated by aqueous acid, they can be separated from other organic compounds by extraction using a separatory funnel. **Extraction separates compounds based on solubility differences.** When an amine is protonated by aqueous acid, its solubility properties change.

For example, when cyclohexylamine is treated with aqueous HCl, it is protonated, forming an ammonium salt. Because the ammonium salt is ionic, it is soluble in water, but insoluble in organic solvents. A similar acid–base reaction does not occur with other organic compounds like alcohols, which are much less basic.

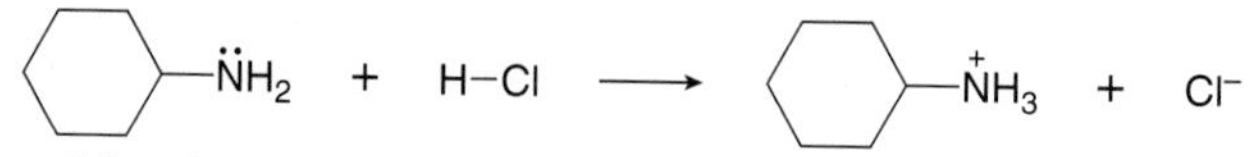

cyclohexylamine
- insoluble in H_2O
- soluble in CH_2Cl_2

cyclohexylammonium chloride
- soluble in H_2O
- insoluble in CH_2Cl_2

This difference in acid–base chemistry can be used to separate cyclohexylamine and cyclohexanol by the stepwise extraction procedure illustrated in Figure 25.8.

Figure 25.8 Separation of cyclohexylamine and cyclohexanol by an extraction procedure

Step [1] Dissolve cyclohexylamine and cyclohexanol in CH_2Cl_2.

Step [2] Add 10% HCl solution to form two layers.

Step [3] Separate the layers.

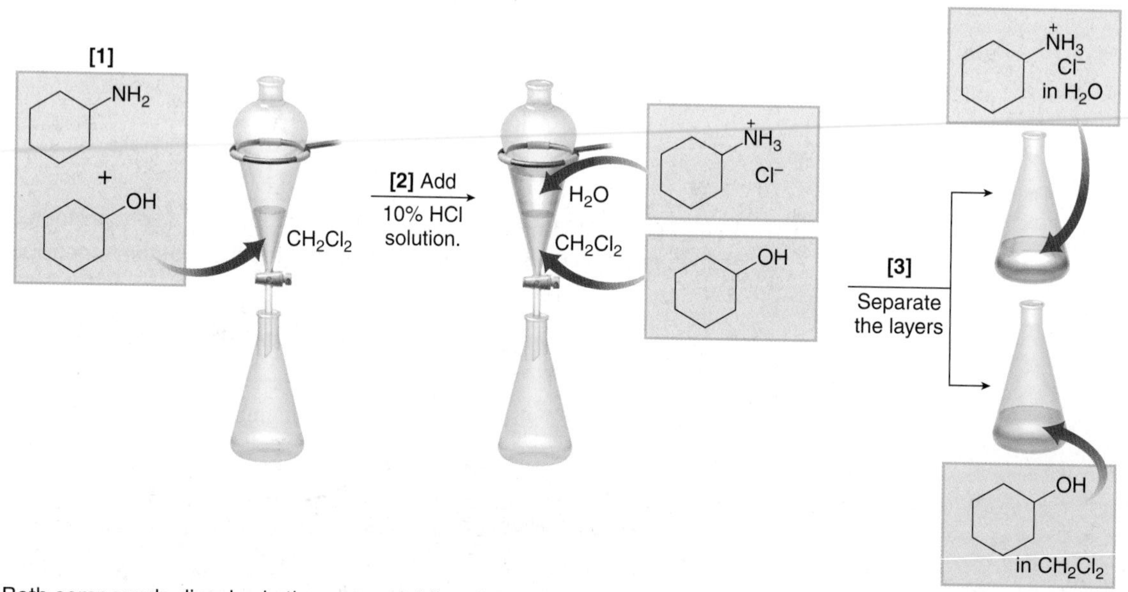

- Both compounds dissolve in the organic solvent CH_2Cl_2.

- Adding 10% aqueous HCl solution forms two layers. When the two layers are mixed, the HCl protonates the amine (RNH_2) to form $RNH_3^+Cl^-$, which dissolves in the aqueous layer.
- The cyclohexanol remains in the CH_2Cl_2 layer.

- Draining the lower layer out the bottom stopcock separates the two layers.
- Cyclohexanol (dissolved in CH_2Cl_2) is in one flask. The ammonium salt, $RNH_3^+Cl^-$ (dissolved in water), is in another flask.

- **An amine can be separated from other organic compounds by converting it to a water-soluble ammonium salt by an acid–base reaction.**

Thus, the water-soluble salt $C_6H_{11}NH_3^+Cl^-$ (obtained by protonation of $C_6H_{11}NH_2$) can be separated from water-insoluble cyclohexanol by an aqueous extraction procedure.

Problem 25.19 Draw the products of each acid–base reaction. Indicate whether equilibrium favors the reactants or products.

a. $CH_3CH_2CH_2CH_2-NH_2$ + HCl ⇌

b. C_6H_5COOH + $(CH_3)_2NH$ ⇌

c. 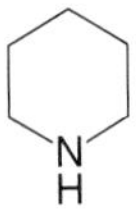 + H_2O ⇌

Many antihistamines and decongestants are sold as their ammonium salts.

Many water-insoluble amines with useful medicinal properties are sold as their water-soluble ammonium salts, which are more easily transported through the body in the aqueous medium of the blood. Benadryl, formed by treating diphenhydramine with HCl, is an over-the-counter antihistamine that is used to relieve the itch and irritation of skin rashes and hives.

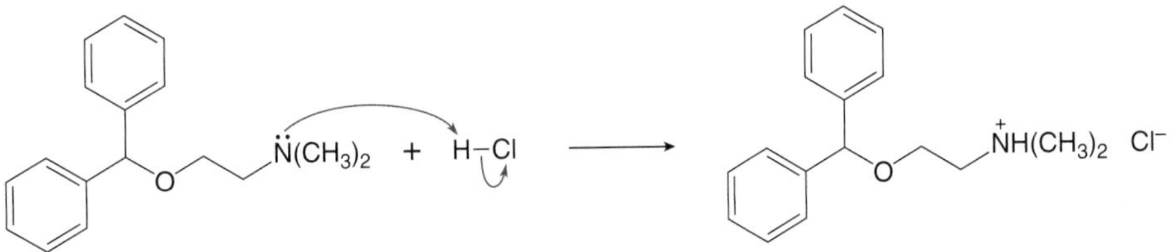

diphenhydramine
water insoluble

ammonium salt
Benadryl
(diphenhydramine hydrochloride)
water soluble

Problem 25.20 Write out steps to show how each of the following pairs of compounds can be separated by an extraction procedure.

a. 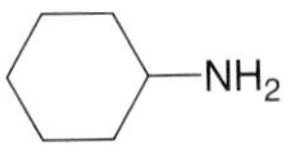 and 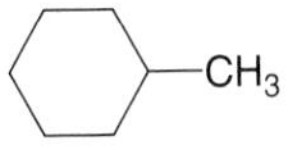

b. $(CH_3CH_2CH_2CH_2)_3N$ and $(CH_3CH_2CH_2CH_2)_2O$

25.10 Relative Basicity of Amines and Other Compounds

The relative acidity of different compounds can be compared using their pK_a values. The relative *basicity* of different compounds (such as amines) can be compared using the pK_a values of their *conjugate acids.*

- **The weaker the conjugate acid, the higher its pK_a and the stronger the base.**

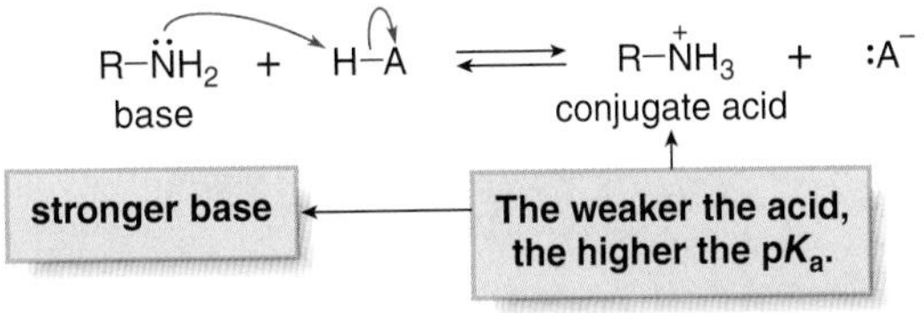

To compare the basicity of two compounds, keep in mind the following:

- **Any factor that increases the electron density on the N atom increases an amine's basicity.**
- **Any factor that decreases the electron density on N decreases an amine's basicity.**

25.10A Comparing an Amine and NH_3

Because alkyl groups are electron donating, they increase the electron density on nitrogen, which makes an amine like $CH_3CH_2NH_2$ more basic than NH_3. In fact, the pK_a of $CH_3CH_2NH_3^+$ is higher than the pK_a of NH_4^+, so **$CH_3CH_2NH_2$ is a stronger base than NH_3.**

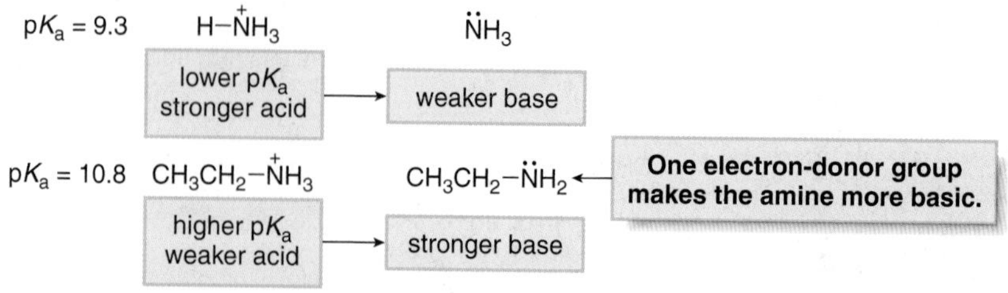

The relative basicity of 1°, 2°, and 3° amines depends on additional factors, and will not be considered in this text.

- **Primary (1°), 2°, and 3° alkylamines are more basic than NH_3 because of the electron-donating inductive effect of the R groups.**

Problem 25.21 Which compound in each pair is more basic: (a) $(CH_3)_2NH$ and NH_3; (b) $CH_3CH_2NH_2$ and $ClCH_2CH_2NH_2$?

25.10B Comparing an Alkylamine and an Arylamine

To compare an alkylamine ($CH_3CH_2NH_2$) and an arylamine ($C_6H_5NH_2$, aniline), we must look at the availability of the nonbonded electron pair on N. With $CH_3CH_2NH_2$, the electron pair is localized on the N atom. With an arylamine, however, the electron pair is now delocalized on the benzene ring. This *decreases* the electron density on N, and makes $C_6H_5NH_2$ less basic than $CH_3CH_2NH_2$.

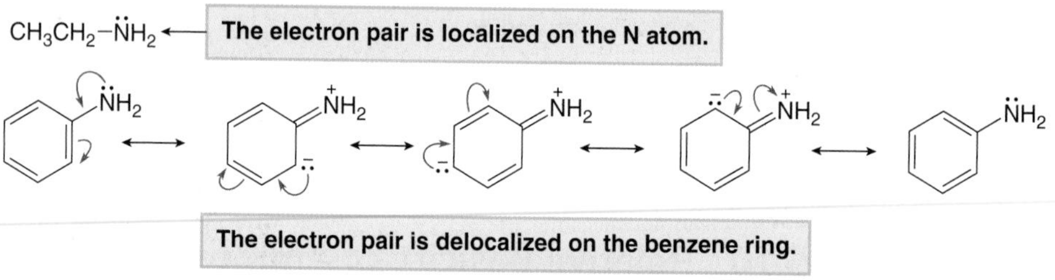

Once again, pK_a values support this reasoning. Because the pK_a of $CH_3CH_2NH_3^+$ is higher than the pK_a of $C_6H_5NH_3^+$, **$CH_3CH_2NH_2$ is a stronger base than $C_6H_5NH_2$.**

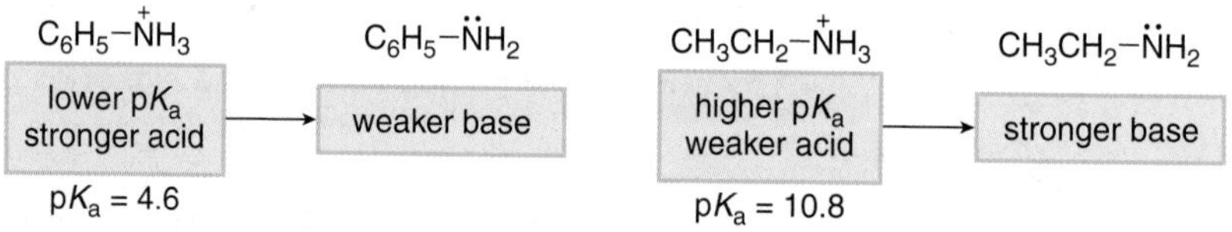

- **Arylamines are less basic than alkylamines because the electron pair on N is delocalized.**

Substituted anilines are more or less basic than aniline depending on the nature of the substituent.

- **Electron-donor groups add electron density to the benzene ring, making the arylamine more basic than aniline.**

D = electron-donor group

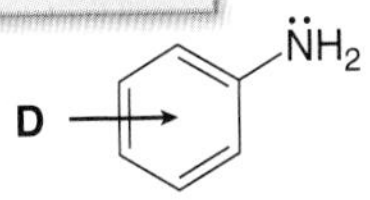

D makes the amine more basic than aniline.

D
$-NH_2$
$-OH$
$-OR$
$-NHCOR$
$-R$

- **Electron-withdrawing groups remove electron density from the benzene ring, making the arylamine less basic than aniline.**

W = electron-withdrawing group

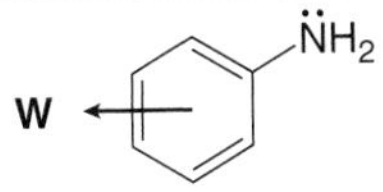

W makes the amine less basic than aniline.

W	
$-X$	$-CN$
$-CHO$	$-SO_3H$
$-COR$	$-NO_2$
$-COOR$	$-NR_3^+$
$-COOH$	

The effect of electron-donating and electron-withdrawing groups on the acidity of substituted benzoic acids was discussed in Section 19.11.

Whether a substituent donates or withdraws electron density depends on the balance of its inductive and resonance effects (Section 18.6 and Figure 18.7).

Sample Problem 25.3

Rank the following compounds in order of increasing basicity.

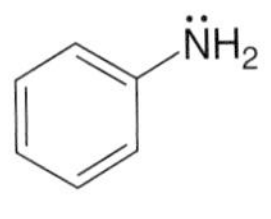

aniline

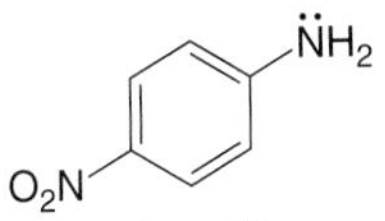

p-nitroaniline

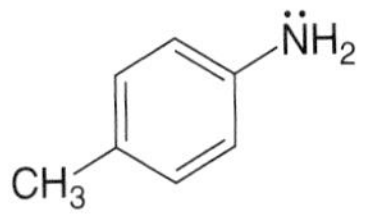

p-methylaniline (*p*-toluidine)

Solution

***p*-Nitroaniline: NO_2** is an electron-withdrawing group, making the amine **less basic** than aniline.

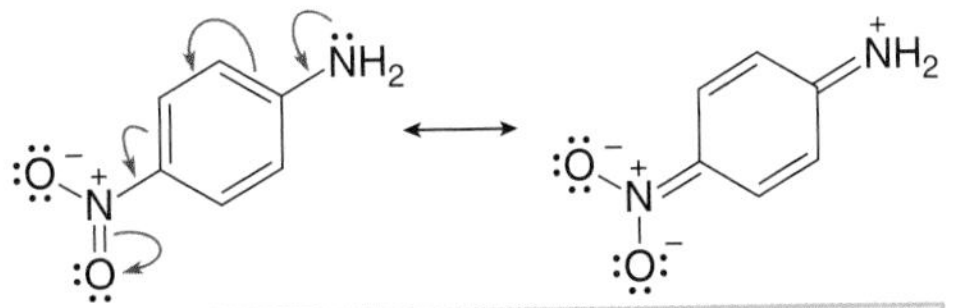

The lone pair on N is delocalized on the O atom, decreasing the basicity of the amine.

***p*-Methylaniline:** CH_3 has an electron-donating inductive effect, making the amine **more basic** than aniline.

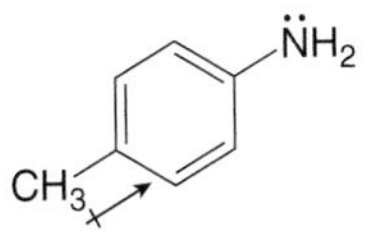

CH_3 inductively donates electron density, increasing the basicity of the amine.

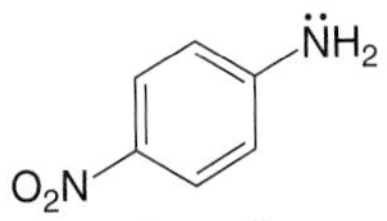

p-nitroaniline

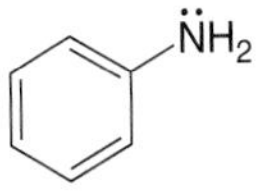

aniline

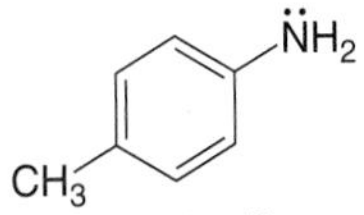

p-methylaniline (*p*-toluidine)

Increasing basicity →

Figure 25.9
Electrostatic potential plots of substituted anilines

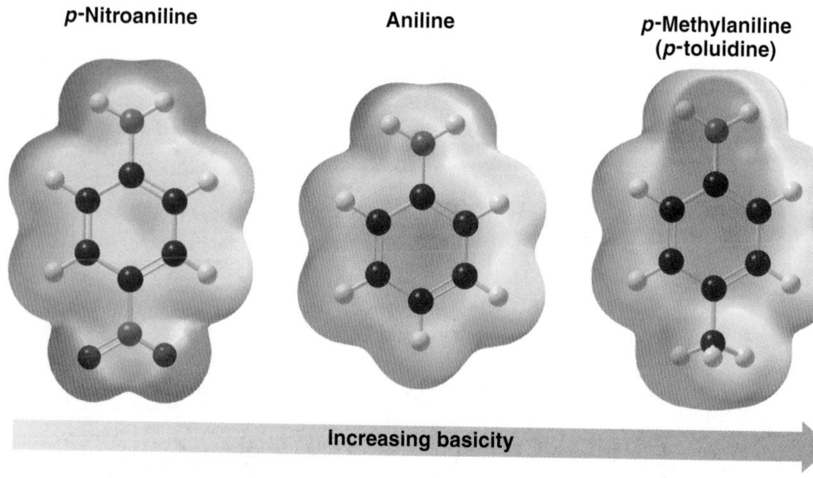

The NH_2 group gets more electron rich as the para substituent changes from $NO_2 \rightarrow H \rightarrow CH_3$. This is indicated by the color change around NH_2 (from green to yellow to red) in the electrostatic potential plot.

The electrostatic potential plots in Figure 25.9 demonstrate that the electron density of the nitrogen atoms in these anilines increases in the order shown.

Problem 25.22 Rank the compounds in each group in order of increasing basicity.

a.

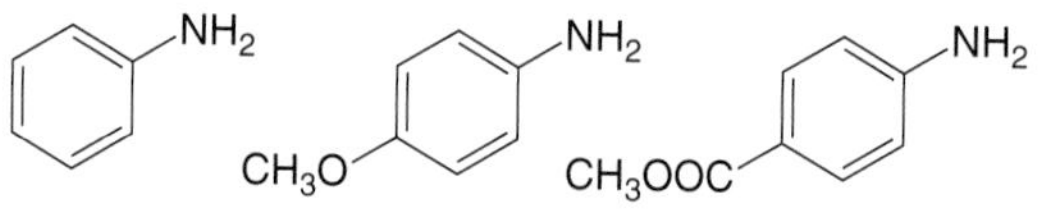

b.

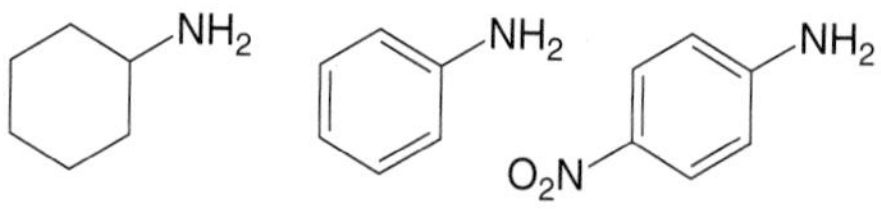

25.10C Comparing an Alkylamine and an Amide

To compare the basicity of an alkylamine (RNH_2) and an amide ($RCONH_2$), we must once again compare the availability of the nonbonded electron pair on nitrogen. With RNH_2, the electron pair is localized on the N atom. With an amide, however, the electron pair is delocalized on the carbonyl oxygen by resonance. This *decreases* the electron density on N, making **an amide much less basic than an alkylamine.**

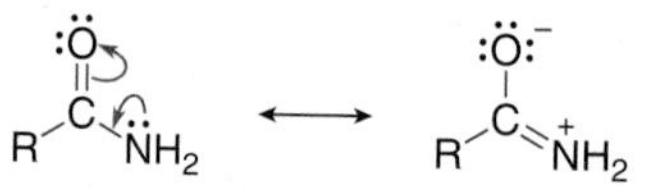

The electron pair on N is delocalized on O by resonance.

- Amides are much less basic than amines because the electron pair on N is delocalized.

In fact, amides are not much more basic than any carbonyl compound. When an amide is treated with acid, **protonation occurs at the carbonyl oxygen, *not* the nitrogen,** because the resulting cation is resonance stabilized. The product of protonation of the NH_2 group cannot be resonance stabilized.

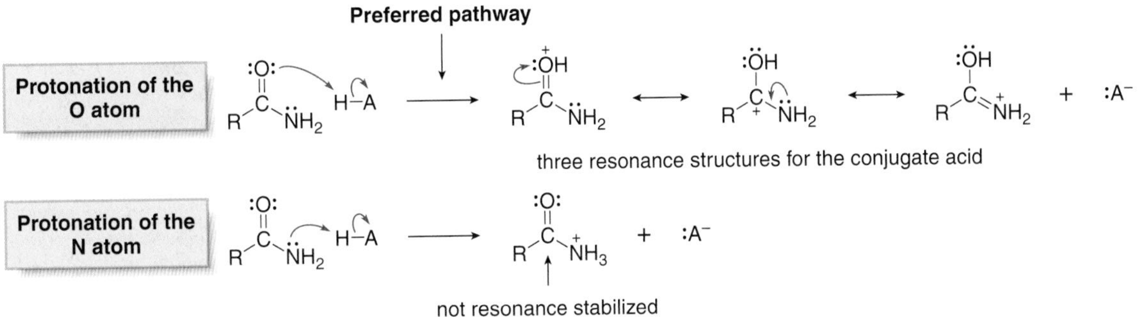

Problem 25.23 Rank the following compounds in order of increasing basicity.

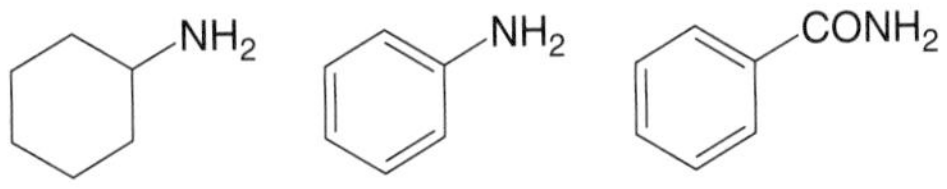

25.10D Heterocyclic Aromatic Amines

To determine the relative basicity of nitrogen heterocycles that are also aromatic, you must know whether the nitrogen lone pair is part of the aromatic π system.

For example, pyridine and pyrrole are both aromatic, but the nonbonded electron pair on the N atom in these compounds is located in different orbitals. Recall from Section 17.8C that the **lone pair of electrons in pyridine occupies an sp^2 hybridized orbital,** perpendicular to the π bonds of the molecule, so it is *not* part of the aromatic system, whereas that of pyrrole resides in a *p* orbital, making it part of the aromatic system. **The lone pair on pyrrole, therefore, is delocalized on all of the atoms of the five-membered ring,** making pyrrole a much weaker base than pyridine.

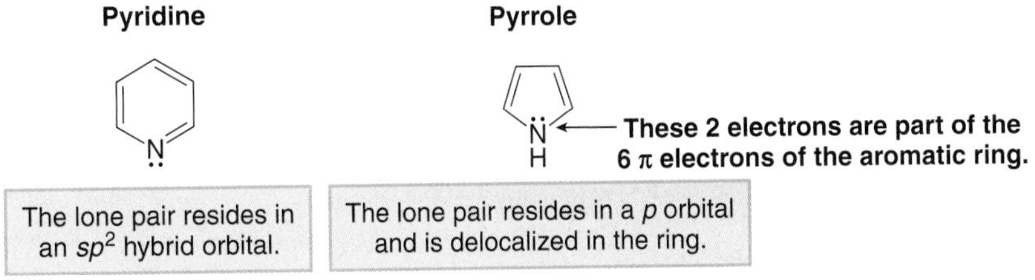

Protonation of pyrrole occurs at a ring carbon, not the N atom, as noted in Problem 17.50.

As a result, the pK_a of the conjugate acid of pyrrole is much less than that for the conjugate acid of pyridine.

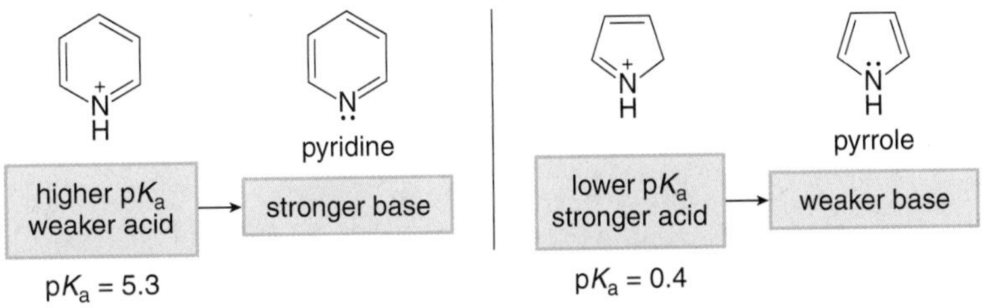

- **Pyrrole is much less basic than pyridine because its lone pair of electrons is part of the aromatic π system.**

25.10E Hybridization Effects

The effect of hybridization on the acidity of an H–A bond was first discussed in Section 2.5D.

The hybridization of the orbital that contains an amine's lone pair also affects its basicity. This is illustrated by comparing the basicity of **piperidine** and **pyridine,** two nitrogen heterocycles. The lone pair in piperidine resides in an sp^3 hybrid orbital that has 25% *s*-character. The lone pair in pyridine resides in an sp^2 hybrid orbital that has 33% *s*-character.

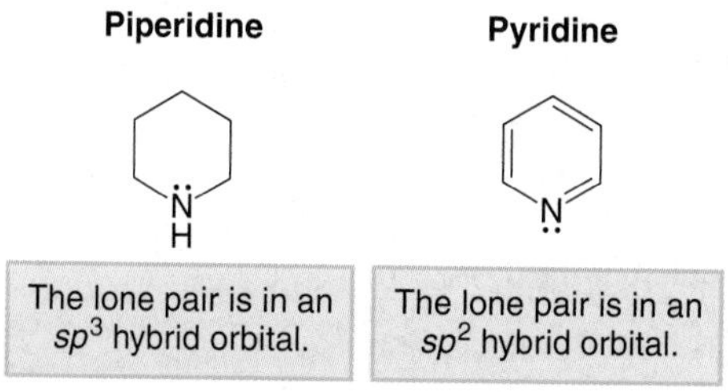
Piperidine
Pyridine
The lone pair is in an sp^3 hybrid orbital.
The lone pair is in an sp^2 hybrid orbital.

- **The higher the percent *s*-character of the orbital containing the lone pair, the more tightly the lone pair is held, and the weaker the base.**

Pyridine is a weaker base than piperidine because its nonbonded pair of electrons resides in an sp^2 hybrid orbital. Although pyridine is an aromatic amine, its lone pair is *not* part of the delocalized π system, so its basicity is determined by the hybridization of its N atom. As a result, the pK_a value for the conjugate acid of pyridine is much lower than that for the conjugate acid of piperidine, making pyridine the weaker base.

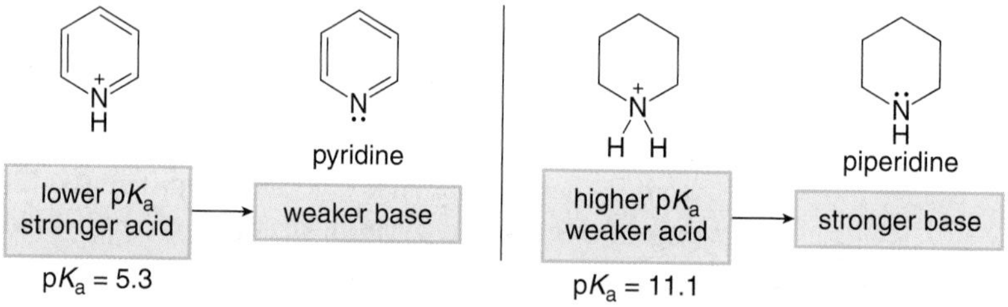
pyridine
lower pK_a
stronger acid
weaker base
pK_a = 5.3
piperidine
higher pK_a
weaker acid
stronger base
pK_a = 11.1

Problem 25.24 Which nitrogen atom in each compound is more basic?

a. 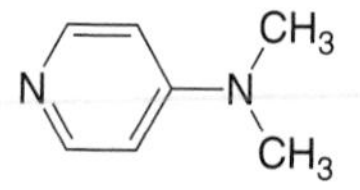
CH3
N
N
CH3

DMAP
4-(*N,N*-dimethylamino)pyridine

b. 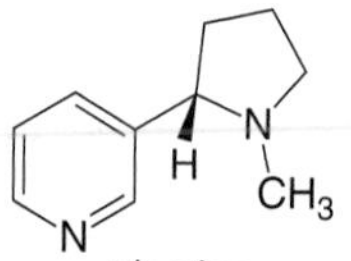
N
H
CH3
N

nicotine

25.10F Summary

Acid–base chemistry is central to many processes in organic chemistry, so it has been a constant theme throughout this text. Tables 25.2 and 25.3 organize and summarize the acid–base principles discussed in Section 25.10. The principles in these tables can be used to determine the most basic site in a molecule that has more than one nitrogen atom, as shown in Sample Problem 25.4.

Table 25.2 Factors That Determine Amine Basicity

Factor	Example
[1] **Inductive effects:** Electron-donating groups bonded to N increase basicity.	• RNH_2, R_2NH, and R_3N are more basic than NH_3.
[2] **Resonance effects:** Delocalizing the lone pair on N decreases basicity.	• Arylamines ($C_6H_5NH_2$) are less basic than alkylamines (RNH_2). • Amides ($RCONH_2$) are much less basic than amines (RNH_2).
[3] **Aromaticity:** Having the lone pair on N as part of the aromatic π system decreases basicity.	• Pyrrole is less basic than pyridine. 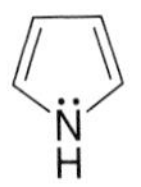 less basic 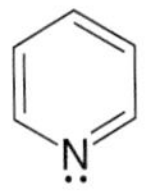 more basic
[4] **Hybridization effects:** Increasing the percent *s*-character in the orbital with the lone pair decreases basicity.	• Pyridine is less basic than piperidine. 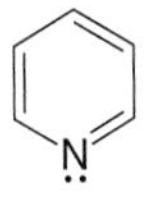 less basic 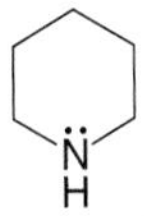 more basic

Table 25.3 Table of pK_a Values of Some Representative Organic Nitrogen Compounds

	Compound	pK_a of the conjugate acid	Comment
Ammonia	NH_3	9.3	
Alkylamines	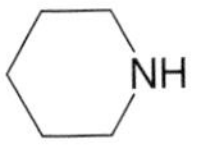	11.1	Alkylamines have pK_a values of ~10–11.
	$(CH_3CH_2)_2NH$	11.1	
	$(CH_3CH_2)_3N$	11.0	
	$CH_3CH_2NH_2$	10.8	
Arylamines	*p*-$CH_3OC_6H_4NH_2$	5.3	The pK_a *decreases* as the electron density of the benzene ring *decreases*.
	p-$CH_3C_6H_4NH_2$	5.1	
	$C_6H_5NH_2$	4.6	
	p-$NO_2C_6H_4NH_2$	1.0	
Heterocyclic aromatic amines	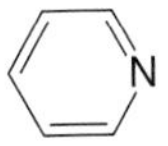	5.3	The pK_a depends on whether the lone pair on N is localized or delocalized.
	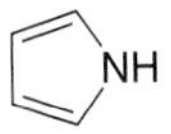	0.4	
Amides	$RCONH_2$	–1	

Sample Problem 25.4 Which N atom in chloroquine is the strongest base?

Since 1945 chloroquine has been used to treat malaria, an infectious disease caused by a protozoan parasite that is spread by the *Anopheles* mosquito.

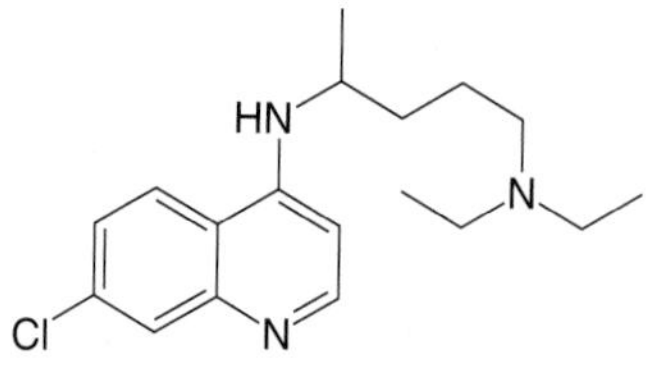

chloroquine

Solution

Examine the nitrogen atoms in chloroquine, labeled N1, N2, and N3, and recall that decreasing the electron density on N decreases basicity.

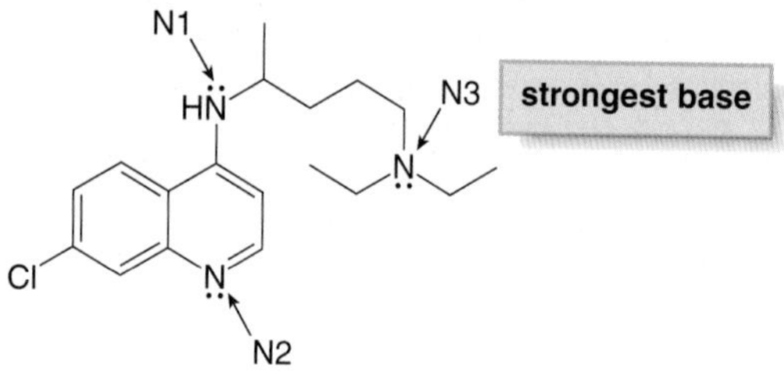

- N1 is bonded to an aromatic ring, so its lone pair is delocalized in the ring like aniline, decreasing basicity.
- The lone pair is localized on N2, but N2 is sp^2 hybridized. Increasing percent *s*-character decreases basicity.
- N3 has a localized lone pair and is sp^3 hybridized, making it the most basic site in the molecule.

Problem 25.25 Which N atom in each drug is more basic?

a. 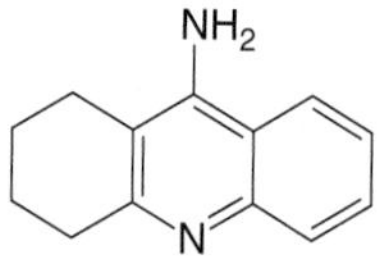

tacrine
drug used to treat
Alzheimer's disease

b. 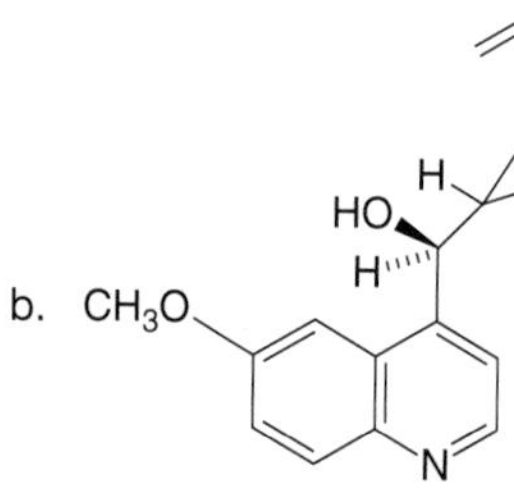

quinine
antimalarial drug

c. 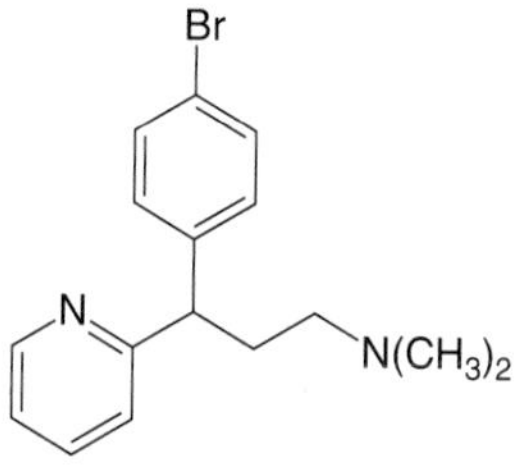

brompheniramine
antihistamine

25.11 Amines as Nucleophiles

Amines react as nucleophiles with electrophilic carbon atoms. The details of these reactions have been described in Chapters 21 and 22, so they are summarized here only to emphasize the similar role that the amine nitrogen plays.

- **Amines attack carbonyl groups to form products of nucleophilic addition or substitution.**

The nature of the product depends on the carbonyl electrophile. These reactions are limited to 1° and 2° amines, because only these compounds yield neutral organic products.

[1] Reaction of 1° and 2° amines with aldehydes and ketones (Sections 21.11–21.12)

Aldehydes and ketones react with 1° amines to form **imines** and with 2° amines to form **enamines.** Both reactions involve nucleophilic addition of the amine to the carbonyl group to form a carbinolamine, which then loses water to form the final product.

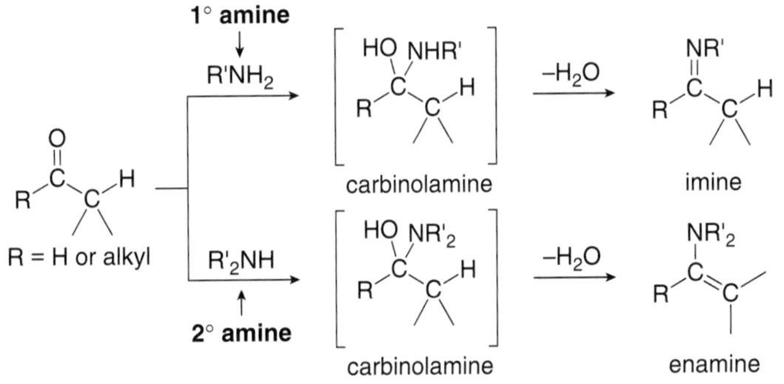

[2] Reaction of NH_3 and 1° and 2° amines with acid chlorides and anhydrides (Sections 22.8–22.9)

Acid chlorides and anhydrides react with NH_3, 1° amines, and 2° amines to form **1°, 2°, and 3° amides,** respectively. These reactions involve attack of the nitrogen nucleophile on the carbonyl group followed by elimination of a leaving group (Cl^- or $RCOO^-$). The overall result of this reaction is substitution of the leaving group by the nitrogen nucleophile.

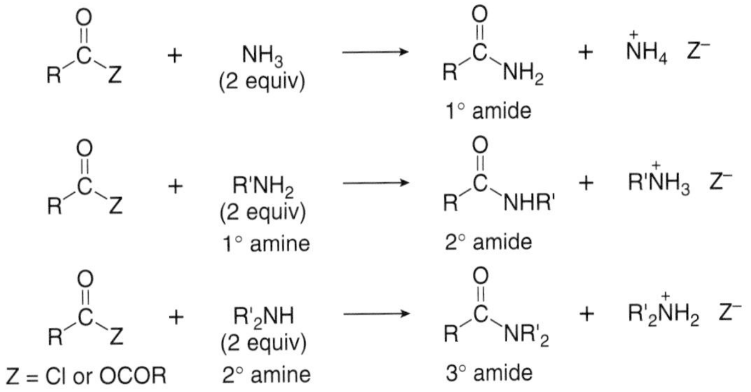

Problem 25.26 Draw the products formed when each carbonyl compound reacts with the following amines: [1] $CH_3CH_2CH_2NH_2$; [2] $(CH_3CH_2)_2NH$.

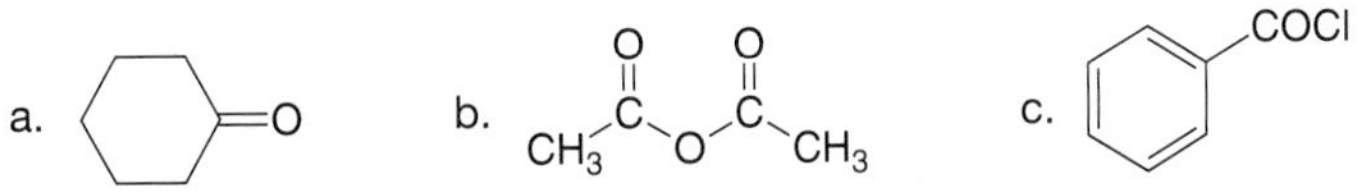

The conversion of amines to amides is useful in the synthesis of substituted anilines. For example, aniline itself does not undergo Friedel–Crafts reactions (Section 18.10B). Instead, its basic lone pair on N reacts with the Lewis acid ($AlCl_3$) to form a deactivated complex that does not undergo further reaction.

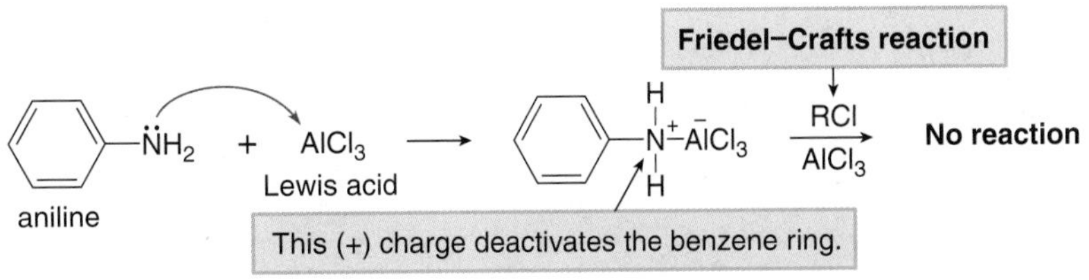

The N atom of an amide, however, is much less basic than the N atom of an amine, so it does not undergo a similar Lewis acid–base reaction with $AlCl_3$. A three-step reaction sequence involving an intermediate amide can thus be used to form the products of the Friedel–Crafts reaction.

[1] **Convert the amine (aniline) into an amide (acetanilide).**

[2] **Carry out the Friedel–Crafts reaction.**

[3] **Hydrolyze the amide** to generate the free amino group.

This three-step procedure is illustrated in Figure 25.10. In this way, **the amide serves as a protecting group for the NH_2 group,** in much the same way that *tert*-butyldimethylsilyl ethers and acetals are used to protect alcohols and carbonyls, respectively (Sections 20.12 and 21.15).

Problem 25.27 Devise a synthesis of each compound from aniline ($C_6H_5NH_2$).

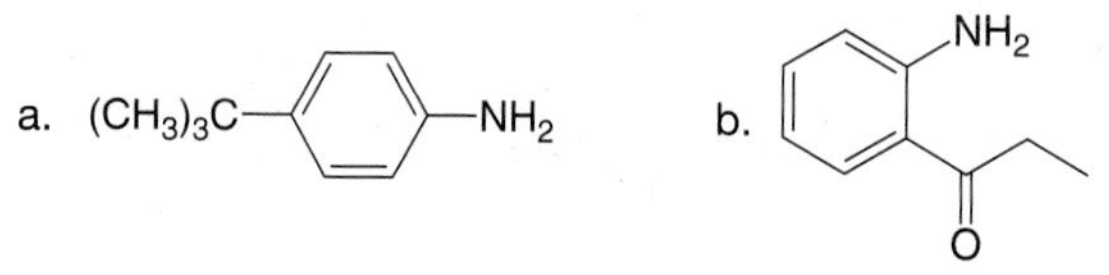

Figure 25.10 An amide as a protecting group for an amine

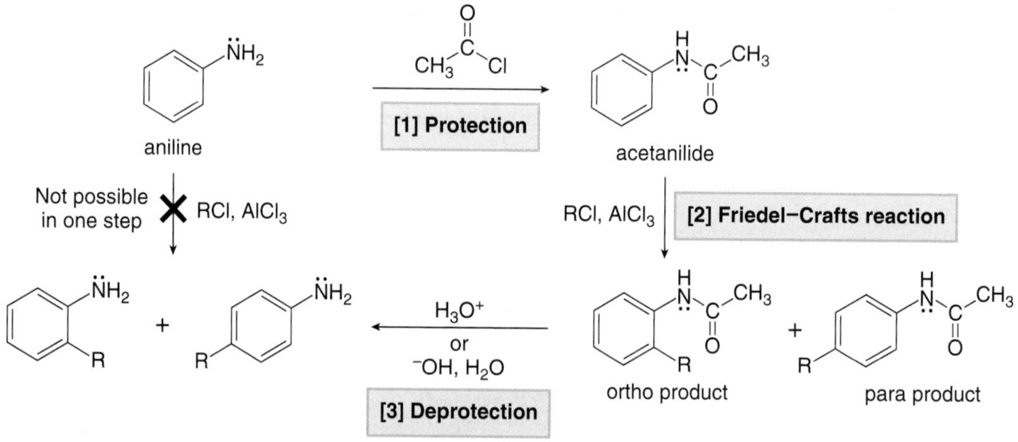

A three-step sequence uses an amide as a protecting group.

[1] Treatment of aniline with acetyl chloride (CH_3COCl) forms an amide (acetanilide).

[2] Acetanilide, having a much less basic N atom compared to aniline, undergoes electrophilic aromatic substitution under Friedel–Crafts conditions, forming a mixture of ortho and para products.

[3] Hydrolysis of the amide forms the Friedel–Crafts substitution products.

25.12 Hofmann Elimination

Amines, like alcohols, contain a poor leaving group. To undergo a β elimination reaction, for example, a 1° amine would need to lose the elements of NH_3 across two adjacent atoms. The leaving group, $^-NH_2$, is such a strong base, however, that this reaction does not occur.

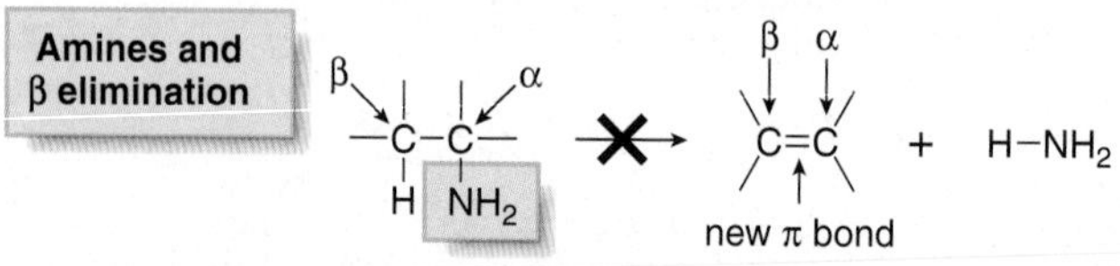

Problem: $^-NH_2$ is a poor leaving group.

The only way around this obstacle is to convert $^-NH_2$ into a better leaving group. The most common method to accomplish this is called a **Hofmann elimination,** which converts an amine into a quaternary ammonium salt prior to β elimination.

25.12A Details of the Hofmann Elimination

The **Hofmann elimination** converts an amine into an alkene.

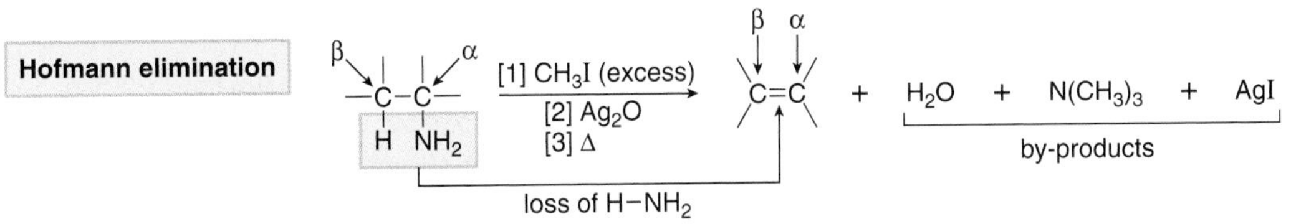
Hofmann elimination
β
α
H NH2
[1] CH3I (excess)
[2] Ag2O
[3] Δ
C=C
+ H2O + N(CH3)3 + AgI
by-products
loss of H–NH2

The Hofmann elimination consists of three steps, as shown for the conversion of propylamine to propene.

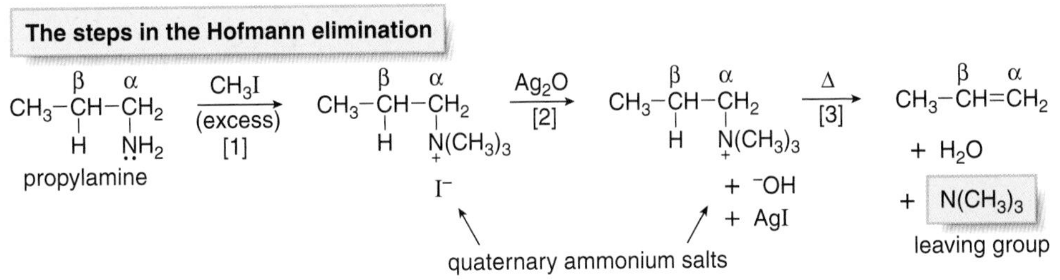
The steps in the Hofmann elimination
CH3–CH–CH2
H NH2
propylamine
CH3I
(excess)
[1]
N(CH3)3
I⁻
Ag2O
[2]
+ ⁻OH
+ AgI
Δ
[3]
CH3–CH=CH2
+ H2O
+ N(CH3)3
leaving group
quaternary ammonium salts

- In Step [1], the amine reacts as a nucleophile in an S_N2 reaction with excess CH_3I to form a quaternary ammonium salt. **The $N(CH_3)_3$ group thus formed is a much better leaving group than $^-NH_2$.**
- Step [2] converts one ammonium salt into another one with a different anion. The silver(I) oxide, Ag_2O, replaces the I^- anion with ^-OH, a strong base.
- When the ammonium salt is heated in Step [3], **^-OH removes a proton from the β carbon atom,** forming the new π bond of the alkene. The mechanism of elimination is **E2,** so:

> - **All bonds are broken and formed in a single step.**
> - **Elimination occurs through an anti periplanar geometry—that is, H and $N(CH_3)_3$ are oriented on opposite sides of the molecule.**

The general E2 mechanism for the Hofmann elimination is shown in Mechanism 25.1.

Mechanism 25.1 The E2 Mechanism for the Hofmann Elimination

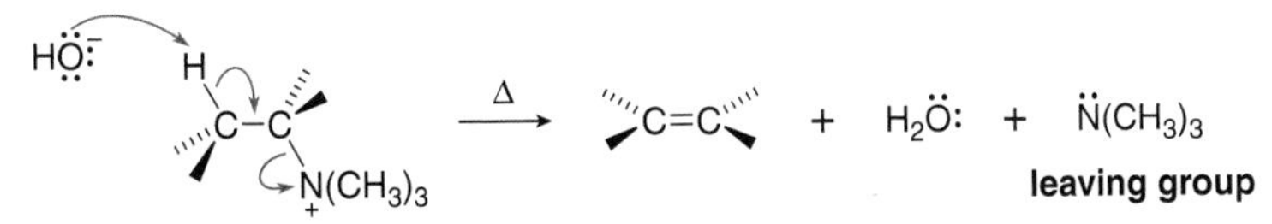
HÖ:⁻
H
N(CH3)3
Δ
C=C
+ H2Ö: + N(CH3)3
leaving group

anti periplanar arrangement of H and $N(CH_3)_3$

All Hofmann elimination reactions result in the formation of a new π bond between the α and β carbon atoms, as shown for cyclohexylamine and 2-phenylethylamine.

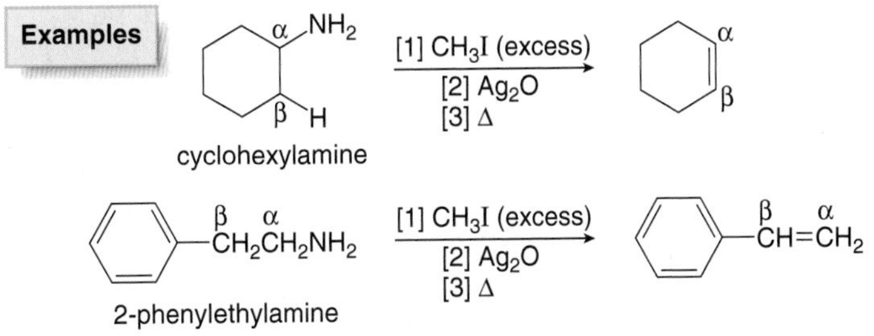
Examples
NH2
H
cyclohexylamine
[1] CH3I (excess)
[2] Ag2O
[3] Δ
CH2CH2NH2
2-phenylethylamine
CH=CH2

To help remember the reagents needed for the steps of the Hofmann elimination, keep in mind what happens in each step.

- **Step [1]** makes a good leaving group by forming a quaternary ammonium salt.
- **Step [2]** provides the strong base, ^{-}OH, needed for elimination.
- **Step [3]** is the E2 elimination that forms the new π bond.

Problem 25.28 Draw an energy diagram for the following reaction. Label the axes, the starting materials, E_a, and $\Delta H°$. Assume the reaction is exothermic. Draw a structure for the likely transition state.

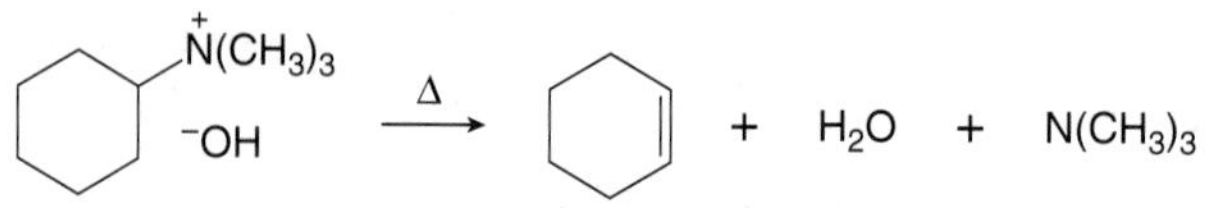

Problem 25.29 Draw the product formed by treating each compound with excess CH_3I, followed by Ag_2O, and then heat.

a. $CH_3CH_2CH_2CH_2{-}NH_2$ b. $(CH_3)_2CHNH_2$ c. 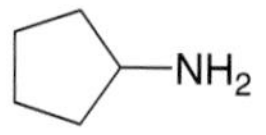

25.12B Regioselectivity of the Hofmann Elimination

There is one major difference between a Hofmann elimination and other E2 eliminations.

- **When constitutional isomers are possible, the major alkene has the *less* substituted double bond in a Hofmann elimination.**

For example, Hofmann elimination of the elements of H and $N(CH_3)_3$ from 2-methylcyclopentanamine yields two constitutional isomers: the disubstituted alkene **A** (the major product) and the trisubstituted alkene **B** (the minor product).

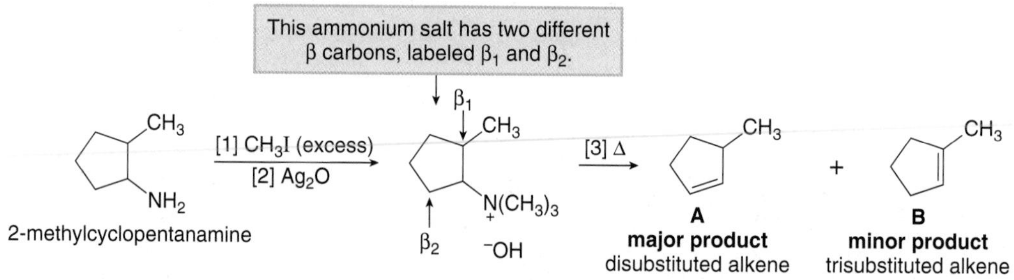

This regioselectivity distinguishes a Hofmann elimination from other E2 eliminations, which form the more substituted double bond by the Zaitsev rule (Section 8.5). This result is sometimes explained by the size of the leaving group, $N(CH_3)_3$. **In a Hofmann elimination, the base removes a proton from the less substituted, more accessible β carbon atom, because of the bulky leaving group on the nearby α carbon.**

Sample Problem 25.5 Draw the major product formed from Hofmann elimination of the following amine.

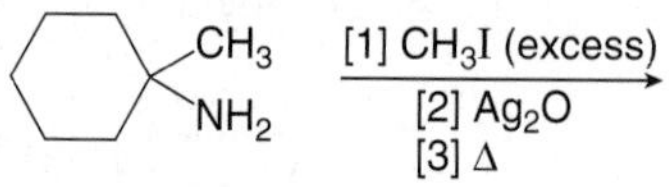

Solution

The amine has three β carbons but two of them are identical, so two alkenes are possible. Draw elimination products by forming alkenes having a C=C between the α and β carbons. The major product has the **less substituted double bond**—that is, the alkene with the C=C between the α and β_1 carbons in this example.

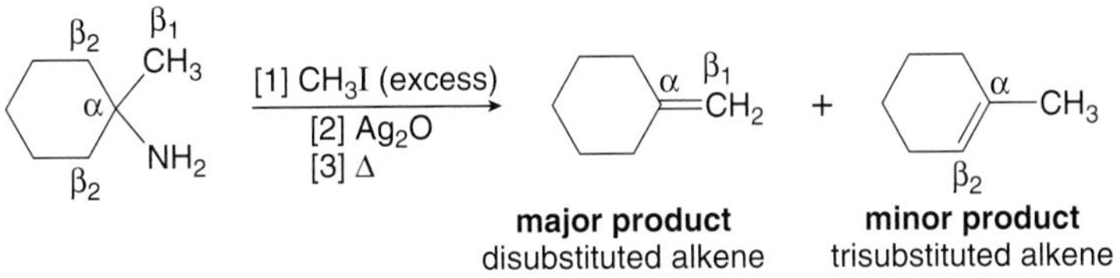

Figure 25.11 contrasts the products formed by E2 elimination reactions using an alkyl halide and an amine as starting materials. Treatment of the alkyl halide (2-bromopentane) with base forms the more substituted alkene as the major product, following the **Zaitsev rule.** In contrast, the three-step Hofmann sequence of an amine (2-pentanamine) forms the less substituted alkene as major product.

Figure 25.11
A comparison of E2 elimination reactions using alkyl halides and amines

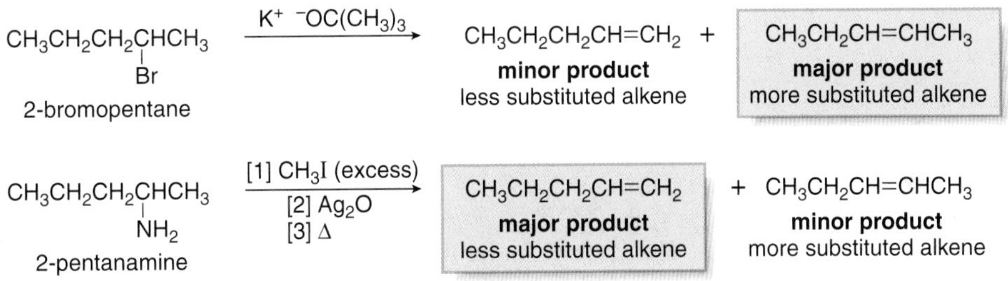

Problem 25.30 Draw the major product formed by treating each amine with excess CH_3I, followed by Ag_2O, and then heat.

a. 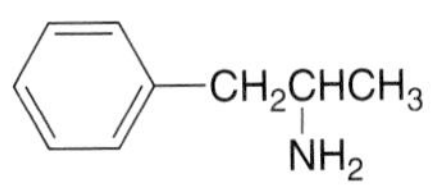

b. 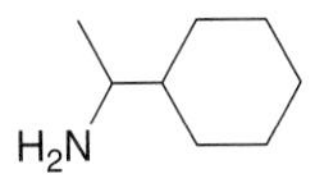

c. 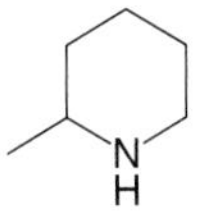

Problem 25.31 Draw the major product formed in each reaction.

a. 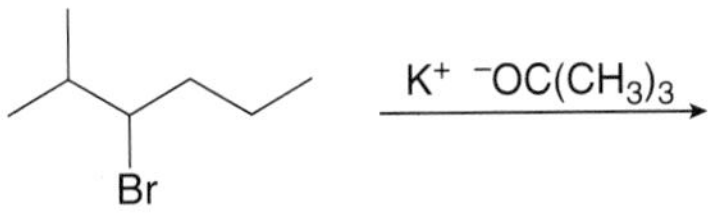

c. 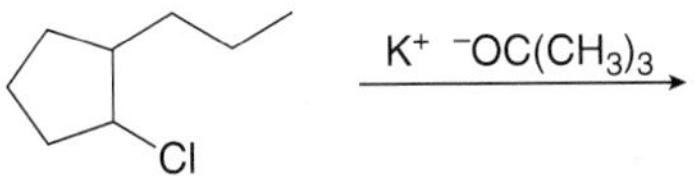

b. 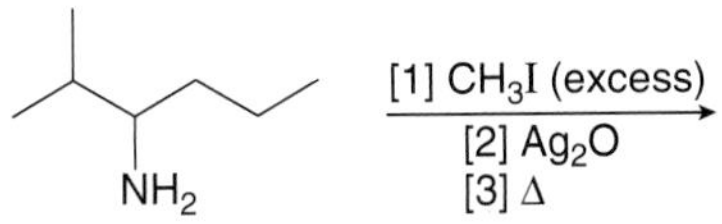

d. 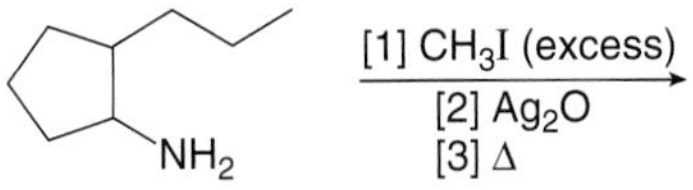

25.13 Reaction of Amines with Nitrous Acid

Nitrous acid, HNO_2, is a weak, unstable acid formed from $NaNO_2$ and a strong acid like HCl.

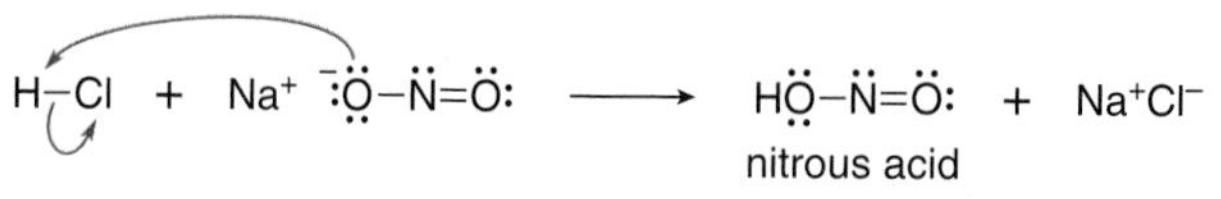

In the presence of acid, nitrous acid decomposes to **^+NO, the nitrosonium ion.** This electrophile then goes on to react with the nucleophilic nitrogen atom of amines to form **diazonium salts ($RN_2^+Cl^-$)** from 1° amines and ***N*-nitrosamines ($R_2NN=O$)** from 2° amines.

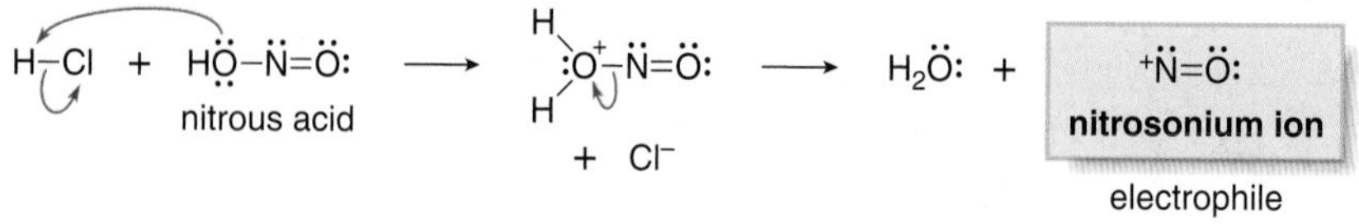

25.13A Reaction of ^+NO with 1° Amines

Nitrous acid reacts with 1° alkylamines and arylamines to form **diazonium salts.** This reaction is called **diazotization.**

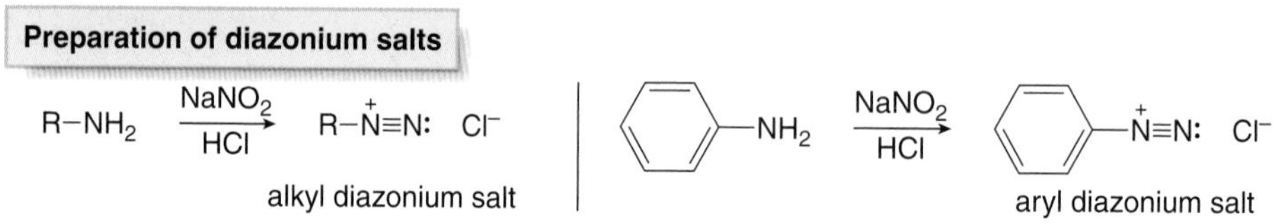

The mechanism for this reaction consists of many steps. It begins with nucleophilic attack of the amine on the nitrosonium ion, and it can conceptually be divided into two parts: formation of an ***N*-nitrosamine,** followed by loss of H_2O, as shown in Mechanism 25.2.

Mechanism 25.2 Formation of a Diazonium Salt from a 1° Amine

Part [1] Formation of an *N*-nitrosamine

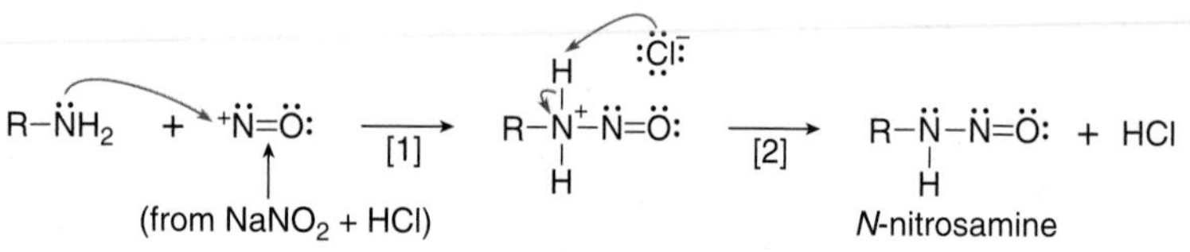

- In Part [1], the amine is converted to an ***N*-nitrosamine** by nucleophilic attack of the amino group on ^+NO, followed by loss of a proton.

Part [2] Loss of H_2O to form the diazonium salt

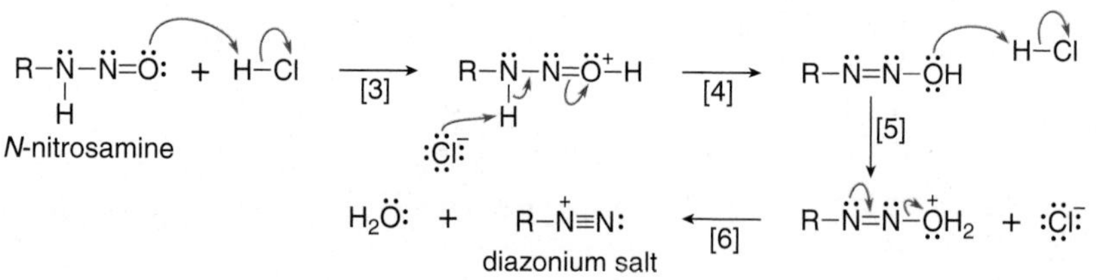

- In Part [2], three proton transfer reactions lead to loss of H_2O in Step [6] and formation of the diazonium ion.

Alkyl diazonium salts are generally not useful compounds. They readily decompose below room temperature to form carbocations with loss of N_2, a very good leaving group. These carbocations usually form a complex mixture of substitution, elimination, and rearrangement products.

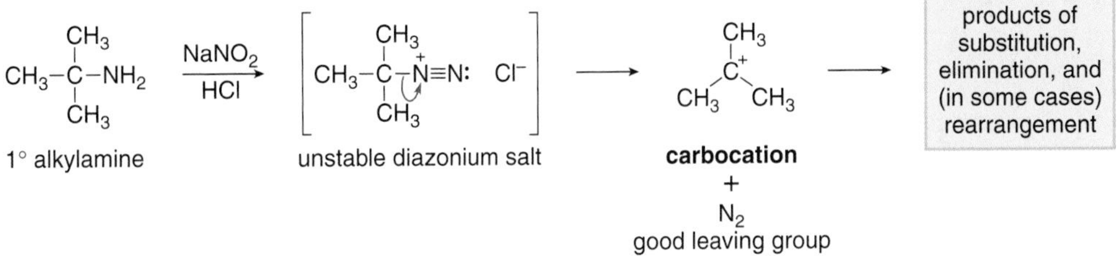

Care must be exercised in handling diazonium salts, because they can explode if allowed to dry.

On the other hand, **aryl diazonium salts are very useful synthetic intermediates.** Although they are rarely isolated and are generally unstable above 0 °C, they are useful starting materials in two general kinds of reactions described in Section 25.14.

25.13B Reaction of ^+NO with 2° Amines

Secondary alkylamines and arylamines react with nitrous acid to form *N*-nitrosamines.

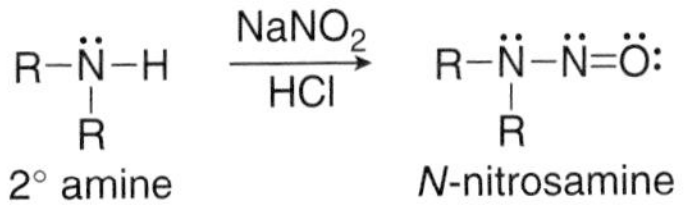

As mentioned in Section 7.16, many *N*-nitrosamines are potent carcinogens found in some food and tobacco smoke. Nitrosamines in food are formed in the same way they are formed in the laboratory: **reaction of a 2° amine with the nitrosonium ion,** formed from nitrous acid (HNO_2). Mechanism 25.3 is shown for the conversion of dimethylamine [$(CH_3)_2NH$] to *N*-nitrosodimethylamine [$(CH_3)_2NN{=}O$].

Mechanism 25.3 Formation of an *N*-Nitrosamine from a 2° Amine

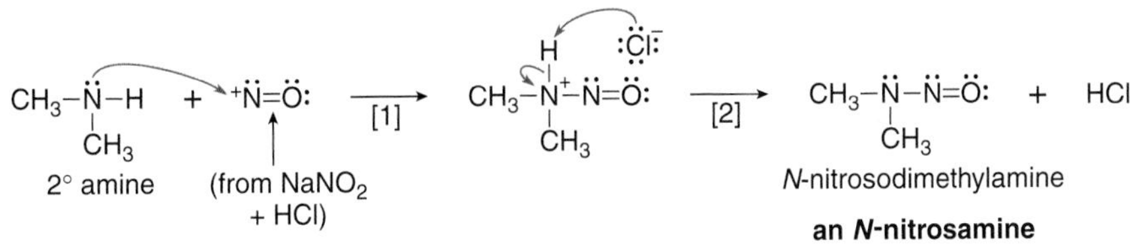

- The amine is converted to an ***N*-nitrosamine** by nucleophilic attack of the amino group on ^+NO, followed by loss of a proton.

Problem 25.32 Draw the product formed when each compound is treated with $NaNO_2$ and HCl.

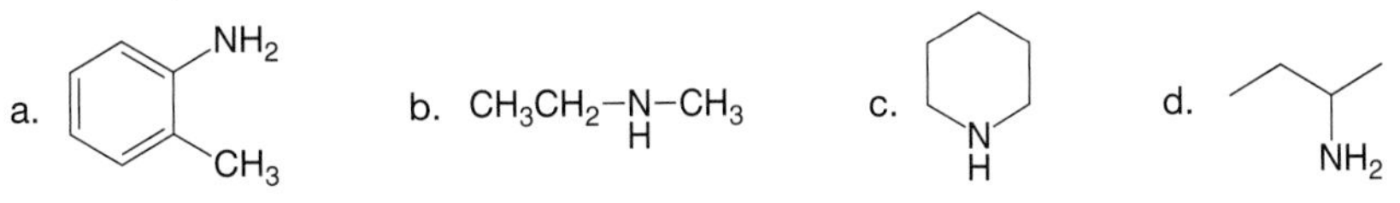

25.14 Substitution Reactions of Aryl Diazonium Salts

Aryl diazonium salts undergo two general reactions.

- **Substitution** of N_2 by an atom or a group of atoms Z forms a variety of substituted benzenes.

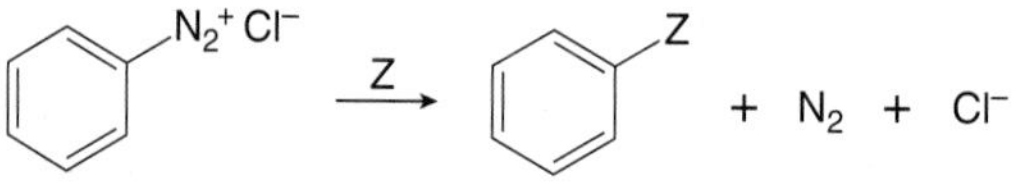

- **Coupling** of a diazonium salt with another benzene derivative forms an **azo compound,** a compound containing a nitrogen–nitrogen double bond.

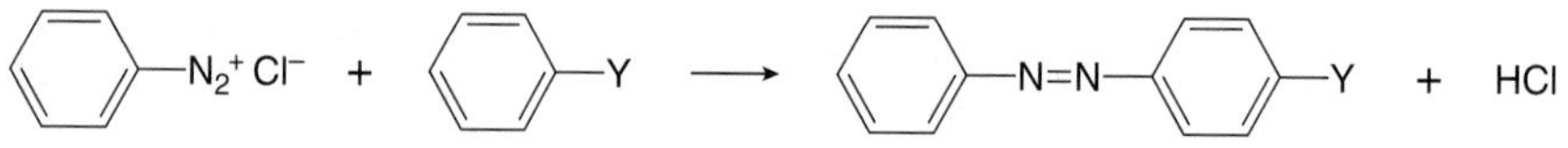

azo compound

Y = NH_2, NHR, NR_2, OH (a strong electron-donor group)

25.14A Specific Substitution Reactions

Aryl diazonium salts react with a variety of reagents to form products in which Z (an atom or group of atoms) replaces N_2, a very good leaving group. The mechanism of these reactions varies with the identity of Z, so we will concentrate on the products of the reactions, not the mechanisms.

General substitution reaction

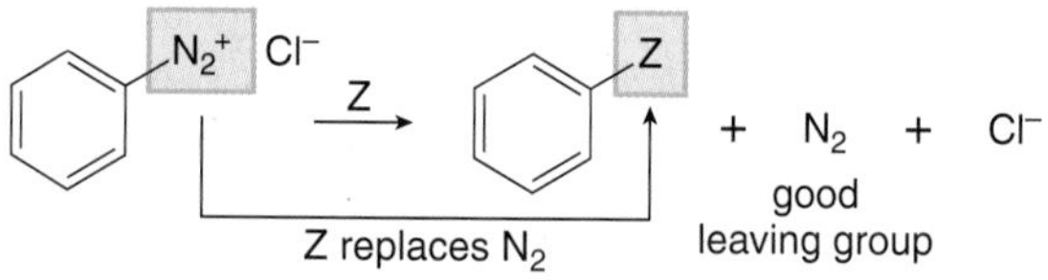

[1] Substitution by OH—Synthesis of phenols

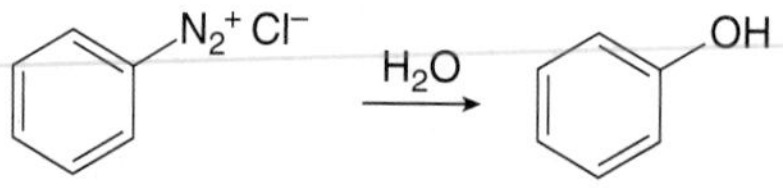

phenol

A diazonium salt reacts with H_2O to form a **phenol.**

[2] Substitution by Cl or Br—Synthesis of aryl chlorides and bromides

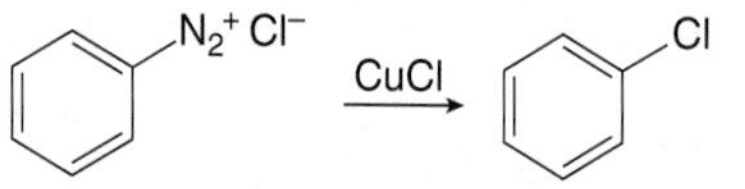

aryl chloride

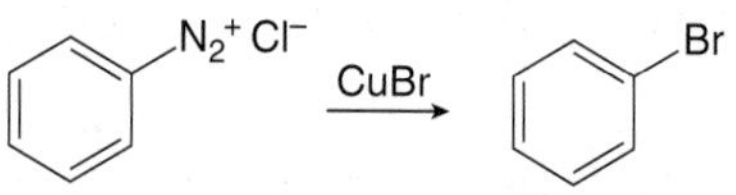

aryl bromide

A diazonium salt reacts with copper(I) chloride or copper(I) bromide to form an **aryl chloride** or **aryl bromide,** respectively. This is called the **Sandmeyer reaction.** It provides an alternative to direct chlorination and bromination of an aromatic ring using Cl_2 or Br_2 and a Lewis acid catalyst.

[3] Substitution by F—Synthesis of aryl fluorides

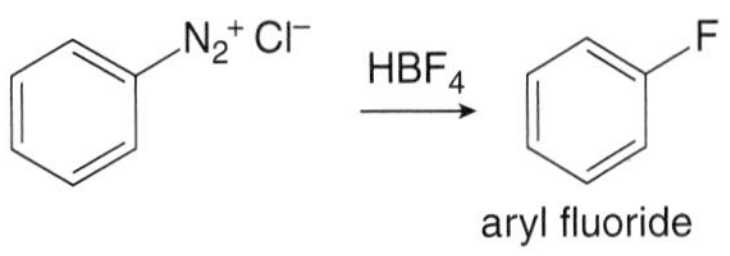

A diazonium salt reacts with fluoroboric acid (HBF_4) to form an **aryl fluoride.** This is a useful reaction because aryl fluorides cannot be produced by direct fluorination with F_2 and a Lewis acid catalyst, as F_2 reacts too violently (Section 18.3).

[4] Substitution by I—Synthesis of aryl iodides

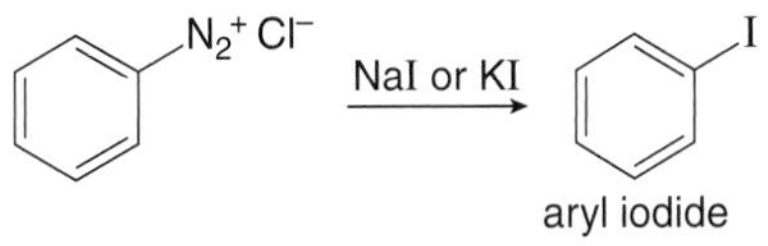

A diazonium salt reacts with sodium or potassium iodide to form an aryl iodide. This, too, is a useful reaction because aryl iodides cannot be produced by direct iodination with I_2 and a Lewis acid catalyst, as I_2 reacts too slowly (Section 18.3).

[5] Substitution by CN—Synthesis of benzonitriles

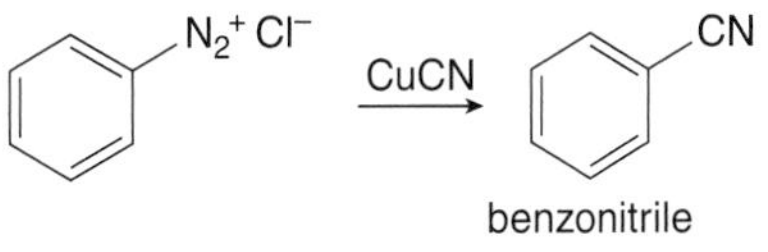

A diazonium salt reacts with copper(I) cyanide to form a benzonitrile. Because a cyano group can be hydrolyzed to a carboxylic acid, reduced to an amine or aldehyde, or converted to a ketone with organometallic reagents, this reaction provides easy access to a wide variety of benzene derivatives using chemistry described in Section 22.18.

[6] Substitution by H—Synthesis of benzene

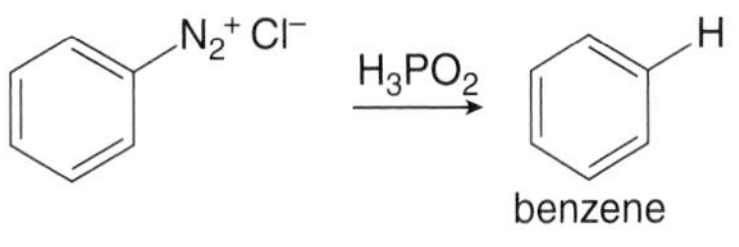

A diazonium salt reacts with hypophosphorus acid (H_3PO_2) to form benzene. This reaction has limited utility because it reduces the functionality of the benzene ring by replacing N_2 with a hydrogen atom. Nonetheless, this reaction *is* useful in synthesizing compounds that have substitution patterns that are not available by other means.

For example, it is not possible to synthesize 1,3,5-tribromobenzene from benzene by direct bromination. Because Br is an ortho, para director, bromination with Br_2 and $FeBr_3$ will not add Br substituents meta to each other on the ring.

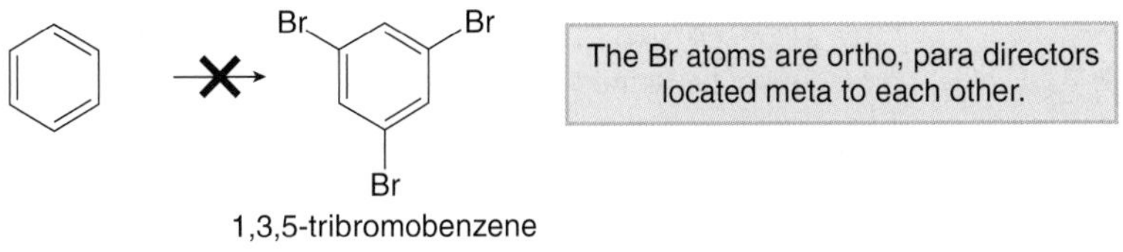

It is possible, however, to add three Br atoms meta to each other when aniline is the starting material. Because an NH_2 group is a very powerful ortho, para director, three Br atoms are introduced in a single step on halogenation (Section 18.10A). Then, the NH_2 group can be removed by diazotization and reaction with H_3PO_2.

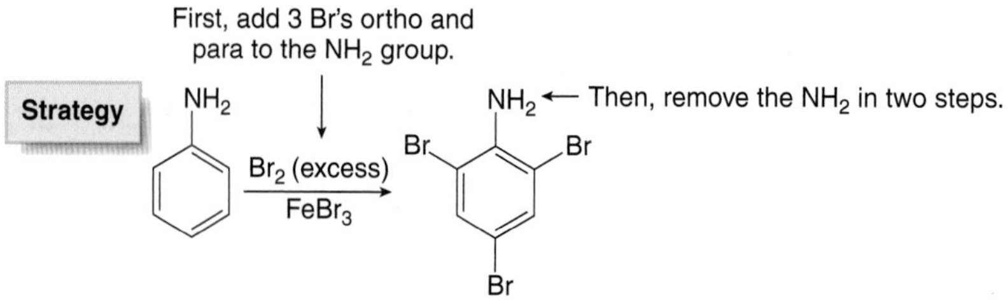

The complete synthesis of 1,3,5-tribromobenzene from benzene is outlined in Figure 25.12.

Figure 25.12 The synthesis of 1,3,5-tribromobenzene from benzene

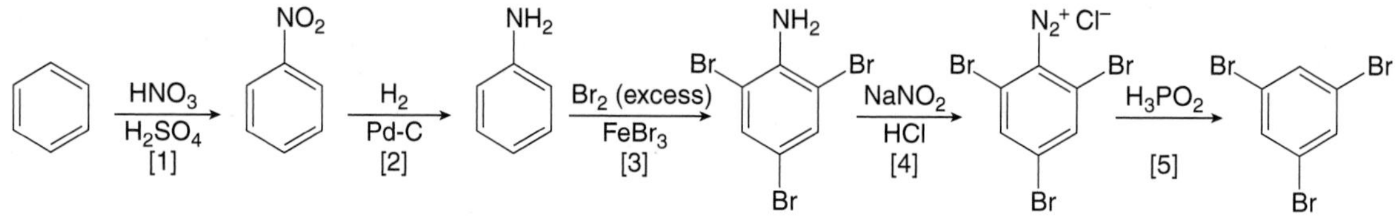

- Nitration followed by reduction forms aniline ($C_6H_5NH_2$) from benzene (Steps [1] and [2]).
- Bromination of aniline yields the tribromo derivative in Step [3].
- The NH_2 group is removed by a two-step process: diazotization with $NaNO_2$ and HCl (Step [4]), followed by substitution of the diazonium ion by H with H_3PO_2.

25.14B Using Diazonium Salts in Synthesis

Diazonium salts provide easy access to many different benzene derivatives. Keep in mind the following four-step sequence, because it will be used to synthesize many substituted benzenes.

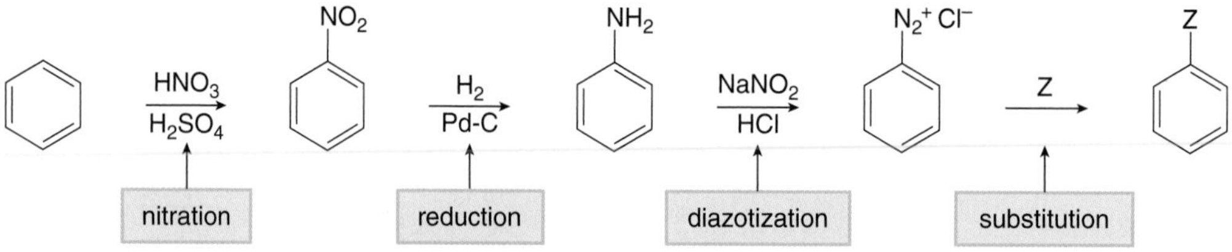

Sample Problems 25.6 and 25.7 apply these principles to two different multistep syntheses.

Sample Problem 25.6 Synthesize *m*-chlorophenol from benzene.

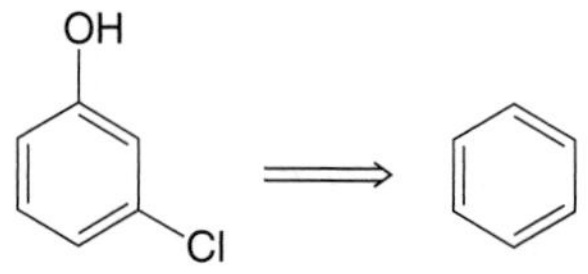

Solution

Both OH and Cl are ortho, para directors, but they are located meta to each other. The OH group must be formed from a diazonium salt, which can be made from an NO_2 group by a stepwise method.

Retrosynthetic Analysis

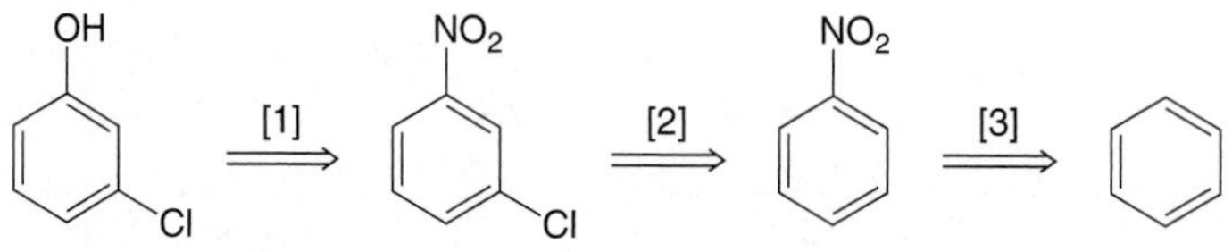

Working backwards:

- [1] Form the OH group from NO_2 by a three-step procedure using a diazonium salt.
- [2] Introduce Cl meta to NO_2 by halogenation.
- [3] Add the NO_2 group by nitration.

Synthesis

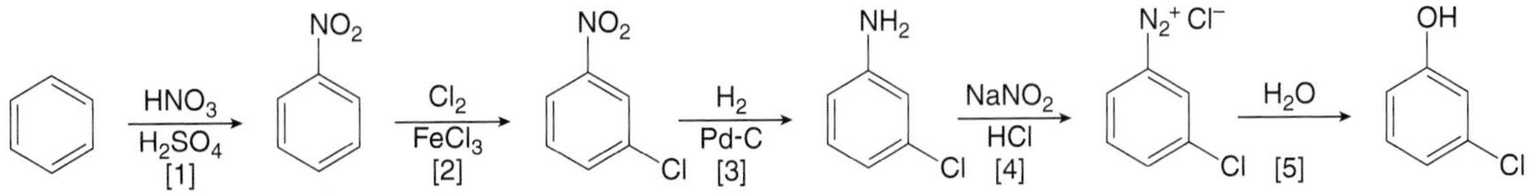

- Nitration followed by chlorination meta to the NO_2 group forms the meta disubstituted benzene (Steps [1]–[2]).
- Reduction of the nitro group followed by diazotization forms the diazonium salt in Step [4], which is then converted to the desired phenol by treatment with H_2O (Step [5]).

Sample Problem 25.7

Synthesize *p*-bromobenzaldehyde from benzene.

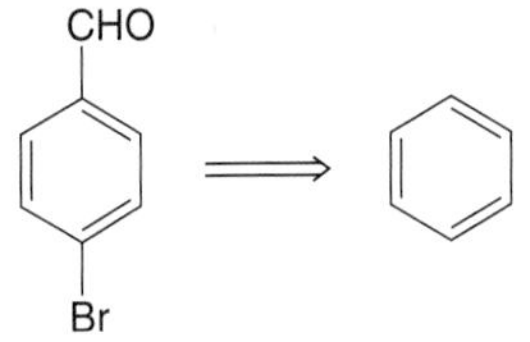

Solution

Because the two groups are located para to each other and Br is an ortho, para director, Br should be added to the ring first. To add the CHO group, recall that it can be formed from CN by reduction.

Retrosynthetic Analysis

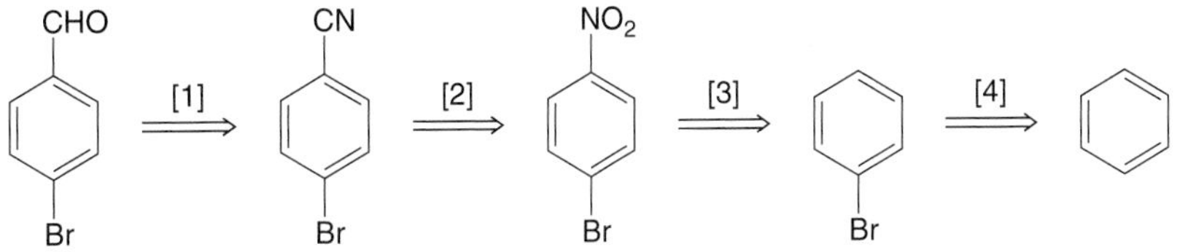

Working backwards:

- [1] Form the CHO group by reduction of CN.
- [2] Prepare the CN group from an NO_2 group by a three-step sequence using a diazonium salt.
- [3] Introduce the NO_2 group by nitration, para to the Br atom.
- [4] Introduce Br by bromination with Br_2 and $FeBr_3$.

Synthesis

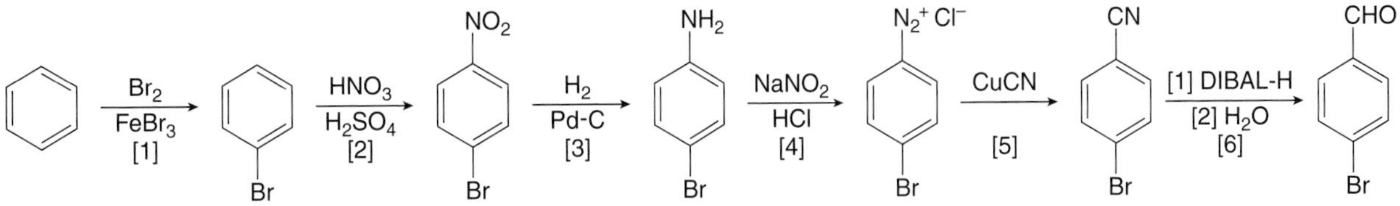

- Bromination followed by nitration forms a disubstituted benzene with two para substituents (Steps [1]–[2]), which can be separated from its undesired ortho isomer.
- Reduction of the NO_2 group followed by diazotization forms the diazonium salt in Step [4], which is converted to a nitrile by reaction with CuCN (Step [5]).
- Reduction of the CN group with DIBAL-H (a mild reducing agent) forms the CHO group and completes the synthesis.

Problem 25.33 Draw the product formed in each reaction.

a. 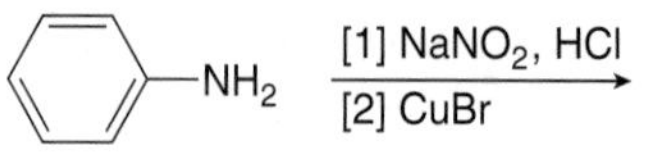

NH2
[1] NaNO2, HCl
[2] CuBr

c. 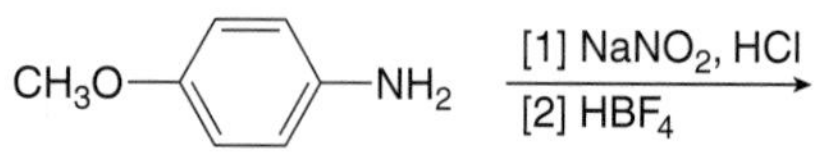

CH3O
NH2
[1] NaNO2, HCl
[2] HBF4

b. 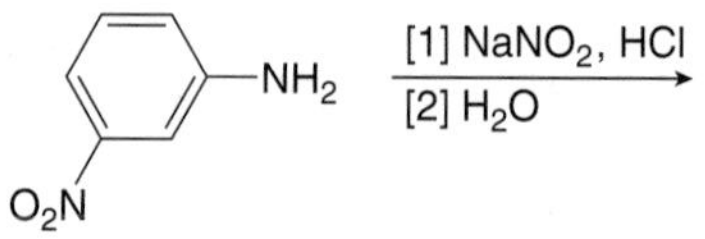

NH2
O2N
[1] NaNO2, HCl
[2] H2O

d. 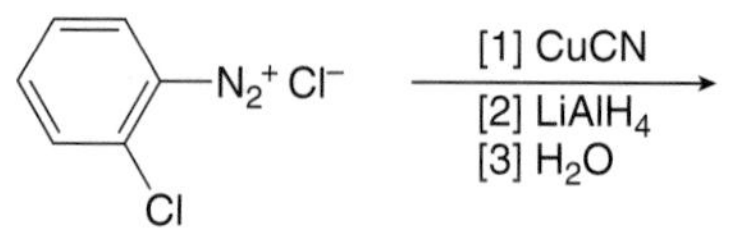

N2+ Cl−
Cl
[1] CuCN
[2] LiAlH4
[3] H2O

Problem 25.34 Devise a synthesis of each compound from benzene.

a. 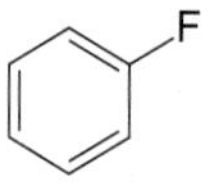

F

b. 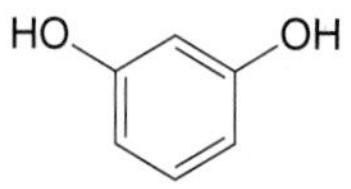

HO
OH

c. 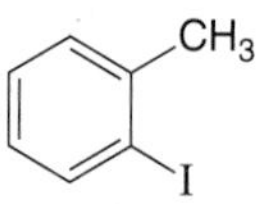

CH3
I

d. 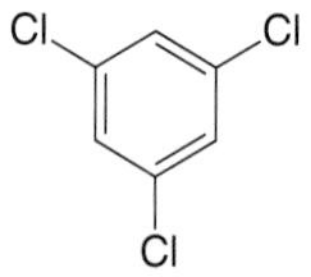

Cl
Cl
Cl

25.15 Coupling Reactions of Aryl Diazonium Salts

The second general reaction of diazonium salts is **coupling.** When a diazonium salt is treated with an aromatic compound that contains a strong electron-donor group, the two rings join together to form an **azo compound,** a compound with a nitrogen–nitrogen double bond.

Azo coupling

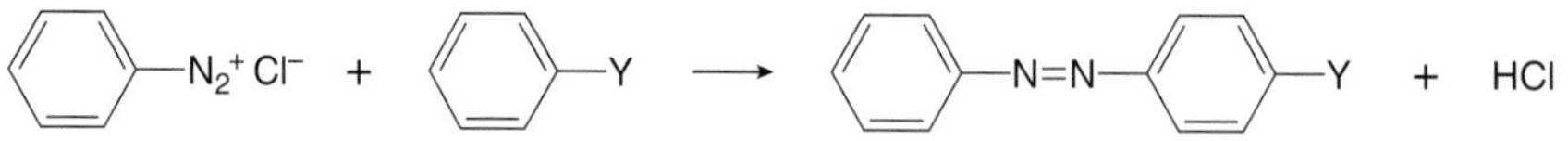

N2+ Cl−
+
Y
N=N
Y
+ HCl

Y = NH_2, NHR, NR_2, OH (a strong electron-donor group)

azo compound

Synthetic dyes are described in more detail in Section 25.16.

Azo compounds are highly conjugated, rendering them colored (Section 16.15). Many of these compounds, such as the azo compound "butter yellow," are synthetic dyes. Butter yellow was once used to color margarine.

Example

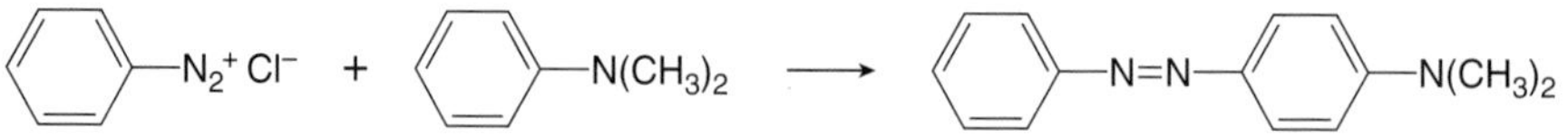

N2+ Cl−
+
N(CH3)2
N=N
N(CH3)2

a yellow azo dye "butter yellow"

This reaction is another example of **electrophilic aromatic substitution,** with the **diazonium salt acting as the electrophile.** Like all electrophilic substitutions (Section 18.2), the mechanism has two steps: addition of the electrophile (the diazonium ion) to form a resonance-stabilized carbocation, followed by deprotonation, as shown in Mechanism 25.4.

Mechanism 25.4 Azo Coupling

Step [1] Addition of the diazonium ion to form a carbocation

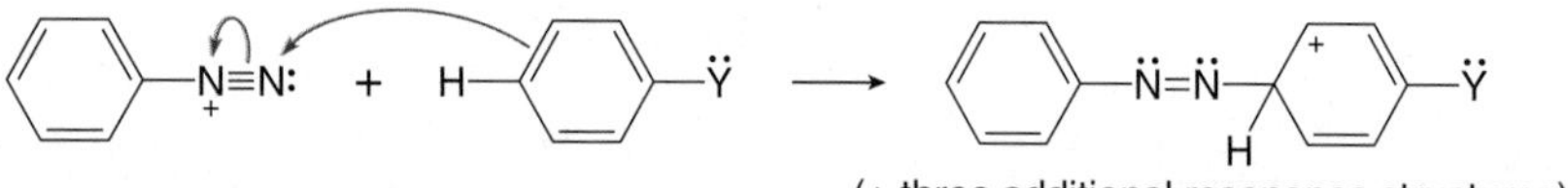

N≡N:
+
H
Y
N=N
H
Y

(+ three additional resonance structures) resonance-stabilized carbocation

- The electrophilic diazonium ion reacts with the electron-rich benzene ring to form a resonance-stabilized carbocation in Step [1]. (Only one resonance structure is drawn.)

Step [2] Loss of a proton to re-form the aromatic ring

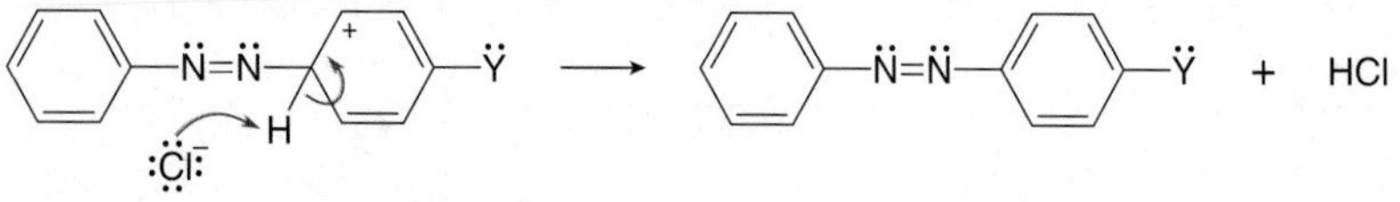

N=N
Y
H
:Cl:−
N=N
Y
+ HCl

- Loss of a proton regenerates the aromatic ring.

Because a diazonium salt is weakly electrophilic, the reaction occurs only when the benzene ring has **a strong electron-donor group Y, where Y = NH_2, NHR, NR_2, or OH.** Although these groups activate both the ortho and para positions, para substitution occurs unless the para position already has another substituent present.

To determine what starting materials are needed to synthesize a particular azo compound, always divide the molecule into two components: **one has a benzene ring with a diazonium ion, and one has a benzene ring with a very strong electron-donor group.**

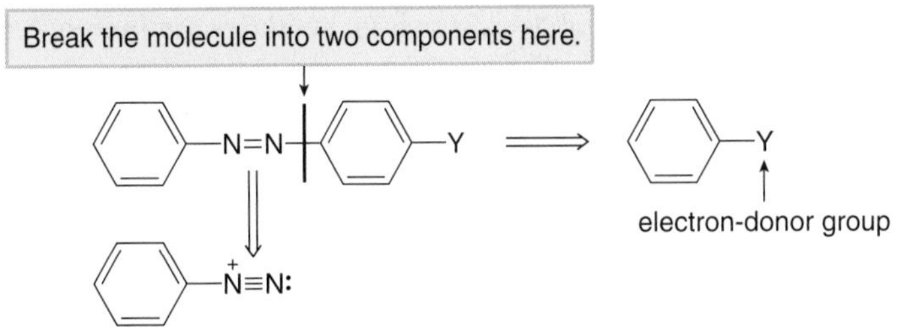

Sample Problem 25.8 What starting materials are needed to synthesize the following azo compound?

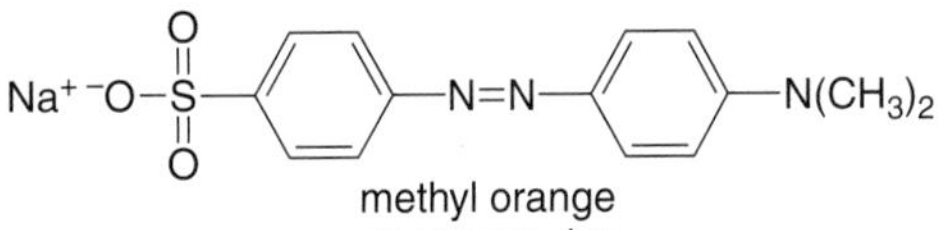

methyl orange
an orange dye

Solution

Both benzene rings in methyl orange have a substituent, but only one group, $N(CH_3)_2$, is a strong electron donor. In determining the two starting materials, the **diazonium ion must be bonded to the ring that is *not* bonded to $N(CH_3)_2$.**

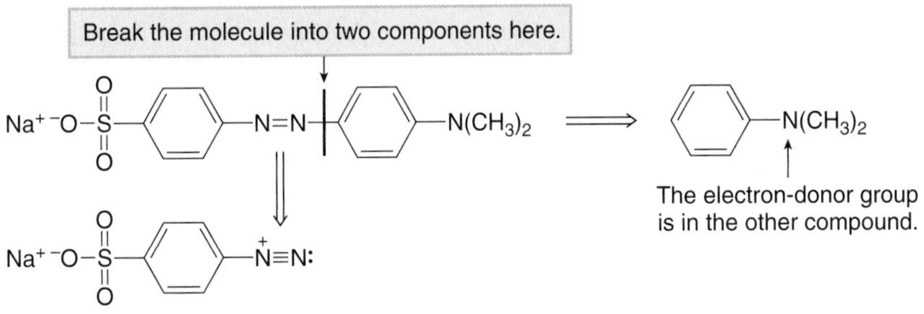

Problem 25.35 Draw the product formed when $C_6H_5N_2^+Cl^-$ reacts with each compound.

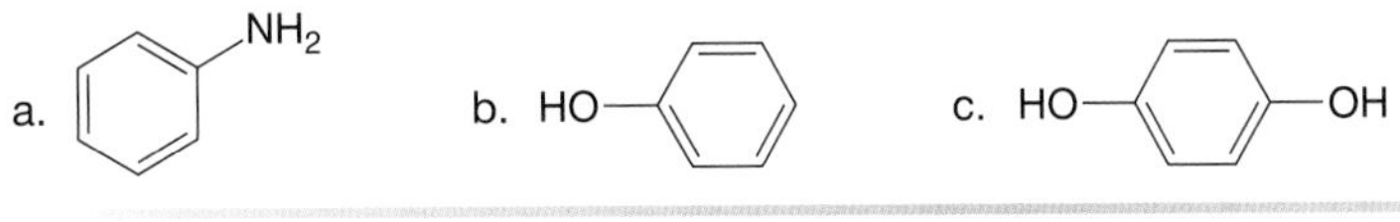

Problem 25.36 What starting materials are needed to synthesize each azo compound?

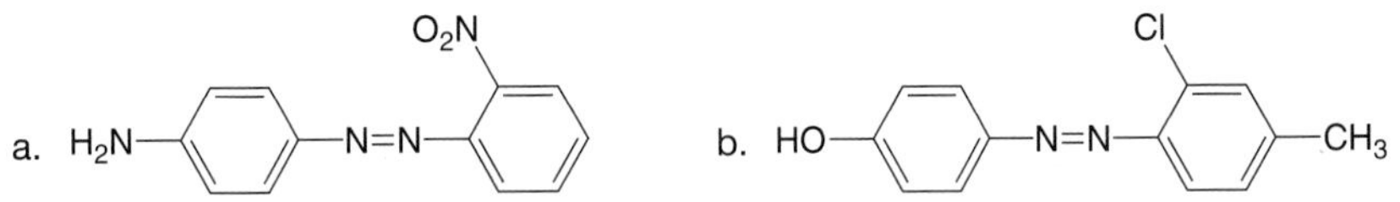

25.16 Application: Synthetic Dyes

Azo compounds have two important applications: as dyes and as sulfa drugs, the first synthetic antibiotics (Section 25.17).

25.16A Natural and Synthetic Dyes

Until 1856, all dyes were natural in origin, obtained from plants, animals, or minerals. Three natural dyes known for centuries are **indigo, tyrian purple,** and **alizarin.**

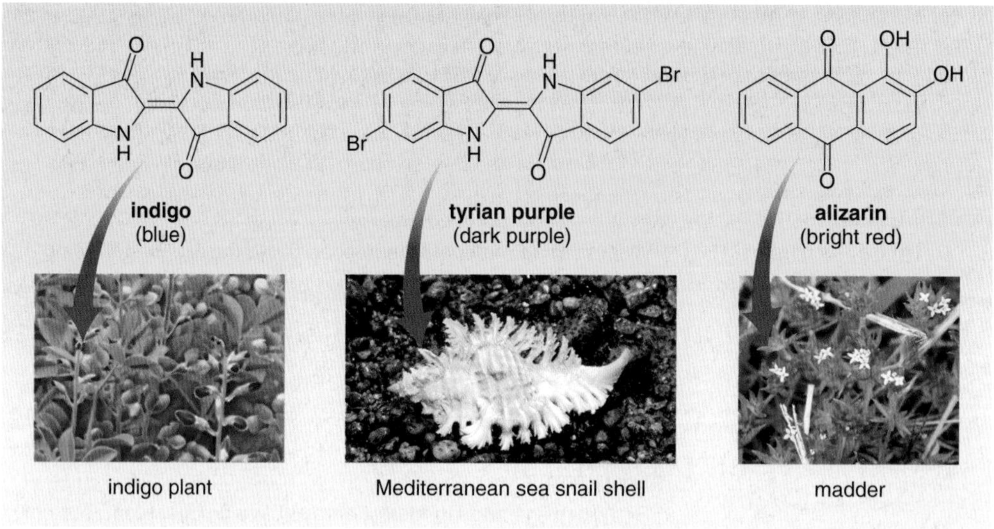

The blue dye **indigo,** derived from the plant *Indigofera tinctoria,* has been used in India for thousands of years. Traders introduced it to the Mediterranean area and then to Europe. **Tyrian purple,** a natural dark purple dye obtained from the mucous gland of a Mediterranean snail of the genus *Murex,* was a symbol of royalty before the collapse of the Roman empire. **Alizarin,** a bright red dye obtained from madder root (*Rubia tinctorum*), a plant native to India and northeastern Asia, has been found in cloth entombed with Egyptian mummies.

A purple shawl dyed with Perkin's mauveine

Because all three of these dyes were derived from natural sources, they were difficult to obtain, making them expensive and available only to the privileged. This all changed when William Henry Perkin, an 18-year-old student with a makeshift home laboratory, serendipitously prepared a purple dye, which would later be called mauveine, during his failed attempt to synthesize the antimalarial drug quinine. Mauveine is a mixture of two compounds that differ in the presence of only one methyl group on one of the aromatic rings.

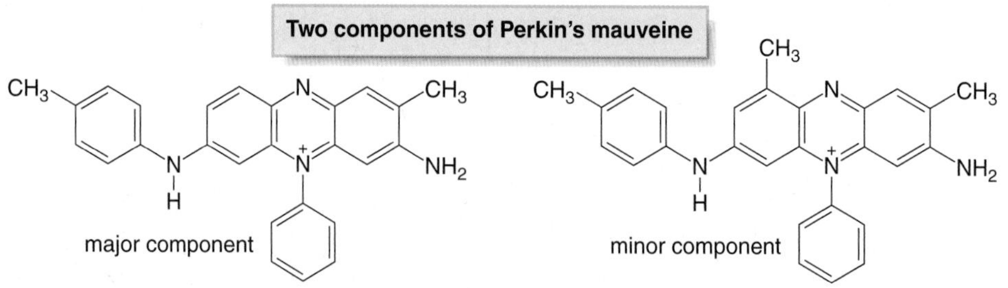

Perkin's discovery marked the beginning of the chemical industry. He patented the dye and went on to build a factory to commercially produce it on a large scale. This event began the surge of research in organic chemistry, not just in the synthesis of dyes, but in the production of perfumes, anesthetics, inks, and drugs as well. Perkin was a wealthy man when he retired at the age of 36 to devote the rest of his life to basic chemical research. The most prestigious award given by the American Chemical Society is named the Perkin Medal in his honor.

Many common synthetic dyes, such as alizarine yellow R, para red, and Congo red, are **azo compounds,** prepared by the diazonium coupling reaction described in Section 25.15.

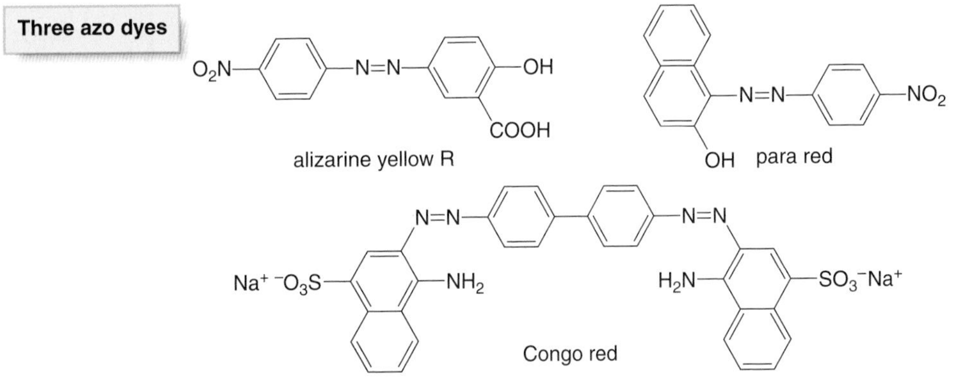

Although natural and synthetic dyes are quite varied in structure, **all of them are colored because they are highly conjugated.** A molecule with eight or more π bonds in conjugation absorbs light in the visible region of the electromagnetic spectrum (Section 16.15A), taking on the color from the visible spectrum that it does *not* absorb.

Problem 25.37 (a) What two components are needed to prepare para red by azo coupling? (b) What two components are needed to prepare alizarine yellow R?

25.16B How Dyes Bind to Fabric

To be classified as a dye, a compound must be colored *and* it must bind to fabric. There are many ways for this binding to occur. Compounds that bind to fabric by some type of attractive forces are called **direct dyes.** These attractive forces may involve electrostatic interactions, van der Waals forces, hydrogen bonding, or sometimes, even covalent bonding. The type of interaction depends on the structure of the dye and the fiber. Thus, a compound that is good for dyeing wool or silk, both polyamides, may be poor for dyeing cotton, a carbohydrate (Figure 22.4).

Wool and silk contain charged functional groups, such as NH_3^+ and COO^-. Because of this, they bind to ionic dyes by electrostatic interactions. For example, positively charged NH_3^+ groups bonded to the protein backbone are electrostatically attracted to anionic groups in a dye like methyl orange.

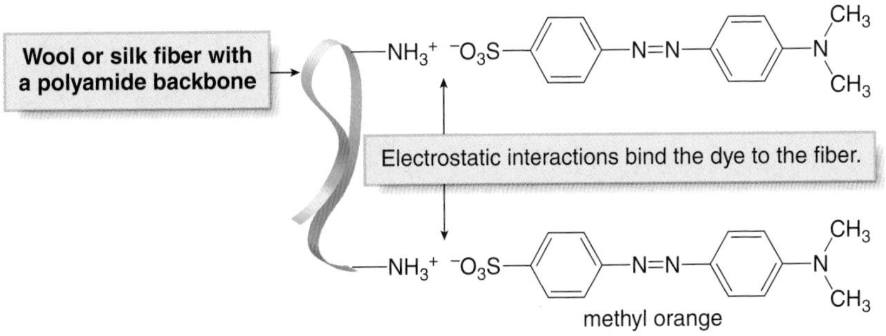

Cotton, on the other hand, binds dyes by hydrogen bonding interactions with its many OH groups. Thus, Congo red is bound to the cellulose backbone by hydrogen bonds.

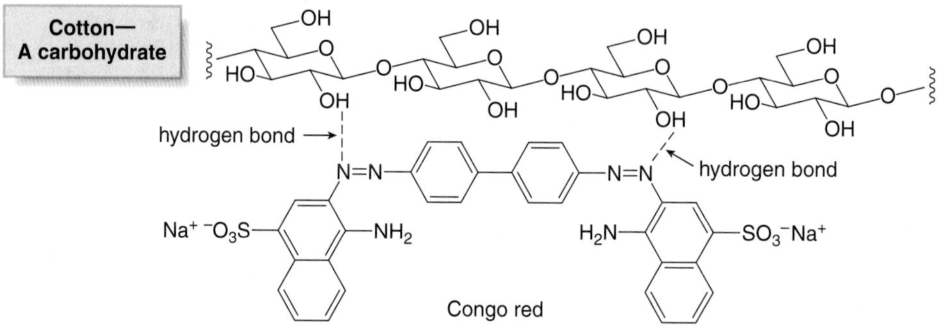

Problem 25.38 Explain why Dacron, a polyester first discussed in Section 22.16B, does not bind well with an anionic dye such as methyl orange.

25.17 Application: Sulfa Drugs

Although they may seem quite unrelated, the synthesis of colored dyes led to the development of the first synthetic antibiotics. Much of the early effort in this field was done by the German chemist Paul Ehrlich, who worked with synthetic dyes and used them to stain tissues. This led him on a search for dyes that were lethal to bacteria without affecting other tissue cells, hoping that these dyes could treat bacterial infections. For many years this effort was unsuccessful.

Then, in 1935, Gerhard Domagk, a German physician working for a dye manufacturer, first used a synthetic dye as a drug to kill bacteria. His daughter had contracted a streptococcal infection, and as she neared death, he gave her **prontosil,** an azo dye that inhibited the growth of certain bacteria in mice. His daughter recovered, and the modern era of synthetic antibiotics was initiated. For his pioneering work, Domagk was awarded the Nobel Prize in Physiology or Medicine in 1939.

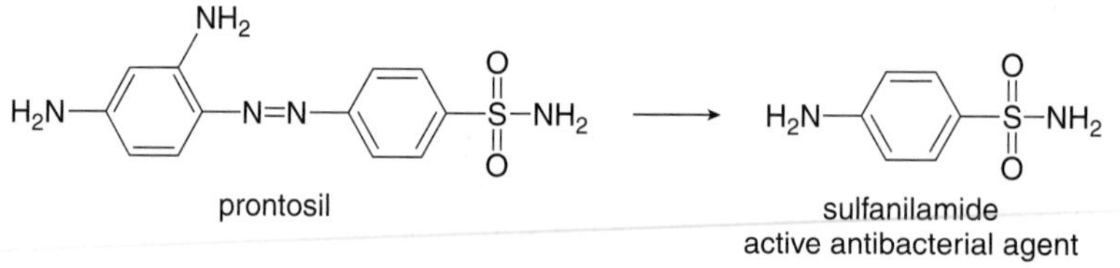

Prontosil and other sulfur-containing antibiotics are collectively called **sulfa drugs.** Prontosil is not the active agent itself. In cells, it is metabolized to **sulfanilamide,** the active drug. To understand how sulfanilamide functions as an antibacterial agent we must examine **folic acid,** which microorganisms synthesize from *p*-aminobenzoic acid.

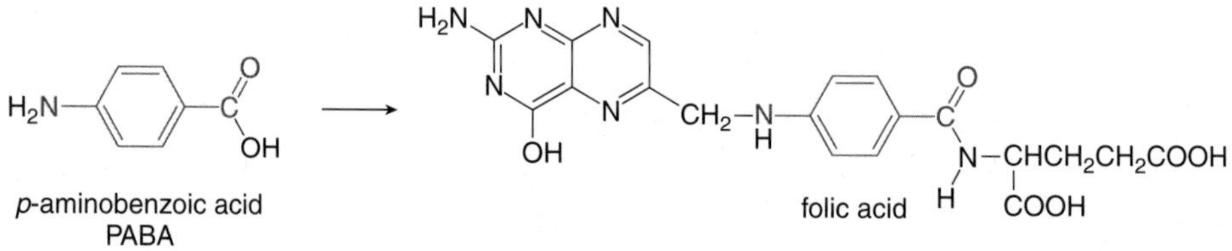

Sulfanilamide and *p*-aminobenzoic acid are similar in size and shape and have related functional groups. Thus, when sulfanilamide is administered, bacteria attempt to use it in place of *p*-aminobenzoic acid to synthesize folic acid. Derailing folic acid synthesis means that the bacteria cannot grow and reproduce. Sulfanilamide only affects bacterial cells, though, because humans do not synthesize folic acid, and must obtain it from their diets.

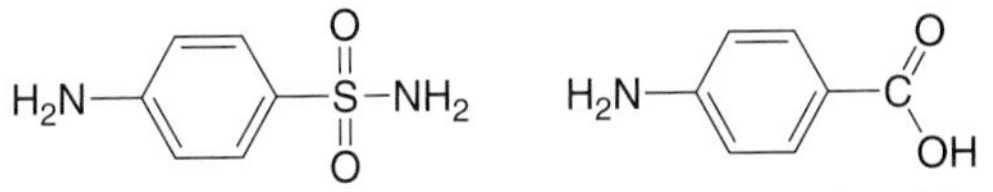

These compounds are similar in size and shape.

Many other compounds of similar structure have been prepared and are still widely used as antibiotics. The structures of two other sulfa drugs are shown in Figure 25.13.

Figure 25.13
Two common sulfa drugs

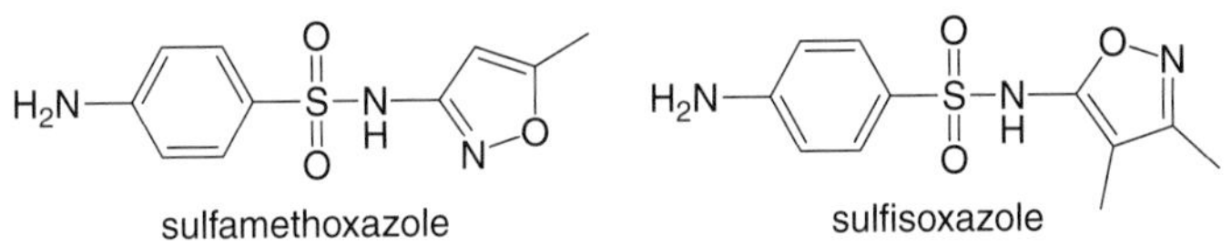

- Sulfamethoxazole is the sulfa drug in Bactrim, and sulfisoxazole is sold as Gantrisin. Both drugs are commonly used in the treatment of ear and urinary tract infections.

KEY CONCEPTS

Amines

General Facts

- Amines are organic nitrogen compounds having the general structure RNH_2, R_2NH, or R_3N, with a lone pair of electrons on N (25.1).
- Amines are named using the suffix *-amine* (25.3).
- All amines have polar C – N bonds. Primary (1°) and 2° amines have polar N – H bonds and are capable of intermolecular hydrogen bonding (25.4).
- The lone pair on N makes amines strong organic bases and nucleophiles (25.8).

Summary of Spectroscopic Absorptions (25.5)

Mass spectra	Molecular ion	Amines with an odd number of N atoms give an odd molecular ion.
IR absorptions	N – H	3300–3500 cm^{-1} (two peaks for RNH_2, one peak for R_2NH)
^{1}H NMR absorptions	NH	0.5–5 ppm (no splitting with adjacent protons)
	CH – N	2.3–3.0 ppm (deshielded C_{sp^3} – H)
^{13}C NMR absorption	C – N	30–50 ppm

Comparing the Basicity of Amines and Other Compounds (25.10)

- Alkylamines (RNH_2, R_2NH, and R_3N) are more basic than NH_3 because of the electron-donating R groups (25.10A).
- Alkylamines (RNH_2) are more basic than arylamines ($C_6H_5NH_2$), which have a delocalized lone pair from the N atom (25.10B).
- Arylamines with electron-donor groups are more basic than arylamines with electron-withdrawing groups (25.10B).
- Alkylamines (RNH_2) are more basic than amides ($RCONH_2$), which have a delocalized lone pair from the N atom (25.10C).
- Aromatic heterocycles with a localized electron pair on N are more basic than those with a delocalized lone pair from the N atom (25.10D).
- Alkylamines with a lone pair in an sp^3 hybrid orbital are more basic than those with a lone pair in an sp^2 hybrid orbital (25.10E).

Preparation of Amines (25.7)

[1] Direct nucleophilic substitution with NH_3 and amines (25.7A)

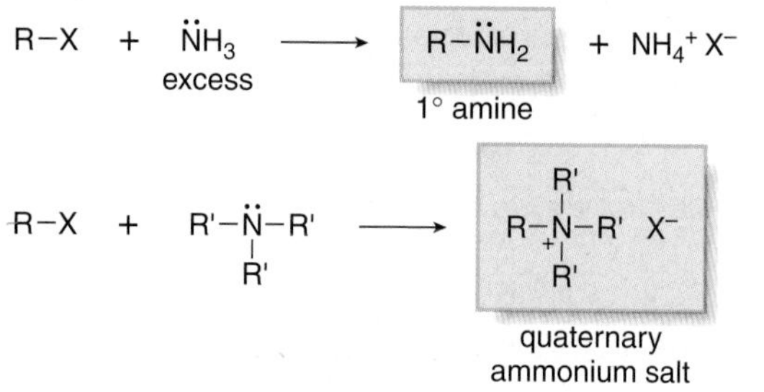
R–X + NH3 excess → R–NH2 + NH4+ X–
1° amine
R–X + R'–N–R' R' → R–N+–R' R' R' X–
quaternary ammonium salt

- The mechanism is S_N2.
- The reaction works best for CH_3X or RCH_2X.
- The reaction works best to prepare 1° amines and quaternary ammonium salts.

[2] Gabriel synthesis (25.7A)

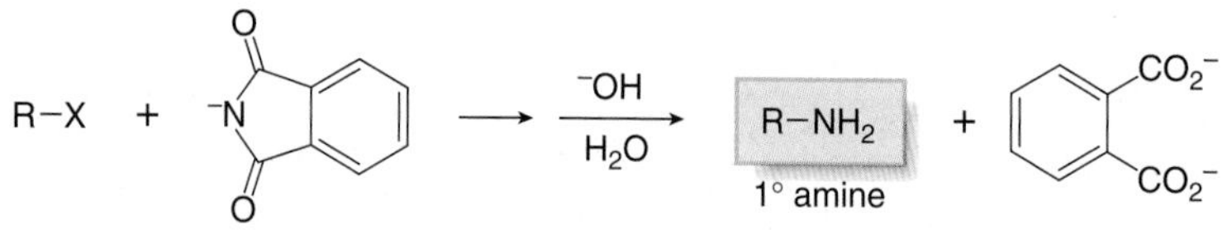
R–X
–OH
H2O
R–NH2
1° amine
CO2–
CO2–

- The mechanism is S_N2.
- The reaction works best for CH_3X or RCH_2X.
- Only 1° amines can be prepared.

[3] Reduction methods (25.7B)

a. From nitro compounds

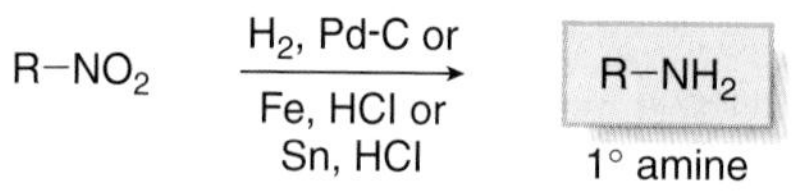
R–NO2
H2, Pd-C or
Fe, HCl or
Sn, HCl
R–NH2
1° amine

b. From nitriles

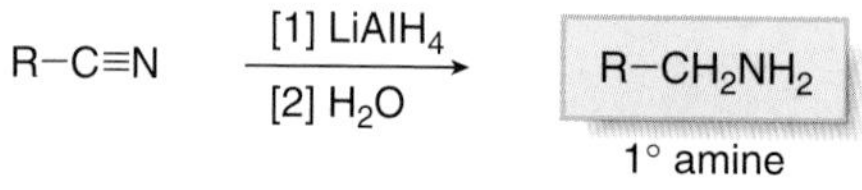
R–C≡N
[1] LiAlH4
[2] H2O
R–CH2NH2
1° amine

c. From amides

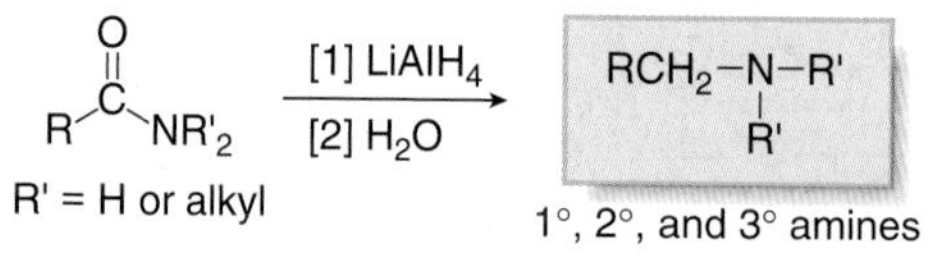
NR'2
R' = H or alkyl
[1] LiAlH4
[2] H2O
RCH2–N–R'
R'
1°, 2°, and 3° amines

[4] Reductive amination (25.7C)

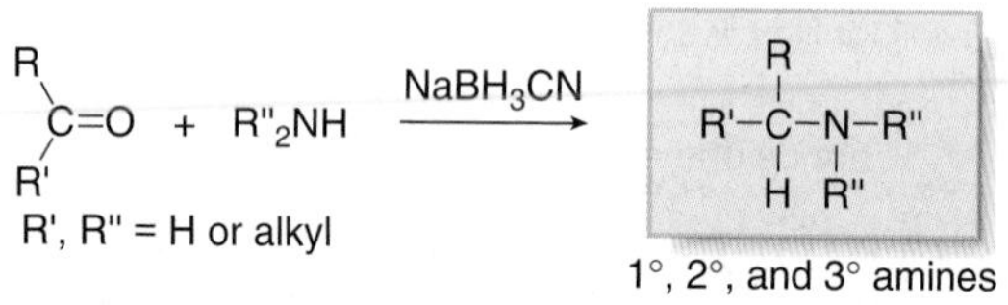
C=O + R''2NH
R', R'' = H or alkyl
NaBH3CN
R'–C–N–R''
1°, 2°, and 3° amines

- Reductive amination adds one alkyl group (from an aldehyde or ketone) to a nitrogen nucleophile.
- Primary (1°), 2°, and 3° amines can be prepared.

Reactions of Amines

[1] Reaction as a base (25.9)

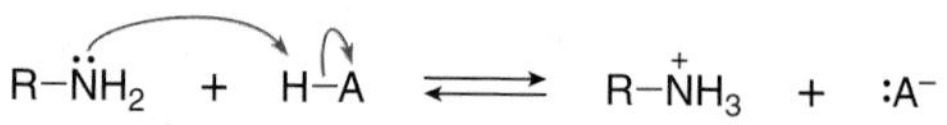
R–NH2 + H–A ⇌ R–NH3+ + :A–

[2] Nucleophilic addition to aldehydes and ketones (25.11)

With 1° amines:

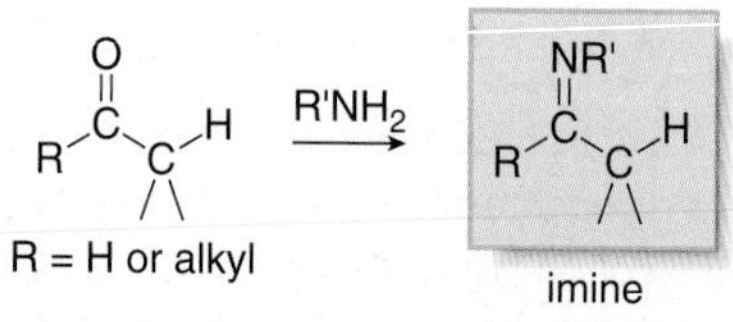
R'NH2
R = H or alkyl
imine

With 2° amines:

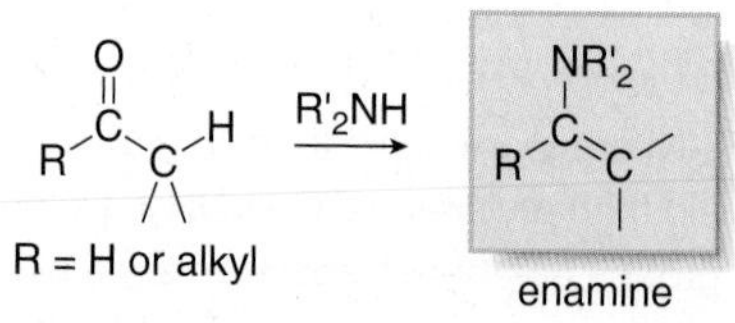
R'2NH
R = H or alkyl
enamine

[3] Nucleophilic substitution with acid chlorides and anhydrides (25.11)

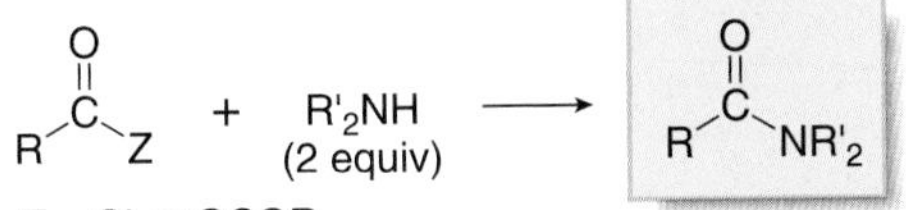
R'$_2$NH
(2 equiv)

Z = Cl or OCOR
R' = H or alkyl

1°, 2°, and 3° amides

[4] Hofmann elimination (25.12)

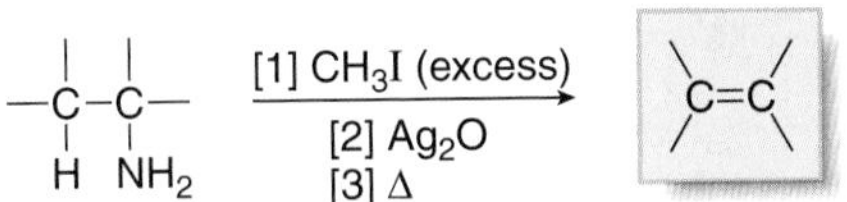
[1] CH_3I (excess)
[2] Ag_2O
[3] Δ

alkene

- The less substituted alkene is the major product.

[5] Reaction with nitrous acid (25.13)

With 1° amines:

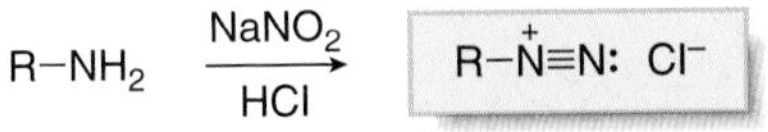
$NaNO_2$
HCl

alkyl diazonium salt

With 2° amines:

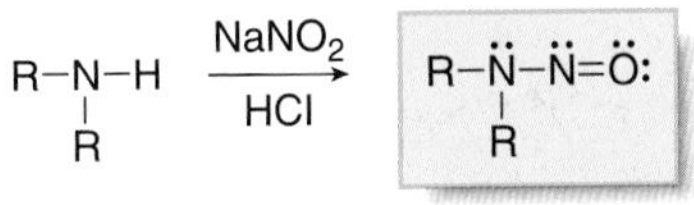
$NaNO_2$
HCl

N-nitrosamine

Reactions of Diazonium Salts

[1] Substitution reactions (25.14)

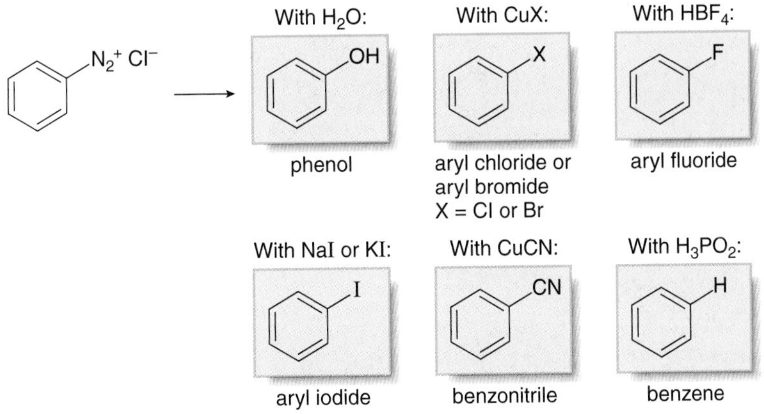
With H_2O:
With CuX:
With HBF_4:
phenol
aryl chloride or
aryl bromide
X = Cl or Br
aryl fluoride
With NaI or KI:
With CuCN:
With H_3PO_2:
aryl iodide
benzonitrile
benzene

[2] Coupling to form azo compounds (25.15)

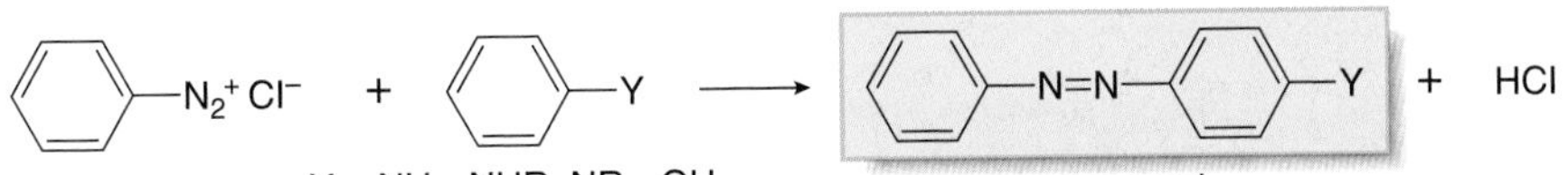

Y = NH_2, NHR, NR_2, OH
(a strong electron-
donor group)

azo compound

PROBLEMS

Problems Using Three-Dimensional Models

25.39 Give a systematic or common name for each compound.

a. 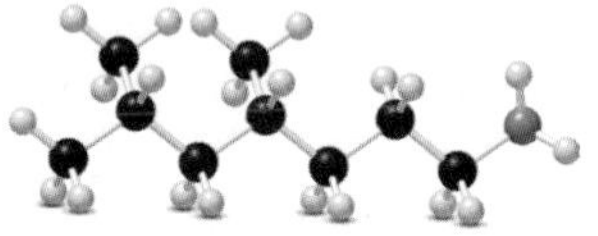

b. 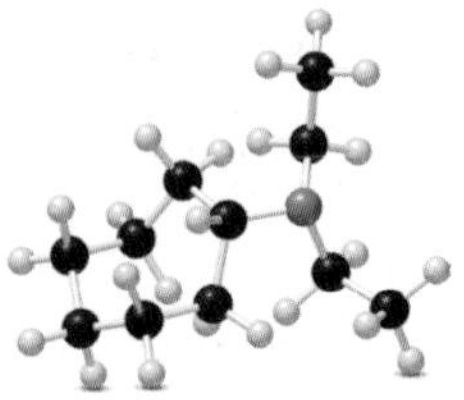

25.40 Which compound is the stronger base?

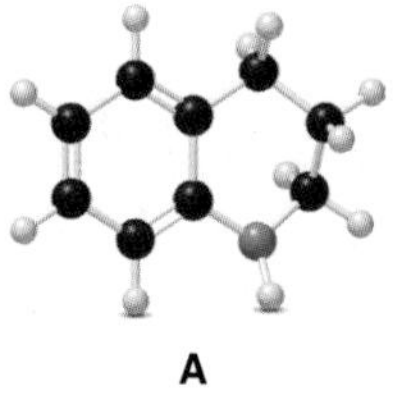

A

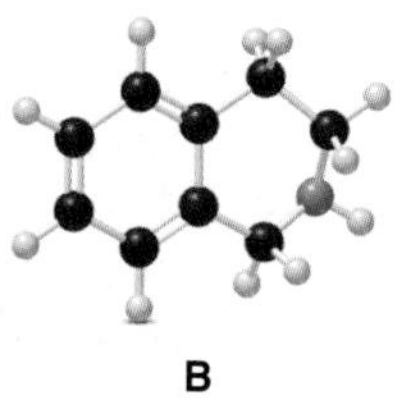

B

25.41 Varenicline (trade name Chantix) is a drug used to help smokers quit their habit. (a) Which N atom in varenicline is most basic? Explain your choice. (b) What product is formed when varenicline is treated with HCl?

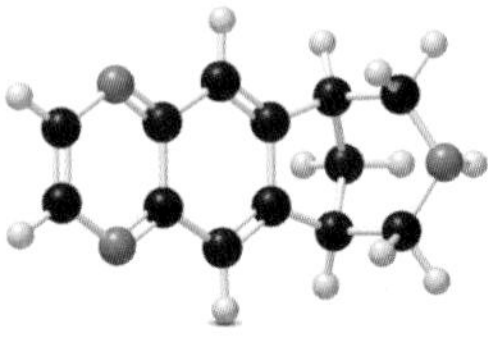

varenicline

Nomenclature

25.42 Give a systematic or common name for each compound.

a. $CH_3NHCH_2CH_2CH_2CH_3$

b. 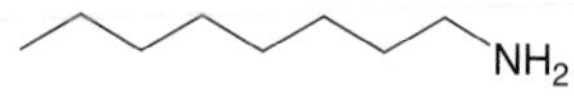
NH2

c. 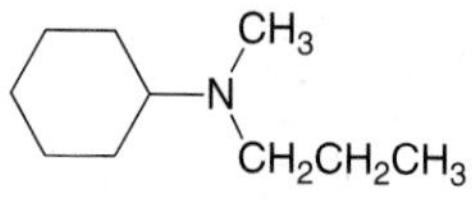
CH3
N
CH2CH2CH3

d. $(CH_3CH_2CH_2)_3N$

e. $(C_6H_5)_2NH$

f. 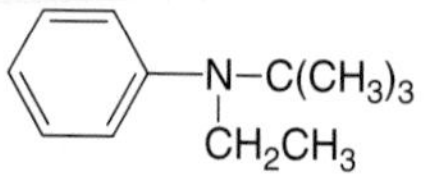
N–C(CH3)3
CH2CH3

g. 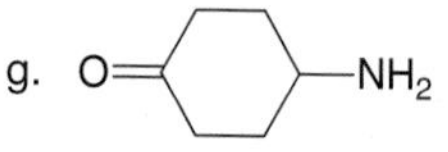
O
NH2

h. 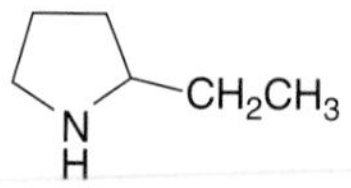
N
H
CH2CH3

i. $CH_3CH_2CH_2CH(NH_2)CH(CH_3)_2$

j. 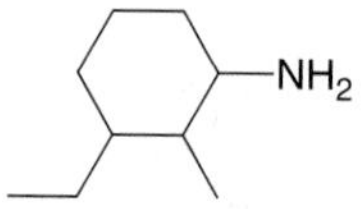
NH2

25.43 Draw the structure that corresponds to each name.

a. cyclobutylamine
b. *N*-isobutylcyclopentylamine
c. tri-*tert*-butylamine
d. *N*,*N*-diisopropylaniline
e. *N*-methylpyrrole
f. *N*-methylcyclopentylamine
g. *cis*-2-aminocyclohexanol
h. 3-methyl-2-hexanamine
i. 2-*sec*-butylpiperidine
j. (2*S*)-2-heptanamine

25.44 Draw all constitutional isomers of molecular formula $C_4H_{11}N$, and give an acceptable name for each amine.

Chiral Compounds

25.45 How many stereogenic centers are present in each compound? Draw all possible stereoisomers.

a. 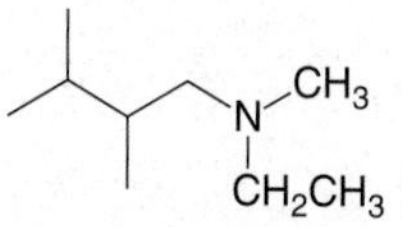
N
CH3
CH2CH3

b. 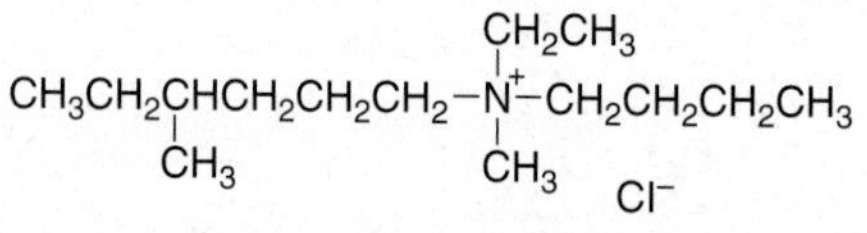
CH2CH3
CH3CH2CHCH2CH2CH2–N+–CH2CH2CH2CH3
CH3
CH3
Cl–

Basicity

25.46 Which compound in each pair is the stronger base?

a. $(CH_3CH_2)_2NH$ or 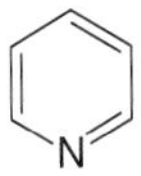

b. $(CH_3CH_2)_2NH$ or $(ClCH_2CH_2)_2NH$

25.47 Rank the compounds in each group in order of increasing basicity.

a. NH_3 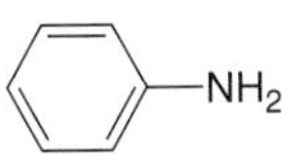 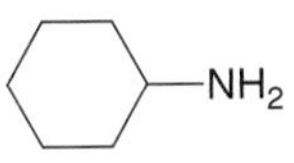

c. 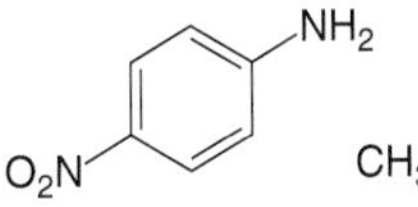 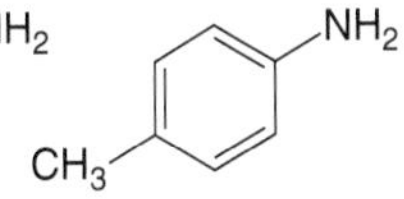 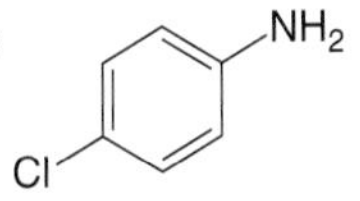

b. 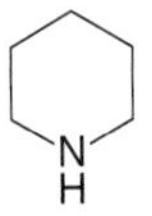 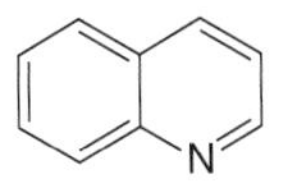 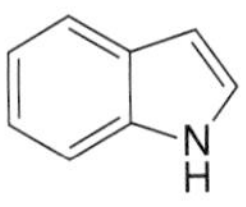

d. $C_6H_5NH_2$ $(C_6H_5)_2NH$ 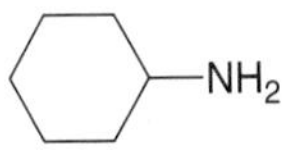

25.48 How does the pK_a of the conjugate acid of benzylamine ($C_6H_5CH_2NH_2$) compare to the pK_a's of the conjugate acids of cyclohexanamine (10.7) and aniline (4.6)? Explain your choice.

25.49 Decide which N atom in each molecule is most basic and draw the product formed when each compound is treated with CH_3CO_2H. Benazepril (trade name Lotensin) is a β blocker used to treat high blood pressure and congestive heart failure. Abilify is the trade name for aripiprazole, a drug used to treat depression, schizophrenia, and bipolar disorders.

a. 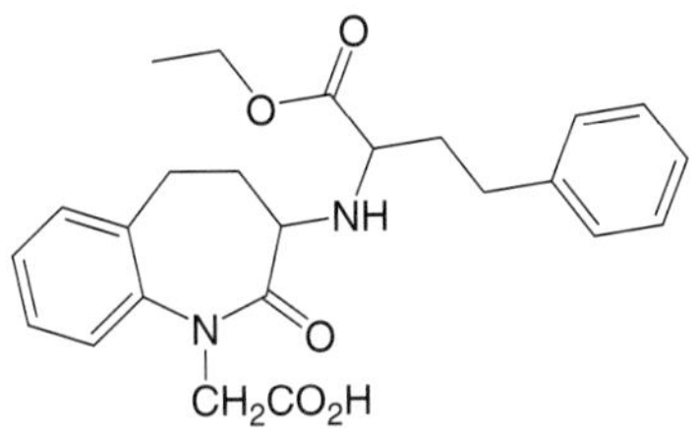

benazepril

b. 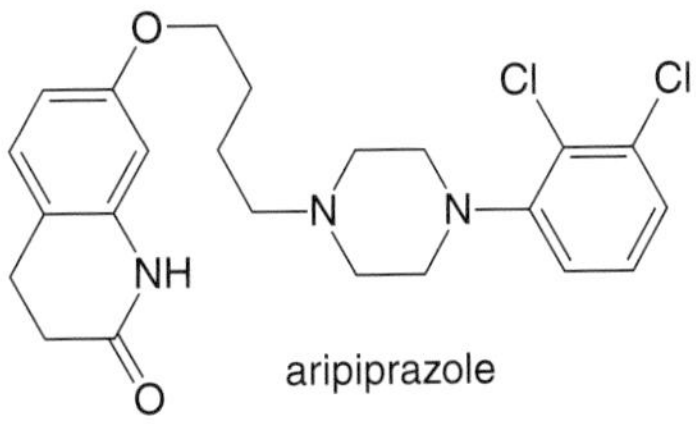

aripiprazole

25.50 Rank the nitrogen atoms in each compound in order of increasing basicity. Isoniazid is a drug used to treat tuberculosis, whereas histamine (Section 25.6B) causes the runny nose and watery eyes associated with allergies.

a. 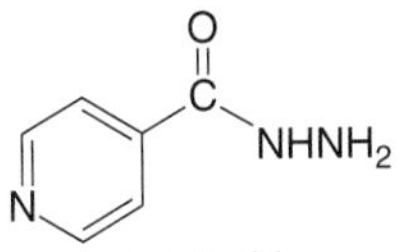

isoniazid

b. 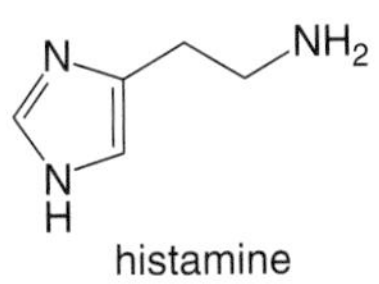

histamine

25.51 Explain why *m*-nitroaniline is a stronger base than *p*-nitroaniline.

25.52 Explain the observed difference in the pK_a values of the conjugate acids of amines **A** and **B.**

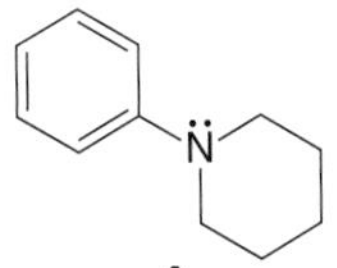

A
pK_a = 5.2

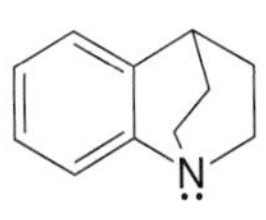

B
pK_a = 7.29

25.53 Why is pyrrole more acidic than pyrrolidine?

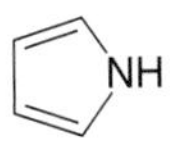

pyrrole
pK_a = 23

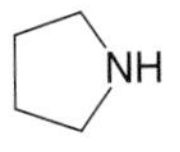

pyrrolidine
pK_a = 44

Preparation of Amines

25.54 How would you prepare 3-phenyl-1-propanamine ($C_6H_5CH_2CH_2CH_2NH_2$) from each compound?

a. $C_6H_5CH_2CH_2CH_2Br$
b. $C_6H_5CH_2CH_2Br$
c. $C_6H_5CH_2CH_2CH_2NO_2$
d. $C_6H_5CH_2CH_2CONH_2$
e. $C_6H_5CH_2CH_2CHO$

25.55 What amide(s) can be used to prepare each amine by reduction?

a. $(CH_3CH_2)_2NH$ b. 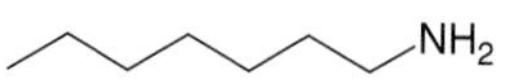 c. 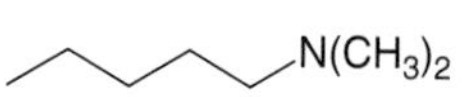 d. 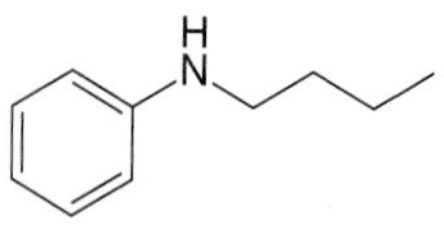

25.56 What carbonyl and nitrogen compounds are needed to make each compound by reductive amination? When more than one set of starting materials is possible, give all possible methods.

a. 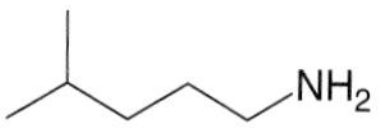 b. 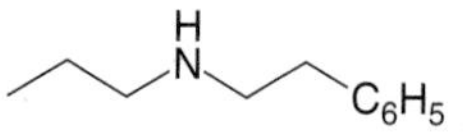 c. $(CH_3CH_2CH_2)_2N(CH_2)_2CH(CH_3)_2$ d. 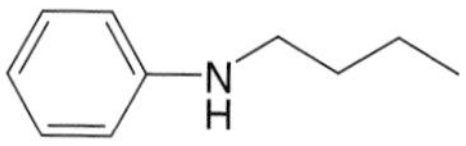

25.57 Draw the product of each reductive amination reaction.

a. 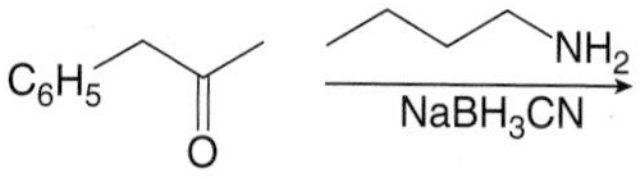 c. 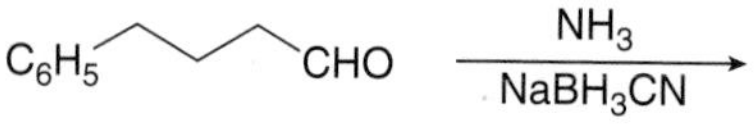

b. 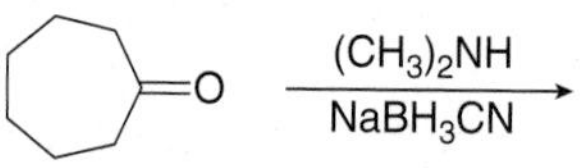 d. 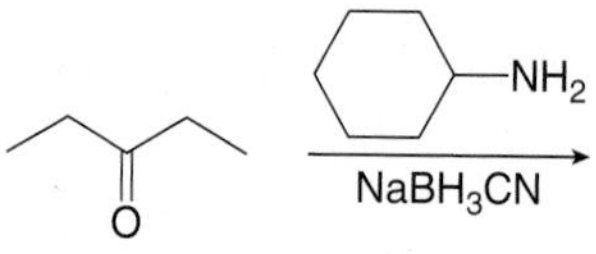

25.58 How would you prepare benzylamine ($C_6H_5CH_2NH_2$) from each compound? In some cases, more than one step is required.

a. $C_6H_5CH_2Br$
b. C_6H_5CN
c. $C_6H_5CONH_2$
d. C_6H_5CHO
e. $C_6H_5CH_3$
f. C_6H_5COOH
g. $C_6H_5NH_2$
h. benzene

Extraction

25.59 How would you separate toluene ($C_6H_5CH_3$), benzoic acid (C_6H_5COOH), and aniline ($C_6H_5NH_2$) by an extraction procedure?

Reactions

25.60 What products are formed when *N*-ethylaniline ($C_6H_5NHCH_2CH_3$) is treated with each reagent?

a. HCl
b. CH_3COOH
c. $(CH_3)_2C{=}O$
d. CH_2O, $NaBH_3CN$
e. CH_3I (excess)
f. CH_3I (excess), followed by Ag_2O and Δ
g. CH_3CH_2COCl
h. The product in (g), then HNO_3, H_2SO_4
i. The product in (g), then [1] $LiAlH_4$; [2] H_2O
j. The product in (h), then H_2, Pd-C

25.61 Draw the products formed when *p*-methylaniline (*p*-$CH_3C_6H_4NH_2$) is treated with each reagent.

a. HCl
b. CH_3COCl
c. $(CH_3CO)_2O$
d. excess CH_3I
e. $(CH_3)_2C{=}O$
f. CH_3COCl, $AlCl_3$
g. CH_3COOH
h. $NaNO_2$, HCl
i. Step (b), then CH_3COCl, $AlCl_3$
j. CH_3CHO, $NaBH_3CN$

25.62 Draw the products formed when each amine is treated with [1] CH_3I (excess); [2] Ag_2O; [3] Δ. Indicate the major product when a mixture results.

a. $CH_3(CH_2)_6NH_2$ b. 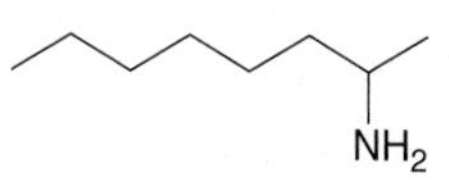 c. 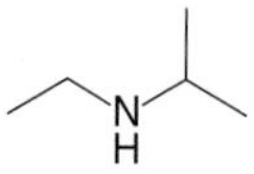 d. 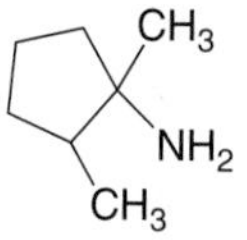 e. 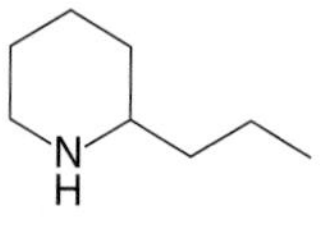

25.63 What reagents are needed to convert acetophenone ($C_6H_5COCH_3$) into each compound? In some cases, more than one step is required.

a. 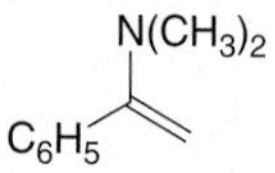 c. 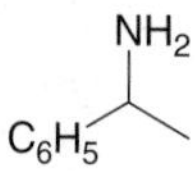 e. 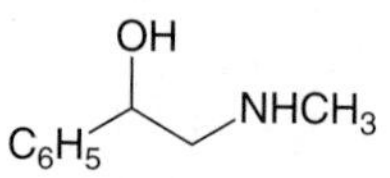

b. 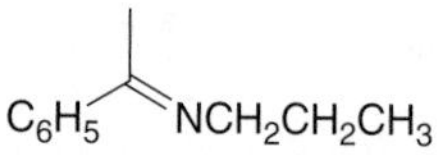 d. 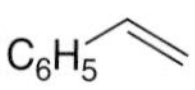 f. 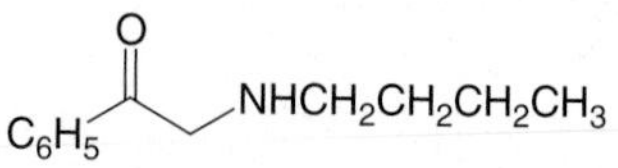

25.64 Answer the following questions about benzphetamine, a habit-forming diet pill sold under the trade name Didrex.

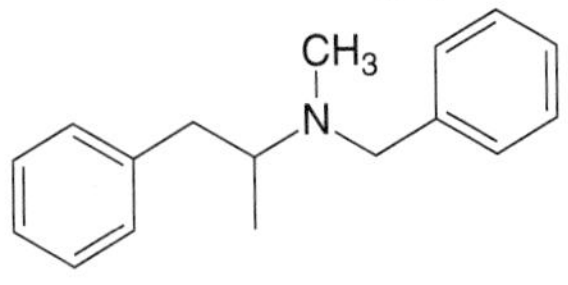

benzphetamine

a. Label the stereogenic center(s).
b. What amide(s) can be reduced to form benzphetamine?
c. What carbonyl compound and amine can be used to make benzphetamine by reductive amination? Draw all possible methods.
d. What products are formed by Hofmann elimination from benzphetamine? Label the major product.

25.65 Draw the organic products formed in each reaction.

a. 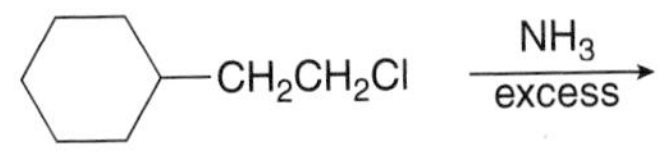

b. 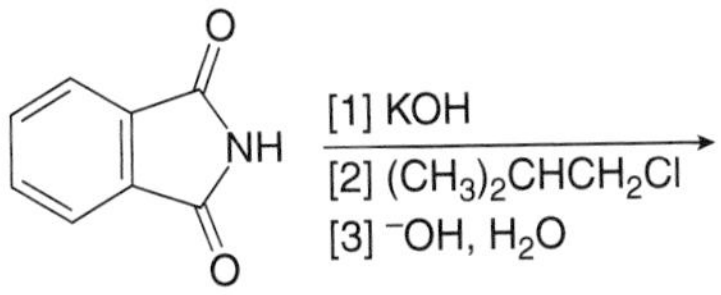

c. 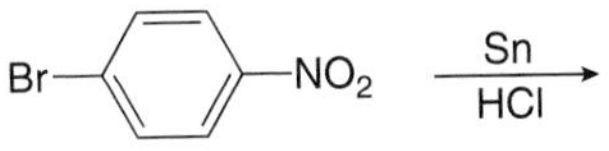

d. 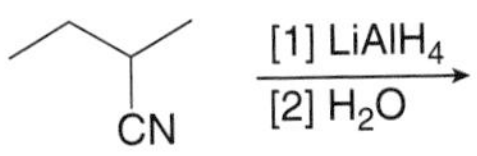

e. 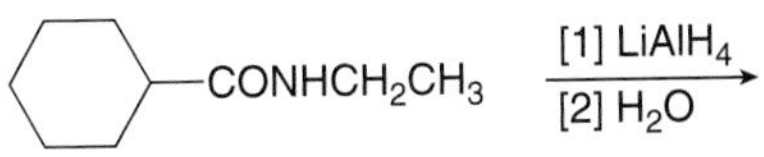

f. $C_6H_5CH_2CH_2NH_2$ + $(C_6H_5CO)_2O$
(2 equiv)

g. 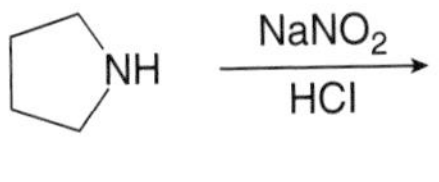

h. 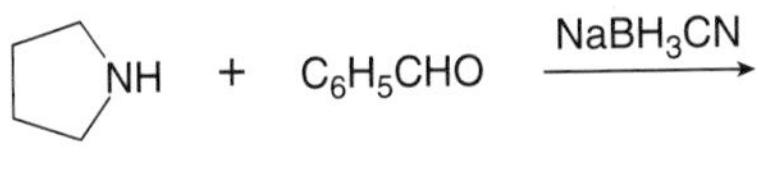

i. 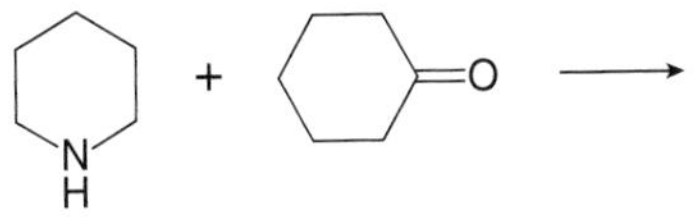

j. $CH_3CH_2CH_2–N(H)–CH(CH_3)_2$ $\xrightarrow{\text{[1] } CH_3I \text{ (excess)}; \text{ [2] } Ag_2O; \text{ [3] } \Delta}$

25.66 What is the major Hofmann elimination product formed from each amine?

a. 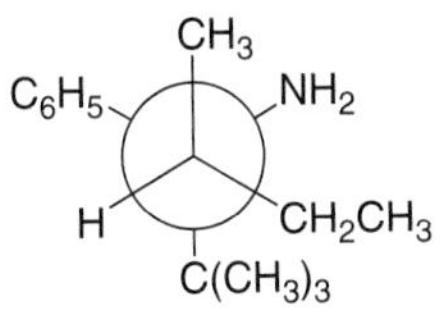

b. 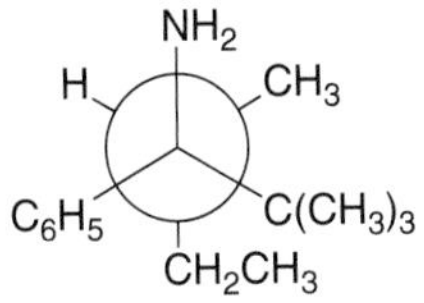

c. 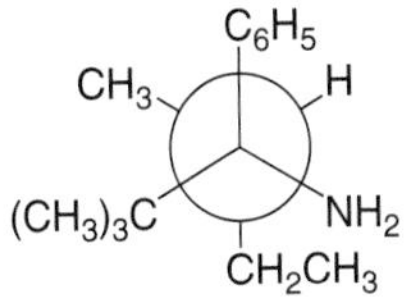

25.67 Identify the intermediates (**A**–**C**) in the following reaction sequence, which was used to prepare racemic ofloxacin. One enantiomer of the product, levofloxacin, is an antibiotic used to treat severe bacterial infections that have not responded to other drugs.

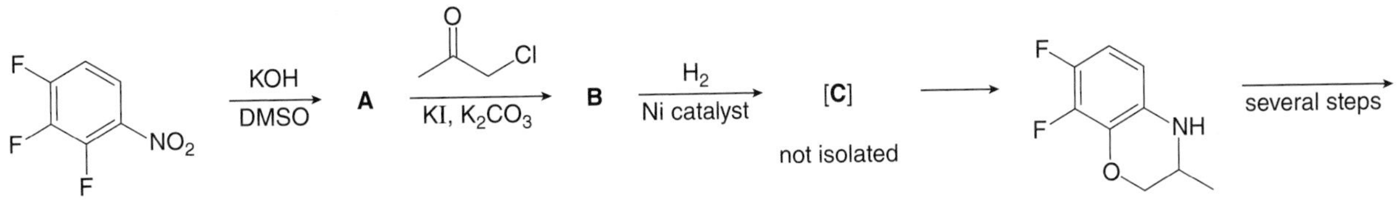

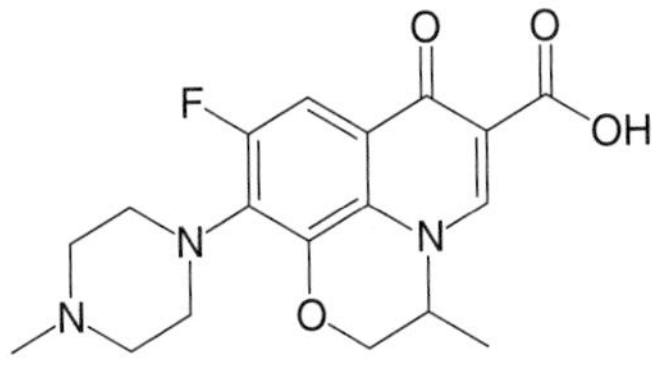

ofloxacin

25.68 Draw the product formed when **A** is treated with each reagent.

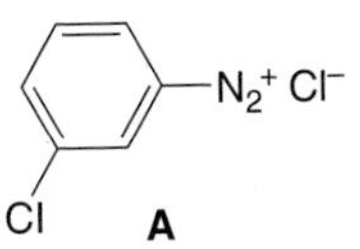

A

a. H_2O
b. H_3PO_2
c. CuCl
d. CuBr
e. CuCN
f. HBF_4
g. NaI
h. $C_6H_5NH_2$
i. C_6H_5OH
j. KI

25.69 A chiral amine **A** having the *R* configuration undergoes Hofmann elimination to form an alkene **B** as the major product. **B** is oxidatively cleaved with ozone, followed by CH_3SCH_3, to form $CH_2=O$ and $CH_3CH_2CH_2CHO$. What are the structures of **A** and **B?**

Mechanism

25.70 Draw a stepwise mechanism for each reaction.

a. 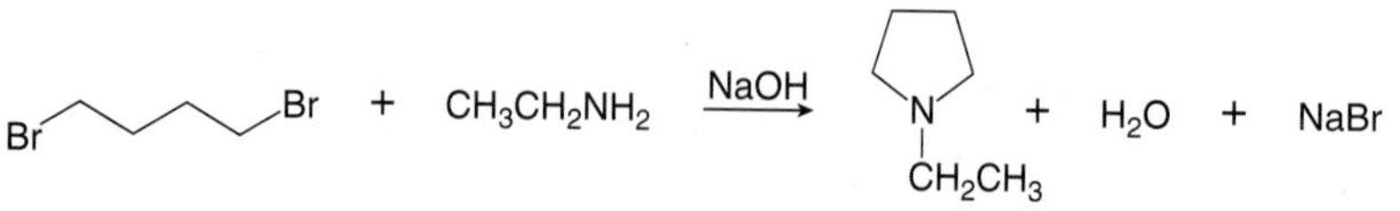

b. 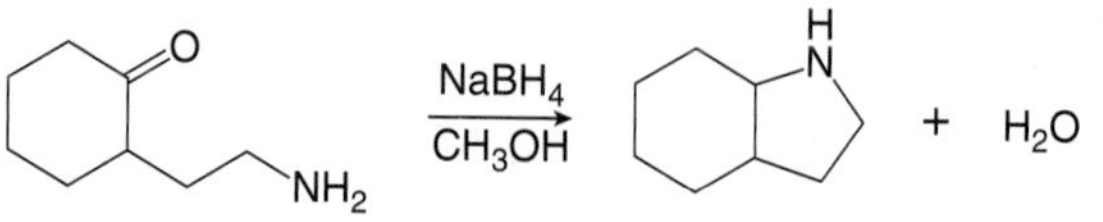

25.71 Draw a stepwise mechanism for the following reaction.

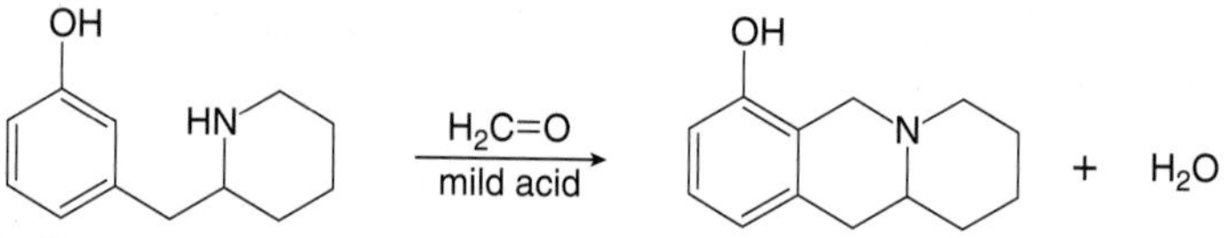

25.72 Alkyl diazonium salts are unstable even at low temperature. They decompose to form carbocations, which go on to form products of substitution, elimination, and (sometimes) rearrangement. Keeping this in mind, draw a stepwise mechanism that forms all of the following products.

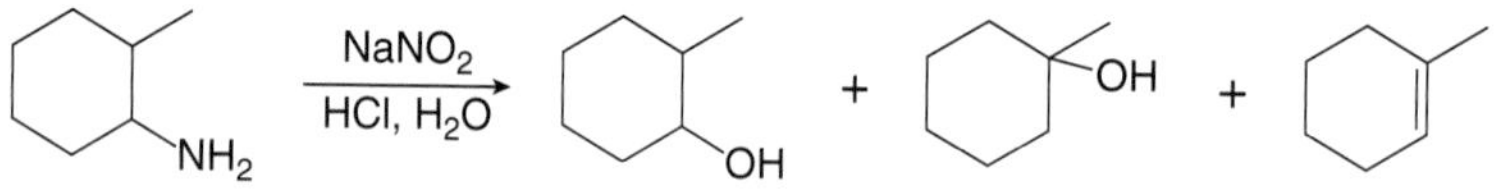

25.73 Tertiary (3°) aromatic amines react with $NaNO_2$ and HCl to afford products of electrophilic aromatic substitution. Draw a stepwise mechanism for this nitrosation reaction and explain why it occurs only on benzene rings with strong ortho, para activating groups.

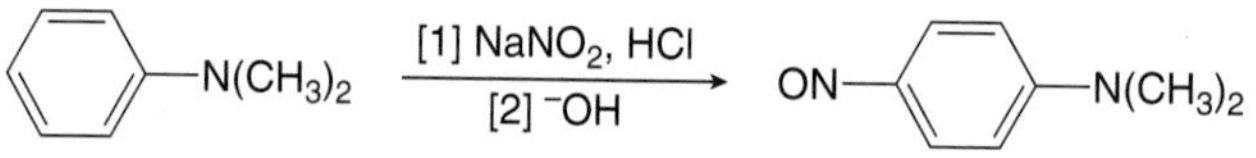

Synthesis

25.74 Devise a stepwise reaction sequence to convert 4-phenyl-2-butanone ($PhCH_2CH_2COCH_3$) into each alkene: (a) $PhCH_2CH_2CH{=}CH_2$; (b) $PhCH_2CH{=}CHCH_3$.

25.75 Devise a synthesis of each compound from benzene. You may use any other organic or inorganic reagents.

a. 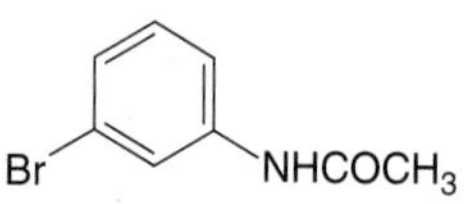

c. 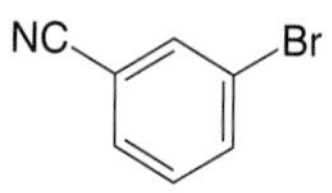

e. 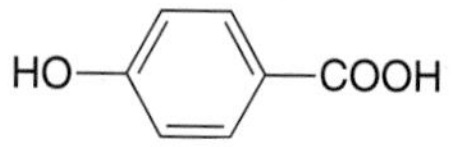

b. 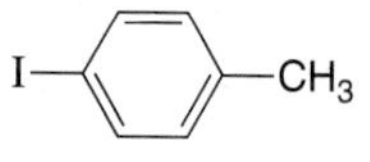

d. 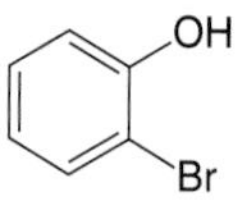

f. 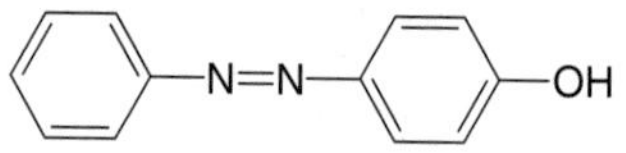

25.76 Devise a synthesis of each compound from aniline ($C_6H_5NH_2$) as starting material.

a. 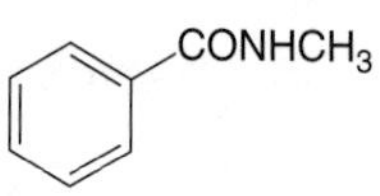

b. 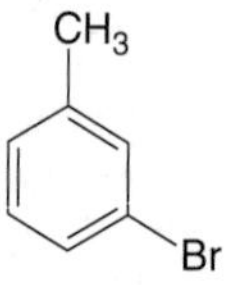

c. 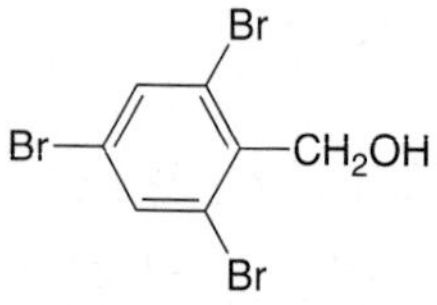

d. 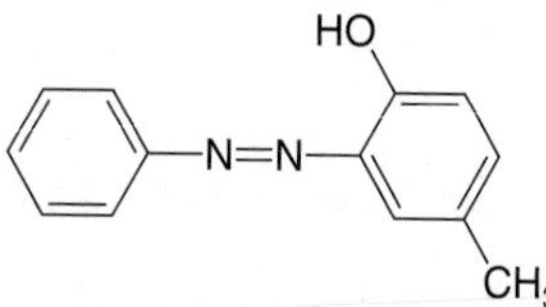

25.77 Devise at least three different methods to prepare *N*-methylbenzylamine ($PhCH_2NHCH_3$) from benzene, any one-carbon organic compounds, and any required reagents.

25.78 Safrole, which is isolated from sassafras (Problem 21.33), can be converted to the illegal stimulant MDMA (3,4-methylenedioxymethamphetamine, "Ecstasy") by a variety of methods. (a) Devise a synthesis that begins with safrole and uses a nucleophilic substitution reaction to introduce the amine. (b) Devise a synthesis that begins with safrole and uses reductive amination to introduce the amine.

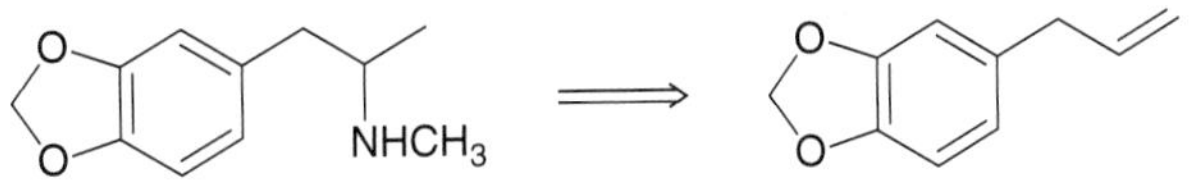

MDMA safrole

25.79 Devise a synthesis of the hallucinogen mescaline (Section 25.6) from each starting material.

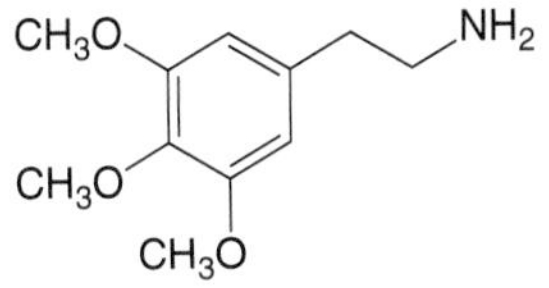
mescaline

a. 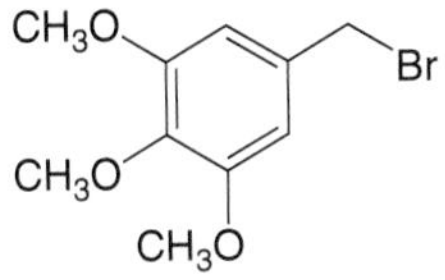

b. 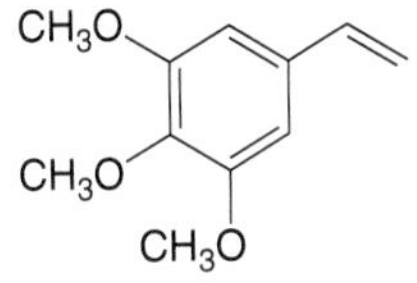

c. 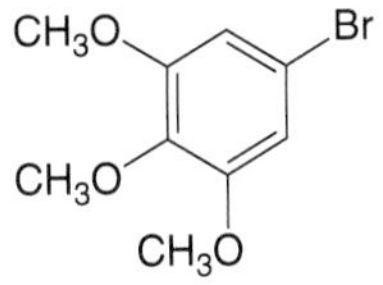

25.80 Synthesize each compound from benzene. Use a diazonium salt as one of the synthetic intermediates.

a. 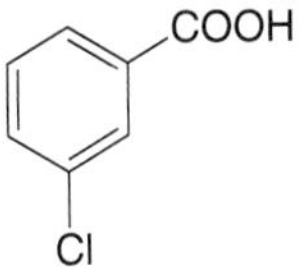

c. 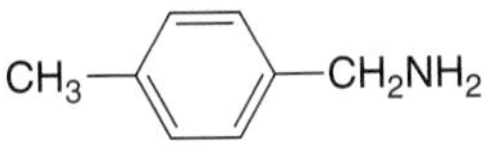

e. 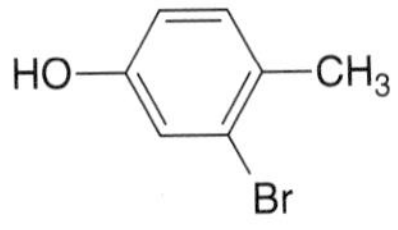

b. 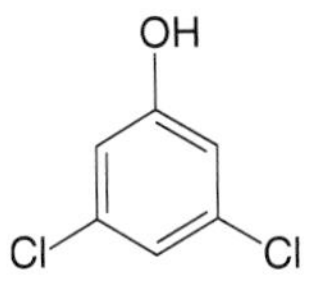

d. 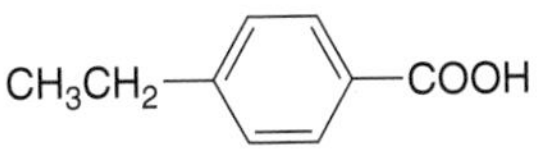

f. 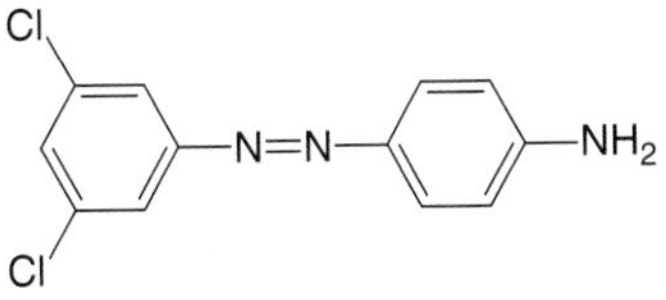

25.81 Devise a synthesis of each biologically active compound from benzene.

a. 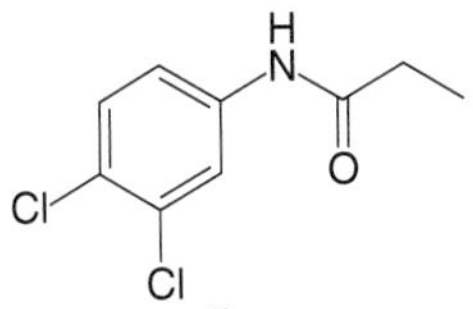
propanil
(herbicide)

b. 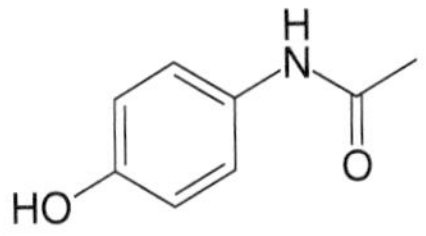
acetaminophen
(analgesic)

c. 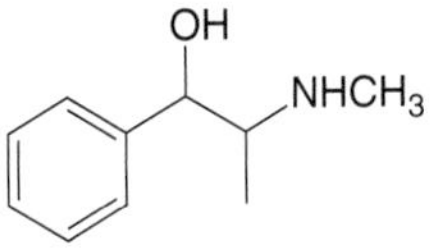
pseudoephedrine
(nasal decongestant)

25.82 Devise a synthesis of each compound from benzene, any organic alcohols having three carbons or fewer, and any required reagents.

a. 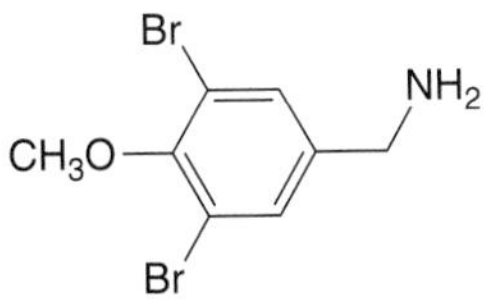

c. 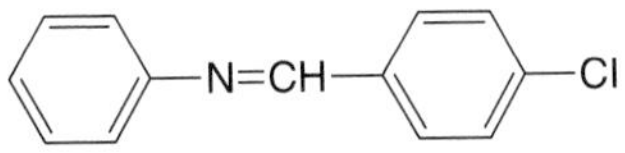

e. 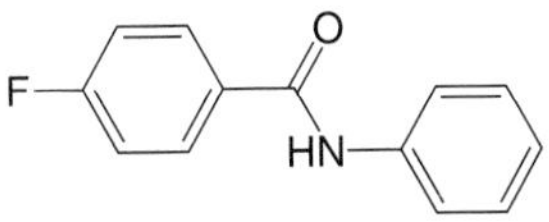

b. 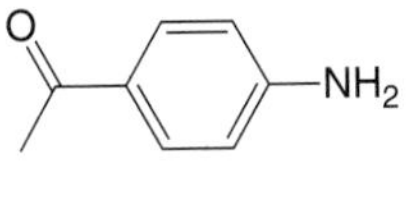

d. 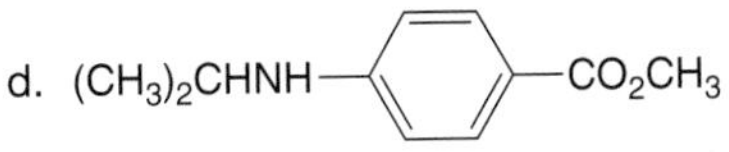

f. 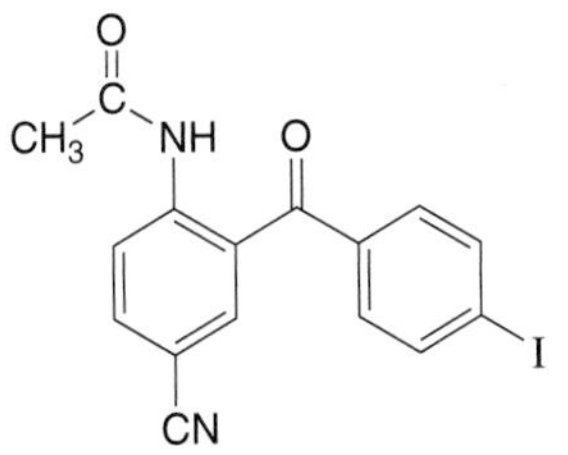

Spectroscopy

25.83 Draw the structures of the eight isomeric amines that have a molecular ion in the mass spectrum at $m/z = 87$ and show two peaks in their IR spectra at 3300–3500 cm^{-1}.

25.84 Three isomeric compounds, **A, B,** and **C,** all have molecular formula $C_8H_{11}N$. The ^1H NMR and IR spectral data of **A, B,** and **C** are given below. What are their structures?

Compound **A:** IR peak at 3400 cm^{-1}

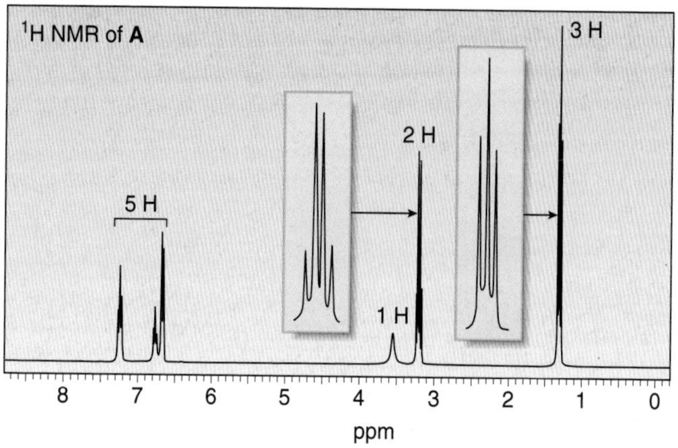

Compound **B:** IR peak at 3310 cm^{-1}

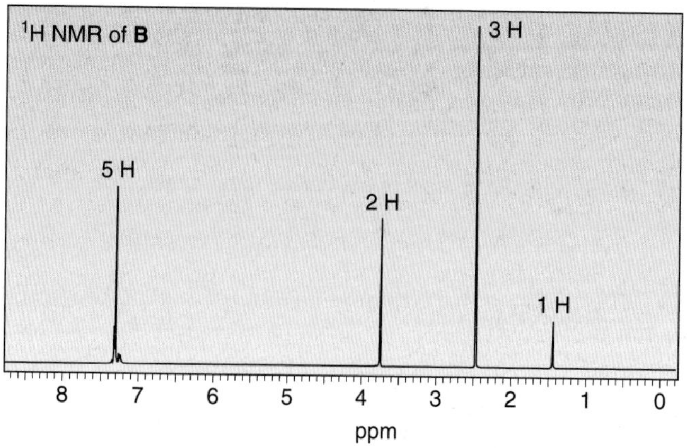

Compound **C:** IR peaks at 3430 and 3350 cm^{-1}

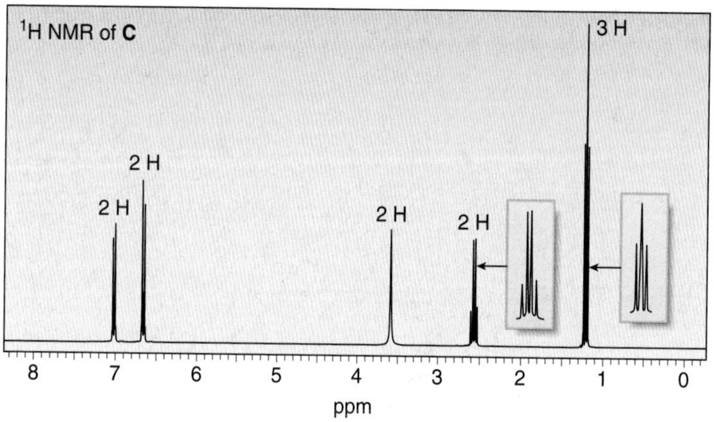

25.85 Treatment of compound **D** with $LiAlH_4$ followed by H_2O forms compound **E. D** shows a molecular ion in its mass spectrum at $m/z = 71$ and IR absorptions at 3600–3200 and 2263 cm^{-1}. **E** shows a molecular ion in its mass spectrum at $m/z = 75$ and IR absorptions at 3636 and 3600–3200 cm^{-1}. Propose structures for **D** and **E** from these data and the given ^1H NMR spectra.

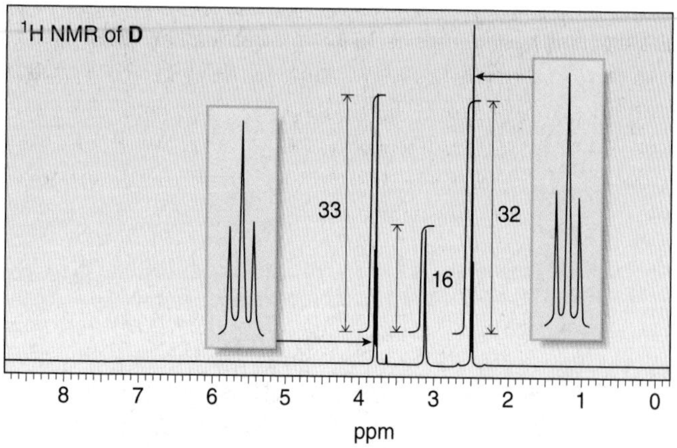

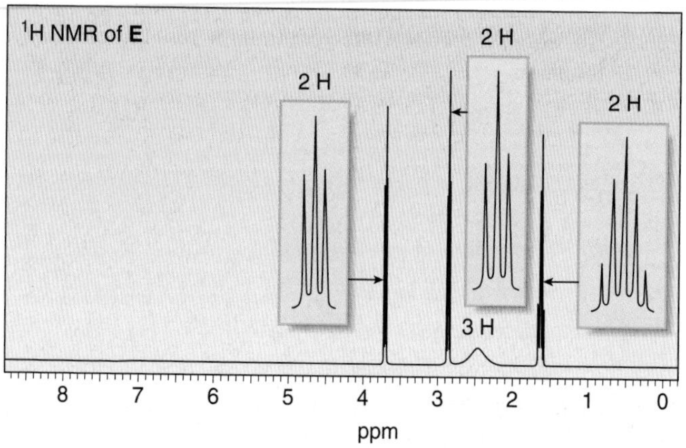

Challenge Problems

25.86 The pK_a of the conjugate acid of guanidine is 13.6, making it one of the strongest neutral organic bases. Offer an explanation.

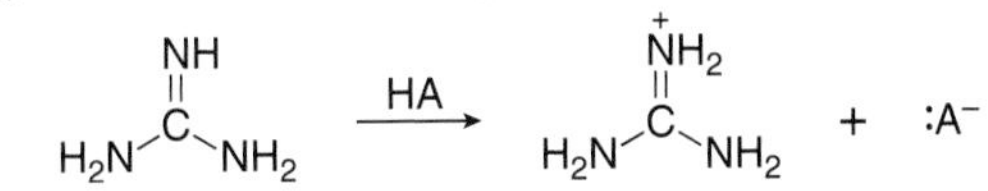

guanidine pK_a = 13.6

25.87 Rank the following compounds in order of increasing basicity and explain the order you chose.

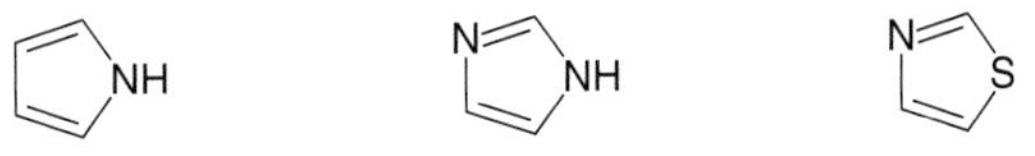

pyrrole imidazole thiazole

25.88 Draw the product **Y** of the following reaction sequence. **Y** was an intermediate in the remarkable synthesis of cyclooctatetraene by Wilstatter in 1911.

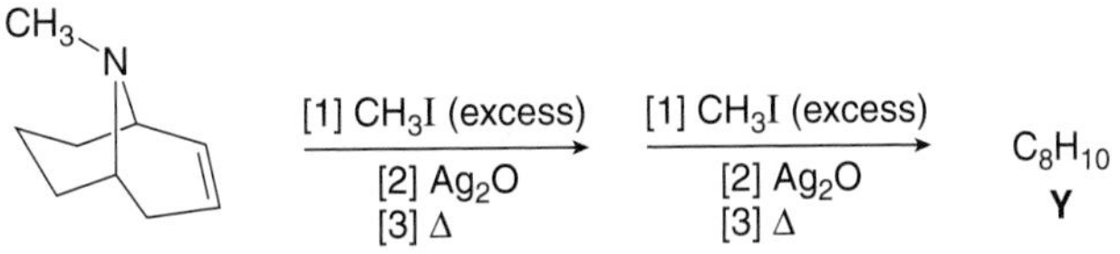

25.89 Devise a synthesis of each compound from the given starting material(s). Albuterol is a bronchodilator and proparacaine is a local anesthetic.

a.

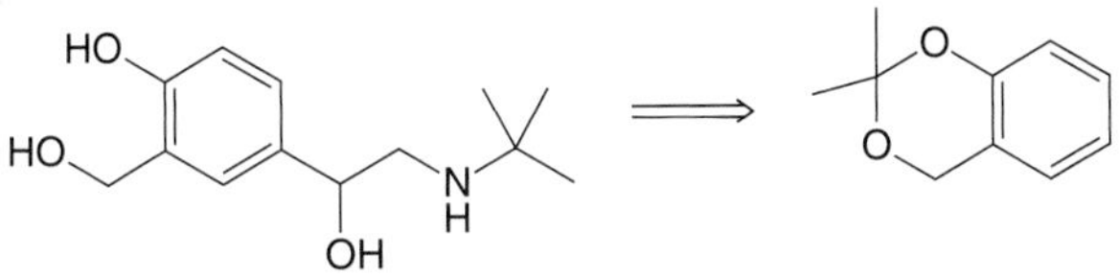

albuterol

b.

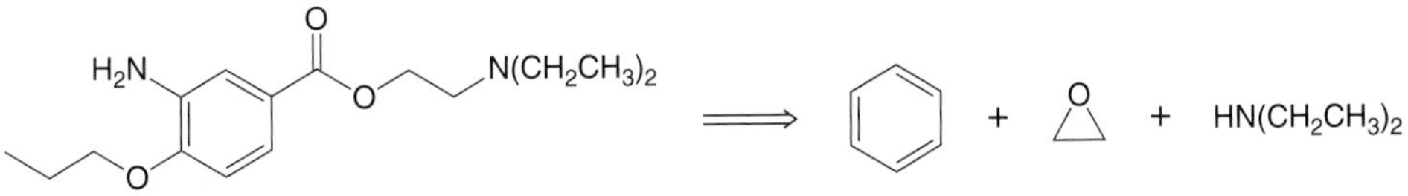

proparacaine

25.90 Heating compound **X** with aqueous formaldehyde forms **Y** ($C_{17}H_{23}NO$), which has been converted to a mixture of lupinine and epilupinine, alkaloids isolated from lupin, a perennial ornamental plant commonly seen on the roadside in parts of Alaska. Identify **Y** and explain how it is formed.

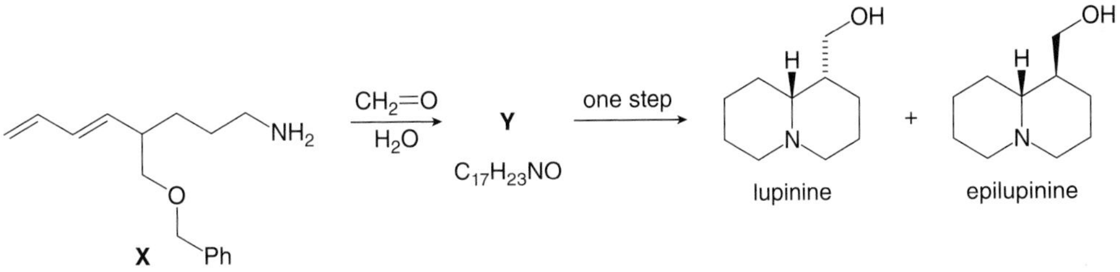

X lupinine epilupinine

26 Carbon–Carbon Bond-Forming Reactions in Organic Synthesis

26.1 Coupling reactions of organocuprate reagents
26.2 Suzuki reaction
26.3 Heck reaction
26.4 Carbenes and cyclopropane synthesis
26.5 Simmons–Smith reaction
26.6 Metathesis

Bombykol is a sex pheromone secreted by the female silkworm moth *Bombyx mori* to attract mates. Bombykol's structure was elucidated in 1959 using 6.4 mg of material obtained from 500,000 silkworm moths. One step in an efficient synthesis of bombykol is the Suzuki reaction, a stereospecific carbon–carbon bond-forming reaction between a vinylborane and a vinyl halide to form a conjugated diene. In Chapter 26, we learn how to prepare a variety of substrates using novel carbon–carbon bond-forming reactions.

To form the carbon skeletons of complex molecules, organic chemists need an extensive repertoire of carbon–carbon bond-forming reactions. In Chapter 20, for example, we learned about the reactions of organometallic reagents—organolithium reagents, Grignard reagents, and organocuprates—with carbonyl substrates. In Chapters 23 and 24, we studied the reactions of nucleophilic enolates that form new carbon–carbon bonds.

Chapter 26 presents more carbon–carbon bond-forming reactions that are especially useful tools in organic synthesis. While previous chapters have concentrated on the reactions of one or two functional groups, the reactions in this chapter utilize a variety of starting materials and conceptually different reactions that form many types of products. All follow one central theme—they form new carbon–carbon bonds under mild conditions, making them versatile synthetic methods.

26.1 Coupling Reactions of Organocuprate Reagents

Several carbon–carbon bond-forming reactions involve the coupling of an organic halide (R'X) with an organometallic reagent or alkene. Three useful reactions are discussed in Sections 26.1–26.3:

[1] Reaction of an organic halide with an organocuprate reagent (Section 26.1)

$$\text{R'–X} + \underset{\text{organocuprate}}{\text{R}_2\text{CuLi}} \longrightarrow \underset{\text{new C–C bond}}{\text{R'–R}} + \text{RCu} + \text{LiX}$$

[2] Suzuki reaction: Reaction of an organic halide with an organoboron reagent in the presence of a palladium catalyst (Section 26.2)

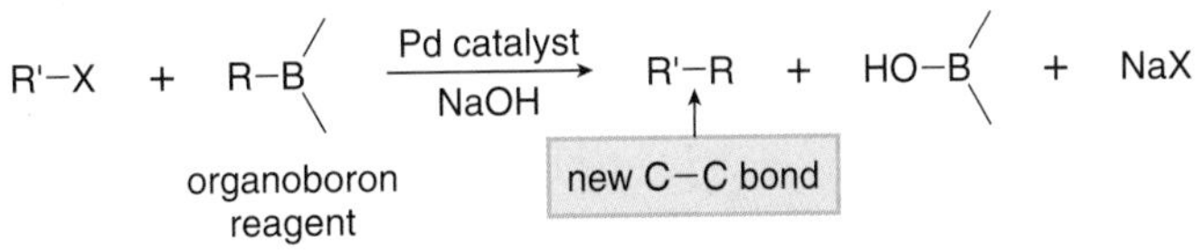

R'–X + R–B
Pd catalyst
NaOH
R'–R + HO–B + NaX
organoboron reagent
new C–C bond

[3] Heck reaction: Reaction of an organic halide with an alkene in the presence of a palladium catalyst (Section 26.3)

A complete list of reactions that form C–C bonds appears in Appendix D.

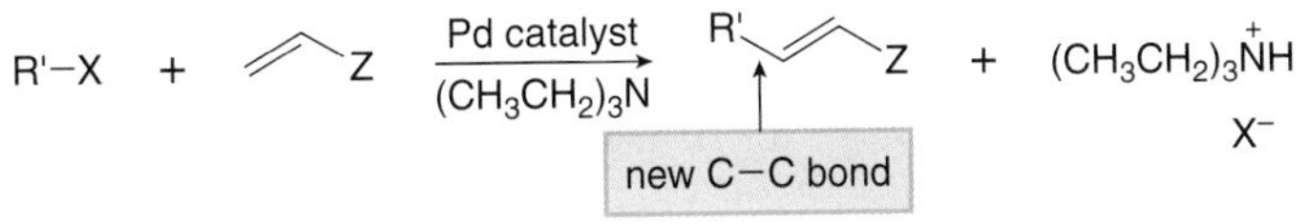

R'–X +
Z
Pd catalyst
$(CH_3CH_2)_3N$
R'
Z
+ $(CH_3CH_2)_3\overset{+}{N}H$
X^-
new C–C bond

26.1A General Features of Organocuprate Coupling Reactions

In addition to their reactions with acid chlorides, epoxides, and α,β-unsaturated carbonyl compounds (Sections 20.13–20.15), organocuprate reagents (R_2CuLi) also react with organic halides R'–X to form coupling products R–R' that contain a new C–C bond. Only one R group of the organocuprate is transferred to form the product, while the other becomes part of RCu, a reaction by-product.

General reaction

$$\text{R'–X} + \underset{\text{organocuprate}}{\text{R}_2\text{CuLi}} \longrightarrow \underset{\text{new C–C bond}}{\text{R'–R}} + \underbrace{\text{RCu} + \text{LiX}}_{\text{by-products}}$$

A variety of organic halides can be used, including methyl and 1° alkyl halides, as well as vinyl and aryl halides that contain X bonded to an sp^2 hybridized carbon. Some cyclic 2° alkyl halides give reasonable yields of product, but 3° alkyl halides are too sterically hindered. The halogen X in R'X may be Cl, Br, or I.

Examples

[1] 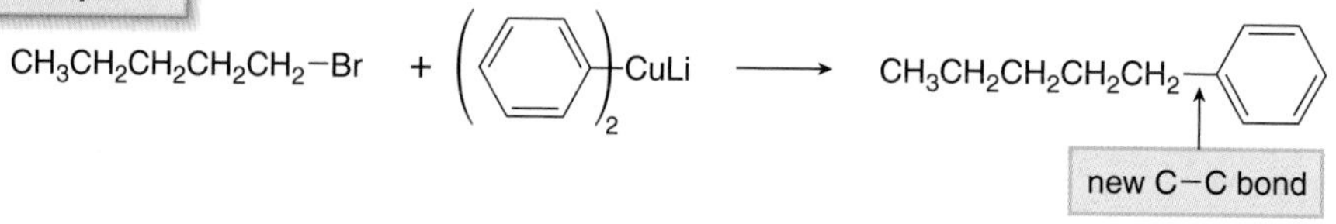

[2] 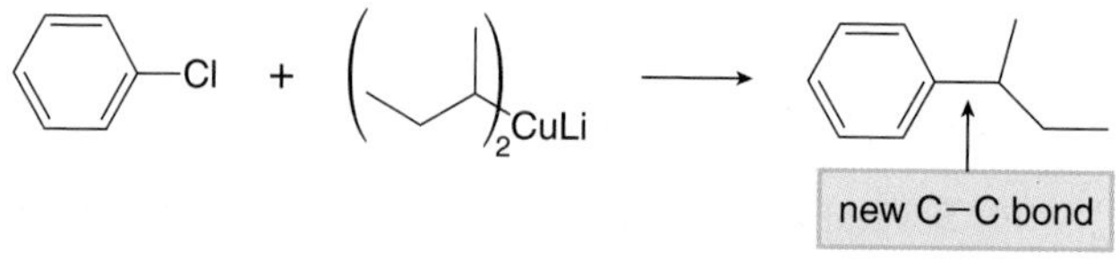

[3] 

trans-1-bromo-1-hexene *trans*-2-heptene

Coupling reactions with vinyl halides are **stereospecific.** For example, reaction of *trans*-1-bromo-1-hexene with $(CH_3)_2CuLi$ forms *trans*-2-heptene as the only stereoisomer (Equation [3]).

Problem 26.1 Draw the product of each coupling reaction.

a. 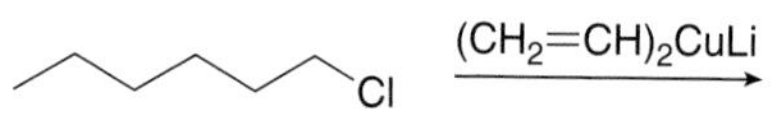

c. 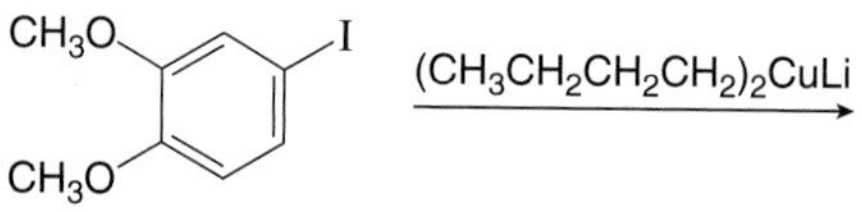

b. 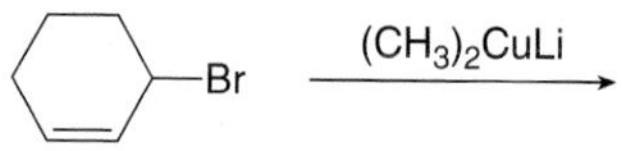

d. 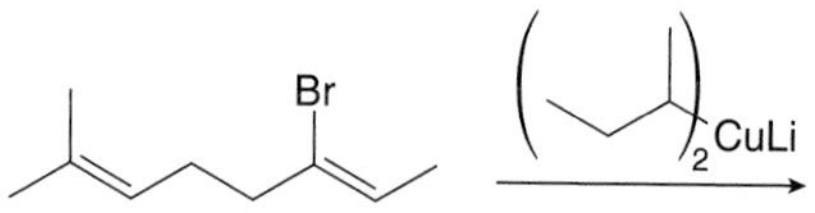

Problem 26.2 Identify reagents **A** and **B** in the following reaction scheme. This synthetic sequence was used to prepare the C_{18} juvenile hormone (Figure 20.6).

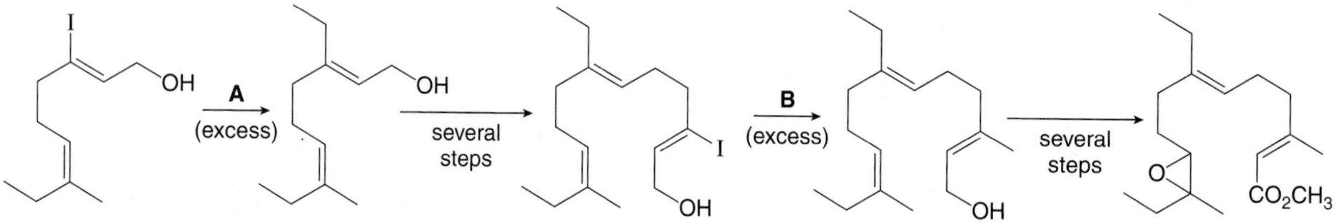

C_{18} juvenile hormone

26.1B Using Organocuprate Couplings to Synthesize Hydrocarbons

Since organocuprate reagents (R_2CuLi) are prepared in two steps from alkyl halides (RX), this method ultimately converts two organic halides (RX and R'X) into a hydrocarbon R–R' with a new carbon–carbon bond. A hydrocarbon can often be made by two different routes, as shown in Sample Problem 26.1.

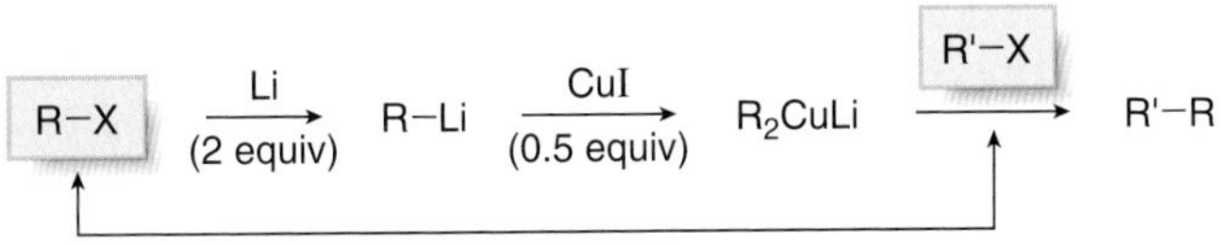
R–X
Li
(2 equiv)
R–Li
CuI
(0.5 equiv)
R₂CuLi
R'–X
R'–R

Two organic halides are needed as starting materials.

Sample Problem 26.1 Devise a synthesis of 1-methylcyclohexene from 1-bromocyclohexene and CH_3I.

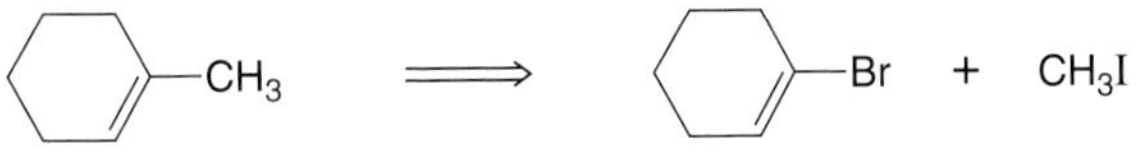
CH₃
Br
+
CH₃I

1-methylcyclohexene 1-bromocyclohexene

Solution

In this example, either halide can be used to form an organocuprate, which can then be coupled with the second halide.

Possibility [1]

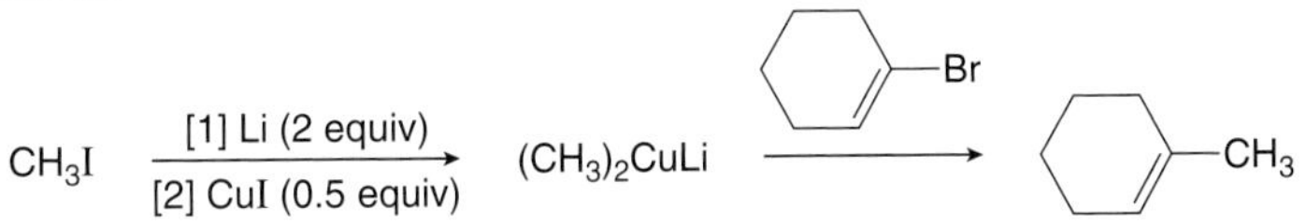
CH₃I
[1] Li (2 equiv)
[2] CuI (0.5 equiv)
(CH₃)₂CuLi
Br
CH₃

Possibility [2]

Br
[1] Li (2 equiv)
[2] CuI (0.5 equiv)
CuLi
2
CH₃I
CH₃

Problem 26.3 Synthesize each product from the given starting materials using an organocuprate coupling reaction.

a.

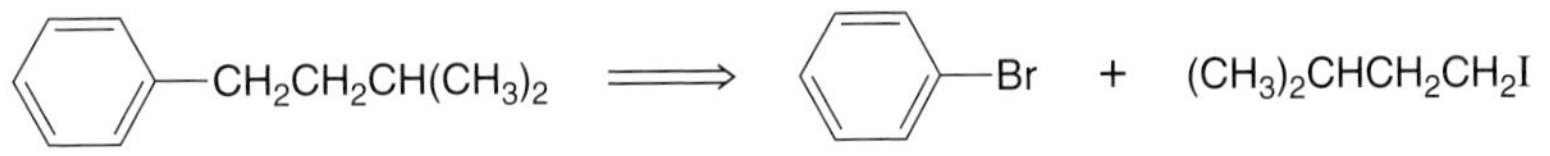
CH₂CH₂CH(CH₃)₂
Br
+
(CH₃)₂CHCH₂CH₂I

b.

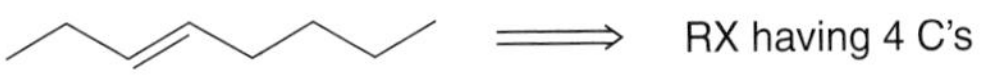
RX having 4 C's

c.

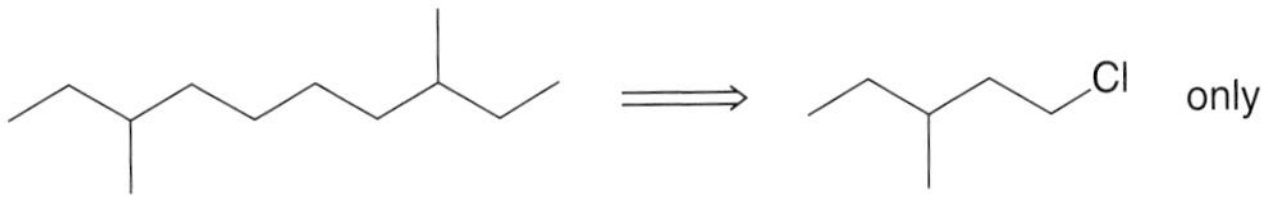
Cl
only

The mechanism of this reaction is not fully understood, and it may vary with the identity of R' in R'–X. Since coupling occurs with organic halides having the halogen X on either an sp^3 or sp^2 hybridized carbon, an S_N2 mechanism cannot explain all the observed results.

26.2 Suzuki Reaction

The **Suzuki reaction** is the first of two reactions that utilize a palladium catalyst and proceed by way of an intermediate organopalladium compound. The second is the Heck reaction (Section 26.3).

26.2A General Features of Reactions with Pd Catalysts

Reactions with palladium compounds share many common features with reactions involving other transition metals. During a reaction, palladium is coordinated to a variety of groups called **ligands,** which donate electron density to (or sometimes withdraw electron density from) the metal. A common electron-donating ligand is a **phosphine,** such as triphenylphosphine, tri(*o*-tolyl)phosphine, or tricyclohexylphosphine.

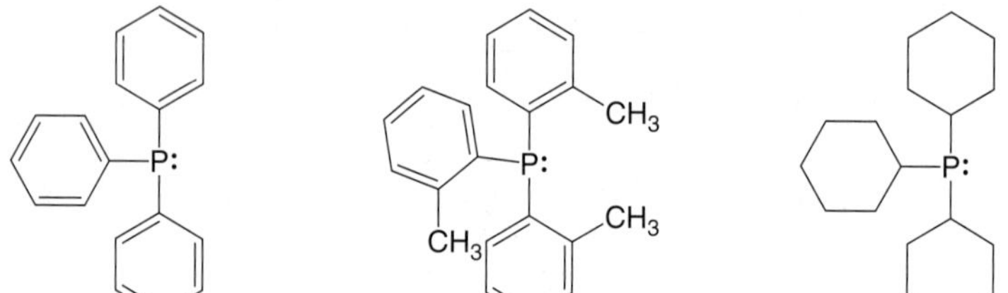

PPh_3 triphenylphosphine | **P(*o*-tolyl)$_3$** tri(*o*-tolyl)phosphine abbreviated as **PAr_3** Ar = an aryl group | **PCy_3** tricyclohexylphosphine

A general ligand bonded to a metal is often designated as **L.** Pd bonded to four ligands is denoted as PdL_4.

Ac is the abbreviation for an acetyl group, **$CH_3C=O$,** so OAc (or $^-$OAc) is the abbreviation for acetate, **$CH_3CO_2^-$.**

Organopalladium compounds—compounds that contain a carbon–palladium bond—are generally prepared in situ during the course of a reaction, from another palladium reagent such as $Pd(OAc)_2$ or $Pd(PPh_3)_4$. In most useful reactions only a catalytic amount of palladium reagent is utilized.

Two common processes, called **oxidative addition** and **reductive elimination,** dominate many reactions of palladium compounds.

- ***Oxidative addition* is the addition of a reagent (such as RX) to a metal, often increasing the number of groups around the metal by two.**

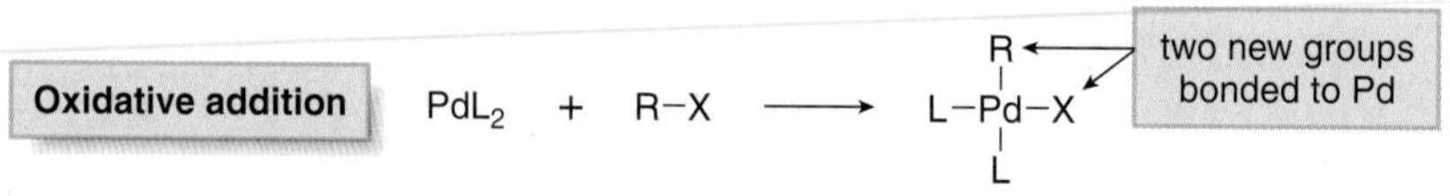

organopalladium compound

- ***Reductive elimination* is the elimination of two groups that surround the metal, often forming new C–H or C–C bonds.**

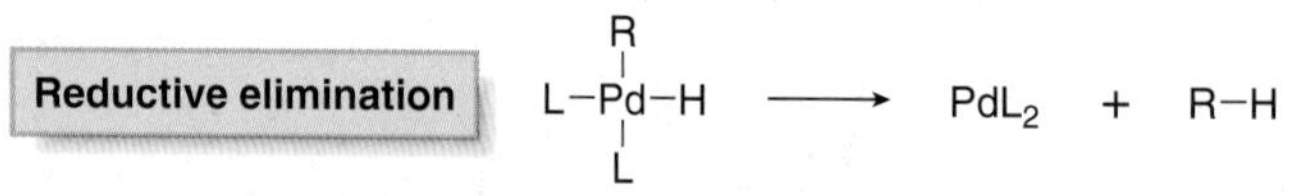

organopalladium compound

Reaction mechanisms with palladium compounds are often multistep. During the course of a reaction, the identity of some groups bonded to Pd will be known with certainty, while the identity of other ligands might not be known. Consequently, only the crucial reacting groups around a metal are usually drawn and the other ligands are not specified.

26.2B Details of the Suzuki Reaction

The **Suzuki reaction** is a palladium-catalyzed coupling of an organic halide (R'X) with an organoborane (RBY_2) to form a product (R–R') with a new C–C bond. $Pd(PPh_3)_4$ is the typical palladium catalyst, and the reaction is carried out in the presence of a base such as NaOH or $NaOCH_2CH_3$.

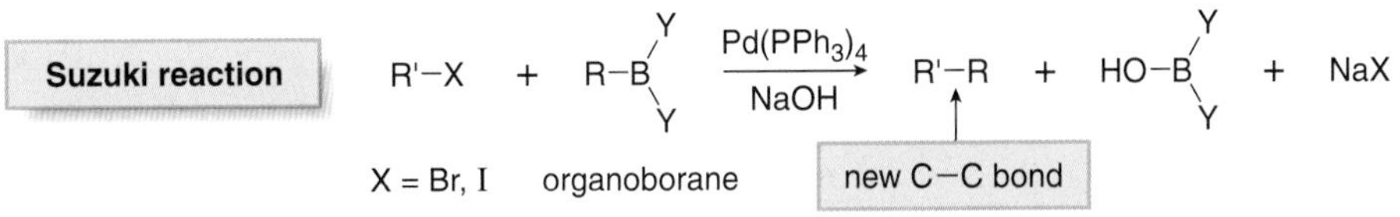

Vinyl halides and aryl halides, both of which contain a halogen X bonded directly to an sp^2 hybridized carbon, are most often used, and the halogen is usually Br or I. The Suzuki reaction is completely **stereospecific,** as shown in Example [3]; a cis vinyl halide and a trans vinylborane form a *cis,trans*-1,3-diene.

Examples

[1] [2] [3]

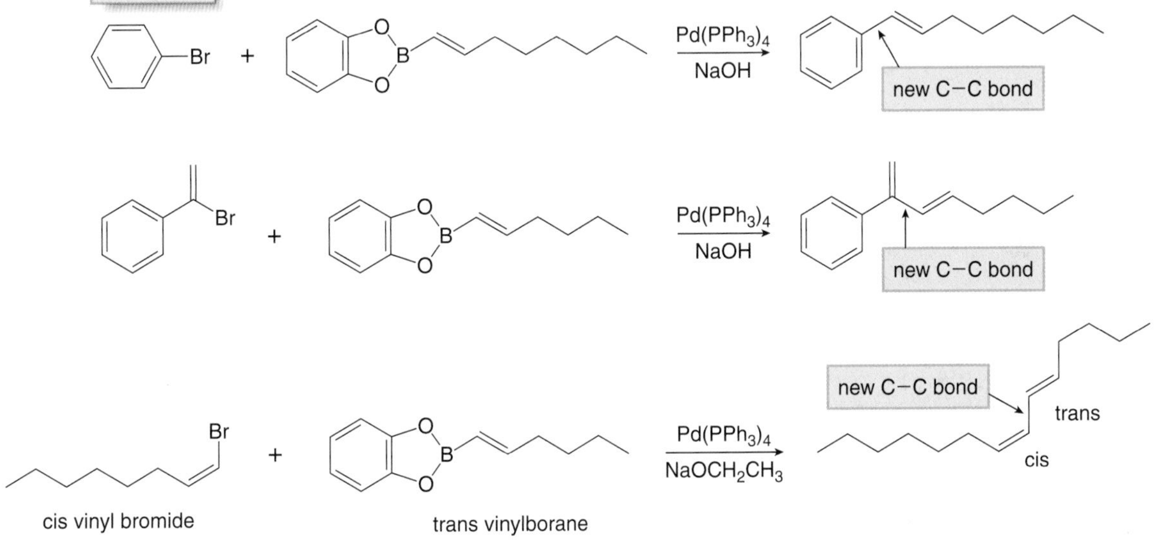

The organoboranes used in the Suzuki reaction are prepared from two sources.

- **Vinylboranes,** which have a boron atom bonded to a carbon–carbon double bond, are prepared by hydroboration of an alkyne using catecholborane, a commercially available reagent. **Hydroboration adds the elements of H and B in a syn fashion to form a trans vinylborane.** With terminal alkynes, hydroboration always places the boron atom on the *less substituted* terminal carbon.

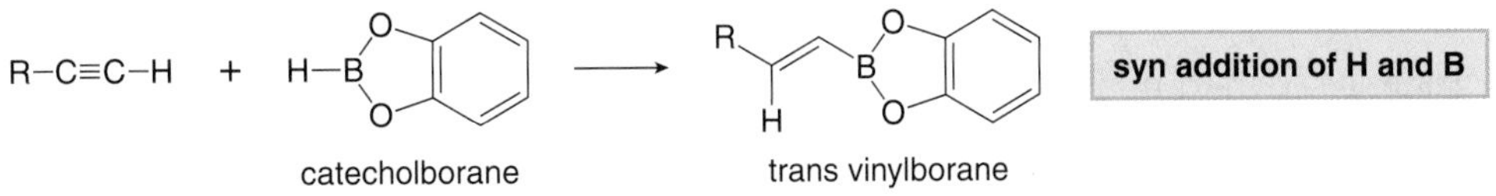

- **Arylboranes,** which have a boron atom bonded to a benzene ring, are prepared from organolithium reagents by reaction with trimethyl borate [$B(OCH_3)_3$].

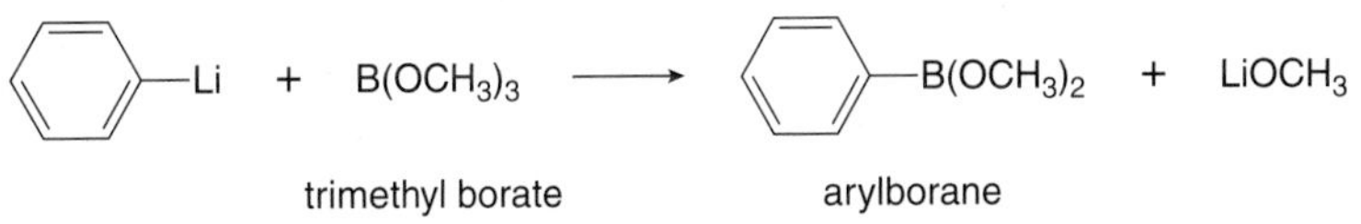

Problem 26.4 Draw the product of each reaction.

a. 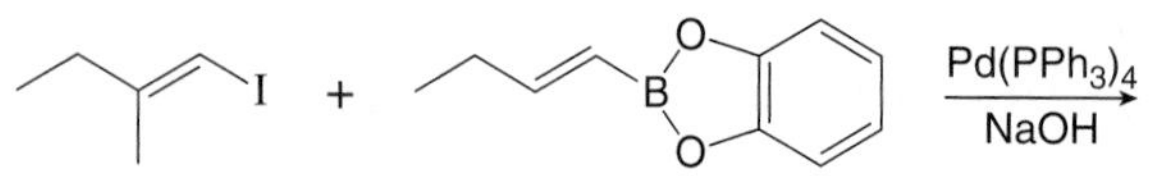
I
B
O
O
$Pd(PPh_3)_4$
NaOH

b. 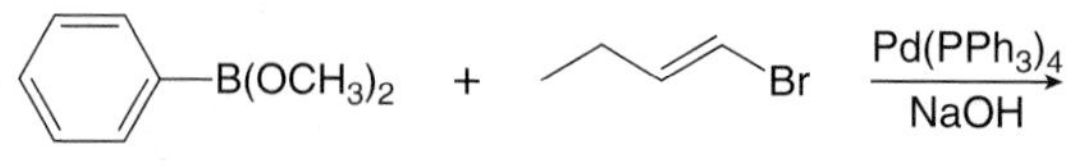
$B(OCH_3)_2$
Br
$Pd(PPh_3)_4$
NaOH

c. 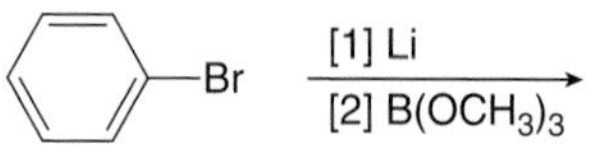
Br
[1] Li
[2] $B(OCH_3)_3$

d. 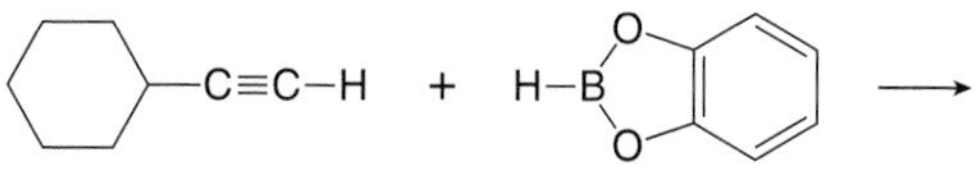
C≡C–H
H–B
O
O

Problem 26.5 One step in the synthesis of the nonsteroidal anti-inflammatory drug rofecoxib (trade name Vioxx, Section 30.6) involves Suzuki coupling of **A** and **B.** What product is formed in this reaction?

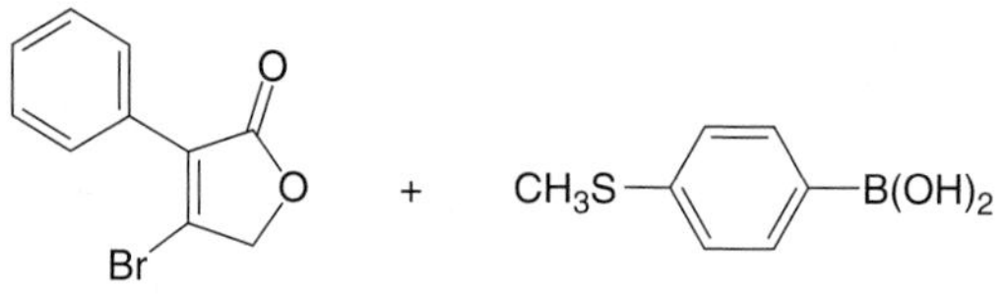
O
O
Br
CH_3S
$B(OH)_2$

A **B**

The mechanism of the Suzuki reaction can be conceptually divided into three parts: oxidative addition of R'–X to the palladium catalyst, transfer of an alkyl group from the organoborane to palladium, and reductive elimination of R–R', forming a new carbon–carbon bond. A general halide R'–X and organoborane $R-BY_2$ are used to illustrate this process in Mechanism 26.1. Since the palladium reagent is regenerated during reductive elimination, only a catalytic amount of palladium is needed.

Mechanism 26.1 Suzuki Reaction

Part [1] Formation of an organopalladium compound by oxidative addition

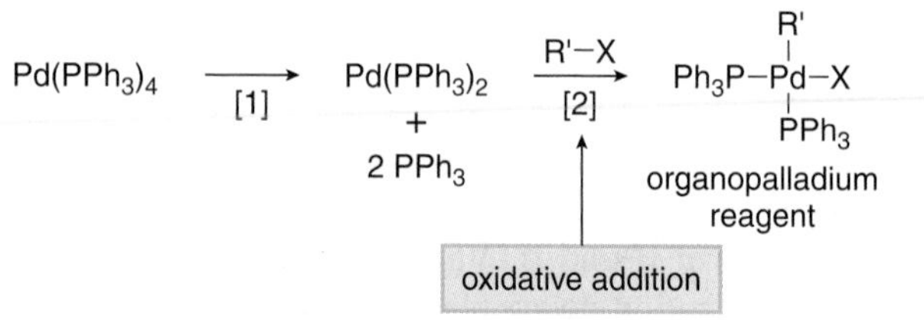
$Pd(PPh_3)_4$
[1]
$Pd(PPh_3)_2$
+
2 PPh_3
R'–X
[2]
R'
Ph_3P–Pd–X
PPh_3
organopalladium reagent
oxidative addition

- Loss of two triphenylphosphine ligands followed by oxidative addition forms an organopalladium compound.
- The organopalladium compound $(Ph_3P)_2Pd(R')X$ bears no net charge, and by convention, organometallic chemists generally omit formal charges on the phosphorus ligands and the metal.

Part [2] Transfer of an alkyl group from boron to palladium

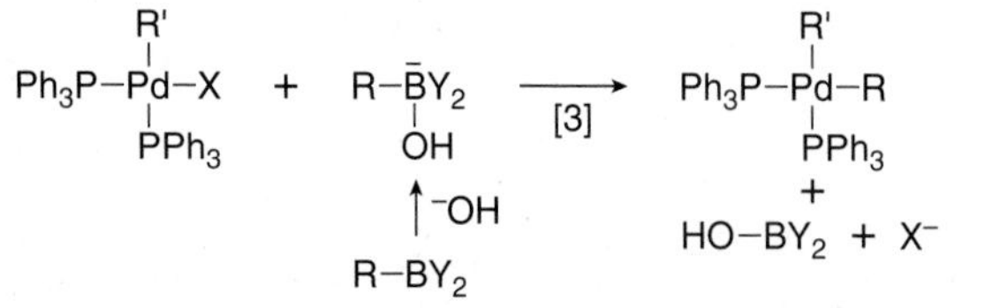
R'
Ph_3P–Pd–X
PPh_3
+
$R-\bar{B}Y_2$
OH
^-OH
$R-BY_2$
[3]
R'
Ph_3P–Pd–R
PPh_3
+
$HO-BY_2$ + X^-

- Reaction of the organoborane $R-BY_2$ with ^-OH forms a nucleophilic boron intermediate that transfers an alkyl group from boron to palladium in Step [3].

Part [3] Reductive elimination

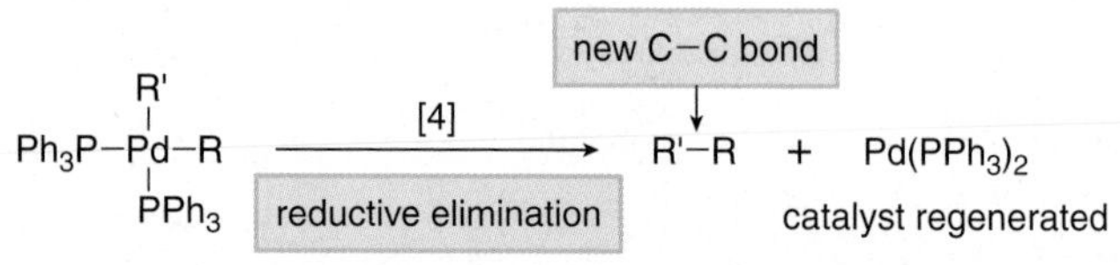
new C–C bond
R'
Ph_3P–Pd–R
PPh_3
[4]
reductive elimination
R'–R + $Pd(PPh_3)_2$
catalyst regenerated

- Reductive elimination of R–R' forms the coupling product.
- The palladium catalyst $Pd(PPh_3)_2$ is regenerated so the cycle can repeat.

Figure 26.1 Synthesis of two natural products using the Suzuki reaction

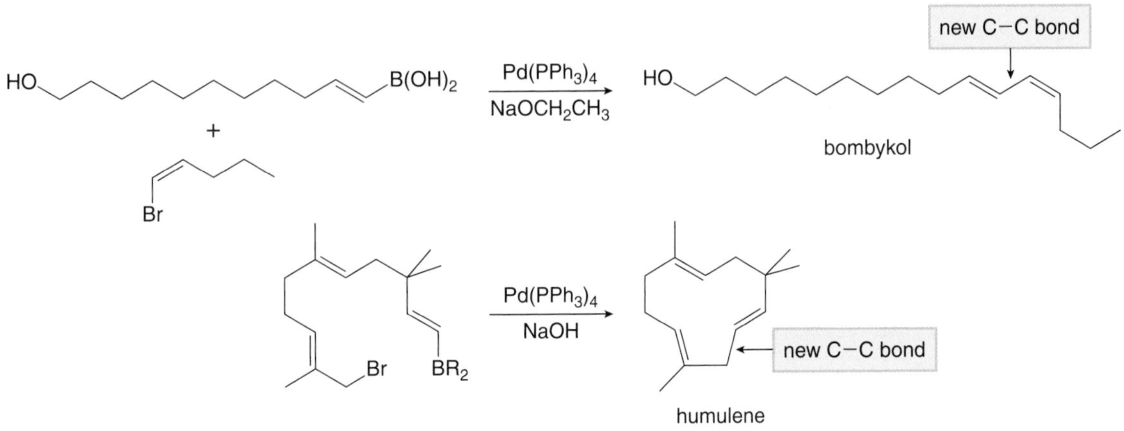

The Suzuki reaction was a key step in the synthesis of **bombykol,** the sex pheromone of the female silkworm moth and the chapter-opening molecule, and **humulene,** a lipid isolated from hops, as shown in Figure 26.1. The synthesis of humulene illustrates that an intramolecular Suzuki reaction can form a ring. Sample Problem 26.2 shows how a conjugated diene can be prepared from an alkyne and vinyl halide using a Suzuki reaction.

Sample Problem 26.2

Devise a synthesis of (1*Z*,3*E*)-1-phenyl-1,3-octadiene from 1-hexyne and (*Z*)-2-bromostyrene using a Suzuki coupling.

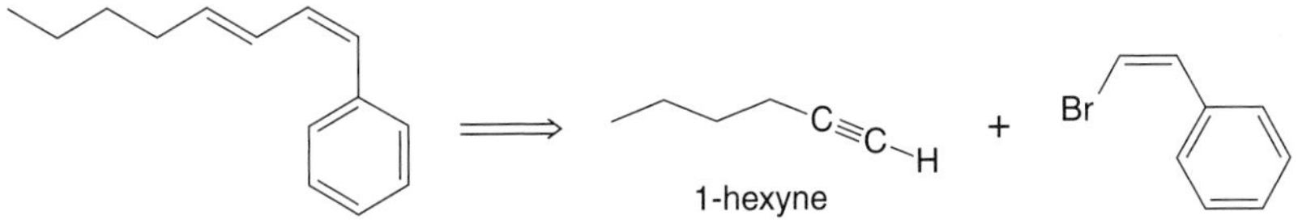

(1*Z*,3*E*)-1-phenyl-1,3-octadiene (*Z*)-2-bromostyrene

Solution

This synthesis can be accomplished in two steps. Hydroboration of 1-hexyne with catecholborane forms a vinylborane. Coupling of this vinylborane with (*Z*)-2-bromostyrene gives the desired 1,3-diene. The *E* configuration of the vinylborane and the *Z* configuration of the vinyl bromide are both retained in the product.

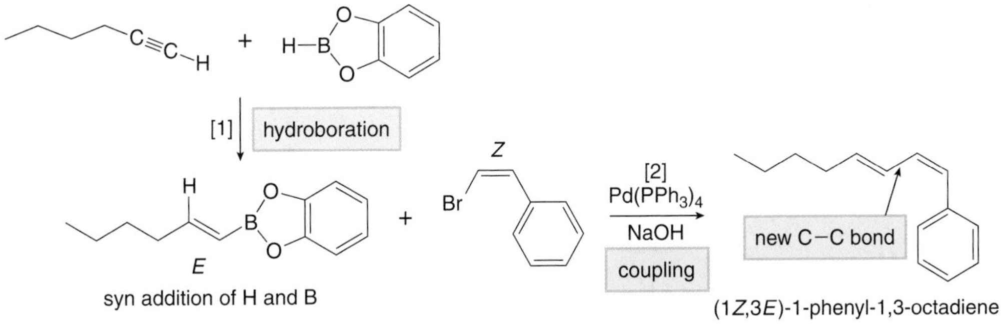

Problem 26.6

Synthesize each compound from the given starting materials.

a. 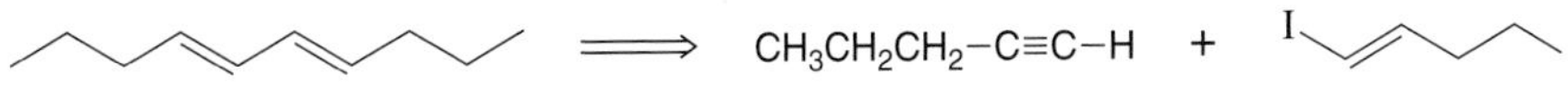

b. 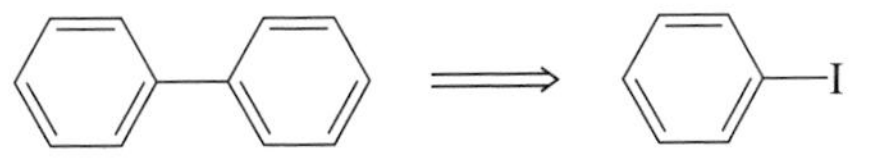

c. 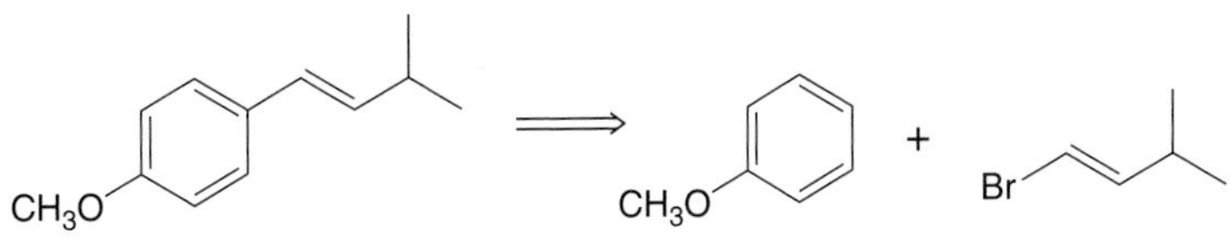

26.3 Heck Reaction

Richard Heck and Akira Suzuki won the 2010 Nobel Prize in Chemistry for the discovery of the carbon–carbon bond-forming reactions detailed in Sections 26.2 and 26.3.

The **Heck reaction is a palladium-catalyzed coupling of a vinyl or aryl halide with an alkene to form a more highly substituted alkene with a new C–C bond.** Palladium(II) acetate [$Pd(OAc)_2$] in the presence of a triarylphosphine [P(*o*-tolyl)$_3$] is the typical catalyst, and the reaction is carried out in the presence of a base such as triethylamine. The Heck reaction is a **substitution reaction** in which one H atom of the alkene starting material is replaced by the R' group of the vinyl or aryl halide.

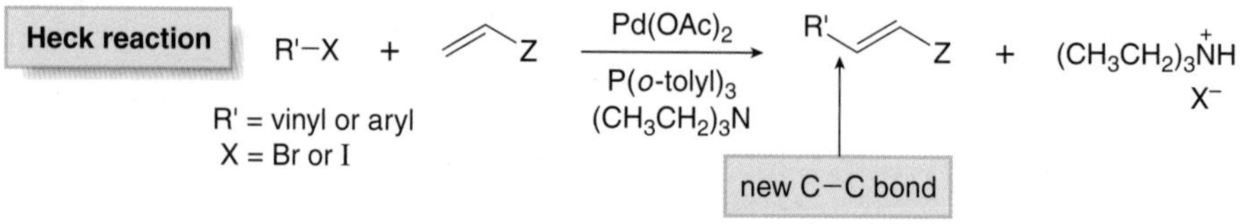

The alkene component is typically ethylene or a monosubstituted alkene ($CH_2{=}CHZ$), and the halogen X is usually Br or I. When Z = Ph, COOR, or CN in a monosubstituted alkene, **the new C–C bond is formed on the *less* substituted carbon to afford a trans alkene.** When a vinyl halide is used as the organic halide, the reaction is **stereospecific,** as shown in Example [3]; the trans stereochemistry of the vinyl iodide is retained in the product.

Examples

[1]

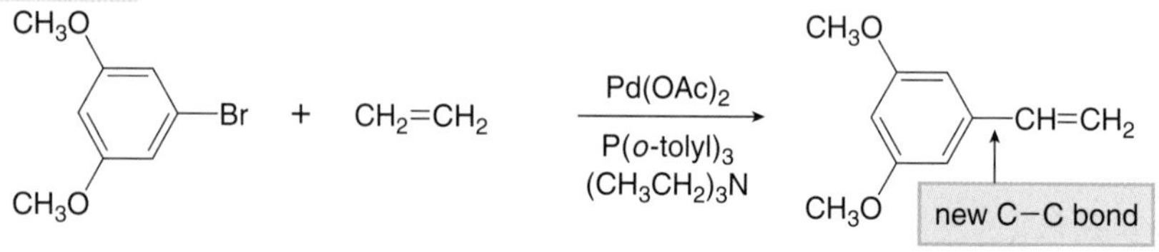

[2]

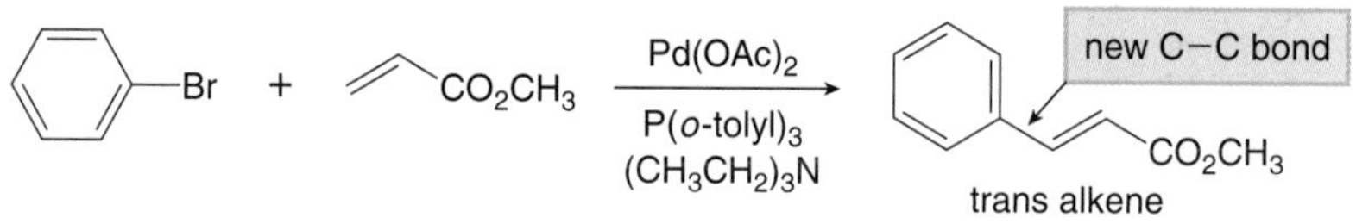

[3]

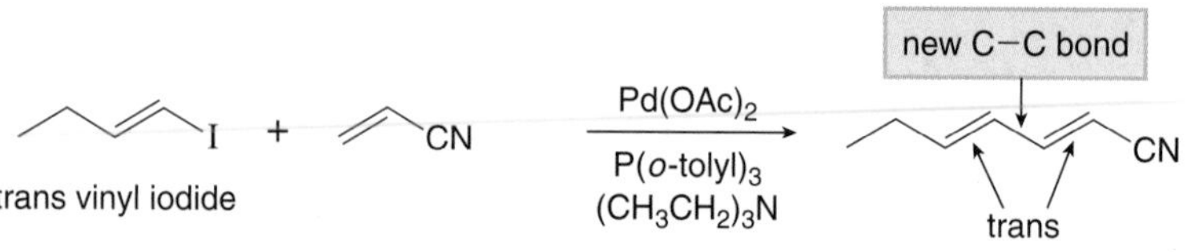

Problem 26.7 Draw the coupling product formed when each pair of compounds is treated with $Pd(OAc)_2$, P(*o*-tolyl)$_3$, and $(CH_3CH_2)_3N$.

a.

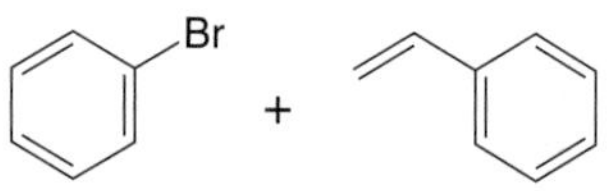

c.

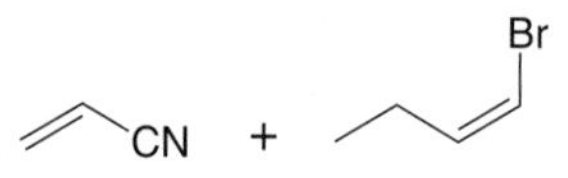

b.

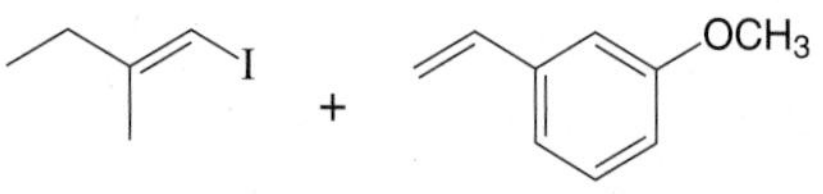

d.

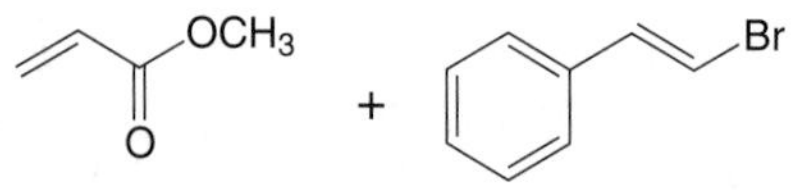

To use the Heck reaction in synthesis, you must determine what alkene and what organic halide are needed to prepare a given compound. To work backwards, locate the double bond with the aryl, COOR, or CN substituent, and break the molecule into two components at the end of the C=C not bonded to one of these substituents. Sample Problem 26.3 illustrates this retrosynthetic analysis.

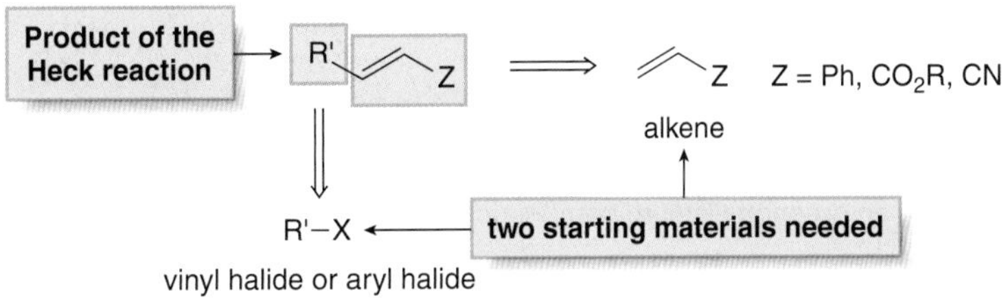

Sample Problem 26.3 What starting materials are needed to prepare each alkene using a Heck reaction?

a. 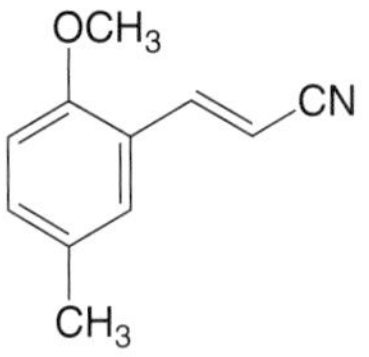

b. 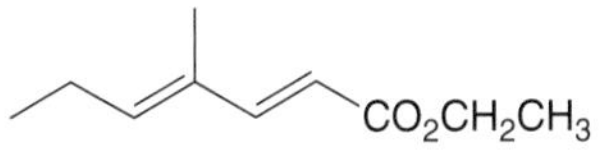

Solution

To prepare an alkene of general formula R'CH=CHZ by the Heck reaction, two starting materials are needed—an alkene (CH_2=CHZ) and a vinyl or aryl halide (R'X).

Form this new C–C bond.

a. 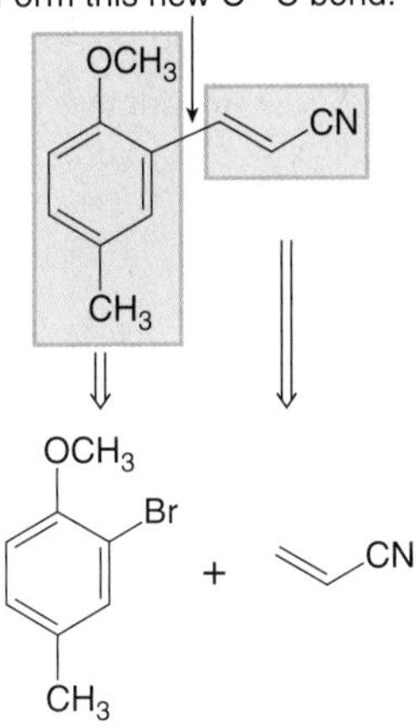

Form this new C–C bond.

b. 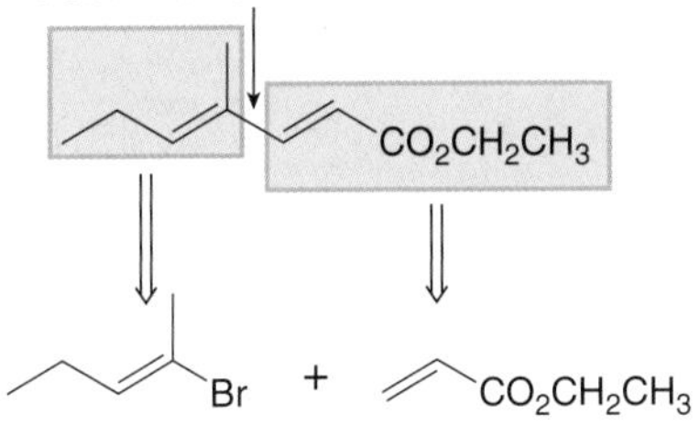

Problem 26.8 What starting materials are needed to prepare each compound using a Heck reaction?

a. 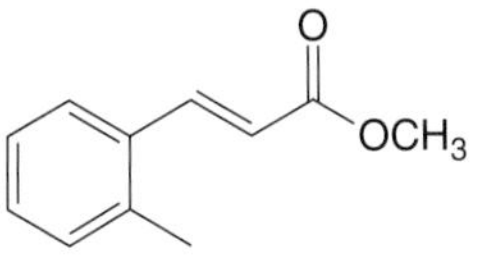

b. 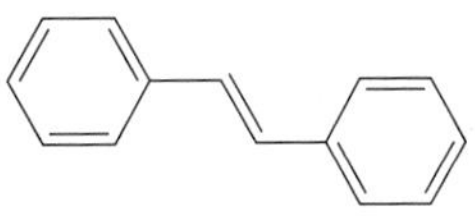

c. 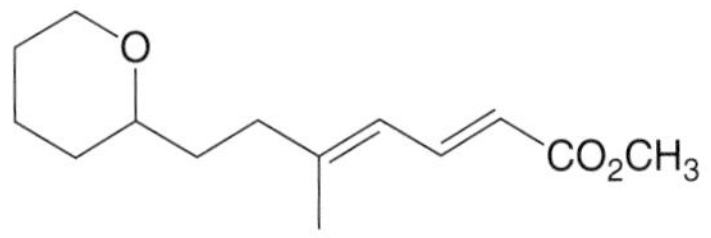

The actual palladium catalyst in the Heck reaction is thought to contain a palladium atom bonded to two tri(*o*-tolyl)phosphine ligands, abbreviated as $Pd(PAr_3)_2$. In this way it resembles the divalent palladium catalyst used in the Suzuki reaction. The mechanism of the Heck reaction conceptually consists of three parts: oxidative addition of the halide R'X to the palladium catalyst, addition of the resulting organopalladium reagent to the alkene, and two successive eliminations. A general organic halide R'X and alkene $CH_2{=}CHZ$ are used to illustrate the process in Mechanism 26.2.

Mechanism 26.2 Heck Reaction

Step [1] Formation of an organopalladium compound by oxidative addition

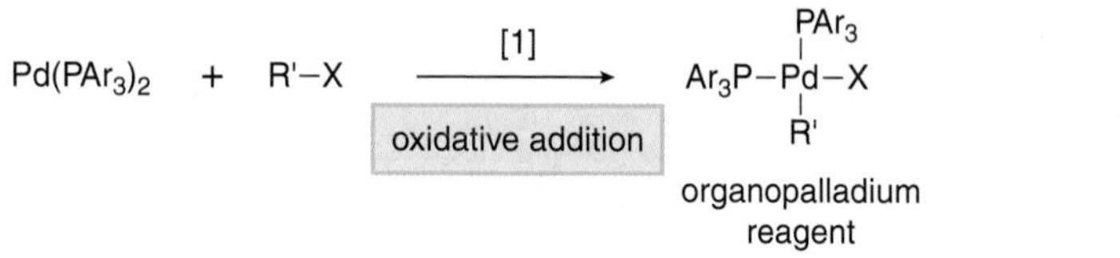

- Oxidative addition of R'X forms an organopalladium compound.

Step [2] Addition of R' and Pd to the double bond

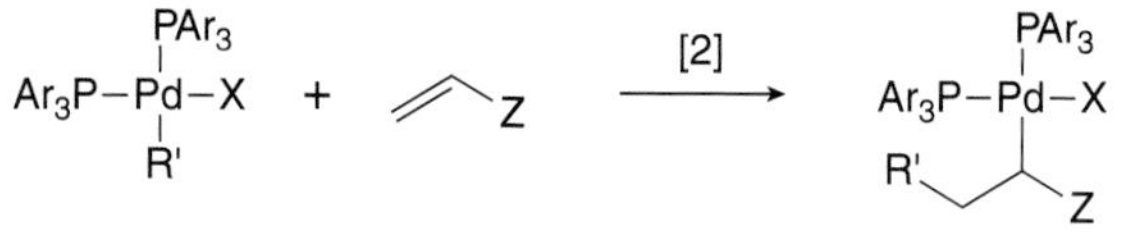

- Addition of R' and Pd to the π bond places the Pd on the carbon with the Z substituent.

Steps [3]–[4] Two successive eliminations

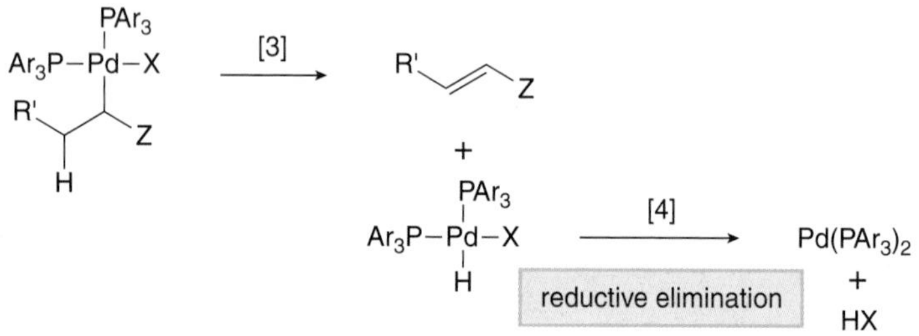

- Elimination of H and Pd forms the alkene in Step [3] and transfers a hydrogen to Pd.
- Reductive elimination of HX regenerates the palladium catalyst $Pd(PAr_3)_2$ in Step [4].

26.4 Carbenes and Cyclopropane Synthesis

Another method of carbon–carbon bond formation involves the conversion of alkenes to cyclopropane rings using **carbene** intermediates.

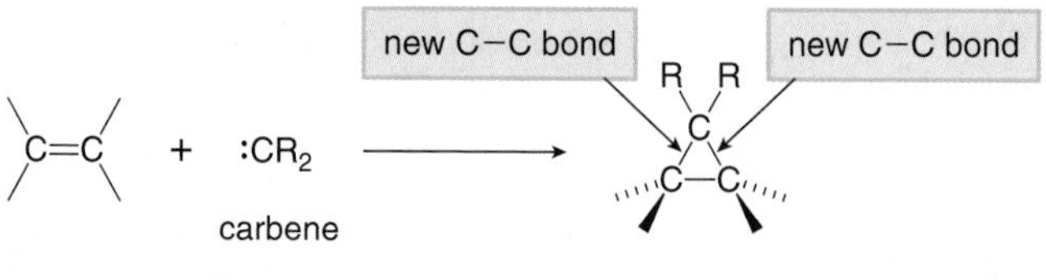

Pyrethrin I and **decamethrin** both contain cyclopropane rings. Pyrethrin I is a naturally occurring biodegradable insecticide obtained from chrysanthemums, whereas **decamethrin** is a more potent synthetic analogue that is widely used as an insecticide in agriculture.

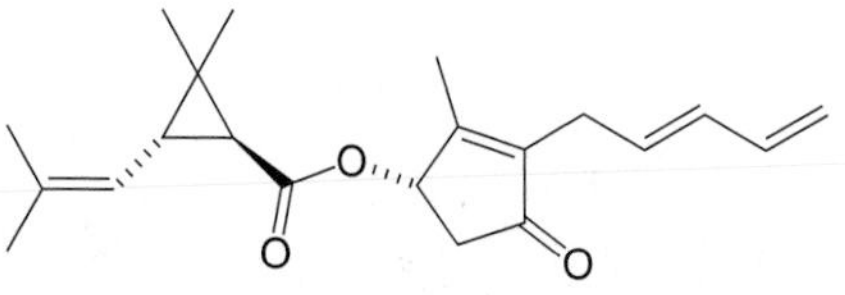

pyrethrin I

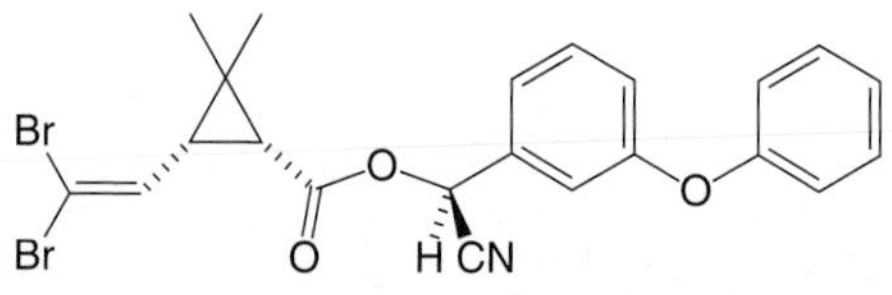

decamethrin

26.4A Carbenes

A *carbene*, R_2C:, is a neutral reactive intermediate that contains a divalent carbon surrounded by six electrons—the lone pair and two each from the two R groups. These three groups make the carbene carbon ***sp^2* hybridized,** with a vacant *p* orbital extending above and below the plane containing the C and the two R groups. The lone pair of electrons occupies an sp^2 hybrid orbital.

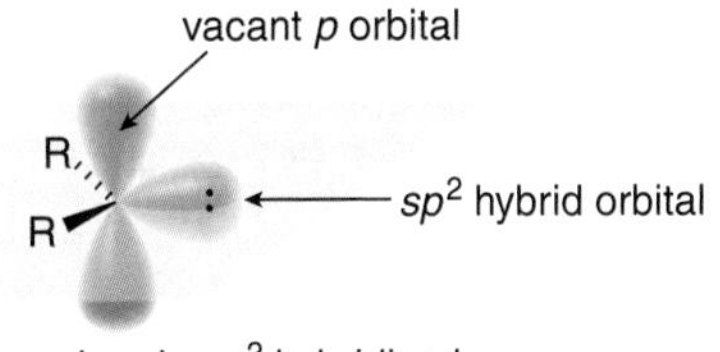

The carbene carbon is sp^2 hybridized.

Carbenes share two features in common with carbocations and carbon radicals.

- **A carbene is highly reactive since carbon does not have an octet of electrons.**
- **A carbene is electron deficient, and so it behaves as an electrophile.**

26.4B Preparation and Reactions of Dihalocarbenes

Dihalocarbenes, $:CX_2$, are especially useful reactive intermediates since they are readily prepared from trihalomethanes (CHX_3) by reaction with a strong base. For example, treatment of chloroform, $CHCl_3$, with $KOC(CH_3)_3$ forms dichlorocarbene, $:CCl_2$.

$$\underset{\text{chloroform}}{CHCl_3} \xrightarrow{KOC(CH_3)_3} \underset{\text{dichlorocarbene}}{:CCl_2} + (CH_3)_3COH + KCl$$

Dichlorocarbene is formed by a two-step process that results in the elimination of the elements of H and Cl from the *same* carbon, as shown in Mechanism 26.3. Loss of two elements from the same carbon is called **α elimination,** to distinguish it from the β eliminations discussed in Chapter 8, in which two elements are lost from *adjacent* carbons.

Mechanism 26.3 Formation of Dichlorocarbene

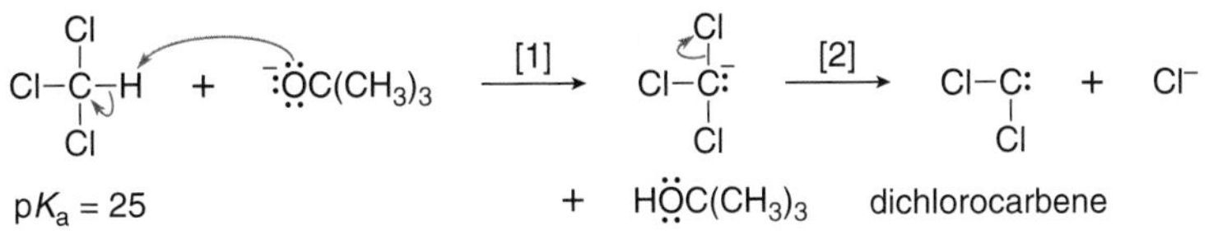

- Three electronegative Cl atoms acidify the C – H bond of $CHCl_3$ so that it can be removed by a strong base to form a carbanion in Step [1].
- Elimination of Cl^- in Step [2] forms the carbene.

Since dihalocarbenes are electrophiles, they readily react with double bonds to afford cyclopropanes, forming two new carbon–carbon bonds.

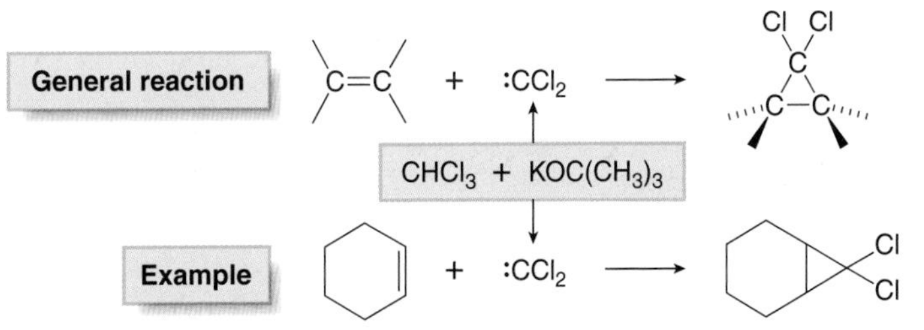

Cyclopropanation is a concerted reaction, so both C−C bonds are formed in a single step, as shown in Mechanism 26.4.

Mechanism 26.4 Addition of Dichlorocarbene to an Alkene

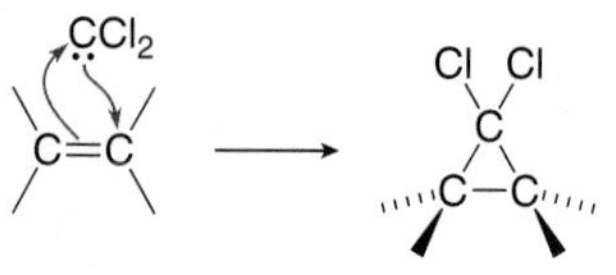

Carbene addition occurs in a **syn** fashion from either side of the planar double bond. The relative position of substituents in the alkene reactant is retained in the cyclopropane product. **Carbene addition is thus a stereospecific reaction,** since cis and trans alkenes yield different stereoisomers as products, as illustrated in Sample Problem 26.4.

Sample Problem 26.4 Draw the products formed when *cis*- and *trans*-2-butene are treated with $CHCl_3$ and $KOC(CH_3)_3$.

Solution

To draw each product, add the carbene carbon from either side of the alkene, and keep all substituents in their original orientations. The **cis** methyl groups in *cis*-2-butene become **cis** substituents in the cyclopropane. Addition from either side of the alkene yields the same compound—**an achiral meso compound that contains two stereogenic centers.**

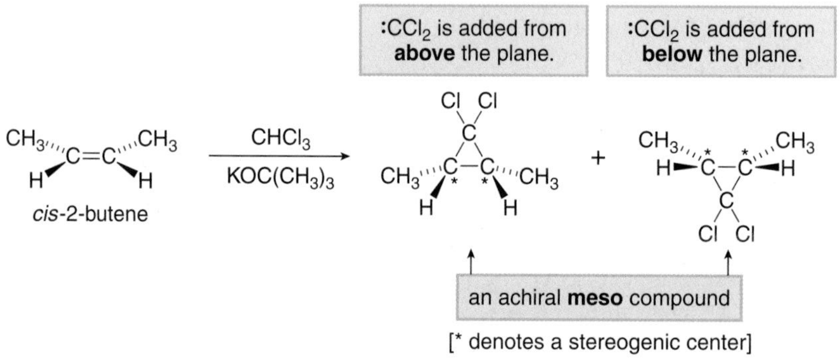

The **trans** methyl groups in *trans*-2-butene become **trans** substituents in the cyclopropane. Addition from either side of the alkene yields an equal amount of two enantiomers—**a racemic mixture.**

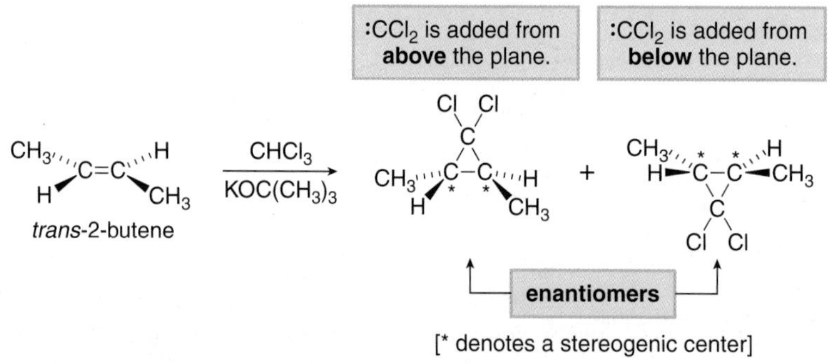

Problem 26.9 Draw all stereoisomers formed when each alkene is treated with $CHCl_3$ and $KOC(CH_3)_3$.

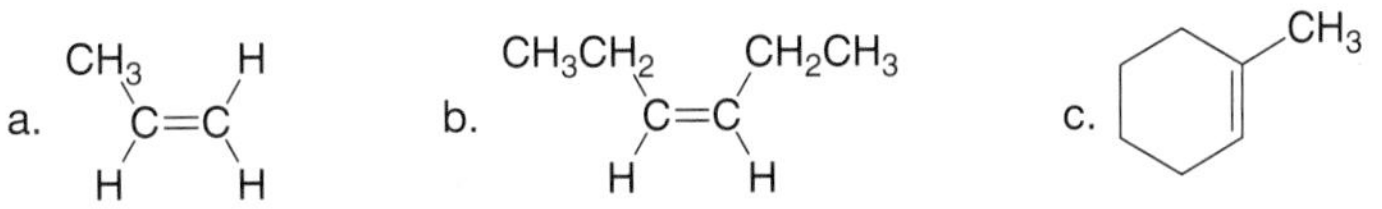

a.
CH3
H
C=C
H
H
b.
CH3CH2
CH2CH3
C=C
H
H
c.
CH3

Finally, dihalo cyclopropanes can be converted to dialkyl cyclopropanes by reaction with organocuprates (Section 26.1). For example, cyclohexene can be converted to a bicyclic product having four new C–C bonds by the following two-step sequence: cyclopropanation with dibromocarbene ($:CBr_2$) and reaction with lithium dimethylcuprate, $LiCu(CH_3)_2$.

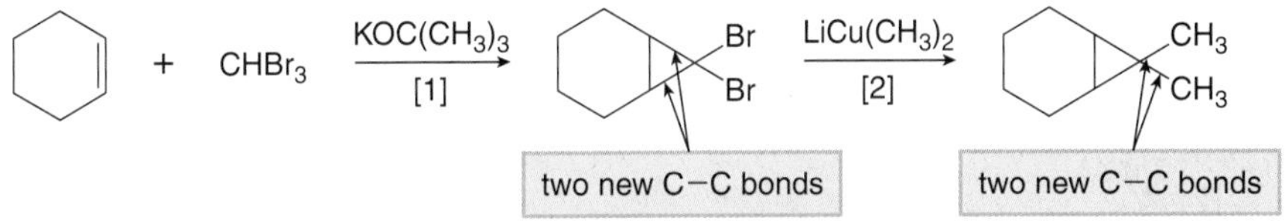

+
CHBr3
KOC(CH3)3
[1]
Br
Br
LiCu(CH3)2
[2]
CH3
CH3
two new C–C bonds
two new C–C bonds

Problem 26.10 What reagents are needed to convert 2-methylpropene [$(CH_3)_2C=CH_2$] to each compound? More than one step may be required.

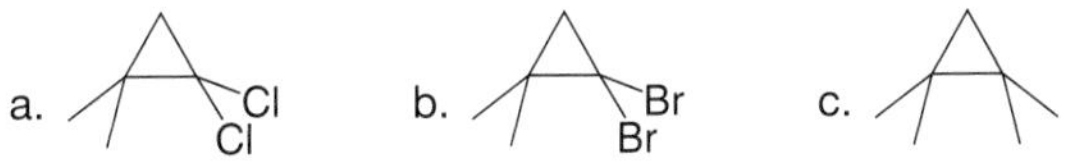

a.
Cl
Cl
b.
Br
Br
c.

26.5 Simmons–Smith Reaction

Although the reaction of dihalocarbenes with alkenes gives good yields of halogenated cyclopropanes, this is not usually the case with **methylene, $:CH_2$,** the simplest carbene. Methylene is readily formed by heating diazomethane, CH_2N_2, which decomposes and loses N_2, but the reaction of $:CH_2$ with alkenes often affords a complex mixture of products. Thus, this reaction cannot be reliably used for cyclopropane synthesis.

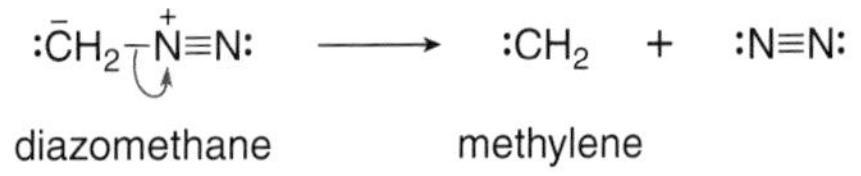

:CH2–N≡N:
:CH2
+
:N≡N:
diazomethane
methylene

Nonhalogenated cyclopropanes can be prepared by the reaction of an alkene with diiodomethane, CH_2I_2, in the presence of a copper-activated zinc reagent called zinc–copper couple [Zn(Cu)]. This process, the **Simmons–Smith reaction,** is named for H. E. Simmons and R. D. Smith, DuPont chemists who discovered the reaction in 1959.

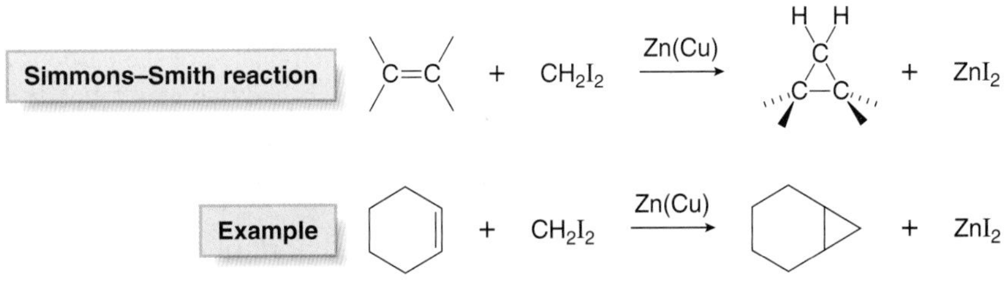

Simmons–Smith reaction
C=C
+
CH2I2
Zn(Cu)
H H
C
C–C
+
ZnI2
Example
+
CH2I2
Zn(Cu)
+
ZnI2

The Simmons–Smith reaction does not involve a free carbene. Rather, the reaction of CH_2I_2 with Zn(Cu) forms (iodomethyl)zinc iodide, which transfers a CH_2 group to an alkene, as shown in Mechanism 26.5.

Mechanism 26.5 Simmons–Smith Reaction

Step [1] Formation of the Simmons–Smith reagent

$$CH_2I_2 \xrightarrow[\text{[1]}]{Zn(Cu)} ICH_2{-}Zn{-}I$$

(iodomethyl)zinc iodide
Simmons–Smith reagent

- Reaction of CH_2I_2 with zinc–copper couple forms ICH_2ZnI, the **Simmons–Smith reagent.** Since the CH_2 group is bonded to the metal and does not exist as a free carbene, this intermediate is called a ***carbenoid.***

Step [2] Formation of the cyclopropane ring

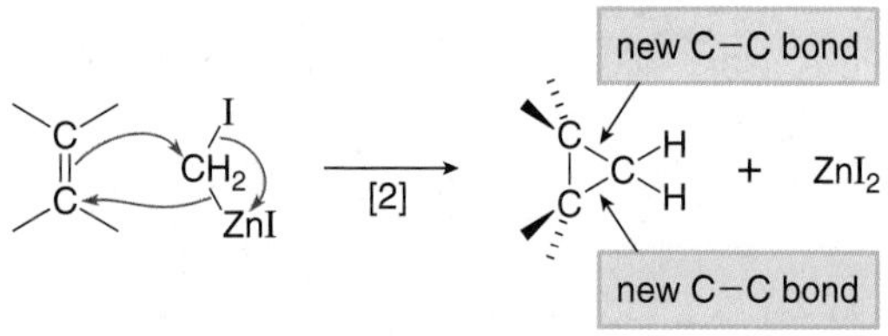
new C–C bond
[2]
+ ZnI2
new C–C bond

- The Simmons–Smith reagent transfers a CH_2 group to the alkene, forming two new C–C bonds in a single step.

The Simmons–Smith reaction is stereospecific. The relative position of substituents in the alkene reactant is *retained* in the cyclopropane product, as shown for the conversion of *cis*-3-hexene to *cis*-1,2-diethylcyclopropane.

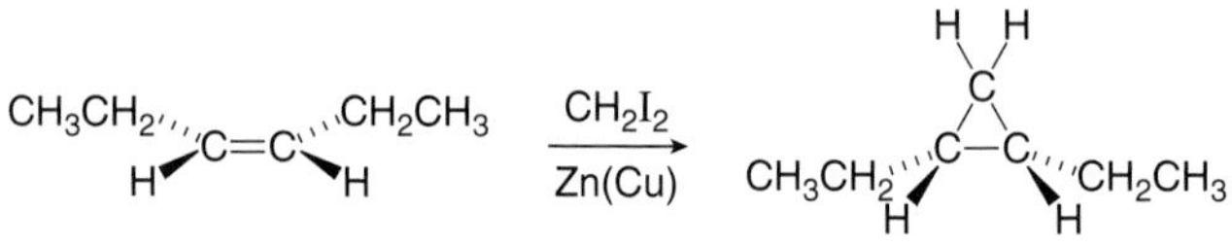
CH2I2
Zn(Cu)

cis-3-hexene *cis*-1,2-diethylcyclopropane

Problem 26.11 What product is formed when each alkene is treated with CH_2I_2 and Zn(Cu)?

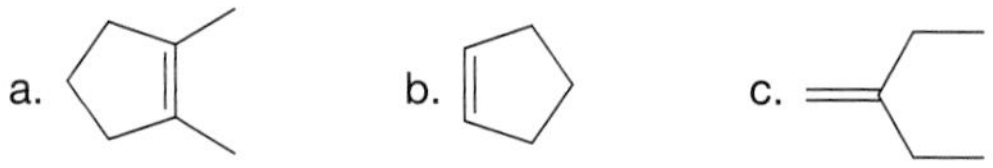
a.
b.
c.

Problem 26.12 What stereoisomers are formed when *trans*-3-hexene is treated with CH_2I_2 and Zn(Cu)?

26.6 Metathesis

Recall from Section 10.1 that **olefin** is another name for an **alkene.**

The word *metathesis* is derived from the Greek words *meta* (change) and *thesis* (position). The 2005 Nobel Prize in Chemistry was awarded to Robert Grubbs of the California Institute of Technology, Yves Chauvin of the Institut Français du Pétrole, and Richard Schrock of the Massachusetts Institute of Technology for their work on olefin metathesis.

Alkene metathesis, more commonly called **olefin metathesis,** is a reaction between two alkene molecules that results in the interchange of the carbons of their double bonds. Two σ and two π bonds are broken and two new σ and two new π bonds are formed.

Olefin metathesis

$$RCH{=}CH_2 + RCH{=}CH_2 \xrightarrow{\text{catalyst}} RCH{=}CHR + CH_2{=}CH_2$$

Olefin metathesis occurs in the presence of a complex transition metal catalyst that contains a carbon–metal double bond. The metal is typically ruthenium (Ru), tungsten (W), or molybdenum (Mo). In a widely used catalyst, called **Grubbs catalyst,** the metal is Ru.

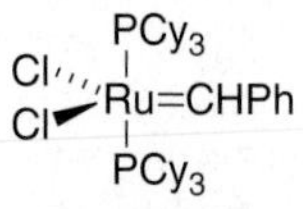
PCy3
Cl
Cl
Ru=CHPh
PCy3

Grubbs catalyst

Olefin metathesis is an equilibrium process and, with many alkene substrates, a mixture of starting material and two or more alkene products is present at equilibrium, making the reaction useless for preparative purposes. With terminal alkenes, however, one metathesis product is $CH_2{=}CH_2$ (a gas), which escapes from the reaction mixture and drives the equilibrium to the right. As a result, monosubstituted alkenes ($RCH{=}CH_2$) and 2,2-disubstituted alkenes ($R_2C{=}CH_2$) are excellent metathesis substrates because high yields of a single alkene product are obtained, as shown in Equations [1] and [2].

[1] $2\ CH_3CH_2CH_2CH{=}CH_2 \xrightarrow{Cl_2(Cy_3P)_2Ru{=}CHPh} CH_3CH_2CH_2CH{=}CHCH_2CH_2CH_3 + CH_2{=}CH_2$ (*E* and *Z*)

[2]

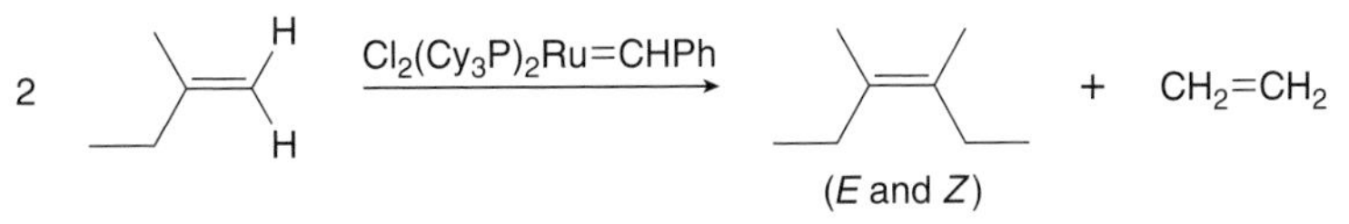

To draw the products of any metathesis reaction:

[1] Arrange two molecules of the starting alkene adjacent to each other as in Figure 26.2 where styrene ($PhCH{=}CH_2$) is used as the starting material.

[2] Then, break the double bonds in the starting material and form two new double bonds using carbon atoms that were *not* previously bonded to each other in the starting alkenes.

There are always two ways to arrange the starting alkenes (Pathways [1] and [2] in Figure 26.2). In this example, the two products of the reaction, $PhCH{=}CHPh$ and $CH_2{=}CH_2$ are formed in the first reaction pathway (Pathway [1]), while starting material is re-formed in the second pathway (Pathway [2]). Whenever the starting alkene is regenerated, it can go on to form product when the catalytic cycle is repeated.

Problem 26.13 Draw the products formed when each alkene is treated with Grubbs catalyst.

a. 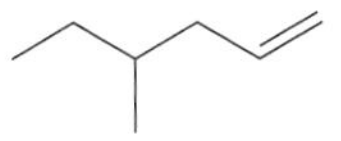

b. 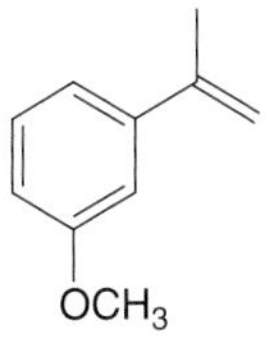

c. 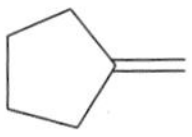

Figure 26.2 Drawing the products of olefin metathesis using styrene ($PhCH{=}CH_2$) as starting material

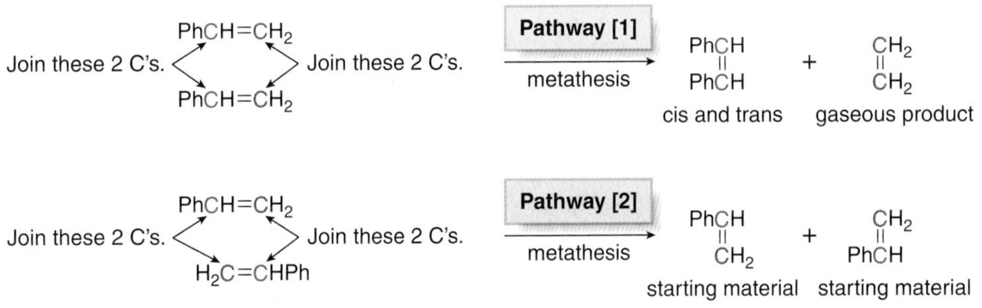

- Overall reaction: $2\ PhCH{=}CH_2 \rightarrow PhCH{=}CHPh + CH_2{=}CH_2$.
- There are always two ways to join the C's of a single alkene together to form metathesis products (Pathways [1] and [2]).
- When like C's of the alkene substrate are joined in the first reaction (Pathway [1]), $PhCH{=}CHPh$ (in a cis and trans mixture) and $CH_2{=}CH_2$ are formed. Since $CH_2{=}CH_2$ escapes as a gas from the reaction mixture, only $PhCH{=}CHPh$ is isolated as product.
- When unlike C's of $PhCH{=}CH_2$ are joined in the second reaction (Pathway [2]), starting material is formed, which can re-enter the catalytic cycle to form product by the first pathway.
- In this way, a single constitutional isomer, $PhCH{=}CHPh$, is isolated with two new C–C bonds.

Problem 26.14 What products are formed when *cis*-2-pentene undergoes metathesis? Use this reaction to explain why metathesis of a 1,2-disubstituted alkene (RCH=CHR') is generally not a practical method for alkene synthesis.

The mechanism for olefin metathesis is complex, and involves **metal–carbene intermediates—intermediates that contain a metal–carbon double bond.** The mechanism is drawn for the reaction of a terminal alkene ($RCH=CH_2$) with Grubbs catalyst, abbreviated as **Ru=CHPh,** to form RCH=CHR and $CH_2=CH_2$. To begin metathesis, Grubbs catalyst reacts with the alkene substrate to form two new metal–carbenes **A** and **B** by a two-step process: addition of Ru=CHPh to the alkene to yield two different metallocyclobutanes (Step [1]), followed by elimination to form **A** and **B** (Steps [2a] and [2b]). The alkene by-products formed in this process (RCH=CHPh and $PhCH=CH_2$) are present in only a small amount since Grubbs reagent is used catalytically.

Formation of the metal–carbene complexes needed for metathesis

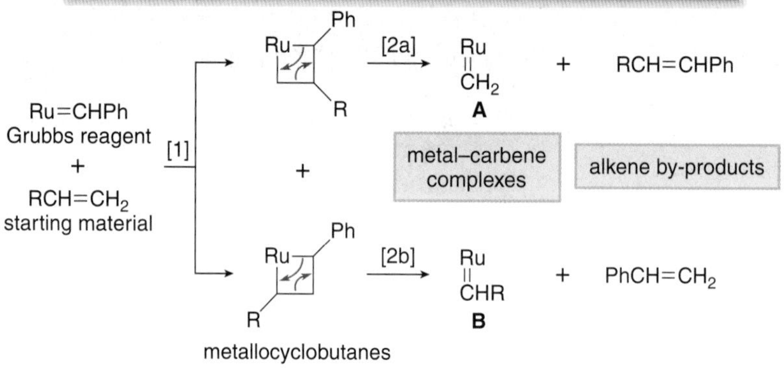

Each of these metal–carbene intermediates **A** and **B** then reacts with more starting alkene to form metathesis products, as shown in Mechanism 26.6. This mechanism is often written in a circle to emphasize the catalytic cycle. The mechanism demonstrates how two molecules of $RCH=CH_2$ are converted to RCH=CHR and $CH_2=CH_2$.

Mechanism 26.6 Olefin Metathesis: 2 $RCH=CH_2 \rightarrow RCH=CHR + CH_2=CH_2$

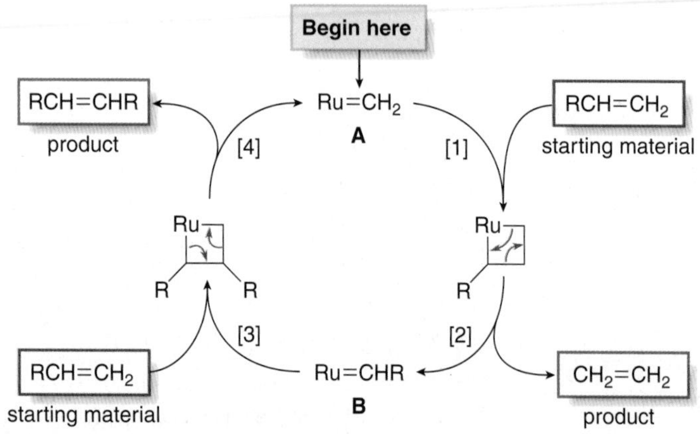

- Reaction of $Ru=CH_2$ with the alkene $RCH=CH_2$ forms a metallocyclobutane in Step [1], which eliminates $CH_2=CH_2$, a metathesis product, in Step [2]. Ru can bond to either the more or less substituted end of the alkene ($RCH=CH_2$), but product is formed only when Ru bonds to the *more* substituted C, as shown.
- Metal–carbene complex **B,** also formed in Step [2], adds to alkene $RCH=CH_2$ to form another metallocyclobutane, which decomposes to RCH=CHR, the second metathesis product, in Step [4]. Ru can bond to either the more or less substituted end of the alkene, but product is formed only when Ru bonds to the *less* substituted C, as shown.
- Since **A** is also formed in Step [4], the catalyst is regenerated and the cycle can begin again.
- The mechanism can be written beginning with reagent **A** or **B,** and all steps are equilibria.

A metathesis reaction that forms a ring is called **ring-closing metathesis (RCM).**

When a diene is used as starting material, ring closure occurs. These reactions are typically run in very dilute solution so that the two reactive ends of the *same* molecule have a higher probability of finding each other for reaction than two functional groups in *different* molecules. These high-dilution conditions thus favor ***intra*molecular** rather than *inter*molecular metathesis.

Ring-closing metathesis

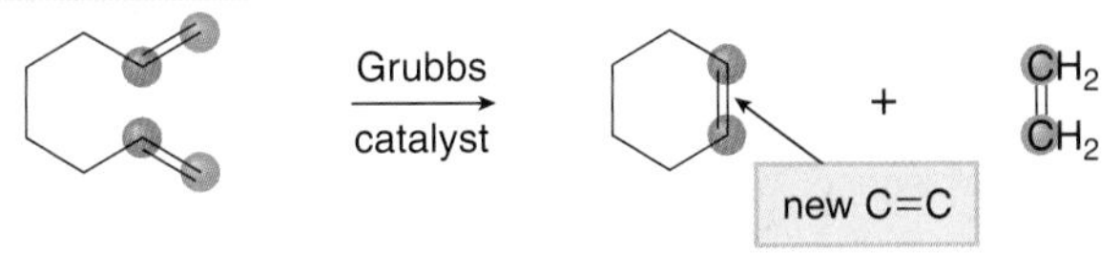

Examples

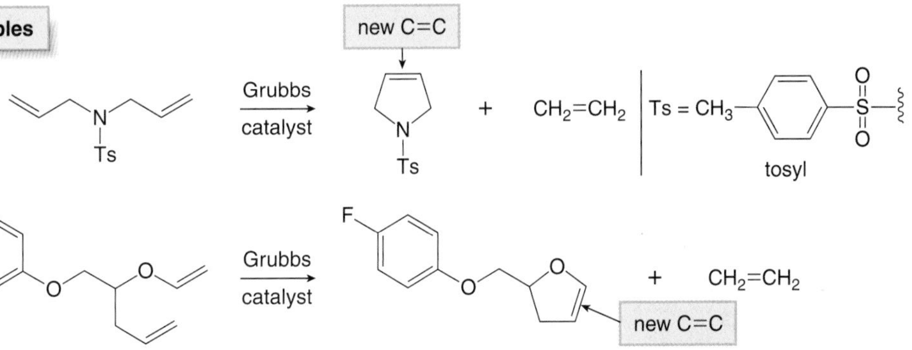

Because metathesis catalysts are compatible with the presence of many functional groups (such as OH, OR, and C=O) and because virtually any ring size can be prepared, metathesis has been used to prepare many complex natural products (Figure 26.3).

Figure 26.3

Ring-closing metathesis in the synthesis of epothilone A and Sch38516

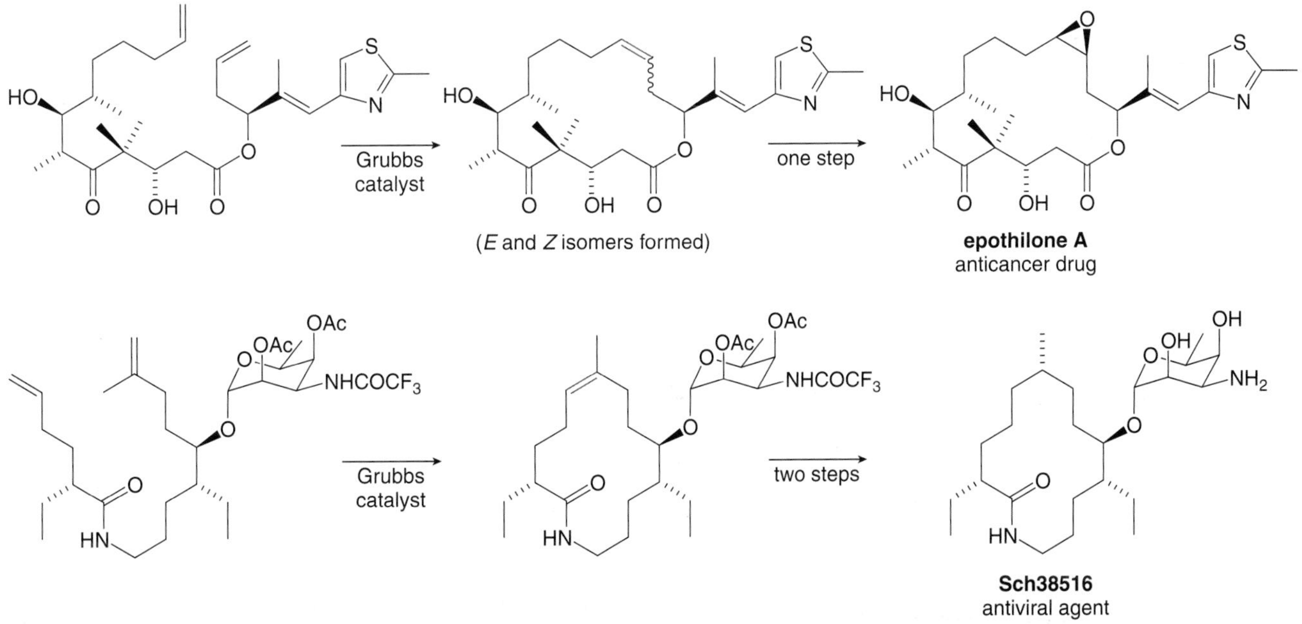

- **Epothilone A,** a promising anticancer agent, was first isolated from soil bacteria collected from the banks of the Zambezi River in South Africa.
- **Sch38516** is an antiviral agent active against influenza A.
- The new C–C bonds formed during metathesis are indicated in red. In both metathesis reactions, $CH_2{=}CH_2$ is also formed.

Problem 26.15 Draw the product formed from ring-closing metathesis of each compound.

a. 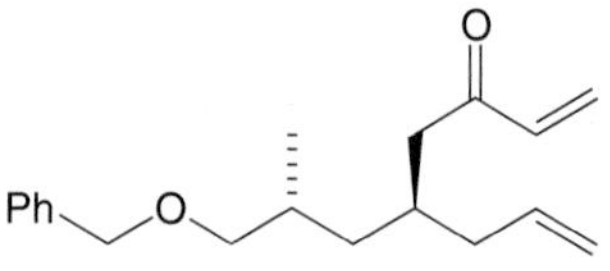
Ph
O
O

b. 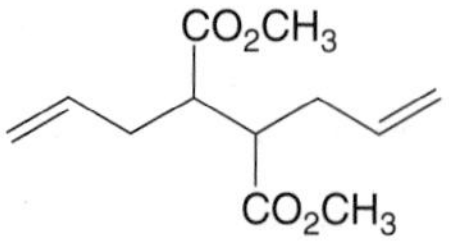
CO2CH3
CO2CH3

Problem 26.16 What product is formed by ring-closing metathesis of compound **V,** a key intermediate in the synthesis of ingenol, a complex naturally occurring compound that exhibits antileukemic and anti-HIV activity?

Ingenol is isolated from the milky liquid obtained from *Euphorbia ingens,* a large cactus commonly called the candelabra tree, which is native to dry areas in southern Africa.

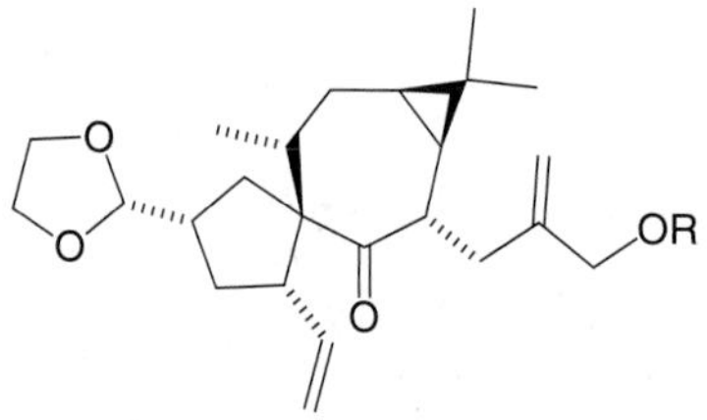
O
O
OR
O

V

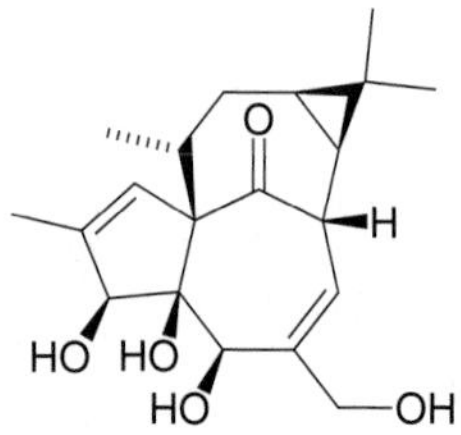
O
O
H
HO HO
HO
OH

ingenol

Sample Problem 26.5 What starting material is needed to synthesize each compound by a ring-closing metathesis reaction?

a. 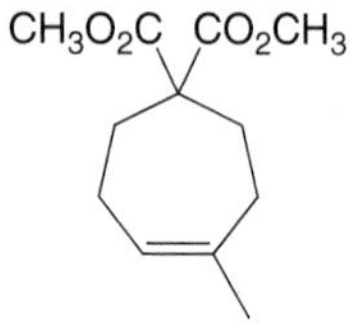
CH3O2C CO2CH3

b. 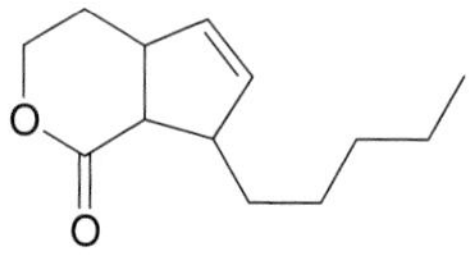
O
O

Solution

To work in the retrosynthetic direction, cleave the C=C in the product, and bond each carbon of the original alkene to a CH_2 group using a double bond.

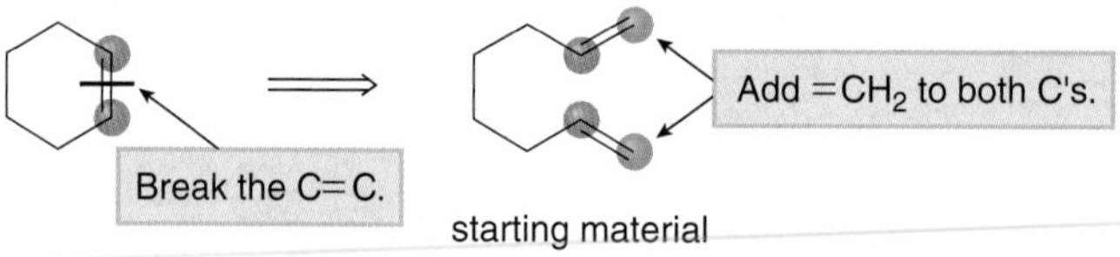
Break the C=C.
Add =CH2 to both C's.

starting material

The resulting compound has a carbon chain with two terminal alkenes.

a. 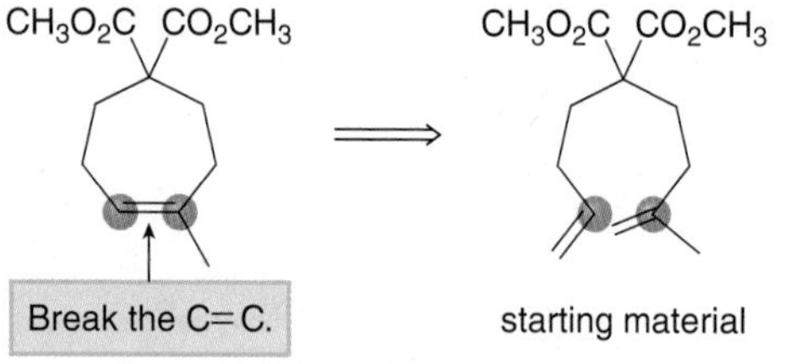
CH3O2C CO2CH3
CH3O2C CO2CH3
Break the C=C.
starting material

b. 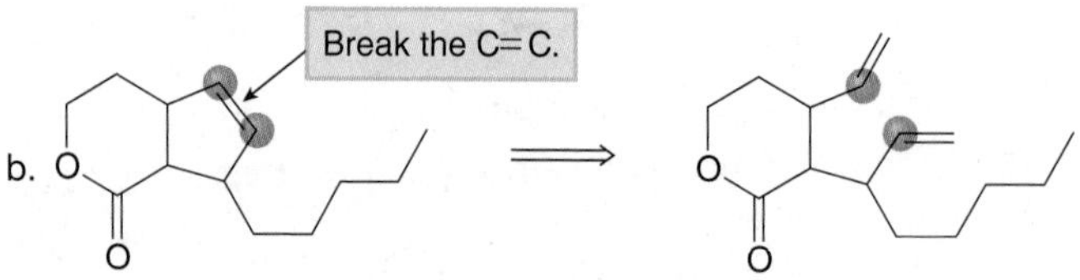
Break the C=C.
O
O
O
O

starting material

Problem 26.17 What starting material is needed to synthesize each compound by a ring-closing metathesis reaction?

a. 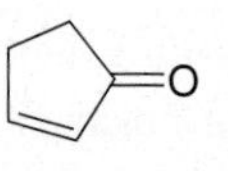
O

b. 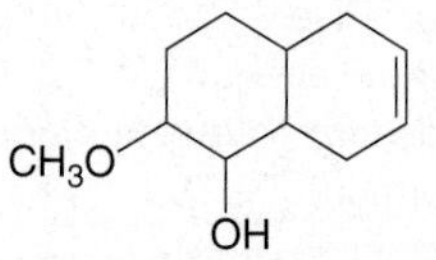
CH3O
OH

c. 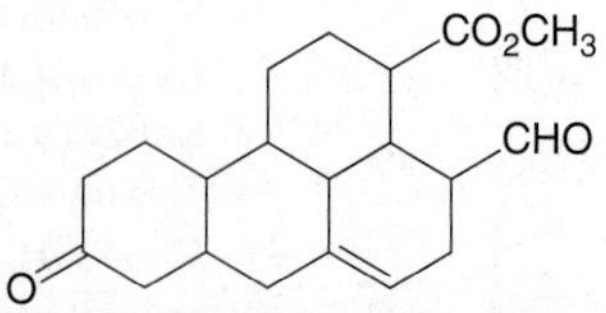
CO2CH3
CHO
O

KEY CONCEPTS

Carbon–Carbon Bond-Forming Reactions in Organic Synthesis

Coupling Reactions

[1] Coupling reactions of organocuprate reagents (26.1)

R'–X + R2CuLi
X = Cl, Br, I
R'–R
+ RCu
+ LiX

- R'X can be CH_3X, RCH_2X, 2° cyclic halides, vinyl halides, and aryl halides.
- X may be Cl, Br, or I.
- With vinyl halides, coupling is stereospecific.

[2] Suzuki reaction (26.2)

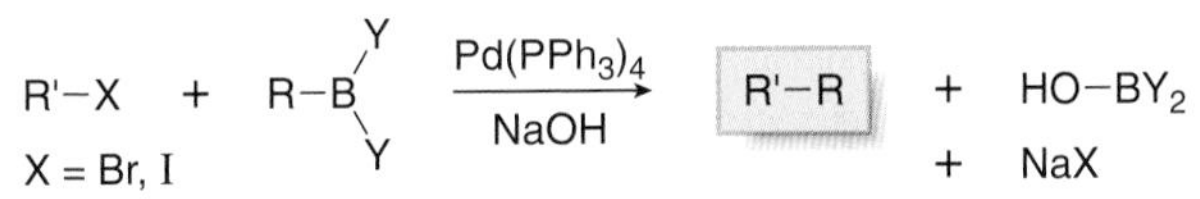
R'–X + R–B
Y
Y
X = Br, I
Pd(PPh3)4
NaOH
R'–R
+ HO–BY2
+ NaX

- R'X is most often a vinyl halide or aryl halide.
- With vinyl halides, coupling is stereospecific.

[3] Heck reaction (26.3)

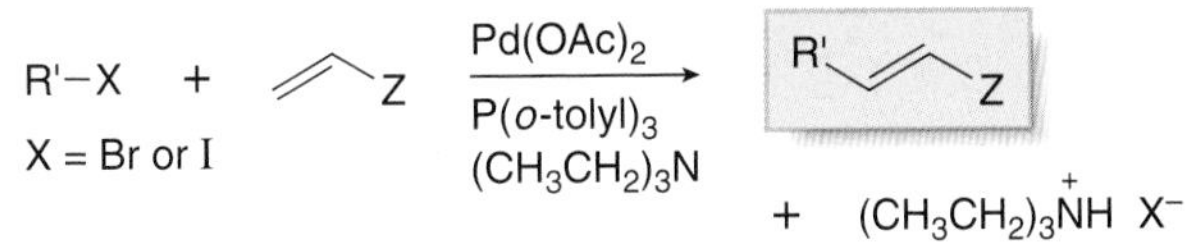
R'–X +
Z
X = Br or I
Pd(OAc)2
P(o-tolyl)3
(CH3CH2)3N
R'
Z
+ (CH3CH2)3NH X⁻

- R'X is a vinyl halide or aryl halide.
- Z = H, Ph, COOR, or CN.
- With vinyl halides, coupling is stereospecific.
- The reaction forms trans alkenes.

Cyclopropane Synthesis

[1] Addition of dihalocarbenes to alkenes (26.4)

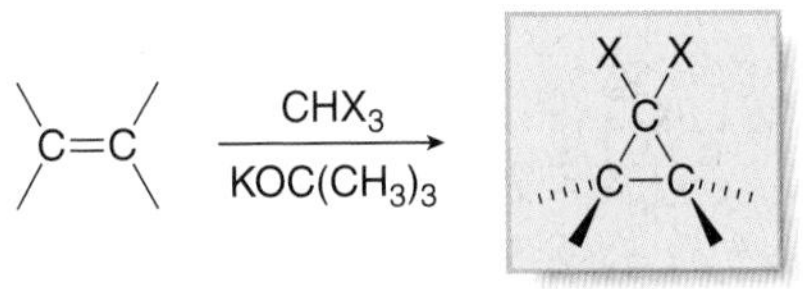
C=C
CHX3
KOC(CH3)3
X X
C
C–C

- The reaction occurs with syn addition.
- The position of substituents in the alkene is retained in the cyclopropane.

[2] Simmons–Smith reaction (26.5)

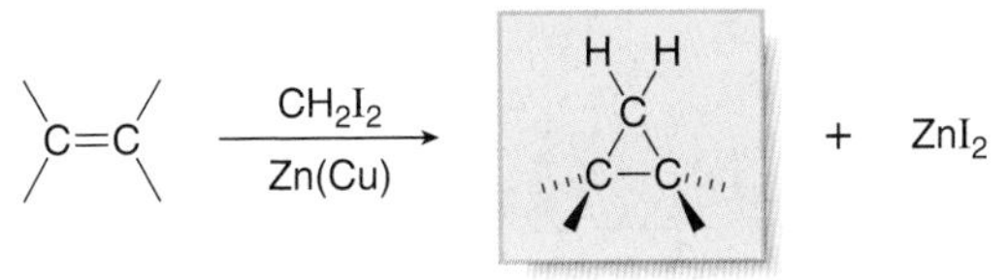
C=C
CH2I2
Zn(Cu)
H H
C
C–C
+ ZnI2

- The reaction occurs with syn addition.
- The position of substituents in the alkene is retained in the cyclopropane.

Metathesis (26.6)

[1] Intermolecular reaction

2 RCH=CH2
Grubbs
catalyst
RCH=CHR
+ CH2=CH2

- Metathesis works best when $CH_2{=}CH_2$, a gas that escapes from the reaction mixture, is one of the products formed.

[2] Intramolecular reaction

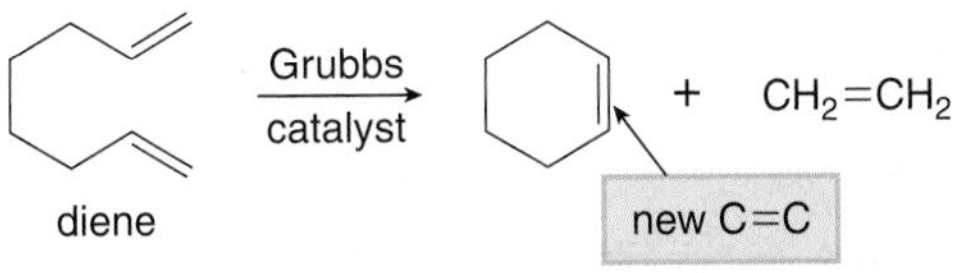
Grubbs
catalyst
+ CH2=CH2
diene
new C=C

- Ring-closing metathesis forms rings of any size from diene starting materials.

PROBLEMS

Problems Using Three-Dimensional Models

26.18 In addition to organic halides, alkyl tosylates (R'OTs, Section 9.13) also react with organocuprates (R_2CuLi) to form coupling products R–R'. When 2° alkyl tosylates are used as starting materials (R_2CHOTs), inversion of the configuration at a stereogenic center results. Keeping this in mind, draw the product formed when each compound is treated with $(CH_3)_2CuLi$.

a. 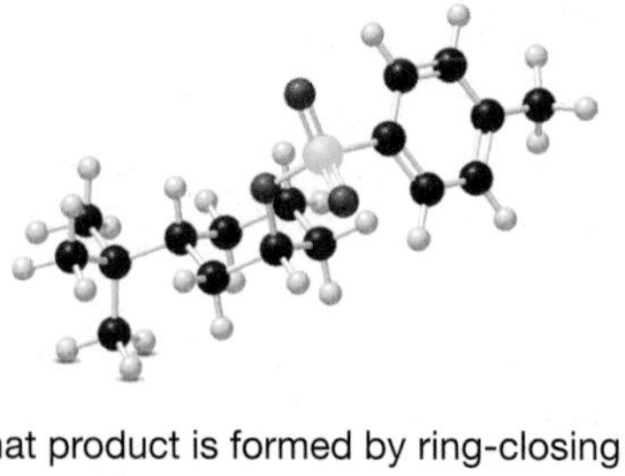

b. 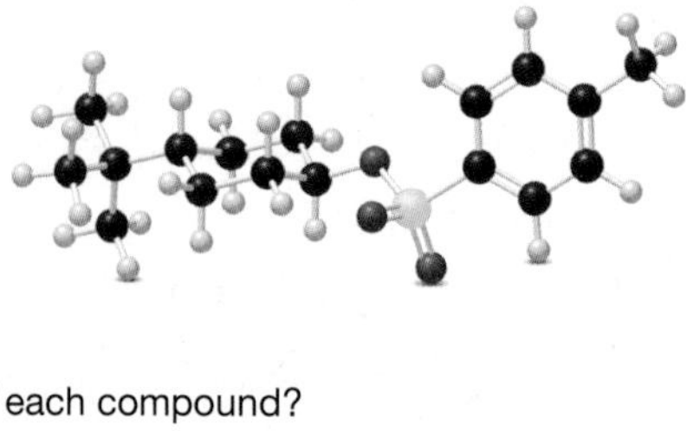

26.19 What product is formed by ring-closing metathesis of each compound?

a. 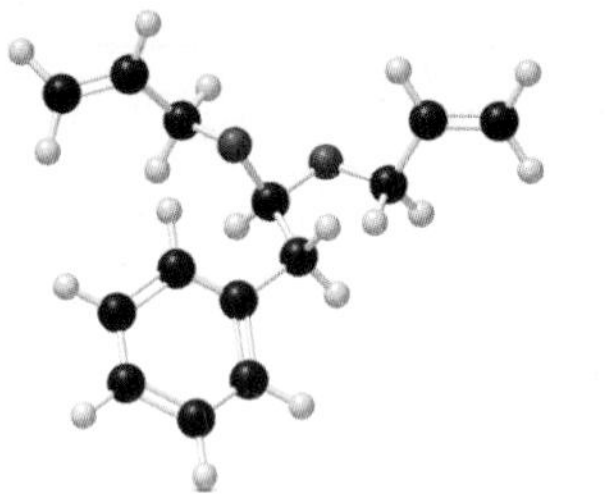

b. 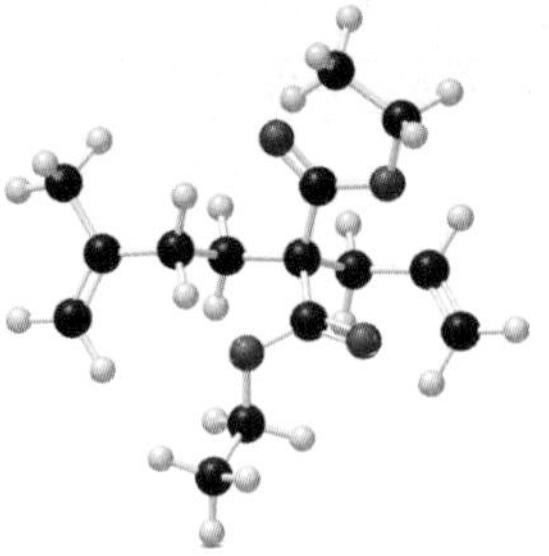

Coupling Reactions

26.20 Draw the products formed in each reaction.

a. 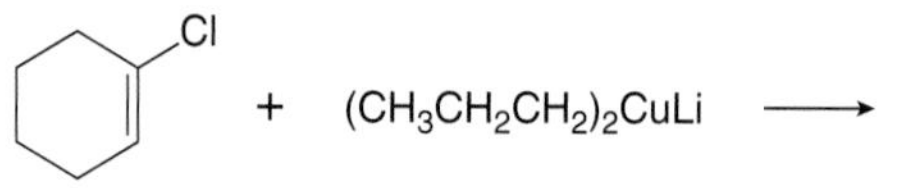

b. 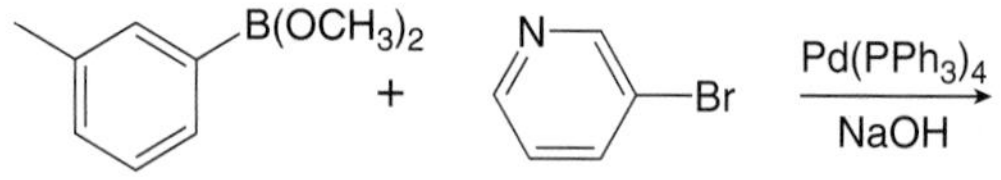

c. 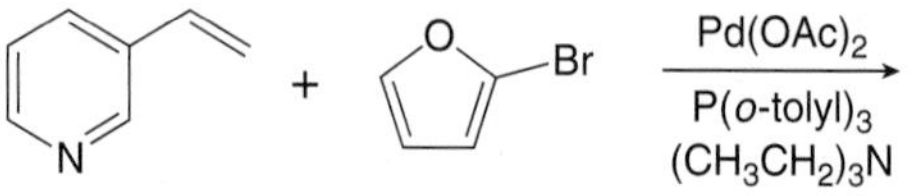

d. 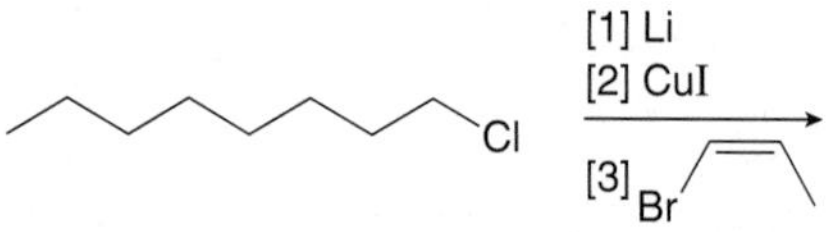

e. 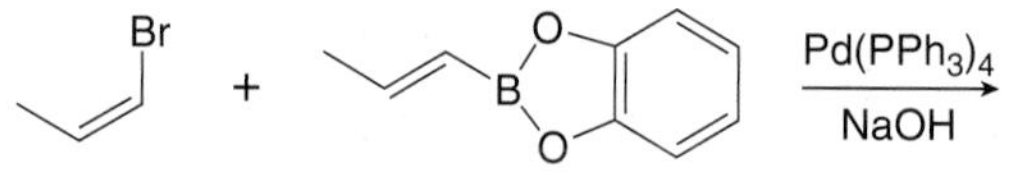

f. 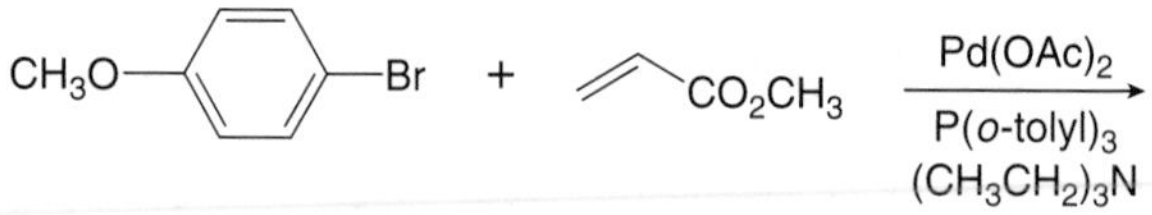

g. 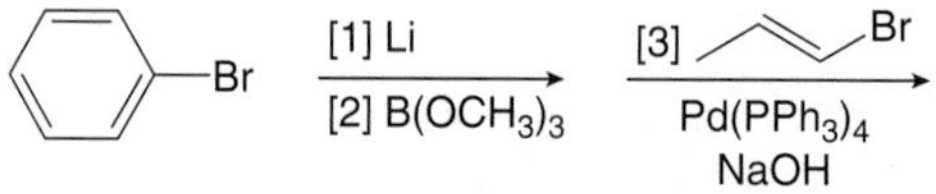

h. 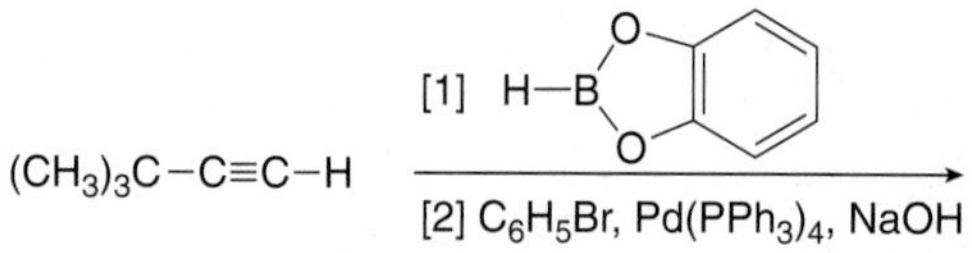

26.21 What organic halide is needed to convert lithium divinylcuprate [$(CH_2{=}CH)_2CuLi$] to each compound?

a. 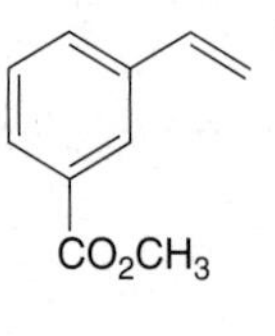

b. 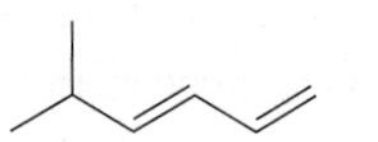

c. 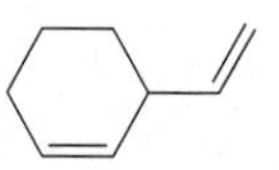

d. 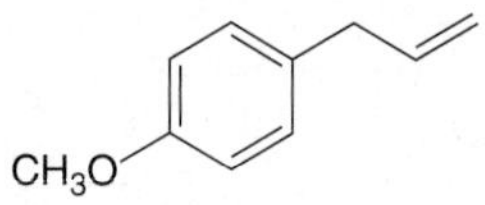

26.22 How can you convert ethynylcyclohexane to dienes **A–C** using a Suzuki reaction? You may use any other organic compounds and inorganic reagents. Is it possible to synthesize diene **D** using a Suzuki reaction? Explain why or why not.

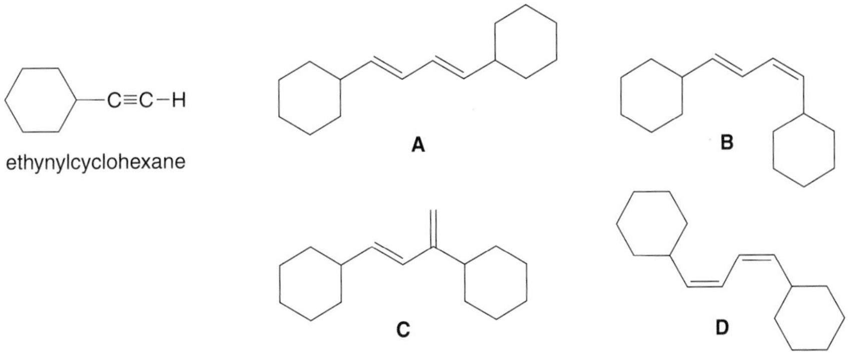

26.23 What compound is needed to convert styrene ($C_6H_5CH{=}CH_2$) to each product using a Heck reaction?

a. 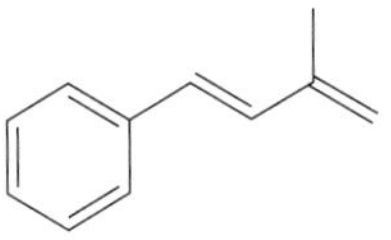 b. 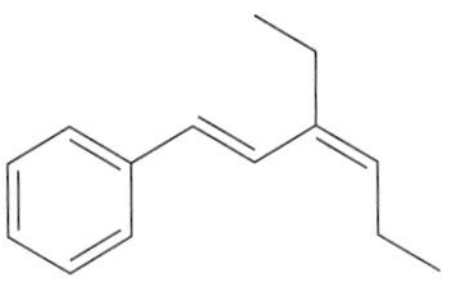 c. 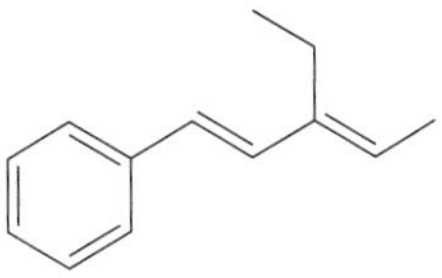

26.24 What steps are needed to convert 1-butene ($CH_3CH_2CH{=}CH_2$) to octane [$CH_3(CH_2)_6CH_3$] using a coupling reaction with an organocuprate reagent? All carbon atoms in octane must come from 1-butene.

Cyclopropanes

26.25 Draw the products (including stereoisomers) formed in each reaction.

a. 

c. 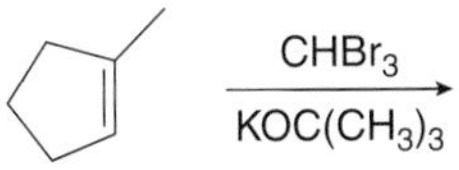

e. 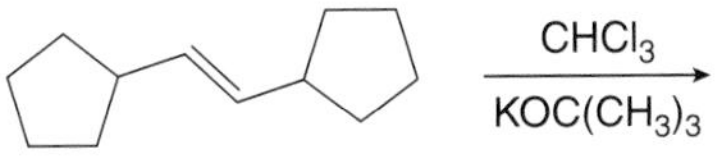

b. 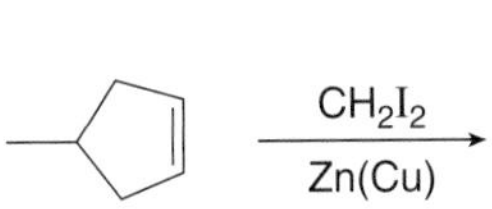

d. 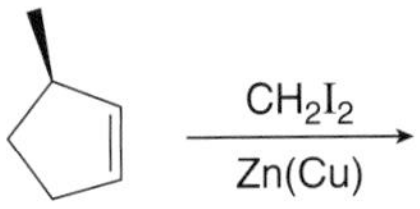

f. 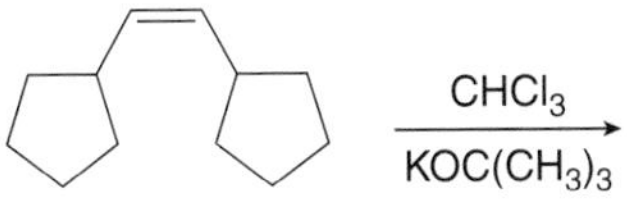

26.26 Treatment of cyclohexene with $C_6H_5CHI_2$ and Zn(Cu) forms two stereoisomers of molecular formula $C_{13}H_{16}$. Draw their structures and explain why two compounds are formed.

Metathesis

26.27 What ring-closing metathesis product is formed when each substrate is treated with Grubbs catalyst under high-dilution conditions?

a. 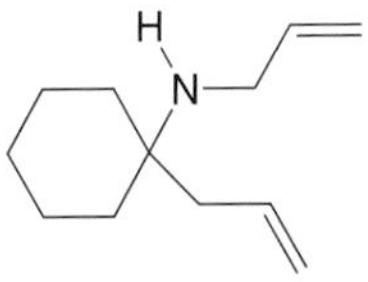

b. 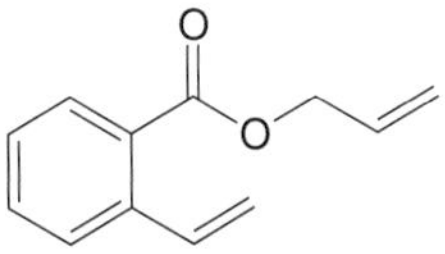

c. 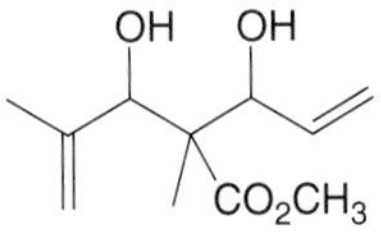

26.28 What starting material is needed to prepare each compound by a ring-closing metathesis reaction?

a. 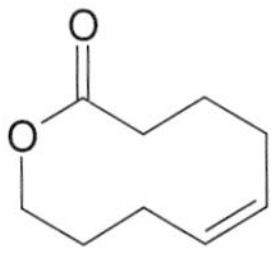

b. 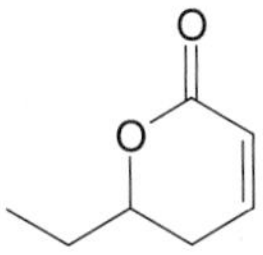

c. 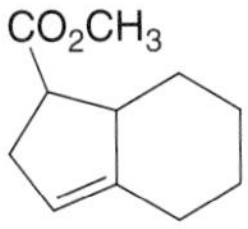

26.29 Metathesis reactions can be carried out with two *different* alkene substrates in one reaction mixture. Depending on the substitution pattern around the C=C, the reaction may lead to one major product or a mixture of many products. For each pair of alkene substrates, draw all metathesis products formed. (Disregard any starting materials that may also be present at equilibrium.) With reference to the three examples, discuss when alkene metathesis with two different alkenes is a synthetically useful reaction.

a. $CH_3CH_2CH{=}CH_2$ + $CH_3CH_2CH_2CH{=}CH_2$

b. 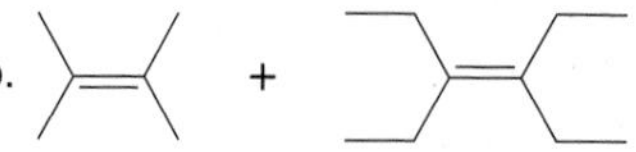

c. 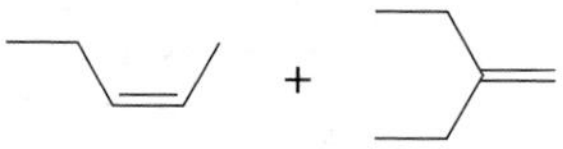

26.30 Draw the structure of the two products of molecular formula $C_{15}H_{26}O_2$ formed when **M** is treated with Grubbs catalyst under high-dilution conditions.

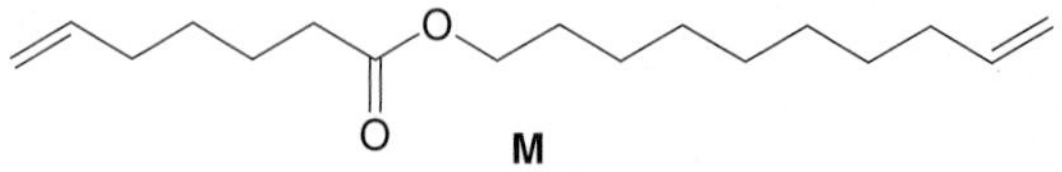

M

26.31 When certain cycloalkenes are used in metathesis reactions, ring-opening metathesis polymerization (ROMP) occurs to form a high molecular weight polymer, as shown with cyclopentene as the starting material. The reaction is driven to completion by relief of strain in the cycloalkene.

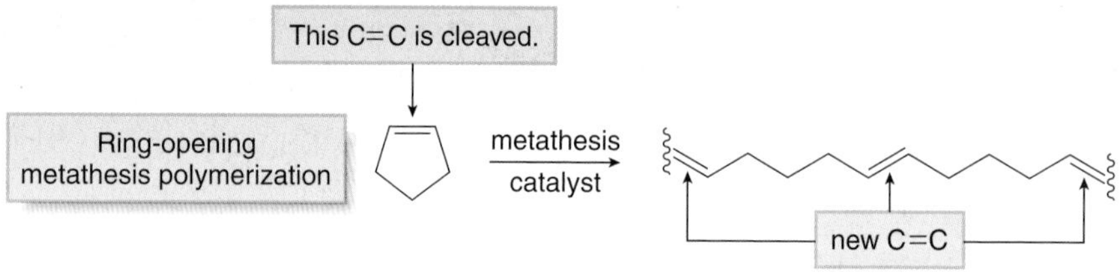

What products are formed by ring-opening metathesis polymerization of each alkene?

a. 

b. 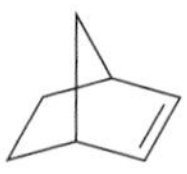

c. 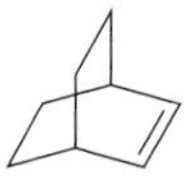

General Reactions

26.32 Draw the products formed in each reaction.

a. 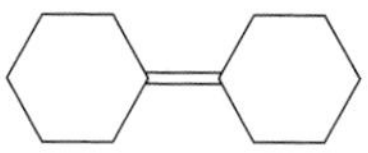 $\xrightarrow[KOC(CH_3)_3]{CHBr_3}$

b. 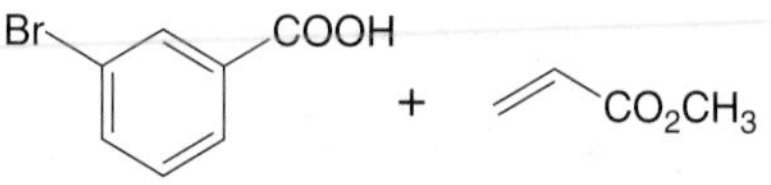

$\xrightarrow{Pd(OAc)_2}$ P(*o*-tolyl)$_3$, $(CH_3CH_2)_3N$

c. 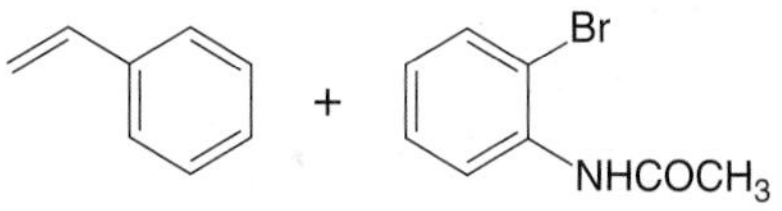

$\xrightarrow{Pd(OAc)_2}$ P(*o*-tolyl)$_3$, $(CH_3CH_2)_3N$

d. 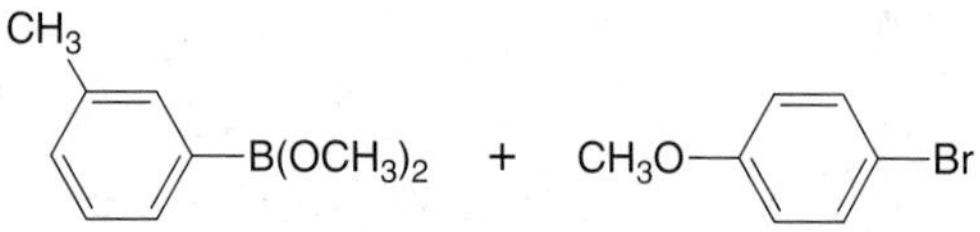

$\xrightarrow[NaOH]{Pd(PPh_3)_4}$

e. 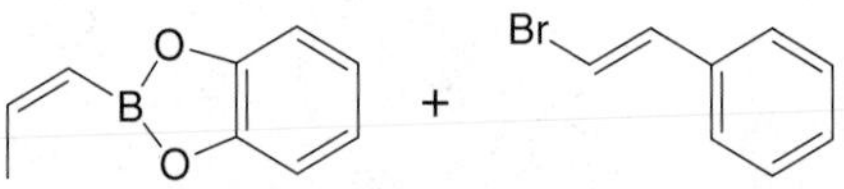

$\xrightarrow[NaOH]{Pd(PPh_3)_4}$

f. 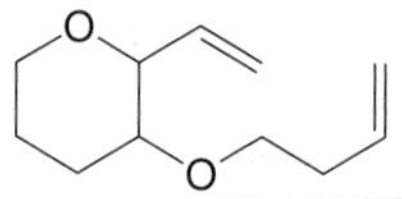

$\xrightarrow[catalyst]{Grubbs}$

g. 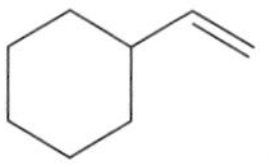 $\xrightarrow[Zn(Cu)]{CH_2I_2}$

h. The product in (a) $\xrightarrow{(CH_3)_2CuLi}$

i. 

[1] Li
[2] CuI
[3] 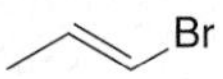

j. $CH_3CH_2{-}C{\equiv}C{-}H$
[1] 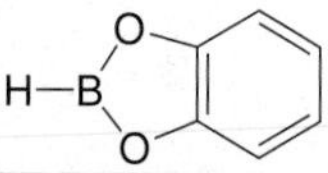

[2] 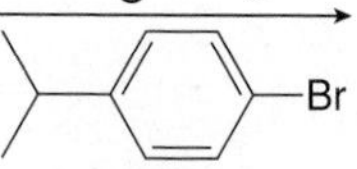

$Pd(PPh_3)_4$
NaOH

Mechanisms

26.33 In addition to using CHX_3 and base to synthesize dihalocarbenes (Section 26.4), dichlorocarbene ($:CCl_2$) can be prepared by heating sodium trichloroacetate. Draw a stepwise mechanism for this reaction.

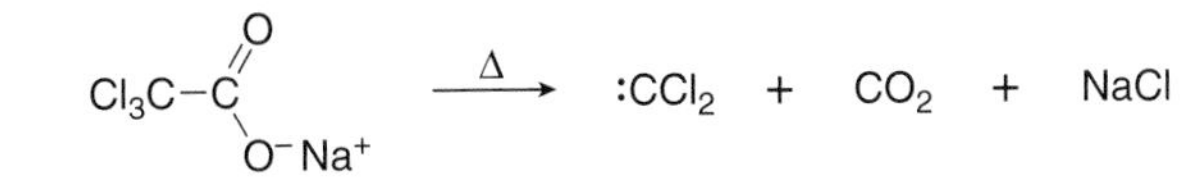

sodium trichloroacetate

26.34 Draw a stepwise mechanism for the following reaction.

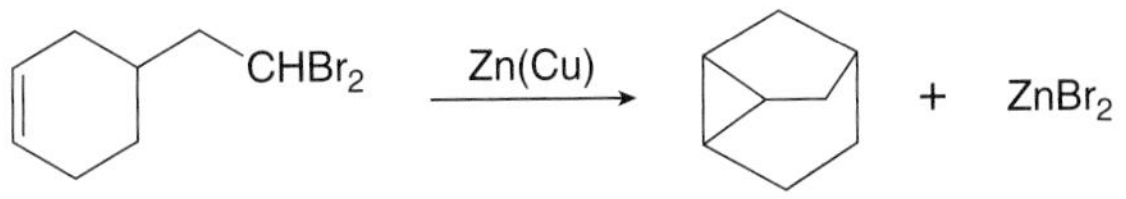

26.35 Sulfur ylides, like the phosphorus ylides of Chapter 21, are useful intermediates in organic synthesis, as shown in Problem 21.77. Methyl *trans*-chrysanthemate, an intermediate in the synthesis of the insecticide pyrethrin I (Section 26.4), can be prepared from diene **A** and a sulfur ylide. Draw a stepwise mechanism for this reaction.

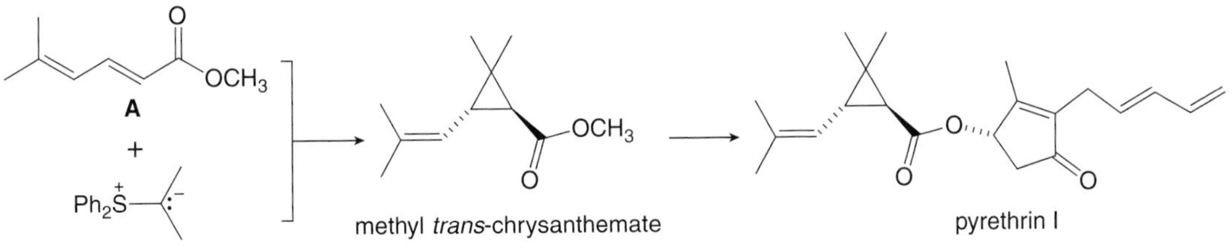

A, a sulfur ylide, methyl *trans*-chrysanthemate, pyrethrin I

26.36 Although diazomethane (CH_2N_2) is often not a useful reagent for preparing cyclopropanes, other diazo compounds give good yields of more complex cyclopropanes. Draw a stepwise mechanism for the conversion of diazo compound **A** to **B,** an intermediate in the synthesis of sirenin, the sperm attractant produced by the female gametes of the water mold *Allomyces.*

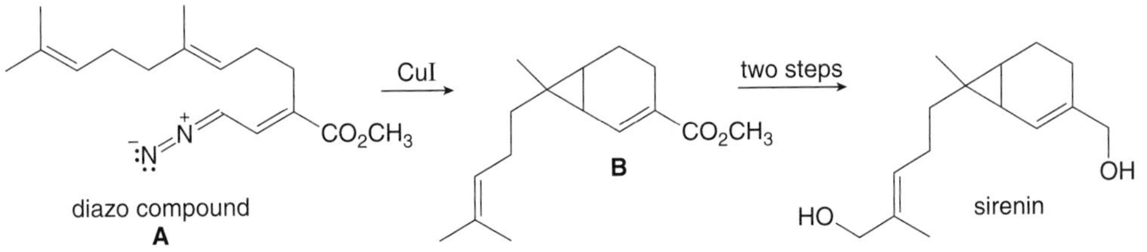

diazo compound **A**, **B**, sirenin — sperm attractant of the female water mold

26.37 The reaction of cyclohexene with iodobenzene under Heck conditions forms **E,** a coupling product with the new phenyl group on the allylic carbon, but none of the "expected" coupling product **F** with the phenyl group bonded directly to the carbon–carbon double bond.

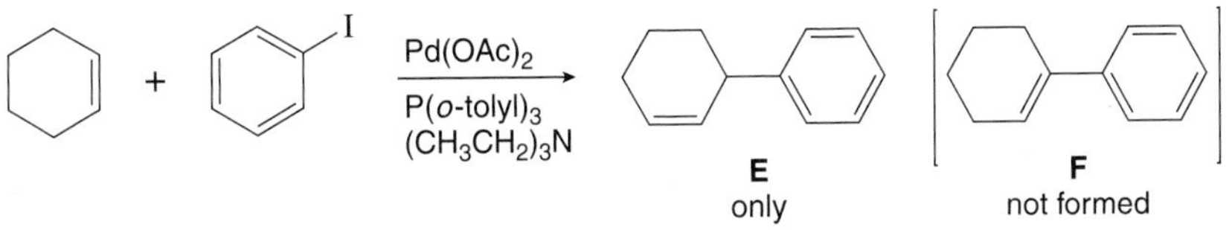

E only, **F** not formed

a. Draw a stepwise mechanism that illustrates how **E** is formed.

b. Step [2] in Mechanism 26.2 proceeds with syn addition of Pd and R' to the double bond. What does the formation of **E** suggest about the stereochemistry of the elimination reaction depicted in Step [3] of Mechanism 26.2?

Synthesis

26.38 Devise a synthesis of diene **A** from (*Z*)-2-bromostyrene as the only organic starting material. Use a Suzuki reaction in one step of the synthesis.

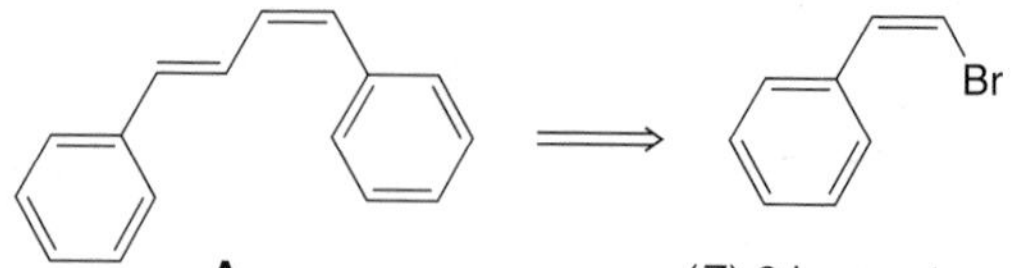

A (*Z*)-2-bromostyrene

26.39 Devise a synthesis of (1*E*)-1-phenyl-1-hexene ($CH_3CH_2CH_2CH_2CH{=}CHPh$) using hydrocarbons having ≤ 6 C's and a Suzuki reaction as one of the steps.

26.40 Devise a synthesis of the given trans vinylborane, which can be used for bombykol synthesis (Figure 26.1). All of the carbon atoms in the vinylborane must come from acetylene, 1,9-nonanediol, and catecholborane.

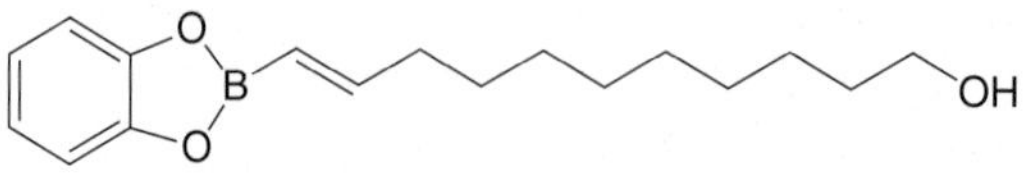

26.41 Devise a synthesis of each compound using a Heck reaction as one step. You may use benzene, $CH_2{=}CHCO_2Et$, organic alcohols having two carbons or fewer, and any required inorganic reagents.

a. 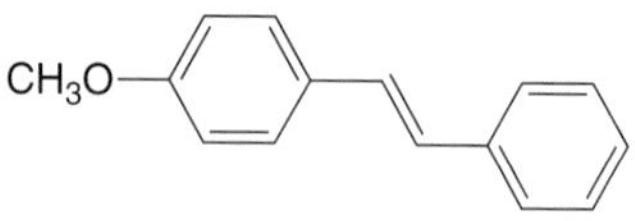

b. 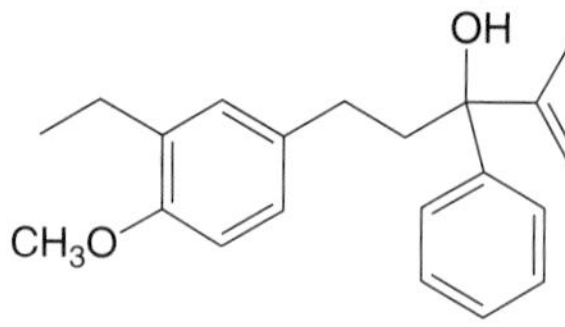

26.42 Devise a synthesis of each compound from cyclohexene and any required organic or inorganic reagents.

a. 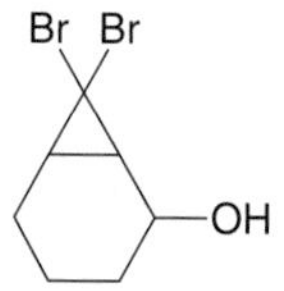

b. 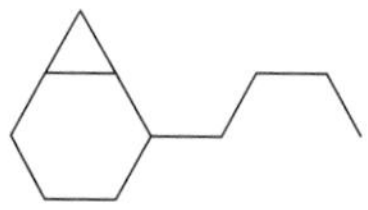

c. 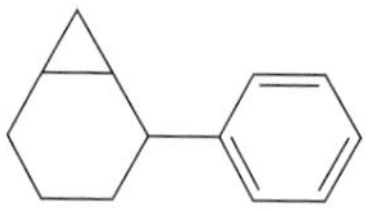

26.43 Devise a synthesis of each compound from benzene. You may also use any organic compounds having four carbons or fewer, and any required inorganic reagents.

a. 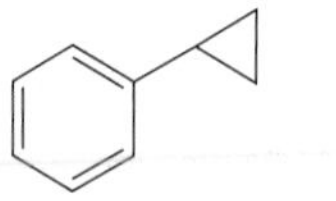

b. 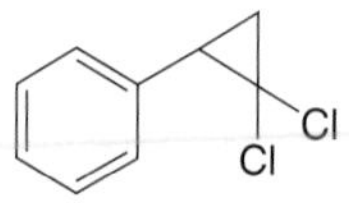

c. 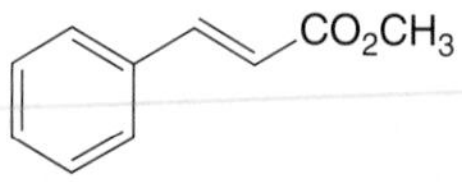

d. 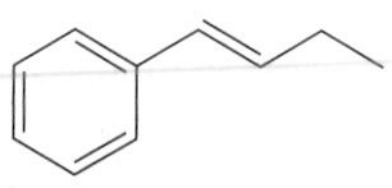

26.44 Devise a synthesis of each substituted cyclopropane. Use acetylene (HC≡CH) as a starting material in parts (a) and (b), and cyclohexanone as a starting material in parts (c) and (d). You may use any other organic compounds and any needed reagents.

a. 

+ enantiomer

b. 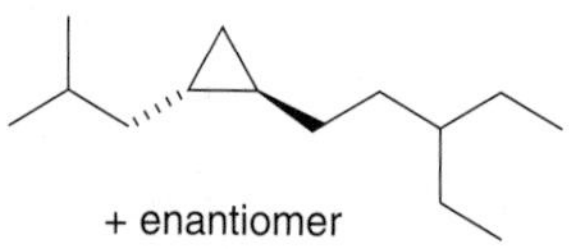

+ enantiomer

c. 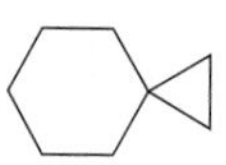

d. 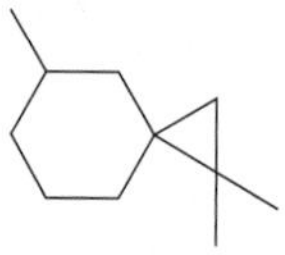

26.45 Biaryls, compounds containing two aromatic rings joined by a C–C bond, can often be efficiently made by two different Suzuki couplings; that is, either aromatic ring can be used to form the organoborane needed for coupling. In some cases, however, only one route is possible. With this in mind, synthesize each of the following biaryls using benzene as the starting material for each aromatic ring. When more than one route is possible, draw both of them. You may use any required organic or inorganic reagents.

a. 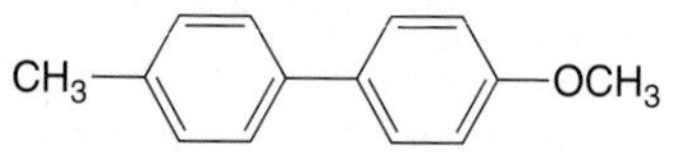

b. 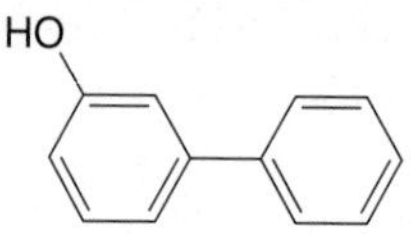

c. 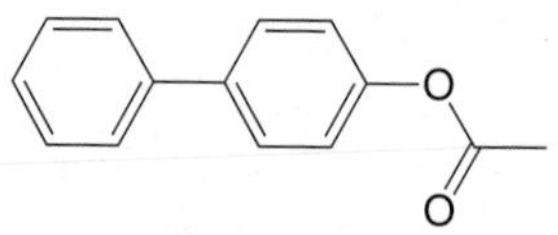

26.46 Draw the product formed from the ring-closing metathesis of each compound. Then, devise a synthesis of each metathesis starting material using any of the following compounds: $CH_2(CO_2Et)_2$, alcohols with less than five carbons, and any needed organic and inorganic reagents.

a. 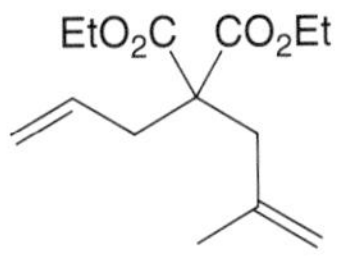

b. 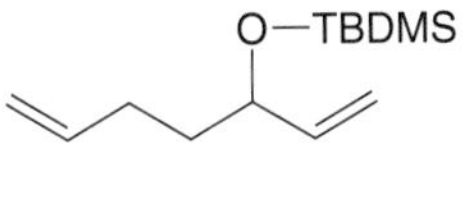

26.47 Draw the product formed from the ring-closing metathesis of each compound. Then, devise a synthesis of each metathesis starting material from benzene, alcohols with less than five carbons, and any needed organic and inorganic reagents.

a. 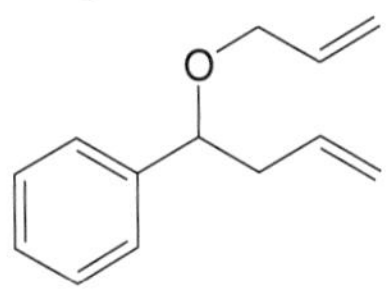

b. 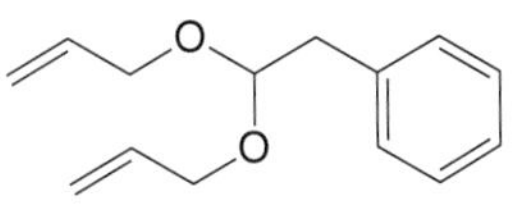

26.48 What reagents are needed to carry out transformations [1]–[3] in the synthesis of aldehyde **A? A** can be converted to the antitumor agent maytansine in several steps.

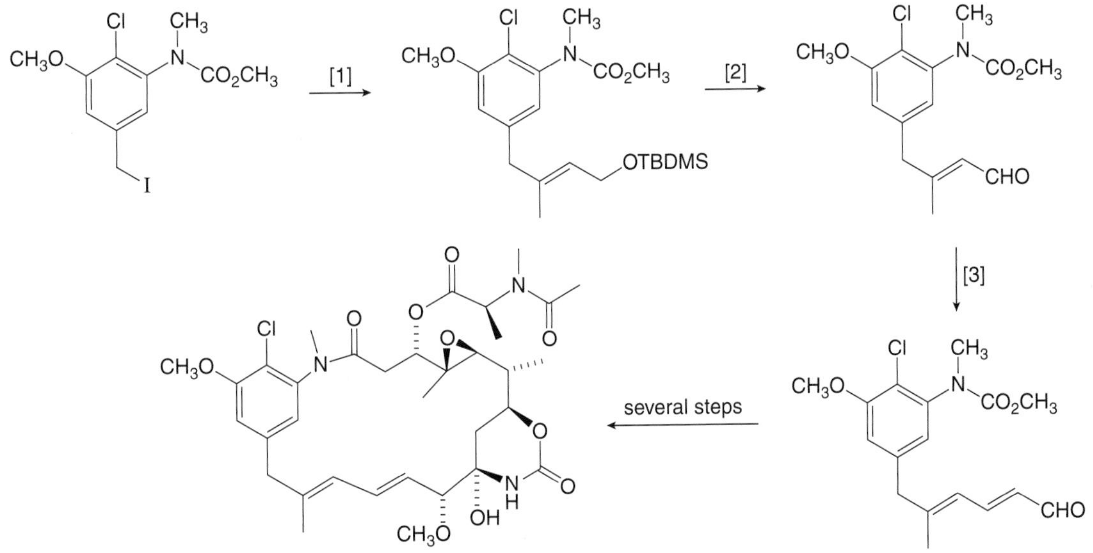

maytansine

A

26.49 Devise a synthesis of each of the following compounds. Besides inorganic reagents, you may use hydrocarbons and halides having ≤ 6 C's, and $CH_2=CHCOOCH_3$ as starting materials. Each synthesis must use at least one of the carbon–carbon bond-forming reactions in this chapter.

a. 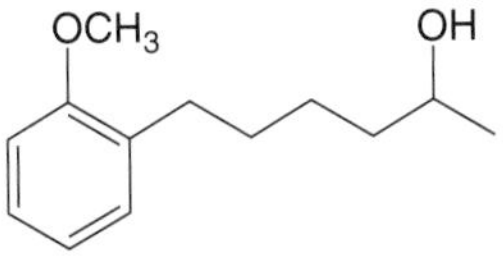

(two enantiomers)

c. 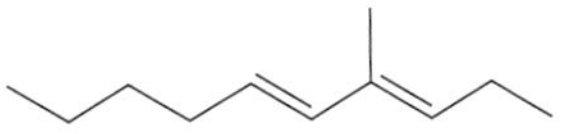

e. 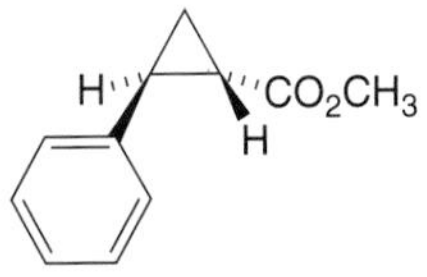

(+ enantiomer)

b. 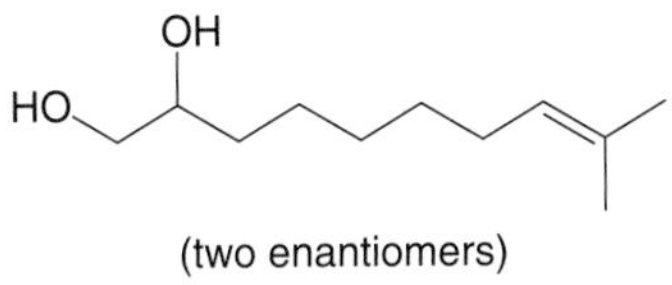

(two enantiomers)

d. 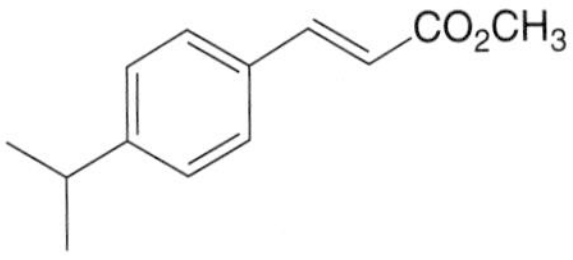

f. 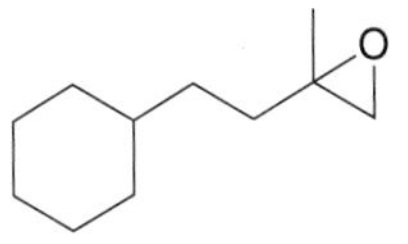

(two enantiomers)

Challenge Problems

26.50 Many variations of ring-closing metathesis have now been reported. For example, tandem ring-opening–ring-closing metathesis can occur with cyclic alkenes that contain two additional carbon–carbon double bonds. In this reaction, the cycloalkene is cleaved, and two new rings are formed. [1] What compounds are formed in this tandem reaction with the following substrates? [2] Devise a synthesis of the substrate in part (b) that uses a Diels–Alder reaction with diethyl maleate as the dienophile.

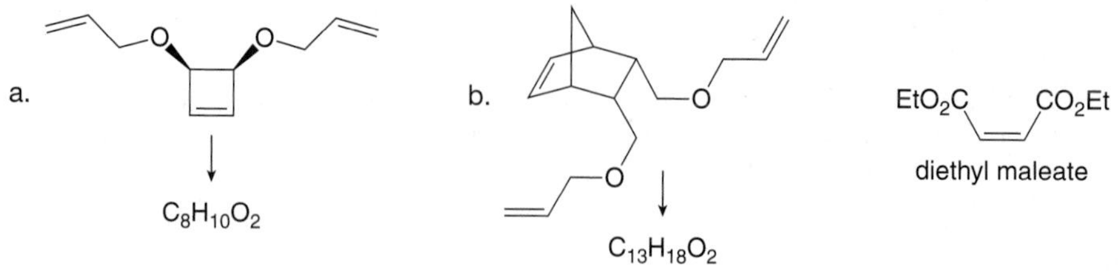

26.51 The following conversion, carried out in the presence of Grubbs catalyst and ethylene gas, involves a cascade of metathesis reactions. Draw a reaction sequence that illustrates how the reactant is converted to the product **Z,** and indicate where each labeled atom in the reactant ends up in **Z.**

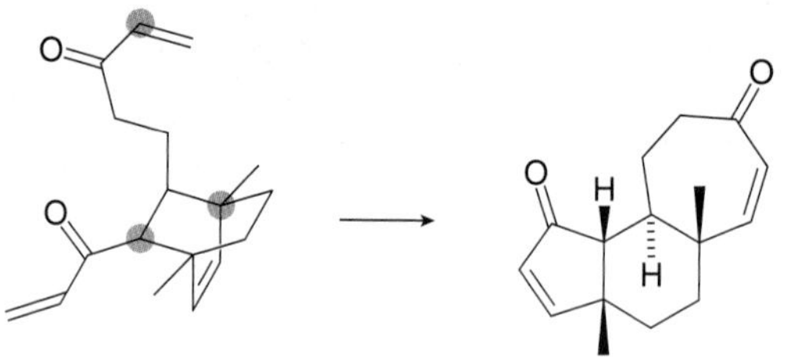

Z

26.52 Suzuki coupling of aryl iodide **A** and vinylborane **B** affords compound **C,** which is converted to **D** in the presence of aqueous acid. Identify compounds **C** and **D** and draw a stepwise mechanism for the conversion of **C** to **D.**

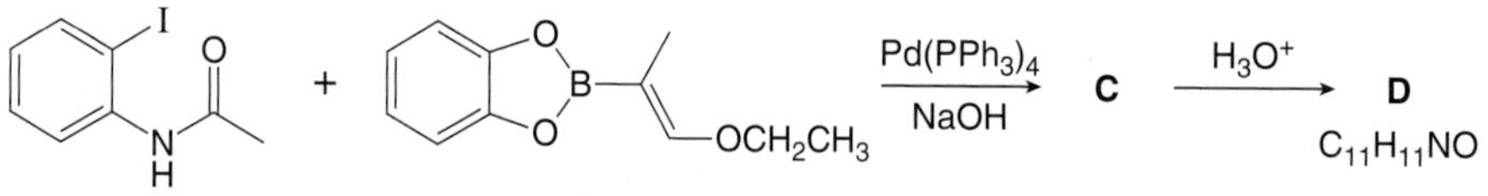

A **B**

26.53 Dimethyl cyclopropanes can be prepared by the reaction of an α,β-unsaturated carbonyl compound **X** with two equivalents of a Wittig reagent **Y.** Draw a stepwise mechanism for this reaction.

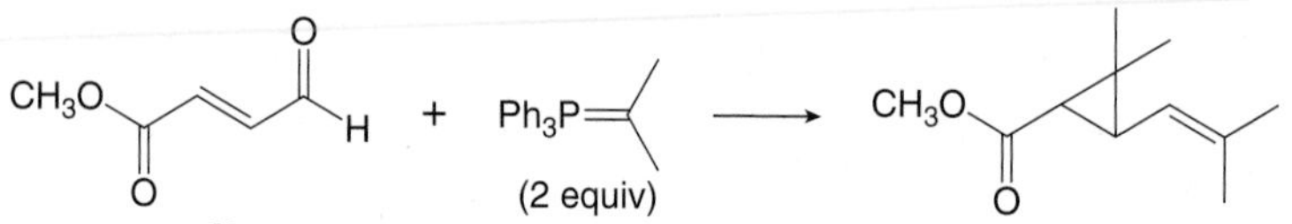

X **Y**

26.54 Dienynes undergo metathesis to afford fused bicyclic ring systems. (a) Explain how **A** is converted to **B.** (b) Keeping this reaction in mind, draw the two products formed by dienyne metathesis of **C.**

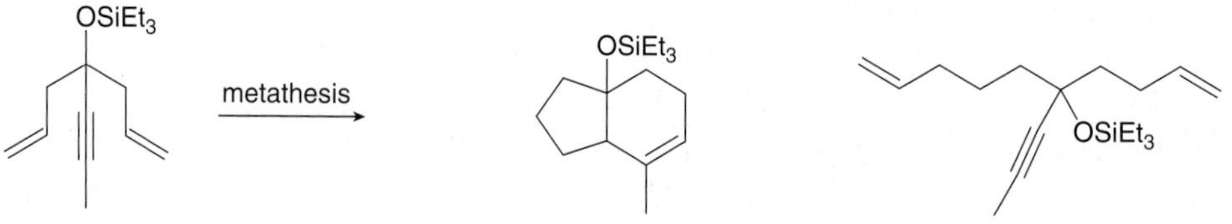

A **B** **C**

Pericyclic Reactions

27

27.1 Types of pericyclic reactions
27.2 Molecular orbitals
27.3 Electrocyclic reactions
27.4 Cycloaddition reactions
27.5 Sigmatropic rearrangements
27.6 Summary of rules for pericyclic reactions

Periplanone B, an unusual diepoxide with a 10-membered ring, is a potent sex pheromone of the female American cockroach. Although periplanone B was isolated in 1952, its structure was not determined until 1976 using 200 μg of material obtained from more than 75,000 female cockroaches. This structure was confirmed by synthesis in 1979, and several subsequent syntheses have been reported. Key steps in an elegant 1984 synthesis of periplanone B involve pericyclic reactions, a group of powerful, stereospecific reactions discussed in Chapter 27.

Many of the reactions thus far encountered in our study of organic chemistry occur by way of reactive intermediates—cations, anions, and radicals. For example, the S_N1 reaction in Chapter 7 and electrophilic aromatic substitutions in Chapter 18 involve carbocations, while the aldol and Claisen reactions in Chapter 24 occur via enolate anions. Other reactions, such as the halogenation of alkanes and the polymerization of alkenes discussed in Chapter 15, take place via radical intermediates.

In Chapter 27, we learn about a small but versatile group of reactions, **pericyclic reactions,** which occurs in a concerted process—all bonds are broken and formed in a single step—with a cyclic transition state. The Diels–Alder reaction in Chapter 16 is an example of one type of pericyclic reaction. Pericyclic reactions involve π bonds, and they are governed by a set of rules that allows us to predict the identity and stereochemistry of the products formed. Consequently, pericyclic reactions are valuable tools for synthesizing organic molecules.

27.1 Types of Pericyclic Reactions

Although most organic reactions take place by way of ionic or radical intermediates, a number of useful reactions occur in one-step processes that do *not* form reactive intermediates.

- **A pericyclic reaction is a concerted reaction that proceeds through a cyclic transition state.**

Stereospecific reactions were first discussed in Chapter 10.

Pericyclic reactions require light or heat and are completely stereospecific; that is, a particular stereoisomer of the reactant forms a particular stereoisomer of the product. There are three categories of pericyclic reactions: **electrocyclic reactions, cycloadditions,** and **sigmatropic rearrangements.**

An **electrocyclic reaction** is a reversible reaction that can involve ring closure or ring opening of one molecule of reactant to form one molecule of product.

- **An electrocyclic ring closure is an intramolecular reaction that forms a cyclic product containing one more σ bond and one fewer π bond than the reactant.**

1,3,5-hexatriene
3 π bonds

1,3-cyclohexadiene
2 π bonds

- **An electrocyclic ring opening is a reaction in which a σ bond of a cyclic reactant is cleaved to form a conjugated product with one more π bond.**

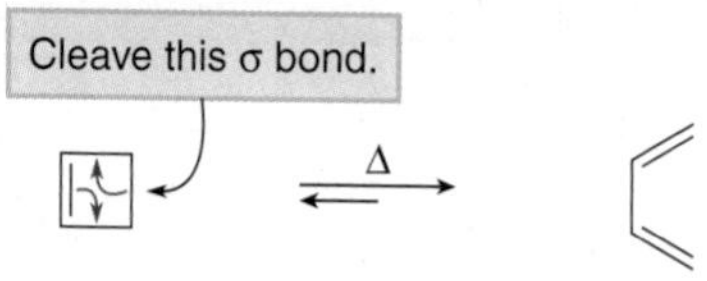

cyclobutene
1 π bond

1,3-butadiene
2 π bonds

Cycloaddition reactions form a ring. The Diels–Alder reaction in Chapter 16 is one example of a cycloaddition.

- **A cycloaddition is a reaction between two compounds with π bonds to form a cyclic product with two new σ bonds.**

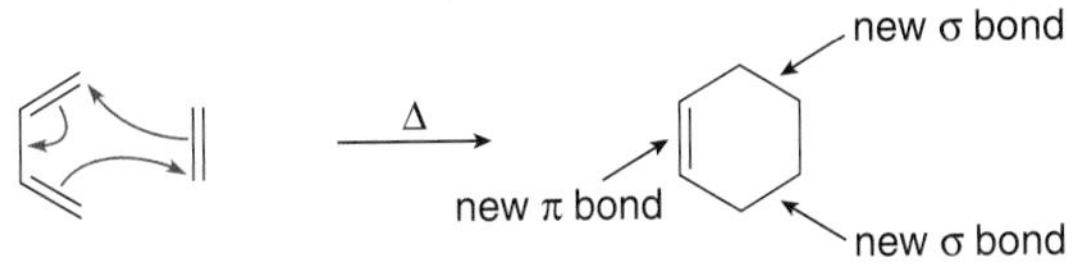

In contrast to electrocyclic reactions and cycloadditions, in which the number of π bonds differs in the reactants and products, the number of π bonds does *not* change in a **sigmatropic rearrangement.**

- **A sigmatropic rearrangement is a reaction in which a σ bond is broken in the reactant, the π bonds rearrange, and a σ bond is formed in the product.**

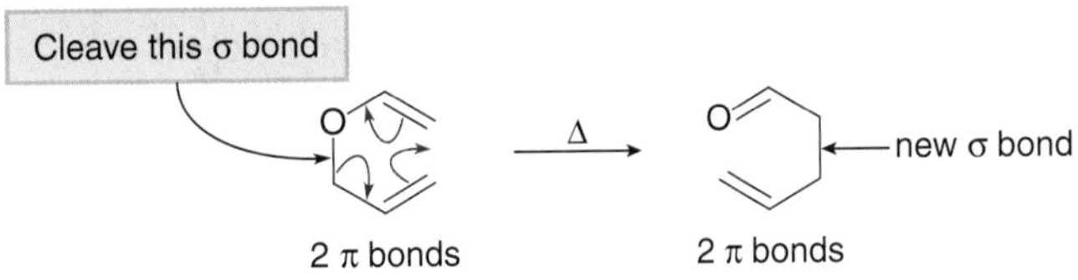

Hoffmann and Fukui received the 1981 Nobel Prize in Chemistry for developing theories that explain the course of pericyclic reactions.

Two features determine the course of the reactions: the number of π bonds involved and whether the reaction occurs in the presence of heat (thermal conditions) or light (photochemical conditions). These reactions follow a set of rules based on orbitals and symmetry first proposed by R. B. Woodward and Roald Hoffmann in 1965, and derived from theory described by Kenichi Fukui in 1954.

To understand pericyclic reactions we must review and expand upon what we learned about the molecular orbitals of systems with π bonds in Chapter 17.

Problem 27.1 Classify each reaction as an electrocyclic reaction, a cycloaddition, or a sigmatropic rearrangement. Label the σ bonds that are broken or formed in each reaction.

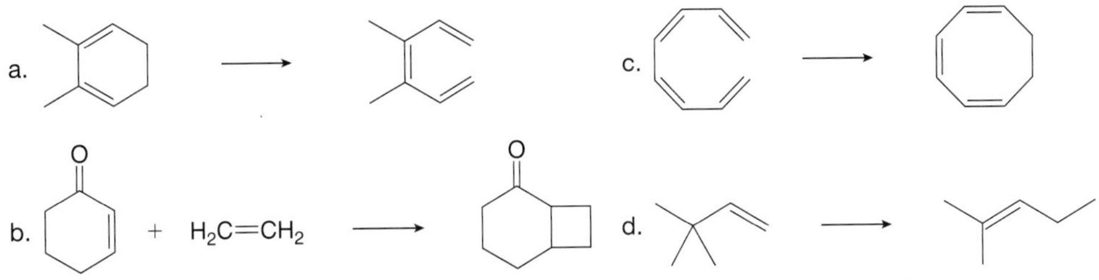

27.2 Molecular Orbitals

In Section 17.9 we learned that molecular orbital (MO) theory describes bonds as the mathematical combination of atomic orbitals that forms a new set of orbitals called **molecular orbitals (MOs). The number of atomic orbitals used *equals* the number of molecular orbitals formed.**

Since pericyclic reactions involve π bonds, let's examine the molecular orbitals that result from *p* orbital overlap in ethylene, 1,3-butadiene, and 1,3,5-hexatriene, molecules that contain one, two, and three π bonds, respectively. Keep in mind that the two lobes of a *p* orbital are opposite in phase, with a node of electron density at the nucleus.

27.2A Ethylene

The π bond in ethylene ($CH_2{=}CH_2$) is formed by side-by-side overlap of two *p* orbitals on adjacent carbons. Two *p* orbitals can combine in two different ways. As shown in Figure 27.1, when two *p* orbitals of similar phase overlap, a π bonding molecular orbital (designated as ψ_1) results. Two electrons occupy this lower-energy bonding molecular orbital. When two *p* orbitals of opposite phase combine, a π* antibonding molecular orbital (designated as ψ_2*) results. A destabilizing node between the orbitals occurs when two orbitals of opposite phase combine.

Figure 27.1
The π and π* molecular orbitals of ethylene

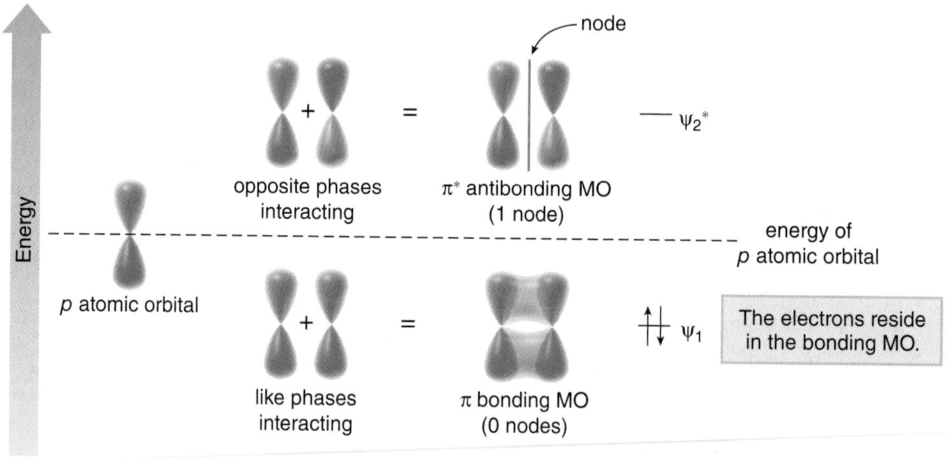

27.2B 1,3-Butadiene

The two π bonds of 1,3-butadiene ($CH_2{=}CH{-}CH{=}CH_2$) are formed by overlap of four *p* orbitals on four adjacent carbons. As shown in Figure 27.2, four *p* orbitals can combine in four different ways to form four molecular orbitals designated as ψ_1–ψ_4. Two are bonding molecular orbitals (ψ_1 and ψ_2), and two are antibonding molecular orbitals (ψ_3* and ψ_4*). The two bonding MOs are lower in energy than the *p* orbitals from which they are formed, whereas the two antibonding MOs are higher in energy than the *p* orbitals from which they are formed. **As the number of bonding interactions decreases and the number of nodes increases, the energy of the molecular orbital increases.**

- In the ground-state electronic arrangement, the four π electrons occupy the two bonding molecular orbitals.

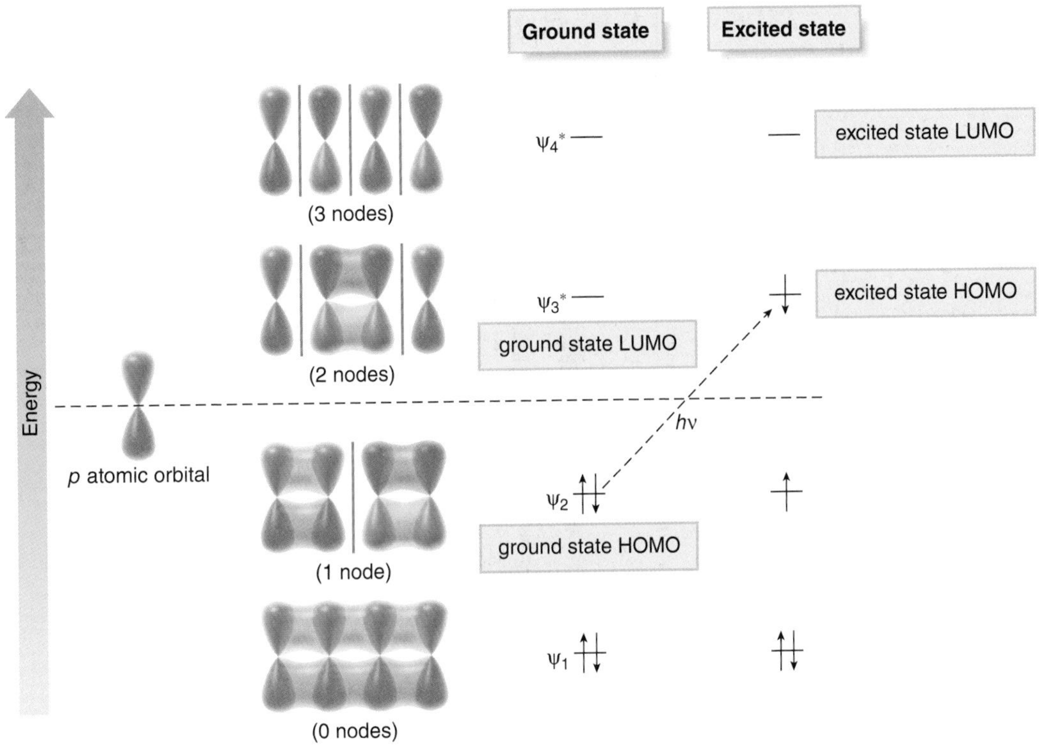

Figure 27.2
The four π molecular orbitals of 1,3-butadiene

- The two lowest energy molecular orbitals, ψ_1 and ψ_2, are bonding MOs.
- The two highest energy molecular orbitals, ψ_3* and ψ_4*, are antibonding MOs.

Also recall from Section 17.9:

- **The highest energy orbital that contains electrons is called the highest occupied molecular orbital (HOMO). In the ground state of 1,3-butadiene, ψ_2 is the HOMO.**
- **The lowest energy orbital that contains no electrons is called the lowest unoccupied molecular orbital (LUMO). In the ground state of 1,3-butadiene, ψ_3* is the LUMO.**

The thermal reactions discussed in Section 27.3 utilize reactants in their ground state electronic configuration.

When 1,3-butadiene absorbs light of appropriate energy, an electron is promoted from ψ_2 (the HOMO) to ψ_3* (the LUMO) to form a higher energy electronic configuration, the **excited state.** In the excited state, the HOMO is now ψ_3*. **In the photochemical reactions in Section 27.3, the reactant is in its excited state.** As a result, the HOMO is ψ_3* and the LUMO is ψ_4* for 1,3-butadiene.

All conjugated dienes can be described by a set of molecular orbitals that are similar to those drawn in Figure 27.2 for 1,3-butadiene.

Problem 27.2 For each molecular orbital in Figure 27.2, count the number of bonding interactions (interactions between adjacent orbitals of similar phase) and the number of nodes. (a) How do these two values compare for a bonding molecular orbital? (b) How do these two values compare for an antibonding molecular orbital?

27.2C 1,3,5-Hexatriene

The three π bonds of 1,3,5-hexatriene ($CH_2{=}CH{-}CH{=}CH{-}CH{=}CH_2$) are formed by overlap of six *p* orbitals on six adjacent carbons. As shown in Figure 27.3, six *p* orbitals can combine in six different ways to form six molecular orbitals designated as ψ_1–ψ_6. Three are bonding molecular orbitals (ψ_1–ψ_3), and three are antibonding molecular orbitals (ψ_4*–ψ_6*).

Figure 27.3 The six π molecular orbitals of 1,3,5-hexatriene

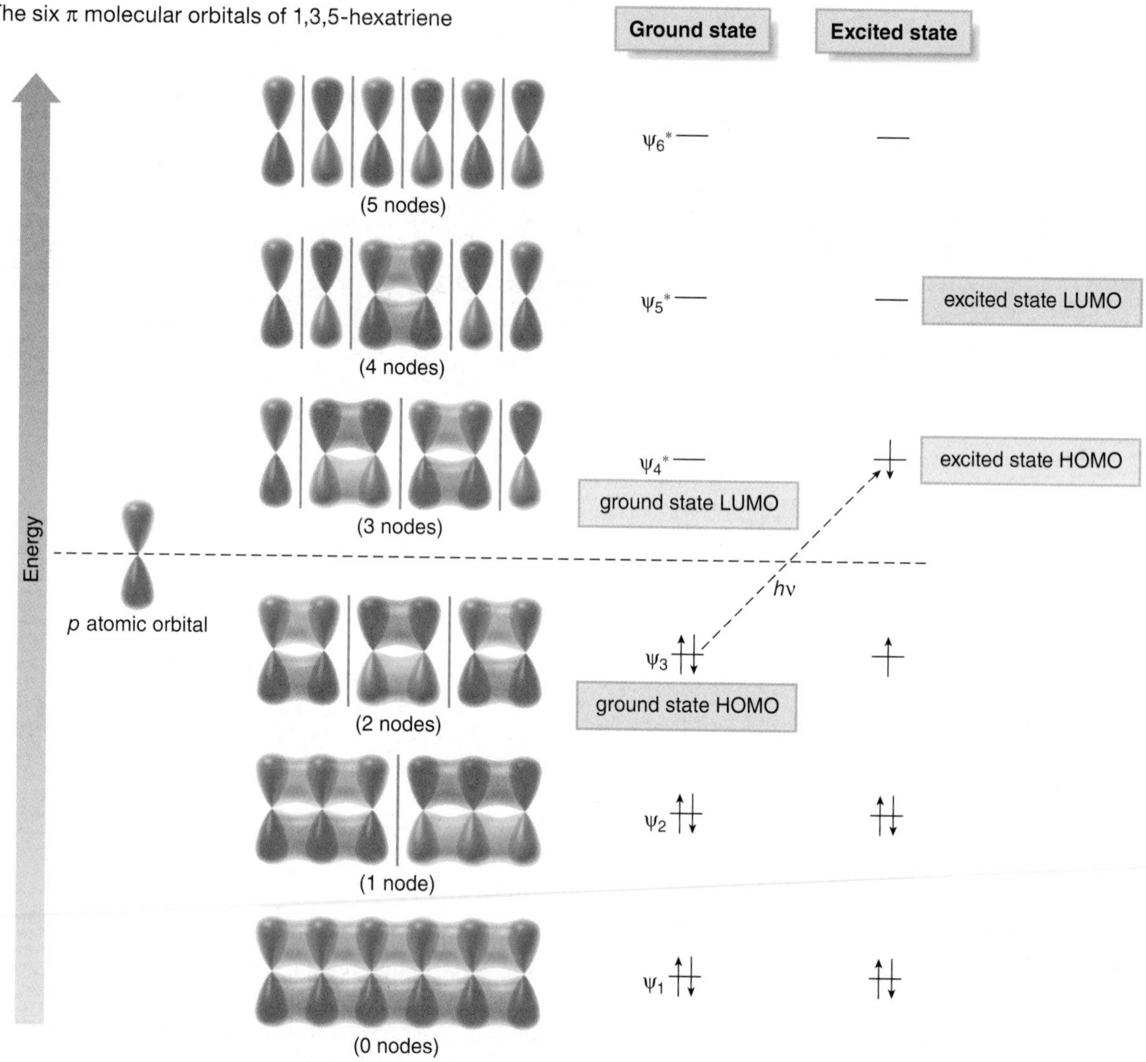

In the ground state electronic configuration, the six π electrons occupy the three bonding MOs, ψ_3 is the HOMO, and ψ_4* is the LUMO. In the excited state, which results from promotion of an electron from ψ_3 to ψ_4*, ψ_4* is the HOMO and ψ_5* is the LUMO.

Problem 27.3 (a) Using Figure 27.2 as a guide, draw the molecular orbitals for 2,4-hexadiene. (b) Label the HOMO and the LUMO in the ground state. (c) Label the HOMO and the LUMO in the excited state.

Problem 27.4 (a) How many π molecular orbitals are present in 1,3,5,7,9-decapentaene ($CH_2{=}CH{-}CH{=}CH{-}CH{=}CH{-}CH{=}CH{-}CH{=}CH_2$)? (b) How many are bonding MOs and how many are antibonding MOs? (c) How many nodes are present in ψ_1? (d) How many nodes are present in ψ_{10}*?

27.3 Electrocyclic Reactions

An electrocyclic reaction is a reversible reaction that involves ring closure of a conjugated polyene to a cycloalkene, or ring opening of a cycloalkene to a conjugated polyene. For example, ring closure of 1,3,5-hexatriene forms 1,3-cyclohexadiene, a product with one more σ bond and one fewer π bond than the reactant. Ring opening of cyclobutene forms 1,3-butadiene, a product with one fewer σ bond and one more π bond than the reactant.

Ring-closing reaction

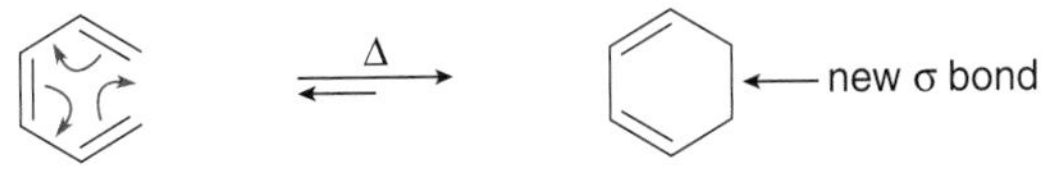

1,3,5-hexatriene 1,3-cyclohexadiene

Ring-opening reaction

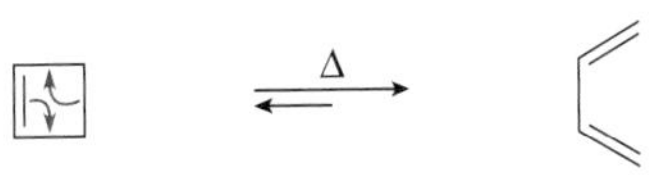

cyclobutene 1,3-butadiene

Arrows may be drawn in a clockwise or counterclockwise direction to show the flow of electrons.

- **To draw the product in each reaction, use curved arrows and begin at a π bond. Move the π electrons to an adjacent carbon–carbon bond and continue in a cyclic fashion.**

In a ring-forming reaction, this process forms a new σ bond that now joins the ends of the conjugated polyene. In a ring-opening reaction, this process breaks a σ bond to form a conjugated polyene with one more π bond.

Whether the reactant or product predominates at equilibrium depends on the ring size of the cyclic compound. Generally, a six-membered ring is favored over an acyclic triene at equilibrium. In contrast, an acyclic diene is favored over a strained four-membered ring.

Problem 27.5 Use curved arrows and draw the product of each electrocyclic reaction.

a. 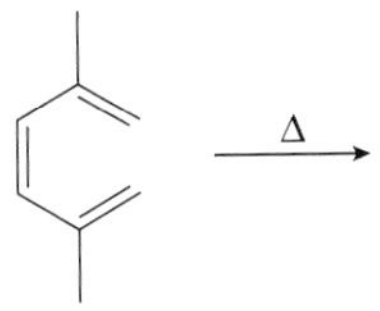

b. 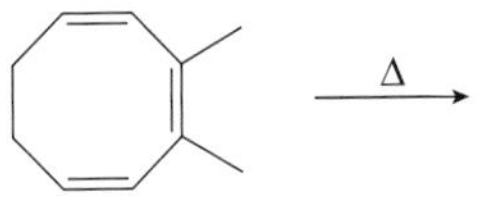

c. 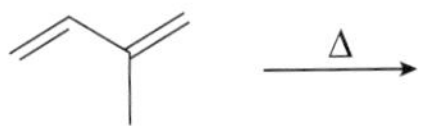

27.3A Stereochemistry and Orbital Symmetry

Electrocyclic reactions are completely stereospecific. For example, ring closure of (2*E*,4*Z*,6*E*)-2,4,6-octatriene yields a single product with cis methyl groups on the ring. Ring opening of *cis*-3,4-dimethylcyclobutene forms a single conjugated diene with one *Z* alkene and one *E* alkene.

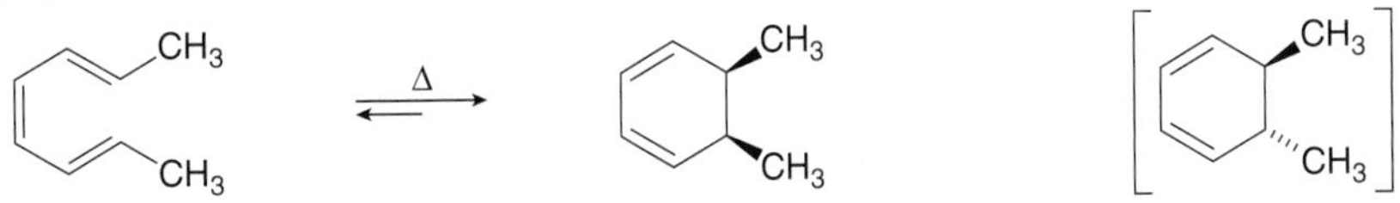

(2*E*,4*Z*,6*E*)-2,4,6-octatriene *cis*-5,6-dimethyl-1,3-cyclohexadiene NOT formed

cis product only

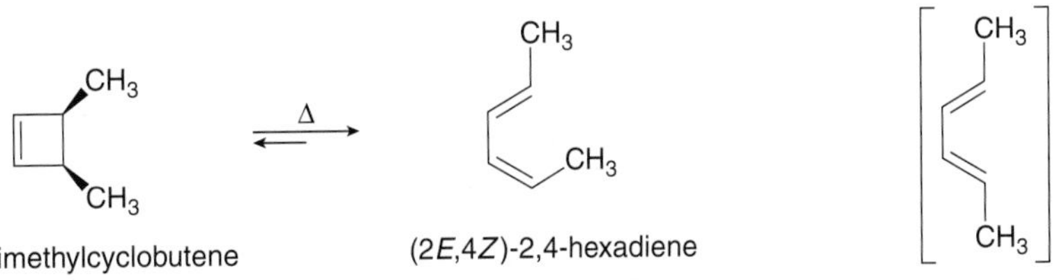

cis-3,4-dimethylcyclobutene (2*E*,4*Z*)-2,4-hexadiene NOT formed

(2*E*,4*Z*) diene only

Moreover, the stereochemistry of the product of an electrocyclic reaction depends on whether the reaction is carried out under thermal or photochemical reaction conditions—that is, with heat or light, respectively. Cyclization of (2*E*,4*E*)-2,4-hexadiene with heat forms a cyclobutene with trans methyl groups, whereas cyclization with light forms a cyclobutene with cis methyl groups.

Electrocyclic ring closure generally forms either an achiral meso compound or a mixture of chiral enantiomers. When enantiomers form, only one enantiomer is drawn in these reactions.

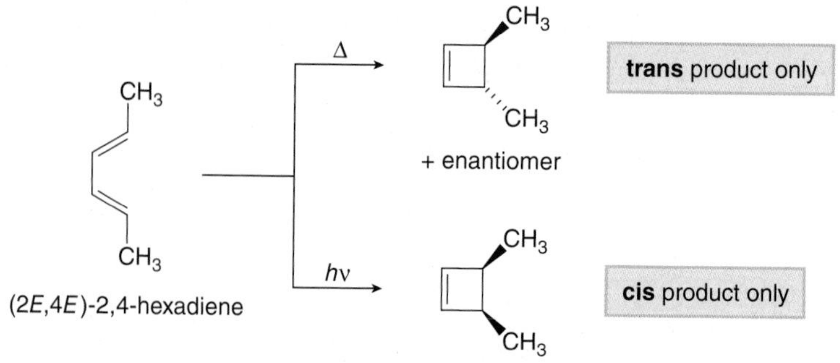

To understand these results, we must focus on the HOMO of the acyclic conjugated polyene that is either the reactant or product in an electrocyclic reaction. In particular, we must examine the *p* orbitals on the terminal carbons of the HOMO, and determine whether like phases of the orbitals are on the same side or on opposite sides of the molecule.

- An electrocyclic reaction occurs only when like phases of orbitals can overlap to form a bond. Such a reaction is *symmetry allowed.*
- An electrocyclic reaction cannot occur between lobes of opposite phase. Such a reaction is *symmetry forbidden.*

To form a bond, the *p* orbitals on the terminal carbons must rotate so that like phases can interact to form the new σ bond. Two modes of rotation are possible.

- When like phases of the *p* orbitals are on the same side of the molecule, the two orbitals must rotate in opposite directions—one clockwise and one counterclockwise. Rotation in opposite directions is said to be *disrotatory.*

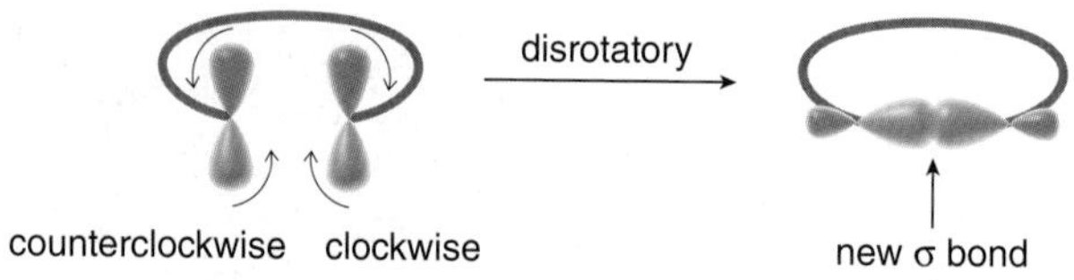

- When like phases of the *p* orbitals are on opposite sides of the molecule, the two orbitals must rotate in the same direction—both clockwise or both counterclockwise. Rotation in the same direction is said to be *conrotatory.*

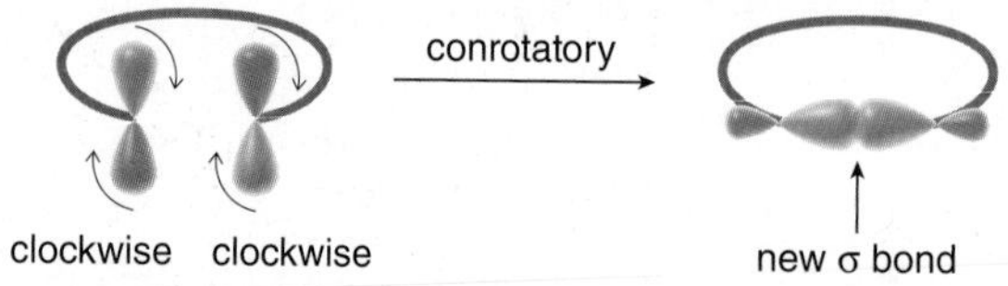

27.3B Thermal Electrocyclic Reactions

To explain the stereochemistry observed in electrocyclic reactions, we must examine the symmetry of the molecular orbital that contains the most loosely held π electrons. In a thermal reaction, we consider the **HOMO of the ground state electronic configuration.** Rotation occurs in a disrotatory or conrotatory fashion so that like phases of the *p* orbitals on the terminal carbons of this molecular orbital combine.

- **The number of double bonds in the conjugated polyene determines whether rotation is conrotatory or disrotatory.**

Two examples illustrate different outcomes.

Thermal electrocyclic ring closure of (2*E*,4*Z*,6*E*)-2,4,6-octatriene yields a single product with cis methyl groups on the ring.

Only the *p* orbitals on the terminal carbons of the HOMO are drawn for clarity.

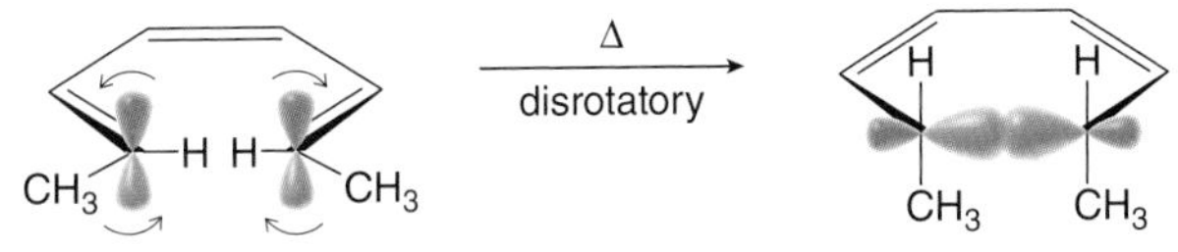

counterclockwise clockwise

ground state HOMO of (2*E*,4*Z*,6*E*)-2,4,6-octatriene

cis-5,6-dimethyl-1,3-cyclohexadiene

cis product

Cyclization occurs in a disrotatory fashion because the HOMO of a conjugated triene has like phases of the outermost *p* orbitals on the *same* side of the molecule (Figure 27.3). A disrotatory ring closure is symmetry allowed because like phases of the *p* orbitals overlap to form the new σ bond of the ring. In the disrotatory ring closure, both methyl groups are pushed *down* (or *up*), making them *cis* in the product.

This is a specific example of the general process observed for conjugated polyenes with an *odd* number of π bonds. The HOMO of a conjugated polyene with an odd number of π bonds has like phases of the outermost *p* orbitals on the *same* side of the molecule. As a result:

- **Thermal electrocyclic reactions occur in a *disrotatory* fashion for a conjugated polyene with an *odd* number of π bonds.**

In contrast, thermal electrocyclic ring closure of (2*E*,4*E*)-2,4-hexadiene forms a cyclobutene with trans methyl groups.

The conrotatory ring closure of (2*E*,4*E*)-2,4-hexadiene is drawn with two clockwise rotations. The conrotatory ring closure could also be drawn with two counterclockwise rotations, leading to the enantiomer of the trans product drawn. Both enantiomers are formed in equal amounts.

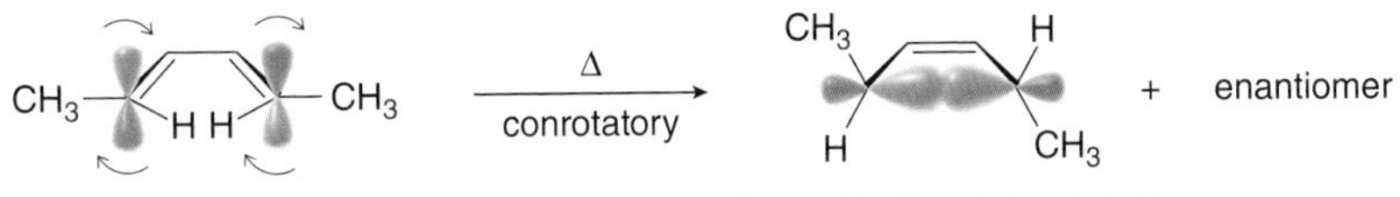

clockwise clockwise

ground state HOMO of (2*E*,4*E*)-2,4-hexadiene

trans-3,4-dimethylcyclobutene

trans product

Cyclization occurs in a conrotatory fashion because the HOMO of a conjugated diene has like phases of the outermost *p* orbitals on *opposite* sides of the molecule (Figure 27.2). A conrotatory ring closure is symmetry allowed because like phases of the *p* orbitals overlap to form the new σ bond of the ring. In the conrotatory ring closure, one methyl group is pushed *down* and one methyl group is pushed *up,* making them *trans* in the product.

This is a specific example of the general process observed for conjugated polyenes with an *even* number of π bonds. The HOMO of a conjugated polyene with an even number of π bonds has like phases of the outermost *p* orbitals on *opposite* sides of the molecule. As a result:

- **Thermal electrocyclic reactions occur in a *conrotatory* fashion for a conjugated polyene with an *even* number of π bonds.**

Since electrocyclic reactions are reversible, **electrocyclic ring-opening reactions follow the same rules** as electrocyclic ring closures. Thus, thermal ring opening of *cis*-3,4-dimethylcyclobutene—which ring opens to a diene with an *even* number of π bonds—occurs in a conrotatory fashion to form (2*E*,4*Z*)-2,4-hexadiene as the only product.

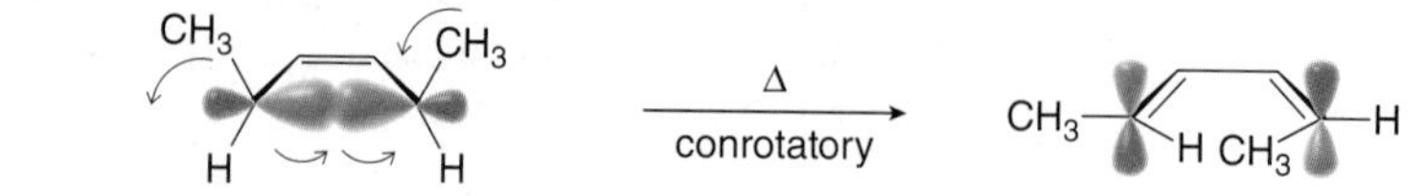

counterclockwise counterclockwise

cis-3,4-dimethylcyclobutene (2*E*,4*Z*)-2,4-hexadiene

Sample Problem 27.1 Draw the product of each thermal electrocyclic ring closure.

a. 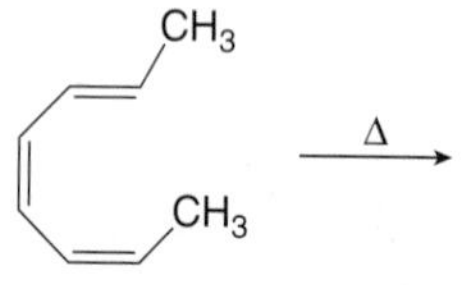

(2*E*,4*Z*,6*Z*)-2,4,6-octatriene

b. 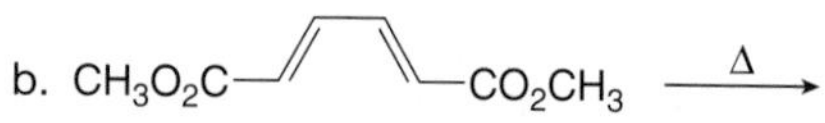

B

Solution

Count the number of π bonds in the conjugated polyene to determine the mode of ring closure in a thermal electrocyclic reaction.

- A conjugated polyene with an **odd** number of π bonds undergoes **disrotatory** cyclization.
- A conjugated polyene with an **even** number of π bonds undergoes **conrotatory** cyclization.

a. (2*E*,4*Z*,6*Z*)-2,4,6-Octatriene contains three π bonds. The HOMO of a conjugated polyene with an odd number of π bonds has like phases of the outermost *p* orbitals on the *same* side of the molecule, and this results in disrotatory cyclization.

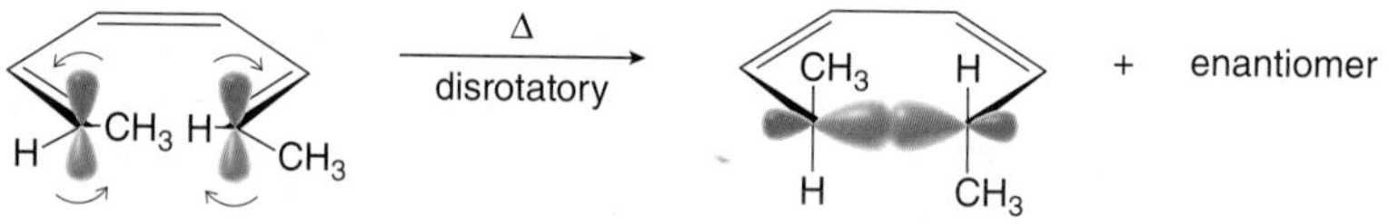

counterclockwise clockwise

(2*E*,4*Z*,6*Z*)-2,4,6-octatriene

trans-5,6-dimethyl-1,3-cyclohexadiene

trans product

b. Diene **B** contains two π bonds. The HOMO of a conjugated polyene with an even number of π bonds has like phases of the outermost *p* orbitals on *opposite* sides of the molecule, and this results in conrotatory cyclization.

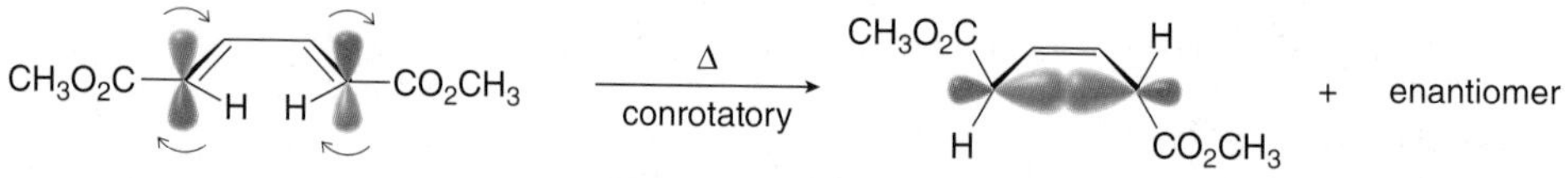

clockwise clockwise

B

trans product

Problem 27.6 What product is formed when each compound undergoes thermal electrocyclic ring opening or ring closure? Label each process as conrotatory or disrotatory and clearly indicate the stereochemistry around tetrahedral stereogenic centers and double bonds.

a. 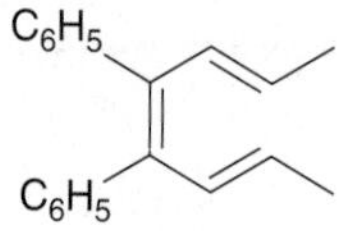

b. 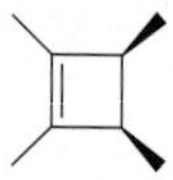

Problem 27.7 What cyclic product is formed when each decatetraene undergoes thermal electrocyclic ring closure?

a. 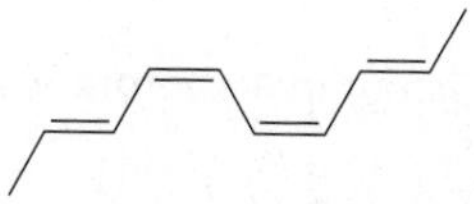

b. 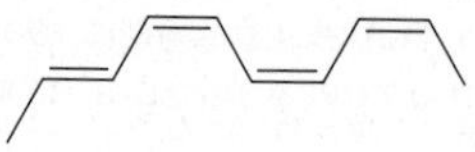

27.3C Photochemical Electrocyclic Reactions

Photochemical electrocyclic reactions follow similar principles as those detailed in thermal reactions with one important difference. **In photochemical reactions, we must consider the orbitals of the HOMO of the *excited* state to determine the course of the reaction.** As a photon is absorbed, an electron in the ground state HOMO is excited to the ground state LUMO. As a result, the excited state HOMO is one energy level higher than before (see Figures 27.2 and 27.3). The excited state HOMO has the *opposite* orientation of the outermost *p* orbitals compared to the HOMO of the ground state. As a result, **the method of ring closure of a photochemical electrocyclic reaction is *opposite* to that of a thermal electrocyclic reaction for the same number of π bonds.**

Photochemical electrocyclic ring closure of (2*E*,4*Z*,6*E*)-2,4,6-octatriene yields a cyclic product with trans methyl groups on the ring.

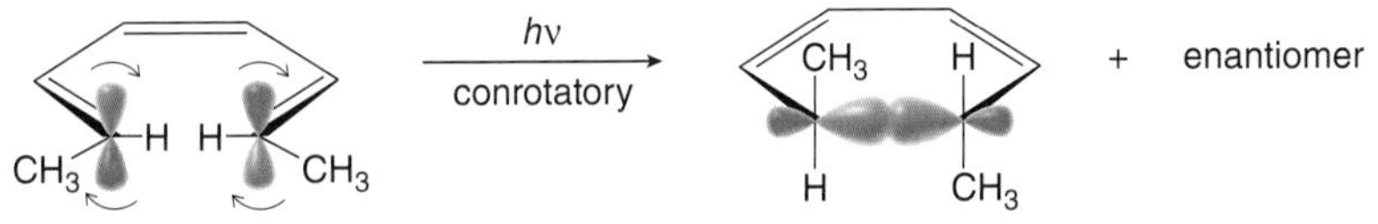

clockwise clockwise

excited state HOMO of
(2*E*,4*Z*,6*E*)-2,4,6-octatriene

trans-5,6-dimethyl-1,3-cyclohexadiene
trans product

Cyclization occurs in a conrotatory fashion because the excited state HOMO of a conjugated triene has like phases of the outermost *p* orbitals on the *opposite* sides of the molecule (Figure 27.3). In the conrotatory ring closure, one methyl group is pushed *down* and one methyl group is pushed *up,* making them *trans* in the product. This is a specific example of the general process observed for conjugated polyenes with an *odd* number of π bonds.

- **Photochemical electrocyclic reactions occur in a *conrotatory* fashion for a conjugated polyene with an *odd* number of π bonds.**

Photochemical electrocyclic ring closure of (2*E*,4*E*)-2,4-hexadiene forms a cyclobutene with cis methyl groups.

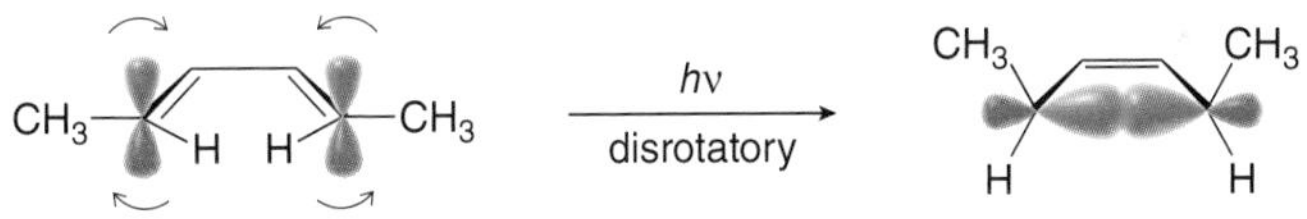

clockwise counterclockwise

excited state HOMO of
(2*E*,4*E*)-2,4-hexadiene

cis-3,4-dimethylcyclobutene
cis product

Cyclization occurs in a disrotatory fashion because the excited state HOMO of a conjugated diene has like phases of the outermost *p* orbitals on the *same* side of the molecule (Figure 27.3). In the disrotatory ring closure, both methyl groups are pushed *down* (or *up*), making them *cis* in the product. This is a specific example of the general process observed for conjugated polyenes with an *even* number of π bonds.

- **Photochemical electrocyclic reactions occur in a *disrotatory* fashion for a conjugated polyene with an *even* number of π bonds.**

Problem 27.8 What product is formed when each compound in Problem 27.6 undergoes photochemical electrocyclic ring opening or ring closure? Label each process as conrotatory or disrotatory and clearly indicate the stereochemistry around tetrahedral stereogenic centers and double bonds.

Vitamin D (Problem 27.9) regulates calcium absorption, so adequate vitamin D levels are needed for proper bone growth. Vitamin D-fortified milk sold in the United States is produced by exposing milk to ultraviolet light.

Problem 27.9 Vitamin D_3, the most abundant of the D vitamins, is synthesized from 7-dehydrocholesterol, a compound found in milk and fatty fish such as salmon and mackerel. When the skin is exposed to sunlight, a photochemical electrocyclic ring opening forms provitamin D_3, which is then converted to vitamin D_3 by a sigmatropic rearrangement (Section 27.5). Draw the structure of provitamin D_3.

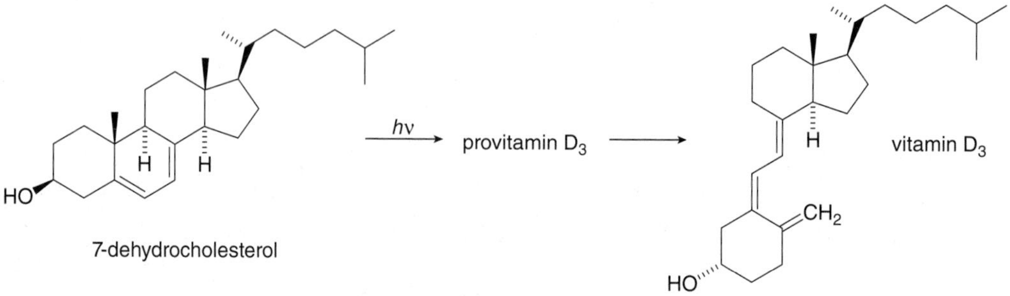

27.3D Summary of Electrocyclic Reactions

Table 27.1 summarizes the rules, often called the **Woodward–Hoffmann rules,** for electrocyclic reactions under thermal or photochemical reaction conditions. The number of π bonds refers to the acyclic conjugated polyene that is either the reactant or product of an electrocyclic reaction.

Table 27.1 Woodward–Hoffmann Rules for Electrocyclic Reactions

Number of π bonds	Thermal reaction	Photochemical reaction
Even	Conrotatory	Disrotatory
Odd	Disrotatory	Conrotatory

Sample Problem 27.2 Identify **A** and **B** in the following reaction sequence. Label each process as conrotatory or disrotatory.

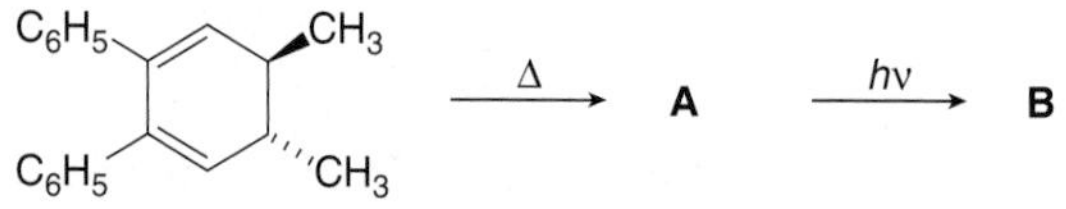

Solution

Ring opening of a cyclohexadiene forms a hexatriene with **three** π bonds. A conjugated polyene with an odd number of π bonds undergoes a thermal electrocyclic reaction in a disrotatory fashion (Table 27.1). The resulting hexatriene (**A**) then undergoes a photochemical electrocyclic reaction in a conrotatory fashion to form a cyclohexadiene with cis methyl groups (**B**).

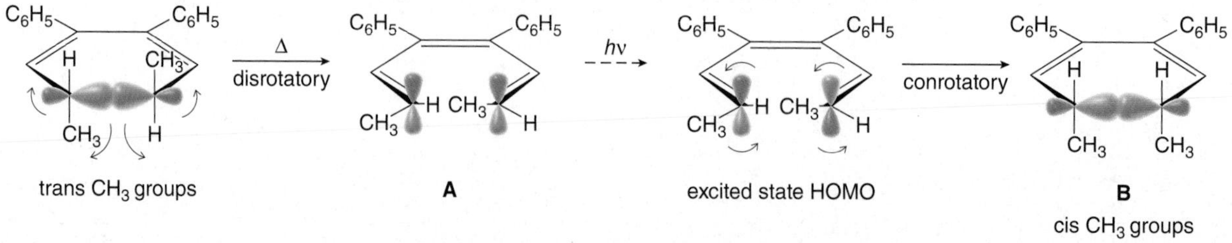

Problem 27.10 Draw the product formed when each triene undergoes electrocyclic reaction under [1] thermal conditions; [2] photochemical conditions.

a.  b. 

Problem 27.11 What product would be formed by the disrotatory cyclization of the given triene? Would this reaction occur under photochemical or thermal conditions?

27.4 Cycloaddition Reactions

A cycloaddition is a reaction between two compounds with π bonds to form a cyclic product with two new σ bonds. Like electrocyclic reactions, cycloadditions are concerted, stereospecific reactions, and the course of the reaction is determined by the symmetry of the molecular orbitals of the reactants.

Cycloadditions can be initiated by heat (thermal conditions) or light (photochemical conditions). Cycloadditions are identified by the number of π electrons in the two reactants.

The Diels–Alder reaction is a thermal [4 + 2] cycloaddition that occurs between a diene with four π electrons and an alkene (dienophile) with two π electrons (Sections 16.12–16.14).

[4 + 2] Cycloaddition

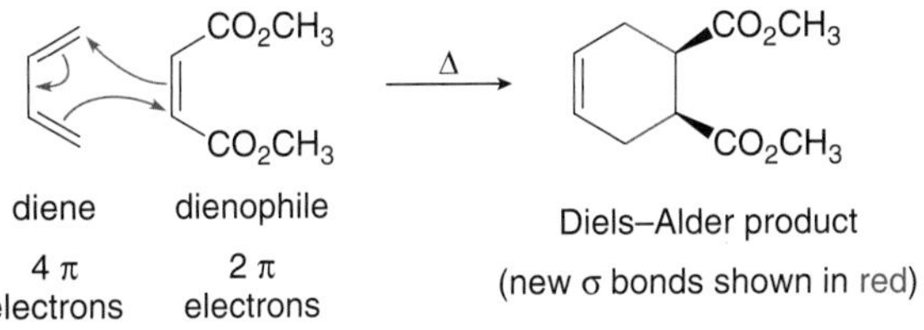
CO_2CH_3
CO_2CH_3
Δ
CO_2CH_3
CO_2CH_3
diene
dienophile
4 π electrons
2 π electrons
Diels–Alder product
(new σ bonds shown in red)

A photochemical [2 + 2] cycloaddition occurs between two alkenes, each with two π electrons, to form a cyclobutane. Thermal [2 + 2] cycloadditions do *not* take place.

[2 + 2] Cycloaddition

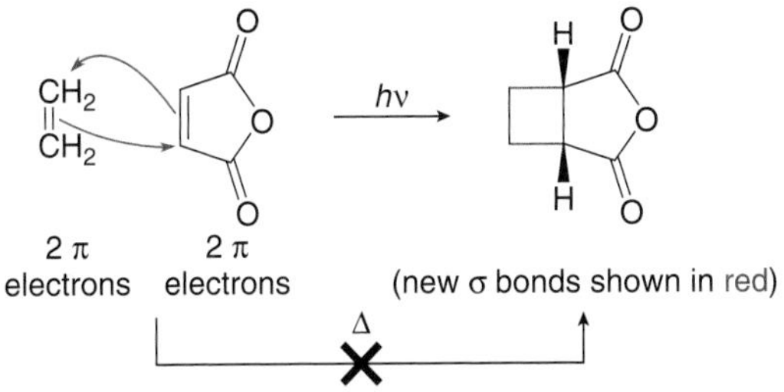
CH_2
CH_2
O
O
O
hν
H
H
O
O
O
2 π electrons
2 π electrons
(new σ bonds shown in red)
Δ

Sample Problem 27.3 What type of cycloaddition is shown in each equation?

a. 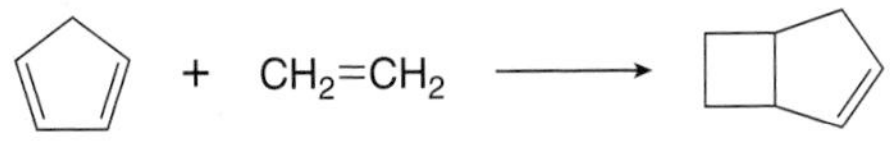
+ $CH_2{=}CH_2$

b. 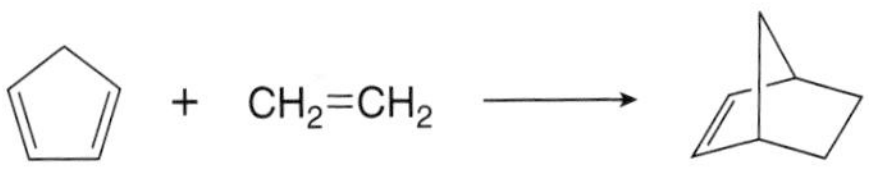
+ $CH_2{=}CH_2$

Solution

Count the number of π electrons *involved in each reactant* to classify the cycloaddition.

a. [2 + 2] Cycloaddition

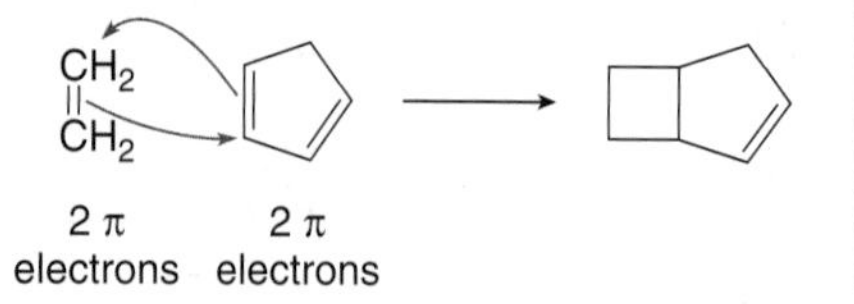

CH2
CH2
2 π
electrons
2 π
electrons

b. [4 + 2] Cycloaddition

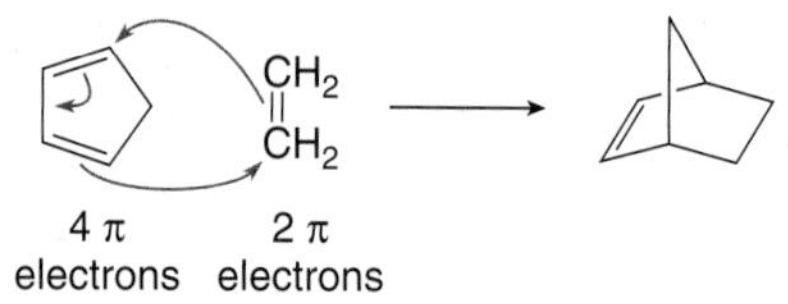

CH2
CH2
4 π
electrons
2 π
electrons

Problem 27.12 Consider cycloheptatrienone and ethylene, and draw a possible product formed from each type of cycloaddition: (a) [2 + 2]; (b) [4 + 2]; (c) [6 + 2].

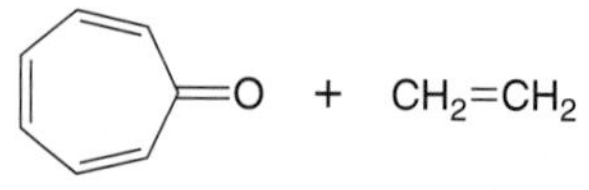

O
+
CH2=CH2

cycloheptatrienone

27.4A Orbital Symmetry and Cycloadditions

To understand cycloaddition reactions, we examine the *p* orbitals of the terminal carbons of both reactants. Bonding can take place only when like phases of both sets of *p* orbitals can combine. Two modes of reaction are possible.

- **A suprafacial cycloaddition occurs when like phases of the *p* orbitals of both reactants are on the same side of the π system, so that two bonding interactions result.**

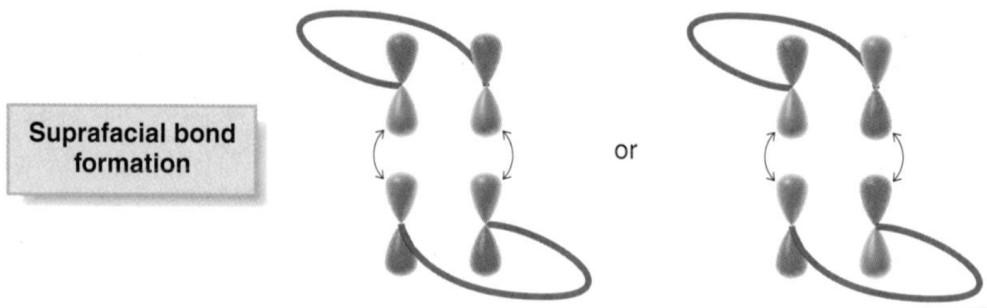

Suprafacial bond formation
or

- **An antarafacial cycloaddition occurs when one π system must twist to align like phases of the *p* orbitals of the terminal carbons of the reactants.**

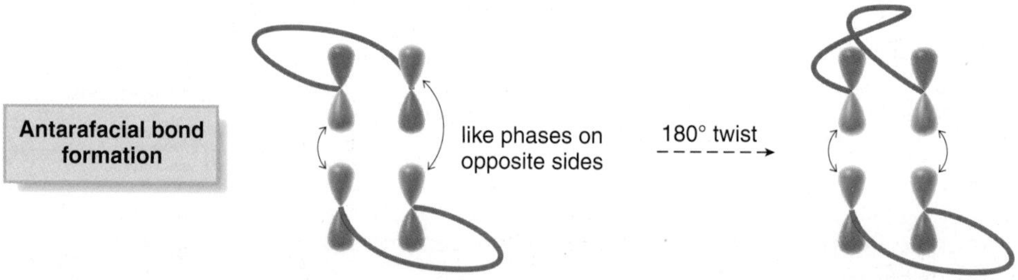

Antarafacial bond formation
like phases on opposite sides
180° twist

Because of the geometrical constraints of small rings, **cycloadditions that form four- or six-membered rings must take place by suprafacial pathways.**

Since cycloaddition involves the donation of electron density from one reactant to another, one reactant donates its most loosely held electrons—those occupying its HOMO—to a vacant orbital that can accept electrons—the LUMO—of the second reactant. The HOMO of either reactant can be used for analysis.

- **In a cycloaddition we examine the bonding interactions of the HOMO of one component with the LUMO of the second component.**

27.4B [4 + 2] Cycloadditions

To examine the course of a [4 + 2] cycloaddition, let's arbitrarily choose the HOMO of the diene and the LUMO of the alkene, and look at the symmetry of the *p* orbitals on the terminal carbons of both components. Since two bonding interactions result from overlap of the like phases of both sets of *p* orbitals, **a [4 + 2] cycloaddition occurs readily by suprafacial reaction under thermal conditions.**

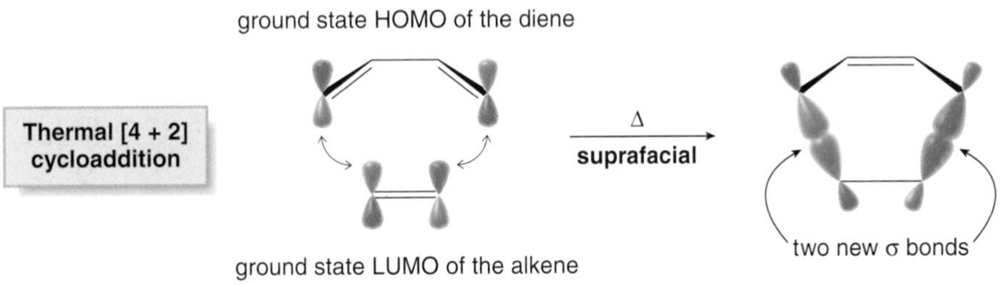
ground state HOMO of the diene
Thermal [4 + 2] cycloaddition
Δ
suprafacial
two new σ bonds
ground state LUMO of the alkene

This is a specific example of a general cycloaddition involving an odd number of π bonds (three π bonds total, two from the diene and one from the alkene).

- **Thermal cycloadditions involving an *odd* number of π bonds proceed by a *suprafacial* pathway.**

In Section 16.13, we learned that the stereochemistry of the dienophile is retained in the Diels–Alder product.

Because a Diels–Alder reaction follows a concerted, suprafacial pathway, the **stereochemistry of the diene is retained in the Diels–Alder product.** As a result, reaction of (2*E*,4*E*)-2,4-hexadiene with ethylene forms a cyclohexene with cis substituents (Reaction [1]), whereas reaction of (2*E*,4*Z*)-2,4-hexadiene with ethylene forms a cyclohexene with trans substituents (Reaction [2]).

[1]
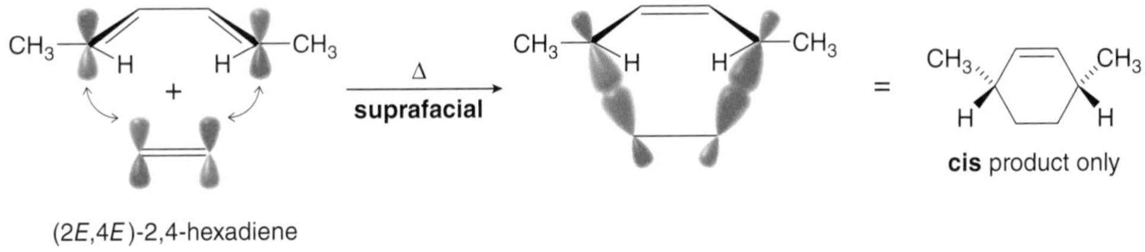
CH_3
H
H
CH_3
+
Δ
suprafacial
=
cis product only
(2E,4E)-2,4-hexadiene

[2]
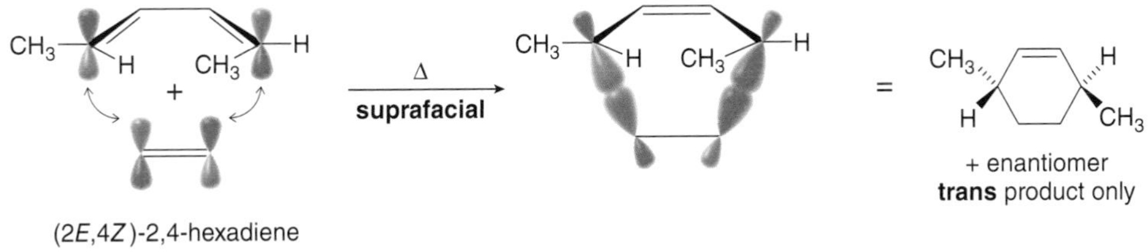
CH_3
H
CH_3
H
+
Δ
suprafacial
=
+ enantiomer
trans product only
(2E,4Z)-2,4-hexadiene

Problem 27.13 Show that a thermal suprafacial addition is symmetry allowed in a [4 + 2] cycloaddition by using the HOMO of the alkene and the LUMO of the diene.

Problem 27.14 Draw the product (including stereochemistry) formed from each pair of reactants in a thermal [4 + 2] cycloaddition reaction.

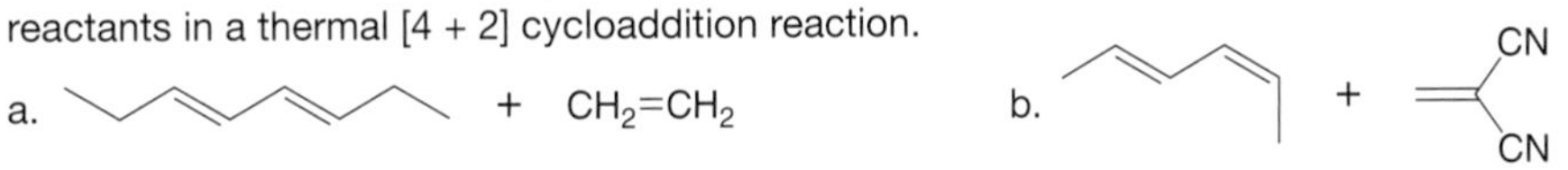
a.
+ $CH_2{=}CH_2$
b.
+
CN
CN

Reserpine (Problem 27.15) is isolated from the roots of *Rauwolfia serpentina,* a plant used for centuries in traditional Indian medicine for the treatment of mental disorders and venomous bites.

Problem 27.15 (a) Draw the product of the following [4 + 2] cycloaddition, which was carried out in the early stages of the synthesis of the alkaloid reserpine (Problem 22.91). Indicate the stereochemistry at any newly formed stereogenic centers. (b) Draw the *p* orbitals of the alkene and the terminal carbons of the conjugated diene, and show how the orientation of the reactants and orbital overlap lead to the observed stereochemistry.

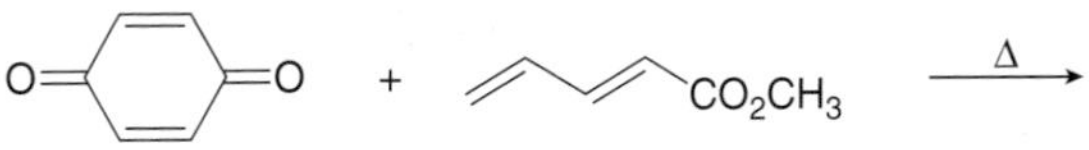
O
O
+
CO_2CH_3
Δ

27.4C [2 + 2] Cycloadditions

In contrast to a [4 + 2] cycloaddition, a [2 + 2] cycloaddition does *not* occur under thermal conditions, but *does* take place photochemically. This result is explained by examining the symmetry of the HOMO and LUMO of the alkene reactants.

In a thermal [2 + 2] cycloaddition, like phases of the *p* orbitals on only one set of terminal carbons can overlap. For like phases to overlap on the other terminal carbon, the molecule must twist to allow for an antarafacial pathway. This process cannot occur to form small rings.

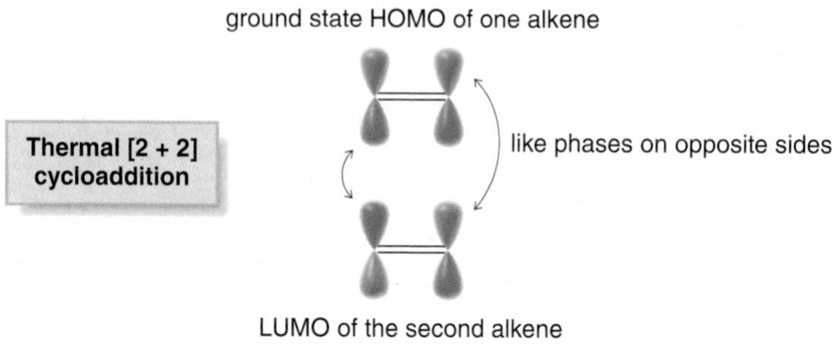

In a photochemical [2 + 2] cycloaddition, light energy promotes an electron from the ground state HOMO to form the excited state HOMO (designated as ψ_2^* in Figure 27.1). Interaction of this excited state HOMO with the LUMO of the second alkene then allows for overlap of the like phases of both sets of *p* orbitals. Two bonding interactions result and the reaction occurs by a suprafacial pathway.

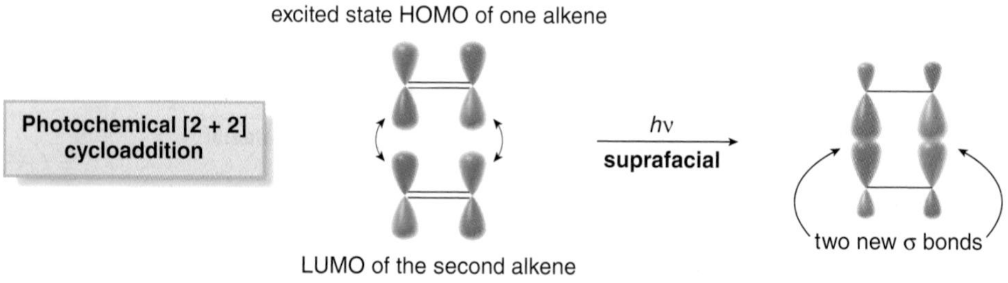

This is a specific example of a general cycloaddition involving an even number of π bonds (two π bonds total, one from each alkene).

- **Photochemical cycloadditions involving an *even* number of π bonds proceed by a *suprafacial* pathway.**

Problem 27.16 Draw the product formed in each cycloaddition.

a. 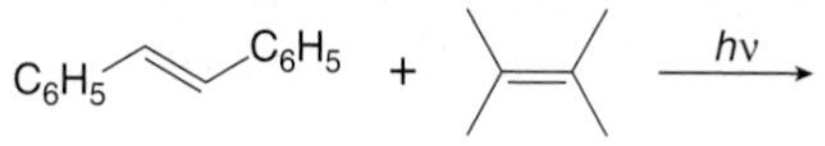

b. 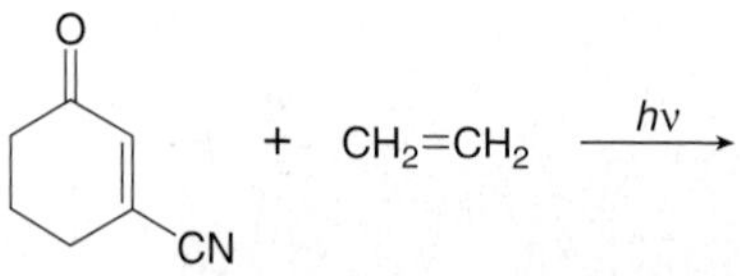

27.4D Summary of Cycloaddition Reactions

Table 27.2 summarizes the Woodward–Hoffmann rules that govern cycloaddition reactions. The number of π bonds refers to the total number of π bonds from both components of the cycloaddition. For a given number of π bonds, the mode of cycloaddition is always *opposite* in thermal and photochemical reactions.

Table 27.2 Woodward–Hoffmann Rules for Cycloaddition Reactions

Number of π bonds	Thermal reaction	Photochemical reaction
Even	Antarafacial	Suprafacial
Odd	Suprafacial	Antarafacial

Problem 27.17 Using the Woodward–Hoffmann rules, predict the stereochemical pathway for each cycloaddition: (a) a [6 + 4] photochemical reaction; (b) an [8 + 2] thermal reaction.

Problem 27.18 Using orbital symmetry, explain why a Diels–Alder reaction does not take place under photochemical reaction conditions.

27.5 Sigmatropic Rearrangements

A sigmatropic rearrangement is an intramolecular pericyclic reaction in which a σ bond is broken in a reactant, the π bonds rearrange, and a new σ bond is formed in the product. In a sigmatropic rearrangement, the number of π bonds in the reactant and product is constant, and the σ bonds broken and formed are **allylic** C–H, C–C, or C–Z bonds (Z = N, O, or S). A sigmatropic rearrangement that results in cleavage and formation of a C–H bond is shown.

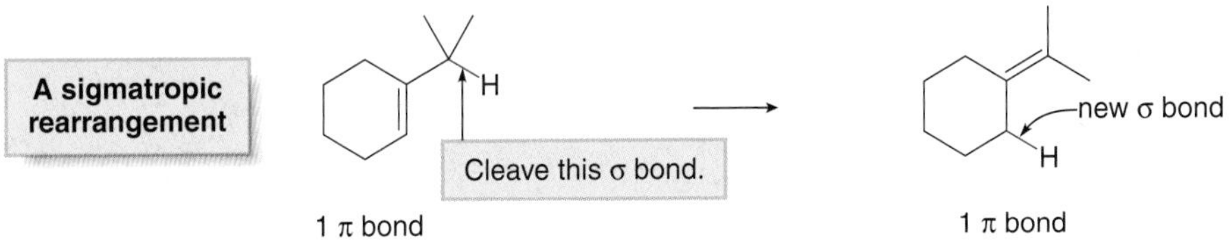

Sigmatropic rearrangements are characterized by a set of numbers in brackets, [*n*,*m*], to indicate the location of the new σ bond relative to the broken σ bond. To designate a sigmatropic rearrangement:

- **Locate the σ bond broken in the reactant and label both atoms in the bond with "1's."**
- **Locate the new σ bond in the product, and count the number of atoms from the broken σ bond to the new σ bond for each fragment.**
- **Place both numbers in brackets, with the lower number first. In a rearrangement involving a C–H bond, the first number is always "1."**

For example, a [3,3] sigmatropic rearrangement converts diene **A** into diene **B** when an allylic C–C bond in **A** is broken and a new allylic C–C bond is formed in **B.**

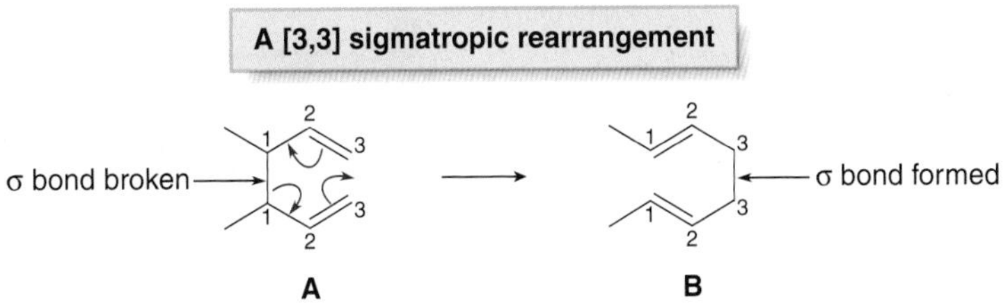

Sample Problem 27.4 What type of sigmatropic rearrangement is illustrated in each equation?

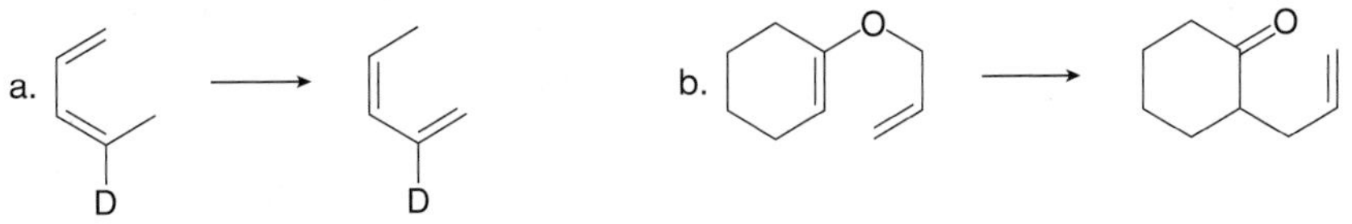

Solution

Locate the atoms in the broken σ bond and label them with 1's. Locate the atoms in the new σ bond, and count the number of atoms from the bond broken to the bond formed. When a C–H bond is broken, the first number in the [*n*,*m*] designation must be 1, since the H atom is bonded to no other atom.

a. A C–H bond is broken on the allylic C and a new C–H bond is formed on C5, so the reaction is a **[1,5] sigmatropic rearrangement.**

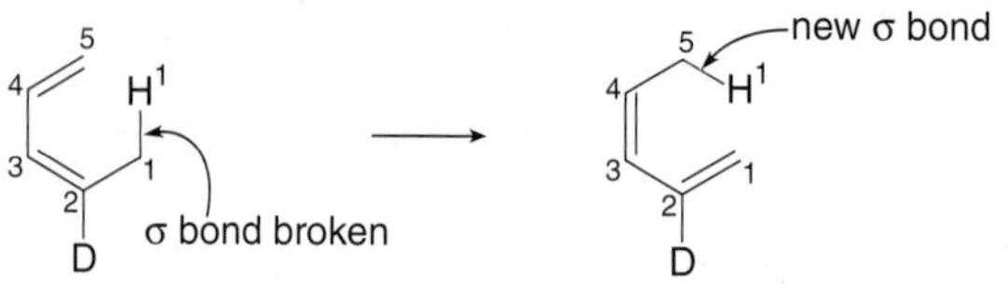

b. The reaction is a **[3,3] sigmatropic rearrangement,** because a C–O σ bond is broken and a new allylic C–C σ bond is formed between carbons that are three atoms removed from the broken bond.

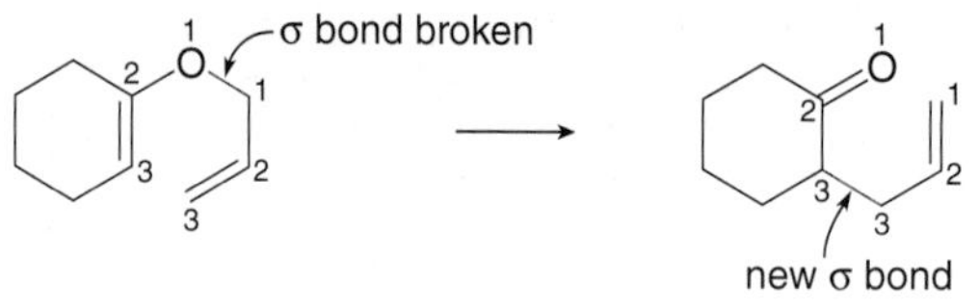

Problem 27.19 What type of sigmatropic rearrangement is illustrated in each equation?

a. 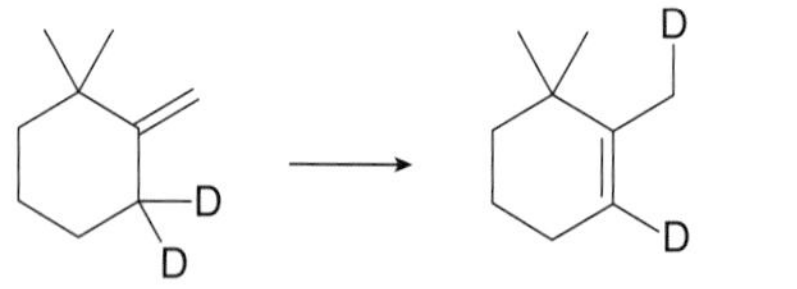

b. 

27.5A Sigmatropic Rearrangements and Orbital Symmetry

The stereochemistry of a sigmatropic rearrangement, like that of other pericyclic reactions, is determined by the symmetry of the orbitals involved in the reaction. In sigmatropic rearrangements, we consider the orbitals of the σ bond that is broken and the terminal *p* orbital of the π bond at which the new σ bond forms. Two modes of rearrangement are possible: **suprafacial** and **antarafacial.**

- **In a suprafacial rearrangement, the new σ bond forms on the *same* side of the π system as the broken σ bond.**

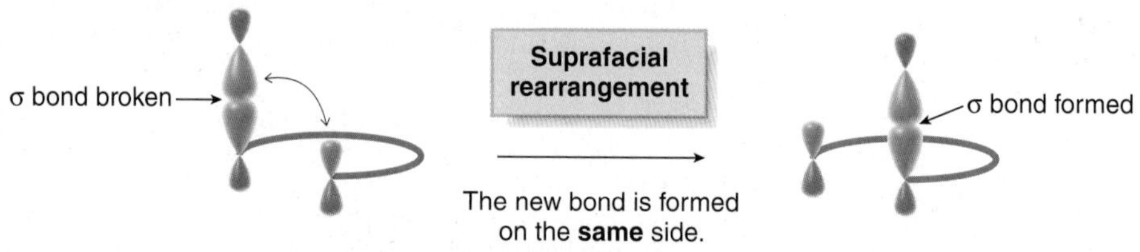

- **In an antarafacial rearrangement, the new σ bond forms on the *opposite* side of the π system as the broken σ bond.**

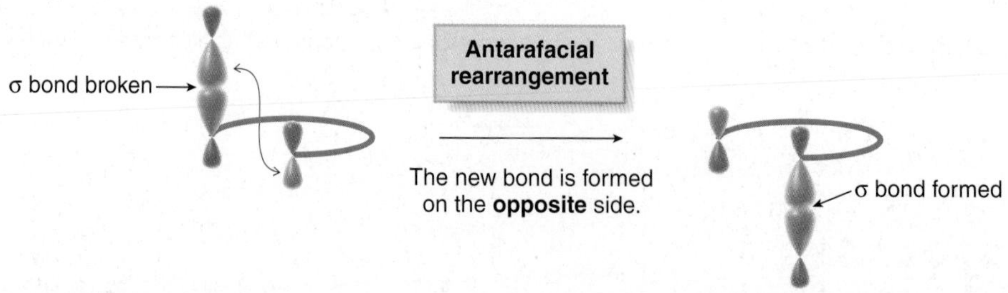

Sigmatropic rearrangements can occur under thermal or photochemical conditions, and follow the same rules observed in cycloaddition reactions. With sigmatropic rearrangements we count the total number of electron pairs in the σ bond that is broken and the π bonds that rearrange (Table 27.3). Because sigmatropic rearrangements involve cyclic transition states and small rings have geometrical constraints, **reactions involving six atoms or fewer must take place by suprafacial pathways.**

Table 27.3 Woodward–Hoffmann Rules for Sigmatropic Rearrangements

Number of electron pairs	Thermal reaction	Photochemical reaction
Even	Antarafacial	Suprafacial
Odd	Suprafacial	Antarafacial

For example, a [1,5] sigmatropic rearrangement of **X** to **Y** involves three electron pairs, one from the σ bond that is broken and two from the π bonds that rearrange.

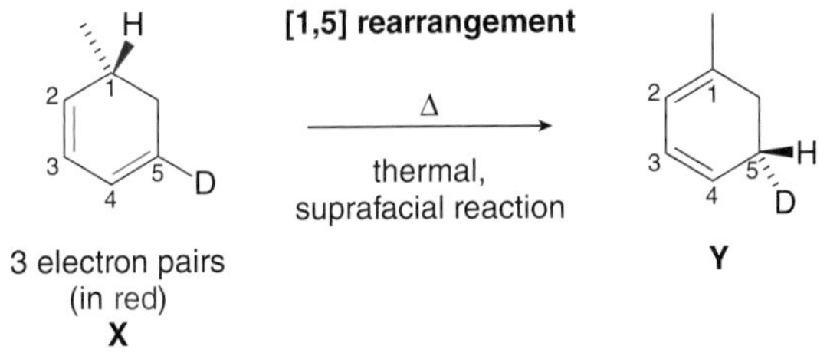

According to Table 27.3, this reaction must occur in a suprafacial mode under thermal conditions and in an antarafacial mode under photochemical conditions. Since this reaction involves only six atoms (including the H atom that migrates), it must take place under thermal conditions in a suprafacial fashion.

Sample Problem 27.5 Classify the following sigmatropic rearrangement and determine whether it takes place readily under thermal or photochemical reaction conditions.

Solution

First, classify the rearrangement as in Sample Problem 27.4: Label the atoms in the broken σ bond with 1's, locate the new σ bond, and count the number of atoms from the bond broken to the bond formed. Then, count the number of electron pairs involved in the reaction, and use Table 27.3 to determine the stereochemical pathway of the reaction. Keep in mind that reactions involving six atoms or fewer must take place by suprafacial pathways.

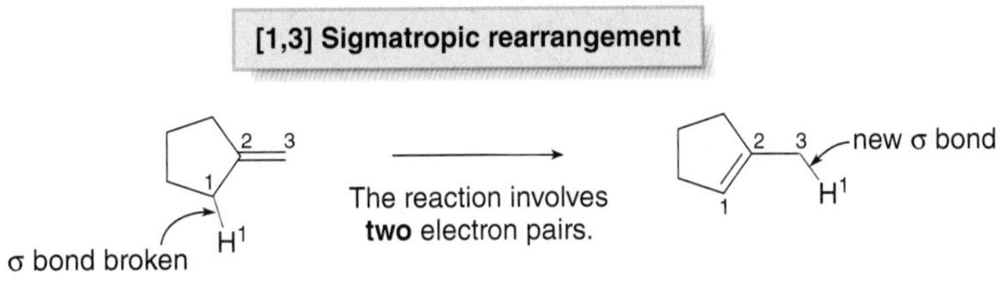

This reaction is a [1,3] sigmatropic rearrangement, involving two electron pairs: the C–H σ bond broken and one π bond. Since the reaction involves four atoms, it must take place via a suprafacial pathway, which occurs under photochemical conditions.

Problem 27.20 (a) What product is formed from the [1,7] sigmatropic rearrangement of a deuterium in the following triene? (b) Does this reaction proceed in a suprafacial or antarafacial manner under thermal conditions? (c) Does this reaction proceed in a suprafacial or antarafacial manner under photochemical conditions?

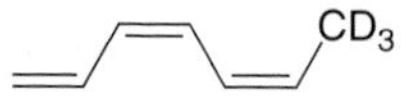

27.5B [3,3] Sigmatropic Rearrangements

Two widely used [3,3] sigmatropic rearrangements in organic synthesis are the **Cope rearrangement** of a 1,5-diene to an isomeric 1,5-diene, and the **Claisen rearrangement** of an unsaturated ether to a γ,δ-unsaturated carbonyl compound.

Cope rearrangement

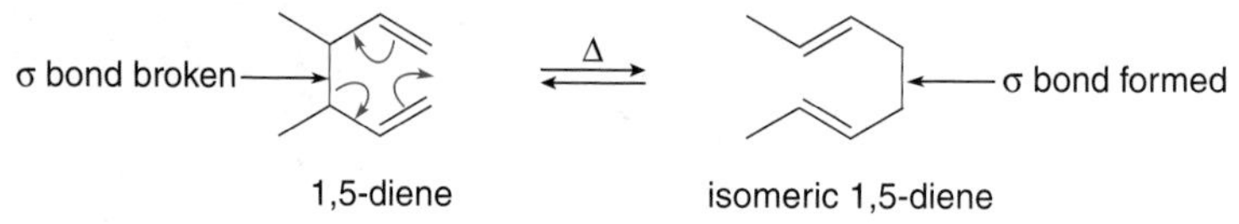

Claisen rearrangement

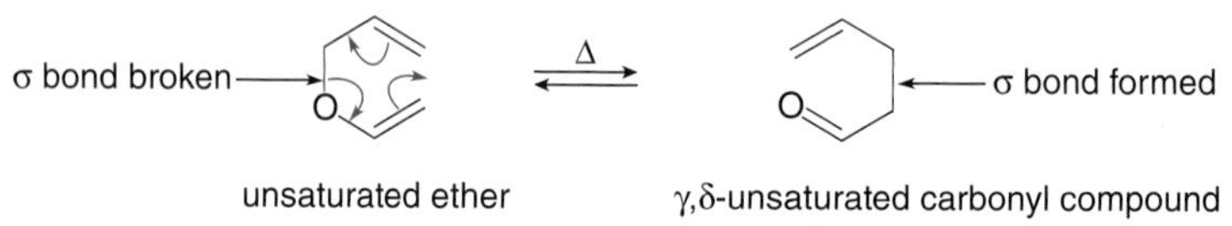

Both reactions involve three electron pairs—two π bonds and one σ bond—and six atoms, and take place readily in a **suprafacial pathway under thermal conditions.**

Cope Rearrangement

Since a Cope rearrangement involves isomeric 1,5-dienes as reactant and product, the more stable diene is favored at equilibrium. Useful Cope rearrangements occur when the reactant 1,5-diene is considerably less stable than the product, as in the case of *cis*-1,2-divinylcyclobutane, which rearranges to 1,5-cyclooctadiene with loss of strain from the cyclobutane ring.

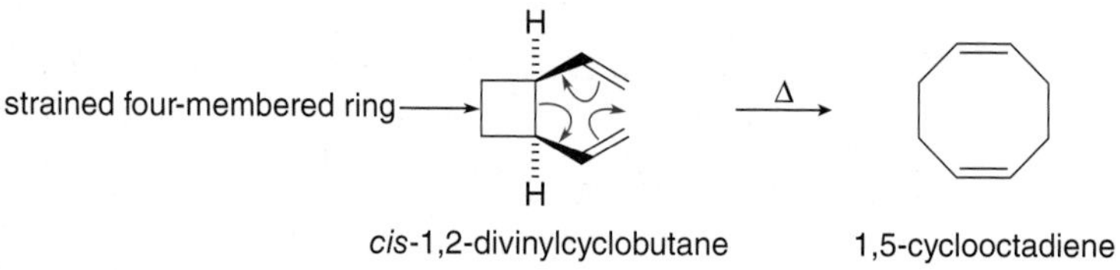

The **oxy-Cope rearrangement** is an especially powerful variation of a Cope rearrangement using an unsaturated alcohol. [3,3] Sigmatropic rearrangement forms an enol initially, which then tautomerizes to form a carbonyl group.

oxy-Cope rearrangement

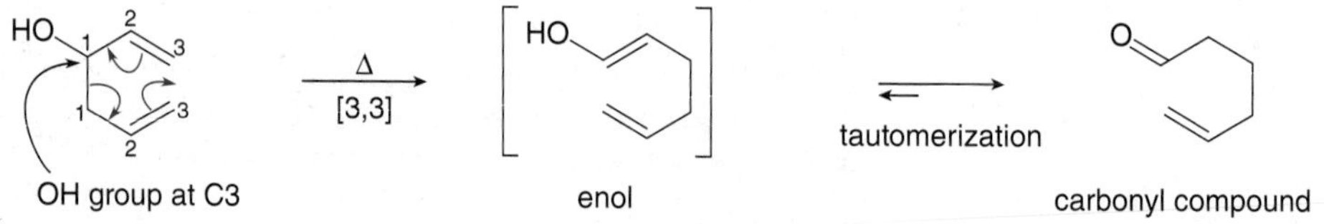

Example

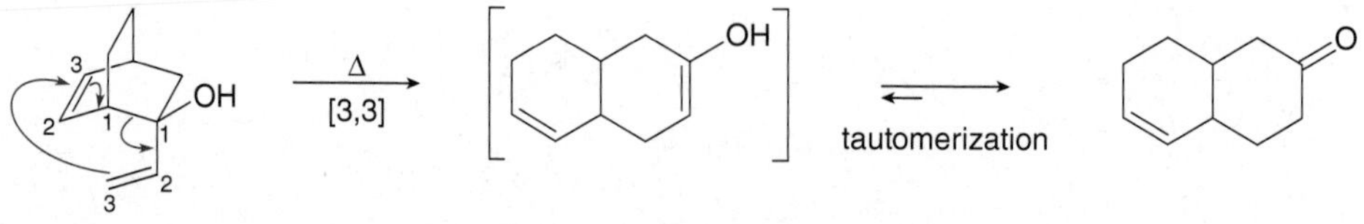

Moreover, ***anionic*** **oxy-Cope rearrangements** often give high yields of rearranged product under very mild reaction conditions. In an anionic oxy-Cope rearrangement, the unsaturated alcohol reactant is first treated with strong base, usually KH in the presence of 18-crown-6 (Section 9.5B), to form an alkoxide. [3,3] Sigmatropic rearrangement then yields a resonance-stabilized enolate, which is protonated to form a carbonyl product.

Anionic oxy-Cope rearrangement

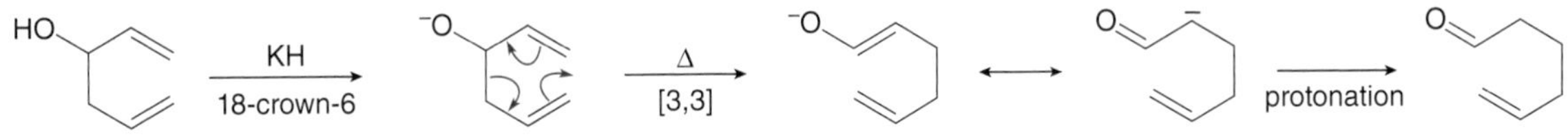

alkoxide resonance-stabilized enolate

Problem 27.21 What product is formed from the Cope or oxy-Cope rearrangement of each starting material?

a. 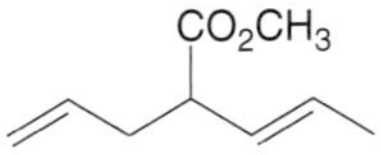

b. 
c. 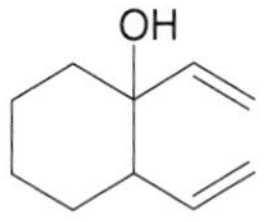

Problem 27.22 One step in the synthesis of periplanone B, the chapter-opening molecule, involved anionic oxy-Cope rearrangement of the following unsaturated alcohol. Draw the product that results after protonation of the intermediate enolate.

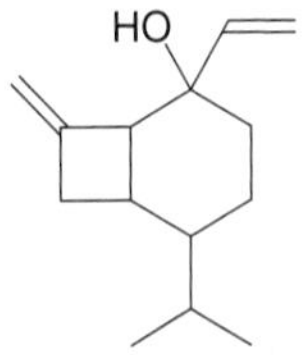

Claisen Rearrangement

A Claisen rearrangement is a [3,3] sigmatropic rearrangement of an unsaturated ether, either an allyl vinyl ether or an allyl aryl ether. With an allyl vinyl ether, a γ,δ-unsaturated carbonyl compound is formed directly by the concerted rearrangement. With an allyl aryl ether, Claisen rearrangement initially generates a cyclohexadienone intermediate, which tautomerizes to a phenol that contains an allyl group ortho to the OH group.

Examples

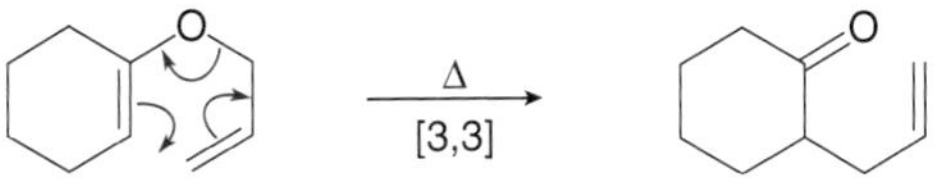

allyl vinyl ether γ,δ unsaturated carbonyl compound

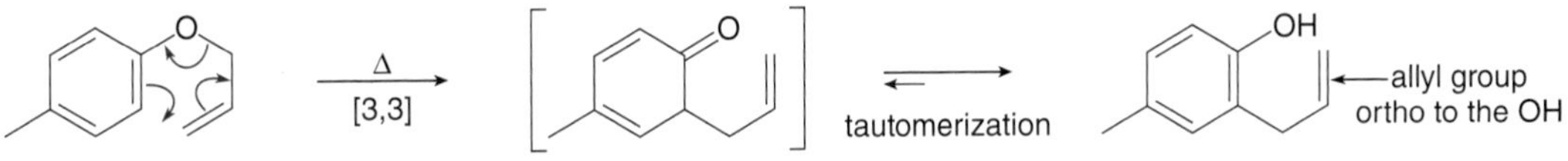

allyl aryl ether cyclohexadienone phenol

Problem 27.23 What product is formed from the Claisen rearrangement of each starting material?

a. 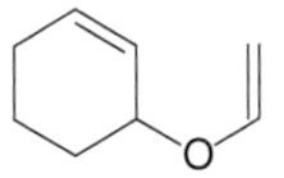

b. 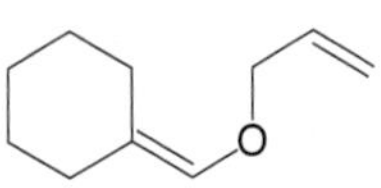

c. 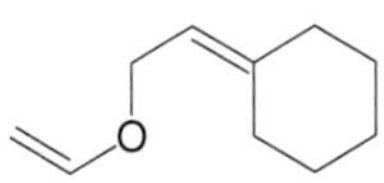

Problem 27.24 (a) What product is formed by the Claisen rearrangement of compound **Z?** (b) Using what you have learned about ring-closing metathesis in Chapter 26, draw the product formed when the product in part (a) is treated with Grubbs catalyst. These two reactions are key steps in the synthesis of garsubellin A, a biologically active natural product that stimulates the synthesis of the neurotransmitter acetylcholine. Compounds of this sort may prove to be useful drugs for the treatment of neurodegenerative diseases such as Alzheimer's disease.

Garsubellin A (Problem 27.24) is isolated from the wood of *Garcinia subelliptica,* a tree grown in Okinawa, Japan.

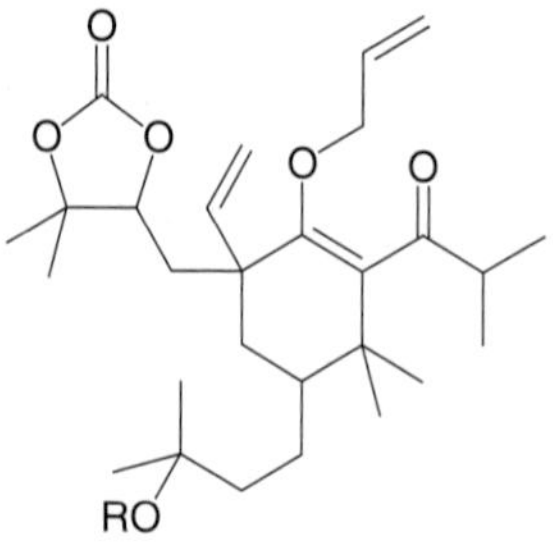

Z

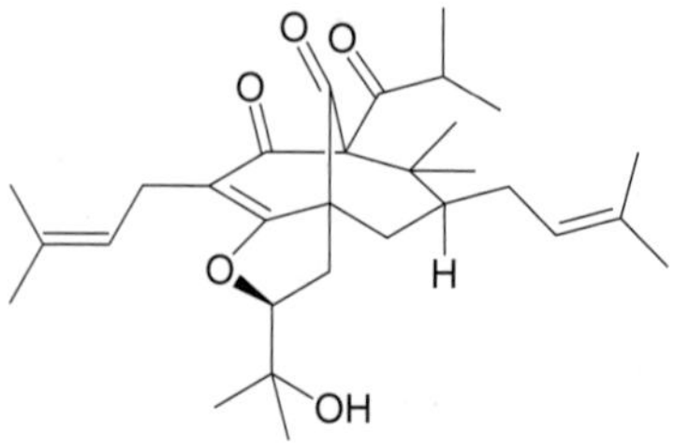

garsubellin A

27.6 Summary of Rules for Pericyclic Reactions

Table 27.4 summarizes the rules that govern pericyclic reactions, and in truth, this table holds a great deal of information. To keep track of this information, it may be helpful to **learn one row in the table only,** and then note the result when one or more conditions change. For example,

- A *thermal* reaction involving an *even* number of electron pairs is *conrotatory* or *antarafacial.*
- If *one* of the reaction conditions changes—either from thermal to photochemical or from an even to an odd number of electron pairs—the stereochemistry of the reaction changes to disrotatory or suprafacial.
- If *both* reaction conditions change—that is, a photochemical reaction with an odd number of electron pairs—the stereochemistry does *not* change.

Table 27.4 Summary of the Stereochemical Rules for Pericyclic Reactions

Reaction conditions	Number of electron pairs	Stereochemistry
Thermal	Even	Conrotatory or antarafacial
	Odd	Disrotatory or suprafacial
Photochemical	Even	Disrotatory or suprafacial
	Odd	Conrotatory or antarafacial

Problem 27.25 Using the Woodward–Hoffmann rules in Table 27.4, predict the stereochemistry of each reaction.

a. a [6 + 4] thermal cycloaddition
b. photochemical electrocyclic ring closure of 1,3,5,7,9-decapentaene
c. a [4 + 4] photochemical cycloaddition
d. a thermal [5,5] sigmatropic rearrangement

KEY CONCEPTS

Pericyclic Reactions

Electrocyclic Reactions (27.3)

Woodward–Hoffmann rules for electrocyclic reactions

Number of π bonds	Thermal reaction	Photochemical reaction
Even	Conrotatory	Disrotatory
Odd	Disrotatory	Conrotatory

Examples

The stereochemistry of a thermal electrocyclic reaction is opposite to that of a photochemical electrocyclic reaction.

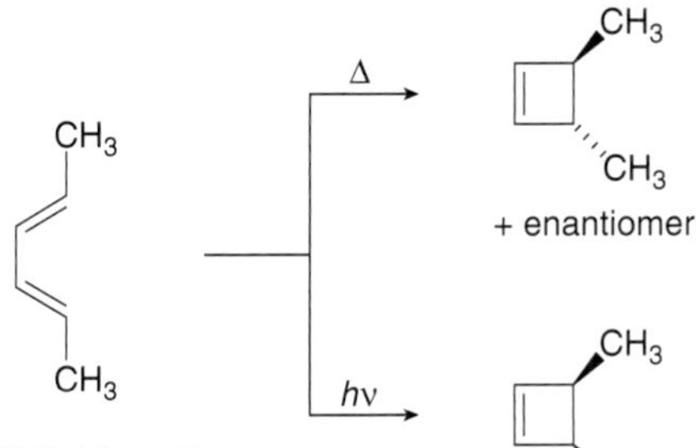
Δ
hν
CH_3
+ enantiomer

(2*E*,4*E*)-2,4-hexadiene
2 π bonds

- A thermal electrocyclic reaction with an even number of π bonds occurs in a conrotatory fashion.
- A photochemical electrocyclic reaction with an even number of π bonds occurs in a disrotatory fashion.

Cycloaddition Reactions (27.4)

Woodward–Hoffmann rules for cycloaddition reactions

Number of π bonds	Thermal reaction	Photochemical reaction
Even	Antarafacial	Suprafacial
Odd	Suprafacial	Antarafacial

Examples

[1] A thermal [4 + 2] cycloaddition takes place in a suprafacial fashion with an odd number of π bonds. An antarafacial photochemical [4 + 2] cycloaddition to form a six-membered ring cannot occur, because of the geometrical constraints of forming a six-membered ring.

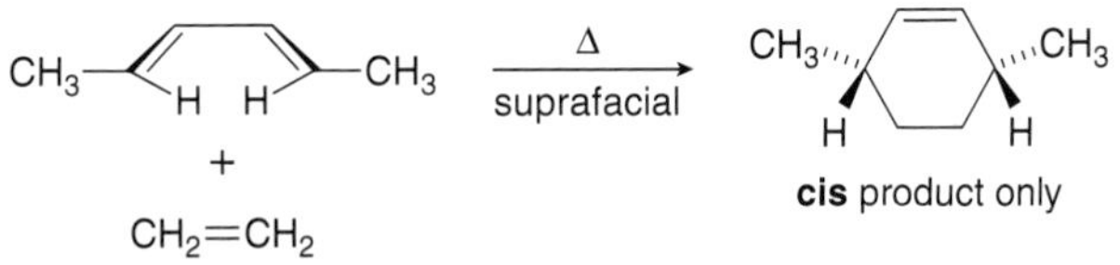
Δ
suprafacial
$CH_2{=}CH_2$
cis product only

[2] A photochemical [2 + 2] cycloaddition takes place in a suprafacial fashion with an even number of π bonds. An antarafacial thermal [2 + 2] cycloaddition to form a four-membered ring cannot occur, because of the geometrical constraints of forming a four-membered ring.

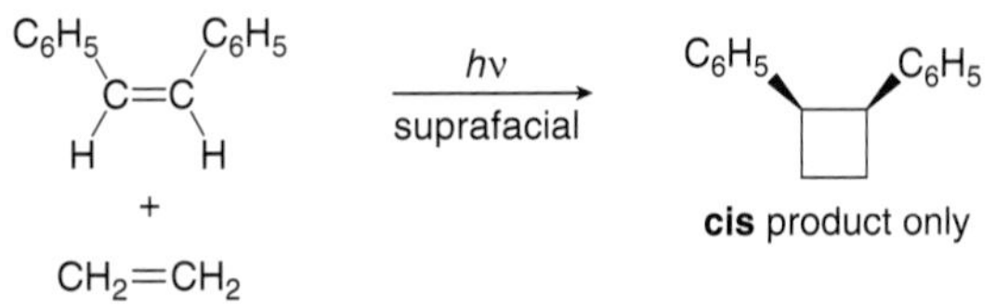
hν
suprafacial
C_6H_5
$CH_2{=}CH_2$
cis product only

Sigmatropic Rearrangements (27.5)

Woodward–Hoffmann rules for sigmatropic rearrangements

Number of electron pairs	Thermal reaction	Photochemical reaction
Even	Antarafacial	Suprafacial
Odd	Suprafacial	Antarafacial

Examples

[1] A **Cope rearrangement** is a thermal [3,3] sigmatropic rearrangement that converts a 1,5-diene into an isomeric 1,5-diene.

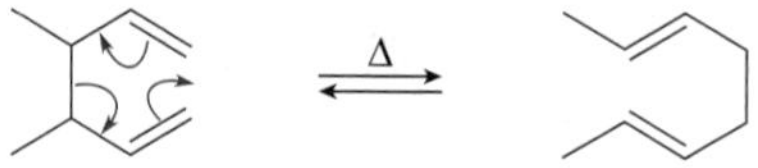

1,5-diene isomeric 1,5-diene

[2] An **oxy-Cope rearrangement** is a thermal [3,3] sigmatropic rearrangement that converts a 1,5-dien-3-ol into a δ,ε-unsaturated carbonyl compound, after tautomerization of an intermediate enol.

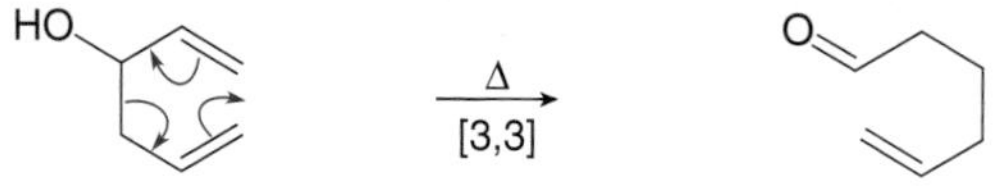

1,5-dien-3-ol δ,ε-unsaturated carbonyl compound

[3] A **Claisen rearrangement** is a thermal [3,3] sigmatropic rearrangement that converts an unsaturated ether into a γ,δ-unsaturated carbonyl compound.

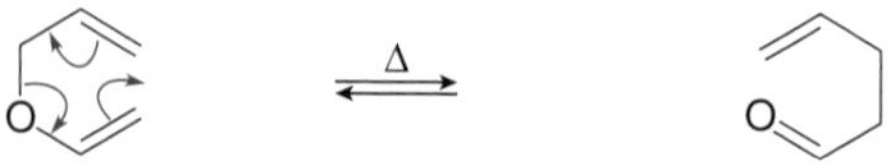

unsaturated ether γ,δ-unsaturated carbonyl compound

PROBLEMS

Problems Using Three-Dimensional Models

27.26 (a) What product is formed when each compound undergoes a thermal electrocyclic ring opening? (b) What product is formed when each compound undergoes a photochemical electrocyclic ring opening?

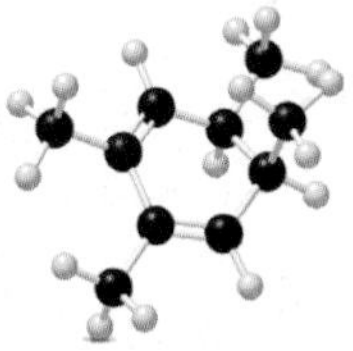

A

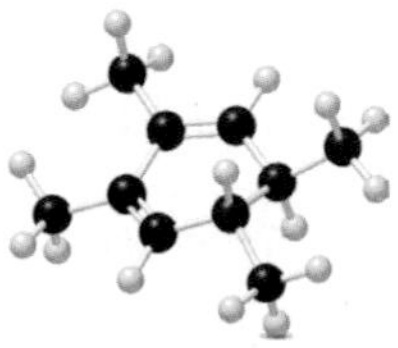

B

27.27 What product is formed by the [3,3] sigmatropic rearrangement of each compound?

a. 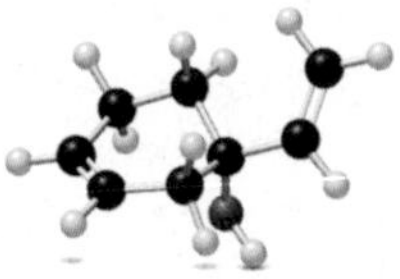

b. 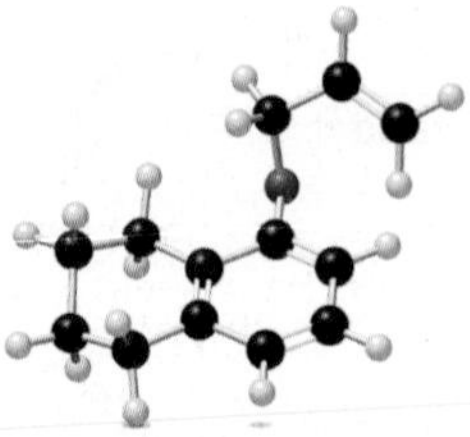

Types of Pericyclic Reactions

27.28 Classify each pericyclic reaction as an electrocyclic reaction, cycloaddition, or sigmatropic rearrangement. Indicate whether the stereochemistry is conrotatory, disrotatory, suprafacial, or antarafacial.

a. 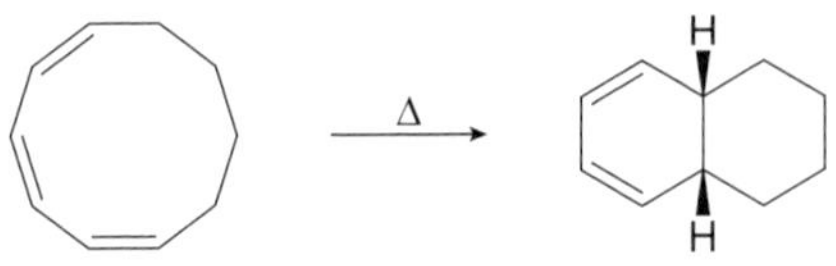

b. 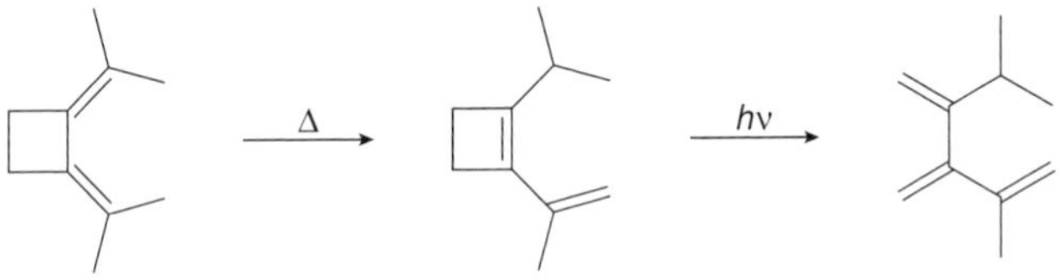

c. 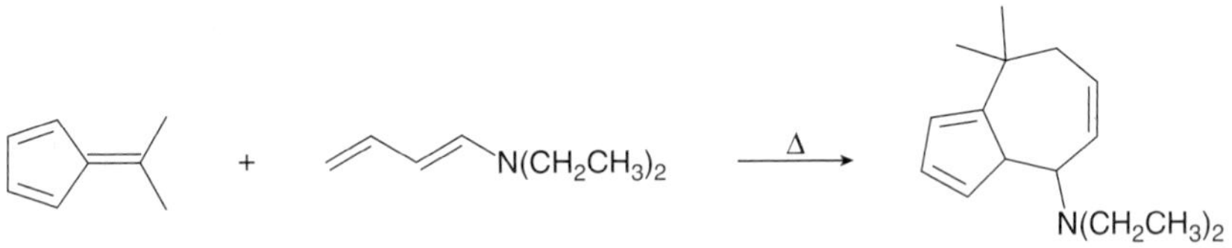

Electrocyclic Reactions

27.29 What product is formed when each compound undergoes thermal electrocyclic ring opening or ring closure? Label each process as conrotatory or disrotatory and clearly indicate the stereochemistry around tetrahedral stereogenic centers and double bonds.

a. 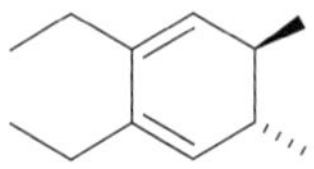

b. 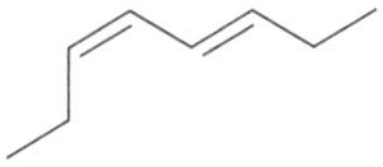

27.30 What product is formed when each compound in Problem 27.29 undergoes photochemical electrocyclic reaction? Label each process as conrotatory or disrotatory and clearly indicate the stereochemistry around tetrahedral stereogenic centers and double bonds.

27.31 What cyclic product is formed when each decatetraene undergoes photochemical electrocyclic ring closure?

a. 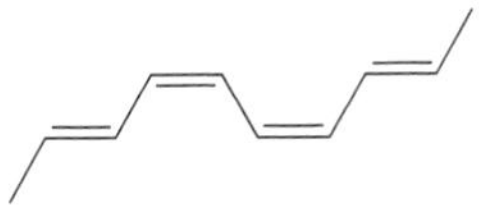

b. 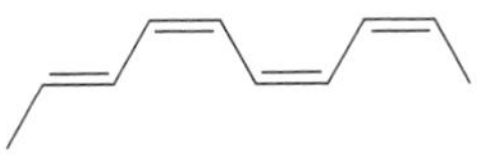

27.32 Draw the product of each electrocyclic reaction.

a. the thermal electrocyclic ring closure of (2*E*,4*Z*,6*Z*)-2,4,6-nonatriene
b. the photochemical electrocyclic ring closure of (2*E*,4*Z*,6*Z*)-2,4,6-nonatriene
c. the thermal electrocyclic ring opening of *cis*-5-ethyl-6-methyl-1,3-cyclohexadiene
d. the photochemical electrocyclic ring opening of *trans*-5-ethyl-6-methyl-1,3-cyclohexadiene

27.33 Consider the following electrocyclic ring closure. Does the product form by a conrotatory or disrotatory process? Would this reaction occur under photochemical or thermal conditions?

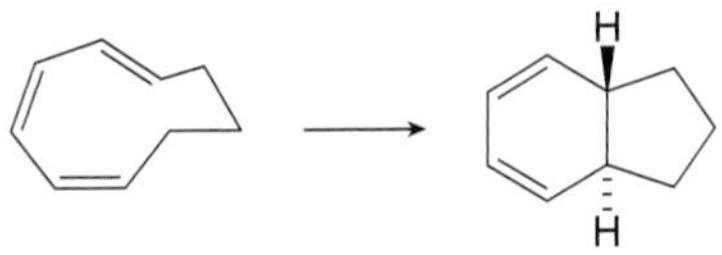

27.34 Draw the product formed when diene **M** undergoes disrotatory cyclization. Indicate the stereochemistry at new sp^3 hybridized carbons. Will the reaction occur under thermal or photochemical conditions?

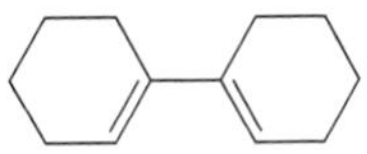

M

27.35 (a) What product is formed when triene **N** undergoes thermal electrocyclic ring closure? (b) What product is formed when triene **N** undergoes photochemical ring closure? (c) Label each process as conrotatory or disrotatory.

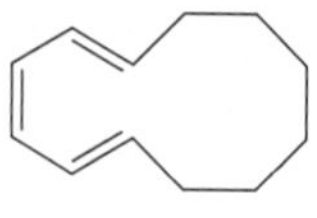

N

27.36 The bicyclic alkene **P** can be prepared by thermal electrocyclic ring closure from cyclodecadiene **Q** or by photochemical electrocyclic ring closure from cyclodecadiene **R.** Draw the structures of **Q** and **R,** and indicate the stereochemistry of the process by which each reaction occurs.

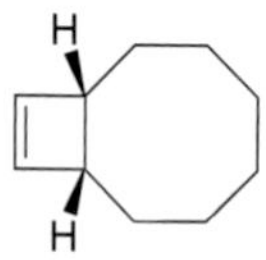

P

Cycloaddition Reactions

27.37 What type of cycloaddition occurs in Reaction [1]? Draw the product of a similar process in Reaction [2]. Would you predict that these reactions occur under thermal or photochemical conditions?

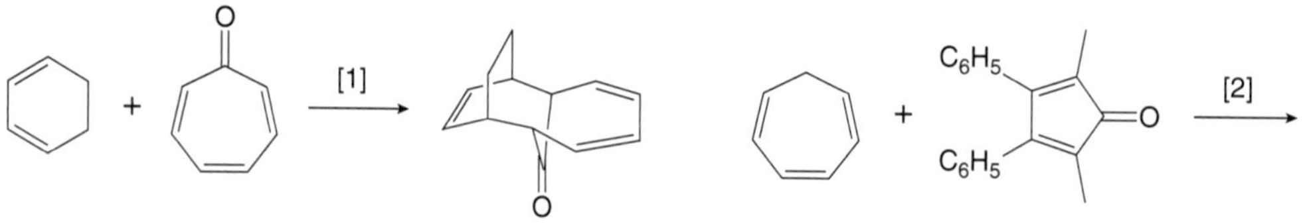

27.38 Draw the product of each Diels–Alder reaction and indicate the stereochemistry at all stereogenic centers.

a. 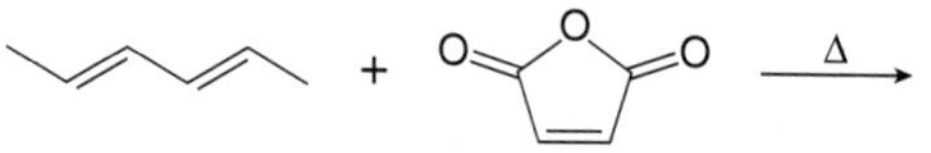

b. 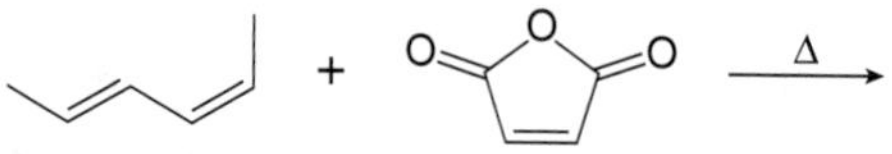

27.39 What cycloaddition products are formed in each reaction? Indicate the stereochemistry of each product.

a. 2 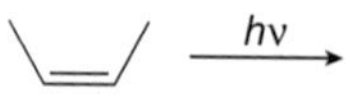

b. 2 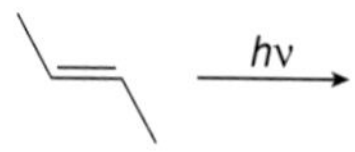

27.40 What starting materials are needed to synthesize each compound by a thermal [4 + 2] cycloaddition?

a. 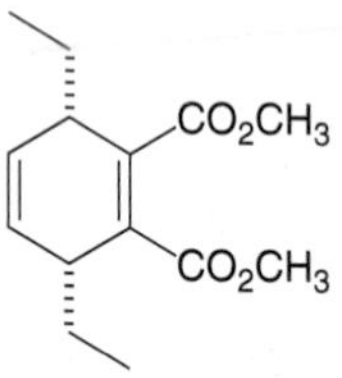

b. 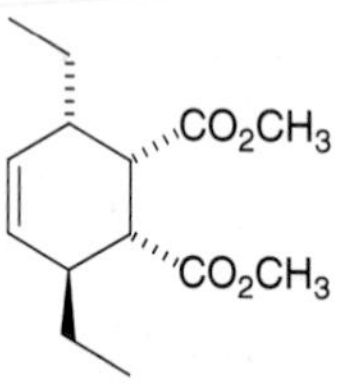

c. 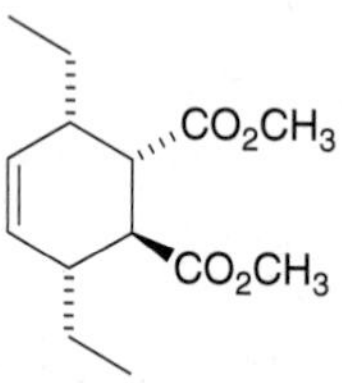

27.41 Explain why heating 1,3-butadiene forms 4-vinylcyclohexene but not 1,5-cyclooctadiene.

27.42 How can **X** be prepared from a constitutional isomer by a series of [2 + 2] cycloaddition reactions? Interest in molecules that contain several cyclobutane rings fused together has been fueled by the discovery of pentacycloanammoxic acid methyl ester, a lipid isolated from the membrane of organelles in the bacterium *Candidatus Brocadia anammoxidans.* The role of this unusual natural product is as yet unknown.

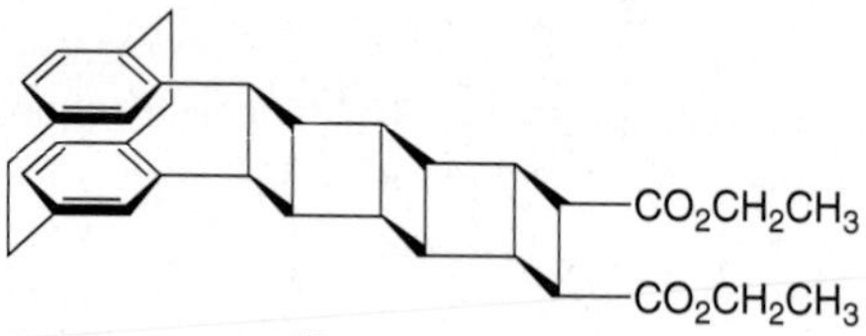

X

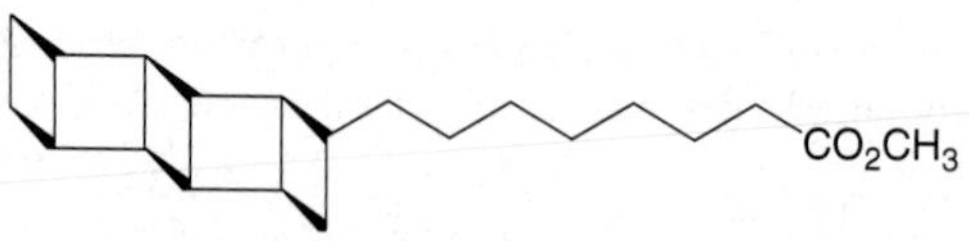

pentacycloanammoxic acid methyl ester

Sigmatropic Rearrangements

27.43 What type of sigmatropic rearrangement is illustrated in each reaction?

a. 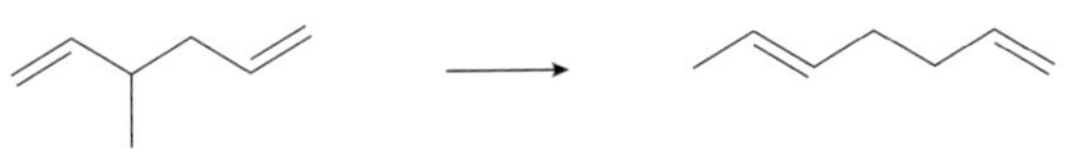

c. 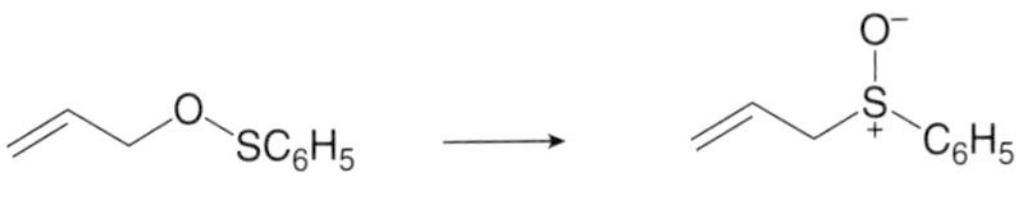

b. 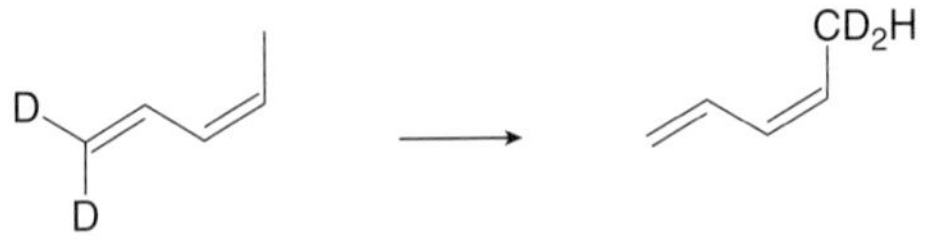

27.44 Draw the product of the [3,3] sigmatropic rearrangement of each compound.

a. 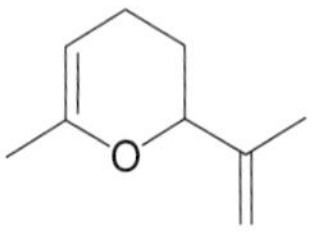

b. 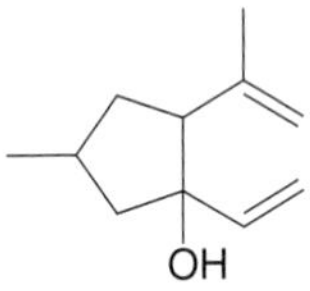

c. 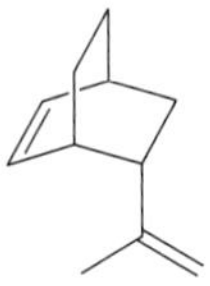

27.45 A solution of 5-methyl-1,3-cyclopentadiene rearranges at room temperature to a mixture containing 1-methyl-, 2-methyl-, and 5-methyl-1,3-cyclopentadiene. (a) Show how both isomeric products are formed from the starting material by a sigmatropic rearrangement involving a C–H bond. (b) Explain why 2-methyl-1,3-cyclopentadiene is not formed directly from 5-methyl-1,3-cyclopentadiene by a [1,3] rearrangement.

27.46 What product is formed from the [5,5] sigmatropic rearrangement of the following unsaturated ether?

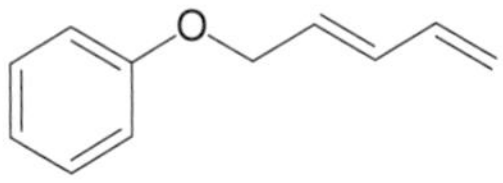

27.47 Draw structures for **A, B,** and **C** in the following reaction sequence and identify the process that converts **B** to **C.**

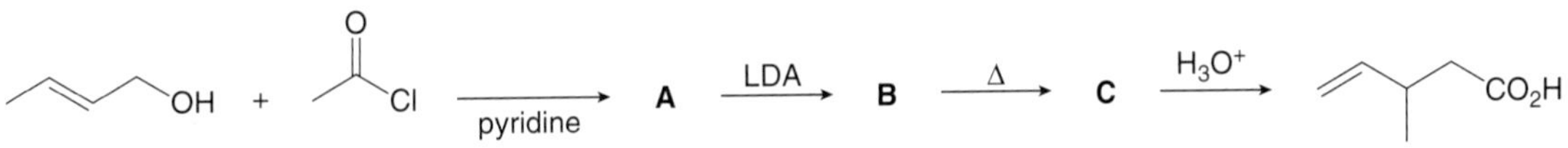

General Pericyclic Reactions

27.48 What type of pericyclic reaction is illustrated in each reaction?

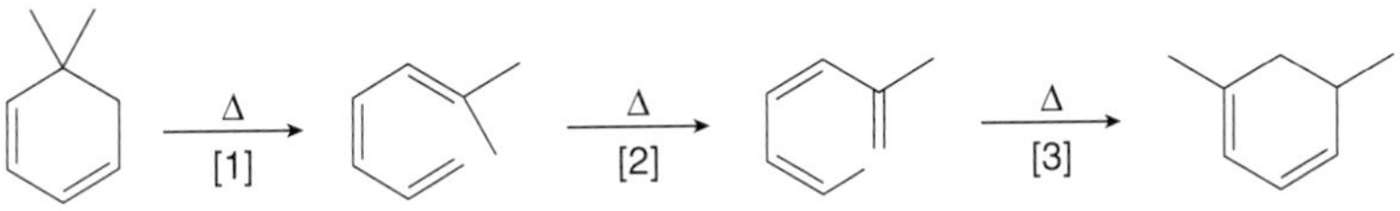

27.49 Draw the product formed (including stereochemistry) in each pericyclic reaction.

a. 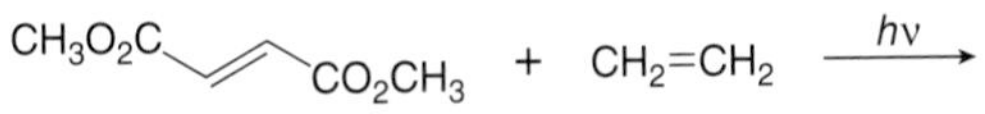

c. 2 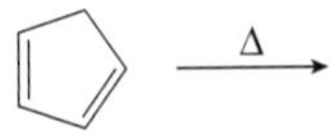

b. 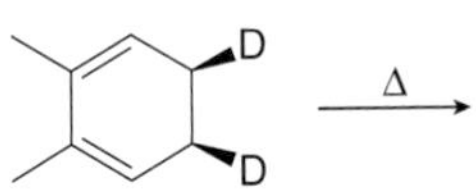

d. 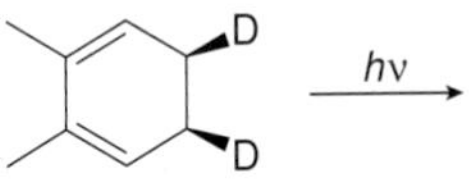

27.50 Draw the products of each reaction.

a. 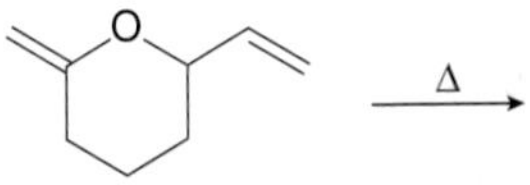

c. 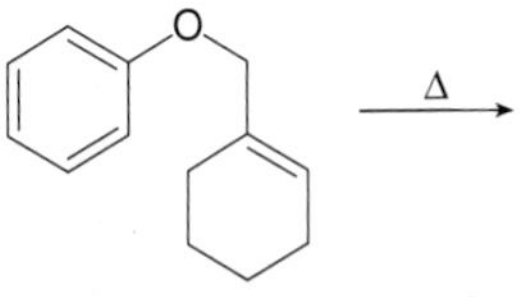

b. 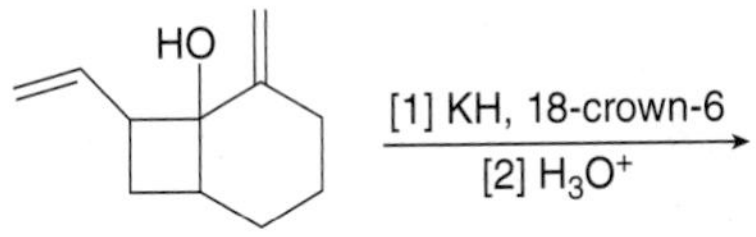

d. 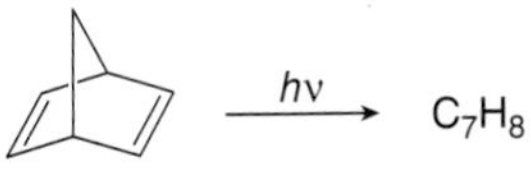

Mechanisms

27.51 When both carbons ortho to the aryl oxygen are not bonded to hydrogen, an allyl aryl ether rearranges to a para-substituted phenol. Draw a stepwise mechanism for the following reaction, which contains two [3,3] sigmatropic rearrangements.

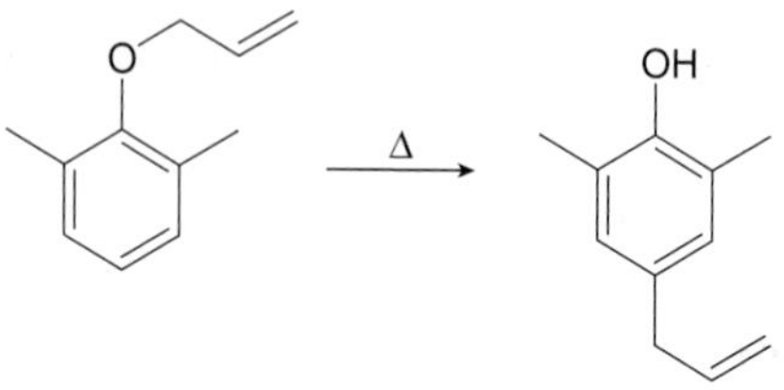

27.52 Draw a stepwise, detailed mechanism for the following reaction.

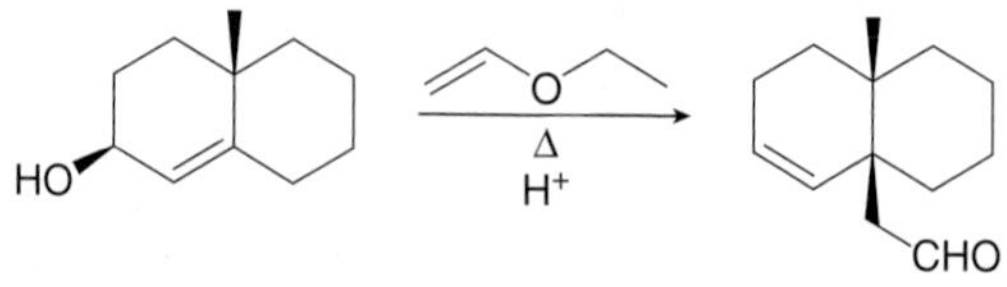

27.53 Show how the following starting material is converted to the given product by a series of two pericyclic reactions. Account for the observed stereochemistry.

27.54 Show how the following starting material is converted to the given product by a series of two pericyclic reactions. Account for the observed stereochemistry.

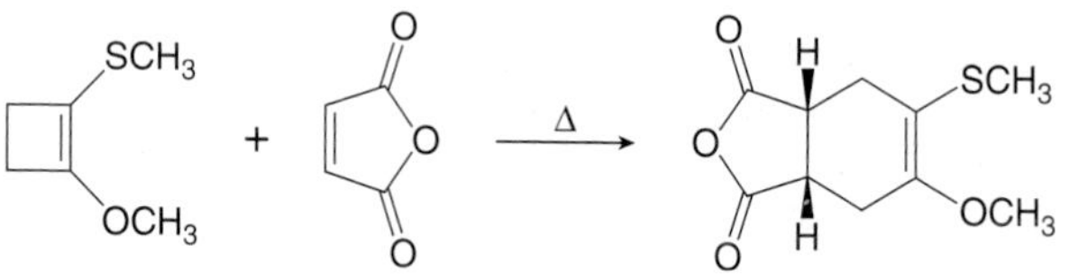

27.55 Draw a stepwise, detailed mechanism for the following reaction.

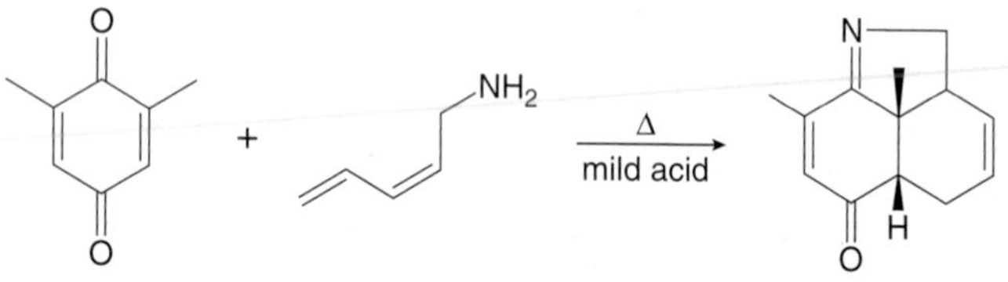

Challenge Problems

27.56 What product is formed by [3,3] sigmatropic rearrangement of the following compound? Clearly indicate the stereochemistry around all tetrahedral stereogenic centers.

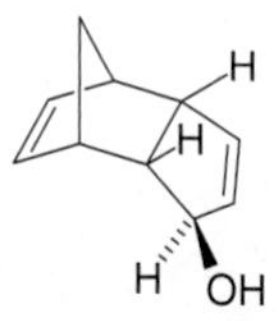

27.57 Draw a stepwise mechanism for the Carroll rearrangement, a reaction that prepares a γ,δ-unsaturated carbonyl compound from a β-keto ester and allylic alcohol in the presence of base.

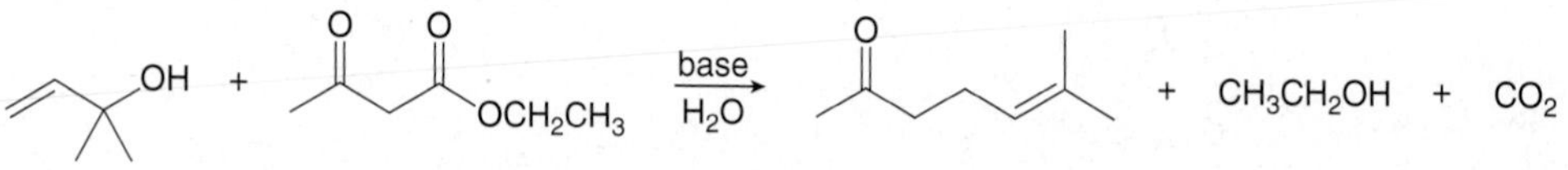

27.58 The endiandric acids comprise a group of unsaturated carboxylic acids isolated from a tree that grows in the rain forests of eastern Australia. The methyl esters of endiandric acids D and E have been prepared from polyene **Y** by a series of two successive electrocyclic reactions: thermal ring closure of the conjugated tetraene followed by ring closure of the resulting conjugated triene. (a) Draw the structures (including stereochemistry) of the methyl esters of endiandric acids D and E. (b) The methyl ester of endiandric acid E undergoes an intramolecular [4 + 2] cycloaddition to form the methyl ester of endiandric acid A. Propose a possible structure for endiandric acid A.

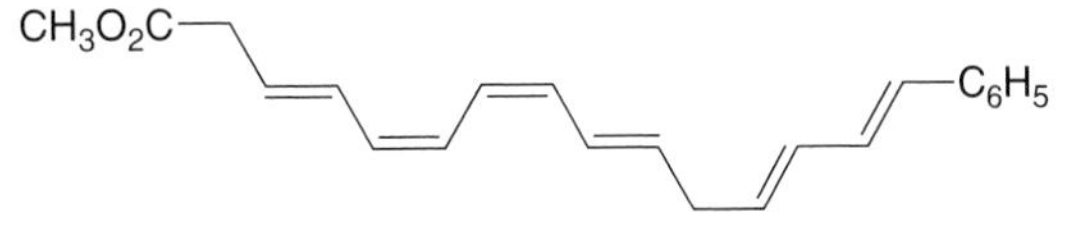

Y

27.59 [4 + 2] Cycloadditions with *o*-quinones such as **B** are often complex because a variety of products are possible.

a. Draw arrows to illustrate how each product is formed when **B** reacts with styrene, and label the "diene" and "dienophile" components.

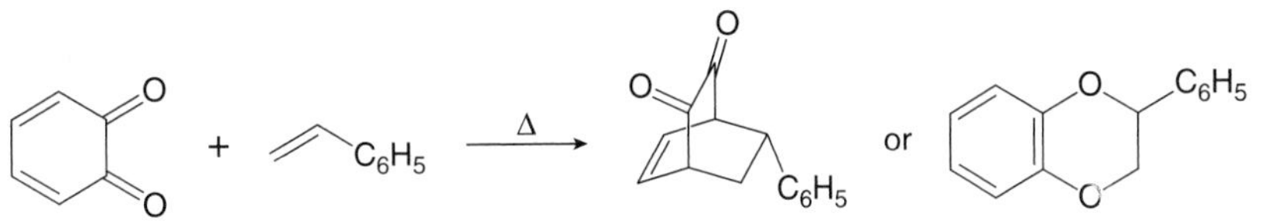

o-quinone **B** styrene

b. Draw arrows to illustrate how each product is formed when **B** reacts with 1,3-butadiene, and label the "diene" and "dienophile" components.

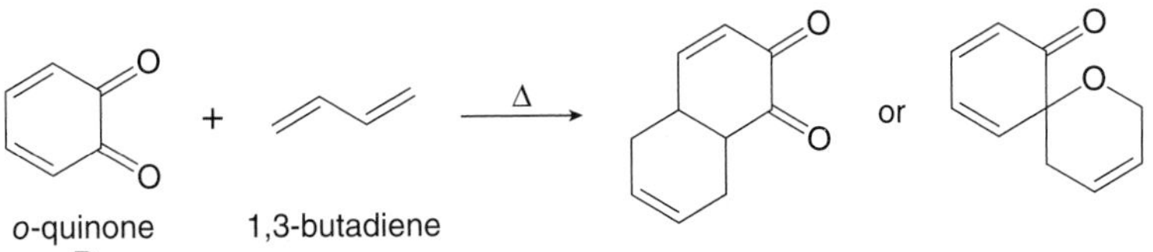

o-quinone **B** 1,3-butadiene

c. *o*-Quinone **C** reacts with diene **D** to form heterocycle **E** by a process that involves a cycloaddition followed by a [3,3] sigmatropic rearrangement. Use curved arrows to illustrate how this two-step sequence occurs. **E** is *not* formed directly from **C** by a Diels–Alder reaction.

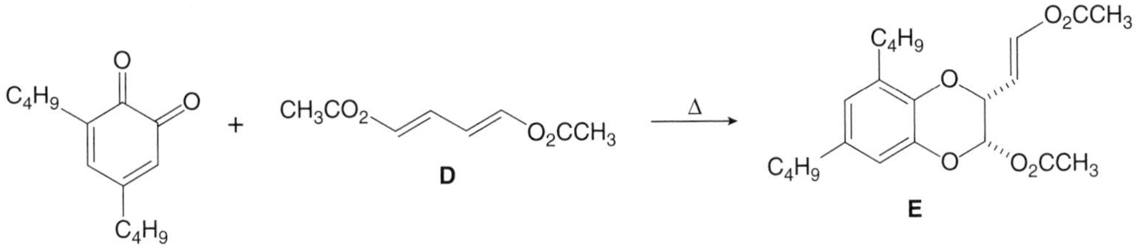

C

28 Carbohydrates

28.1 Introduction
28.2 Monosaccharides
28.3 The family of D-aldoses
28.4 The family of D-ketoses
28.5 Physical properties of monosaccharides
28.6 The cyclic forms of monosaccharides
28.7 Glycosides
28.8 Reactions of monosaccharides at the OH groups
28.9 Reactions at the carbonyl group—Oxidation and reduction
28.10 Reactions at the carbonyl group—Adding or removing one carbon atom
28.11 The Fischer proof of the structure of glucose
28.12 Disaccharides
28.13 Polysaccharides
28.14 Other important sugars and their derivatives

Lactose, a carbohydrate formed from two simple sugars, glucose and galactose, is the principal sugar in dairy products. Many individuals, mainly of Asian and African descent, lack adequate amounts of the enzyme lactase necessary to digest and absorb lactose. This condition, lactose intolerance, is associated with abdominal cramping and recurrent diarrhea, and is precipitated by the ingestion of milk and dairy products. Individuals who are lactose intolerant can drink lactose-free milk. Tablets that contain the lactase enzyme can also be taken when ice cream or other milk products are ingested. In Chapter 28, we learn about the structure, synthesis, and properties of carbohydrates like lactose.

Chapters 28, 29, and 30 discuss ***biomolecules*****, organic compounds found in biological systems.** You have already learned many facts about these compounds in previous chapters while you studied other organic compounds having similar properties. In Chapter 10 (Alkenes), for example, you learned that the presence of double bonds determines whether a fatty acid is part of a fat or an oil. In Chapter 19 (Carboxylic Acids and the Acidity of the O–H Bond), you learned that amino acids are the building blocks of proteins.

Chapter 28 focuses on carbohydrates, the largest group of biomolecules in nature, comprising ~50% of the earth's biomass. Chapter 29 concentrates on proteins (and the amino acids that compose them), whereas Chapter 30 explores lipids. These compounds are all organic molecules, so many of the same principles and chemical reactions that you have already studied will be examined once again. But, as you will see, each class of compound has its own unique features that we must learn as well.

28.1 Introduction

Carbohydrates were given their name because their molecular formulas could be written as $C_n(H_2O)_n$, making them **hydrates of carbon.**

Carbohydrates such as glucose and cellulose were discussed in Sections 5.1, 6.4, and 21.17.

Although the metabolism of lipids provides more energy per gram than the metabolism of carbohydrates, glucose is the preferred source when a burst of energy is needed during exercise. Glucose is water soluble, so it can be quickly and easily transported through the bloodstream to the tissues.

Carbohydrates, commonly referred to as sugars and starches, are polyhydroxy aldehydes and ketones, or compounds that can be hydrolyzed to them. The cellulose in plant stems and tree trunks and the chitin in the exoskeletons of arthropods and mollusks are both complex carbohydrates. Four examples are shown in Figure 28.1. They include not only glucose and cellulose, but also doxorubicin (an anticancer drug) and 2'-deoxyadenosine 5'-monophosphate (a nucleotide base from DNA), both of which have a carbohydrate moiety as part of a larger molecule.

Carbohydrates are storehouses of chemical energy. They are synthesized in green plants and algae by **photosynthesis,** a process that uses the energy from the sun to convert carbon dioxide and water into glucose and oxygen. This energy is released when glucose is metabolized. The oxidation of glucose is a multistep process that forms carbon dioxide, water, and a great deal of energy (Section 6.4).

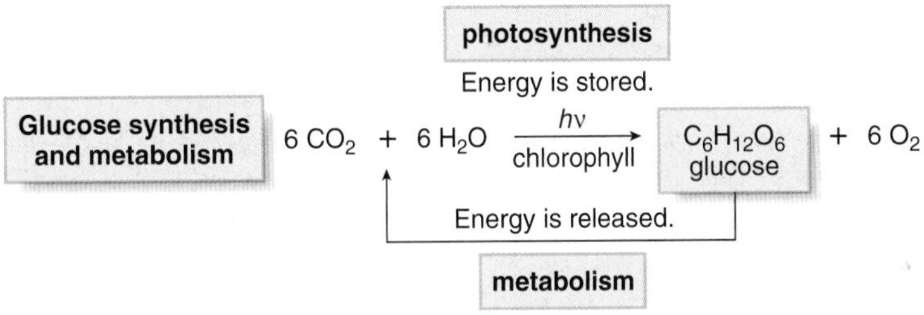

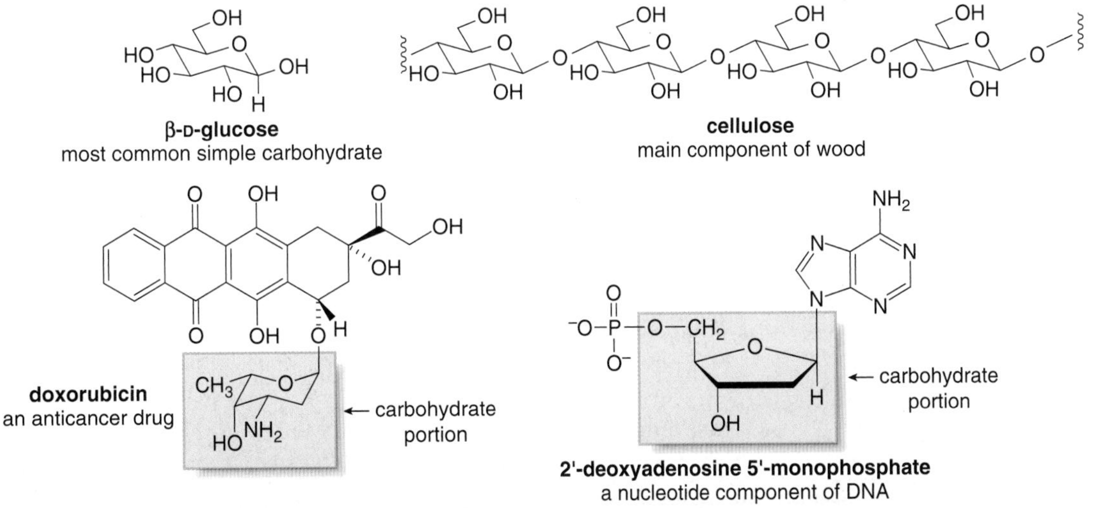

Figure 28.1 Some examples of carbohydrates

These compounds illustrate the structural diversity of carbohydrates. **Glucose** is the most common simple sugar, whereas **cellulose,** which comprises wood, plant stems, and grass, is the most common carbohydrate in the plant world. **Doxorubicin,** an anticancer drug that has a carbohydrate ring as part of its structure, has been used in the treatment of leukemia, Hodgkin's disease, and cancers of the breast, bladder, and ovaries. **2'-Deoxyadenosine 5'-monophosphate** is one of the four nucleotides that form DNA.

28.2 Monosaccharides

The simplest carbohydrates are called **monosaccharides** or **simple sugars. Monosaccharides have three to seven carbon atoms** in a chain, with a **carbonyl group** at either the terminal carbon (C1) or the carbon adjacent to it (C2). In most carbohydrates, each of the remaining carbon atoms has a **hydroxy group.** Monosaccharides are often drawn vertically, with the carbonyl group at the top.

General structure of a monosaccharide

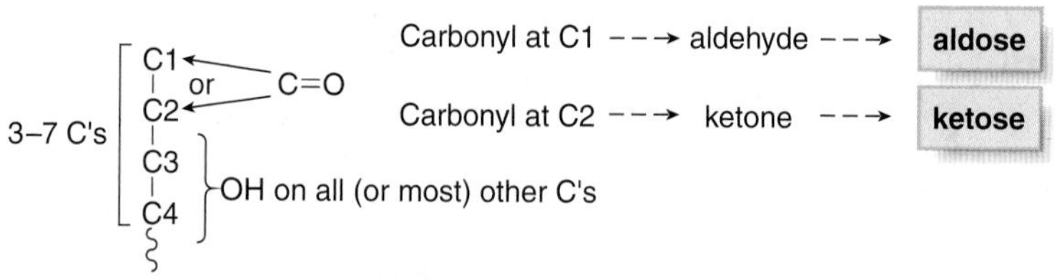

- **Monosaccharides with an aldehyde carbonyl group at C1 are called aldoses.**
- **Monosaccharides with a ketone carbonyl group at C2 are called ketoses.**

D-Fructose is almost twice as sweet as normal table sugar (sucrose) with about the same number of calories per gram. "Lite" food products use only half as much fructose as sucrose for the same level of sweetness, and so they have fewer calories.

Several examples of simple carbohydrates are shown. D-Glyceraldehyde and dihydroxyacetone have the same molecular formula, so they are **constitutional isomers,** as are D-glucose and D-fructose.

Examples

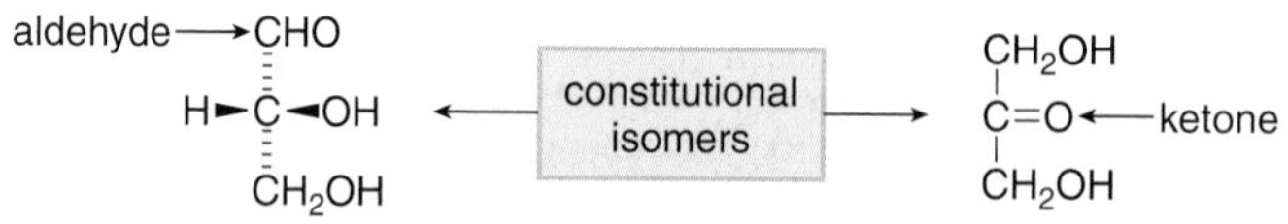

D-glyceraldehyde
an **aldose**

dihydroxyacetone
a **ketose**

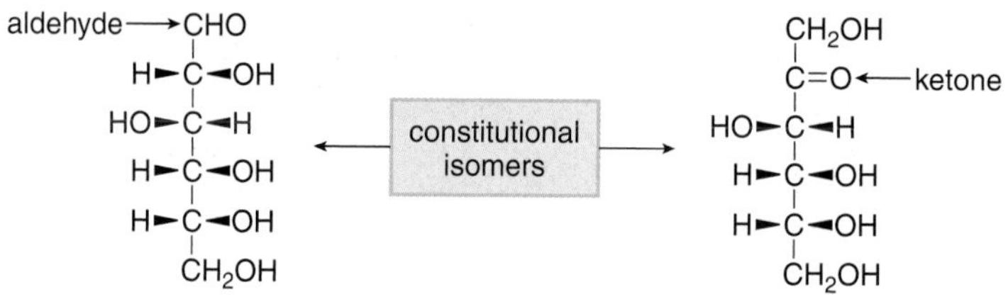

D-glucose
an **aldose**
(the most common simple sugar)

D-fructose
a **ketose**

Dihydroxyacetone is the active ingredient in many artificial tanning agents.

All carbohydrates have common names. The simplest aldehyde, glyceraldehyde, and the simplest ketone, dihydroxyacetone, are the only monosaccharides whose names do not end in the suffix ***-ose.*** (The prefix "D-" is explained in Section 28.2C.)

A monosaccharide is called:

- **a triose if it has 3 C's;**
- **a tetrose if it has 4 C's;**
- **a pentose if it has 5 C's;**
- **a hexose if it has 6 C's, and so forth.**

These terms are then combined with the words *aldose* and *ketose* to indicate both the number of carbon atoms in the monosaccharide and whether it contains an aldehyde or ketone. Thus, glyceraldehyde is an aldotriose (three C atoms and an aldehyde), glucose is an aldohexose (six C atoms and an aldehyde), and fructose is a ketohexose (six C atoms and a ketone).

Problem 28.1 Draw the structure of (a) a ketotetrose; (b) an aldopentose; (c) an aldotetrose.

28.2A Fischer Projection Formulas

A striking feature of carbohydrate structure is the presence of stereogenic centers. **All carbohydrates except for dihydroxyacetone contain one or more stereogenic centers.**

The simplest aldehyde, glyceraldehyde, has one stereogenic center, so there are two possible **enantiomers.** Only the enantiomer with the *R* configuration occurs naturally.

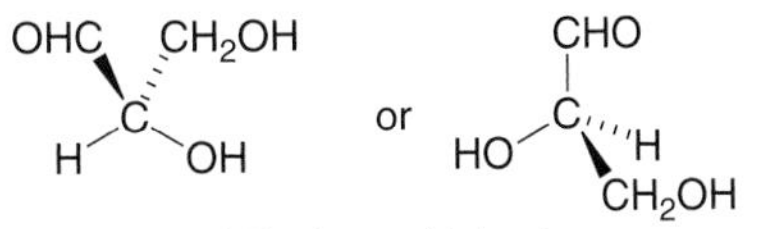

(*R*)-glyceraldehyde
naturally occurring enantiomer

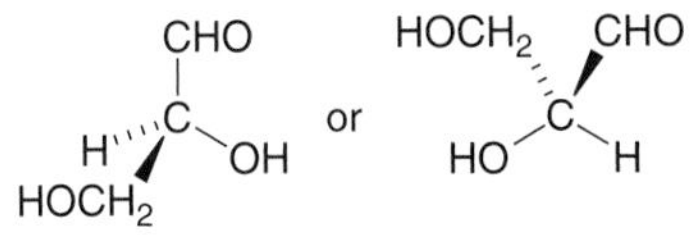

(*S*)-glyceraldehyde

The stereogenic centers in sugars are often depicted following a different convention than is usually seen for other stereogenic centers. Instead of drawing a tetrahedron with two bonds in the plane, one in front of the plane, and one behind it, the **tetrahedron is tipped so that horizontal bonds come forward (drawn on wedges) and vertical bonds go behind (on dashed lines).** This structure is then abbreviated by a **cross formula,** also called a **Fischer projection formula.** In a Fischer projection formula:

- **A carbon atom is located at the intersection of the two lines of the cross.**
- **The horizontal bonds come forward, on wedges.**
- **The vertical bonds go back, on dashed lines.**
- **In a carbohydrate, the aldehyde or ketone carbonyl is put at or near the top.**

Using a Fischer projection formula, (*R*)-glyceraldehyde becomes:

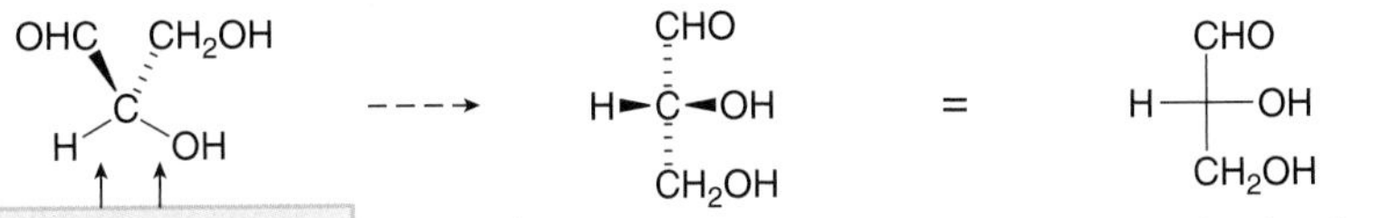
Tip these bonds forward.

(*R*)-glyceraldehyde

- Horizontal bonds come forward.
- Vertical bonds go back.

Fischer projection formula
(*R*)-glyceraldehyde

Do not rotate a Fischer projection formula in the plane of the page, because you might inadvertently convert a compound into its enantiomer. When using Fischer projections it is usually best to convert them to structures with wedges and dashes, and then manipulate them. Although a Fischer projection formula can be used for the stereogenic center in any compound, it is most commonly used for monosaccharides.

Sample Problem 28.1 Convert each compound to a Fischer projection formula.

a. 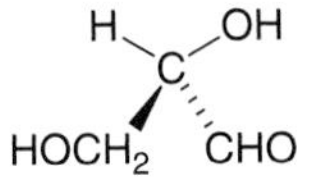

b. 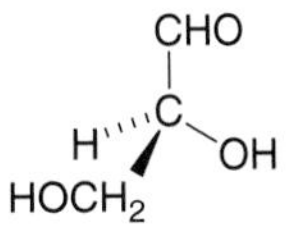

Solution

Rotate and re-draw each molecule to place the horizontal bonds in front of the plane and the vertical bonds behind the plane. Then use a cross to represent the stereogenic center.

a. 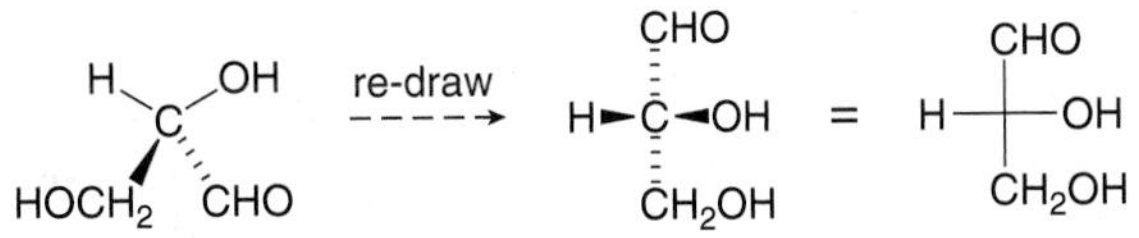

b. 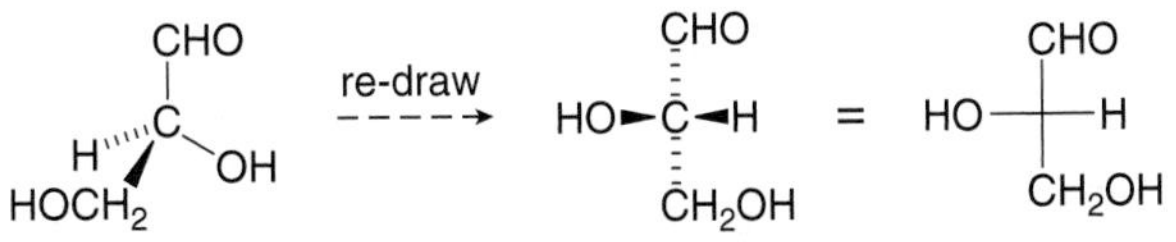

Problem 28.2 Draw each stereogenic center using a Fischer projection formula.

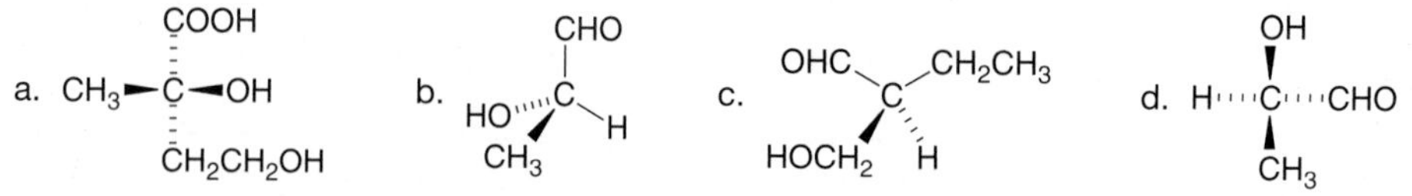
a. CH_3 C OH COOH CH_2CH_2OH
b. CHO HO C H CH_3
c. OHC C CH_2CH_3 $HOCH_2$ H
d. H C CHO OH CH_3

R,S designations can be assigned to any stereogenic center drawn as a Fischer projection formula in the following manner:

[1] Assign priorities (1 → 4) to the four groups bonded to the stereogenic center using the rules detailed in Section 5.6.

[2] When the lowest priority group occupies a vertical bond—that is, it projects *behind* the plane on a dashed line—tracing a circle in the clockwise direction (from priority group 1 → 2 → 3) gives the *R* configuration. Tracing a circle in the counterclockwise direction gives the *S* configuration.

[3] When the lowest priority group occupies a horizontal bond—that is, it projects *in front* of the plane on a wedge—reverse the answer obtained in Step [2] to designate the configuration.

Sample Problem 28.2 Re-draw each Fischer projection formula using wedges and dashes for the stereogenic center, and label the center as *R* or *S*.

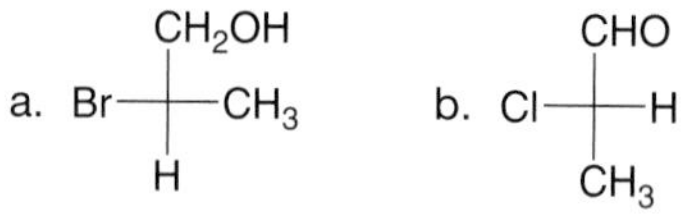
a. Br CH_2OH CH_3 H
b. Cl CHO H CH_3

Solution

For each molecule:

[1] Convert the Fischer projection formula to a representation with wedges and dashes.

[2] Assign priorities (Section 5.6).

[3] Determine *R* or *S* in the usual manner. Reverse the answer if priority group [4] is oriented forward (on a wedge).

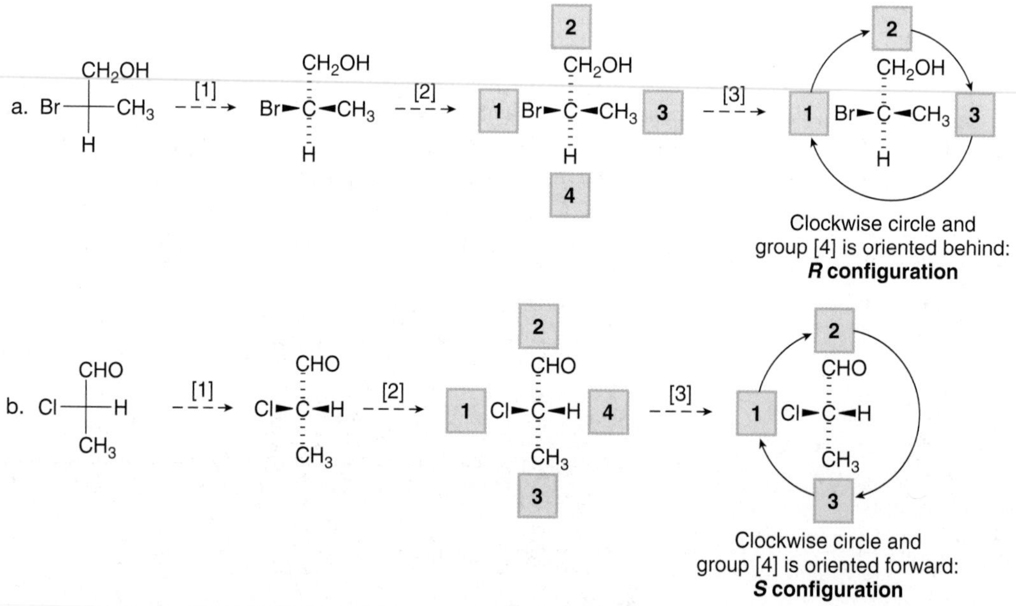
a.
[1]
[2]
[3]
Clockwise circle and group [4] is oriented behind: **R configuration**
b.
Clockwise circle and group [4] is oriented forward: **S configuration**

Problem 28.3 Label each stereogenic center as *R* or *S*.

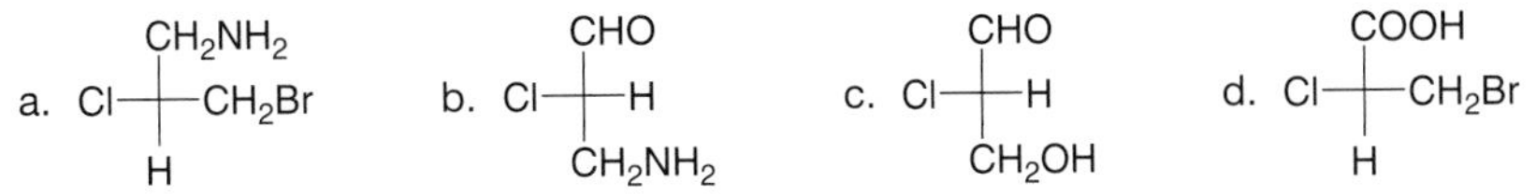
a. Cl CH2NH2 CH2Br H
b. Cl CHO H CH2NH2
c. Cl CHO H CH2OH
d. Cl COOH CH2Br H

28.2B Monosaccharides with More Than One Stereogenic Center

The number of possible stereoisomers of a monosaccharide increases exponentially with the number of stereogenic centers present. **An aldohexose has four stereogenic centers, and so it has $2^4 = 16$ possible stereoisomers,** or eight pairs of enantiomers.

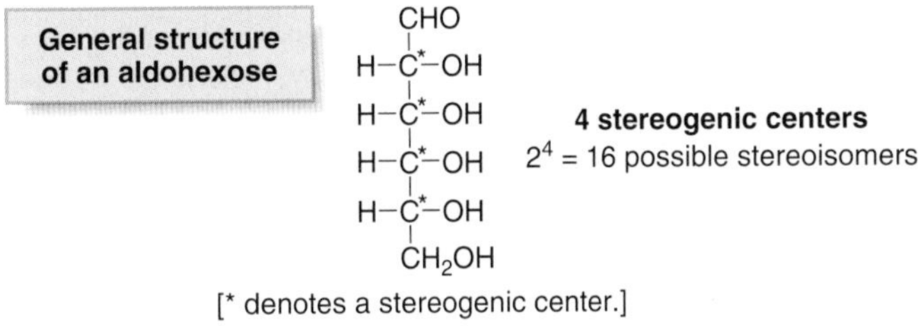
General structure of an aldohexose
4 stereogenic centers
2^4 = 16 possible stereoisomers
[* denotes a stereogenic center.]

Fischer projection formulas are also used for compounds like aldohexoses that contain several stereogenic centers. In this case, the molecule is drawn with a vertical carbon skeleton and the stereogenic centers are stacked one above another. Using this convention, **all horizontal bonds project forward (on wedges).**

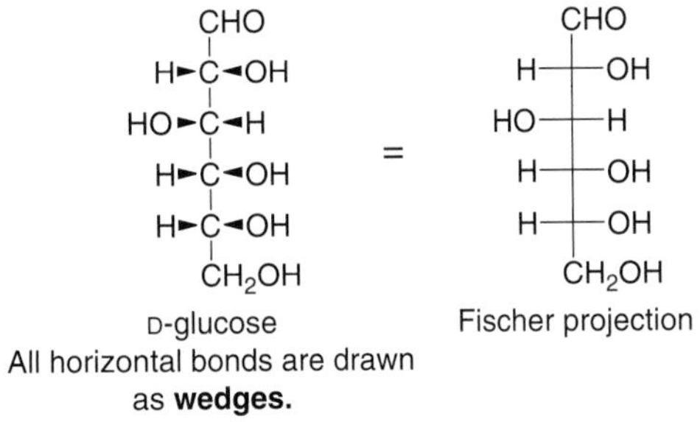
D-glucose
All horizontal bonds are drawn as **wedges.**
Fischer projection

Although Fischer projections are commonly used to depict monosaccharides with many stereogenic centers, care must be exercised in using them since they do not give a true picture of the three-dimensional structures they represent. Because each stereogenic center is drawn in the less stable eclipsed conformation, the Fischer projection of glucose really represents the molecule in a cylindrical conformation, as shown in Figure 28.2.

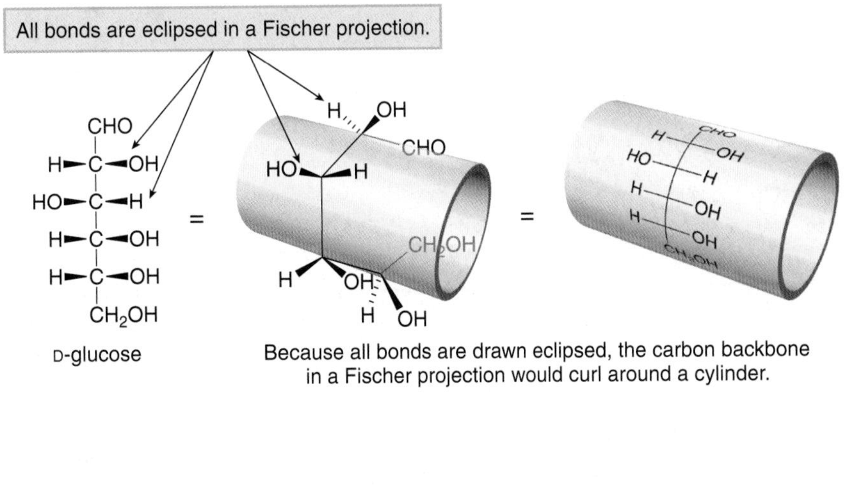
All bonds are eclipsed in a Fischer projection.
D-glucose
Because all bonds are drawn eclipsed, the carbon backbone in a Fischer projection would curl around a cylinder.

Figure 28.2 A Fischer projection and the 3-D structure of glucose

Sample Problem 28.3 Convert the ball-and-stick model to a Fischer projection.

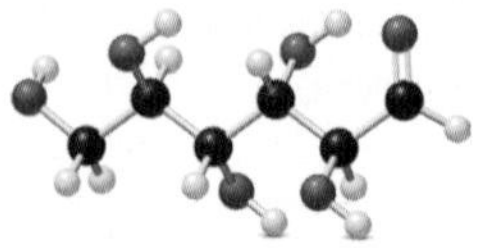

Solution

Since the ball-and-stick model is shown in the more stable staggered conformation, it must be converted to the less stable eclipsed conformation used in a Fischer projection. First, re-draw the model as a skeletal structure (**A**), and rotate it to place the carbonyl group at the top (**B**). To convert the all-staggered form to the all-eclipsed form, rotate around the bonds in **B** to swing two carbons (labeled in red) 180°, forming **C.** Re-draw **C** so that all bonds to H and OH on the four stereogenic centers are drawn on wedges, forming **D.** Groups that are on wedges in **C** are on the left side of the carbon skeleton in **D,** and groups on dashed bonds in **C** are on the right side of the carbon skeleton in **D.** Finally, replace the wedges with crosses to form the Fischer projection.

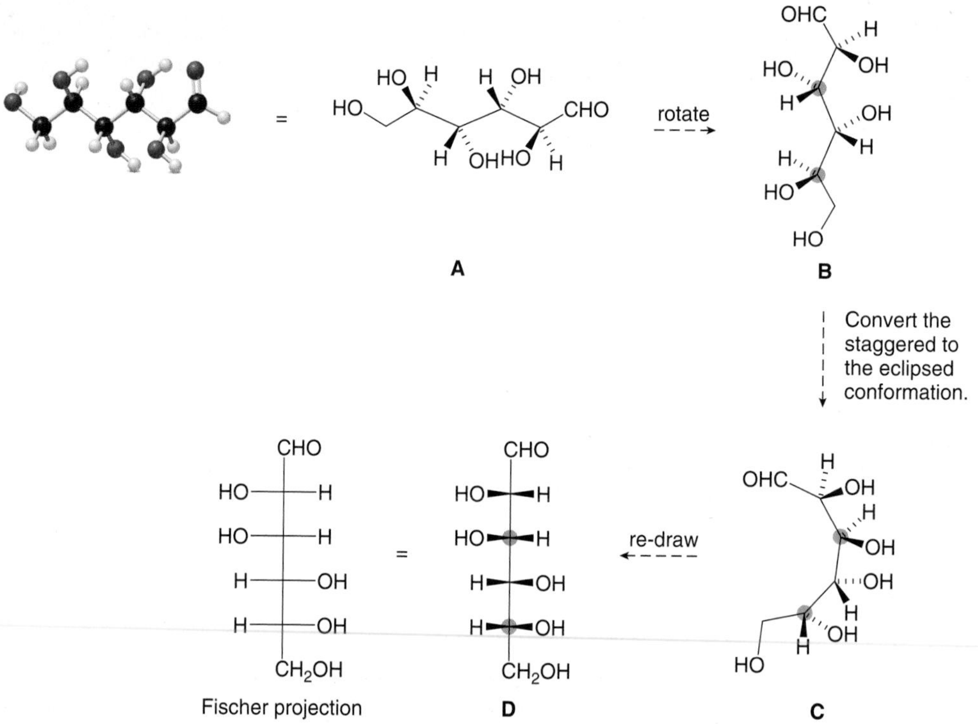

Problem 28.4 Convert the ball-and-stick model to a Fischer projection.

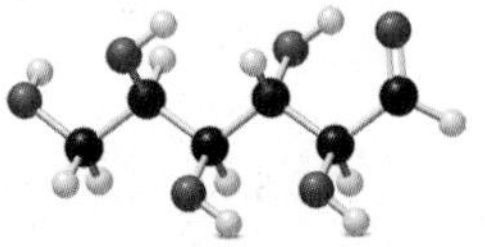

Problem 28.5 Assign *R,S* designations to each stereogenic center in glucose.

28.2C D and L Monosaccharides

Although the prefixes *R* and *S* can be used to designate the configuration of stereogenic centers in monosaccharides, an older system of nomenclature uses the prefixes D- and L-, instead. Naturally occurring glyceraldehyde with the *R* configuration is called the **D-isomer.** Its enantiomer, (*S*)-glyceraldehyde, is called the **L-isomer.**

Fischer projections for the enantiomers of glyceraldehyde

CHO
H—OH
CH2OH
CHO
HO—H
CH2OH

(*R*)-glyceraldehyde
D-glyceraldehyde

(*S*)-glyceraldehyde
L-glyceraldehyde

The letters D and L are used to label all monosaccharides, even those with multiple stereogenic centers. **The configuration of the stereogenic center *farthest* from the carbonyl group determines whether a monosaccharide is D- or L-.**

- **A D-sugar has the OH group on the stereogenic center farthest from the carbonyl on the right in a Fischer projection (like D-glyceraldehyde).**
- **An L-sugar has the OH group on the stereogenic center farthest from the carbonyl on the left in a Fischer projection (like L-glyceraldehyde).**

The two designations, D and *d,* refer to very different phenomena. The "D" designates the configuration around a stereogenic center. In a D monosaccharide, the OH group on the stereogenic center farthest from the carbonyl group is on the right in a Fischer projection. The "*d,*" on the other hand, is an abbreviation for "dextrorotatory;" that is, a *d*-compound rotates the plane of polarized light in the clockwise direction. A D-sugar may be dextrorotatory or it may be levorotatory. **There is no direct correlation between D and *d* or L and *l*.**

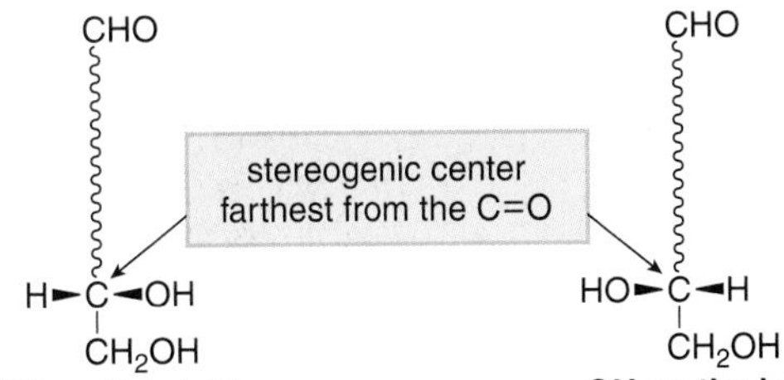
CHO
stereogenic center farthest from the C=O
H—C—OH
CH2OH
CHO
HO—C—H
CH2OH

OH on the right
D-sugar

OH on the left
L-sugar

Glucose and all other naturally occurring sugars are D-sugars. L-Glucose, a compound that does not occur in nature, is the enantiomer of D-glucose. L-Glucose has the opposite configuration at *every* stereogenic center.

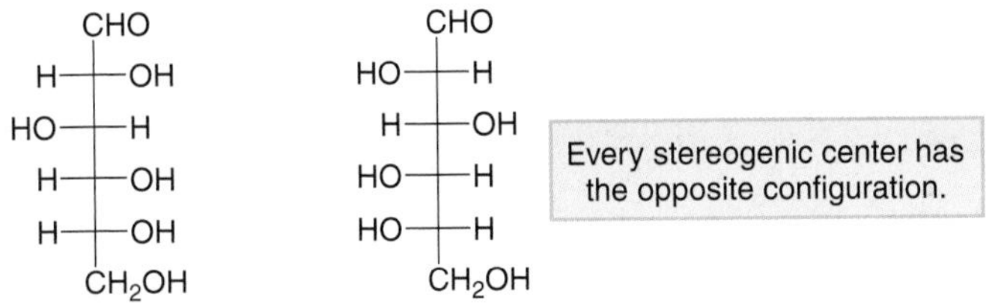
CHO
H—OH
HO—H
H—OH
H—OH
CH2OH
CHO
HO—H
H—OH
HO—H
HO—H
CH2OH
Every stereogenic center has the opposite configuration.

D-glucose
naturally occurring enantiomer

L-glucose

Problem 28.6 (a) Label compounds **A, B,** and **C** as D- or L-sugars. (b) How are compounds **A** and **B** related? **A** and **C? B** and **C?** Choose from enantiomers, diastereomers, or constitutional isomers.

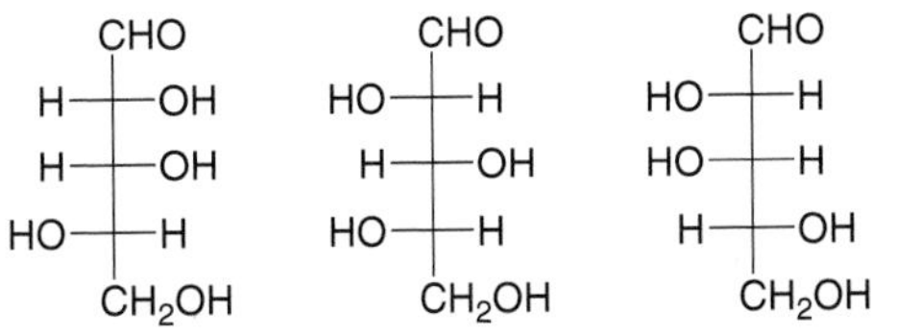
CHO
H—OH
H—OH
HO—H
CH2OH
CHO
HO—H
H—OH
HO—H
CH2OH
CHO
HO—H
HO—H
H—OH
CH2OH

A **B** **C**

28.3 The Family of D-Aldoses

Beginning with D-glyceraldehyde, one may formulate other D-aldoses having four, five, or six carbon atoms by adding carbon atoms (each bonded to H and OH), one at a time, between C1 and C2. Two D-aldotetroses can be formed from D-glyceraldehyde, one with the new OH group on the right and one with the new OH group on the left. Their names are D-erythrose and D-threose. They are two diastereomers, each with two stereogenic centers.

The common name of each monosaccharide indicates both the number of atoms it contains and the configuration at each of the stereogenic centers. Because the common names are firmly entrenched in the chemical literature, no systematic method has ever been established to name these compounds.

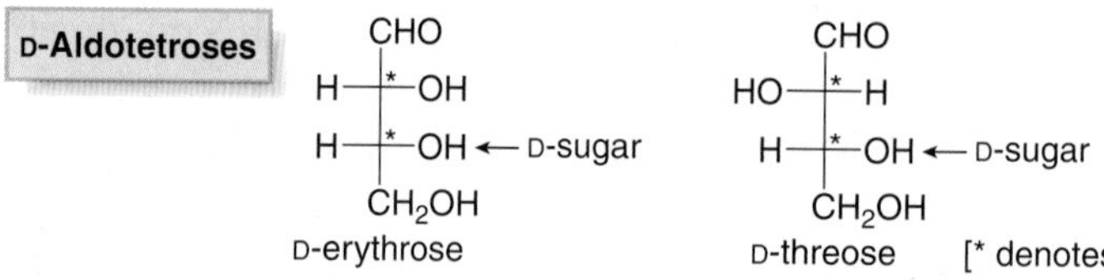

[* denotes a stereogenic center.]

Because each aldotetrose has two stereogenic centers, there are 2^2 or four possible stereoisomers. D-Erythrose and D-threose are two of them. The other two are their enantiomers, called L-erythrose and L-threose, respectively. The configuration around each stereogenic center is exactly the opposite in its enantiomer. All four stereoisomers of the D-aldotetroses are shown in Figure 28.3.

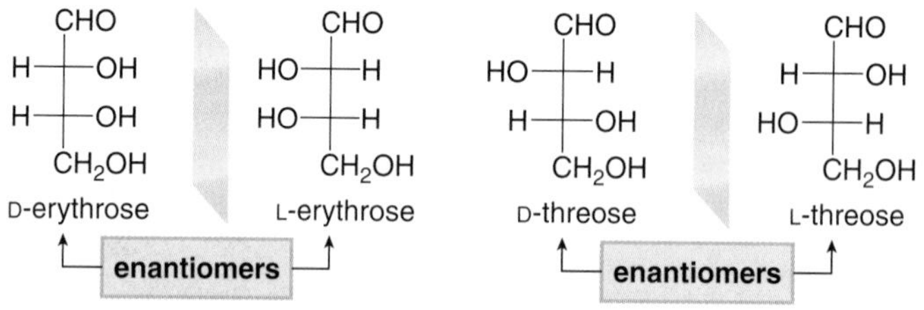

Figure 28.3 The four stereoisomeric aldotetroses

D-Ribose, D-arabinose, and D-xylose are all common aldopentoses in nature. D-Ribose is the carbohydrate component of RNA, the polymer that translates the genetic information of DNA for protein synthesis.

To continue forming the family of D-aldoses, we must add another carbon atom (bonded to H and OH) just below the carbonyl of either tetrose. Because there are two D-aldotetroses to begin with, and there are two ways to place the new OH (right or left), there are now four D-aldopentoses: D-ribose, D-arabinose, D-xylose, and D-lyxose. Each aldopentose now has three stereogenic centers, so there are $2^3 = 8$ possible stereoisomers, or four pairs of enantiomers. The D-enantiomer of each pair is shown in Figure 28.4.

Finally, to form the D-aldohexoses, we must add another carbon atom (bonded to H and OH) just below the carbonyl of all the aldopentoses. Because there are four D-aldopentoses to begin with, and there are two ways to place the new OH (right or left), there are now eight D-aldohexoses. Each aldohexose now has four stereogenic centers, so there are $2^4 = 16$ possible stereoisomers, or eight pairs of enantiomers. Only the D-enantiomer of each pair is shown in Figure 28.4.

The tree of D-aldoses (Figure 28.4) is arranged in pairs of compounds that are bracketed together. Each pair of compounds, such as D-glucose and D-mannose, has the same configuration around all of its stereogenic centers except for one.

Figure 28.4
The family of D-aldoses having three to six carbon atoms

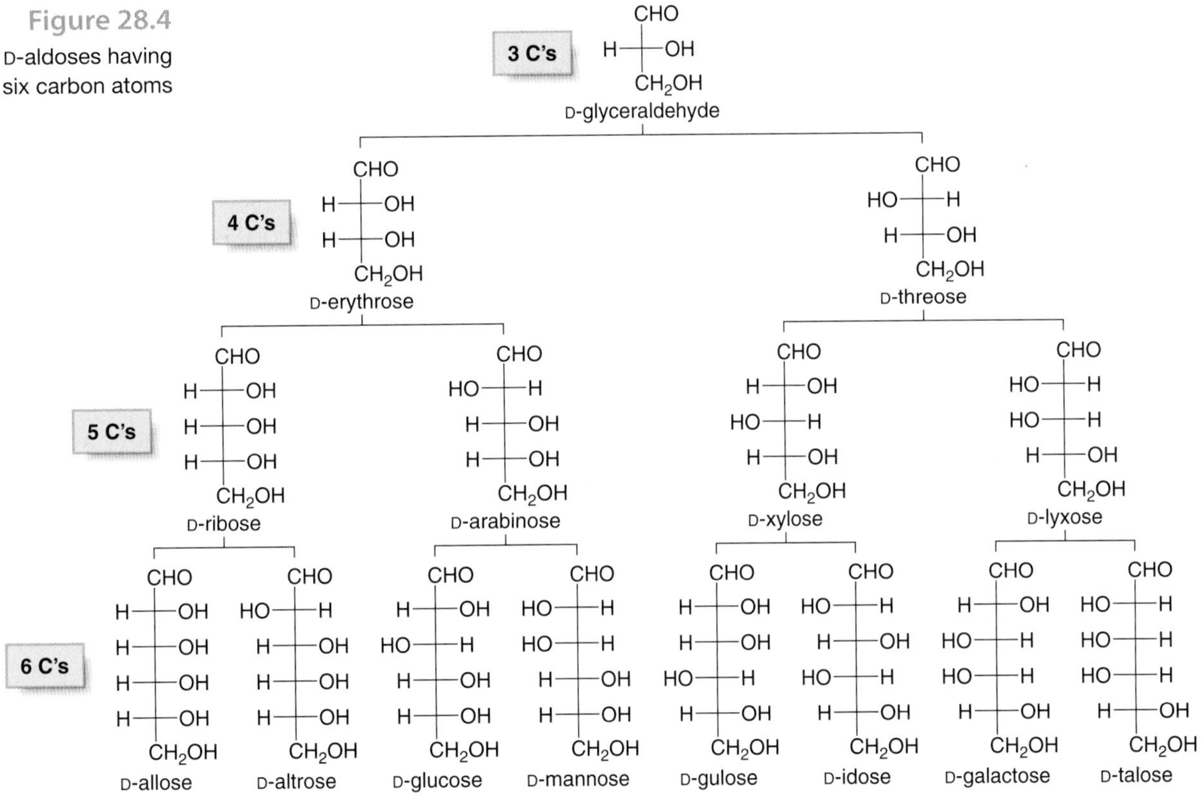

Of the D-aldohexoses, only D-glucose and D-galactose are common in nature. **D-Glucose is by far the most abundant of all D-aldoses.** D-Glucose comes from the hydrolysis of starch and cellulose, and D-galactose comes from the hydrolysis of fruit pectins.

- **Two diastereomers that differ in the configuration around one stereogenic center only are called *epimers*.**

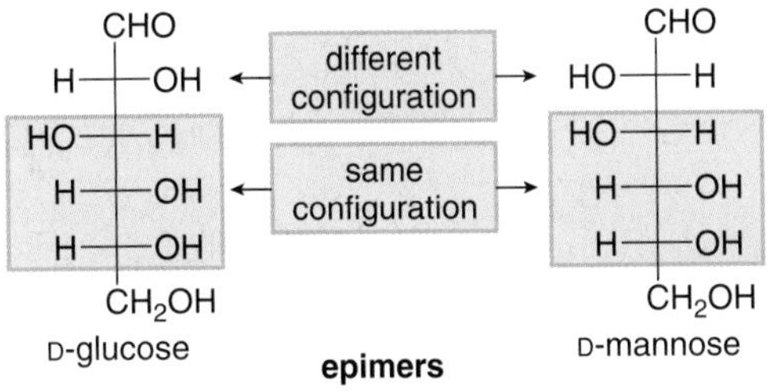

Problem 28.7 How many different aldoheptoses are there? How many are D-sugars? Draw all D-aldoheptoses having the *R* configuration at C2 and C3.

Problem 28.8 Draw two possible epimers of D-erythrose. Name each of these compounds using Figure 28.4.

28.4 The Family of D-Ketoses

The family of D-ketoses, shown in Figure 28.5, is formed from dihydroxyacetone by adding a new carbon (bonded to H and OH) between C2 and C3. Having a carbonyl group at C2 decreases the number of stereogenic centers in these monosaccharides, so that there are only four D-ketohexoses. The most common naturally occurring ketose is D-fructose.

Problem 28.9 Referring to the structures in Figures 28.4 and 28.5, classify each pair of compounds as enantiomers, epimers, diastereomers but not epimers, or constitutional isomers of each other.

a. D-allose and L-allose
b. D-altrose and D-gulose
c. D-galactose and D-talose
d. D-mannose and D-fructose
e. D-fructose and D-sorbose
f. L-sorbose and L-tagatose

Problem 28.10 a. Draw the enantiomer of D-fructose.
b. Draw an epimer of D-fructose at C4. What is the name of this compound?
c. Draw an epimer of D-fructose at C5. What is the name of this compound?

Problem 28.11 Referring to Figure 28.5, which D-ketohexoses have the *S* configuration at C3?

Figure 28.5 The family of D-ketoses having three to six carbon atoms

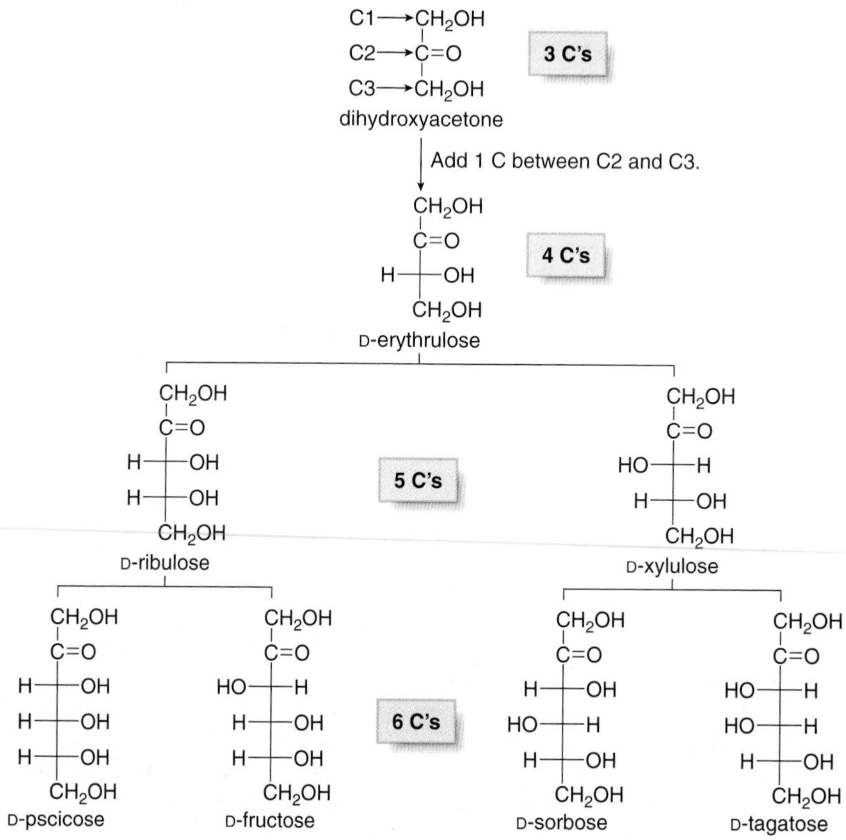

28.5 Physical Properties of Monosaccharides

Monosaccharides have the following physical properties:

- They are all **sweet tasting,** but their relative sweetness varies a great deal.
- They are polar compounds with **high melting points.**
- The presence of so many polar functional groups capable of hydrogen bonding makes them **water soluble.**
- Unlike most other organic compounds, monosaccharides are so polar that they are **insoluble in organic solvents like diethyl ether.**

28.6 The Cyclic Forms of Monosaccharides

Although the monosaccharides in Figures 28.4 and 28.5 are drawn as acyclic carbonyl compounds containing several hydroxy groups, the hydroxy and carbonyl groups of monosaccharides can undergo intramolecular cyclization reactions to form **hemiacetals** having either five or six atoms in the ring. This process was first discussed in Section 21.16.

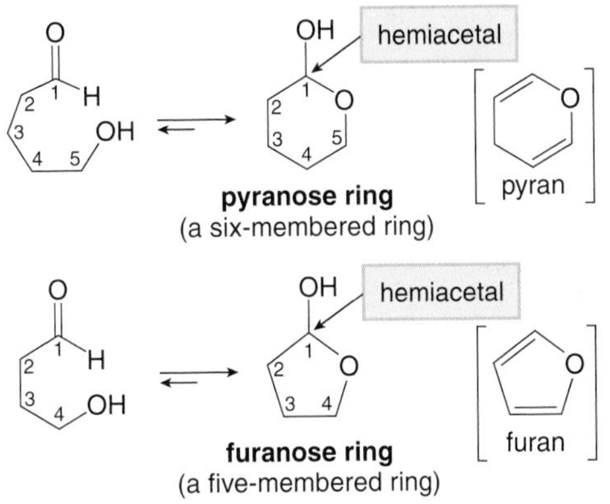

- **A six-membered ring containing an O atom is called a *pyranose* ring.**
- **A five-membered ring containing an O atom is called a *furanose* ring.**

Cyclization of a hydroxy carbonyl compound always forms a stereogenic center at the hemiacetal carbon, called the **anomeric carbon.** The two hemiacetals are called **anomers.**

- **Anomers are stereoisomers of a cyclic monosaccharide that differ in the position of the OH group at the hemiacetal carbon.**

In forming a pyranose ring:

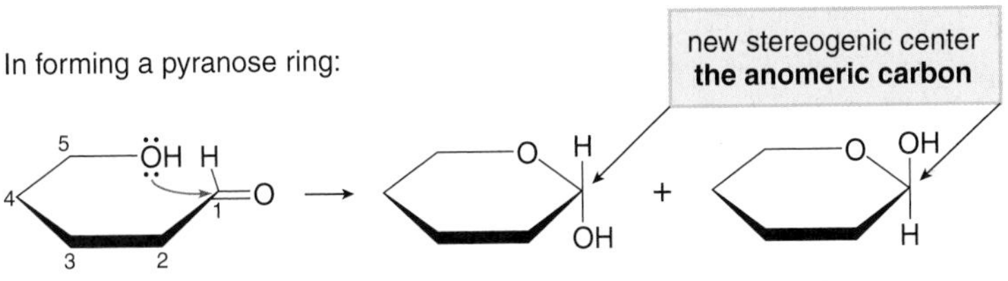

two anomers formed by cyclization

Cyclization forms the more stable ring size in a given molecule. **The most common monosaccharides, the aldohexoses like glucose, typically form a pyranose ring,** so our discussion begins with forming a cyclic hemiacetal from D-glucose.

28.6A Drawing Glucose as a Cyclic Hemiacetal

Which of the five OH groups in glucose is at the right distance from the carbonyl group to form a six-membered ring? The **O atom on the stereogenic center farthest from the carbonyl** (C5) is six atoms from the carbonyl carbon, placing it in the proper position for cyclization to form a pyranose ring.

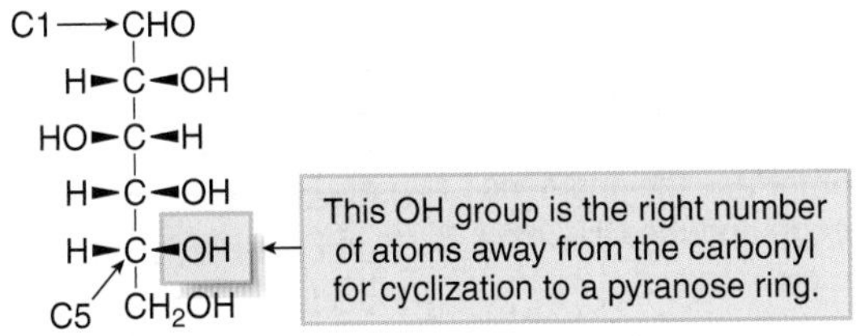

D-glucose

To translate the acyclic form of glucose into a cyclic hemiacetal, we must draw the hydroxy aldehyde in a way that suggests the position of the atoms in the new ring, and then draw the ring. **By convention the O atom in the new pyranose ring is drawn in the upper right-hand corner of the six-membered ring.**

Rotating the groups on the bottom stereogenic center in **A** places all six atoms needed for the ring (including the OH) in a vertical line (**B**). Re-drawing this representation as a Fischer projection makes the structure appear less cluttered (**C**). Twisting this structure and rotating it 90° forms **D.** Structures **A–D** are four different ways of drawing the same acyclic structure of D-glucose.

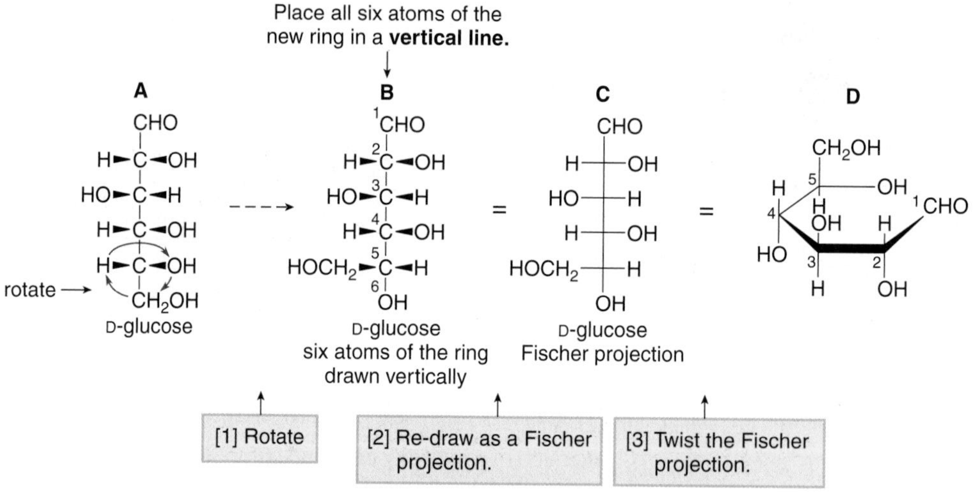

We are now set to draw the cyclic hemiacetal formed by nucleophilic attack of the OH group on C5 on the aldehyde carbonyl. Because cyclization creates a new stereogenic center, there are **two cyclic forms of D-glucose,** an **α anomer** and a **β anomer.** All the original stereogenic centers maintain their configuration in both of the products formed.

- **The α anomer of a D monosaccharide has the OH group drawn *down,* trans to the CH_2OH group at C5. The α anomer of D-glucose is called α-D-glucose, or α-D-glucopyranose (to emphasize the six-membered ring).**
- **The β anomer of a D monosaccharide has the OH group drawn *up,* cis to the CH_2OH group at C5. The β anomer is called β-D-glucose, or β-D-glucopyranose (to emphasize the six-membered ring).**

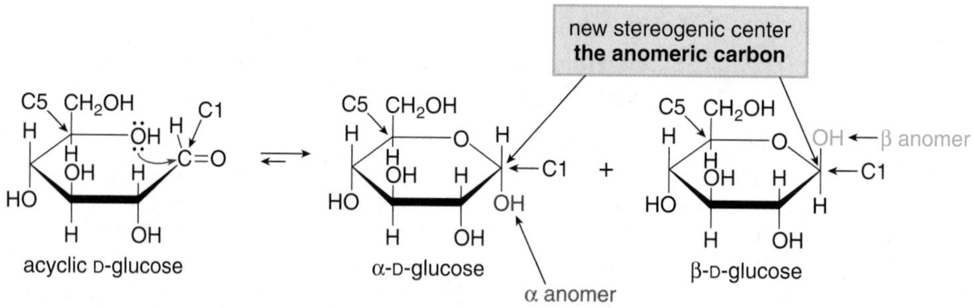

The **α anomer** in any monosaccharide has the anomeric OH group and the CH_2OH group **trans.** The **β anomer** has the anomeric OH group and the CH_2OH group **cis.**

These flat, six-membered rings used to represent the cyclic hemiacetals of glucose and other sugars are called **Haworth projections.** The cyclic forms of glucose now have **five stereogenic centers, the four from the starting hydroxy aldehyde and the new anomeric carbon.** α-D-Glucose and β-D-glucose are **diastereomers,** because only the anomeric carbon has a different configuration.

The mechanism for this transformation is exactly the same as the mechanism that converts a hydroxy aldehyde to a cyclic hemiacetal (Mechanism 21.11). The acyclic aldehyde and two cyclic hemiacetals are all in equilibrium. Each cyclic hemiacetal can be isolated and crystallized separately, but when any one compound is placed in solution, an equilibrium mixture of all three forms results. This process is called **mutarotation.** At equilibrium, the mixture has 37% of the α anomer, 63% of the β anomer, and only trace amounts of the acyclic hydroxy aldehyde, as shown in Figure 28.6.

Figure 28.6
The three forms of glucose

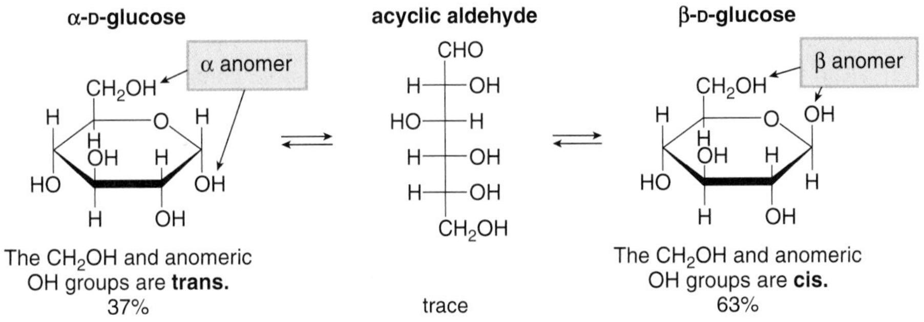
α-D-glucose
α anomer
CH_2OH
The CH_2OH and anomeric OH groups are **trans.**
37%
acyclic aldehyde
CHO
CH_2OH
trace
β-D-glucose
β anomer
CH_2OH
The CH_2OH and anomeric OH groups are **cis.**
63%

28.6B Haworth Projections

To convert an acyclic monosaccharide to a Haworth projection, follow a stepwise procedure.

How To Draw a Haworth Projection from an Acyclic Aldohexose

Example Convert D-mannose to a Haworth projection.

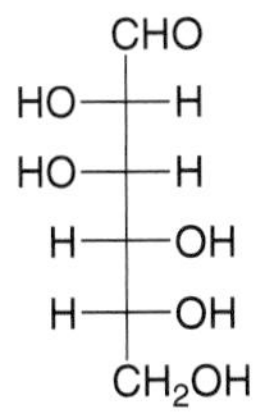
CHO
CH_2OH
D-mannose

Step [1] Place the O atom in the upper right corner of a hexagon, and add the CH_2OH group on the first carbon counterclockwise from the O atom.

- For **D-sugars,** the CH_2OH group is drawn **up.** For **L-sugars,** the CH_2OH group is drawn **down.**

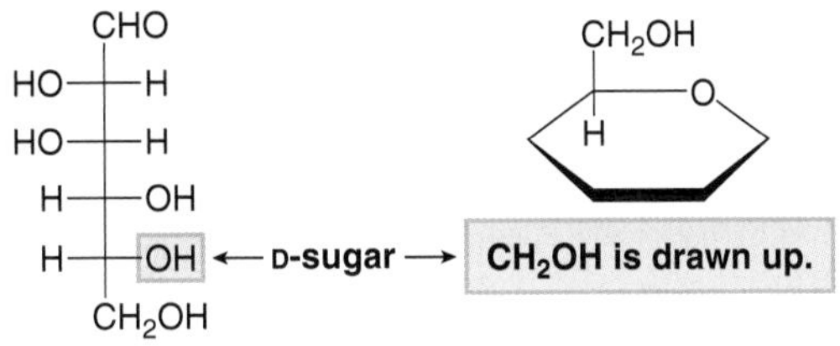
CHO
CH_2OH
D-sugar
CH_2OH is drawn up.
D-mannose

Step [2] Place the anomeric carbon on the first carbon clockwise from the O atom.

- For an **α anomer,** the **OH** is drawn **down** in a D-sugar.
- For a **β anomer,** the **OH** is drawn **up** in a D-sugar.

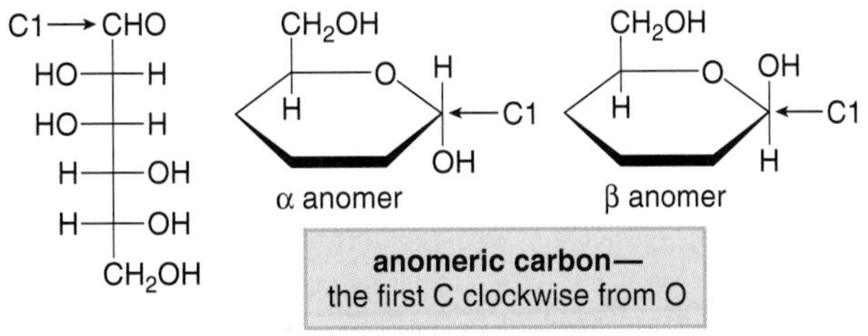
C1
CHO
CH_2OH
α anomer
β anomer
anomeric carbon—
the first C clockwise from O

- Remember: The carbonyl carbon becomes the anomeric carbon (a new stereogenic center).

—Continued

How To, continued . . .

Step [3] Add the substituents at the three remaining stereogenic centers clockwise around the ring.

- The substituents on the **right side** of the Fischer projection are drawn **down.**
- The substituents on the **left** are drawn **up.**

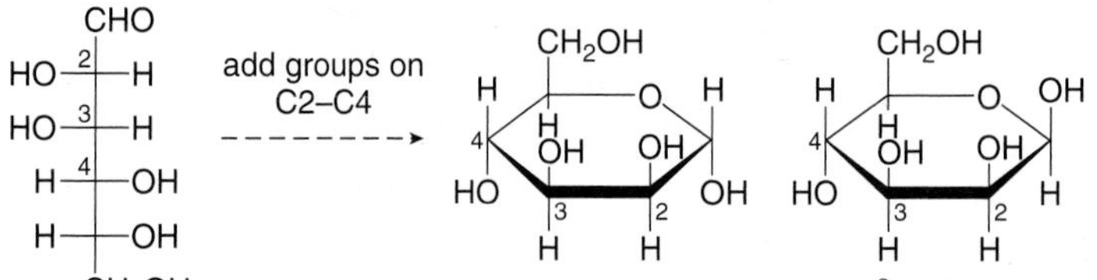
add groups on
C2–C4

α anomer β anomer

Problem 28.12 Convert each aldohexose to the indicated anomer using a Haworth projection.

a. Draw the α anomer of:

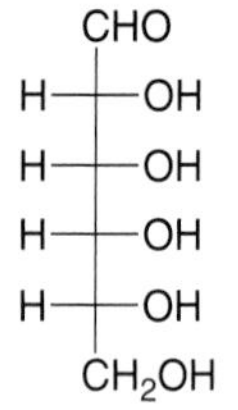

b. Draw the α anomer of:

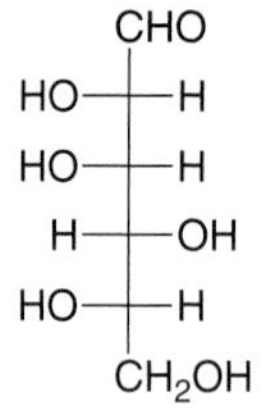

c. Draw the β anomer of:

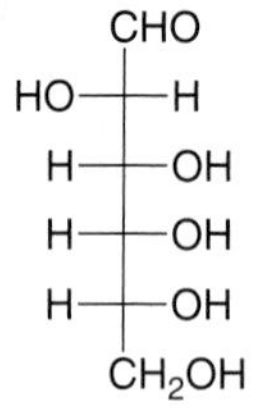

Sample Problem 28.4 shows how to convert a Haworth projection back to the acyclic form of a monosaccharide. It doesn't matter whether the hemiacetal is the α or β anomer, because both anomers give the *same* hydroxy aldehyde.

Sample Problem 28.4 Convert the following Haworth projection to the acyclic form of the aldohexose.

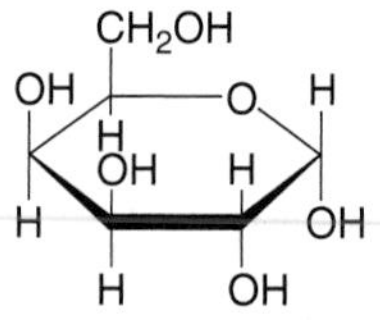

Solution

To convert the substituents to the acyclic form, start at the pyranose O atom, and work in a ***counterclockwise*** fashion around the ring, and from bottom-to-top along the chain.

[1] Draw the carbon skeleton, placing the CHO on the top and the CH_2OH on the bottom.

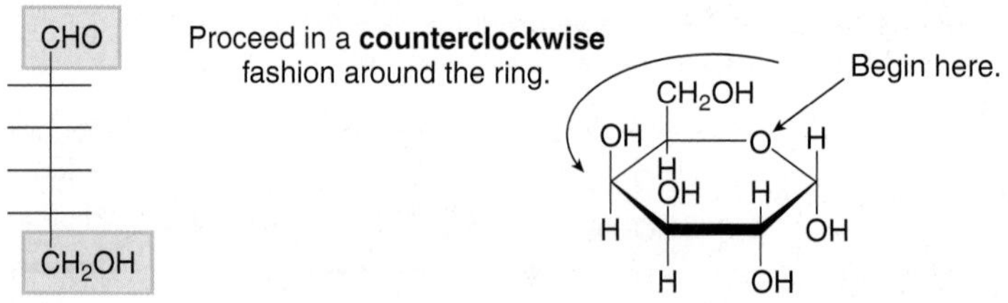
Proceed in a **counterclockwise** fashion around the ring.
Begin here.

[2] Classify the sugar as D- or L-.

- The CH_2OH is drawn **up,** so it is a **D-sugar.**
- A D-sugar has the OH group on the bottom stereogenic center on the **right.**

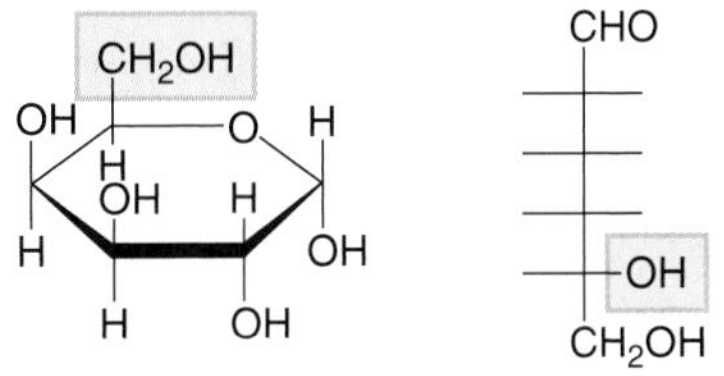

[3] Add the three other stereogenic centers.

- **Up** substituents go on the **left.**
- **Down** substituents go on the **right.**

The anomeric C becomes the C=O.

Answer:

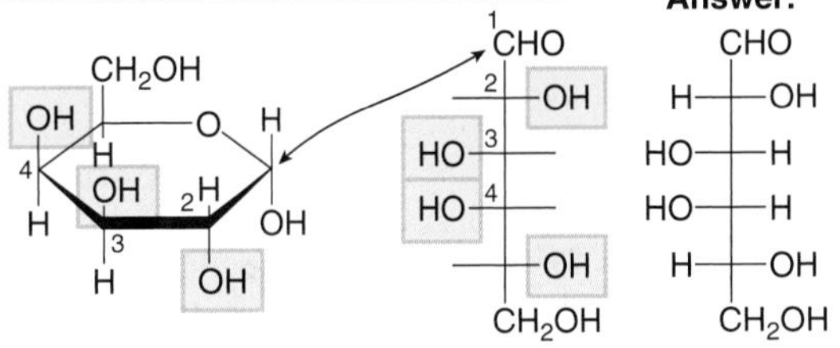

Problem 28.13 Convert each Haworth projection to its acyclic form.

a. 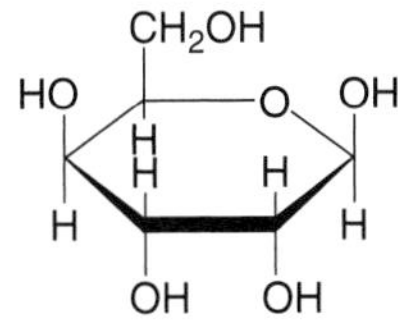

b. 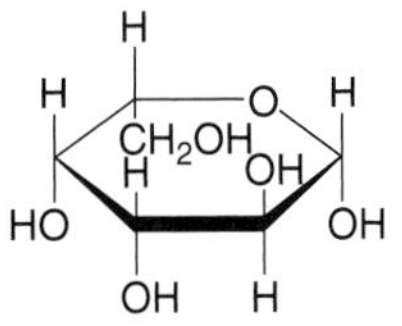

28.6C Three-Dimensional Representations for D-Glucose

Because the chair form of a six-membered ring gives the truest picture of its three-dimensional shape, we must learn to convert Haworth projections into chair forms.

To convert a Haworth projection to a chair form:

- **Draw the pyranose ring with the O atom as an "up" atom.**
- **The "up" substituents in a Haworth projection become the "up" bonds (either axial or equatorial) on a given carbon atom on a puckered six-membered ring.**
- **The "down" substituents in a Haworth projection become the "down" bonds (either axial or equatorial) on a given carbon atom on a puckered six-membered ring.**

As a result, the three-dimensional chair form of β-D-glucose is drawn in the following manner:

Make the O atom an "up" atom.

Three-dimensional chair form for β-D-glucose

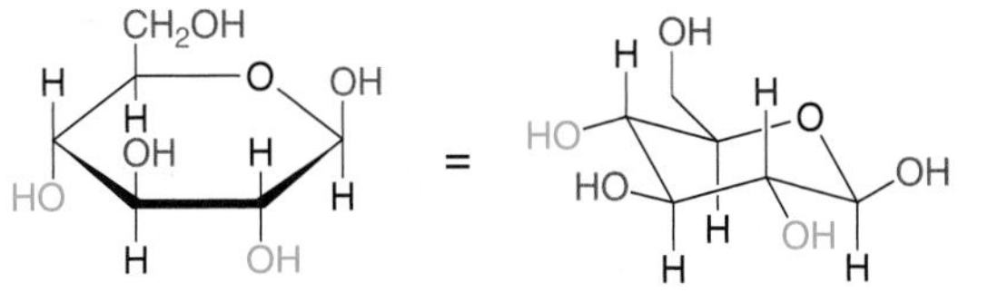

- "Up" substituents are labeled in red.
- "Down" substituents are labeled in blue.

Figure 28.7 Three-dimensional representations for both anomers of D-glucose

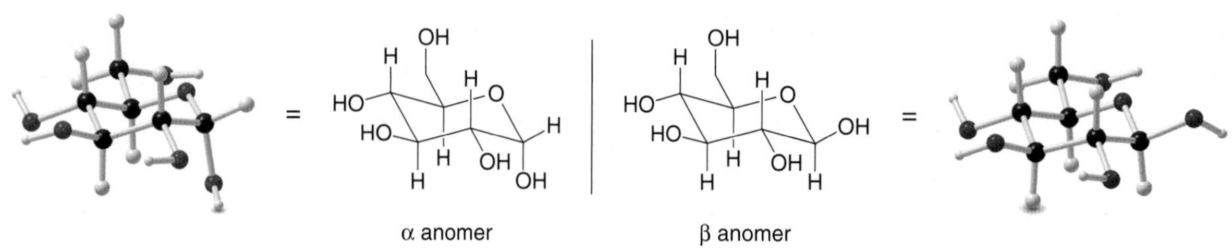
α anomer
β anomer

Glucose has all substituents larger than a hydrogen atom in the more roomy equatorial positions, making it the most stable and thus most prevalent monosaccharide. The β anomer is the major isomer at equilibrium, moreover, because the hemiacetal OH group is in the equatorial position, too. Figure 28.7 shows both anomers of D-glucose drawn as chair conformations.

Problem 28.14 Convert each Haworth projection in Problem 28.13 to a three-dimensional representation using a chair pyranose ring.

28.6D Furanoses

Honey was the first and most popular sweetening agent until it was replaced by sugar (from sugarcane) in modern times. Honey is a mixture consisting largely of D-fructose and D-glucose.

Certain monosaccharides—notably aldopentoses and ketohexoses—predominantly form furanose rings, rather than pyranose rings, in solution. The same principles apply to drawing these structures as for drawing pyranose rings, except the ring size is one atom smaller.

- Cyclization always forms a new stereogenic center at the anomeric carbon, so two different anomers are possible. For a D-sugar, the OH group is drawn down in the α anomer and up in the β anomer.
- Use the same drawing conventions for adding substituents to the five-membered ring. With D-sugars, the CH_2OH group is drawn up.

With D-ribose, the OH group used to form the five-membered furanose ring is located on C4. Cyclization yields two anomers at the new stereogenic center, which are called **α-D-ribofuranose** and **β-D-ribofuranose.**

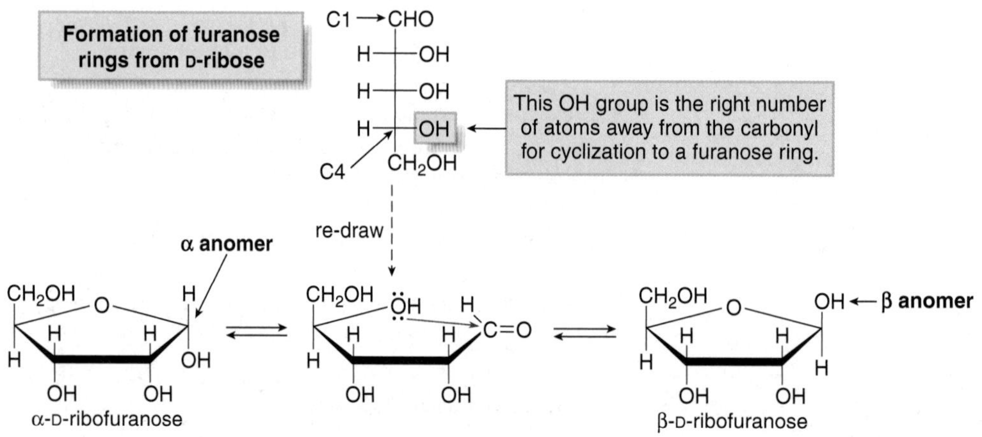
Formation of furanose rings from D-ribose
This OH group is the right number of atoms away from the carbonyl for cyclization to a furanose ring.
re-draw
α anomer
β anomer
α-D-ribofuranose
β-D-ribofuranose

The same procedure can be used to draw the furanose form of D-fructose, the most common ketohexose. Because the carbonyl group is at C2 (instead of C1, as in the aldoses), the OH group at C5 reacts to form the hemiacetal in the five-membered ring. Two anomers are formed.

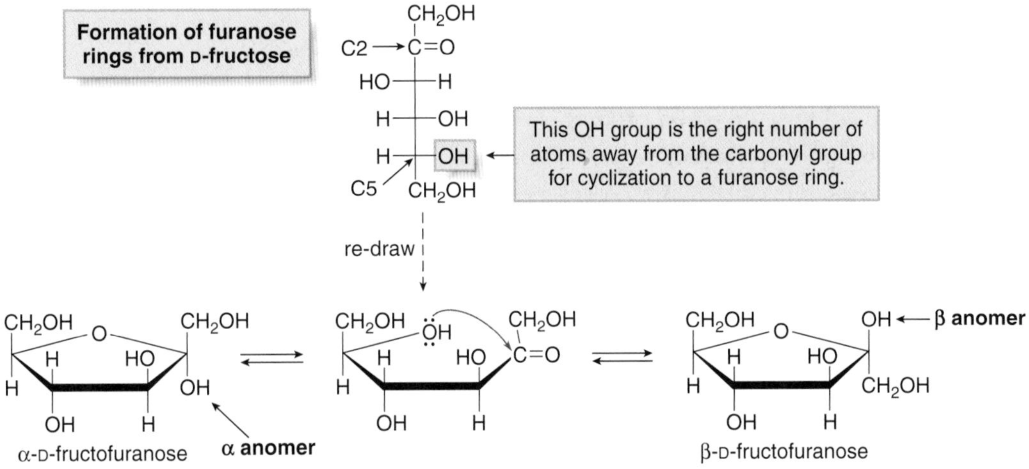
Formation of furanose rings from D-fructose
C2
C5
This OH group is the right number of atoms away from the carbonyl group for cyclization to a furanose ring.
re-draw
α-D-fructofuranose
α anomer
β anomer
β-D-fructofuranose

Problem 28.15 Aldotetroses exist in the furanose form. Draw both anomers of D-erythrose.

28.7 Glycosides

Keep in mind the difference between a hemiacetal and an acetal:

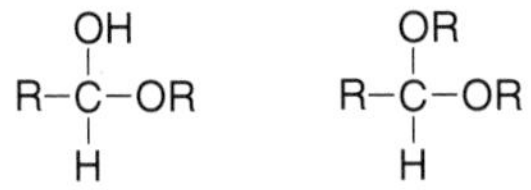

hemiacetal
- one OH group
- one OR group

acetal
- two OR groups

Because monosaccharides exist in solution in an equilibrium between acyclic and cyclic forms, they undergo three types of reactions:

- **Reaction of the hemiacetal**
- **Reaction of the hydroxy groups**
- **Reaction of the carbonyl group**

Even though the acyclic form of a monosaccharide may be present in only trace amounts, the equilibrium can be tipped in its favor by Le Châtelier's principle (Section 9.8). Suppose, for example, that the carbonyl group of the acyclic form reacts with a reagent, thus depleting its equilibrium concentration. The equilibrium will then shift to compensate for the loss, thus producing more of the acyclic form, which can react further.

Note, too, that monosaccharides have two different types of OH groups. Most are "regular" alcohols, and as such, undergo reactions characteristic of alcohols. The anomeric OH group, on the other hand, is part of a hemiacetal, giving it added reactivity.

28.7A Glycoside Formation

Treatment of a monosaccharide with an alcohol and HCl converts the hemiacetal into an acetal called a **glycoside.** For example, treatment of α-D-glucose with CH_3OH and HCl forms two glycosides that are diastereomers at the acetal carbon. The α and β labels are assigned in the same way as anomers: with a D-sugar, an α glycoside has the new OR group (OCH_3 group in this example) down, and a β glycoside has the new OR group up.

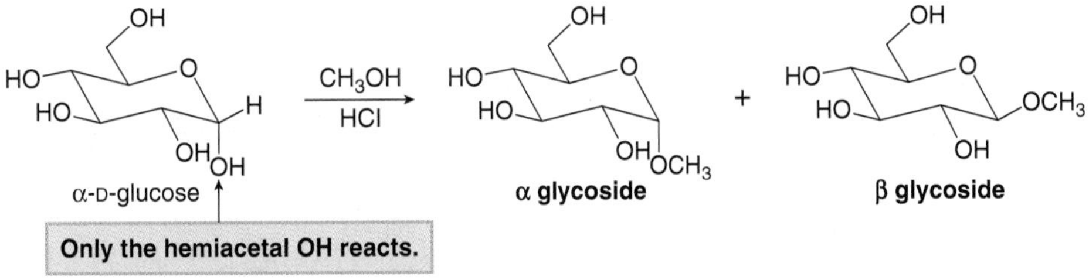
α-D-glucose
CH_3OH
HCl
α glycoside
β glycoside
Only the hemiacetal OH reacts.

Mechanism 28.1 explains why a single anomer forms two glycosides. The reaction proceeds by way of a **planar carbocation,** which undergoes nucleophilic attack from two different directions to give a mixture of diastereomers. Because both α- and β-D-glucose form the same planar carbocation, each yields the same mixture of two glycosides.

Mechanism 28.1 Glycoside Formation

Steps [1]–[2] Protonation and loss of the leaving group

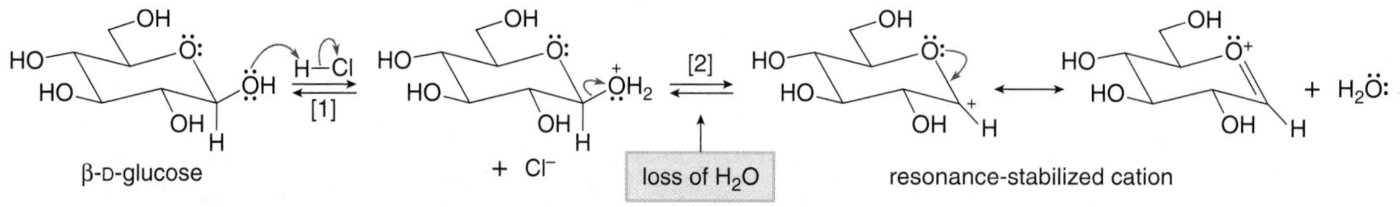

- Protonation of the hemiacetal OH group, followed by **loss of H_2O,** forms a resonance-stabilized cation (Steps [1] and [2]).

Steps [3]–[4] Nucleophilic attack and deprotonation

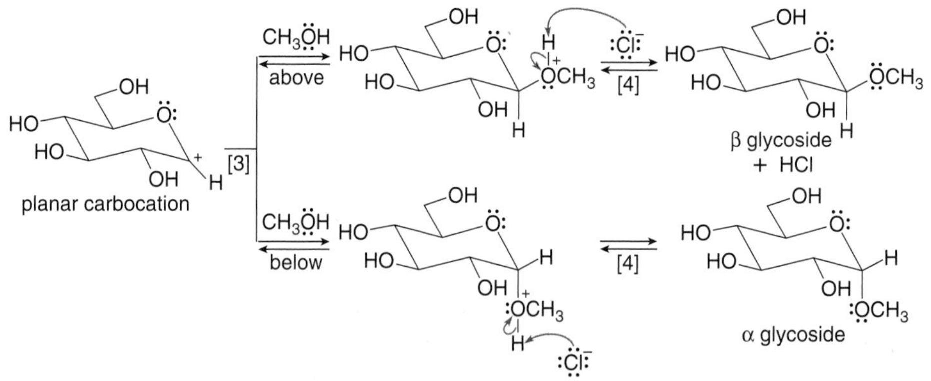

- **Nucleophilic attack of CH_3OH** on the planar carbocation occurs from both sides to yield α and β glycosides after loss of a proton (Steps [3] and [4]).

The mechanism also explains why only the hemiacetal OH group reacts. Protonation of the hemiacetal OH, followed by loss of H_2O, forms a resonance-stabilized carbocation in Step [2]. A resonance-stabilized carbocation is not formed by loss of H_2O from any other OH group.

Unlike cyclic hemiacetals, **glycosides are acetals, and so they do not undergo mutarotation.** When a single glycoside is dissolved in H_2O, it is *not* converted to an equilibrium mixture of α and β glycosides.

- **Glycosides are acetals with an alkoxy group (OR) bonded to the anomeric carbon.**

Problem 28.16 What glycosides are formed when each monosaccharide is treated with CH_3CH_2OH, HCl: (a) β-D-mannose; (b) α-D-gulose; (c) β-D-fructose?

28.7B Glycoside Hydrolysis

Because glycosides are acetals, **they are hydrolyzed with acid and water to cyclic hemiacetals and a molecule of alcohol.** A mixture of two anomers is formed from a single glycoside. For example, treatment of methyl α-D-glucopyranoside with aqueous acid forms a mixture of α- and β-D-glucose and methanol.

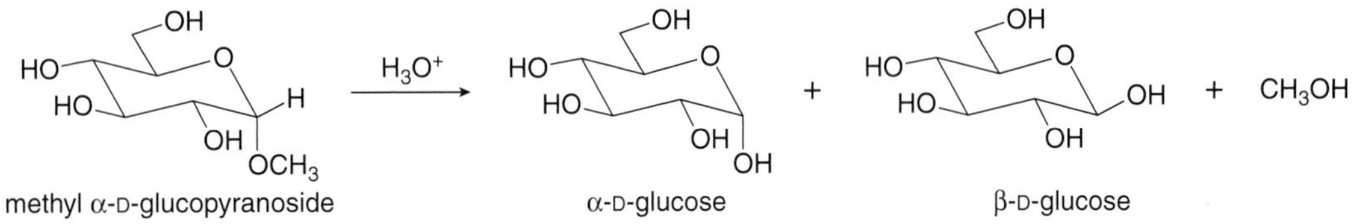

The mechanism for glycoside hydrolysis is just the reverse of glycoside formation. It involves two parts: **formation of a planar carbocation,** followed by **nucleophilic attack of H_2O** to form anomeric hemiacetals, as shown in Mechanism 28.2.

Mechanism 28.2 Glycoside Hydrolysis

Steps [1]–[2] Protonation and loss of the leaving group

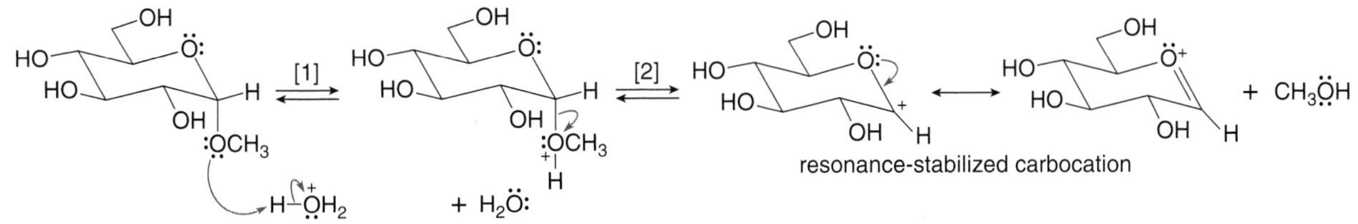

- Protonation of the acetal OCH_3 group, followed by **loss of CH_3OH,** forms a resonance-stabilized cation (Steps [1] and [2]).

Steps [3]–[4] Nucleophilic attack and deprotonation

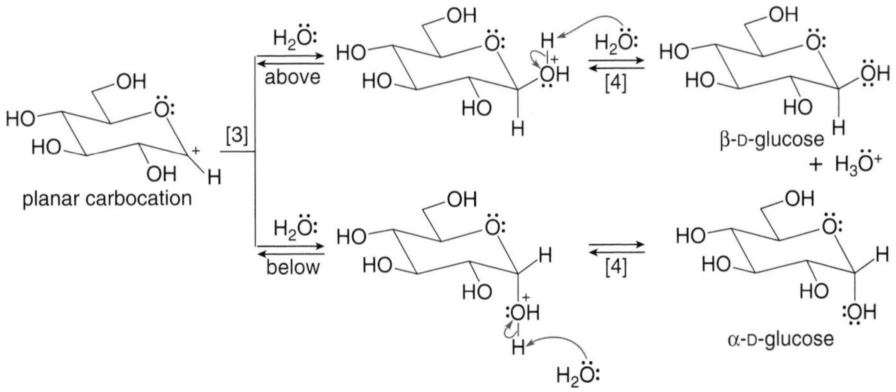

- **Nucleophilic attack of H_2O** on the planar carbocation occurs from both sides to yield α and β anomers after loss of a proton (Steps [3] and [4]).

Problem 28.17 Draw a stepwise mechanism for the following reaction.

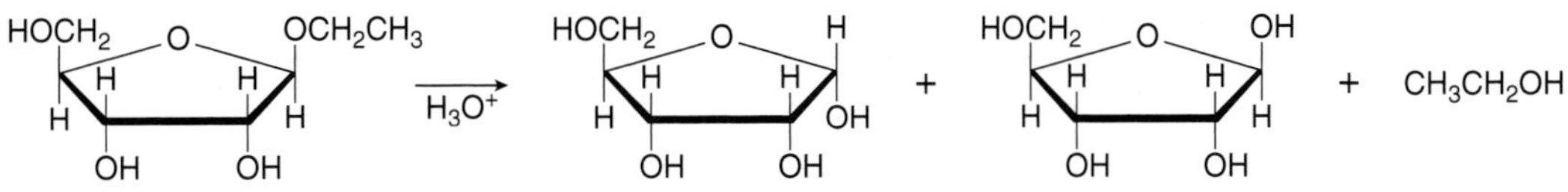

28.7C Naturally Occurring Glycosides

The berries of the black nightshade plant (*Solanum nigrum*) are a source of the poisonous alkaloid solanine.

Salicin and **solanine** are two naturally occurring compounds that contain glycoside bonds as part of their structure. Salicin is an analgesic isolated from willow bark, and solanine is a poisonous compound isolated from the berries of the deadly nightshade plant. Solanine is also produced in the leaves, stem, and green spots on the skin of potatoes as a defense against insects and predators. It is believed that the role of the sugar rings in both salicin and solanine is to increase their water solubility.

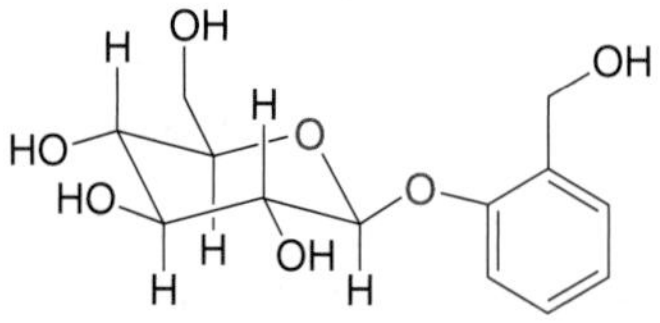

salicin

[The O atoms that are part of the glycoside bonds are drawn in red.]

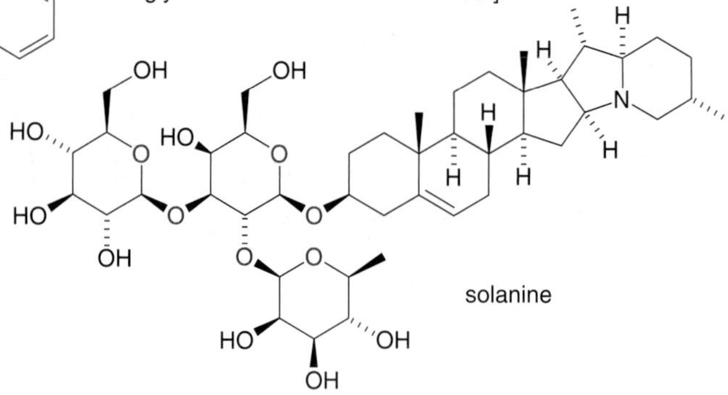

solanine

Glycosides are common in nature. All disaccharides and polysaccharides are formed by joining monosaccharides together with glycosidic linkages. These compounds are discussed in detail beginning in Section 28.12.

Problem 28.18 (a) Label all the O atoms that are part of a glycoside in rebaudioside A. Rebaudioside A, marketed under the trade name Truvia, is a sweet glycoside obtained from the stevia plant, which has been used for centuries in Paraguay to sweeten foods. (b) The alcohol or phenol formed from the hydrolysis of a glycoside is called an **aglycon.** What aglycon and monosaccharides are formed by the hydrolysis of rebaudioside A?

Rebaudioside A, a naturally occurring glycoside about 400 times sweeter than table sugar, is obtained from the leaves of the stevia plant, a shrub native to Central and South America.

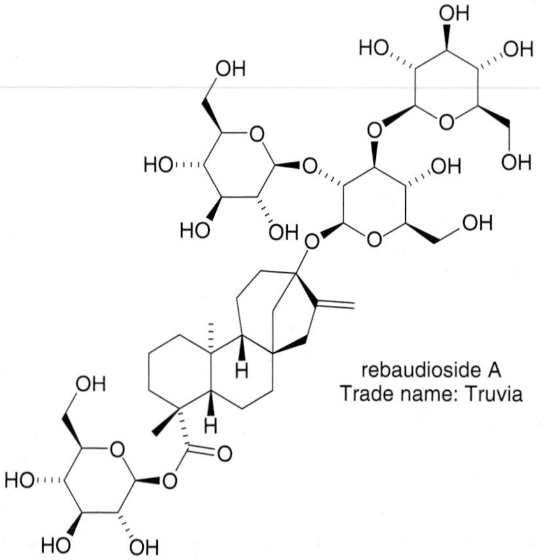

rebaudioside A
Trade name: Truvia

28.8 Reactions of Monosaccharides at the OH Groups

Because monosaccharides contain OH groups, they undergo reactions typical of alcohols—that is, they are converted to **ethers** and **esters.** Because the cyclic hemiacetal form of a monosaccharide contains an OH group, this form of a monosaccharide must be drawn as the starting material for any reaction that occurs at an OH group.

All OH groups of a cyclic monosaccharide are converted to ethers by treatment with base and an alkyl halide. For example, α-D-glucose reacts with silver(I) oxide (Ag_2O, a base) and excess CH_3I to form a pentamethyl ether.

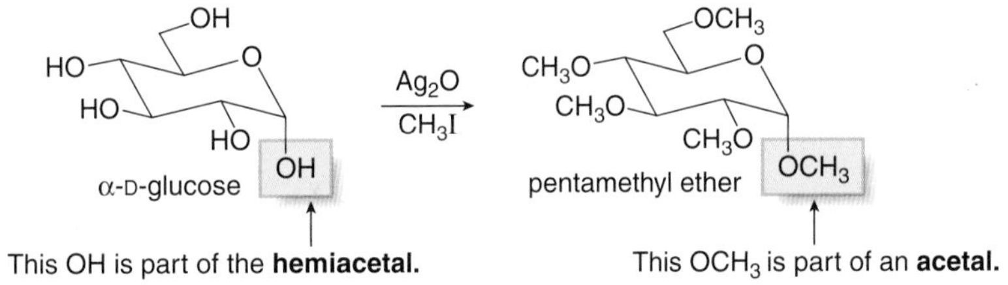
Ag2O
CH3I
α-D-glucose
pentamethyl ether
This OH is part of the **hemiacetal.**
This OCH3 is part of an **acetal.**

Ag_2O removes a proton from each alcohol, forming an alkoxide (RO^-), which then reacts with CH_3I in an S_N2 reaction. Because no C–O bonds are broken, the configuration of all substituents in the starting material is **retained,** forming a single product.

The product contains two different types of ether bonds. There are four "regular" ethers formed from the "regular" hydroxyls. The new ether from the hemiacetal is now part of an **acetal**—that is, a **glycoside.**

The four ether bonds that are *not* part of the acetal do not react with any reagents except strong acids like HBr and HI (Section 9.14). **The acetal ether, on the other hand, is hydrolyzed with aqueous acid** (Section 28.7B). Aqueous hydrolysis of a single glycoside (like the pentamethyl ether of α-D-glucose) yields both anomers of the product monosaccharide.

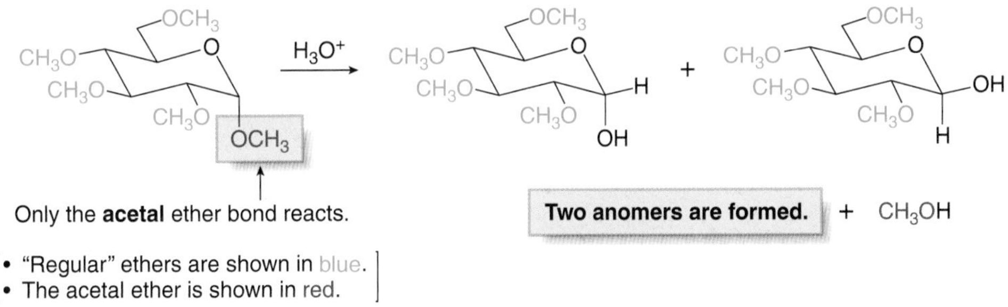
H3O+
Only the **acetal** ether bond reacts.
Two anomers are formed.
+ CH3OH
• "Regular" ethers are shown in blue.
• The acetal ether is shown in red.

The OH groups of monosaccharides can also be converted to esters. For example, treatment of β-D-glucose with either acetic anhydride or acetyl chloride in the presence of pyridine (a base) converts all OH groups into acetate esters.

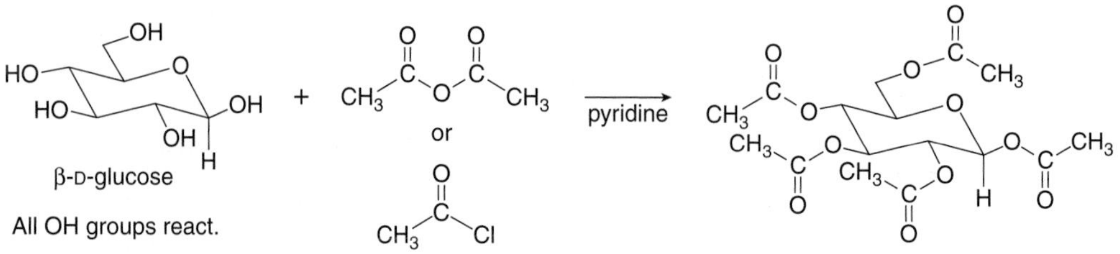

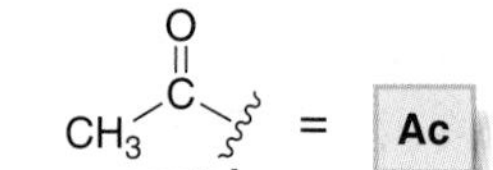
acetyl

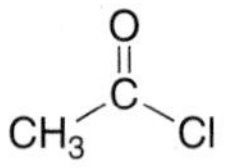
AcCl

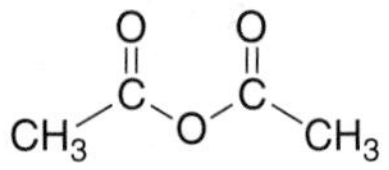
Ac_2O

Since it is cumbersome and tedious to draw in all the atoms of the esters, the abbreviation **Ac** is used for the acetyl group, **$CH_3C{=}O$.** The esterification of β-D-glucose can then be written as follows:

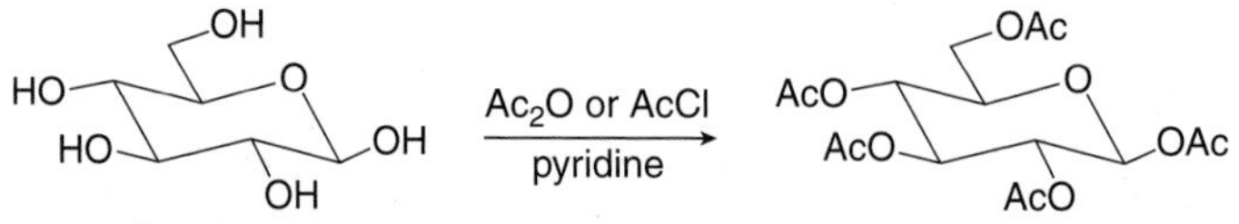

β-D-glucose

Monosaccharides are so polar that they are insoluble in common organic solvents, making them difficult to isolate and use in organic reactions. Monosaccharide derivatives that have five ether or ester groups in place of the OH groups, however, are readily soluble in organic solvents.

Problem 28.19 Draw the products formed when β-D-galactose is treated with each reagent.

a. $Ag_2O + CH_3I$
b. $NaH + C_6H_5CH_2Cl$
c. The product in (b), then H_3O^+
d. Ac_2O + pyridine
e. C_6H_5COCl + pyridine
f. The product in (c), then C_6H_5COCl + pyridine

28.9 Reactions at the Carbonyl Group—Oxidation and Reduction

Oxidation and reduction reactions occur at the carbonyl group of monosaccharides, so they all begin with the monosaccharide drawn in the acyclic form. We will confine our discussion to aldoses as starting materials.

28.9A Reduction of the Carbonyl Group

Glucitol occurs naturally in some fruits and berries. It is sometimes used as a substitute for sucrose (table sugar). With six polar OH groups capable of hydrogen bonding, glucitol is readily hydrated. It is used as an additive to prevent certain foods from drying out.

Like other aldehydes, the **carbonyl group of an aldose is reduced to a 1° alcohol using $NaBH_4$.** This alcohol is called an **alditol.** For example, reduction of D-glucose with $NaBH_4$ in CH_3OH yields glucitol (also called sorbitol).

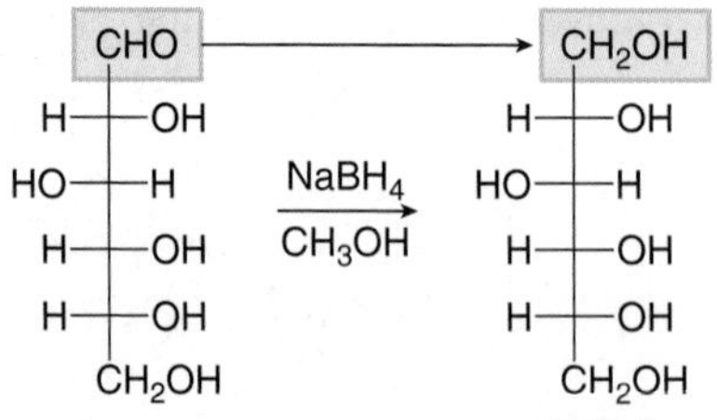

D-glucose glucitol (sorbitol)

Problem 28.20 A 2-ketohexose is reduced with $NaBH_4$ in CH_3OH to form a mixture of D-galactitol and D-talitol. What is the structure of the 2-ketohexose?

28.9B Oxidation of Aldoses

Aldoses contain 1° and 2° alcohols and an aldehyde, all of which are oxidizable functional groups. Two different types of oxidation reactions are particularly useful—oxidation of the aldehyde to a carboxylic acid (an **aldonic acid**) and oxidation of both the aldehyde and the 1° alcohol to a diacid (an **aldaric acid**).

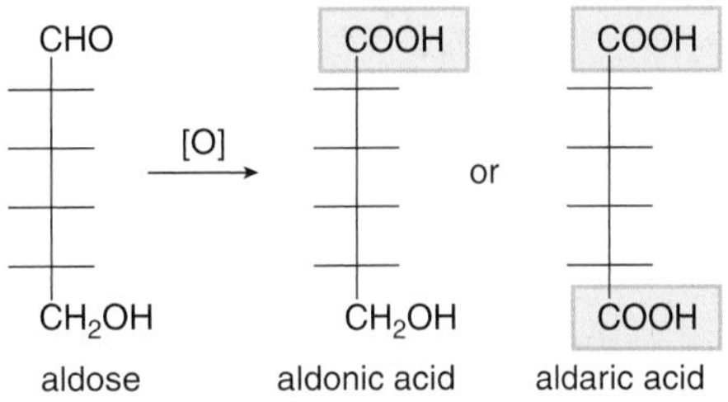

CHO
[O]
COOH
or
COOH
CH2OH
CH2OH
COOH
aldose
aldonic acid
aldaric acid

[1] Oxidation of the aldehyde to a carboxylic acid

The aldehyde carbonyl is the most easily oxidized functional group in an aldose, and so a variety of reagents oxidize it to a carboxy group, forming an **aldonic acid.**

Three reagents used for this process produce a characteristic color change because the oxidizing agent is reduced to a colored product that is easily visible. As described in Section 20.8, **Tollens reagent** oxidizes aldehydes to carboxylic acids using Ag_2O in NH_4OH, and forms a mirror of Ag as a by-product. **Benedict's** and **Fehling's reagents** use a blue Cu^{2+} salt as an oxidizing agent, which is reduced to Cu_2O, a brick-red solid. Unfortunately, none of these reagents gives a high yield of aldonic acid. When the aldonic acid is needed to carry on to other reactions, $\mathbf{Br_2 + H_2O}$ is used as the oxidizing agent.

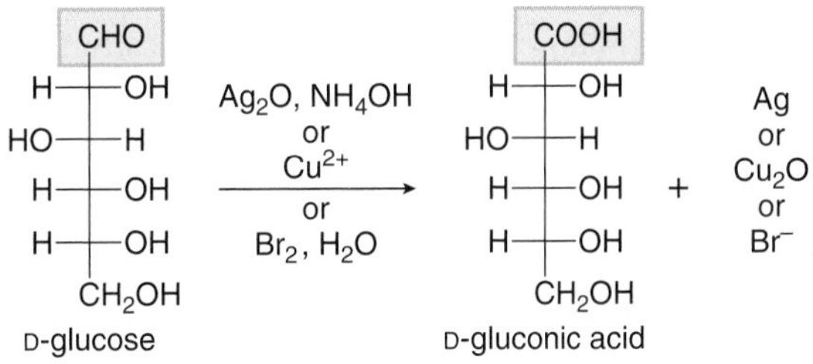

CHO
H—OH
HO—H
H—OH
H—OH
CH2OH
D-glucose
Ag2O, NH4OH
or
Cu2+
or
Br2, H2O
COOH
H—OH
HO—H
H—OH
H—OH
CH2OH
D-gluconic acid
+
Ag
or
Cu2O
or
Br−

- **Any carbohydrate that exists as a *hemiacetal* is in equilibrium with a small amount of acyclic aldehyde, so it is oxidized to an aldonic acid.**
- **Glycosides are acetals, not hemiacetals, so they are *not* oxidized to aldonic acids.**

Carbohydrates that can be oxidized with Tollens, Benedict's, or Fehling's reagent are called **reducing sugars.** Those that do not react with these reagents are called **nonreducing sugars.** Figure 28.8 shows examples of reducing and nonreducing sugars.

Figure 28.8 Examples of reducing and nonreducing sugars

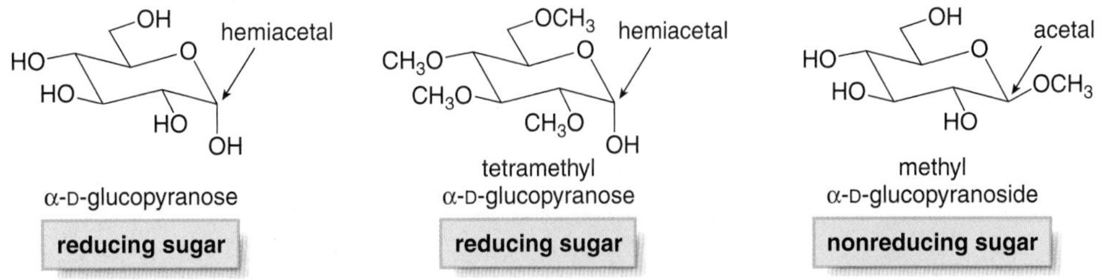

OH
hemiacetal
HO
HO
HO
OH
α-D-glucopyranose
reducing sugar
OCH3
hemiacetal
CH3O
CH3O
CH3O
OH
tetramethyl
α-D-glucopyranose
reducing sugar
OH
acetal
HO
HO
HO
OCH3
methyl
α-D-glucopyranoside
nonreducing sugar

- Carbohydrates containing a hemiacetal are in equilibrium with an acyclic aldehyde, making them reducing sugars.
- Glycosides are acetals, so they are *not* in equilibrium with any acyclic aldehyde, making them nonreducing sugars.

Problem 28.21 Classify each compound as a reducing or nonreducing sugar.

a. 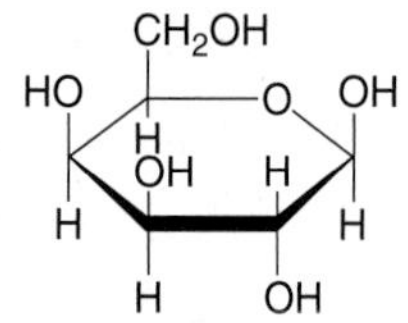

b. 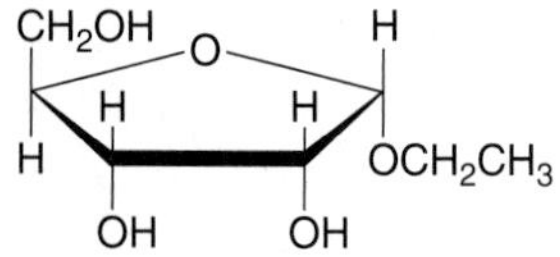

c. 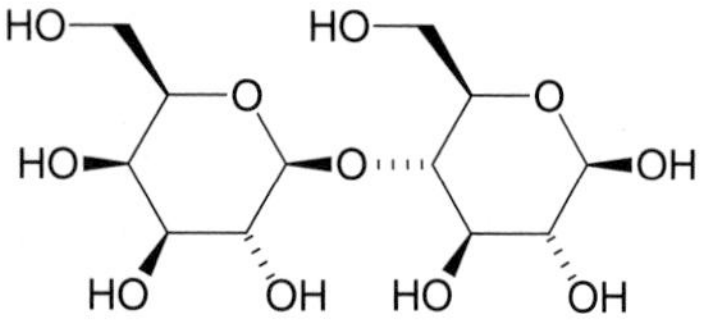

lactose

[2] Oxidation of both the aldehyde and 1° alcohol to a diacid

Both the aldehyde and 1° alcohol of an aldose are oxidized to carboxy groups by treatment with warm nitric acid, forming an **aldaric acid.** Under these conditions, D-glucose is converted to D-glucaric acid.

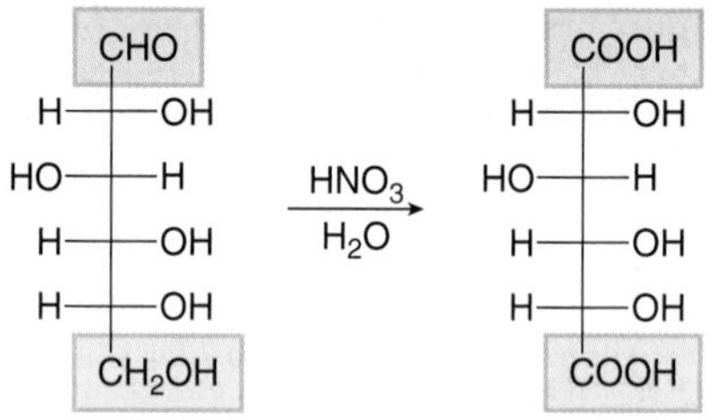

D-glucose

D-glucaric acid
an aldaric acid

Because aldaric acids have identical functional groups on both terminal carbons, some aldaric acids contain a plane of symmetry, making them achiral molecules. For example, oxidation of D-allose forms an achiral, optically inactive aldaric acid. This contrasts with D-glucaric acid formed from glucose, which has no plane of symmetry, and is thus still optically active.

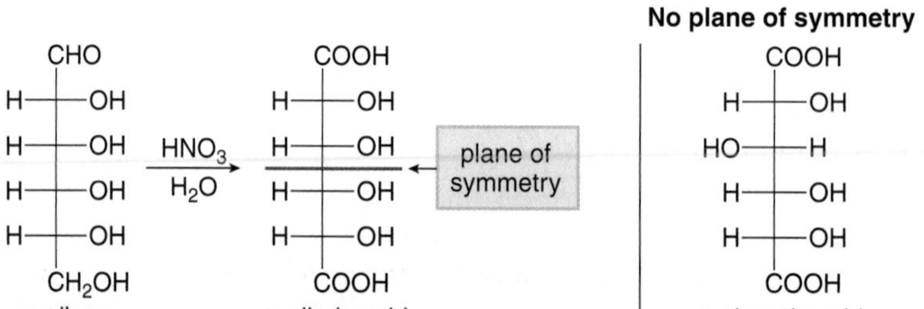

D-allose — D-allaric acid — D-glucaric acid

an achiral diacid **a chiral diacid**

Problem 28.22 Draw the products formed when D-arabinose is treated with each reagent: (a) Ag_2O, NH_4OH; (b) Br_2, H_2O; (c) HNO_3, H_2O.

Problem 28.23 Which aldoses are oxidized to optically inactive aldaric acids: (a) D-erythrose; (b) D-lyxose; (c) D-galactose?

28.10 Reactions at the Carbonyl Group—Adding or Removing One Carbon Atom

Two common procedures in carbohydrate chemistry result in adding or removing one carbon atom from the skeleton of an aldose. The **Wohl degradation** shortens an aldose chain by one carbon, whereas the **Kiliani–Fischer synthesis** lengthens it by one. Both reactions involve cyanohydrins as intermediates. Recall from Section 21.9 that cyanohydrins are formed from aldehydes by addition of the elements of HCN. Cyanohydrins can also be re-converted to carbonyl compounds by treatment with base.

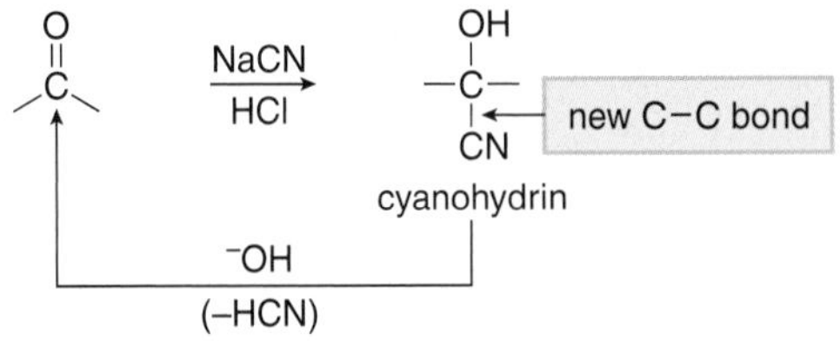

- **Forming a cyanohydrin adds one carbon to a carbonyl group.**
- **Re-converting a cyanohydrin to a carbonyl compound removes one carbon.**

28.10A The Wohl Degradation

The Wohl degradation is a stepwise procedure that shortens the length of an aldose chain by cleavage of the C1 – C2 bond. As a result, an aldohexose is converted to an aldopentose having the same configuration at its bottom three stereogenic centers (C3 – C5). For example, the Wohl degradation converts D-glucose into D-arabinose.

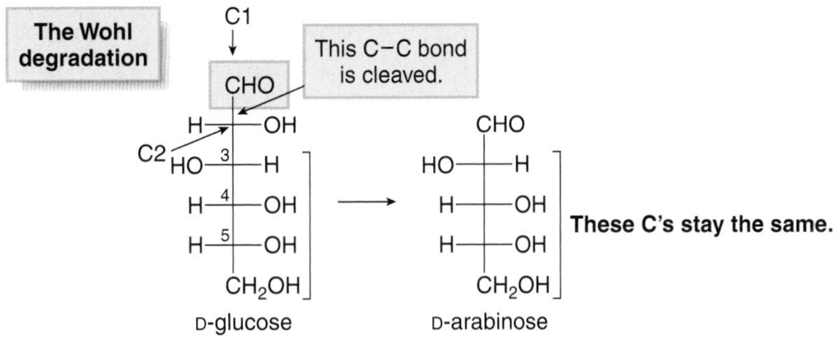

The Wohl degradation consists of three steps, illustrated here beginning with D-glucose.

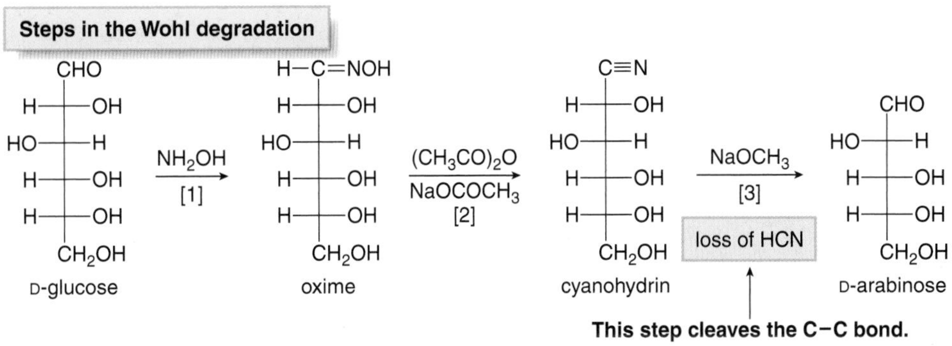

[1] Treatment of D-glucose with hydroxylamine (NH_2OH) forms an **oxime** by nucleophilic addition. This reaction is analogous to the formation of imines discussed in Section 21.11.

[2] Dehydration of the oxime to a nitrile occurs with acetic anhydride and sodium acetate. The nitrile product is a cyanohydrin.

[3] **Treatment of the cyanohydrin with base results in loss of the elements of HCN to form an aldehyde having one fewer carbon.**

The Wohl degradation converts a stereogenic center at C2 in the original aldose to an sp^2 hybridized C=O. As a result, a pair of aldoses that are epimeric at C2, such as D-galactose and D-talose, yield the same aldose (D-lyxose, in this case) upon Wohl degradation.

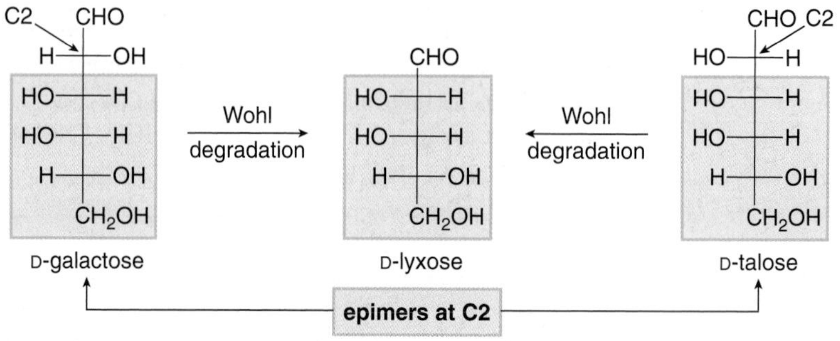

Problem 28.24 What two aldoses yield D-xylose on Wohl degradation?

28.10B The Kiliani–Fischer Synthesis

The Kiliani–Fischer synthesis lengthens a carbohydrate chain by adding one carbon to the aldehyde end of an aldose, thus forming a new stereogenic center at C2 of the product. The product consists of epimers that differ only in their configuration about the one new stereogenic center. For example, the Kiliani–Fischer synthesis converts D-arabinose into a mixture of D-glucose and D-mannose.

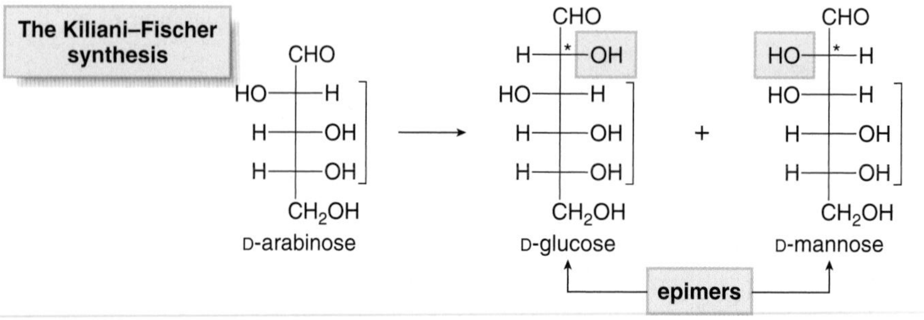

[* denotes the new stereogenic center.]

The Kiliani–Fischer synthesis, shown here beginning with D-arabinose, consists of three steps. "Squiggly" lines are meant to indicate that two different stereoisomers are formed at the new stereogenic center. As with the Wohl degradation, the key intermediate is a cyanohydrin.

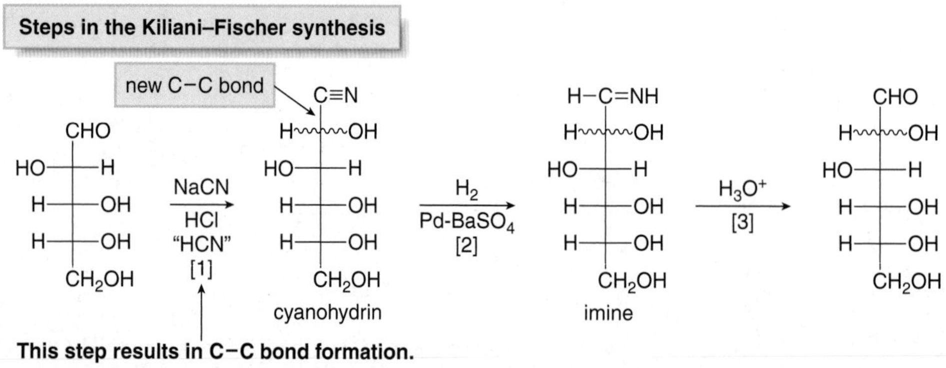

[1] Treating an aldose with NaCN and HCl adds the elements of HCN to the carbonyl group, forming a **cyanohydrin** and a new carbon–carbon bond. Because the sp^2 hybridized carbonyl carbon is converted to an sp^3 hybridized carbon with four different groups, a new stereogenic center is formed in this step.

[2] Reduction of the nitrile with H_2 and Pd-$BaSO_4$, a poisoned Pd catalyst, forms an **imine.**

[3] Hydrolysis of the imine with aqueous acid forms an aldehyde that has one more carbon than the aldose that began the sequence.

Note that the **Wohl degradation and the Kiliani–Fischer synthesis are conceptually opposite transformations.**

- **The Wohl degradation *removes* a carbon atom from the aldehyde end of an aldose. Two aldoses that are epimers at C2 form the same product.**
- **The Kiliani–Fischer synthesis *adds* a carbon to the aldehyde end of an aldose, forming two epimers at C2.**

Problem 28.25 What aldoses are formed when the following aldoses are subjected to the Kiliani–Fischer synthesis: (a) D-threose; (b) D-ribose; (c) D-galactose?

28.10C Determining the Structure of an Unknown Monosaccharide

The reactions in Sections 28.9–28.10 can be used to determine the structure of an unknown monosaccharide, as shown in Sample Problem 28.5.

Sample Problem 28.5 A D-aldopentose **A** is oxidized to an optically inactive aldaric acid with HNO_3. **A** is formed by the Kiliani–Fischer synthesis of a D-aldotetrose **B,** which is also oxidized to an optically inactive aldaric acid with HNO_3. What are the structures of **A** and **B?**

Solution

Use each fact to determine the relative orientation of the OH groups in the D-aldopentose.

Fact [1] **A D-aldopentose A is oxidized to an optically *inactive* aldaric acid with HNO_3.**

An optically inactive aldaric acid must contain a **plane of symmetry.** There are only two ways to arrange the OH groups in a five-carbon D-aldaric acid, for this to be the case. Thus, only two structures are possible for **A,** labeled **A'** and **A''.**

Possible optically inactive D-aldaric acids:

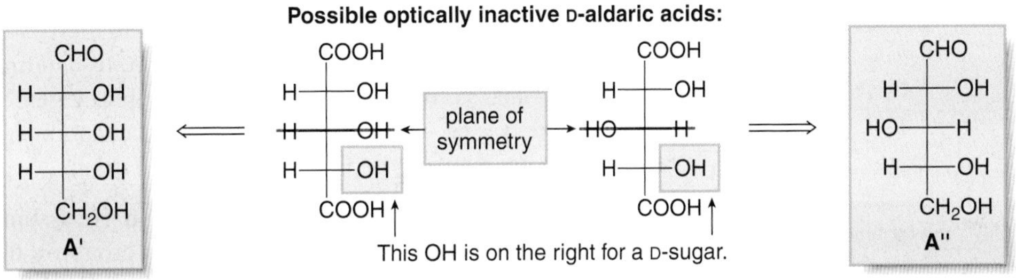

Fact [2] **A is formed by the Kiliani–Fischer synthesis from a D-aldotetrose B.**

A' and **A''** are each prepared from a D-aldotetrose (**B'** and **B''**) that has the same configuration at the bottom two stereogenic centers.

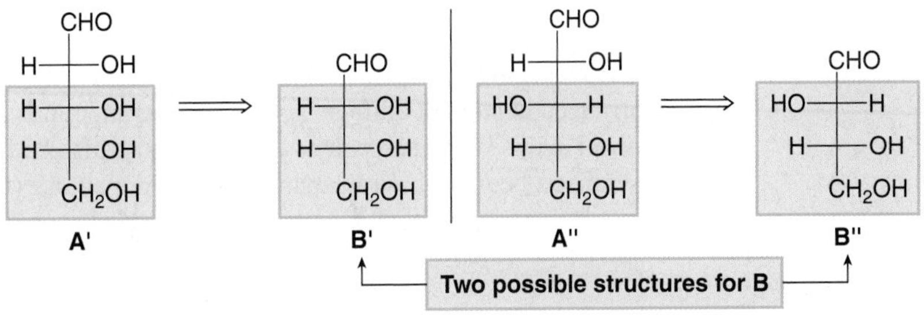

Fact [3] **The D-aldotetrose is oxidized to an optically *inactive* aldaric acid upon treatment with HNO_3.**

Only the aldaric acid from **B'** has a plane of symmetry, making it optically inactive. Thus, **B'** is the correct structure for the D-aldotetrose **B,** and therefore **A'** is the structure of the D-aldopentose **A.**

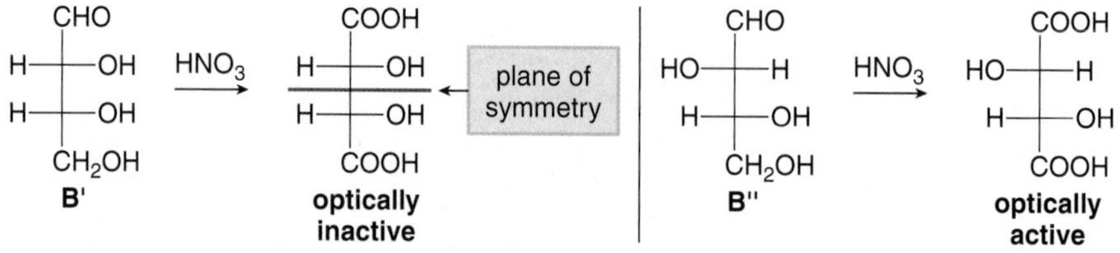
CHO
H OH
H OH
CH2OH
B'
HNO3
COOH
H OH
H OH
COOH
optically inactive
plane of symmetry
CHO
HO H
H OH
CH2OH
B''
HNO3
COOH
HO H
H OH
COOH
optically active

Answer:

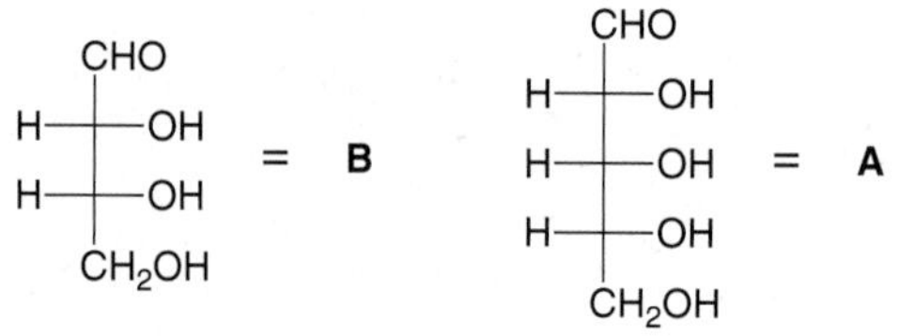
CHO
H OH
H OH
CH2OH
= B
CHO
H OH
H OH
H OH
CH2OH
= A

Problem 28.26 D-Aldopentose **A** is oxidized to an optically inactive aldaric acid. On Wohl degradation, **A** forms an aldotetrose **B** that is oxidized to an optically active aldaric acid. What are the structures of **A** and **B?**

28.11 The Fischer Proof of the Structure of Glucose

The Fischer proof is remarkable because it was done at a time when determining melting points and optical rotations were the most sophisticated techniques available to the chemist.

Both Fischer projections and the Kiliani–Fischer synthesis are named after **Emil Fischer,** a noted chemist of the late nineteenth and early twentieth centuries, who received the Nobel Prize in Chemistry in 1902 for his work in carbohydrate chemistry. Fischer's most elegant work is the subject of Section 28.11.

In 1891, only 10 years after the tetrahedral structure of carbon was proposed, Fischer determined the *relative* configuration of the four stereogenic centers in naturally occurring (+)-glucose. This body of work is called the **Fischer proof** of the structure of glucose.

Because glucose has four stereogenic centers, there are $2^4 = 16$ possible stereoisomers, or eight pairs of enantiomers. In 1891, there was no way to determine the ***absolute* configuration** of (+)-glucose—that is, the *exact* three-dimensional arrangement of the four stereogenic centers. Because there was no way to distinguish between enantiomers, Fischer could only determine the ***relative* arrangement of the OH groups *to each other.***

In 1951, the technique of X-ray crystallography confirmed that (+)-glucose had the D configuration, as assumed by Fischer more than 50 years earlier.

Because of this, Fischer began with an assumption. He assumed that naturally occurring glucose had the **D configuration**—namely, that the OH group on the stereogenic center farthest from the aldehyde was oriented on the *right* in a Fischer projection. He then set out to determine the orientation of all other OH groups relative to it. Thus, the Fischer proof determined which of the eight D-aldohexoses was (+)-glucose.

The strategy used by Fischer is similar to that used in Sample Problem 28.5, in which the structure of an aldopentose is determined by piecing together different facts. The Fischer proof is much more complicated, though, because the relative orientation of more stereogenic centers had to be determined.

The reasoning behind the Fischer proof is easier to follow if the eight possible D-aldohexoses are arranged in pairs of epimers at C2. These compounds are labeled **1–8** in Figure 28.9. When organized in this way, each pair of epimers would also be formed as the products of a Kiliani–Fischer synthesis beginning with a particular D-aldopentose (lettered **A–D** in Figure 28.9).

Figure 28.9 The D-aldopentoses and D-aldohexoses needed to illustrate the Fischer proof

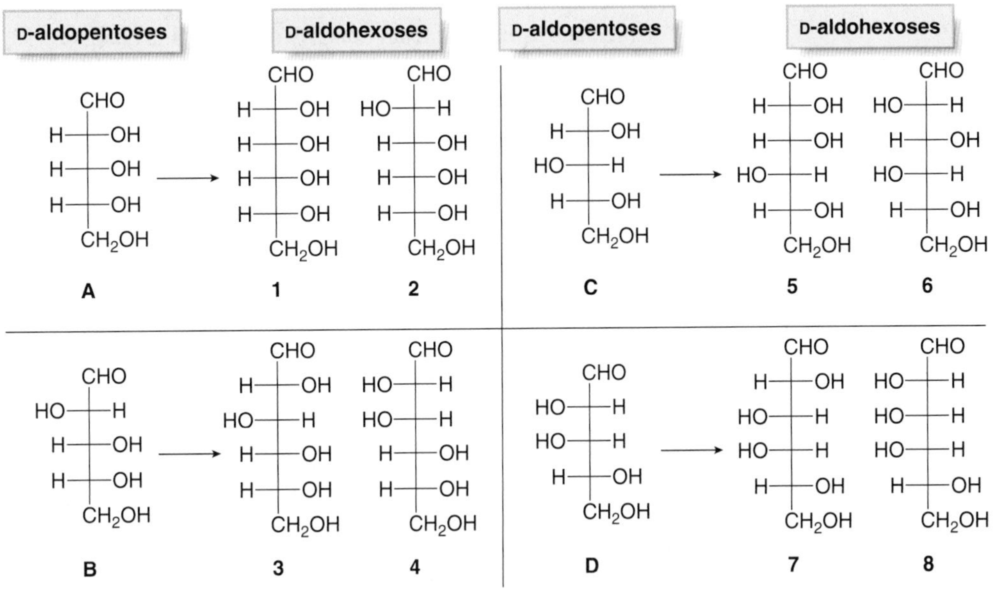

- The aldohexoses (**1–8**) are arranged in pairs of epimers at C2.
- Kiliani–Fischer synthesis using aldopentoses **A–D** forms each pair of epimers.

To follow the steps in the Fischer proof, we must determine what information can be obtained from each experimental result.

Fact [1] **Kiliani–Fischer synthesis of arabinose, an aldopentose, forms glucose and mannose.**

Because the Kiliani–Fischer synthesis forms two epimers at C2, glucose and mannose have the same configurations at three stereogenic centers (C3–C5), but opposite configurations at C2. Thus, glucose and mannose are either **1** and **2, 3** and **4, 5** and **6,** or **7** and **8.**

Glucose and mannose are epimers at C2.

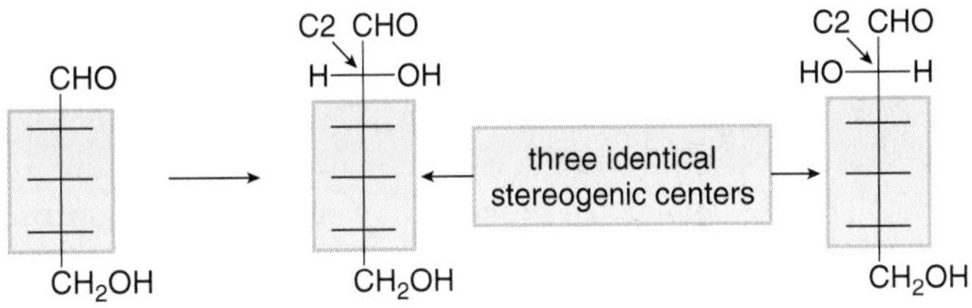

Fact [2] **Glucose and mannose are both oxidized to optically active aldaric acids.**

Because an optically active aldaric acid does not have a plane of symmetry, any aldohexose that forms an aldaric acid with a plane of symmetry can be eliminated.

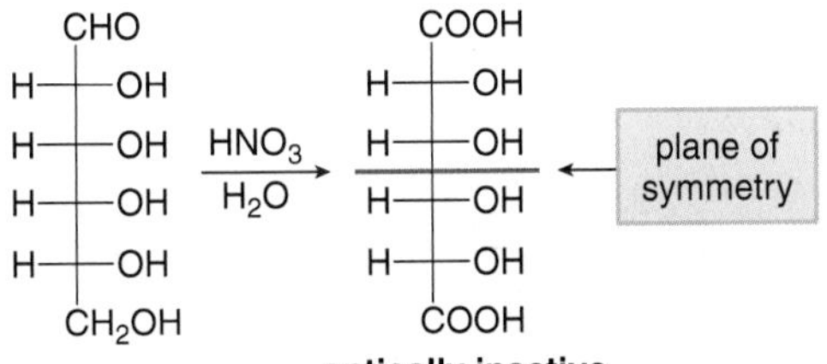

1

optically inactive aldaric acid

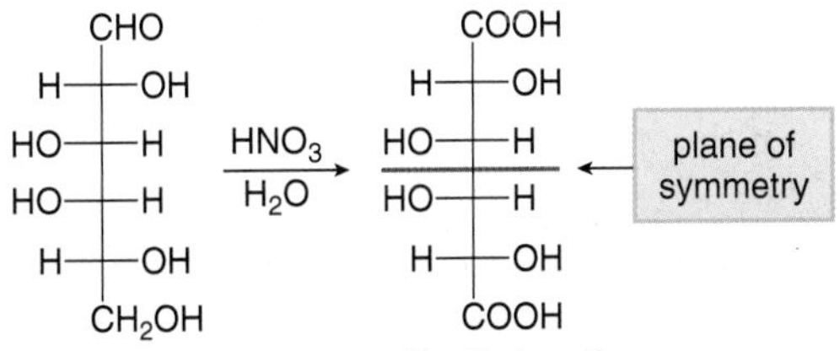

7

optically inactive aldaric acid

- Thus, aldohexoses **1** (and therefore its epimer **2**) and **7** (and its epimer **8**) can be eliminated, so that glucose and mannose are one of two pairs of epimers: either **3** and **4,** or **5** and **6.**

Fact [3] Arabinose is oxidized to an optically active aldaric acid.

We can now narrow down the possible structures for arabinose, the aldopentose that forms glucose and mannose from the Kiliani–Fischer synthesis (Fact [1]).

- Because glucose and mannose are epimers **3** and **4** or **5** and **6** (Fact [2]), arabinose must be either **B** or **C.**
- Because oxidation of **C** forms an optically *inactive* aldaric acid, arabinose must have structure **B,** an aldopentose that gives an optically active aldaric acid.

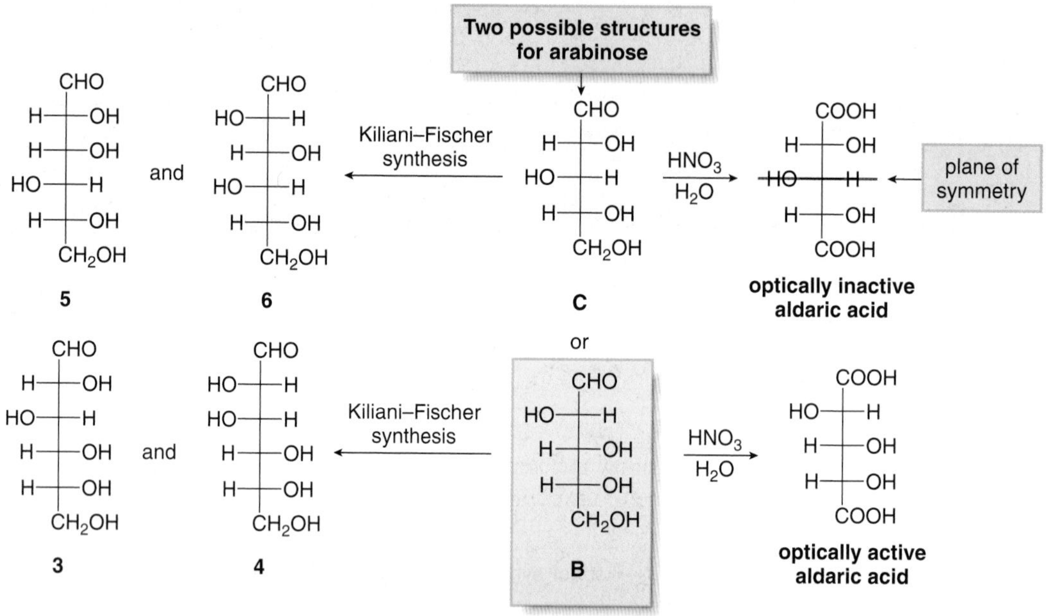

This must be arabinose.

- Thus, glucose and mannose are structures **3** and **4,** but, with the given information, it is not possible to decide which is glucose and which is mannose.

Fact [4] When the functional groups on the two end carbons of glucose are interchanged, glucose is converted to a different aldohexose.

To determine whether glucose had structure **3** or **4,** a method was devised to interchange the two functional groups at the ends of an aldohexose. The CHO at C1 was converted to CH_2OH, and the CH_2OH at C6 was converted to CHO.

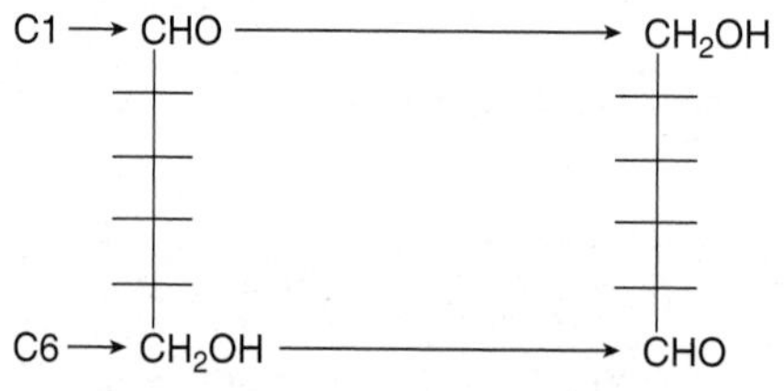

The results of this process are different for compounds **3** and **4.** Compound **4** gives a compound that is identical to itself, whereas compound **3** gives a compound that is different from itself.

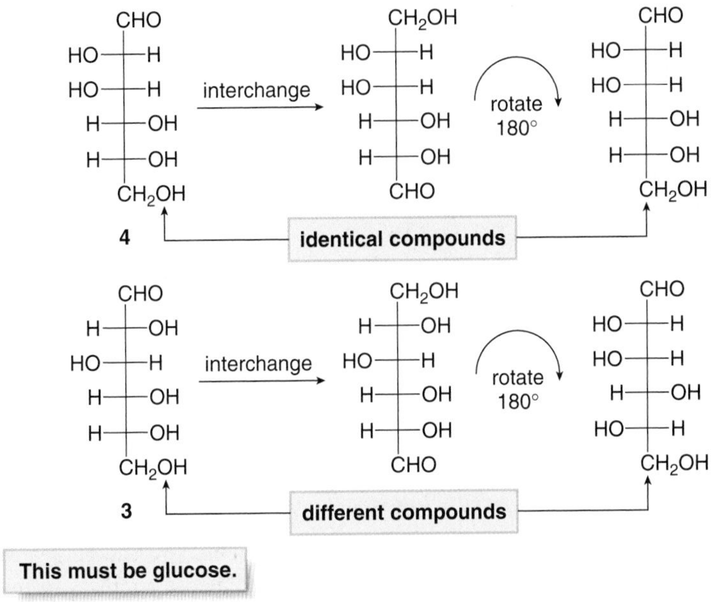
CHO
HO–H
HO–H
H–OH
H–OH
CH₂OH
4
interchange
CH₂OH
HO–H
HO–H
H–OH
H–OH
CHO
rotate 180°
CHO
HO–H
HO–H
H–OH
H–OH
CH₂OH
identical compounds
CHO
H–OH
HO–H
H–OH
H–OH
CH₂OH
3
interchange
CH₂OH
H–OH
HO–H
H–OH
H–OH
CHO
rotate 180°
CHO
HO–H
HO–H
H–OH
HO–H
CH₂OH
different compounds
This must be glucose.

- Because glucose gives a different aldohexose after the two end groups are interchanged, it must have structure **3,** and mannose must have structure **4. The proof is complete.**

Problem 28.27 Besides D-mannose, only one other D-aldohexose yields itself when the CHO and CH_2OH groups on the end carbon atoms are interchanged. What is the name and structure of this D-aldohexose?

Problem 28.28 A D-aldohexose **A** is formed from an aldopentose **B** by the Kiliani–Fischer synthesis. Reduction of **A** with $NaBH_4$ forms an optically inactive alditol. Oxidation of **B** forms an optically active aldaric acid. What are the structures of **A** and **B?**

28.12 Disaccharides

Disaccharides contain two monosaccharides joined together by a glycosidic linkage. The **general features of a disaccharide** include the following:

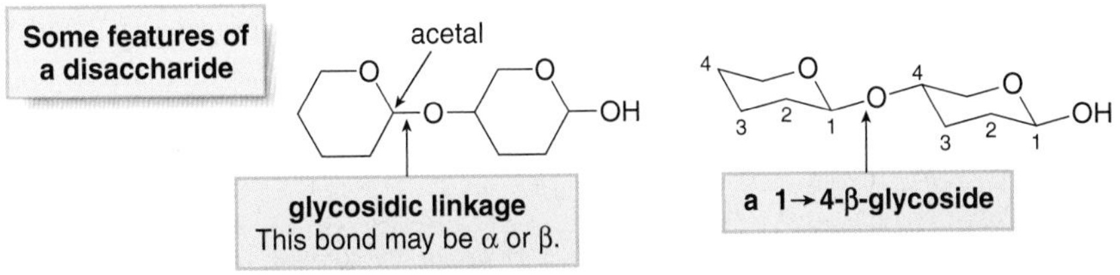
Some features of a disaccharide
acetal
O
O
O
OH
glycosidic linkage
This bond may be α or β.
4
O
3
2
1
O
4
O
OH
3
2
1
a 1→4-β-glycoside

[1] Two monosaccharide rings may be five- or six-membered, but six-membered rings are much more common. The two rings are connected by an O atom that is part of an acetal, called a **glycosidic linkage,** which may be oriented α or β.

[2] The **glycoside is formed from the anomeric carbon of one monosaccharide and any OH group on the other monosaccharide.** All disaccharides have **one acetal,** together with either a hemiacetal or another acetal.

[3] With pyranose rings, the carbon atoms in each ring are numbered beginning with the anomeric carbon. The most common disaccharides contain two monosaccharides in which the hemiacetal carbon of one ring (Cl) is joined to C4 of the other ring.

The three most abundant disaccharides are **maltose, lactose,** and **sucrose.**

28.12A Maltose

Maltose gets its name from malt, the liquid obtained from barley and other cereal grains.

Maltose, a disaccharide formed by the hydrolysis of starch, is found in germinated grains such as barley. Maltose contains two glucose units joined together by a 1→4-α-glycoside bond.

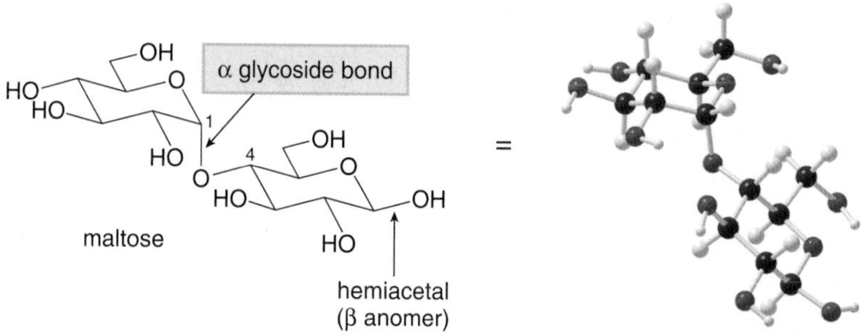

α glycoside bond
maltose
hemiacetal
(β anomer)

Because one glucose ring of maltose still contains a hemiacetal, it exists as a mixture of α and β anomers. Only the β anomer is shown. Maltose exhibits two properties of all carbohydrates that contain a hemiacetal: it undergoes **mutarotation,** and it reacts with oxidizing agents, making it a **reducing sugar.**

Hydrolysis of maltose forms two molecules of glucose. The **C1 – O** bond is cleaved in this process, and a mixture of glucose anomers forms. The mechanism for this hydrolysis is exactly the same as the mechanism for glycoside hydrolysis in Section 28.7B.

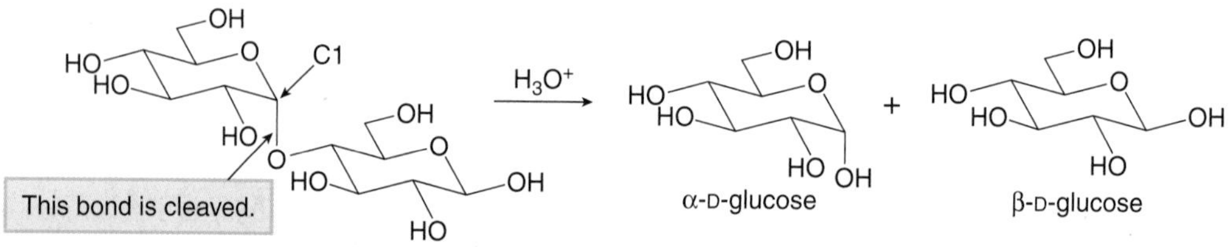

C1
This bond is cleaved.
H_3O^+
α-D-glucose
β-D-glucose

Problem 28.29 Draw the α anomer of maltose. What products are formed on hydrolysis of this form of maltose?

28.12B Lactose

Milk contains the disaccharide lactose.

As noted in the chapter opener, **lactose** is the principal disaccharide found in milk from both humans and cows. Unlike many mono- and disaccharides, lactose is not appreciably sweet. Lactose consists of **one galactose** and **one glucose unit,** joined by a **1→4-β-glycoside bond** from the anomeric carbon of galactose to C4 of glucose.

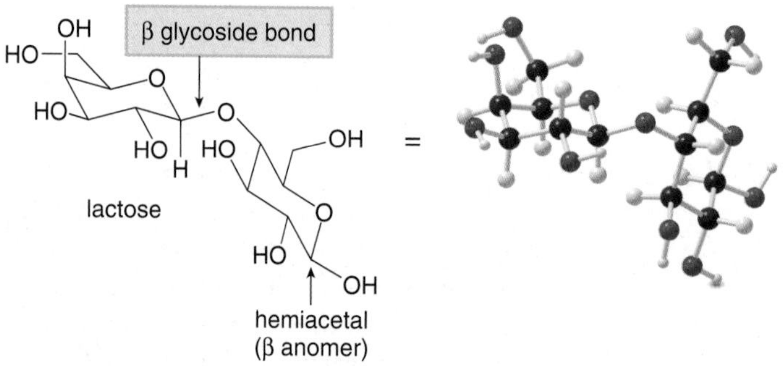

β glycoside bond
lactose
hemiacetal
(β anomer)

Like maltose, lactose also contains a hemiacetal, so it exists as a mixture of α and β anomers. The β anomer is drawn. Lactose undergoes **mutarotation,** and it reacts with oxidizing agents, making it a **reducing sugar.**

Lactose is digested in the body by first cleaving the 1→4-β-glycoside bond using the enzyme *lactase.* Individuals who are lactose intolerant no longer produce lactase, and so they are unable to digest and absorb lactose.

Problem 28.30 Cellobiose, a disaccharide obtained by the hydrolysis of cellulose, is composed of two glucose units joined together in a 1→4-β-glycoside bond. What is the structure of cellobiose?

28.12C Sucrose

Sucrose, the disaccharide found in sugarcane and used as table sugar (Figure 28.10), is the most common disaccharide in nature. It contains **one glucose unit** and **one fructose unit.**

The structure of sucrose has several features that make it different from maltose and lactose. First of all, sucrose contains one six-membered ring (glucose) and one five-membered ring (fructose), whereas both maltose and lactose contain two six-membered rings. In sucrose the six-membered glucose ring is joined by an α-glycosidic bond to C2 of a fructofuranose ring. The numbering in a fructofuranose is different from the numbering in a pyranose ring. The anomeric carbon is now designated as C2, so the anomeric carbons of the glucose and fructose rings are both used to form the glycosidic linkage.

Figure 28.10 Sucrose

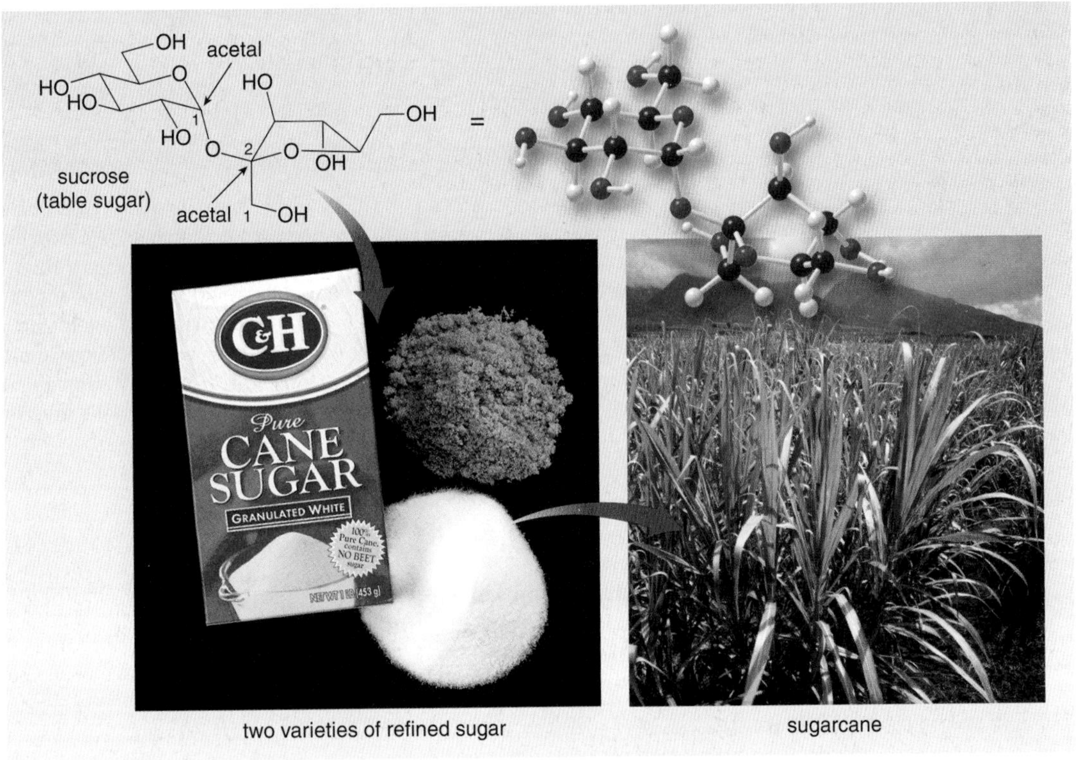

As a result, **sucrose contains two acetals but no hemiacetal.** Sucrose, therefore, is a **nonreducing sugar** and **it does not undergo mutarotation.**

Sucrose's pleasant sweetness has made it a widely used ingredient in baked goods, cereals, bread, and many other products. It is estimated that the average American ingests 100 lb of sucrose annually. Like other carbohydrates, however, sucrose contains many calories. To reduce caloric intake while maintaining sweetness, a variety of artificial sweeteners have been developed. These include sucralose, aspartame, and saccharin (Figure 28.11). These compounds are much sweeter than sucrose so only a small amount of each compound is needed to achieve the same level of perceived sweetness.

Figure 28.11
Artificial sweeteners

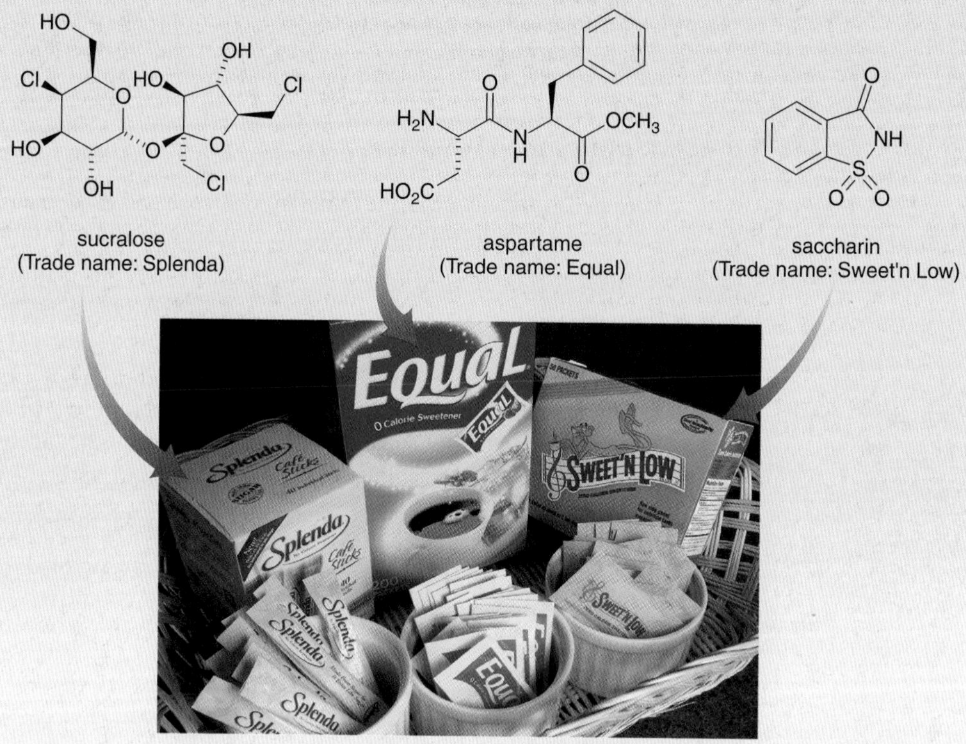
sucralose
(Trade name: Splenda)
aspartame
(Trade name: Equal)
saccharin
(Trade name: Sweet'n Low)
Equal
Splenda
Sweet'N Low

The sweetness of these three artificial sweeteners was discovered accidentally. The sweetness of sucralose was discovered in 1976 when a chemist misunderstood his superior, and so he *tasted* rather than *tested* his compound. Aspartame was discovered in 1965 when a chemist licked his dirty fingers in the lab and tasted its sweetness. Saccharin, the oldest known artificial sweetener, was discovered in 1879 by a chemist who failed to wash his hands after working in the lab. Saccharin was not used extensively until sugar shortages occurred during World War I. Although there were concerns in the 1970s that saccharin causes cancer, there is no proven link between cancer occurrence and saccharin intake at normal levels.

28.13 Polysaccharides

Polysaccharides contain three or more monosaccharides joined together. Three prevalent polysaccharides in nature are **cellulose, starch,** and **glycogen,** each of which consists of repeating glucose units joined by different glycosidic bonds.

28.13A Cellulose

The structure of cellulose was discussed previously in Section 5.1.

Cellulose is found in the cell walls of nearly all plants, where it gives support and rigidity to wood and plant stems. Cotton is essentially pure cellulose.

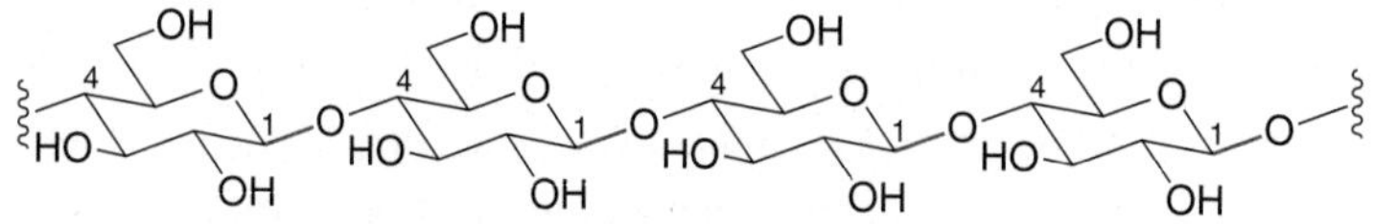

cellulose

The 1→4-β-glycosidic bonds are shown in red.

Ball-and-stick models showing the three-dimensional structures of cellulose and starch were given in Figure 5.2.

Cellulose is an unbranched polymer composed of repeating glucose units joined in a 1→4-β-glycosidic linkage. The β-glycosidic linkage creates long linear chains of cellulose molecules that stack in sheets, creating an extensive three-dimensional array. A network of intermolecular hydrogen bonds between the chains and sheets means that only the few OH groups on the surface are available to hydrogen bond to water, making this very polar compound water insoluble.

Cellulose acetate, a cellulose derivative, is made by treating cellulose with acetic anhydride and sulfuric acid. The resulting product has acetate esters in place of every OH group. Cellulose acetate is spun into fibers that are used for fabrics called *acetates,* which have a deep luster and satin appearance.

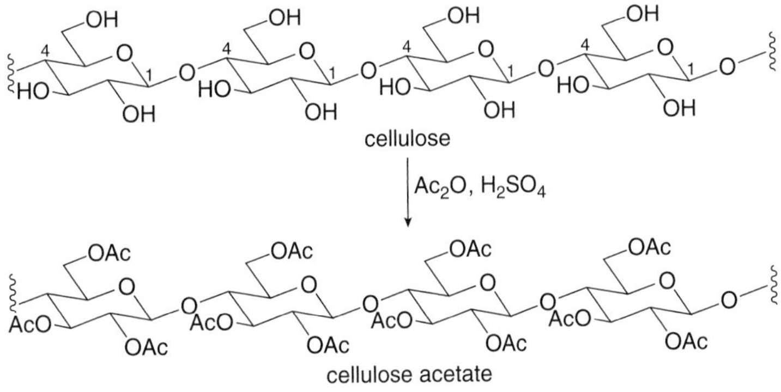
cellulose
Ac_2O, H_2SO_4
cellulose acetate

Cellulose can be hydrolyzed to glucose by cleaving all of the β-glycosidic bonds, yielding both anomers of glucose.

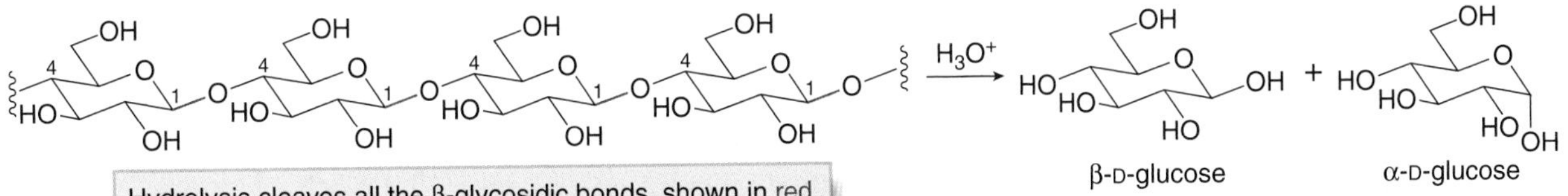
H_3O^+
β-D-glucose
α-D-glucose

Hydrolysis cleaves all the β-glycosidic bonds, shown in red.

A **β-glycosidase** is the general name of an enzyme that hydrolyzes a β-glycoside linkage.

In cells, the hydrolysis of cellulose is accomplished by an enzyme called a **β-glucosidase,** which cleaves all the β-glycoside bonds formed from glucose. Humans do not possess this enzyme, and therefore cannot digest cellulose. Ruminant animals, on the other hand, such as cattle, deer, and camels, have bacteria containing a β-glucosidase in their digestive systems, so they can derive nutritional benefit from eating grass and leaves.

28.13B Starch

Starch is the main carbohydrate found in the seeds and roots of plants. Corn, rice, wheat, and potatoes are common foods that contain a great deal of starch.

Starch is a polymer composed of repeating glucose units joined in α-glycosidic linkages. Both starch and cellulose are polymers of glucose, but starch contains α glycoside bonds, whereas cellulose contains β glycoside bonds. The two common forms of starch are **amylose** and **amylopectin.**

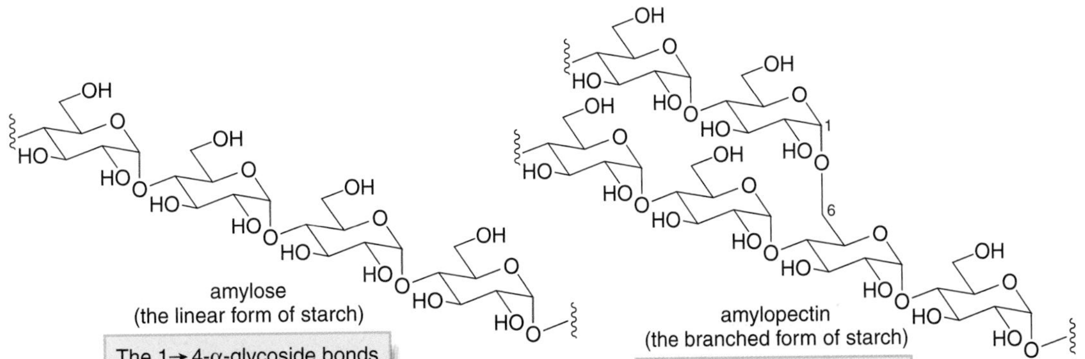
amylose
(the linear form of starch)
amylopectin
(the branched form of starch)

The 1→4-α-glycoside bonds are shown in red.

The 1→6-α-glycoside bond is shown in red.

Amylose, which comprises about 20% of starch molecules, has an unbranched skeleton of glucose molecules with **1→4-α-glycoside bonds.** Because of this linkage, an amylose chain adopts a helical arrangement, giving it a very different three-dimensional shape from the linear chains of cellulose. Amylose was first described in Section 5.1.

Amylopectin, which comprises about 80% of starch molecules, likewise consists of a backbone of glucose units joined in **α-glycosidic bonds,** but it also contains considerable branching along the chain. The linear linkages of amylopectin are formed by **1→4-α-glycoside bonds,** similar to amylose. The branches are linked to the chain with **1→6-α-glycosidic linkages.**

Both forms of starch are water soluble. Because the OH groups in these starch molecules are not buried in a three-dimensional network, they are more available for hydrogen bonding with water molecules, leading to greater water solubility than cellulose has.

The ability of amylopectin to form branched polymers is a unique feature of carbohydrates. Other types of polymers in the cell, such as the proteins discussed in Chapter 29, occur in nature only as linear molecules.

α-Glycosidase is the general name of an enzyme that hydrolyzes an α-glycoside linkage.

Both amylose and amylopectin are hydrolyzed to glucose with cleavage of the glycosidic bonds. The human digestive system has the necessary **α-glucosidase** enzymes needed to catalyze this process. Bread and pasta made from wheat flour, rice, and corn tortillas are all sources of starch that are readily digested.

28.13C Glycogen

Glycogen is the major form in which polysaccharides are stored in animals. Glycogen, a polymer of glucose containing **α-glycosidic bonds,** has a branched structure similar to amylopectin, but the branching is much more extensive.

Glycogen is stored principally in the liver and muscle. When glucose is needed for energy in the cell, glucose units are hydrolyzed from the ends of the glycogen polymer, and then further metabolized with the release of energy. Because glycogen has a highly branched structure, there are many glucose units at the ends of the branches that can be cleaved whenever the body needs them.

Problem 28.31 Draw the structure of: (a) a polysaccharide formed by joining D-mannose units in 1→4-β-glycosidic linkages; (b) a polysaccharide formed by joining D-glucose units in 1→6-α-glycosidic linkages. The polysaccharide in (b) is dextran, a component of dental plaque.

28.14 Other Important Sugars and Their Derivatives

Many other examples of simple and complex carbohydrates with useful properties exist in the biological world. In Section 28.14, we examine some carbohydrates that contain nitrogen atoms.

28.14A Amino Sugars and Related Compounds

Amino sugars contain an NH_2 group instead of an OH group at a non-anomeric carbon. The most common amino sugar in nature, **D-glucosamine,** is formally derived from D-glucose by replacing the OH at C2 with NH_2. Although it is not classified as a drug, and therefore not regulated by the Food and Drug Administration, glucosamine is available in many over-the-counter treatments for osteoarthritis. Glucosamine is thought to promote the repair of deteriorating cartilage in joints.

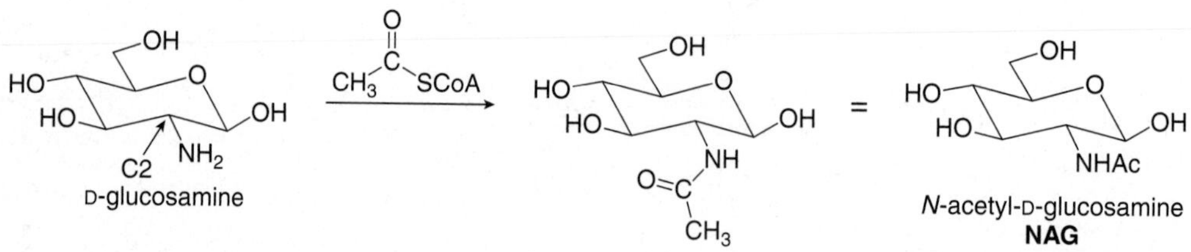

The rigidity of a crab shell is due to chitin, a high molecular weight carbohydrate molecule. Chitin-based coatings have found several commercial applications, such as extending the shelf life of fruits. Processing plants now convert the shells of crabs, lobsters, and shrimp to chitin and various derivatives for use in many consumer products.

Acetylation of glucosamine with acetyl CoA (Section 22.17) forms ***N*-acetyl-D-glucosamine,** abbreviated as **NAG. Chitin,** the second most abundant carbohydrate polymer, is a polysaccharide formed from NAG units joined together in **1→4-β-glycosidic linkages.** Chitin is identical in structure to cellulose, except that each OH group at C2 is now replaced by $NHCOCH_3$. The exoskeletons of lobsters, crabs, and shrimp are composed of chitin. Like those of cellulose, chitin chains are held together by an extensive network of hydrogen bonds, forming water-insoluble sheets.

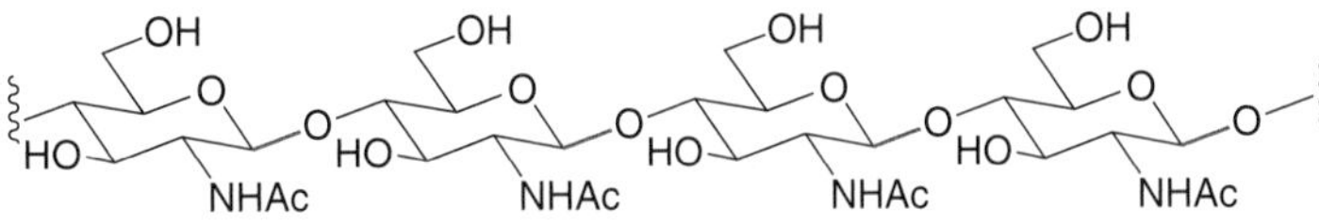

chitin
a polysaccharide composed of NAG units

The 1→4-β-glycosidic bonds are shown in red.

Several trisaccharides containing amino sugars are potent antibiotics used in the treatment of certain severe and recurrent bacterial infections. These compounds, such as tobramycin and amikacin, are called **aminoglycoside antibiotics.**

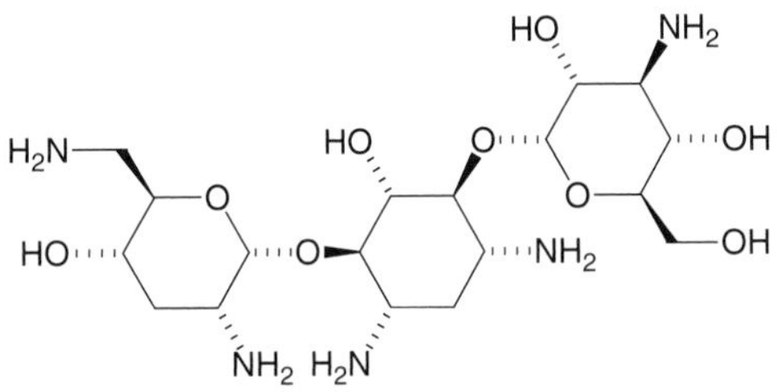

tobramycin

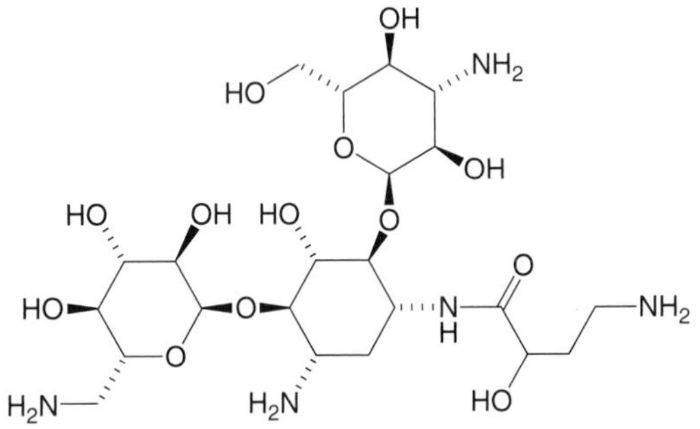

amikacin

Problem 28.32 Treating chitin with H_2O, ^-OH hydrolyzes its amide linkages, forming a compound called chitosan. What is the structure of chitosan? Chitosan has been used in shampoos, fibers for sutures, and wound dressings.

28.14B *N*-Glycosides

***N*-Glycosides** are formed when a monosaccharide is reacted with an amine in the presence of mild acid (Reactions [1] and [2]).

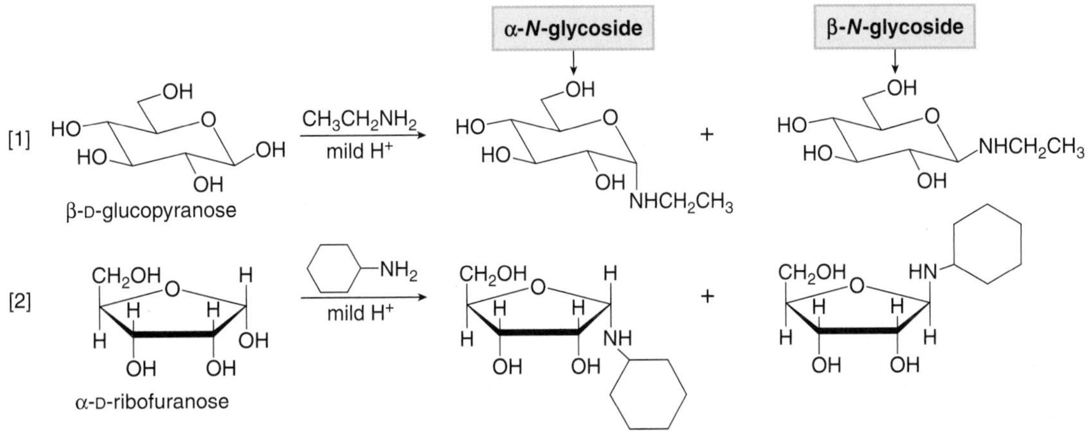

The mechanism of *N*-glycoside formation is analogous to the mechanism for glycoside formation, and both anomers of the *N*-glycoside are formed as products.

Problem 28.33 Draw the products of each reaction.

a. 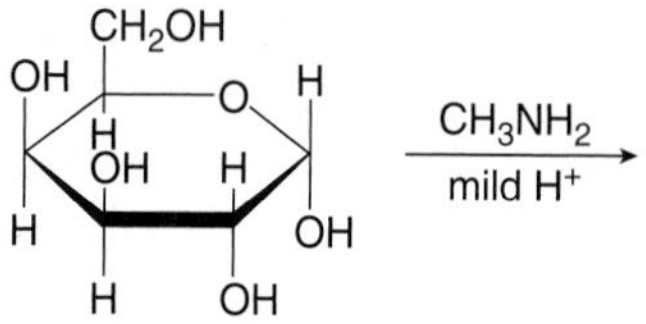

b. 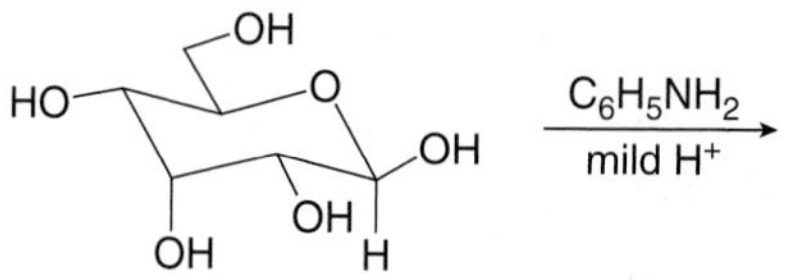

Problem 28.34 Draw a stepwise mechanism for the conversion of β-D-glucose to both anomers of *N*-ethyl glucopyranoside, the equation written in Reaction [1].

The prefix ***deoxy*** means "without oxygen."

The *N*-glycosides of two sugars, **D-ribose** and **2-deoxy-D-ribose,** are especially noteworthy, because they form the building blocks of RNA and DNA, respectively. 2-Deoxyribose is so named because it lacks an OH group at C2 of ribose.

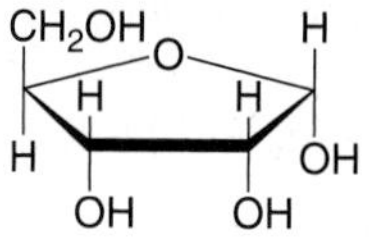

D-ribose

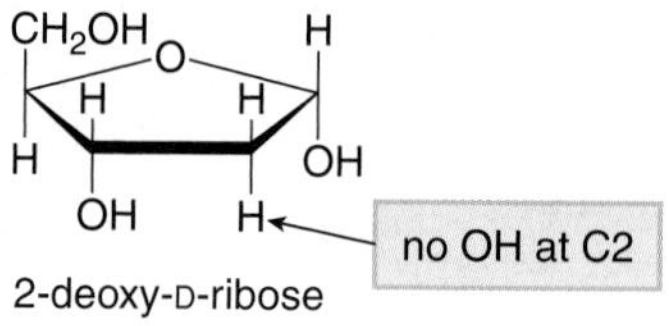

2-deoxy-D-ribose

- **Reaction of D-ribose with certain amine heterocycles forms *N*-glycosides called ribonucleosides.**
- **This same reaction of 2-deoxy-D-ribose forms deoxyribonucleosides.**

An example of a **ribonucleoside** and a **deoxyribonucleoside** are drawn. These *N*-glycosides have the β orientation. Numbering in the sugar ring begins at the anomeric carbon (1'), and proceeds in a clockwise fashion around the ring.

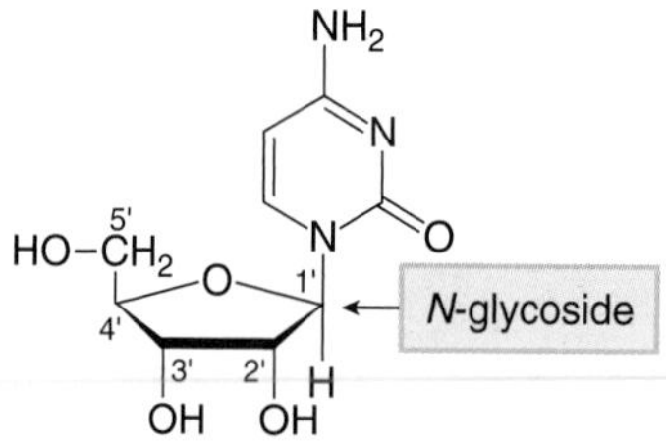

cytidine

a ribonucleoside

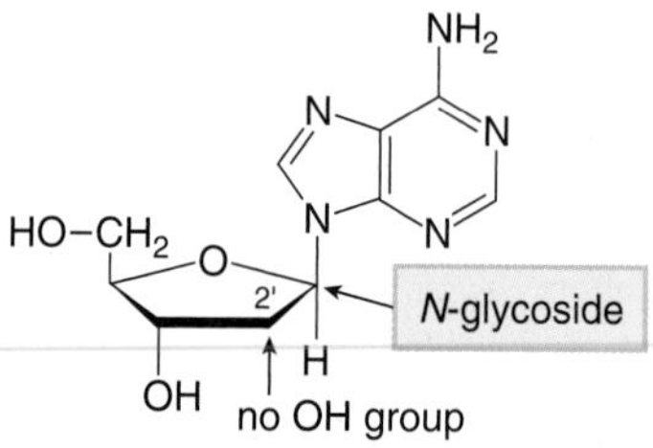

2-deoxyadenosine

a deoxyribonucleoside

Only five common nitrogen heterocycles are used to form these nucleosides. Three compounds have one ring, and are derived from a nitrogen heterocycle called **pyrimidine.** Two are bicyclic, and are derived from a nitrogen heterocycle called **purine.** These five amines are referred to as ***bases.*** Each base is designated by a one-letter abbreviation, as shown in the names and structures drawn. Note that uracil (U) occurs only in ribonucleosides and thymine (T) occurs only in deoxyribonucleosides.

- Each nucleoside has two parts, a sugar and a base, joined together by a β *N*-glycosidic linkage.

The five nitrogen heterocycles used to form nucleosides

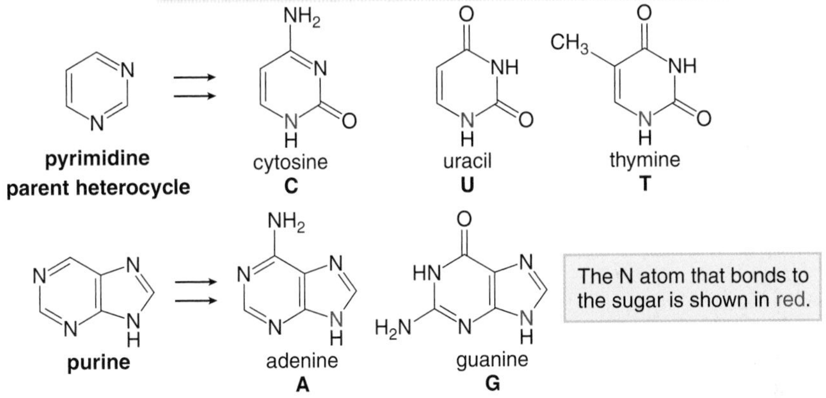

pyrimidine
parent heterocycle
cytosine
C
uracil
U
thymine
T
purine
adenine
A
guanine
G
The N atom that bonds to the sugar is shown in red.

When one OH group of the sugar nucleus is bonded to a phosphate, the derivatives are called **ribonucleotides** and **deoxyribonucleotides.**

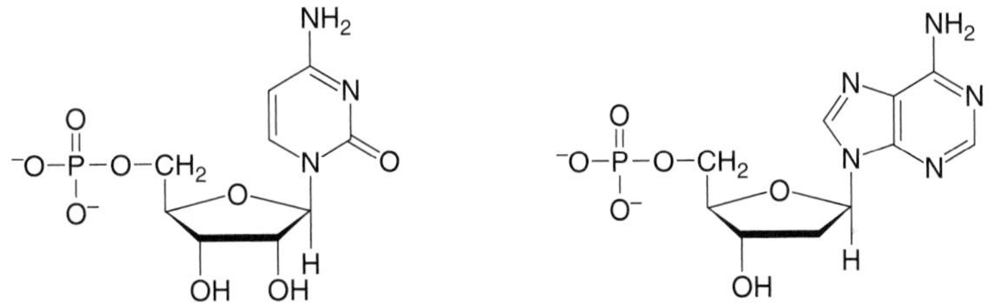

cytidine monophosphate

a ribonucleotide

deoxyadenosine monophosphate

a deoxyribonucleotide

- Ribonucleotides are the building blocks of the polymer ribonucleic acid, or RNA, the messenger molecules that convert genetic information into proteins.
- Deoxyribonucleotides are the building blocks of the polymer deoxyribonucleic acid, or DNA, the molecules that are responsible for the storage of all genetic information.

Figure 28.12 Short segments of RNA and DNA

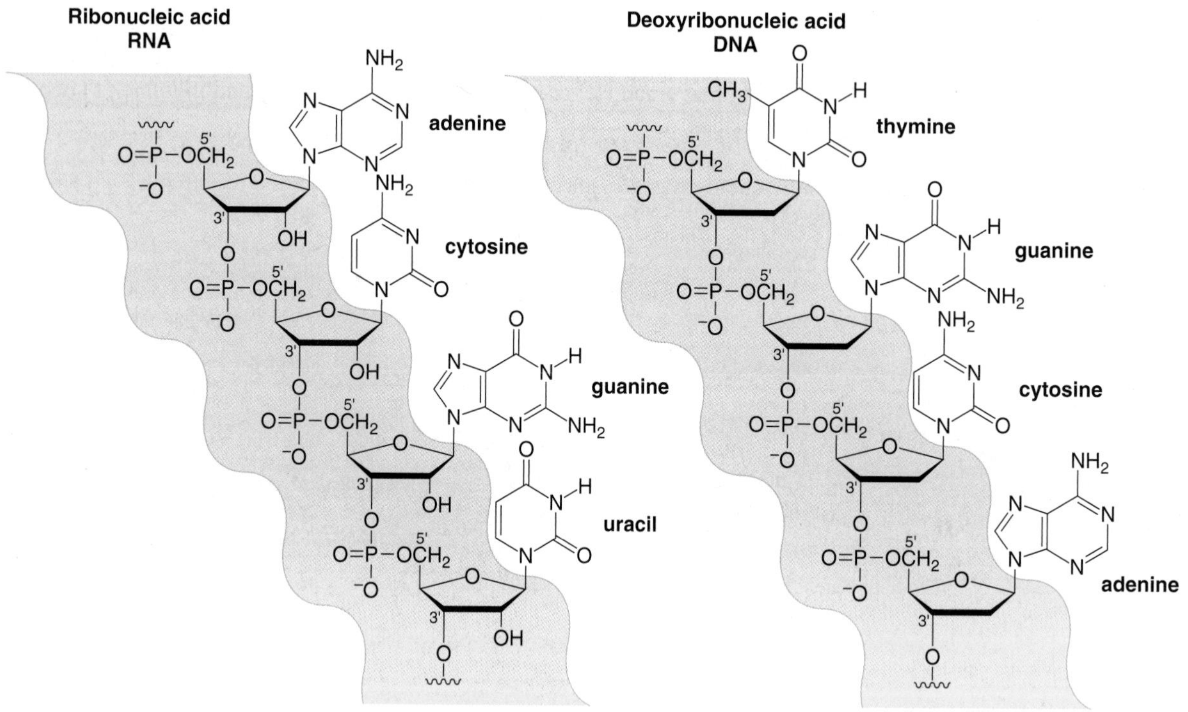

Short segments of both RNA and DNA are shown in Figure 28.12. Note the central role of the sugar moiety in both RNA and DNA. The sugar residues are bonded to two phosphate groups, thus connecting the chain of RNA or DNA together. The sugar residues are also bonded to the nitrogen base via the anomeric carbon.

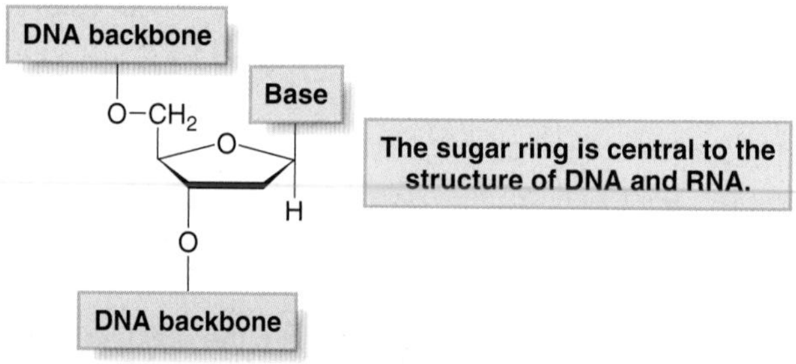

DNA is composed of two polynucleotide strands that wind around each other to form a double helix, resembling a spiral ladder. The sides of the ladder are composed of the sugar–phosphate backbone of the polymer and the rungs are composed of the bases, as shown in Figure 28.13.

The nitrogen bases on one strand of DNA hydrogen bond to nitrogen bases on the other strand. A purine base on one strand hydrogen bonds with a pyrimidine base on the other strand. Two types of bases, called **base pairs,** hydrogen bond to each other: adenine hydrogen bonds with thymine (A–T) and cytosine hydrogen bonds with guanine (C–G). Although much more can be said about the intricate structure of DNA, our discussion will end here since the focus of this chapter is carbohydrates, not nucleic acids.

Problem 28.35 Draw the structures of the nucleosides formed from each of the following components: (a) ribose + uracil; (b) 2-deoxyribose + guanine

Problem 28.36 (a) Why can't two purine bases (A and G) form a base pair and hydrogen bond to each other on two strands of DNA in the double helix? (b) Why is hydrogen bonding between guanine and cytosine more favorable than hydrogen bonding between guanine and thymine?

Figure 28.13 DNA—A double helix

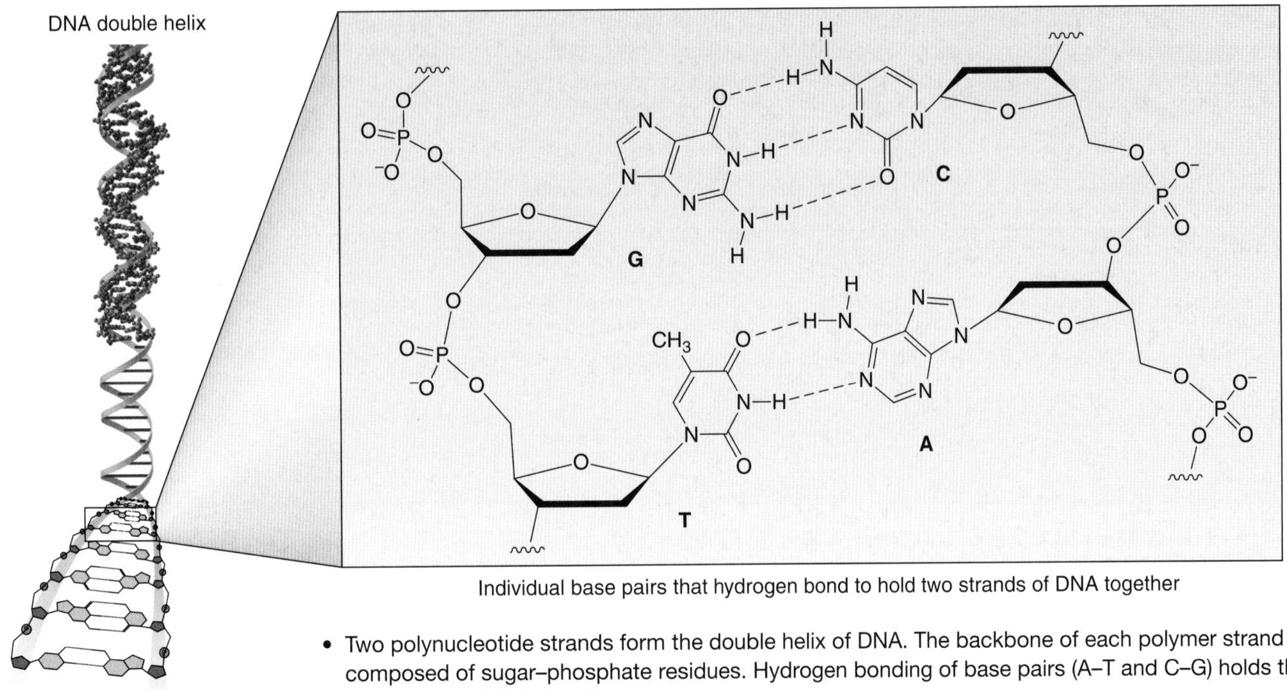

Individual base pairs that hydrogen bond to hold two strands of DNA together

- Two polynucleotide strands form the double helix of DNA. The backbone of each polymer strand is composed of sugar–phosphate residues. Hydrogen bonding of base pairs (A–T and C–G) holds the two strands of DNA together.

KEY CONCEPTS

Carbohydrates

Important Terms

- **Aldose** A monosaccharide containing an aldehyde (28.2)
- **Ketose** A monosaccharide containing a ketone (28.2)
- **D-Sugar** A monosaccharide with the OH bonded to the stereogenic center farthest from the carbonyl group drawn on the right in the Fischer projection (28.2C)
- **Epimers** Two diastereomers that differ in configuration around one stereogenic center only (28.3)
- **Anomers** Monosaccharides that differ in configuration at the hemiacetal OH group (28.6)
- **Glycoside** An acetal derived from a monosaccharide hemiacetal (28.7)

Acyclic, Haworth, and 3-D Representations for D-Glucose (28.6)

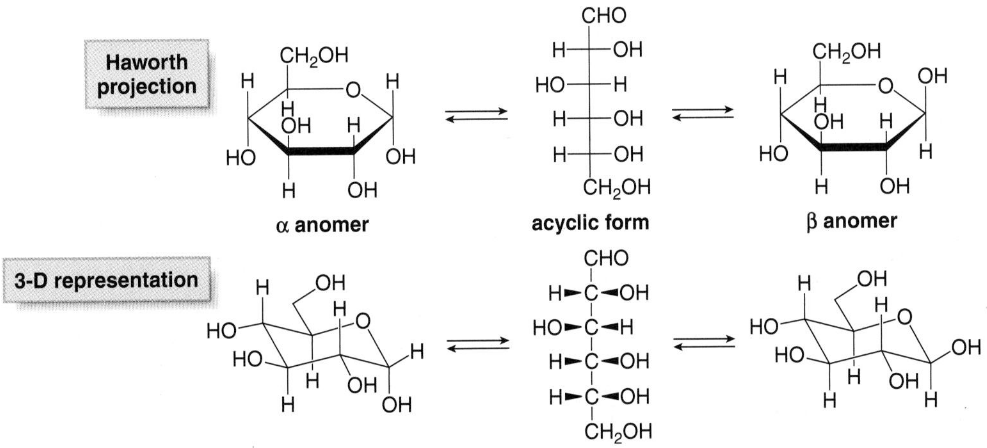

Reactions of Monosaccharides Involving the Hemiacetal

[1] Glycoside formation (28.7A)

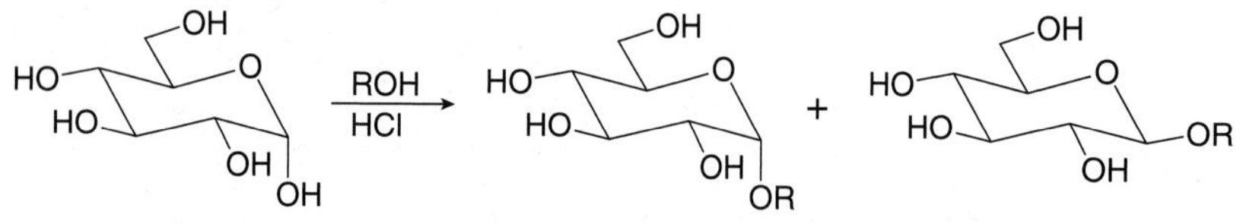

α-D-glucose — α glycoside — β glycoside

- Only the hemiacetal OH reacts.
- A mixture of α and β glycosides forms.

[2] Glycoside hydrolysis (28.7B)

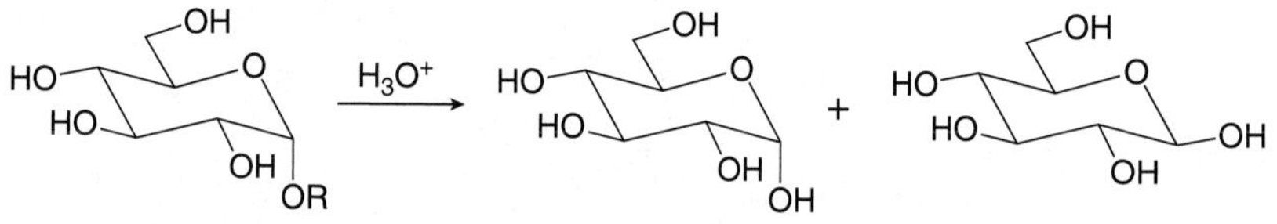

α anomer + ROH β anomer

- A mixture of α and β anomers forms.

Reactions of Monosaccharides at the OH Groups

[1] Ether formation (28.8)

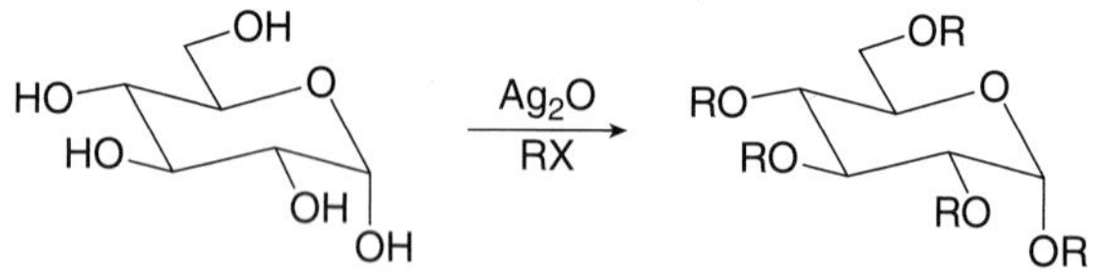

- All OH groups react.
- The stereochemistry at all stereogenic centers is retained.

[2] Ester formation (28.8)

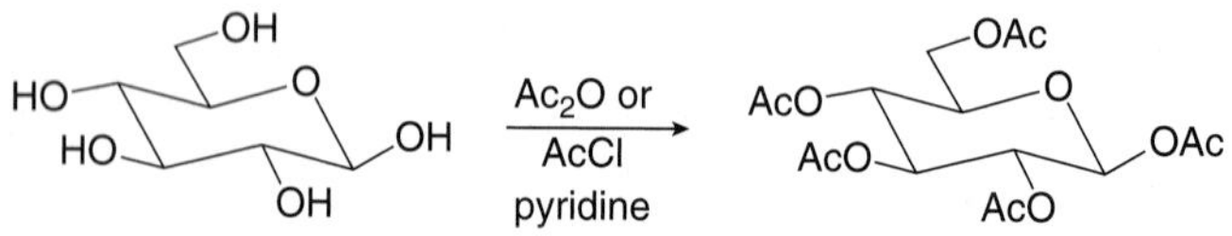

- All OH groups react.
- The stereochemistry at all stereogenic centers is retained.

Reactions of Monosaccharides at the Carbonyl Group

[1] Oxidation of aldoses (28.9B)

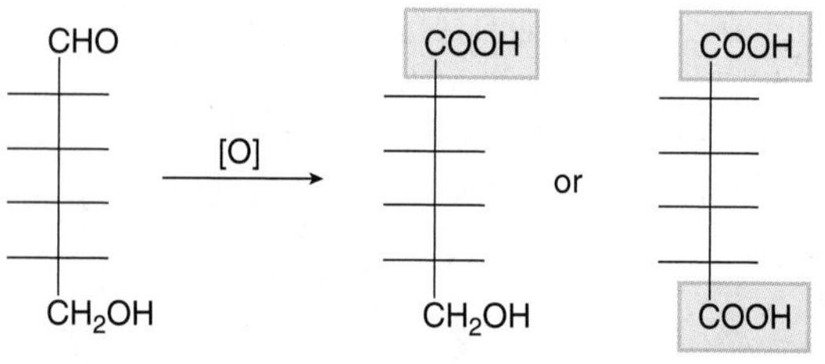

aldose — aldonic acid — aldaric acid

- Aldonic acids are formed using:
  - Ag_2O, NH_4OH
  - Cu^{2+}
  - Br_2, H_2O
- Aldaric acids are formed with HNO_3, H_2O.

[2] Reduction of aldoses to alditols (28.9A)

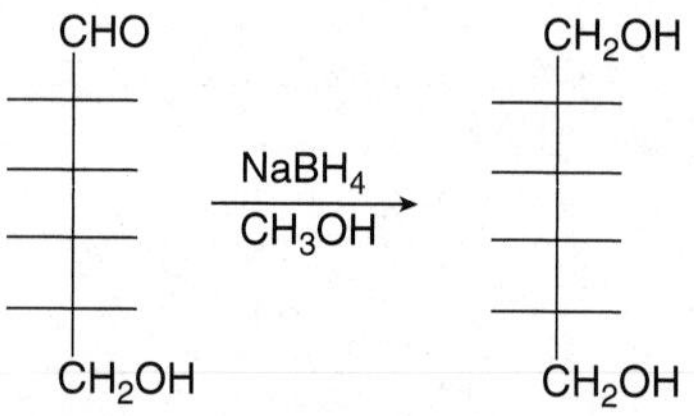

aldose — alditol

[3] Wohl degradation (28.10A)

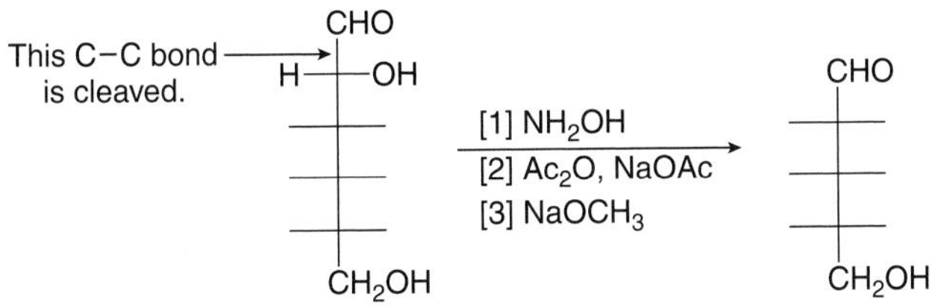

- The C1 – C2 bond is cleaved to shorten an aldose chain by one carbon.
- The stereochemistry at all other stereogenic centers is retained.
- Two epimers at C2 form the same product.

[4] Kiliani–Fischer synthesis (28.10B)

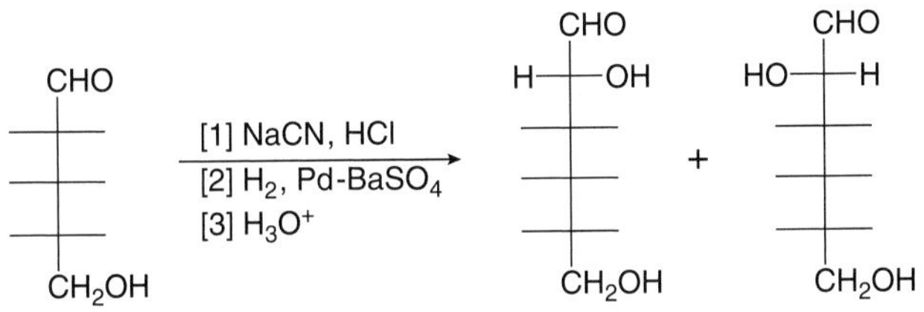

- One carbon is added to the aldehyde end of an aldose.
- Two epimers at C2 are formed.

Other Reactions

[1] Hydrolysis of disaccharides (28.12)

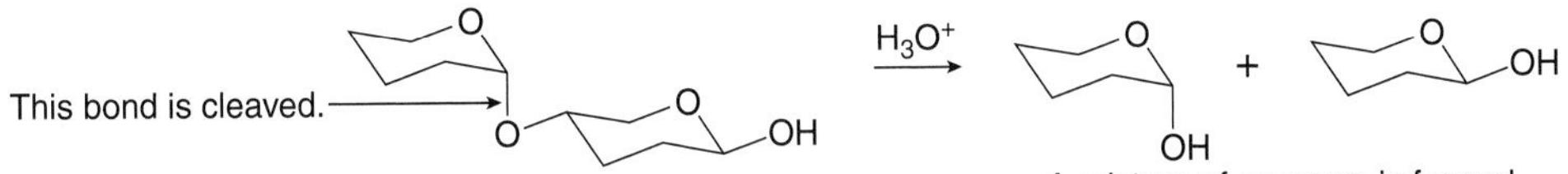

A mixture of anomers is formed.

[2] Formation of *N*-glycosides (28.14B)

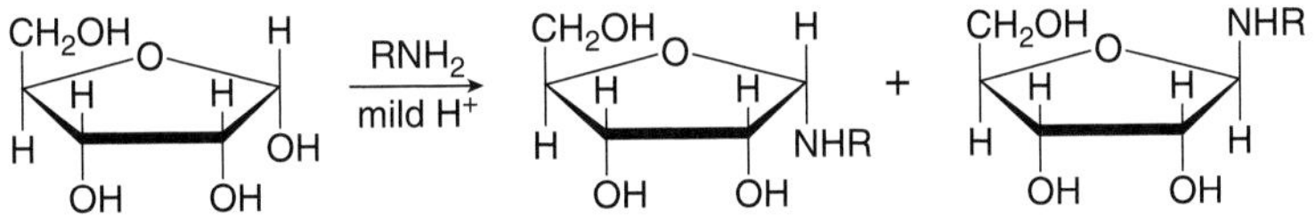

- Two anomers are formed.

PROBLEMS

Problems Using Three-Dimensional Models

28.37 Convert each ball-and-stick model to a Fischer projection.

a. 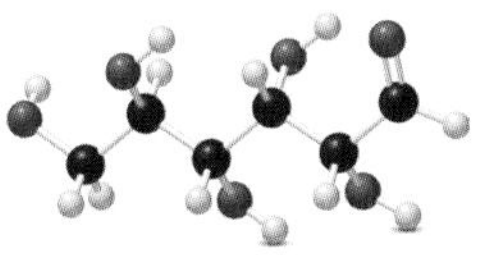

b. 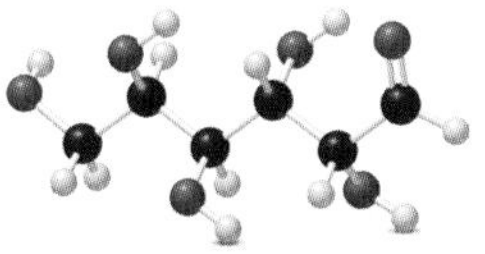

28.38 (a) Convert each cyclic monosaccharide into a Fischer projection of its acyclic form. (b) Name each monosaccharide. (c) Label the anomer as α or β.

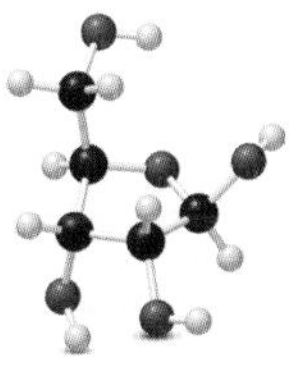

A

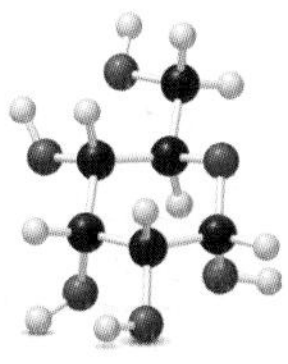

B

Fischer Projections

28.39 Classify each compound as identical to **A** or its enantiomer.

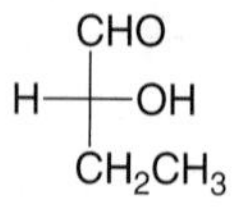

A

a. 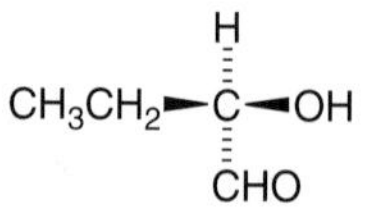

b. 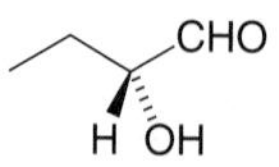

c. 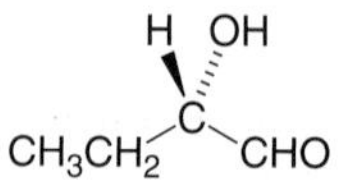

d. 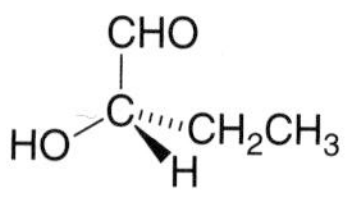

28.40 Convert each compound to a Fischer projection and label each stereogenic center as *R* or *S*.

a. 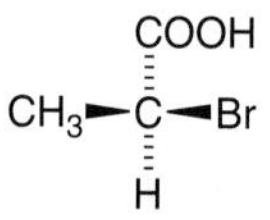

c. 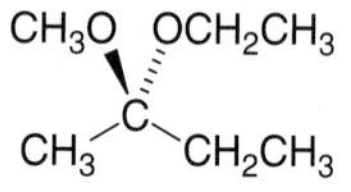

e. 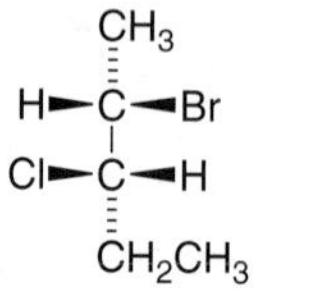

g. 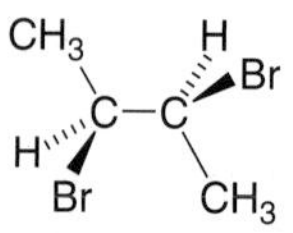

b. 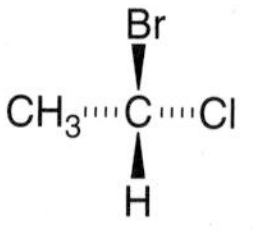

d. 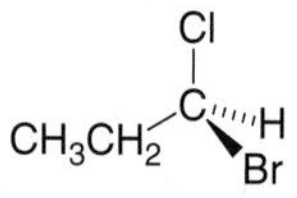

f. 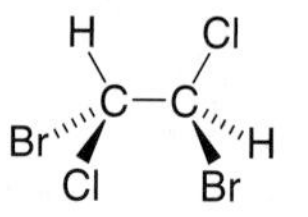

h. 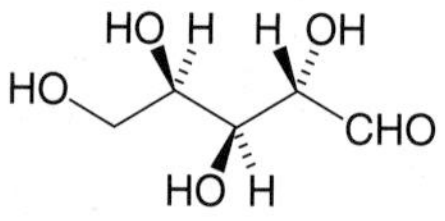

Monosaccharide Structure and Stereochemistry

28.41 Draw the C4 epimer of D-xylose and name the monosaccharide.

28.42 For D-arabinose:

a. Draw its enantiomer.

b. Draw an epimer at C3.

c. Draw a diastereomer that is not an epimer.

d. Draw a constitutional isomer that still contains a carbonyl group.

28.43 Consider the following six compounds (**A–F**).

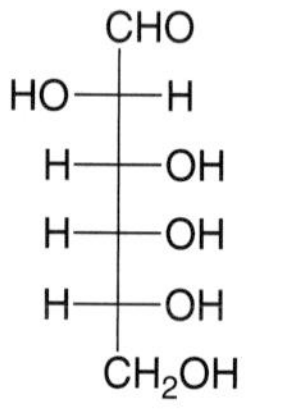

A

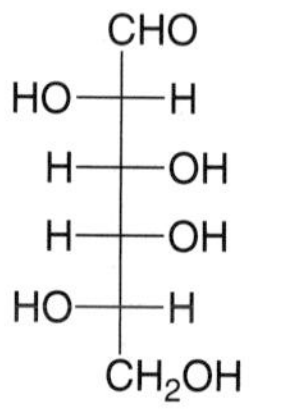

B

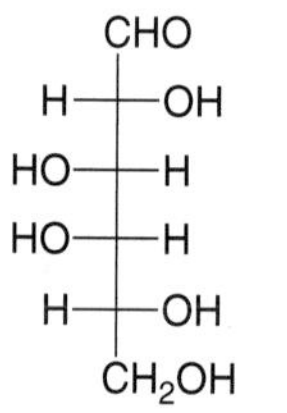

C

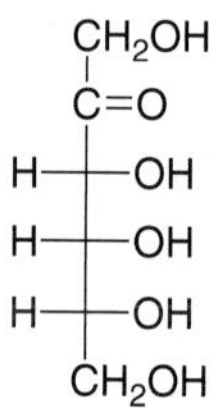

D

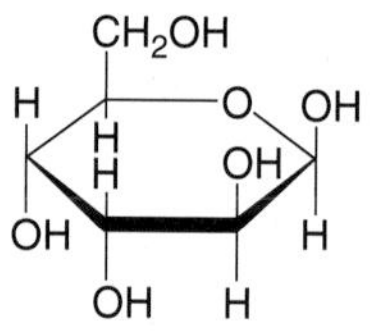

E

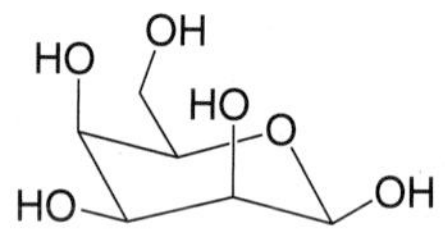

F

How are the two compounds in each pair related? Choose from enantiomers, epimers, diastereomers but not epimers, constitutional isomers, and identical compounds.

a. **A** and **B** b. **A** and **C** c. **B** and **C** d. **A** and **D** e. **E** and **F**

28.44 Consider the monosaccharide aldopentoses **A** and **B,** drawn below.

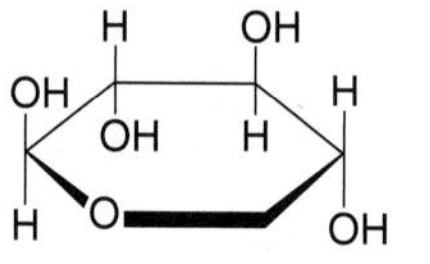

A

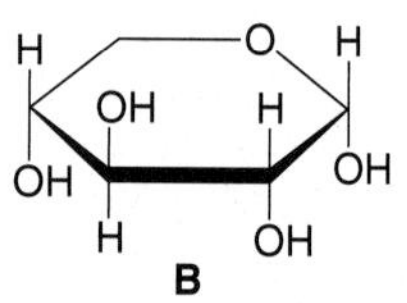

B

a. Which of the following terms describe **A** and **B:** epimers, anomers, enantiomers, diastereomers, and reducing sugars?

b. Draw the acyclic form of both **A** and **B,** and name each compound.

28.45 Draw a Haworth projection for each compound using the structures in Figures 28.4 and 28.5.

a. β-D-talopyranose b. β-D-mannopyranose c. α-D-galactopyranose d. α-D-ribofuranose e. α-D-tagatofuranose

28.46 Draw both pyranose anomers of each aldohexose using a three-dimensional representation with a chair pyranose. Label each anomer as α or β.

a. 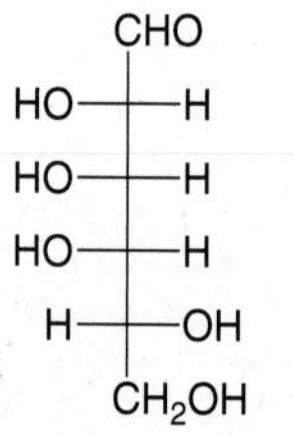

b. 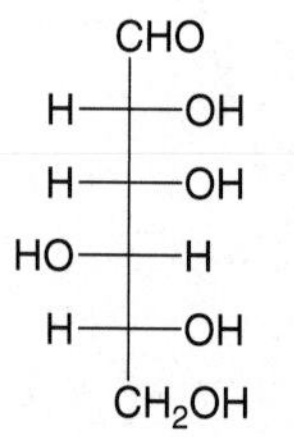

c. 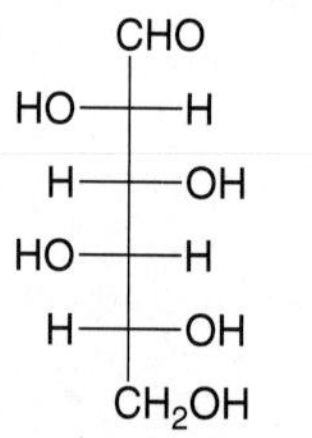

28.47 Convert each cyclic monosaccharide into its acyclic form.

a. 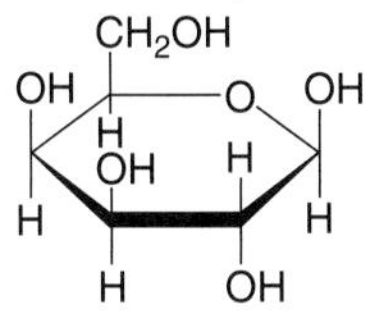

c. 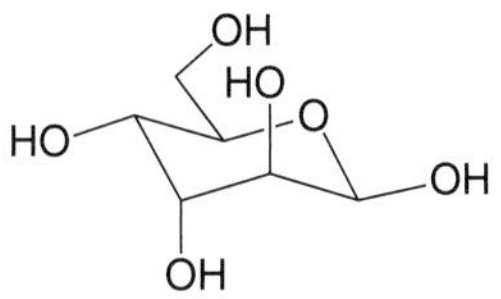

e. 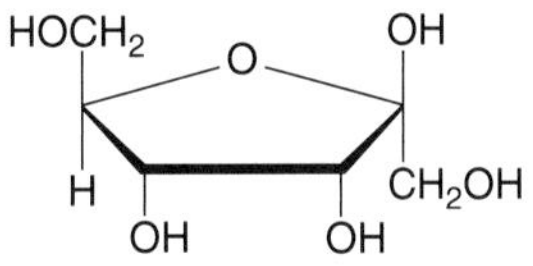

b. 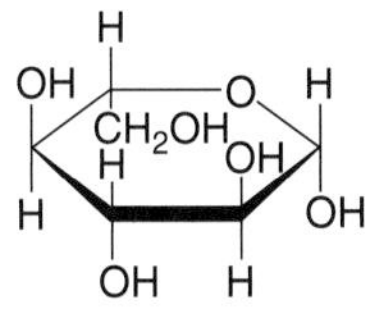

d. 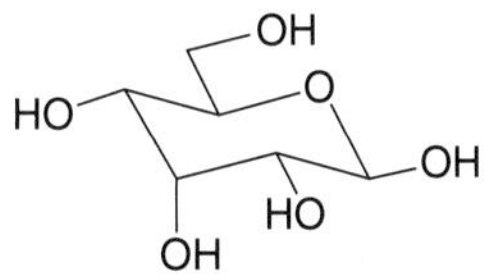

f. 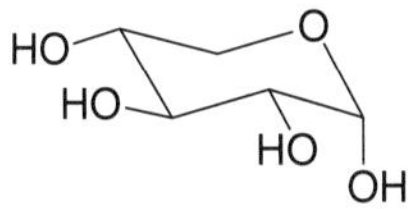

28.48 D-Arabinose can exist in both pyranose and furanose forms.

a. Draw the α and β anomers of D-arabinofuranose.
b. Draw the α and β anomers of D-arabinopyranose.

28.49 The most stable conformation of the pyranose ring of most D-aldohexoses places the largest group, CH_2OH, in the equatorial position. An exception to this is the aldohexose D-idose. Draw the two possible chair conformations of either the α or β anomer of D-idose. Explain why the more stable conformation has the CH_2OH group in the axial position.

Monosaccharide Reactions

28.50 Draw the products formed when α-D-gulose is treated with each reagent.

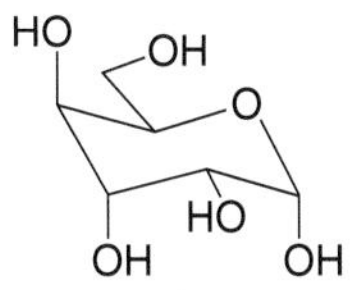

D-gulose

a. CH_3I, Ag_2O
b. CH_3OH, HCl
c. $C_6H_5CH_2Cl$, Ag_2O
d. $C_6H_5CH_2OH$, HCl
e. Ac_2O, pyridine
f. C_6H_5COCl, pyridine
g. The product in (a), then H_3O^+
h. The product in (b), then Ac_2O, pyridine
i. The product in (g), then $C_6H_5CH_2Cl$, Ag_2O
j. The product in (d), then CH_3I, Ag_2O

28.51 Draw the products formed when D-altrose is treated with each reagent.

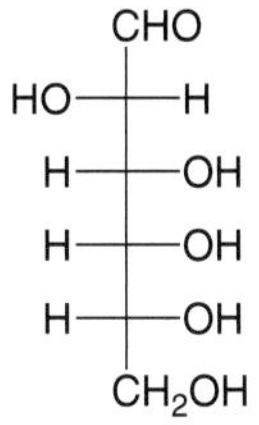

D-altrose

a. CH_3OH, HCl
b. $(CH_3)_2CHOH$, HCl
c. $NaBH_4$, CH_3OH
d. Br_2, H_2O
e. HNO_3, H_2O
f. [1] NH_2OH; [2] $(CH_3CO)_2O$, $NaOCOCH_3$; [3] $NaOCH_3$
g. [1] NaCN, HCl; [2] H_2, Pd-$BaSO_4$; [3] H_3O^+
h. CH_3I, Ag_2O
i. Ac_2O, pyridine
j. $C_6H_5CH_2NH_2$, mild H^+

28.52 What aglycon and monosaccharides are formed when salicin and solanine (Section 28.7C) are each hydrolyzed with aqueous acid?

28.53 What two aldohexoses yield D-arabinose upon Wohl degradation?

28.54 What products are formed when each compound is subjected to a Kiliani–Fischer synthesis?

a. 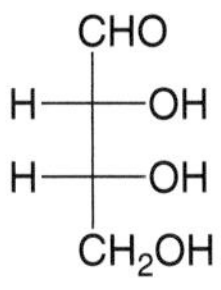

b. 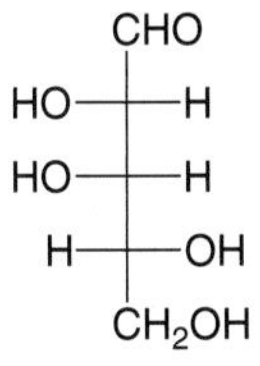

c. 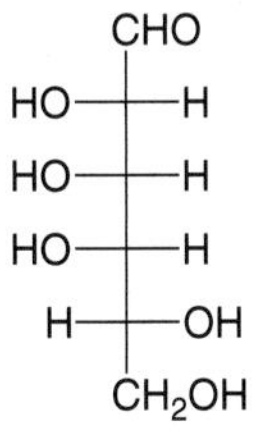

28.55 How would you convert D-glucose into each compound? More than one step is required.

a. 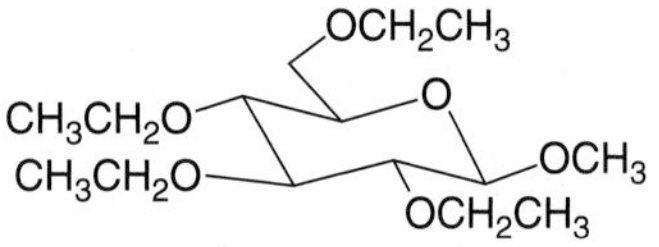

+ α anomer

b. 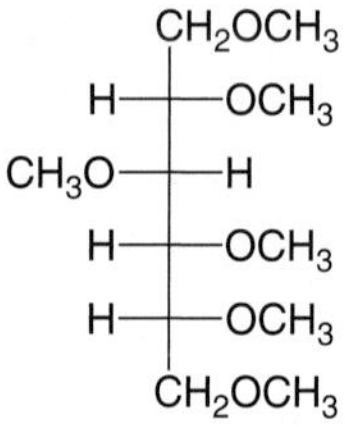

c. 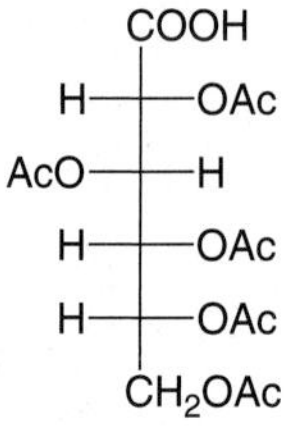

28.56 Which D-aldopentoses are reduced to optically inactive alditols using $NaBH_4$, CH_3OH?

28.57 What products are formed when each compound is treated with aqueous acid?

a. 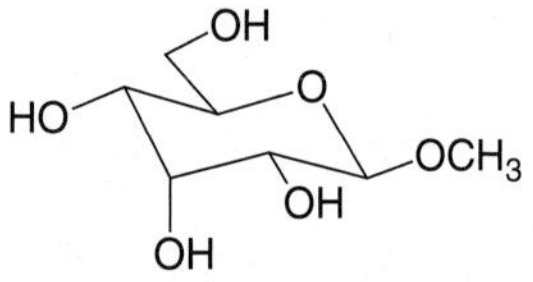

b. 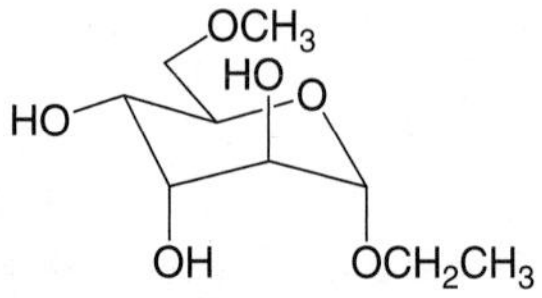

c. 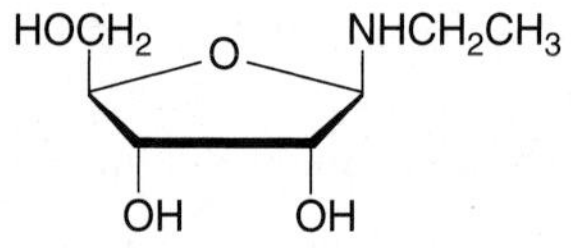

Mechanisms

28.58 Draw a stepwise mechanism for the acid-catalyzed interconversion of two glucose anomers by mutarotation.

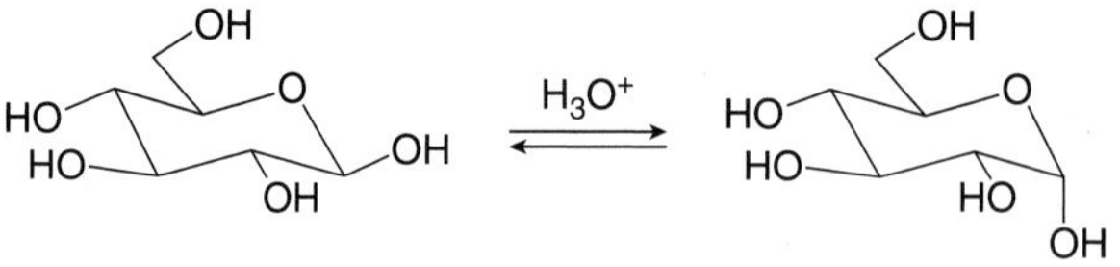

28.59 Draw a stepwise mechanism for the following reaction.

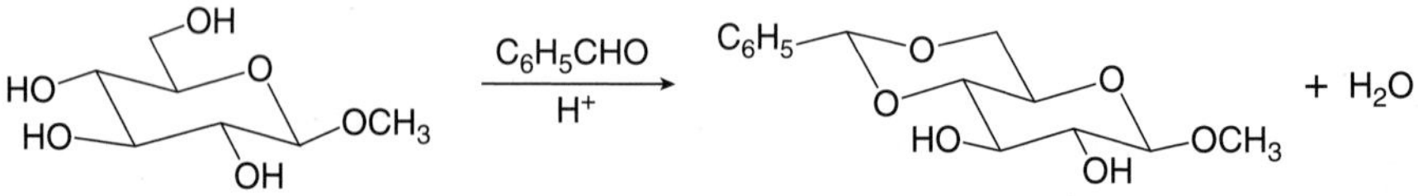

28.60 Draw a stepwise mechanism for the following hydrolysis.

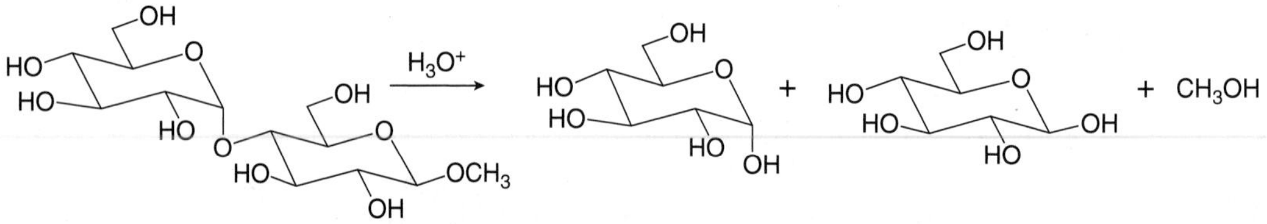

28.61 In the oxidation of D-allose to D-allonic acid, a lactone having the general structure **A** is isolated. Draw a stepwise mechanism to account for the formation of **A.** Use wedges and dashes to indicate the stereochemistry of all stereogenic centers in **A.**

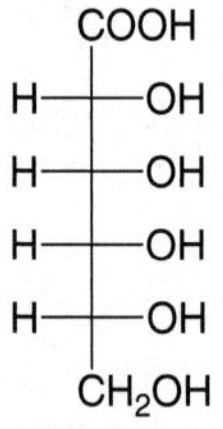

D-allonic acid

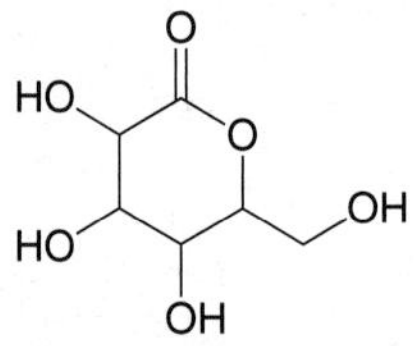

A

28.62 The following isomerization reaction, drawn using D-glucose as starting material, occurs with all aldohexoses in the presence of base. Draw a stepwise mechanism that illustrates how each compound is formed.

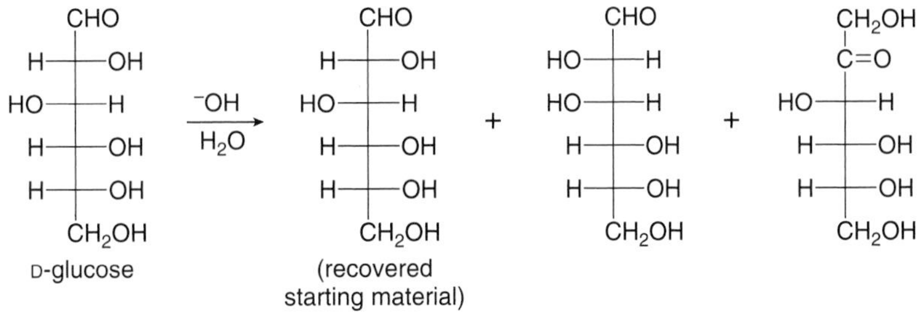

Identifying Monosaccharides

28.63 Which D-aldopentose is oxidized to an optically active aldaric acid and undergoes the Wohl degradation to yield a D-aldotetrose that is oxidized to an optically active aldaric acid?

28.64 What other D-aldopentose forms the same alditol as D-arabinose when reduced with $NaBH_4$ in CH_3OH?

28.65 Identify compounds **A–D.** A D-aldopentose **A** is oxidized with HNO_3 to an optically inactive aldaric acid **B. A** undergoes the Kiliani–Fischer synthesis to yield **C** and **D. C** is oxidized to an optically active aldaric acid. **D** is oxidized to an optically inactive aldaric acid.

28.66 A D-aldopentose **A** is reduced to an optically active alditol. Upon Kiliani–Fischer synthesis, **A** is converted to two D-aldohexoses, **B** and **C. B** is oxidized to an optically inactive aldaric acid. **C** is oxidized to an optically active aldaric acid. What are the structures of **A–C?**

28.67 A D-aldohexose **A** is reduced to an optically active alditol **B** using $NaBH_4$ in CH_3OH. **A** is converted by Wohl degradation to an aldopentose **C,** which is reduced to an optically inactive alditol **D. C** is converted by Wohl degradation to aldotetrose **E,** which is oxidized to an optically active aldaric acid **F.** When the two ends of aldohexose **A** are interconverted, a different aldohexose **G** is obtained. What are the structures of **A–G?**

Disaccharides and Polysaccharides

28.68 Draw the structure of a disaccharide formed from two galactose units joined by a 1→4-β-glycosidic linkage.

28.69 Draw the structure of a disaccharide formed from two mannose units joined by a 1→4-α-glycosidic linkage.

28.70 Identify the lettered compounds in the following reactions.

a.

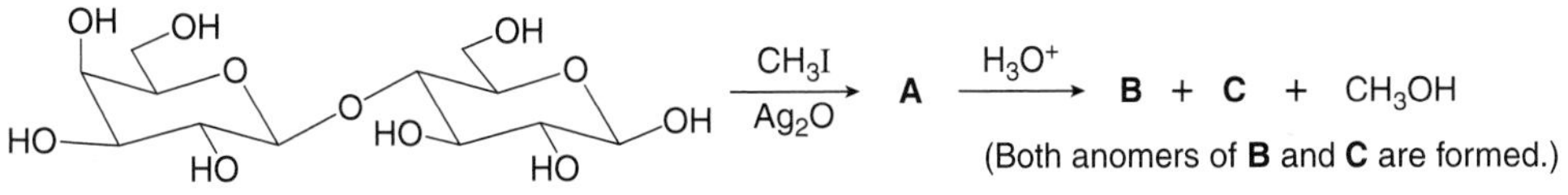

b.

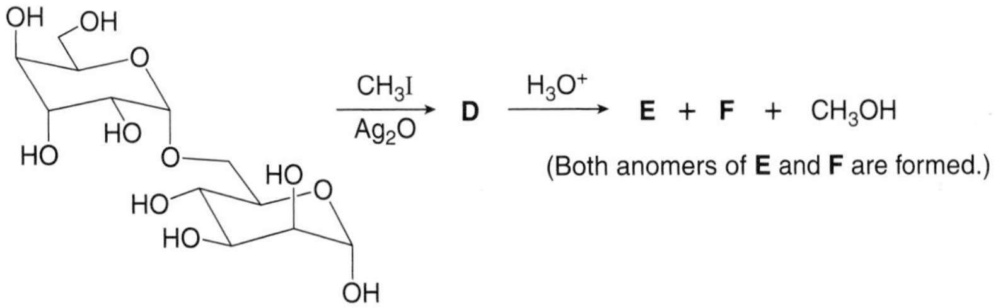

28.71 For each disaccharide in Problem 28.70:

a. Identify the glycosidic linkage.
b. Classify the glycosidic bond as α or β and use numbers to designate its location.
c. Classify each disaccharide as reducing or nonreducing.

28.72 Consider the tetrasaccharide stachyose drawn below. Stachyose is found in white jasmine, soybeans, and lentils. Because humans cannot digest it, its consumption causes flatulence.

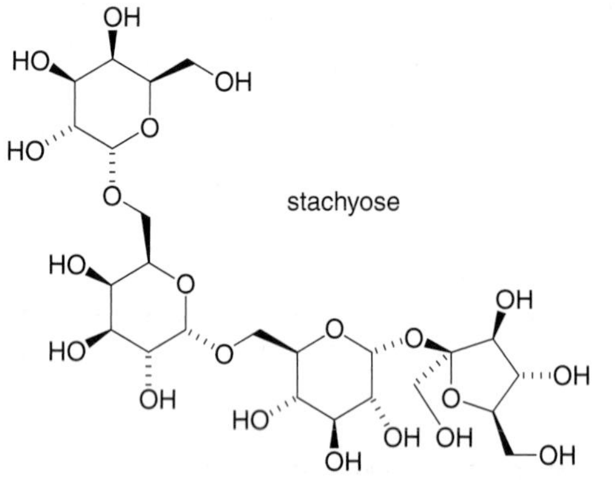

a. Label all glycoside bonds.
b. Classify each glycosidic linkage as α or β and use numbers to designate its location between two rings (e.g., 1→4-β).
c. What products are formed when stachyose is hydrolyzed with H_3O^+?
d. Is stachyose a reducing sugar?
e. What product is formed when stachyose is treated with excess CH_3I, Ag_2O?
f. What products are formed when the product in (e) is treated with H_3O^+?

28.73 Deduce the structure of the disaccharide isomaltose from the following data.

[1] Hydrolysis yields D-glucose exclusively.

[2] Isomaltose is cleaved with α-glycosidase enzymes.

[3] Isomaltose is a reducing sugar.

[4] Methylation with excess CH_3I, Ag_2O and then hydrolysis with H_3O^+ forms two products:

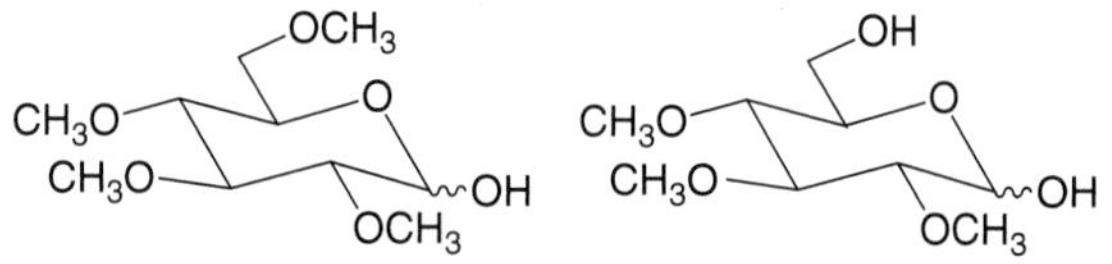

(Both anomers are present.)

28.74 Deduce the structure of the disaccharide trehalose from the following data. Trehalose is the "blood sugar" of the insect world. It is found in bacterial spores, fungi, and many insects whose natural environment has large variations in temperature.

[1] Hydrolysis yields D-glucose exclusively.

[2] Trehalose is hydrolyzed by α-glycosidase enzymes.

[3] Trehalose is a nonreducing sugar.

[4] Methylation with excess CH_3I, Ag_2O, followed by hydrolysis with H_3O^+, forms only one product:

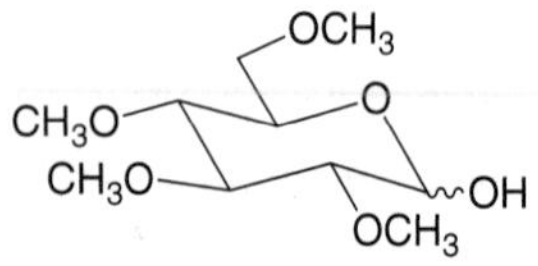

(both anomers)

28.75 Draw the structure of each of the following compounds:

a. a polysaccharide formed by joining D-glucosamine in 1→6-α-glycosidic linkages
b. a disaccharide formed by joining D-mannose and D-glucose in a 1→4-β-glycosidic linkage using mannose's anomeric carbon
c. an α-*N*-glycoside formed from D-arabinose and $C_6H_5CH_2NH_2$
d. a ribonucleoside formed from D-ribose and thymine

Challenge Problems

28.76 (a) Draw the more stable chair form of fucose, an essential monosaccharide needed in the diet and a component of carbohydrates on mammalian and plant cell surfaces. (b) Classify fucose as a D- or L-monosaccharide. (c) What two structural features are unusual in fucose?

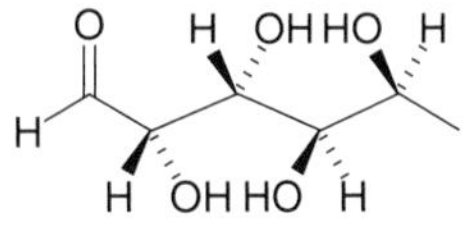

fucose

28.77 As we have seen in Chapter 28, monosaccharides can be drawn in a variety of ways, and in truth, often a mixture of cyclic compounds is present in a solution. Identify each monosaccharide, including its proper D,L designation, drawn in a less-than-typical fashion.

a. 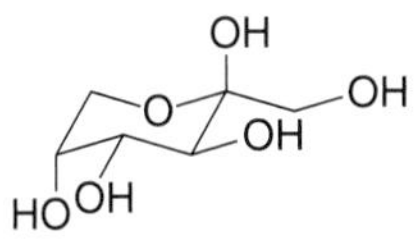

b. 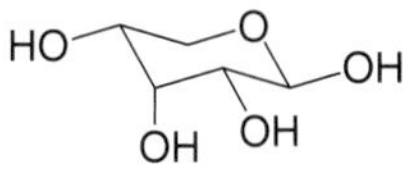

c. 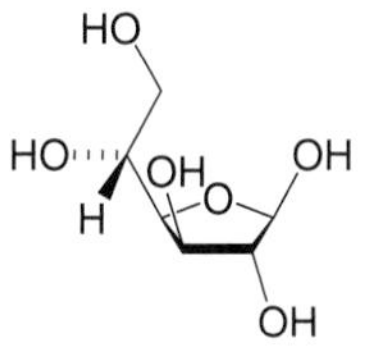

d. 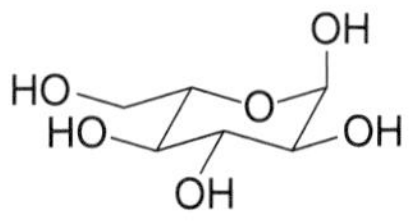

28.78 Draw a stepwise mechanism for the following reaction.

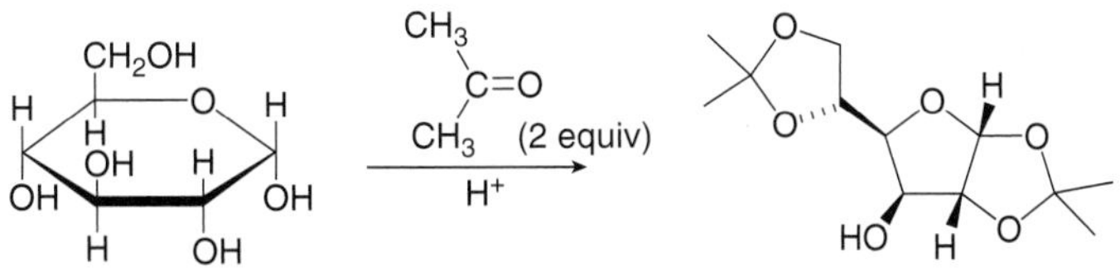

28.79 Deduce the structure of the trisaccharide (**X**) from the given information.

[1] Methylation with excess CH_3I, Ag_2O and then hydrolysis with H_3O^+ forms three products.

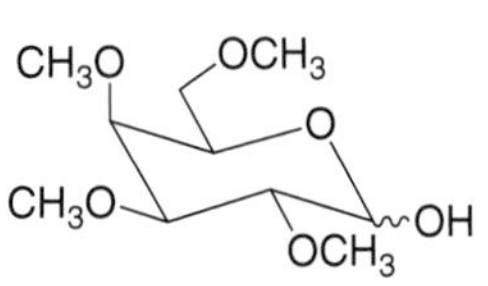

2,3,4,6-tetra-*O*-methyl-D-galactose

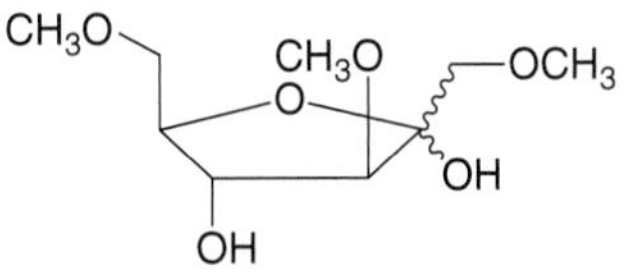

1,3,6-tri-*O*-methyl-D-fructose

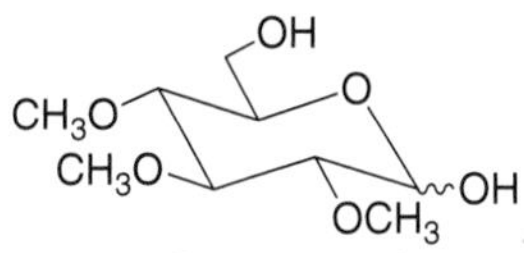

2,3,4-tri-*O*-methyl-D-glucose

(Both anomers of each compound are formed.)

[2] **X** is cleaved with a β-glycosidase enzyme to give a disaccharide and D-galactose.

[3] **X** is cleaved with an α-glycosidase enzyme to give a disaccharide and D-fructose.

29 Amino Acids and Proteins

29.1 Amino acids
29.2 Synthesis of amino acids
29.3 Separation of amino acids
29.4 Enantioselective synthesis of amino acids
29.5 Peptides
29.6 Peptide sequencing
29.7 Peptide synthesis
29.8 Automated peptide synthesis
29.9 Protein structure
29.10 Important proteins

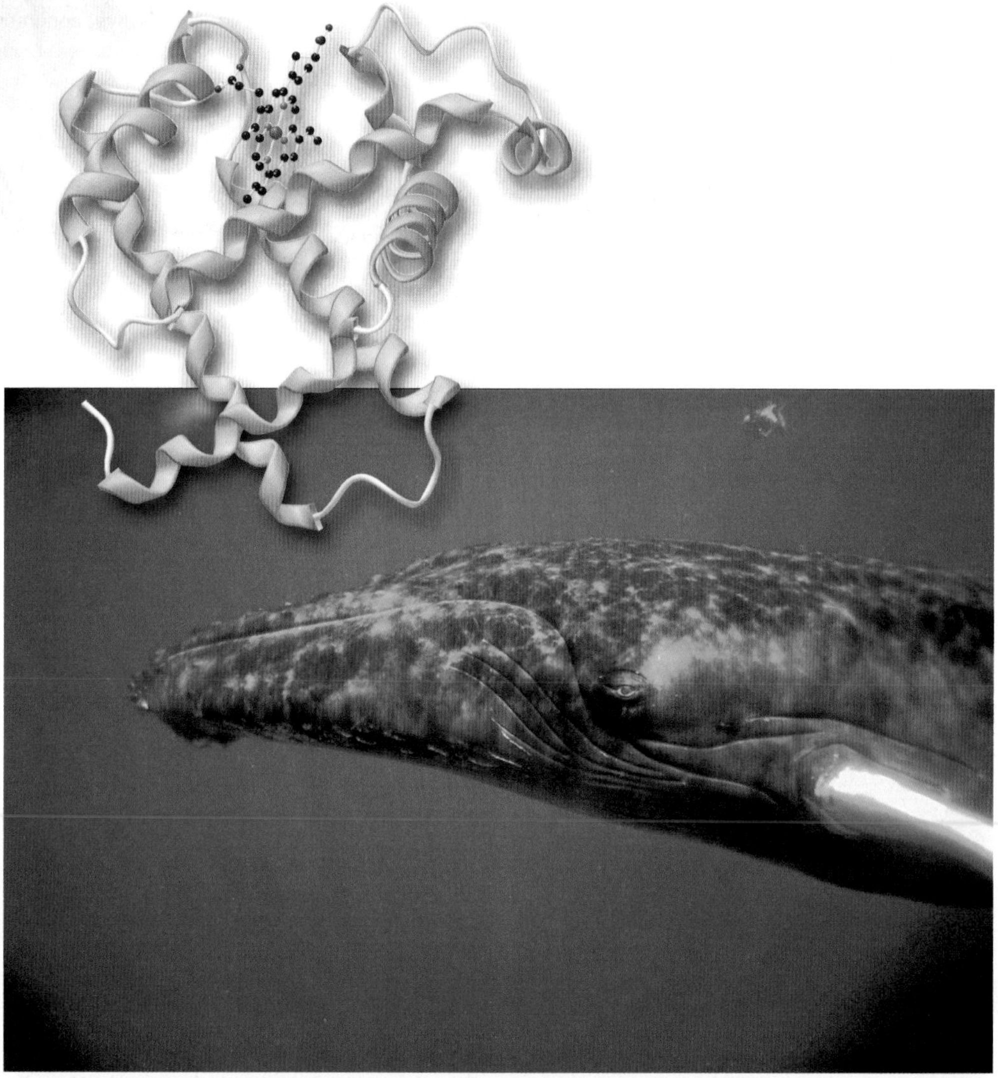

Myoglobin is a globular protein that contains 153 amino acids joined together, as well as a non-protein portion called a heme unit. The heme group consists of a large nitrogen heterocycle complexed with the Fe^{2+} cation. The Fe^{2+} cation binds oxygen in the blood and stores it in tissues. Whales have a particularly high myoglobin concentration in their muscles. It serves as an oxygen reservoir for the whale while it is submerged for long periods of time. In Chapter 29, we discuss the properties of proteins and the amino acids from which they are synthesized.

Of the four major groups of biomolecules—lipids, carbohydrates, nucleic acids, and proteins—proteins have the widest array of functions. **Keratin** and **collagen,** for example, are part of a large group of structural proteins that form long insoluble fibers, giving strength and support to tissues. Hair, horns, hooves, and fingernails are all made up of keratin. **Collagen** is found in bone, connective tissue, tendons, and cartilage. **Enzymes** are proteins that catalyze and regulate all aspects of cellular function. **Membrane proteins** transport small organic molecules and ions across cell membranes. **Insulin,** the hormone that regulates blood glucose levels, **fibrinogen** and **thrombin,** which form blood clots, and **hemoglobin,** which transports oxygen from the lungs to tissues, are all proteins.

In Chapter 29 we discuss proteins and their primary components, the amino acids.

29.1 Amino Acids

Amino acids were first discussed in Section 19.14.

Naturally occurring amino acids have an amino group (NH_2) bonded to the α carbon of a carboxy group (COOH), and so they are called **α-amino acids.**

- **All proteins are polyamides formed by joining amino acids together.**

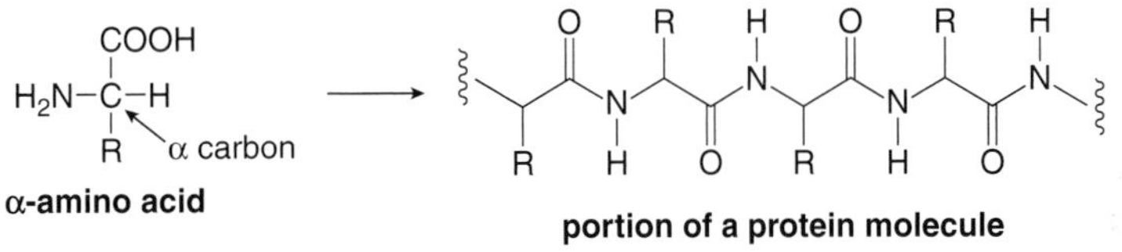
COOH
H2N–C–H
R
α carbon
O R H O R H
N N N
R H O R H O

α-amino acid

portion of a protein molecule

29.1A General Features of α-Amino Acids

The 20 amino acids that occur naturally in proteins differ in the identity of the R group bonded to the α carbon. The R group is called the **side chain** of the amino acid.

The simplest amino acid, called glycine, has R = H. **All other amino acids (R ≠ H) have a stereogenic center on the α carbon.** As is true for monosaccharides, the prefixes D and L are used to designate the configuration at the stereogenic center of amino acids. Common, naturally occurring amino acids are called **L-amino acids.** Their enantiomers, D-amino acids, are rarely found in nature. These general structures are shown in Figure 29.1. According to *R,S* designations, all L-amino acids except cysteine have the ***S*** **configuration.**

All amino acids have common names. These names can be represented by either a one-letter or a three-letter abbreviation. Figure 29.2 is a listing of the 20 naturally occurring amino acids, together with their abbreviations. Note the variability in the R groups. A side chain can be a simple alkyl group, or it can have additional functional groups such as OH, SH, COOH, or NH_2.

- **Amino acids with an additional COOH group in the side chain are called acidic amino acids.**
- **Those with an additional basic N atom in the side chain are called basic amino acids.**
- **All others are neutral amino acids.**

Figure 29.1 The general features of an α-amino acid

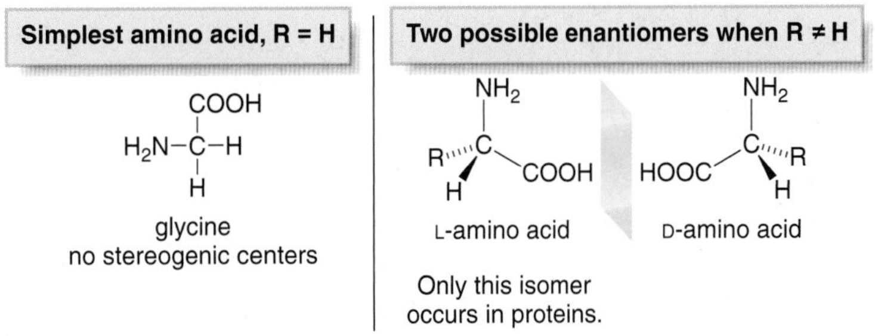
Simplest amino acid, R = H
COOH
H2N–C–H
H
glycine
no stereogenic centers
Two possible enantiomers when R ≠ H
NH2
R C COOH
H
L-amino acid
NH2
HOOC C R
H
D-amino acid
Only this isomer
occurs in proteins.

Figure 29.2 The 20 naturally occurring amino acids

Neutral amino acids

Name	Structure	Abbreviations	Name	Structure	Abbreviations
Alanine	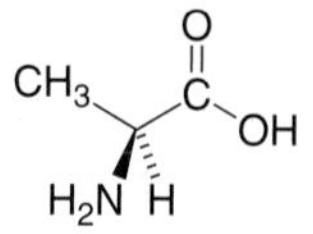	Ala A	Phenylalanine*	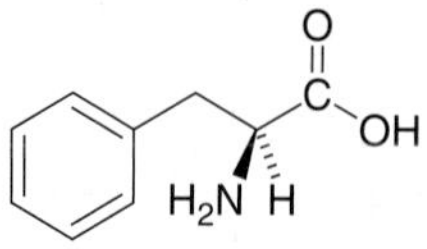	Phe F
Asparagine	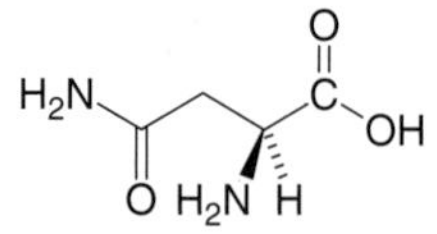	Asn N	Proline	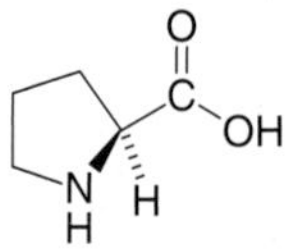	Pro P
Cysteine	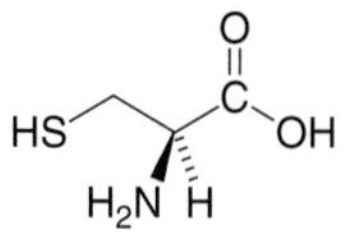	Cys C	Serine	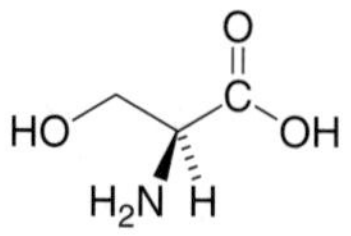	Ser S
Glutamine	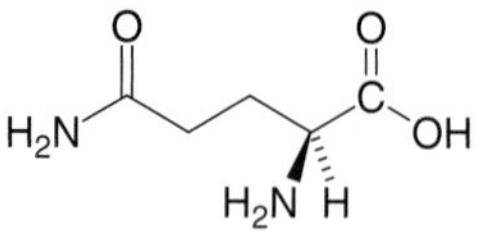	Gln Q	Threonine*	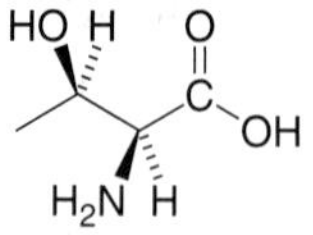	Thr T
Glycine	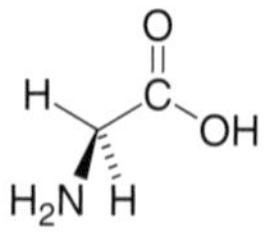	Gly G	Tryptophan*	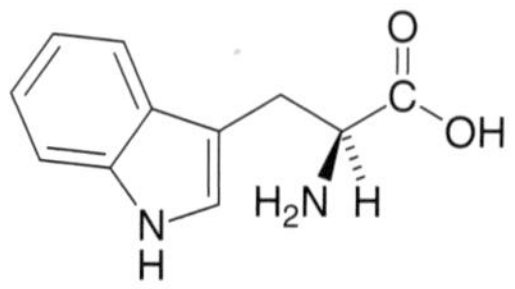	Trp W
Isoleucine*	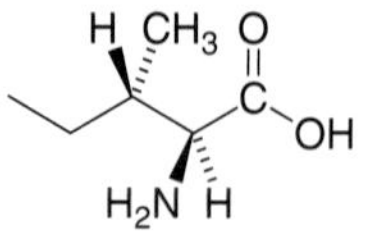	Ile I	Tyrosine	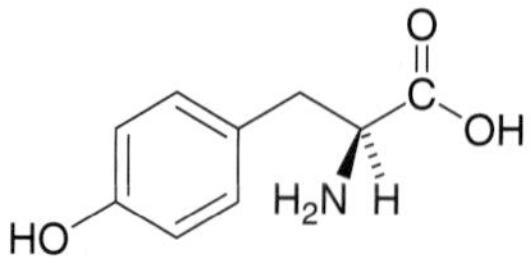	Tyr Y
Leucine*	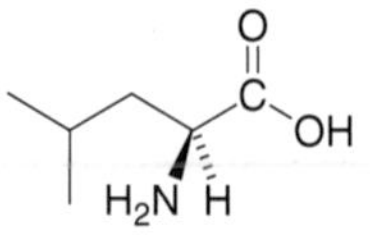	Leu L	Valine*	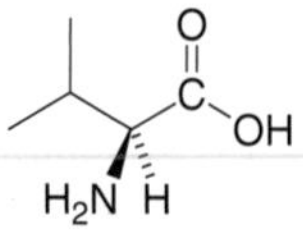	Val V
Methionine*	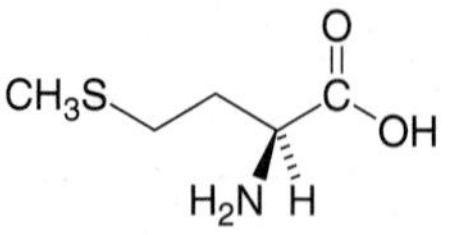	Met M			

Acidic amino acids

Name	Structure	Abbreviations
Aspartic acid	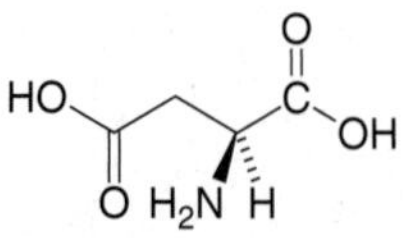	Asp D
Glutamic acid	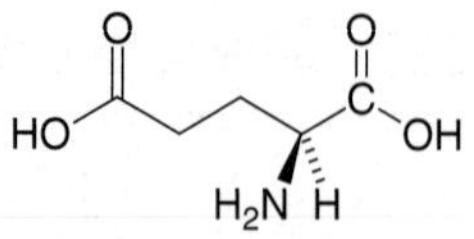	Glu E

Basic amino acids

Name	Structure	Abbreviations
Arginine*	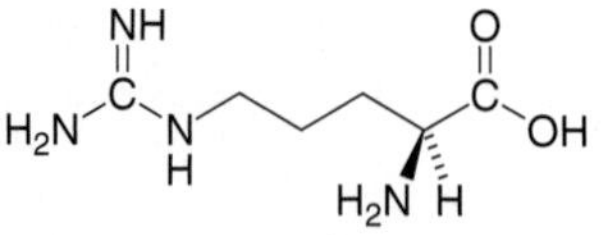	Arg R
Histidine*	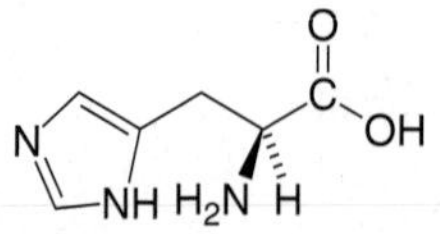	His H
Lysine*	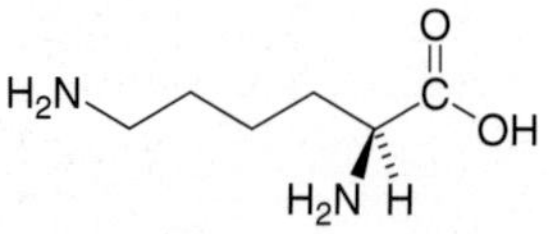	Lys K

Essential amino acids are labeled with an asterisk (*).

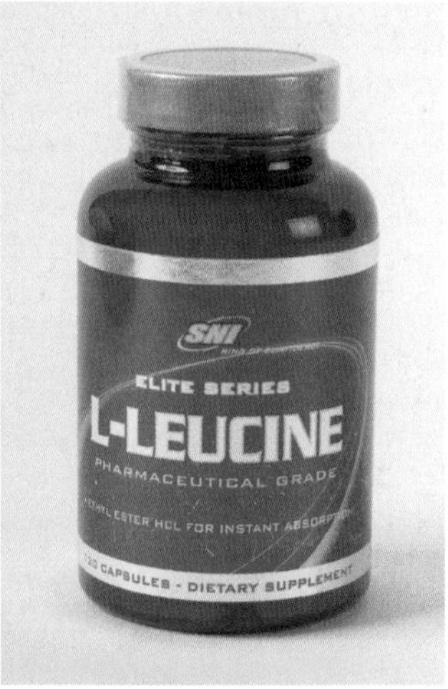

The essential amino acid leucine is sold as a dietary supplement that is used by body builders to help prevent muscle loss and heal muscle tissue after injury.

Look closely at the structures of proline, isoleucine, and threonine.

- **All amino acids are 1° amines except for proline,** which has its N atom in a five-membered ring, making it a **2° amine.**
- **Isoleucine** and **threonine** contain an additional stereogenic center at the β carbon, so there are four possible stereoisomers, only one of which is naturally occurring.

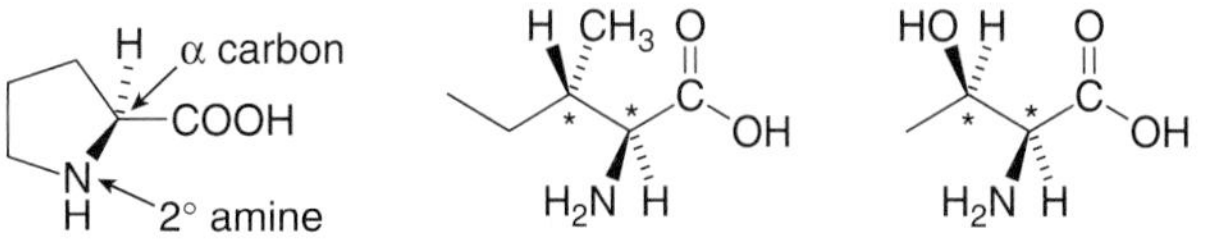

L-proline L-isoleucine L-threonine

[* denotes a stereogenic center.]

Humans can synthesize only 10 of these 20 amino acids. The remaining 10 are called **essential amino acids** because they must be obtained from the diet. These are labeled with an asterisk in Figure 29.2.

Problem 29.1 Draw the other three stereoisomers of L-isoleucine, and label the stereogenic centers as *R* or *S*.

29.1B Acid–Base Behavior

Recall from Section 19.14B that an amino acid has both an acidic and a basic functional group, so proton transfer forms a salt called a **zwitterion.**

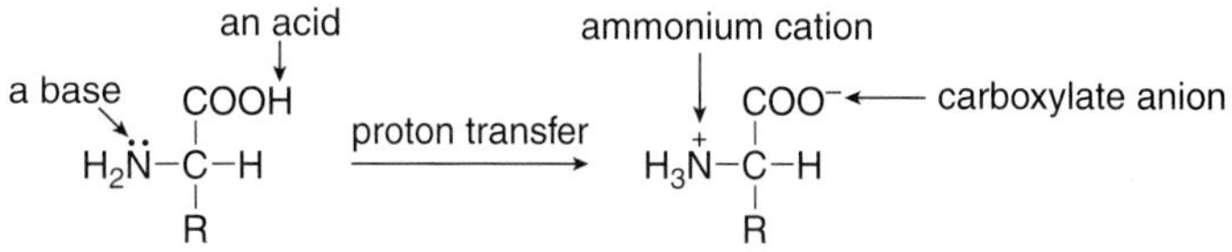

The zwitterion is neutral.

This neutral form of an amino acid does ***not*** really exist.

This salt is the neutral form of an amino acid.

This form exists at **pH ≈ 6.**

- **Amino acids do not exist to any appreciable extent as uncharged neutral compounds. They exist as salts, giving them high melting points and making them water soluble.**

Amino acids exist in different charged forms, as shown in Figure 29.3, depending on the pH of the aqueous solution in which they are dissolved. For neutral amino acids, the overall charge is +1, 0, or –1. Only at pH ~6 does the zwitterionic form exist.

The –COOH and $-NH_3^+$ groups of an amino acid are ionizable, because they can lose a proton in aqueous solution. As a result, they have different pK_a values. The pK_a of the –COOH group is typically ~2, whereas that of the $-NH_3^+$ group is ~9, as shown in Table 29.1.

Some amino acids, such as aspartic acid and lysine, have acidic or basic side chains. These additional ionizable groups complicate somewhat the acid–base behavior of these amino acids. Table 29.1 lists the pK_a values for these acidic and basic side chains as well.

Figure 29.3 How the charge of a neutral amino acid depends on the pH

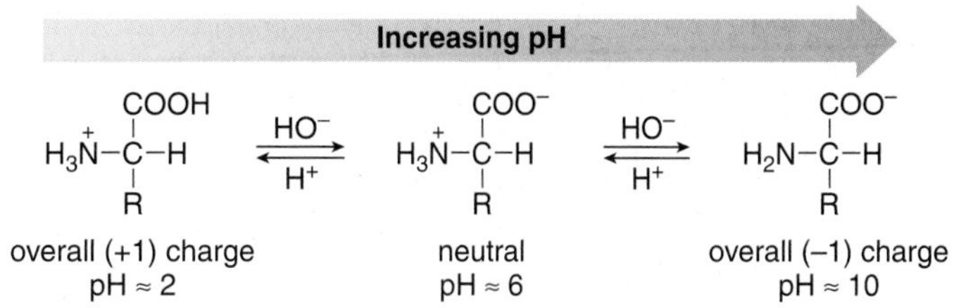

Table 29.1 pK_a Values for the Ionizable Functional Groups of an α-Amino Acid

Amino acid	α-COOH	α-NH_3^+	Side chain	p*I*
Alanine	2.35	9.87	—	6.11
Arginine	2.01	9.04	12.48	10.76
Asparagine	2.02	8.80	—	5.41
Aspartic acid	2.10	9.82	3.86	2.98
Cysteine	2.05	10.25	8.00	5.02
Glutamic acid	2.10	9.47	4.07	3.08
Glutamine	2.17	9.13	—	5.65
Glycine	2.35	9.78	—	6.06
Histidine	1.77	9.18	6.10	7.64
Isoleucine	2.32	9.76	—	6.04
Leucine	2.33	9.74	—	6.04
Lysine	2.18	8.95	10.53	9.74
Methionine	2.28	9.21	—	5.74
Phenylalanine	2.58	9.24	—	5.91
Proline	2.00	10.60	—	6.30
Serine	2.21	9.15	—	5.68
Threonine	2.09	9.10	—	5.60
Tryptophan	2.38	9.39	—	5.88
Tyrosine	2.20	9.11	10.07	5.63
Valine	2.29	9.72	—	6.00

Table 29.1 also lists the isoelectric points (p*I*) for all of the amino acids. Recall from Section 19.14C that the **isoelectric point is the pH at which an amino acid exists primarily in its neutral form,** and that it can be calculated from the average of the pK_a values of the α-COOH and α-NH_3^+ groups (for neutral amino acids only).

Problem 29.2 What form exists at the isoelectric point of each of the following amino acids: (a) valine; (b) leucine; (c) proline; (d) glutamic acid?

Problem 29.3 Explain why the pK_a of the $-NH_3^+$ group of an α-amino acid is lower than the pK_a of the ammonium ion derived from a 1° amine (RNH_3^+). For example the pK_a of the $-NH_3^+$ group of alanine is 9.7 but the pK_a of $CH_3NH_3^+$ is 10.63.

29.2 Synthesis of Amino Acids

Amino acids can be prepared in a variety of ways in the laboratory. Three methods are described, each of which is based on reactions learned in previous chapters.

29.2A S_N2 Reaction of α-Halo Acids with NH_3

The most direct way to synthesize an α-amino acid is by **S_N2 reaction of an α-halo carboxylic acid with a large excess of NH_3.**

General reaction

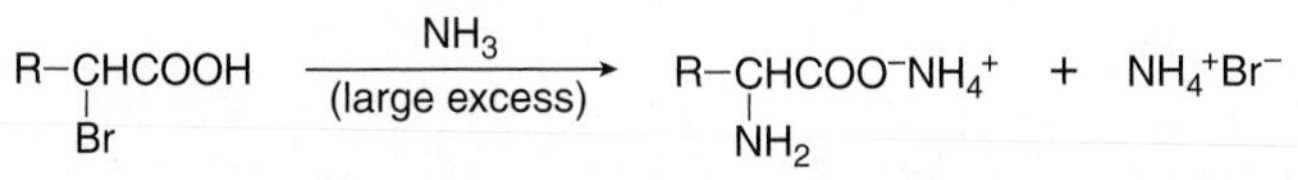
R–CHCOOH
Br
NH3
(large excess)
R–CHCOO⁻NH4⁺ + NH4⁺Br⁻
NH2

Example

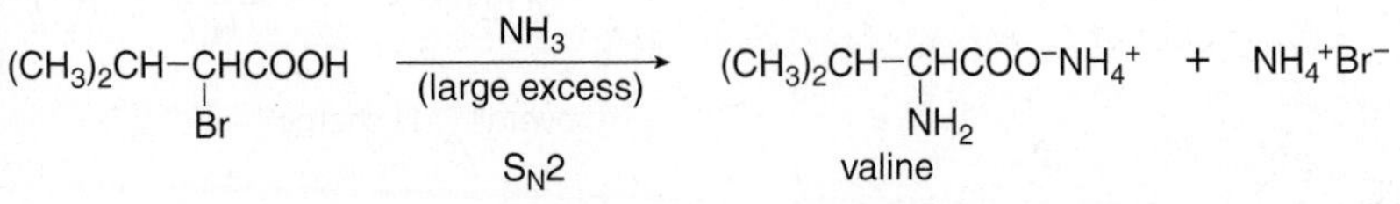
(CH3)2CH–CHCOOH
Br
NH3
(large excess)
SN2
(CH3)2CH–CHCOO⁻NH4⁺ + NH4⁺Br⁻
NH2
valine

Although the alkylation of ammonia with simple alkyl halides does not generally afford high yields of 1° amines (Section 25.7A), this reaction using α-halo carboxylic acids does form the desired amino acids in good yields. In this case, the amino group in the product is both less basic and more sterically crowded than other 1° amines, so that a single alkylation occurs and the desired amino acid is obtained.

Problem 29.4 What α-halo carbonyl compound is needed to synthesize each amino acid: (a) glycine; (b) isoleucine; (c) phenylalanine?

29.2B Alkylation of a Diethyl Malonate Derivative

The second method for preparing amino acids is based on the malonic ester synthesis. Recall from Section 23.9 that this synthesis converts diethyl malonate to a carboxylic acid with a new alkyl group on its α carbon atom.

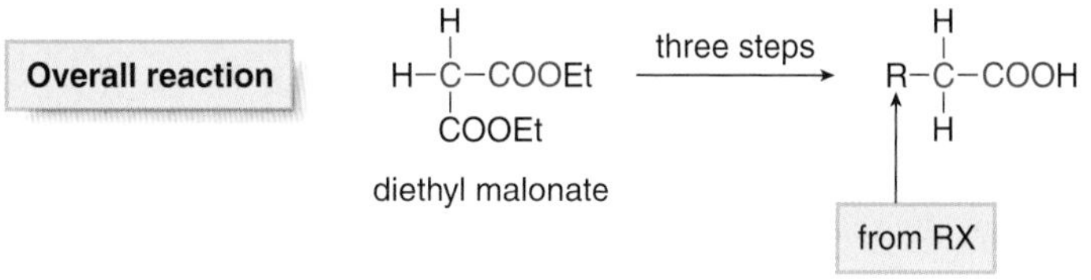

This reaction can be adapted to the synthesis of α-amino acids by using a commercially available derivative of diethyl malonate as starting material. This compound, **diethyl acetamidomalonate,** has a nitrogen atom on the α carbon, which ultimately becomes the NH_2 group on the α carbon of the amino acid.

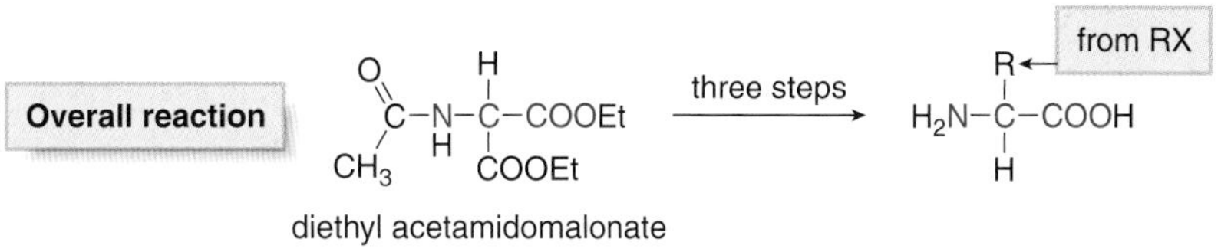

The malonic ester synthesis consists of three steps, and so does this variation to prepare an amino acid.

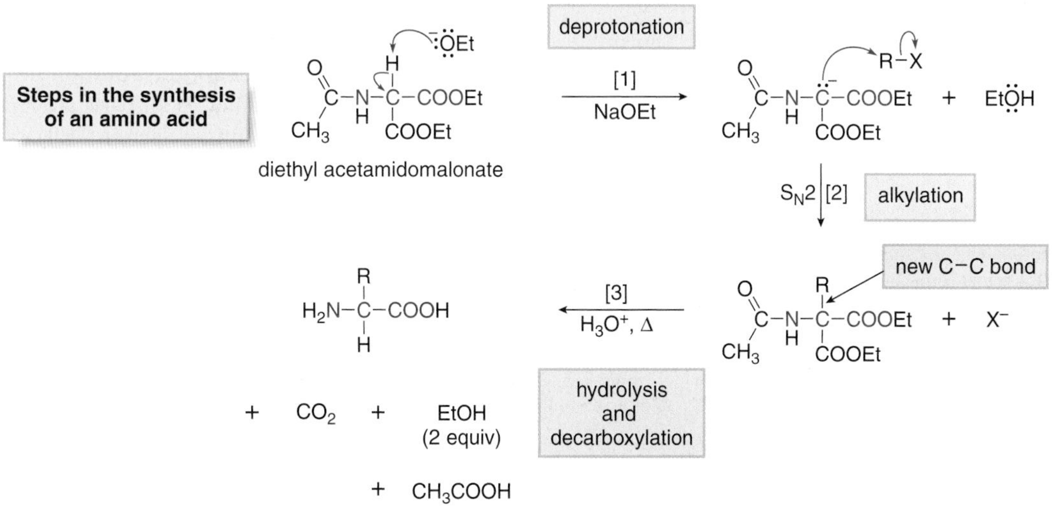

[1] **Deprotonation** of diethyl acetamidomalonate with NaOEt forms an enolate by removal of the acidic proton between the two carbonyl groups.

[2] **Alkylation** of the enolate with an unhindered alkyl halide (usually CH_3X or RCH_2X) forms a substitution product with a new R group on the α carbon.

[3] Heating the alkylation product with aqueous acid results in **hydrolysis** of both esters and the amide, followed by **decarboxylation** to form the amino acid.

Phenylalanine, for example, can be synthesized as follows:

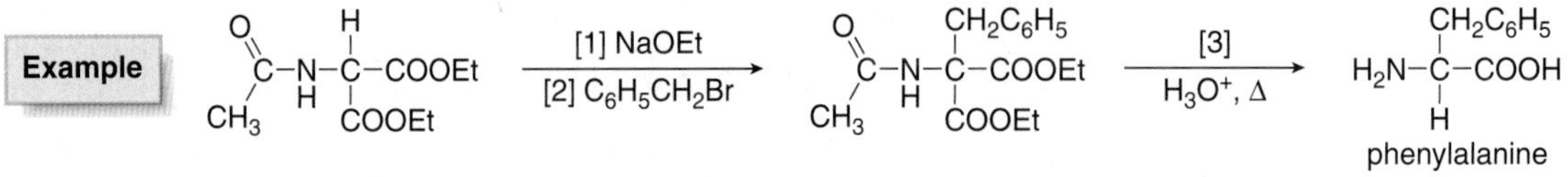

Problem 29.5 The enolate derived from diethyl acetamidomalonate is treated with each of the following alkyl halides. After hydrolysis and decarboxylation, what amino acid is formed: (a) CH_3I; (b) $(CH_3)_2CHCH_2Cl$; (c) $CH_3CH_2CH(CH_3)Br$?

Problem 29.6 What amino acid is formed when $CH_3CONHCH(CO_2Et)_2$ is treated with the following series of reagents: [1] NaOEt; [2] $CH_2{=}O$; [3] H_3O^+, Δ?

29.2C Strecker Synthesis

The third method, the **Strecker amino acid synthesis,** converts an aldehyde into an amino acid by a two-step sequence that adds one carbon atom to the aldehyde carbonyl. Treating an aldehyde with NH_4Cl and NaCN first forms an **α-amino nitrile,** which can then be hydrolyzed in aqueous acid to an amino acid.

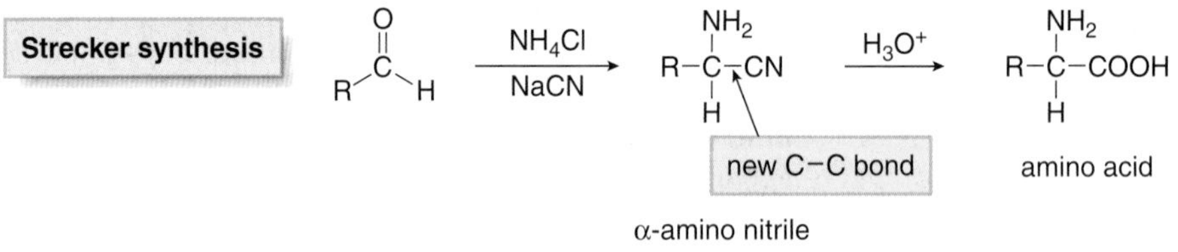

The Strecker synthesis of alanine, for example, is as follows:

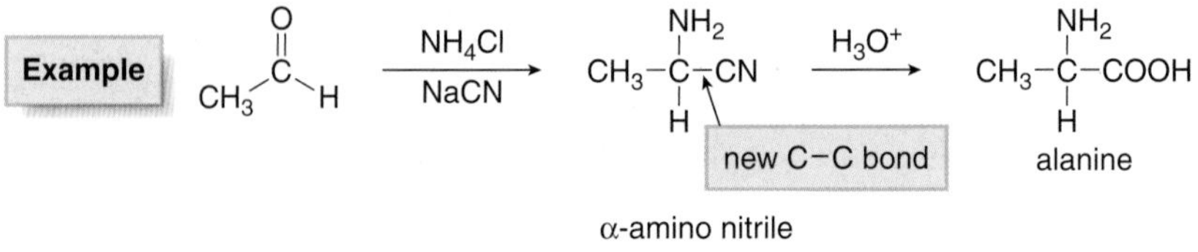

Mechanism 29.1 for the formation of the α-amino nitrile from an aldehyde (the first step in the Strecker synthesis) consists of two parts: **nucleophilic addition of NH_3** to form an imine, followed by **addition of cyanide** to the C=N bond. Both parts are related to earlier mechanisms involving imines (Section 21.11) and cyanohydrins (Section 21.9).

Mechanism 29.1 Formation of an α-Amino Nitrile

Part [1] Nucleophilic attack of NH_3 to form an imine

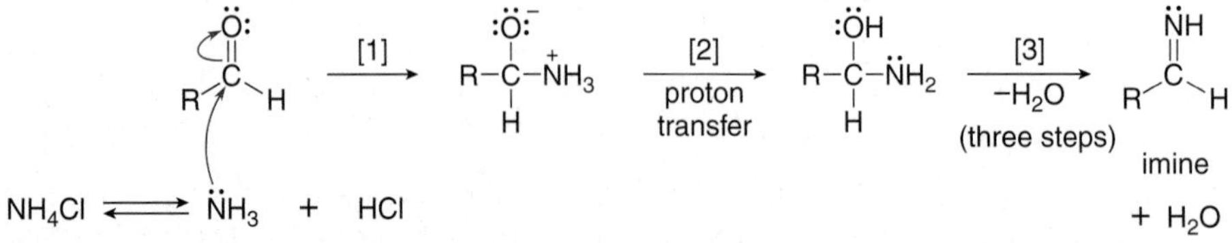

- **Part [1]** Nucleophilic attack of NH_3 followed by proton transfer and loss of H_2O forms an imine. Loss of H_2O occurs by the same three-step process outlined in Mechanism 21.5.

Part [2] Nucleophilic attack of ^-CN to form an α-amino nitrile

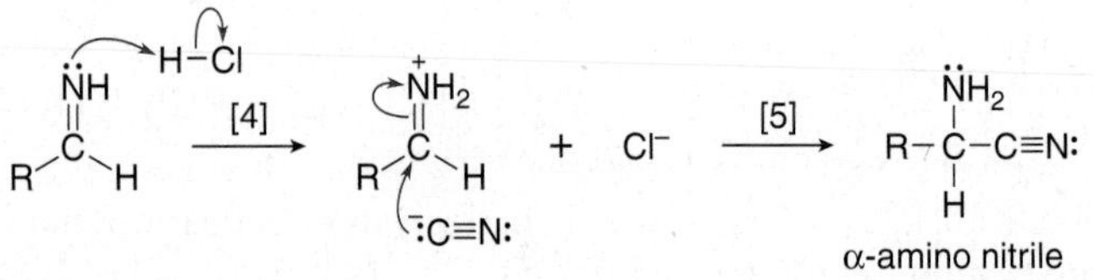

- **Part [2]** Protonation of the imine followed by nucleophilic attack of ^-CN gives the α-amino nitrile.

The details of the second step of the Strecker synthesis, the hydrolysis of a nitrile (RCN) to a carboxylic acid (RCOOH), have already been presented in Section 22.18A.

Figure 29.4 shows how the amino acid methionine can be prepared by all three methods in Section 29.2.

Problem 29.7 What aldehyde is needed to synthesize each amino acid by the Strecker synthesis: (a) valine; (b) leucine; (c) phenylalanine?

Problem 29.8 Draw the products of each reaction.

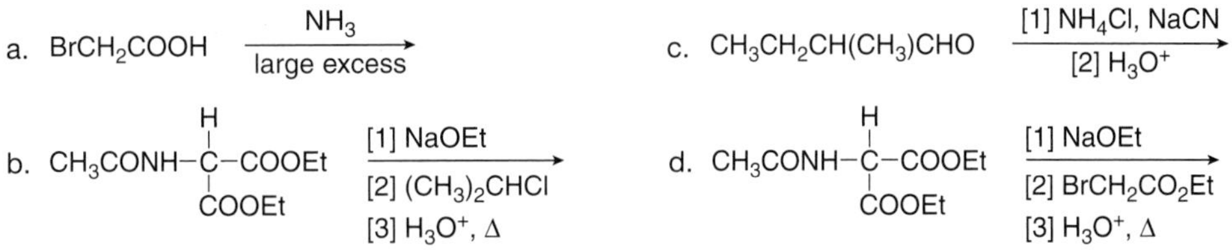
a. $BrCH_2COOH$
NH_3
large excess
c. $CH_3CH_2CH(CH_3)CHO$
[1] NH_4Cl, NaCN
[2] H_3O^+
b.
[1] NaOEt
[2] $(CH_3)_2CHCl$
[3] H_3O^+, Δ
d.
[1] NaOEt
[2] $BrCH_2CO_2Et$
[3] H_3O^+, Δ

Figure 29.4
The synthesis of methionine by three different methods

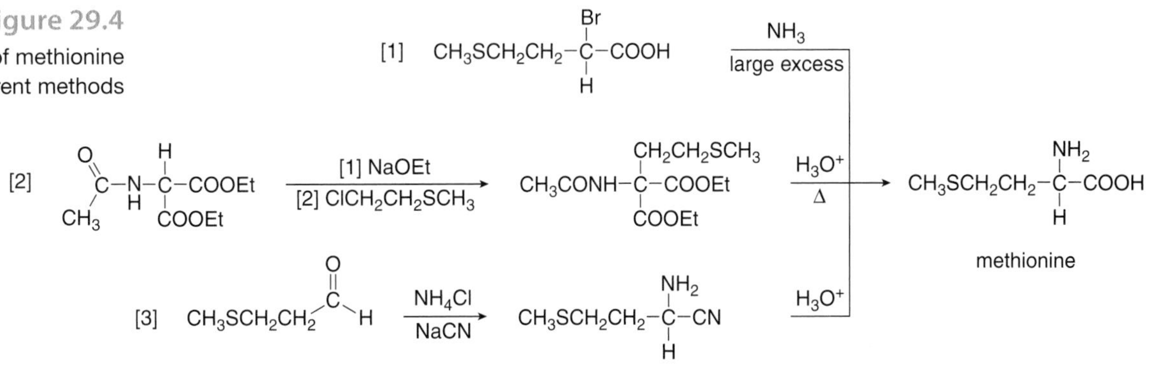
[1]
NH_3
large excess
[2]
[1] NaOEt
[2] $ClCH_2CH_2SCH_3$
H_3O^+
Δ
[3]
NH_4Cl
NaCN
H_3O^+
methionine

Three methods of amino acid synthesis:

[1] S_N2 reaction using an α-halo carboxylic acid
[2] Alkylation of diethyl acetamidomalonate
[3] Strecker synthesis

29.3 Separation of Amino Acids

No matter which of the preceding methods is used to synthesize an amino acid, all three yield a racemic mixture. Naturally occurring amino acids exist as a single enantiomer, however, so the two enantiomers obtained must be separated if they are to be used in biological applications. This is not an easy task. Two enantiomers have the same physical properties, so they cannot be separated by common physical methods, such as distillation or chromatography. Moreover, they react in the same way with achiral reagents, so they cannot be separated by chemical reactions either.

Nonetheless, strategies have been devised to separate two enantiomers using physical separation techniques and chemical reactions. We examine two different strategies in Section 29.3. Then, in Section 29.4, we will discuss a method that affords optically active amino acids without the need for separation.

- **The separation of a racemic mixture into its component enantiomers is called *resolution*. Thus, a racemic mixture is *resolved* into its component enantiomers.**

29.3A Resolution of Amino Acids

The oldest, and perhaps still the most widely used method to separate enantiomers exploits the following fact: **enantiomers have the *same* physical properties, but diastereomers have *different* physical properties.** Thus, a racemic mixture can be resolved using the following general strategy.

[1] **Convert a pair of enantiomers into a pair of diastereomers,** which are now separable because they have different melting points and boiling points.

[2] **Separate the diastereomers.**

[3] **Re-convert each diastereomer into the original enantiomer,** now separated from the other.

This general three-step process is illustrated in Figure 29.5.

Figure 29.5 Resolution of a racemic mixture by converting it to a mixture of diastereomers

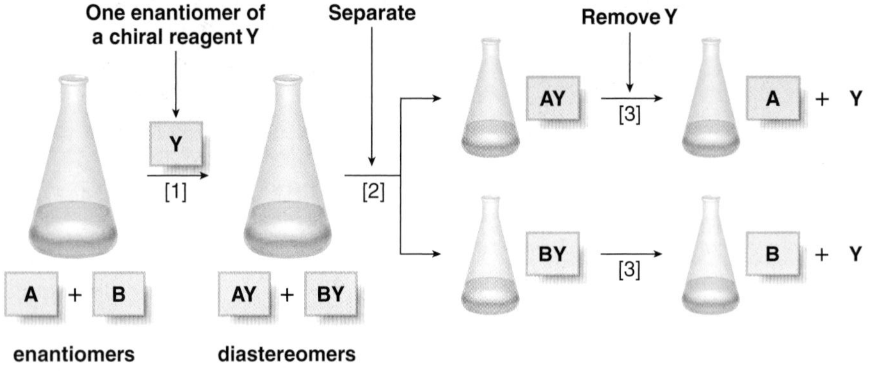

Enantiomers A and B can be separated by reaction with a single enantiomer of a chiral reagent, Y. The process of resolution requires three steps:

[1] Reaction of enantiomers **A** and **B** with **Y** forms two diastereomers, **AY** and **BY.**

[2] Diastereomers **AY** and **BY** have different physical properties, so they can be separated by physical methods such as fractional distillation or crystallization.

[3] **AY** and **BY** are then re-converted to **A** and **B** by a chemical reaction. The two enantiomers **A** and **B** are now separated from each other, and resolution is complete.

To resolve a racemic mixture of amino acids such as (*R*)- and (*S*)-alanine, the racemate is first treated with acetic anhydride to form ***N*-acetyl amino acids.** Each of these amides contains one stereogenic center and they are still enantiomers, so they are *still inseparable.*

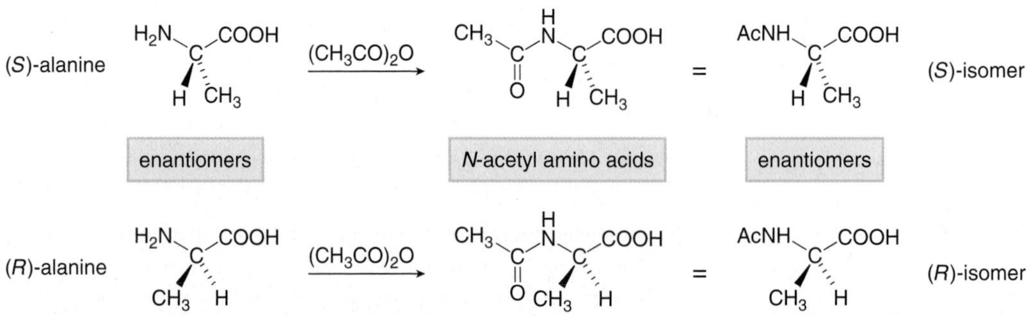

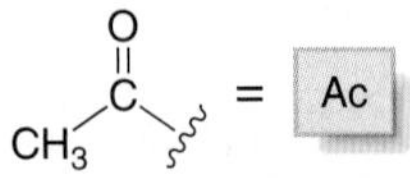

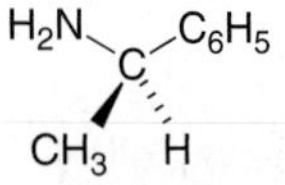

(*R*)-α-methylbenzylamine

a resolving agent

Both enantiomers of *N*-acetyl alanine have a free carboxy group that can react with an amine in an acid–base reaction. **If a chiral amine is used, such as (*R*)-α-methylbenzylamine, the two salts formed are diastereomers, *not* enantiomers.** Diastereomers can be physically separated from each other, so the compound that converts enantiomers into diastereomers is called a **resolving agent.** Either enantiomer of the resolving agent can be used.

How To Use (*R*)-α-Methylbenzylamine to Resolve a Racemic Mixture of Amino Acids

Step [1] React both enantiomers with the *R* isomer of the chiral amine.

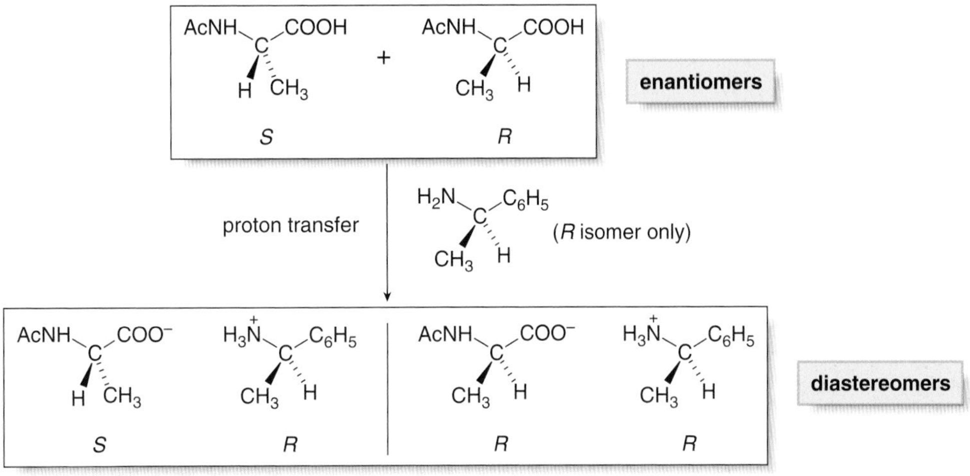

These salts have the *same* configuration around one stereogenic center, but the *opposite* configuration about the other stereogenic center.

Step [2] Separate the diastereomers.

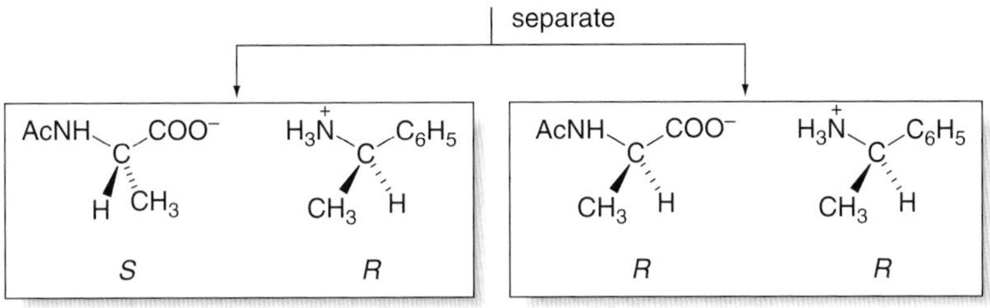

Step [3] Regenerate the amino acid by hydrolysis of the amide.

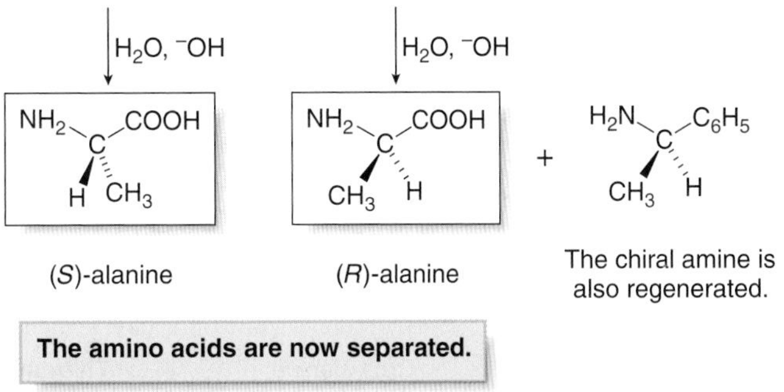

Step [1] is just an acid–base reaction in which the racemic mixture of *N*-acetyl alanines reacts with the same enantiomer of the resolving agent, in this case (*R*)-α-methylbenzylamine. The salts that form are **diastereomers, *not* enantiomers,** because they have the same configuration about one stereogenic center, but the opposite configuration about the other stereogenic center.

In **Step [2],** the diastereomers are separated by some physical technique, such as crystallization or distillation.

In **Step [3],** the amides can be hydrolyzed with aqueous base to regenerate the amino acids. The amino acids are now separated from each other. The optical activity of the amino acids can be measured and compared to their known rotations to determine the purity of each enantiomer.

Problem 29.9 Which of the following amines can be used to resolve a racemic mixture of amino acids?

a. $C_6H_5CH_2CH_2NH_2$

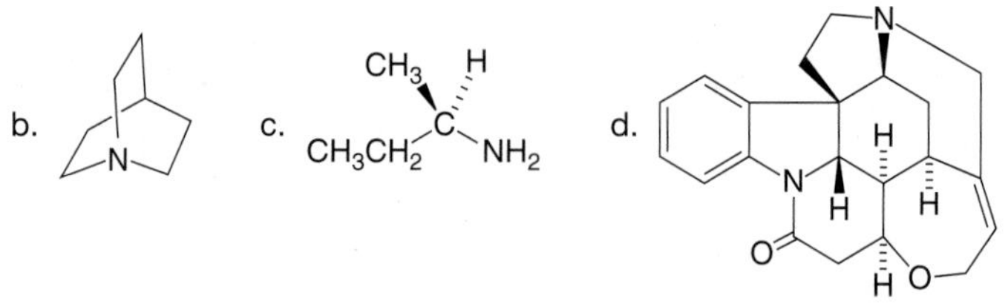

strychnine
(a powerful poison)

Problem 29.10 Write out a stepwise sequence that shows how a racemic mixture of leucine enantiomers can be resolved into optically active amino acids using (*R*)-α-methylbenzylamine.

29.3B Kinetic Resolution of Amino Acids Using Enzymes

A second strategy used to separate amino acids is based on the fact that two enantiomers react differently with chiral reagents. An **enzyme** is typically used as the chiral reagent.

To illustrate this strategy, we begin again with the two enantiomers of *N*-acetyl alanine, which were prepared by treating a racemic mixture of (*R*)- and (*S*)-alanine with acetic anhydride (Section 29.3A). Enzymes called **acylases** hydrolyze amide bonds, such as those found in *N*-acetyl alanine, but only for amides of L-amino acids. Thus, when a racemic mixture of *N*-acetyl alanines is treated with an acylase, only the amide of L-alanine (the *S* stereoisomer) is hydrolyzed to generate L-alanine, whereas the amide of D-alanine (the *R* stereoisomer) is untouched. The reaction mixture now consists of one amino acid and one *N*-acetyl amino acid. Because they have different functional groups with different physical properties, they can be physically separated.

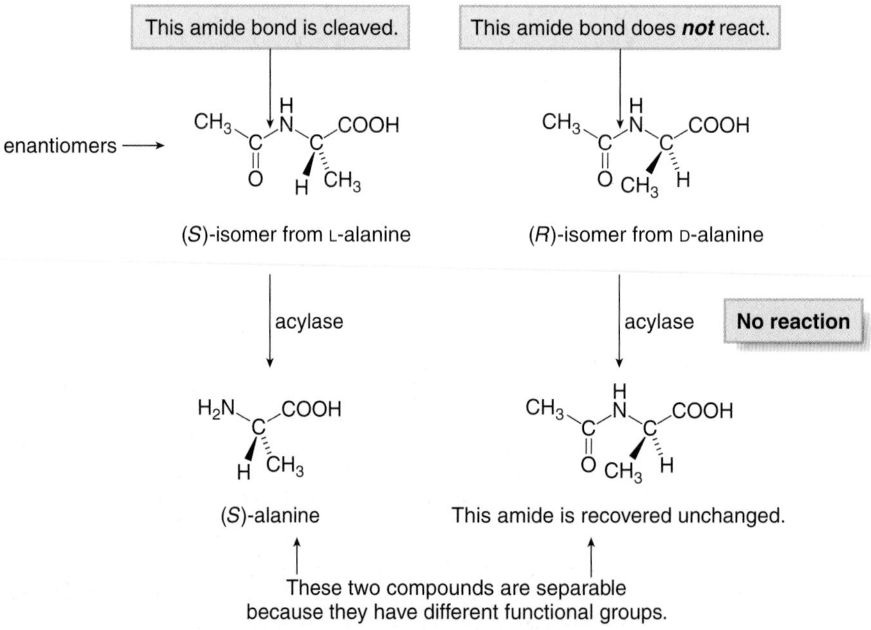

- **Separation of two enantiomers by a chemical reaction that selectively occurs for only one of the enantiomers is called *kinetic resolution.***

Problem 29.11 Draw the organic products formed in the following reaction.

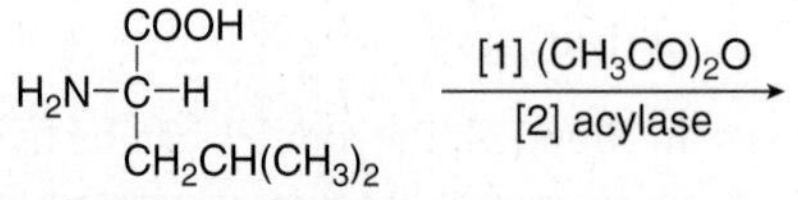

(mixture of enantiomers)

29.4 Enantioselective Synthesis of Amino Acids

Although the two methods introduced in Section 29.3 for resolving racemic mixtures of amino acids make enantiomerically pure amino acids available for further research, half of the reaction product is useless because it has the undesired configuration. Moreover, each of these procedures is costly and time-consuming.

If we use a chiral reagent to synthesize an amino acid, however, it is possible to favor the formation of the desired enantiomer over the other, without having to resort to a resolution. For example, single enantiomers of amino acids have been prepared by using **enantioselective (or asymmetric) hydrogenation reactions.** The success of this approach depends on finding a chiral catalyst, in much the same way that a chiral catalyst is used for the Sharpless asymmetric epoxidation (Section 12.15).

The necessary starting material is an alkene. Addition of H_2 to the double bond forms an *N*-acetyl amino acid with a new stereogenic center on the α carbon to the carboxy group. With proper choice of a chiral catalyst, the naturally occurring *S* configuration can be obtained as product.

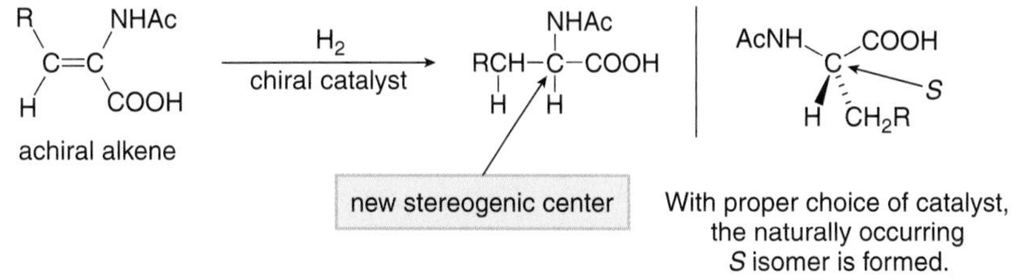

Several chiral catalysts with complex structures have now been developed for this purpose. Many contain **rhodium** as the metal, complexed to a chiral molecule containing one or more phosphorus atoms. One example, abbreviated simply as **Rh*,** is drawn below.

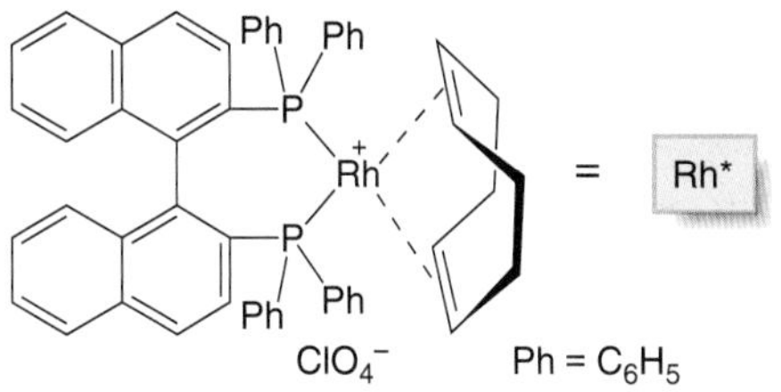

chiral hydrogenation catalyst

Ryoji Noyori shared the 2001 Nobel Prize in Chemistry for developing methods for asymmetric hydrogenation reactions using the chiral BINAP catalyst.

This catalyst is synthesized from a rhodium salt and a phosphorus compound, 2,2'-bis(diphenylphosphino)-1,1'-binaphthyl **(BINAP).** It is the BINAP moiety (Figure 29.6) that makes the catalyst chiral.

Figure 29.6
The structure of BINAP

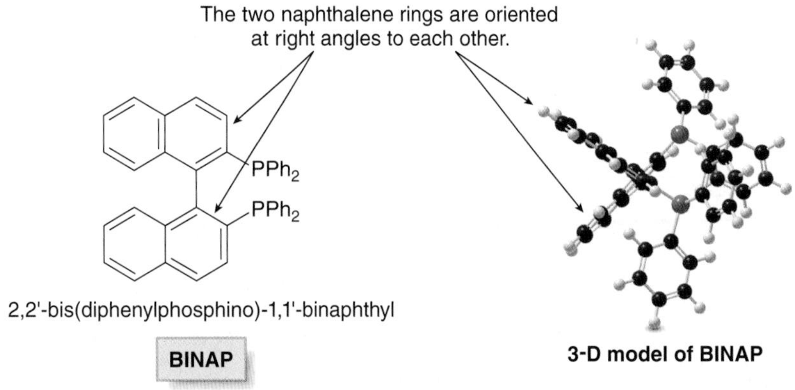

Twistoflex and helicene (Section 17.5) are two more aromatic compounds whose shape makes them chiral.

BINAP is one of a small number of molecules that is chiral even though it has no tetrahedral stereogenic centers. Its shape makes it a chiral molecule. The two naphthalene rings of the BINAP molecule are oriented at almost 90° to each other to minimize steric interactions between the hydrogen atoms on adjacent rings. This rigid three-dimensional shape makes BINAP non-superimposable on its mirror image, and thus it is a chiral compound.

The following graphic shows how enantioselective hydrogenation can be used to synthesize a single stereoisomer of phenylalanine. Treating achiral alkene **A** with H_2 and the chiral rhodium catalyst Rh* forms the *S* isomer of *N*-acetyl phenylalanine in 100% *ee*. Hydrolysis of the acetyl group on nitrogen then yields a single enantiomer of phenylalanine.

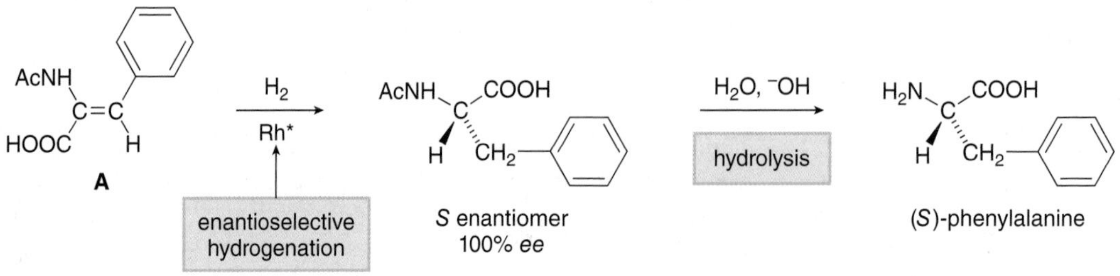

Problem 29.12 What alkene is needed to synthesize each amino acid by an enantioselective hydrogenation reaction using H_2 and Rh*: (a) alanine; (b) leucine; (c) glutamine?

29.5 Peptides

When amino acids are joined together by amide bonds, they form larger molecules called **peptides** and **proteins.**

- A *dipeptide* has two amino acids joined together by *one* amide bond.
- A *tripeptide* has three amino acids joined together by *two* amide bonds.

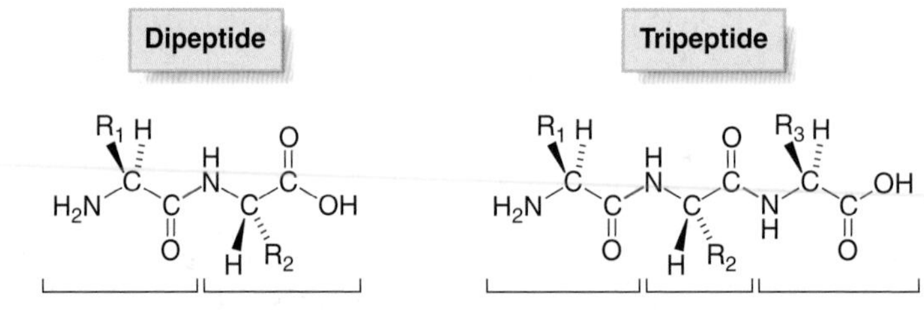

Two amino acids joined together. Three amino acids joined together.
[Amide bonds are drawn in red.]

Polypeptides and **proteins** both have many amino acids joined together in long linear chains, but the term **protein** is usually reserved for polymers of more than 40 amino acids.

- The amide bonds in peptides and proteins are called *peptide bonds.*
- The individual amino acids are called *amino acid residues.*

29.5A Simple Peptides

To form a dipeptide, the amino group of one amino acid forms an amide bond with the carboxy group of another amino acid. Because each amino acid has both an amino group and a carboxy group, **two different dipeptides can be formed.** This is illustrated with alanine and cysteine.

[1] **The COOH group of alanine can combine with the NH_2 group of cysteine.**

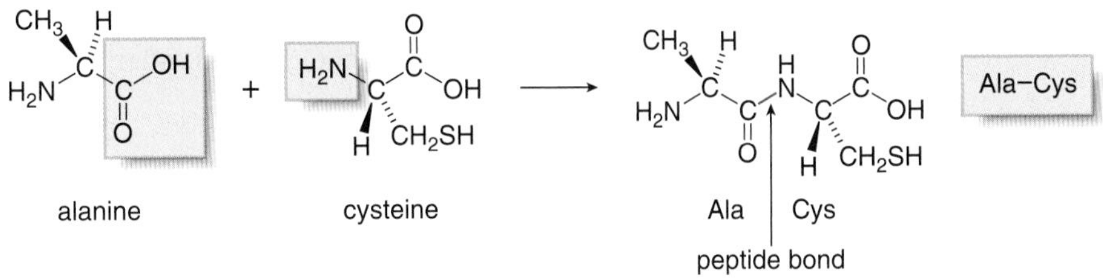
alanine
cysteine
Ala–Cys
Ala
Cys
peptide bond

[2] **The COOH group of cysteine can combine with the NH_2 group of alanine.**

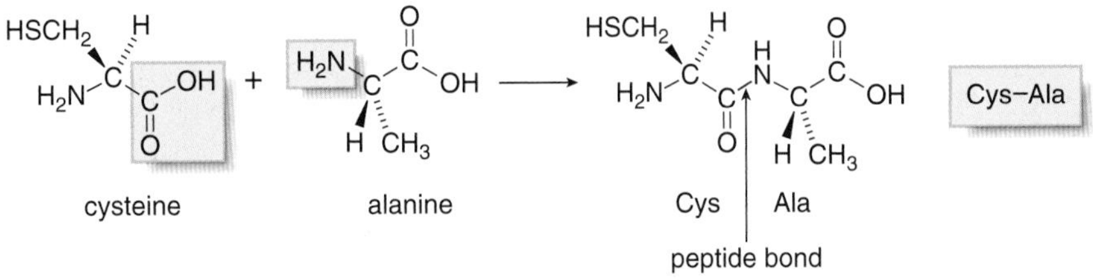
cysteine
alanine
Cys–Ala
Cys
Ala
peptide bond

These compounds are **constitutional isomers** of each other. Both have a free amino group at one end of their chains and a free carboxy group at the other.

- **The amino acid with the free amino group is called the *N-terminal amino acid.***
- **The amino acid with the free carboxy group is called the *C-terminal amino acid.***

By convention, **the N-terminal amino acid is always written at the left end of the chain and the C-terminal amino acid at the right.** The peptide can be abbreviated by writing the one- or three-letter symbols for the amino acids in the chain from the N-terminal to the C-terminal end. Thus, Ala–Cys has alanine at the N-terminal end and cysteine at the C-terminal end, whereas Cys–Ala has cysteine at the N-terminal end and alanine at the C-terminal end. Sample Problem 29.1 shows how this convention applies to a tripeptide.

Sample Problem 29.1

Draw the structure of the following tripeptide, and label its N-terminal and C-terminal amino acids: Ala–Gly–Ser.

Solution

Draw the structures of the amino acids in order from **left to right,** placing the COOH of one amino acid *next* to the NH_2 group of the adjacent amino acid. Always draw the **NH_2 group on the *left*** and the **COOH group on the *right.*** Then, join adjacent COOH and NH_2 groups together in amide bonds to form the tripeptide.

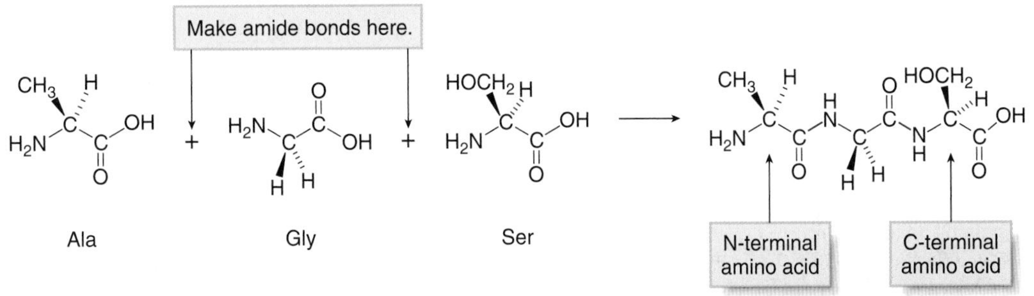
Make amide bonds here.
Ala
Gly
Ser
N-terminal amino acid
C-terminal amino acid

tripeptide **Ala–Gly–Ser**
[The new peptide bonds are drawn in red.]

The N-terminal amino acid is **alanine,** and the C-terminal amino acid is **serine.**

The tripeptide in Sample Problem 29.1 has one N-terminal amino acid, one C-terminal amino acid, and two peptide bonds.

- **No matter how many amino acid residues are present, there is only *one* N-terminal amino acid and *one* C-terminal amino acid.**
- **For *n* amino acids in the chain, the number of amide bonds is *n* – 1.**

Problem 29.13 Draw the structure of each peptide. Label the N-terminal and C-terminal amino acids and all amide bonds.

a. Val–Glu b. Gly–His–Leu c. M–A–T–T

Problem 29.14 Name each peptide using both the one-letter and the three-letter abbreviations for the names of the component amino acids.

a. 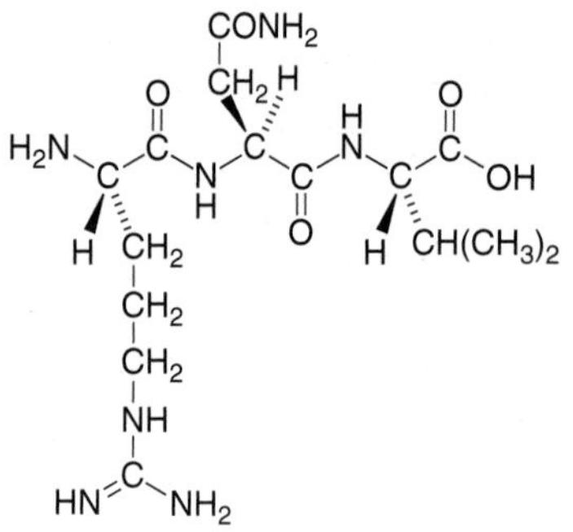

b. 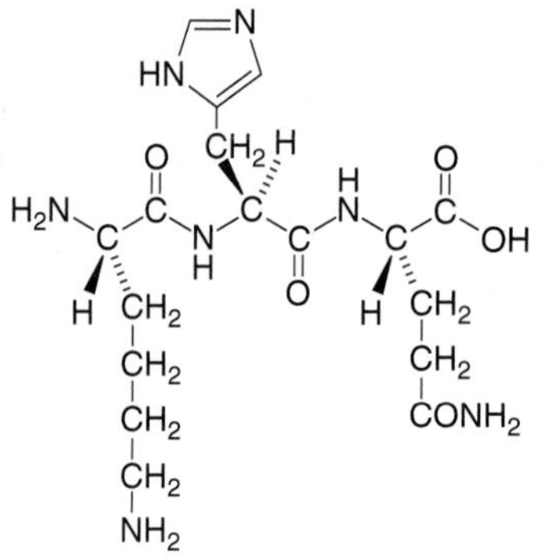

Problem 29.15 How many different tripeptides can be formed from three different amino acids?

29.5B The Peptide Bond

The carbonyl carbon of an amide is ***sp*² hybridized** and has **trigonal planar** geometry. A second resonance structure can be drawn that delocalizes the nonbonded electron pair on the N atom. Amides are more resonance stabilized than other acyl compounds, so the resonance structure having the C=N makes a significant contribution to the hybrid.

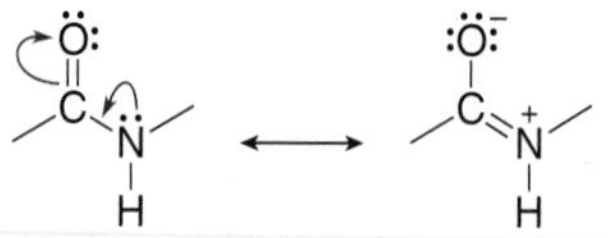

two resonance structures for the peptide bond

Resonance stabilization has important consequences. Rotation about the C–N bond is restricted because it has partial double bond character. As a result, there are two possible conformations.

Two conformations of the peptide bond

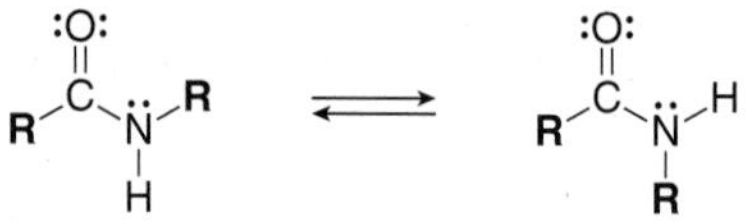

s-trans *s*-cis

Recall from Section 16.6 that 1,3-butadiene can also exist as *s*-cis and *s*-trans conformations. In 1,3-butadiene, the *s*-cis conformation has the two double bonds on the same side of the single bond (dihedral angle = 0°), whereas the *s*-trans conformation has them on opposite sides (dihedral angle = 180°).

- **The *s*-trans conformation has the two R groups oriented on *opposite* sides of the C–N bond.**
- **The *s*-cis conformation has the two R groups oriented on the *same* side of the C–N bond.**
- **The *s*-trans conformation of a peptide bond is typically more stable than the *s*-cis, because the *s*-trans has the two bulky R groups located farther from each other.**

The planar geometry of the peptide bond is analogous to the planar geometry of ethylene (or any other alkene), where the double bond between sp^2 hybridized carbon atoms makes all of the bond angles ~120° and puts all six atoms in the same plane.

A second consequence of resonance stabilization is that **all six atoms involved in the peptide bond lie in the same plane.** All bond angles are ~120° and the C=O and N–H bonds are oriented 180° from each other.

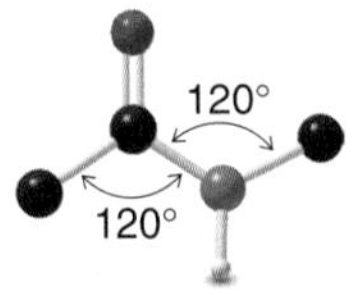

120°
120°

These six atoms lie in a plane.

The structure of a tetrapeptide illustrates the results of these effects in a long peptide chain.

- **The *s*-trans arrangement makes a long chain with a zigzag arrangement.**
- **In each peptide bond, the N–H and C=O bonds lie parallel and at 180° with respect to each other.**

A tetrapeptide

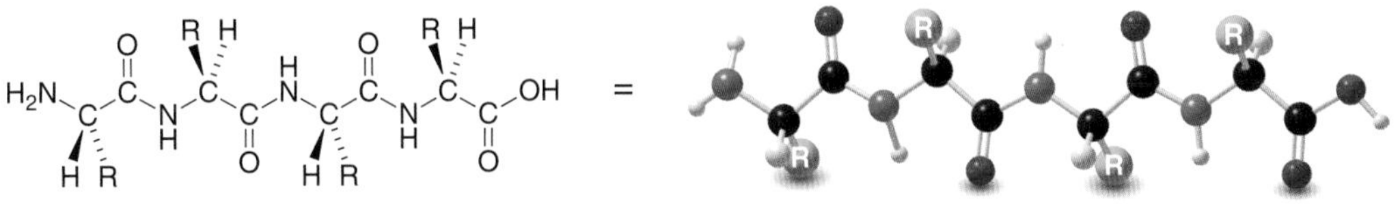

H2N
OH
R

29.5C Interesting Peptides

Even relatively simple peptides can have important biological functions. **Bradykinin,** for example, is a peptide hormone composed of nine amino acids. It stimulates smooth muscle contraction, dilates blood vessels, and causes pain. Bradykinin is a component of bee venom.

Arg–Pro–Pro–Gly–Phe–Ser–Pro–Phe–Arg

bradykinin

Oxytocin and **vasopressin** are nonapeptide hormones, too. Their sequences are identical except for two amino acids, yet this is enough to give them very different biological activities. Oxytocin induces labor by stimulating the contraction of uterine muscles, and it stimulates the flow of milk in nursing mothers. Vasopressin, on the other hand, controls blood pressure by regulating smooth muscle contraction. The N-terminal amino acid in both hormones is a cysteine residue, and the C-terminal residue is glycine. Instead of a free carboxy group, both peptides have an NH_2 group in place of OH, so this is indicated with the additional NH_2 group drawn at the end of the chain.

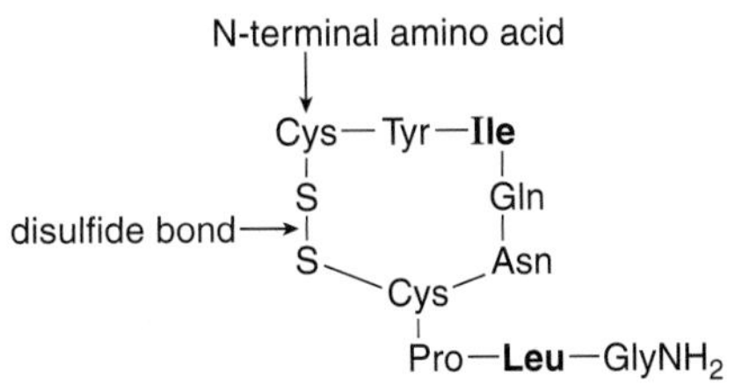

N-terminal amino acid
Cys—Tyr—Ile
S
Gln
disulfide bond
S
Asn
Cys
Pro—Leu—GlyNH2

oxytocin

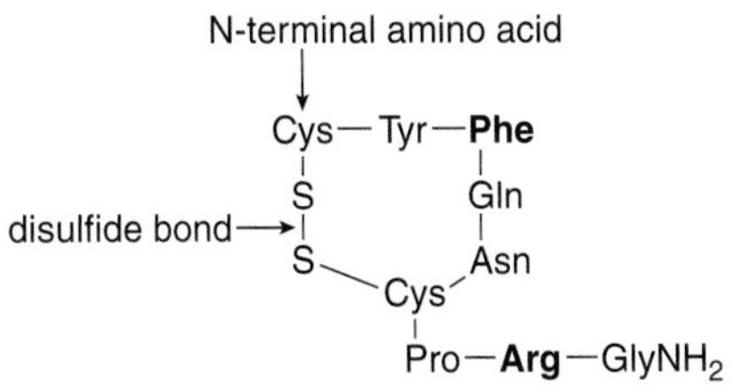

N-terminal amino acid
Cys—Tyr—Phe
S
Gln
disulfide bond
S
Asn
Cys
Pro—Arg—GlyNH2

vasopressin

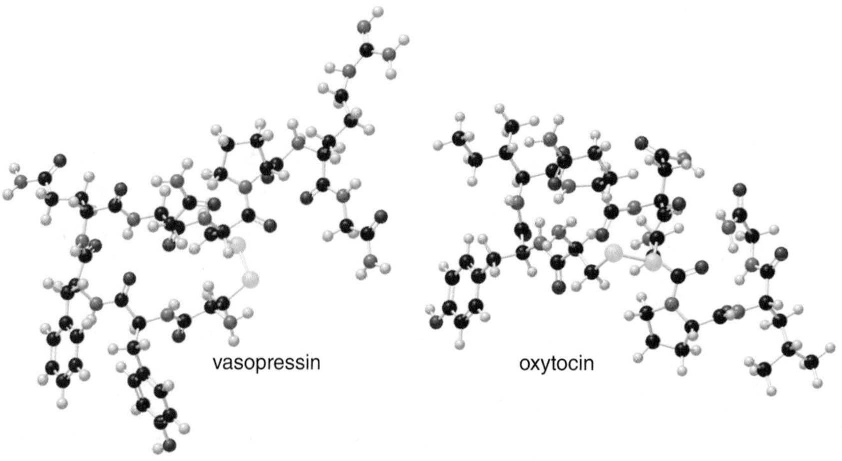

Figure 29.7
Three-dimensional structures of vasopressin and oxytocin

The structure of both peptides includes a **disulfide bond,** a form of covalent bonding in which the –SH groups from two cysteine residues are oxidized to form a sulfur–sulfur bond. In oxytocin and vasopressin, the disulfide bonds make the peptides cyclic. Three-dimensional structures of oxytocin and vasopressin are shown in Figure 29.7.

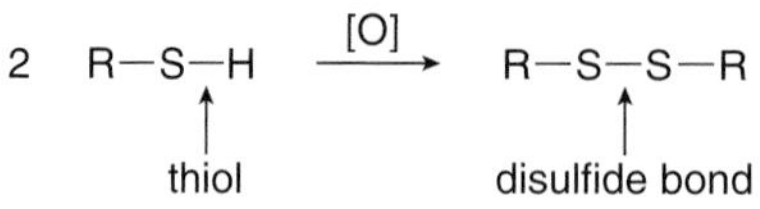

The artificial sweetener **aspartame** (Figure 28.11) is the methyl ester of the dipeptide Asp–Phe. This synthetic peptide is 180 times sweeter (on a gram-for-gram basis) than sucrose (common table sugar). Both of the amino acids in aspartame have the naturally occurring L-configuration. If the D-amino acid is substituted for either Asp or Phe, the resulting compound tastes bitter.

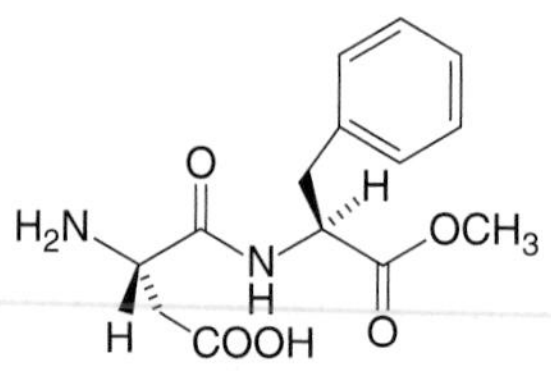

aspartame
the methyl ester of Asp–Phe
a synthetic artificial sweetener

Problem 29.16 Draw the structure of leu-enkephalin, a pentapeptide that acts as an analgesic and opiate, and has the following sequence: Tyr–Gly–Gly–Phe–Leu. (The structure of a related peptide, met-enkephalin, appeared in Section 22.6B.)

Problem 29.17 Glutathione, a powerful antioxidant that destroys harmful oxidizing agents in cells, is composed of glutamic acid, cysteine, and glycine, and has the following structure:

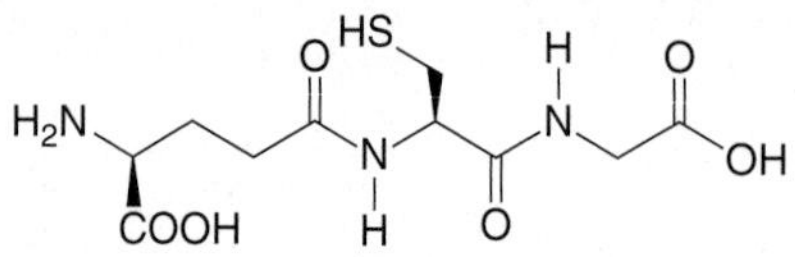

glutathione

a. What product is formed when glutathione reacts with an oxidizing agent?
b. What is unusual about the peptide bond between glutamic acid and cysteine?

29.6 Peptide Sequencing

To determine the structure of a peptide, we must know not only what amino acids comprise it, but also the sequence of the amino acids in the peptide chain. Although mass spectrometry has become an increasingly powerful method for the analysis of high molecular weight proteins (Section 13.4), chemical methods to determine peptide structure are still widely used and presented in this section.

29.6A Amino Acid Analysis

The structure determination of a peptide begins by analyzing the total amino acid composition. The amide bonds are first hydrolyzed by heating with hydrochloric acid for 24 h to form the individual amino acids. The resulting mixture is then separated using high-performance liquid chromatography (HPLC), a technique in which a solution of amino acids is placed on a column and individual amino acids move through the column at characteristic rates, often dependent on polarity.

This process determines both the identity of the individual amino acids and the amount of each present, but it tells nothing about the order of the amino acids in the peptide. For example, complete hydrolysis and HPLC analysis of the tetrapeptide Gly–Gly–Phe–Tyr would indicate the presence of three amino acids—glycine, phenylalanine, and tyrosine—and show that there are twice as many glycine residues as phenylalanine or tyrosine residues. The exact order of the amino acids in the peptide chain must then be determined by additional methods

29.6B Identifying the N-Terminal Amino Acid—The Edman Degradation

To determine the sequence of amino acids in a peptide chain, a variety of procedures are often combined. One especially useful technique is to identify the N-terminal amino acid using the **Edman degradation.** In the Edman degradation, amino acids are cleaved one at a time from the N-terminal end, the identity of the amino acid determined, and the process repeated until the entire sequence is known. Automated sequencers using this methodology are now available to sequence peptides containing up to about 50 amino acids.

The Edman degradation is based on the reaction of the nucleophilic NH_2 group of the N-terminal amino acid with the electrophilic carbon of phenyl isothiocyanate, $C_6H_5N{=}C{=}S$. When the N-terminal amino acid is removed from the peptide chain, two products are formed: **an *N*-phenylthiohydantoin (PTH) and a new peptide with one *fewer* amino acid.**

Edman degradation

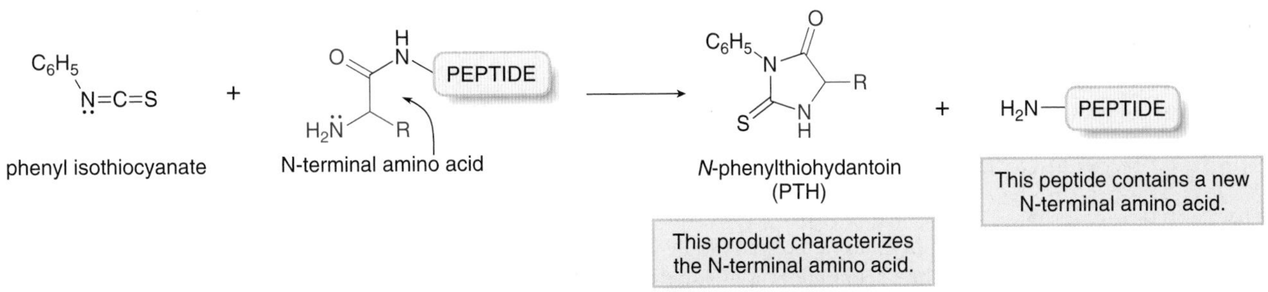

The *N*-phenylthiohydantoin derivative contains the atoms of the N-terminal amino acid. This product identifies the N-terminal amino acid in the peptide because the PTH derivatives of all 20 naturally occurring amino acids are known and characterized. The new peptide formed in the Edman degradation has one amino acid fewer than the original peptide. Moreover, it contains a new N-terminal amino acid, so the process can be repeated.

Mechanism 29.2 illustrates some of the key steps of the Edman degradation. The nucleophilic N-terminal NH_2 group adds to the electrophilic carbon of phenyl isothiocyanate to form an *N*-phenylthiourea, the product of nucleophilic addition (Part [1]). Intramolecular cyclization followed by elimination results in cleavage of the terminal amide bond in Part [2] to form a new peptide with one fewer amino acid. A sulfur heterocycle, called a thiazolinone, is also formed, which rearranges by a multistep pathway (Part [3]) to form an *N*-phenylthiohydantoin. The R group in this product identifies the amino acid located at the N-terminal end.

Mechanism 29.2 Edman Degradation

Part [1] Formation of an *N*-phenylthiourea

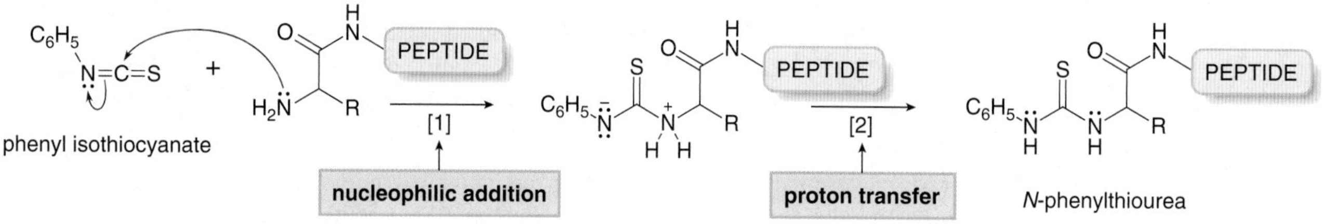

- Addition of the free amino group from the N-terminal amino acid to the electrophilic carbon of phenyl isothiocyanate followed by proton transfer forms an *N*-phenylthiourea.

Part [2] Cleavage of the amide bond from the N-terminal amino acid

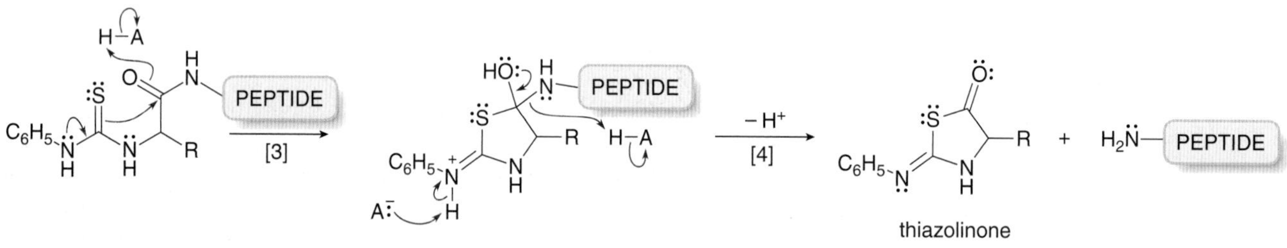

- Nucleophilic addition in Step [3] followed by loss of the amino group in Step [4] forms two products: a five-membered thiazolinone ring and a peptide chain that contains one fewer amino acid than the original peptide.

Part [3] Rearrangement to form an *N*-phenylthiohydantoin (PTH)

- Under the conditions of the reaction, the thiazolinone rearranges by a multistep pathway to form an *N*-phenylthiohydantoin (PTH). This product contains the original N-terminal amino acid.

In theory a protein of any length can be sequenced using the Edman degradation, but in practice, the accumulation of small quantities of unwanted by-products limits sequencing to proteins having fewer than approximately 50 amino acids.

Problem 29.18 Draw the structure of the *N*-phenylthiohydantoin formed by initial Edman degradation of each peptide: (a) Ala–Gly–Phe–Phe; (b) Val–Ile–Tyr.

29.6C Partial Hydrolysis of a Peptide

Additional structural information can be obtained by cleaving some, but not all, of the amide bonds in a peptide. Partial hydrolysis of a peptide with acid forms smaller fragments in a random fashion. Sequencing these peptides and identifying sites of overlap can be used to determine the sequence of the complete peptide, as shown in Sample Problem 29.2.

Sample Problem 29.2 Give the amino acid sequence of a hexapeptide that contains the amino acids Ala, Val, Ser, Ile, Gly, Tyr, and forms the following fragments when partially hydrolyzed with HCl: Gly–Ile–Val, Ala–Ser–Gly, and Tyr–Ala.

Solution

Looking for points of overlap in the sequences of the smaller fragments shows how the fragments should be pieced together. In this example, the fragment Ala–Ser–Gly contains amino acids common to the two other fragments, thus showing how the three fragments can be joined together.

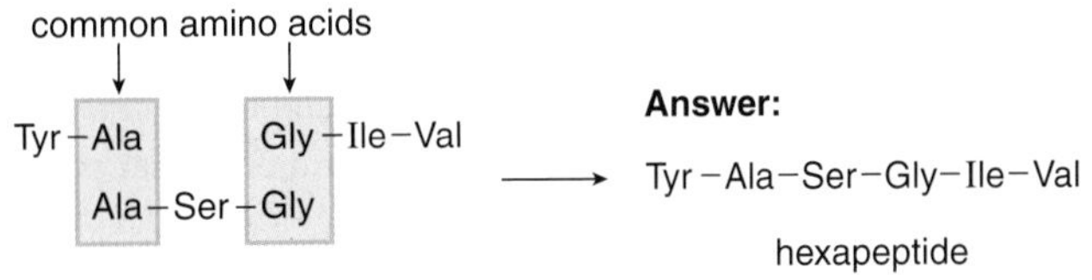
common amino acids
Tyr–Ala
Gly–Ile–Val
Ala–Ser–Gly
Answer:
Tyr–Ala–Ser–Gly–Ile–Val
hexapeptide

Problem 29.19 Give the amino acid sequence of an octapeptide that contains the amino acids Tyr, Ala, Leu (2 equiv), Cys, Gly, Glu, and Val, and forms the following fragments when partially hydrolyzed with HCl: Val–Cys–Gly–Glu, Ala–Leu–Tyr, and Tyr–Leu–Val–Cys.

Peptides can also be hydrolyzed at specific sites using enzymes. The enzyme carboxypeptidase catalyzes the hydrolysis of the amide bond nearest the C-terminal end, forming the C-terminal amino acid and a peptide with one fewer amino acid. In this way, carboxypeptidase is used to identify the C-terminal amino acid.

Other enzymes catalyze the hydrolysis of amide bonds formed with specific amino acids. For example:

- **Trypsin catalyzes the hydrolysis of amides with a carbonyl group that is part of the basic amino acids arginine and lysine.**
- **Chymotrypsin hydrolyzes amides with carbonyl groups that are part of the aromatic amino acids phenylalanine, tyrosine, and tryptophan.**

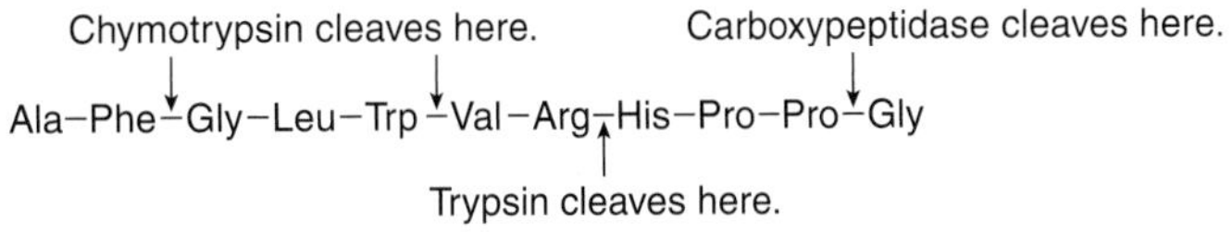
Chymotrypsin cleaves here.
Carboxypeptidase cleaves here.
Ala–Phe–Gly–Leu–Trp–Val–Arg–His–Pro–Pro–Gly
Trypsin cleaves here.

Table 29.2 summarizes these enzyme specificities used in peptide sequencing.

Table 29.2 Cleavage Sites of Specific Enzymes in Peptide Sequencing

Enzyme	Site of cleavage
Carboxypeptidase	Amide bond nearest to the C-terminal amino acid
Chymotrypsin	Amide bond with a carbonyl group from Phe, Tyr, or Trp
Trypsin	Amide bond with a carbonyl group from Arg or Lys

Problem 29.20 (a) What products are formed when each peptide is treated with trypsin? (b) What products are formed when each peptide is treated with chymotrypsin?

[1] Gly–Ala–Phe–Leu–Lys–Ala
[2] Phe–Tyr–Gly–Cys–Arg–Ser
[3] Thr–Pro–Lys–Glu–His–Gly–Phe–Cys–Trp–Val–Val–Phe

Sample Problem 29.3 Deduce the sequence of a pentapeptide that contains the amino acids Ala, Glu, Gly, Ser, and Tyr, from the following experimental data. Edman degradation cleaves Gly from the pentapeptide, and carboxypeptidase forms Ala and a tetrapeptide. Treatment of the pentapeptide with chymotrypsin forms a dipeptide and a tripeptide. Partial hydrolysis forms Gly, Ser, and the tripeptide Tyr–Glu–Ala.

Solution

Use each result to determine the location of an amino acid in the pentapeptide.

Experiment		Result
• Edman degradation identifies the N-terminal amino acid—in this case, Gly.	→	Gly– _ – _ – _ – _
• Carboxypeptidase identifies the C-terminal amino acid (Ala) when it is cleaved from the end of the chain.	→	Gly– _ – _ – _ –Ala
• Chymotrypsin cleaves amide bonds that contain a carbonyl group from an aromatic amino acid—Tyr in this case. Because a dipeptide and tripeptide are obtained after treatment with chymotrypsin, Tyr must be the C-terminal amino acid of either the di- or tripeptide. As a result, Tyr must be either the second or third amino acid in the pentapeptide chain.	→	Gly–Tyr– _ – _ –Ala or Gly– _ –Tyr– _ –Ala
• Partial hydrolysis forms the tripeptide Tyr–Glu–Ala. Because Ala is the C-terminal amino acid, this result identifies the last three amino acids in the chain.	→	Gly– _ –Tyr–Glu–Ala
• The last amino acid, Ser, must be located at the only remaining position, the second amino acid in the pentapeptide, and the complete sequence is determined.	→	Gly–Ser–Tyr–Glu–Ala

Problem 29.21 Deduce the sequence of a heptapeptide that contains the amino acids Ala, Arg, Glu, Gly, Leu, Phe, and Ser, from the following experimental data. Edman degradation cleaves Leu from the heptapeptide, and carboxypeptidase forms Glu and a hexapeptide. Treatment of the heptapeptide with chymotrypsin forms a hexapeptide and a single amino acid. Treatment of the heptapeptide with trypsin forms a pentapeptide and a dipeptide. Partial hydrolysis forms Glu, Leu, Phe, and the tripeptides Gly–Ala–Ser and Ala–Ser–Arg.

29.7 Peptide Synthesis

The synthesis of a specific dipeptide, such as Ala–Gly from alanine and glycine, is complicated because both amino acids have two functional groups. As a result, four products—namely, Ala–Ala, Ala–Gly, Gly–Gly, and Gly–Ala—are possible.

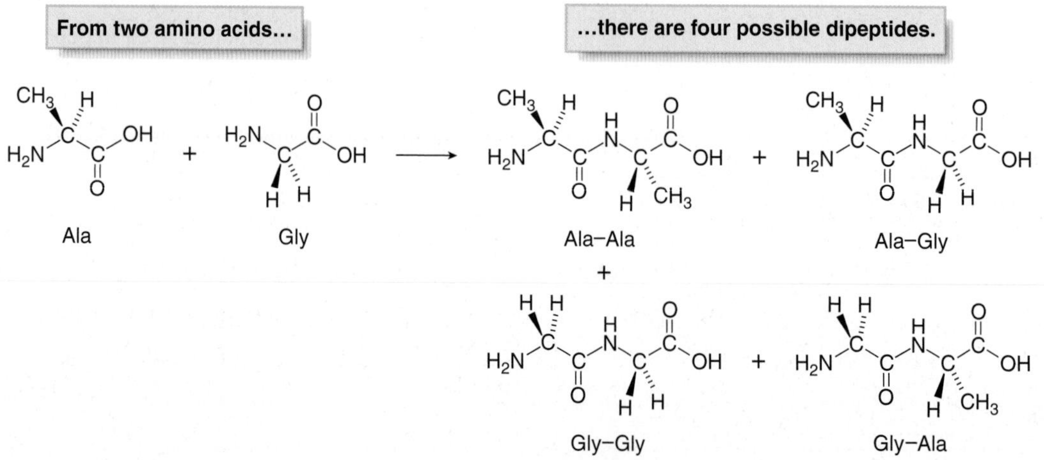

How do we selectively join the COOH group of alanine with the NH_2 group of glycine?

- **Protect the functional groups that we don't want to react, and then form the amide bond.**

How To Synthesize a Dipeptide from Two Amino Acids

Example

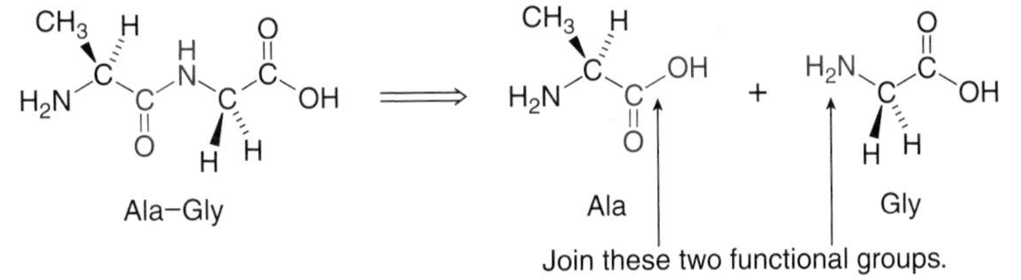
Ala–Gly
Ala
Gly
Join these two functional groups.

Step [1] Protect the NH_2 group of alanine.

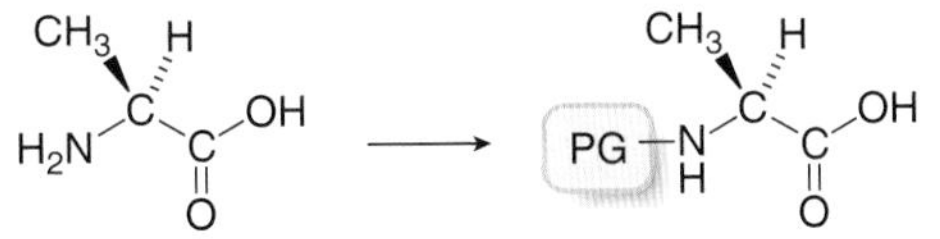

[PG = protecting group]

Ala

Step [2] Protect the COOH group of glycine.

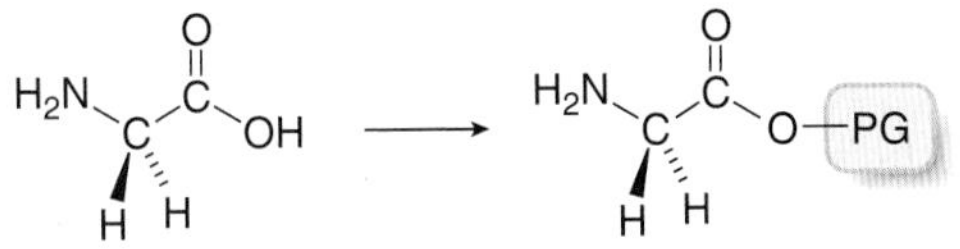

Gly

Step [3] Form the amide bond with DCC.

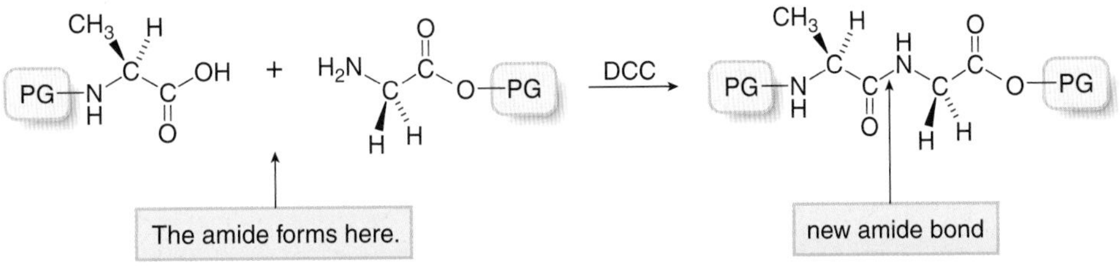
DCC
The amide forms here.
new amide bond

Dicyclohexylcarbodiimide (**DCC**) is a reagent commonly used to form amide bonds (see Section 22.10D). DCC makes the OH group of the carboxylic acid a better leaving group, thus **activating the carboxy group toward nucleophilic attack.**

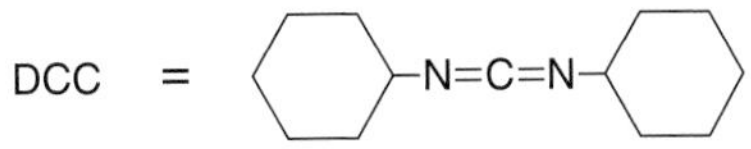

dicyclohexylcarbodiimide

Step [4] Remove one or both protecting groups.

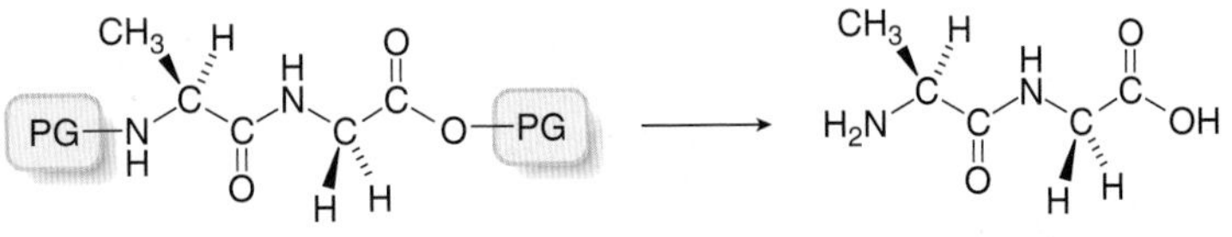

Ala–Gly

Two widely used amino protecting groups convert an amine into a **carbamate,** a functional group having a carbonyl bonded to both an oxygen and a nitrogen atom. Since the N atom of the carbamate is bonded to a carbonyl group, the protected amino group is no longer nucleophilic.

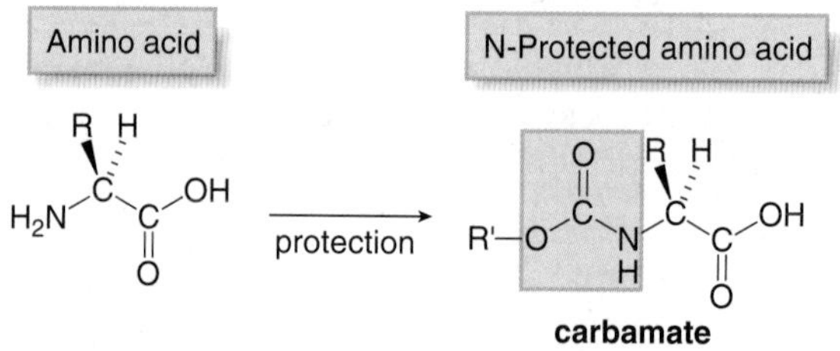

For example, the ***tert*-butoxycarbonyl protecting group,** abbreviated as **Boc,** is formed by reacting the amino acid with di-*tert*-butyl dicarbonate in a nucleophilic acyl substitution reaction.

Adding a Boc protecting group

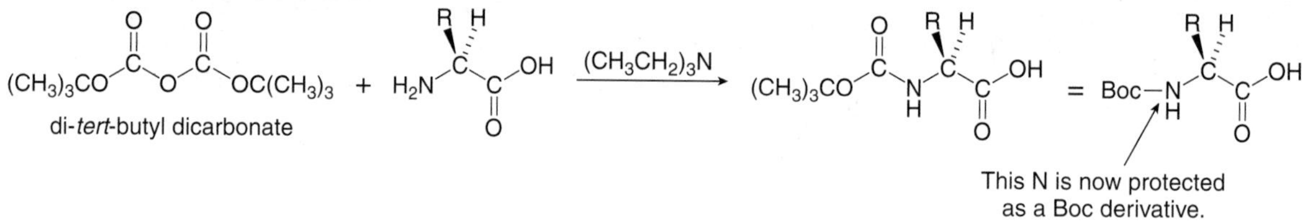

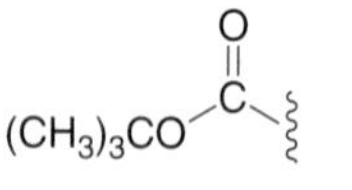

tert-butoxycarbonyl
Boc

To be a useful protecting group, the Boc group must be removed under reaction conditions that do not affect other functional groups in the molecule. It can be removed with an acid such as **trifluoroacetic acid, HCl,** or **HBr.**

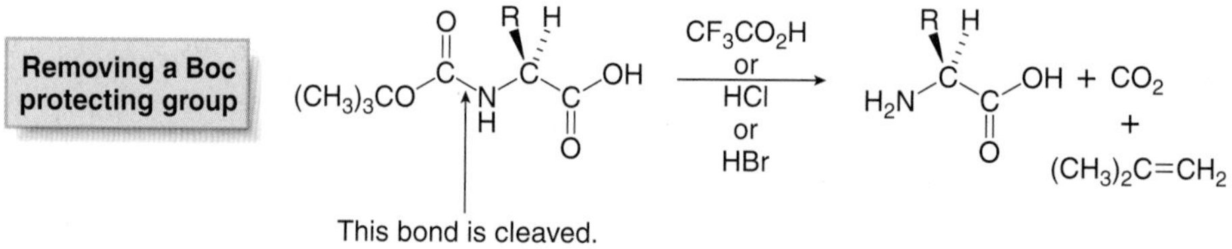

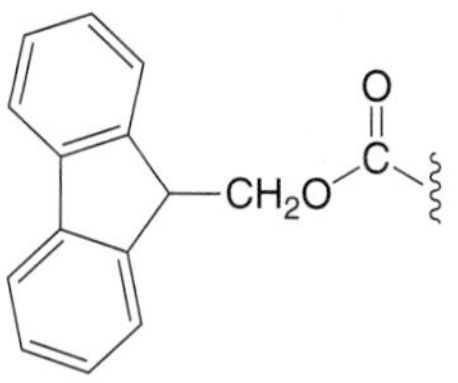

9-fluorenylmethoxycarbonyl
Fmoc

A second amino protecting group, the **9-fluorenylmethoxycarbonyl protecting group,** abbreviated as **Fmoc,** is formed by reacting the amino acid with 9-fluorenylmethyl chloroformate in a nucleophilic acyl substitution reaction.

Adding an Fmoc protecting group

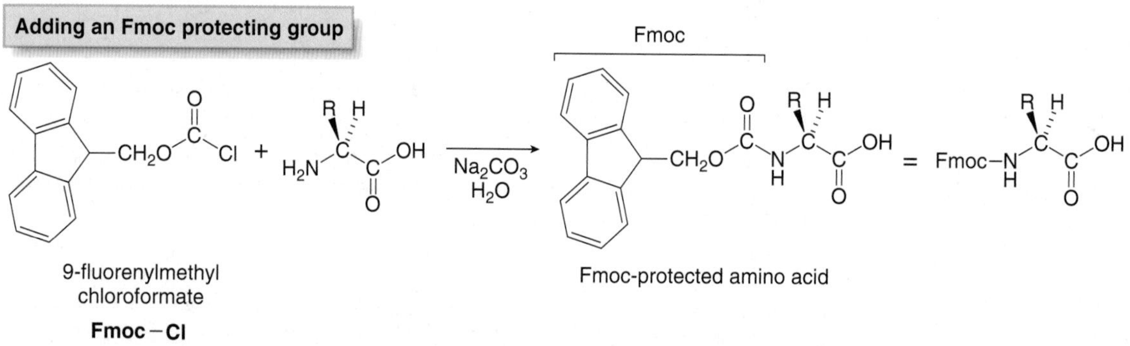

While the Fmoc protecting group is stable to most acids, it can be removed by treatment with base (NH_3 or an amine), to regenerate the free amino group.

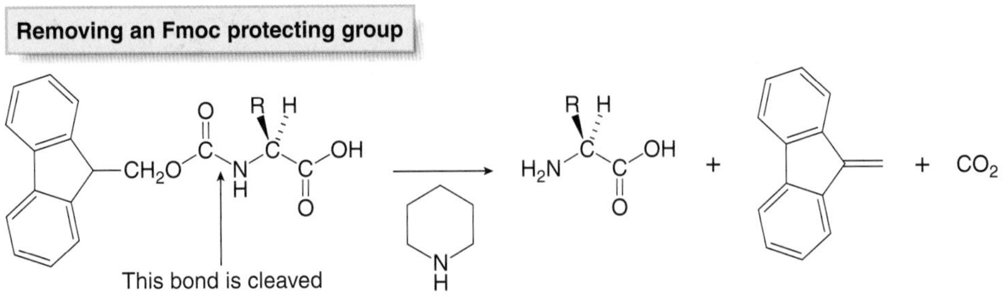
Removing an Fmoc protecting group
This bond is cleaved
+ CO2

The carboxy group is usually protected as a **methyl** or **benzyl ester** by reaction with an alcohol and an acid.

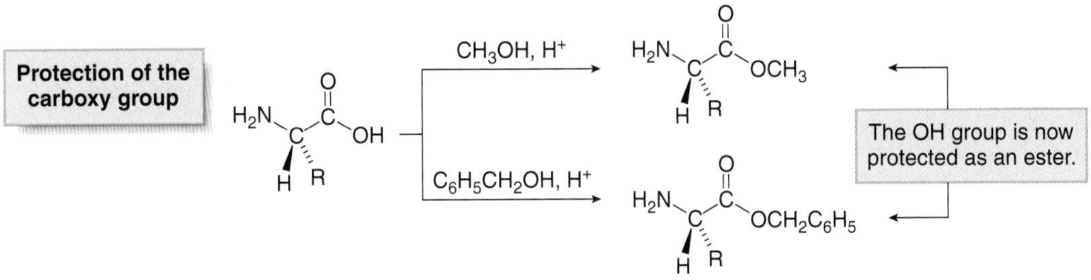
Protection of the carboxy group
CH3OH, H+
C6H5CH2OH, H+
The OH group is now protected as an ester.

These esters are usually removed by hydrolysis with aqueous base.

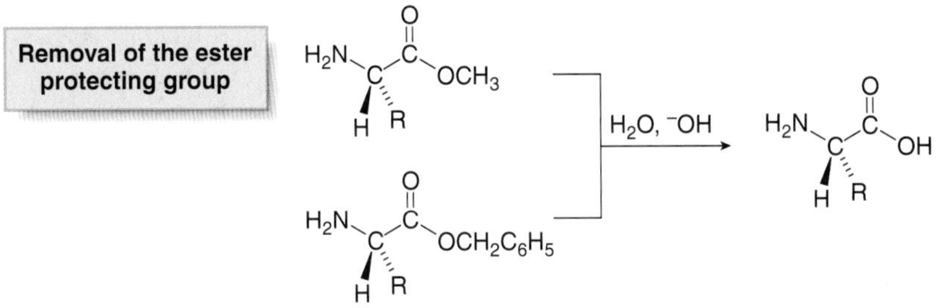
Removal of the ester protecting group
H2O, −OH

One advantage of using a benzyl ester for protection is that it can also be removed with H_2 in the presence of a Pd catalyst. This process is called **hydrogenolysis.** These conditions are especially mild, because they avoid the use of either acid or base. Benzyl esters can also be removed with HBr in acetic acid.

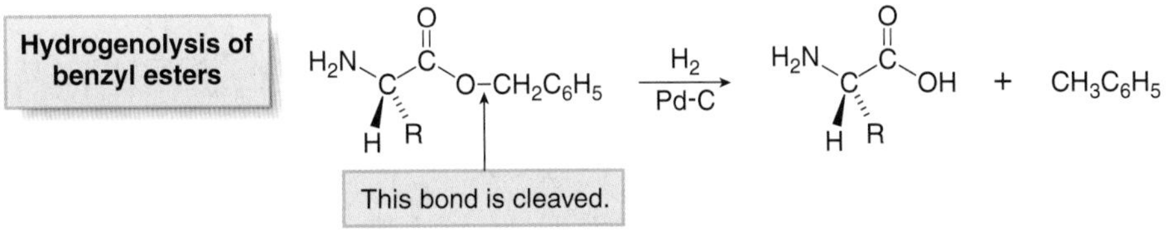
Hydrogenolysis of benzyl esters
H2
Pd-C
+ CH3C6H5
This bond is cleaved.

The specific reactions needed to synthesize the dipeptide Ala–Gly are illustrated in Sample Problem 29.4.

Sample Problem 29.4

Draw out the steps in the synthesis of the dipeptide Ala–Gly.

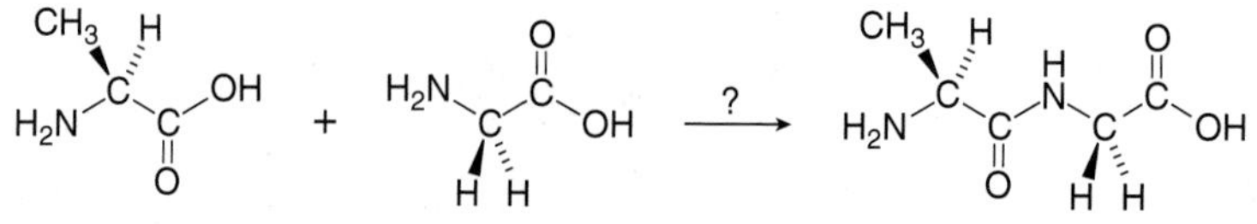

Ala Gly Ala–Gly

Solution

Step [1] Protect the NH_2 group of alanine using a Boc group.

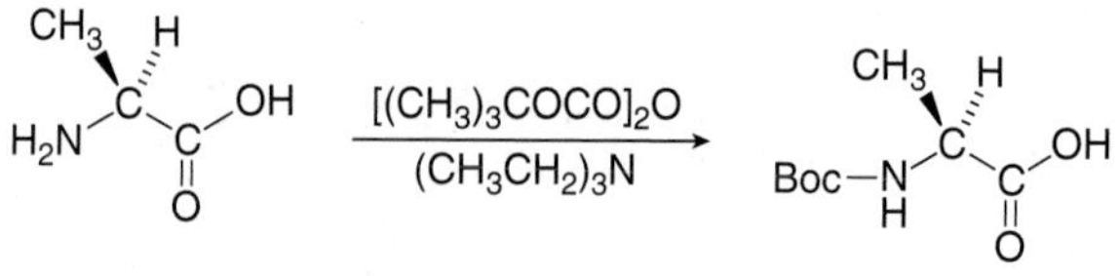
[(CH3)3COCO]2O
(CH3CH2)3N

Ala

Step [2] Protect the COOH group of glycine as a benzyl ester.

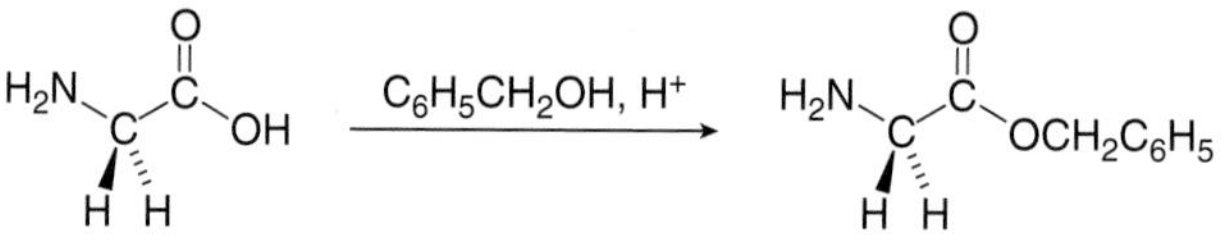
C6H5CH2OH, H+

Gly

Step [3] Form the amide bond with DCC.

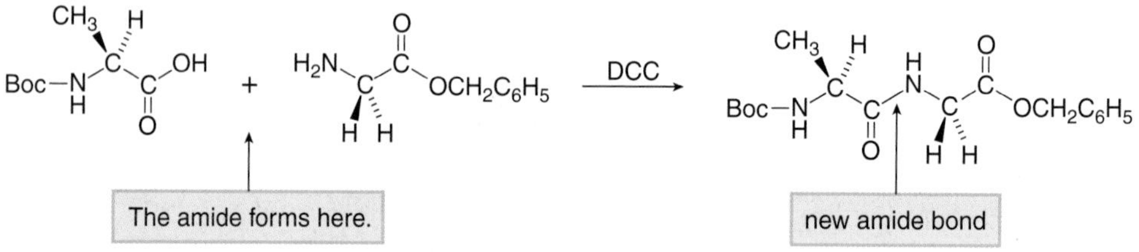
DCC
The amide forms here.
new amide bond

Step [4] Remove one or both protecting groups.

The protecting groups can be removed in a stepwise fashion, or in a single reaction.

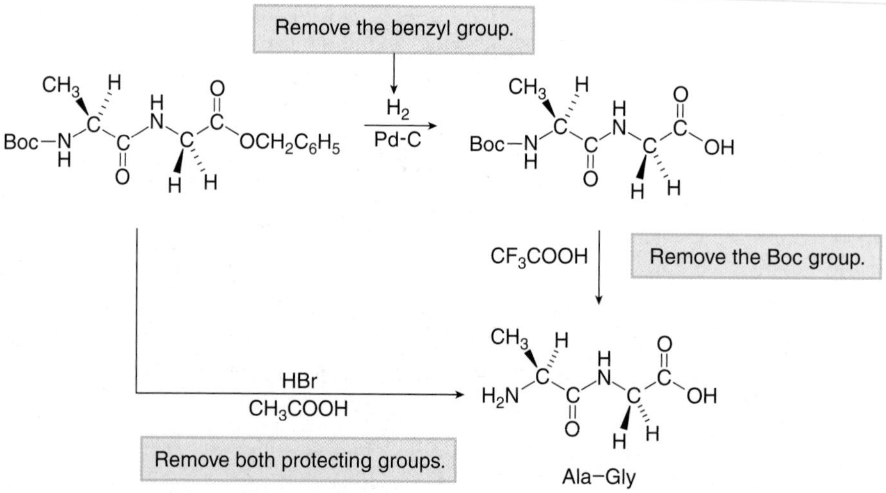
Remove the benzyl group.
H2
Pd-C
CF3COOH
Remove the Boc group.
HBr
CH3COOH
Remove both protecting groups.
Ala–Gly

This method can be applied to the synthesis of tripeptides and even larger polypeptides. After the protected dipeptide is prepared in Step [3], only one of the protecting groups is removed, and this dipeptide is coupled to a third amino acid with one of its functional groups protected, as illustrated in the following equations.

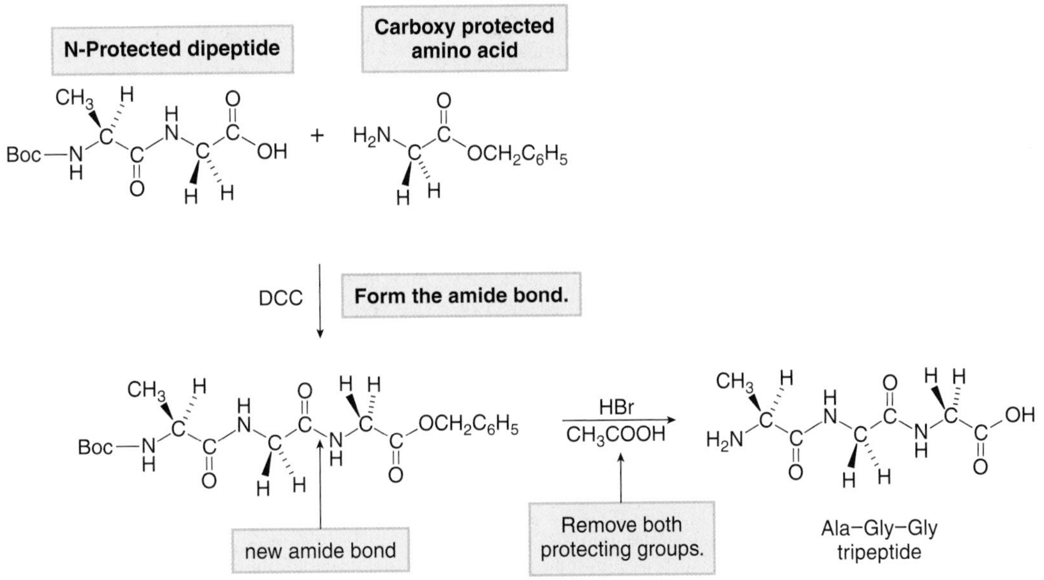
N-Protected dipeptide
Carboxy protected amino acid
DCC
Form the amide bond.
new amide bond
HBr
CH_3COOH
Remove both protecting groups.
Ala–Gly–Gly tripeptide

Problem 29.22 Devise a synthesis of each peptide from amino acid starting materials: (a) Leu–Val; (b) Ala–Ile–Gly; (c) Ala–Gly–Ala–Gly.

Problem 29.23 Devise a synthesis of the following dipeptide from amino acid starting materials.

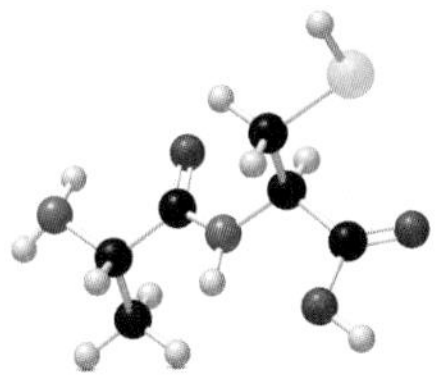

29.8 Automated Peptide Synthesis

The method described in Section 29.7 works well for the synthesis of small peptides. It is extremely time-consuming to synthesize larger proteins by this strategy, however, because each step requires isolation and purification of the product. The synthesis of larger polypeptides is usually accomplished by using the **solid phase technique** originally developed by R. Bruce Merrifield of Rockefeller University.

Development of the solid phase technique earned Merrifield the 1984 Nobel Prize in Chemistry and has made possible the synthesis of many polypeptides and proteins.

In the **Merrifield method** an amino acid is attached to an **insoluble polymer.** Amino acids are sequentially added, one at a time, thereby forming successive peptide bonds. Because impurities and by-products are not attached to the polymer chain, they are removed simply by washing them away with a solvent at each stage of the synthesis.

A commonly used polymer is a **polystyrene derivative** that contains $-CH_2Cl$ groups bonded to some of the benzene rings in the polymer chain. The Cl atoms serve as handles that allow attachment of amino acids to the chain.

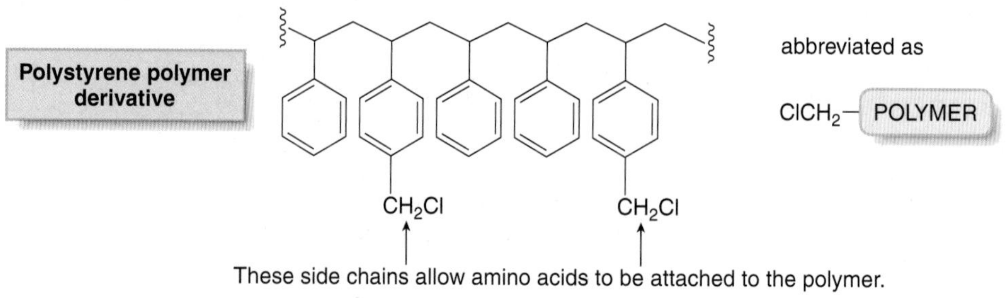
Polystyrene polymer derivative
abbreviated as
ClCH2—POLYMER
CH2Cl
CH2Cl
These side chains allow amino acids to be attached to the polymer.

An Fmoc-protected amino acid is attached to the polymer at its carboxy group by an $\mathbf{S_N2}$ reaction.

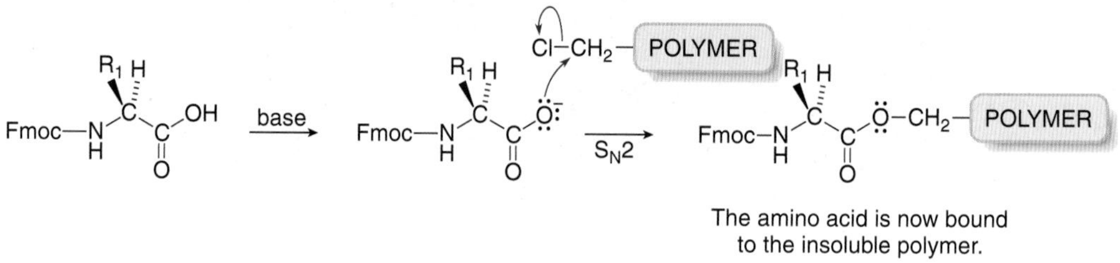
base
SN2
POLYMER
The amino acid is now bound to the insoluble polymer.

Once the first amino acid is bound to the polymer, additional amino acids can be added sequentially. The steps of the solid phase peptide synthesis technique are illustrated in the accompanying scheme. In the last step, HF cleaves the polypeptide chain from the polymer.

How To Synthesize a Peptide Using the Merrifield Solid Phase Technique

Step [1]
Attach an Fmoc-protected amino acid to the polymer.

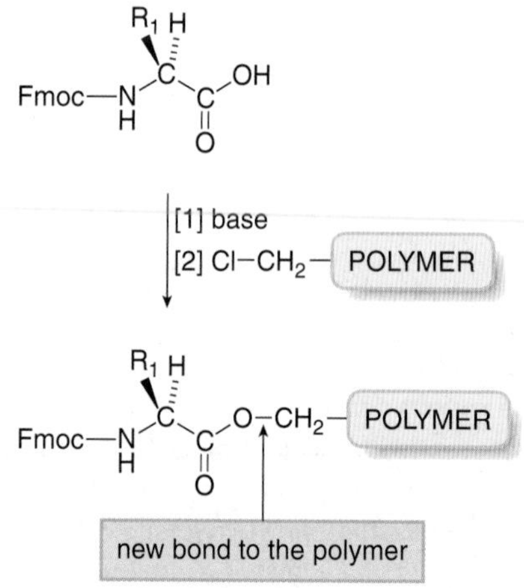
[1] base
[2] Cl–CH2–POLYMER
new bond to the polymer

Step [2]
Remove the protecting group.

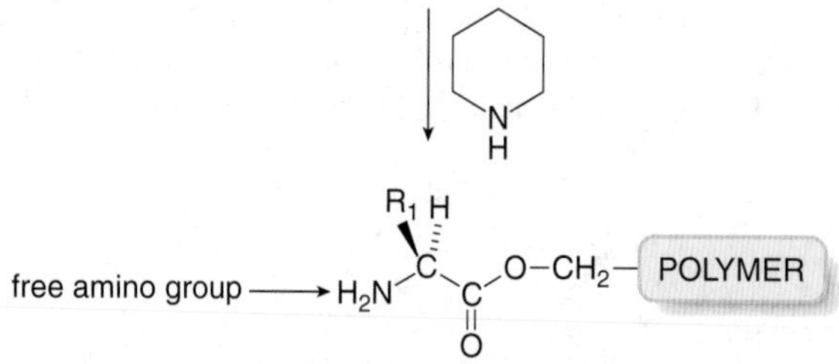
free amino group
POLYMER

How To, continued . . .

Step [3]
Form the amide bond with DCC.

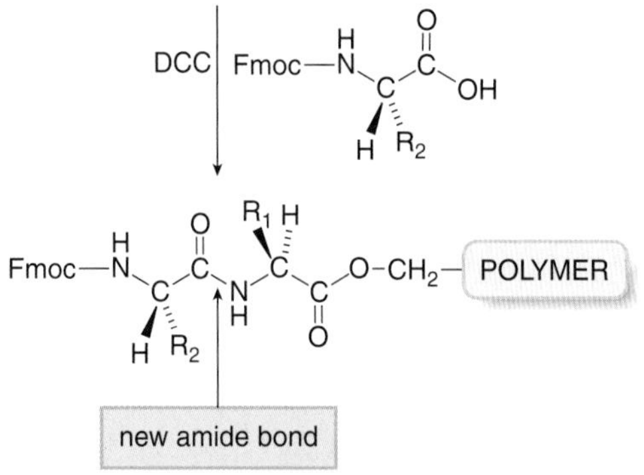

Step [4]
Repeat Steps [2] and [3].

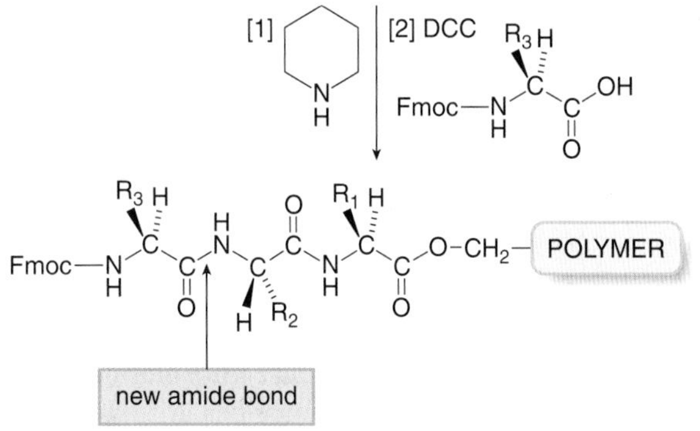

Step [5]
Remove the protecting group and detach the peptide from the polymer.

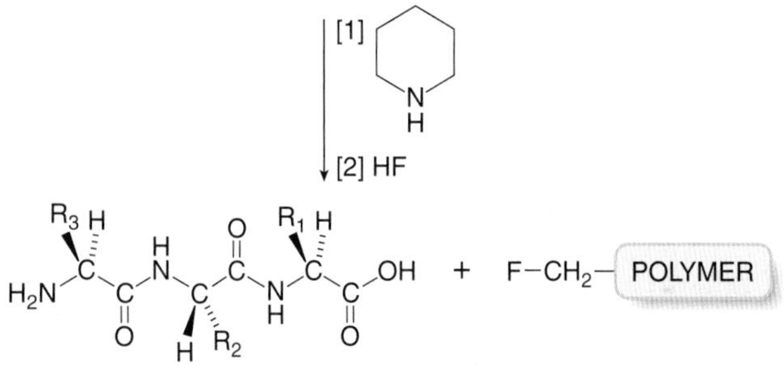

tripeptide

The Merrifield method has now been completely automated, so it is possible to purchase peptide synthesizers that automatically carry out all of the above operations and form polypeptides in high yield in a matter of hours, days, or weeks, depending on the length of the chain of the desired product. For example, the protein ribonuclease, which contains 128 amino acids, has been prepared by this technique in an overall yield of 17%. This remarkable synthesis involved 369 separate reactions, and thus the yield of each individual reaction was > 99%.

Problem 29.24 Outline the steps needed to synthesize the tetrapeptide Ala–Leu–Ile–Gly using the Merrifield technique.

29.9 Protein Structure

Now that you have learned some of the chemistry of amino acids, it's time to study proteins, the large polymers of amino acids that are responsible for so much of the structure and function of all living cells. We begin with a discussion of the **primary, secondary, tertiary, and quaternary structure** of proteins.

29.9A Primary Structure

The *primary structure* of proteins is the particular sequence of amino acids that is joined together by peptide bonds. The most important element of this primary structure is the **amide bond.**

- Rotation around the amide C–N bond is *restricted* because of electron delocalization, and the *s*-trans conformation is the more stable arrangement.
- In each peptide bond, the N–H and C=O bonds are directed 180° from each other.

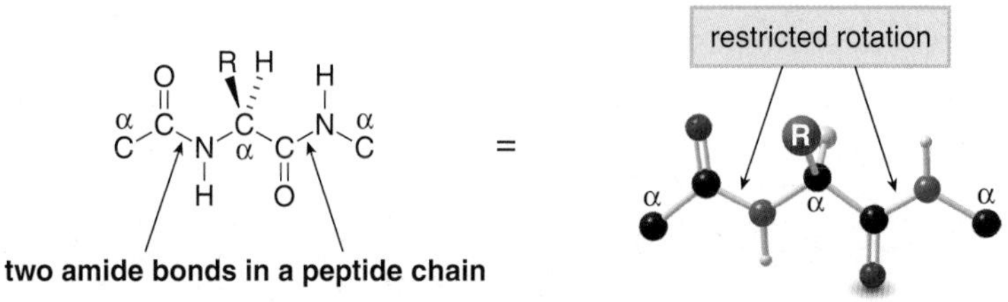

Although rotation about the amide bonds is restricted, **rotation about the other σ bonds in the protein backbone is not.** As a result, the peptide chain can twist and bend into a variety of different arrangements that constitute the secondary structure of the protein.

29.9B Secondary Structure

The three-dimensional conformations of localized regions of a protein are called its secondary structure. These regions arise due to hydrogen bonding between the N–H proton of one amide and C=O oxygen of another. Two arrangements that are particularly stable are called the **α-helix** and the **β-pleated sheet.**

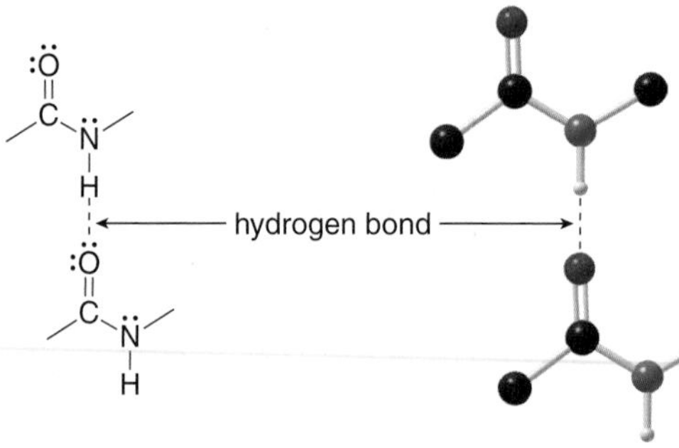

α-Helix

The **α-helix** forms when a peptide chain twists into a right-handed or clockwise spiral, as shown in Figure 29.8. Four important features of the α-helix are as follows:

[1] **Each turn of the helix has 3.6 amino acids.**

[2] **The N–H and C=O bonds point along the axis of the helix.** All C=O bonds point in one direction, and all N–H bonds point in the opposite direction.

[3] **The C=O group of one amino acid is hydrogen bonded to an N–H group four amino acid residues farther along the chain.** Thus, hydrogen bonding occurs between two amino acids ***in the same chain.*** Note, too, that the hydrogen bonds are parallel to the axis of the helix.

[4] The **R groups of the amino acids extend outward** from the core of the helix.

An α-helix can form only if there is rotation about the bonds at the α carbon of the amide carbonyl group, and not all amino acids can do this. For example, proline, the amino acid whose nitrogen atom forms part of a five-membered ring, is more rigid than other amino acids, and its C_α–N bond cannot rotate the necessary amount. Additionally, it has no N–H proton with which to form an intramolecular hydrogen bond to stabilize the helix. Thus, proline cannot be part of an α-helix.

Both the myosin in muscle and α-keratin in hair are proteins composed almost entirely of α-helices.

Figure 29.8 Two different illustrations of the α-helix

a. The right-handed α-helix

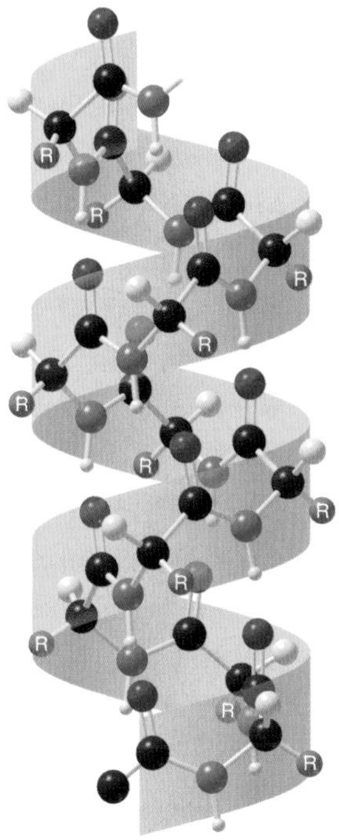

All atoms of the α-helix are drawn in this representation. All C=O bonds are pointing up and all N–H bonds are pointing down.

b. The backbone of the α-helix

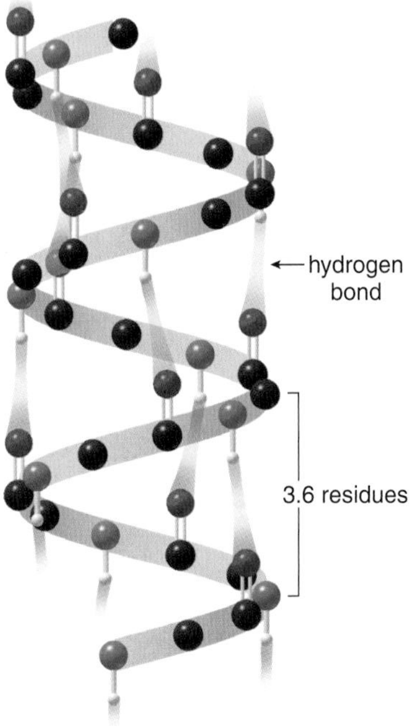

Only the peptide backbone is drawn in this representation. The hydrogen bonds between the C=O and N–H of amino acids four residues away from each other are shown.

β-Pleated Sheet

The **β-pleated sheet** secondary structure forms when two or more peptide chains, called **strands,** line up side-by-side, as shown in Figure 29.9. All β-pleated sheets have the following characteristics:

[1] **The C=O and N–H bonds lie in the plane of the sheet.**

[2] **Hydrogen bonding often occurs between the N–H and C=O groups of nearby amino acid residues.**

[3] The **R groups are oriented above and below the plane** of the sheet, and alternate from one side to the other along a given strand.

Figure 29.9 Three-dimensional structure of the β-pleated sheet

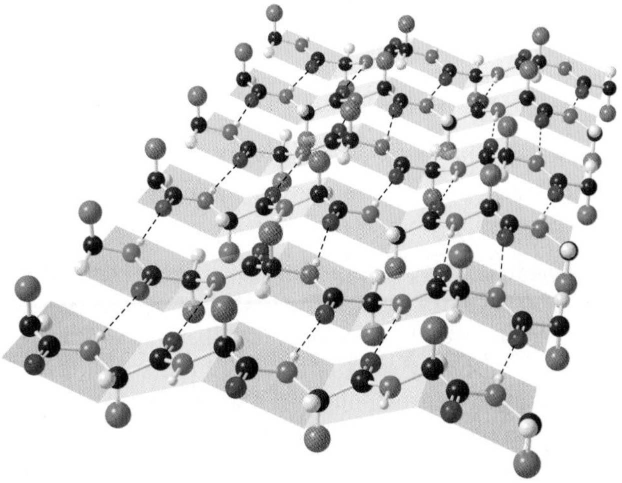

- The β-pleated sheet consists of extended strands of the peptide chains held together by hydrogen bonding. The C=O and N–H bonds lie in the plane of the sheet, and the R groups (shown as orange balls) alternate above and below the plane.

The β-pleated sheet arrangement most commonly occurs with amino acids with small R groups, like alanine and glycine. With larger R groups steric interactions prevent the chains from getting close together and so the sheet cannot be stabilized by hydrogen bonding.

The peptide strands of β-pleated sheets can actually be oriented in two different ways, as shown in Figure 29.10.

- **In a *parallel* β-pleated sheet, the strands run in the *same* direction from the N- to C-terminal amino acid.**
- **In an *antiparallel* β-pleated sheet, the strands run in the *opposite* direction.**

Figure 29.10 The parallel and antiparallel forms of the β-pleated sheet

Parallel β-pleated sheet **Antiparallel β-pleated sheet**

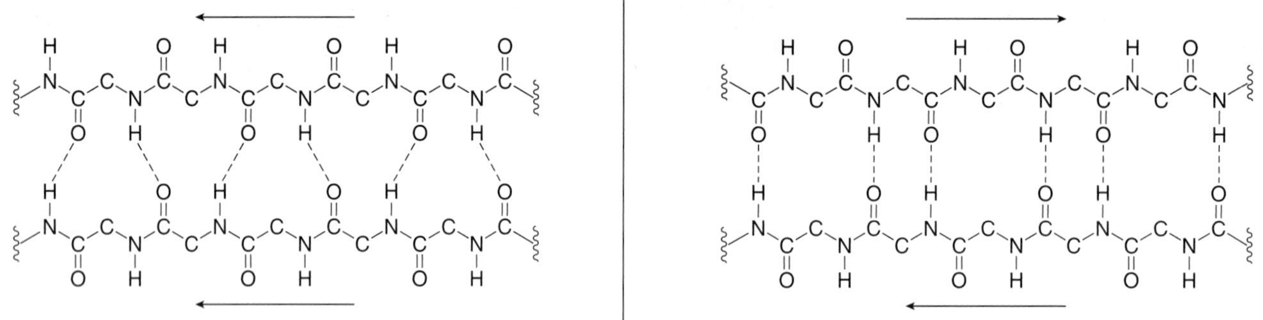

The two peptide chains are arranged in the same direction. Hydrogen bonds occur between N–H and C=O bonds in adjacent chains.

[Note: R groups on the carbon chain are omitted for clarity.]

The two peptide chains are arranged in opposite directions. Hydrogen bonding between the N–H and C=O groups still holds the two chains together.

Most proteins have regions of α-helix and β-pleated sheet, in addition to other regions that cannot be characterized by either of these arrangements. Shorthand symbols are often used to indicate regions of a protein that have α-helix or β-pleated sheet. A **flat helical ribbon** is used for the α-helix, and a **flat wide arrow** is used for the β-pleated sheet. These representations are often used in **ribbon diagrams** to illustrate protein structure.

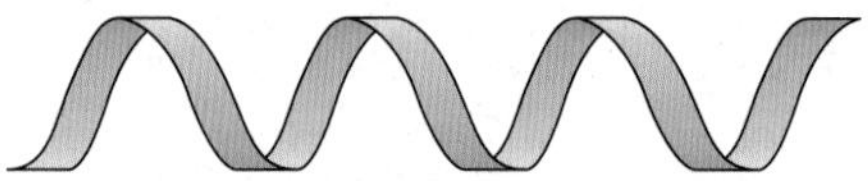

α-helix shorthand

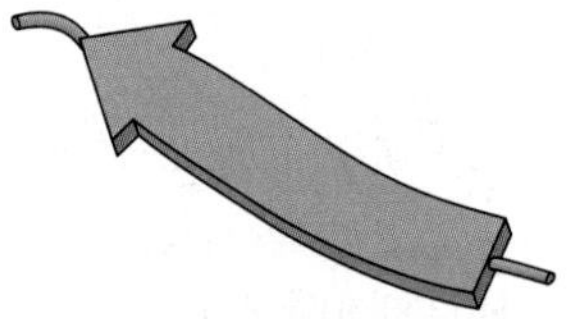

β-pleated sheet shorthand

Proteins are drawn in a variety of ways to illustrate different aspects of their structure. Figure 29.11 illustrates three different representations of the protein lysozyme, an enzyme found in both plants and animals. Lysozyme catalyzes the hydrolysis of bonds in bacterial cell walls, weakening them, often causing the bacteria to burst.

Spider dragline silk is a strong yet elastic protein because it has regions of β-pleated sheet and regions of α-helix (Figure 29.12). α-Helical regions impart elasticity to the silk because the peptide chain is twisted (not fully extended), so it can stretch. β-Pleated sheet regions are almost fully extended, so they can't be stretched further, but their highly ordered three-dimensional structure imparts strength to the silk. Thus, spider silk suits the spider by comprising both types of secondary structure with beneficial properties.

Figure 29.11 Lysozyme

a. Ball-and-stick model
b. Space-filling model
c. Ribbon diagram

(a) The ball-and-stick model of lysozyme shows the protein backbone with color-coded C, N, O, and S atoms. Individual amino acids are most clearly located using this representation. (b) The space-filling model uses color-coded balls for each atom in the backbone of the enzyme and illustrates how the atoms fill the space they occupy. (c) The ribbon diagram shows regions of α-helix and β-sheet that are not clearly in evidence in the other two representations.

Figure 29.12 Different regions of secondary structure in spider silk

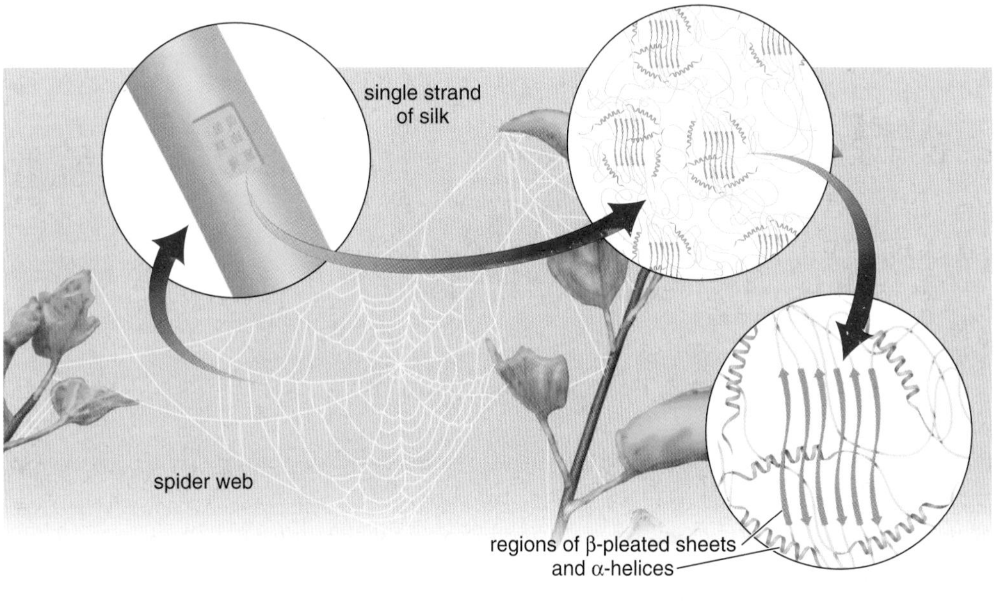
single strand
of silk
spider web
regions of β-pleated sheets
and α-helices

Spider silk has regions of α-helix and β-pleated sheet that make it both strong and elastic. The green coils represent the α-helical regions, and the purple arrows represent the β-pleated sheet regions. The yellow lines represent other areas of the protein that are neither α-helix nor β-pleated sheet.

Problem 29.25 Consider two molecules of a tetrapeptide composed of only alanine residues. Draw the hydrogen bonding interactions that result when these two peptides adopt a parallel β-pleated sheet arrangement. Answer this same question for the antiparallel β-pleated sheet arrangement.

29.9C Tertiary and Quaternary Structure

The three-dimensional shape adopted by the entire peptide chain is called its tertiary structure. A peptide generally folds into a conformation that maximizes its stability. In the aqueous environment of the cell, proteins often fold in such a way as to place a large number of polar and charged groups on their outer surface, to maximize the dipole–dipole and hydrogen bonding interactions with water. This generally places most of the nonpolar side chains in the interior of the protein, where van der Waals interactions between these hydrophobic groups help stabilize the molecule, too.

In addition, polar functional groups hydrogen bond with each other (not just water), and amino acids with charged side chains like $-COO^-$ and $-NH_3^+$ can stabilize tertiary structure by electrostatic interactions.

Finally, **disulfide bonds are the only covalent bonds that stabilize tertiary structure.** As previously mentioned, these strong bonds form by oxidation of two cysteine residues either on the same polypeptide chain or another polypeptide chain of the same protein.

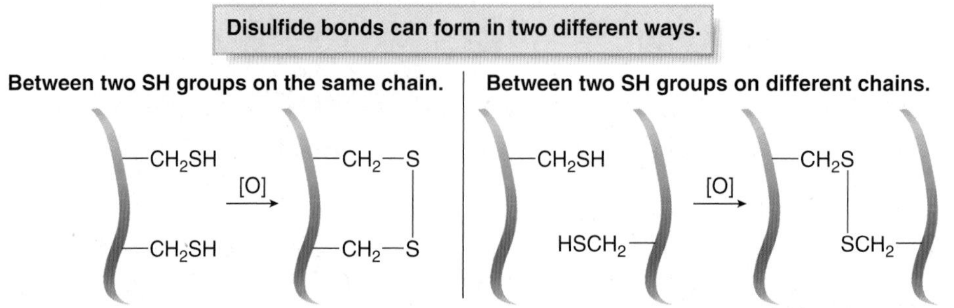

The nonapeptides **oxytocin** and **vasopressin** (Section 29.5C) contain intramolecular disulfide bonds. **Insulin,** on the other hand, consists of two separate polypeptide chains (**A** and **B**) that are covalently linked by two intermolecular disulfide bonds, as shown in Figure 29.13. The **A** chain, which also has an intramolecular disulfide bond, has 21 amino acid residues, whereas the **B** chain has 30.

Figure 29.13
Insulin

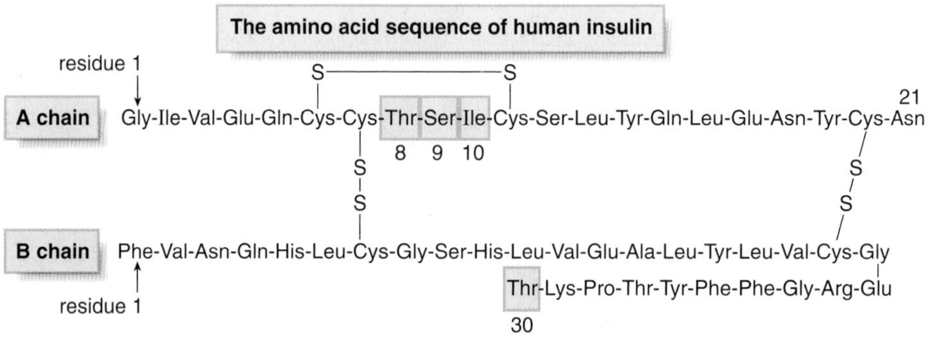

Insulin is a small protein consisting of two polypeptide chains (designated as the **A** and **B** chains) held together by two disulfide bonds. An additional disulfide bond joins two cysteine residues within the **A** chain.

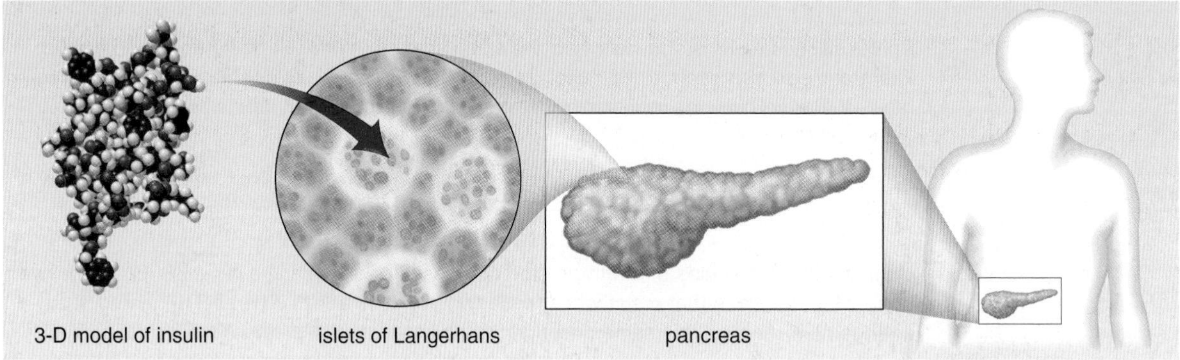

Synthesized by groups of cells in the pancreas called the islets of Langerhans, insulin is the protein that regulates the levels of glucose in the blood. Insufficiency of insulin results in diabetes. Many of the abnormalities associated with this disease can be controlled by the injection of insulin. Until the availability of human insulin through genetic engineering techniques, all insulin used by diabetics was obtained from pigs and cattle. The amino acid sequences of these insulin proteins is slightly different from that of human insulin. Pig insulin differs in one amino acid only, whereas bovine insulin has three different amino acids. This is shown in the accompanying table.

	Chain A			Chain B
Position of residue →	**8**	**9**	**10**	**30**
Human insulin	Thr	Ser	Ile	Thr
Pig insulin	Thr	Ser	Ile	Ala
Bovine insulin	Ala	Ser	Val	Ala

Figure 29.14
The stabilizing interactions in secondary and tertiary protein structure

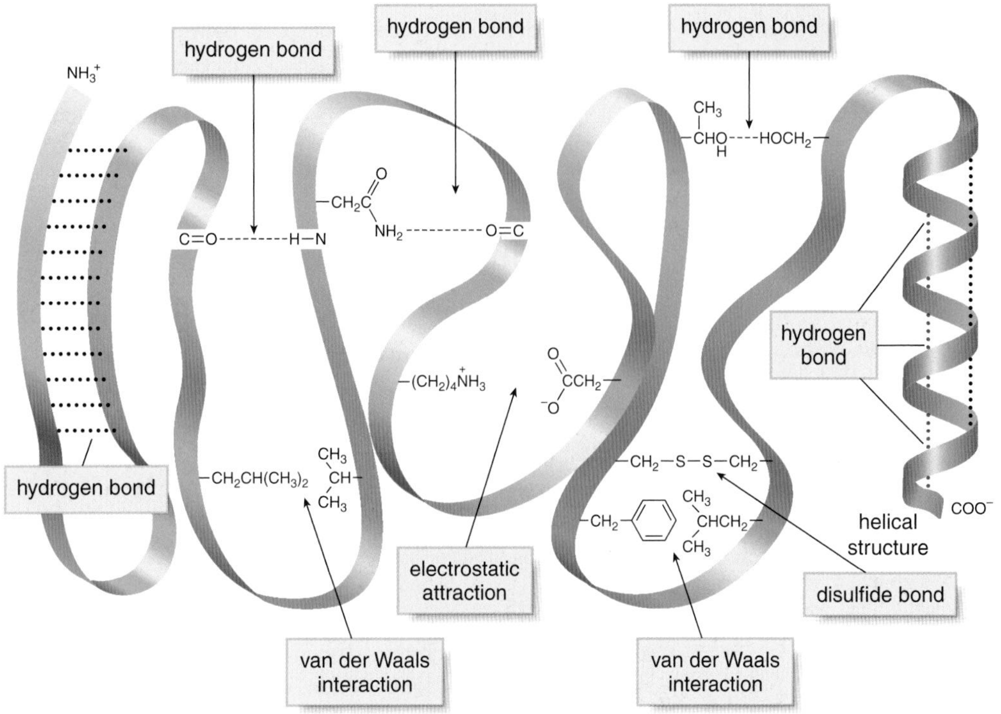

Figure 29.14 schematically illustrates the many different kinds of intramolecular forces that stabilize the secondary and tertiary structures of polypeptide chains.

The shape adopted when two or more folded polypeptide chains aggregate into one protein complex is called the **quaternary structure** of the protein. Each individual polypeptide chain is called a **subunit** of the overall protein. **Hemoglobin,** for example, consists of two α and two β subunits held together by intermolecular forces in a compact three-dimensional shape. The unique function of hemoglobin is possible only when all four subunits are together.

The four levels of protein structure are summarized in Figure 29.15.

Figure 29.15 The primary, secondary, tertiary, and quaternary structure of proteins

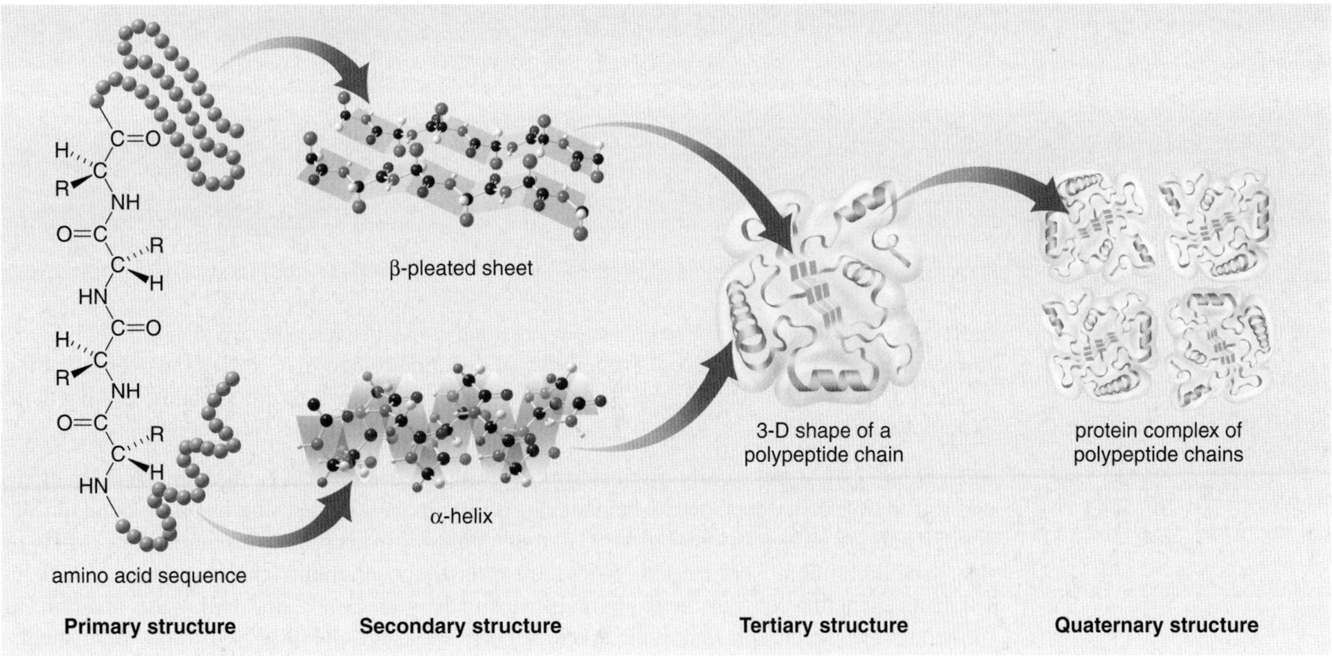

Problem 29.26 What types of stabilizing interactions exist between each of the following pairs of amino acids?

a. Ser and Tyr b. Val and Leu c. two Phe residues

Problem 29.27 The fibroin proteins found in silk fibers consist of large regions of β-pleated sheets stacked one on top of another. (a) Explain why having a glycine at every other residue allows the β-pleated sheets to stack on top of each other. (b) Why are silk fibers insoluble in water?

29.10 Important Proteins

Proteins are generally classified according to their three-dimensional shapes.

- **Fibrous proteins** are composed of long linear polypeptide chains that are bundled together to form rods or sheets. These proteins are insoluble in water and serve structural roles, giving strength and protection to tissues and cells.
- **Globular proteins** are coiled into compact shapes with hydrophilic outer surfaces that make them water soluble. Enzymes and transport proteins are globular to make them soluble in the blood and other aqueous environments in cells.

29.10A α-Keratins

α-Keratins are the proteins found in hair, hooves, nails, skin, and wool. They are composed almost exclusively of long sections of α-helix units, having large numbers of alanine and leucine residues. Because these nonpolar amino acids extend outward from the α-helix, these proteins are very water insoluble. Two α-keratin helices coil around each other, forming a structure called a **supercoil** or **superhelix.** These, in turn, form larger and larger bundles of fibers, ultimately forming a strand of hair, as shown schematically in Figure 29.16.

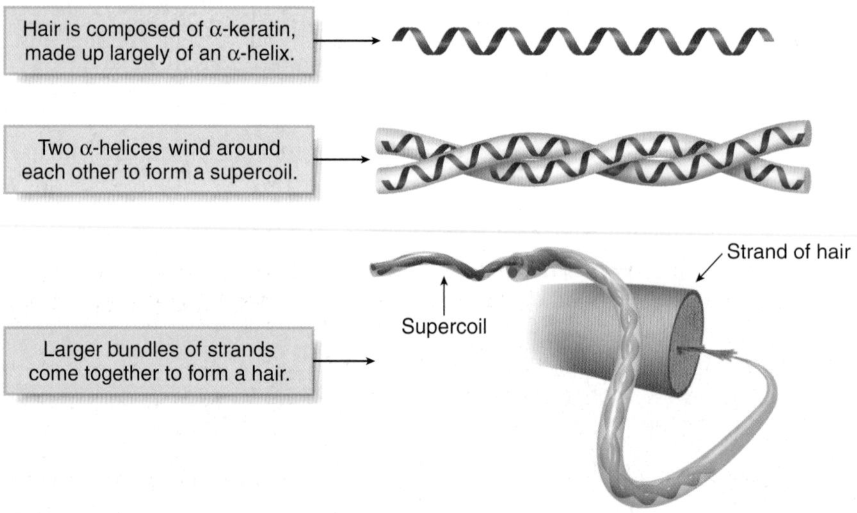
Hair is composed of α-keratin, made up largely of an α-helix.
Two α-helices wind around each other to form a supercoil.
Strand of hair
Supercoil
Larger bundles of strands come together to form a hair.

Figure 29.16 Anatomy of a hair— It begins with α-keratin.

α-Keratins also have a number of cysteine residues, and because of this, disulfide bonds are formed between adjacent helices. The number of disulfide bridges determines the strength of the material. Claws, horns, and fingernails have extensive networks of disulfide bonds, making them extremely hard.

Straight hair can be made curly by cleaving the disulfide bonds in α-keratin, and then rearranging and re-forming them, as shown schematically in Figure 29.17. First, the disulfide bonds in the straight hair are reduced to thiol groups, so the bundles of α-keratin chains are no longer held in their specific "straight" orientation. Then, the hair is wrapped around curlers and treated with an oxidizing agent that converts the thiol groups back to disulfide bonds, now with twists and turns in the keratin backbone. This makes the hair look curly and is the chemical basis for a "permanent."

Figure 29.17
The chemistry of a "permanent"—Making straight hair curly

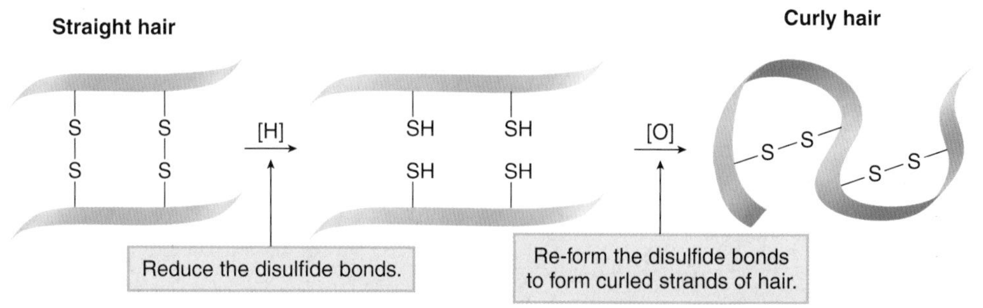

To make straight hair curly, the disulfide bonds holding the α-helical chains together are cleaved by reduction. This forms free thiol groups (–SH). The hair is turned around curlers and then an oxidizing agent is applied. This re-forms the disulfide bonds in the hair, but between different thiol groups, now giving it a curly appearance.

29.10B Collagen

Collagen, the most abundant protein in vertebrates, is found in connective tissues such as bone, cartilage, tendons, teeth, and blood vessels. Glycine and proline account for a large fraction of its amino acid residues, whereas cysteine accounts for very little. Because of the high proline content, it cannot form a right-handed α-helix. Instead, it forms an elongated left-handed helix, and then three of these helices wind around each other to form a right-handed **superhelix** or **triple helix.** The side chain of glycine is only a hydrogen atom, so the high glycine content allows the collagen superhelices to lie compactly next to each other, thus stabilizing the superhelices via hydrogen bonding. Two views of the collagen superhelix are shown in Figure 29.18.

Figure 29.18
Two different representations for the triple helix of collagen

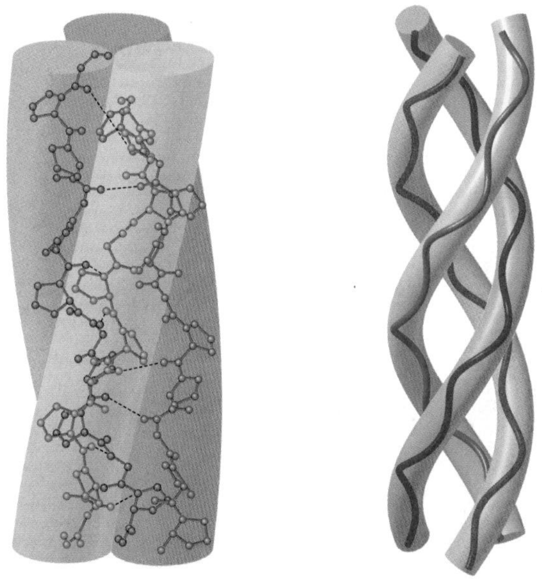

- In collagen, three polypeptide chains having an unusual left-handed helix wind around each other in a right-handed triple helix. The high content of small glycine residues allows the chains to lie close to each other, permitting hydrogen bonding between the chains.

29.10C Hemoglobin and Myoglobin

Hemoglobin and **myoglobin,** two globular proteins, are called **conjugated proteins** because they are composed of a protein unit and a nonprotein molecule called a **prosthetic group.** The prosthetic group in hemoglobin and myoglobin is **heme,** a complex organic compound containing the

Figure 29.19
Protein ribbon diagrams for myoglobin and hemoglobin

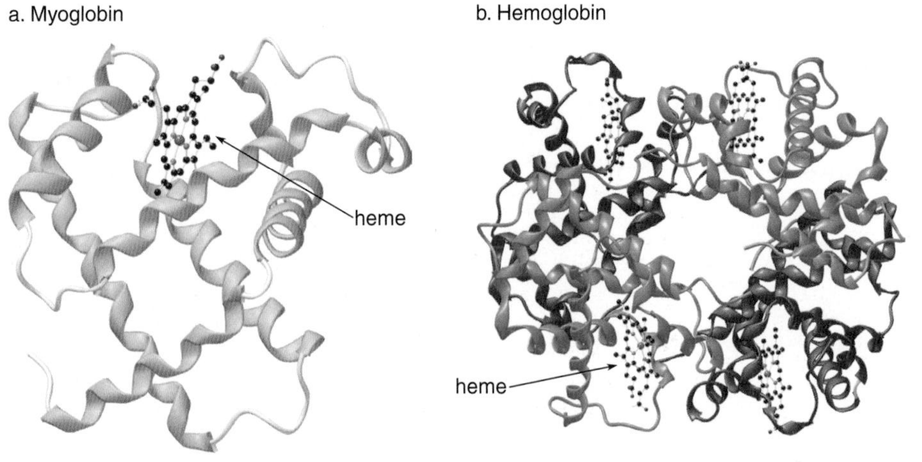

Myoglobin consists of a single polypeptide chain with a heme unit shown in a ball-and-stick model.

Hemoglobin consists of two α and two β chains shown in red and blue, respectively, and four heme units shown in ball-and-stick models.

Fe^{2+} ion complexed with a nitrogen heterocycle called a **porphyrin.** The Fe^{2+} ion of hemoglobin and myoglobin binds oxygen in the blood. Hemoglobin, which is present in red blood cells, transports oxygen to wherever it is needed in the body, whereas myoglobin stores oxygen in tissues. Ribbon diagrams for myoglobin and hemoglobin are shown in Figure 29.19.

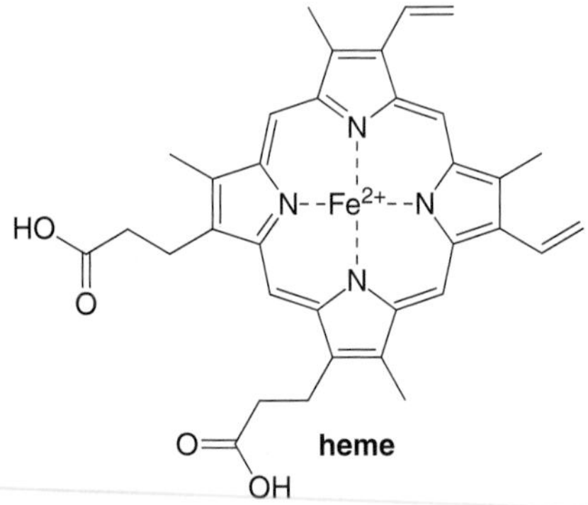

heme

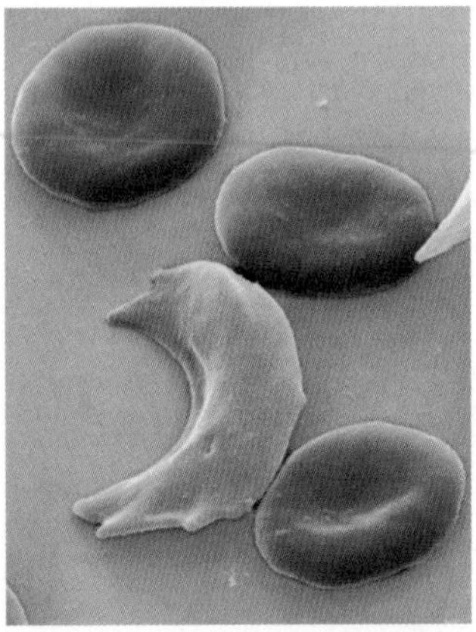

When red blood cells take on a "sickled" shape in persons with sickle cell disease, they occlude capillaries (causing organ injury) and they break easily (leading to profound anemia). This devastating illness results from the change of a single amino acid in hemoglobin. Note the single sickled cell surrounded by three red cells with normal morphology.

Myoglobin, the chapter-opening molecule, has 153 amino acid residues in a single polypeptide chain. It has eight separate α-helical sections that fold back on one another, with the prosthetic heme group held in a cavity inside the polypeptide. Most of the polar residues are found on the outside of the protein so that they can interact with the water solvent. Spaces in the interior of the protein are filled with nonpolar amino acids. Myoglobin gives cardiac muscle its characteristic red color.

Hemoglobin consists of four polypeptide chains (two α subunits and two β subunits), each of which carries a heme unit. Hemoglobin has more nonpolar amino acids than myoglobin. When each subunit is folded, some of these remain on the surface. The van der Waals attraction between these hydrophobic groups is what stabilizes the quaternary structure of the four subunits.

Carbon monoxide is poisonous because it binds to the Fe^{2+} of hemoglobin more strongly than does oxygen. Hemoglobin complexed with CO cannot carry O_2 from the lungs to the tissues. Without O_2 in the tissues for metabolism, cells cannot function, so they die.

The properties of all proteins depend on their three-dimensional shape, and their shape depends on their primary structure—that is, their amino acid sequence. This is particularly well exemplified by comparing normal hemoglobin with **sickle cell hemoglobin,** a mutant variation in which a single amino acid of both β subunits is changed from glutamic acid to valine. The replacement of one acidic amino acid (Glu) with one nonpolar amino acid (Val) changes the shape of hemoglobin, which has profound effects on its function. Deoxygenated red blood cells with sickle cell hemoglobin become elongated and crescent shaped, and they are unusually fragile. As a result, they do not flow easily through capillaries, causing pain and inflammation, and they break open easily, leading to severe anemia and organ damage. The end result is often a painful and premature death.

This disease, called **sickle cell anemia,** is found almost exclusively among people originating from central and western Africa, where malaria is an enormous health problem. Sickle cell hemoglobin results from a genetic mutation in the DNA sequence that is responsible for the synthesis of hemoglobin. Individuals who inherit this mutation from both parents develop sickle cell anemia, whereas those who inherit it from only one parent are said to have the sickle cell trait. They do not develop sickle cell anemia and they are more resistant to malaria than individuals without the mutation. This apparently accounts for this detrimental gene being passed on from generation to generation.

KEY CONCEPTS

Amino Acids and Proteins

Synthesis of Amino Acids (29.2)

[1] From α-halo carboxylic acids by S_N2 reaction

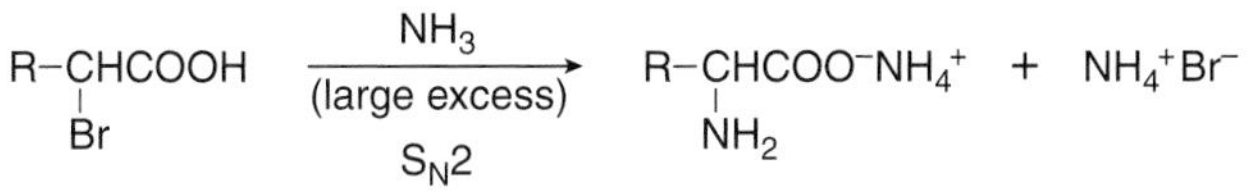
R–CHCOOH
Br
NH3
(large excess)
SN2
R–CHCOO−NH4+ + NH4+Br−
NH2

---

[2] By alkylation of diethyl acetamidomalonate

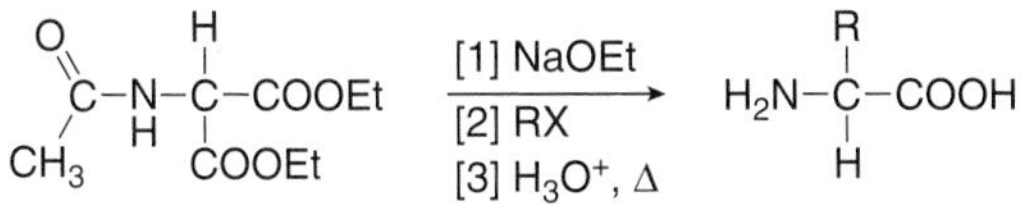
O
C–N–C–COOEt
CH3 H COOEt
H
[1] NaOEt
[2] RX
[3] H3O+, Δ
R
H2N–C–COOH
H

- Alkylation works best with unhindered alkyl halides—that is, CH_3X and RCH_2X.

---

[3] Strecker synthesis

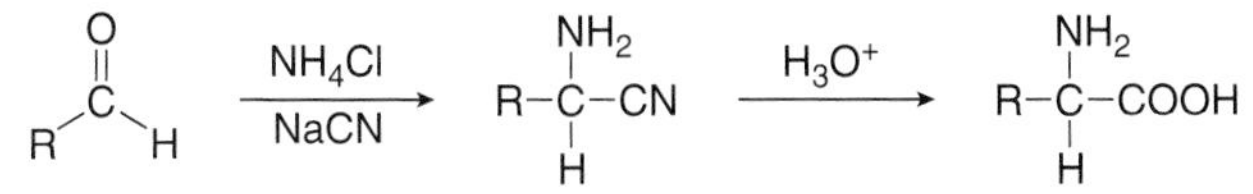
O
C
R H
NH4Cl
NaCN
NH2
R–C–CN
H
H3O+
NH2
R–C–COOH
H

α-amino nitrile

Preparation of Optically Active Amino Acids

[1] Resolution of enantiomers by forming diastereomers (29.3A)

- Convert a racemic mixture of amino acids into a racemic mixture of *N*-acetyl amino acids [(*S*)- and (*R*)-$CH_3CONHCH(R)COOH$].
- Treat the enantiomers with a chiral amine to form a mixture of diastereomers.
- Separate the diastereomers.
- Regenerate the amino acids by protonation of the carboxylate salt and hydrolysis of the *N*-acetyl group.

---

[2] Kinetic resolution using enzymes (29.3B)

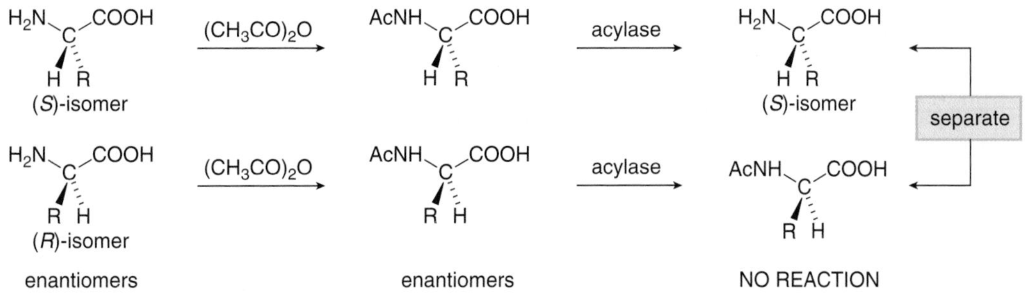
H2N COOH
C
H R
(S)-isomer
(CH3CO)2O
AcNH COOH
C
H R
acylase
H2N COOH
C
H R
(S)-isomer
separate
H2N COOH
C
R H
(R)-isomer
(CH3CO)2O
AcNH COOH
C
R H
acylase
AcNH COOH
C
R H
enantiomers
enantiomers
NO REACTION

[3] By enantioselective hydrogenation (29.4)

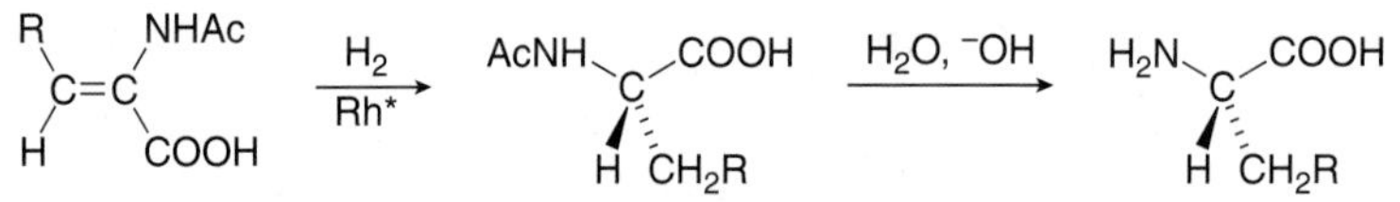

S enantiomer   *S* amino acid

Rh* = chiral Rh hydrogenation catalyst

Summary of Methods Used for Peptide Sequencing (29.6)

- Complete hydrolysis of all amide bonds in a peptide gives the identity and amount of the individual amino acids.
- Edman degradation identifies the N-terminal amino acid. Repeated Edman degradations can be used to sequence a peptide from the N-terminal end.
- Cleavage with carboxypeptidase identifies the C-terminal amino acid.
- Partial hydrolysis of a peptide forms smaller fragments that can be sequenced. Amino acid sequences common to smaller fragments can be used to determine the sequence of the complete peptide.
- Selective cleavage of a peptide occurs with trypsin and chymotrypsin to identify the location of specific amino acids (Table 29.2).

Adding and Removing Protecting Groups for Amino Acids (29.7)

[1] Protection of an amino group as a Boc derivative

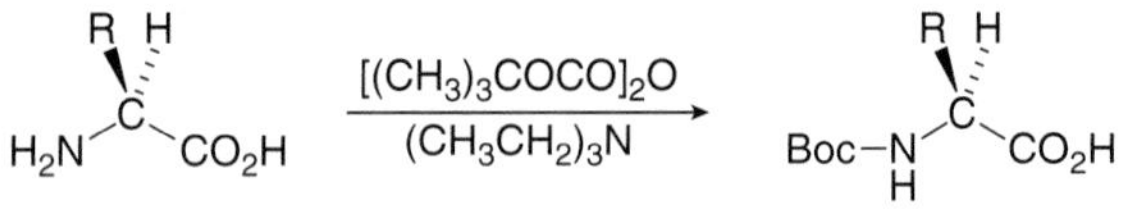

[2] Deprotection of a Boc-protected amino acid

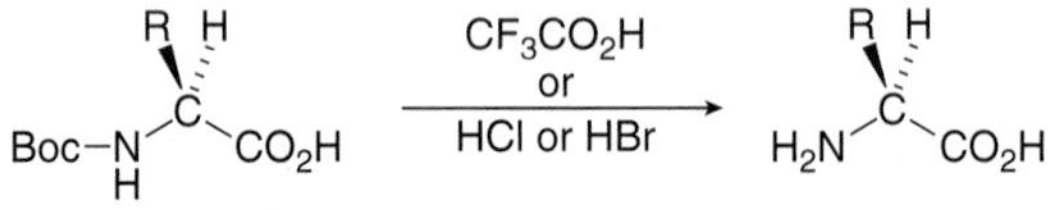

[3] Protection of an amino group as an Fmoc derivative

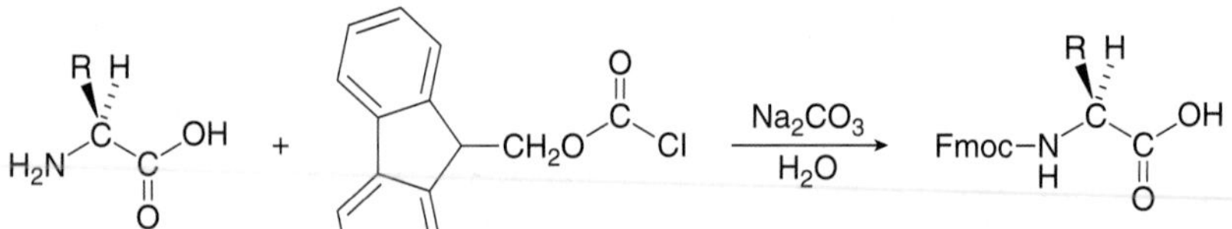

Fmoc–Cl

[4] Deprotection of an Fmoc-protected amino acid

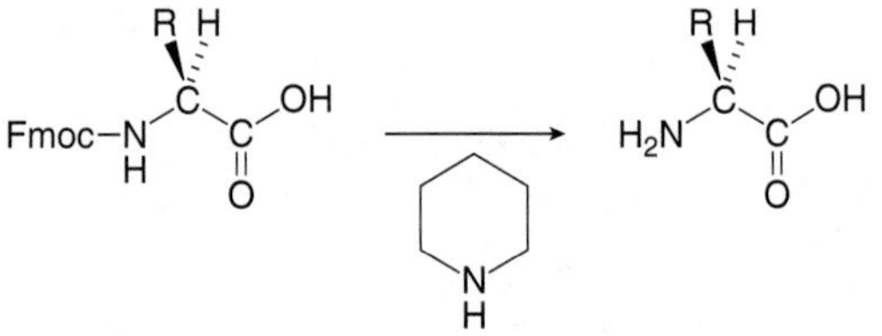

[5] Protection of a carboxy group as an ester

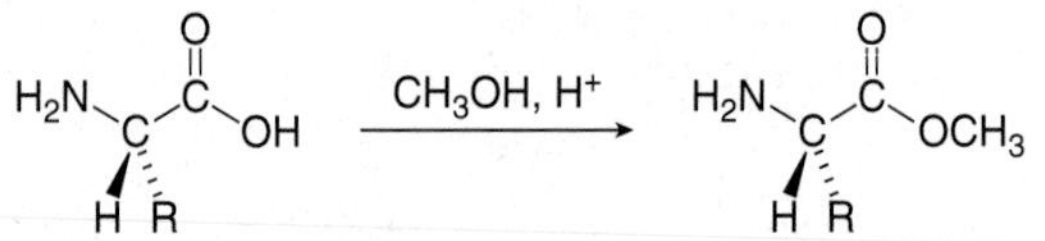

methyl ester

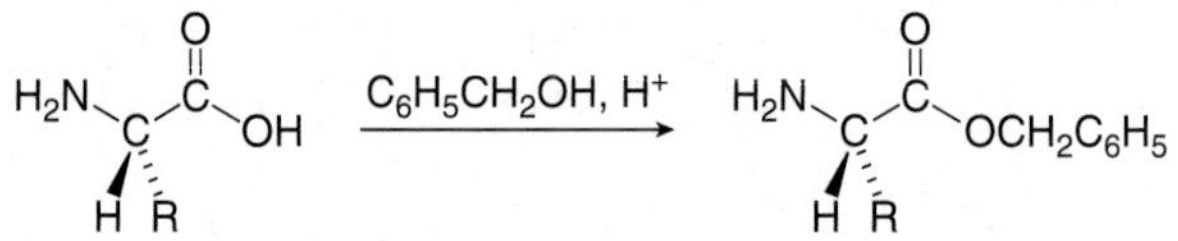

benzyl ester

[6] Deprotection of an ester group

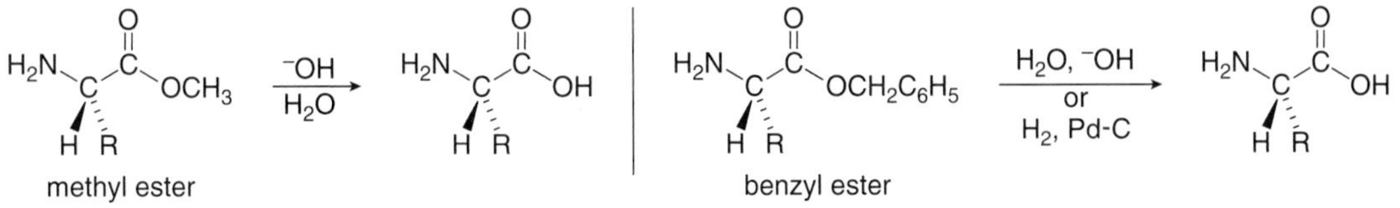

H2N
OCH3
-OH
H2O
OH
H R
methyl ester
OCH2C6H5
H2O, -OH
or
H2, Pd-C
benzyl ester

Synthesis of Dipeptides (29.7)

[1] Amide formation with DCC

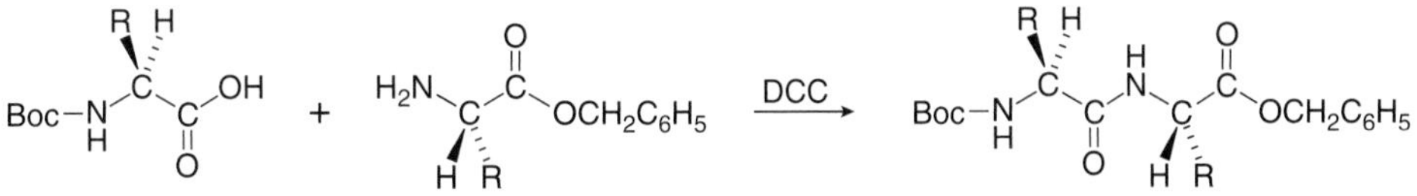

Boc−N
OH
H2N
OCH2C6H5
DCC

[2] Four steps are needed to synthesize a dipeptide:

a. **Protect** the amino group of one amino acid with a Boc or Fmoc group.
b. **Protect** the carboxy group of the second amino acid as an ester.
c. Form the amide bond with **DCC.**
d. **Remove both protecting groups** in one or two reactions.

Summary of the Merrifield Method of Peptide Synthesis (29.8)

[1] Attach an Fmoc-protected amino acid to a polymer derived from polystyrene.
[2] Remove the Fmoc protecting group.
[3] Form the amide bond with a second Fmoc-protected amino acid by using DCC.
[4] Repeat steps [2] and [3].
[5] Remove the protecting group and detach the peptide from the polymer.

PROBLEMS

Problems Using Three-Dimensional Models

29.28 Draw the product formed when the following amino acid is treated with each reagent: (a) CH_3OH, H^+; (b) CH_3COCl, pyridine; (c) HCl (1 equiv); (d) NaOH (1 equiv); (e) $C_6H_5N{=}C{=}S$.

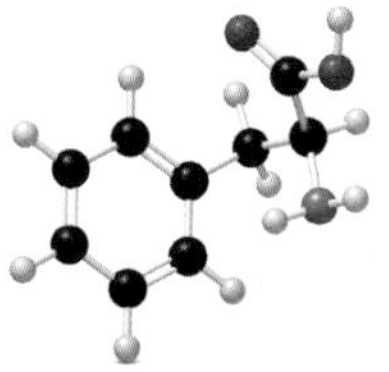

29.29 With reference to the following peptide: (a) Identify the N-terminal and C-terminal amino acids. (b) Name the peptide using one-letter abbreviations. (c) Label all the amide bonds in the peptide backbone.

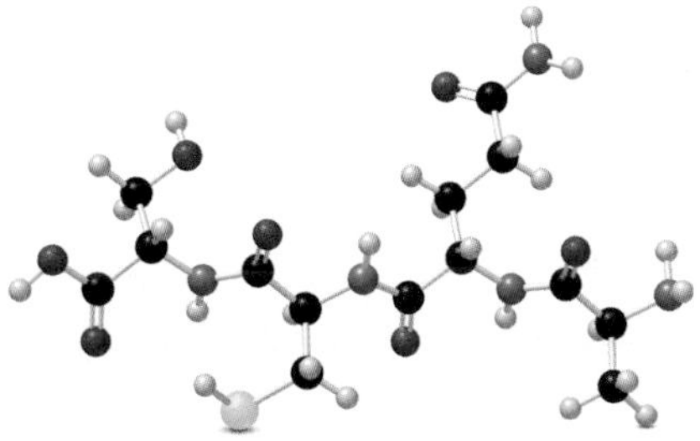

29.30 Devise a synthesis of the following dipeptide from amino acid starting materials.

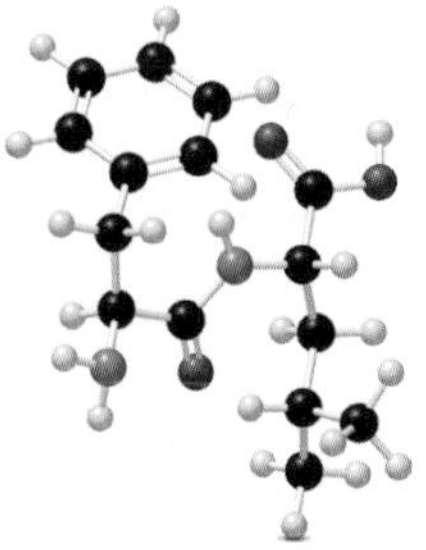

Amino Acids

29.31

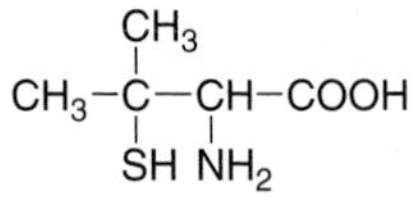

penicillamine

a. (*S*)-Penicillamine, an amino acid that does not occur in proteins, is used as a copper chelating agent to treat Wilson's disease, an inherited defect in copper metabolism. (*R*)-Penicillamine is toxic, sometimes causing blindness. Draw the structures of (*R*)- and (*S*)-penicillamine.

b. What disulfide is formed from oxidation of L-penicillamine?

29.32 Explain why amino acids are insoluble in diethyl ether but *N*-acetyl amino acids are soluble.

29.33 Histidine is classified as a basic amino acid because one of the N atoms in its five-membered ring is readily protonated by acid. Which N atom in histidine is protonated and why?

29.34 Tryptophan is not classified as a basic amino acid even though it has a heterocycle containing a nitrogen atom. Why is the N atom in the five-membered ring of tryptophan not readily protonated by acid?

29.35 What is the structure of each amino acid at its isoelectric point: (a) alanine; (b) methionine; (c) aspartic acid; (d) lysine?

29.36 To calculate the isoelectric point of amino acids having other ionizable functional groups, we must also take into account the pK_a of the additional functional group in the side chain.

For an acidic amino acid (one with an additional acidic OH group):

$$pI = \frac{pK_a\ (\alpha\text{-COOH}) + pK_a\ (\text{second COOH})}{2}$$

For a basic amino acid (one with an additional basic NH group):

$$pI = \frac{pK_a\ (\alpha\text{-NH}_3^+) + pK_a\ (\text{side chain NH})}{2}$$

a. Indicate which pK_a values must be used to calculate the pI of each of the following amino acids: [1] glutamic acid; [2] lysine; [3] arginine.

b. In general, how does the pI of an acidic amino acid compare to that of a neutral amino acid?

c. In general, how does the pI of a basic amino acid compare to the pI of a neutral amino acid?

29.37 What is the predominant form of each of the following amino acids at pH = 1? What is the overall charge on the amino acid at this pH? (a) threonine; (b) methionine; (c) aspartic acid; (d) arginine

29.38 What is the predominant form of each of the following amino acids at pH = 11? What is the overall charge on the amino acid? (a) valine; (b) proline; (c) glutamic acid; (d) lysine

29.39 a. Draw the structure of the tripeptide A–A–A, and label the two ionizable functional groups.

b. What is the predominant form of A–A–A at pH = 1?

c. The pK_a values for the two ionizable functional groups (3.39 and 8.03) differ considerably from the pK_a values of alanine (2.35 and 9.87; see Table 29.1). Account for the observed pK_a differences.

Synthesis and Reactions of Amino Acids

29.40 Draw the organic product formed when the amino acid leucine is treated with each reagent.

a. CH_3OH, H^+
b. CH_3COCl, pyridine
c. $C_6H_5CH_2OH$, H^+
d. Ac_2O, pyridine
e. HCl (1 equiv)
f. NaOH (1 equiv)
g. C_6H_5COCl, pyridine
h. $[(CH_3)_3COCO]_2O$, $(CH_3CH_2)_3N$
i. The product in (d), then $NH_2CH_2COOCH_3$ + DCC
j. The product in (h), then $NH_2CH_2COOCH_3$ + DCC
k. Fmoc–Cl, Na_2CO_3, H_2O
l. $C_6H_5N{=}C{=}S$

29.41 Draw the organic products formed in each reaction.

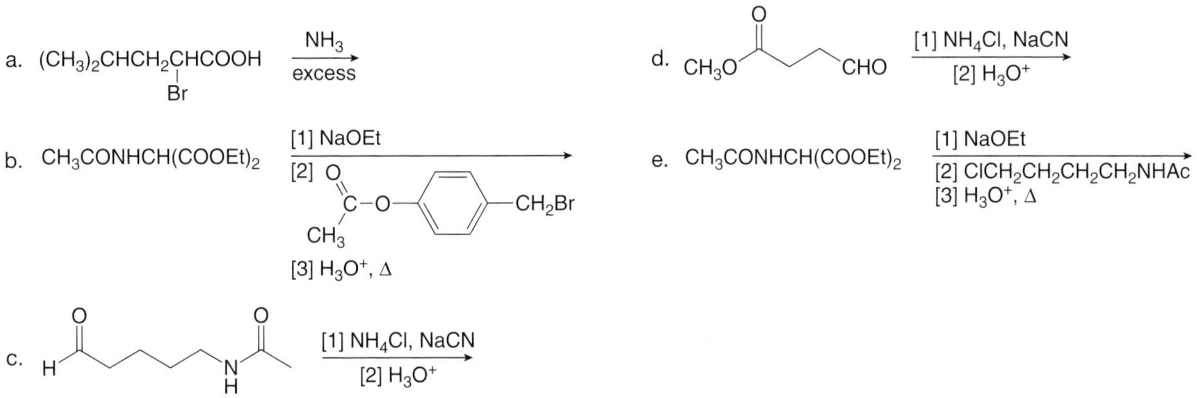
a. (CH3)2CHCH2CHCOOH
Br
NH3
excess
b. CH3CONHCH(COOEt)2
[1] NaOEt
[2] O
C–O
CH2Br
CH3
[3] H3O+, Δ
c. H
N
H
O
O
[1] NH4Cl, NaCN
[2] H3O+
d. CH3O
O
CHO
[1] NH4Cl, NaCN
[2] H3O+
e. CH3CONHCH(COOEt)2
[1] NaOEt
[2] ClCH2CH2CH2CH2NHAc
[3] H3O+, Δ

29.42 What alkyl halide is needed to synthesize each amino acid from diethyl acetamidomalonate: (a) Asn; (b) His; (c) Trp?

29.43 Devise a synthesis of threonine from diethyl acetamidomalonate.

29.44 Devise a synthesis of each amino acid from acetaldehyde (CH_3CHO): (a) glycine; (b) alanine.

29.45 Identify the lettered intermediates in the following reaction scheme. This is an alternative method to synthesize amino acids, based on the Gabriel synthesis of 1° amines (Section 25.7A).

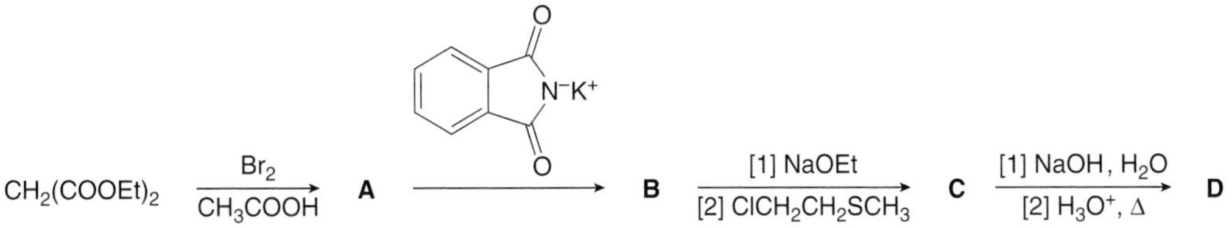
CH2(COOEt)2
Br2
CH3COOH
A
O
N−K+
O
B
[1] NaOEt
[2] ClCH2CH2SCH3
C
[1] NaOH, H2O
[2] H3O+, Δ
D

29.46 Glutamic acid is synthesized by the following reaction sequence. Draw a stepwise mechanism for Steps [1]–[3].

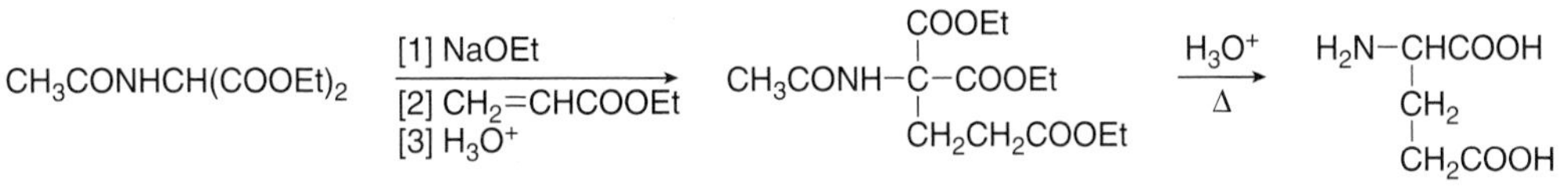
CH3CONHCH(COOEt)2
[1] NaOEt
[2] CH2=CHCOOEt
[3] H3O+
COOEt
CH3CONH–C–COOEt
CH2CH2COOEt
H3O+
Δ
H2N–CHCOOH
CH2
CH2COOH

glutamic acid

29.47 Identify **A–E** in the following reaction sequence. **E** was converted to amphikuemin, the compound secreted by a sea anemone of the genus *Heteractis* that attracts pink anemonefish to live among its stinging tentacles. Amphikuemin is depicted in the three-dimensional model on the cover.

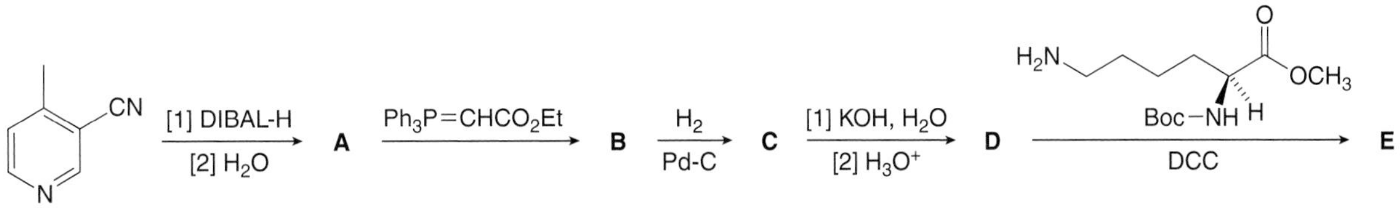
CN
N
[1] DIBAL-H
[2] H2O
A
Ph3P=CHCO2Et
B
H2
Pd-C
C
[1] KOH, H2O
[2] H3O+
D
H2N
O
OCH3
Boc–NH H
DCC
E

Resolution; The Synthesis of Chiral Amino Acids

29.48 Write out a scheme for the resolution of the two enantiomers of the antiplatelet drug clopidogrel with 10-camphorsulfonic acid.

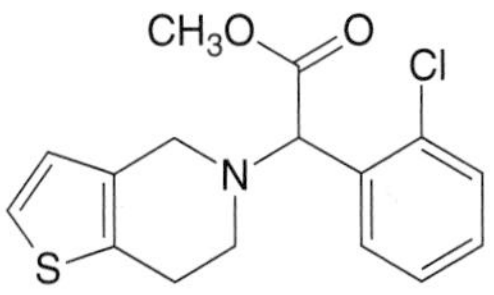
CH3O
O
Cl
N
S

clopidogrel

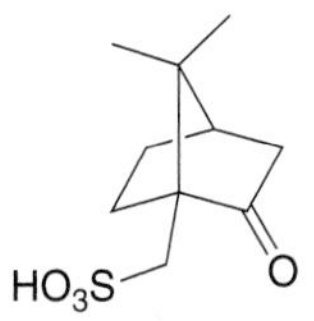
HO3S
O

10-camphorsulfonic acid

29.49 Another strategy used to resolve amino acids involves converting the carboxy group to an ester and then using a *chiral carboxylic acid* to carry out an acid–base reaction at the free amino group. The general plan is drawn below using (*R*)-mandelic acid as resolving agent. Using a racemic mixture of alanine enantiomers and (*R*)-mandelic acid as resolving agent, write out the steps showing how a resolution process would occur.

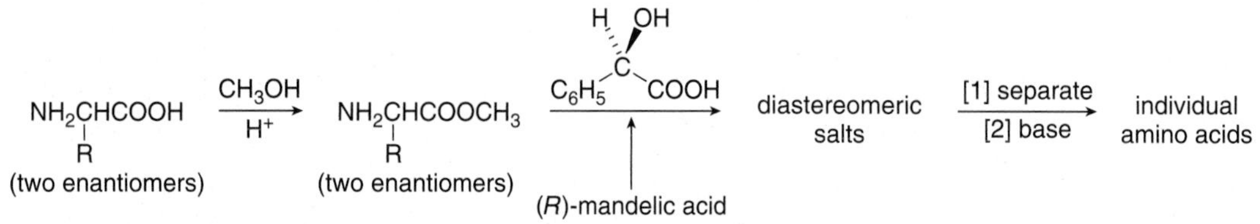
NH2CHCOOH
R
(two enantiomers)
CH3OH
H+
NH2CHCOOCH3
R
(two enantiomers)
H OH
C6H5 COOH
(R)-mandelic acid
diastereomeric salts
[1] separate
[2] base
individual amino acids

29.50 Brucine is a poisonous alkaloid obtained from *Strychnos nux vomica,* a tree that grows in India, Sri Lanka, and northern Australia. Write out a resolution scheme similar to the one given in Section 29.3A, which shows how a racemic mixture of phenylalanine can be resolved using brucine.

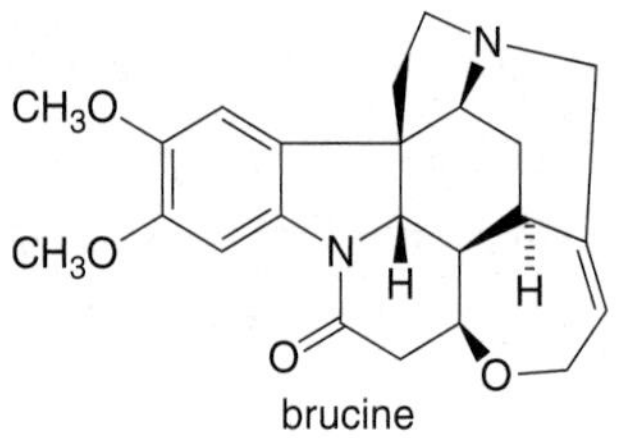
CH3O
CH3O
N
N
H
H
O
O

brucine

29.51 Draw the organic products formed in each reaction.

a. 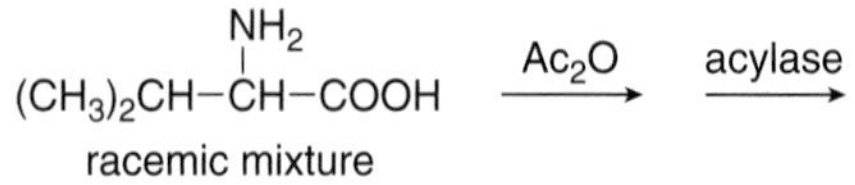
NH2
(CH3)2CH–CH–COOH
racemic mixture
Ac2O
acylase

c. 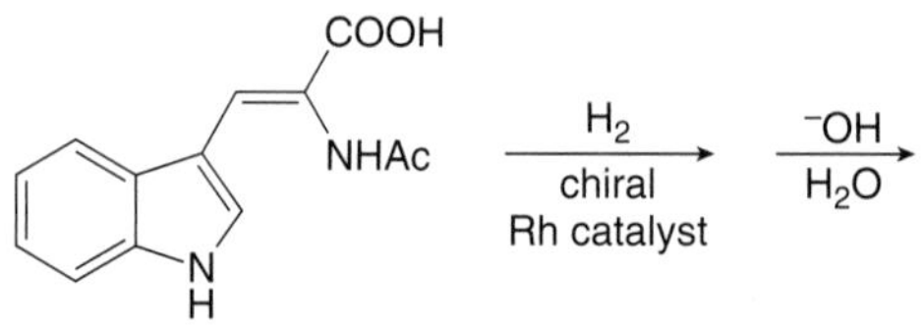
COOH
NHAc
N
H
H2
chiral
Rh catalyst
−OH
H2O

b. 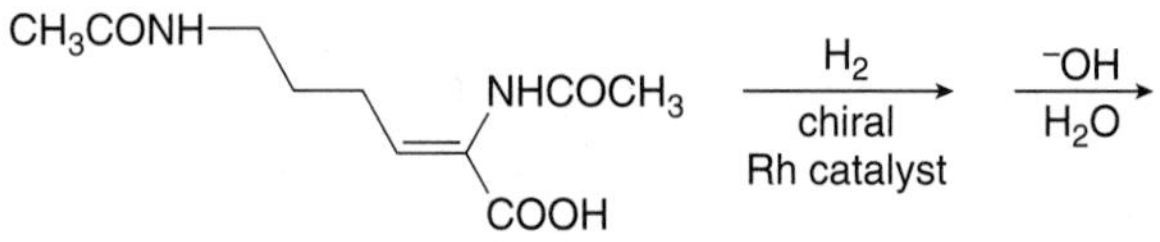
CH3CONH
NHCOCH3
COOH
H2
chiral
Rh catalyst
−OH
H2O

29.52 What two steps are needed to convert **A** to L-dopa, an uncommon amino acid that is effective in treating Parkinson's disease? These two steps are the key reactions in the first commercial asymmetric synthesis using a chiral transition metal catalyst. This process was developed at Monsanto in 1974.

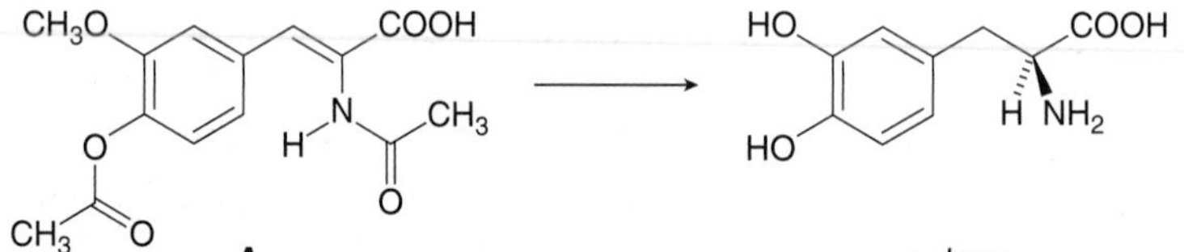
CH3O
COOH
N
H
CH3
O
O
CH3
O
HO
HO
COOH
H NH2

A L-dopa

Peptide Structure and Sequencing

29.53 Draw the structure for each peptide: (a) Phe–Ala; (b) Gly–Gln; (c) Lys–Gly; (d) R–H.

29.54 For the tetrapeptide Asp–Arg–Val–Tyr:

a. Name the peptide using one-letter abbreviations.
b. Draw the structure.
c. Label all amide bonds.
d. Label the N-terminal and C-terminal amino acids.

29.55 Name each peptide using both the three-letter and one-letter abbreviations of the component amino acids.

a. 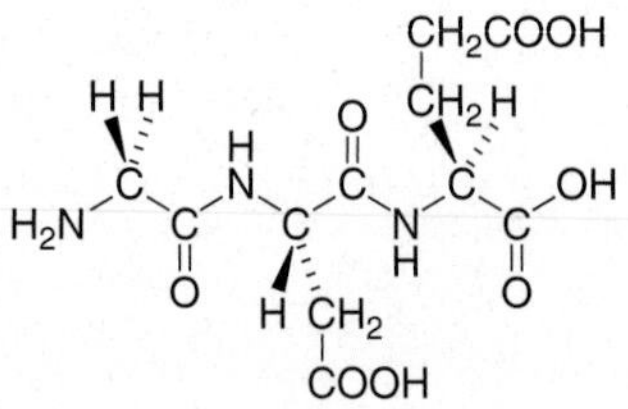
CH2COOH
CH2H
H H
H2N
OH
H CH2
COOH

b. 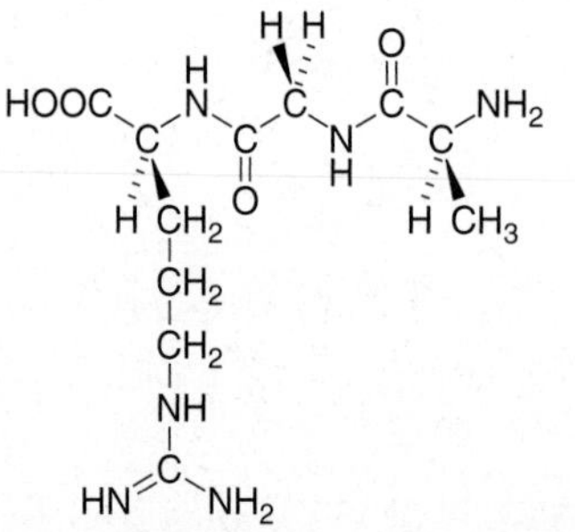
HOOC
NH2
H CH2
CH2
CH2
NH
HN
NH2
H CH3

29.56 Explain why a peptide C–N bond is stronger than an ester C–O bond.

29.57 Draw the *s*-trans and *s*-cis conformations of the peptide bond in the dipeptide Ala–Ala.

29.58 Draw the amino acids and peptide fragments formed when the decapeptide A–P–F–L–K–W–S–G–R–G is treated with each reagent or enzyme: (a) chymotrypsin; (b) trypsin; (c) carboxypeptidase; (d) $C_6H_5N{=}C{=}S$.

29.59 Give the amino acid sequence of each peptide using the fragments obtained by partial hydrolysis of the peptide with acid.

a. a tetrapeptide that contains Ala, Gly, His, and Tyr, which is hydrolyzed to the dipeptides His–Tyr, Gly–Ala, and Ala–His

b. a pentapeptide that contains Glu, Gly, His, Lys, and Phe, which is hydrolyzed to His–Gly–Glu, Gly–Glu–Phe, and Lys–His

29.60 Angiotensin is an octapeptide that narrows blood vessels, thereby increasing blood pressure. ACE inhibitors are a group of drugs used to treat high blood pressure by blocking the synthesis of angiotensin in the body. Angiotensin contains the amino acids Arg (2 equiv), His, Ile, Phe, Pro, Tyr, and Val. Determine the sequence of angiotensin using the following fragments obtained by partial hydrolysis with acid: Ile–His–Pro–Phe, Arg–Arg–Val, Tyr–Ile–His, and Val–Tyr.

29.61 Use the given experimental data to deduce the sequence of an octapeptide that contains the following amino acids: Ala, Gly (2 equiv), His (2 equiv), Ile, Leu, and Phe. Edman degradation cleaves Gly from the octapeptide, and carboxypeptidase forms Leu and a heptapeptide. Partial hydrolysis forms the following fragments: Ile–His–Leu, Gly, Gly–Ala–Phe–His, and Phe–His–Ile.

29.62 An octapeptide contains the following amino acids: Arg, Glu, His, Ile, Leu, Phe, Tyr, and Val. Carboxypeptidase treatment of the octapeptide forms Phe and a heptapeptide. Treatment of the octapeptide with chymotrypsin forms two tetrapeptides, **A** and **B.** Treatment of **A** with trypsin yields two dipeptides, **C** and **D.** Edman degradation cleaves the following amino acids from each peptide: Glu (octapeptide), Glu (**A**), Ile (**B**), Glu (**C**), and Val (**D**). Partial hydrolysis of tetrapeptide **B** forms Ile–Leu in addition to other products. Deduce the structure of the octapeptide and fragments **A–D.**

Peptide Synthesis

29.63 Draw all the products formed in the following reaction.

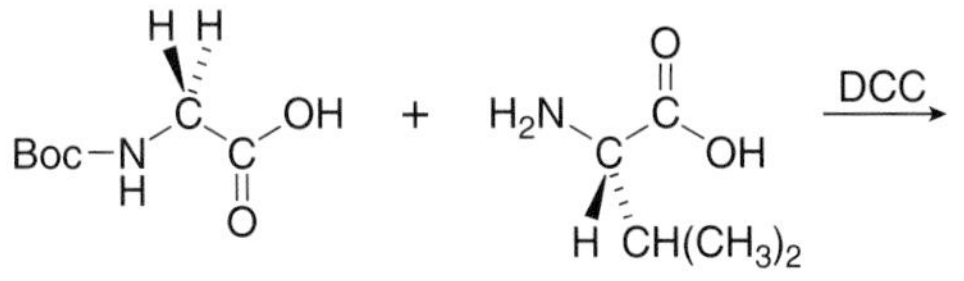

29.64 Draw the organic products formed in each reaction.

a. 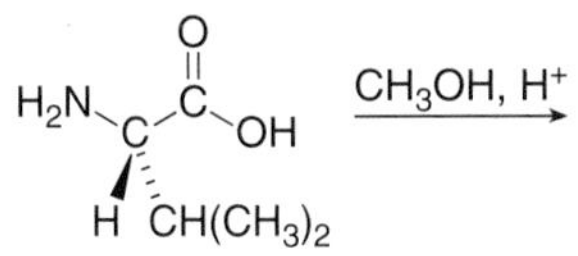

e. 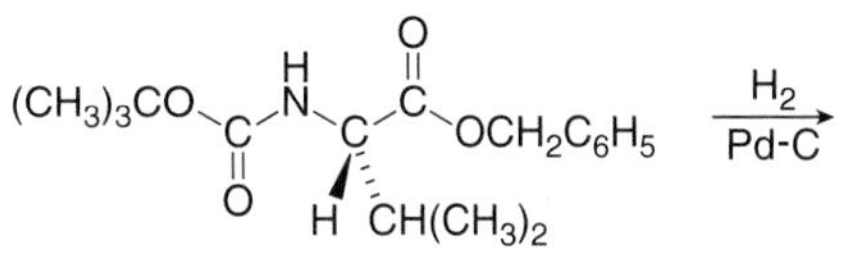

b. 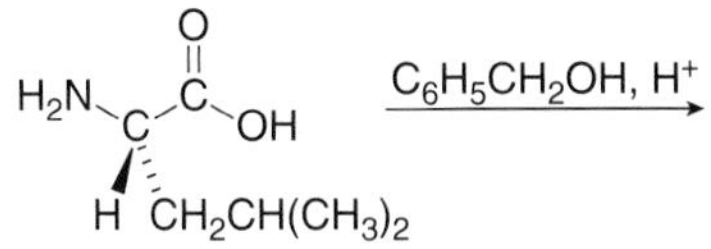

f. starting material in (e) $\xrightarrow[CH_3COOH]{HBr}$

c. NH_2CH_2COOH $\xrightarrow[(CH_3CH_2)_3N]{[(CH_3)_3COCO]_2O}$

g. product in (e) $\xrightarrow{CF_3COOH}$

d. product in (b) + product in (c) $\xrightarrow{DCC}$

h. 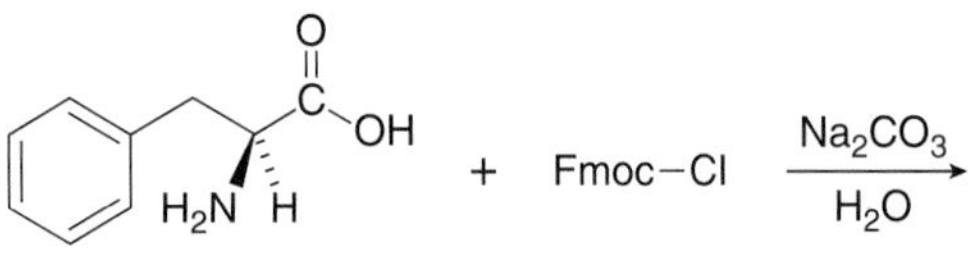

29.65 Draw all the steps in the synthesis of each peptide from individual amino acids: (a) Gly–Ala; (b) Ile–Ala–Phe.

29.66 Write out the steps for the synthesis of each peptide using the Merrifield method: (a) Ala–Leu–Phe–Phe; (b) Phe–Gly–Ala–Ile.

29.67 Another method to form a peptide bond involves a two-step process:

[1] Conversion of a Boc-protected amino acid to a *p*-nitrophenyl ester.

[2] Reaction of the *p*-nitrophenyl ester with an amino acid ester.

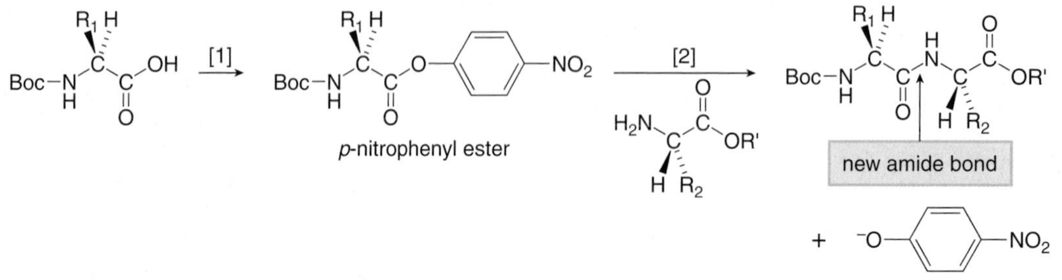
p-nitrophenyl ester
new amide bond

a. Why does a *p*-nitrophenyl ester “activate” the carboxy group of the first amino acid to amide formation?

b. Would a *p*-methoxyphenyl ester perform the same function? Why or why not?

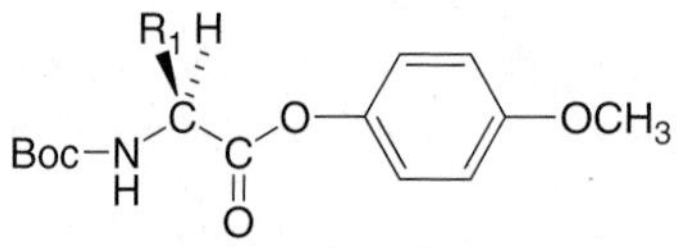

p-methoxyphenyl ester

29.68 In addition to forming an Fmoc-protected amino acid using Fmoc–Cl, an Fmoc protecting group can also be added to an amino group using reagent **A.**

a. Draw the mechanism for the following reaction that adds an Fmoc group to an amino acid.

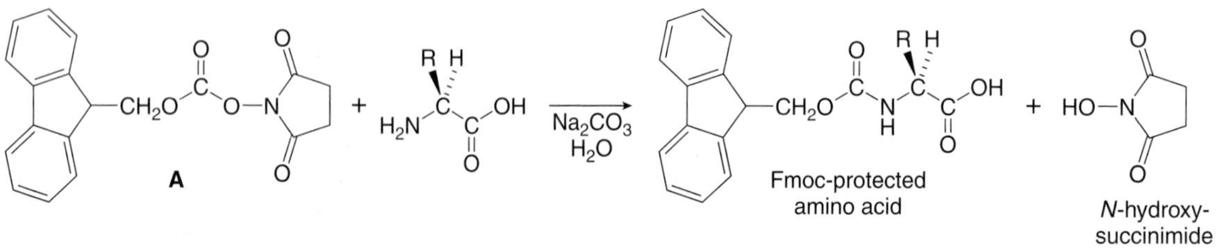
A
Fmoc-protected amino acid
N-hydroxy-succinimide

b. Draw the mechanism for the reaction that removes an Fmoc group from an amino acid under the following conditions:

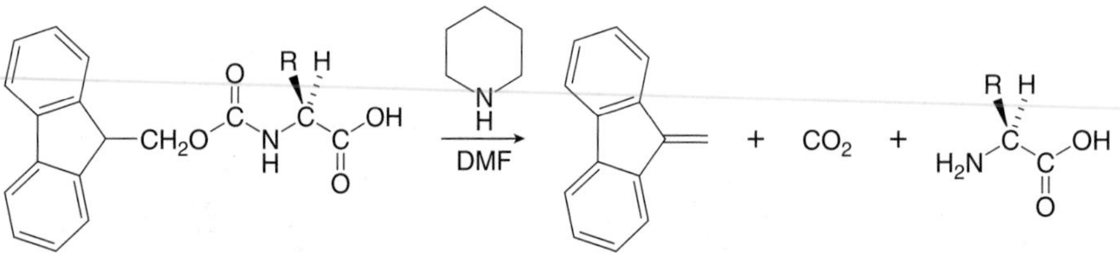

29.69 Many different insoluble polymers, called resins, are currently available for automated peptide synthesis. For example, the Wang resin contains benzene rings substituted with $-CH_2OH$ groups that serve as sites of attachment for amino acids. Propose reaction conditions that would bind an Fmoc-protected amino acid to a Wang resin. What reaction conditions could be used to remove the polypeptide from the resin after the synthesis is complete?

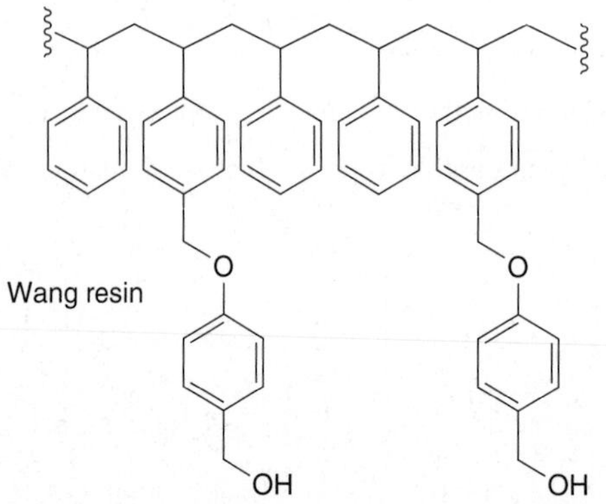
Wang resin

Proteins

29.70 Which of the following amino acids are typically found in the interior of a globular protein, and which are typically found on the surface: (a) phenylalanine; (b) aspartic acid; (c) lysine; (d) isoleucine; (e) arginine; (f) glutamic acid?

29.71 After the peptide chain of collagen has been formed, many of the proline residues are hydroxylated on one of the ring carbon atoms. Why is this process important for the triple helix of collagen?

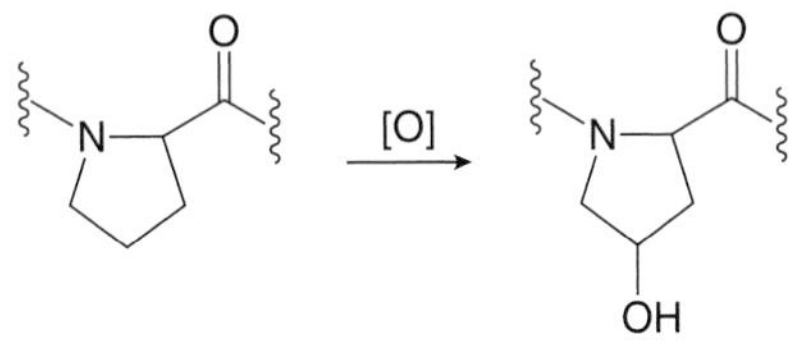

Challenge Problems

29.72 Devise a stepwise synthesis of the tripeptide Val–Leu–Val from 3-methylbutanal [$(CH_3)_2CHCH_2CHO$] as the only organic starting material. You may also use any required inorganic or organic reagents.

29.73 Besides asymmetric hydrogenation (Section 29.4), several other methods are now available for the synthesis of optically active amino acids. How might a reaction like the Strecker synthesis be adapted to the preparation of chiral amino acids?

29.74 The anti-obesity drug orlistat works by irreversibly inhibiting pancreatic lipase, an enzyme responsible for the hydrolysis of triacylglycerols in the intestines, so they are excreted without metabolism. Inhibition occurs by reaction of orlistat with a serine residue of the enzyme, forming a covalently bound, inactive enzyme product. Draw the structure of the product formed during inhibition.

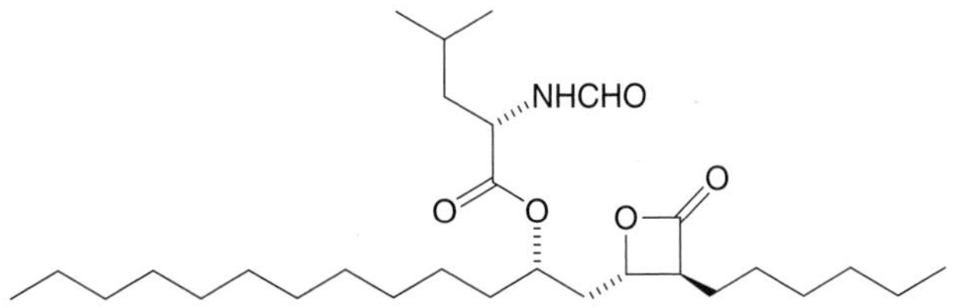

29.75 As shown in Mechanism 29.2, the final steps in the Edman degradation result in rearrangement of a thiazolinone to an *N*-phenylthiohydantoin. Draw a stepwise mechanism for this acid-catalyzed reaction.

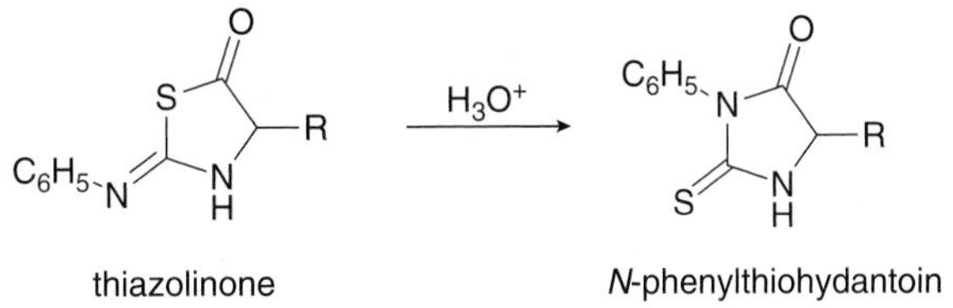

30 Lipids

30.1 Introduction
30.2 Waxes
30.3 Triacylglycerols
30.4 Phospholipids
30.5 Fat-soluble vitamins
30.6 Eicosanoids
30.7 Terpenes
30.8 Steroids

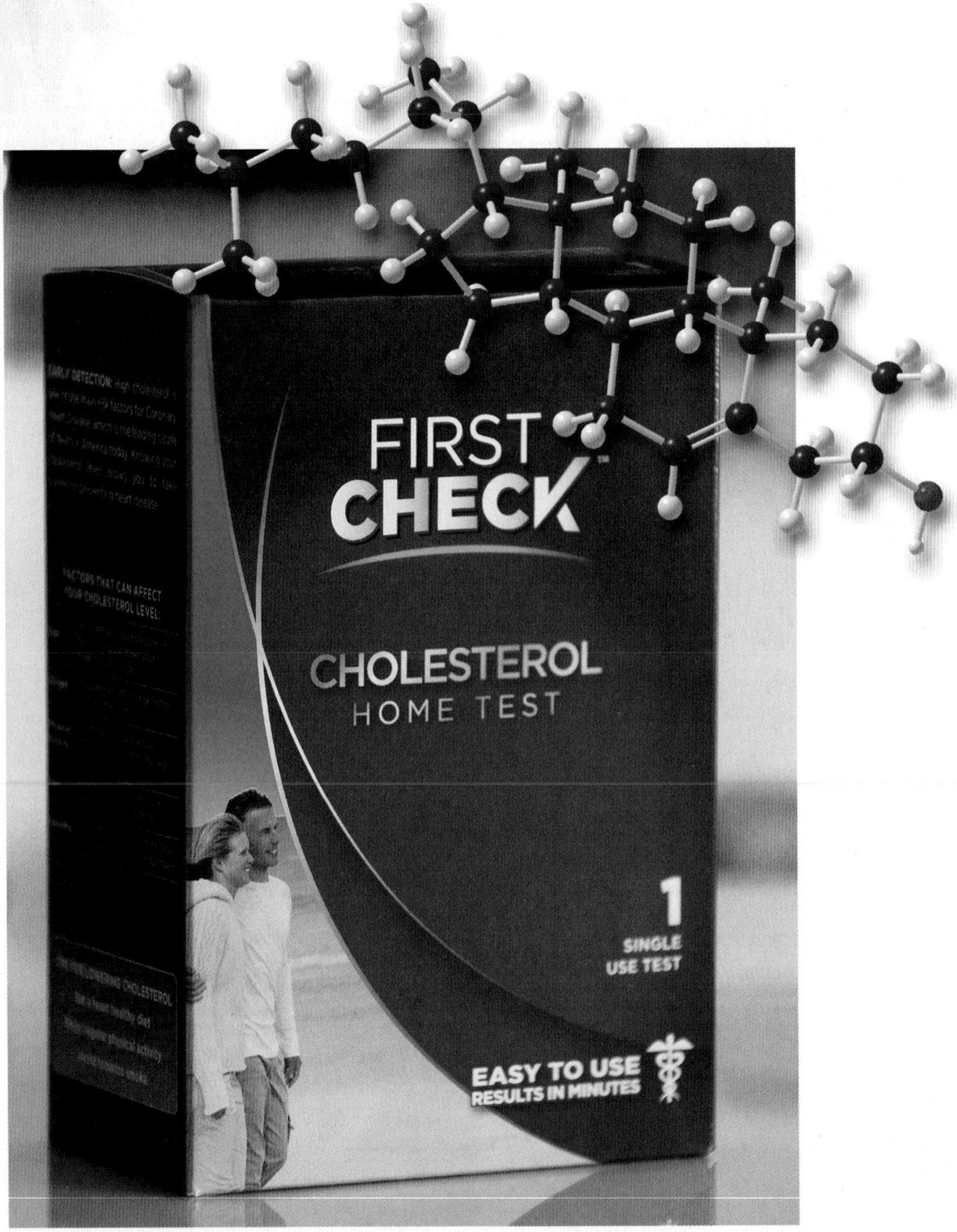

Cholesterol is the most prominent member of the steroid family, a group of organic lipids that contains a tetracyclic structure. Cholesterol is synthesized in the liver and is found in almost all body tissues. It is a vital component for healthy cell membranes and serves as the starting material for the synthesis of all other steroids. But, as the general public now knows well, elevated cholesterol levels can lead to coronary artery disease. For this reason, consumer products are now labeled with their cholesterol content. In Chapter 30, we learn about the properties of cholesterol and other lipids.

We conclude the discussion of the organic molecules in biological systems by turning our attention to **lipids,** biomolecules that are soluble in organic solvents. Unlike the carbohydrates in Chapter 28 and the amino acids and proteins in Chapter 29, lipids contain many carbon–carbon and carbon–hydrogen bonds and few functional groups.

Since lipids are the biomolecules that most closely resemble the hydrocarbons we studied in Chapters 4 and 10, we have already learned many facts that directly explain their properties. Since there is no one functional group that is present in all lipids, however, the chemistry of lipids draws upon knowledge learned in many prior chapters.

30.1 Introduction

The word *lipid* comes from the Greek word ***lipos*** for "fat."

- ***Lipids* are biomolecules that are soluble in organic solvents.**

Lipids are unique among organic molecules because their identity is defined on the basis of a *physical property* and not by the presence of a particular functional group. Because of this, lipids come in a wide variety of structures and they have many different functions in the cell. Three examples are given in Figure 30.1.

The large number of **carbon–carbon and carbon–hydrogen σ bonds in lipids makes them very soluble in organic solvents and insoluble in water.** Monosaccharides (from which carbohydrates are formed) and amino acids (from which proteins are formed), on the other hand, are very polar, so they tend to be water soluble. Because lipids share many properties with hydrocarbons, several features of lipid structure and properties have already been discussed. Table 30.1 summarizes sections of the text where aspects of lipid chemistry were covered previously.

Table 30.1 Summary of Lipid Chemistry Discussed Prior to Chapter 30

Topic	Section	Topic	Section
• Vitamin A	3.5	• Lipid oxidation	15.11
• Soap	3.6	• Vitamin E	15.12
• Phospholipids, the cell membrane	3.7	• Steroid synthesis	16.14
• Lipids Part 1	4.15	• Prostaglandins	19.6
• Leukotrienes	9.16	• Lipid hydrolysis	22.12A
• Fats and oils	10.6	• Soap	22.12B
• Oral contraceptives	11.4	• Cholesteryl esters	22.17
• Hydrogenation of oils	12.4	• Steroid synthesis	24.8

Figure 30.1
Three examples of lipids

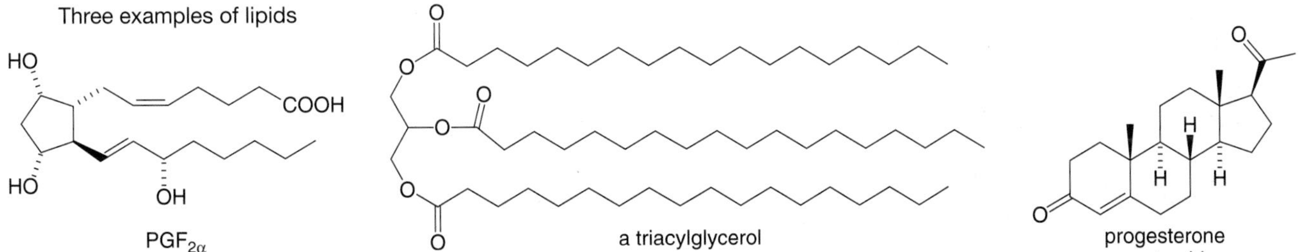

$PGF_{2\alpha}$
a prostaglandin

a triacylglycerol

progesterone
a steroid

All lipids have many C–C and C–H bonds, but there is no one functional group common to all lipids.

Lipids can be categorized as hydrolyzable or nonhydrolyzable.

[1] ***Hydrolyzable lipids*** **can be cleaved into smaller molecules by hydrolysis with water.** Most hydrolyzable lipids contain an ester unit. We will examine three subgroups: waxes, triacylglycerols, and phospholipids.

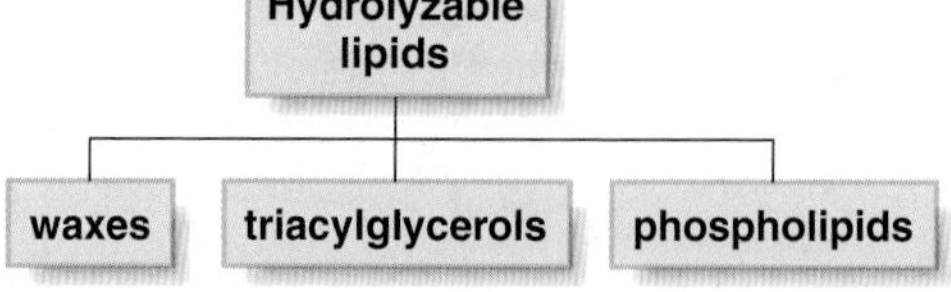

[2] ***Nonhydrolyzable lipids*** **cannot be cleaved into smaller units by aqueous hydrolysis.** Nonhydrolyzable lipids tend to be more varied in structure. We will examine four different types: fat-soluble vitamins, eicosanoids, terpenes, and steroids.

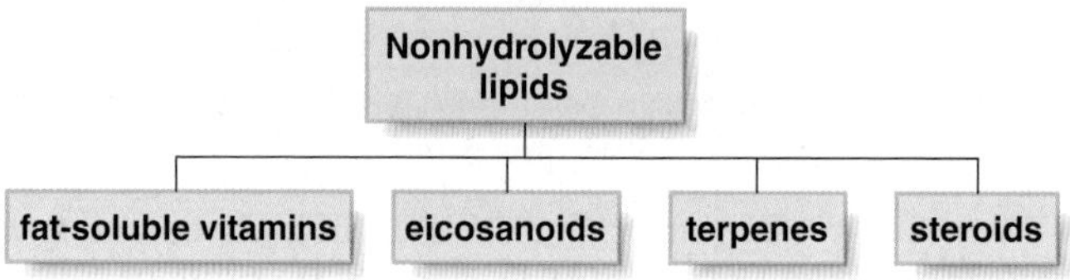

30.2 Waxes

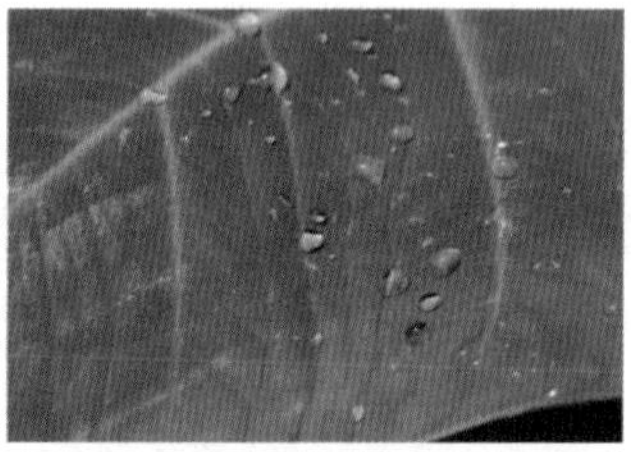

Water beads up on the surface of a leaf because of the leaf's waxy coating.

The seeds of the jojoba plant grown in the southwestern United States are rich in waxes used in cosmetics and personal care products.

Waxes are the simplest hydrolyzable lipids. **Waxes are esters (RCOOR') formed from a high molecular weight alcohol (R'OH) and a fatty acid (RCOOH).**

Because of their long hydrocarbon chains, **waxes are very hydrophobic.** They form a protective coating on the feathers of birds to make them water repellent, and on leaves to prevent water evaporation. **Lanolin,** a wax composed of a complex mixture of high molecular weight esters, coats the wool fibers of sheep. **Spermaceti wax,** isolated from the heads of sperm whales, is largely $CH_3(CH_2)_{14}COO(CH_2)_{15}CH_3$. The three-dimensional structure of this compound shows how small the ester group is compared to the long hydrocarbon chains.

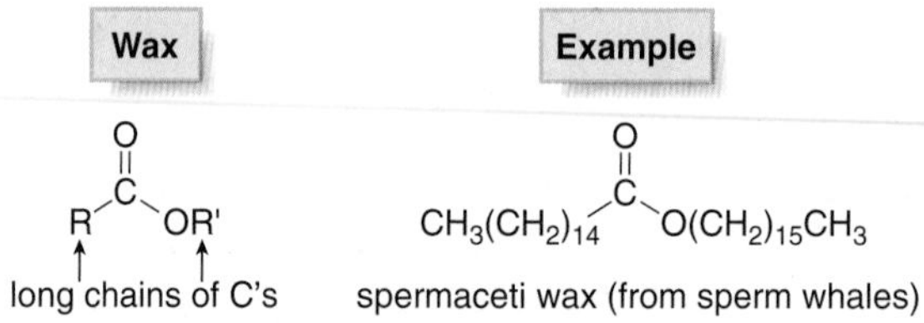

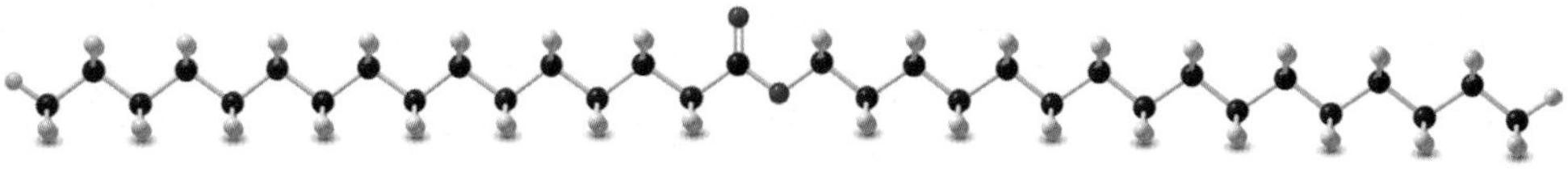

spermaceti wax
3-D structure

Problem 30.1 One component of jojoba oil is a wax formed from eicosenoic acid [$CH_3(CH_2)_7CH{=}CH(CH_2)_9CO_2H$] and $CH_3(CH_2)_7CH{=}CH(CH_2)_8OH$. Draw the structure of the wax, including the cis geometry of both carbon–carbon double bonds.

30.3 Triacylglycerols

Triacylglycerols, or triglycerides, are the most abundant lipids, and for this reason we have already discussed many of their properties in earlier sections of this text.

- **Triacylglycerols are triesters that produce glycerol and three molecules of fatty acid upon hydrolysis.**

Line structures of stearic, oleic, linoleic, and linolenic acids can be found in Table 10.2. Ball-and-stick models of these fatty acids are shown in Figure 10.6.

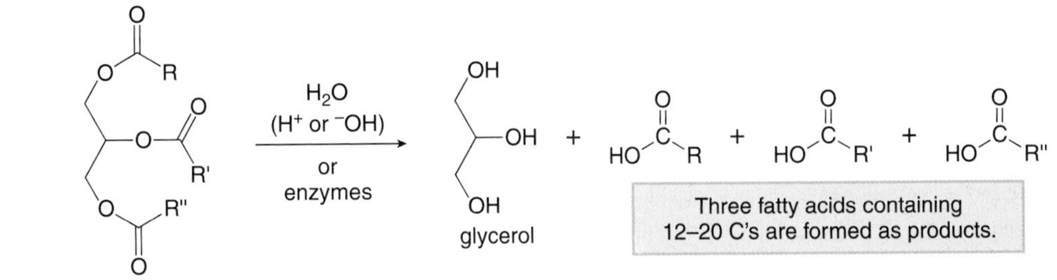
H2O
(H+ or −OH)
or
enzymes
glycerol
Three fatty acids containing 12–20 C's are formed as products.

triacylglycerol
the most common type of lipid

Simple triacylglycerols are composed of three identical fatty acid side chains, whereas **mixed triacylglycerols** have two or three different fatty acids. Table 30.2 lists the most common fatty acids used to form triacylglycerols.

Table 30.2 The Most Common Fatty Acids in Triacylglycerols

Number of C atoms	Number of C=C bonds	Structure	Name	Mp (°C)
		Saturated fatty acids		
12	0	$CH_3(CH_2)_{10}COOH$	lauric acid	44
14	0	$CH_3(CH_2)_{12}COOH$	myristic acid	58
16	0	$CH_3(CH_2)_{14}COOH$	palmitic acid	63
18	0	$CH_3(CH_2)_{16}COOH$	stearic acid	69
20	0	$CH_3(CH_2)_{18}COOH$	arachidic acid	77
		Unsaturated fatty acids		
16	1	$CH_3(CH_2)_5CH=CH(CH_2)_7COOH$	palmitoleic acid	1
18	1	$CH_3(CH_2)_7CH=CH(CH_2)_7COOH$	oleic acid	4
18	2	$CH_3(CH_2)_4(CH=CHCH_2)_2(CH_2)_6COOH$	linoleic acid	–5
18	3	$CH_3CH_2(CH=CHCH_2)_3(CH_2)_6COOH$	linolenic acid	–11
20	4	$CH_3(CH_2)_4(CH=CHCH_2)_4(CH_2)_2COOH$	arachidonic acid	–49

The most common saturated fatty acids are palmitic and stearic acids. The most common unsaturated fatty acid is oleic acid.

Linoleic and linolenic acids are called **essential fatty acids** because we cannot synthesize them and must acquire them in our diets.

What are the characteristics of these fatty acids?

- **All fatty acid chains are unbranched, but they may be saturated or unsaturated.**
- **Naturally occurring fatty acids have an even number of carbon atoms.**
- **Double bonds in naturally occurring fatty acids generally have the *Z* configuration.**
- **The melting point of a fatty acid depends on the degree of unsaturation.**

Fats and oils are triacylglycerols; that is, they are triesters of glycerol and these fatty acids.

- **Fats have higher melting points, making them solids at room temperature.**
- **Oils have lower melting points, making them liquids at room temperature.**

Figure 30.2 Three-dimensional structures of a saturated and unsaturated triacylglycerol

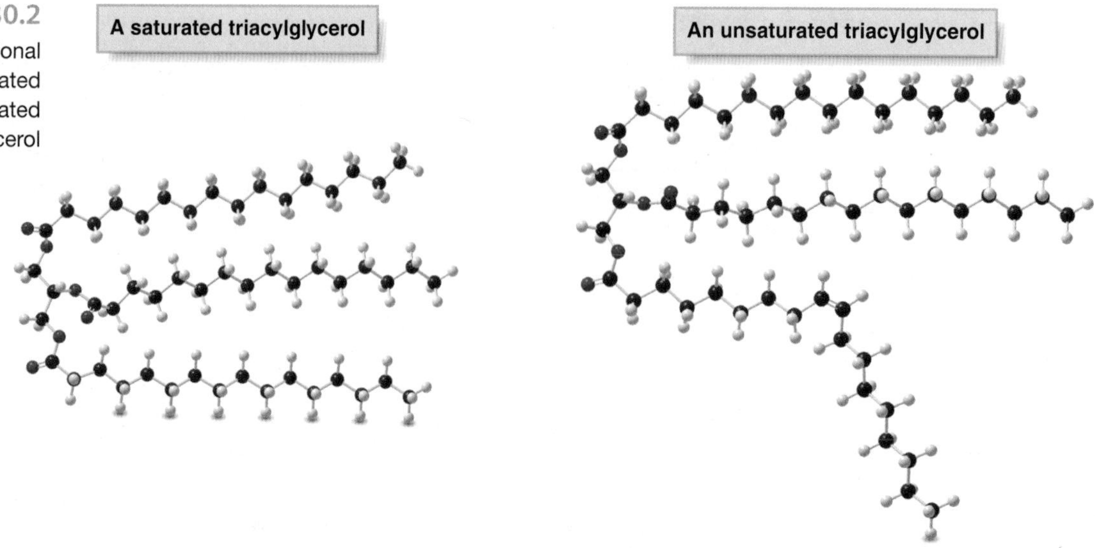

- Three saturated side chains lie parallel to each other, making a compact lipid.
- One *Z* double bond in a fatty acid side chain produces a twist so the lipid is no longer so compact.

Unlike other vegetable oils, oils from palm and coconut trees are very high in saturated fats. Considerable evidence currently suggests that diets high in saturated fats lead to a greater risk of heart disease. For this reason, the demand for coconut and palm oils has decreased considerably in recent years, and many coconut plantations previously farmed in the South Pacific are no longer in commercial operation.

This melting point difference correlates with the number of degrees of unsaturation present in the fatty acid side chains. **As the number of double bonds *increases*, the melting point *decreases*, as it does for the constituent fatty acids as well.**

Three-dimensional structures of a saturated and unsaturated triacylglycerol are shown in Figure 30.2. With no double bonds, the three side chains of the saturated lipid lie parallel to each other, making it possible for this compound to pack relatively efficiently in a crystalline lattice, thus leading to a high melting point. In the unsaturated lipid, however, a single *Z* double bond places a kink in the side chain, making it more difficult to pack efficiently in the solid state, thus leading to a lower melting point.

Solid fats have a relatively high percentage of saturated fatty acids and are generally of animal origin. Liquid oils have a higher percentage of unsaturated fatty acids and are generally of vegetable origin. Table 30.3 lists the fatty acid composition of some common fats and oils.

Table 30.3 Fatty Acid Composition of Some Fats and Oils

Source	% Saturated fatty acids	% Oleic acid	% Linoleic acid
beef	49–62	37–43	2–3
milk	37	33	3
coconut	86	7	–
corn	11–16	19–49	34–62
olive	11	84	4
palm	43	40	8
safflower	9	13	78
soybean	15	20	52

Data from *Merck Index,* 10th ed. Rahway, NJ: Merck and Co.; and Wilson, et al., 1967, *Principles of Nutrition,* 2nd ed. New York: Wiley.

Fish oils, such as cod liver and herring oils, are very rich in polyunsaturated triacylglycerols. These triacylglycerols pack so poorly that they have very low melting points; thus, they remain liquids even in the cold water inhabited by these fish.

The hydrolysis, hydrogenation, and oxidation of triacylglycerols—reactions originally discussed in Chapters 12, 15, and 22—are summarized here for your reference.

[1] **Hydrolysis of triacylglycerols (Section 22.12A)**

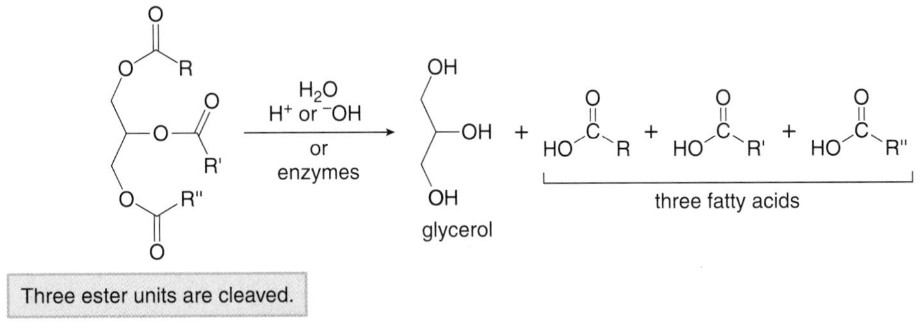
H2O
H+ or -OH
or
enzymes
glycerol
three fatty acids
Three ester units are cleaved.

Hydrolysis of a triacylglycerol with water in the presence of either acid, base, or an enzyme yields glycerol and three fatty acids. This cleavage reaction follows the same mechanism as any other ester hydrolysis (Section 22.11). This reaction is the first step in triacylglycerol metabolism.

[2] **Hydrogenation of unsaturated fatty acids (Section 12.4)**

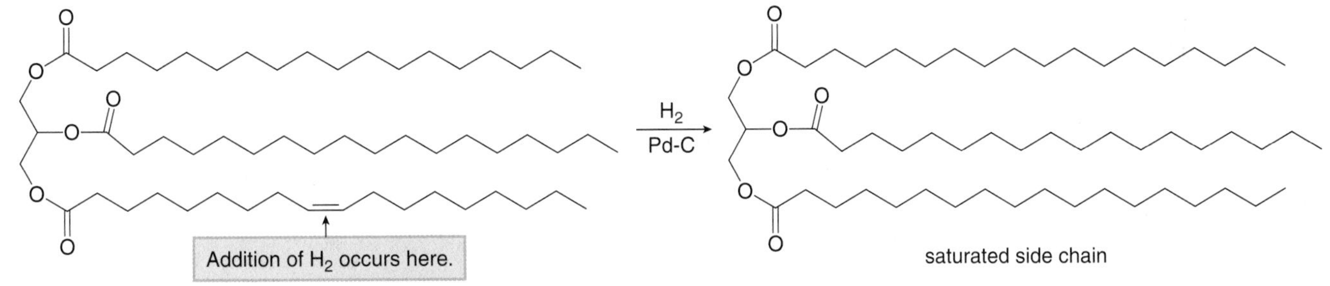
H2
Pd-C
Addition of H2 occurs here.
saturated side chain

The double bonds of an unsaturated fatty acid can be hydrogenated by using H_2 in the presence of a transition metal catalyst. Hydrogenation converts a liquid oil to a solid fat. This process, sometimes called **hardening,** is used to prepare margarine from vegetable oils.

[3] **Oxidation of unsaturated fatty acids (Section 15.11)**

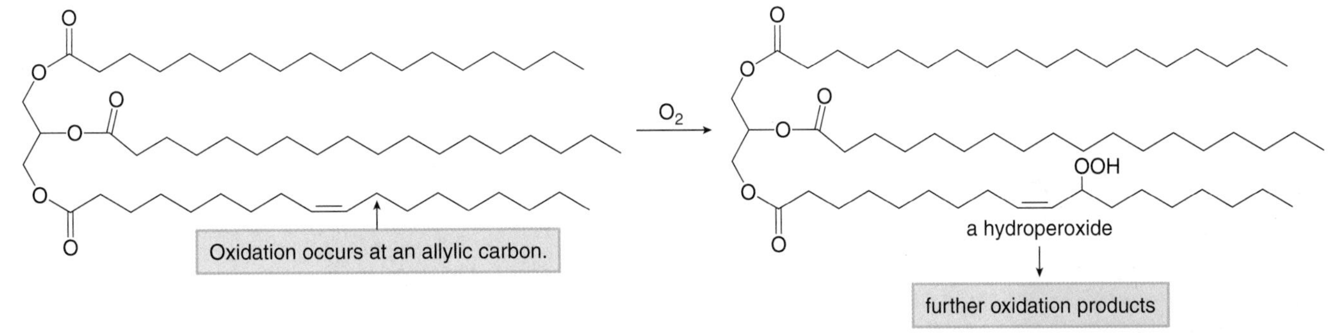
O2
OOH
Oxidation occurs at an allylic carbon.
a hydroperoxide
further oxidation products

Allylic C–H bonds are weaker than other C–H bonds and are thus susceptible to oxidation with molecular oxygen by a radical process. The hydroperoxide formed by this process is unstable, and it undergoes further oxidation to products that often have a disagreeable odor. This oxidation process turns an oil rancid.

In the cell, the principal function of triacylglycerols is energy storage. Complete metabolism of a triacylglycerol yields CO_2 and H_2O, and a great deal of energy. This overall reaction is reminiscent of the combustion of alkanes in fossil fuels, a process that also yields CO_2 and H_2O and provides energy to heat homes and power automobiles (Section 4.14B). Fundamentally both processes convert C–C and C–H bonds to C–O bonds, a highly exothermic reaction.

The average body fat content of men and women is ~20% and ~25%, respectively. (For elite athletes, however, the averages are more like <10% for men and <15% for women.) This stored fat can fill the body's energy needs for two or three months.

Metabolism of a lipid

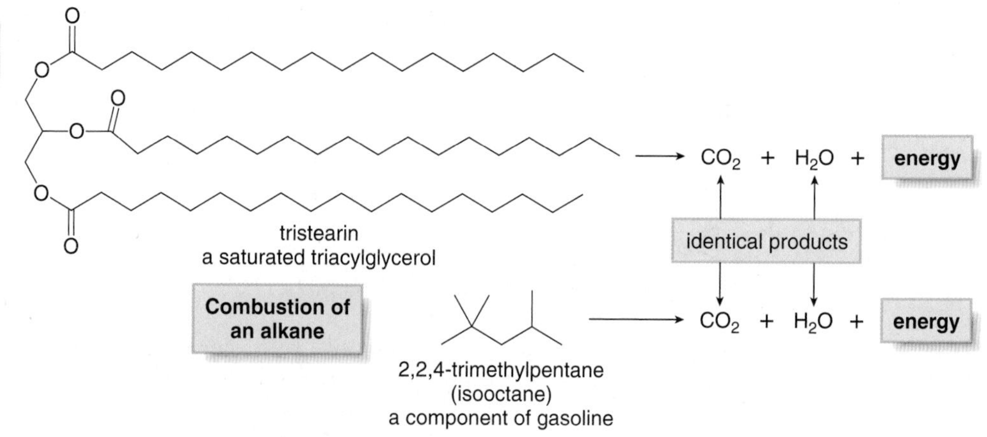
O
O
O
O
O
O
CO_2 + H_2O + energy
tristearin
a saturated triacylglycerol
identical products
Combustion of an alkane
CO_2 + H_2O + energy
2,2,4-trimethylpentane
(isooctane)
a component of gasoline

veggie-POWERED

Carbohydrates provide an energy boost, but only for the short term, such as during strenuous exercise. Our long-term energy needs are met by triacylglycerols, because they store ~38 kJ/g, whereas carbohydrates and proteins store only ~16 kJ/g.

Because triacylglycerols release heat on combustion, they can in principle be used as fuels for vehicles. In fact, coconut oil was used as a fuel during both World War I and World War II, when gasoline and diesel supplies ran short. Since coconut oil is more viscous than petroleum products and freezes at 24 °C, engines must be modified to use it and it can't be used in cold climates. Nonetheless, a limited number of trucks and boats can now use vegetable oils, sometimes blended with diesel, as a fuel source. When the price of crude oil is high, the use of these **biofuels** becomes economically attractive.

Problem 30.2 How would you expect the melting point of eicosapentaenoic acid [$CH_3CH_2(CH{=}CHCH_2)_5(CH_2)_2COOH$] to compare with the melting points of the fatty acids listed in Table 30.2?

Problem 30.3 Draw the products formed when triacylglycerol **A** is treated with each reagent. Rank compounds **A**, **B**, and **C** in order of increasing melting point.

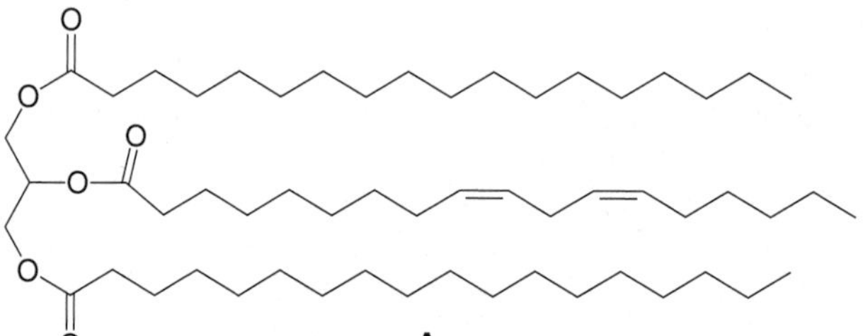
O
O
O
O
O
O

A

a. H_2O, H^+
b. H_2 (excess), Pd-C → **B**
c. H_2 (1 equiv), Pd-C → **C**

The cocoa butter in chocolate is rich in triacylglycerols derived from at least one molecule of oleic acid.

Problem 30.4 The main fatty acid component of the triacylglycerols in coconut oil is lauric acid, $CH_3(CH_2)_{10}COOH$. Explain why coconut oil is a liquid at room temperature even though it contains a large fraction of this saturated fatty acid.

Problem 30.5 Unlike many fats and oils, the cocoa butter used to make chocolate is remarkably uniform in composition. All triacylglycerols contain oleic acid esterified to the 2° OH group of glycerol, and either palmitic acid or stearic acid esterified to the 1° OH groups. Draw the structures of two possible triacylglycerols that compose cocoa butter.

30.4 Phospholipids

Phospholipids are hydrolyzable lipids that contain a phosphorus atom. There are two common types of phospholipids: **phosphoacylglycerols** and **sphingomyelins.** Both classes are found almost exclusively in the cell membranes of plants and animals, as discussed in Section 3.7.

The phosphorus atom in a phosphodiester shares 10 electrons. Recall that third-row elements (such as P and S) can be surrounded by more than eight electrons.

Phospholipids are organic derivatives of phosphoric acid, formed by replacing two of the H atoms by R groups. This type of functional group is called a **phosphodiester,** or a **phosphoric acid diester.** These compounds are phosphorus analogues of carboxylic esters. In cells, the remaining OH group on phosphorus loses its proton, giving the phosphodiester a net negative charge.

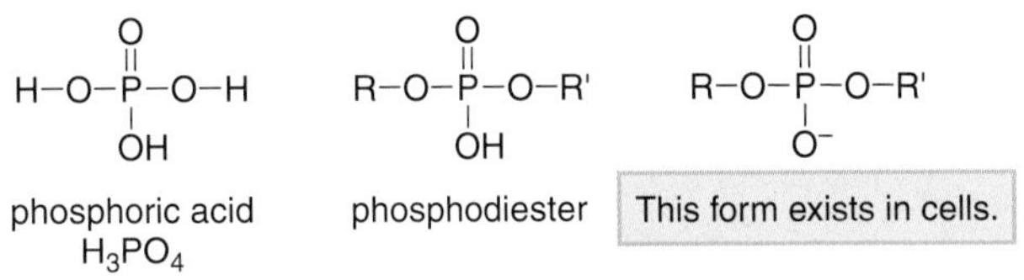

30.4A Phosphoacylglycerols

Phosphoacylglycerols (or phosphoglycerides) are the second most abundant type of lipid. They form the principal lipid component of most cell membranes. Their structure resembles the triacylglycerols of Section 30.3 with one important difference. In phosphoacylglycerols, only two of the hydroxy groups of glycerol are esterified with fatty acids. The third OH group is part of a phosphodiester, which is also bonded to another low molecular weight alcohol.

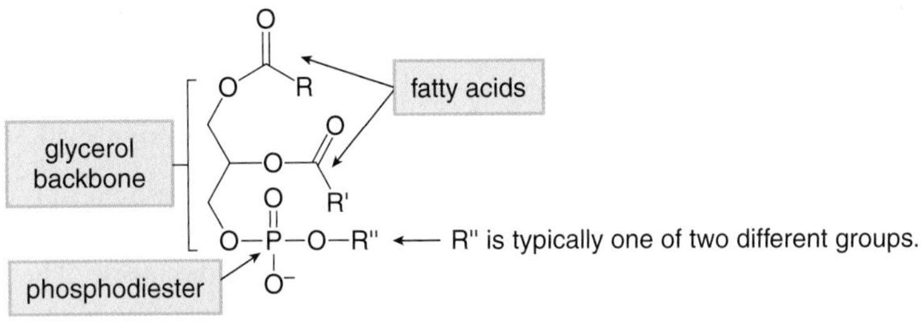

phosphoacylglycerol

There are two prominent types of phosphoacylglycerols. They differ in the identity of the R'' group in the phosphodiester.

- **When R'' = $CH_2CH_2NH_3^+$, the phosphoacylglycerol is called a phosphatidylethanolamine or cephalin.**
- **When R'' = $CH_2CH_2N(CH_3)_3^+$, the phosphoacylglycerol is called a phosphatidylcholine or lecithin.**

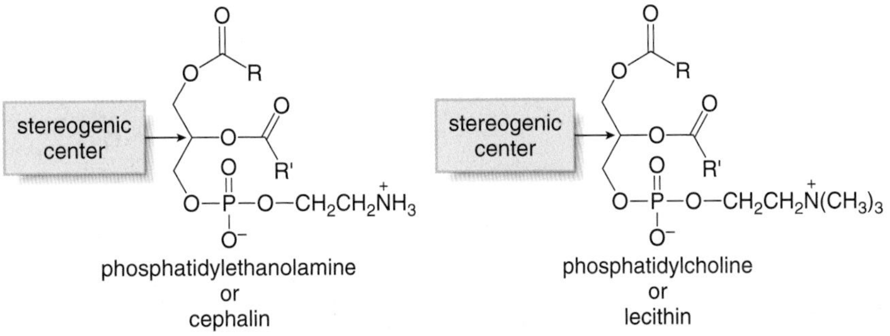

The middle carbon of the glycerol backbone of all of these compounds is a stereogenic center, usually with the *R* configuration.

Figure 30.3
Three-dimensional structure of a phosphoacylglycerol

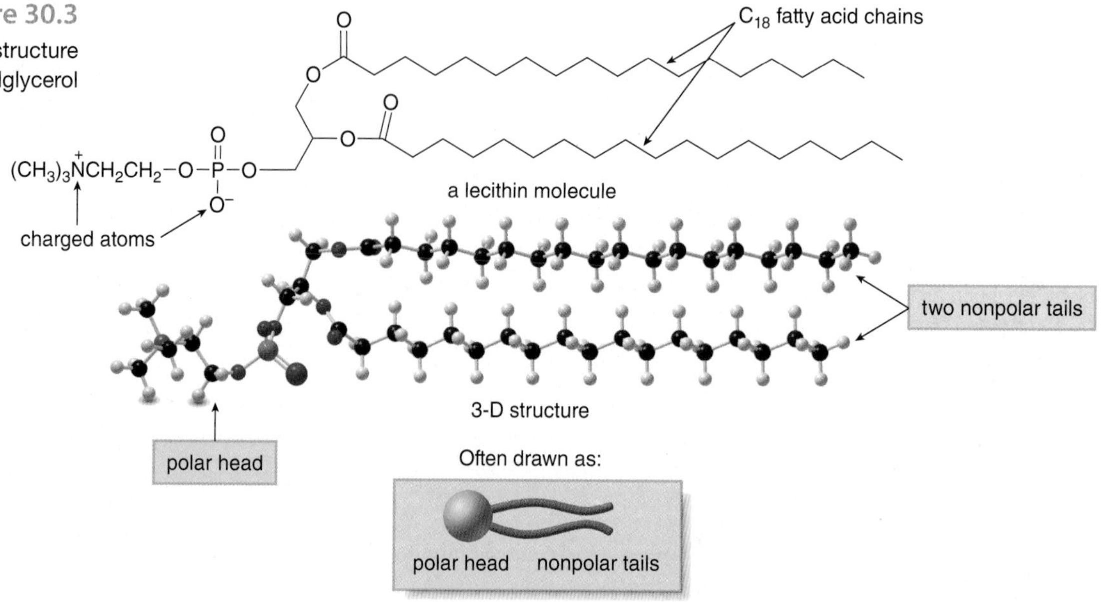
C18 fatty acid chains
(CH3)3NCH2CH2–O–P–O
charged atoms
a lecithin molecule
two nonpolar tails
polar head
3-D structure
Often drawn as:
polar head
nonpolar tails

- A phosphoacylglycerol has two distinct regions: two nonpolar tails due to the long-chain fatty acids, and a very polar head from the charged phosphodiester.

The phosphorus side chain of a phosphoacylglycerol makes it different from a triacylglycerol. The two fatty acid side chains form two nonpolar "tails" that lie parallel to each other, while the phosphodiester end of the molecule is a charged or polar "head." A three-dimensional structure of a phosphoacylglycerol is shown in Figure 30.3.

As discussed in Section 3.7, when these phospholipids are mixed with water, they assemble in an arrangement called a **lipid bilayer.** The ionic heads of the phospholipid are oriented on the outside and the nonpolar tails on the inside. The identity of the fatty acids in the phospholipid determines the rigidity of this bilayer. When the fatty acids are saturated, they pack well in the interior of the lipid bilayer, and the membrane is quite rigid. When there are many unsaturated fatty acids, the nonpolar tails cannot pack as well and the bilayer is more fluid. Thus, important characteristics of this lipid bilayer are determined by the three-dimensional structure of the molecules that comprise it.

Cell membranes are composed of these lipid bilayers (see Figure 3.7). Proteins and cholesterol are embedded in the membranes as well, but the phospholipid bilayer forms the main fabric of the insoluble barrier that protects the cell.

Problem 30.6 Draw the structure of a lecithin containing oleic acid and palmitic acid as the fatty acid side chains.

Problem 30.7 Phosphoacylglycerols should remind you of soaps (Section 3.6). In what ways are these compounds similar?

30.4B Sphingomyelins

Sphingomyelins, the second major class of phospholipids, are derivatives of the amino alcohol **sphingosine,** in much the same way that triacylglycerols and phosphoacylglycerols are derivatives of glycerol. Other notable features of a sphingomyelin include:

- **A phosphodiester at C1.**
- **An amide formed with a fatty acid at C2.**

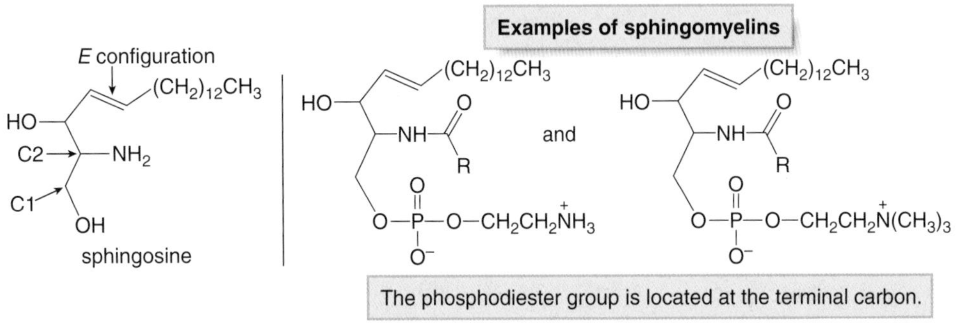

Like phosphoacylglycerols, **sphingomyelins are also a component of the lipid bilayer of cell membranes.** The coating that surrounds and insulates nerve cells, the **myelin sheath,** is particularly rich in sphingomyelins, and is vital for proper nerve function. Deterioration of the myelin sheath as seen in multiple sclerosis leads to disabling neurological problems.

Figure 30.4 compares the structural features of the most common hydrolyzable lipids: a triacylglycerol, a phosphoacylglycerol, and a sphingomyelin.

Problem 30.8 Why are phospholipids, but not triacylglycerols, found in cell membranes?

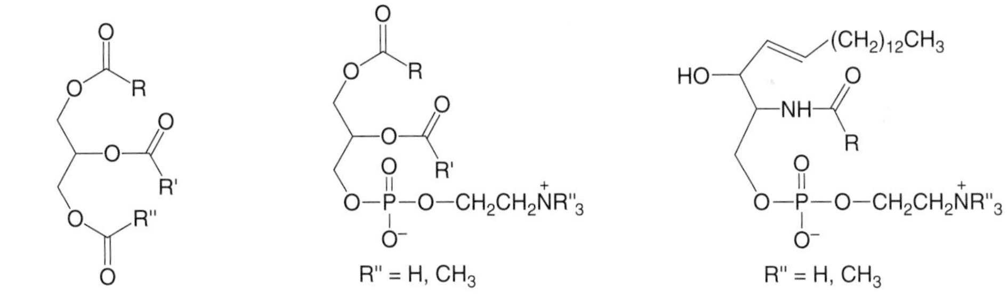

Figure 30.4 A comparison of a triacylglycerol, a phosphoacylglycerol, and a sphingomyelin

- A triacylglycerol has three nonpolar side chains.
- The three OH groups of glycerol are esterified with three fatty acids.

- A phosphoacylglycerol has two nonpolar side chain tails and one ionic head.
- Two OH groups of glycerol are esterified with fatty acids.
- A phosphodiester is located on a terminal carbon.

- A sphingomyelin has two nonpolar side chain tails and one ionic head.
- A sphingomyelin is formed from sphingosine, not glycerol. One of the nonpolar tails is an amide.
- A phosphodiester is located on a terminal carbon.

30.5 Fat-Soluble Vitamins

Vitamins are organic compounds required in small quantities for normal metabolism (Section 3.5). Because our cells cannot synthesize these compounds, they must be obtained in the diet. Vitamins can be categorized as fat soluble or water soluble. **The fat-soluble vitamins are lipids.**

The four fat-soluble vitamins—**A, D, E,** and **K**—are found in fruits and vegetables, fish, liver, and dairy products. Although fat-soluble vitamins must be obtained from the diet, they do not have to be ingested every day. Excess vitamins are stored in fat cells, and then used when needed. Figure 30.5 shows the structure of these vitamins and summarizes their functions.

Figure 30.5 The fat-soluble vitamins

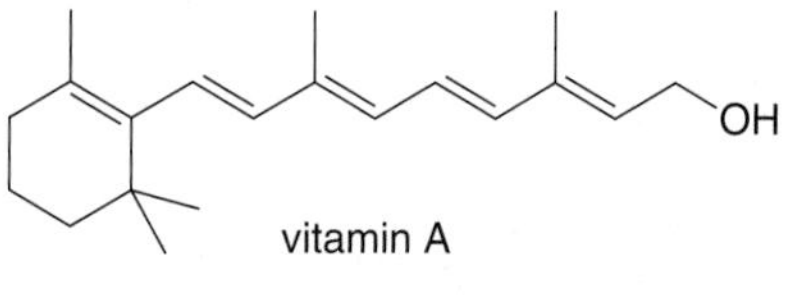

vitamin A

- **Vitamin A** (retinol, Section 3.5) is obtained from fish liver oils and dairy products, and is synthesized from β-carotene, the orange pigment in carrots.
- In the body, vitamin A is converted to 11-*cis*-retinal, the light-sensitive compound responsible for vision in all vertebrates (Section 21.11B). It is also needed for healthy mucous membranes.
- A deficiency of vitamin A causes night blindness, as well as dry eyes and skin.

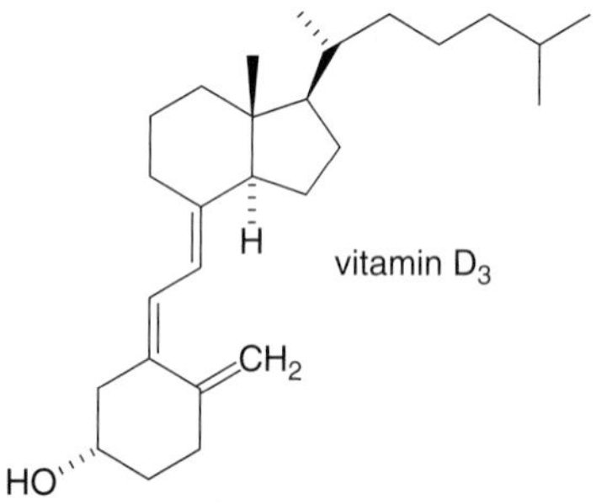

vitamin D_3

- **Vitamin D_3** is the most abundant of the D vitamins. Strictly speaking, it is not a vitamin because it can be synthesized in the body from cholesterol. Nevertheless, it is classified as such, and many foods (particularly milk) are fortified with vitamin D_3 so that we get enough of this vital nutrient.
- Vitamin D helps regulate both calcium and phosphorus metabolism.
- A deficiency of vitamin D causes rickets, a bone disease characterized by knock-knees, spinal curvature, and other deformities.

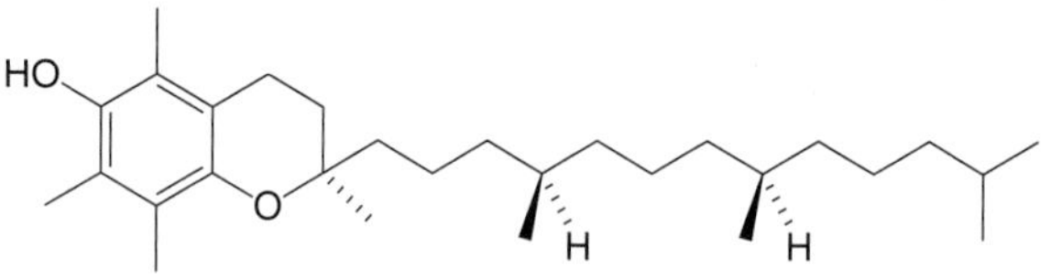

vitamin E
(α-tocopherol)

- The term **vitamin E** refers to a group of structurally similar compounds, the most potent being α-tocopherol (Section 15.12).
- Vitamin E is an antioxidant, so it protects unsaturated side chains in fatty acids from oxidation.
- A deficiency of vitamin E causes numerous neurologic problems.

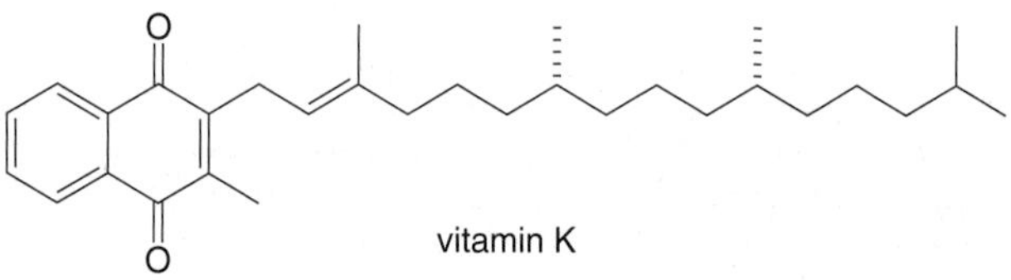

vitamin K

- **Vitamin K** (phylloquinone) regulates the synthesis of prothrombin and other proteins needed for blood to clot.
- A deficiency of vitamin K leads to excessive and sometimes fatal bleeding because of inadequate blood clotting.

Electrostatic potential plots of vitamins A and E (Figure 30.6) show that the electron density is virtually uniform in these compounds. The large regions of nonpolar C–C and C–H bonds tend to obscure small dipoles that occur in the one or two polar bonds, making these vitamins nonpolar and hydrophobic.

Problem 30.9 Explain why regularly ingesting a large excess of a fat-soluble vitamin can lead to severe health problems, whereas ingesting a large excess of a water-soluble vitamin often causes no major health problems.

Figure 30.6
Electrostatic potential plots of vitamins A and E

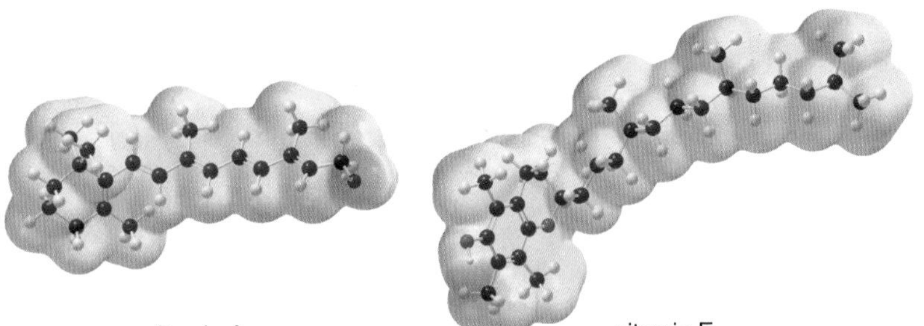

- The electron density is distributed fairly evenly among the carbon atoms of these vitamins due to their many nonpolar C–C and C–H bonds.

30.6 Eicosanoids

The word ***eicosanoid*** is derived from the Greek word *eikosi,* meaning **20.**

The **eicosanoids** are a group of biologically active compounds containing 20 carbon atoms derived from arachidonic acid. The **prostaglandins** (Section 19.6) and the **leukotrienes** (Section 9.16) are two types of eicosanoids. Two others are the **thromboxanes** and **prostacyclins.**

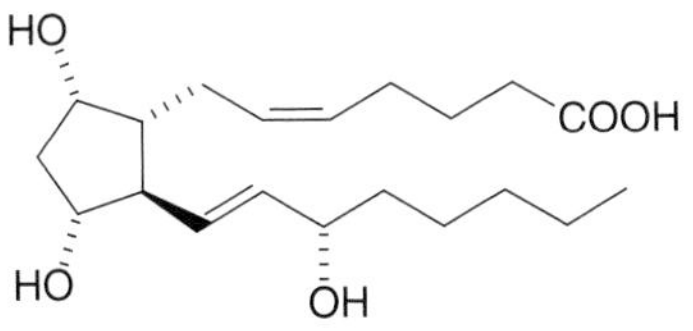

$PGF_{2\alpha}$
a prostaglandin

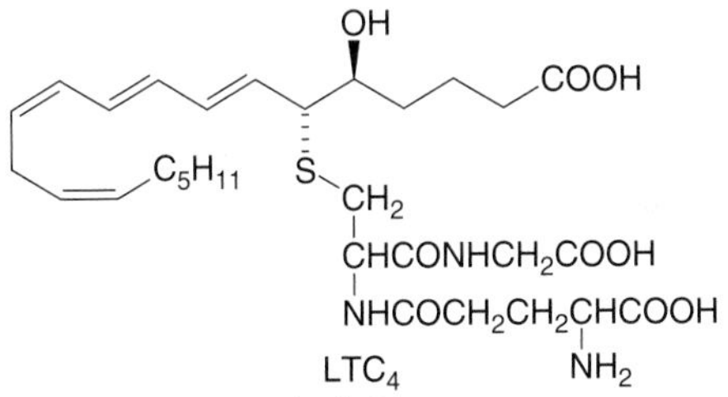

LTC_4
a leukotriene

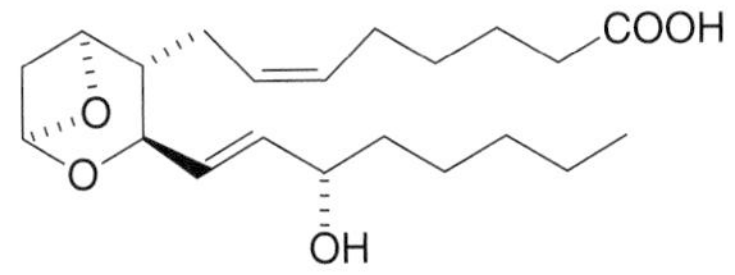

TXA_2
a thromboxane

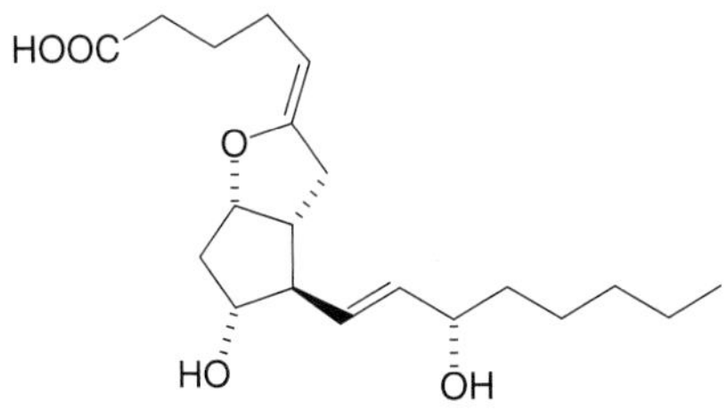

PGI_2
a prostacyclin

All eicosanoids are very potent compounds present in low concentration in cells. They are **local mediators,** meaning that they perform their function in the environment in which they are synthesized. This distinguishes them from **hormones,** which are first synthesized and then transported in the bloodstream to their site of action. Eicosanoids are not stored in cells; rather, they are synthesized from arachidonic acid in response to an external stimulus.

The synthesis of prostaglandins, thromboxanes, and prostacyclins begins with the oxidation of arachidonic acid with O_2 by a **cyclooxygenase** enzyme, which forms an unstable cyclic intermediate, PGG_2. PGG_2 is then converted via different pathways to these three classes of compounds. Leukotrienes are formed by a different pathway, using an enzyme called a **lipoxygenase.** These four paths for arachidonic acid are summarized in Figure 30.7.

Other details of the biosynthesis of leukotrienes and prostaglandins were given in Sections 9.16 and 19.6, respectively.

Each eicosanoid is associated with specific types of biological activity (Table 30.4). In some cases, the effects oppose one another. For example, thromboxanes are vasoconstrictors that trigger blood platelet aggregation, whereas prostacyclins are vasodilators that inhibit platelet aggregation. The levels of these two eicosanoids must be in the right balance for cells to function properly.

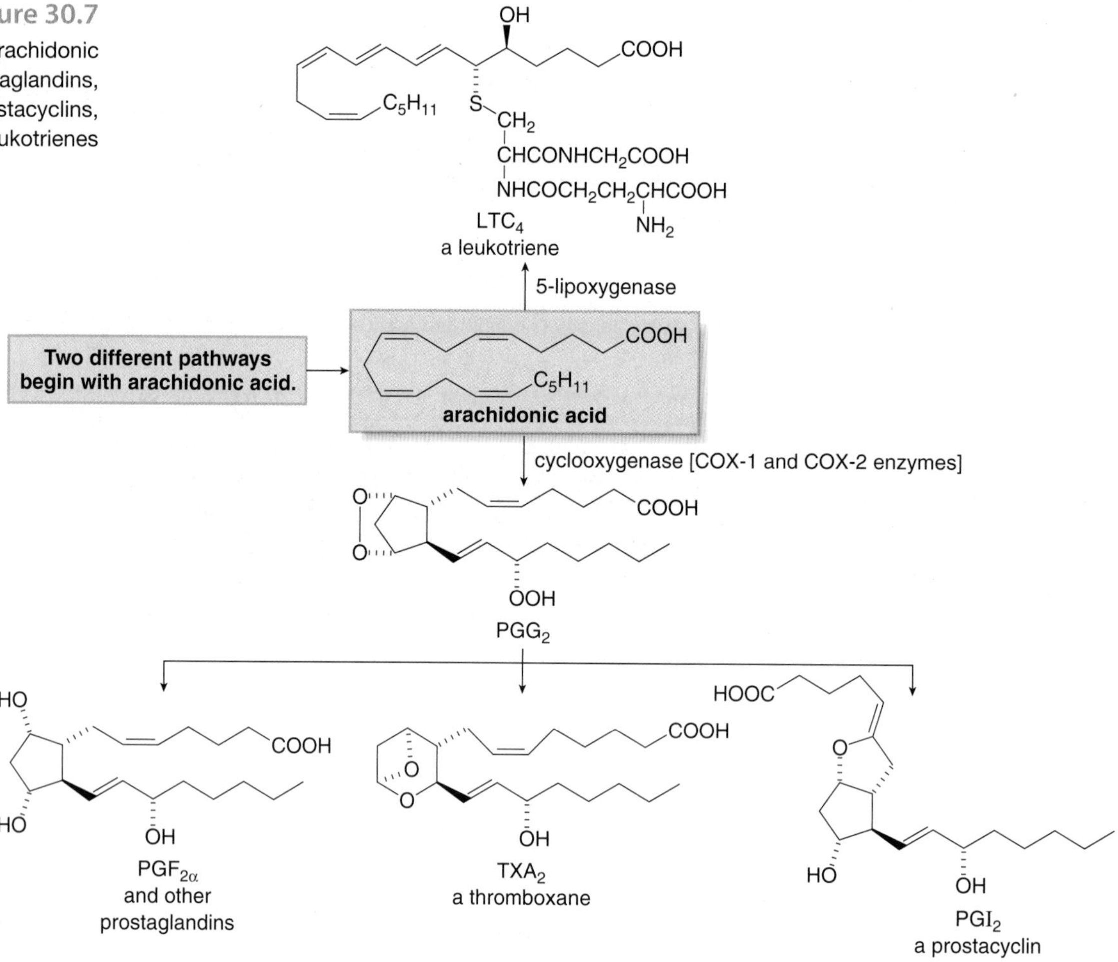

Figure 30.7
The conversion of arachidonic acid to prostaglandins, thromboxanes, prostacyclins, and leukotrienes

Table 30.4 Biological Activity of the Eicosanoids

Eicosanoid	Effect	Eicosanoid	Effect
Prostaglandins	• Lower blood pressure • Inhibit blood platelet aggregation • Control inflammation • Lower gastric secretions • Stimulate uterine contractions • Relax smooth muscles of the uterus	**Thromboxanes**	• Constrict blood vessels • Trigger blood platelet aggregation
		Prostacyclins	• Dilate blood vessels • Inhibit blood platelet aggregation
		Leukotrienes	• Constrict smooth muscle, especially in the lungs

Because of their wide range of biological functions, prostaglandins and their analogues have found several clinical uses. For example, **dinoprostone,** the generic name for **PGE_2,** is administered to relax the smooth muscles of the uterus when labor is induced, and to terminate pregnancies in the early stages.

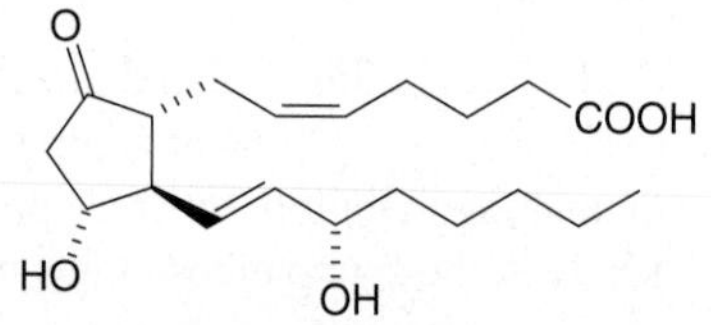

PGE_2
(dinoprostone)

Because prostaglandins themselves are unstable in the body, often having half-lives of only minutes, more stable analogues have been developed that retain their important biological activity longer. For example, **misoprostol,** an analogue of PGE_1, is sold as a mixture of stereoisomers. Misoprostol is administered to prevent gastric ulcers in patients who are at high risk of developing them.

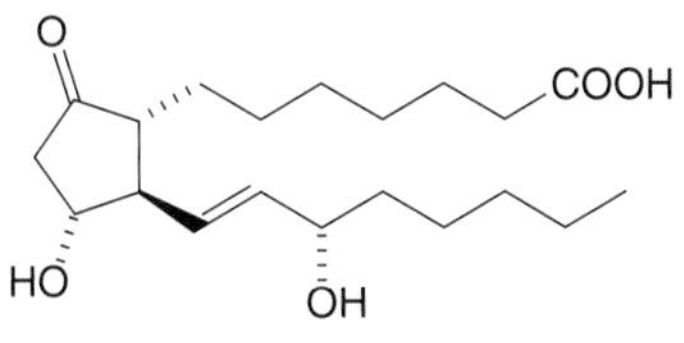

PGE_1

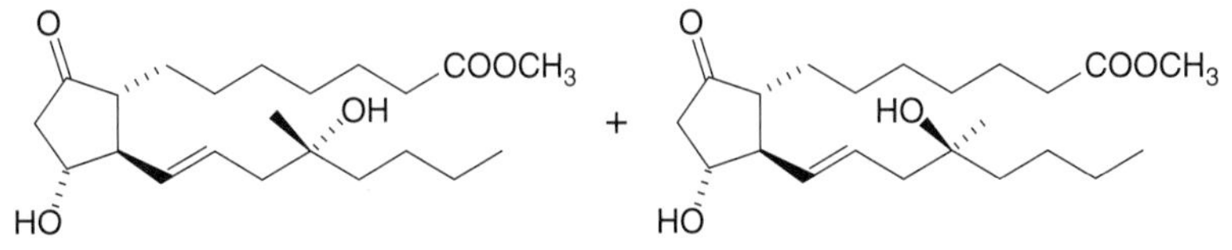

misoprostol
(sold as a mixture of stereoisomers)

Studying the biosynthesis of eicosanoids has led to other discoveries as well. For example, aspirin and other nonsteroidal anti-inflammatory drugs (**NSAIDs**) inactivate the cyclooxygenase enzyme needed for prostaglandin synthesis. In this way, NSAIDs block the synthesis of the prostaglandins that cause inflammation (Section 19.6).

More recently, it has been discovered that two *different* cyclooxygenase enzymes, called **COX-1** and **COX-2,** are responsible for prostaglandin synthesis. COX-1 is involved with the usual production of prostaglandins, but COX-2 is responsible for the synthesis of additional prostaglandins in inflammatory diseases like arthritis. **NSAIDs like aspirin and ibuprofen inactivate both the COX-1 and COX-2 enzymes.** This activity also results in an increase in gastric secretions, making an individual more susceptible to ulcer formation.

A group of anti-inflammatory drugs that block only the COX-2 enzyme was developed in the 1990s. These drugs—**rofecoxib, valdecoxib,** and **celecoxib**—do not cause an increase in gastric secretions, and thus were touted as especially effective NSAIDs for patients with arthritis, who need daily doses of these medications. Unfortunately, both rofecoxib and valdecoxib have now been removed from the market, since their use has been associated with an increased risk of heart attack and stroke.

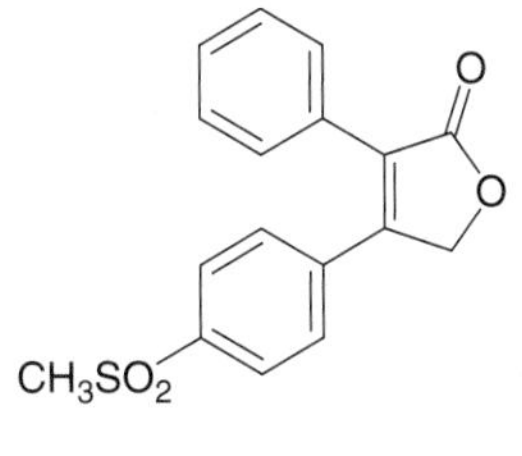

Generic name: rofecoxib
Trade name: Vioxx

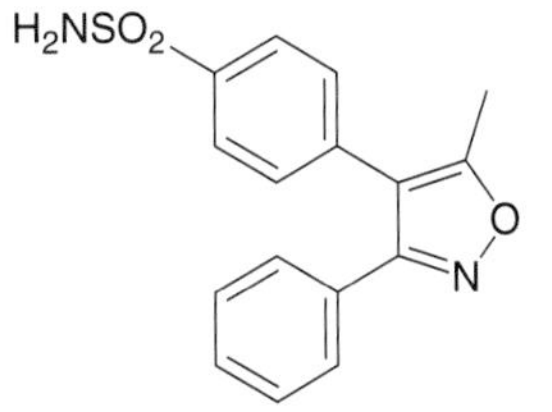

Generic name: valdecoxib
Trade name: Bextra

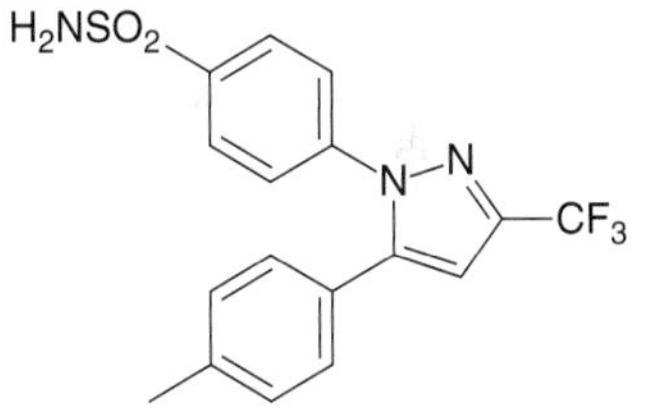

Generic name: celecoxib
Trade name: Celebrex

A COX-3 enzyme was also reported in 2002. Its activity is inhibited by acetaminophen, the active ingredient in the pain reliever Tylenol.

The discovery of drugs that block prostaglandin synthesis illustrates how basic research in organic chemistry can lead to important practical applications. Elucidating the structure and biosynthesis of prostaglandins began as a project in basic research. It has now resulted in a number of applications that benefit many individuals with various illnesses.

Problem 30.10 How are the two isomers of misoprostol related?

30.7 Terpenes

Terpenes **are lipids composed of repeating five-carbon units called isoprene units.** An **isoprene unit** has five carbons: four in a row, with a one-carbon branch on a middle carbon.

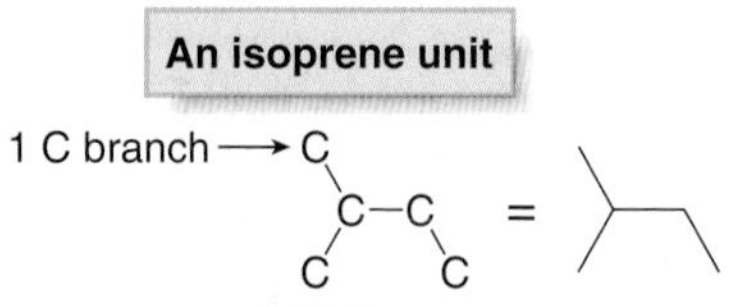

Terpenes are hydrocarbons that may be acyclic or have one or more rings. The term ***terpenoid*** is used for compounds that contain isoprene units as well as an oxygen heteroatom. Many **essential oils,** a group of compounds isolated from plant sources by distillation, are terpenes and terpenoids. Examples include myrcene and menthol.

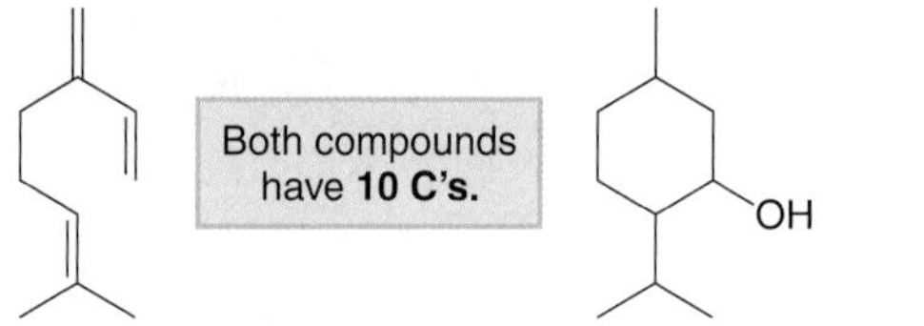

myrcene (isolated from bayberry oil) menthol (isolated from peppermint oil)

30.7A Locating Isoprene Units

bayberry plant (source of myrcene)

peppermint plant (source of menthol)

How do we identify the isoprene units in these molecules? Start at one end of the molecule near a branch point. Then **look for a four-carbon chain with a one-carbon branch.** This forms one isoprene unit. Continue along the chain or around the ring until all the carbons are part of an isoprene unit. Keep in mind the following:

- **An isoprene unit may be composed of C–C σ bonds only, or there may be π bonds at any position.**
- **Isoprene units are always connected by one or more carbon–carbon bonds.**
- **Each carbon atom is part of one isoprene unit only.**
- **Every isoprene unit has five carbon atoms. Heteroatoms may be present but their presence is ignored in locating isoprene units.**

Myrcene and menthol, for example, each have 10 carbon atoms, so they are composed of two isoprene units.

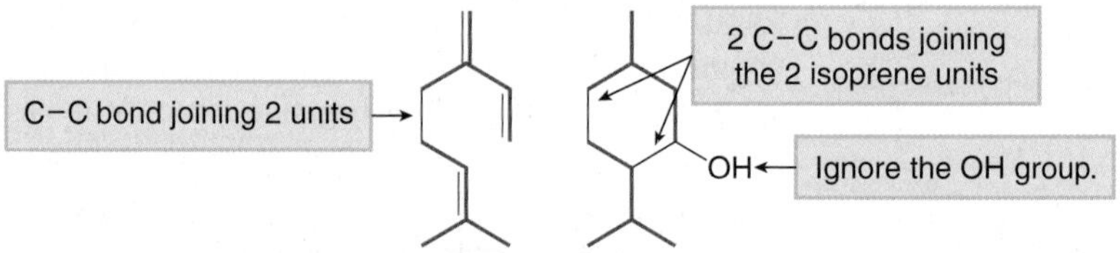

myrcene menthol

Terpenes and terpenoids are classified by the number of isoprene units they contain. A ***monoterpene*** **(or *monoterpenoid*) contains 10 carbons** and has two isoprene units, a ***sesquiterpene*** **(or *sesquiterpenoid*) contains 15 carbons** and has three isoprene units, and so forth. The different terpene classes are summarized in Table 30.5.

Several examples, with the isoprene units labeled in red, are given in Figure 30.8.

Table 30.5 Classes of Terpenes and Terpenoids

Name	Number of C atoms	Number of isoprene units
Monoterpene (Monoterpenoid)	10	2
Sesquiterpene (Sesquiterpenoid)	15	3
Diterpene (Diterpenoid)	20	4
Sesterterpene (Sesterterpenoid)	25	5
Triterpene (Triterpenoid)	30	6
Tetraterpene (Tetraterpenoid)	40	8

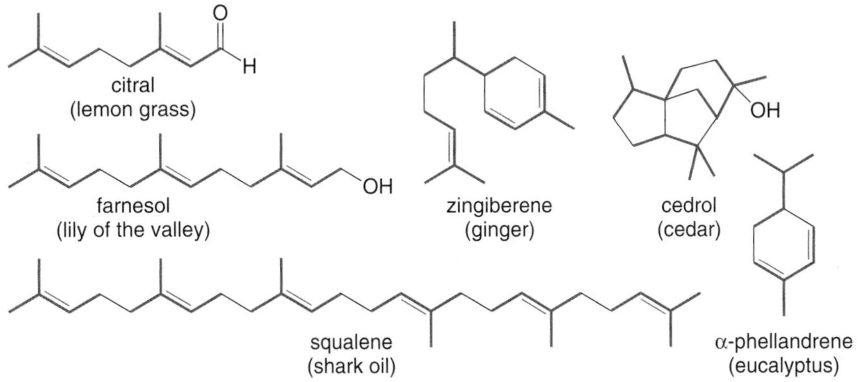
citral
(lemon grass)
farnesol
(lily of the valley)
zingiberene
(ginger)
cedrol
(cedar)
squalene
(shark oil)
α-phellandrene
(eucalyptus)

Figure 30.8 Examples of some common terpenes and terpenoids

- Isoprene units are labeled in red, with C–C bonds (in black) joining two units.
- The source of each terpene or terpenoid is given in parentheses.

Problem 30.11 Locate the isoprene units in each compound.

a. 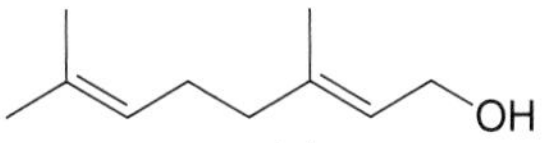
geraniol
(roses and geraniums)

b. 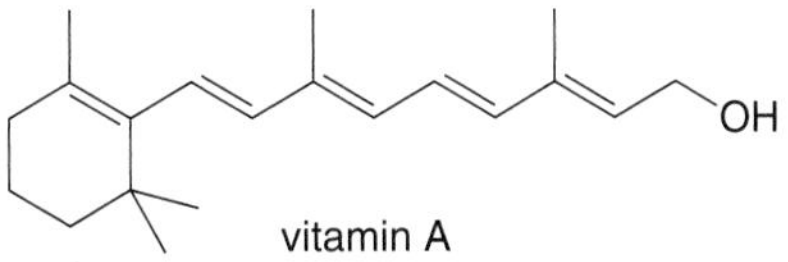
vitamin A

c. 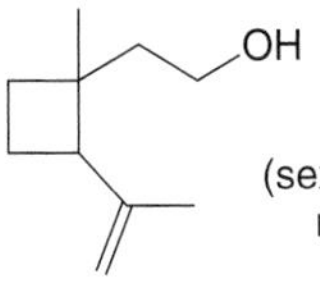
grandisol
(sex pheromone of the male boll weevil)

d. 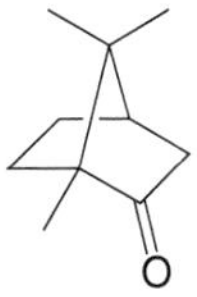
camphor

Problem 30.12 Manoalide, a sesterterpenoid isolated from the Pacific marine sponge *Luffariella veriabilis* by Scheuer and co-workers at the University of Hawai'i at Mānoa, has anti-inflammatory, analgesic, and antifungal properties. Find the isoprene units in manoalide.

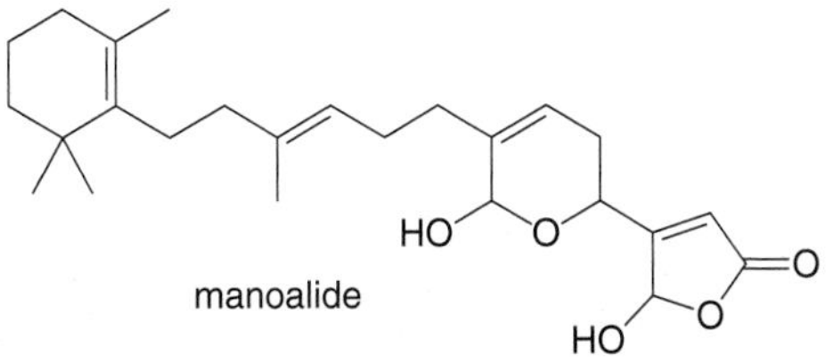
manoalide

Amber, fossilized resin that oozed from trees long ago, contains biformene, as well as many other terpenoids called labdanoids.

Problem 30.13 Locate the isoprene units in biformene, a component of amber, and classify biformene as a monoterpene, sesquiterpene, etc.

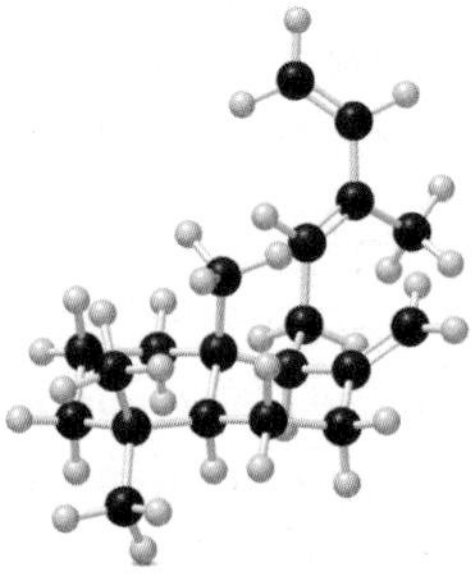

biformene

30.7B The Biosynthesis of Terpenes and Terpenoids

Terpene and terpenoid biosynthesis is an excellent example of how syntheses in nature occur with high efficiency. There are two ways this is accomplished.

[1] **The same reaction is used over and over again to prepare progressively more complex compounds.**

[2] **Key intermediates along the way serve as the starting materials for a wide variety of other compounds.**

All terpenes and terpenoids are synthesized from dimethylallyl diphosphate and isopentenyl diphosphate. Both of these five-carbon compounds are synthesized, in turn, in a multistep process from three molecules of acetyl CoA (Section 22.17).

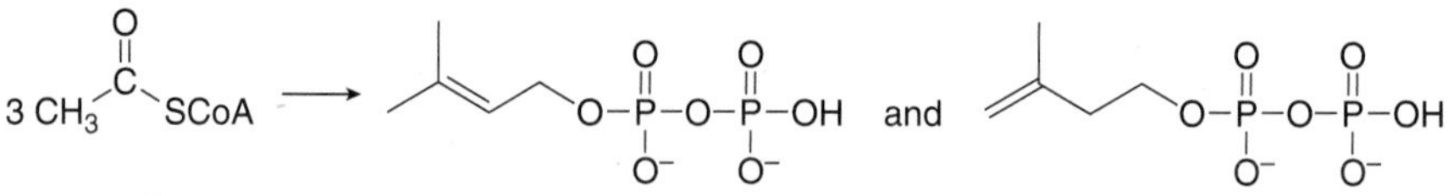

Diphosphate, abbreviated as **OPP,** is often used as a leaving group in biological systems. **It is a good leaving group because it is a weak, resonance-stabilized base.**

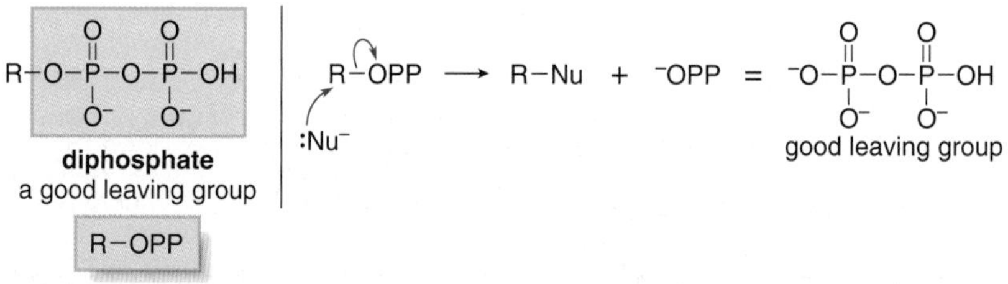

The overall strategy of biosynthesis from dimethylallyl diphosphate and isopentenyl diphosphate is summarized in Figure 30.9.

There are three basic parts:

[1] The two C_5 diphosphates are converted to **geranyl diphosphate, a C_{10} monoterpenoid.** Geranyl diphosphate is the starting material for all other monoterpenes and monoterpenoids.

[2] Geranyl diphosphate is converted to **farnesyl diphosphate, a C_{15} sesquiterpenoid,** by addition of a five-carbon unit. Farnesyl diphosphate is the starting material for all sesquiterpenes, diterpenes, and related terpenoids.

[3] Two molecules of farnesyl diphosphate are converted to **squalene, a C_{30} triterpene.** Squalene is the starting material for all triterpenes and steroids.

Figure 30.9 An outline of terpene and terpenoid biosynthesis

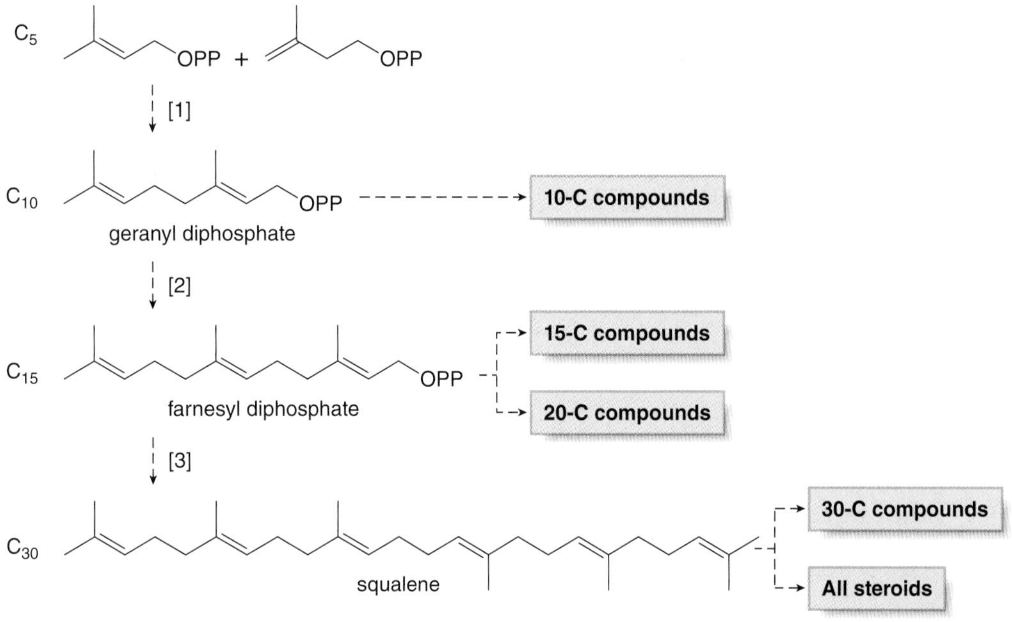

The biological formation of geranyl diphosphate from the two five-carbon diphosphates involves three steps: **loss of the leaving group, nucleophilic attack,** and **loss of a proton,** as shown in Mechanism 30.1.

Mechanism 30.1 Biological Formation of Geranyl Diphosphate

Steps [1]–[2] Loss of the leaving group and nucleophilic attack to form a new C–C bond

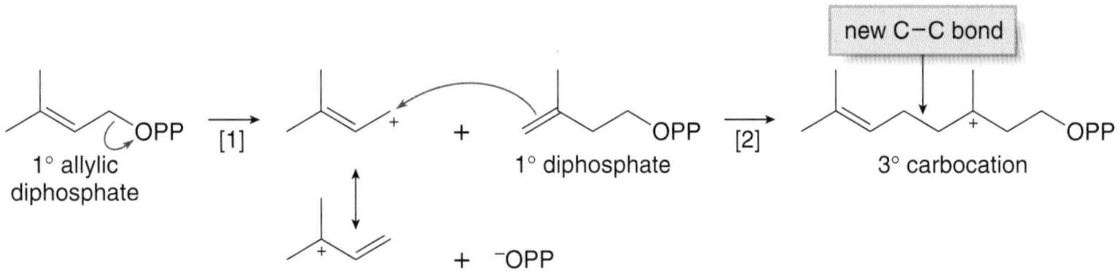

- Loss of the diphosphate leaving group forms a resonance-stabilized carbocation in Step [1], which reacts with the nucleophilic double bond of the 1° diphosphate to form a new C–C bond and a 3° carbocation in Step [2].
- Steps [1] and [2] are analogous to an S_N1 mechanism because the leaving group (^{-}OPP) is lost before the nucleophile (a C=C) attacks.

Step [3] Loss of a proton

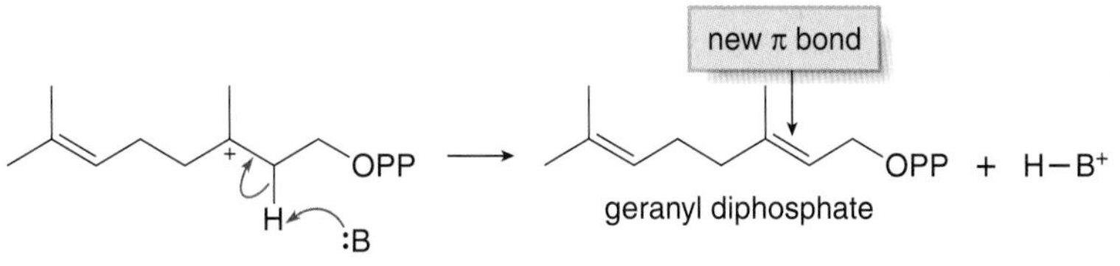

- Loss of a proton forms geranyl diphosphate in Step [3].

The biological conversion of geranyl diphosphate to farnesyl diphosphate involves the same three steps, as shown in Mechanism 30.2.

Mechanism 30.2 Biological Formation of Farnesyl Diphosphate

Steps [1]–[2] Loss of the leaving group and nucleophilic attack to form a new C–C bond

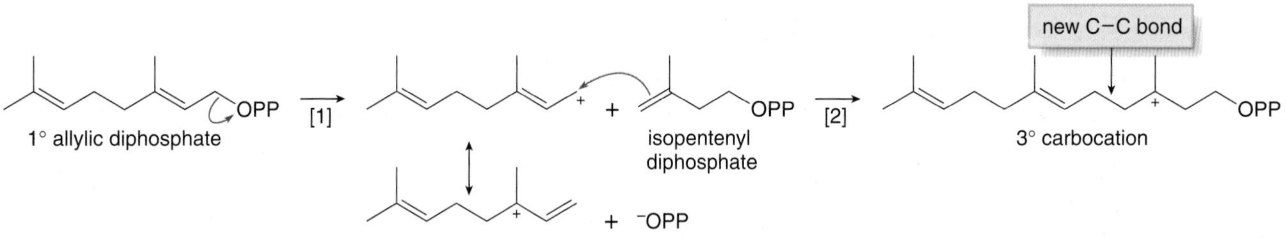

- Loss of the diphosphate leaving group forms a resonance-stabilized carbocation in Step [1], which reacts with isopentenyl diphosphate to form a new C–C bond and a 3° carbocation in Step [2].

Step [3] Loss of a proton

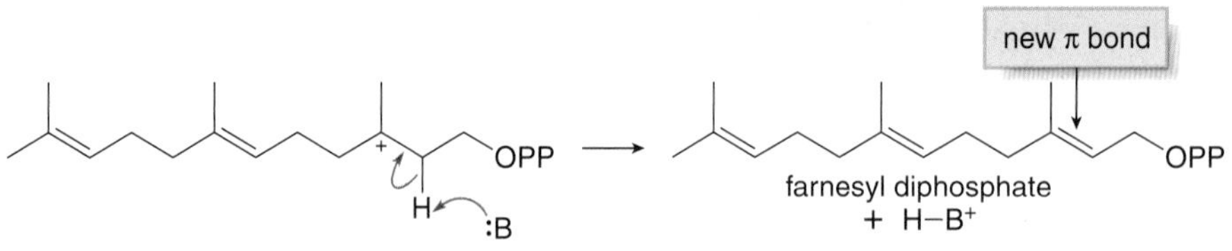

- Loss of a proton forms a new π bond and farnesyl diphosphate in Step [3].

Two molecules of farnesyl diphosphate react to form squalene, from which all other triterpenes and steroids are synthesized.

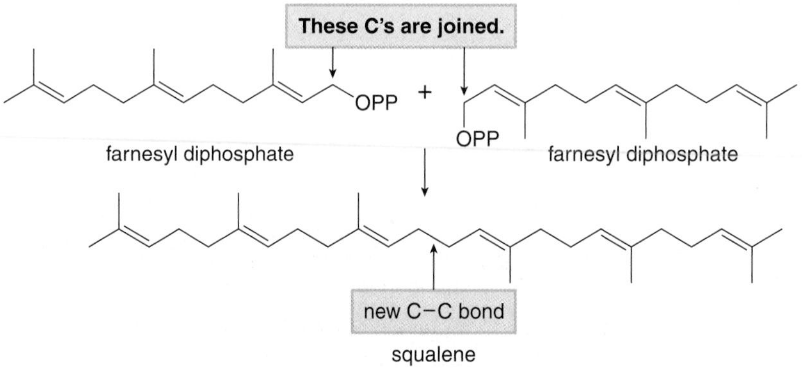

Aqueous hydrolysis of geranyl and farnesyl diphosphates forms the monoterpenoid geraniol and the sesquiterpenoid farnesol, respectively.

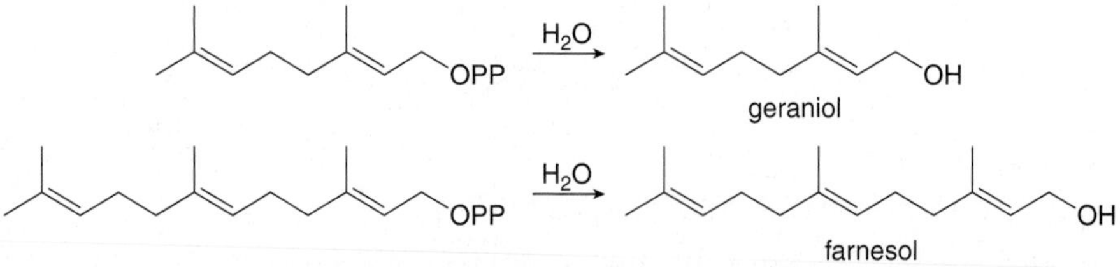

All other terpenes and terpenoids are biologically derived from geranyl and farnesyl diphosphates by a series of reactions. Cyclic compounds are formed by intramolecular reactions involving nucleophilic attack of π bonds on intermediate carbocations. To form some cyclic compounds, the *E* double bond in geranyl diphosphate must first isomerize to an isomeric diphosphate with a *Z* double bond, neryl diphosphate, by the process illustrated in Mechanism 30.3. Isomerization forms a substrate with a leaving group and nucleophilic double bond in close proximity, so that an intramolecular reaction can occur.

Mechanism 30.3 Isomerization of Geranyl Diphosphate to Neryl Diphosphate

Steps [1]–[2] Isomerization of geranyl diphosphate to linalyl diphosphate

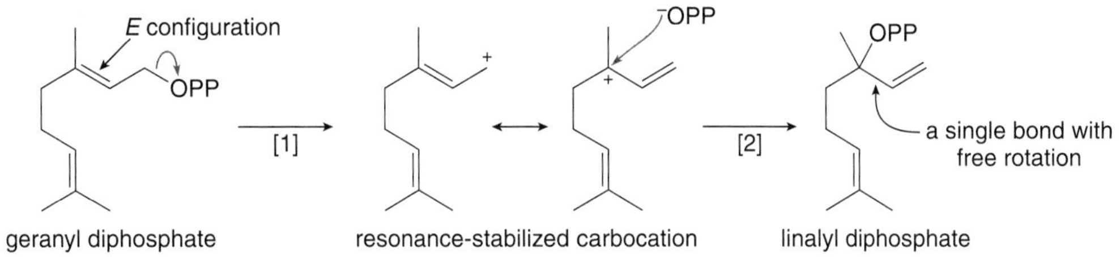

- Loss of the diphosphate leaving group forms a resonance-stabilized carbocation in Step [1], which reacts with the diphosphate anion to form linalyl diphosphate, a constitutional isomer.
- The original *E* double bond is now a single bond that can rotate freely.

Steps [3]–[4] Isomerization of linalyl diphosphate to neryl diphosphate

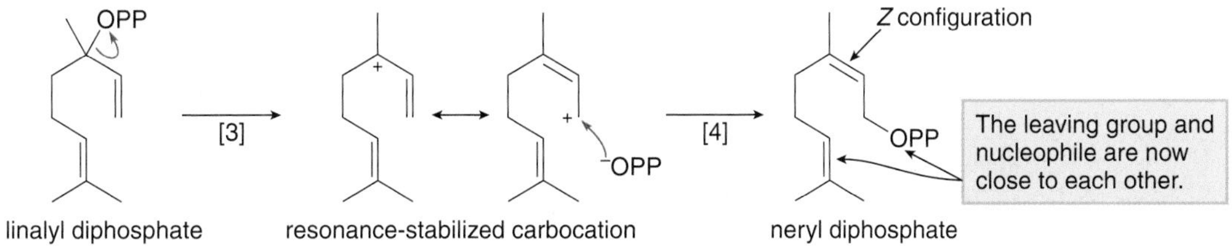

- Loss of the diphosphate leaving group forms a resonance-stabilized carbocation in Step [3]. The only difference in the products of Steps [1] and [3] is the geometry around the internal carbon–carbon double bond.
- Nucleophilic attack with diphosphate forms neryl diphosphate, a stereoisomer of geranyl diphosphate. The diphosphate leaving group of neryl diphosphate is now in closer proximity to the double bond at the other end of the chain, so that intramolecular cyclization can occur.

In the synthesis of α-terpineol or limonene, for example, geranyl diphosphate isomerizes to form neryl diphosphate (Step [1] in the following reaction sequence). Neryl diphosphate then cyclizes to a 3° carbocation by intramolecular attack (Steps [2]–[3]). Nucleophilic attack of water on this carbocation yields the monoterpenoid α-terpineol (Step [4]) or loss of a proton yields the monoterpene limonene (Step [5]).

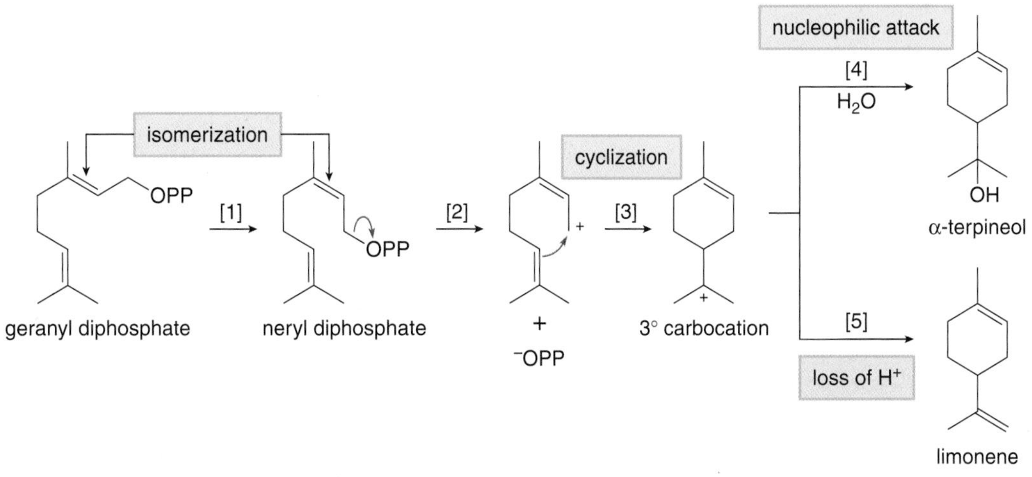

Problem 30.14 Write a stepwise mechanism for the following reaction.

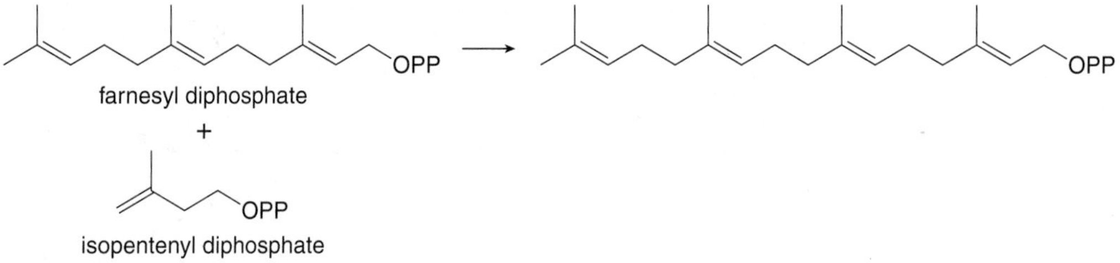

Problem 30.15 Draw a stepwise mechanism for the conversion of geranyl diphosphate to α-terpinene.

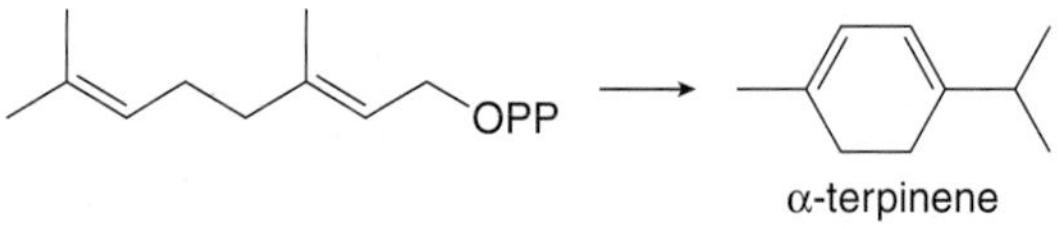

30.8 Steroids

The steroids are a group of tetracyclic lipids, many of which are biologically active.

30.8A Steroid Structure

Steroids are composed of three six-membered rings and one five-membered ring, joined together as drawn. Many steroids also contain two methyl groups, called **angular methyl groups,** at the two ring junctions indicated. The steroid rings are lettered **A, B, C,** and **D,** and the 17 ring carbons are numbered as shown. The two angular methyl groups are numbered C18 and C19.

General steroid skeleton | **Numbering the steroid skeleton**

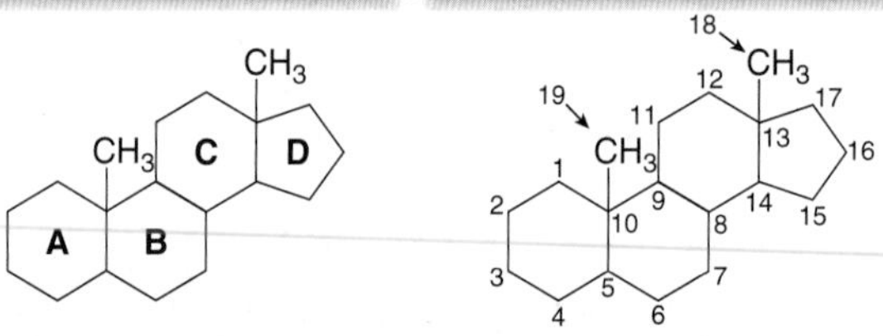

Whenever two rings are fused together, the substituents at the ring fusion can be arranged cis or trans. To see more easily why this is true, consider **decalin,** which consists of two six-membered rings fused together. ***trans*-Decalin** has the two hydrogen atoms at the ring fusion on opposite sides, whereas ***cis*-decalin** has them on the same side.

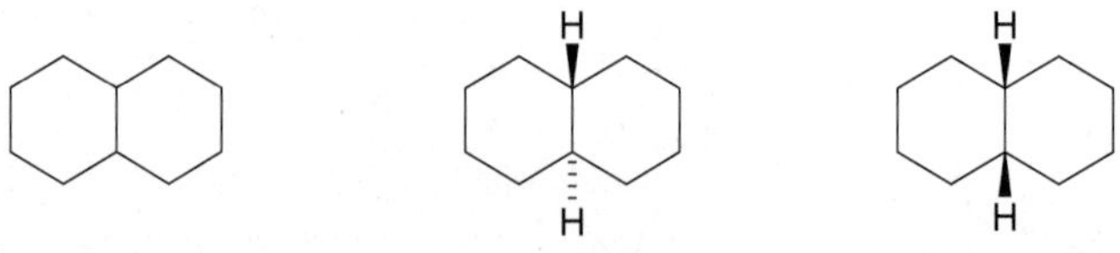

decalin
Two six-membered rings share a C–C bond.

***trans*-decalin**
2 H's on opposite sides

***cis*-decalin**
2 H's on the same side

Three-dimensional structures of these molecules show how different these two possible arrangements actually are. The two rings of *trans*-decalin lie roughly in the same plane, whereas the two rings of *cis*-decalin are almost perpendicular to each other. **The trans arrangement is lower in energy and therefore more stable.**

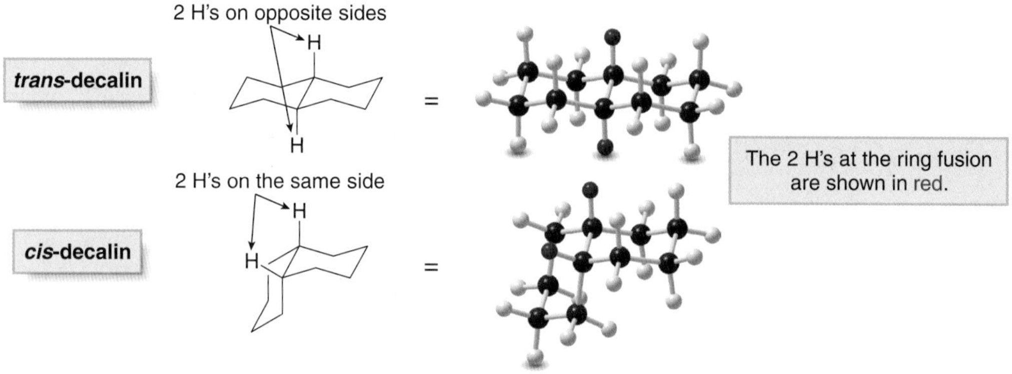

trans-decalin
2 H's on opposite sides
H
H
=
cis-decalin
2 H's on the same side
H
H
=
The 2 H's at the ring fusion are shown in red.

In steroids, each ring fusion could theoretically have the cis or trans configuration, but, by far the most common arrangement is all trans. Because of this, **all four rings of the steroid skeleton lie in the same plane,** and the ring system is fairly rigid. The two angular methyl groups are oriented perpendicular to the plane of the molecule. These methyl groups make one side of the steroid skeleton significantly more hindered than the other, as shown in Figure 30.10.

Although steroids have the same fused-ring arrangement of carbon atoms, they differ in the identity and location of the substituents attached to that skeleton.

Problem 30.16 (a) Draw a skeletal structure of the anabolic steroid 4-androstene-3,17-dione, also called "andro," from the following description. Andro contains the tetracyclic steroid skeleton with carbonyl groups at C3 and C17, a double bond between C4 and C5, and methyl groups bonded to C10 and C13. (b) Add wedges and dashes for all stereogenic centers with the following information: the configuration at C10 is *R*, the configuration at C13 is *S*, and all substituents at ring fusions are trans to each other.

Figure 30.10 The three-dimensional structure of the steroid nucleus

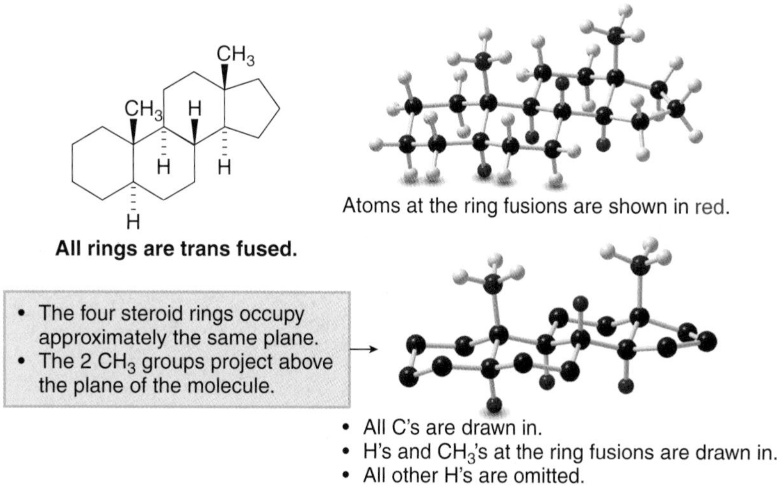

CH3
CH3
H
H
H
H
All rings are trans fused.
Atoms at the ring fusions are shown in red.
• The four steroid rings occupy approximately the same plane.
• The 2 CH3 groups project above the plane of the molecule.
• All C's are drawn in.
• H's and CH3's at the ring fusions are drawn in.
• All other H's are omitted.

30.8B Cholesterol

Cholesterol has also been discussed in Sections 3.4C and 4.15. The role of cholesterol in plaque formation and atherosclerosis was discussed in Section 22.17.

Cholesterol, the chapter-opening molecule, has the tetracyclic carbon skeleton characteristic of steroids. It also has eight stereogenic carbons (seven on rings and one on a side chain), so there are $2^8 = 256$ possible stereoisomers. In nature, however, only the following stereoisomer exists:

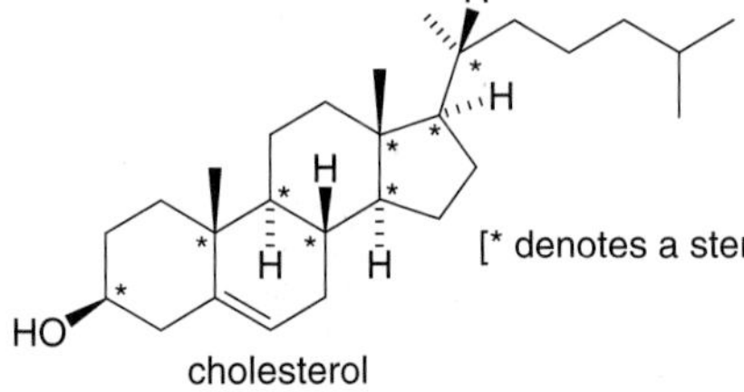

[* denotes a stereogenic center.]

cholesterol

Cholesterol is essential to life because it forms an important component of cell membranes and is the starting material for the synthesis of all other steroids. Humans do not have to ingest cholesterol, because it is synthesized in the liver and then transported to other tissues through the bloodstream. Because cholesterol has only one polar OH group and many nonpolar C–C and C–H bonds, it is insoluble in water (and, thus, in the aqueous medium of the blood).

Konrad Bloch and Feodor Lynen shared the 1964 Nobel Prize in Physiology or Medicine for unraveling the complex transformation of squalene to cholesterol.

Cholesterol is synthesized in the body from squalene, a C_{30} triterpene that is itself prepared from smaller terpenes, as discussed in Section 30.7B. Because the biosynthesis of all terpenes begins with acetyl CoA, every one of the 27 carbon atoms of cholesterol comes from the same two-carbon precursor. The major steps in the conversion of squalene to cholesterol are given in Figure 30.11.

Figure 30.11
The biosynthesis of cholesterol

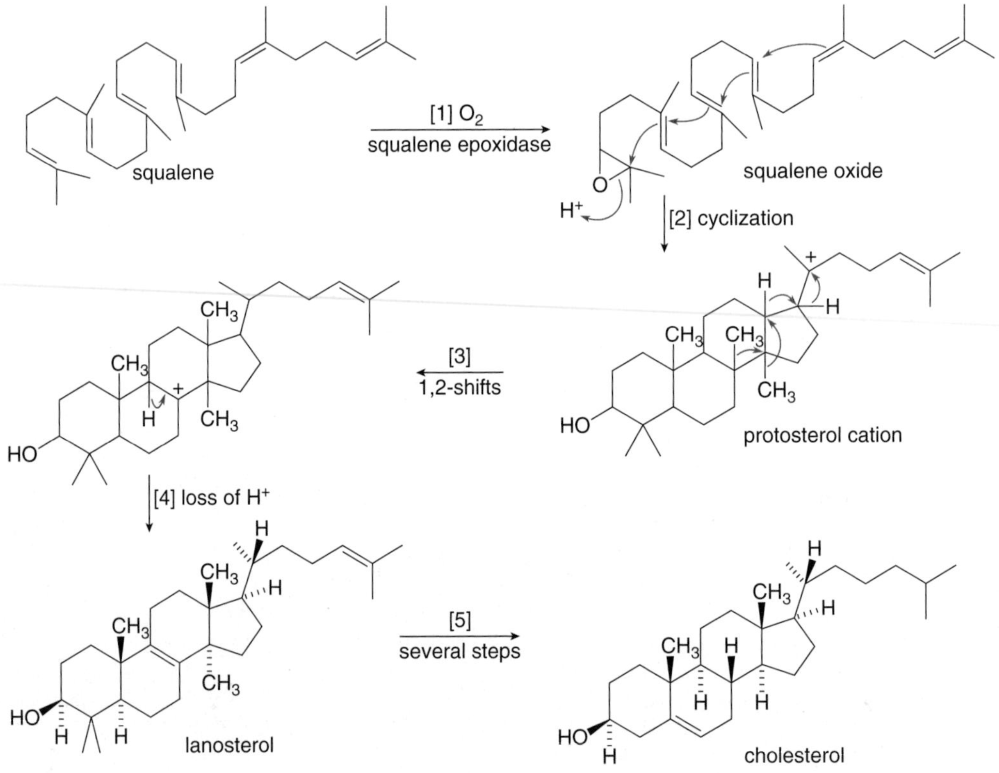

The conversion of squalene to cholesterol consists of five different parts:

[1] **Epoxidation** of squalene with an enzyme, squalene epoxidase, gives squalene oxide, which contains a single epoxide on one of the six double bonds.

[2] **Cyclization** of squalene oxide yields a carbocation, called the protosterol cation. This reaction results in the formation of four new C–C bonds and the tetracyclic ring system.

[3] **The protosterol carbocation rearranges** by a series of 1,2-shifts of either a hydrogen or methyl group to form another 3° carbocation.

[4] **Loss of a proton** gives an alkene called **lanosterol.** Although lanosterol has seven stereogenic centers, a single stereoisomer is formed.

[5] Lanosterol is then converted to cholesterol by a multistep process that results in removal of three methyl groups.

Several drugs called statins are now available to reduce the level of cholesterol in the bloodstream. These compounds act by blocking the biosynthesis of cholesterol at its very early stages. Two examples include atorvastatin (Lipitor) and simvastatin (Zocor), whose structures appear in Figure 30.12.

Problem 30.17 Draw the enantiomer and any two diastereomers of cholesterol. Does the OH group of cholesterol occupy an axial or equatorial position?

Problem 30.18 Treatment of cholesterol with mCPBA results in formation of a single epoxide **A,** with the stereochemistry drawn. Why isn't the isomeric epoxide **B** formed to any extent?

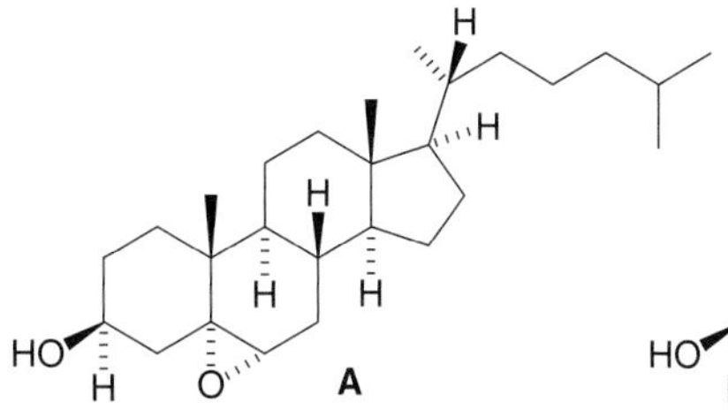

A

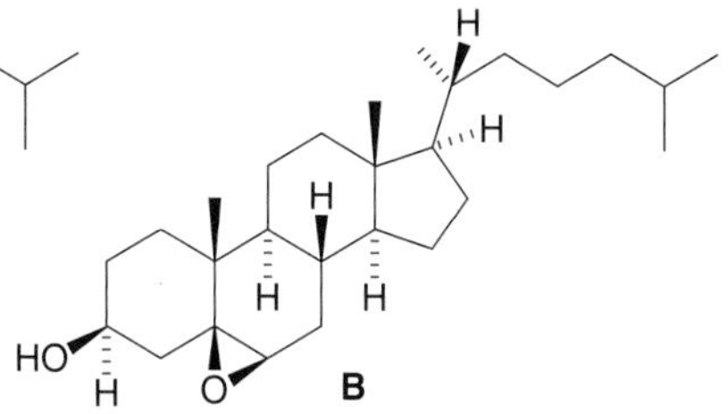

B

Figure 30.12
Two cholesterol-lowering drugs

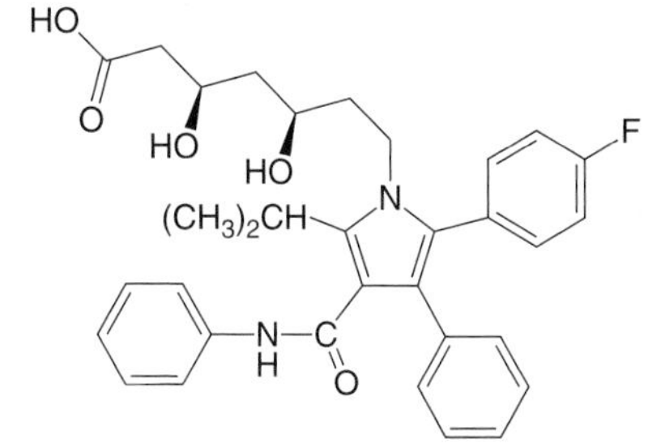

Generic name: atorvastatin
Trade name: Lipitor

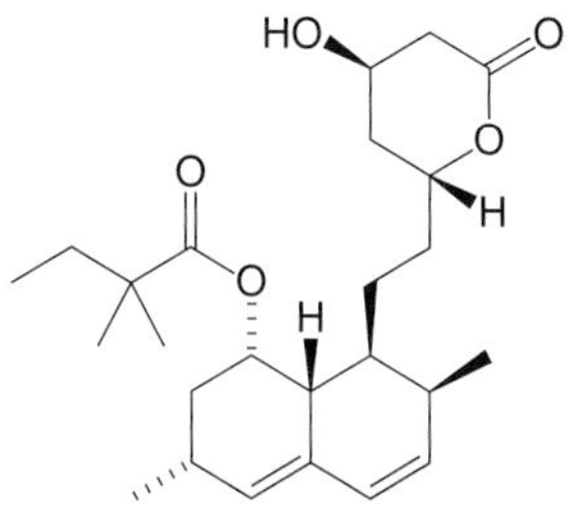

Generic name: simvastatin
Trade name: Zocor

30.8C Other Steroids

Many other important steroids are hormones secreted by the endocrine glands. Two classes are the **sex hormones** and the **adrenal cortical steroids.**

There are two types of female sex hormones, **estrogens** and **progestins.** The male sex hormones are called **androgens.** The most important members of each hormone type are given in Table 30.6.

Table 30.6 The Female and Male Sex Hormones

Structure	Properties
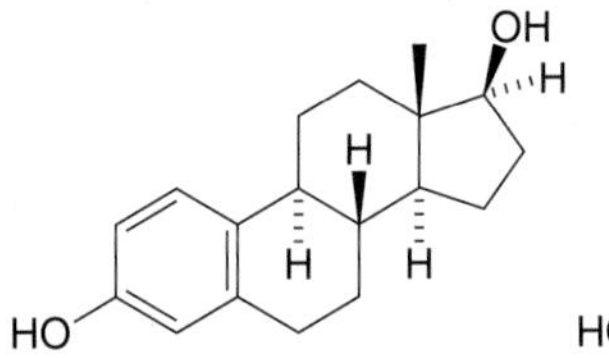 estradiol 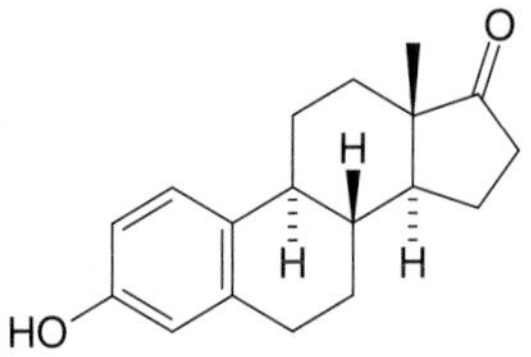 estrone	• **Estradiol** and **estrone** are estrogens synthesized in the ovaries. They control the development of secondary sex characteristics in females and regulate the menstrual cycle.
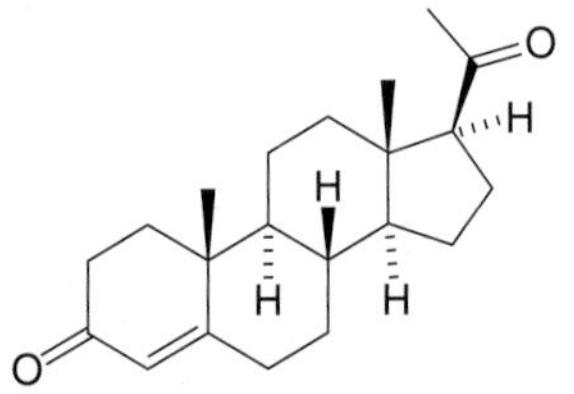 progesterone	• **Progesterone** is often called the "pregnancy hormone." It is responsible for the preparation of the uterus for implantation of a fertilized egg.
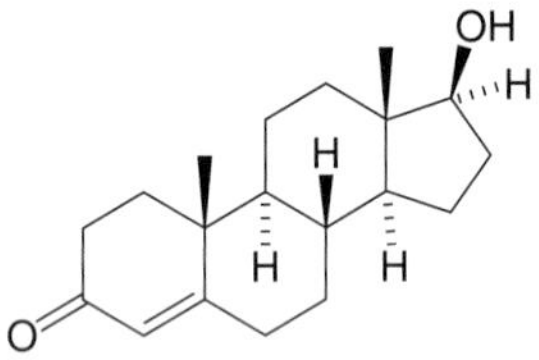 testosterone 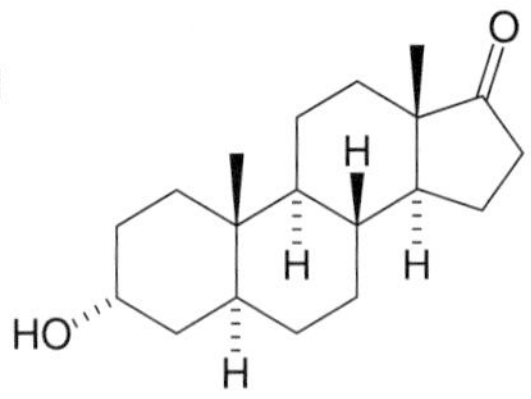 androsterone	• **Testosterone** and **androsterone** are androgens synthesized in the testes. They control the development of secondary sex characteristics in males.

Synthetic analogues of these steroids have found important uses, such as in oral contraceptives, first mentioned in Section 11.4.

Synthetic oral contraceptives

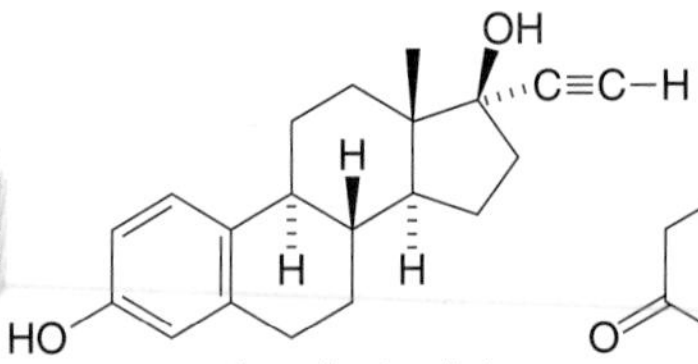
ethynylestradiol

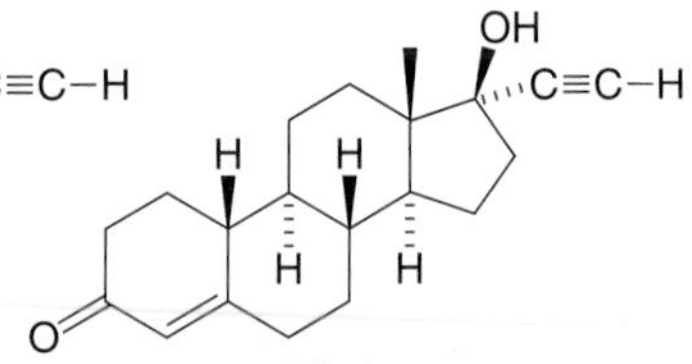
norethindrone

Some body builders use anabolic steroids to increase muscle mass. Long-term or excessive use can cause many health problems, including high blood pressure, liver damage, and cardiovascular disease.

Synthetic androgen analogues, called **anabolic steroids,** promote muscle growth. They were first developed to help individuals whose muscles had atrophied from lack of use following surgery. They have since come to be used by athletes and body builders, although their use is not permitted in competitive sports. Many physical and psychological problems result from their prolonged use.

Anabolic steroids, such as stanozolol, nandrolone, and tetrahydrogestrinone have the same effect on the body as testosterone, but they are more stable, so they are not metabolized as quickly. Tetrahydrogestrinone (also called THG or The Clear), the performance-enhancing drug used by track star Marion Jones during the 2000 Sydney Olympics, was considered a "designer steroid" because it was initially undetected in urine tests for doping. After its chemical structure and properties were determined, it was added to the list of banned anabolic steroids in 2004.

Anabolic steroids

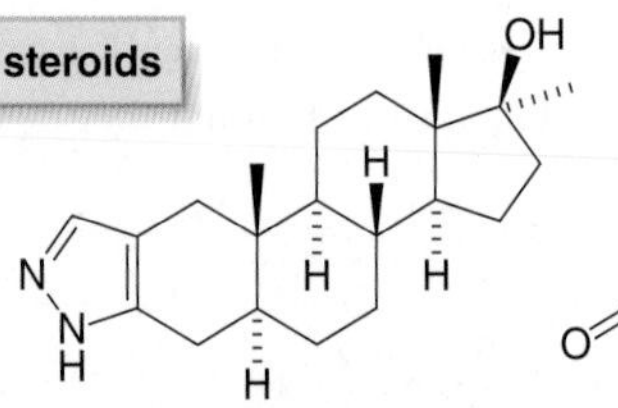
stanozolol

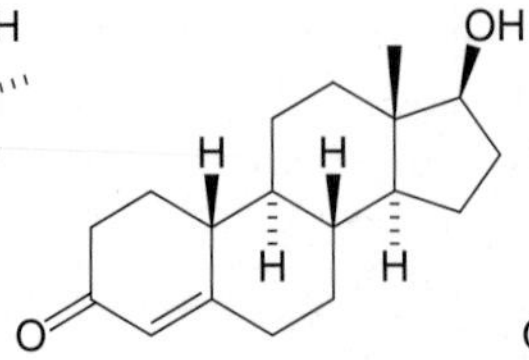
nandrolone

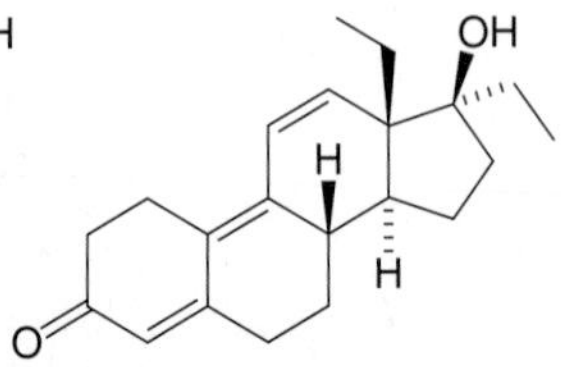
tetrahydrogestrinone

A second group of steroid hormones includes the **adrenal cortical steroids.** Three examples of these hormones are **cortisone, cortisol,** and **aldosterone.** All of these compounds are synthesized in the outer layer of the adrenal gland. Cortisone and cortisol serve as anti-inflammatory agents and they also regulate carbohydrate metabolism. Aldosterone regulates blood pressure and volume by controlling the concentration of Na^+ and K^+ in body fluids.

Three adrenal cortical steroids

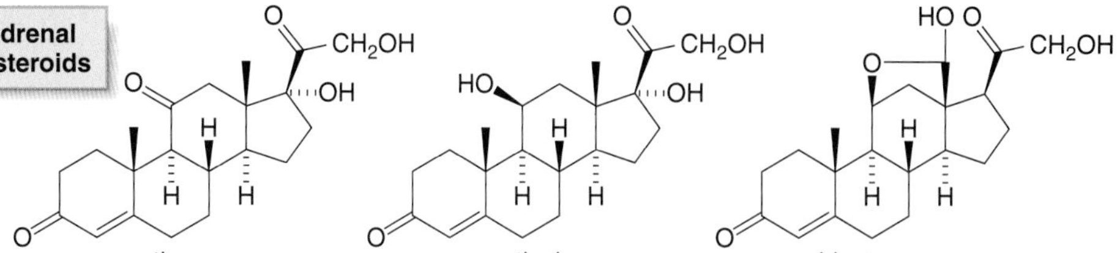

cortisone cortisol aldosterone

KEY CONCEPTS

Lipids

Hydrolyzable Lipids

[1] **Waxes** (30.2)—Esters formed from a long-chain alcohol and a long-chain carboxylic acid.

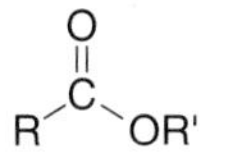

R, R' = long chains of C's

[2] **Triacylglycerols** (30.3)—Triesters of glycerol with three fatty acids.

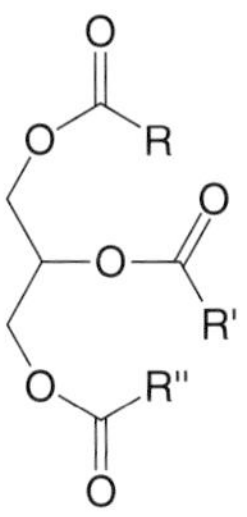

R, R', R'' = alkyl groups with 11–19 C's

[3] **Phospholipids** (30.4)

a. Phosphatidylethanolamine (cephalin)

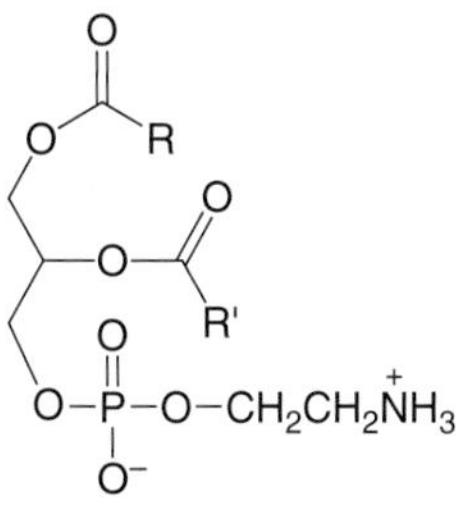

R, R' = long carbon chain

b. Phosphatidylcholine (lecithin)

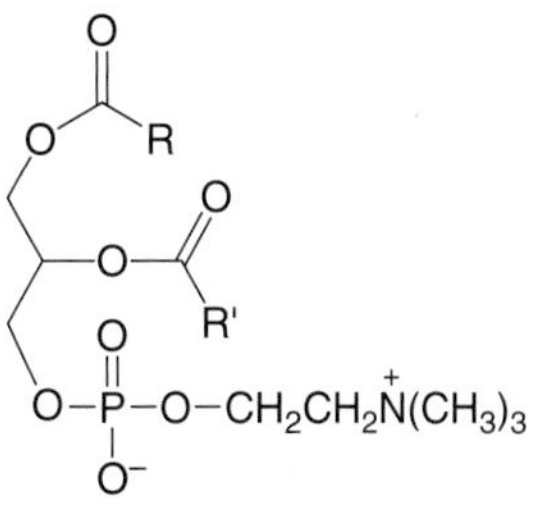

R, R' = long carbon chain

c. Sphingomyelin

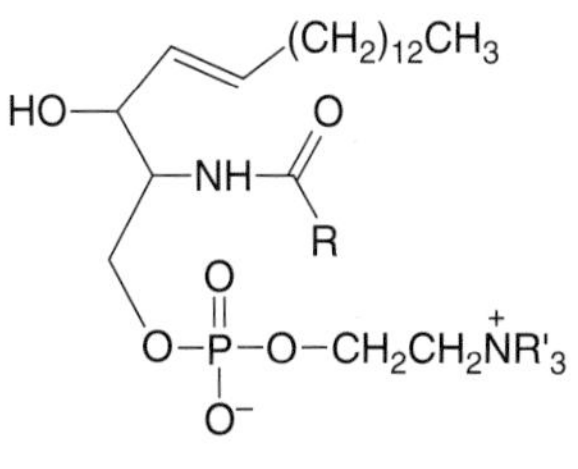

R = long carbon chain
R' = H or CH_3

Nonhydrolyzable Lipids

[1] **Fat-soluble vitamins** (30.5)—Vitamins A, D, E, and K.

[2] **Eicosanoids** (30.6)—Compounds containing 20 C's derived from arachidonic acid. There are four types: prostaglandins, thromboxanes, prostacyclins, and leukotrienes.

[3] **Terpenes** (30.7)—Lipids composed of repeating 5 C units called isoprene units.

Isoprene unit	Types of terpenes			
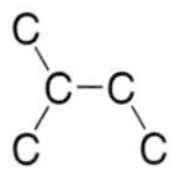	[1] monoterpene	10 C's	[4] sesterterpene	25 C's
	[2] sesquiterpene	15 C's	[5] triterpene	30 C's
	[3] diterpene	20 C's	[6] tetraterpene	40 C's

[4] **Steroids** (30.8)—Tetracyclic lipids composed of three six-membered and one five-membered ring.

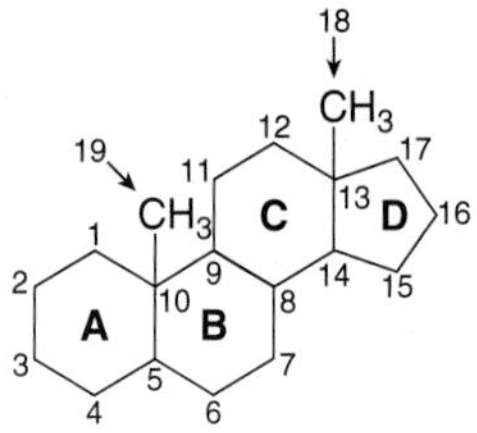

PROBLEMS

Problems Using Three-Dimensional Models

30.19 Locate the isoprene units in each compound.

a. 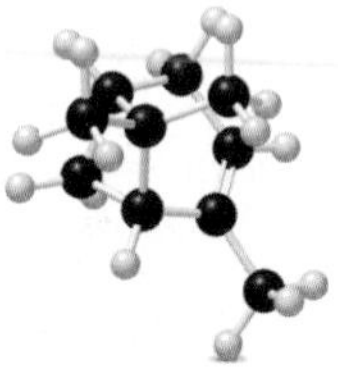

α-pinene

b. 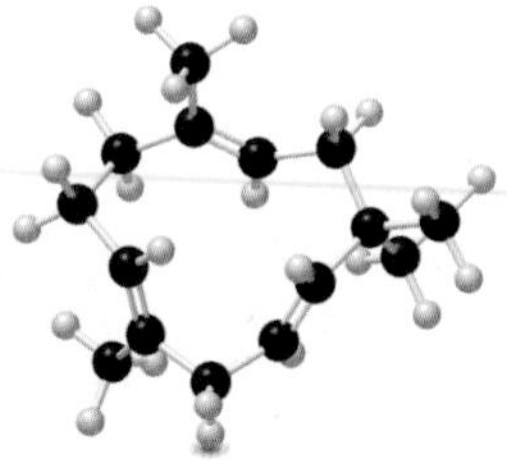

humulene

30.20 Convert each ball-and-stick model to a skeletal structure that clearly shows the stereochemistry at the ring fusion of these decalin derivatives.

a. 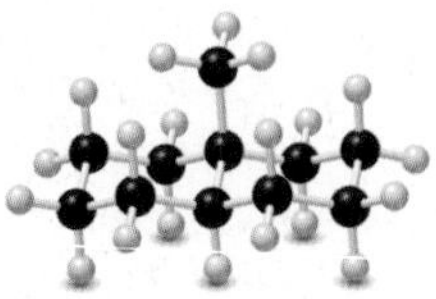

b. 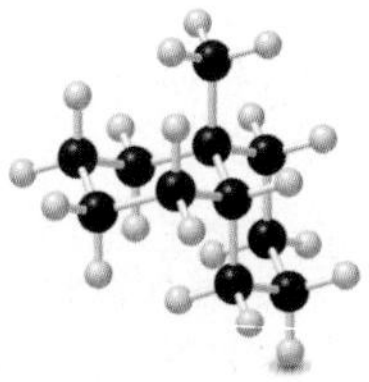

30.21 Convert the ball-and-stick model of androsterone to (a) a skeletal structure using wedges and dashes around all stereogenic centers; and (b) a three-dimensional representation using chair cyclohexane rings.

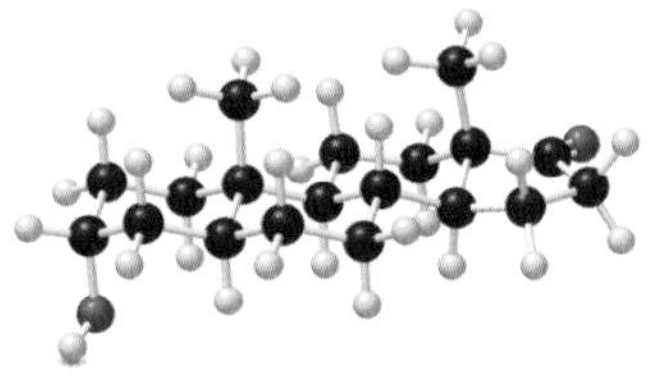

androsterone

Waxes, Triacylglycerols, and Phospholipids

30.22 One component of lanolin, the wax that coats sheep's wool, is derived from cholesterol and stearic acid. Draw its structure, including the correct stereochemistry at all stereogenic centers.

30.23 Draw all possible constitutional isomers of a triacylglycerol formed from one mole each of palmitic, oleic, and linoleic acids. Locate the tetrahedral stereogenic centers in each constitutional isomer.

30.24 What is the structure of an optically inactive triacylglycerol that yields two moles of oleic acid and one mole of palmitic acid when hydrolyzed in aqueous acid?

30.25 Triacylglycerol **L** yields compound **M** when treated with excess H_2, Pd-C. Ozonolysis of **L** ([1] O_3; [2] $(CH_3)_2S$) affords compounds **N – P.** What is the structure of **L?**

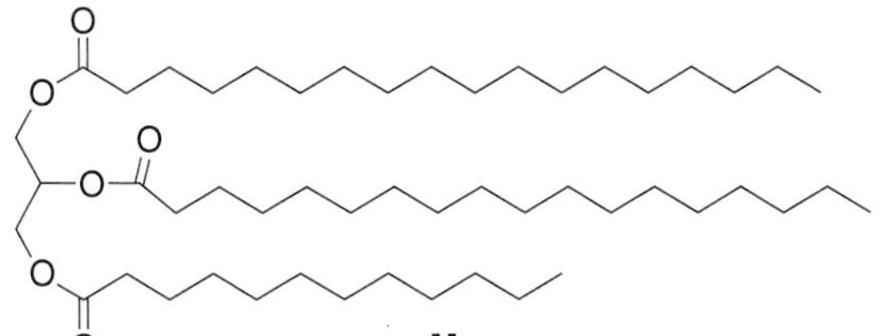

M

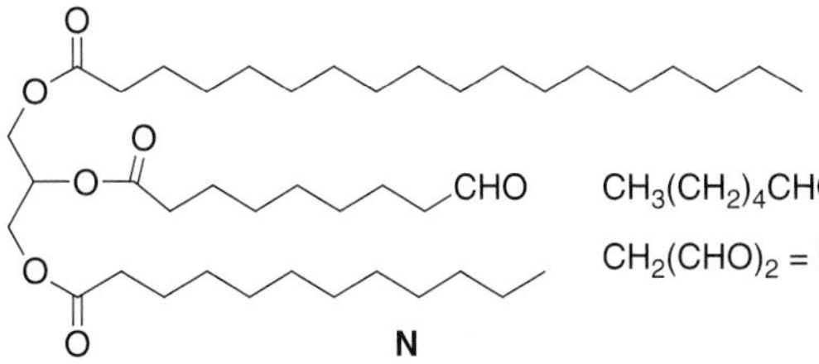

N

$CH_3(CH_2)_4CHO$ = **O**

$CH_2(CHO)_2$ = **P**

30.26 Draw the structure of the following phospholipids:

a. a cephalin formed from two molecules of stearic acid

b. a sphingomyelin formed from palmitic acid

Prostaglandins

30.27 A difficult problem in the synthesis of $PGF_{2\alpha}$ is the introduction of the OH group at C15 in the desired configuration.

a. Label this stereogenic center as *R* or *S*.

b. A well known synthesis of $PGF_{2\alpha}$ involves reaction of **A** with $Zn(BH_4)_2$, a metal hydride reagent similar in reactivity to $NaBH_4$, to form two isomeric products, **B** and **C.** Draw their structures and indicate their stereochemical relationship.

c. Suggest a reagent to convert **A** to the single stereoisomer **X.**

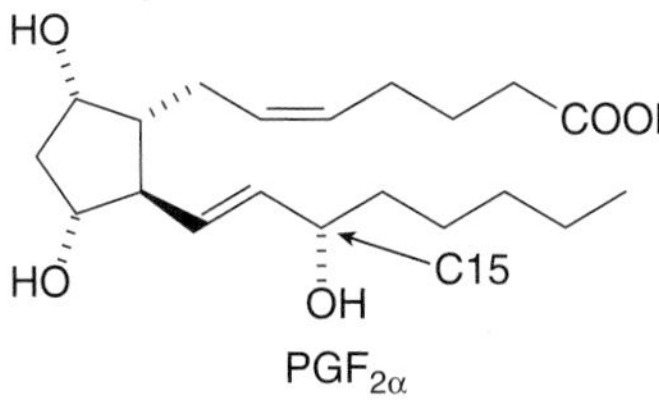

$PGF_{2\alpha}$

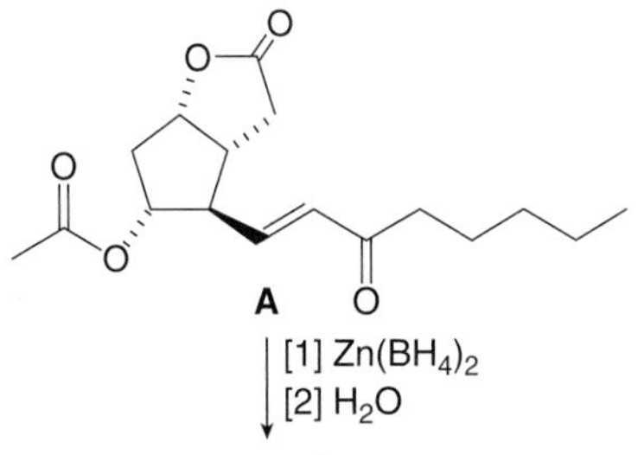

B and **C**

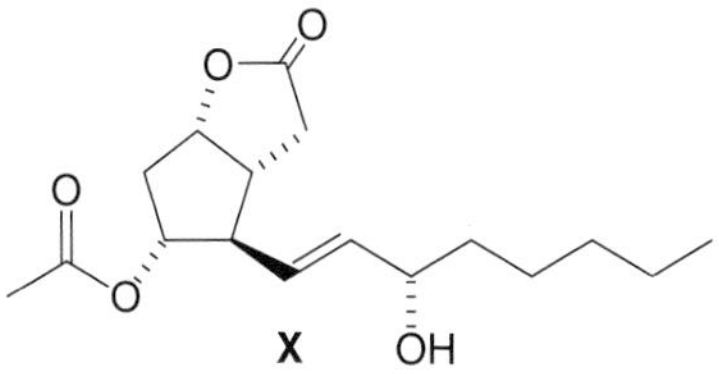

Terpenes and Terpenoids

30.28 Locate the isoprene units in each compound.

a. 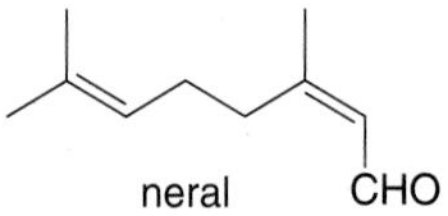

neral

e. 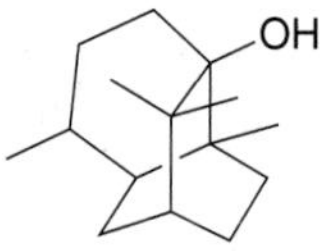

patchouli alcohol

g. 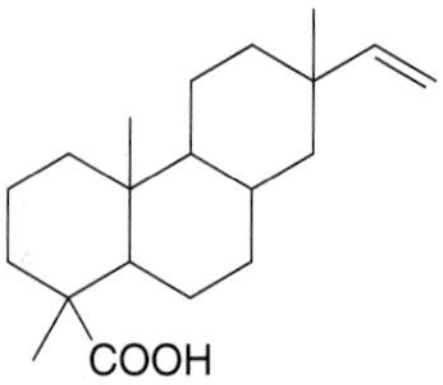

dextropimaric acid

b. 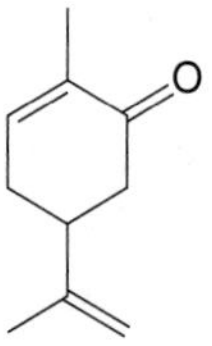

carvone

f. 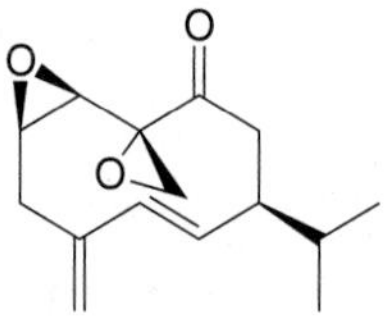

periplanone B

h. 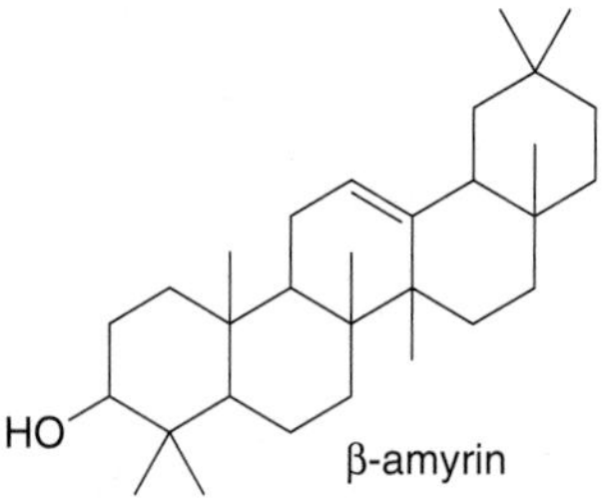

β-amyrin

c. 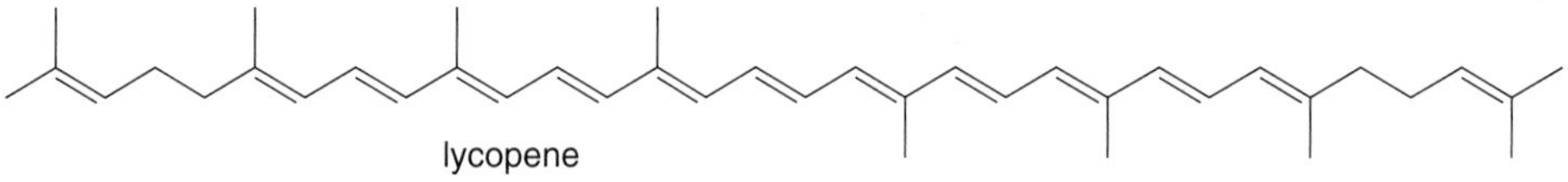

lycopene

d. 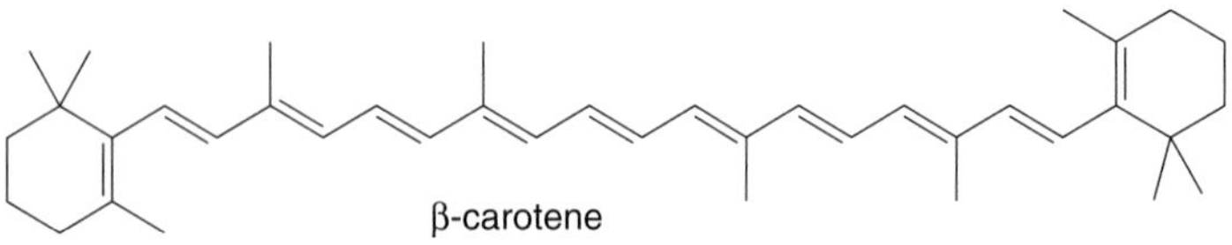

β-carotene

30.29 Classify each terpene and terpenoid in Problem 30.28 (e.g., as a monoterpene, sesquiterpene, etc.).

30.30 An isoprene unit can be thought of as having a head and a tail. The "head" of the isoprene unit is located at the end of the chain nearest the branch point, and the "tail" is located at the end of the carbon chain farthest from the branch point. Most isoprene units are connected together in a "head-to-tail" fashion, as illustrated. For both lycopene (Problem 30.28), and squalene (Figure 30.9), decide which isoprene units are connected in a head-to-tail fashion and which are not.

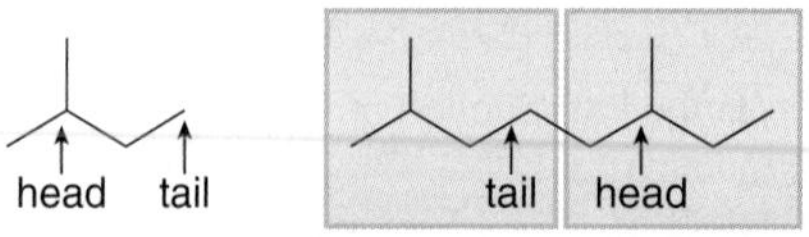

These two isoprene units are connected in a head-to-tail fashion.

30.31 Draw a stepwise mechanism for the conversion of neryl diphosphate to α-pinene. α-Pinene is a component of pine oil and rosemary oil.

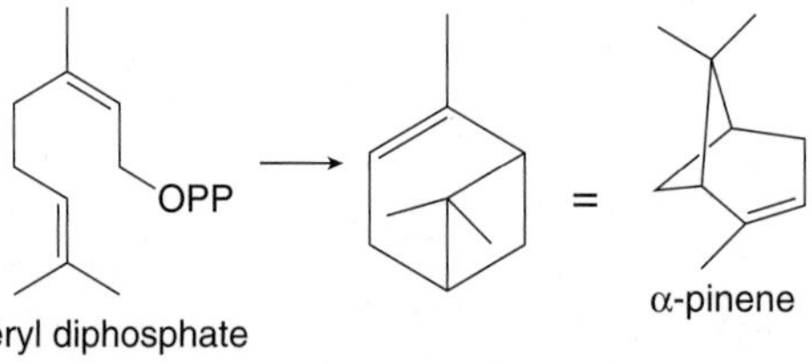

neryl diphosphate α-pinene

30.32 Flexibilene is a terpene isolated from *Sinularia flexibilis,* a soft coral found in the Indian Ocean. Draw a stepwise mechanism for the formation of flexibilene from farnesyl diphosphate and isopentenyl diphosphate. What is unusual about the cyclization that forms the 15-membered ring of flexibilene?

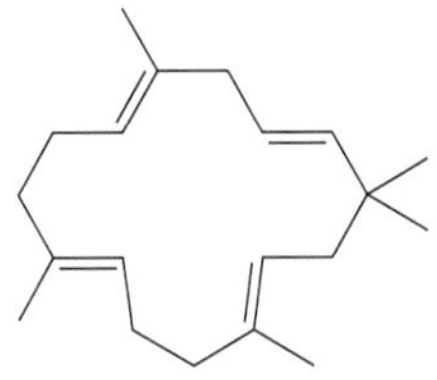

flexibilene

30.33 The biosynthesis of lanosterol from squalene has intrigued chemists since its discovery. It is now possible, for example, to synthesize polycyclic compounds from acyclic or monocyclic precursors by reactions that form several C–C bonds in a single reaction mixture.

a. Draw a stepwise mechanism for the following reaction.

b. Show how **X** can be converted to 16,17-dehydroprogesterone. (*Hint:* See Figure 24.5 for a related conversion.)

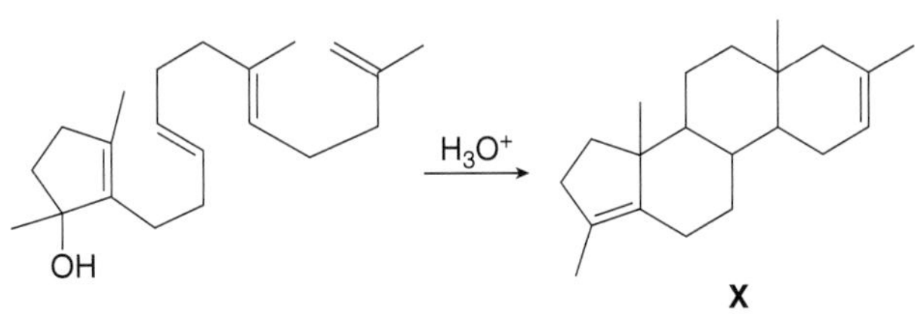

X

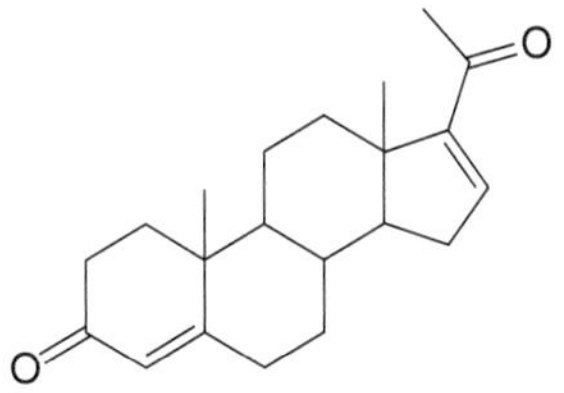

16,17-dehydroprogesterone

Steroids

30.34 Draw three-dimensional structures for each alcohol. Label the OH groups as occupying axial or equatorial positions.

a. 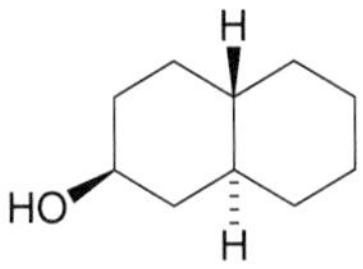

b. 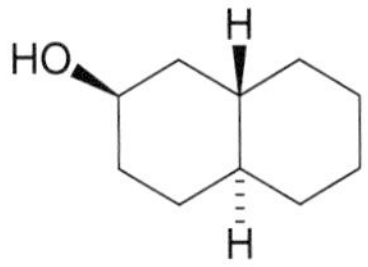

c. 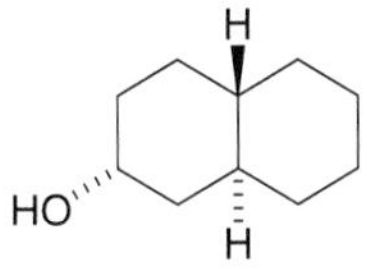

d. 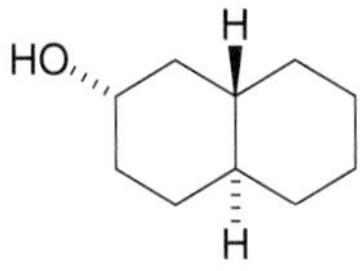

30.35 Axial alcohols are oxidized faster than equatorial alcohols by PCC and other Cr^{6+} oxidants. Which OH group in each compound is oxidized faster?

a. 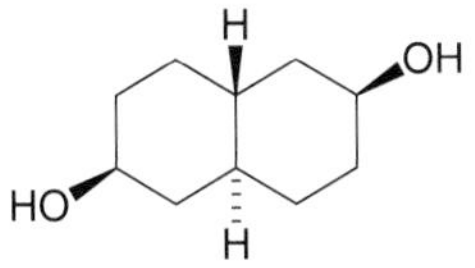

b. 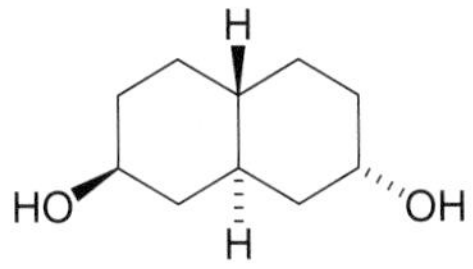

30.36 (a) Draw a skeletal structure of the anabolic steroid methenolone from the following description. Methenolone contains the tetracyclic steroid skeleton with a carbonyl group at C3, a hydroxyl at C17, a double bond between C1 and C2, and methyl groups bonded to C1, C10, and C13. (b) Add wedges and dashes for all stereogenic centers with the following information: the configuration at C10 is *R,* the configuration at C13 is *S,* the configuration at C17 is *S,* and all substituents at ring fusions are trans to each other. (c) Draw the structure of Primobolan, the product formed when methenolone is treated with $CH_3(CH_2)_5COCl$ and pyridine. Primobolan is an anabolic steroid that can be taken orally or by injection and has been used illegally by well-known Major League Baseball players.

30.37 a. Draw a three-dimensional structure for the following steroid.

b. What is the structure of the single stereoisomer formed by reduction of this ketone with H_2, Pd-C? Explain why only one stereoisomer is formed.

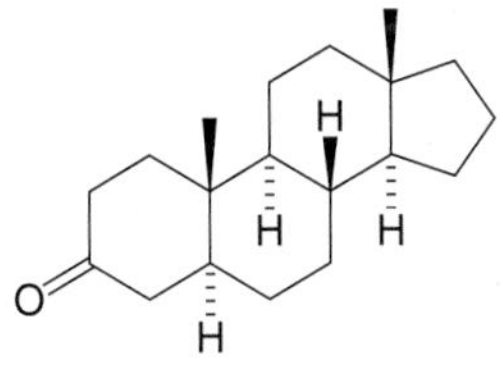

30.38 Draw the products formed when cholesterol is treated with each reagent. Indicate the stereochemistry around any stereogenic centers in the product.

a. CH_3COCl
b. H_2, Pd-C
c. PCC
d. oleic acid, H^+
e. [1] BH_3•THF; [2] H_2O_2, ^-OH

Challenge Problems

30.39 Draw a stepwise mechanism for the following conversion, which forms camphene. Camphene is a component of camphor and citronella oils.

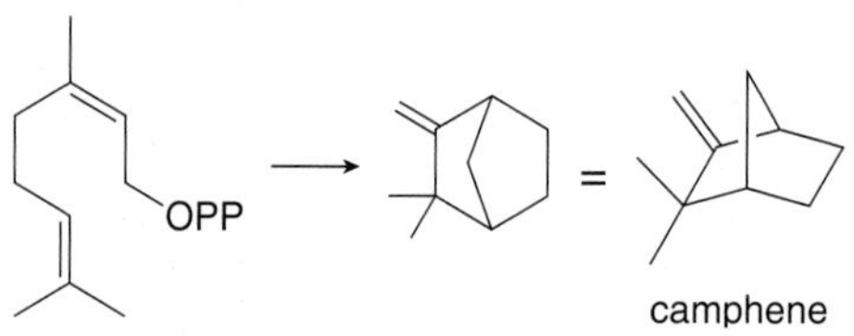

30.40 Draw a stepwise mechanism for the following reaction.

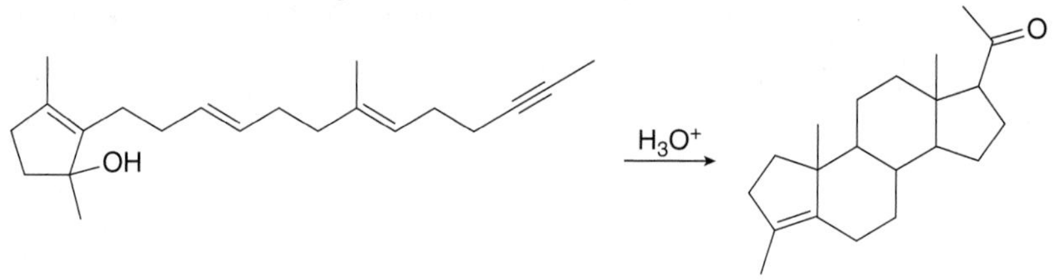

30.41 Farnesyl diphosphate is cyclized to sesquiterpene **A,** which is then converted to the bicyclic product epi-aristolochene. Write a stepwise mechanism for both reactions.

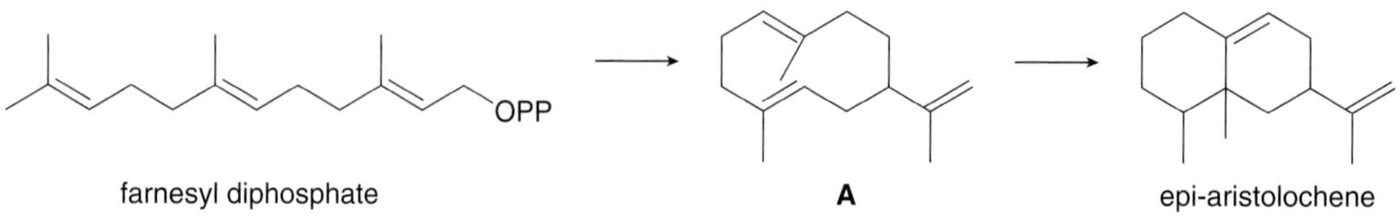

Synthetic Polymers

31

31.1 Introduction
31.2 Chain-growth polymers—Addition polymers
31.3 Anionic polymerization of epoxides
31.4 Ziegler–Natta catalysts and polymer stereochemistry
31.5 Natural and synthetic rubbers
31.6 Step-growth polymers—Condensation polymers
31.7 Polymer structure and properties
31.8 Green polymer synthesis
31.9 Polymer recycling and disposal

Polyethylene terephthalate (PET) is a synthetic polymer formed by the reaction of ethylene glycol ($HOCH_2CH_2OH$) and terephthalic acid. Because PET is lightweight and impervious to air and moisture, it is commonly used for transparent soft drink containers. PET is also used to produce synthetic fibers, sold under the trade name of Dacron. Of the six most common synthetic polymers, PET is the most easily recycled, in part because beverage bottles that bear the recycling code "1" are composed almost entirely of PET. Recycled polyethylene terephthalate is used for fleece clothing and carpeting. In Chapter 31, we learn about the preparation and properties of synthetic polymers like polyethylene terephthalate.

Chapter 31 discusses polymers, large organic molecules composed of repeating units—called **monomers**—that are covalently bonded together. Polymers occur naturally, as in the polysaccharides and proteins of Chapters 28 and 29, respectively, or they are synthesized in the laboratory.

This chapter concentrates on **synthetic polymers,** and expands on the material already presented in Chapters 15 and 22. Thousands of synthetic polymers have now been prepared. While some exhibit properties that mimic naturally occurring compounds, many others have unique properties. Although all polymers are large molecules, the size and branching of the polymer chain and the identity of the functional groups all contribute to determining an individual polymer's properties, thus making it suited for a particular product.

31.1 Introduction

A **polymer** is a large organic molecule composed of repeating units—called **monomers**—that are covalently bonded together. The word *polymer* is derived from the Greek words *poly* + *meros* meaning "many parts."

Polymerization is the joining together of monomers to make polymers.

Synthetic polymers are perhaps more vital to the fabric of modern society than any other group of compounds prepared in the laboratory. Nylon backpacks and polyester clothing, car bumpers and CD cases, milk jugs and grocery bags, artificial heart valves and condoms—all these products and innumerable others are made of synthetic polymers. Since 1976, the U.S. production of synthetic polymers has exceeded its steel production. Figure 31.1 illustrates several consumer products and the polymers from which they are made.

Synthetic polymers can be classified as chain-growth or step-growth polymers.

- **Chain-growth polymers, also called addition polymers, are prepared by chain reactions.**

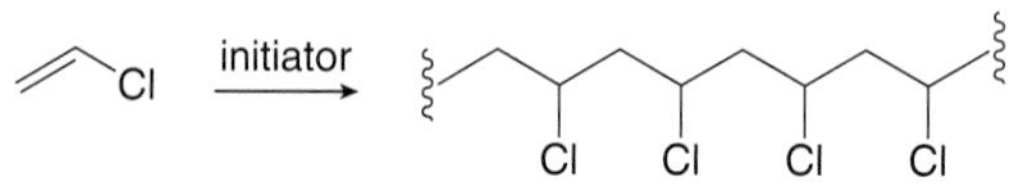
Cl
initiator
Cl Cl Cl Cl

vinyl chloride — poly(vinyl chloride)

monomer — **polymer**

These compounds are formed by adding monomers to the growing end of a polymer chain. The conversion of vinyl chloride to poly(vinyl chloride) is an example of chain-growth polymerization. These reactions were introduced in Section 15.14.

Figure 31.1 Polymers in some common consumer products

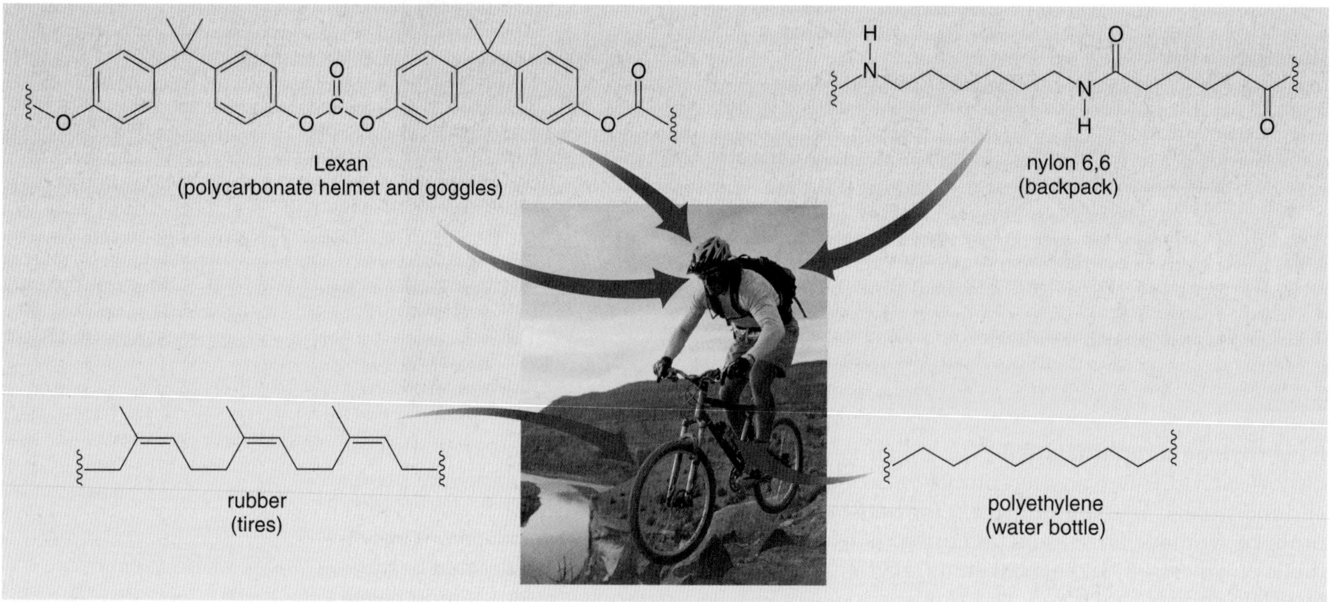
Lexan
(polycarbonate helmet and goggles)
nylon 6,6
(backpack)
rubber
(tires)
polyethylene
(water bottle)

- We are surrounded by synthetic polymers in our daily lives. This cyclist rides on synthetic rubber tires, drinks from a polyethylene water bottle, wears a protective Lexan helmet and goggles, and uses a lightweight nylon backpack.

- **Step-growth polymers, also called condensation polymers, are formed when monomers containing two functional groups come together and lose a small molecule such as H_2O or HCl.**

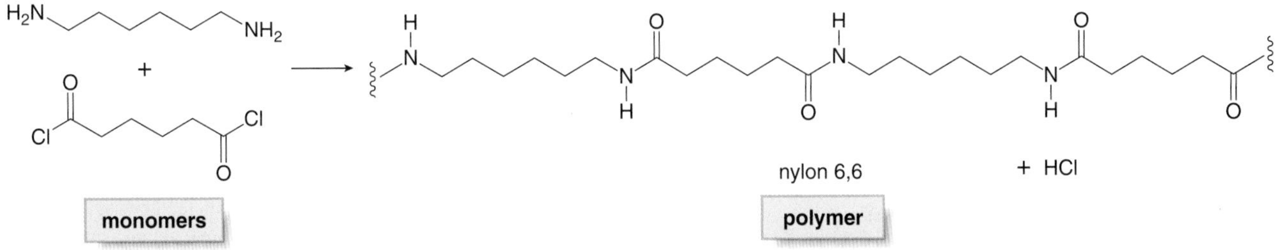
monomers
nylon 6,6
+ HCl
polymer

In this method, any two reactive molecules can combine, so the monomer is not necessarily added to the end of a growing chain. Step-growth polymerization is used to prepare polyamides and polyesters, as discussed in Section 22.16.

In contrast to many of the organic molecules encountered in Chapters 1–27, which have molecular weights much less than 1000 grams per mole (g/mol), polymers generally have high molecular weights, ranging from 10,000 to 1,000,000 grams per mole (g/mol). Synthetic polymers are really mixtures of individual polymer chains of varying lengths, so the reported molecular weight is an average value based on the average size of the polymer chain.

By convention, we often simplify the structure of a polymer by placing brackets around the repeating unit that forms the chain, as shown in Figure 31.2.

Problem 31.1 Give the shorthand structures of poly(vinyl chloride) and nylon 6,6 in Section 31.1.

Figure 31.2 Drawing a polymer in a shorthand representation

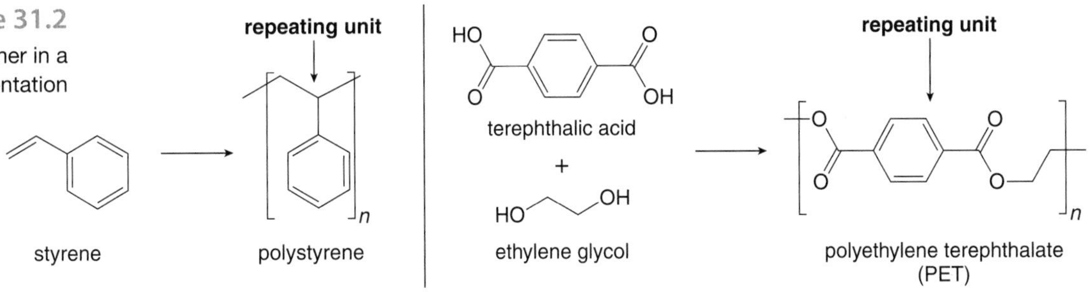
repeating unit
styrene
polystyrene
terephthalic acid
ethylene glycol
repeating unit
polyethylene terephthalate
(PET)

31.2 Chain-Growth Polymers—Addition Polymers

Chain-growth polymerization is a chain reaction that converts an organic starting material, usually an alkene, to a polymer via a reactive intermediate—a radical, cation, or anion.

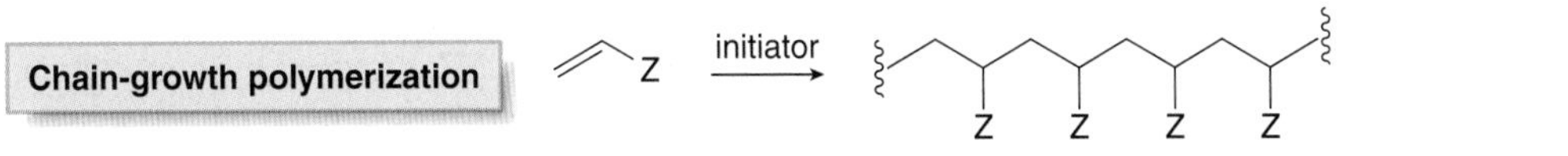
Chain-growth polymerization
initiator

- The alkene can be ethylene ($CH_2{=}CH_2$) or a derivative of ethylene ($CH_2{=}CHZ$ or $CH_2{=}CZ_2$).
- The substituent Z (in part) determines whether radicals, cations, or anions are formed as intermediates.
- An initiator—a radical, cation, or anion—is needed to begin polymerization.
- Since chain-growth polymerization is a chain reaction, the mechanism involves initiation, propagation, and termination (Section 15.4).

In most chain-growth polymerizations, an initiator adds to the carbon–carbon double bond of one monomer to form a reactive intermediate, which then reacts with another molecule of monomer to build the chain. Polymerization of $CH_2{=}CHZ$ results in a carbon chain having the Z substituents on every other carbon atom.

Problem 31.2 What polymer is formed by chain-growth polymerization of each monomer?

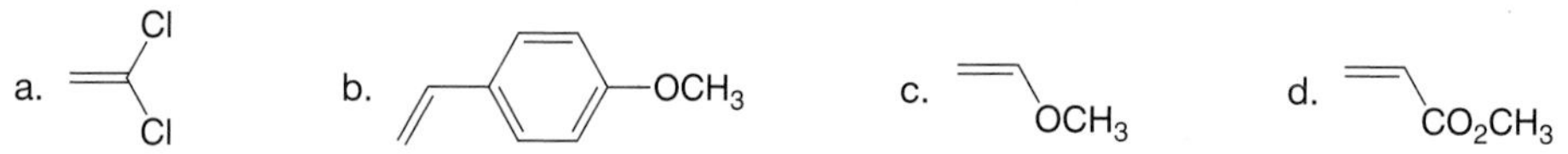

31.2A Radical Polymerization

Radical polymerization of alkenes was first discussed in Section 15.14, and is included here to emphasize its relationship to other methods of chain-growth polymerization. The initiator is often a peroxy radical (RO·), formed by cleavage of the weak O–O bond in an organic peroxide, ROOR. Mechanism 31.1 is written with styrene ($CH_2{=}CHPh$) as the starting material.

Mechanism 31.1 Radical Polymerization of $CH_2{=}CHPh$

Part [1] Initiation: Formation of a carbon radical in two steps

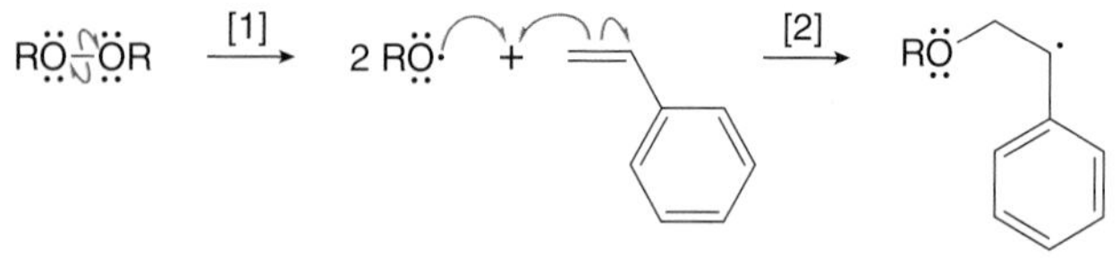

- Homolysis of the weak O–O bond of the peroxide forms RO·, which then adds to a molecule of monomer to form a carbon radical.

Part [2] Propagation: Growth of the polymer chain by C–C bond formation

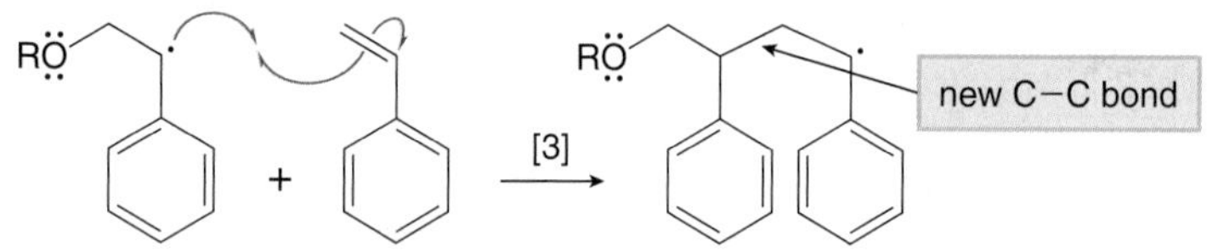

Repeat Step [3] over and over.

- In Step [3], the carbon radical formed during initiation adds to another alkene molecule to form a new C–C bond and another carbon radical. Addition gives the more substituted carbon radical—that is, the **unpaired electron is always located on the carbon atom having the phenyl substituent.**
- Step [3] occurs repeatedly, thus growing the polymer chain.

Part [3] Termination: Removal of radicals by formation of a σ bond

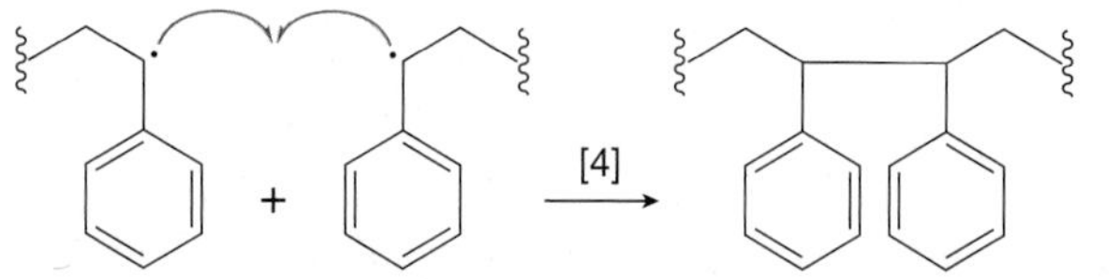

- To terminate the chain, two radicals can combine to form a stable bond, thus ending the polymerization process.

Radical polymerization of $CH_2{=}CHZ$ is favored by Z substituents that stabilize a radical by electron delocalization. Each addition step occurs to put the intermediate radical on the carbon bearing the Z substituent. With styrene as the starting material, the intermediate radical is benzylic and highly resonance stabilized. Figure 31.3 shows several monomers used in radical polymerization reactions.

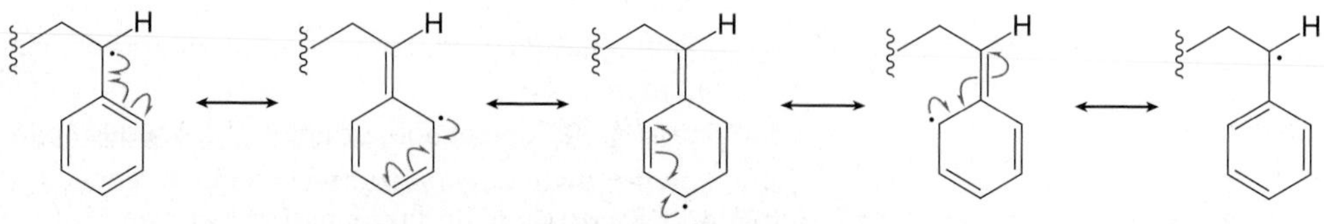

five resonance structures for the benzylic radical

Figure 31.3
Monomers used in radical polymerization reactions

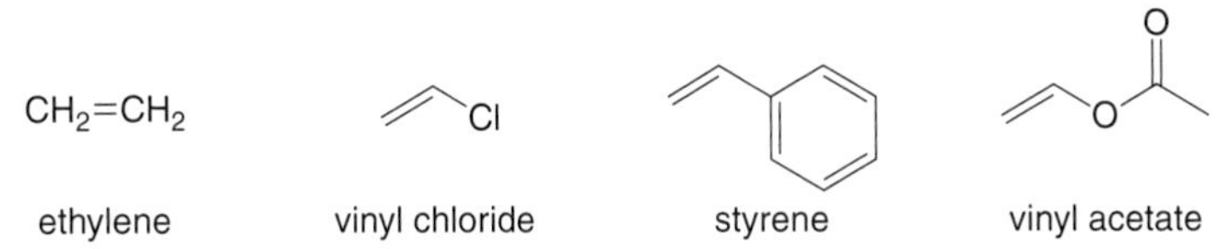
CH2=CH2
Cl
O
O
ethylene
vinyl chloride
styrene
vinyl acetate

Problem 31.3 What polymer is formed by the radical polymerization of each monomer?

a. $CH_2=C(CH_3)CO_2CH_3$ b. $CH_2=C(CH_3)CN$

Problem 31.4 Draw the mechanism for the radical polymerization of vinyl acetate ($CH_2=CHOCOCH_3$) using $(CH_3)_3CO-OC(CH_3)_3$ as the initiator.

Chain termination can occur by radical coupling, as shown in Mechanism 31.1. Chain termination can also occur by **disproportionation,** a process in which a hydrogen atom is transferred from one polymer radical to another, forming a new C–H bond on one polymer chain, and a double bond on the other.

Disproportionation—One method of chain termination

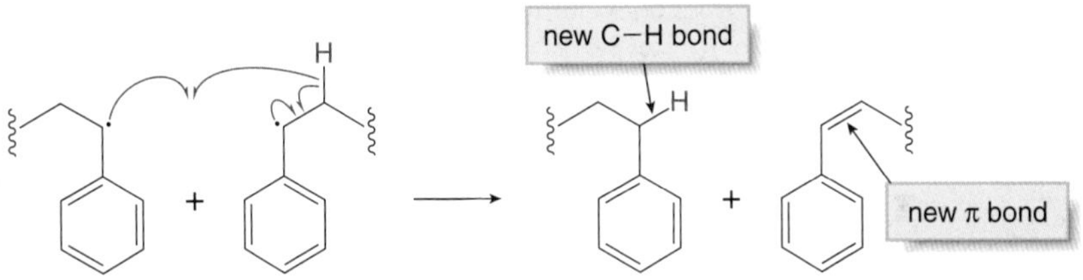
H
new C–H bond
H
new π bond

31.2B Chain Branching

HDPE is used in milk containers and water jugs, whereas LDPE is used in plastic bags and insulation.

The choice of reaction parameters greatly affects the properties of a synthetic polymer. In Section 15.14, we learned that there are two common types of polyethylene—**high-density polyethylene (HDPE) and low-density polyethylene (LDPE).** High-density polyethylene, which consists of long chains of CH_2 groups joined together in a linear fashion, is strong and hard because the linear chains pack well, resulting in strong van der Waals interactions. Low-density polyethylene, on the other hand, consists of long carbon chains with many branches along the chain. Branching prohibits the chains from packing well, so LDPE has weaker intermolecular interactions, making it a much softer, pliable material.

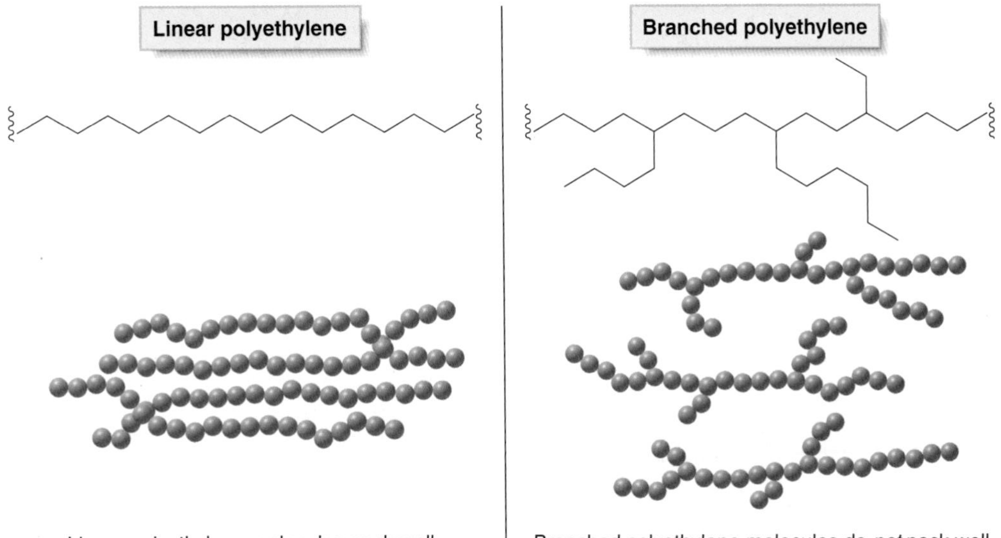
Linear polyethylene
Branched polyethylene

Linear polyethylene molecules pack well. Branched polyethylene molecules do *not* pack well.

Branching occurs when a radical on one growing polyethylene chain abstracts a hydrogen atom from a CH_2 group in another polymer chain, as shown in Mechanism 31.2. The new 2° radical then continues chain propagation by adding to another molecule of ethylene, thus forming a branch point.

Mechanism 31.2 Forming Branched Polyethylene During Radical Polymerization

Step [1] Abstraction of a hydrogen atom

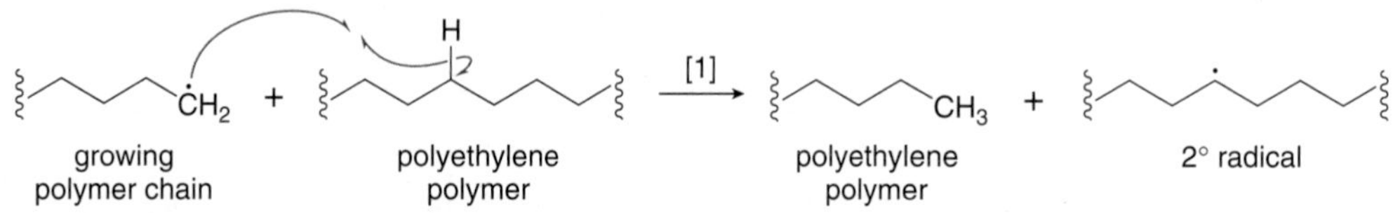

- Abstraction of a hydrogen atom from an existing polymer chain forms a 2° radical in the middle of the polymer chain.

Step [2] Growth of the polymer chain forming a branch point

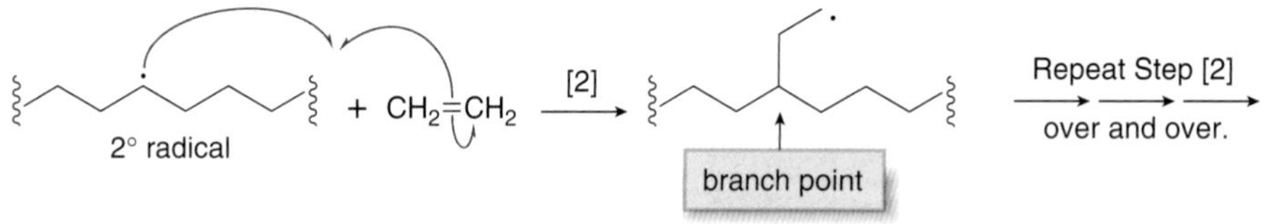

- Addition of the radical to another molecule of ethylene forms a new radical and a branch point along the polymer chain. Step [2] occurs repeatedly, and a long branch grows off the original polymer chain.

Problem 31.5 Explain why radical polymerization of styrene forms branched chains with 4° carbons as in **A,** but none with 3° carbons as in **B.**

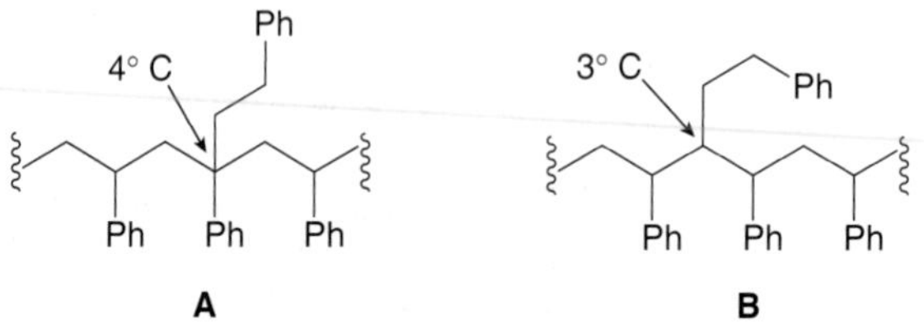

31.2C Ionic Polymerization

Chain-growth polymerization can also occur by way of cationic or anionic intermediates. **Cationic polymerization is an example of electrophilic addition to an alkene involving carbocations.** Cationic polymerization occurs with alkene monomers that have substituents capable of stabilizing intermediate carbocations, such as alkyl groups or other electron-donor groups. The initiator is an electrophile such as a proton source or Lewis acid.

Mechanism 31.3 illustrates cationic polymerization of the general monomer $CH_2{=}CHZ$ using $BF_3{\cdot}H_2O$, the Lewis acid–base complex formed from BF_3 and H_2O, as the initiator.

Mechanism 31.3 Cationic Polymerization of $CH_2{=}CHZ$

Part [1] Initiation: Formation of a carbocation

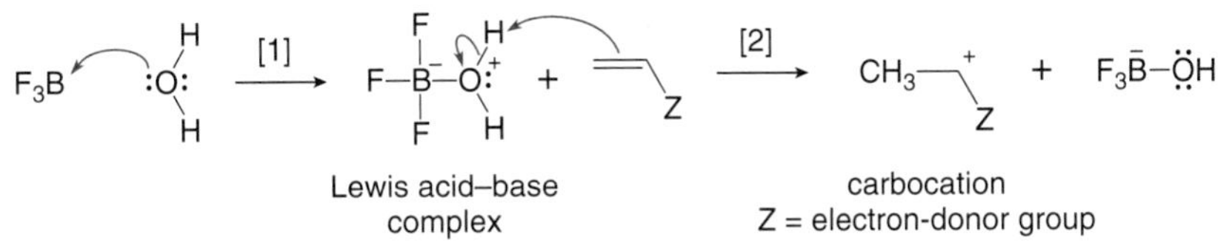
[1]
[2]
Lewis acid–base complex
carbocation
Z = electron-donor group

- Electrophilic addition of H^+ from $BF_3{\cdot}H_2O$ forms a carbocation.

Part [2] Propagation: Growth of the polymer chain by C–C bond formation

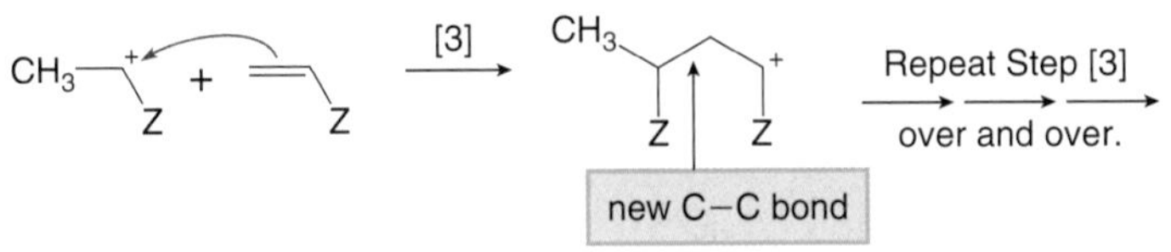
[3]
Repeat Step [3]
over and over.
new C–C bond

- In Step [3], the carbocation adds to another alkene molecule to form a new C–C bond. Addition always forms a carbocation stabilized by an electron-donating Z substituent.
- Step [3] occurs repeatedly, thus growing the polymer chain.

Part [3] Termination: Loss of a proton

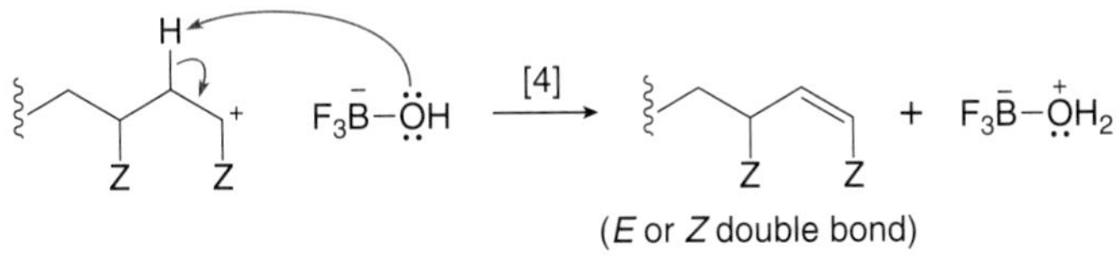
[4]
(*E* or *Z* double bond)

- Loss of a proton forms a new π bond to terminate the chain.

Since cationic polymerization involves carbocations, addition follows Markovnikov's rule to form the more stable, more substituted carbocation. Chain termination can occur by a variety of pathways, such as loss of a proton to form an alkene. Examples of alkene monomers that undergo cationic polymerization are shown in Figure 31.4.

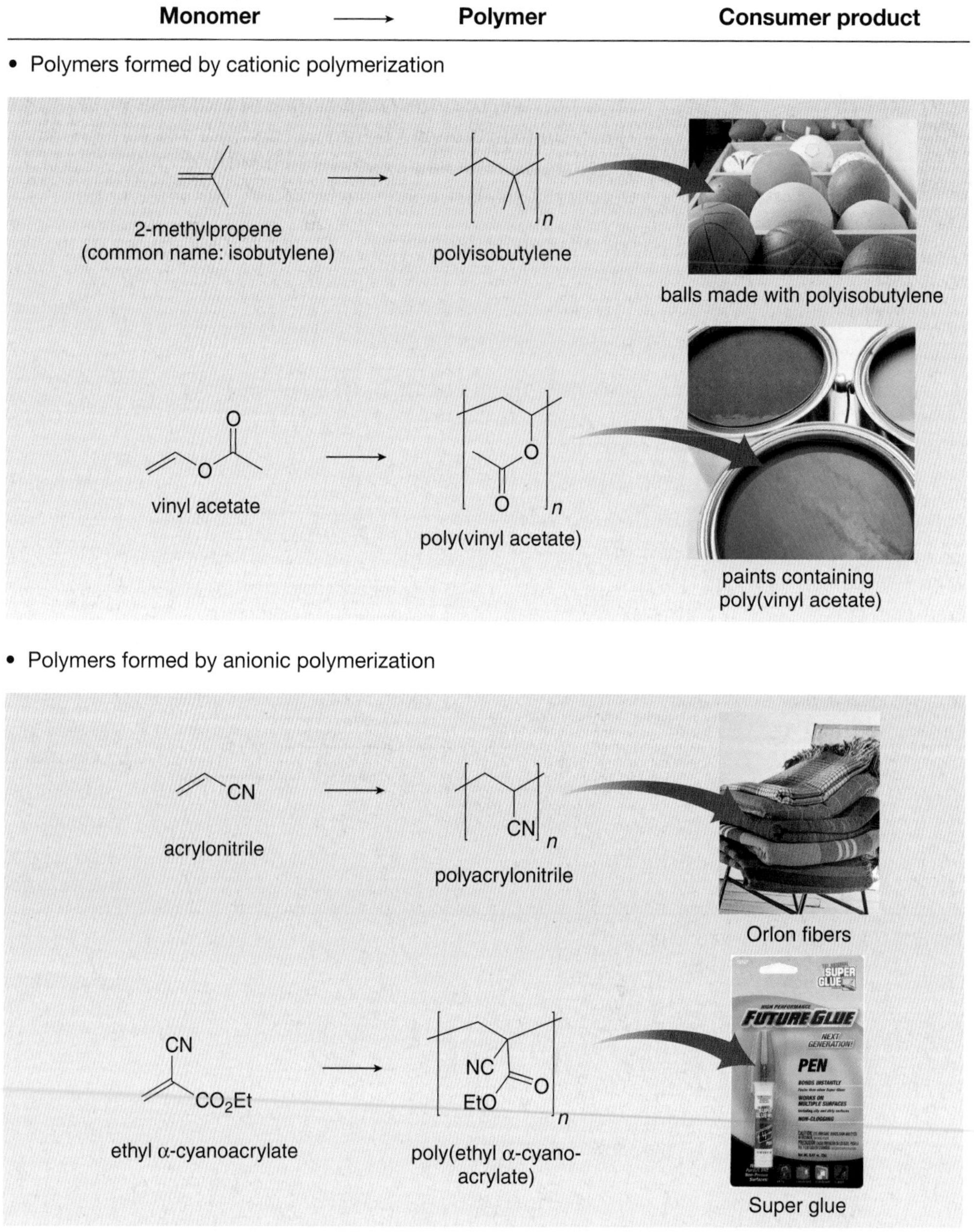
Monomer
Polymer
Consumer product
• Polymers formed by cationic polymerization
2-methylpropene
(common name: isobutylene)
polyisobutylene
balls made with polyisobutylene
vinyl acetate
poly(vinyl acetate)
paints containing poly(vinyl acetate)
• Polymers formed by anionic polymerization
acrylonitrile
polyacrylonitrile
Orlon fibers
ethyl α-cyanoacrylate
poly(ethyl α-cyanoacrylate)
Super glue
FUTURE GLUE
PEN

Figure 31.4 Common polymers formed by ionic chain-growth polymerization

- A chain-growth polymer is named by adding the prefix *poly* to the name of the monomer from which it is made. When the name of the monomer contains two words, this name is enclosed in parentheses and preceded by the prefix *poly.*

Problem 31.6 Explain why cationic polymerization is an effective method of polymerizing $CH_2=C(CH_3)_2$ but not $CH_2=CH_2$.

Although alkenes readily react with electron-deficient radicals and electrophiles, alkenes do not generally react with anions and other nucleophiles. Consequently, **anionic polymerization takes place only with alkene monomers that contain electron-withdrawing groups** such as COR, COOR, or CN, which can stabilize an intermediate negative charge. The initiator is a strong nucleophile, such as an organolithium reagent, RLi. Mechanism 31.4 illustrates anionic polymerization of the general monomer $CH_2=CHZ$.

Mechanism 31.4 Anionic Polymerization of $CH_2=CHZ$

Part [1] Initiation: Formation of a carbanion

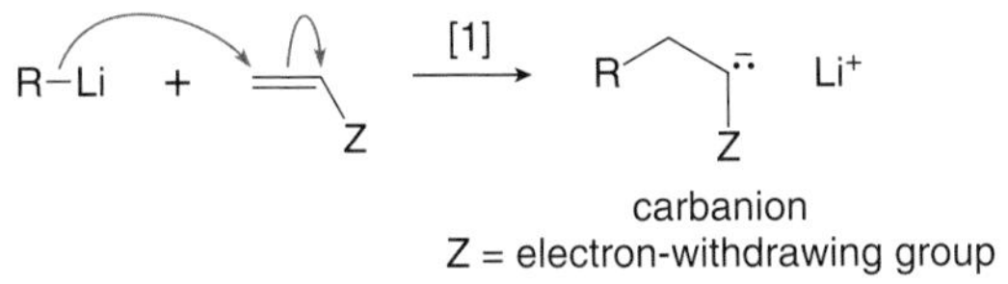

- Nucleophilic addition of RLi forms a carbanion stabilized by an electron-withdrawing group Z.

Part [2] Propagation: Growth of the polymer chain by C–C bond formation

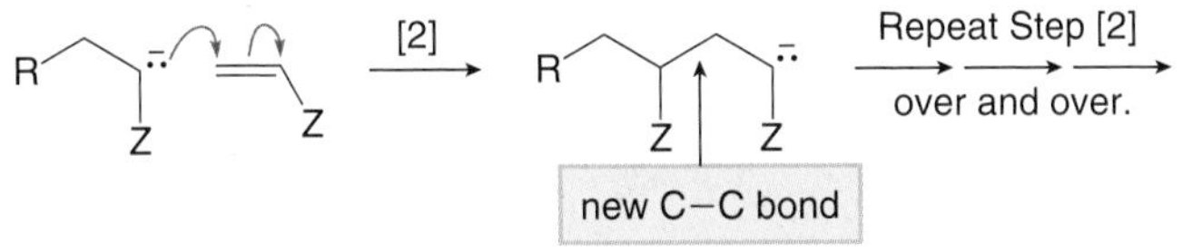

- In Step [2], the carbanion adds to another alkene molecule to form a new C–C bond. Addition always forms a carbanion adjacent to the Z substituent.
- Step [2] occurs repeatedly, thus growing the polymer chain.

Part [3] Termination: Addition of a proton source to stop the chain

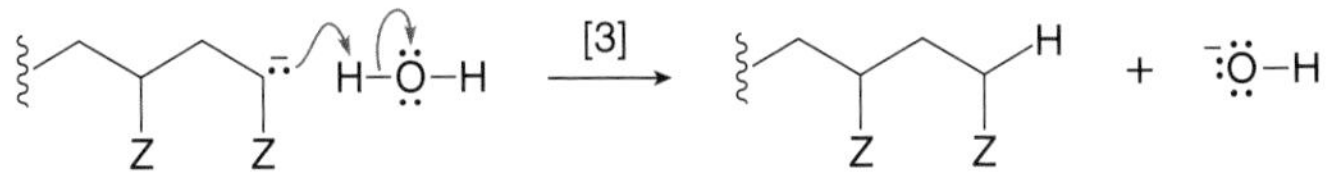

- Addition of H_2O (or another electrophile) terminates the chain by a Brønsted–Lowry acid–base reaction.

In contrast to other types of chain-growth polymerization, there are no efficient methods of terminating the chain mechanism in anionic polymerization. The reaction continues until all the initiator and monomer have been consumed, so that the end of each polymer chain contains a carbanion (Step [2] in Mechanism 31.4). Anionic polymerization is often called **living polymerization** because polymerization will begin again if more monomer is added at this stage. To terminate anionic polymerization an electrophile such as H_2O or CO_2 must be added. Examples of alkene monomers that undergo anionic polymerization are shown in Figure 31.4.

Problem 31.7 Which method of ionic polymerization—cationic or anionic—is preferred for each monomer? Explain your choices.

a. $CH_2=C(CH_3)COOCH_3$ b. $CH_2=CHCH_3$ c. $CH_2=CHOC(CH_3)_3$ d. $CH_2=CHCOCH_3$

Problem 31.8 Draw a stepwise mechanism for the conversion of acrylonitrile ($CH_2=CHC\equiv N$) to polyacrylonitrile, $-[CH_2CHC\equiv N]_n-$, using butyllithium (BuLi) as the initiator and CO_2 as the electrophile to terminate the chain.

Problem 31.9 Explain why styrene ($CH_2=CHPh$) can be polymerized to polystyrene by all three methods of chain-growth polymerization.

31.2D Copolymers

All polymers discussed thus far are **homopolymers,** because they have been prepared by the polymerization of a single monomer. **Copolymers, on the other hand, are polymers prepared by joining two or more monomers (X and Y) together.**

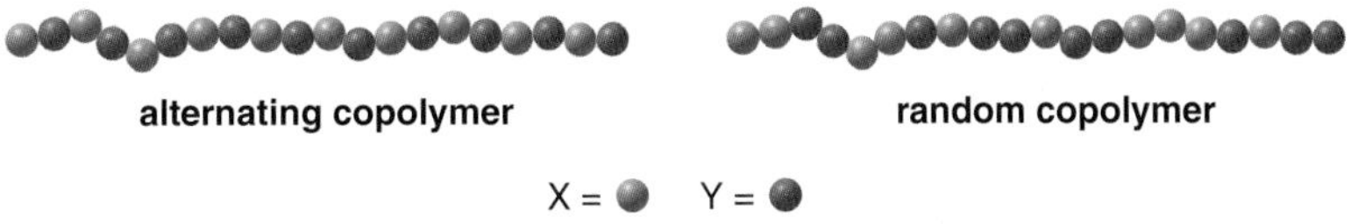

- An *alternating copolymer* is formed when X and Y alternate regularly along the chain.
- A *random copolymer* is formed when X and Y are randomly distributed along the chain.

The structure of the copolymer depends on the relative amount and reactivity of **X** and **Y,** as well as the conditions used for polymerization.

Several copolymers are commercially important and used in a wide range of consumer products. For example, the copolymer of vinyl chloride and vinylidene chloride forms **Saran,** the film used in the well-known plastic food wrap. Copolymerization of 1,3-butadiene and styrene forms **styrene–butadiene rubber (SBR),** the polymer used almost exclusively in automobile tires.

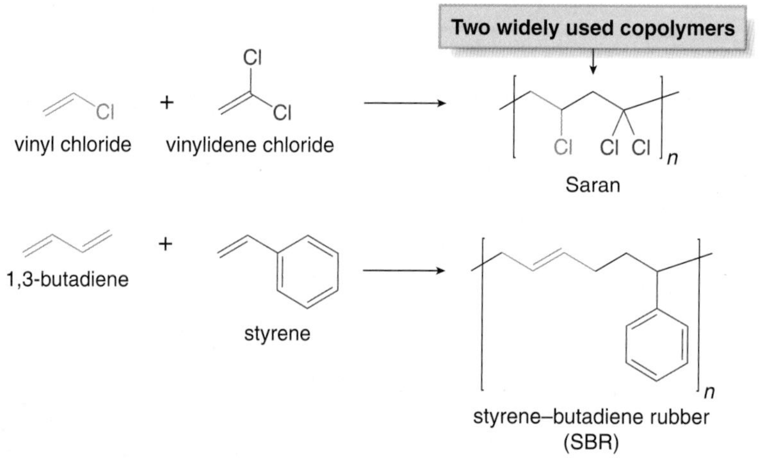

Problem 31.10 Draw the alternating copolymer formed from each set of monomers.

a. $CH_2=CHPh$ and $CH_2=CHCN$ b. $F_2C=CFCF_3$ and $CH_2=CF_2$

Problem 31.11 Draw the mechanism for the radical copolymerization of $CH_2=CHCH=CH_2$ and $CH_2=CHPh$ to form styrene–butadiene rubber, $-[CH_2CH=CHCH_2CH_2CHPh]_n-$.

31.3 Anionic Polymerization of Epoxides

Alkene monomers are the most common starting materials in chain-growth polymerizations, but epoxides can also serve as starting materials, forming **polyethers.** The strained three-membered ring of an epoxide is readily opened with a nucleophile (such as ^-OH or ^-OR) to form an alkoxide, which can then ring open another epoxide monomer to build the polymer chain. Unlike the other methods of chain-growth polymerization that join monomers together with C–C bonds, this process forms **new C–O bonds** in the polymer backbone.

For example, the ring opening of ethylene oxide with a ^-OH initiator affords an alkoxide nucleophile, which propagates the chain by reacting with more ethylene oxide. This process yields **poly(ethylene glycol), PEG,** a polymer used in lotions and creams. The many C–O bonds in these polymers make them highly water soluble.

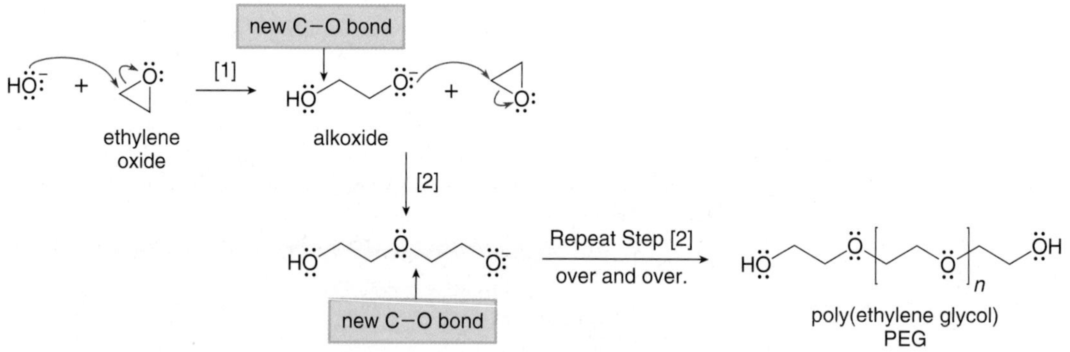

The ring opening of epoxides with nucleophiles was first discussed in Section 9.15.

Under anionic conditions, the ring opening follows an S_N2 mechanism. Thus, the ring opening of an unsymmetrical epoxide occurs at the more accessible, less substituted carbon.

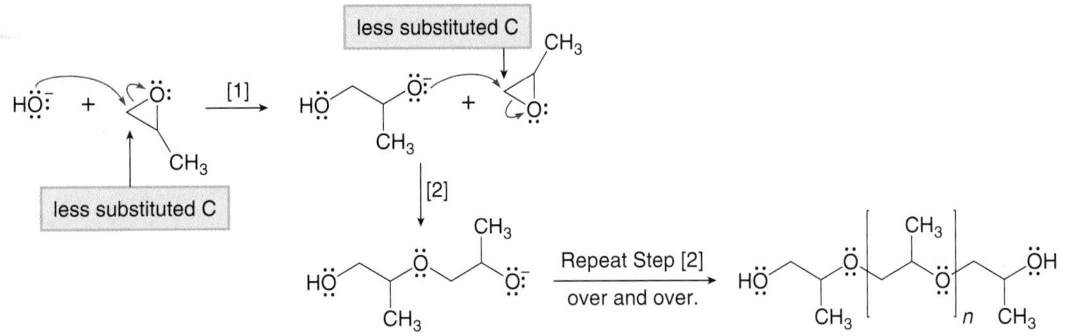

Problem 31.12 What polymer is formed by anionic polymerization of each monomer?

a. 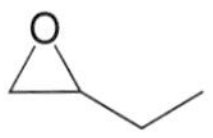 b. 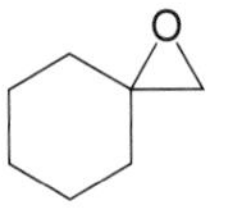

31.4 Ziegler–Natta Catalysts and Polymer Stereochemistry

Polymers prepared from monosubstituted alkene monomers ($CH_2{=}CHZ$) can exist in three different configurations, called **isotactic, syndiotactic,** and **atactic:**

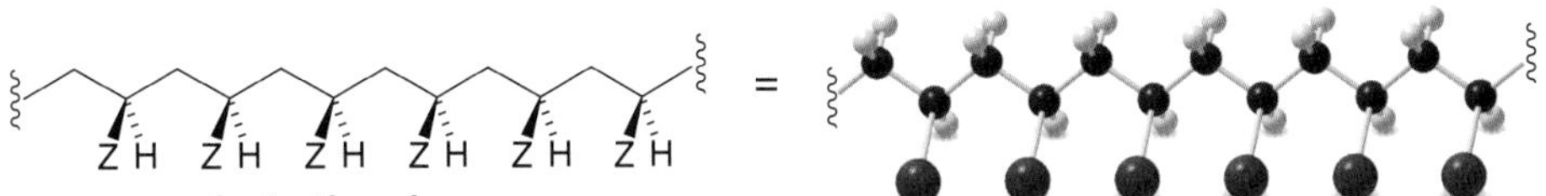

isotactic polymer

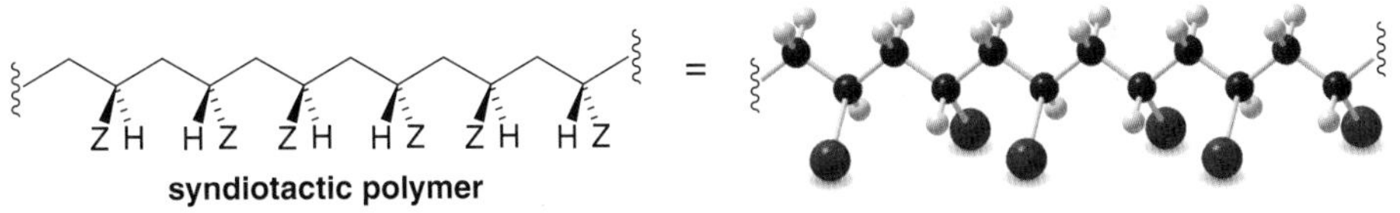

syndiotactic polymer

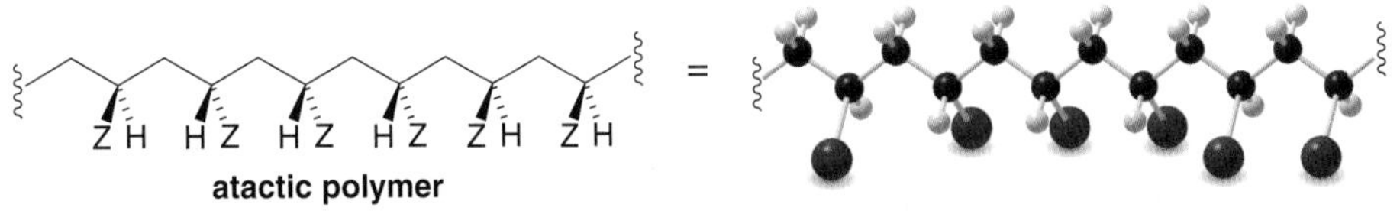

atactic polymer

- An *isotactic* polymer has all Z groups on the same side of the carbon backbone.
- A *syndiotactic* polymer has the Z groups alternating from one side of the carbon chain to the other.
- An *atactic* polymer has the Z groups oriented randomly along the polymer chain.

The more regular arrangement of the Z substituents in isotactic and syndiotactic polymers allows them to pack together better, making the polymer stronger and more rigid. In contrast, the chains of an atactic polymer tend to pack less closely together, resulting in a lower melting, softer polymer. Radical polymerization often affords an atactic polymer, but the particular reaction conditions can greatly affect the stereochemistry of the polymer formed.

In 1953, Karl Ziegler and Giulio Natta developed a new method of polymerizing alkene monomers using a metal catalyst to promote chain-growth polymerization. These catalysts, now called **Ziegler–Natta catalysts,** offer two advantages over other methods of chain-growth polymerization.

- **The stereochemistry of the polymer is easily controlled. Polymerization affords isotactic, syndiotactic, or atactic polymers depending on the catalyst.**
- **Long, linear chains of polymer are prepared without significant branching. Radicals are not formed as reactive intermediates, so intermolecular hydrogen abstraction, which leads to chain branching, does not occur.**

Ziegler and Natta received the 1963 Nobel Prize in Chemistry for their pioneering work on polymerization catalysts.

Many different Ziegler–Natta catalysts are used for polymerization, but most consist of an organoaluminum compound such as $(CH_3CH_2)_2AlCl$ and $TiCl_4$, a Lewis acid. The active catalyst is thought to be an alkyl titanium compound, formed by transfer of an ethyl group from $(CH_3CH_2)_2AlCl$ to $TiCl_4$, although many mechanistic details are not known with certainty. It is generally agreed that the alkene monomer coordinates to an alkyl titanium complex, and then inserts into the Ti–C bond to form a new carbon–carbon bond, as shown in Mechanism 31.5.

Mechanism 31.5 Ziegler–Natta Polymerization of $CH_2=CH_2$

Step [1] Formation of the catalyst

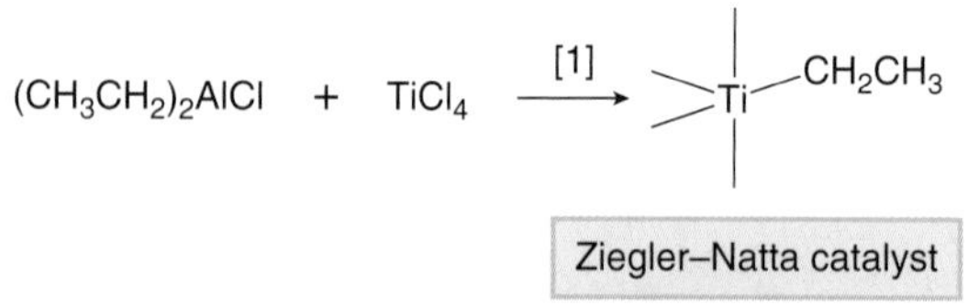
(CH3CH2)2AlCl
+
TiCl4
[1]
Ti
CH2CH3
Ziegler–Natta catalyst

- Reaction of the organoaluminum compound with $TiCl_4$ forms a Ziegler–Natta catalyst with a Ti–C bond.

Steps [2] and [3] Growth of the polymer chain by C–C bond formation

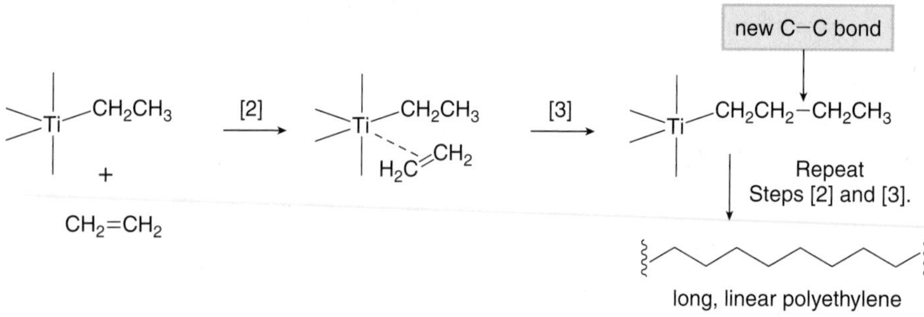
Ti
CH2CH3
+
CH2=CH2
[2]
H2C
CH2
[3]
new C–C bond
CH2CH2–CH2CH3
Repeat
Steps [2] and [3].
long, linear polyethylene

- An alkene monomer coordinates with the titanium catalyst in Step [2].
- Insertion of $CH_2=CH_2$ into the Ti–C bond forms a new C–C bond in Step [3].
- Repeating Steps [2] and [3] again and again yields the long polymer chain.

Dyneema, the strongest fabric known, is made of ultra high-density polyethylene, and is used for ropes, nets, bulletproof vests, and crash helmets.

The Ziegler–Natta polymerization of ethylene forms **high-density polyethylene, HDPE,** composed of long linear carbon chains that pack closely together, forming a rigid polymer. By using specialized manufacturing techniques that force the polymer chains to pack closely in the solid phase as a set of linear extended chains, this material is converted to ultra high-density polyethylene, a synthetic organic material stronger than steel.

Recently developed Ziegler–Natta polymerizations utilize zirconium complexes that are soluble in the reaction solvents typically used, and so they are **homogeneous catalysts.** Reactions that use these soluble catalysts are called **coordination polymerizations.**

31.5 Natural and Synthetic Rubbers

Locating isoprene units in terpenes was discussed in Section 30.7.

Natural rubber is a terpene composed of repeating isoprene units, in which all the double bonds have the *Z* configuration. Because natural rubber is a hydrocarbon, it is water insoluble, and thus useful for waterproofing. The *Z* double bonds cause bends and kinks in the polymer chain, making it a soft material.

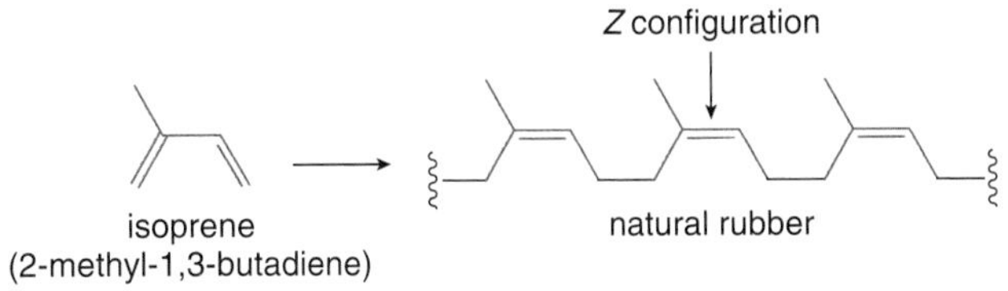

Natural rubber is obtained from latex that oozes from cuts made to the bark of the rubber tree. Waterproof latex is the rubber tree's natural protection, exuded in response to an injury. Although rubber was produced exclusively in Brazil until the late 1800s, today most of the world's rubber comes from plantations in Southeast Asia, Sri Lanka, and Indonesia.

The polymerization of isoprene under radical conditions forms a stereoisomer of natural rubber called **gutta-percha,** in which all the double bonds have the *E* configuration. Gutta-percha is also a naturally occurring polymer, although considerably less common than its *Z* stereoisomer. Polymerization of isoprene with a Ziegler–Natta catalyst forms natural rubber with all the double bonds having the desired *Z* configuration.

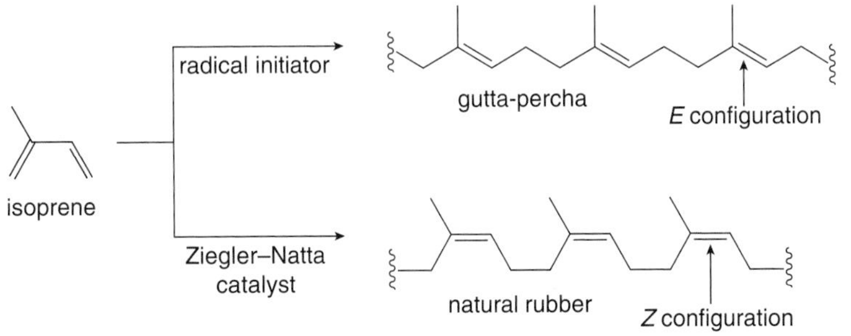

Natural rubber is too soft to be a useful material for most applications. Moreover, when natural rubber is stretched, the chains become elongated and slide past each other until the material pulls apart. In 1839, Charles Goodyear discovered that mixing hot rubber with sulfur produced a stronger and more elastic material. This process, called **vulcanization,** results in cross-linking of the hydrocarbon chains by disulfide bonds, as shown in Figure 31.5. When the polymer is stretched, the chains no longer can slide past each other and tearing does not occur. Vulcanized rubber is an ***elastomer,* a polymer that stretches when stressed but then returns to its original shape when the stress is alleviated.**

Figure 31.5
Vulcanized rubber

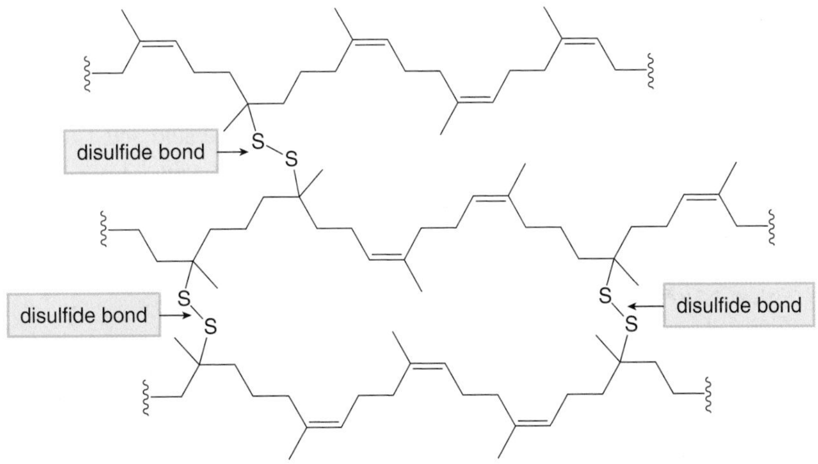

- Vulcanized rubber contains many disulfide bonds that cross-link the hydrocarbon chains together.

Gutta-percha, a much harder material than natural rubber obtained from latex, is used in golf ball casings.

The degree of cross-linking affects the rubber's properties. Harder rubber used for automobile tires has more cross-linking than the softer rubber used for rubber bands.

Other synthetic rubbers can be prepared by the polymerization of different 1,3-dienes using Ziegler–Natta catalysts. For example, the polymerization of 1,3-butadiene affords (*Z*)-poly(1,3-butadiene), and the polymerization of 2-chloro-1,3-butadiene yields neoprene, a polymer used in wet suits and tires.

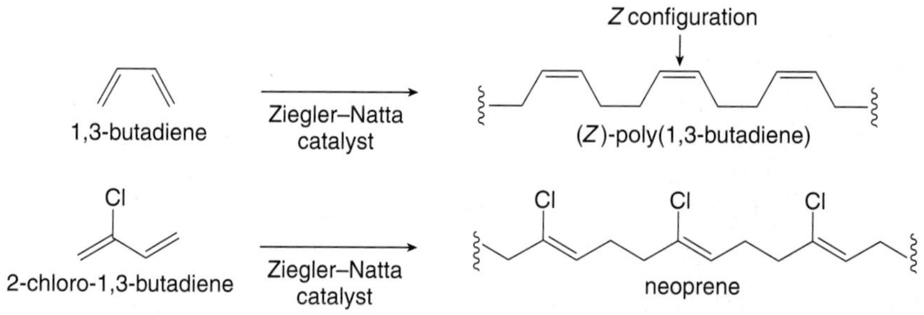

Problem 31.13 Assign the *E* or *Z* configuration to the double bonds in neoprene. Draw a stereoisomer of neoprene in which all the double bonds have the opposite configuration.

Problem 31.14 The polymerization of $CH_2{=}CHCH{=}CH_2$ under radical conditions affords products **A** and **B.** Draw a mechanism that accounts for their formation.

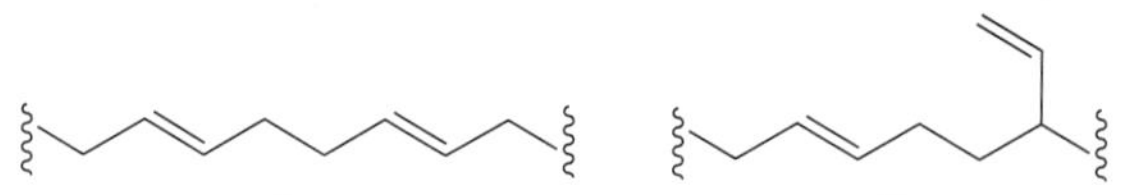

A **B**

31.6 Step-Growth Polymers—Condensation Polymers

Step-growth polymers, the second major class of polymers, are formed when monomers containing two functional groups come together and lose a small molecule such as H_2O or HCl. Commercially important step-growth polymers include:

- **Polyamides**
- **Polyesters**
- **Polyurethanes**
- **Polycarbonates**
- **Epoxy resins**

31.6A Polyamides

Nylon 6,6 is used in many products including parachutes and clothing.

Nylons are polyamides formed by step-growth polymerization. In Section 22.16A, we learned that **nylon 6,6** can be prepared by the reaction of a diacid chloride and a diamine. Nylon 6,6 can also be prepared by heating adipic acid and 1,6-diaminohexane. A Brønsted–Lowry acid–base reaction forms a diammonium salt, which loses H_2O at high temperature. In both methods, each starting material has two identical functional groups.

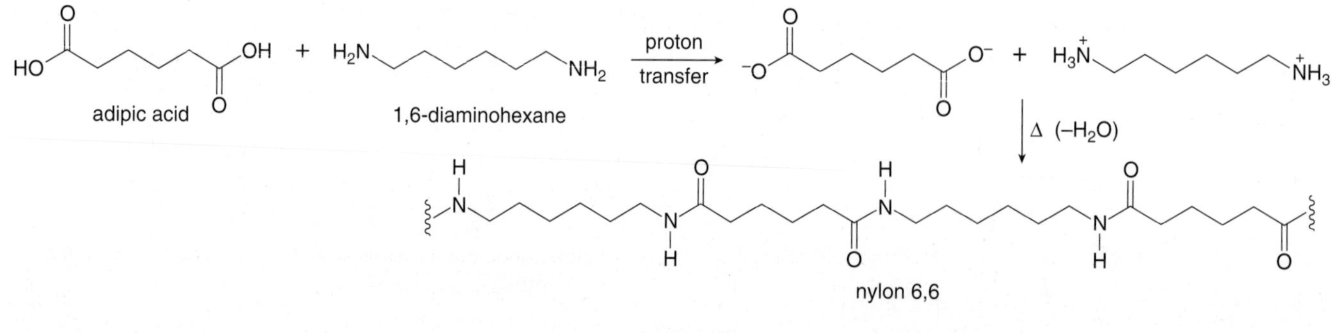

Nylon 6, trade name **Perlon,** is used to make rope and tire cord.

Nylon 6 is another polyamide, which is made by heating an aqueous solution of ε-caprolactam. The seven-membered ring of the lactam (a cyclic amide) is opened to form 6-aminohexanoic acid, the monomer that reacts with more lactam to form the polyamide chain. This step-growth polymerization thus begins with a single difunctional monomer that has two *different* functional groups, NH_2 and COOH.

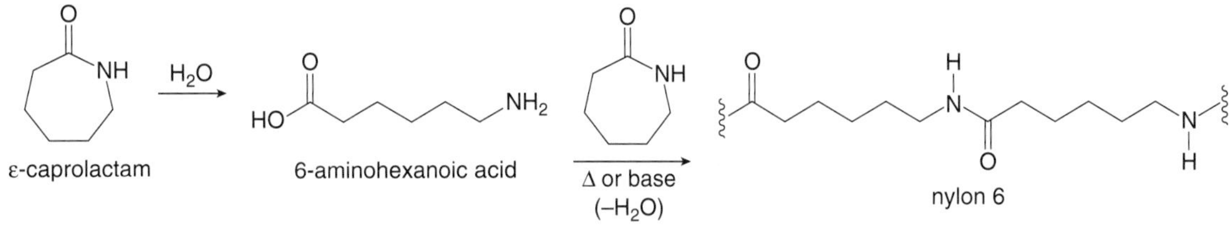
ε-caprolactam
H2O
6-aminohexanoic acid
Δ or base
(–H2O)
nylon 6

ARMADILLO TECHNOLOGY
Armadillo bicycle tires reinforced with Kevlar are hard to pierce with sharp objects, so a cyclist rarely gets a flat tire.

Kevlar is a polyamide formed from terephthalic acid and 1,4-diaminobenzene. The aromatic rings of the polymer backbone make the chains less flexible, resulting in a very strong material. Kevlar is light in weight compared to other materials that are similar in strength, so it is used in many products, such as bulletproof vests, army helmets, and the protective clothing used by firefighters.

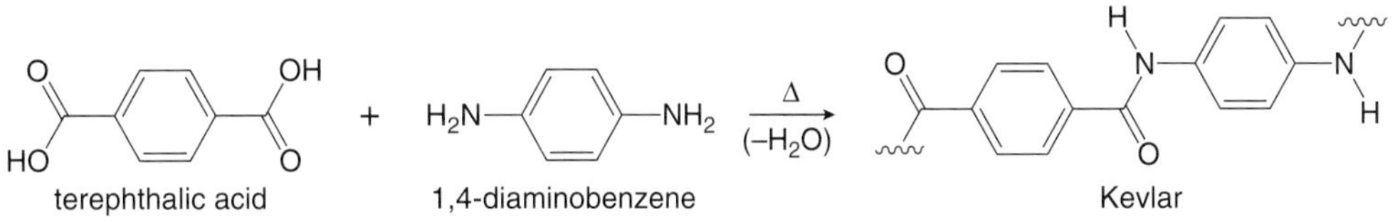
terephthalic acid
1,4-diaminobenzene
Δ
(–H2O)
Kevlar

Problem 31.15 What polyamide is formed from each monomer or pair of monomers?

a. 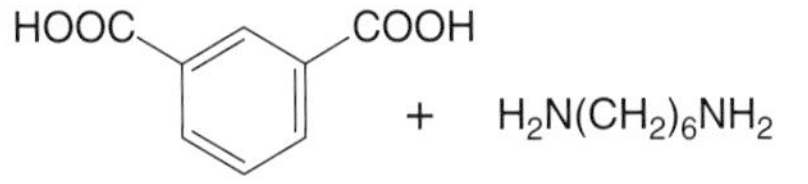
+ H2N(CH2)6NH2

b. 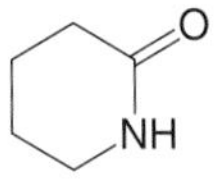

c. 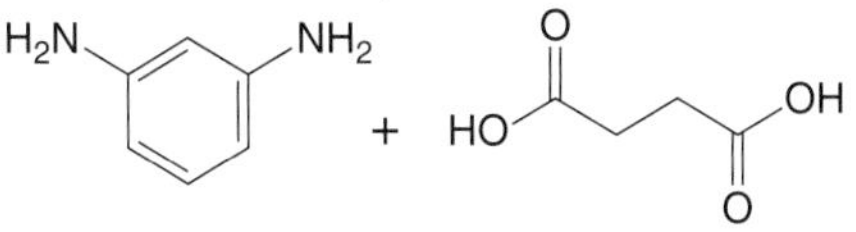

31.6B Polyesters

Polyesters are formed by step-growth polymerization using nucleophilic acyl substitution reactions, as we learned in Section 22.16B. For example, the reaction of terephthalic acid and ethylene glycol forms **polyethylene terephthalate (PET),** the chapter-opening molecule.

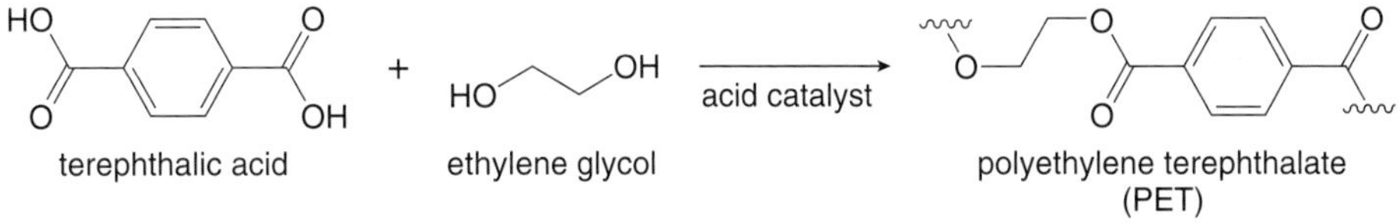
terephthalic acid
ethylene glycol
acid catalyst
polyethylene terephthalate
(PET)

Although PET is a very stable material, some polyesters are more readily hydrolyzed to carboxylic acids and alcohols in aqueous medium, making them suited for applications in which slow degradation is useful. For example, copolymerization of glycolic acid and lactic acid forms a copolymer used by surgeons in dissolving sutures. Within weeks, the copolymer is hydrolyzed to the monomers from which it was prepared, which are metabolized readily by the body. These sutures are used internally to hold tissues together while healing and scar formation occur.

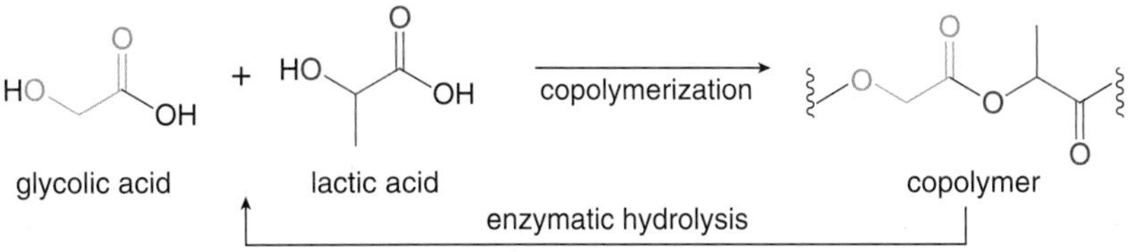
glycolic acid
lactic acid
copolymerization
copolymer
enzymatic hydrolysis

Problem 31.16 Polyethylene terephthalate is also prepared by the transesterification of dimethyl terephthalate with ethylene glycol. Draw the mechanism for this nucleophilic acyl substitution.

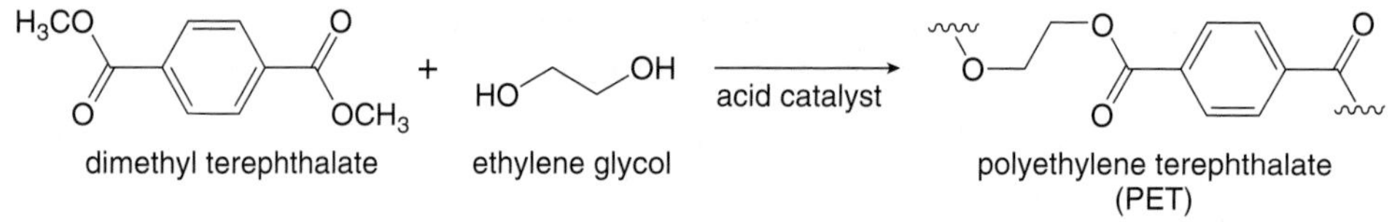

Problem 31.17 The first synthetic fibers were prepared by the step-growth polymerization of $HOOC(CH_2)_4COOH$ and $HOCH_2CH_2OH$. Draw the structure of this polymer and suggest reasons why it is less suitable than either nylon 6,6 or PET for use in consumer products.

31.6C Polyurethanes

A **urethane** (also called a **carbamate**) is a compound that contains a carbonyl group bonded to both an OR group and an NHR (or NR_2) group (Section 29.7). Urethanes are prepared by the nucleophilic addition of an alcohol to the carbonyl group of an **isocyanate, RN=C=O.**

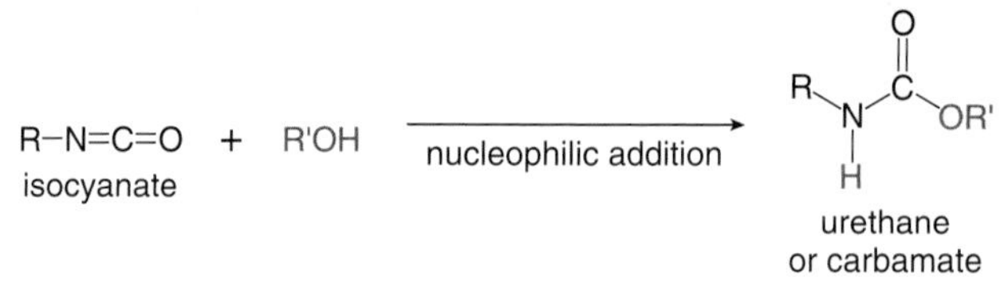

Polyurethanes are polymers formed by the reaction of a diisocyanate and a diol.

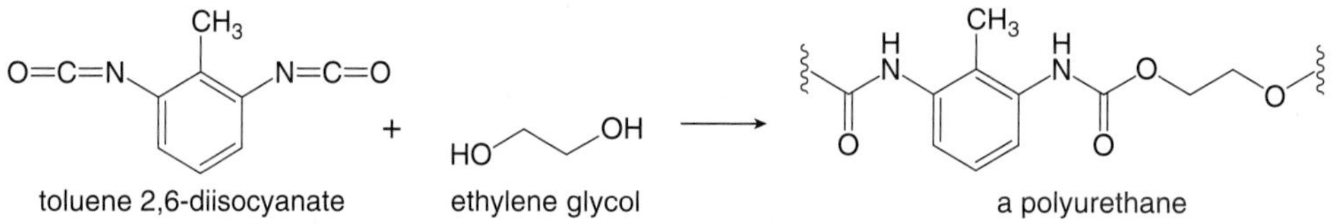

A well-known polyurethane is **spandex,** a strong and flexible polymer that illustrates how the macroscopic properties of a polymer depend on its structure at the molecular level. Spandex was first used in women's corsets, girdles, and support hose, but is now routinely used in both men's and women's active wear. Spandex is strong and lends "support" to the wearer, but it also stretches. Spandex is lighter in weight than many other elastic polymers, and it does not break down when exposed to perspiration and detergents. On the molecular level, it has rigid regions that are joined together by soft, flexible segments. The flexible regions allow the polymer to expand and then recover its original shape. The rigid regions strengthen the polymer.

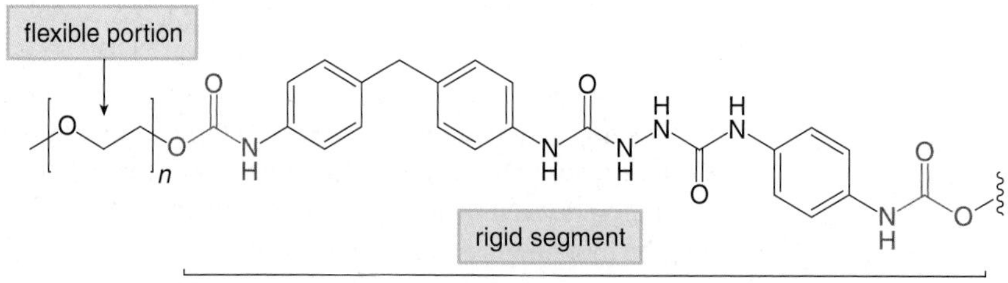

spandex
Trade name: **Lycra**
[The urethane units are indicated in red.]

31.6D Polycarbonates

Although it is not acutely toxic, bisphenol A (BPA) mimics the body's own hormones and disrupts normal endocrine functions. Concern over low-dose exposure by infants has led to a voluntary phase-out of BPA-based polymers in infant formula packaging.

A **carbonate** is a compound that contains a carbonyl group bonded to two OR groups. Carbonates can be prepared by the reaction of phosgene ($Cl_2C{=}O$) with two equivalents of an alcohol (ROH).

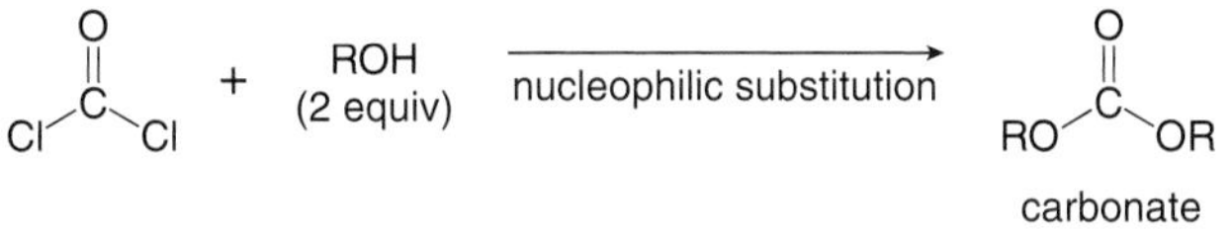

Polycarbonates are formed from phosgene and a diol. The most widely used polycarbonate is **Lexan,** a lightweight, transparent material that is formed from phosgene and bisphenol A, and used in bike helmets, goggles, catcher's masks, and bulletproof glass.

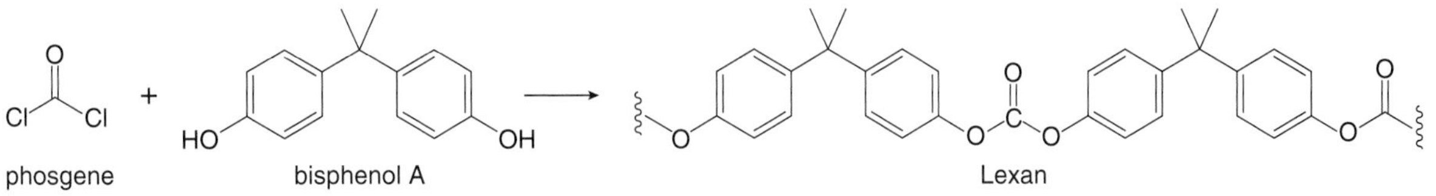

Problem 31.18 Lexan can also be prepared by the acid-catalyzed reaction of diphenyl carbonate with bisphenol A. Draw a stepwise mechanism for this process.

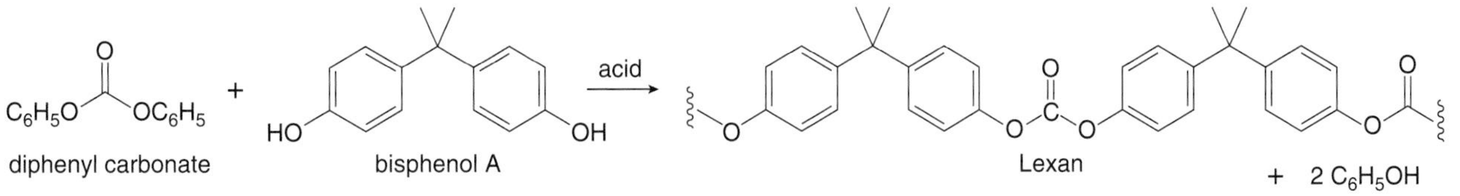

31.6E Epoxy Resins

Epoxy resins represent a class of step-growth polymer familiar to anyone who has used "epoxy" to glue together a broken object. An epoxy resin consists of two components: a fluid **prepolymer** composed of short polymer chains with reactive epoxides on each end, and a **hardener,** usually a diamine or triamine that ring opens the epoxides and cross-links the chains together. The prepolymer is formed by reacting two difunctional monomers, bisphenol A and epichlorohydrin.

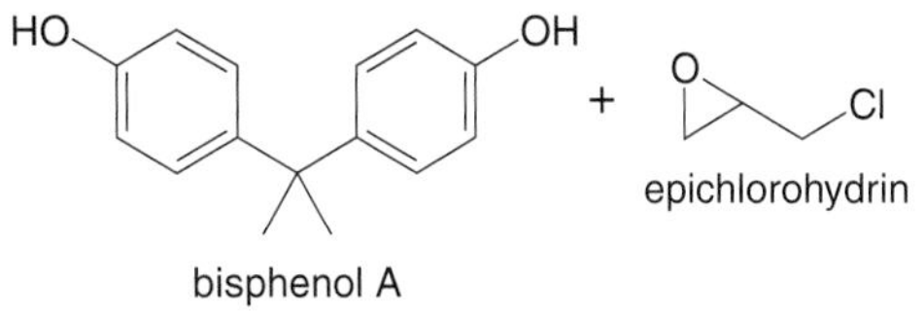

Bisphenol A has two nucleophilic OH groups, while epichlorohydrin has polar C–O and C–Cl bonds that can react with two different nucleophiles. The general reaction of epichlorohydrin with nucleophiles is given in the accompanying equation. Nucleophilic attack on the strained epoxide ring affords an alkoxide that displaces chloride by an intramolecular S_N2 reaction, forming a new epoxide. Ring opening with a second nucleophile gives a 2° alcohol.

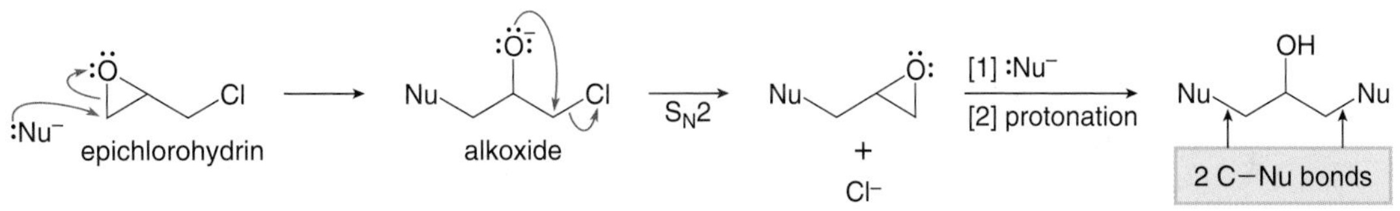

Figure 31.6 Formation of an epoxy resin from a prepolymer and a hardening agent

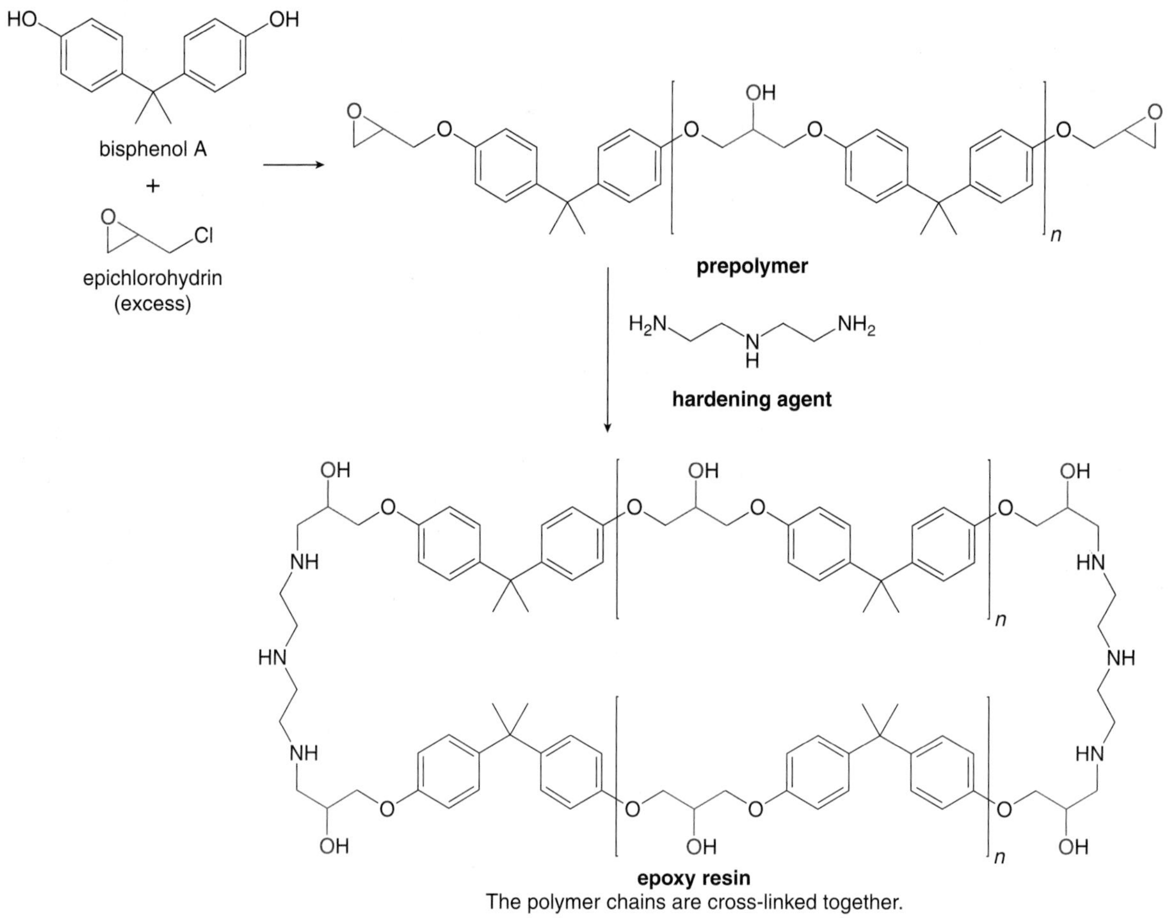

When bisphenol A is treated with excess epichlorohydrin, this stepwise process continues until all the phenolic OH groups have been used in ring-opening reactions, leaving epoxy groups on both ends of the polymer chains. This constitutes the fluid **prepolymer,** as shown in Figure 31.6.

When the prepolymer is mixed with a diamine or triamine (the **hardener**), the reactive epoxide rings can be opened by the nucleophilic amino groups to cross-link polymer chains together, causing the polymer to harden. A wide range of epoxy resins is commercially prepared by this process, making them useful for adhesives and coatings. The longer and more extensively cross-linked the polymer chains, the harder the resin.

Problem 31.19 (a) Draw the structure of the prepolymer **A** formed from 1,4-dihydroxybenzene and excess epichlorohydrin. (b) Draw the structure of the cross-linked polymer **B** formed when **A** is treated with $H_2NCH_2CH_2CH_2NH_2$ as the hardening agent.

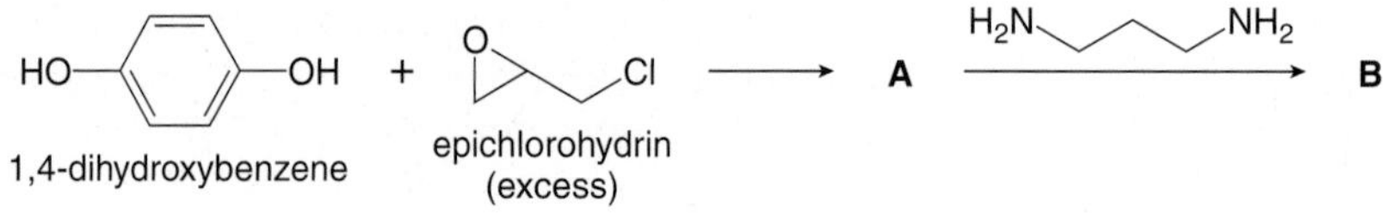

31.7 Polymer Structure and Properties

While the chemistry of polymer synthesis can be explained by the usual themes of organic reactions, the large size of polymer molecules gives them some unique physical properties compared to small organic molecules.

Linear and branched polymers do not form crystalline solids because their long chains prevent efficient packing in a crystal lattice. Most polymer chains have **crystalline regions** and **amorphous regions:**

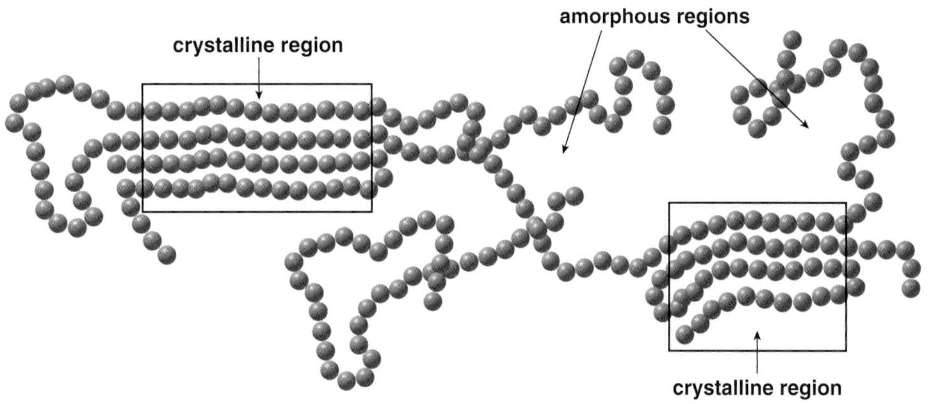

- **Ordered crystalline regions,** called **crystallites,** are places where sections of the polymer chain lie in close proximity and are held together by intermolecular interactions. Ordered regions of polyethylene, $-[CH_2CH_2]_n-$, are held together by van der Waals interactions, whereas ordered regions of nylon chains are held together by intermolecular hydrogen bonding.
- **Amorphous regions** are places where the polymer chains are randomly arranged, resulting in weak intermolecular interactions.

Crystalline regions impart toughness to a polymer, while amorphous regions impart flexibility. The greater the crystallinity of a polymer—that is, the larger the percentage of ordered regions—the harder the polymer. Branched polymers are generally more amorphous and, since branching prevents chains from packing closely, they are softer, too.

Two temperatures, T_g and T_m, often characterize a polymer's behavior on heating:

- **T_g, the glass transition temperature, is the temperature at which a hard amorphous polymer becomes soft.**
- **T_m, the melt transition temperature, is the temperature at which the crystalline regions of the polymer melt to become amorphous. More ordered polymers have higher T_m values.**

Thermoplastics are polymers that can be melted and then molded into shapes that are retained when the polymer is cooled. Although they have high T_g values and are hard at room temperature, heating causes individual polymer chains to slip past each other, causing the material to soften. Polyethylene terephthalate and polystyrene are thermoplastic polymers.

Thermosetting polymers are complex networks of cross-linked polymers. Thermosetting polymers are formed by chemical reactions that occur when monomers are heated together to form a network of covalent bonds. Thermosetting polymers cannot be re-melted to form a liquid phase, because covalent bonds hold the network together. **Bakelite,** a thermosetting polymer prepared from phenol (PhOH) and formaldehyde ($H_2C{=}O$) in the presence of a Lewis acid, is formed by

Figure 31.7
The synthesis of Bakelite from phenol and formaldehyde

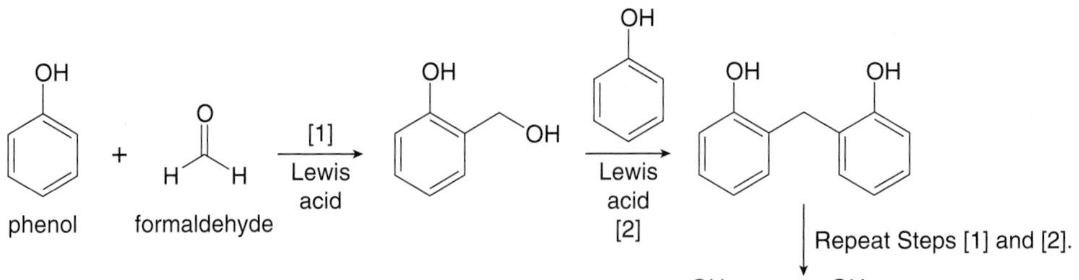

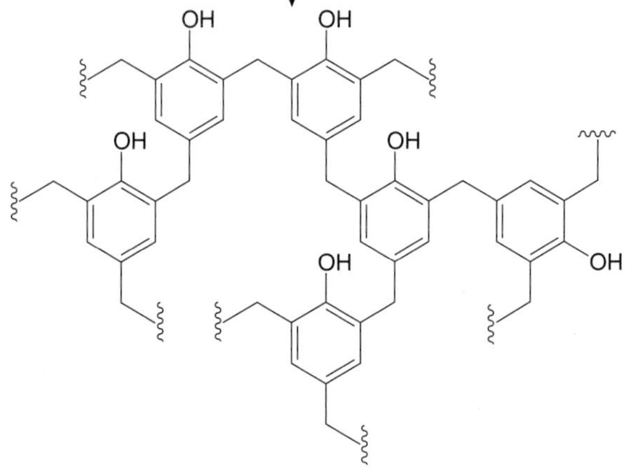

Bakelite

- Bakelite, the first totally synthetic polymeric material, was patented by Leo Baekeland in 1910. Bowling balls are made of Bakelite.

electrophilic aromatic substitution reactions. Since formaldehyde is a reactive electrophile and phenol contains a strongly electron-donating OH group, substitution occurs at all ortho and para positions to the OH group, resulting in a highly cross-linked polymer, shown in Figure 31.7.

Problem 31.20 Draw a stepwise mechanism for Step [2] in Figure 31.7 using $AlCl_3$ as the Lewis acid catalyst.

Sometimes a polymer is too stiff and brittle to be useful in many applications. In this case, a low molecular weight compound called a **plasticizer** is added to soften the polymer and give it flexibility. The plasticizer interacts with the polymer chains, replacing some of the intermolecular interactions between the polymer chains. This lowers the crystallinity of the polymer, making it more amorphous and softer.

Dibutyl phthalate is a plasticizer added to the poly(vinyl chloride) used in vinyl upholstery and garden hoses. Since plasticizers are more volatile than the high molecular weight polymers, they slowly evaporate with time, making the polymer brittle and easily cracked. Plasticizers like dibutyl phthalate that contain hydrolyzable functional groups are also slowly degraded by chemical reactions.

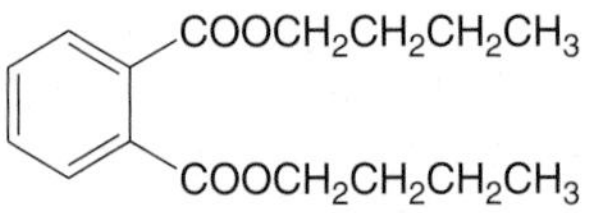

dibutyl phthalate

31.8 Green Polymer Synthesis

One hundred fifty years ago there were no chemical manufacturing plants and no synthetic polymers, and petroleum had little value. Synthetic polymers have transformed the daily lives of many in the modern world, but not without a hefty price. Polymer synthesis and disposal have a tremendous impact on the environment, creating two central issues:

- **Where do polymers come from?** What raw materials are used for polymer synthesis and what environmental consequences result from their manufacture?
- **What happens to polymers once they are used?** How does polymer disposal affect the environment, and what can be done to minimize its negative impact?

31.8A Environmentally Friendly Polymer Synthesis—The Feedstock

In Chapter 12, you were introduced to **green chemistry,** the use of environmentally benign methods to synthesize compounds. Given the billions of pounds of polymers manufactured worldwide each year, there is an obvious need for methods that minimize the environmental impact.

Recall from Section 4.7 that 3% of a barrel of crude oil is used as the feedstock for chemical synthesis.

To date, green polymer synthesis has been approached in a variety of ways:

- **Using starting materials that are derived from renewable sources, rather than petroleum. The starting materials for an industrial process are often called the chemical *feedstock*.**
- **Using safer, less toxic reagents that form fewer by-products.**
- **Carrying out reactions in the absence of solvent or in aqueous solution (instead of an organic solvent).**

Until recently, **the feedstock for all polymer synthesis has been petroleum;** that is, the monomers for virtually all polymer syntheses are made from crude oil, a nonrenewable raw material. As an example, nylon 6,6 is prepared industrially from adipic acid [$HOOC(CH_2)_4COOH$] and 1,6-diaminohexane [$H_2N(CH_2)_6NH_2$], both of which originate from benzene, a product of petroleum refining (Figure 31.8).

Figure 31.8

Synthesis of adipic acid and 1,6-diaminohexane for nylon 6,6 synthesis

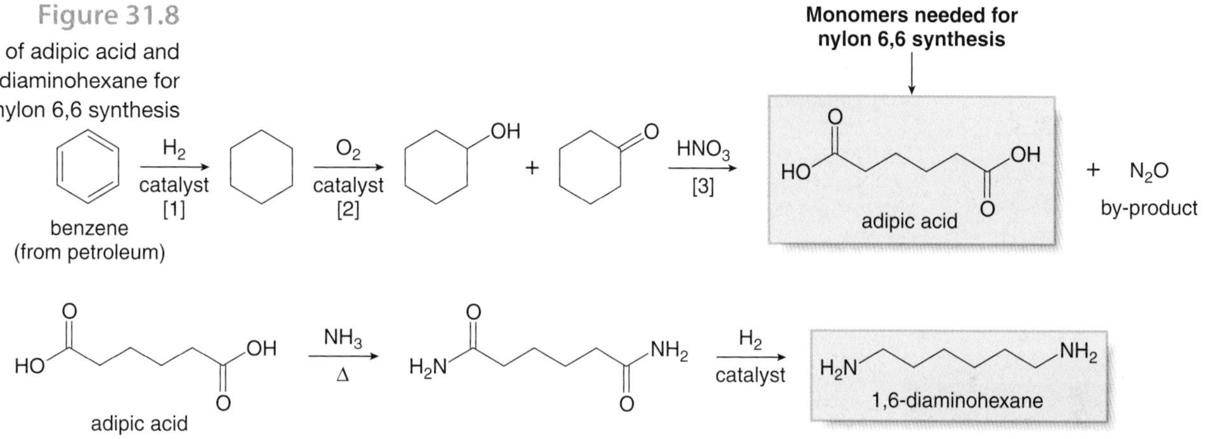

- The synthesis of both monomers needed for nylon 6,6 synthesis begins with benzene, a petroleum product.

Besides beginning with a nonrenewable chemical feedstock, adipic acid synthesis has other problems. The use of benzene, a carcinogen and liver toxin, is undesirable, especially in a large-scale reaction. Moreover, oxidation with HNO_3 in Step [3] produces N_2O as a by-product. N_2O depletes ozone in the stratosphere in much the same way as the CFCs discussed in Chapter 15. In addition, N_2O also absorbs thermal energy from the earth's surface like CO_2, and may therefore contribute to global climate change, as discussed in Section 4.14.

As a result, several research groups are working to develop new methods of monomer synthesis that begin with renewable, more environmentally friendly raw materials and produce fewer hazardous by-products. As an example, chemists at Michigan State University have devised a two-step synthesis of adipic acid from D-glucose, a monosaccharide available from plant sources. The synthesis uses a genetically altered *E. coli* strain (called a **biocatalyst**) to convert D-glucose to (2*Z*,4*Z*)-2,4-hexadienoic acid, which is then hydrogenated to adipic acid. Methods such as this, which avoid starting materials derived from petroleum, are receiving a great deal of attention in the chemical community.

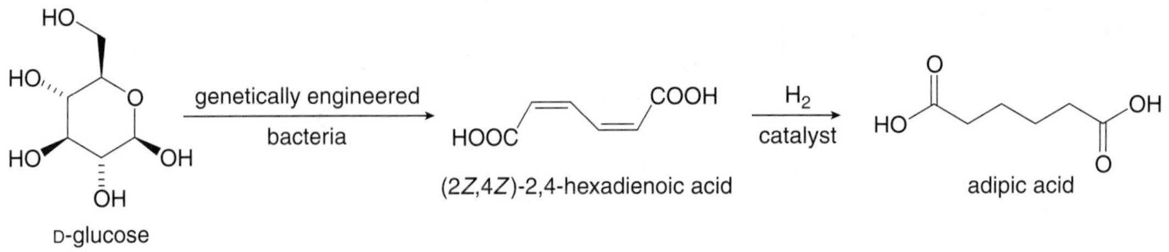

Sorona, DuPont's trade name for **poly(trimethylene terephthalate),** is a large-volume polymer that can now be made at least in part from glucose derived from a renewable plant source such as corn. A biocatalyst converts D-glucose to 1,3-propanediol, which forms poly(trimethylene terephthalate) (PTT) on reaction with terephthalic acid, as shown in Figure 31.9.

In related chemistry, poly(lactic acid) (PLA) is a polymer used in bottles and packaging, and it can also be made into a synthetic fiber (trade name Ingeo) used in clothing and carpets. Poly(lactic acid) is prepared on a large scale by the fermentation of carbohydrates obtained from corn. Fermentation initially yields a cyclic lactone called lactide, derived from two molecules of lactic acid [$CH_3CH(OH)CO_2H$]. Heating lactide with acid forms poly(lactic acid). PLA is an especially attractive polymer choice, because it readily degrades in a landfill.

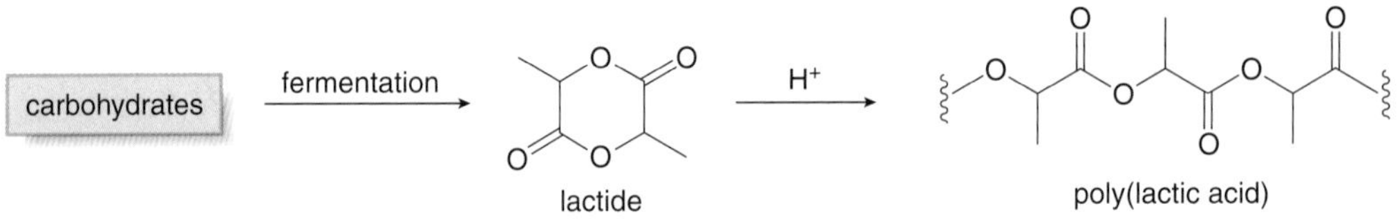

Figure 31.9 A swimsuit made (in part) from corn—The synthesis of poly(trimethylene terephthalate) from 1,3-propanediol derived from corn

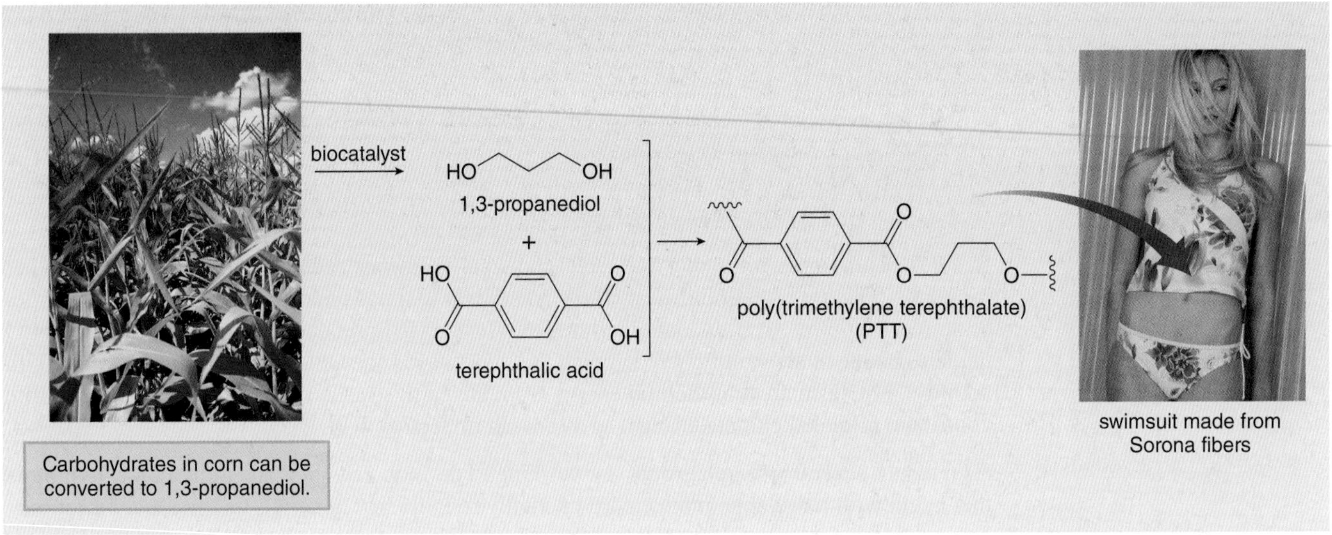

- Poly(trimethylene terephthalate), sold as Sorona by the DuPont Corporation, is made into fibers used in clothing and other materials. Although 1,3-propanediol, one of the monomers needed for its synthesis, has been prepared from petroleum feedstocks in the past, it is now available from a renewable plant source such as corn.

31.8B Polymer Synthesis with Less Hazardous Reagents

Other approaches to green polymer synthesis have concentrated on using less hazardous reagents and avoiding solvents. For example, Lexan can now be prepared by the reaction of bisphenol A with diphenyl carbonate [$(PhO)_2C{=}O$] in the absence of solvent. This process avoids the use of phosgene ($Cl_2C{=}O$, Section 31.6D), an acutely toxic reagent that must be handled with extreme care, as well as the large volume of CH_2Cl_2 typically used as the solvent for the polymerization process.

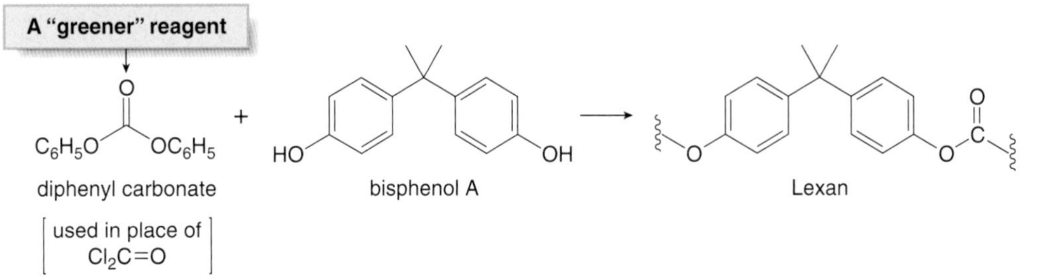
A "greener" reagent
C6H5O
OC6H5
HO
OH
diphenyl carbonate
bisphenol A
Lexan
used in place of
Cl2C=O

Problem 31.21 Thermosetting resins similar to Bakelite (Section 31.7) have also been prepared from renewable feedstocks. One method uses cardinol, the major constituent of the liquid obtained from roasted cashew nutshells. What polymer is obtained when cardinol is treated with formaldehyde ($H_2C{=}O$) in the presence of a proton source?

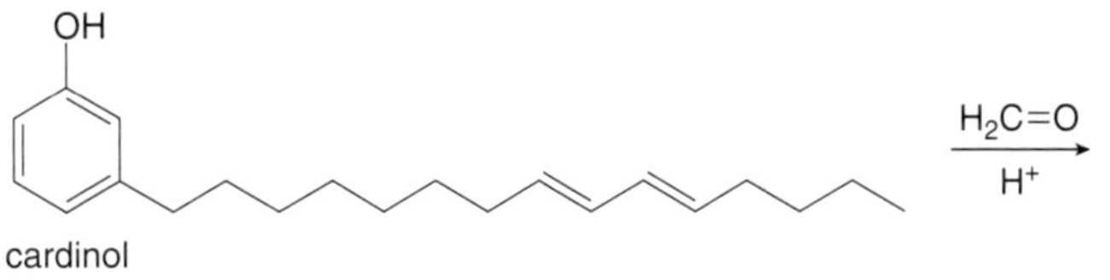
OH
H2C=O
H+
cardinol

31.9 Polymer Recycling and Disposal

The same desirable characteristics that make polymers popular materials for consumer products—durability, strength, and lack of reactivity—also contribute to environmental problems. Polymers do not degrade readily, and as a result, billions of pounds of polymers end up in landfills every year. Estimates suggest that synthetic polymers comprise 11% of solid municipal waste, 30% of which comes from packaging materials.

Two solutions to address the waste problem created by polymers are recycling existing polymer types to make new materials, and using biodegradable polymers that will decompose in a finite and limited time span.

31.9A Polymer Recycling

Although thousands of different synthetic polymers have now been prepared, six compounds, called the **"Big Six,"** account for 76% of the synthetic polymers produced in the United States each year. Each polymer is assigned a recycling code (1–6) that indicates its ease of recycling; **the lower the number, the easier to recycle.** Table 31.1 lists these six most common polymers, as well as the type of products made from each recycled polymer.

Recycling begins with sorting plastics by type, shredding the plastics into small chips, and washing the chips to remove adhesives and labels. After the chips are dried and any metal caps or rings are removed, the polymer chips are melted and molded for reuse.

Table 31.1 Recyclable Polymers

Recycling code	Polymer name	Structure	Recycled product
1	PET Polyethylene terephthalate	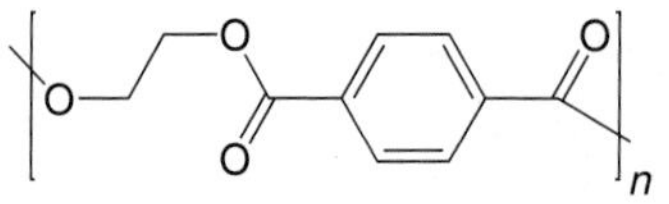	fleece jackets carpeting plastic bottles
2	HDPE High-density polyethylene	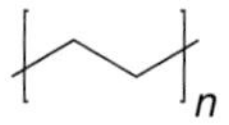	Tyvek insulation sports clothing
3	PVC Poly(vinyl chloride)	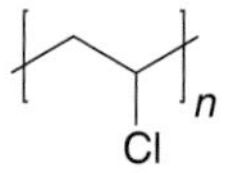	floor mats
4	LDPE Low-density polyethylene	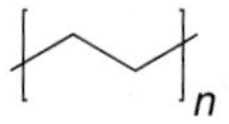	trash bags
5	PP Polypropylene	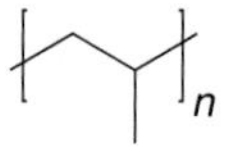	furniture
6	PS Polystyrene	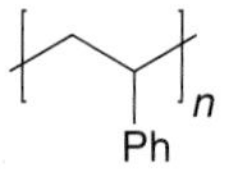	molded trays trash cans

Of the Big Six, only the polyethylene terephthalate (PET) in soft drink bottles and the high-density polyethylene (HDPE) in milk jugs and juice bottles are recycled to any great extent. Since recycled polymers are often still contaminated with small amounts of adhesives and other materials, these recycled polymers are generally not used for storing food or drink products. Recycled HDPE is converted to Tyvek, an insulating wrap used in new housing construction, and recycled PET is used to make fibers for fleece clothing and carpeting. Currently about 23% of all plastics are recycled in the United States.

An alternative recycling process is to re-convert polymers back to the monomers from which they were made, a process that has been successful with acyl compounds that contain C–O or C–N bonds in the polymer backbone. For example, heating polyethylene terephthalate with CH_3OH cleaves the esters of the polymer chain to give ethylene glycol ($HOCH_2CH_2OH$) and dimethyl terephthalate. These monomers then serve as starting materials for more PET. This chemical recycling process is a transesterification reaction that occurs by nucleophilic acyl substitution, as discussed in Chapter 22.

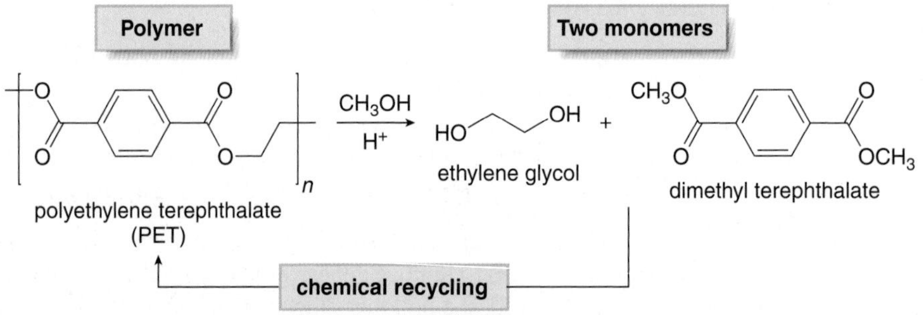

Similarly, treatment of discarded nylon 6 polymer with NH_3 cleaves the polyamide backbone, forming ε-caprolactam, which can be purified and re-converted to nylon 6.

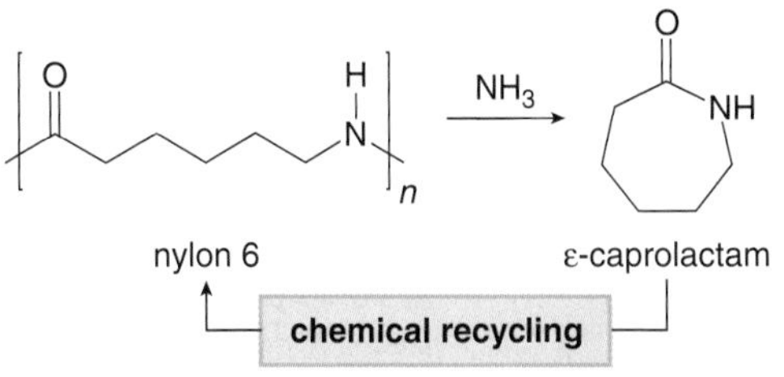

Problem 31.22 Why can't chemical recycling—that is, the conversion of polymer to monomers and re-conversion of monomers to polymer—be done easily with HDPE and LDPE?

Problem 31.23 Organic polymers can also be incinerated as a means of disposal. (a) What products are formed on combustion of polyethylene? (b) What products are formed on combustion of polyethylene terephthalate? (c) Are these reactions exothermic or endothermic? (See Sections 6.4 and 30.3 for related reactions.) (d) Propose a reason why HDPE and PET must be separated from poly(vinyl chloride) prior to incineration.

31.9B Biodegradable Polymers

Another solution to the accumulation of waste polymers in landfills is to design and use polymers that are biodegradable.

- **Biodegradable polymers are polymers that can be degraded by microorganisms—bacteria, fungi, or algae—naturally present in the environment.**

Several biodegradable polyesters have now been developed. For example, the **polyhydroxyalkanoates (PHAs)** are polymers of 3-hydroxy carboxylic acids, such as 3-hydroxybutyric acid or 3-hydroxyvaleric acid.

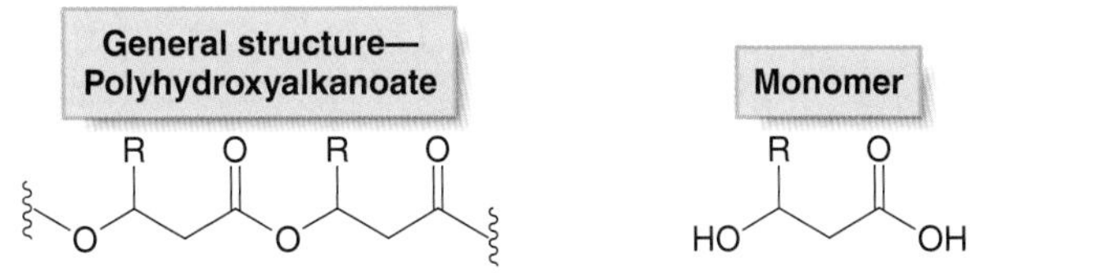

PHA

3-hydroxy carboxylic acid

R = CH_3, 3-hydroxybutyric acid
R = CH_2CH_3, 3-hydroxyvaleric acid

The two most common PHAs are **polyhydroxybutyrate (PHB)** and a copolymer of **polyhydroxybutyrate** and **polyhydroxyvalerate (PHBV).** PHAs can be used as films, fibers, and coatings for hot beverage cups made of paper.

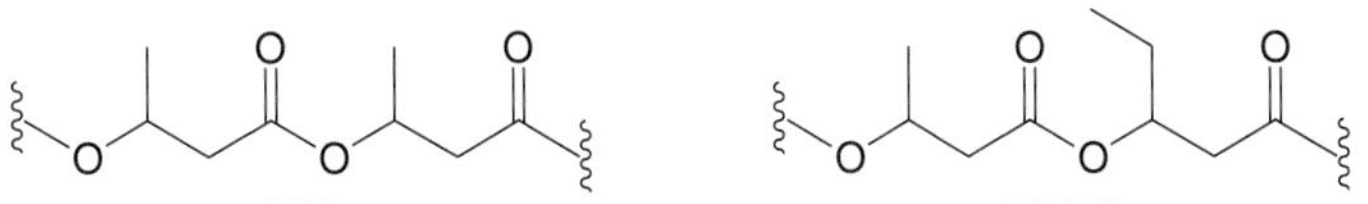

PHB **PHBV**

Bacteria in the soil readily degrade PHAs, and in the presence of oxygen, the final degradation products are CO_2 and H_2O. The rate of degradation depends on moisture, temperature, and pH. Degradation is slower in enclosed landfills that are lined and covered.

PHAs are bioplastics. PHAs are not synthesized from petroleum products, and they are degraded by soil microorganisms to CO_2 and H_2O.

An additional advantage of the polyhydroxyalkanoates is that the polymers can be produced by fermentation. Certain types of bacteria produce PHAs for energy storage when they are grown in glucose solution in the absence of specific nutrients. The polymer forms as discrete granules within the bacterial cell, and it is then removed by extraction to give a white powder that can be melted and modified into a variety of different products.

Biodegradable polyamides have also been prepared from amino acids. For example, aspartic acid can be converted to polyaspartate, abbreviated as **TPA** (thermal polyaspartate). TPA is commonly used as an alternative to poly(acrylic acid), which is used to line the pumps and boilers of wastewater treatment facilities.

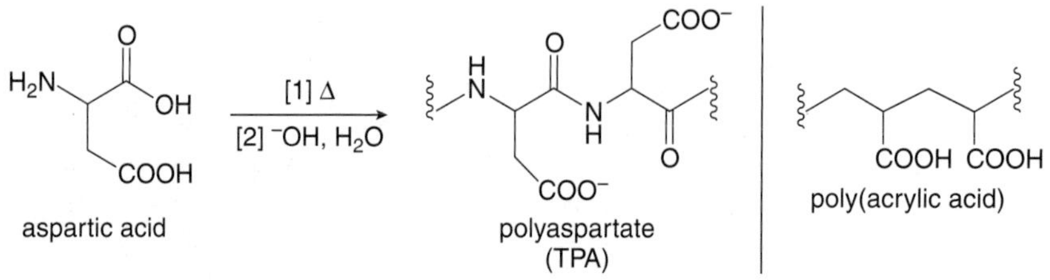

Problem 31.24 What polymers are formed from each monomer?

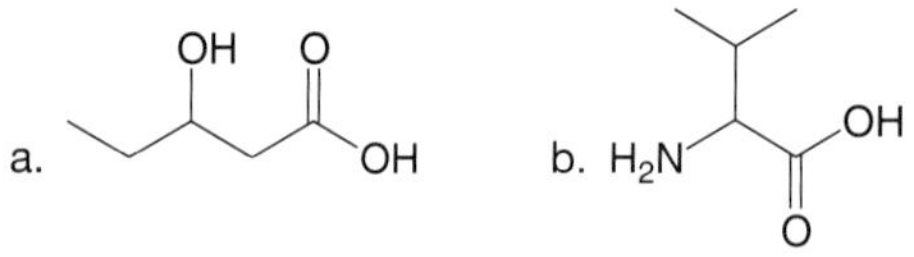

KEY CONCEPTS

Synthetic Polymers

Chain-Growth Polymers—Addition Polymers

[1] Chain-growth polymers with alkene starting materials (31.2)

- General reaction:

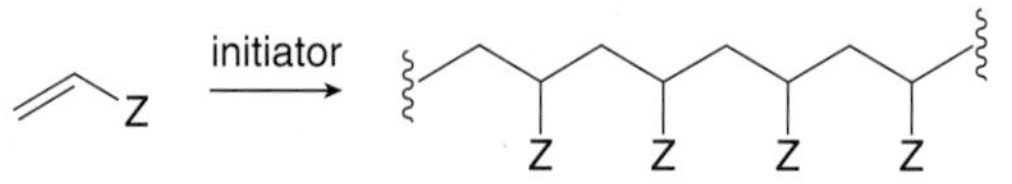

- Mechanism—three possibilities, depending in part on the identity of Z:

Type	Identity of Z	Initiator	Comments
[1] radical polymerization	Z stabilizes a radical. Z = R, Ph, Cl, etc.	A source of radicals (ROOR)	Termination occurs by radical coupling or disproportionation. Chain branching occurs.
[2] cationic polymerization	Z stabilizes a carbocation. Z = R, Ph, OR, etc.	H–A or a Lewis acid ($BF_3 + H_2O$)	Termination occurs by loss of a proton.
[3] anionic polymerization	Z stabilizes a carbanion. Z = Ph, COOR, COR, CN, etc.	An organolithium reagent (R–Li)	Termination occurs only when an acid or other electrophile is added.

[2] Chain-growth polymers with epoxide starting materials (31.3)

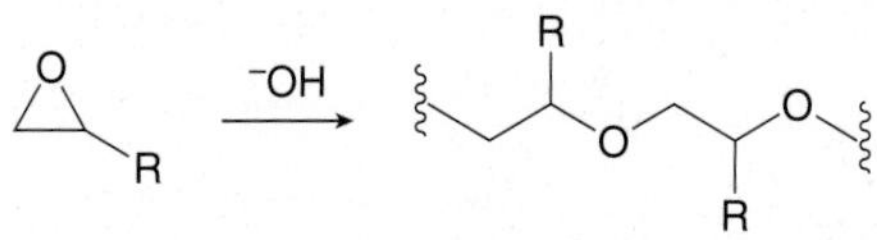

- The mechanism is S_N2.
- Ring opening occurs at the less substituted carbon of the epoxide.

Examples of Step-Growth Polymers—Condensation Polymers (31.6)

Polyamides

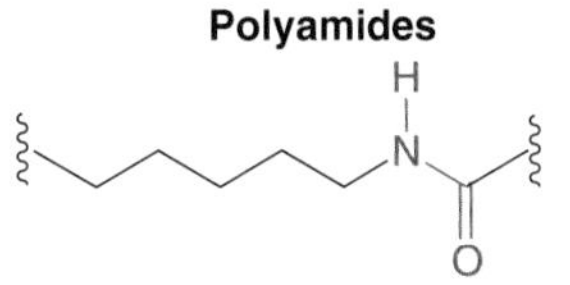

nylon 6

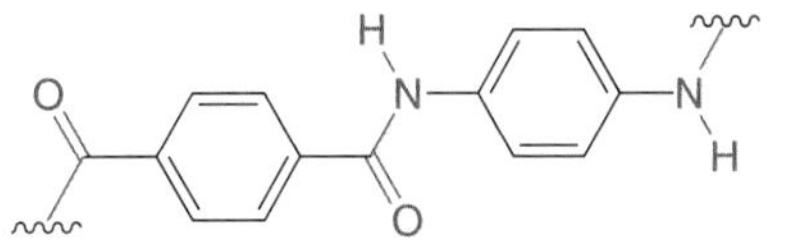

Kevlar

Polyesters

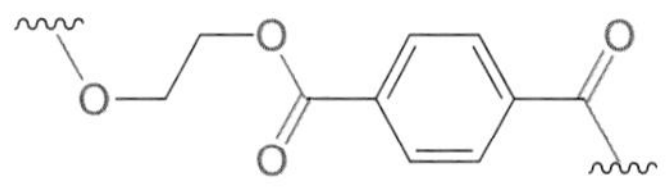

polyethylene terephthalate

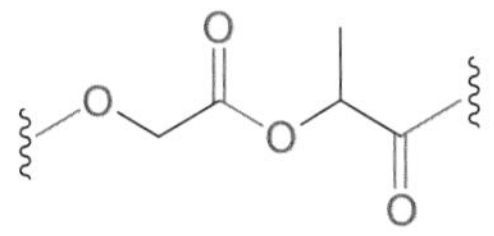

copolymer of
glycolic and lactic acids

Polyurethanes

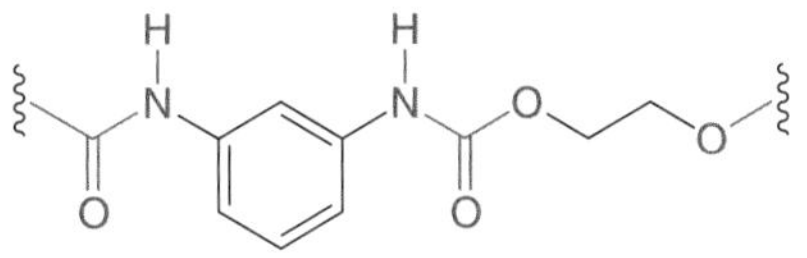

a polyurethane

Polycarbonates

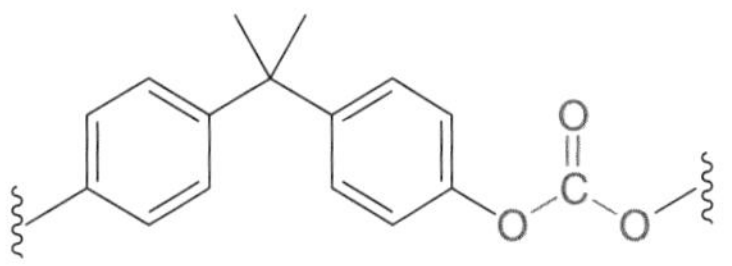

Lexan

[Key functional groups are indicated in red.]

Structure and Properties

- Polymers prepared from monomers having the general structure $CH_2=CHZ$ can be isotactic, syndiotactic, or atactic depending on the identity of Z and the method of preparation (31.4).
- Ziegler–Natta catalysts form polymers without significant branching. Polymers can be isotactic, syndiotactic, or atactic depending on the catalyst. Polymers prepared from 1,3-dienes have the *E* or *Z* configuration depending on the catalyst (31.4, 31.5).
- Most polymers contain ordered crystalline regions and less ordered amorphous regions (31.7). The greater the crystallinity, the harder the polymer.
- Elastomers are polymers that stretch and can return to their original shape (31.5).
- Thermoplastics are polymers that can be molded, shaped, and cooled such that the new form is preserved (31.7).
- Thermosetting polymers are composed of complex networks of covalent bonds so they cannot be re-melted to form a liquid phase (31.7).

PROBLEMS

Problems Using Three-Dimensional Models

31.25 Draw the structure of the polymer formed by chain-growth polymerization of each monomer.

a. 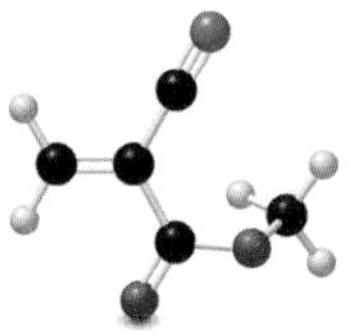

b. 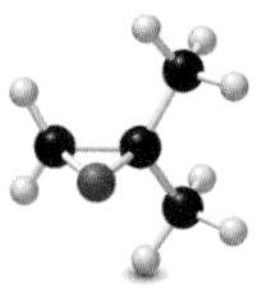

31.26 What monomer(s) are used to prepare each polymer or copolymer?

a. 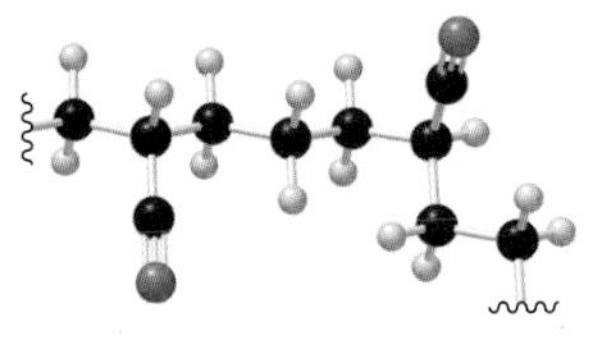

b. 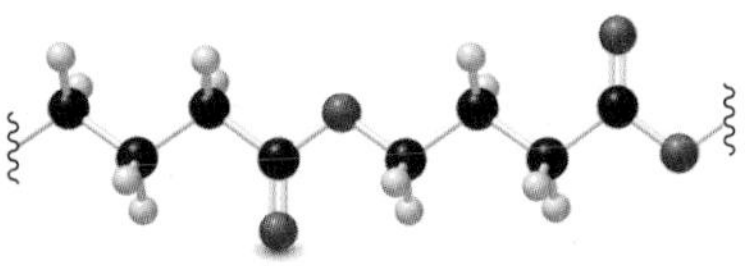

31.27 Draw the structure of the polymer formed by step-growth polymerization of each monomer or pair of monomers.

a. 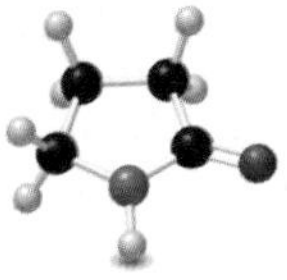

b. 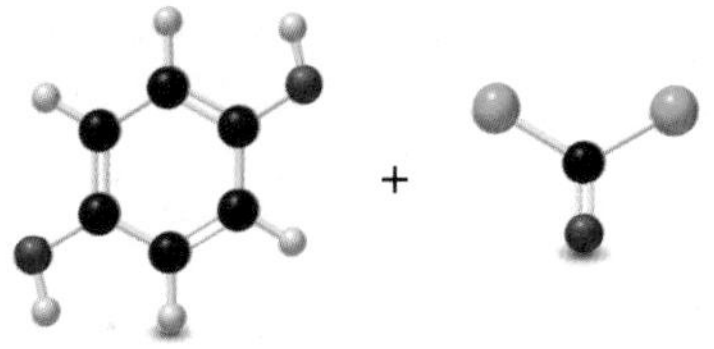

Polymer Structure and Properties

31.28 Draw the structure of the polymer formed by chain-growth polymerization of each monomer.

a. 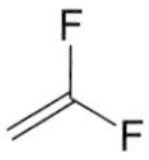
b. 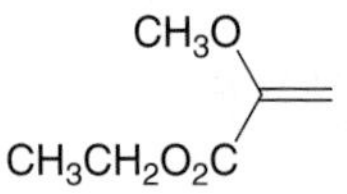
c. 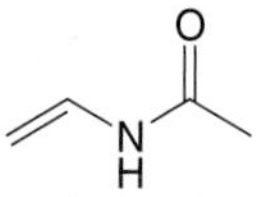
d. 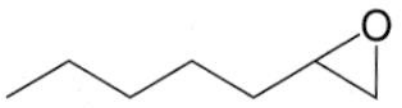

31.29 Draw the structure of the alternating copolymer formed from each pair of monomers.

a. 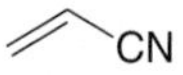 and 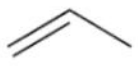

b. 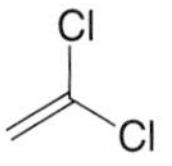 and 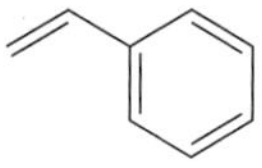

c. 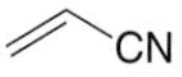 and 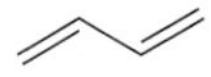

d. 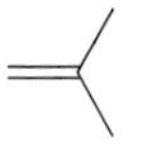 and 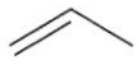

e. 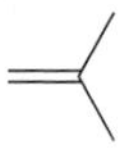 and 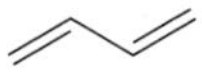

31.30 What monomer(s) are used to prepare each polymer or copolymer?

a. 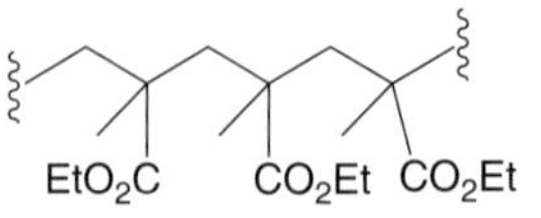

b. 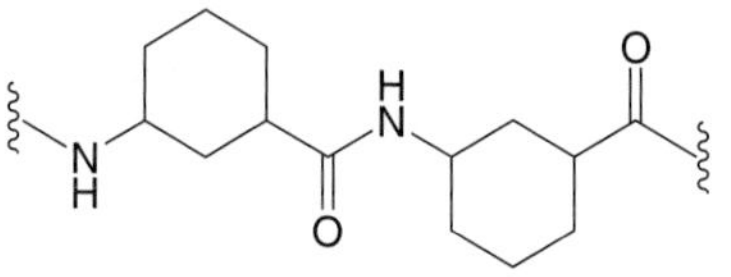

c. 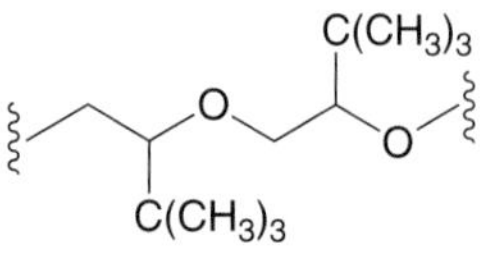

d. 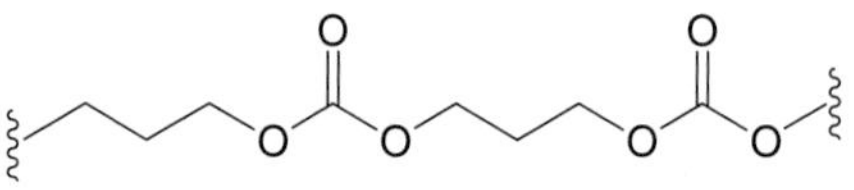

31.31 Draw each polymer in Problem 31.30 using the shorthand representation shown in Figure 31.2.

31.32 Draw a short segment of each polymer: (a) isotactic poly(vinyl chloride); (b) syndiotactic polyacrylonitrile; (c) atactic polystyrene.

31.33 Draw the structure of the polymer that results from anionic polymerization of *p*-trichloromethylstyrene ($CCl_3C_6H_4CH{=}CH_2$) using ethylene oxide as the electrophile to terminate the chain.

31.34 Draw the structure of the polymer formed by step-growth polymerization of each monomer or pair of monomers.

a. 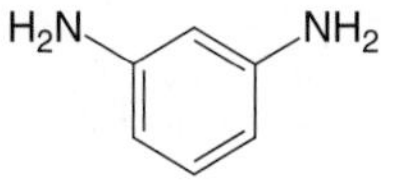 and 

b. 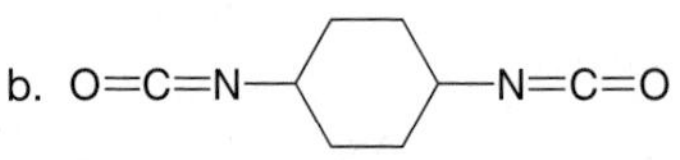 and 

c. 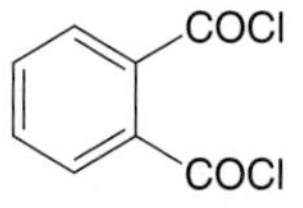 and 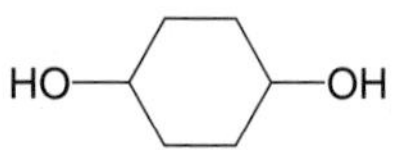

d. 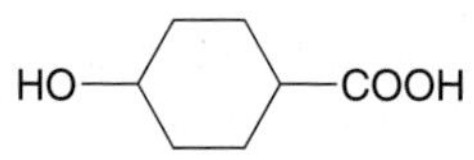

31.35 **ABS,** a widely produced copolymer used for high-impact applications like car bumpers and crash helmets, is formed from three monomers—acrylonitrile ($CH_2{=}CHCN$), 1,3-butadiene ($CH_2{=}CH{-}CH{=}CH_2$), and styrene ($CH_2{=}CHPh$). Draw a possible structure for ABS.

31.36 Draw the structures of **Quiana** and **Nomex,** two commercially available step-growth polymers formed from the given monomers. Nomex is a strong polymer used in aircraft tires and microwave transformers. Quiana has been used to make wrinkle-resistant fabrics.

a. 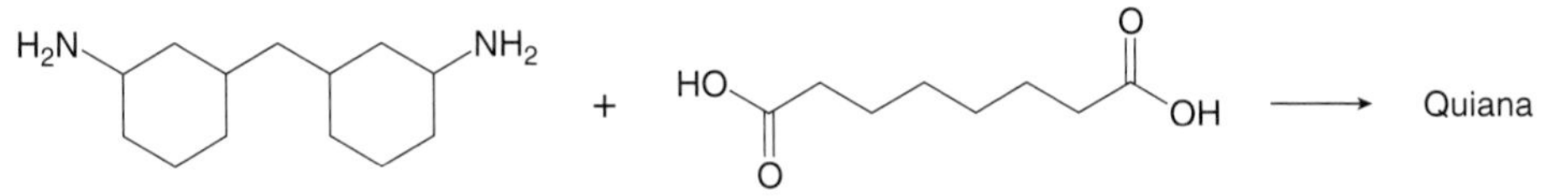

b. 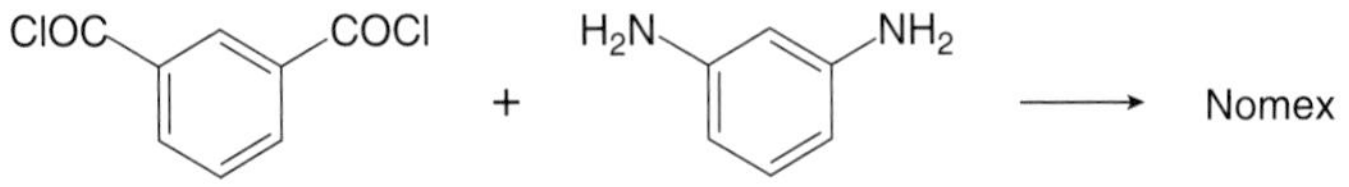

31.37 Kevlar (Section 31.6A) is a very stiff polymer because its backbone contains many aromatic rings and its polymer chains are extensively hydrogen bonded to each other. Draw a short segment of two Kevlar chains, and indicate how the chains are hydrogen bonded to each other.

31.38 Explain the differences observed in the T_g and T_m values for each pair of polymers: (a) polyester **A** and PET; (b) polyester **A** and nylon 6,6. (c) How would you expect the T_m value for Kevlar (Section 31.6A) to compare with the T_m value for nylon 6,6? Explain your prediction.

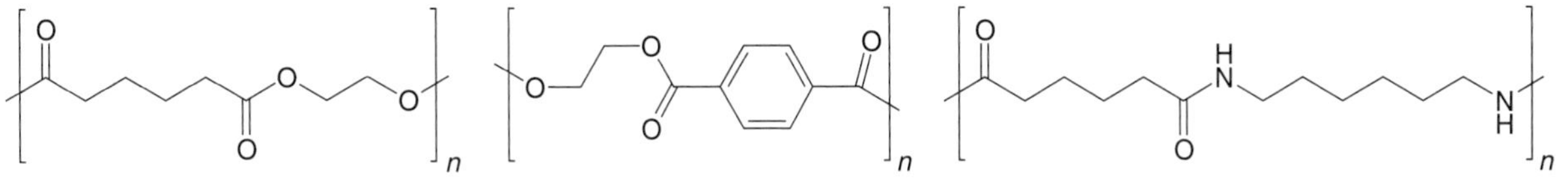

polyester **A**
$T_g < 0$ °C
$T_m = 50$ °C

PET
$T_g = 70$ °C
$T_m = 265$ °C

nylon 6,6
$T_g = 53$ °C
$T_m = 265$ °C

31.39 Explain why diester **A** is now often used as a plasticizer in place of dibutyl phthalate.

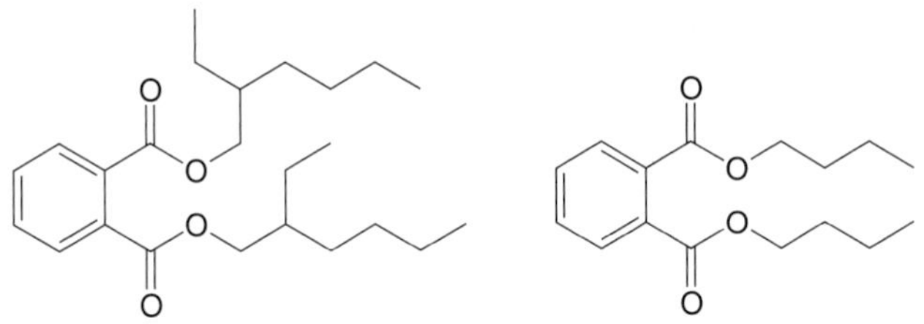

A dibutyl phthalate

Mechanism

31.40 Draw a stepwise mechanism for the polymerization of isoprene to gutta-percha using $(CH_3)_3CO-OC(CH_3)_3$ as the initiator.

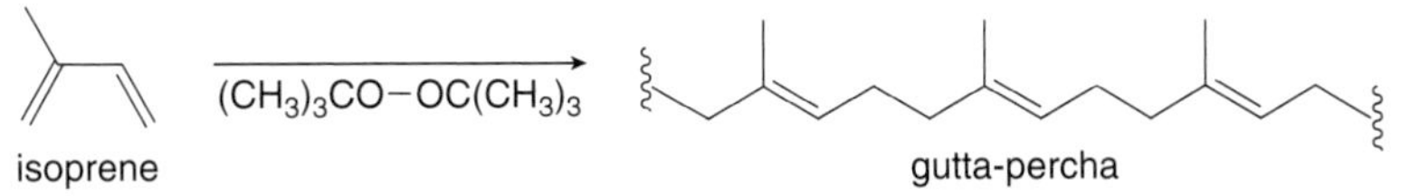

isoprene gutta-percha

31.41 Cationic polymerization of 3-phenylpropene ($CH_2=CHCH_2Ph$) affords **A** as the major product rather than **B.** Draw a stepwise mechanism to account for this observation.

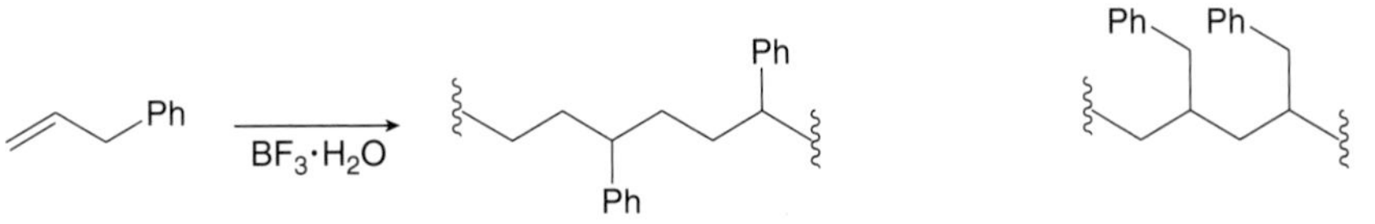

A
major product

B

31.42 Explain why acrylonitrile ($CH_2{=}CHCN$) undergoes cationic polymerization more slowly than 3-butenenitrile ($CH_2{=}CHCH_2CN$).

31.43 Draw a stepwise mechanism for the anionic polymerization of styrene ($CH_2{=}CHPh$) to form polystyrene $-[CH_2CHPh]_n-$ using BuLi as the initiator. Use CO_2 as the electrophile that terminates the chain mechanism.

31.44 Although styrene undergoes both cationic and anionic polymerization equally well, one method is often preferred with substituted styrenes. Which method is preferred with each compound? Explain.

a. 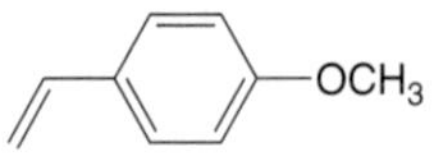
b. 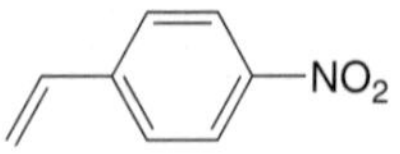
c. 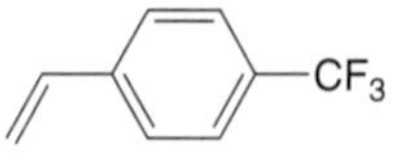
d. 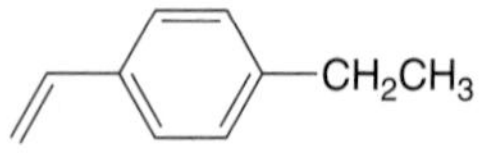

31.45 Rank the following compounds in order of increasing ability to undergo anionic chain-growth polymerization.

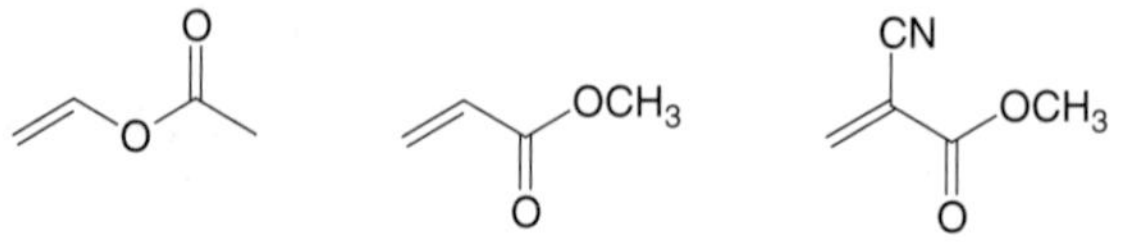

31.46 In the presence of H_3O^+, 2-methylpropene oxide undergoes chain-growth polymerization such that nucleophilic attack occurs at the more substituted end of the epoxide. Draw a stepwise mechanism for this process, and explain this regioselectivity.

Nucleophilic attack occurs here.

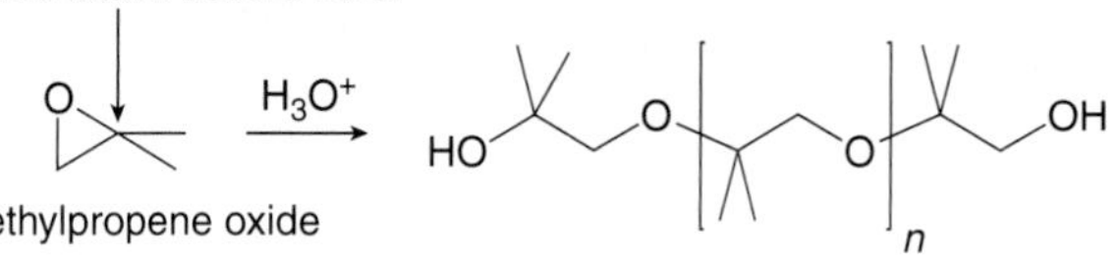

2-methylpropene oxide

31.47 Draw a stepwise mechanism for the conversion of dihalide **A** and 1,4-cyclohexanediol to polyether **B** in the presence of $AlCl_3$.

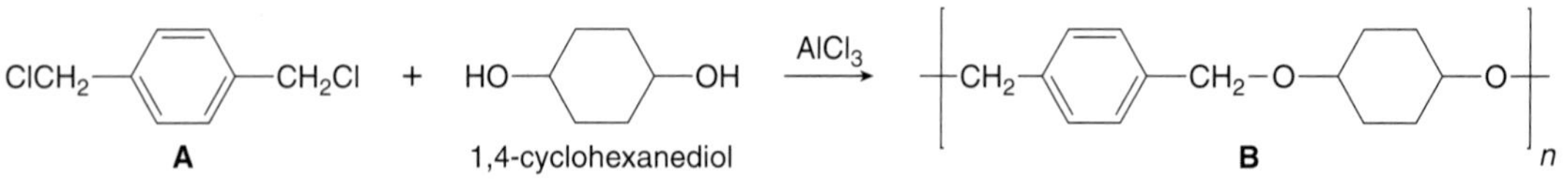

A 1,4-cyclohexanediol **B**

31.48 Draw a stepwise mechanism for the following reaction, which is used to prepare bisphenol A (BPA), a widely used monomer in polymer synthesis.

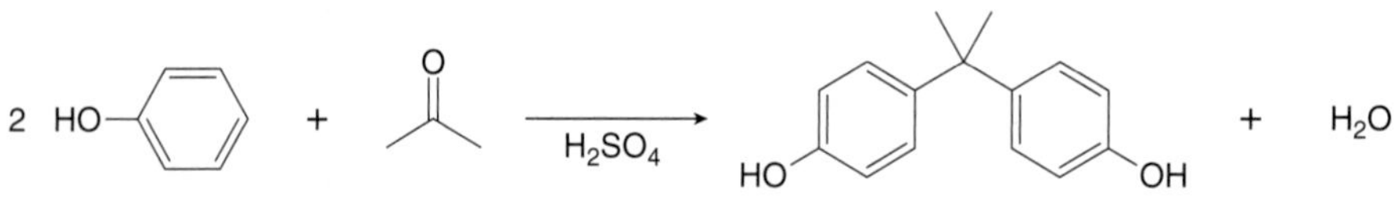

bisphenol A

31.49 Draw a stepwise mechanism for the reaction of an alcohol with an isocyanate to form a urethane.

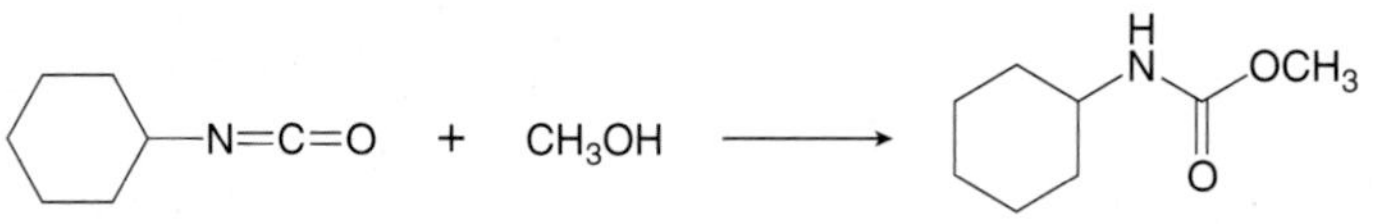

a urethane

Reactions and Synthesis

31.50 Draw the products of each reaction.

a. 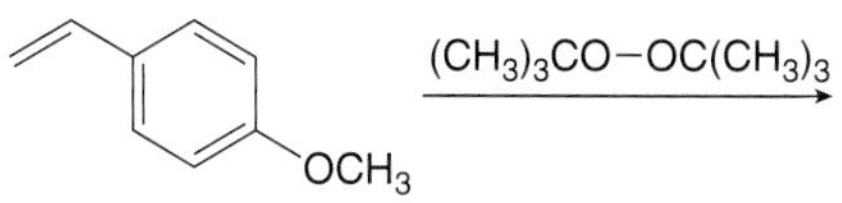
(CH3)3CO–OC(CH3)3
OCH3

b. 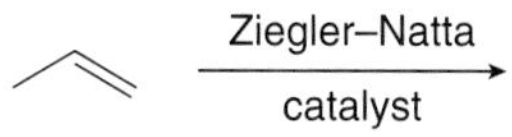
Ziegler–Natta
catalyst

c. 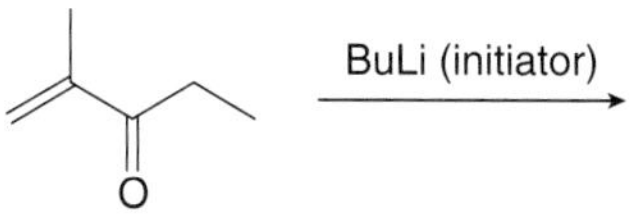
BuLi (initiator)
O

d. 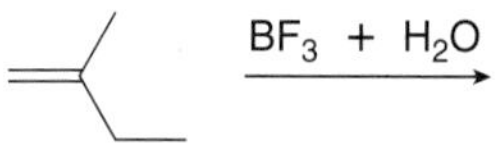
BF3 + H2O

e. 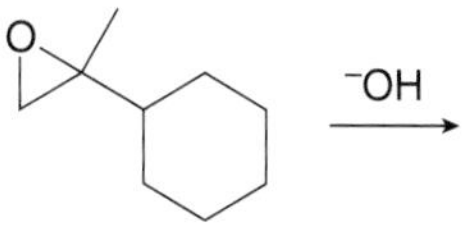
O
⁻OH

f. 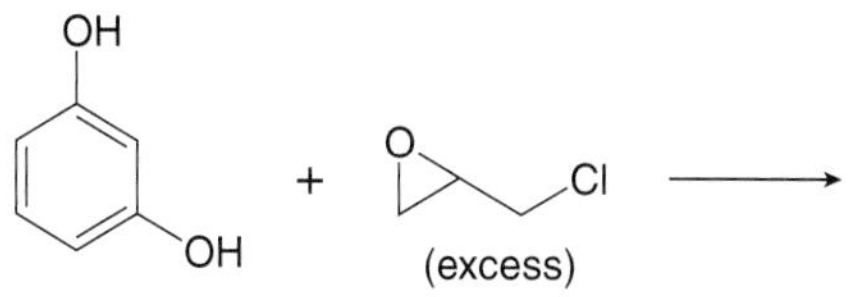
OH
OH
+
O
Cl
(excess)

g. 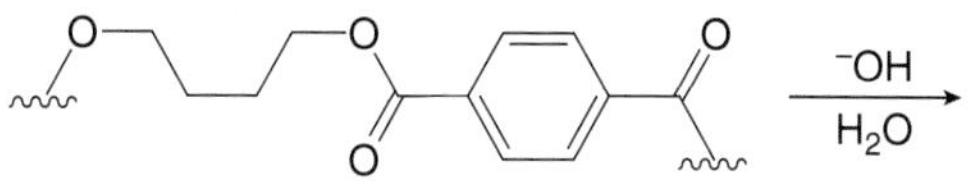
O
O
O
O
⁻OH
H2O

h. 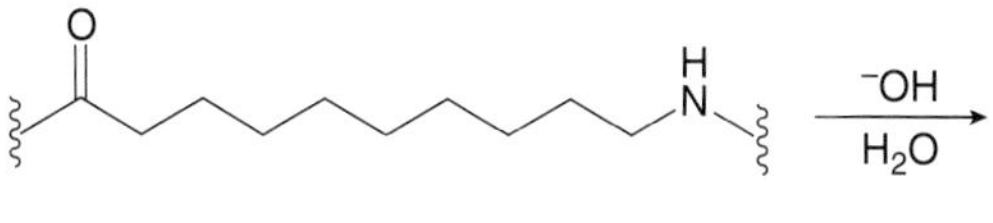
O
H
N
⁻OH
H2O

i. 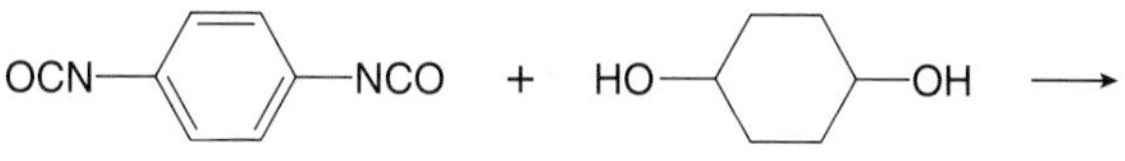
OCN
NCO
+
HO
OH

j. 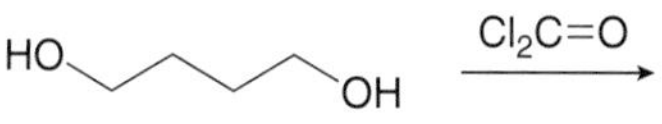
HO
OH
Cl2C=O

31.51 Explain why aqueous NaOH solution can be stored indefinitely in polyethylene bottles, but spilling aqueous base on a polyester shirt or nylon stockings quickly makes a hole.

31.52 What epoxy resin is formed by the following reaction sequence?

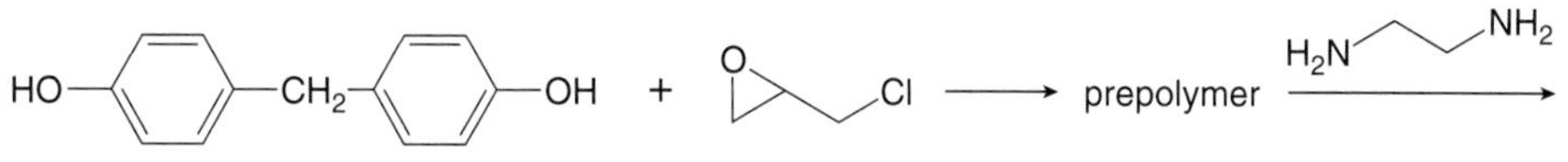
HO
CH2
OH
+
O
Cl
prepolymer
H2N
NH2

31.53 (a) Explain why poly(vinyl alcohol) cannot be prepared by the radical polymerization of vinyl alcohol ($CH_2=CHOH$). (b) Devise a stepwise synthesis of poly(vinyl alcohol) from vinyl acetate ($CH_2=CHOCOCH_3$). (c) How can poly(vinyl alcohol) be converted to poly(vinyl butyral), a polymer used in windshield safety glass?

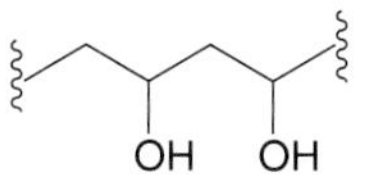
OH
OH

poly(vinyl alcohol)

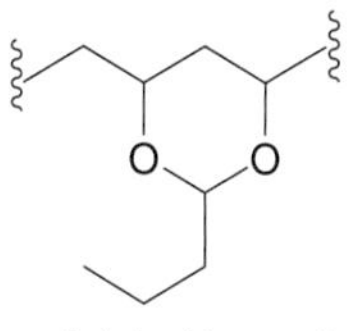
O
O

poly(vinyl butyral)

31.54 Although 1,3-propanediol ($HOCH_2CH_2CH_2OH$) can now be prepared from carbohydrate feedstocks (Section 31.8), it can also be prepared from petroleum feedstocks. Devise a synthesis of $HOCH_2CH_2CH_2OH$ from $CH_3CH=CH_2$, a product of petroleum refining.

31.55 Devise a synthesis of terephthalic acid and ethylene glycol, the two monomers needed for polyethylene terephthalate synthesis, from the given starting materials.

terephthalic acid

ethylene glycol

31.56 The reaction of *p*-cresol with $CH_2{=}O$ resembles the reaction of phenol (PhOH) with $CH_2{=}O$, except that the resulting polymer is thermoplastic but not thermosetting. Draw the structure of the polymer formed, and explain why the properties of these two polymers are so different.

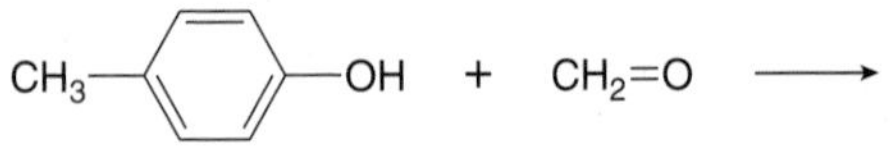

p-cresol

Biological Applications

31.57 In addition to glycolic and lactic acids (Section 31.6B), dissolving sutures can also be prepared from each of the following lactone monomers. Draw the structure of the polymer formed from each monomer.

a. 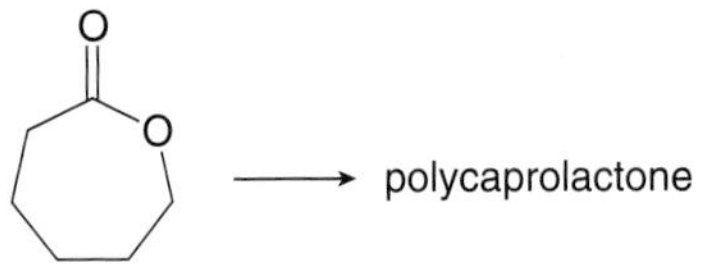

ε-caprolactone

b. 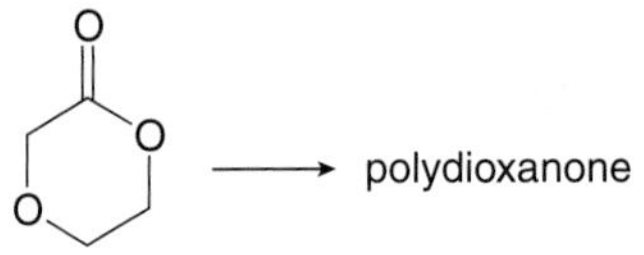

p-dioxanone

31.58 Compound **A** is a novel poly(ester amide) copolymer that can be used as a bioabsorbable coating for the controlled release of drugs. **A** is a copolymer of four monomers, two of which are amino acids or amino acid derivatives. The body's enzymes recognize the naturally occurring amino acids in the polymer backbone, allowing for controlled enzymatic breakdown of the polymer and steady release of an encapsulated drug. Identify the four monomers used to synthesize **A;** then use Figure 29.2 to name the two amino acids.

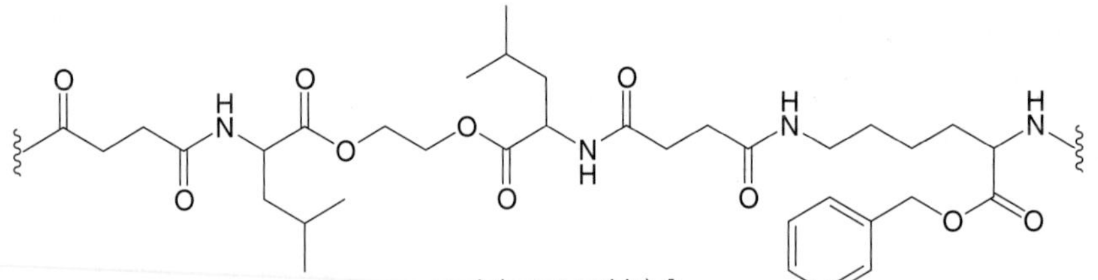

poly(ester amide) **A**

31.59 Researchers at Rutgers University have developed biocompatible polymers that degrade into nonsteroidal anti-inflammatory drugs. For example, the reaction of two equivalents of benzyl salicylate and one equivalent of sebacoyl chloride forms a poly(anhydride ester) called PolyAspirin, which hydrolyzes to salicylic acid (an anti-inflammatory agent) and sebacic acid, which is excreted. This technology can perhaps be used for localized drug delivery at specific sites of injury. What is the structure of PolyAspirin?

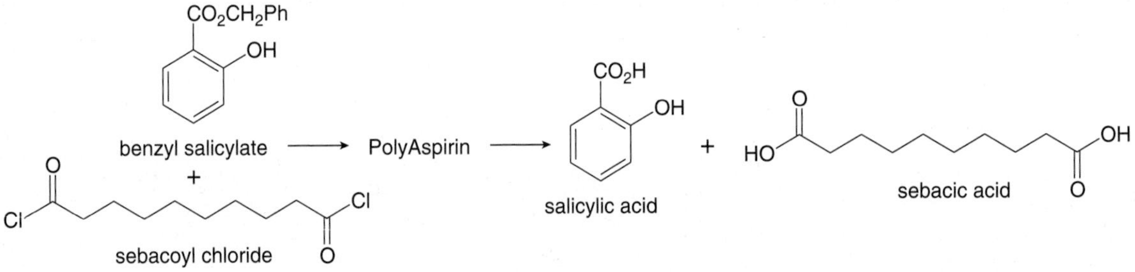

Challenge Questions

31.60 Melmac, a thermosetting polymer formed from melamine and formaldehyde ($CH_2=O$), is used to make dishes and countertops. Draw a stepwise mechanism for the condensation of one mole of formaldehyde with two moles of melamine, which begins the synthesis of Melmac.

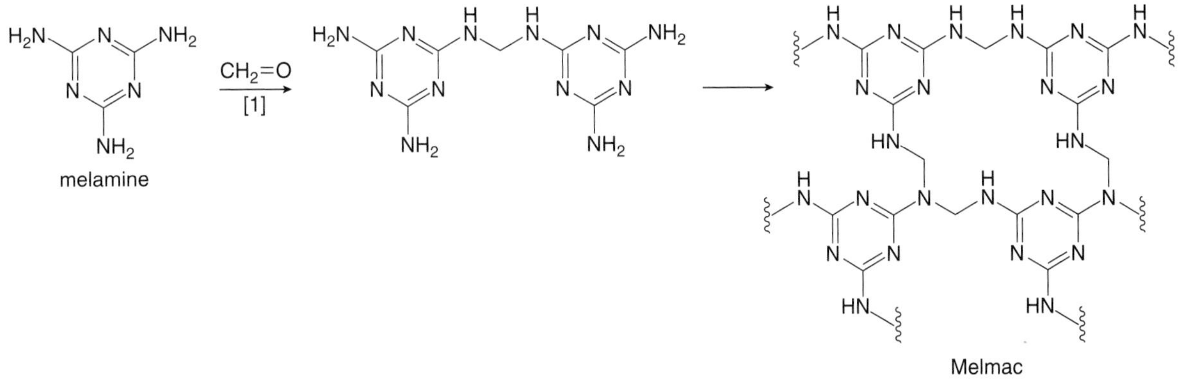

31.61 Although chain branching in radical polymerizations can occur by intermolecular H abstraction as shown in Mechanism 31.2, chain branching can also occur by intramolecular H abstraction to form branched polyethylene that contains butyl groups as branches.

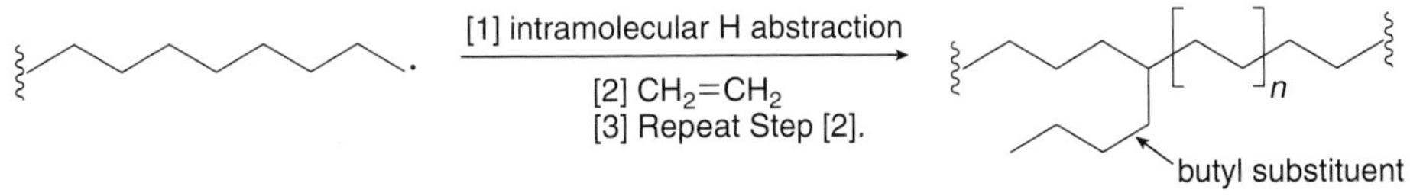

a. Draw a stepwise mechanism that illustrates which H must be intramolecularly abstracted to form butyl substituents.

b. Suggest a reason why the abstraction of this H is more facile than the abstraction of other H's.

31.62 The reaction of urea [$(NH_2)_2C=O$] and formaldehyde ($CH_2=O$) forms a highly cross-linked polymer used in foams. Suggest a structure for this polymer. [*Hint:* Examine the structures of Bakelite (Figure 31.7) and Melmac (Problem 31.60).]

APPENDIX

A pK$_a$ Values for Selected Compounds

Compound	pK$_a$
HI	−10
HBr	−9
H_2SO_4	−9
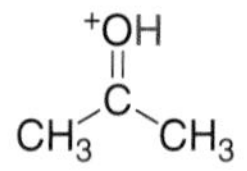	−7.3
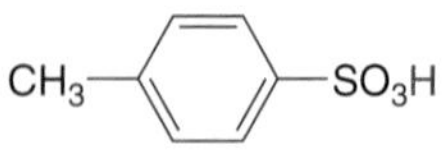	−7
HCl	−7
$[(CH_3)_2OH]^+$	−3.8
$[CH_3OH_2]^+$	−2.5
H_3O^+	−1.7
CH_3SO_3H	−1.2
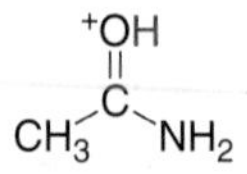	0.0
CF_3COOH	0.2
CCl_3COOH	0.6
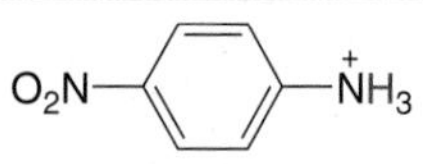	1.0
$Cl_2CHCOOH$	1.3
H_3PO_4	2.1
FCH_2COOH	2.7
$ClCH_2COOH$	2.8
$BrCH_2COOH$	2.9
ICH_2COOH	3.2
HF	3.2
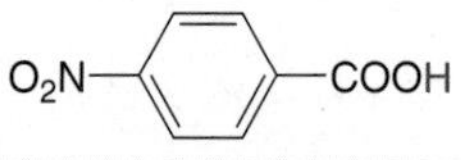	3.4
HCOOH	3.8

Compound	pK$_a$
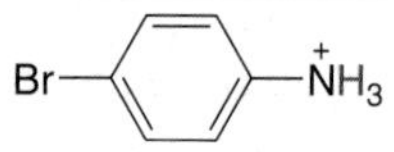	3.9
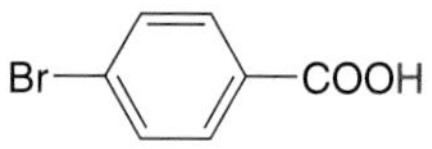	4.0
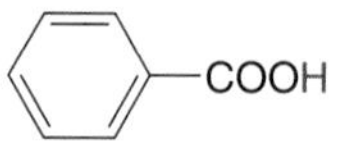	4.2
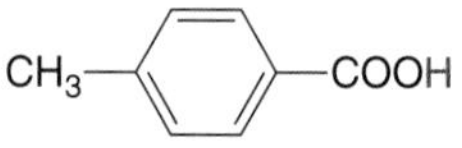	4.3
	4.5
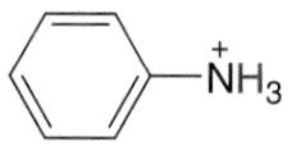	4.6
CH_3COOH	4.8
$(CH_3)_3CCOOH$	5.0
	5.1
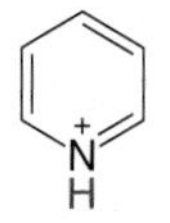	5.3
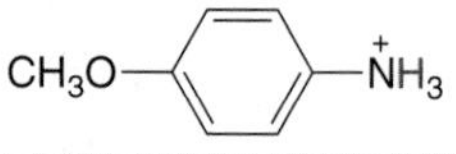	5.3
H_2CO_3	6.4
H_2S	7.0
	7.1
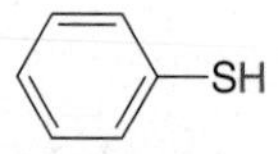	7.8

Compound	pK_a
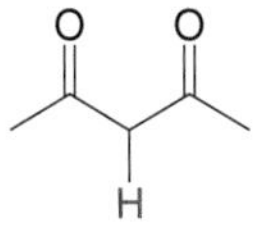	8.9
$HC{\equiv}N$	9.1
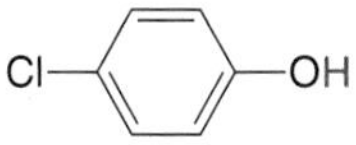	9.4
NH_4^+	9.4
$H_3\overset{+}{N}CH_2COO^-$	9.8
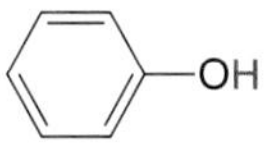	10.0
	10.2
HCO_3^-	10.2
CH_3NO_2	10.2
	10.3
CH_3CH_2SH	10.5
$[(CH_3)_3NH]^+$	10.6
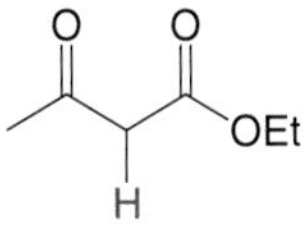	10.7
$[CH_3NH_3]^+$	10.7
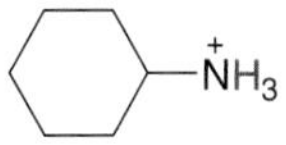	10.7
$[(CH_3)_2NH_2]^+$	10.7
CF_3CH_2OH	12.4
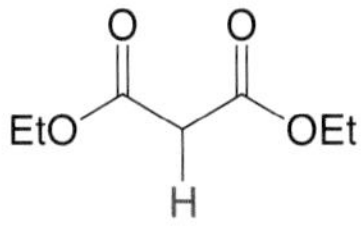	13.3
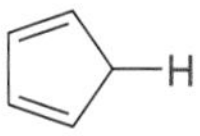	15
CH_3OH	15.5
H_2O	15.7
CH_3CH_2OH	16
CH_3CONH_2	16
CH_3CHO	17
$(CH_3)_3COH$	18
$(CH_3)_2C{=}O$	19.2
$CH_3CO_2CH_2CH_3$	24.5
$HC{\equiv}CH$	25
$CH_3C{\equiv}N$	25
$CHCl_3$	25
$CH_3CON(CH_3)_2$	30
H_2	35
NH_3	38
CH_3NH_2	40
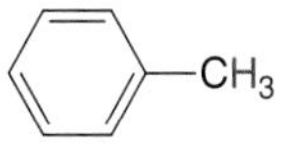	41
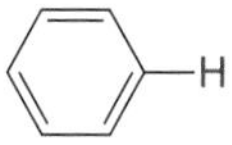	43
$CH_2{=}CHCH_3$	43
$CH_2{=}CH_2$	44
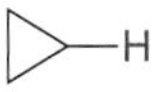	46
CH_4	50
CH_3CH_3	50

APPENDIX B
Nomenclature

Although the basic principles of nomenclature are presented in the body of this text, additional information is often needed to name many complex organic compounds. Appendix B concentrates on three topics:

- **Naming alkyl substituents that contain branching**
- **Naming polyfunctional compounds**
- **Naming bicyclic compounds**

Naming Alkyl Substituents That Contain Branching

Alkyl groups that contain any number of carbons and no branches are named as described in Section 4.4A: change the *-ane* ending of the parent alkane to the suffix *-yl.* Thus the seven-carbon alkyl group $CH_3CH_2CH_2CH_2CH_2CH_2CH_2-$ is called *heptyl.*

When an alkyl substituent also contains branching, follow a stepwise procedure:

[1] Identify the longest carbon chain of the alkyl group that begins at the point of attachment to the parent. Begin numbering at the point of attachment and use the suffix *-yl* to indicate an alkyl group.

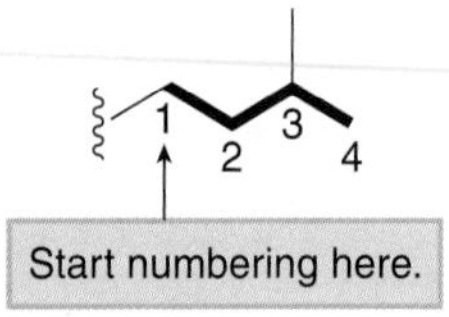

4 C's in the chain - - - → butyl group

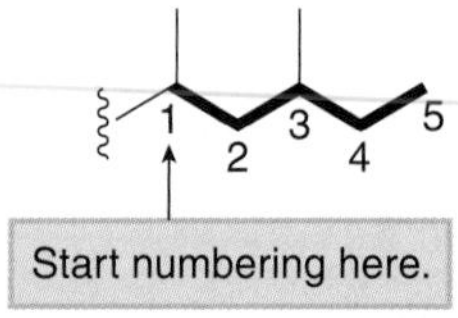

5 C's in the chain - - - → pentyl group

[2] Name all branches off the main alkyl chain and use the numbers from Step [1] to designate their location.

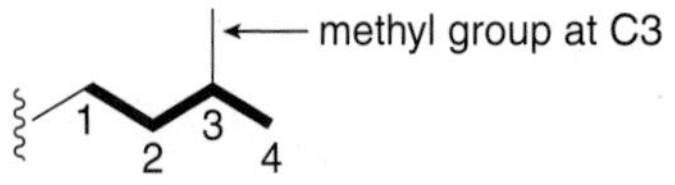

3-methylbutyl

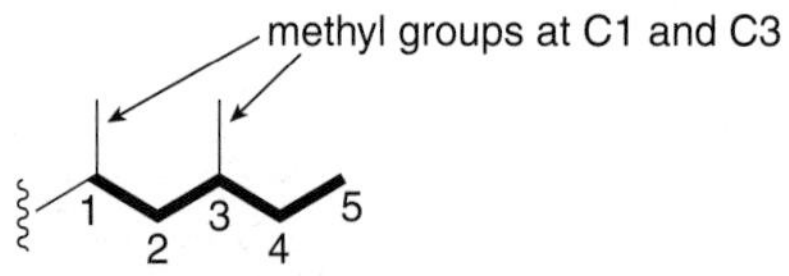

1,3-dimethylpentyl

[3] Set the entire name of the substituent in parentheses, and alphabetize this substituent name by the first letter of the complete name.

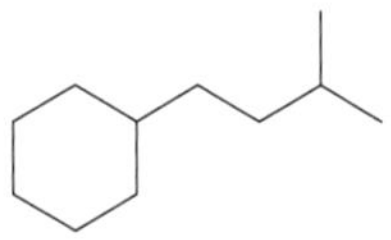

(3-methylbutyl)cyclohexane

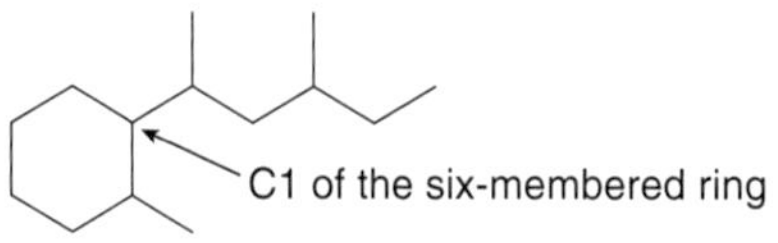
C1 of the six-membered ring

1-(1,3-dimethylpentyl)-2-methylcyclohexane

- Alphabetize the **d** of **d**imethylpentyl before the **m** of **m**ethyl.
- Number the ring to give the lower number to the first substituent alphabetically: place the dimethylpentyl group at C1.

Naming Polyfunctional Compounds

Many organic compounds contain more than one functional group. When one of those functional groups is halo (X−) or alkoxy (RO−), these groups are named as substituents as described in Sections 7.2 and 9.3B. To name other polyfunctional compounds, we must learn which functional group is assigned a higher priority in the rules of nomenclature. Two steps are usually needed:

[1] **Name a compound using the suffix of the highest priority group,** and name other functional groups as *substituents*. Table B.1 lists the common functional groups in order of decreasing priority, as well as the prefixes needed when a functional group must be named as a substituent.

[2] Number the carbon chain to give the lower number to the highest priority functional group that can be named as a suffix, and then follow all other rules of nomenclature. Examples are shown in Figure B.1.

Table B.1 Summary of Functional Group Nomenclature

(Increasing priority ↑)

Functional group	Suffix	Substituent name (prefix)
Carboxylic acid	-oic acid	carboxy
Ester	-oate	alkoxycarbonyl
Amide	-amide	amido
Nitrile	-nitrile	cyano
Aldehyde	-al	oxo (=O) or formyl (−CHO)
Ketone	-one	oxo
Alcohol	-ol	hydroxy
Amine	-amine	amino
Alkene	-ene	alkenyl
Alkyne	-yne	alkynyl
Alkane	-ane	alkyl
Ether	—	alkoxy
Halide	—	halo

Polyfunctional compounds that contain C−C double and triple bonds have characteristic suffixes to identify them, as shown in Table B.2. The higher priority functional group is assigned the lower number.

Figure B.1
Examples of nomenclature of polyfunctional compounds

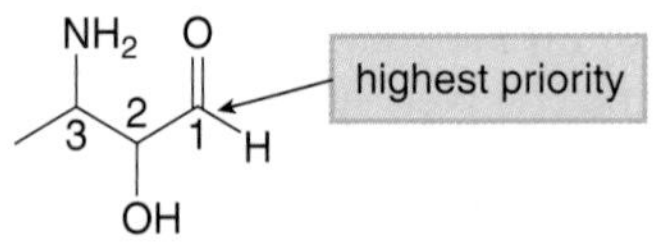

3-amino-2-hydroxybutanal

[Name as a derivative of an aldehyde since CHO is the highest priority functional group.]

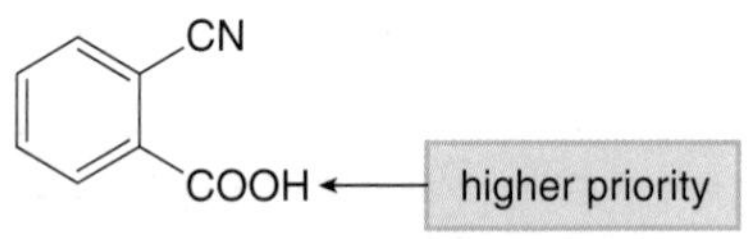

o-cyanobenzoic acid

[Name as a derivative of benzoic acid since COOH is the higher priority functional group.]

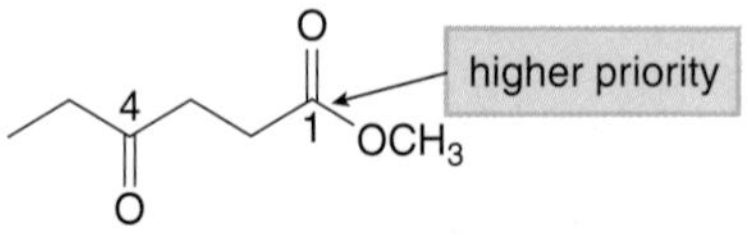

methyl 4-oxohexanoate

[Name as a derivative of an ester since COOR is the higher priority functional group.]

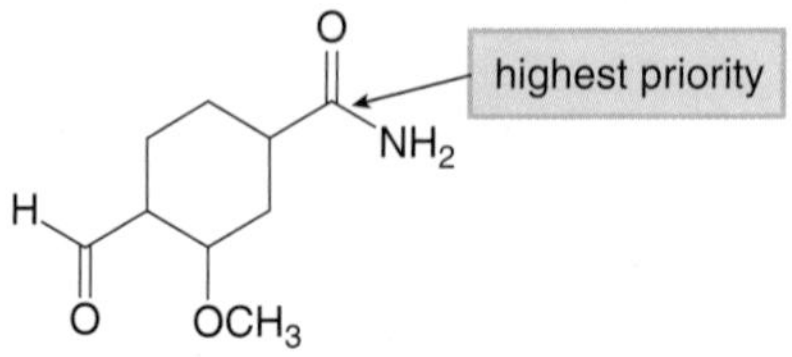

4-formyl-3-methoxycyclohexanecarboxamide

[Name as a derivative of an amide since $CONH_2$ is the highest priority functional group.]

Table B.2 Naming Polyfunctional Compounds with C–C Double and Triple Bonds

Functional groups	Suffix	Example
C=C and OH	enol	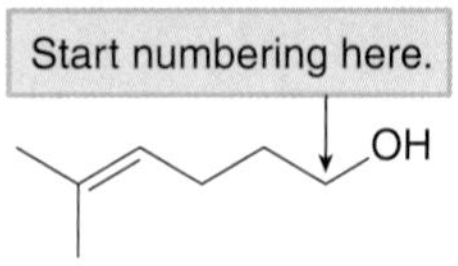 5-methyl-4-hexen-1-ol
C=C + C=O (ketone)	enone	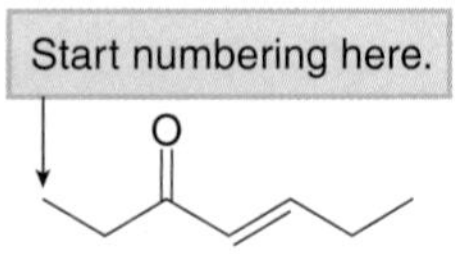 (4*E*)-4-hepten-3-one
C=C + C≡C	enyne	Start numbering here. ↓ $HC{\equiv}CCH_2CH_2CH{=}CH_2$ 1-hexen-5-yne

Naming Bicyclic Compounds

Bicyclic ring systems—compounds that contain two rings that share one or two carbon atoms—can be bridged, fused, or spiro.

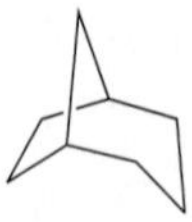
bridged ring

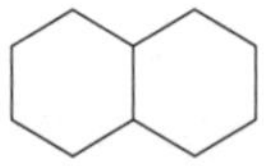
fused ring

spiro ring

- **A bridged ring system contains two rings that share two non-adjacent carbons.**
- **A fused ring system contains two rings that share a common carbon–carbon bond.**
- **A spiro ring system contains two rings that share one carbon atom.**

Fused and bridged ring systems are named as bicyclo[*x.y.z*]alkanes, where the parent alkane corresponds to the total number of carbons in both rings. The numbers *x, y,* and *z* refer to the number of carbons that join the shared carbons together, written in order of *decreasing* size. For a fused ring system, *z* always equals zero, because the two shared carbons are directly joined together. The shared carbons in a bridged ring system are called the **bridgehead carbons.**

8 C's in the ring system

↓

bicyclooctane

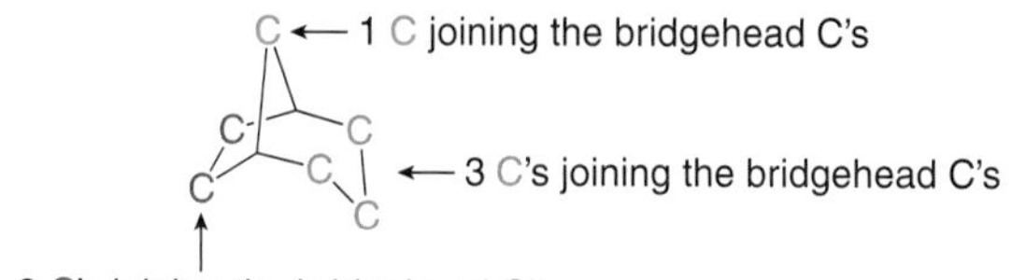
1 C joining the bridgehead C's
3 C's joining the bridgehead C's
2 C's joining the bridgehead C's

Name: bicyclo[3.2.1]octane

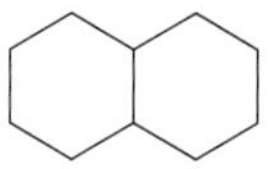

10 C's in the ring system

↓

bicyclodecane

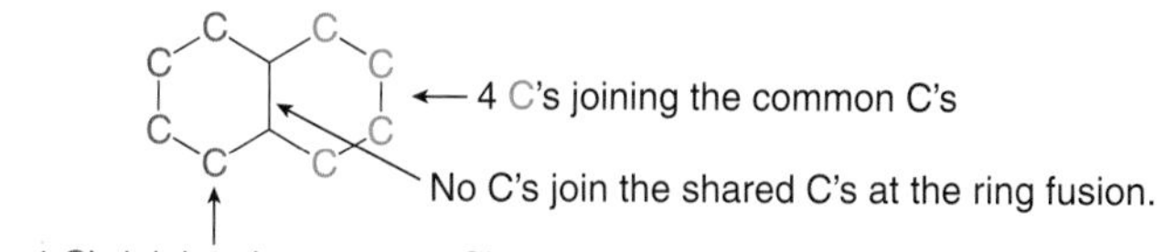
4 C's joining the common C's
No C's join the shared C's at the ring fusion.
4 C's joining the common C's

Name: bicyclo[4.4.0]decane

Rings are numbered beginning at a *shared* carbon, and continuing around the *longest* bridge first, then the next longest, and so forth.

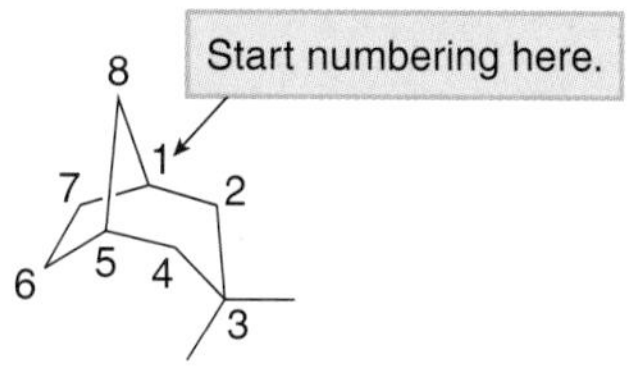
Start numbering here.
8
1
2
3
4
5
6
7

3,3-dimethylbicyclo[3.2.1]octane

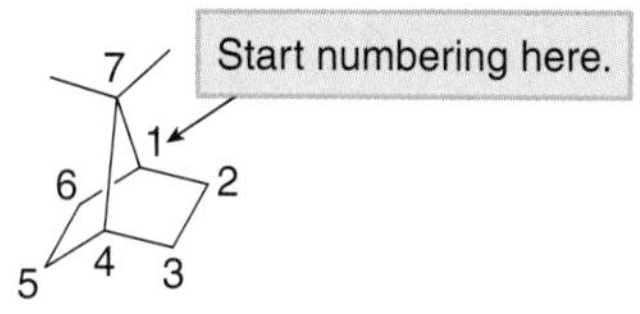
Start numbering here.
7
1
2
3
4
5
6

7,7-dimethylbicyclo[2.2.1]heptane

Spiro ring systems are named as spiro[*x.y*]alkanes where the parent alkane corresponds to the total number of carbons in both rings, and *x* and *y* refer to the number of carbons that join the shared carbon (the spiro carbon), written in order of *increasing* size. When substituents are present, the rings are numbered beginning with a carbon *adjacent* to the spiro carbon in the *smaller* ring.

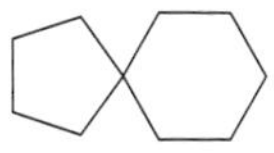

10 C's in the ring system

Name: spiro[4.5]decane

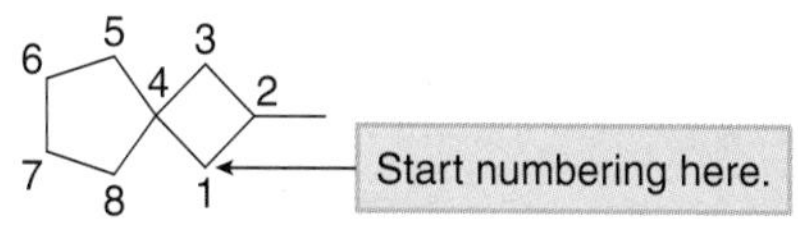
Start numbering here.
1
2
3
4
5
6
7
8

8 C's in the ring system

Name: 2-methylspiro[3.4]octane

APPENDIX C

Bond Dissociation Energies for Some Common Bonds [A–B → A· + ·B]

Bond	$\Delta H°$ kJ/mol	(kcal/mol)
H – Z bonds		
H – F	569	(136)
H – Cl	431	(103)
H – Br	368	(88)
H – I	297	(71)
H – OH	498	(119)
Z – Z bonds		
H – H	435	(104)
F – F	159	(38)
Cl – Cl	242	(58)
Br – Br	192	(46)
I – I	151	(36)
HO – OH	213	(51)
R – H bonds		
CH_3 – H	435	(104)
CH_3CH_2 – H	410	(98)
$CH_3CH_2CH_2$ – H	410	(98)
$(CH_3)_2CH$ – H	397	(95)
$(CH_3)_3C$ – H	381	(91)
$CH_2{=}CH$ – H	435	(104)
$HC{\equiv}C$ – H	523	(125)
$CH_2{=}CHCH_2$ – H	364	(87)
C_6H_5 – H	460	(110)
$C_6H_5CH_2$ – H	356	(85)
R – R bonds		
CH_3 – CH_3	368	(88)
CH_3 – CH_2CH_3	356	(85)
CH_3 – $CH{=}CH_2$	385	(92)
CH_3 – $C{\equiv}CH$	489	(117)

Bond	$\Delta H°$ kJ/mol	(kcal/mol)
R – X bonds		
CH_3 – F	456	(109)
CH_3 – Cl	351	(84)
CH_3 – Br	293	(70)
CH_3 – I	234	(56)
CH_3CH_2 – F	448	(107)
CH_3CH_2 – Cl	339	(81)
CH_3CH_2 – Br	285	(68)
CH_3CH_2 – I	222	(53)
$(CH_3)_2CH$ – F	444	(106)
$(CH_3)_2CH$ – Cl	335	(80)
$(CH_3)_2CH$ – Br	285	(68)
$(CH_3)_2CH$ – I	222	(53)
$(CH_3)_3C$ – F	444	(106)
$(CH_3)_3C$ – Cl	331	(79)
$(CH_3)_3C$ – Br	272	(65)
$(CH_3)_3C$ – I	209	(50)
R – OH bonds		
CH_3 – OH	389	(93)
CH_3CH_2 – OH	393	(94)
$CH_3CH_2CH_2$ – OH	385	(92)
$(CH_3)_2CH$ – OH	401	(96)
$(CH_3)_3C$ – OH	401	(96)
Other bonds		
$CH_2{=}CH_2$	635	(152)
$HC{\equiv}CH$	837	(200)
$O{=}C{=}O$	535	(128)
O_2	497	(119)

APPENDIX D

Reactions That Form Carbon–Carbon Bonds

Section	Reaction
11.11A	S_N2 reaction of an alkyl halide with an acetylide anion, $^{-}C{\equiv}CR$
11.11B	Opening of an epoxide ring with an acetylide anion, $^{-}C{\equiv}CR$
15.14	Radical polymerization of an alkene
16.12	Diels–Alder reaction
18.5	Friedel–Crafts alkylation
18.5	Friedel–Crafts acylation
20.10	Reaction of an aldehyde or ketone with a Grignard or organolithium reagent
20.13A	Reaction of an acid chloride with a Grignard or organolithium reagent
20.13A	Reaction of an ester with a Grignard or organolithium reagent
20.13B	Reaction of an acid chloride with an organocuprate reagent
20.14A	Reaction of a Grignard reagent with CO_2
20.14B	Reaction of an epoxide with an organometallic reagent
20.15	Reaction of an α,β-unsaturated carbonyl compound with an organocuprate reagent
21.9	Cyanohydrin formation
21.10	Wittig reaction to form an alkene
22.18	S_N2 reaction of an alkyl halide with NaCN
22.18C	Reaction of a nitrile with a Grignard or organolithium reagent
23.8	Direct enolate alkylation using LDA and an alkyl halide
23.9	Malonic ester synthesis to form a carboxylic acid
23.10	Acetoacetic ester synthesis to form a ketone
24.1	Aldol reaction to form a β-hydroxy carbonyl compound or an α,β-unsaturated carbonyl compound
24.2	Crossed aldol reaction
24.3	Directed aldol reaction
24.5	Claisen reaction to form a β-keto ester
24.6	Crossed Claisen reaction to form a β-dicarbonyl compound
24.7	Dieckmann reaction to form a five- or six-membered ring
24.8	Michael reaction to form a 1,5-dicarbonyl compound
24.9	Robinson annulation to form a 2-cyclohexenone
25.14	Reaction of a diazonium salt with CuCN
26.1	Coupling of an organocuprate reagent (R_2CuLi) with an organic halide (R'X)
26.2	The palladium-catalyzed Suzuki reaction of an organic halide with an organoborane
26.3	The palladium-catalyzed Heck reaction of a vinyl or aryl halide with an alkene
26.4	Addition of a dihalocarbene to an alkene to form a cyclopropane
26.5	Simmons–Smith reaction of an alkene with CH_2I_2 and Zn(Cu) to form a cyclopropane
26.6	Olefin metathesis
27.3	Electrocyclic reactions
27.4	Cycloaddition reactions
27.5	Sigmatropic rearrangements
28.10B	Kiliani–Fischer synthesis of an aldose
29.2B	Alkylation of diethyl acetamidomalonate to form an amino acid
29.2C	Strecker synthesis of an amino acid
31.2	Chain-growth polymerization
31.4	Polymerization using Ziegler–Natta catalysts

APPENDIX

E Characteristic IR Absorption Frequencies

Bond	Functional group	Wavenumber (cm^{-1})	Comment
O–H			
	• ROH	3600–3200	broad, strong
	• RCOOH	3500–2500	very broad, strong
N–H			
	• RNH_2	3500–3300	two peaks
	• R_2NH	3500–3300	one peak
	• $RCONH_2$, RCONHR	3400–3200	one or two peaks; N–H bending also observed at 1640 cm^{-1}
C–H			
	• C_{sp}–H	3300	sharp, often strong
	• C_{sp^2}–H	3150–3000	medium
	• C_{sp^3}–H	3000–2850	strong
	• C_{sp^2}–H of RCHO	2830–2700	one or two peaks
C≡C		2250	medium
C≡N		2250	medium
C=O			strong
	• RCOCl	1800	
	• $(RCO)_2O$	1800, 1760	two peaks
	• RCOOR	1745–1735	increasing $\tilde{\nu}$ with decreasing ring size
	• RCHO	1730	
	• R_2CO	1715	increasing $\tilde{\nu}$ with decreasing ring size
	• R_2CO, conjugated	1680	
	• RCOOH	1710	
	• $RCONH_2$, RCONHR, $RCONR_2$	1680–1630	increasing $\tilde{\nu}$ with decreasing ring size
C=C			
	• Alkene	1650	medium
	• Arene	1600, 1500	medium
C=N		1650	medium

APPENDIX

F

Characteristic NMR Absorptions

^{1}H NMR Absorptions

Compound type	Chemical shift (ppm)
Alcohol	
R–O–H	1–5
R–C(H)–O–	3.4–4.0
Aldehyde	
R–C(=O)–H	9–10
Alkane	0.9–2.0
RCH_3	~0.9
R_2CH_2	~1.3
R_3CH	~1.7
Alkene	
C=C–H *sp*^{2} C–H	4.5–6.0
C=C–C–H allylic *sp*^{3} C–H	1.5–2.5
Alkyl halide	
R–C(H)–F	4.0–4.5
R–C(H)–Cl	3.0–4.0
R–C(H)–Br	2.7–4.0
R–C(H)–I	2.2–4.0
Alkyne	
–C≡C–H	~2.5

Compound type	Chemical shift (ppm)
Amide	
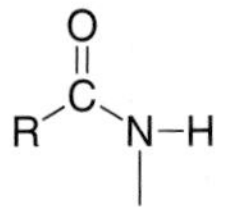	7.5–8.5
Amine	
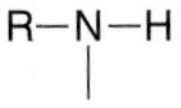	0.5–5.0
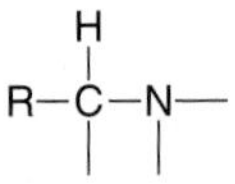	2.3–3.0
Aromatic compound	
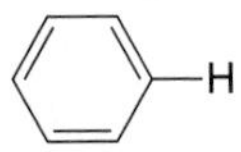 *sp*^{2} C–H	6.5–8
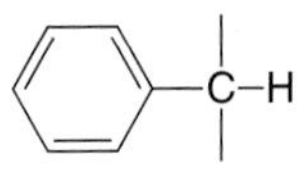 benzylic *sp*^{3} C–H	1.5–2.5
Carbonyl compound	
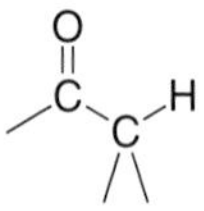 *sp*^{3} C–H on the α carbon	2.0–2.5
Carboxylic acid	
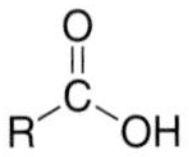	10–12
Ether	
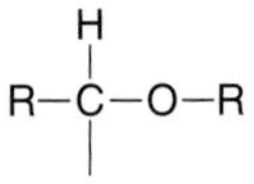	3.4–4.0

^{13}C NMR Absorptions

Carbon type	Structure	Chemical shift (ppm)
Alkyl, *sp*^{3} hybridized C	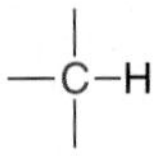	5–45
Alkyl, *sp*^{3} hybridized C bonded to N, O, or X	 Z = N, O, X	30–80
Alkynyl, *sp* hybridized C	—C≡C—	65–100
Alkenyl, *sp*^{2} hybridized C	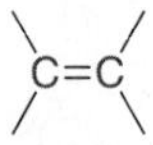	100–140
Aryl, *sp*^{2} hybridized C	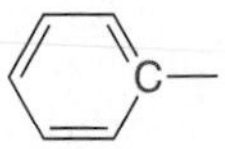	120–150
Carbonyl C	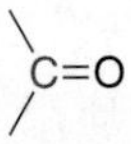	160–210

APPENDIX G

General Types of Organic Reactions

Substitution Reactions

[1] Nucleophilic substitution at an sp^3 hybridized carbon atom

a. Alkyl halides (Chapter 7)

$$\text{R–X} + \text{:Nu}^- \longrightarrow \text{R–Nu} + \text{X:}^-$$

(:Nu⁻ = nucleophile)

b. Alcohols (Section 9.11)

$$\text{R–OH} + \text{HX} \longrightarrow \text{R–X} + H_2O$$

c. Ethers (Section 9.14)

$$\text{R–OR'} + \text{HX} \longrightarrow \text{R–X} + \text{R'–X} + H_2O$$

X = Br or I

d. Epoxides (Section 9.15)

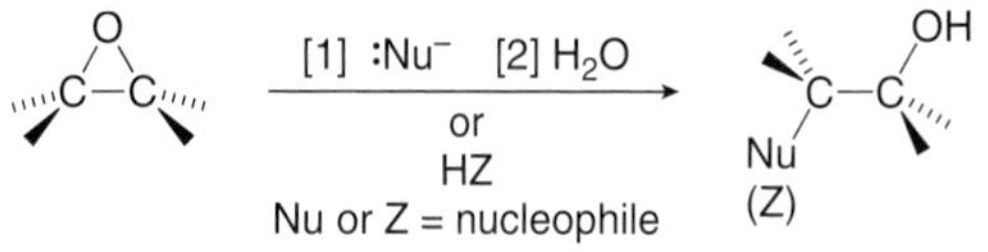

[2] Nucleophilic acyl substitution at an sp^2 hybridized carbon atom

Carboxylic acids and their derivatives (Chapter 22)

Z = OH, Cl, OCOR, OR', NR'$_2$

[3] Radical substitution at an sp^3 hybridized C – H bond

Alkanes (Section 15.3)

$$\text{R–H} + X_2 \xrightarrow{h\nu \text{ or } \Delta} \text{R–X} + \text{HX}$$

[4] Electrophilic aromatic substitution

Aromatic compounds (Chapter 18)

[5] Nucleophilic aromatic substitution

Aromatic compounds (Chapter 18)

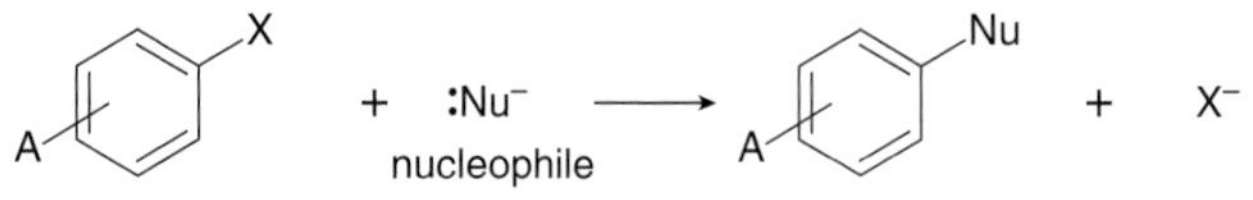

X = F, Cl, Br, I
A = H or electron-withdrawing group

Elimination Reactions

β Elimination at an *sp*³ hybridized carbon atom

a. Alkyl halides
(Chapter 8)

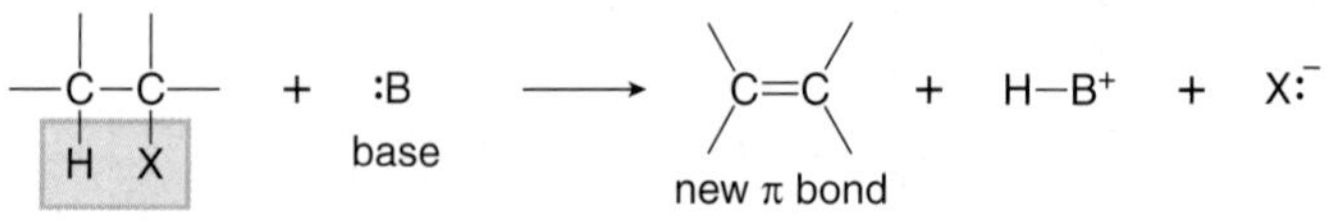

b. Alcohols
(Section 9.8)

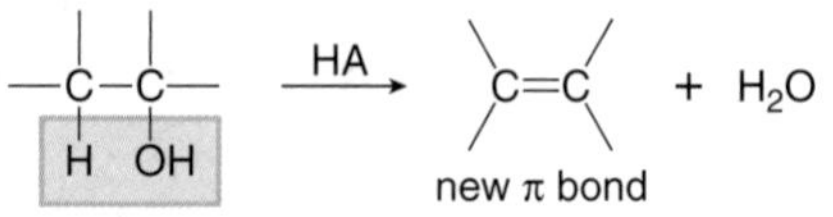

Addition Reactions

[1] Electrophilic addition to carbon–carbon multiple bonds

a. Alkenes
(Chapter 10)

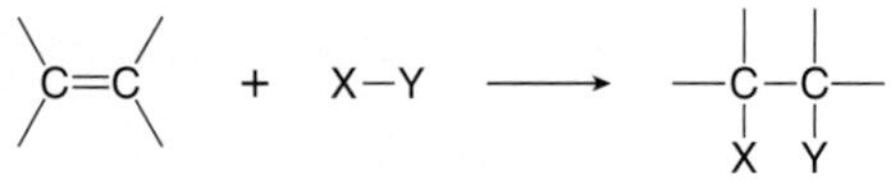

b. Alkynes
(Section 11.6)

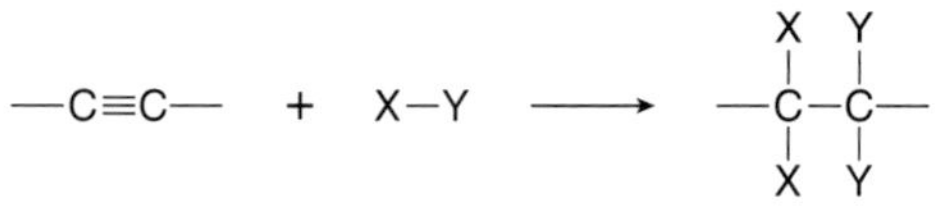

[2] Nucleophilic addition to carbon–oxygen multiple bonds

Aldehydes and ketones
(Chapter 21)

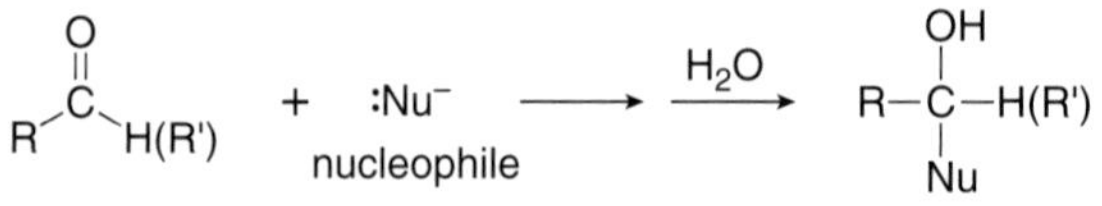

APPENDIX H

How to Synthesize Particular Functional Groups

Acetals

- Reaction of an aldehyde or ketone with two equivalents of an alcohol (21.14)

Acid chlorides

- Reaction of a carboxylic acid with thionyl chloride (22.10)

Alcohols

- Nucleophilic substitution of an alkyl halide with ^{-}OH or H_2O (9.6)
- Hydration of an alkene (10.12)
- Hydroboration–oxidation of an alkene (10.16)
- Reduction of an epoxide with $LiAlH_4$ (12.6)
- Reduction of an aldehyde or ketone (20.4)
- Hydrogenation of an α,β-unsaturated carbonyl compound with H_2 + Pd-C (20.4C)
- Enantioselective reduction of an aldehyde or ketone with the chiral CBS reagent (20.6)
- Reduction of an acid chloride with $LiAlH_4$ (20.7)
- Reduction of an ester with $LiAlH_4$ (20.7)
- Reduction of a carboxylic acid with $LiAlH_4$ (20.7)
- Reaction of an aldehyde or ketone with a Grignard or organolithium reagent (20.10)
- Reaction of an acid chloride with a Grignard or organolithium reagent (20.13)
- Reaction of an ester with a Grignard or organolithium reagent (20.13)
- Reaction of an organometallic reagent with an epoxide (20.14B)

Aldehydes

- Hydroboration–oxidation of a terminal alkyne (11.10)
- Oxidative cleavage of an alkene with O_3 followed by Zn or $(CH_3)_2S$ (12.10)
- Oxidation of a 1° alcohol with PCC (12.12)
- Oxidation of a 1° alcohol with $HCrO_4^-$, Amberlyst A-26 resin (12.13)
- Reduction of an acid chloride with $LiAlH[OC(CH_3)_3]_3$ (20.7)
- Reduction of an ester with DIBAL-H (20.7)
- Hydrolysis of an acetal (21.14B)
- Hydrolysis of an imine or enamine (21.12B)
- Reduction of a nitrile (22.18B)

Alkanes

- Catalytic hydrogenation of an alkene with H_2 + Pd-C (12.3)
- Catalytic hydrogenation of an alkyne with two equivalents of H_2 + Pd-C (12.5A)
- Reduction of an alkyl halide with $LiAlH_4$ (12.6)

- Reduction of a ketone to a methylene group (CH_2)—the Wolff–Kishner or Clemmensen reaction (18.15B)
- Protonation of an organometallic reagent with H_2O, ROH, or acid (20.9)
- Coupling of an organocuprate reagent (R_2CuLi) with an alkyl halide, R'X (26.1)
- Simmons–Smith reaction of an alkene with CH_2I_2 and Zn(Cu) to form a cyclopropane (26.5)

Alkenes

- Dehydrohalogenation of an alkyl halide with base (8.3)
- Dehydration of an alcohol with acid (9.8)
- Dehydration of an alcohol using $POCl_3$ and pyridine (9.10)
- β Elimination of an alkyl tosylate with base (9.13)
- Catalytic hydrogenation of an alkyne with H_2 + Lindlar catalyst to form a cis alkene (12.5B)
- Dissolving metal reduction of an alkyne with Na, NH_3 to form a trans alkene (12.5C)
- Wittig reaction (21.10)
- β Elimination of an α-halo carbonyl compound with Li_2CO_3, LiBr, and DMF (23.7C)
- Hofmann elimination of an amine (25.12)
- Coupling of an organocuprate reagent (R_2CuLi) with an organic halide, R'X (26.1)
- The palladium-catalyzed Suzuki reaction of a vinyl or aryl halide with a vinyl- or arylborane (26.2)
- The palladium-catalyzed Heck reaction of a vinyl or aryl halide with an alkene (26.3)
- Olefin metathesis (26.6)

Alkyl halides

- Reaction of an alcohol with HX (9.11)
- Reaction of an alcohol with $SOCl_2$ or PBr_3 (9.12)
- Cleavage of an ether with HBr or HI (9.14)
- Hydrohalogenation of an alkene with HX (10.9)
- Halogenation of an alkene with X_2 (10.13)
- Hydrohalogenation of an alkyne with two equivalents of HX (11.7)
- Halogenation of an alkyne with two equivalents of X_2 (11.8)
- Radical halogenation of an alkane (15.3)
- Radical halogenation at an allylic carbon (15.10)
- Radical addition of HBr to an alkene (15.13)
- Electrophilic addition of HX to a 1,3-diene (16.10)
- Radical halogenation of an alkyl benzene (18.14)
- Halogenation α to a carbonyl group (23.7)
- Addition of a dihalocarbene to an alkene to form a dihalocyclopropane (26.4)

Alkynes

- Dehydrohalogenation of an alkyl dihalide with base (11.5)
- S_N2 reaction of an alkyl halide with an acetylide anion, $^-C{\equiv}CR$ (11.11)

Amides

- Reaction of an acid chloride with NH_3 or an amine (22.8)
- Reaction of an anhydride with NH_3 or an amine (22.9)
- Reaction of a carboxylic acid with NH_3 or an amine and DCC (22.10)
- Reaction of an ester with NH_3 or an amine (22.11)

Amines

- Nucleophilic aromatic substitution (18.13)
- Reduction of a nitro group (18.15C)
- Reduction of an amide with $LiAlH_4$ (20.7B)
- Reduction of a nitrile (22.18B)
- S_N2 reaction using NH_3 or an amine (25.7A)
- Gabriel synthesis (25.7A)
- Reductive amination of an aldehyde or ketone (25.7C)

Amino acids

- S_N2 reaction of an α-halo carboxylic acid with excess NH_3 (29.2A)
- Alkylation of diethyl acetamidomalonate (29.2B)
- Strecker synthesis (29.2C)
- Enantioselective hydrogenation using a chiral catalyst (29.4)

Anhydrides

- Reaction of an acid chloride with a carboxylate anion (22.8)
- Dehydration of a dicarboxylic acid (22.10)

Aryl halides

- Halogenation of benzene with $X_2 + FeX_3$ (18.3)
- Reaction of a diazonium salt with CuCl, CuBr, HBF_4, NaI, or KI (25.14A)

Carboxylic acids

- Oxidative cleavage of an alkyne with ozone (12.11)
- Oxidation of a 1° alcohol with CrO_3 (or a similar Cr^{6+} reagent), H_2O, H_2SO_4 (12.12B)
- Oxidation of an alkyl benzene with $KMnO_4$ (18.15A)
- Oxidation of an aldehyde (20.8)
- Reaction of a Grignard reagent with CO_2 (20.14A)
- Hydrolysis of a cyanohydrin (21.9)
- Hydrolysis of an acid chloride (22.8)
- Hydrolysis of an anhydride (22.9)
- Hydrolysis of an ester (22.11)
- Hydrolysis of an amide (22.13)
- Hydrolysis of a nitrile (22.18A)
- Malonic ester synthesis (23.9)

Cyanohydrins

- Addition of HCN to an aldehyde or ketone (21.9)

1,2-Diols

- Anti dihydroxylation of an alkene with a peroxyacid, followed by ring opening with ^{-}OH or H_2O (12.9A)
- Syn dihydroxylation of an alkene with $KMnO_4$ or OsO_4 (12.9B)

Enamines

- Reaction of an aldehyde or ketone with a 2° amine (21.12)

Epoxides

- Intramolecular S_N2 reaction of a halohydrin using base (9.6)
- Epoxidation of an alkene with mCPBA (12.8)
- Enantioselective epoxidation of an allylic alcohol with the Sharpless reagent (12.15)

Esters

- S_N2 reaction of an alkyl halide with a carboxylate anion, $RCOO^-$ (7.19)
- Reaction of an acid chloride with an alcohol (22.8)
- Reaction of an anhydride with an alcohol (22.9)
- Fischer esterification of a carboxylic acid with an alcohol (22.10)

Ethers

- Williamson ether synthesis—S_N2 reaction of an alkyl halide with an alkoxide, ^-OR (9.6)
- Reaction of an alkyl tosylate with an alkoxide, ^-OR (9.13)
- Addition of an alcohol to an alkene in the presence of acid (10.12)
- Anionic polymerization of epoxides to form polyethers (31.3)

Halohydrins

- Reaction of an epoxide with HX (9.15)
- Addition of X and OH to an alkene (10.15)

Imine

- Reaction of an aldehyde or ketone with a 1° amine (21.11)

Ketones

- Hydration of an alkyne with H_2O, H_2SO_4, and $HgSO_4$ (11.9)
- Oxidative cleavage of an alkene with O_3 followed by Zn or $(CH_3)_2S$ (12.10)
- Oxidation of a 2° alcohol with any Cr^{6+} reagent (12.12, 12.13)
- Friedel–Crafts acylation (18.5)
- Reaction of an acid chloride with an organocuprate reagent (20.13)
- Hydrolysis of an imine or enamine (21.12B)
- Hydrolysis of an acetal (21.14B)
- Reaction of a nitrile with a Grignard or organolithium reagent (22.18C)
- Acetoacetic ester synthesis (23.10)

Nitriles

- S_N2 reaction of an alkyl halide with NaCN (7.19, 22.18)
- Reaction of an aryl diazonium salt with CuCN (25.14A)

Phenols

- Reaction of an aryl diazonium salt with H_2O (25.14A)
- Nucleophilic aromatic substitution (18.13)

Glossary

A

Absolute configuration (Section 28.11): The exact three-dimensional arrangement of the stereogenic centers in a molecule.

Acetal (Section 21.14): A compound having the general structure $R_2C(OR')_2$, where R = H, alkyl, or aryl. Acetals are used as protecting groups for aldehydes and ketones.

Acetoacetic ester synthesis (Section 23.10): A stepwise method that converts ethyl acetoacetate into a ketone having one or two carbons bonded to the α carbon.

Acetylation (Section 22.9): A reaction that transfers an acetyl group (CH_3CO-) from one atom to another.

Acetyl coenzyme A (Section 22.17): A biochemical thioester that acts as an acetylating reagent. Acetyl coenzyme A is often referred to as acetyl CoA.

Acetyl group (Section 21.2E): A substituent having the structure $-COCH_3$.

Acetylide anion (Sections 11.11, 20.9B): An anion formed by treating a terminal alkyne with a strong base. Acetylide anions have the general structure $R-C\equiv C^-$.

Achiral molecule (Section 5.3): A molecule that is superimposable upon its mirror image. An achiral molecule is not chiral.

Acid chloride (Sections 20.1, 22.1): A compound having the general structure RCOCl.

Acidity constant (Section 2.3): A value symbolized by K_a that represents the strength of an acid (HA). The larger the K_a, the stronger the acid.

$$K_a = \frac{[H_3O^+][A{:}^-]}{[H-A]}$$

Active site (Section 6.11): The region of an enzyme that binds the substrate.

Acyclic alkane (Section 4.1): A compound with the general formula C_nH_{2n+2}. Acyclic alkanes are also called saturated hydrocarbons because they contain the maximum number of hydrogen atoms per carbon.

Acylation (Sections 18.5A, 22.17): A reaction that transfers an acyl group from one atom to another.

Acyl chloride (Section 18.5A): A compound having the general structure RCOCl. Acyl chlorides are also called acid chlorides.

Acyl group (Section 18.5A): A substituent having the general structure $RCO-$.

Acylium ion (Section 18.5B): A positively charged electrophile having the general structure $(R-C\equiv O)^+$, formed when the Lewis acid $AlCl_3$ ionizes the carbon–halogen bond of an acid chloride.

Acyl transfer reaction (Section 22.17): A reaction that transfers an acyl group from one atom to another.

1,2-Addition (Sections 16.10, 20.15): An addition reaction to a conjugated system that adds groups across two adjacent atoms.

1,4-Addition (Sections 16.10, 20.15): An addition reaction that adds groups to the atoms in the 1 and 4 positions of a conjugated system. 1,4-Addition is also called conjugate addition.

Addition polymer (Section 31.1): A polymer prepared by a chain reaction that adds a monomer to the growing end of a polymer chain. Addition polymers are also called chain-growth polymers.

Addition reaction (Sections 6.2C, 10.8): A reaction in which elements are added to a starting material. In an addition reaction, a π bond is broken and two σ bonds are formed.

Aglycon (Section 28.7C): The alcohol formed from hydrolysis of a glycoside.

Alcohol (Section 9.1): A compound having the general structure ROH. An alcohol contains a hydroxy group (OH group) bonded to an sp^3 hybridized carbon atom.

Aldaric acid (Section 28.9B): The dicarboxylic acid formed by the oxidation of the aldehyde and the primary alcohol of an aldose.

Aldehyde (Section 11.10): A compound having the general structure RCHO, where R = H, alkyl, or aryl.

Alditol (Section 28.9A): A compound formed by the reduction of the aldehyde of an aldose to a primary alcohol.

Aldol condensation (Section 24.1B): An aldol reaction in which the initially formed β-hydroxy carbonyl compound loses water by dehydration.

Aldol reaction (Section 24.1A): A reaction in which two molecules of an aldehyde or ketone react with each other in the presence of base to form a β-hydroxy carbonyl compound.

Aldonic acid (Section 28.9B): A compound formed by the oxidation of the aldehyde of an aldose to a carboxylic acid.

Aldose (Section 28.2): A monosaccharide comprised of a polyhydroxy aldehyde.

Aliphatic (Section 3.2A): A compound or portion of a compound made up of $C-C$ σ and π bonds but not aromatic bonds.

Alkaloid (Section 25.6A): A basic, nitrogen-containing compound isolated from a plant source.

Alkane (Section 4.1): An aliphatic hydrocarbon having only $C-C$ and $C-H$ σ bonds.

Alkene (Section 8.2A): An aliphatic hydrocarbon that contains a carbon–carbon double bond.

Alkoxide (Sections 8.1, 9.6): An anion having the general structure RO^-, formed by deprotonating an alcohol with a base.

Alkoxy group (Section 9.3B): A substituent containing an alkyl group bonded to an oxygen (RO group).

Alkylation (Section 23.8): A reaction that transfers an alkyl group from one atom to another.

Alkyl group (Section 4.4A): A group formed by removing one hydrogen from an alkane. Alkyl groups are named by replacing the suffix *-ane* of the parent alkane with *-yl.*

Alkyl halide (Section 7.1): A compound containing a halogen atom bonded to an sp^3 hybridized carbon atom. Alkyl halides have the general molecular formula $C_nH_{2n+1}X$.

1,2-Alkyl shift (Section 9.9): The rearrangement of a less stable carbocation to a more stable carbocation by the shift of an alkyl group from one carbon atom to an adjacent carbon atom.

Alkyl tosylate (Section 9.13): A compound having the general structure $ROSO_2C_6H_4CH_3$. Alkyl tosylates are also called tosylates and are abbreviated as ROTs.

Alkyne (Section 8.10): An aliphatic hydrocarbon that contains a carbon–carbon triple bond.

Allyl carbocation (Section 16.1B): A carbocation that has a positive charge on the atom adjacent to a carbon–carbon double bond. An allyl carbocation is resonance stabilized.

Allyl group (Section 10.3C): A substituent having the structure $-CH_2-CH=CH_2$.

Allylic bromination (Section 15.10A): A radical substitution reaction in which bromine replaces a hydrogen atom on the carbon adjacent to a carbon–carbon double bond.

Allylic carbon (Section 15.10): A carbon atom bonded to a carbon–carbon double bond.

Allylic halide (Section 7.1): A molecule containing a halogen atom bonded to the carbon atom adjacent to a carbon–carbon double bond.

Allyl radical (Section 15.10): A radical that has an unpaired electron on the carbon adjacent to a carbon–carbon double bond. An allyl radical is resonance stabilized.

Alpha (α) carbon (Sections 8.1, 19.2B): In an elimination reaction, the carbon that is bonded to the leaving group. In a carbonyl compound, the carbon that is bonded to the carbonyl carbon.

Ambident nucleophile (Section 23.3C): A nucleophile that has two reactive sites.

Amide (Sections 20.1, 22.1): A compound having the general structure $RCONR'_2$, where R' = H or alkyl.

Amide base (Sections 8.10, 23.3B): A nitrogen-containing base formed by deprotonating an amine or ammonia.

Amine (Sections 21.11, 25.1): A basic organic nitrogen compound having the general structure RNH_2, R_2NH, or R_3N. An amine has a nonbonded pair of electrons on the nitrogen atom.

α-Amino acid (Sections 19.14A, 29.1): A compound having the general structure $RCH(NH_2)COOH$. α-Amino acids are the building blocks of proteins.

Amino acid residue (Section 29.5): The individual amino acids in peptides and proteins.

Amino group (Section 25.3D): A substituent having the structure $-NH_2$.

α-Amino nitrile (Section 29.2C): A compound having the general structure $RCH(NH_2)C{\equiv}N$.

Amino sugar (Section 28.14A): A carbohydrate that contains an NH_2 group instead of a hydroxy group at a non-anomeric carbon.

Ammonium salt (Section 25.1): A compound containing a positively charged nitrogen with four σ bonds; for example, $R_4N^+X^-$.

Angle strain (Section 4.11): An increase in the energy of a molecule resulting when the bond angles of the sp^3 hybridized atoms deviate from the optimum tetrahedral angle of 109.5°.

Angular methyl group (Section 30.8A): A methyl group located at the ring junction of two fused rings of the steroid skeleton.

Anhydride (Section 22.1): A compound having the general structure $(RCO)_2O$.

Aniline (Section 25.3C): A compound having the structure $C_6H_5NH_2$.

Anion (Section 1.2): A negatively charged ion that results from a neutral atom gaining one or more electrons.

Anionic polymerization (Section 31.2C): Chain-growth polymerization of alkenes substituted by electron-withdrawing groups that stabilize intermediate anions.

Annulation (Section 24.9): A reaction that forms a new ring.

Annulene (Section 17.8A): A hydrocarbon containing a single ring with alternating double and single bonds.

α Anomer (Section 28.6): The stereoisomer of a cyclic monosaccharide in which the anomeric OH and the CH_2OH groups are trans. In a D monosaccharide, the hydroxy group on the anomeric carbon is drawn down.

β Anomer (Section 28.6): The stereoisomer of a cyclic monosaccharide in which the anomeric OH and the CH_2OH groups are cis. In a D monosaccharide, the hydroxy group on the anomeric carbon is drawn up.

Anomeric carbon (Section 28.6): The stereogenic center at the hemiacetal carbon of a cyclic monosaccharide.

Antarafacial reaction (Section 27.4): A pericyclic reaction that occurs on opposite sides of the two ends of the π electron system.

Anti addition (Section 10.8): An addition reaction in which the two parts of a reagent are added from opposite sides of a double bond.

Antiaromatic compound (Section 17.7): An organic compound that is cyclic, planar, completely conjugated, and has $4n$ π electrons.

Antibonding molecular orbital (Section 17.9A): A high-energy molecular orbital formed when two atomic orbitals of opposite phase overlap.

Anti conformation (Section 4.10): A staggered conformation in which the two larger groups on adjacent carbon atoms have a dihedral angle of 180°.

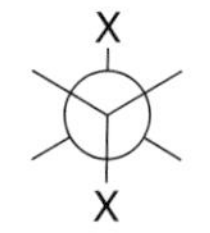

Anti dihydroxylation (Section 12.9A): The addition of two hydroxy groups to opposite faces of a double bond.

Antioxidant (Section 15.12): A compound that stops an oxidation from occurring.

Anti periplanar (Section 8.8A): In an elimination reaction, a geometry where the β hydrogen and the leaving group are on opposite sides of the molecule.

Aromatic compound (Section 17.1): A planar, cyclic organic compound that has p orbitals on all ring atoms and a total of $4n + 2$ π electrons in the orbitals.

Aryl group (Section 17.3D): A substituent formed by removing one hydrogen atom from an aromatic ring.

Aryl halide (Sections 7.1, 18.3): A molecule such as C_6H_5X, containing a halogen atom X bonded to an aromatic ring.

Asymmetric carbon (Section 5.3): A carbon atom that is bonded to four different groups. An asymmetric carbon is also called a stereogenic center, a chiral center, or a chirality center.

Asymmetric reaction (Sections 12.15, 20.6A, 29.4): A reaction that converts an achiral starting material into predominantly one enantiomer.

Atactic polymer (Section 31.4): A polymer having the substituents randomly oriented along the carbon backbone of an elongated polymer chain.

Atomic number (Section 1.1): The number of protons in the nucleus of an element.

Atomic weight (Section 1.1): The weighted average of the mass of all isotopes of a particular element. The atomic weight is reported in atomic mass units (amu).

Axial bonds (Section 4.12A): Bonds located above or below and perpendicular to the plane of the chair conformation of cyclohexane. Three axial bonds point upwards (on the up carbons) and three axial bonds point downwards (on the down carbons).

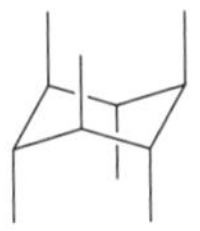

Azo compound (Section 25.15): A compound having the general structure RN=NR'.

B

Backside attack (Section 7.11C): Approach of a nucleophile from the side opposite the leaving group.

Barrier to rotation (Section 4.10): The energy difference between the lowest and highest energy conformations of a molecule.

Base peak (Section 13.1): The peak in the mass spectrum having the greatest abundance value.

Basicity (Section 7.8): A measure of how readily an atom donates its electron pair to a proton.

Benedict's reagent (Section 28.9B): A reagent for oxidizing aldehydes to carboxylic acids using a Cu^{2+} salt, forming brick-red Cu_2O as a side product.

Benzoyl group (Section 21.2E): A substituent having the structure $-COC_6H_5$.

Benzyl group (Section 17.3D): A substituent having the structure $C_6H_5CH_2-$.

Benzylic halide (Sections 7.1, 18.14): A compound such as $C_6H_5CH_2X$, containing a halogen atom X bonded to a carbon that is bonded to a benzene ring.

Benzyne (Section 18.13B): A reactive intermediate formed by elimination of HX from an aryl halide.

Beta (β) carbon (Sections 8.1, 19.2B): In an elimination reaction, the carbon adjacent to the carbon with the leaving group. In a carbonyl compound, the carbon located two carbons from the carbonyl carbon.

Bimolecular reaction (Sections 6.9B, 7.10, 7.13A): A reaction in which the concentration of both reactants affects the reaction rate and both terms appear in the rate equation. In a bimolecular reaction, two reactants are involved in the only step or the rate-determining step.

Biodegradable polymer (Section 31.9B): A polymer that can be degraded by microorganisms naturally present in the environment.

Biomolecule (Section 3.9): An organic compound found in a biological system.

Boat conformation of cyclohexane (Section 4.12B): An unstable conformation adopted by cyclohexane that resembles a boat. The instability of the boat conformation results from torsional strain and steric strain. The boat conformation of cyclohexane is 30 kJ/mol less stable than the chair conformation.

Boiling point (Section 3.4A): The temperature at which molecules in the liquid phase are converted to the gas phase. Molecules with stronger intermolecular forces have higher boiling points. Boiling point is abbreviated as bp.

Bond dissociation energy (Section 6.4): The amount of energy needed to homolytically cleave a covalent bond.

Bonding (Section 1.2): The joining of two atoms in a stable arrangement. Bonding is a favorable process that leads to lowered energy and increased stability.

Bonding molecular orbital (Section 17.9A): A low-energy molecular orbital formed when two atomic orbitals of similar phase overlap.

Bond length (Section 1.7A): The average distance between the centers of two bonded nuclei. Bond lengths are reported in picometers (pm).

Branched-chain alkane (Section 4.1A): An acyclic alkane that has alkyl substituents bonded to the parent carbon chain.

Bridged ring system (Section 16.13D): A bicyclic ring system in which the two rings share non-adjacent carbon atoms.

Bromination (Sections 10.13, 15.6, 18.3): The reaction of a compound with bromine.

Bromohydrin (Section 10.15): A compound having a bromine and a hydroxy group on adjacent carbon atoms.

Brønsted–Lowry acid (Section 2.1): A proton donor, symbolized by HA. A Brønsted–Lowry acid must contain a hydrogen atom.

Brønsted–Lowry base (Section 2.1): A proton acceptor, symbolized by :B. A Brønsted–Lowry base must be able to form a bond to a proton by donating an available electron pair.

C

^{13}C NMR spectroscopy (Section 14.1): A form of nuclear magnetic resonance spectroscopy used to determine the type of carbon atoms in a molecule.

Cahn–Ingold–Prelog system of nomenclature (Section 5.6): The system of designating a stereogenic center as either *R* or *S* according to the arrangement of the four groups attached to the center.

Carbamate (Sections 29.7, 31.6): A functional group containing a carbonyl group bonded to both an oxygen and a nitrogen atom. A carbamate is also called a urethane.

Carbanion (Section 2.5D): An ion with a negative charge on a carbon atom.

Carbene (Section 26.4): A neutral reactive intermediate having the general structure $:CR_2$. A carbene contains a divalent carbon surrounded by six electrons, making it a highly reactive electrophile that adds to C−C double bonds.

Carbinolamine (Section 21.7B): An unstable intermediate having a hydroxy group and an amine group on the same carbon. A carbinolamine is formed during the addition of an amine to a carbonyl group.

Carbocation (Section 7.13C): A positively charged carbon atom. A carbocation is sp^2 hybridized and trigonal planar, and contains a vacant *p* orbital.

Carbohydrate (Sections 21.17, 28.1): A polyhydroxy aldehyde or ketone or a compound that can be hydrolyzed to a polyhydroxy aldehyde or ketone.

Carbonate (Section 31.6D): A compound having the general structure $(RO)_2C=O$.

Carbon backbone (Section 3.1): The C−C and C−H σ bond framework that makes up the skeleton of an organic molecule.

Carbon NMR spectroscopy (Section 14.1): A form of nuclear magnetic resonance spectroscopy used to determine the type of carbon atoms in a molecule.

Carbonyl group (Sections 3.2C, 11.9, 20.1): A functional group that contains a carbon–oxygen double bond (C=O). The polar carbon–oxygen bond makes the carbonyl carbon electrophilic.

Carboxy group (Section 19.1): A functional group having the structure COOH.

Carboxylate anion (Section 19.2C): An anion having the general structure $RCOO^-$, formed by deprotonating a carboxylic acid with a Brønsted–Lowry base.

Carboxylation (Section 20.14): The reaction of an organometallic reagent with CO_2 to form a carboxylic acid after protonation.

Carboxylic acid (Section 19.1): A compound having the general structure RCOOH.

Carboxylic acid derivatives (Section 20.1): Compounds having the general structure RCOZ, which can be synthesized from carboxylic acids. Common carboxylic acid derivatives include acid chlorides, anhydrides, esters, and amides.

Catalyst (Section 6.10): A substance that speeds up the rate of a reaction, but is recovered unchanged at the end of the reaction and does not appear in the product.

Catalytic hydrogenation (Section 12.3): A reduction reaction involving the addition of H_2 to a π bond in the presence of a metal catalyst.

Cation (Section 1.2): A positively charged ion that results from a neutral atom losing one or more electrons.

Cationic polymerization (Section 31.2C): Chain-growth polymerization of alkene monomers involving carbocation intermediates.

CBS reagent (Section 20.6A): A chiral reducing agent formed by reacting an oxazaborolidine with BH_3. CBS reagents predictably give one enantiomer as the major product of ketone reduction.

Cephalin (Section 30.4A): A phosphoacylglycerol in which the phosphodiester alkyl group is $-CH_2CH_2NH_3^+$. Cephalins are also called phosphatidylethanolamines.

Chain-growth polymer (Section 31.1): A polymer prepared by a chain reaction that adds a monomer to the growing end of a polymer chain. Chain-growth polymers are also called addition polymers.

Chain mechanism (Section 15.4A): A reaction mechanism that involves repeating steps.

Chair conformation of cyclohexane (Section 4.12A): A stable conformation adopted by cyclohexane that resembles a chair. The stability of the chair conformation results from the elimination of angle strain (all C–C–C bond angles are 109.5°) and torsional strain (all groups on adjacent carbon atoms are staggered).

Chemical shift (Section 14.1B): The position of an absorption signal on the *x* axis in an NMR spectrum relative to the reference signal of tetramethylsilane.

Chirality center (Section 5.3): A carbon atom bonded to four different groups. A chirality center is also called a chiral center, a stereogenic center, and an asymmetric center.

Chiral molecule (Section 5.3): A molecule that is not superimposable upon its mirror image.

Chlorination (Sections 10.14, 15.5, 18.3): The reaction of a compound with chlorine.

Chlorofluorocarbons (Sections 7.4, 15.9): Synthetic alkyl halides having the general molecular formula CF_xCl_{4-x}. Chlorofluorocarbons, abbreviated as CFCs, were used as refrigerants and aerosol propellants and contribute to the destruction of the ozone layer.

Chlorohydrin (Section 10.15): A compound having a chlorine and a hydroxy group on adjacent carbon atoms.

Chromate ester (Section 12.12A): An intermediate in the chromium-mediated oxidation of an alcohol having the general structure $R-O-CrO_3H$.

***s*-Cis** (Sections 16.6, 29.5B): The conformation of a 1,3-diene that has the two double bonds on the same side of the single bond that joins them.

Cis isomer (Sections 4.13B, 8.2B): An isomer of a ring or double bond that has two groups on the same side of the ring or double bond.

Claisen reaction (Section 24.5): A reaction between two molecules of an ester in the presence of base to form a β-keto ester.

Claisen rearrangement (Section 27.5): A [3,3] sigmatropic rearrangement of an unsaturated ether to a γ,δ-unsaturated carbonyl compound.

α Cleavage (Section 13.3B): A fragmentation in mass spectrometry that results in cleavage of a carbon–carbon bond. With aldehydes and ketones, α cleavage results in breaking the bond between the carbonyl carbon and the carbon adjacent to it. With alcohols, α cleavage occurs by breaking a bond between an alkyl group and the carbon that bears the OH group.

Clemmensen reduction (Section 18.15B): A method to reduce aryl ketones to alkyl benzenes using Zn(Hg) in the presence of a strong acid.

Coenzyme (Section 12.13): A compound that acts with an enzyme to carry out a biochemical process.

Combustion (Section 4.14B): An oxidation–reduction reaction, in which an alkane or other organic compound reacts with oxygen to form CO_2 and H_2O, releasing energy.

Common name (Section 4.6): The name of a molecule that was adopted prior to and therefore does not follow the IUPAC system of nomenclature.

Compound (Section 1.2): The structure that results when two or more elements are joined together in a stable arrangement.

Concerted reaction (Sections 6.3, 7.11B): A reaction in which all bond forming and bond breaking occurs in one step.

Condensation polymer (Sections 22.16A, 31.1): A polymer formed when monomers containing two functional groups come together with loss of a small molecule such as water or HCl. Condensation polymers are also called step-growth polymers.

Condensation reaction (Section 24.1B): A reaction in which a small molecule, often water, is eliminated during the reaction process.

Condensed structure (Section 1.8A): A shorthand representation of the structure of a compound in which all atoms are drawn in but bonds and lone pairs are usually omitted. Parentheses are used to denote similar groups bonded to the same atom.

Configuration (Section 5.2): A particular three-dimensional arrangement of atoms.

Conformations (Section 4.9): The different arrangements of atoms that are interconverted by rotation about single bonds.

Conjugate acid (Section 2.2): The compound that results when a base gains a proton in a proton transfer reaction.

Conjugate addition (Sections 16.10, 20.15): An addition reaction that adds groups to the atoms in the 1 and 4 positions of a conjugated system. Conjugate addition is also called 1,4-addition.

Conjugate base (Section 2.2): The compound that results when an acid loses a proton in a proton transfer reaction.

Conjugated diene (Section 16.1A): A compound that contains two carbon–carbon double bonds joined by a single σ bond. Pi (π) electrons are delocalized over both double bonds. Conjugated dienes are also called 1,3-dienes.

Conjugated protein (Section 29.10C): A structure composed of a protein unit and a non-protein molecule.

Conjugation (Section 16.1): The overlap of *p* orbitals on three or more adjacent atoms.

Conrotatory rotation (Section 27.3): Rotation of *p* orbitals in the same direction during electrocyclic ring closure or ring opening.

Constitutional isomers (Sections 1.4, 4.1A, 5.2): Two compounds that have the same molecular formula, but differ in the way the atoms are connected to each other. Constitutional isomers are also called structural isomers.

Coordination polymerization (Section 31.4): A polymerization reaction that uses a homogeneous catalyst that is soluble in the reaction solvents typically used.

Cope rearrangement (Section 27.5): A [3,3] sigmatropic rearrangement of a 1,5-diene to an isomeric 1,5-diene.

Copolymer (Section 31.2D): A polymer prepared by joining two or more different monomers together.

Core electrons (Section 1.1): The electrons in the inner shells of orbitals. Core electrons are not usually involved in the chemistry of a particular element.

Counterion (Section 2.1): An ion that does not take part in a reaction and is opposite in charge to the ion that does take part in the reaction. A counterion is also called a spectator ion.

Coupling constant (Section 14.6A): The frequency difference, measured in Hz, between the peaks in a split NMR signal.

Coupling reaction (Section 25.15): A reaction that forms a bond between two discrete molecules.

Covalent bond (Section 1.2): A bond that results from the sharing of electrons between two nuclei. A covalent bond is a two-electron bond.

Crossed aldol reaction (Section 24.2): An aldol reaction in which the two reacting carbonyl compounds are different. A crossed aldol reaction is also called a mixed aldol reaction.

Crossed Claisen reaction (Section 24.6): A Claisen reaction in which the two reacting esters are different.

Crown ether (Section 3.7B): A cyclic ether containing multiple oxygen atoms. Crown ethers bind specific cations depending on the size of their central cavity.

Curved arrow notation (Section 1.6A): A convention that shows the movement of an electron pair. The tail of the arrow begins at the electron pair and the head points to where the electron pair moves.

Cyanide anion (Section 21.9A): An anion having the structure $^{-}C{\equiv}N$.

Cyano group (Section 22.1): A functional group consisting of a carbon–nitrogen triple bond ($C{\equiv}N$).

Cyanohydrin (Section 21.9): A compound having the general structure $RCH(OH)C{\equiv}N$. A cyanohydrin results from the addition of HCN across the carbonyl of an aldehyde or a ketone.

Cycloaddition (Section 27.1): A pericyclic reaction between two compounds with π bonds to form a cyclic product with two new σ bonds.

Cycloalkane (Sections 4.1, 4.2): A compound that contains carbons joined in one or more rings. Cycloalkanes with one ring have the general formula C_nH_{2n}.

Cyclopropanation (Section 26.4): An addition reaction to a carbon–carbon double bond that forms a cyclopropane.

D

D-Sugar (Section 28.2C): A sugar with the hydroxy group on the stereogenic center farthest from the carbonyl on the right side in the Fischer projection formula.

Decalin (Section 30.8A): Two fused six-membered rings. *cis*-Decalin has the hydrogen atoms at the ring fusion on the same side of the rings, whereas *trans*-decalin has the hydrogen atoms at the ring fusion on opposite sides of the rings.

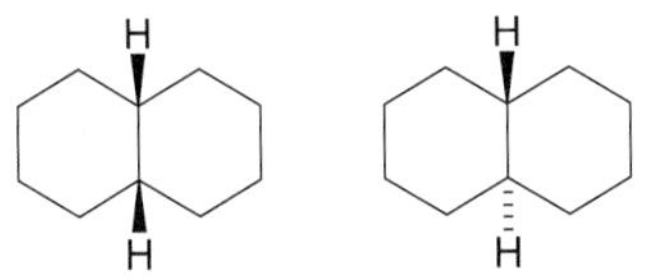

Decarboxylation (Section 23.9A): Loss of CO_2 through cleavage of a carbon–carbon bond.

Degenerate orbitals (Section 17.9B): Orbitals (either atomic or molecular) having the same energy.

Degree of unsaturation (Section 10.2): A ring or a π bond in a molecule. The number of degrees of unsaturation compares the number of hydrogens in a compound to that of a saturated hydrocarbon containing the same number of carbons.

Dehydration (Sections 9.8, 22.10B): A reaction that results in the loss of the elements of water from the reaction components.

Dehydrohalogenation (Section 8.1): An elimination reaction in which the elements of hydrogen and halogen are lost from a starting material.

Delta (δ) scale (Section 14.1B): A common scale of chemical shifts used in NMR spectroscopy in which the absorption due to tetramethylsilane (TMS) occurs at zero parts per million.

Deoxy (Section 28.14B): A prefix that means without oxygen.

Deoxyribonucleoside (Section 28.14B): An *N*-glycoside formed by the reaction of D-2-deoxyribose with certain amine heterocycles.

Deoxyribonucleotide (Section 28.14B): A DNA building block having a deoxyribose and either a purine or pyrimidine base joined together by an *N*-glycosidic linkage, and a phosphate bonded to a hydroxy group of the sugar nucleus.

Deprotection (Section 20.12): A reaction that removes a protecting group, regenerating a functional group.

Deshielding effects (Section 14.3A): An effect in NMR caused by a decrease in electron density, thus increasing the strength of the magnetic field felt by the nucleus. Deshielding shifts an absorption downfield.

Dextrorotatory (Section 5.12A): Rotating plane-polarized light in the clockwise direction. The rotation is labeled *d* or (+).

1,3-Diacid (Section 23.9A): A compound containing two carboxylic acids separated by a single carbon atom. 1,3-Diacids are also called β-diacids.

Dialkylamide (Section 23.3B): An amide base having the general structure R_2N^-.

Diastereomers (Section 5.7): Stereoisomers that are not mirror images of each other. Diastereomers have the same *R,S* designation for at least one stereogenic center and the opposite *R,S* designation for at least one of the other stereogenic centers.

Diastereotopic protons (Section 14.2C): Two hydrogen atoms on the same carbon such that substitution of either hydrogen with a group Z forms diastereomers. The two hydrogen atoms are not equivalent and give two NMR signals.

1,3-Diaxial interaction (Section 4.13A): A steric interaction between two axial substituents of the chair form of cyclohexane. Larger axial substituents create unfavorable 1,3-diaxial interactions, destabilizing a cyclohexane conformation.

Diazonium salt (Section 25.13A): An ionic salt having the general structure $(R-N\equiv N)^+Cl^-$.

Diazotization reaction (Section 25.13A): A reaction that converts 1° alkylamines and arylamines to diazonium salts.

1,3-Dicarbonyl compound (Section 23.2): A compound containing two carbonyl groups separated by a single carbon atom.

1,4-Dicarbonyl compound (Section 24.4): A dicarbonyl compound in which the carbonyl groups are separated by three single bonds. 1,4-Dicarbonyl compounds can undergo intramolecular reactions to form five-membered rings.

1,5-Dicarbonyl compound (Section 24.4): A dicarbonyl compound in which the carbonyl groups are separated by four single bonds. 1,5-Dicarbonyl compounds can undergo intramolecular reactions to form six-membered rings.

Dieckmann reaction (Section 24.7): An intramolecular Claisen reaction of a diester to form a ring, typically a five- or six-membered ring.

Diels–Alder reaction (Section 16.12): An addition reaction between a 1,3-diene and a dienophile to form a cyclohexene ring.

1,3-Diene (Section 16.1A): A compound containing two carbon–carbon double bonds joined by a single σ bond. Pi (π) electrons are delocalized over both double bonds. 1,3-Dienes are also called conjugated dienes.

Dienophile (Section 16.12): The alkene component in a Diels–Alder reaction that reacts with a 1,3-diene.

Dihedral angle (Section 4.9): The angle that separates a bond on one atom from a bond on an adjacent atom.

Dihydroxylation (Section 12.9): Addition of two hydroxy groups to a double bond to form a 1,2-diol.

Diol (Section 9.3A): A compound possessing two hydroxy groups. Diols are also called glycols.

Dipeptide (Section 29.5): Two amino acids joined together by one amide bond.

Diphosphate (Section 30.7B): A good leaving group that is often used in biological systems. Diphosphate is abbreviated as OPP.

Dipole (Section 1.12): A separation of electronic charge.

Dipole–dipole interaction (Section 3.3B): An attractive intermolecular interaction between the permanent dipoles of polar molecules. The dipoles of adjacent molecules align so that the partial positive and partial negative charges are in close proximity.

Directed aldol reaction (Section 24.3): A crossed aldol reaction in which the enolate of one carbonyl compound is formed, followed by addition of the second carbonyl compound.

Disaccharide (Section 28.12): A carbohydrate containing two monosaccharide units joined together by a glycosidic linkage.

Disproportionation (Section 31.2): A method of chain termination in radical polymerization involving the transfer of a hydrogen atom from one polymer radical to another, forming a new C−H bond on one polymer chain and a new double bond on the other.

Disrotatory rotation (Section 27.3): Rotation of *p* orbitals in opposite directions during electrocyclic ring closure or ring opening.

Dissolving metal reduction (Section 12.2): A reduction reaction using alkali metals as a source of electrons and liquid ammonia as a source of protons.

Disubstituted alkene (Section 8.2A): An alkene that has two alkyl groups and two hydrogens bonded to the carbons of the double bond ($R_2C=CH_2$ or $RCH=CHR$).

Disulfide (Section 29.5C): A compound having the general structure RSSR', often formed between the side chain of two cysteine residues.

Diterpene (Section 30.7A): A terpene that contains 20 carbons and four isoprene units. A diterpenoid contains at least one oxygen atom as well.

Doublet (Section 14.6): An NMR signal that is split into two peaks of equal area, caused by one nearby nonequivalent proton.

Doublet of doublets (Section 14.8): A splitting pattern of four peaks observed when a signal is split by two different nonequivalent protons.

Downfield shift (Section 14.1B): In an NMR spectrum, a term used to describe the relative location of an absorption signal. A downfield shift means the signal is shifted to the left in the spectrum to higher chemical shift on the δ scale.

E

***E,Z* System of nomenclature** (Section 10.3B): A system for unambiguously naming alkene stereoisomers by assigning priorities to the two groups on each carbon of the double bond. The *E* isomer has the two higher priority groups on opposite sides of the double bond, and the *Z* isomer has them on the same side.

E1 mechanism (Sections 8.3, 8.6): An elimination mechanism that goes by a two-step process involving a carbocation intermediate. E1 is an abbreviation for "Elimination Unimolecular."

E1cB mechanism (Section 24.1B): A two-step elimination mechanism that goes by a carbanion intermediate. E1cB stands for "Elimination Unimolecular, Conjugate Base."

E2 mechanism (Sections 8.3, 8.4): An elimination mechanism that goes by a one-step concerted process, in which both reactants are involved in the transition state. E2 is an abbreviation for "Elimination Bimolecular."

Eclipsed conformation (Section 4.9): A conformation of a molecule where the bonds on one carbon are directly aligned with the bonds on the adjacent carbon.

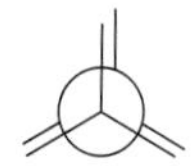

Edman degradation (Section 29.6B): A procedure used in peptide sequencing in which amino acids are cleaved one at a time from the N-terminal end, the identity of the amino acid determined, and the process repeated until the entire sequence is known.

Eicosanoids (Section 30.6): A group of biologically active compounds containing 20 carbon atoms derived from arachidonic acid.

Elastomer (Section 31.5): A polymer that stretches when stressed but then returns to its original shape.

Electrocyclic ring closure (Section 27.1): An intramolecular pericyclic reaction that forms a cyclic product containing one more σ bond and one fewer π bond than the reactant.

Electrocyclic ring-opening reaction (Section 27.1): A pericyclic reaction in which a σ bond of a cyclic reactant is cleaved to form a conjugated product with one more π bond.

Electromagnetic radiation (Section 13.5): Radiant energy having dual properties of both waves and particles. The electromagnetic spectrum contains the complete range of electromagnetic radiation, arbitrarily divided into different regions.

Electron-donating inductive effect (Section 7.14A): An inductive effect in which an electropositive atom or polarizable group donates electron density through σ bonds to another atom.

Electronegativity (Section 1.12): A measure of an atom's attraction for electrons in a bond. Electronegativity indicates how much a particular atom "wants" electrons.

Electron-withdrawing inductive effect (Sections 2.5, 7.14A): An inductive effect in which a nearby electronegative atom pulls electron density towards itself through σ bonds.

Electrophile (Section 2.8): An electron-deficient compound, often symbolized by E^+, which can accept a pair of electrons from an electron-rich compound, forming a covalent bond. Lewis acids are electrophiles.

Electrophilic addition reaction (Section 10.9): An addition reaction in which the first step of the mechanism involves addition of the electrophilic end of a reagent to a π bond.

Electrophilic aromatic substitution (Section 18.1): A characteristic reaction of benzene in which a hydrogen atom on the ring is replaced by an electrophile.

Electrospray ionization (Section 13.4C): A method for ionizing large biomolecules in a mass spectrometer. Electrospray ionization is abbreviated as ESI.

Electrostatic potential map (Section 1.12): A color-coded map that illustrates the distribution of electron density in a molecule. Electron-rich regions are indicated in red and electron-deficient regions are indicated in blue. Regions of intermediate electron density are shown in orange, yellow, and green.

α Elimination (Section 26.4): An elimination reaction involving the loss of two elements from the same atom.

β Elimination (Section 8.1): An elimination reaction involving the loss of elements from two adjacent atoms.

Elimination reaction (Sections 6.2B, 8.1): A chemical reaction in which elements of the starting material are "lost" and a π bond is formed.

Enamine (Section 21.12): A compound having an amine nitrogen atom bonded to a carbon–carbon double bond [$R_2C{=}CH(NR'_2)$].

Enantiomeric excess (Section 5.12D): A measurement of how much one enantiomer is present in excess of the racemic mixture. Enantiomeric excess (*ee*) is also called optical purity; *ee* = % of one enantiomer – % of the other enantiomer.

Enantiomers (Section 5.3): Stereoisomers that are mirror images but are not superimposable upon each other. Enantiomers have the exact opposite *R,S* designation at every stereogenic center.

Enantioselective reaction (Sections 12.15, 20.6A, 29.4): A reaction that affords predominantly or exclusively one enantiomer. Enantioselective reactions are also called asymmetric reactions.

Enantiotopic protons (Section 14.2C): Two hydrogen atoms on the same carbon such that substitution of either hydrogen with a group Z forms enantiomers. The two hydrogen atoms are equivalent and give a single NMR signal.

Endo position (Section 16.13D): A position of a substituent on a bridged bicyclic compound in which the substituent is closer to the longer bridge that joins the two carbons common to both rings.

Endothermic reaction (Section 6.4): A reaction in which the energy of the products is higher than the energy of the reactants. In an endothermic reaction, energy is absorbed and the $\Delta H°$ is a positive value.

Energy diagram (Section 6.7): A schematic representation of the energy changes that take place as reactants are converted to products. An energy diagram indicates how readily a reaction proceeds, how many steps are involved, and how the energies of the reactants, products, and intermediates compare.

Energy of activation (Section 6.7): The energy difference between the transition state and the starting material. The energy of activation, symbolized by E_a, is the minimum amount of energy needed to break bonds in the reactants.

Enolate (Sections 20.15, 23.3): A resonance-stabilized anion formed when a base removes an α hydrogen from the α carbon to a carbonyl group.

Enol tautomer (Sections 9.1, 11.9, 20.15): A compound having a hydroxy group bonded to a carbon–carbon double bond. An enol tautomer [such as $CH_2{=}C(OH)CH_3$] is in equilibrium with its keto tautomer [$(CH_3)_2C{=}O$].

Enthalpy change (Section 6.4): The energy absorbed or released in a reaction. Enthalpy change is symbolized by $\Delta H°$ and is also called the heat of reaction.

Entropy (Section 6.6): A measure of the randomness in a system. The more freedom of motion or the more disorder present, the higher the entropy. Entropy is denoted by the symbol $S°$.

Entropy change (Section 6.6): The change in the amount of disorder between reactants and products in a reaction. The entropy change is denoted by the symbol $\Delta S°$. $\Delta S° = S°_{products} - S°_{reactants}$.

Enzyme (Section 6.11): A biochemical catalyst composed of at least one chain of amino acids held together in a very specific three-dimensional shape.

Enzyme–substrate complex (Section 6.11): A structure having a substrate bonded to the active site of an enzyme.

Epoxidation (Section 12.8): Addition of a single oxygen atom to an alkene to form an epoxide.

Epoxide (Section 9.1): A cyclic ether having the oxygen atom as part of a three-membered ring. Epoxides are also called oxiranes.

Epoxy resin (Section 31.6E): A step-growth polymer formed from a fluid prepolymer and a hardener that cross-links polymer chains together.

Equatorial bonds (Section 4.12A): Bonds located in the plane of the chair conformation of cyclohexane (around the equator). Three equatorial bonds point slightly upward (on the down carbons) and three equatorial bonds point slightly downward (on the up carbons).

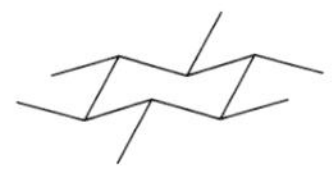

Equilibrium constant (Section 6.5A): A mathematical expression, denoted by the symbol K_{eq}, which relates the amount of starting material and product at equilibrium. K_{eq} = [products]/[starting materials].

Essential oil (Section 30.7): A class of terpenes isolated from plant sources by distillation.

Ester (Sections 20.1, 22.1): A compound having the general structure RCOOR'.

Esterification (Section 22.10C): A reaction that converts a carboxylic acid or a derivative of a carboxylic acid to an ester.

Ether (Section 9.1): A functional group having the general structure ROR'.

Ethynyl group (Section 11.2): An alkynyl substituent having the structure $-C{\equiv}C-H$.

Excited state (Sections 1.9B, 16.15A): A high-energy electronic state in which one or more electrons have been promoted to a higher energy orbital by absorption of energy.

Exo position (Section 16.13D): A position of a substituent on a bridged bicyclic compound in which the substituent is closer to the shorter bridge that joins the two carbons common to both rings.

Exothermic reaction (Section 6.4): A reaction in which the energy of the products is lower than the energy of the reactants. In an exothermic reaction, energy is released and the $\Delta H°$ is a negative value.

Extraction (Section 19.12): A laboratory method to separate and purify a mixture of compounds using solubility differences and acid–base principles.

F

Fat (Sections 10.6B, 30.3): A triacylglycerol that is solid at room temperature and composed of fatty acid side chains with a high degree of saturation.

Fatty acid (Sections 10.6A, 19.6): A long-chain carboxylic acid having between 12 and 20 carbon atoms.

Fehling's reagent (Section 28.9B): A reagent for oxidizing aldehydes to carboxylic acids using a Cu^{2+} salt as an oxidizing agent, forming brick-red Cu_2O as a by-product.

Fibrous proteins (Section 29.10): Long linear polypeptide chains that are bundled together to form rods or sheets.

Fingerprint region (Section 13.6B): The region in an IR spectrum at $< 1500\ cm^{-1}$. The region often contains a complex set of peaks and is unique for every compound.

First-order rate equation (Sections 6.9B, 7.10): A rate equation in which the reaction rate depends on the concentration of only one reactant.

Fischer esterification (Section 22.10C): An acid-catalyzed esterification reaction between a carboxylic acid and an alcohol to form an ester.

Fischer projection formula (Section 28.2A): A method for representing stereogenic centers with the stereogenic carbon at the intersection of vertical and horizontal lines. Fischer projections are also called cross formulas.

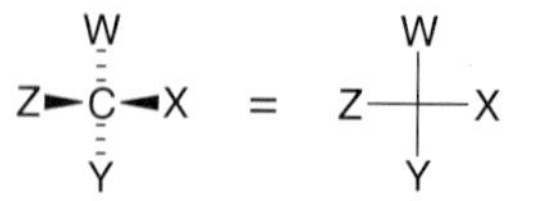

Fishhook (Section 6.3B): A half-headed curved arrow used in a reaction mechanism to denote the movement of a single electron.

Flagpole hydrogens (Section 4.12B): Hydrogens in the boat conformation of cyclohexane that are on either end of the "boat" and are forced into close proximity to each other.

Formal charge (Section 1.3C): The electronic charge assigned to individual atoms in a Lewis structure. The formal charge is calculated by subtracting an atom's unshared electrons and half of its shared electrons from the number of valence electrons that a neutral atom would possess.

Formyl group (Section 21.2E): A substituent having the structure –CHO.

Four-centered transition state (Section 10.16): A transition state that involves four atoms.

Fragment (Section 13.1): Radicals and cations formed by the decomposition of the molecular ion in a mass spectrometer.

Freons (Sections 7.4, 15.9): Chlorofluorocarbons consisting of simple halogen-containing organic compounds that were once commonly used as refrigerants.

Frequency (Section 13.5): The number of waves passing a point per unit time. Frequency is reported in cycles per second (s^{-1}), which is also called hertz (Hz). Frequency is abbreviated with the Greek letter nu (ν).

Friedel–Crafts acylation (Section 18.5A): An electrophilic aromatic substitution reaction in which benzene reacts with an acid chloride in the presence of a Lewis acid to give a ketone.

Friedel–Crafts alkylation (Section 18.5A): An electrophilic aromatic substitution reaction in which benzene reacts with an alkyl halide in the presence of a Lewis acid to give an alkyl benzene.

Frontside attack (Section 7.11C): Approach of a nucleophile from the same side as the leaving group.

Full-headed curved arrow (Section 6.3B): An arrow used in a reaction mechanism to denote the movement of a pair of electrons.

Functional group (Section 3.1): An atom or group of atoms with characteristic chemical and physical properties. The functional group is the reactive part of the molecule.

Functional group interconversion (Section 11.12): A reaction that converts one functional group into another.

Functional group region (Section 13.6B): The region in an IR spectrum at $\geq 1500\ cm^{-1}$. Common functional groups show one or two peaks in this region, at a characteristic frequency.

Furanose (Section 28.6): A cyclic five-membered ring of a monosaccharide containing an oxygen atom.

Fused ring system (Section 16.13D): A bicyclic ring system in which the two rings share one bond and two adjacent atoms.

G

Gabriel synthesis (Section 25.7A): A two-step method that converts an alkyl halide into a primary amine using a nucleophile derived from phthalimide.

Gas chromatography (Section 13.4B): An analytical technique that separates the components of a mixture based on their boiling points and the rate at which their vapors travel through a column.

Gauche conformation (Section 4.10): A staggered conformation in which the two larger groups on adjacent carbon atoms have a dihedral angle of 60°.

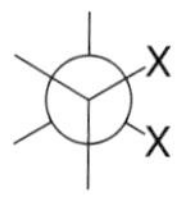

GC–MS (Section 13.4B): An analytical instrument that combines a gas chromatograph (GC) and a mass spectrometer (MS) in sequence.

***gem*-Diol** (Section 21.13): A compound having the general structure $R_2C(OH)_2$. *gem*-Diols are also called hydrates.

Geminal dihalide (Section 8.10): A compound that has two halogen atoms on the same carbon atom.

Gibbs free energy (Section 6.5A): The free energy of a molecule. Gibbs free energy is denoted by the symbol $G°$.

Gibbs free energy change (Section 6.5A): The overall energy difference between reactants and products. The Gibbs free energy change is denoted by the symbol $\Delta G°$. $\Delta G° = G°_{products} - G°_{reactants}$.

Globular proteins (Section 29.10): Polypeptide chains that are coiled into compact shapes with hydrophilic outer surfaces that make them water soluble.

Glycol (Section 9.3A): A compound possessing two hydroxy groups. Glycols are also called diols.

Glycosidase (Section 28.13B): An enzyme that hydrolyzes glycosidic linkages. An α-glycosidase hydrolyzes only α-glycosidic linkages.

Glycoside (Section 28.7A): A monosaccharide with an alkoxy group bonded to the anomeric carbon.

***N*-Glycoside** (Section 28.14B): A monosaccharide containing a nitrogen bonded to the anomeric carbon.

Glycosidic linkage (Section 28.12): An acetal linkage formed between an OH group on one monosaccharide and the anomeric carbon on a second monosaccharide.

Green chemistry (Sections 12.13, 31.8): The use of environmentally benign methods to synthesize compounds.

Grignard reagent (Section 20.9): An organometallic reagent having the general structure RMgX.

Ground state (Sections 1.9B, 16.15A): The lowest energy arrangement of electrons for an atom.

Group number (Section 1.1): The number above a particular column in the periodic table. Group numbers are represented by either an Arabic (1 to 8) or Roman (I to VIII) numeral followed by the letter A or B. The group number of a second-row element is equal to the number of valence electrons in that element.

Grubbs catalyst (Section 26.6): A widely used ruthenium catalyst for olefin metathesis that has the structure $Cl_2(Cy_3P)_2Ru{=}CHPh$.

Guest molecule (Section 9.5B): A small molecule that can bind to a larger host molecule.

H

^{1}H NMR spectroscopy (Section 14.1): A form of nuclear magnetic resonance spectroscopy used to determine the number and type of hydrogen atoms in a molecule. ^{1}H NMR is also called proton NMR spectroscopy.

Half-headed curved arrow (Section 6.3B): An arrow used in a reaction mechanism to denote the movement of a single electron. A half-headed curved arrow is also called a fishhook.

α-Halo aldehyde or ketone (Section 23.7): An aldehyde or ketone with a halogen atom bonded to the α carbon.

Haloform reaction (Section 23.7B): A halogenation reaction of a methyl ketone ($RCOCH_3$) with excess halogen, which results in formation of $RCOO^-$ and CHX_3 (haloform).

Halogenation (Sections 10.13, 15.3, 18.3): The reaction of a compound with a halogen.

Halohydrin (Sections 9.6, 10.15): A compound that has a hydroxy group and a halogen atom on adjacent carbon atoms.

Halonium ion (Section 10.13): A positively charged halogen atom. A bridged halonium ion contains a three-membered ring and is formed in the addition of a halogen (X_2) to an alkene.

Hammond postulate (Section 7.15): A postulate that states that the transition state of a reaction resembles the structure of the species (reactant or product) to which it is closer in energy.

Haworth projection (Section 28.6A): A representation of the cyclic form of a monosaccharide in which the ring is drawn flat.

Head-to-tail polymerization (Section 15.14B): A mechanism of radical polymerization in which the more substituted radical of the growing polymer chain always adds to the less substituted end of the new monomer.

Heat of hydrogenation (Section 12.3A): The $\Delta H°$ of a catalytic hydrogenation reaction equal to the amount of energy released by hydrogenating a π bond.

Heat of reaction (Section 6.4): The energy absorbed or released in a reaction. Heat of reaction is symbolized by $\Delta H°$ and is also called the change in enthalpy.

Heck reaction (Section 26.3): The palladium-catalyzed coupling of a vinyl or aryl halide with an alkene to form a more highly substituted alkene with a new carbon–carbon bond.

α-Helix (Section 29.9B): A secondary structure of a protein formed when a peptide chain twists into a right-handed or clockwise spiral.

Heme (Section 29.10C): A complex organic compound containing an Fe^{2+} ion coordinated with a porphyrin.

Hemiacetal (Section 21.14A): A compound that contains an alkoxy group and a hydroxy group bonded to the same carbon atom.

Hertz (Section 13.5): A unit of frequency measuring the number of waves passing a point per second.

Heteroatom (Section 3.1): An atom other than carbon or hydrogen. Common heteroatoms in organic chemistry are nitrogen, oxygen, sulfur, phosphorus, and the halogens.

Heterocycle (Section 9.3B): A cyclic compound containing a heteroatom as part of the ring.

Heterolysis (Section 6.3A): The breaking of a covalent bond by unequally dividing the electrons between the two atoms in the bond. Heterolysis generates charged intermediates. Heterolysis is also called heterolytic cleavage.

Hexose (Section 28.2): A monosaccharide containing six carbons.

Highest occupied molecular orbital (Section 17.4B): The molecular orbital with the highest energy that also contains electrons. The highest occupied molecular orbital is abbreviated as HOMO.

High-resolution mass spectrometer (Section 13.4A): A mass spectrometer that can measure mass-to-charge ratios to four or more decimal places. High-resolution mass spectra are used to determine the molecular formula of a compound.

Hofmann elimination (Section 25.12): An E2 elimination reaction that converts an amine into a quaternary ammonium salt as the leaving group. The Hofmann elimination gives the less substituted alkene as the major product.

Homologous series (Section 4.1B): A group of compounds that differ by only a CH_2 group in the chain.

Homolysis (Section 6.3A): The breaking of a covalent bond by equally dividing the electrons between the two atoms in the bond. Homolysis generates uncharged radical intermediates. Homolysis is also called homolytic cleavage.

Homopolymer (Section 31.2D): A polymer prepared from a single monomer.

Hooke's law (Section 13.7): A physical law that can be used to calculate the frequency of a bond vibration from the strength of the bond and the masses of the atoms attached to it.

Host–guest complex (Section 9.5B): The complex that is formed when a small guest molecule binds to a larger host molecule.

Host molecule (Section 9.5B): A large molecule that can bind a smaller guest molecule.

Hückel's rule (Section 17.7): A principle that states for a compound to be aromatic, it must be cyclic, planar, completely conjugated, and have $4n + 2$ π electrons.

Hybridization (Section 1.9B): The mathematical combination of two or more atomic orbitals (having different shapes) to form the same number of hybrid orbitals (all having the same shape).

Hybrid orbital (Section 1.9B): A new orbital that results from the mathematical combination of two or more atomic orbitals. The hybrid orbital is intermediate in energy compared to the atomic orbitals that were combined to form it.

Hydrate (Sections 12.12B, 21.13): A compound having the general structure $R_2C(OH)_2$. Hydrates are also called *gem*-diols.

Hydration (Sections 10.12, 21.9A): Addition of the elements of water to a molecule.

Hydride (Section 12.2): A negatively charged hydrogen ion ($H{:}^-$).

1,2-Hydride shift (Section 9.9): Rearrangement of a less stable carbocation to a more stable carbocation by the shift of a hydrogen atom from one carbon atom to an adjacent carbon atom.

Hydroboration (Section 10.16): The addition of the elements of borane (BH_3) to an alkene or alkyne.

Hydrocarbon (Sections 3.2A, 4.1): A compound made up of only the elements of carbon and hydrogen.

Hydrogen bonding (Section 3.3B): An attractive intermolecular interaction that occurs when a hydrogen atom bonded to an O, N, or F atom is electrostatically attracted to a lone pair of electrons on an O, N, or F atom in another molecule.

Hydrogenolysis (Section 29.7): A reaction that cleaves a σ bond using H_2 in the presence of a metal catalyst.

α Hydrogens (Section 23.1): The hydrogen atoms on the carbon bonded to the carbonyl carbon atom (the α carbon).

Hydrohalogenation (Section 10.9): An electrophilic addition of hydrogen halide (HX) to an alkene or alkyne.

Hydrolysis (Section 21.9A): A cleavage reaction with water.

Hydroperoxide (Section 15.11): An organic compound having the general structure ROOH.

Hydrophilic (Section 3.4C): Attracted to water. The polar portion of a molecule that interacts with polar water molecules is hydrophilic.

Hydrophobic (Section 3.4C): Not attracted to water. The nonpolar portion of a molecule that is not attracted to polar water molecules is hydrophobic.

β-Hydroxy carbonyl compound (Section 24.1A): An organic compound having a hydroxy group on the carbon β to the carbonyl group.

Hydroxy group (Section 9.1): The OH functional group.

Hyperconjugation (Section 7.14B): The overlap of an empty *p* orbital with an adjacent σ bond.

I

Imide (Section 25.7A): A compound having a nitrogen atom between two carbonyl groups.

Imine (Sections 21.7B, 21.11A): A compound with the general structure $R_2C{=}NR'$. Imines are also called Schiff bases.

Iminium ion (Section 21.11A): A resonance-stabilized cation having the general structure $(R_2C{=}NR'_2)^+$, where R' = H or alkyl.

Inductive effect (Sections 2.5B, 7.14A): The pull of electron density through σ bonds caused by electronegativity differences of atoms.

Infrared (IR) spectroscopy (Section 13.6): An analytical technique used to identify the functional groups in a molecule based on their absorption of electromagnetic radiation in the infrared region.

Initiation (Section 15.4A): The initial step in a chain mechanism that forms a reactive intermediate by cleavage of a bond.

Inscribed polygon method (Section 17.10): A method to predict the relative energies of cyclic, completely conjugated compounds to determine which molecular orbitals are filled or empty. The inscribed polygon is also called a Frost circle.

Integration (Section 14.5): The area under an NMR signal that is proportional to the number of absorbing nuclei that give rise to the signal.

Intermolecular forces (Section 3.3): The types of interactions that exist between molecules. Functional groups determine the type and strength of these forces. Intermolecular forces are also called noncovalent interactions or nonbonded interactions.

Internal alkene (Section 10.1): An alkene that has at least one carbon atom bonded to each end of the double bond.

Internal alkyne (Section 11.1): An alkyne that has one carbon atom bonded to each end of the triple bond.

Inversion of configuration (Section 7.11C): The opposite relative stereochemistry of a stereogenic center in the starting material and product of a chemical reaction. In a nucleophilic substitution reaction, inversion results when the nucleophile and leaving group are in the opposite position relative to the three other groups on carbon.

Iodoform test (Section 23.7B): A test for the presence of methyl ketones, indicated by the formation of the yellow precipitate, CHI_3, via the haloform reaction.

Ionic bond (Section 1.2): A bond that results from the transfer of electrons from one element to another. Ionic bonds result from strong electrostatic interactions between ions with opposite charges. The transfer of electrons forms stable salts composed of cations and anions.

Ionophore (Section 3.7B): An organic molecule that can form a complex with cations so they may be transported across a cell membrane. Ionophores have a hydrophobic exterior and a hydrophilic central cavity that complexes the cation.

Isocyanate (Section 31.6C): A compound having the general structure $RN{=}C{=}O$.

Isoelectric point (Sections 19.14C, 29.1A): The pH at which an amino acid exists primarily in its neutral zwitterionic form. Isoelectric point is abbreviated as p*I*.

Isolated diene (Section 16.1A): A compound containing two carbon–carbon double bonds joined by more than one σ bond.

Isomers (Sections 1.4A, 4.1A, 5.1): Two different compounds that have the same molecular formula.

Isoprene unit (Section 30.7): A five-carbon unit with four carbons in a row and a one-carbon branch on one of the middle carbons.

Isotactic polymer (Section 31.4): A polymer having all the substituents on the same side of the carbon backbone of an elongated polymer chain.

Isotope (Section 1.1): Two or more atoms of the same element having the same number of protons in the nucleus but a different number of neutrons. Isotopes have the same atomic number but different mass numbers.

IUPAC system of nomenclature (Section 4.3): A systematic method for naming compounds developed by the International Union of Pure and Applied Chemistry.

K

K_a (Section 2.3): The symbol that represents the acidity constant of an acid HA. The larger the K_a, the stronger the acid.

$$K_a = \frac{[H_3O^+][A:^-]}{[H{-}A]}$$

K_{eq} (Section 2.3): The equilibrium constant. K_{eq} = [products]/[starting materials].

Kekulé structures (Section 17.1): Two equilibrating structures for benzene. Each structure contains a six-membered ring and three π bonds alternating with σ bonds around the ring.

Ketal (Section 21.14): A compound having the general structure $R_2C(OR')_2$, where R = alkyl or aryl. Ketals are derived from ketones and constitute a subclass of acetals.

β-Keto ester (Section 23.10): A compound containing a ketone carbonyl on the carbon β to the ester carbonyl group.

Ketone (Section 11.9): A compound with two alkyl groups bonded to the $C{=}O$ carbon atom, having the general structures $R_2C{=}O$ or RCOR'.

Ketose (Section 28.2): A monosaccharide comprised of a polyhydroxy ketone.

Keto tautomer (Section 11.9): A tautomer of a ketone that has a $C{=}O$ and a hydrogen bonded to the α carbon. The keto tautomer is in equilibrium with the enol tautomer.

Kiliani–Fischer synthesis (Section 28.10B): A reaction that lengthens the carbon chain of an aldose by adding one carbon to the carbonyl end.

Kinetic enolate (Section 23.4): The enolate that is formed the fastest—generally the less substituted enolate.

Kinetic product (Section 16.11): In a reaction that can give more than one product, the product that is formed the fastest.

Kinetic resolution (Section 29.3B): The separation of two enantiomers by a chemical reaction that selectively occurs for only one of the enantiomers.

Kinetics (Section 6.5): The study of chemical reaction rates.

L

L-Sugar (Section 28.2C): A sugar with the hydroxy group on the stereogenic center farthest from the carbonyl on the left side in the Fischer projection formula.

Lactam (Section 22.1): A cyclic amide in which the carbonyl carbon–nitrogen σ bond is part of a ring. A β-lactam contains the carbon–nitrogen σ bond in a four-membered ring.

Lactol (Section 21.16): A cyclic hemiacetal.

Lactone (Section 22.1): A cyclic ester in which the carbonyl carbon–oxygen σ bond is part of a ring.

Le Châtelier's principle (Section 9.8D): The principle that a system at equilibrium will react to counteract any disturbance to the equilibrium.

Leaving group (Section 7.6): An atom or group of atoms (Z) that is able to accept the electron density of the C−Z bond during a substitution or elimination reaction.

Leaving group ability (Section 7.7): A measure of how readily a leaving group (Z) can accept the electron density of the C−Z bond during a substitution or elimination reaction.

Lecithin (Section 30.4A): A phosphoacylglycerol in which the phosphodiester alkyl group is $-CH_2CH_2N(CH_3)_3^+$. Lecithins are also called phosphatidylcholines.

Leukotriene (Section 9.16): An unstable and potent biomolecule synthesized in cells by the oxidation of arachidonic acid. Leukotrienes are responsible for biological conditions such as asthma.

Levorotatory (Section 5.12A): Rotating plane-polarized light in the counterclockwise direction. The rotation is labeled *l* or (–).

Lewis acid (Section 2.8): An electron pair acceptor.

Lewis acid–base reaction (Section 2.8): A reaction that results when a Lewis base donates an electron pair to a Lewis acid.

Lewis base (Section 2.8): An electron pair donor.

Lewis structure (Section 1.3): A representation of a molecule that shows the position of covalent bonds and nonbonding electrons. In Lewis structures, unshared electrons are represented by dots and a two-electron covalent bond is represented by a solid line. Lewis structures are also called electron dot structures.

Ligand (Section 26.2A): A group coordinated to a metal, which donates electron density to or sometimes withdraws electron density from the metal.

"Like dissolves like" (Section 3.4C): The principle that compounds dissolve in solvents having similar kinds of intermolecular forces; that is, polar compounds dissolve in polar solvents and nonpolar compounds dissolve in nonpolar solvents.

Lindlar catalyst (Section 12.5B): A catalyst for the hydrogenation of an alkyne to a cis alkene. The Lindlar catalyst is Pd adsorbed onto $CaCO_3$ with lead(II) acetate and quinoline.

Lipid (Sections 4.15, 30.1): A biomolecule with a large number of C−C and C−H σ bonds that is soluble in organic solvents and insoluble in water.

Lone pair of electrons (Section 1.2): A pair of valence electrons that is not shared with another atom in a covalent bond. Lone pairs are also called unshared or nonbonded pairs of electrons.

Lowest unoccupied molecular orbital (Section 17.9B): The molecular orbital with the lowest energy that does not contain electrons. The lowest unoccupied molecular orbital is abbreviated as the LUMO.

M

M peak (Section 13.1): The peak in the mass spectrum that corresponds to the mass of the molecular ion. The M peak is also called the molecular ion peak or the parent peak.

M + 1 peak (Section 13.1): The peak in the mass spectrum that corresponds to the mass of the molecular ion plus one. The M + 1 peak is caused by the presence of isotopes that increase the mass of the molecular ion.

M + 2 peak (Section 13.2): The peak in the mass spectrum that corresponds to the mass of the molecular ion plus two. The M + 2 peak is caused by the presence of isotopes, typically of a chlorine or a bromine atom.

Macrocyclic lactone (Section 22.6A): A cyclic ester contained in a large ring. Macrocyclic lactones are also called macrolides.

Macrolide (Section 22.6A): A cyclic ester contained in a large ring. Macrolides are also called macrocyclic lactones.

Magnetic resonance imaging (MRI) (Section 14.12): A form of NMR spectroscopy used in medicine.

Malonic ester synthesis (Section 23.9A): A stepwise method that converts diethyl malonate into a carboxylic acid having one or two carbons bonded to the α carbon.

Markovnikov's rule (Section 10.10): The rule that states in the addition of HX to an unsymmetrical alkene, the H atom bonds to the less substituted carbon atom.

Mass number (Section 1.1): The total number of protons and neutrons in the nucleus of a particular atom.

Mass spectrometry (Section 13.1): An analytical technique used for measuring the molecular weight and determining the molecular formula of an organic molecule.

Mass-to-charge ratio (Section 13.1): A ratio of the mass to the charge of a molecular ion or fragment. Mass-to-charge ratio is abbreviated as *m/z*.

Megahertz (Section 14.1A): A unit used for the frequency of the RF radiation in NMR spectroscopy. Megahertz is abbreviated as MHz; 1 MHz = 10^6 Hz.

Melting point (Section 3.4B): The temperature at which molecules in the solid phase are converted to the liquid phase. Molecules with stronger intermolecular forces and higher symmetry have higher melting points. Melting point is abbreviated as mp.

Merrifield method (Section 29.8): A method for synthesizing polypeptides using insoluble polymer supports.

Meso compound (Section 5.8): An achiral compound that contains two or more tetrahedral stereogenic centers.

Meta director (Section 18.7): A substituent on a benzene ring that directs a new group to the meta position during electrophilic aromatic substitution.

Meta isomer (Section 17.3B): A 1,3-disubstituted benzene ring. Meta substitution is abbreviated as *m*-.

Metal hydride reagent (Section 12.2): A reagent containing a polar metal–hydrogen bond that places a partial negative charge on the hydrogen and acts as a source of hydride ions ($H:^-$).

Metathesis (Section 26.6): A reaction between two alkene molecules that results in the interchange of the carbons of their double bonds.

Methylation (Section 7.12): A reaction in which a CH_3 group is transferred from one compound to another.

Methylene group (Sections 4.1B, 10.3C): A CH_2 group bonded to a carbon chain ($-CH_2-$) or part of a double bond ($CH_2=$).

1,2-Methyl shift (Section 9.9): Rearrangement of a less stable carbocation to a more stable carbocation by the shift of a methyl group from one carbon atom to an adjacent carbon atom.

Micelles (Section 3.6): Spherical droplets formed by soap molecules having the ionic heads on the surface and the nonpolar tails packed together in the interior. Grease and oil dissolve in the interior nonpolar region.

Michael acceptor (Section 24.8): The α,β-unsaturated carbonyl compound in a Michael reaction.

Michael reaction (Section 24.8): A reaction in which a resonance-stabilized carbanion (usually an enolate) adds to the β carbon of an α,β-unsaturated carbonyl compound.

Mixed aldol reaction (Section 24.2): An aldol reaction between two different carbonyl compounds. A mixed aldol reaction is also called a crossed aldol reaction.

Mixed anhydride (Section 22.1): An anhydride with two different alkyl groups bonded to the carbonyl carbon atoms.

Molecular ion (Section 13.1): The radical cation having the general structure $M^{+\bullet}$, formed by the removal of an electron from an organic molecule. The molecular ion is also called the parent ion.

Molecular orbital theory (Section 17.9A): A theory that describes bonds as the mathematical combination of atomic orbitals to form a new set of orbitals called molecular orbitals. Molecular orbital theory is also called MO theory.

Molecular recognition (Section 9.5B): The ability of a host molecule to recognize and bind specific guest molecules.

Molecule (Section 1.2): A compound containing two or more atoms bonded together with covalent bonds.

Monomers (Sections 5.1, 15.14): Small organic compounds that can be covalently bonded to each other (polymerized) in a repeating pattern.

Monosaccharide (Section 28.2): A simple sugar having three to seven carbon atoms.

Monosubstituted alkene (Section 8.2A): An alkene that has one alkyl group and three hydrogens bonded to the carbons of the double bond ($RCH=CH_2$).

Monoterpene (Section 30.7A): A terpene that contains 10 carbons and two isoprene units. A monoterpenoid also contains at least one oxygen atom.

Multiplet (Section 14.6C): An NMR signal that is split into more than seven peaks.

Mutarotation (Section 28.6A): The process by which a pure anomer of a monosaccharide equilibrates to a mixture of both anomers when placed in solution.

N

***n* + 1 rule** (Section 14.6C): The rule that an NMR signal for a proton with *n* nearby nonequivalent protons will be split into *n* + 1 peaks.

Natural product (Section 7.19): A compound isolated from a natural source.

Newman projection (Section 4.9): An end-on representation of the conformation of a molecule. The Newman projection shows the three groups bonded to each carbon atom in a particular C−C bond, as well as the dihedral angle that separates the groups on each carbon.

or

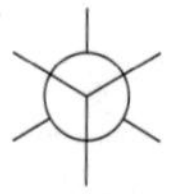

Nitration (Section 18.4): An electrophilic aromatic substitution reaction in which benzene reacts with $^+NO_2$ to give nitrobenzene, $C_6H_5NO_2$.

Nitrile (Sections 22.1, 22.18): A compound having the general structure $RC\equiv N$.

Nitronium ion (Section 18.4): An electrophile having the structure $^+NO_2$.

***N*-Nitrosamine** (Sections 7.16, 25.13B): A compound having the general structure $R_2N-N=O$. Nitrosamines are formed by the reaction of a secondary amine with ^+NO.

Nitrosonium ion (Section 25.13): An electrophile having the structure ^+NO.

NMR peak (Section 14.6A): The individual absorptions in a split NMR signal due to nonequivalent nearby protons.

NMR signal (Section 14.6A): The entire absorption due to a particular kind of proton in an NMR spectrum.

NMR spectrometer (Section 14.1A): An analytical instrument that measures the absorption of RF radiation by certain atomic nuclei when placed in a strong magnetic field.

Nonbonded pair of electrons (Section 1.2): A pair of valence electrons that is not shared with another atom in a covalent bond. Nonbonded electrons are also called unshared or lone pairs of electrons.

Nonbonding molecular orbital (Section 17.10): A molecular orbital having the same energy as the atomic orbitals that formed it.

Nonnucleophilic base (Section 7.8B): A base that is a poor nucleophile due to steric hindrance resulting from the presence of bulky groups.

Nonpolar bond (Section 1.12): A covalent bond in which the electrons are equally shared between the two atoms.

Nonpolar molecule (Section 1.13): A molecule that has no net dipole. A nonpolar molecule has either no polar bonds or multiple polar bonds whose dipoles cancel.

Nonreducing sugar (Section 28.9B): A carbohydrate that cannot be oxidized by Tollens, Benedict's, or Fehling's reagent.

Normal alkane (Section 4.1A): An acyclic alkane that has all of its carbons in a row. A normal alkane is an "*n*-alkane" or a straight-chain alkane.

Nuclear magnetic resonance spectroscopy (Section 14.1): A powerful analytical tool that can help identify the carbon and hydrogen framework of an organic molecule.

Nucleophile (Sections 2.8, 7.6): An electron-rich compound, symbolized by $:Nu^-$, which donates a pair of electrons to an electron-deficient compound, forming a covalent bond. Lewis bases are nucleophiles.

Nucleophilic acyl substitution (Sections 20.2B, 22.1): Substitution of a leaving group by a nucleophile at a carbonyl carbon.

Nucleophilic addition (Section 20.2A): Addition of a nucleophile to the electrophilic carbon of a carbonyl group followed by protonation of the oxygen.

Nucleophilic aromatic substitution (Section 18.13): A substitution reaction of an aryl halide with a strong nucleophile.

Nucleophilicity (Section 7.8A): A measure of how readily an atom donates an electron pair to other atoms.

Nucleophilic substitution (Section 7.6): A reaction in which a nucleophile replaces the leaving group in a molecule.

Nucleoside (Section 28.14B): A biomolecule having a sugar and either a purine or pyrimidine base joined together by an *N*-glycosidic linkage.

Nucleotide (Section 28.14B): A biomolecule having a sugar and either a purine or pyrimidine base joined together by an *N*-glycosidic linkage, and a phosphate bonded to a hydroxy group of the sugar nucleus.

O

Observed rotation (Section 5.12A): The angle that a sample of an optically active compound rotates plane-polarized light. The angle is denoted by the symbol α and is measured in degrees (°).

Octet rule (Section 1.2): The general rule governing the bonding process for second-row elements. Through bonding, second-row elements attain a complete outer shell of eight valence electrons.

Oil (Sections 10.6B, 30.3): A triacylglycerol that is liquid at room temperature and composed of fatty acid side chains with a high degree of unsaturation.

Olefin (Section 10.1): An alkene; a compound possessing a carbon–carbon double bond.

Optically active (Section 5.12A): Able to rotate the plane of plane-polarized light as it passes through a solution of a compound.

Optically inactive (Section 5.12A): Not able to rotate the plane of plane-polarized light as it passes through a solution of a compound.

Optical purity (Section 5.12D): A measurement of how much one enantiomer is present in excess of the racemic mixture. Optical purity is also called enantiomeric excess (*ee*); *ee* = % of one enantiomer – % of the other enantiomer.

Orbital (Section 1.1): A region of space around the nucleus of an atom that is high in electron density. There are four different kinds of orbitals, called *s, p, d,* and *f.*

Order of a rate equation (Section 6.9B): The sum of the exponents of the concentration terms in the rate equation of a reaction.

Organoborane (Section 10.16): A compound that contains a carbon–boron bond. Organoboranes have the general structure RBH_2, R_2BH, or R_3B.

Organocopper reagent (Section 20.9): An organometallic reagent having the general structure R_2CuLi. Organocopper reagents are also called organocuprates.

Organolithium reagent (Section 20.9): An organometallic reagent having the general structure RLi.

Organomagnesium reagent (Section 20.9): An organometallic reagent having the general structure RMgX. Organomagnesium reagents are also called Grignard reagents.

Organometallic reagent (Section 20.9): A reagent that contains a carbon atom bonded to a metal.

Organopalladium compound (Section 26.2): An organometallic compound that contains a carbon–palladium bond.

Organophosphorus reagent (Section 21.10A): A reagent that contains a carbon–phosphorus bond.

Ortho isomer (Section 17.3B): A 1,2-disubstituted benzene ring. Ortho substitution is abbreviated as *o*-.

Ortho, para director (Section 18.7): A substituent on a benzene ring that directs a new group to the ortho and para positions during electrophilic aromatic substitution.

Oxaphosphetane (Section 21.10B): An intermediate in the Wittig reaction consisting of a four-membered ring containing a phosphorus–oxygen bond.

Oxazaborolidine (Section 20.6A): A heterocycle possessing a boron, a nitrogen, and an oxygen. An oxazaborolidine can be used to form a chiral reducing agent.

Oxidation (Sections 4.14A, 12.1): A process that results in a loss of electrons. For organic compounds, oxidation results in an increase in the number of C–Z bonds or a decrease in the number of C–H bonds; Z = an element more electronegative than carbon.

Oxidative addition (Section 26.2A): The addition of a reagent to a metal, often increasing the number of groups around the metal by two.

Oxidative cleavage (Section 12.10): An oxidation reaction that breaks both the σ and π bonds of a multiple bond to form two oxidized products.

Oxime (Section 28.10A): A compound having the general structure $R_2C{=}NOH$.

Oxirane (Section 9.1): A cyclic ether having the oxygen atom as part of a three-membered ring. Oxiranes are also called epoxides.

Oxy-Cope rearrangement (Section 27.5): A [3,3] sigmatropic rearrangement of a 1,5-dien-3-ol to a δ,ε-unsaturated carbonyl compound.

Ozonolysis (Section 12.10): An oxidative cleavage reaction in which a multiple bond reacts with ozone (O_3) as the oxidant.

P

Para isomer (Section 17.3B): A 1,4-disubstituted benzene ring. Para substitution is abbreviated as *p*-.

Parent ion (Section 13.1): The radical cation having the general structure $M^{+\bullet}$, formed by the removal of an electron from an organic molecule. The parent ion is also called the molecular ion.

Parent name (Section 4.4): The portion of the IUPAC name of an organic compound that indicates the number of carbons in the longest continuous chain in the molecule.

Pentose (Section 28.2): A monosaccharide containing five carbons.

Peptide bond (Section 29.5): The amide bond in peptides and proteins.

Peptides (Sections 22.6B, 29.5): Low molecular weight polymers of less than 40 amino acids joined together by amide linkages.

Percent *s*-character (Section 1.11B): The fraction of a hybrid orbital due to the *s* orbital used to form it. As the percent *s*-character increases, a bond becomes shorter and stronger.

Percent transmittance (Section 13.6B): A measure of how much electromagnetic radiation passes through a sample of a compound and how much is absorbed.

Pericyclic reaction (Section 27.1): A concerted reaction that proceeds through a cyclic transition state.

Peroxide (Section 15.2): A reactive organic compound with the general structure ROOR. Peroxides are used as radical initiators by homolysis of the weak O–O bond.

Peroxyacid (Section 12.7): An oxidizing agent having the general structure RCO_3H.

Peroxy radical (Section 15.11): A radical having the general structure ROO·.

Petroleum (Section 4.7): A fossil fuel containing a complex mixture of compounds, primarily hydrocarbons with 1 to 40 carbon atoms.

Phenol (Sections 9.1, 15.12): A compound such as C_6H_5OH, which contains a hydroxy group bonded to a benzene ring.

Phenyl group (Section 17.3D): A group formed by removal of one hydrogen from benzene, abbreviated as C_6H_5- or Ph–.

Pheromone (Section 4.1): A chemical substance used for communication in an animal or insect species.

Phosphatidylcholine (Section 30.4A): A phosphoacylglycerol in which the phosphodiester alkyl group is $-CH_2CH_2N(CH_3)_3^+$. Phosphatidylcholines are also called lecithins.

Phosphatidylethanolamine (Section 30.4A): A phosphoacylglycerol in which the phosphodiester alkyl group is $-CH_2CH_2NH_3^+$. Phosphatidylethanolamines are also called cephalins.

Phosphoacylglycerols (Section 30.4A): A lipid having a glycerol backbone with two of the hydroxy groups esterified with fatty acids and the third hydroxy group as part of a phosphodiester.

Phosphodiester (Section 30.4): A functional group having the general formula $ROPO_2OR'$ formed by replacing two of the H atoms in phosphoric acid (H_3PO_4) with alkyl groups.

Phospholipid (Sections 3.7A, 30.4): A hydrolyzable lipid that contains a phosphorus atom.

Phosphonium salt (Section 21.10A): An organophosphorus reagent with a positively charged phosphorus and a suitable counterion; for example, $R_4P^+X^-$. Phosphonium salts are converted to ylides upon treatment with a strong base.

Phosphorane (Section 21.10A): A phosphorus ylide; for example, $Ph_3P{=}CR_2$.

Photon (Section 13.5): A particle of electromagnetic radiation.

Pi (π) bond (Section 1.10B): A bond formed by side-by-side overlap of two *p* orbitals where electron density is not concentrated on the axis joining the two nuclei. Pi (π) bonds are generally weaker than σ bonds.

pK_a (Section 2.3): A logarithmic scale of acid strength. $pK_a = -\log K_a$. The smaller the pK_a, the stronger the acid.

Plane of symmetry (Section 5.3): A mirror plane that cuts a molecule in half, so that one half of the molecule is the mirror reflection of the other half.

Plane-polarized light (Section 5.12A): Light that has an electric vector that oscillates in a single plane. Plane-polarized light, also called polarized light, arises from passing ordinary light through a polarizer.

Plasticizer (Section 31.7): A low molecular weight compound added to a polymer to give it flexibility.

β-Pleated sheet (Section 29.9B): A secondary structure of a protein formed when two or more peptide chains line up side by side.

Poisoned catalyst (Section 12.5B): A hydrogenation catalyst with reduced activity that allows selective reactions to occur. The Lindlar catalyst is a poisoned Pd catalyst that converts alkynes to cis alkenes.

Polar aprotic solvent (Section 7.8C): A polar solvent that is incapable of intermolecular hydrogen bonding because it does not contain an O–H or N–H bond.

Polar bond (Section 1.12): A covalent bond in which the electrons are unequally shared between the two atoms. Unequal sharing of electrons results from bonding between atoms of different electronegativity values, usually with a difference of ≥ 0.5 units.

Polarimeter (Section 5.12A): An instrument that measures the degree that a compound rotates plane-polarized light.

Polarity (Section 1.12): A characteristic that results from a dipole. The polarity of a bond is indicated by an arrow with the head of the arrow pointing toward the negative end of the dipole and the tail with a perpendicular line through it at the positive end of the dipole. The polarity of a bond can also be indicated by the symbols δ^+ and δ^-.

Polarizability (Section 3.3B): A measure of how the electron cloud around an atom responds to changes in its electronic environment.

Polar molecule (Section 1.13): A molecule that has a net dipole. A polar molecule has either one polar bond or multiple polar bonds whose dipoles reinforce.

Polar protic solvent (Section 7.8C): A polar solvent that is capable of intermolecular hydrogen bonding because it contains an O–H or N–H bond.

Polyamide (Sections 22.16A, 31.6A): A step-growth polymer that contains many amide bonds. Nylon 6,6 and nylon 6 are polyamides.

Polycarbonate (Section 31.6C): A step-growth polymer that contains many $-OC({=}O)O-$ bonds in its backbone, often formed by reaction of $Cl_2C{=}O$ with a diol.

Polycyclic aromatic hydrocarbon (Sections 9.17, 17.5): An aromatic hydrocarbon containing two or more benzene rings that share carbon–carbon bonds. Polycyclic aromatic hydrocarbons are abbreviated as PAHs.

Polyene (Section 16.7): A compound that contains three or more double bonds.

Polyester (Sections 22.16B, 31.6B): A step-growth polymer consisting of many ester bonds between diols and dicarboxylic acids.

Polyether (Sections 9.5B, 31.3): A compound that contains two or more ether linkages.

Polymer (Sections 5.1, 15.14): A large molecule composed of smaller monomer units covalently bonded to each other in a repeating pattern.

Polymerization (Section 15.14A): The chemical process that joins together monomers to make polymers.

Polysaccharide (Section 28.13): A carbohydrate containing three or more monosaccharide units joined together by glycosidic linkages.

Polyurethane (Section 31.6C): A step-growth polymer that contains many $-NHC({=}O)O-$ bonds in its backbone, formed by reaction of a diisocyanate and a diol.

Porphyrin (Section 29.10C): A nitrogen-containing heterocycle that can complex metal ions.

Primary (1°) alcohol (Section 9.1): An alcohol having the general structure RCH_2OH.

Primary (1°) alkyl halide (Section 7.1): An alkyl halide having the general structure RCH_2X.

Primary (1°) amide (Section 22.1): An amide having the general structure $RCONH_2$.

Primary (1°) amine (Sections 21.11, 25.1): An amine having the general structure RNH_2.

Primary (1°) carbocation (Section 7.14): A carbocation having the general structure RCH_2^+.

Primary (1°) carbon (Section 4.1A): A carbon atom that is bonded to one other carbon atom.

Primary (1°) hydrogen (Section 4.1A): A hydrogen that is bonded to a 1° carbon.

Primary protein structure (Section 29.9A): The particular sequence of amino acids joined together by peptide bonds.

Primary (1°) radical (Section 15.1): A radical having the general structure $RCH_2\cdot$.

Propagation (Section 15.4A): The middle part of a chain mechanism in which one reactive particle is consumed and another is generated. Propagation repeats until a termination step occurs.

Prostaglandin (Section 4.15): A class of lipids containing 20 carbons, a five-membered ring, and a COOH group. Prostaglandins possess a wide range of biological activities.

Prosthetic group (Section 29.10C): The non-protein unit of a conjugated protein.

Protecting group (Section 20.12): A blocking group that renders a reactive functional group unreactive so that it does not interfere with another reaction.

Protection (Section 20.12): The reaction that blocks a reactive functional group with a protecting group.

Proteins (Sections 22.6B, 29.5): High molecular weight polymers of 40 or more amino acids joined together by amide linkages.

Proton (Section 2.1): A positively charged hydrogen ion (H^+).

Proton NMR spectroscopy (Section 14.1): A form of nuclear magnetic resonance spectroscopy used to determine the number and type of hydrogen atoms in a molecule.

Proton transfer reaction (Section 2.2): A Brønsted–Lowry acid–base reaction; a reaction that results in the transfer of a proton from an acid to a base.

Purine (Section 28.14B): A bicyclic aromatic heterocycle having two nitrogens in each of the rings.

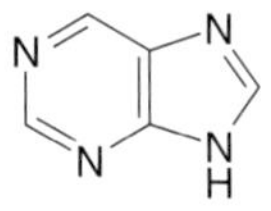

Pyranose (Section 28.6): A cyclic six-membered ring of a monosaccharide containing an oxygen atom.

Pyrimidine (Section 28.14B): A six-membered aromatic heterocycle having two nitrogens in the ring.

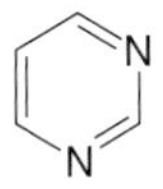

Q

Quantum (Section 13.5): The discrete amount of energy associated with a particle of electromagnetic radiation (i.e., a photon).

Quartet (Section 14.6C): An NMR signal that is split into four peaks having a relative area of 1:3:3:1, caused by three nearby nonequivalent protons.

Quaternary (4°) carbon (Section 4.1A): A carbon atom that is bonded to four other carbon atoms.

Quaternary protein structure (Section 29.9C): The shape adopted when two or more folded polypeptide chains aggregate into one protein complex.

Quintet (Section 14.6C): An NMR signal that is split into five peaks caused by four nearby nonequivalent protons.

R

R,S **System of nomenclature** (Section 5.6): A system of nomenclature that distinguishes the stereochemistry at a tetrahedral stereogenic center by assigning a priority to each group connected to the stereogenic center. *R* indicates a clockwise orientation of the three highest priority groups and *S* indicates a counterclockwise orientation of the three highest groups. The system is also called the Cahn–Ingold–Prelog system.

Racemic mixture (Section 5.12B): An equal mixture of two enantiomers. A racemic mixture, also called a racemate, is optically inactive.

Racemization (Section 7.13C): The formation of equal amounts of two enantiomers from an enantiomerically pure starting material.

Radical (Sections 6.3B, 15.1): A reactive intermediate with a single unpaired electron, formed by homolysis of a covalent bond.

Radical anion (Section 12.5C): A reactive intermediate containing both a negative charge and an unpaired electron.

Radical cation (Section 13.1): A species with an unpaired electron and a positive charge, formed in a mass spectrometer by the bombardment of a molecule with an electron beam.

Radical inhibitor (Section 15.2): A compound that prevents radical reactions from occurring. Radical inhibitors are also called radical scavengers.

Radical initiator (Section 15.2): A compound that contains an especially weak bond that serves as a source of radicals.

Radical polymerization (Section 15.14B): A radical chain reaction involving the polymerization of alkene monomers by adding a radical to a π bond.

Radical scavenger (Section 15.2): A compound that prevents radical reactions from occurring. Radical scavengers are also called radical inhibitors.

Rate constant (Section 6.9B): A constant that is a fundamental characteristic of a reaction. The rate constant, symbolized by *k*, is a complex mathematical term that takes into account the dependence of a reaction rate on temperature and the energy of activation.

Rate-determining step (Section 6.8): In a multistep reaction mechanism, the step with the highest energy transition state.

Rate equation (Section 6.9B): An equation that shows the relationship between the rate of a reaction and the concentration of the reactants. The rate equation depends on the mechanism of the reaction and is also called the rate law.

Reaction coordinate (Section 6.7): The *x* axis in an energy diagram that represents the progress of a reaction as it proceeds from reactant to product.

Reaction mechanism (Section 6.3): A detailed description of how bonds are broken and formed as a starting material is converted to a product.

Reactive intermediate (Sections 6.3, 10.18): A high-energy unstable intermediate formed during the conversion of a stable starting material to a stable product.

Reciprocal centimeter (Section 13.6A): The unit for wavenumber, which is used to report frequency in IR spectroscopy.

Reducing sugar (Section 28.9B): A carbohydrate that can be oxidized by Tollens, Benedict's, or Fehling's reagent.

Reduction (Sections 4.14A, 12.1): A process that results in the gain of electrons. For organic compounds, reduction results in a decrease in the number of C–Z bonds or an increase in the number of C–H bonds; Z = an element more electronegative than carbon.

Reductive amination (Section 25.7C): A two-step method that converts aldehydes and ketones into amines.

Reductive elimination (Section 26.2A): The elimination of two groups that surround a metal, often forming new carbon–hydrogen or carbon–carbon bonds.

Regioselective reaction (Section 8.5): A reaction that yields predominantly or exclusively one constitutional isomer when more than one constitutional isomer is possible.

Resolution (Section 29.3): The separation of a racemic mixture into its component enantiomers.

Resonance (Section 14.1A): In NMR spectroscopy, when an atomic nucleus absorbs RF radiation and spin flips to a higher energy state.

Resonance hybrid (Sections 1.6C, 16.4): A structure that is a weighted composite of all possible resonance structures. The resonance hybrid shows the delocalization of electron density due to the different locations of electrons in individual resonance structures.

Resonance structures (Sections 1.6, 16.2): Two or more structures of a molecule that differ in the placement of π bonds and nonbonded electrons. The placement of atoms and σ bonds stays the same.

Retention of configuration (Section 7.11C): The same relative stereochemistry of a stereogenic center in the reactant and the product of a chemical reaction.

Retention time (Section 13.4B): The length of time required for a component of a mixture to travel through a chromatography column.

Retro Diels–Alder reaction (Section 16.14B): The reverse of a Diels–Alder reaction in which a cyclohexene is cleaved to give a 1,3-diene and an alkene.

Retrosynthetic analysis (Section 10.18): Working backwards from a product to determine the starting material from which it is made.

RF radiation (Section 14.1A): Radiation in the radiofrequency region of the electromagnetic spectrum, characterized by long wavelength and low frequency and energy.

Ribonucleoside (Section 28.14B): An *N*-glycoside formed by the reaction of D-ribose with certain amine heterocycles.

Ribonucleotide (Section 28.14B): An RNA building block having a ribose and either a purine or pyrimidine base joined together by an *N*-glycosidic linkage, and a phosphate bonded to a hydroxy group of the sugar nucleus.

Ring-closing metathesis (Section 26.6): An intramolecular olefin metathesis reaction using a diene starting material, which results in ring closure.

Ring current (Section 14.4): A circulation of π electrons in an aromatic ring caused by the presence of an external magnetic field.

Ring flipping (Section 4.12B): A stepwise process in which one chair conformation of cyclohexane interconverts with a second chair conformation.

Ring-opening metathesis polymerization (Problem 26.31): An olefin metathesis reaction that forms a high molecular weight polymer from certain cyclic alkenes.

Robinson annulation (Section 24.9): A ring-forming reaction that combines a Michael reaction with an intramolecular aldol reaction to form a 2-cyclohexenone.

Rule of endo addition (Section 16.13D): The rule that the endo product is preferred in a Diels–Alder reaction.

S

Sandmeyer reaction (Section 25.14A): A reaction between an aryl diazonium salt and a copper(I) halide to form an aryl halide (C_6H_5Cl or C_6H_5Br).

Saponification (Section 22.11B): Basic hydrolysis of an ester to form an alcohol and a carboxylate anion.

Saturated fatty acid (Section 10.6A): A fatty acid having no carbon–carbon double bonds in its long hydrocarbon chain.

Saturated hydrocarbon (Section 4.1): A compound that contains only C−C and C−H σ bonds and no rings, thus having the maximum number of hydrogen atoms per carbon.

Schiff base (Section 21.11A): A compound having the general structure $R_2C{=}NR'$. A Schiff base is also called an imine.

Secondary (2°) alcohol (Section 9.1): An alcohol having the general structure R_2CHOH.

Secondary (2°) alkyl halide (Section 7.1): An alkyl halide having the general structure R_2CHX.

Secondary (2°) amide (Section 22.1): An amide having the general structure RCONHR'.

Secondary (2°) amine (Sections 21.11, 25.1): An amine having the general structure R_2NH.

Secondary (2°) carbocation (Section 7.14): A carbocation having the general structure R_2CH^+.

Secondary (2°) carbon (Section 4.1A): A carbon atom that is bonded to two other carbon atoms.

Secondary (2°) hydrogen (Section 4.1A): A hydrogen that is attached to a 2° carbon.

Secondary protein structure (Section 29.9B): The three-dimensional conformations of localized regions of a protein.

Secondary (2°) radical (Section 15.1): A radical having the general structure $R_2CH\cdot$.

Second-order rate equation (Sections 6.9B, 7.10): A rate equation in which the reaction rate depends on the concentration of two reactants.

Separatory funnel (Section 19.12): An item of laboratory glassware used for extractions.

Septet (Section 14.6C): An NMR signal that is split into seven peaks caused by six nearby nonequivalent protons.

Sesquiterpene (Section 30.7A): A terpene that contains 15 carbons and three isoprene units. A sesquiterpenoid also contains at least one oxygen atom.

Sesterterpene (Section 30.7A): A terpene that contains 25 carbons and five isoprene units. A sesterterpenoid also contains at least one oxygen atom.

Sextet (Section 14.6C): An NMR signal that is split into six peaks caused by five nearby nonequivalent protons.

Sharpless asymmetric epoxidation (Section 12.15): An enantioselective oxidation reaction that converts the double bond of an allylic alcohol to a predictable enantiomerically enriched epoxide.

Sharpless reagent (Section 12.15): The reagent used in the Sharpless asymmetric epoxidation. The Sharpless reagent consists of *tert*-butyl hydroperoxide, a titanium catalyst, and one enantiomer of diethyl tartrate.

Shielding effects (Section 14.3A): An effect in NMR caused by small induced magnetic fields of electrons in the opposite direction to the applied magnetic field. Shielding decreases the strength of the magnetic field felt by the nucleus and shifts an absorption upfield.

1,2-Shift (Section 9.9): Rearrangement of a less stable carbocation to a more stable carbocation by the shift of a hydrogen atom or an alkyl group from one carbon atom to an adjacent carbon atom.

Sigma (σ) bond (Section 1.9A): A cylindrically symmetrical bond that concentrates the electron density on the axis that joins two nuclei. All single bonds are σ bonds.

Sigmatropic rearrangement (Section 27.1): A pericyclic reaction in which a σ bond is broken in the reactant, the π bonds rearrange, and a σ bond is formed in the product.

Silyl ether (Section 20.12): A common protecting group for an alcohol in which the O−H bond is replaced by an O−Si bond.

Simmons–Smith reaction (Section 26.5): Reaction of an alkene with CH_2I_2 and Zn(Cu) to form a cyclopropane.

Singlet (Section 14.6A): An NMR signal that occurs as a single peak.

Skeletal structure (Section 1.8B): A shorthand representation of the structure of an organic compound in which carbon atoms and the hydrogen atoms bonded to them are omitted. All heteroatoms and the hydrogens bonded to them are drawn in. Carbon atoms are assumed to be at the junction of any two lines or at the end of a line.

S_N1 mechanism (Sections 7.10, 7.13): A nucleophilic substitution mechanism that goes by a two-step process involving a carbocation intermediate. S_N1 is an abbreviation for "Substitution Nucleophilic Unimolecular."

S_N2 mechanism (Sections 7.10, 7.11): A nucleophilic substitution mechanism that goes by a one-step concerted process, where both reactants are involved in the transition state. S_N2 is an abbreviation for "Substitution Nucleophilic Bimolecular."

Soap (Sections 3.6, 22.12B): The carboxylate salts of long-chain fatty acids prepared by the basic hydrolysis or saponification of a triacylglycerol.

Solubility (Section 3.4C): A measure of the extent to which a compound dissolves in a liquid.

Solute (Section 3.4C): The compound that is dissolved in a liquid solvent.

Solvent (Section 3.4C): The liquid component into which the solute is dissolved.

Specific rotation (Section 5.12C): A standardized physical constant for the amount that a chiral compound rotates plane-polarized light. Specific rotation is denoted by the symbol [α] and defined using a specific sample tube length (*l* in dm), concentration (*c* in g/mL), temperature (25 °C), and wavelength (589 nm). $[\alpha] = \alpha/(l \times c)$

Spectator ion (Section 2.1): An ion that does not take part in a reaction and is opposite in charge to the ion that does take part in a reaction. A spectator ion is also called a counterion.

Spectroscopy (Section 13.1): An analytical method using the interaction of electromagnetic radiation with molecules to determine molecular structure.

Sphingomyelin (Section 30.4B): A hydrolyzable phospholipid derived from sphingosine.

Spin flip (Section 14.1A): In NMR spectroscopy, when an atomic nucleus absorbs RF radiation and its magnetic field flips relative to the external magnetic field.

Spin–spin splitting (Section 14.6): Splitting of an NMR signal into peaks caused by nonequivalent protons on the same carbon or adjacent carbons.

Spiro ring system (Problem 23.63, Appendix B): A compound having two rings that share a single carbon atom.

Staggered conformation (Section 4.9): A conformation of a molecule in which the bonds on one carbon bisect the R−C−R bond angle on the adjacent carbon.

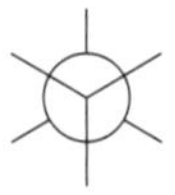

Step-growth polymer (Sections 22.16A, 31.1): A polymer formed when monomers containing two functional groups come together with loss of a small molecule such as water or HCl. Step-growth polymers are also called condensation polymers.

Stereochemistry (Sections 4.9, 5.1): The three-dimensional structure of molecules.

Stereogenic center (Section 5.3): A site in a molecule at which the interchange of two groups forms a stereoisomer. A carbon bonded to four different groups is a tetrahedral stereogenic center. A tetrahedral stereogenic center is also called a chirality center, a chiral center, or an asymmetric center.

Stereoisomers (Sections 4.13B, 5.1): Two isomers that differ only in the way the atoms are oriented in space.

Stereoselective reaction (Section 8.5): A reaction that yields predominantly or exclusively one stereoisomer when two or more stereoisomers are possible.

Stereospecific reaction (Section 10.14): A reaction in which each of two stereoisomers of a starting material yields a particular stereoisomer of a product.

Steric hindrance (Section 7.8B): A decrease in reactivity resulting from the presence of bulky groups at the site of a reaction.

Steric strain (Section 4.10): An increase in energy resulting when atoms in a molecule are forced too close to one another.

Steroid (Sections 16.14C, 30.8): A tetracyclic lipid composed of three six-membered rings and one five-membered ring.

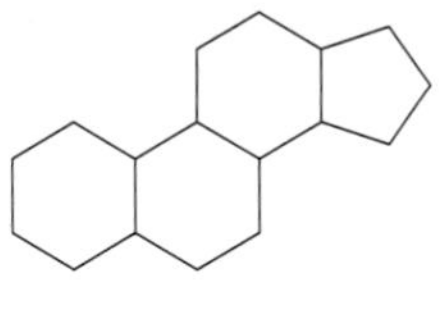

Straight-chain alkane (Section 4.1A): An acyclic alkane that has all of its carbons in a row. Straight-chain alkanes are also called normal alkanes.

Strecker amino acid synthesis (Section 29.2C): A reaction that converts an aldehyde into an α-amino acid by way of an α-amino nitrile.

Structural isomers (Sections 4.1A, 5.2): Two compounds that have the same molecular formula but differ in the way the atoms are connected to each other. Structural isomers are also called constitutional isomers.

Substituent (Section 4.4): A group or branch attached to the longest continuous chain of carbons in an organic molecule.

Substitution reaction (Section 6.2A): A reaction in which an atom or a group of atoms is replaced by another atom or group of atoms. Substitution reactions involve σ bonds: one σ bond breaks and another is formed at the same atom.

Substrate (Section 6.11): An organic molecule that is transformed by the action of an enzyme.

Sulfonate anion (Section 19.13): An anion having the general structure RSO_3^-, formed by deprotonating a sulfonic acid with a Brønsted–Lowry base.

Sulfonation (Section 18.4): An electrophilic aromatic substitution reaction in which benzene reacts with $^+SO_3H$ to give a benzenesulfonic acid, $C_6H_5SO_3H$.

Sulfonic acid (Section 19.13): A compound having the general structure RSO_3H.

Suprafacial reaction (Section 27.4): A pericyclic reaction that occurs on the same side of the two ends of the π electron system.

Suzuki reaction (Section 26.2): The palladium-catalyzed coupling of an organic halide (R'X) with an organoborane (RBY_2) to form a product R−R'.

Symmetrical anhydride (Section 22.1): An anhydride that has two identical alkyl groups bonded to the carbonyl carbon atoms.

Symmetrical ether (Section 9.1): An ether with two identical alkyl groups bonded to the oxygen.

Syn addition (Section 10.8): An addition reaction in which two parts of a reagent are added from the same side of a double bond.

Syn dihydroxylation (Section 12.9B): The addition of two hydroxy groups to the same face of a double bond.

Syndiotactic polymer (Section 31.4): A polymer having the substituents alternating from one side of the backbone of an elongated polymer chain to the other.

Syn periplanar (Section 8.8): In an elimination reaction, a geometry in which the β hydrogen and the leaving group are on the same side of the molecule.

Systematic name (Section 4.3): The name of a molecule indicating the compound's chemical structure. The systematic name is also called the IUPAC name.

T

Target compound (Section 11.12): The final product of a synthetic scheme.

Tautomerization (Sections 11.9, 23.2A): The process of converting one tautomer into another.

Tautomers (Section 11.9): Constitutional isomers that are in equilibrium and differ in the location of a double bond and a hydrogen atom.

Terminal alkene (Section 10.1): An alkene that has the double bond at the end of the carbon chain.

Terminal alkyne (Section 11.1): An alkyne that has the triple bond at the end of the carbon chain.

C-Terminal amino acid (Section 29.5A): The amino acid at the end of a peptide chain with a free carboxy group.

N-Terminal amino acid (Section 29.5A): The amino acid at the end of a peptide chain with a free amino group.

Termination (Section 15.4A): The final step of a chain reaction. In a radical chain mechanism, two radicals combine to form a stable bond.

Terpene (Section 30.7): A hydrocarbon composed of repeating five-carbon isoprene units.

Terpenoid (Section 30.7): A lipid that contains isoprene units as well as at least one oxygen heteroatom.

Tertiary (3°) alcohol (Section 9.1): An alcohol having the general structure R_3COH.

Tertiary (3°) alkyl halide (Section 7.1): An alkyl halide having the general structure R_3CX.

Tertiary (3°) amide (Section 22.1): An amide having the general structure $RCONR'_2$.

Tertiary (3°) amine (Sections 21.11, 25.1): An amine having the general structure R_3N.

Tertiary (3°) carbocation (Section 7.14): A carbocation having the general structure R_3C^+.

Tertiary (3°) carbon (Section 4.1A): A carbon atom that is bonded to three other carbon atoms.

Tertiary (3°) hydrogen (Section 4.1A): A hydrogen that is attached to a 3° carbon.

Tertiary protein structure (Section 29.9C): The three-dimensional shape adopted by an entire peptide chain.

Tertiary (3°) radical (Section 15.1): A radical having the general structure $R_3C\cdot$.

Tesla (Section 14.1A): A unit used to measure the strength of a magnetic field. Tesla is denoted with the symbol "T."

Tetramethylsilane (Section 14.1B): An internal standard used as a reference in NMR spectroscopy. The tetramethylsilane (TMS) reference peak occurs at 0 ppm on the δ scale.

Tetrasubstituted alkene (Section 8.2A): An alkene that has four alkyl groups and no hydrogens bonded to the carbons of the double bond ($R_2C{=}CR_2$).

Tetraterpene (Section 30.7A): A terpene that contains 40 carbons and eight isoprene units. A tetraterpenoid contains at least one oxygen atom as well.

Tetrose (Section 28.2): A monosaccharide containing four carbons.

Thermodynamic enolate (Section 23.4): The enolate that is lower in energy—generally the more substituted enolate.

Thermodynamic product (Section 16.11): In a reaction that can give more than one product, the product that predominates at equilibrium.

Thermodynamics (Section 6.5): A study of the energy and equilibrium of a chemical reaction.

Thermoplastics (Section 31.7): Polymers that can be melted and then molded into shapes that are retained when the polymer is cooled.

Thermosetting polymer (Section 31.7): A complex network of cross-linked polymer chains that cannot be re-melted to form a liquid phase.

Thioester (Section 22.17): A compound with the general structure RCOSR'.

Tollens reagent (Sections 20.8, 28.9B): A reagent that oxidizes aldehydes, and consists of silver(I) oxide in aqueous ammonium hydroxide. A Tollens test is used to detect the presence of an aldehyde.

***p*-Toluenesulfonate** (Section 9.13): A very good leaving group having the general structure $CH_3C_6H_4SO_3^-$ and abbreviated as TsO^-. Compounds containing a *p*-toluenesulfonate leaving group are called alkyl tosylates and are abbreviated ROTs.

Torsional energy (Section 4.9): The energy difference between the staggered and eclipsed conformations of a molecule.

Torsional strain (Section 4.9): An increase in the energy of a molecule caused by eclipsing interactions between groups attached to adjacent carbon atoms.

Tosylate (Section 9.13): A very good leaving group having the general structure $CH_3C_6H_4SO_3^-$, and abbreviated as TsO^-.

***s*-Trans** (Sections 16.6, 29.5B): The conformation of a 1,3-diene that has the two double bonds on opposite sides of the single bond that joins them.

Trans diaxial (Section 8.8B): In an elimination reaction of a cyclohexane, a geometry in which the β hydrogen and the leaving group are trans with both in the axial position.

Trans isomer (Sections 4.13B, 8.3B): An isomer of a ring or double bond that has two groups on opposite sides of the ring or double bond.

Transition state (Section 6.7): An unstable energy maximum as a chemical reaction proceeds from reactants to products. The transition state is at the top of an energy "hill" and can never be isolated.

Triacylglycerol (Sections 10.6, 22.12A, 30.3): A lipid consisting of the triester of glycerol with three long-chain fatty acids. Triacylglycerols are the lipids that comprise animal fats and vegetable oils. Triacylglycerols are also called triglycerides.

Triose (Section 28.2): A monosaccharide containing three carbons.

Triplet (Section 14.6): An NMR signal that is split into three peaks having a relative area of 1:2:1, caused by two nearby nonequivalent protons.

Trisubstituted alkene (Section 8.2A): An alkene that has three alkyl groups and one hydrogen bonded to the carbons of the double bond ($R_2C{=}CHR$).

Triterpene (Section 30.7A): A terpene that contains 30 carbons and six isoprene units. A triterpenoid contains at least one oxygen atom as well.

U

Ultraviolet (UV) light (Section 16.15): Electromagnetic radiation with a wavelength from 200–400 nm.

Unimolecular reaction (Sections 6.9B, 7.10, 7.13A): A reaction that has only one reactant involved in the rate-determining step, so the concentration of only one reactant appears in the rate equation.

α,β-Unsaturated carbonyl compound (Section 20.15): A conjugated compound containing a carbonyl group and a carbon–carbon double bond separated by a single σ bond.

Unsaturated fatty acid (Section 10.6A): A fatty acid having one or more carbon–carbon double bonds in its hydrocarbon chain. In natural fatty acids, the double bonds generally have the *Z* configuration.

Unsaturated hydrocarbon (Section 10.2): A hydrocarbon that has fewer than the maximum number of hydrogen atoms per carbon atom. Hydrocarbons with π bonds or rings are unsaturated.

Unsymmetrical ether (Section 9.1): An ether in which the two alkyl groups bonded to the oxygen are different.

Upfield shift (Section 14.1B): In an NMR spectrum, a term used to describe the relative location of an absorption signal. An upfield shift means a signal is shifted to the right in the spectrum to lower chemical shift.

Urethane (Section 31.6C): A compound that contains a carbonyl group bonded to both an OR group and an NHR (or NR_2) group. A urethane is also called a carbamate.

V

Valence bond theory (Section 17.9A): A theory that describes covalent bonding as the overlap of two atomic orbitals with the electron pair in the resulting bond being shared by both atoms.

Valence electrons (Section 1.1): The electrons in the outermost shell of orbitals. Valence electrons determine the properties of a given element. Valence electrons are more loosely held than the core electrons and thus participate in chemical reactions.

van der Waals forces (Section 3.3B): Very weak intermolecular interactions caused by momentary changes in electron density in molecules. The changes in electron density cause temporary dipoles, which are attracted to temporary dipoles in adjacent molecules. van der Waals forces are also called London forces.

Vicinal dihalide (Section 8.10): A compound that has two halogen atoms on adjacent carbon atoms.

Vinyl group (Section 10.3C): An alkene substituent having the structure $-CH{=}CH_2$.

Vinyl halide (Section 7.1): A molecule containing a halogen atom bonded to the sp^2 hybridized carbon of a carbon–carbon double bond.

Vitamins (Sections 3.5, 30.5): Organic compounds needed in small amounts by biological systems for normal cell function.

VSEPR theory (Section 1.7B): Valence shell electron pair repulsion theory. A theory that determines the three-dimensional shape of a molecule by the number of groups surrounding a central atom. The most stable arrangement keeps the groups as far away from each other as possible.

W

Walden inversion (Section 7.11C): The inversion of a stereogenic center involved in an S_N2 reaction.

Wavelength (Section 13.5): The distance from one point of a wave to the same point on the adjacent wave. Wavelength is abbreviated with the Greek letter lambda (λ).

Wavenumber (Section 13.6A): A unit for the frequency of electromagnetic radiation that is inversely proportional to wavelength. Wavenumber, reported in reciprocal centimeters (cm^{-1}), is used for frequency in IR spectroscopy.

Wax (Sections 4.15, 30.2): A hydrolyzable lipid consisting of an ester formed from a high molecular weight alcohol and a fatty acid.

Williamson ether synthesis (Section 9.6): A method for preparing ethers by reacting an alkoxide (RO^-) with a methyl or primary alkyl halide.

Wittig reaction (Section 21.10): A reaction of a carbonyl group and an organophosphorus reagent that forms an alkene.

Wittig reagent (Section 21.10A): An organophosphorus reagent having the general structure $Ph_3P{=}CR_2$.

Wohl degradation (Section 28.10A): A reaction that shortens the carbon chain of an aldose by removing one carbon from the aldehyde end.

Wolff–Kishner reduction (Section 18.15B): A method to reduce aryl ketones to alkyl benzenes using hydrazine (NH_2NH_2) and strong base (KOH).

Woodward–Hoffmann rules (Section 27.3): A set of rules based on orbital symmetry used to explain the stereochemical course of pericyclic reactions.

Y

Ylide (Section 21.10A): A chemical species that contains two oppositely charged atoms bonded to each other, and both atoms have octets of electrons.

Z

Zaitsev rule (Section 8.5): In a β elimination reaction, a rule that states that the major product is the alkene with the most substituted double bond.

Ziegler–Natta catalysts (Section 31.4): Polymerization catalysts prepared from an organoaluminum compound and a Lewis acid such as $TiCl_4$, which afford polymer chains without significant branching and with controlled stereochemistry.

Zwitterion (Sections 19.14B, 29.1B): A neutral compound that contains both a positive and negative charge.

Credits

Prologue

Figure 1a: © Comstock/Punchstock RF; **1b:** © Corbis Premium RF/Alamy; **1c:** © Steven May/Alamy; **1d:** © Layne Kennedy/Corbis; **2 (top):** © Kevin Lee; **(bottom):** © Florent Charpin; **3:** © photo M. Boyer–www.kudalaut.eu.

Chapter 1

Opener: © Organics Image Library/Alamy RF**; p. 12:** © Jill Braaten; **p. 19 (both):** © Steve Gschmeissner/Photo Researchers, Inc.; **p. 28:** Courtesy John Somerville; **p. 32:** © CD 16/Author's Image RF; **p. 33:** © The McGraw-Hill Companies, Inc./Elite Images; **p. 39 (top):** © Corbis/RF; **p. 39 (bottom) & p. 41:** © PhotoDisc/Getty RF; **p. 48:** © Cristina Pedrazzini/Photo Researchers, Inc.

Chapter 2

Opener: © Jill Braaten; **p. 60:** © Fancy Photography/Veer RF; **pp. 69, 70:** © The McGraw-Hill Companies, Inc./Jill Braaten, photographer; **p. 74:** © Wilmer Stratton; **2.7:** © National Geographic/Getty Images.

Chapter 3

Opener: © S. Aubert/univ. Grenoble; **p. 89:** Courtesy of Gebauer Company, Cleveland, Ohio; **p. 91:** © Jill Braaten; **p. 93 (top):** © Andrew Syred/Photo Researchers, Inc.; **p.93 (bottom):** © Martin Harvey/Corbis; **p. 103 (top):** © Comstock/PunchStock RF; **p. 93 (bottom):** © The McGraw-Hill Companies, Inc./Mary Reeg; **p. 104:** © Digital Vision/Getty RF.

Chapter 4

Opener: © Bettmann/Corbis; **p. 121(top):** © God of Insects; **p. 121 (bottom):** © Douglas Peebles/Corbis; **p. 124:** © Jill Braaten; **p. 125:** © Daniel C. Smith; **4.5:** © PhotoDisc RF; **p. 136:** © The McGraw-Hill Companies, Inc./Jill Braaten, photographer; **p. 157:** © PhotoDisc RF; **p. 158:** © Eric Couture, courtesy Canadian Shark Research Laboratory.

Chapter 5

Opener: © Shallenberger Photography; **5.1 (starch):** © Jim Erickson/Corbis; **5.1 (wheat):** © PhotoDisc/Getty RF; **5.1 (cotton plant):** © Corbis/RF; **5.1 (cotton fabric) & p. 170:** © Daniel C. Smith; **p. 173:** © The McGraw-Hill Companies, Inc./Jill Braaten, photographer; **p. 174:** © Mark W. Skinner @ USDA PLANTS; **p. 177:** © Gerry Ellis/Minden Pictures; p. 182: © Photo Researchers, Inc.; **p. 187:** © The McGraw-Hill Companies, Inc./Jill Braaten, photographer; **pp. 195, 196 (caraway seed):** © The McGraw-Hill Companies, Inc./Elite Images; **p. 196 (spearmint leaves):** © David Sieren/Visuals Unlimited, Inc.

Chapter 6

Opener: © UpperCut Images/Alamy RF; **p. 225(top):** © Jack Star/PhotoLink/ Getty RF; **p. 225 (bottom):** © The McGraw-Hill Companies, Inc./Jill Braaten, photographer.

Chapter 7

Opener: © Randy Morse/Animals Animals–Earth Scenes; **p. 243 (top):** © Michael Guiry; **p. 243 (bottom):** Time Magazine June 30, 1947 in the collection of Beverly Naidus, www.artsforchange.org; **p. 246:** © Jill Braaten; **p. 260:** © Jill Braaten; **p. 271:** © The McGraw-Hill Companies, Inc./Elite Images; **p. 279:** © The McGraw-Hill Companies, Inc./Elite Images.

Chapter 8

Opener: © Comstock/Punchstock RF; **p. 291:** © The McGraw-Hill Companies, Inc./Jill Braaten, photographer; **p. 293:** © Steven P. Lynch RF; **p. 299:** Forest & Kim Starr.

Chapter 9

Opener: Photo collection of Dr. James P. McVey, NOAA Sea Grant Program; **p. 326:** © Jill Braaten; **9.4 (corn):** © Jupiterimages RF; **9.4 (ethanol):** Photo by Mark Wilson/Getty Images; **p. 333:** The Boston Medical Library in the Francis A. Countway Library of Medicine; **p. 345:** © Henriette Kress; **p. 361:** © The McGraw-Hill Companies, Inc./Jill Braaten, photographer; **p. 363:** © The McGraw-Hill Companies, Inc./John Thoeming, photographer.

Chapter 10

Opener: © Jill Braaten; **p. 379:** © Daniel C. Smith; **10.5 (carrots):** © Corbis/ RF; **10.5 (ginger root):** © The McGraw-Hill Companies, Inc./Jill Braaten, photographer; **10.5 (apples):** © PhotoDisc RF; **10.5 (oranges):** © Iconotec/ Alamer and Cali, photographers RF; **pp. 382, 384:** © JIll Braaten; **p. 395:** © 1998 Richard Megna, Fundamental Photographs, NYC; **10.17:** © Henriette Kress.

Chapter 11

Opener: © The McGraw-Hill Companies, Inc./Chris Kerrigan, photographer; **11.3:** © Arachnokulture; **p. 433:** © Michael G. Moye.

Chapter 12

Opener: © Royalty Free/Corbis; **p. 451 (peanut butter & label), 12.4 (both):** © The McGraw-Hill Companies, Inc./Elite Images; **p. 453:** PhotoLink/Getty Images RF; **p. 454:** © 1998 Richard Megna, Fundamental Phogoraphers, NYC; **p. 459:** USDA APHIS PPQ Archives, www.forestryimages.org; **p. 463:** © Comstock Images/Punchstock RF; **12.10:** © The McGraw-Hill Companies, Inc./Elite Images; **p. 472:** © PhotoDisc/Getty RF.

Chapter 13

Opener: Library of Congress; **p. 492:** © Ted Kinsman/Photo Researchers, Inc.; **p. 505:** © Andrew McClenaghan/Photo Researchers, Inc.

Chapter 14

Opener: © Carlos F. Barbas, III; **p. 545:** © Brand X Pictures/PunchStock RF; **14.15a:** James Rosato, RT (R) (MR) (CT)/MRI Applications Specialist Brigham and Women's Hospital, Boston MA; **14.15b:** With permission, Daniel C. Smith. Spectra courtesy of the Chemistry Department at Rutgers University.

Chapter 15

Opener: © Jill Braaten; **p. 573 (propane):** © The McGraw-Hill Companies, Inc./ Jill Braaten, photographer; **p. 573 (ozone):** NASA Ozone Watch; **p. 578:** © The McGraw-Hill Companies, Inc./Elite Images; **p. 579:** © Royalty-Free/Corbis; **p. 582:** © The McGraw-Hill Companies, Inc./Jill Braaten, photographer; **table 15.2 (blood bag):** © Image Source/Getty RF; **table 15.2 (syringes):** © Royalty-Free/Corbis; **table 15.2 (dental floss):** © Jill Braaten.

Chapter 16

Opener: © Stockbyte Silver/Getty Images RF; **p. 602:** © Franz-Marc-Frei/ Corbis; **16.8:** Stephen Frank/Getty Images RF; **p. 612:** © Puna Organics, Pahoa, Hawaii, Sept. 2011; **p. 620:** © C Squared Studios/Getty Images RF; **p. 621:** © The McGraw-Hill Companies, Inc./Jill Braaten, photographer.

Chapter 17

Opener: © The McGraw-Hill Companies, Inc./Jill Braaten, photographer; **17.3 (cigarette smoke):** PhotoAlto/PictureQuest RF; **17.3 (tobacco plant):** Photo by Bob Nichols, USDA Natural Resources Conservation Service; **p. 646:** Daniel C. Smith; **p. 647:** Forest & Kim Starr; **p. 655 (diamonds):** © Charles O'Rear/Corbis; **p. 655 (graphite):** © Lester V. Bergman/Corbis; **p. 656:** © Getty Images RF.

Chapter 18

Opener: © Bill Aron/Photo Edit, Inc.; **p. 670:** © Time Life Pictures/Getty Images; **18.4:** © Rene Dulhoste/Photo Researchers, Inc.; **p. 703:** © The McGraw-Hill Companies, Inc./Jill Braaten, photographer.

Chapter 19

Opener: Dr. Steven J. Wolf; **p. 725:** © Ryman Cabannes/Photocuisine/Corbis; **p. 726:** © Biopix.dx http://www.biopix.dk; **p. 738:** © Photodisc Green/Getty RF; **p. 742:** © John A. Raineri.

Chapter 20

Opener:© Photodisc/Alamy RF; **p. 755:** © Gerald D. Carr, PhD; **p. 762:** © M.K. Ranjitsinh/Photo Researchers, Inc.; **p. 765:** © John Kaprielian/Photo Researchers, Inc.; **p. 766:** © PhotoDisc/Getty RF; **p. 771:** © The McGraw-Hill Companies, Inc./photographer Joe Franek; **p. 778:** © George Grall/National Geographic/Getty Images; **p. 780:** © Iconotec.com/Pepiera Tom Canabi Hugo RF.

Chapter 21

Opener: © Richo Cech, Horizon Herbs, LLC; **21.6 & p. 824:** © The McGraw-Hill Companies, Inc./Jill Braaten, photographer; **p. 825:** Daniel C. Smith; **p. 841:** © Bill Beatty/Visuals Unlimited, Inc.

Chapter 22

Opener & p. 871 (fruit): © Jill Braaten; **(coca plant):** © blickwinkel/Alamy; **p. 876:** © The McGraw-Hill Companies, Inc./Joe Franek, photographer; **p. 877:** Photo by Scott Bauer/USDA; **p. 878:** © Coby Schal/NC State University; **p. 888:** © The McGraw-Hill Companies, Inc./Jill Braaten, photographer; **p. 889:** © Jill Braaten; **p. 893:** Image courtesy of The Advertising Archives; **p. 894:** © Jill Braaten.

Chapter 23

Opener: © Colin Young-Wolff/Alamy; **pp. 923, 930:** © The McGraw-Hill Companies, Inc./Joe Franek, photographer; **p. 935:** © The McGraw-Hill Companies, Inc./Mary Reeg, photographer; **p. 942:** © Margareta Taute/Visuals Unlimited, Inc.

Chapter 24

Opener: © Jill Braaten; **24.4:** © William Weber/Visuals Unlimited, Inc.; **p. 964 (ground root) & p. 965:** © Jill Braaten; **p. 970:** © The McGraw-Hill Companies, Inc./Jill Braaten, photographer.

Chapter 25

Opener: © James Forte/Getty Images/RF; **25.5 (nightshade):** © Werner Arnold; **(tobacco):** © Creatas Images RF; **25.5 (hemlock):** © Steven P. Lynch RF; **p. 998:** Daniel C. Smith; **p. 1007:** © The McGraw-Hill Companies, Inc./Jill Braaten, photographer; **p. 1014:** James Gathany/CDC; **p. 1028 (indigo plant):** © Kirsten Soderlind/Corbis; **p. 1028 (sea snail):** © Kirsten Soderlind/Corbis; **p. 1028 (madder):** Photograph by Paul Redfearn/Ozarks Regional Herbarium/ Southwest Missouri State University; **p. 1028 (purple shawl):** © Science & Society Picture Library.

Chapter 26

Opener: © Degginger E.R./Animals Animals/Earth Scenes; **p. 1052:** © The McGraw-Hill Companies, Inc./John Thoeming, photographer; **p. 1060:** © Ross Warner/Alamy.

Chapter 27

Opener: © Kim Taylor/npl/Minden Pictures; **p. 1080:** © The McGraw-Hill Companies, Inc./Mary Reeg, photographer; **p. 1083:** © blickwinkel/Alamy; **p. 1090:** © Marina Khaytarova TopTropicals.com.

Chapter 28

Opener: © The McGraw-Hill Companies, Inc./Mary Reeg, photographer; **p. 1100 (syrup):** © The McGraw-Hill Companies, Inc./Jill Braaten, photographer; **p. 1100 (tanning cream):** © The McGraw-Hill Companies, Inc./Elite Images; **p. 1114:** © Brand X Pictures/PunchStock RF; **p. 1118 (top):** © Nature Picture Library/ Alamy; **p. 1118 (bottom):** © inga spence/Alamy; **p. 1130 (top, maltose):** © Vol. 3/PhotoDisc/Getty RF; **p. 1130 (bottom, milk):** © The McGraw-Hill Companies, Inc./Elite Images; **28.10 (left):** © The McGraw-Hill Companies, Inc./Elite Images; **28.10 (right):** © David Muench/Corbis; 28.11: © The McGraw-Hill Companies, Inc./Jill Braaten, photographer; **p. 1135:** © Comstock Images/PictureQuest RF.

Chapter 29

Opener: © Royalty-Free/Corbis; **p. 1151:** © Jill Braaten; **p. 1184:** © Eye of Science/Photo Researchers, Inc.

Chapter 30

Opener: © Jill Braaten; **p. 1196 (top):** © Daniel C. Smith; (bottom): USDA, ARS, National Genetic Resources Program; **p. 1198 (coconut trees):** © Royalty-Free/Corbis; **p. 1198 (oils):** © The McGraw-Hill Companies, Inc./Elite Images; **p. 1198 (fish):** © Rick Price/Corbis; **p. 1200 (top):** © AP/Wide World Photos; **p. 1200 (bottom):** © PhotoDisc/Getty RF; **p. 1208 (top):** © Henriette Kress; **(bottom):** © PhotoDisc/Getty RF; **p. 1210:** © Thomas J. Abercrombie/Getty Images; **p. 1218:** © Comstock/JupiterImages RF.

Chapter 31

Opener: © The McGraw-Hill Companies, Inc./Jill Braaten, photographer; **31.1:** © Getty Images; **31.4 (balls):** © Dynamicgraphics/JupiterImages RF; **31.4 (paint):** © Royalty-Free/Corbis; **31.4 (fibers):** © Fernando Bengoe/Corbis; **31.4 (glue):** © The McGraw-Hill Companies, Inc./John Thoeming, photographer; **p. 1236:** DSM Dyneema; **p. 1237:** © Bob Krist/Corbis; **p. 1239:** © The McGraw-Hill Companies, Inc./John Thoeming, photographer; **p. 1244:** © The McGraw-Hill Companies, Inc./John Thoeming, photographer; **31.9 (corn):** © Royalty-Free/ Corbis; **31.9 (swimsuit):** DuPont; **p. 1249 (both):** Ecoflex/www.basf.de/ecoflex.

Spectra Art

Chapters 13, 14, 16, 17, 18, 19, 20, 21, 23, 25: Spectra courtesy of the Chemistry Department at Rutgers University.

Index

Page numbers followed by f indicate figures; those followed by t indicate tables. An A– before page numbers indicates appendix pages.

A

- ABS, 1252
- Abyssomicin C, 987
- Acebutolol, 117
- Acetal(s)
  - conversion to hemiacetals, 840–841
  - cyclic, 837
    - in carbohydrates, 845–846
    - conversion of cyclic hemiacetal to, 844–845
  - glycosides, 1115–1118
  - hydrolysis of, 840–841
  - as protecting groups, 841–842
  - structure of, 1115
  - synthesis of
    - addition of alcohols to aldehydes and ketones, 837–841
    - from hemiacetals, 838–839, 844–845
  - terminology of, 837
- Acetaldehyde
  - aldol reaction of, 955, 958, 960
  - ethanol oxidized to, 470
  - structure of, 810
- Acetamide, 56, 85, 860, 865, 869f
- Acetaminophen, 57, 879, 891, 910, 1039, 1207
- Acetanilide, 749
- Acetate
  - bond length in, 604
  - formation from acetaldehyde oxidation, 470
  - as nucleophile, 253–255, 262
  - resonance structures of, 71, 71f, 597, 731, 733f
- Acetic acid, 725
  - acidity of, 70–71, 74, 731, 733f, 734
  - as Brønsted–Lowry acid, 59f
  - deprotonation of, 730
  - dimers, 723f
  - electrostatic potential plot of, 71f, 719, 719f
  - in ethyl acetate formation, 228
  - glacial, 725
  - halogenation of carbonyl compounds in, 929
  - melting point of, 99
  - NMR spectrum of, 544
  - pK_a of, 730
  - as polar protic solvent, 250f
  - structure of, 721t, 860
- Acetic anhydride, 860, 865, 1119
- Acetic benzoic anhydride, 865
- Acetoacetic ester synthesis, 935, 940–943, 971
- Acetone
  - acidity of, 71
  - aldol reactions of, 961
  - bonding of, 42
  - as Brønsted–Lowry base, 59f
  - dipoles in adjacent molecules, 94
  - odor of, 815
  - as polar aprotic solvent, 251, 251f
  - solubility of, 100
  - structure and bonding of, 42, 588, 811, 815
  - surface area and boiling point of, 96, 97f
  - uses of, 815
- Acetone enolate, 921f, 927f
- Acetonitrile
  - acidity of, 71
  - deprotonation of, 66
  - as polar aprotic solvent, 251f
  - structure of, 867f
- *p*-Acetophenetidin, 910
- Acetophenone, 764
  - aldol reaction of, 958
  - structure of, 811
- *N*-Acetyl amino acids, 1156–1158
- Acetylation, 880
- Acetyl chloride, 860, 864, 1119
- Acetylcholine, 895
- Acetyl coenzyme A (acetyl CoA), 895, 897, 1209, 1210, 1216
- 1-Acetylcyclohexene, 946
- 2-Acetylcyclopentanone, 986
- 1-Acetylcyclopentene, 983
- Acetylene
  - acetylide anion formation from, 436–437
  - in acid–base reactions, 65–66
  - acidity of, 72, 73f
  - bond angles, 417
  - bond dissociation energies of, 418
  - bonds in, 41–42, 42f, 42t
  - combustion of, 420
  - deprotonation of, 436
  - disparlure synthesis from, 460, 460f
  - electrostatic potential map of, 422, 422f
  - functional group in, 88, 89t
  - Lewis structure, 16
  - molecular shape of, 26
  - nomenclature, 419
- *N*-Acetyl-D-glucosamine (NAG), 897, 1134–1135
- Acetyl group, 812, 1046, 1120
- Acetylide anions, 65–66
  - conversion of terminal alkynes to, 431
  - formation by deprotonation of terminal alkynes, 423
  - as organometallic compounds, 773
  - reactions with alkyl halides, 431–433, 433f
  - reactions with epoxides, 434
  - retrosynthetic analysis with, 436–437
  - synthesis from acetylene, 436–437
  - in synthesis of disparlure, 460, 460f
- Acetylsalicylic acid, 58, 726, 879, 891. *See also* Aspirin
- Achiral carbocation, 392
- Achiral enolate, 927
- Achiral epoxides, 461
- Achiral intermediate, 397
- Achiral meso compound, 186, 188, 398, 398f
- Achiral molecules, 171–173, 173f
  - halogenation of, 570t, 571
  - optical inactivity of, 190
- Achiral product, 391
- Achiral reactant, 358, 391
- Achiral starting material, 459, 471
- Acid(s)
  - amino. *See* Amino acids
  - Brønsted–Lowry
    - carboxylic acids, 729–734
    - description of, 59–60
    - reactions of, 60–62
  - carboxylic. *See* Carboxylic acid(s)
  - as catalysts, 228
  - common, 74
  - conjugate, 60–62, 247–248, 247t
  - dehydration of alcohols to alkenes in strong, 338–343
  - as electron pair acceptors, 59, 62, 77
  - in epoxide ring-opening reactions, 359–361
  - Lewis, 77–79
  - origin of word, 59
  - as proton donors, 59
  - reaction of ethers with strong, 355–356
  - strength, 62–74
  - sulfonic, 741
- Acid–base reactions
  - Brønsted–Lowry, 60–62, 265
  - description, 60–62
  - Lewis, 77–79, 245
  - organometallic reagents and, 773–774
  - predicting outcome of, 65–66
- Acid chlorides
  - acidity/basicity of, 863, 863t
  - boiling point of, 869t
  - functional group in, 91t
  - IR spectra of, 870, 870t
  - leaving group, 757
  - melting point of, 869t
  - nomenclature of, 864, 867t
  - nucleophilic substitution reactions, 757
  - odor of, 876
  - physical properties of, 869t
  - pK_a, 863t
  - reactions of, 876–878, 892t
    - conversion to amides, 877, 1015
    - conversion to anhydrides, 876, 877
    - conversion to carboxylic acids, 876, 878
    - conversion to esters, 876
    - Friedel–Crafts acylation reactions, 672
    - with organometallic reagents, 784–786
  - reduction of, 766–767
  - solubility of, 869t
  - stability of, 863
  - structure and bonding of, 754, 860, 862–863
  - synthesis from carboxylic acids, 880f, 881
- Acidity
  - basicity, inverse relationship with, 63, 63t
  - of carbon–hydrogen bonds, 67, 68
  - of carboxylic acids, 729, 730–735, 733f
  - determining relative acidity of protons, 73–74
  - electronegativity and, 67–70
  - factors affecting, 66–74
    - element effects, 67–69, 73f
    - hybridization effects, 72, 72f, 73f
    - inductive effects, 69–70, 70f, 73f
    - resonance effects, 70–71, 71f, 73f
  - periodic trends in, 67–69
- Acidity constant (K_a), 62–63
- Acid rain, 74
- Acrolein, 613f
- Acrylic acid, 583
- Acrylonitrile, 551, 1232f
- Activation energy. *See* Energy of activation (E_a)
- Active methylene compounds, 962, 972, 973
- Active site, enzyme, 229, 229f
- Acyclic alkanes
  - branched-chain, 122
  - conformations of, 137–144
    - butane, 141–144, 141f, 143f
    - ethane, 137–144, 139f, 140f
  - constitutional isomers, 122–124, 125t
  - having more than five carbon atoms, 124, 125t
  - having one to five carbon atoms, 121–124, 125t
  - homologous series, 124, 125t
  - molecular formula, 121, 125, 125t
  - naming, 128–132
  - normal (*n*) (straight-chain), 124–125, 125t
  - structure, 121–122
  - torsional and steric strain energies in, 143t
- Acyclovir, 946
- Acylases, 1158
- Acylation
  - definition of, 672
  - Friedel–Crafts. *See* Friedel–Crafts acylation
- Acyl derivatives, 754
- Acyl group, 672, 812, 864, 865, 866
- Acylium ion, 491, 674
- Acyl transfer reactions, 895–896, 896f
- Addition polymers. *See* Chain-growth polymers
- Addition reactions, A–13
  - in alkenes, 385–406
    - anti addition, 386, 392, 393t, 395, 396, 399
    - halogenation, 386f, 395–398, 398f
    - halohydrin formation, 386f, 398–401, 400t
    - hydration, 386f, 394–395, 405–406
    - hydroboration–oxidation, 386f, 401–406, 402f, 403f, 405f, 405t

hydrohalogenation, 386–393, 386f, 388f, 390f, 393t
overview of, 385–386, 386f
stereochemistry of, 386, 391–393, 393f, 393t
syn addition, 386, 392, 393t, 402, 404
allylic bromination, 576
anti additions, 452, 454, 461, 462
carbene addition, 1054
conjugate, 972
in conjugated dienes
Diels–Alder reaction, 610–619, 611f
electrophilic, 606–608
kinetic versus thermodynamic product, 608–610
description of, 208
dihydroxylation, 461–463
epoxidation, 458–461, 471–473
exothermic reactions, 387, 387f
in nucleophilic aromatic substitution, 695–699
oxidative, 1046, 1048, 1052
radical reactions, 576, 579–582
syn additions, 447, 452, 458, 460, 460f, 461, 462–463, 1054
Adenine, 1137, 1138f
S-Adenosylmethionine (SAM), 260, 261
-adiene (suffix), 376
Adipic acid, 1238, 1245, 1246
Adipoyl chloride, 893
Adrenal cortical steroids, 1217, 1219
Adrenaline, 261–262, 261f, 997
Advil. *See* Ibuprofen
Aerosol propellant, 243, 573
Agent Orange, 670f
Aglycon, 1118
-al (suffix), 809
Alanine, 110
abbreviation for, 742t
acid–base reactions of, 743–744, 744f
in dipeptide synthesis, 1168–1169, 1172
enantiomers of, 175f, 1156–1158
isoelectric point of, 744, 1152t
in peptide formation, 1161
pK_a values for, 1152t
structure of, 1150f
Albuterol, 174, 361, 361f, 852, 1041
Alcohol dehydrogenase, 470
Alcoholic beverages, 331, 444
Alcohols, 324–371
alkene preparation by acid-catalyzed dehydration, 384
allylic, epoxidation of, 471–473
boiling point of, 331t
bonding in, 326
classification of, 325
dehydration reactions of, 338–345
alkene synthesis in, 338–345
of β-hydroxy carbonyl compounds, 958
carbocation rearrangements in, 341–343
dehydration to alkenes, 338–345, 341f
E1 mechanism in, 339–340
E2 mechanism in, 340, 344
enthalpy change in, 340, 341f
Le Châtelier's principle in, 340
in phosphorus oxychloride and pyridine, 344–345
in strong acid, 338–343
electrostatic potential maps, 326f
elimination reactions, 336–345, 354, 355f
ether formation from, 395
fragmentation pattern in mass spectrum, 491
Friedel–Crafts alkylation of, 676
functional group, 88, 90t
β-hydroxy carbonyl compounds, 955–966
infrared (IR) spectra of, 502
interesting examples, 331–332, 332f
leaving groups of, 337, 344–347, 349–352, 354
melting point of, 331t
NMR spectra of, 538–539
nomenclature, 327–328
common names, 328
for cyclic alcohols, 327, 327f
IUPAC system, 327, 328
nucleophilicity of, 273
oxidation of, 457f, 466–471
patchouli, 345f
physical properties of, 330–331, 331t
as polar protic solvents, 250, 250f, 275
primary (1°), 406
classification as, 325
conversion to alkyl halides with HX, 345–347, 350f
conversion to alkyl halides with phosphorus tribromide, 350, 350t
conversion to alkyl halides with thionyl chloride, 349, 350t
dehydration by E2 mechanism, 340
hydrogen bonding extent, 330
from nucleophilic addition to aldehydes, 767
oxidation to carboxylic acids, 466, 467–468, 728
from reactions of aldehydes with organometallic reagents, 774–775
from reduction of acid chlorides, 766–767
from reduction of aldehydes, 450, 759, 760, 761
from reduction of carboxylic acid derivatives, 759
from reduction of carboxylic acids, 769
from reduction of esters, 766–767
from reduction of monosaccharides, 1120
racemic mixture of, 404
reactions of
conversion to alkyl halides with HX, 345–348, 350t
conversion to alkyl halides with thionyl chloride and phosphorus tribromide, 349–350, 350t
conversion to alkyl tosylates, 352
elimination reactions, 336–345
general features, 336–337
nucleophilic substitution reactions, 336–337, 345–354, 355f
summary of, 354, 355f
secondary (2°), 406
classification as, 325
conversion to alkyl halides with HX, 345–348, 350t
conversion to alkyl halides with phosphorus tribromide, 350, 350t
conversion to alkyl halides with thionyl chloride, 349, 350t
dehydration by E1 mechanism, 339–340
hydrogen bonding extent, 330
oxidation to ketones, 466, 467
from reactions of aldehydes with organometallic reagents, 774–775
from reduction of ketones, 450, 759, 760, 761
solubility, 331t
structure of, 325, 326
substitution reactions, 336–337, 345–354, 355f
synthesis of, 333–335
from alkyl halides, 334–335
hydration of alkene, 394–395
hydroboration–oxidation of alkenes, 401–405
by nucleophilic substitution reaction, 334–335
reactions of organometallic reagents with aldehydes and ketones, 774–775, 822–823
reactions of organometallic reagents with epoxides, 787–788
reduction of epoxides, 455–456, 456f
tertiary (3°)
classification as, 325
conversion to alkyl halides with HX, 345–348, 350t
dehydration by E1 mechanism, 339–340
hydrogen bonding extent, 330
from reaction of esters and acid chlorides with organometallic reagents, 783–785
from reaction of ketones with organometallic reagents, 774–775
Aldaric acids, 1121, 1122, 1125–1128
D-aldaric acids, 1125
-aldehyde (suffix), 810
Aldehyde dehydrogenase, 470
Aldehyde group, as electron-withdrawing group, 680
Aldehydes. *See also* Carbonyl compounds
aldol reactions of, 955–967
boiling point of, 813t
carbohydrates, 845–846
electrostatic potential map of, 755, 755f
fragmentation pattern in mass spectrum, 491
functional group in, 91t
hydration of, 835–837
kinetics of hydrate formation, 836–837
thermodynamics of hydrate formation, 835–836
hydroxy
cyclization of, 843, 846
β-hydroxy, synthesis in aldol reactions, 955–966
intramolecular cyclization of, 843, 846
IR spectra, 813–814, 813f, 814f
melting point of, 813t
NMR spectra, 815, 815f
nomenclature, 809–810, 812
common names, 810, 810f
IUPAC system, 809, 810f
nucleophilic addition reactions, 756, 761, 807–846
carbanion addition, 822–823
cyanide addition, 823–824
hydride addition, 821–822
mechanism of, 819–820
nucleophiles in, 820, 821f
primary amine addition, 830–832, 834f
secondary amine addition, 833–834, 834f
odors of, 816, 816f
oxidation reactions, 758–759, 771
to carboxylic acid, 1121–1122
physical properties of, 812, 813t
pK_a, 922t
polyhydroxy, 845–846
protecting groups for, 841–842
reactions of
with amines, 1015
at α carbon, 818–819
at carbonyl carbon, 818, 819
halogenation at α carbon, 928–932, 931f
with organometallic reagents, 775–777, 822–823
reactivity of, 756
reduction of, 821–822
to alcohols, 450, 759, 760, 761
reductive amination to amines, 1002–1005
solubility of, 813t
structure of, 754, 808
synthesis of, 816–818
alcohol oxidation, 466, 467–468
carboxylic acid reduction, 759
hydroboration–oxidation of alkynes, 430–431, 817
hydrolysis of acetals, 840–841
hydrolysis of imines and enamines, 834
oxidation of primary alcohols, 817
oxidative cleavage of alkenes, 463–464, 817
reduction of acid chlorides, 766
reduction of acid chlorides and esters, 817
reduction of esters, 766
reduction of nitriles, 900
unreactivity to nucleophilic substitution, 758
Wittig reaction, 825–830
Alditol, 1120
Aldohexoses, 1126–1129
D-aldohexoses, 1106–1107, 1107f, 1127f
Haworth projections of, 1111–1113
pyranose ring of, 1109
stereogenic centers of, 1103, 1106
Aldol reactions
crossed, 960–963
synthetically useful reactions, 961–962, 962f
useful transformations of aldol products, 962, 963f
dehydration of aldol product, 958–959
directed, 963–965, 964f
features of, 955–957, 956f
intramolecular, 965–967, 966f
in Robinson annulation, 974–978
mechanism of, 955–956
retrosynthetic analysis using, 959–960
Aldonic acid, 1121
D-Aldopentoses, 1106, 1107f, 1126, 1127f
Aldoses
D-aldose family, 1106–1107, 1107f
in Kiliani–Fischer synthesis, 1123, 1124–1125
oxidation of, 1121–1122
reduction of, 1120
structure of, 1100
in Wohl degradation, 1123–1124

Aldosterone, 1219
Aldotetroses
D-aldotetroses, 1106, 1106f, 1107f, 1125, 1126
stereoisomers of, 1106, 1106f
Aldrin, 626
Alendronic acid (Fosamax), 19
Aleve. *See* Naproxen
Aliphatic carboxylic acids, 734–735
Aliphatic hydrocarbons, 88, 121. *See also* Alkanes; Alkenes; Alkynes
Aliskiren, 175, 481
Alizarin, 1028
Alizarine yellow R, 1029
Alkaloids, 988, 995, 996f
Alkanes, 120–165
acyclic
branched-chain, 122
conformations of, 137–144, 139f, 140f, 141f, 143f
constitutional isomers, 122–124, 125t
having more than five carbon atoms, 124, 125t
having one to five carbon atoms, 121–124, 125t
homologous series, 124, 125t
molecular formula, 121, 125, 125t
normal (*n*) (straight-chain), 124–125, 125t
structure of, 121–122
torsional and steric strain energies in, 143t
boiling point of, 136, 137t
bonds in, 88
combustion of, 155–156
cycloalkanes
molecular formula, 121, 125
naming, 132–134, 133f, 134f
structure, 121, 125, 145f
substituted, 148–154, 150f, 153f
definition of, 121
fossil fuels, 135–136
halo, 240
halogenation, 562–572
of achiral starting material, 570t, 571
bromination, 566–568, 568f
of chiral starting material, 570t, 571–572
chlorination, 563–567, 569–572, 569f
energy changes during, 565, 565f
mechanism of, 563–565
in organic synthesis, 570
stereochemistry of, 570–572, 570t
infrared (IR) spectra of, 500, 501
melting point of, 136, 137t
naming, 128–132
nomenclature, 125–135, 130f
common names, 134–135, 135f
IUPAC system, 128–134, 130f
substituents, 127
nonreactivity of, 89
oxidation of, 154–156
physical properties, 136, 137t
radical reactions, 561
solubility of, 136, 137t
synthesis of
reduction of alkenes, 445, 445f, 447–450
reduction of alkyl halides, 455, 774
reduction of alkynes, 445f, 452–453, 455f
Alkene oxides, 329, 330
Alkenes, 372–415
addition reactions, 385–406
anti addition, 386, 392, 393t, 395, 396, 399
halogenation, 386f, 395–398, 398f
halohydrin formation, 386f, 398–401, 400t
hydration, 386f, 394–395, 405–406
hydroboration–oxidation, 386f, 401–406, 402f, 403f, 405f, 405t
hydrohalogenation, 386–393, 386f, 388f, 390f, 393t
overview of, 385–386, 386f
stereochemistry of, 386, 391–393, 393f, 393t
syn addition, 386, 392, 393t, 402, 404
amino acid synthesis from, 1159–1160
boiling point of, 380
bonds in, 88
classification of, 291–292, 291f
constitutional isomers of, 338
conversion to alkynes, 421–422
conversion to cyclopropane, 1052–1055
in coupling reactions with organic halides (Heck reaction), 1043, 1050–1055
cyclopropane synthesis in Simmons–Smith reaction, 1055–1056
degrees of unsaturation, calculating, 374–376, 449–450
dehydration of alcohols to, 338–345
diastereomers of, 292–293
dihydroxylation of, 461–463
disubstituted, 291, 291f, 298, 299–300, 301, 303, 307–308
double bonds in, 291–293, 373, 374t
restricted rotation around, 292–293, 292f
electrophiles, reactions with, 109
electrostatic potential plots, 385, 385f
epoxidation of, 457f, 458–459
fatty acids, 372, 382–383, 383f, 383t
Friedel–Crafts alkylation of, 676
functional group in, 88, 89t
hybrid orbitals in, 291, 294
hydrogenation of, 447–452
alkene stability and, 447–448, 448f
cis and trans isomers compared, 447, 448f
degrees of unsaturation, determination of, 449–450
mechanism of catalytic hydrogenation, 448–449
infrared (IR) spectra of, 500, 501
interesting examples, 380, 381f
internal, 373
lipids, 382–384
melting point of, 380, 382, 383t
metathesis, 1056–1060, 1057f, 1059f
molecular formula of, 374
monomers in polymerization, 582–585, 583t
monosubstituted, 291, 291f, 298
NMR spectra of, 536–538, 538f
nomenclature, 376–379
common names, 379, 379f
IUPAC system, 376–377
for stereoisomers, 377–379
organic synthesis, 407–408
oxidative cleavage of, 457f, 463–465, 817
physical properties of, 380
polymerization of, 1227–1234, 1235–1236
radical reactions, 561, 579–582
reduction of, 445, 445f, 447–450
solubility of, 380
stability of, 293–294, 447–448, 448f
stereoisomers of, 292–294
alkyne reduction and, 452–455
synthesis of, 384–385
amine conversion, 1016–1019
comparison of methods, 829–830
dehydration of alcohols, 384
dehydrohalogenation of alkyl halides with strong base, 384
elimination reactions, 384–385
by elimination reactions, 289–290
by Hofmann elimination reaction, 1016–1019
reduction of alkynes to cis alkenes, 452, 453, 455f
reduction of alkynes to trans alkenes, 452, 454–455, 455f
substituted alkenes in Heck reaction, 1050
Wittig reaction, 825–830
terminal, 373
tetrasubstituted, 291
trisubstituted, 291, 291f, 299–300, 303, 307–308
Alkenols, 377
Alkoxides, 290
electron density plot, 920, 921f
in ether synthesis, 335
protonation of, 763, 765, 767, 775, 784, 788
Alkoxy group, 90t, 329
Alkylamines
basicity of, 1008–1011, 1013t
reaction with nitrous acid, 1020–1021
Alkylation reactions
in acetoacetic ester synthesis, 935, 940–943
of diethyl malonate derivative, 1153–1154, 1155f
of enolates, 933–936
general features of, 933–934
tamoxifen synthesis, 935
of unsymmetrical ketones, 934–935
Friedel–Crafts. *See* Friedel–Crafts alkylation
in malonic ester synthesis, 936–940
polyalkylation, 691
Alkyl benzenes
electron density of, 679–680
halogenation of, 699–701
oxidation of, 701–702, 728
sulfonation of, 671
synthesis of
Friedel–Crafts alkylation, 667f, 672–673
by reduction of aryl ketones, 702–703
Alkylborane
formation by hydroboration, 401–404
oxidation of, 404–405, 406
Alkyl bromides
mass spectrum of, 489, 489f
synthesis of, 579–582
Alkyl chlorides
in Friedel–Crafts alkylation reactions, 673, 675–676
mass spectrum of, 488, 488f
Alkyl diazonium salts, 1020–1021
Alkyl group, 127, 128, 241, 245, 379, 672, 865, 866
in alkyl tosylates, 352
carbon radical stability and, 559–560, 560f
as electron-donating group, 678, 679, 681
in ethers, 328–329
nomenclature
in alcohols, 328
for branching molecules, A-3–4
in ethers, 328–329
polarizable, 678
stabilization of carbonyl group by, 835
Alkyl halides
acetylide anion reactions with, 431–433, 433f
alkane formation from, 774
allylic halides, 239, 239f
aryl halides, 239, 239f, 277
benzylic halides, 239, 239f
classification of, 239–240, 239f, 312
conversion of alcohols to, 345–351
with HX, 345–348, 350t
importance of, 351
with thionyl chloride and phosphorus tribromide, 349–350, 350t
conversion to carboxylic acids, 787
conversion to primary amines, 1001
coupling reaction with organocuprates, 1044
dehydrohalogenation with strong base, 384
in direct enolate alkylation, 933–935
elimination reactions, 244, 288–323
E1 mechanism, 311–315
E2 mechanism, 297–298, 298t, 305–306, 311–315, 1019, 1019f
examples, 239f, 242–244, 242f
functional group, 90t
mass spectrometry of, 488–489, 488f, 489f
molecular formula of, 239
in monosaccharides conversion to ethers, 1119
nomenclature, 240–241, 241f
common names, 241
IUPAC, 240, 241f
nucleophiles, reactions with, 109
nucleophilic substitution reactions, 245–280
alcohol synthesis, 334–335
alkyl halide structure and, 258, 266, 272, 272f
with ammonia or amines to form amines, 999
ether synthesis, 334–335
S_N1 mechanism, 310–315
S_N2 mechanism, 311–315
physical properties, 241–242, 242t
polar carbon–halogen bond, 244, 244f
primary (1°)
acetylide anion reactions with, 431–432
classification as, 239
E2 elimination reactions, 297, 298, 312f
example of, 239f
S_N2 substitution reactions, 258, 272, 272f, 312f
synthesis of, 345
reaction mechanism, determining type of, 311–315, 312f–313f
reduction of, 455–456, 456f

secondary (2°)
acetylide anion reactions with, 432
classification as, 239
E1 elimination reactions, 303, 313f
E2 elimination reactions, 297, 313f
example of, 239f
S_N1 substitution reactions, 266, 272, 272f, 313f
S_N2 substitution reactions, 258, 272, 272f, 313f
synthesis of, 345
synthesis of
halogenation of alkanes, 562–570
hydrohalogenation of alkenes, 386–393, 393t
tertiary (3°)
acetylide anion reaction with, 432
classification as, 239
E1 elimination reactions, 303, 304, 312f
E2 elimination reactions, 297, 298, 312f
example of, 239f
S_N1 substitution reactions, 264, 266, 272, 272f, 312f
synthesis of, 345, 348
unreactive, 239, 239f
vinyl halides, 239, 239f, 277
1,2-Alkyl shift, 341
Alkylthio group, 90t
Alkyl titanium compound, 1236
Alkyl tosylates, 352–354, 355f, 384
conversion of alcohols to, 352, 354
reactions of, 353
Alkynes, 416–443
addition reactions
halogenation, 423f, 426
hydration, 423f, 427–429
hydroboration–oxidation, 423f, 429–431
hydrohalogenation, 423f, 424–426
overview of, 422
boiling point of, 419
bond dissociation energies of, 418
bonds in, 88
cycloalkynes, 418
degrees of unsaturation, 417
deprotonation of, 423–424, 423t
examples, 420–421, 420f, 421f
functional group in, 88, 89t
hydroboration of, 1047, 1049
hydroboration–oxidation of, 423f, 429–431
infrared (IR) spectra of, 500, 501
internal
definition of, 417
hydration of, 427
hydroboration–oxidation of, 430
oxidative cleavage of, 465, 728
synthesis in acetylide anion reactions with alkyl halides, 431–433
melting point of, 419
molecular formula of, 417
nomenclature, 418–419
oxidative cleavage of, 457f, 465–466, 728
physical properties of, 419
reduction of, 445, 445f, 452–455, 455f
to alkanes, 445f, 452–453, 455f
to cis alkene, 452, 453, 455f
to trans alkene, 452, 454–455, 455f
solubility of, 419
structure of, 417–418
synthesis of, 421–422, 436–437
from alkenes, 421–422
by dehydrohalogenation, 310–311, 311f
from dihalides, 421–422
E2 elimination reactions, 289, 310–311, 311f
multistep, 436–437
terminal
definition of, 417
hydration of, 427
hydroboration–oxidation, 430–431
hydrohalogenation, 424
oxidative cleavage of, 465, 728
reaction as an acid, 422–423
synthesis in acetylide anion reactions with alkyl halides, 431–433
triple bond of, 417–418
D-Allaric acid, 1122
Allegra. *See* Fexofenadine
Allicin, 125
D-Allonic acid, 1144
D-Allose, 1107f, 1122
Allyl aryl ether, 1089
Allyl group, 379
Allylic alcohol
aldol reactions of, 963f
epoxidation of, 471–473
synthesis from α,β-unsaturated carbonyl compounds, 789
Allylic carbocations, 607
as conjugated system, 594, 595
electrostatic potential plot, 596, 596f
NMR spectra of, 597, 597f
resonance of, 596–597, 596f
resonance-stabilized, 607
Allylic carbon
oxidation of, 451, 451f
radical halogenation at, 574–577
bromination, 575–577
product mixtures in, 576–577
in triacylglycerols, 451, 451f
Allylic halides, 239, 239f
Allylic substitution, 576
Allyl radical, 574–577, 578f
Allyl vinyl ether, 1089
Alpha (α) carbon, 289–290, 721, 724, 741, 742
of aldehydes and ketones, 810, 818–819
substitution reactions of carbonyl compounds at the α carbon, 915–953
Alpha (α) cleavage, 491
Alpha (α) elimination reaction, 1053
Alpha (α) helix, 1176, 1177f, 1178, 1178f, 1179f, 1181f
Alpha (α) hydrogens, 916, 920, 929–930, 960, 961, 962, 963, 969
Altocid. *See* Methoprene
D-Altrose, 1107f
Aluminum chloride, in Friedel–Crafts alkylations, 672–678, 691–692
Alzheimer's disease, 90, 965, 1014, 1090
Amberlyst A-26 resin, 469
Ambident nucleophile, 924
-amide (suffix), 866, 867t
Amide bond, 1160, 1176
Amides
basicity of, 863t, 1010–1011, 1013t
boiling point of, 869t
cyclic, 861
functional group in, 91t
hydrolysis of, 890
infrared (IR) spectra of, 503
interesting examples, 871–872
IR spectra of, 869–870, 870t
leaving group, 757
melting point of, 869t
nitrogen bases, 75, 75f
NMR spectra of, 870
nomenclature, 866, 867t
nucleophilic substitution reactions, 757
physical properties of, 868, 869f, 869t
pK_a, 863t, 922t
primary (1°), 861, 866, 868–869, 877, 879, 885, 898
as protecting group for an amine, 1016, 1016f
proteins, 871–872
reduction to amines, 769, 1001
secondary (2°), 861, 866, 868–869, 877, 879, 885
solubility of, 869t
stability of, 863
structure and bonding of, 754, 860, 861
synthesis of
from acid chlorides, 877, 1015
from anhydrides, 879, 1015
from carboxylic acids, 880f, 883–885
from esters, 885
tautomers, 898–899
term usage, 923
tertiary (3°), 861, 866, 877, 879, 885, 921
Amide tautomer, 898–899
Amikacin, 1135
-amine (suffix), 991–992
Amine oxide, 462
Amines, 988–1041
aromatic
basicity of heterocyclic, 1011, 1013t
nomenclature, 992
basicity of, 989, 1005–1014, 1013t
aromaticity effects on, 1011, 1013t
hybridization effects on, 1012, 1013t
inductive effects on, 1013t
pK_a values, 1005, 1007–1008, 1013t
relative to other compounds, 1007–1014, 1013t
resonance effects of, 1013t
boiling point of, 993t
classification of, 989
electrostatic potential plots of, 990, 990f
functional group, 90t
general molecular formula for, 994
infrared (IR) spectra of, 503
interesting examples, 995–998
derivatives of 2-phenylethylamine, 997–998, 997f
histamine and antihistamines, 996
simple amines and alkaloids, 995, 996f
IR spectra of, 994, 994f
mass spectra of, 994, 994f
melting point of, 993t
nitrosamine formation, 271
NMR spectra of, 995, 995f
nomenclature of, 991–993
as nucleophiles, 989, 1014–1016
odors of, 995
physical properties of, 993, 993t
primary (1°)
addition to aldehydes and ketones, 830–832, 832f, 834f
amino acids, 1151
from direct nucleophilic substitution, 999–1000
Gabriel synthesis, 1000–1001
IR spectra of, 994, 994f
nomenclature, 991
reactions with acid chlorides and anhydrides, 1015
reactions with aldehydes and ketones, 1015
reactions with nitrous acid, 1020–1021
from reduction of amides, 1001
from reduction of nitriles, 1001
from reduction of nitro compounds, 1001
structure of, 989
synthesis from reduction of nitriles, 900
protecting group for, 1016, 1016f
reactions of
with acid chlorides, 877, 1015
with aldehydes and ketones, 1015
with anhydrides, 879, 1015
with carboxylic acids, 880f, 883–885
conversion to alkenes, 1016–1019
conversion to amides, 1015
with esters, 885
general features, 1005
Hofmann elimination, 1016–1019
with monosaccharides, 1135
with nitrous acid, 1020–1021
secondary (2°)
addition to aldehydes and ketones, 833–834, 834f
from direct nucleophilic substitution, 999
IR spectra of, 994, 994f
nomenclature, 991–992
proline, 1151
reactions with acid chlorides and anhydrides, 1015
reactions with aldehydes and ketones, 1015
reaction with nitrous acid, 1021
from reduction of amides, 1001
structure of, 989
separation from other organic compounds, 1006–1007, 1006f
solubility of, 993t
spectroscopic properties of, 994–995, 994f, 995f
structure and bonding of, 989–991
synthesis of, 998–1005
direct nucleophilic substitution reactions, 999
Gabriel synthesis, 1000–1001
reduction of amides, 769, 1001
reduction of nitriles, 1001
reduction of nitro compounds, 1001
reductive amination of aldehydes and ketones, 1002–1005
tertiary (3°)
from direct nucleophilic substitution, 999
IR spectra of, 994, 994f
nomenclature, 991–992
from reduction of amides, 1001
structure of, 989

Amino acids, 109–110, 741–744, 1149–1160. *See also* Peptides; Proteins
abbreviations for, 742t, 1150f
N-acetyl, 1156–1158
acid–base behavior of, 743–744, 744f, 1151–1152, 1151f, 1152t
α-amino acids, 741, 1149, 1149f
D-amino acids, 742, 1149, 1149f
L-amino acids, 742, 1149, 1149f
analysis of peptide composition, 1165
enantiomers of, 1149, 1149f
separation of, 1155–1158
essential, 742, 1151
general features of, 1149, 1149f, 1151
isoelectric points, 744
naturally occurring, 1149, 1150f
peptide synthesis from, 1168–1175
pK_a values, 1151, 1152, 1152t
representative examples, 742t
resolution of
by conversion to diastereomers, 1155–1158, 1156f
kinetic, using enzymes, 1158
separation of, 1155–1158
stereogenic center of, 1149, 1151
structure of, 741, 1149, 1149f, 1150f, 1151
synthesis of, 1152–1155
alkylation of diethyl malonate derivative, 1153–1154, 1155f
enantioselective hydrogenation, 1159–1160
reaction of α-halo acids with ammonia, 1152–1153, 1155f
Strecker synthesis, 1154–1155, 1155f
zwitterion form, 743, 1151
Aminobenzene, 634. *See also* Aniline
p-Aminobenzoic acid (PABA), 621, 714, 1030–1031
Aminoglycoside antibiotics, 1135
Amino group, 90t, 992
as activating group, 691
as electron-donating group, 679–680, 680f
inductive effect of, 678
nitro reduction to, 703
as ortho, para director, 688
resonance effect of, 679
6-Aminohexanoic acid, 1239
α-Amino nitrile, 1154–1155
Amino sugars, 1134–1135
Ammonia
basicity of, 1008
boiling point, 454
in dissolving metal reductions, 446, 454
hybrid orbitals in, 38, 38f
molecular shape, 27
pK_a of, 64
reactions with
acid chlorides, 877, 1015
alkyl halides to form amines, 999
anhydrides, 879, 1015
esters, 885
α-halo acids, 1152–1153
Ammonium cation, of amino acids, 743
Ammonium salt
in amine extraction process, 1006–1007
enantiomers, 990
in Hofmann elimination reaction, 1016–1018
synthesis of, 989–990, 999
Amoxicillin, 3, 56, 200, 872
Amphetamine, 76, 81, 199, 1002
Amphikuemin, 5f, 6
Amphiprion perideraion, 5f, 6
Amygdalin, 203, 824–825
Amylopectin, 1133–1134
Amylose, 168f, 1133–1134
β-Amyrin, 1222
Anabolic steroids, 1218
Analgesics, 593, 726, 879, 934, 943
Anastrozole, 897, 951
Androgens, 1217
Androsterone, 1218t
-ane (suffix), 124, 127, 128, 132, 135, 376
Anemonefish, 5–6, 5f
Anesthetics, 89, 242f, 333, 703, 715
Angiotensin, 182
Angle strain, 144–146
in epoxide, 326, 337
Angstrom (Å), 25
Angular methyl groups, 1214–1215
Anhydrides
acidity/basicity of, 863t
boiling point of, 869t
cyclic, 861, 881
derivation of term, 865
IR spectra of, 870t
melting point of, 869t
mixed, 861, 865
nomenclature, 865, 867t
physical properties of, 869t
pK_a, 863t
reactions of, 878–880, 892t
acetylation, 880
with ammonia or amines to form amides, 1015
conversion to amides, 879
conversion to carboxylic acids, 879
conversion to esters, 879
solubility of, 869t
stability of, 863
structure and bonding of, 860–861, 863
symmetrical, 861, 865
synthesis of
from acid chlorides, 876, 877
dehydration of dicarboxylic acids, 881
Aniline, 628, 1009
basicity of, 1009
electrophilic aromatic substitution reaction, 670, 688, 690
electrostatic potential plot of, 680f, 1010f
nomenclature and, 635
polyhalogenation of, 690
protection of, 1016f
resonance structures, 679
structure of, 634, 992
synthesis of
electrophilic aromatic substitution reaction, 670
by nitrobenzene reduction, 703
Anionic oxy-Cope rearrangements, 1089
Anionic polymerization, 1232–1233, 1232f
of epoxides, 1234–1235
Anions
acetate, 71, 71f
carbanion, 72, 210–211, 210f
cyclopentadienyl, 647–649, 654, 654f
definition of, 8
enolate, 22
naked, 251
radical, 454
salt formation, 12
solvation by hydrogen bonding, 250
Anisole, 356
Annulation
origin of word, 974
Robinson, 974–978
Annulenes, 643–644
18-annulene, 557
Anomeric carbon, 1109–1114, 1116, 1129–1131, 1136
Anomers, 1110–1115, 1114f
Antabuse, 470
Antarafacial bond formation, 1082
Antarafacial rearrangement, 1086–1087, 1087t
Anthracene, 644
Anti addition, 386, 392, 393t, 395, 396, 399, 452, 454, 461, 462
Antiaromatic compounds, 641, 642, 648, 650
Antibiotics
aminoglycoside, 1135
cephalosporins, 872
chloramphenicol, 174
ionophores, 107–108
β-lactam, 483, 505, 872, 891–892
penicillin(s), 483, 505, 872, 876–877, 891–892
Antibonding molecular orbital, 651, 651f, 652f, 653
Anticancer drugs
aromatase inhibitors, 897
doxorubicin, 1099f
epothilone A, 1059f
illudin-S, 942
imatinib mesylate, 872
tamoxifen, 915, 935
Anti conformation, 141f, 142–144, 143f, 292f
Antidepressant, 260, 665, 670f, 678, 998
Antifreeze, 332f
Antihistamines, 633, 670f, 996, 1007, 1014
Anti-inflammatory drugs
aspirin, 58, 76, 224, 279, 279f, 726, 727, 1207
ibuprofen, 126, 157, 195, 703, 706, 762f, 954, 971, 1207
nabumetone, 943
naproxen, 195, 934
nonsteroidal anti-inflammatory drugs (NSAIDs), 1207
Antimalarial drugs, 299f, 405, 405f, 647, 932, 1014
Antimicrobials. *See also* Antibiotics
sulfa drugs, 1030–1031, 1031f
Antioxidants, 237, 578–579
Anti periplanar geometry, 305–308, 306f
Antiseptics, 246
Antiviral agents, 91, 1059f
Applied magnetic field, 516, 518, 526, 530
Aprotic solvents, polar, 251, 251f, 275, 276t, 297, 298t, 925
D-Arabinose, 1106, 1107f, 1123
Arachidic acid, 1197t
Arachidonic acid, 590, 592
leukotriene synthesis by oxidation of, 362
prostaglandin synthesis from, 727
structure of, 102, 1197t
synthesis of eicosanoids from, 1205, 1206f
Arene, 631
Arene oxide, 164
Arginine
isoelectric point for, 1152t
pK_a values for, 1152t
structure of, 1150f
Aricept. *See* Donepezil
Arimidex. *See* Anastrozole
Aripiprazole, 1035
Aromatase inhibitors, 897
Aromatic compounds, 630–634
background on, 631
bonding and antibonding orbitals, 650–651
buckminsterfullerene, 655–656
charged, 647–649
electrophilic substitution. *See* Electrophilic aromatic substitution reactions
examples, 643–649
charged compounds, 647–649
heterocycles, 644–647, 646f
multiple rings, 644
single ring, 643–644
Hückel's rule, 640–643
basis of, 650–653
interesting, 637–638, 638f
molecular orbitals, 650–653, 651f, 652f
nomenclature, 634–636
predicting aromaticity using inscribed polygon method, 653–655, 654f
reactions of, 665–717
electrophilic aromatic substitution, 666–695
nucleophilic aromatic substitution, 695–699
spectroscopic properties, 636, 636t, 637f
Aromaticity, effect on basicity of amines, 1011, 1013t
Arrows
curved, 21–22, 60, 61, 210, 211, 211t, 212, 245
double-headed, 19, 60–61, 211t
equilibrium, 60–61
half-headed, 559
open, 434
use in describing organic reactions, 211–212, 211t
Artemisinin, 203, 405, 405f
Artificial sweeteners, 1131, 1132f, 1164
Arylamines
basicity of, 1008–1010, 1013t
reaction with nitrous acid, 1020–1021
Arylboranes, 1047
Aryl bromides, synthesis from aryl diazonium salts, 1022
Aryl chlorides
examples of biologically active, 670f
reactivity of, 696
synthesis from aryl diazonium salts, 1022
Aryl diazonium salt, 1020–1027
Aryl fluorides, synthesis from aryl diazonium salts, 1023
Aryl groups, 635
Aryl halides, 239, 239f, 277
coupling reactions
with alkene, 1050–1051
with organoborane, 1047
examples of biologically active, 670f
nucleophilic aromatic substitution, 695–699
reactivity of, 674
synthesis of
from aryl diazonium salts, 1022, 1023
halogenation of benzene, 667f, 669–670
Aryl iodides, synthesis from aryl diazonium salts, 1023

Aryl ketones, reduction to alkyl benzenes, 702–703
Ascorbic acid, 86, 103
Asparagine
 isoelectric point for, 1152t
 pK_a values for, 1152t
 structure of, 1150f
Asparagopsis taxiformis, 238
Aspartame, 907, 1131, 1132f, 1164
Aspartic acid, 1151, 1250
 isoelectric point for, 1152t
 pK_a values for, 1152t
 structure of, 1150f
Aspirin, 58, 76, 879, 908
 crossing of cell membrane, 76
 derivation of word, 726
 mechanism of action, 224, 726, 727
 mode of action, 1207
 proton transfer reaction, 76
 structure, 726
 synthesis of, 279, 279f, 726
Asthma, 361–362
Asymmetric carbon. *See* Stereogenic centers
Asymmetric reaction, 471
Asymmetric reduction, 763
Atactic polymer, 1235–1236
-ate (suffix), 722, 865, 867t
Atenolol, 83, 90
Atherosclerosis, 896, 896f
Atmosphere
 carbon dioxide concentration in, 156, 156f
 ozone layer destruction, 243
Atomic mass unit (amu), 8
Atomic number, 8
Atomic orbitals, number of, 1072
Atomic symbol, 9
Atomic weight, 8
Atom mass, infrared (IR) absorption and, 498, 498f, 499
Atoms
 components of, 8
 excited state, 35
 ground state, 35
Atorvastatin, 1217, 1217f
Atropine, 995, 996f
Automated peptide synthesis, 1173–1175
Avobenzone, 33, 116, 970
Avocado, 104
Axial bond, 167
Axial hydrogens, 146–147, 146f, 148f
Aziridines, 371
Azo compound
 applications of, 1028–1031
  dyes, 1028–1031
  sulfa drugs, 1030–1031, 1031f
 formation of, 1023, 1026–1027
Azo coupling, 1022, 1026–1027
AZT (azidodeoxythymidine), 4, 659
Azulene, 658

B

Backside attack, in nucleophilic substitution reactions, 256–257, 273
Baekeland, Leo, 1243, 1244f
Baeyer, Adolf von, 125
Baeyer strain theory, 144
Bakelite, 1243–1244, 1244f
Ball-and-stick model
 of acyclic alkanes, 121–122
 of molecular shape, 25–28
Barbituric acid, 125
Barrier to rotation, 143
Base(s)
 for alkyne deprotonation, 423, 423t
 for alkyne synthesis by dehydrohalogenation, 310, 310f
 Brønsted–Lowry
  description of, 59–60
  reactions of, 60–62
  substitution reactions with alkyl halides, 244
 common, 75, 75f
 conjugate, 60–62
 dehydration of β-hydroxy carbonyl compounds with, 958
 as electron pair donors, 59, 62, 77
 in elimination reactions, 289–290, 290t, 309t
  in E1 elimination reactions, 303, 303t, 309, 309t
  in E2 elimination reactions, 296, 296f, 298t, 309, 309t
 enolate formation with, 922–923, 923t
 hydrides, 75f
 Lewis, 77–79
 nitrogen, 75, 75f
 nonnucleophilic, 249
 organometallic reagents, 772, 773–774
 oxygen, 75, 75f
 as proton acceptors, 59
 strong, 75
 used to deprotonate carboxylic acids, 730, 731t
 weak as good leaving group in nucleophilic substitution reactions, 246–248
Base pairs, 1138, 1139f
Base peak, in mass spectrum, 485
Bases, nucleoside, 1137–1138, 1138f
Basicity
 acidity, inverse relationship with, 63, 63t
 of amines, 989, 1005–1014, 1013t
 of carboxylic acid derivatives, 862–863, 863t
 of carboxylic acids, 729
 leaving group ability and, 246–248
 nucleophilicity compared to, 249, 250, 251
 periodic trends in, 67–69
Basketane, 135f
Beeswax, 157, 157f
Benadryl, 1007
Benazepril, 1035
Benedict's reagent, 1121
Bent molecular shape
 alcohols, 326
 description of, 27–28
 ethers, 326
 polarity and, 47
Benzaldehyde
 aldol reactions of, 961, 962, 962f
 electron density of, 680, 680f
 resonance structures of, 679
 secondary alcohol formed from, 776
 structure of, 810
Benzalkonium chloride, 286
Benzamide, structure of, 866
Benzene, 55, 88, 89t, 115, 494, 630–634
 as annulene, 643
 background on, 631
 in BTX mixture, 637
 p-chlorostyrene synthesis from, 705–706
 conjugation of, 641
 degrees of unsaturation, 631, 632
 electrostatic potential plot of, 633, 633f, 680f
 Friedel–Crafts acylation of, 667f, 672–678, 702f, 707
 Friedel–Crafts alkylation of, 667f, 672–678, 702f, 705
 halogenation of, 667f, 669–670, 694
 heat of hydrogenation, 639–640, 639f
 hybridization and orbitals, 633
 lack of addition reactivity, 631, 640, 666
 metabolism of, 164
 molecular orbitals of, 652–653, 652f
 nitration of, 667f, 670–671, 694
 p-nitrobenzoic acid synthesis from, 705
 NMR spectrum of, 525, 526t, 527f, 643
 pi (π) electrons of, 632, 633, 642, 650, 666, 668
 in polymer synthesis, 1245, 1245f
 resonance, 632
 resonance structures, 598
 stability, 639–640, 642
 structure of, 632–633
 substitution reactions, 631, 640, 666–678. *See also* Electrophilic aromatic substitution reactions
 sulfonation of, 667f, 670, 671
 synthesis from aryl diazonium salts, 1023
 synthesis of bromonitrobenzene from, 694
 synthesis of *m*-bromoaniline from, 704
 synthesis of *o*-nitrotoluene from, 694–695
 synthesis of 1,3,5-tribromobenzene from, 1023–1024, 1024f
 trisubstituted benzene synthesis from, 706–707
Benzenecarbaldehyde. *See* Benzaldehyde
Benzene derivatives
 disubstituted, 692–693
  electrophilic aromatic substitution reactions of, 692–693
  halogenation of, 692–693
  nitration of, 693
  synthesis of, 694–695
 drugs containing benzene ring, 638f
 interesting examples, 637–638, 637f, 638f
 NMR spectra, 539–540, 540f
 nomenclature, 634–636
  aromatic rings as substituents, 635
  disubstituted, 634
  monosubstituted, 634
  polysubstituted, 635
 spectroscopic properties, 636, 636t, 637f
 substituted
  activating and deactivating substituents, 682–686, 685f
  directing effects of substituents, 682–690, 690f
  electrophilic aromatic substitution, 682–686, 685f, 690–692
  electrostatic potential plot of, 680, 680f
  Friedel–Crafts acylation of, 691–692
  Friedel–Crafts alkylation of, 691–692
  halogenation of, 690–691
  inductive effects on, 678–681
  multistep synthesis of, 705–707
  orientation effects on, 686–690
  oxidation of, 701–702
  reduction of, 702–704
  resonance effects on, 679–681
 synthesis of, 694–695, 705–707
  with diazonium salts, 1024–1026
 trisubstituted, synthesis of, 706–707
Benzene ring
 of arylamines, 1008
 NMR spectra of, 525, 526t, 527f, 539–540, 540f
Benzenesulfonic acid, 667f, 670
Benzo[*a*]pyrene, 363, 637, 637f
Benzocaine, 703
Benzoic acid
 acidity of, 735–737, 737f
 deprotonation of, 730
 separation from cyclohexanol by extraction procedure, 738–740, 740f
 structure of, 721t
 substituted, 735–738, 737f
 synthesis of
  by arene oxidation, 701
  by oxidation of alkyl benzenes, 728
Benzoic anhydride, 867t
Benzonitriles, 867t, 1023
Benzophenone, structure of, 811
Benzoquinone, 613f
Benzoyl chloride, 867t
Benzoyl group, 812
Benzyl acetate, 910
2-Benzylbutanoic acid, 938
Benzyl ester, 1171
Benzyl group, 635
Benzylic bromination, 699–701
Benzylic C–H bond, 699, 701–702, 728
Benzylic halides, 239, 239f, 699–701
Benzylic radical, 699–701, 1228
Benzyne, 698–699
Bergstrom, Sune, 727
Beryllium, octet rule exceptions in, 19
Beryllium hydride
 hybrid orbitals in, 37
 molecular shape of, 26
Beta (β) blocker, 90
Beta (β) carbon, 289–290, 306, 721
Beta (β) elimination reactions. *See also* Elimination reactions
 of alcohols, 336–345
 dehydrohalogenation as, 289
 Zaitsev rule, 299–301
Beta (β) lactam(s), 323, 483, 505, 861, 872, 891–892
Bextra. *See* Valdecoxib
BHA (butylated hydroxy anisole), 586
BHT (butylated hydroxy toluene), 578–579
Biaryls, 1066
Bicyclic compounds, naming, A-5–6
Bicyclic product, 614
Bicyclic ring system, bridged, 614–615, 615f
Biformene, 1210
"Big Six" synthetic polymers, 1247–1248, 1248t
Bile acid, 164
Bile salt, 164
Bilobalide, 124
Bimatoprost, 727
Bimolecular elimination. *See* E2 elimination reactions
Bimolecular reactions
 elimination reactions, 295
 in nucleophilic substitution reactions, 253–254
 organic reactions, 226

Biocatalyst, 1245, 1246, 1246f
Biodegradable polymers, 1249–1250
Biofuels, 1200
Biomolecules, 110, 111f, 1099. *See also* Carbohydrates; DNA; Lipids; Proteins
  definition of, 110
  families of, 110
  mass spectra of, 494
Birch reduction, 481
2,2'-Bis(diphenylphosphino)-1,1'-binaphthyl (BINAP), 1159–1160
Bisphenol A (BPA), 1241, 1242f, 1247, 1254
Blattellaquinone, 878
Bloch, Konrad, 1216
Blood alcohol content, measurement of, 468, 469f
Boat form, of cyclohexane, 147, 148, 148f
Boc (*tert*-butoxycarbonyl protecting group), 1170, 1172
Boiling point
  of alcohols, 331t
  of aldehydes and ketones, 813t
  of alkanes, 136, 137t
  of alkenes, 380
  of alkyl halides, 242t
  of alkynes, 419
  of amines, 993t
  of carboxylic acids, 723t
  definition of, 96
  of enantiomers, 192, 192t
  of epoxides, 331t
  of ethers, 331t
  intermolecular forces and, 96–98
  polarizability and, 96, 97f
  of racemic mixtures, 192, 192t
  separation of liquids based on, 97–98, 97f
  surface area and, 96, 97f
Bombykol, 1042, 1049, 1049f
Bond(s) and bonding, 11–13. *See also specific bond types*
  bond angle, 25–28, 28t, 42t
  bond length, 25, 25t, 43–44, 44t
  breaking and making in organic reactions, 209–212, 210f
  covalent, 11, 12–13
  definition of, 11
  double, 16
  ionic, 11–12
  Lewis structures, 13–19
  in nucleophilic substitution reactions, 252–253, 255, 262
  octet rule, 11
  π (pi), 40, 40f, 41, 42f, 42t, 43
  polar, 46–47, 47f
  rotation, 39, 40
  σ (sigma), 34, 36, 39–43, 40f, 42f, 42t
  triple, 16
Bond angles
  in alkynes, 417
  four groups around an atom, 25, 26–28, 28t, 42f
  molecular shape and, 25–28
  three groups around an atom, 25, 26, 28t, 42t
  two groups around an atom, 25, 27f, 41f
Bond cleavage
  heterolytic, 209
  homolytic, 209
  in nucleophilic substitution reactions, 252–253, 255, 262
Bond dissociation energy, 212–215
  in alkynes, 418
  for benzylic C–H bond, 699
  bond length and, 214
  bond strength and, 214–215
  carbon radical stability and, 559–560
  of common bonds, 213t, A–7
  definition of, 212
  enthalpy change calculation from, 214–215
  limitations of, 215
  periodic table trend in, 214
Bonding (shared) electrons, 13, 13f
Bonding energy, entropy and, 219
Bonding molecular orbital, 651, 651f, 652–655, 652f, 654f
Bond length
  average for common bonds, 25t
  in benzene, 632
  bond dissociation energy and, 214
  bond strength and, 43–44, 44t
  in conjugated dienes, 603–604
  percent *s*-character and, 44, 603
  periodic trends in, 25
Bond polarity, 45–47, 47f
Bond strength
  bond dissociation energy and, 214–215
  bond length and, 43–44, 44t
  infrared (IR) absorption and, 498–499, 498f, 500
  percent *s*-character and, 44
9-Borabicyclo[3.3.1]nonane (9-BBN), 403
Borane, 401–404, 405f, 763
Boron, octet rule exceptions in, 19
Boron trifluoride, 26, 37
BPA (bisphenol A), 1241, 1242f, 1247, 1254
Bradykinin, 1163
Brevicomin, 857
Bridged bicyclic ring system, 614–615, 615f
Bridged halonium ion, 396–400, 400t, 426
Bridgehead carbons, A–6
Bromination
  of alkanes, 566–568, 568f
  of alkenes, 579–582
  at allylic C–H bonds, 575–577
    with NBS, 575–577
    product mixtures in, 576–577
    selective, 575–576
    substitution versus addition, 576
  of benzene, 669, 694
  benzylic, 699–701
  chlorination compared, 566–567
  as endothermic reaction, 568
  as exothermic reaction, 582
  polybromination, 690
  of substituted benzenes, 690
  as test for pi (π) bond, 395
Bromine, isotopes of, 489
α-Bromoacetone, 929
3-Bromoacetophenone, 812f
m-Bromoacetophenone, 812f
m-Bromoaniline, 704
o-Bromoaniline, 992
p-Bromobenzaldehyde, synthesis of, 1025
Bromobenzene, 356, 669
4-Bromobutanal, 853
1-Bromobutane, 298
2-Bromobutane, 290, 571–572
1-Bromo-2-butene, 576, 609, 609f
3-Bromo-1-butene, 576, 609, 609f
o-Bromochlorobenzene, 634
1-Bromo-1-chloroethylene, NMR spectrum of, 520
Bromocyclohexane, 391
cis-4-Bromocyclohexanol, 370
trans-4-Bromocyclohexanol, 370
2-Bromocyclohexanone, 932
1-Bromocyclohexene, 1045
3-Bromohexane, 173, 175f
6-Bromo-2-hexanone, 857
1-Bromo-2-hexene, 284
trans-1-Bromo-1-hexene, 1044
Bromohydrins, 399
Bromomethane, 253–255, 258–259, 258f, 259f, 335
2-Bromo-2-methylbutane, 300
cis-1-Bromo-4-methylcyclohexane, 273
1-Bromo-1-methylcyclopentane, 303
2-Bromo-2-methylpropane, 290, 298, 432
Bromonitrobenzene, 694
Bromonium ion, 576
2-Bromopentane, in E2 elimination reaction, 1019, 1019f
1-Bromo-1-phenylpropane, 287
1-Bromopropane
  NMR spectrum of, 535, 535f
  synthesis of, 580
2-Bromopropane, 335
  mass spectrum of, 489, 489f
  NMR spectrum of, 534, 534f
  synthesis of, 568, 580
2-Bromo-1-propene, 628
α-Bromopropiophenone, 930
(*Z*)-2-Bromostyrene, 1049, 1066
N-Bromosuccinimide (NBS), 399, 575–577
1-Bromo-4-*tert*-butylcyclohexane, 321
p-Bromotoluene, 634
Brompheniramine, 1014
Bronchodilator, 174, 333, 361, 361f
Brønsted–Lowry acid
  carboxylic acids, 729–734
  description of, 59–60
  reactions of, 60–62
Brønsted–Lowry base
  alklyl halide and elimination reactions, 244
  description of, 59–60
  in elimination reactions with alkyl halides, 289
  reactions of, 60–62
Brucine, 1190
BTX mixture, 88, 637
Buckminsterfullerene, 655–656
Bufotenin, 998
Bufo toads, 998
Bupropion, 670f, 951
1,2-Butadiene, 441
1,3-Butadiene, 1070, 1075
  conformations of, 1162
  conjugation in, 594–595, 595f, 601
  electrostatic potential plot for, 595, 595f
  HBr addition to, 606–609, 609f
  molecular orbitals of, 1072–1073, 1073f
  polymerization of, 1234, 1238
  resonance structures, 598, 604
  sigma (σ) bond length in, 603–604
  stability of, 642
  ultraviolet absorption, 619
Butanal
  boiling point of, 96
  intermolecular forces in, 95
  melting point of, 98
Butane
  alkene conversion to, 447
  anti conformation, 292f
  conformations of, 141–144, 141f, 143f
  constitutional isomers of, 125t, 127
  eclipsed conformation, 292f
  halogenation of, 571
  molecular formula of, 125t
  as propellant, 573
  rotation about carbon–carbon single bonds of, 292, 292f
  solubility of, 100
  structure of, 122
Butanedioic acid, 722
2,3-Butanediol, 359
Butanenitrile, synthesis from 1-propanol, 351
Butanoic acid, 724f, 725
1-Butanol
  boiling point of, 96
  intermolecular forces in, 95
  melting point of, 98
  naming, 327
2-Butanol
  (2*S*)-2-butanol, conversion to its tosylate, 352
  enantiomers of, 178–180, 762–763
  infrared (IR) spectrum, 502
  stereogenic center of, 175
  synthesis using Grignard reaction, 779–780
tert-Butanol, as polar protic solvent, 250f
2-Butanone, 440
  boiling point of, 812
  infrared (IR) spectrum, 502
  reduction of, 762–763
  structure of, 811
  synthesis of, 942
1-Butene, 318, 374t, 377f
  bond dissociation energy, 624
  halogenation of, 576
2-Butene
  cis-2-butene, 374t, 380, 388, 398, 398f
    carbene addition to, 1054
    epoxidation of, 459
    hydrogenation of, 447–448, 448f
  trans-2-butene, 374t, 380, 398, 398f, 399–400
    from 2-butyne reduction, 454
    carbene addition to, 1054
    epoxidation of, 459
    hydrogenation of, 447–448, 448f
  stereoisomers of, 292–294, 292f, 318
tert-Butoxide, nucleophilicity of, 249
tert-Butoxycarbonyl protecting group (Boc), 1170, 1172
tert-Butoxy group, 329
Butter, 384, 451
Butylamine, mass spectrum of, 994, 994f
(*R*)-*sec*-Butylamine, 204
Butylbenzene, 707
tert-Butylbenzene, 634
Butylcyclohexane, 133f
tert-Butyl cyclohexanecarboxylate, 865
tert-Butylcyclohexane, 150f
cis-4-*tert*-Butylcyclohexanol, 805
4-*tert*-Butylcyclohexanone, 805
tert-Butylcyclopentane, 133
1-*tert*-Butylcyclopentene, 370
tert-Butyldimethylsilyl ether (TBDMS), 782, 783
Butyl group, 127
  sec-butyl group, 127
  tert-butyl group, 127, 150
tert-Butyl hydroperoxide, 456, 471
tert-Butyl iodide, 241
Butyllithium, 75, 827, 924
Butylmagnesium chloride, 792
1-*sec*-Butyl-3-methylcyclohexane, 134f
sec-Butyl methyl ether, 328
tert-Butyl methyl ether (MTBE), 101
  formation of, 395
  as fuel additive, 395, 517
  NMR spectrum of, 517, 519

5-*tert*-Butyl-3-methylnonane, 131
1-Butyne, 441, 443
addition reactions of, 422, 423f
hydrohalogenation of, 423f, 424, 425
2-Butyne, 441, 443, 454
hydration of, 428
infrared (IR) spectrum, 500
Butyric acid, structure of, 721t
γ-Butyrolactone, 908

C

Cadaverine, 995
Caffeine, 115, 550
Cahn–Ingold–Prelog system, 178
Calcitriol, 603, 603f
Calorie (cal), 43
Camphene, 1224
Camphor, 1209
10-Camphorsulfonic acid, 1189
Cancer. *See also* Anticancer drugs
nitrosamines and, 271
polycyclic aromatic hydrocarbons and, 363
Capnellene, 433, 433f
Caproic acid, 718, 721t
ε-Caprolactam, 1239, 1249
ε-Caprolactone, 1256
Capsaicin, 4, 53, 505, 550, 630, 952
Caraway, odor of, 196
-carbaldehyde suffix, 809
Carbamate, 911, 1170, 1240
Carbanions
addition to aldehydes and ketones, 822
electrostatic potential plots, 72, 72f
formation in alkyne reduction, 454–455
nucleophilic addition with, 756, 822
nucleophilic substitution with, 757
vinyl, 455
Carbenes
intermediates in cyclopropane synthesis, 1052–1055
metal–carbene intermediates in metathesis, 1058
preparation of dihalocarbenes, 1053–1055
structure of, 1052, 1053
Carbenoid, 1056
Carbidopa, 48, 49
Carbinolamines, 820, 821f, 830, 831, 833, 1015
Carbocation(s), 21
achiral, 392
allylic, 607
as conjugated system, 594, 595–596
electrostatic potential plot, 596, 596f
NMR spectra of, 597, 597f
resonance of, 596–597
classification, 266
in electrophilic addition reactions, 388–392
in electrophilic aromatic substitution reactions, 667–669, 684, 685f
electrostatic potential maps, 267, 267f
in E1 mechanism, 301, 303, 304–305
energy diagram for formation of, 271f
formation in Lewis acid–base reactions, 79
Hammond postulate, 390, 390f
as Lewis acid, 388
localized versus delocalized, 596f
in nucleophilic substitution reactions, 253
planar, 265, 392, 1116–1117
primary (1°), 266
as reactive intermediate, 343
resonance-stabilized, 425, 428, 491, 596–597, 596f, 597f, 606–607, 609, 667, 669, 695–696
secondary (2°), 266, 673, 675, 676
in S_N1 substitution reactions, 262–270, 271f, 304–305
tertiary (3°), 266, 673, 675, 676
trigonal planar, 264
vinyl, 277, 424–425, 428
Carbocation intermediates, 580
Carbocation rearrangements
conversions of alcohols to alkyl halides, 348
in dehydration of alcohols, 341–343
Friedel–Crafts alkylation, 675–676
in hydration reactions, 394
1,2-shifts, 341–343
1,2-hydride shift, 675–676
1,2-methyl shift, 342
in S_N1 reactions, 348
Carbocation stability, 266–268
of allylic carbocations, 596
conjugation and, 596
in electrophilic aromatic substitution reaction, 684, 685f
Hammond postulate and, 268–271
hyperconjugation and, 267–268
inductive effects and, 267
1,2-shifts and, 341
Carbohydrates, 845–846, 1098–1147
amino sugars, 1134–1135
cellulose, 167, 168f, 169, 169f, 893, 893f, 1099f, 1132–1133
disaccharides, 1129–1131, 1131f, 1132f
energy in, 1099
examples of, 1099, 1099f
glycosides, 1115–1118
N-glycosides, 1135–1138, 1138f
molecular formula of, 1099
monosaccharides. *See* Monosaccharides
natural fibers, 893, 893f
nomenclature, 1100, 1106
polysaccharides, 1132–1134
starch, 167, 168f, 169f, 332, 332f, 1133–1134
Carbon
alpha (α), 289–290, 721, 724, 741, 742
of aldehydes and ketones, 810, 818–819
substitution reactions of carbonyl compounds at the α carbon, 915–953
beta (β), 289–290, 306, 721
bonding of, 12, 13f, 16, 17, 18t, 35–36
charged atom, 33–34
chiral. *See* Stereogenic centers
common nucleophiles, 252t
delta (δ), 721
electron-deficient, 69, 87, 89, 90, 109, 211, 244, 244f
electronegativity value, 772
electrophilic, 244
elemental forms of, 655
excited state, 35
formal charge of, 18t
gamma (γ), 721
ground state, 35
isotopes of, 8, 9f, 492t
mass of, 492t
periodic table entry, 9
primary (1°), 123–124
quaternary (4°), 123–124
radicals, 559–560, 560f
secondary (2°), 123–124
tertiary (3°), 123–124
tetravalence of, 4, 27, 29
valence electrons of, 35
Carbonate, 1241
Carbon backbone (skeleton), 87
Carbon–carbon bonds
bond length and bond strength, 43, 44t
double. *See also* Double bonds
in alkenes, 291–293. *See also* Alkenes
properties of, 374t
radical reactions, 579–582
restricted rotation around, 292–293, 292f
NMR spectra of, 526, 526f, 526t
nonpolar nature of, 45
reactions forming, 1042–1068, A-8
coupling reactions of organocuprates, 1043–1045
cyclopropane synthesis, 1052–1055
Heck reaction, 1043, 1050–1052
metathesis, 1056–1060, 1057f, 1059f
Simmons–Smith reaction, 1055–1056
Suzuki reaction, 1042, 1043, 1046–1049, 1049f
rotation, 39, 40, 137–138
Carbon dioxide
atmospheric concentration of, 156, 156f
electrostatic potential plot for, 47f
global climate change, role in, 156
as nonpolar molecule, 47
reaction of Grignard reagents with, 787
release in combustion reactions, 155
Carbon–halogen bond, polar, 244, 244f
Carbon–hydrogen bonds
acidity of, 67, 68
benzylic, 699, 701–702
bond length and bond strength, 43–44
halogenation of, 574–577
nonpolar nature of, 45
radical reaction with, 561
Carbon monoxide, 1184
Carbon NMR, 515, 543–547
of aldehydes, 815, 815f
of amines, 995
basis of, 543–544
of benzene derivatives, 636, 636t, 637f
of carbocations, 597, 597f
of carboxylic acid derivatives, 870
of carboxylic acids, 724, 725f
characteristic absorptions, A-11
chemical shifts in, 543, 544, 544f, 546, 546t, 597, 597f
examples of spectra, 546f
of ketones, 815
of nitriles, 870
number of signals in, 544–545
position of signals in, 546–547
reference signal, 543
Carbon–oxygen bonds
carbonyl group, 90, 91t
condensed structures containing double, 30, 30f
polar nature of, 46
Carbon skeleton (backbone), 87, 100
Carbon tetrachloride, 99, 100, 242
-carbonyl chloride (suffix), 864, 867t
Carbonyl compounds. *See also specific classes*
classes of, 754
condensation reactions, 954–987
conversion of ozonides to, 463
electron deficiency of, 755
electrostatic potential map of, 755, 755f
formation by oxidation of alcohols, 466
β-hydroxy
synthesis of, in aldol reactions, 955–966
useful transformations of, 962, 963f
leaving groups of, 754, 756, 757–758
pK_a, 920, 921t, 922t
reactions at α carbon, 915–953
acetoacetic ester synthesis, 940–943
enolate alkylation, 933–936
halogenation, 928–932, 931f
malonic ester synthesis, 936–940
racemization, 927, 927f
reactions of
general, 755–758
nucleophilic addition, 756
nucleophilic substitution, 756, 757–758
with organometallic reagents, 775–778, 781–783, 782f
oxidation, 758–759, 771
reduction, 758–770
reactivity, 808
reduction of, 758–770
biological, 765–766
carboxylic acids and derivatives, 766–770
by catalytic hydrogenation, 761
enantioselective, 763–766, 764f
with metal hydride reagents, 760–762, 762f, 770t
stereochemistry of, 762–763
synthesis by hydroboration–oxidation of alkynes, 429–431
tautomers, 898–899
α,β-unsaturated compounds, 788–791
unsymmetrical, enolates of, 925
Carbonyl condensation reactions, 954–987
aldol reactions, 955–967. *See also* Aldol reactions
Claisen reaction, 967–971, 967f
Dieckmann reaction, 971–972
Michael reaction, 972–974, 974f
Robinson annulation, 974–978
Carbonyl groups, 427, 754
conjugated, 814, 814f
as electron-withdrawing group, 613
features of, 862
formation by oxidative cleavage of alkenes, 463–464
as functional group, 90, 91t
hydrogenation of, 450
IR absorption of, 724, 724f, 813–814, 813f, 814f
of monosaccharides, 1100
nucleophilic addition to, 818–820, 821f
reactions of, 1120–1126
reactivity of, 90
stabilization by alkyl groups, 835
tautomers of, 917–918
Carboxy, derivation of term, 719
Carboxy group, 91t, 719
of benzene derivatives, 701–702, 705

Carboxylate anion
of amino acids, 743
formation of, 730, 731
metal salt of, 722, 722f
synthesis of
hydrolysis of amides, 890
hydrolysis of esters, 885–887
hydrolysis of nitriles, 898–899
Carboxylation, 787
Carboxylic acid(s), 718–740
acidity of, 729, 730–735, 733f, 863t, 880
aliphatic, inductive effects in, 734–735
aspirin as, 726–727
basicity of, 729
benzene derivatives, 701–702
boiling point of, 723t
deprotonation of, 730, 731t
diacids, 722, 936–938
as dimers, 723, 723f
dipole–dipole interactions of, 723
electrostatic potential plot, 719, 719f
functional group in, 91t
hydrogen bonding, 723, 723f
interesting examples, 725–726
intermolecular forces, 723, 723f, 723t
IR spectra of, 724, 724f
leaving group, 757
melting point of, 723t
NMR spectra of, 724, 725f
nomenclature of, 720–722, 722f
common names, 721–722, 721t
IUPAC system, 720–722
nucleophilic acyl substitution reactions, 880–885, 880f, 892t
conversion to acid chlorides, 880f, 881
conversion to amides and amines, 880f, 883–885
conversion to cyclic anhydrides, 880f, 881
conversion to esters, 880f, 882–883
nucleophilic substitution reactions, 757
physical properties, 723, 723t, 869t
pK_a of, 863t
protonation of, 729
reactions of
esters synthesis, 880f, 882–883
general features, 729–730
nucleophilic acyl substitution reactions, 880–885, 880f, 892t
reduction, 759, 767, 769
resonance stabilization of, 731–732, 732f, 733f
salts of, 726
separation from other organic compounds, 738–740, 740f
solubility of, 723t
spectroscopic properties, 724, 724f, 725f
stability of, 863
structure and bonding of, 719, 754, 860, 863
substituted benzoic acids, 735–738, 737f
synthesis of, 728–729
conversion of acid chlorides, 876, 878
conversion of anhydrides, 879
hydrolysis of amides, 890
hydrolysis of esters, 885–886
hydrolysis of nitriles, 898–899
malonic ester synthesis, 936–940
oxidation of aldehydes, 759, 771
oxidation of alkyl benzenes, 728
oxidation of alkynes, 728
oxidation of primary (1°) alcohols, 466, 467–468, 728
oxidative cleavage of alkynes, 465
reaction of organometallic reagents with carbon dioxide, 787
-carboxylic acid (suffix), 864
Carboxylic acid derivatives. *See also* Acid chlorides; Amides; Anhydrides; Esters
acidity/basicity of, 862–863, 863t
boiling point of, 869t
IR spectra of, 869–870, 870t
leaving groups of, 861, 863, 863t, 873–874
melting point of, 868, 869t
NMR spectra of, 870
nomenclature of, 864–868, 867t
nucleophilic acyl substitution reactions of, 757
mechanism of, 873–874
relative reactivity, 874–875, 892
summary of, 892, 892t
physical properties of, 869t
reaction of organometallic reagents with, 774, 783–786
reactivity with nucleophiles, 757
reduction of, 759, 766–770
resonance structures of, 862
solubility of, 869t
stability of, 863
structure and bonding of, 754, 860–863
Carboxypeptidase, 1167, 1167t
Carcinogen, 363
Cardinol, 1247
Carotatoxin, 115
β-Carotene, 102–103, 381f, 828, 828f, 1222
Carroll rearrangement, 1096
Carson, Rachel, 243
Carvacrol, 664
Carvone, 196, 664, 1222
Caryophyllene, 317
Cassava, 825
Catalysts. *See also specific catalysts*
acids as, 228
biocatalyst, 1245, 1246, 1246f
chiral, 1159–1160
definition of, 228
energy of activation lowered by, 228, 228f
enzymes, 229, 229f
homogeneous, 1236
hydrogenation, 447
Lewis acid, 347
Lindlar, 453, 455f
metal, 228, 447
palladium, 228, 761. *See also* Palladium-catalyzed reactions
Ziegler–Natta, 1236, 1237
Catalytic amount, 228
Catalytic hydrogenation, 447–449
of aldeyhdes and ketones, 761
Catecholborane, 1047, 1049
Cation(s)
carbocation. *See* Carbocation(s)
counterions, 59
cyclopentadienyl, 648
definition of, 8
radical, 485, 489
salt formation, 12
solvation ion–dipole interactions, 250, 251, 275
spectator ions, 59
tropylium, 649, 654, 654f
Cationic polymerization, 1231–1232, 1232f
CBS reagent, 763–765, 764f
Cedrol, 1209f
Celecoxib (Celebrex), 853, 1207
Cell membrane
cholesterol in, 127–128, 127f, 1216
functions, 105
phospholipids in, 1201–1203
structure of, 105–107, 106f
transport across, 107–108, 108f
Cellobiose, 1131
Cells, 105
Cellulose, 893, 893f
hydrolysis of, 167, 168f, 1133
solubility of, 169
structure of, 167, 168f, 169, 169f, 1099f, 1132–1133
Cellulose acetate, 1133
Cephalexin, 872
Cephalin, 1201
Cephalosporins, 872
Cetylpyridinium chloride (CPC), 246
CFCs. *See* Chlorofluorocarbons (CFCs)
Chain branching, in polymerization, 1229–1230
Chain growth polymerization, 1227–1234
anionic, 1232–1233, 1232f, 1234–1235
cationic, 1231–1232, 1232f
chain branching in, 1229–1230
copolymers, 1233–1234
of epoxides, 1234–1235
ionic, 1231–1233, 1232f
radical, 1228–1229, 1229f
Chain-growth polymers, 1226, 1227–1234
Chain mechanism, 564, 573, 582
Chain termination, 1229
Chair conformation
of cyclohexanes, 145–154, 146f
of glucose, 1114
Charge
Brønsted–Lowry acids and bases, 59f, 60
on carbon atom, 33–34
dipole, 46, 47, 47f
formal, 16–18, 18t
in resonance hybrid, 24
Charged ion, 8
Chauvin, Yves, 1056
Chemical shift
in ^{13}C NMR, 543–544, 544f, 546, 546t, 597, 597f
in ^{1}H NMR
equation for, 518
predicting values of, 524–525
protons on benzene rings, 525, 526t
protons on carbon–carbon double bonds, 526, 526t
protons on carbon–carbon triple bonds, 526, 526t
scale, 517
values for common proton types, 524t
Chiral catalysts, 1159–1160
Chiral drugs, 195
Chirality
basic principles of, 173f
of naturally occurring objects, 173
in substituted cycloalkanes, 188
test for, 171
Chirality center, 172. *See also* Stereogenic centers
Chiral molecules, 170–173, 173f
definition of, 170, 172
halogenation of, 570t, 571–572
optical activity of, 191
Chiral reagent, 1159
Chiral reducing agent, 763
Chitin, 1135
Chloral, 835, 836
Chloral hydrate, 835, 836
Chloramphenicol, 174
Chlorination
of alkanes, 563–567, 565f, 568f, 569–572, 569f
of benzene, 670
bromination compared to, 566–567
of ethane, 563–565, 565f
as exothermic reaction, 565, 565f, 569
mechanism of, 563–564
Chlorine
isotopes of, 488
mass spectra of alkyl chlorides, 488, 489f
2-Chloroacetic acid, 734
Chlorobenzene, 634, 669, 697
2-Chloro-1,3-butadiene, polymerization of, 1238
1-Chlorobutane, synthesis of, 571
2-Chlorobutane
NMR spectrum of, 521
synthesis of, 571
Chlorobutanoic acid, 735
Chlorocyclohexane, chair conformation of, 306–307, 307f
Chlorocyclopentane, 101
Chlorocyclopropane, NMR spectrum of, 520
Chloroethane, 55, 89, 545
Chloroethylene, NMR spectrum of, 520
4-Chloro-1-ethyl-2-propylbenzene, 635
Chlorofluorocarbons (CFCs), 3, 243, 573–574, 574f
Chloroform, 242, 1053
Chlorohydrin, 398, 401f
Chloromethane, 242f
1-Chloro-2-methylbutane, 562
1-Chloro-1-methylcyclohexane, 391
1-Chloro-2-methylcyclohexane
cis-1-chloro-2-methylcyclohexane, 306
trans-1-chloro-2-methylcyclohexane, 306
1-Chloro-3-methylcyclohexane, 391
1-Chloro-1-methylcyclopropane, 319
2-Chloro-5-methylheptane, 240
3-Chloro-3-methylhexane, 391
1-Chloro-2-methylpropane, 241f
o-Chloronitrobenzene, 696
p-Chloronitrobenzene, 695
2-Chloropentane, 519
3-Chloropentane, 519
meta-Chloroperoxybenzoic acid, 457f, 458–460
2-Chloropropanal, 810f
1-Chloropropane, 389, 569, 703
2-Chloropropane, 389, 488, 488f, 569
2-Chloropropene, 424
3-Chloropropenoic acid, NMR spectra of, 536, 537f
α-Chloropropionaldehyde, 810f
2-Chloropyridine, 713
Chloroquine, 1014
p-Chlorostyrene, 705–706
p-Chlorotoluene, 698
Chlorpheniramine, 670f
Cholesterol, 618, 896, 896f, 1194, 1216–1217
biosynthesis of, 1216, 1216f
in cell membranes, 157–158, 157f, 1216
cholesterol-lowering drugs, 1217, 1217f

solubility of, 100, 157
specific rotation of, 193
structure of, 157, 157f, 177, 1216
synthesis stimulation by saturated fats, 384
trans fats and, 452
Cholesteryl esters, 896, 896f
Cholic acid, 164
Choline, 895
Chondrocole A, 244
Chromate ester, 467
Chromium
in blood alcohol screening, 468, 469f
in oxidizing agents, 457, 466–469, 771
Chromium (VI) oxide, 457
Chrysanthemic acid, 545
Churchane, 135f
Churchill, Winston, 243
Chymotrypsin, 1167, 1167t
Ciguatoxin (CTX3C), 753, 768, 768f
Cimetidine, 996
Cinnamaldehyde, 816f, 961
cis (prefix), 377–378
Cis-fused, 614
Cis geometry
alkenes, 374, 374t, 377–378, 392
cycloalkenes, 374
Cis isomers
of 2-butene, 292–293, 292f, 294
of cycloalkanes, 151–154
definition of, 151, 292
of disubstituted cycloalkanes, 188
Cis protons, 536, 537f
Citral, 1209f
Citric acid, 51, 59f
Citronellal, 816f
Citronellol, 513
Claisen reactions, 967–971, 967f
crossed, 969–971
intramolecular, 971–972
Claisen rearrangement, 1089–1090
Claritin. *See* Loratadine
Clemmensen reduction, 702
Clopidogrel, 182, 949, 1189
Clostridium botulinum, 271
^{13}C NMR. *See* Carbon NMR
Cocaine, 83, 116, 871, 995
Cockroach, 121
Cocoa butter, 1200
Coconut oil, 384, 1198, 1200
Codeine, 748, 998
Coenzyme, 470, 765
Coffee, decaffeinated, 242f
Collagen, 1149, 1183, 1183f
Column, in periodic table, 9
Combustion
of acetylene, 420
of alkanes, 155–156
definition of, 155
of triacylglycerols, 1200
Common names
of alcohols, 328
of aldehydes, 810, 810f
of alkanes, 134–135, 135f
of alkenes, 379, 379f
of alkyl halides, 241
of amines, 991–992
of benzene derivatives, 634–635
of carbohydrates, 1100, 1106
of carboxylic acid derivatives, 864
of carboxylic acids, 721–722, 721t
of epoxides, 330
of ethers, 328
of ketones, 811, 812f
of nitriles, 867, 867f
Compounds
examples of, 11
formation of, 11
ionic, 12
Concentration, reaction rate and, 225, 226–227
Concerted reaction, 209, 295
Condensation polymer. *See also* Step-growth polymers
nylon, 893
polyesters, 894
Condensation reactions
carbonyl, 954–987
definition of, 958
Condensed structures, 29–30, 29f, 30f
Configuration
inversion in alkyl tosylate reactions, 353, 354
retention of
in chlorination, 572
in conversion of alcohols to alkyl tosylates, 352, 354
in oxidation of alkylborane, 404
in S_N2 reactions, 256–258, 257f, 273
of stereoisomers, 170
Conformations
of acyclic alkanes, 137–144
butane, 141–144, 141f, 143f
ethane, 137–141, 139f, 140f
anti, 141f, 142–144, 143f
of cycloalkanes, 144–154
disubstituted, 151–154
monosubstituted, 148–150
of cyclohexane(s), 145–154
boat, 147, 148, 148f
chair, 145–154, 146f
disubstituted cyclohexane, 151–154, 153f
monosubstituted cyclohexane, 148–150, 150f
ring-flipping, 147–148, 148f
definition of, 138
eclipsed, 138–144, 139f, 140f, 141f, 143f, 143t, 306f
free energy change and, 218
gauche, 141f, 142, 143f, 143t
staggered, 138–144, 139f, 140f, 141f, 143f, 306, 306f
Congo red, 1029, 1030
Coniine, 995, 996f
Conivaptan, 858
Conjugate acid, 60–62, 247–248, 247t
Conjugate addition, 606, 972, 973
Conjugate base, 60–62, 63t, 64
Conjugated dienes, 602–621
addition reactions
Diels–Alder reaction, 610–619, 611f
electrophilic, 606–608
kinetic versus thermodynamic product, 608–610
carbon–carbon bond length in, 603–604
conformation of
s-cis, 601–602
s-trans, 601–602
electrostatic plot for, 595, 595f
hydrogenation of, 604–605
interesting examples of, 602–603
stability of, 604–605, 605f
stereoisomers of, 601–602
synthesis in Suzuki reaction, 1049
ultraviolet (UV) light absorption, 619–621, 620f
Conjugated double bond, 958
Conjugated proteins, 1183
Conjugated systems
allylic carbocation, 594, 595–596
1,3-dienes, 594–595, 595f
Conjugation, 593–629
definition of, 594
β-dicarbonyl compounds, 917
effect on carbonyl group IR absorption, 814, 814f
Hückel's rule and, 641
Conrotatory, 1076
Constitutional isomers
of alkanes, 122–124, 125t
of alkenes, 338
definition of, 18
of dipeptides, 1161
in elimination reactions, 290
features of, 169
ketone and aldehyde, 430
of monosaccharides, 1100
stereoisomers compared, 170f
tautomers, 427
Cope rearrangements, 1088–1089
Copolymers, 1233–1234
Copper
electronegativity value of, 772
organocuprate reagents, 772, 773, 1043–1045
Copper(I) cyanide, 1023
Core electrons, 10
Corey, E. J., 362, 764, 859
Corn
ethanol production from, 332, 332f
use in green polymer synthesis, 1246, 1246f
Coronary artery disease, 157, 182, 384
Cortisol, 1219
Cortisone, 618, 816, 984, 1219
Cotton
binding dyes to, 1030
cellulose in, 1132
structure of, 893, 893f
Coumarin, 984
Counterions, 59
Coupling constant, 530, 536
Coupling reactions
alkenes with organic halides (Heck reaction), 1043, 1050–1052
of aryl diazonium salts, 1022, 1026–1027
of organocuprate reagents, 1043–1045
Covalent bonding
description of, 11, 12–13
in Lewis structures, 13–16
Covalent molecules
boiling points of, 96
intermolecular forces, 92–95, 93f, 95t
melting points of, 98
solubility of, 101f
COX-1, 1206f, 1207
COX-2, 1206f, 1207
COX-3, 1207
CPC (cetylpyridinium chloride), 246
Cracking, 380
Crafts, James, 667
CRCs (chlorofluorocarbons), 243, 573–574, 574f
Creatine, 52
p-Cresol, 716, 1256
Crossed aldol reactions, 960–963
synthetically useful reactions, 961–962, 961f
with two different aldehydes, both having α H atoms, 960
useful transformations of aldol products, 962, 963f
Crossed Claisen reactions, 969–971
Cross formula, 1101
Crown ethers, 107, 333–334, 333f
Crude oil, 135–136, 135f
Crutzen, Paul, 573
Crystallites, 1243
CTX3C (ciguatoxin), 753, 768, 768f
Cubane, 135f, 145
Cucumber aldehyde, 812
Curcumin, 663
Curved arrow notation, 21–22, 60, 61, 210, 211, 211t, 212, 245
Cyanide
addition to aldehydes and ketones, 823–824
addition to imine, 1154
α-Cyano carbonyl compounds, 962
2-Cyanocyclohexanecarboxylic acid, 867f
Cyano group, 824
of nitriles, 861, 867
Cyanohydrins
in Kiliani–Fischer synthesis, 1123, 1124
naturally occurring derivatives, 824–825
synthesis by cyanide addition to aldehydes and ketones, 823–824
in Wohl degradation, 1123
Cyclic anhydrides, 861, 881
Cyclic compounds
entropy decrease with formation of, 219
stereogenic centers in, 176–177
Cyclic ethers, 329
Cyclization, of hydroxy aldehydes, 843, 846
Cyclo- (prefix), 125, 132
Cycloaddition reactions, 1081–1085. *See also* Diels–Alder reaction
[2 + 2] cycloadditions, 1081, 1084
[4 + 2] cycloadditions, 1083
description of, 1071
orbital symmetry and, 1082
Woodward–Hoffmann rules, 1084–1085, 1085t
Cycloalkanes
conformations of, 144–154
disubstituted, 151–154
monosubstituted, 148–150
disubstituted, 187–188
molecular formula, 121, 125, 374
naming, 132–134, 133f, 134f
NMR spectra, 520
stereoisomers, 151–154
structure of, 121, 125, 145f
substituted, 148–154, 150f, 153f
Cycloalkenes, 373
cis and trans geometry of, 374
nomenclature, 377, 377f
Cycloalkynes, 418
Cyclobutadiene, 641–642, 650, 654–655
Cyclobutane
conformation, 144
structure of, 125, 145f
Cyclobutene, 1070, 1075
1-Cyclobutylhexane, 133f
Cyclodecane, structure of, 145f
α-Cyclogeraniol, 415
Cycloheptane, structure of, 145f
1,3,5-Cycloheptatriene, 641, 649
Cycloheptatrienone, 1082
1,3-Cyclohexadiene, 641, 1070, 1075
heat of hydrogenation, 639
stability of, 642
ultraviolet absorption, 619

Cyclohexanamine, 628. *See also* Cyclohexylamine
Cyclohexane(s)
  conformations of, 145–154
    boat, 147, 148, 148f
    chair, 145–154, 146f, 306–308, 307f
    disubstituted cyclohexane, 151–154, 153f
    free energy change and, 218
    monosubstituted cyclohexane, 148–150, 150f
    ring-flipping, 147–148, 148f, 152
  conversion to cyclohexene, 570
  E2 elimination in, 306–308
  in mango, 121
  NMR spectrum, 539
  skeletal structures, 31
  structure of, 121, 125, 132
Cyclohexanecarbonyl chloride, structure of, 864
Cyclohexanediols, 461
  1,4-cyclohexanediol, 1254
  cis-1,2-cyclohexanediol, 462
1,3-Cyclohexanedione, 749
Cyclohexanol, 853
  cyclohexane formation from, 408
  dehydration of, 344, 406
  1,2-dibromocyclohexane synthesis from, 407–408
  separation from benzoic acid by extraction procedure, 738–740, 740f
  separation of cyclohexylamine from, 1006–1007, 1006f
  synthesis from cyclohexene, 394
Cyclohexanone, 513, 793
  aldol reactions of, 962, 963f
  alkylation of, 934
  conversion to alkene, 829–830
  enolate formation from, 920
  halogenation of, 932
  nucleophilic addition reactions, 820, 821f
  structure, 588
  tertiary alcohol formed from, 776
2-Cyclohexanone, synthesis of, 932
Cyclohexene
  addition reactions of, 386f, 391, 394, 395
  bromination of, 575
  1,2-dibromocyclohexane synthesis from, 406
  dihydroxylation of, 461
  heat of hydrogenation, 639
  as Lewis base, 79
  stereoisomers, 613
  synthesis
    cyclohexane conversion, 570
    from cyclohexanol, 408
    by dehydration of cyclohexanol, 344
  as synthetic intermediate, 408
2-Cyclohexen-1-ol, 370
3-Cyclohexen-1-ol, 370
2-Cyclohexenone, 557, 855
  formation in Robinson annulation, 975–978
  reduction of, 761
Cyclohexylamine, 991
  ammonium salt of, 1006–1007, 1006f
  in Hofmann elimination reaction, 1017
  separation from cyclohexanol, 1006–1007, 1006f
Cyclononatetraenyl anion, 660
Cyclononatetraenyl cation, 660
Cyclononatetraenyl radical, 660
1,5-Cyclooctadiene, 1088
Cyclooctane, 196, 196f
Cyclooctatetraene, 641, 643, 660
Cyclooctene, cis and trans isomers of, 374
Cyclooctyne, 418
Cyclooxygenase, 727, 1205, 1206f, 1207
Cyclopentadiene, 614–615, 617, 648
Cyclopentadienyl anion, 647–649
Cyclopentadienyl cation, 648
Cyclopentadienyl radical, 648
Cyclopentane, structure of, 125, 145f
Cyclopentanecarboxylic acid, 939
cis-1,2-Cyclopentanediol, 462
trans-1,2-Cyclopentanediol, 328
Cyclopentanol, 101
Cyclopentanone, 853
Cyclopentene, chlorination of, 396
Cyclopropane(s)
  conformation, 144
  dihalo to dialkyl conversion, 1055
  NMR spectrum of, 520
  structure of, 125
  synthesis of
    in Simmons–Smith reaction, 1055–1056
    using carbene intermediates, 1052–1055
Cyclopropenone, 855
Cyclopropenyl radical, 659
Cysteine
  abbreviation for, 742t
  isoelectric point for, 1152t
  in peptide formation, 1161
  pK_a values for, 1152t
  structure of, 1150f
Cytidine, 1136
Cytidine monophosphate, 1137
Cytosine, 1137, 1138f

D

2,4-D (2,4-dichlorophenoxyacetic acid herbicide), 670f
Darunavir, 858
Darvon. *See* Propoxyphene
DBN (1,5-diazabicyclo[4.3.0]non-5-ene), 296, 296f, 311
DBU (1,8-diazabicyclo[5.4.0]undec-7-ene), 85, 296, 311
DCC. *See* Dicyclohexylcarbodiimide
d (dextrorotatory) compounds, 191, 1105
DDE (dichlorodiphenyldichloroethylene), 288, 290
DDT (dichlorodiphenyltrichloroethane), 4, 224, 243, 714
  biological effects of, 288
  DDE formed from, 288
  degradation of, 290
Dean–Stark trap, 837, 838f
(2*Z*,4*Z*)-2,4-Decadienoic acid, 1245–1246
Decalin, 165, 480, 1214–1215
Decamethrin, 1052
Decane, 120, 125t
Decarboxylation, 1153
  of β-acids, 937
  of β-keto acids, 937
  in malonic ester synthesis, 937–939
DEET, 877
Dehydrating agent, 884
Dehydration reactions
  of alcohols to alkenes, 338–345
    acid-catalyzed, 384
    alkene synthesis in, 338–345
    carbocation rearrangements in, 341–343
    E1 mechanism in, 339–340
    E2 mechanism in, 340, 344
    enthalpy change in, 340, 341f
    Le Châtelier's principle in, 340
    in phosphorus oxychloride and pyridine, 344–345
    in strong acid, 338–343
  of aldol product, 958–959
  defined, 338
  dicarboxylic acid conversion to cyclic anhydrides, 881
  as β-elimination reaction, 338
  fragmentation pattern in mass spectrum, 491
7-Dehydrocholesterol, 1080
Dehydrohalogenation
  alkene synthesis by, 289
  of alkyl halides with strong base, 384
  alkyne synthesis by, 310–311, 311f
  bases commonly used in, 290, 290t
  drawing products of, 290
  E1 mechanism of, 301
  E2 mechanism of, 295, 300
16,17-Dehydroprogesterone, 1223
Delocalization, resonance, 71
Delta (δ) carbon, 721
Delta (δ) scale, 517
Dementia, 90, 965
Demerol. *See* Meperidine
Dendrobates histrionicus (poison dart frog), 421, 421f
Deoxy (prefix), 1136
2-Deoxyadenosine, 1136
Deoxyadenosine monophosphate, 110, 1099f, 1137
2-Deoxy-D-ribose, 1136
Deoxyribonucleic acid (DNA), 110, 111f, 1137–1138, 1138f, 1139f
Deoxyribonucleosides, 1136–1137
Deoxyribonucleotides, 1137
Deprotection, 781
Deprotonation
  in acetoacetic ester synthesis, 941
  of acetylene, 436
  of alkyne, 423–424, 423t, 428
  of carboxylic acids, 730, 731t
  of diethyl acetamidomalonate, 1153
  in direct enolate alkylation, 933
  in glycoside formation, 1116
  in halogenation at α carbon of carbonyl compounds, 929–931
  in malonic ester synthesis, 938
  racemization at α carbon of carbonyl compounds, 927
  in tautomerization, 918
Deshielding effects, in NMR, 522–524, 523f, 526t, 527f
DET (diethyl tartrate), 471–472
Detergents, 105
Deuterium, 8
Deuterochloroform, 516f
Dexamethasone, 326
Dextropimaric acid, 1222
Dextrorotatory *(d)*, 191, 1105
DHA, 480
Di- (prefix), 130, 328
Diabetes, 815
Diacids, 722, 936–938
  formation from monosaccharide oxidation, 1121, 1122
  in nylon synthesis, 893, 1238
Diacon. *See* Methoprene
Dialkylborane, 402
Diamine, in nylon synthesis, 893, 1238
1,4-Diaminobenzene, 1239
1,6-Diaminohexane, 1238, 1245, 1245f
Diamond, 655
Diastereomers, 183–184, 185f, 823
  alkenes, 374t, 377–378
  of 2-butene, 292–294, 292f
  definition of, 184
  disubstituted cycloalkanes, 187–188
  epimers, 1107
  of glucose, 1110, 1111f
  halogenation reactions and, 572
  of monosaccharides, 1107
  NMR spectrum of, 520–522
  nucleophilic substitution reactions and, 274
  physical properties of, 194, 194f
  separation of amino acid enantiomers into, 1155–1157, 1156f
1,3-Diaxial interactions, 150
Diazepam, structure, 638f
Diazomethane, 1055
Diazonium ions, 271
Diazonium salts
  alkyl, 1020
  aryl, 1020–1027
  coupling reactions of, 1022, 1026–1027
  explosiveness of, 1021
  formation from primary amines, 1020–1021
  substitution reactions of, 1022–1026
    synthesis of aryl chlorides and bromides, 1022
    synthesis of aryl fluorides, 1023
    synthesis of aryl iodides, 1023
    synthesis of benzene, 1023
    synthesis of benzonitriles, 1023
    synthesis of phenols, 1022
  uses in synthesis, 1024–1026
Diazotization, 1020, 1024
DIBAL-H (diisobutylaluminum hydride), 766–768, 768f, 770t, 900–901
Dibromobenzene
  meta-, 634, 636, 637f
  ortho-, 634, 636, 637f
  para-, 634, 636, 637f
1,4-Dibromobutane, 939
2,2-Dibromobutane, 424–425, 441
2,3-Dibromobutane, 173, 185–186, 186f
Dibromocarbene, 1055
1,2-Dibromocyclohexane, synthesis from cyclohexanol, 407–408
1,3-Dibromocyclopentane, 187–188
2,3-Dibromopentane, stereoisomers of, 183–184, 185f, 187
Dibutyl phthalate, 1244, 1253
Dicarbonyl compounds, 464
  aldol reactions with, 965–966
  1,4-dicarbonyl compounds, 965
  1,5-dicarbonyl compounds, 966, 966f
    in Robinson annulation, 975
  β-dicarbonyl compounds, 961–962, 961f
    pK_a values, 921, 922t
    synthesis in crossed Claisen reactions, 970
    tautomers, 917
2,5-Dichloroaniline, 635
4,4'-Dichlorobiphenyl, 101
Dichlorocarbene, 1053
1,2-Dichlorocyclopentane, 396
Dichlorodifluoromethane, 573
Dichlorodiphenyldichloroethylene. *See* DDE

Dichlorodiphenyltrichloroethane. *See* DDT
1,1-Dichloroethylene, NMR spectrum of, 520
Dichloromethane, 242f, 466
as solvent in extraction procedure, 738, 738f, 740f
2,4-Dichlorophenoxyacetic acid herbicide (2,4-D), 670f
trans-1,3-Dichloropropene, 538
Dictyopterene, 480
Dicyclohexylcarbodiimide (DCC), 880f, 884–885, 1169, 1172, 1173
Dicyclohexylurea, 884
Dicyclopentadiene, 617
Dieckmann reaction, 971–972
Dieldrin, 626
Diels–Alder reaction, 610–619
diene reactivity in, 612
dienophile reactivity in, 612–13
drawing product of, 611–612
features of, 610
retro, 617
retrosynthetic analysis of product, 616–617
rule of endo addition, 614–616
rules governing, 612–616
stereospecificity of, 613–614
in steroid synthesis, 618
tetrodotoxin synthesis, 611, 611f
as thermal [4 + 2] cycloaddition, 1081
as thermal reaction, 610
Dienes, 376
conjugated. *See* Conjugated dienes
Cope rearrangements, 1088
isolated, 594–595, 595f, 605, 605f, 606
in metathesis, 1059
ozonolysis of, 464
reactivity, 612
1,3-Dienes, 594–595, 595f. *See also* Conjugated dienes
polymerization of, 1238
synthesis in Suzuki reaction, 1049
Dienophiles
cis, 611, 612–613, 614, 617
cyclic, 612, 614
Diels–Alder reaction, 610–617
reactivity of, 612–613
stereochemistry, 613–614
trans, 612, 613
Diesel fuel, composition of hydrocarbons in, 136
Diesters
in Dieckmann reaction, 971–972
1,3-diesters, pK_a of, 922t
1,6-diesters, in Dieckmann reaction, 971
1,7-diesters, in Dieckmann reaction, 971
β-diesters
as active methylene compounds, 962
synthesis in crossed Claisen reaction, 970
Diethyl acetamidomalonate, 1153
Diethylamine, 102, 877
Diethyl carbonate, in crossed Claisen reaction, 970
cis-1,2-Diethylcyclopropane, 1056
Diethyl ether, 89
as anesthetic, 243f, 333
boiling point of, 812
in extraction procedures, 738
infrared (IR) spectrum, 502
naming, 328
solubility of, 102, 118
as solvent, 99, 355, 738
Diethyl maleate, 1068
Diethyl malonate, 961, 962, 962f, 970
alkylation of derivatives, 1153–1154, 1155f
conversion to a carboxylic acid, 936–939
N, N-Diethyl-*m*-toluamide, 877
Diethyl oxalate, 985
Diethyl tartrate (DET), 471–472
Digoxin, 807, 845
Dihalides, 311, 311f
alkyne synthesis from, 421–422
Dihalocarbenes, 1053–1055
Dihedral angle, 138, 139f, 140f, 142, 143f, 305
Dihydroxyacetone, 1100, 1101, 1108, 1108f
1,4-Dihydroxybenzene, 1242
Dihydroxylation, 457f, 461–463
anti, 461–462
syn, 461, 462–463
1,4-Dihydroxymethylcyclohexane, 894
6,7-Dihydroxy-2-nonanone, 857
Diiodomethane, 1055
Diisobutylaluminum hydride (DIBAL-H), 766–768, 768f, 770t, 900–901
Diisocyanate, 1240
Diisopropylamine, 923, 991
β-Diketone, pK_a of, 922t
Dimers, carboxylic acids as, 723, 723f
2,2-Dimethoxy-1,3-cyclopentane-dicarbaldehyde, 818
1,2-Dimethoxyethane, 518
5,5-Dimethoxy-2-pentanone, 854
Dimethylacetylene dicarboxylate, 629
Dimethylallyl diphosphate, 1210
4-(*N, N*-Dimethylamino)pyridine, 1012
N, N-Dimethylbenzamide, 866
1,3-Dimethylbenzene, 693
2,3-Dimethylbutanal, 809
3,3-Dimethyl-2-butanol, 341, 342
2,2-Dimethyl-3-butenal, 812
Dimethyl carbonate, 802
cis-3,4-Dimethylcyclobutene, 1075, 1078, 1079
trans-3,4-Dimethylcyclobutene, 1077
cis-5,6-Dimethyl-1,3-cyclohexadiene, 1075, 1077
trans-5,6-Dimethyl-1,3-cyclohexadiene, 1078, 1079
1,2-Dimethylcyclohexane, 134f
1,3-Dimethylcyclohexane, 133
1,4-Dimethylcyclohexane, 151–153, 153f
2,2-Dimethyl-1,3-cyclohexanedione, 946
5,5-Dimethyl-1,3-cyclohexanedione, 946
2,2-Dimethylcyclohexanone, 934, 935
2,6-Dimethylcyclohexanone, 934
1,2-Dimethylcyclohexene, 392, 393f
1,6-Dimethylcyclohexene, 377f
1,2-Dimethylcyclopentane, 151, 170f
1,3-Dimethylcyclopentane, 194
Dimethylcyclopropanes, 202, 520
Dimethyl ether
isomers of, 18
NMR spectrum of, 545
Dimethylformamide (DMF), 557
boiling point of, 97
as solvent, 251f, 932
2,5-Dimethyl-3-heptyne, 419f
2,5-Dimethyl-2,3-hexadiene, 443
4,5-Dimethylhexanoic acid, 720
2,4-Dimethyl-3-hexanone, 793
2,4-Dimethylhexanoyl chloride, 868
2,5-Dimethyl-3-hexyne, 443
6,6-Dimethyl-3-octyne, 419
2,2-Dimethyloxirane, 330, 360
2,3-Dimethyloxirane, 359
2,3-Dimethylpentane, 130f, 490
2,2-Dimethylpropane (neopentane), 93, 93f, 98, 123
2,2-Dimethylpropanoic acid, 734
Dimethyl sulfide, conversion of ozonide to carbonyl compounds, 463–465
Dimethyl sulfoxide (DMSO), 19
aqueous, 399
as polar aprotic solvent, 251f, 277
as solvent for alkyne synthesis, 310, 311f
Dimethyl terephthalate, 1240, 1248
1,3-Dinitriles
active methylene compounds, 962
pK_a, 922t
Dinoprostone, 1206
-dioic acid (suffix), 722
-diol (suffix), 328
Diol epoxide, 363
Diols, 328
1,2-diol formation by dihydroxylation, 461–463
gem-diol, 835–837
p-Dioxanone, 1256
Dioxybenzone, 116
Dipeptides
constitutional isomers of, 1161
synthesis of, 1160–1161, 1172
Diphenhydramine, 285, 633, 1007
Diphenyl carbonate, 1241, 1247
Diphosphate, as leaving group, 1210–1213
Dipole, 46, 47, 47f
in alkenes, 380
temporary, 93–94
Dipole–dipole interactions, 94, 95t
of aldehydes and ketones, 812
of alkyl halides, 241
of carbonyl compounds, 868
of carboxylic acids, 723
of nitriles, 868
in polar aprotic solvents, 251, 275
Dipole moment, infrared (IR) absorption and, 500
Directed aldol reactions, 963–965, 964f
Disaccharides, 1129–1131
artificial sweeteners, 1131, 1132f
general features, 1129
lactose, 1098, 1130
maltose, 1130
sucrose, 1131, 1131f
Discodermolide, 204
Disorder, entropy as measure of, 218
Disparlure, synthesis of, 459–461, 460f
Disproportionation, 1229
Disrotatory, 1076
Dissolving metal reductions, 446, 454
Distillation, of crude petroleum, 135, 135f
Distillation apparatus, 97–98, 97f
trans-1,2-Disubstituted cycloalkanes, 358, 359
Disulfide bonds
in α-keratins, 1182, 1183f
in peptides, 1164
in tertiary structure of proteins, 1180, 1180f, 1181f
in vulcanized rubber, 1237, 1237f
Di-*tert*-butyl dicarbonate, 1170
cis-1,2-Divinylcyclobutane, 1088
Diynes, 418
DMAP, 1012
DMF. *See* Dimethylformamide
DMSO. *See* Dimethyl sulfoxide
DNA, 110, 111f, 1137–1138, 1138f, 1139f
Dobutamine, 991
Docetaxel, 911
Dodecahedrane, 134, 145, 629
Dodecane, 125t
Domagk, Gerhard, 1030
Donepezil, 90, 965
Dopamine, 7, 997–998, 997f
Double bonds. *See also* Alkenes
in alkenes, 88, 89t, 291–293
in alkyl halides, 239
bond length and bond strength, 43, 44t
components of carbon-carbon, 40, 40f
in condensed structures, 30, 30f
conjugated, 598, 958
degrees of unsaturation, calculating, 449–450
effect on melting point of fatty acids, 380
in functional group, 88, 89t
hydrogenation of, 450–451, 451f
Lewis structure, 16
nitrogen–nitrogen, 1026
NMR spectra of, 526, 526t, 527f
pi (π) bonds, 88, 90
planar, 392, 397, 402, 404
properties of, 374t
radical reactions with, 561, 579–582
in resonance structure, 20, 23, 24
resonance structures
conjugated, 598
major contributor, 599–600, 604
minor contributors, 599–600, 604
with one atom more electronegative than the other, 598, 599
rotation restriction, 40, 292–293, 292f, 374t
in trans fats, 451–452
in triacylglycerols, 384, 1197–1199, 1197t
in unsaturated fatty acids, 372, 382
Z configuration, 382
Double dagger notation, 221
Double-headed arrow, 19, 60–61, 211t
Doublet, NMR spectrum, 529–530, 531t, 532t, 533, 534
Doublet of doublets, NMR spectrum, 537, 538f
Doxorubicin, 1099f
Dyes
azo compounds, 1026, 1028–1031
binding to fabric, 1029–1030
direct, 1029
natural and synthetic, 1028–1029
sulfa drugs, 1030–1031
Dyneema, 1236

E

E (prefix), 378–379
E, Z system of nomenclature, 378–379
E1cB elimination reactions, 958
Eclipsed conformation, 138–144, 139f, 140f, 141f, 143f, 143t, 292f, 306f
E configuration, double bond, 1237–1238

Ecteinascidia turbinata, 5, 5f
Edman degradation, 1165–1166
E1 elimination reactions, 301–304
  acid-catalyzed dehydration of alcohols, 384
  base in, 303, 303t, 309
  characteristics of, 303t
  dehydration of secondary and tertiary alcohols, 339–340
  E2 mechanism compared, 302, 309, 309t, 311–315, 312f–313f
  energy diagram for, 302, 302f
  kinetics of, 301, 303t
  leaving group in, 302, 303t
  rate of reaction, 303, 303t
  regioselectivity of, 303
  S_N1 substitution reactions compared, 304–305, 311–315, 312f–313f
  S_N2 substitution reactions compared, 311–315, 312f–313f
  solvent for, 303t
  two-step mechanism, 301–302, 303t
E2 elimination reactions
  acetylide anion reactions with alkyl halides, 432
  alkyl halide identity in, 295–299, 298t
  alkyl tosylate reactions, 353
  alkyne synthesis, 310–311, 421–422
  anti periplanar geometry in, 305–308, 306f
  base in, 296, 296f, 298t, 309
  characteristics of, 298t
  dehydration of alcohols, 340, 344
  dehydrohalogenation of alkyl halides, 384
  E1 mechanism compared, 302, 309, 309t, 311–315, 312f–313f
  energy diagram of, 295, 295f
  in Hofmann elimination, 1017–1019, 1019f
  kinetics of, 295, 298t
  leaving group in, 297, 298t
  one-step mechanism, 295–297, 298t
  organic synthesis examples, 299f
  rate of reaction, 297
  regioselectivity of, 299
  S_N1 and S_N2 substitution reactions compared, 311–315, 312f–313f
  solvent for, 297, 298t
  stereochemistry of, 305–309, 306f
  stereoselectivity of, 300
  syn periplanar geometry in, 305, 306f
  trans diaxial geometry in, 306–308, 307f
  Zaitsev rule, 299–301, 307
Effexor. *See* Venlafaxine
E-85 fuel, 332, 332f
Ehrlich, Paul, 1030
Eicosane
  constitutional isomers of, 125t
  molecular formula, 125t
Eicosanoids, 1205–1207
  biological activity of, 1205, 1206t
  biosynthesis of, 1205, 1206f, 1207
  derivation of word, 1205
E isomer, 378
Elaidic acid, 412
Elastomer, 1237
Electrocyclic reaction, 1075–1081
  description of, 1070, 1075
  photochemical, 1079–1080
  stereochemistry and orbital symmetry, 1075–1076
  thermal, 1077–1078
  Woodward–Hoffmann rules for, 1080, 1080t
Electrocyclic ring closure, 1070, 1075–1079
Electrocyclic ring opening, 1070, 1075, 1078
Electromagnetic radiation, 494–495, 495f
Electromagnetic spectrum, 494, 495f
Electron cloud, 8
Electron-deficient sites/species, 46, 47f, 62, 87, 89, 90, 108–109, 211, 755
Electron density, delocalization, 71
Electron-donating groups, 267, 678–681, 684–685, 690, 734–736, 737f
Electron dot representation. *See* Lewis structures
Electronegativity
  acidity trends and, 67–70
  bond polarity and, 45–46
  definition of, 45
  inductive effects on substituted benzenes, 678
  oxidation and, 154
  periodic trends in, 45, 45f
  values for common elements, 45f
Electron pair acceptor, 59, 77
Electron pair donor, 59, 77
Electron pairs
  in Brønsted–Lowry acid–base definition, 59
  Lewis acids and bases, 77–79
  movement of, 60, 210
Electron-poor sites/species, 77
Electron-rich sites/species, 46, 47f, 62, 77, 108–109, 385
Electrons
  bonded (shared), 13
  core, 10
  delocalized, 19, 23, 596, 600–601, 605, 631
  density of, 10, 34, 46, 46f, 92–93
  excited state, 619–620
  ground state, 619–620
  in Lewis structure, 13–15
  lone pairs. *See* Lone pairs
  nonbonded (unshared), 13, 13f
  number of, 8, 11
  in resonance structures, 19–24
  unpaired, 209
  valence, 11–13, 18t
Electron-withdrawing groups, 267, 613, 678–681, 684–685, 691, 692, 695–697, 734–737, 737f
Electrophiles, 90
  alkyne reactions with, 422
  carbocations as, 210, 211
  Lewis acid, 78
  meaning of term, 78
  radicals as, 211
  reactivity of, 108–109
Electrophilic addition reactions, A–13
  of conjugated dienes
    kinetic versus thermodynamic products, 608–610, 609f
    1,2- versus 1,4-addition, 606–608
  energy diagram for, 388, 388f
  halogenation of alkynes, 426
  hydration of alkenes, 394–395, 405–406
  hydrohalogenation of alkenes, 386–393, 386f, 387f, 388f, 390f, 393f, 393t
  hydrohalogenation of alkynes, 424–425
  Markovnikov's rule on, 389–391, 390f, 393t
  stereochemistry of, 391–393, 393f, 393t
Electrophilic aromatic substitution reactions, 666–695, A–13
  azo coupling, 1026–1027
  energy changes in, 668, 668f
  examples of, 667f
  Friedel–Crafts acylation, 667f, 672–678, 677f, 691–692, 702–703, 707
  Friedel–Crafts alkylation, 667f, 672–678, 691–692, 702–703, 705, 706
  halogenation, 667f, 669–670, 690–691, 692–693
  mechanism of, 667–668
  nitration, 667f, 670–671, 694–695
  of substituted benzenes, 678–695
    disubstituted benzenes, 692–693
    limitations on reactions, 691–692
    rate of reactions, 684, 685, 685f
  sulfonation, 667f, 670–671
Electrophilic carbon, in alkyl halides, 244
Electrospray ionization (ESI), 494
Electrostatic interactions, 11–12, 92
Electrostatic potential plot
  of acetic acid, 71f, 719, 719f
  of acetylene, 422, 422f
  of alcohol, 326f
  of alkoxide, 920, 921f
  of amines, 990, 990f
  of benzene, 633, 633f
  of carbanions, 72f
  of carbocations, 267, 267f
    localized and delocalized, 596, 596f
  of carbon dioxide, 47f
  description of, 46
  of dienes, 595, 595f
  of enolate, 920, 921f
  of epoxide, 326f
  of ethanol, 70f, 71f
  of ether, 326f
  of ethylene, 385, 385f
  of formaldehyde, 755, 755f
  of halomethanes, 244f
  of methyl chloride, 46, 46f
  of pyridine and pyrrole, 646, 646f
  of substituted anilines, 1010, 1010f
  of 2,2,2-trifluoroethanol, 70f
  of vitamins A and E, 1204, 1205f
  of water, 47f
Elements, periodic table, 9–11, 9f
Elemicin, 113
Eleostearic acid, 412
Elimination reactions, A–13
  of alcohols, 336–345, 354, 355f
  alkene synthesis, 289–290, 384–385
  of alkyl halides, 244, 288–323
  alkyne synthesis, 289, 421–422
  alpha (α), 1053
  beta (β), 289
  bimolecular, 294, 295. *See also* E2 elimination reactions
  description of, 207
  elimination, unimolecular, conjugate base (E1cB) mechanism, 958
  features of, 289–290
  mechanisms of, 294–295
    E1. *See* E1 elimination reactions
    E2. *See* E2 elimination reactions
    E1 and E2 compared, 302, 309, 309t, 311–315, 312f–313f
  reductive, 1046, 1048, 1052
  stereochemistry, 305–309
  unimolecular, 294, 301. *See also* E1 elimination reactions
  Zaitsev rule on, 299–301, 303
Enalapril, 200, 1003
Enals, 812
Enamines
  hydrolysis of, 834
  synthesis of
    from aldehydes and ketones, 821f, 833–834, 834f
    amine reaction with aldehydes and ketones, 1015
Enanthotoxin, 28
Enantiomeric excess, 192–193, 472, 764
Enantiomers
  of amino acids, 742, 1149, 1149f
    separation of, 1155–1158, 1156f
  of an ammonium salt, 990
  in carbonyl reductions, 762–763
  chemical properties of, 195–196
  chiral drugs, 195
  of cyclic compounds, 176
  definition of, 172, 184
  dienophile, 613
  disubstituted cycloalkanes, 188
  drawing, 175, 175f
  in electrophilic addition to alkenes, 391–393, 393f
  enantioselective reactions, 471–472
  enantiotopic protons, 520–522
  in enolate alkylation, 934
  from epoxidation of alkenes, 459, 461
  in epoxide ring opening reactions, 358–359
  formation in halogenation of alkenes, 395, 396, 397
  halogenation reactions and, 571–572
  in halohydrin formation, 399–400
  in hydroboration–oxidation reactions, 404
  labeling stereogenic centers with *R* or *S*, 178–182, 179f, 181f, 187
  of monosaccharides, 1101, 1103, 1106, 1106f
  in nucleophilic substitution reactions, 256, 264–265
  optical purity, 192–193
  in organometallic reagent reactions, 777
  physical properties, 190–194, 192t, 194f
  racemic mixture of, 191–192, 192t, 391–392
  sense of smell and, 196, 196f
  three-dimensional representations for, 175f
Enantioselective reactions, 471–472
  amino acid synthesis, 1159–1160
  biological reduction, 765–766
  carbonyl reductions, 763–766, 764f
Enantiotopic protons, NMR signals of, 520–522
Enclomiphene, 411
Endergonic reaction, 219
Endiandric acids, 1097
Endo addition, 614–616, 616f
Endothermic reaction
  bond breakage and, 212–213
  bromination, 568
  dehydration of alcohols, 341f
  energy diagram of, 221f
  enthalpy change and, 219
  reaction rate, 269–270
  transition state in, 269–270, 269f
-ene (suffix), 376
Energy
  nonrenewable, 136
  of photons, 494, 495
  release in bond formation, 211
  torsional, 140–141
  units of measurement, 43

Energy barrier, 220, 221, 224, 225, 295, 302
Energy change
  during the chlorination of ethane, 565, 565f
  during radical addition of HBr, 582
Energy diagrams, 219–224, 221f, 222f, 224f
  for carbocation formation, 270f
  for chlorination of ethane, 565f
  for E1 elimination reactions, 302, 302f
  for E2 elimination reactions, 295, 295f
  for electrophilic addition of HBr to 1,3-butadiene, 609, 609f
  for electrophilic additions, 388, 388f
  for electrophilic aromatic substitution, 668, 668f
  for halogenations, 565f, 568f, 569f
  for rate of electrophilic aromatic substitution of substituted benzenes, 685, 685f
  for S_N1 substitution reactions, 263, 263f, 271f
  for S_N2 substitution reactions, 255, 255f, 259f
  for two-step reaction mechanisms, 222–224, 224f
Energy of activation (E_a)
  catalysts and, 228, 228f
  definition of, 220
  energy barrier height determined by, 221
  in energy diagrams, 220–224, 221f, 222f, 224f
  in exothermic reactions, 270, 270f
  rate constant, relationship to, 226
  reaction rate and, 225
  transition state energy effect on, 269
Enol(s), 916–919
  hydroxy group of, 325
  reaction mechanism, 919
  resonance structures, 919
  synthesis of, 790
    hydration of alkyne, 427–429
    hydroboration–oxidation of alkyne, 429–430
  tautomers, 917–918
-enol (suffix), A–5
Enolate(s), 818, 916, 919–926
  achiral, 927
  in aldol reactions, 956, 956f, 957, 958, 960, 961, 962f, 963, 965, 966
  alkylation, 933–936
    general features of, 933–934
    tamoxifen synthesis, 935
    of unsymmetrical ketones, 934–935
  in Claisen reactions, 967–971
  electrostatic potential plot of, 920, 921f
  examples, 921
  kinetic, 925, 934, 963
  in Michael reaction, 972–974, 974f
  reactions of, 924, 928, 933–936
  resonance-stabilized, 958, 968, 973
  resonance structures, 919
  in Robinson annulation, 974–978
  synthesis of, 790
    with bases, 922–923, 923t
    from carbonyl compounds, 919
    from esters, 921
    from tertiary amides, 921
  thermodynamic, 926, 935
  of unsymmetrical carbonyl compounds, 925–926
Enolate anion, 22
Enol tautomers, 427–429, 899, 917–918
-enone (suffix), A–5
Enones, 812
Entacapone, 56
Enthalpy change ($\Delta H°$), 212–215
  calculation from bond dissociation energies, 214–215
  in dehydration of alcohols, 340, 341f
  E1 elimination reactions, 302, 302f
  in energy diagrams, 220–224, 221f, 222f, 224f
  free energy change, relation to, 218–219
  negative, 212, 219
  positive, 212, 219
Entropy ($S°$), 218–219
Entropy change ($\Delta S°$), 218–219
Environmental Protection Agency, 469
-enyne (suffix), A–5
Enynes, 418
Enzymes, 229, 229f, 1149
  active site of, 229, 229f
  catalytic action of, 229, 229f
  in kinetic resolution of amino acids, 1158
  in oxidation reactions, 470
  in peptide sequencing, 1167, 1167t
Enzyme–substrate complex, 229, 229f
Ephedrine, 174, 200
Epi-aristolochene, 1224
Epichlorohydrin, 370, 1241–1242, 1242f
Epilupinine, 1041
Epimers
  definition of, 1107
  of monosaccharides, 1107, 1124, 1126–1127
Epinephrine, 261–262, 261f, 997
Eplerenone, 334
Epothilone A, 1059f
Epoxidation, 457f, 458–461
  in anti dihydroxylation, 461
  Sharpless, 471–473
  of squalene, 1216f, 1217
  stereochemistry of, 458–459
  in synthesis of disparlure, 459–461, 460f
Epoxide(s), 287
  achiral, 461
  angle strain, 326, 337
  anionic polymerization of, 1234–1235
  applications, 361–363
  boiling point of, 331t
  bonding, 326
  electrostatic potential plot of, 326f
  interesting examples, 334
  leaving group, 337
  melting point of, 331t
  nomenclature, 329–330
  physical properties of, 330–331, 331t
  reactions of, 357–361
    with acetylide anions, 434
    with acids HZ, 359–361, 360f, 361f
    general features, 337
    with organometallic reagents, 787–788
    reduction, 455–456, 456f
    with strong nucleophiles, 357–359
  reduction of, 455–456, 456f
  ring opening reactions, 1234–1235
    with acids, 359–361
    enantiomers in, 358–359
    nucleophilic substitution reactions, 357–361
    regioselectivity of, 360
  solubility of, 331t
  structure of, 325, 326
  synthesis of, 336
Epoxy (prefix), 329
Epoxyalkane, 329
1,2-Epoxycyclohexane, 329, 358
1,2-Epoxy-2-methylpropane, 329
cis-2,3-Epoxypentane, 329
Epoxy resins, 1241–1242, 1242f
Equal. *See* Aspartame
Equations for organic reactions, writing, 206, 206f
Equatorial bond, 167
Equatorial hydrogens, 146–147, 146f, 148f
Equilibrium, 216–217, 217f, 217t
  acid–base reactions, 65–66
  direction of, 225
  nucleophilic substitution and, 248
Equilibrium arrow, 60–61, 211t
Equilibrium constant (K_{eq}), 216–218, 217f, 217t, 225
Ergot, 677
Erlotinib, 438
Erythrose, 201
  D-erythrose, 1106, 1106f, 1107f
  L-erythrose, 1106, 1106f
D-Erythrulose, 1108f
ESI (electrospray ionization), 494
Esmolol, 84
Essential amino acids, 742
Essential fatty acids, 382
Essential oils, 1208
Esterification, 237
  Fischer, 882–883, 894
Esters
  acidity/basicity of, 863t
  boiling point of, 869t
  cholesteryl, 896, 896f
  chromate, 467
  cyclic, 861
  enolates from, 921
  functional group in, 91t
  general structure of, 382
  interesting examples, 871
  IR spectra of, 870t
  leaving group, 757
  melting point of, 869t
  nomenclature of, 865, 867t
  nucleophilic substitution reactions, 757
  odors of, 871
  physical properties of, 869t
  pK_a, 863t, 922t
  polyesters, 894
  reactions of, 885–889, 892t
    with ammonia and amines to form amides, 885
    carboxylic acid preparation by malonic ester synthesis, 936–940
    Claisen reaction, 967–971, 967f
    hydrolysis to carboxylic acids, 885–886
    lipid hydrolysis, 887–889
    methyl ketone preparation by acetoacetic ester synthesis, 936, 940–943
  reaction with organometallic reagents, 783–785
  reduction of, 766–768
  solubility of, 869t
  stability of, 863
  structure and bonding of, 754, 860, 863
  synthesis of
    from acid chlorides, 876
    from anhydrides, 879
    from carboxylic acids, 880f, 882–883
    from monosaccharides, 1119–1120
  thioesters, 895–896
  in triacylglycerols, 382
  waxes, 1196
Estradiol, 53, 164, 803
  analogs of, 420
  function in body, 1218t
  structure of, 420, 1218t
  synthesis of, 298, 299f
Estragole, 715
Estrogens, 1217, 1218t
Estrone, 717
  function in the body, 1218t
  structure of, 783, 1218t
  synthesis of
    from chlorohydrin, 401f
    in Diels–Alder reactions, 618
    using Micheal reaction, 974, 974f
Eth- (prefix), 127
Ethambutol, 53, 260, 260f
Ethanal. *See* Acetaldehyde
Ethane
  acidity of, 72, 73f
  bond dissociation energy, 624
  bonds in, 38–39, 42t
  carbon–carbon bond length in, 603
  chlorination of, 563–565, 565f
  conformations of, 137–141, 139f, 140f
  formation from ethylene and hydrogen, 228
  molecular formula, 122, 125t
  nonreactivity of, 87, 88
  structure of, 87, 88, 121
Ethanedioic acid, 722
1,2-Ethanediol, 328
Ethanol, 116
  in acid–base reactions, 65–66
  acidity of, 65–66, 69, 70, 71, 731, 733f
  in alcoholic beverages, 331, 444
  description, 2
  electrostatic potential plot, 70f, 71f
  in ethyl acetate formation, 228
  isomers of, 18
  NMR spectrum of, 519, 538, 539f
  oxidation of, 470–471
  pK_a of, 731, 733f
  as polar protic solvent, 250f
  preparation from ethylene, 381f
  production by fermentation of carbohydrates, 331–332, 332f
  reactivity of, 88
  as renewable fuel source, 332, 332f
  sodium ethoxide production from, 335
  solubility of, 100
  structure of, 88
Ethene, 379. *See also* Ethylene
Ethers
  boiling point of, 331t
  bonding of, 326
  Claisen rearrangement, 1089
  crown, 107, 333–334, 333f
  cyclic, 329
  electrostatic potential maps, 326f
  formation by alcohol addition to alkenes, 395
  functional group, 90t
  infrared (IR) spectra of, 502
  interesting examples, 333–334, 333f
  leaving group, 337
  melting point of, 331t
  nomenclature, 328–329

physical properties of, 330–331, 331t
preparation by nucleophilic substitution reaction, 280
reactions of
alkyl halide formation, 355–356
general features, 337
with strong acid, 355–356
simple and complex, 328–329
solubility of, 331t
structure of, 325, 326
symmetrical, 325, 334
synthesis of
from alkyl halides, 334–335
from monosaccharides, 1119–1120
by nucleophilic substitution reactions, 334–335
Williamson ether synthesis, 334, 335
unsymmetrical, 325, 334
Ethoxide, 65–66, 71, 249, 732, 733f
Ethoxy group, 329
4-Ethoxyoctane, 329
Ethyl acetate
in Claisen reaction, 967, 969
formation from acetic acid and ethanol, 228
as solvent, 882
structure of, 865
synthesis of, 882
Ethyl acetoacetate, 924, 945
conversion to ketone, 940–942
synthesis in Claisen reaction, 967
Ethyl α-cyanoacrylate, 1232f
N-Ethylaniline, 992
Ethylbenzene, 634
bromination of, 699
styrene synthesis from, 701
Ethyl benzoate, 867t, 969
Ethyl butanoate, 871
Ethyl chloride, 89, 241
Ethyl chloroformate, in crossed Claisen reaction, 970
Ethyl chrysanthemate, 909
Ethylcyclobutane, 134f
N-Ethylcyclohexanamine, 1004
2-Ethylcyclohexanecarbaldehyde, 809
2-Ethylcyclohexanone, 934
4-Ethyl-3,4-dimethyloctane, 130f
5-Ethyl-2,6-dimethyloctane, 130
Ethylene, 379
acidity of, 72, 73f
bond dissociation energies, 418
bonds of, 39–40, 40f, 42t, 373
bromine addition to, 631
as Brønsted–Lowry base, 59f
electrostatic potential plot, 385, 385f
ethane formation from, 228
fruit ripening and, 291
functional group in, 88, 89t
in Heck reaction, 1050
as industrial starting material, 380, 381f
Lewis structure, 15–16
molecular shape of, 26
monomers in polymerization, 582–583
pK_a of, 64
polymerization of, 1230, 1236
preparation from petroleum, 380
structure of, 1229f
synthesis from alkyl tosylates, 353
Ethylene glycol, 840
acetal formation from, 837
in antifreeze, 332f
formation from PET recycling, 1248
naming, 328
in polyester synthesis, 894
in polyethylene terephthalate (PET), 1225, 1227f, 1239–1240, 1256
in polyurethane synthesis, 1240
preparation from ethylene, 381f
structure of, 332f
Ethylene oxide, 330, 1234–1235
1-Ethyl-2-fluorocyclopentane, 241f
N-Ethylformamide, 866
Ethyl formate, in crossed Claisen reactions, 969
Ethyl group, 128
2-Ethyl-1-heptene, 376
Ethyl 2,4-hexadienoate, 985
Ethyl isopropyl ketone, 812f
1-Ethyl-3-methylcyclohexane, 133
Ethyl methyl ether, 532
Ethyl methyl ketone, 811
4-Ethyl-5-methyloctane, 130f
N-Ethyl-*N*-methylcyclopenatanamine, 992
N-Ethyl-*N*-methylcyclopentylamine, 992
Ethyl *p*-aminobenzoate, 703
3-Ethylpentane, bromination of, 567
2-Ethyl-1-pentene, 391
Ethyl phenylacetate, 910
Ethyl *p*-nitrobenzoate, 703
Ethyl propanoate, 497, 498f
Ethyl tosylate, 353
Ethyne, 419. *See also* Acetylene
Ethynylcyclohexane, 419f, 1063
Ethynylestradiol, 416, 420, 420f, 777, 777f, 783, 1218
Ethynyl group, 419
Etoposide, 851
Excited state
of atom, 35
of electron, 619–620
Exergonic reaction, 219
Exo product, 614, 615–616, 616f
Exothermic reactions
addition reaction, 387, 387f
bond formation and, 212–213, 215
chlorination, 565, 565f, 569
energy diagram of, 220, 221f
enthalpy change and, 219
hydrogenation, 447
reaction rate, 270
transition state in, 269, 270, 270f
Extraction, 738–740, 738f, 740f
for separation of amines, 1006–1007, 1006f
Ezetimibe, 198, 765

F

Fabric, binding of dyes to, 1029–1030
α-Farnesene, 381f
Farnesol, 1209f, 1212
Farnesyl diphosphate, 1210, 1211f, 1212, 1214, 1224
Fats, 384, 450–452, 887–889
body content of, 1200
degree of unsaturation, 450–451
fatty acid composition, 1198, 1198t
melting point of, 384, 1197–1198
saturated, 384
trans, 451–452
Fat-soluble vitamins, 1204, 1204f, 1205f
Fatty acids
characteristics of, 1197
composition in fats and oils, 1198, 1198t
essential, 382, 1197
melting point of, 382, 383t
omega-3, 383, 384
oxidation of, 888, 1199
saturated, 372, 382, 451–452, 1197–1199, 1197t, 1198t
synthesis in lipid hydrolysis, 888
thioesters of, 896
trans, 451–452
triacylglycerol formation and, 110
in triacylglycerols, 382, 384, 1197–1200, 1197t
unsaturated, 372, 382, 1197–1199, 1197t, 1198t
Feedstock, 1245
Fehling's reagent, 1121
Femara. *See* Letrozole
Fenfluramine, 82
Fenn, Dr. John, 494
Fentanyl, 118
Fermentation, alcohol production by, 331–332, 332f
Ferulic acid, 628
Fexofenadine, 53, 996
Fibers
natural, 893, 893f
synthetic, 893–894
Fibrinogen, 1149
Fibrous proteins, 1182
Fingerprint, of IR spectrum, 497, 497f, 498f, 499
First-order kinetics, 227
of E1 elimination reactions, 301, 303t
of nucleophilic substitution reactions, 253–254
of S_N1 substitution reactions, 262
First-order rate equation, 227, 253, 254
Fischer, Emil, 1126
Fischer esterification, 882–883, 894
Fischer projection formulas, 1101–1105, 1103f
Fischer proof of the structure of glucose, 1126–1129, 1127f
Fishhook notation, 210, 211t
Five-membered rings, synthesis of
in Dieckmann reaction, 971
in intramolecular aldol reactions, 965–967
Flagpole hydrogens, 148, 148f
Flat helical ribbon, shorthand for α-helix, 1178
Flat polygons, 188
Flat wide arrow, shorthand for β-pleated sheet, 1178
Fleming, Sir Alexander, 483
Flexibilene, 1223
Flosal, 961
9-Fluorenylmethoxycarbonyl protecting group (Fmoc), 1170, 1174–1175
Fluorine
polarizability, 93–94
valence electrons of, 12
Fluorocyclohexane, 234
Fluoromethane, polarizability and boiling point of, 96, 97f
m-Fluoronitrobenzene, 634
Fluoxetine, 3, 81, 195, 260, 260f, 697, 998
Fmoc (9-fluorenylmethoxycarbonyl protecting group), 1171, 1174–1175
Folic acid, 1030–1031
Formal charge, 16–18, 18t
Formaldehyde, 16
aldol reactions of, 961, 962
Bakelite preparation from, 1243–1244, 1244f
electrostatic potential map of, 755, 755f
formation from methanol oxidation, 470
hydration of, 835
primary alcohol formed from, 776
structure of, 810, 815
uses of, 815
Formaldehyde hydrate, 835
Formalin, 815
Formic acid, 64, 125, 470, 721t, 725
Formyl group, 812
Fosamax (alendronic acid), 19
Fossil fuels, 74, 135–136, 156
Four-centered transition state, 402
Fragmentation, 485, 489–491, 490f
Free energy change ($\Delta G°$), 216–219, 217f, 217t
Frequency
of electromagnetic radiation, 494–495, 495f
of infrared radiation, 496–497
Friedel, Charles, 667
Friedel–Crafts acylation, 667f, 672–678, 707
alkyl benzene synthesis, 702–703, 702f
of benzene, 667f, 702f
electrophilic aromatic substitution reaction, 667f
general features of, 672
intramolecular, 677–678, 677f
ketone synthesis, 667f, 672, 702–703
limitations of, 691–692
mechanism of, 674
Friedel–Crafts alkylation, 667f, 672–678, 705, 706
of alcohols, 676
of alkenes, 676
in alkyl benzene synthesis, 672–673, 702–703, 703f
of benzene, 667f, 702f
carbon/carbocation rearrangements, 675–676
electrophilic aromatic substitution reaction, 667f
general features of, 672
intramolecular reactions, 678
limitations in, 691–692
mechanism of, 673–674
polyalkylation, 691
unreactive halides, 674
Frontalin, 473, 473f
Frontside attack, in nucleophilic substitution reactions, 256
Frost circle, 653
Fructofuranose ring, 1131
Fructose
D-fructose, 1100, 1108f, 1114, 1115
stereogenic centers, 174
in sucrose, 1131
Fucose, 1147
Fuels, renewable, 332, 332f
Fugu, 5, 5f
Fukui, Kenichi, 1071
Full-headed curved arrow, 210, 210f, 211t
Fumaric acid, 119, 613
Functional groups, 87–92. *See also specific functional groups*
compounds containing a C=O group, 90–92, 91t
compounds containing a C–Z σ bond, 89, 90t
definition of, 87
drawing connection to carbon skeleton, 87
fragmentation pattern in mass spectrum, 491
grouping organic compounds by, 88
hydrocarbons, 88–89, 89t
importance of, 91

infrared (IR) spectrometry and, 496, 497, 498f, 499–500, 499f, 499t
intermolecular forces and, 92
nomenclature of, A-4
nucleophilic substitutions and, 278, 278t
reactivity and, 108–109
synthesis of, A-14–17
Funk, Casimir, 102
Funnel, separatory, 738, 738f
Furan, 659, 1109
Furanose(s), 1114–1115
Furanose rings, 1109, 1114–1115
Fused bicyclic system, 615f
Fused ring system, 614, 615f

G

Gabapentin, 177
Gabriel synthesis of primary (1°) amines, 1000–1001
Galactose, 1130
α-D-galactose, 846
D-galactose, 1107f, 1124
in lactose, 229, 229f
structure, 163
Wohl degradation, 1124
Gamma (γ) carbon, 721
Gamma (γ) hydroxybutyric acid (GHB), 726
Garlic, 125
Garsubellin A, 1090
Gas chromatography–mass spectrometry (GC–MS), 492–494, 493f
Gasohol, 332, 332f
Gasoline
additives
benzene, 88
BTX mixture, 637
ethanol, 332
high-octane, 517, 637
MTBE, 101
combustion of, 155
composition of hydrocarbons in, 135, 136
isooctane in, 205
octane and, 88, 101
oxidation of isooctane, 205, 215
refining, 135f
Gauche conformation, 141f, 142, 143f, 143t
GC–MS (gas chromatography–mass spectrometry), 492–494, 493f
Geckos, 93
Geminal dichloride, 421
Geminal dihalide, 310
alkyne synthesis from, 421–422
synthesis in hydrohalogenation of alkynes, 424
Geminal protons, 536
Generic name, 126
Geranial, 816f
Geraniol, 473, 1209, 1212
Geranyl diphosphate, 1210–1211, 1211f, 1212, 1213
GHB [gamma (γ) hydroxybutyric acid], 726
Gibberellic acid, 983
Gibbs free energy ($G°$), 216
Ginger, 612
Ginkgo biloba, 124, 718
Ginkgolide B, 859, 887
Glacial acetic acid, 725
Gleevec, 872
Globular proteins, 1182
D-Glucaric acid, 1122
Glucitol, 1120
Glucopyranose
α-D-glucopyranose, 1121f
β-D-glucopyranose, 1135
Glucosamine, 897
D-glucosamine, 1134
Glucose, 845–846
acyclic aldehyde, 1110, 1111f
anomers of, 1110, 1111f, 1113–1114, 1113f
in complex carbohydrates, 110
conversion to ester, 1119–1120
conversion to ether, 1119–1120
diastereomers of, 1110, 1111f
drawing as cyclic hemiacetal, 1109–1110, 1111f
energy in, 1099
Fischer projection of, 1103, 1103f
Fischer proof of structure of, 1126–1129, 1127f
D-glucose, 1100, 1103, 1105, 1107, 1107f, 1109–1110, 1111f, 1114, 1114f, 1120, 1122–1124, 1126, 1145, 1245
α-D-glucose, 846, 1110, 1111f, 1115–1117, 1119, 1130, 1133
β-D-glucose, 846, 857, 1099f, 1110, 1111f, 1113, 1116–1117, 1120, 1130, 1133
L-glucose, 1105
glycoside formation from, 1115–1116
in honey, 1114
from hydrolysis
of cellulose, 1133
of glycosides, 1117
of maltose, 1130
of starch, 167, 1134
in lactose, 229, 229f
oxidation of, 205, 215, 219, 1121–1122
reduction of carbonyl group, 1120
structure, 110, 163, 168f
three-dimensional representations for D-glucose, 1114f
Wohl degradation, 1123
Glucosidase
α-glucosidase, 1134
β-glucosidase, 1133
Glutamic acid, 752
abbreviation for, 742t
isoelectric point for, 1152t
pK_a values for, 1152t
structure of, 1150f
Glutamine
isoelectric point for, 1152t
pK_a values for, 1152t
structure of, 1150f
Glutaric anhydride, 714
Glutathione, 1164
Glyceraldehyde
enantiomers of, 1101–1102, 1105
D-glyceraldehyde, 1100, 1106, 1107f
L-glyceraldehyde, 1105
(*R*)-glyceraldehyde, 1101, 1105
(*S*)-glyceraldehyde, 1101, 1105
optical activity, 191
Glycerol
naming, 328
synthesis in lipid hydrolysis, 888
in triacylglycerols, 382
Glycine, 742
abbreviation for, 742t
in dipeptide synthesis, 1168–1169, 1172
isoelectric point for, 1152t
pK_a values for, 1152t
structure of, 1149f, 1150f
zwitterion form, 85
Glycogen, 1134
Glycolic acid, 16, 70, 1239
Glycols, 328, 461
Glycopeptide transpeptidase, 891
Glycoside(s), 1115–1118
formation, 1115–1116
α glycoside, 1115–1117
β glycoside, 1115–1117
hydrolysis of, 1117
naturally occurring, 1118
N-Glycoside(s), 1135–1138, 1138f
α-*N*-glycoside, 1135
β-*N*-glycoside, 1135
Glycosidic bond/linkage
in disaccharides, 1129–1131
α-glycosidic linkage, 1131, 1133–1134
1→4-α-glycosidic bond, 1130, 1133–1134
1→6-α-glycosidic bond, 1133–1134
β-glycosidic linkage, 1130, 1132–1133, 1135, 1136
1→4-β-glycosidic bond, 1130, 1132, 1135
in polysaccharides, 1132–1134
Goodyear, Charles, 1237
Grandisol, 1209
Graphite, 655
Green chemistry, 469–470
Amberlyst A-26 resin and, 469
definition of, 469
green polymer synthesis, 1244–1247, 1245f, 1246f
Grignard, Victor, 772
Grignard products, retrosynthetic analysis of, 778–781
Grignard reagents, 772
addition to nitriles, 901
organic synthesis with, 792–795
preparation of, 772
reaction as base, 774
reaction with α,β-unsaturated carbonyl compounds, 790
reaction with aldehydes and ketones, 775–778, 822–823
reaction with carbon dioxide, 787
reaction with epoxides, 787–788
reaction with esters and acid chlorides, 784–786
Ground state
of atom, 35
of electron, 619–620
Group, in periodic table, 9
Group number, 9, 11
Grubbs, Robert, 1056
Grubbs catalyst, 1055–1059, 1059f
Guanidine, 1041
Guanine, 1137, 1138f
D-Gulose, 1107f
Gutta-percha, 1237, 1238, 1253
Gypsy moth, 459

H

Half-headed curved arrow, 210, 210f, 211t, 559
Halides. *See also* Alkyl halides; Aryl halides; Hydrogen halides; Vinyl halides
allylic, 239, 239f
benzylic, 699–701
methyl
S_N2 substitution reactions, 258, 272
organic
coupling reaction with organocuprate reagents, 1043–1045
coupling with alkenes (Heck reaction), 1043, 1050–1052
coupling with organoboron reagents (Suzuki reaction), 1043, 1046–1049
unreactive, 674
α-Halo aldehyde or ketone, synthesis of, 928–932
Halo alkane, 240
α-Halo carbonyl compounds
reactions of, 932
synthesis of, 928–931
α-Halo carboxylic acids, amino acid synthesis from, 1152–1153, 1155f
Halocyclohexanes, E2 elimination in, 306–308
Haloethanes, 165
Haloform, 930–931
Haloform reaction, 930–931
Halogenation
of activated benzenes, 690–691
of alkanes, 562–572
of achiral starting material, 570t, 571
bromination, 566–568, 568f
of chiral starting material, 570t, 571–572
chlorination, 563–567, 569–572, 569f
energy changes during, 565, 565f
mechanism of, 563–565
in organic synthesis, 570
stereochemistry of, 570–572, 570t
of alkenes, 386f, 395–398, 398f
of alkyl benzenes, 699–701
of alkynes, 426
of benzene, 667f, 669–670, 694
of carbonyl compounds, at α carbon, 928–932, 931f
in acid, 929, 931f
in base, 929–930, 931f
electrophilic aromatic substitution reaction, 667f, 669–670, 690–691, 692–693
haloform reaction, 930–931
monohalogenation, 562
polyhalogenation, 690
stereochemistry of, 396–398
transition states in, 565f, 567, 568f, 569, 569f
Halogens
in alkyl halides. *See* Alkyl halides
common nucleophiles, 252t
as electron-withdrawing groups, 680–681, 685
polarizable, 395
Halo group, 90t
Halohydrin
epoxide synthesis from, 336
synthesis from alkenes, 386f, 398–400, 400t
mechanism of, 398–399, 400t
regioselectivity of, 399–400, 400t
stereochemistry of, 399–400, 400t
use in organic synthesis, 401
Halomethanes, electrostatic potential map of, 244f
Halomon, 240
Halonium ion, bridged, 396–400, 400t, 426
Halothane, 242f, 333

Hammond postulate, 268–271, 303, 390, 390f, 425, 568, 696
electrophilic aromatic substitution reaction, 684
features of, 269–270
S_N1 substitution reactions, 268, 270–271
Handedness, 167, 170, 173
Hansen's disease (leprosy), 166, 177
Hardener, 1241–1242, 1242f
Hardening, 451, 1199
Haworth projections, 1110, 1111–1113
HCFCs (hydrochlorofluorocarbons), 573
HDL particles (high density lipoproteins), 896
HDPE (high-density polyethylene), 582, 1229, 1236, 1248, 1248t
Heat of hydrogenation, 447–448, 604–605
benzene, 639–640, 639f
Heat of reaction, 212. *See also* Enthalpy change
Heck, Richard, 1050
Heck reaction, 1043, 1050–1052
Helicene, 638, 638f
Helium, electronic configuration of, 10
Helminthosporal, 986
Heme, 1148, 1183–1184
Hemiacetal(s)
in carbohydrates, 845–846
conversion to acetals, 838–839
conversion to carbonyl compounds, 841
cyclic
conversion to cyclic acetals, 844–845
structure, 842
synthesis of, 843–844
monosaccharides, 1109–1115
structure of, 842
synthesis of, 838–839, 840
Hemibrevetoxin B, 89
Hemlock water dropwort, 28
Hemoglobin, 1149
sickle cell, 1184–1185
structure, 1181, 1184, 1184f
Heptalene, 658
Heptanal, 961
Heptane
constitutional isomers of, 125t
molecular formula, 125t
2,6-Heptanedione, 966
2-Heptanone, synthesis of, 941–942
trans-2-Heptene, 1044
Herbicides, 670, 670f
Heroin, 200, 510, 880
Heteractis crispa, 5f, 6
Heteroatom(s), 4
in condensed structures, 29
definition of, 87
in functional groups, 87, 108–109
in skeletal structures, 31, 33, 34
stereogenic centers, 174
Heterocycle(s), 329
aromatic, 644–647, 646f
nitrogen, 992
Heterocyclic aromatic amines, basicity of, 1011, 1013t
Heterogeneous reaction mixture, 447
Heterolysis (heterolytic cleavage)
carbocation formation, 262, 270
description, 209
in E1 elimination reactions, 301
reactive intermediates of, 210–211, 210f
in two-step reaction mechanism, 223
Hexachloroethane, 196
2,4-Hexadiene, 602, 642
(2*E*,4*Z*)-2,4-Hexadiene, 1075, 1076, 1077, 1078, 1079
1,3-Hexadiyne, 419f
Hexamethylenediamine, 893
Hexamethylphosphoramide (HMPA), 251f
Hexane, 120, 455f
constitutional isomers of, 125t
infrared (IR) spectrum, 501
mass spectrum of, 486, 486f, 489–490, 490f
molecular formula, 125t
skeletal structures, 31
as solvent, 99
solvent in extraction procedure, 738
2,5-Hexanedione, aldol reactions of, 965–966
Hexanoic acid, 718, 749
2-Hexanol, conversion to other compounds, 792
Hexaphenylethane, 592
1,3,5-Hexatriene, 640, 642, 1070, 1075
molecular orbitals of, 1074, 1074f
1-Hexene, infrared (IR) spectrum of, 501
3-Hexene, 455f
cis-3-hexene, 377–378, 1056
trans-3-hexene, 378
1-Hexyne, 501, 1049
3-Hexyne, 455f
HFCs (hydrofluorocarbons), 573
High density lipoproteins (HDLs), 896
High-density polyethylene (HDPE), 582, 1229, 1236, 1248, 1248t
Highest occupied molecular orbital (HOMO), 652, 1073
High-performance liquid chromatography (HPLC), 1165
Hinckley, Robert, 333
Histamine, 646–647, 996, 1035
Histidine
isoelectric point for, 1152t
pK_a values for, 1152t
structure of, 1150f
Histrionicotoxin, 113, 421, 421f
HMPA (hexamethylphosphoramide), 251f
^{1}H NMR. *See* Proton NMR
Hoffman, Felix, 726
Hoffmann, Roald, 1071
Hofmann elimination, 1016–1019
HOMO, 1077, 1079
Homogeneous catalysts, 1236
Homologous series, 124, 125t
Homolysis (homolytic cleavage)
of allylic C–H bond, 575
bond dissociation energy for, 212
chlorination of alkanes, 563, 564, 566
description, 209
endothermic nature of, 212, 213
entropy increase with, 219
radical formation, 561
reactive intermediates of, 210–211, 210f
Homopolymers, 1233
Honey, 1114
Honeycomb, 157
Hooke's law, 498, 498f
Hormones. *See also specific hormones*
local mediators distinct from, 1205
peptide, 1163, 1164f
sex, 1216t, 1217, 1218, 1218t
Host–guest complex, 333
Housane, 135f
5-HPETE (5-hydroperoxyeicosatetraenoic acid), 362, 590, 623
Hückel, Erich, 641
Hückel's rule, 640–643, 650–653
Humulene, 1049, 1049f
Hybridization, 34–43, 633
conjugated systems and, 600–601
definition of, 35
Hybridization effects
on acidity, 72, 72f, 73f
on basicity of amines, 1012, 1013t
Hybrid orbitals, 34–43
percent *s*-character, 44, 72, 294
sp orbitals, 35–37, 37f, 41, 42f, 42t
in alkynes, 417, 418, 422, 423
percent *s*-character, 72
sp^2 orbitals, 35–37, 37f, 39, 40, 40f, 42t
in alkenes, 291, 294
in aromatic heterocycles, 644–645, 646f
in benzene, 633
carbon radical, 559
carboxy group, 719
percent *s*-character, 72
sp^3 orbitals, 35–39, 36f, 38f, 42t
in acyclic alkanes, 121
in alkenes, 294
percent *s*-character, 72
superscripts, meaning of, 37
Hydrates
oxidation of, 468
synthesis from aldehydes and ketones, 835–837
kinetics, 836–837
thermodynamics, 835–836
Hydration
of aldehydes and ketones, 835–837
kinetics, 836–837
thermodynamics, 835–836
of alkenes, 386f, 394–395, 405–406
definition of, 824
hydroboration–oxidation compared, 405–406
Hydrazine, in Wolff–Kishner reduction, 702
Hydrides
as base, 75, 75f
metal hydride reagents
reducing agents, 446, 760–762, 766–770, 770t
reduction of aldehydes and ketones, 760–761
reduction of nitrile, 900
nucleophilic addition with, 756, 761
nucleophilic substitution with, 757
reduction of ketones and aldehydes, 760–762, 762f, 770t, 821–822
1,2-Hydride shift, 341–343, 675–676
Hydroboration
of alkenes, 401–403
of alkynes, 1047, 1049
definition of, 401
mechanism of, 402
regioselectivity of, 403, 405t
Hydroboration–oxidation reactions
of alkenes, 386f, 401–406
mechanism of, 401–404
regioselectivity of, 403, 405t
stereochemistry of, 402, 404, 405t
hydration compared, 405–406
synthesis of artemisinin, 405, 405f
Hydrocarbons
aliphatic, 88, 121
aromatic, 88–89, 630–634
definition of, 88
functional groups in, 88–89, 89t
infrared (IR) absorptions in, 500–501
oxidation and reduction of, 445, 445f
polycyclic aromatic (PAH), 363
saturated, 121
synthesis in organocuprate couplings, 1045
unsaturated, 374. *See also* Alkenes
Hydrochloric acid
elimination in nylon synthesis, 893
in epoxide ring opening reactions, 359, 360, 360f
as Lewis acid, 79
pK_a of, 66
for removal of Boc protecting group, 1170
Hydrochlorofluorocarbons (HCFCs), 573
Hydrofluorocarbons (HFCs), 573
Hydrogen
addition to alkenes, 447–452
addition to alkynes, 452–454, 455f
alpha (α), 916, 920, 929–930, 960, 961, 962, 963, 969
covalent bond formation by, 12–13, 13f
electronic configuration, 10
isotopes of, 8, 492t
mass of, 492t
octet rule exceptions, 18
primary (1°), 123–124
as reducing agent, 446. *See also* Hydrogenation
secondary (2°), 123–124
sigma (σ) bond in molecular hydrogen, 34
tertiary (3°), 123–124
Hydrogenation
of aldeyhdes and ketones, 761
of alkenes, 447–452
alkene stability and, 447–448, 448f
cis and trans isomers compared, 447, 448f
degrees of unsaturation, determination of, 449–450
mechanism of catalytic hydrogenation, 448–449
alkene stability and, 447–448, 448f
catalytic, 447–449
of conjugated dienes, 604–605
enantioselective synthesis of amino acids, 1159–1160
as exothermic reactions, 447
heat of, 447–448, 604–605, 639–640, 639f
of oils, 450–452, 451f
of unsaturated fatty acids, 1199
Hydrogen bonding
in alcohols, 330
in amides, 868, 869f
in amines, 993
anion solvation by, 250
in carboxylic acids, 723, 723f
in DNA, 110, 111f, 1138, 1139f
intramolecular in β-dicarbonyl compounds, 917
in polar protic solvents, 250, 275
solubility and, 101f
strength of, 94, 95t
in water, 94
Hydrogen bromide, for removal of Boc protecting group, 1170
Hydrogen chloride. *See* Hydrochloric acid
Hydrogen cyanide, 16, 825
Hydrogen fluoride, 14
Hydrogen halides
addition to alkenes, 386–393, 386f, 387f, 393t
addition to alkynes, 423f, 424–426
alcohol conversion to alkyl halides, 345–348
reactivity of, 347
Hydrogen ions (H^+), Brønsted–Lowry acid definition and, 59

Hydrogenolysis
of benzyl esters, 1171
in peptide synthesis, 1171–1172
Hydrogen peroxide, as oxidizing agent, 456
Hydrohalogenation
of alkenes, 386–393, 386f
Markovnikov's rule, 389–391, 390f, 393t
mechanism of, 386–389, 387f, 388f, 393t
stereochemistry of, 391–393, 393f, 393t
of alkynes, 423f, 424–426
Markovnikov's rule, 424, 425
Hydrolysis
of acetals, 840–841
in acetoacetate ester synthesis, 940, 941
of amides, 890
in amino acid synthesis, 1153
base-promoted, 886–887
definition of, 824
of esters, 885–889
acid-catalyzed, 885
applications of, 887–889
base-promoted, 886–887
glucose formation by, 1117, 1130, 1133, 1134
of imines and enamines, 834
of lipids, 887–889, 1196
in malonic ester synthesis, 936, 938
of nitriles, 898–899
partial of peptides, 1167–1168
of starch, 332, 332f
of triacylglycerols, 1199
Hydronium ion, formal charge on, 17
Hydroperoxide(s), 577, 578f, 1199
5-Hydroperoxyeicosatetraenoic acid (5-HPETE), 362, 590, 623
Hydrophilic, 100, 102, 104
Hydrophobic, 100, 102, 104, 157, 1196
Hydroxide
as Brønsted–Lowry base, 84
nucleophile in alcohol synthesis, 335
oxygen bases, 75, 75f
α-Hydroxy acids, 70
Hydroxy aldehyde
cyclization of, 843, 846
β-hydroxy, synthesis in aldol reactions, 955–966
intramolecular cyclization of, 843, 846
o-Hydroxybenzaldehyde, 984
Hydroxybenzene, 634. *See also* Phenol
o-Hydroxybenzoic acid, 752
p-Hydroxybenzoic acid, 752
3-Hydroxybutanal, 955
4-Hydroxybutanal, 843
2-Hydroxybutanedioic acid, 752
4-Hydroxybutanoic acid, 726, 908
3-Hydroxybutyric acid, 1249
γ-Hydroxybutyric acid (GHB), 726
β-Hydroxy carbonyl compounds
synthesis of, in aldol reactions, 955–966
useful transformations of, 962, 963f
3-Hydroxy carboxylic acids, 1249
Hydroxy group, 90t
of alcohols, 325, 337
of enols, 325
of ethanol, 88
hydrophilic nature of, 100
IR absorption, 502, 724, 724f
of monosaccharides, 1100, 1119–1120
NMR absorption, 724, 725f
OH proton, NMR spectra of, 538–539, 539f
of phenols, 325
6-Hydroxy-2-hexanone, 841
Hydroxylamine, 1123
5-Hydroxypentanal, 843
5-Hydroxy-2-pentanone, 781–783, 782f
N-Hydroxysuccinimide, 1192
3-Hydroxyvaleric acid, 1249
(–)-Hyoscyamine, 953
Hyperconjuation, 267–268
Hypertension, 90
Hypophosphorus acid, 1023

I

Ibuprofen, 83, 113, 949
anti-inflammatory action of, 157, 954
enantiomers, 195
mode of action, 1207
synthesis of, 703, 762f, 954, 971
systematic name of, 126
-ic acid (suffix), 721, 864, 866, 867
-ide (suffix), 241
D-Idose, 1107f
Iejimalide B, 411
Illudin-S, 942
Imatinib mesylate, 872
Imidazole, 782, 783
Imidazolide, 906
Imides, in Gabriel synthesis of primary amines, 1000
Imidic amide tautomer, 898–899
Imines, 769, 1124, 1125
hydrolysis of, 834
reduction to amines, 1002
synthesis of
from aldehydes and ketones, 830–832, 832f, 834f, 1015, 1154
from nucleophilic addition reactions, 820, 821f
reduction of nitriles, 900–901
Iminium ion, 831, 833, 834f
Indene, 660
Indigo, 1028
Indole, 717
Inductive effects
on acidity, 69–70, 70f, 73f
in aliphatic carboxylic acids, 736–735
on basicity of amines, 1013t
in carbocation stability, 267
definition of, 69
electron-donating, 678–681
electron-withdrawing, 69, 678–681
on substituted benzenes, 678–681
-ine (suffix), 240–241
Influenza, 91
Infrared (IR) absorptions/spectra
of aldehydes, 813–814, 814f
of amines, 994, 994f
atom mass and, 498–499, 498f
of benzene derivatives, 636t
bond strength and, 498–499, 499f, 500
of carboxylic acid derivatives, 869–870, 870t
of carboxylic acids, 724, 724f
characteristic frequencies, A–9
functional groups and, 496, 497, 499–500, 499f, 499t, 500–505
of hydrocarbons, 500–501
important, 499, 499t
of ketones, 813–814
of nitriles, 869
of nitrogen-containing compounds, 503
of oxygen-containing compounds, 502
percent *s*-character and, 500
vibration of bonds and, 496, 498–500
wavenumber scale of, 496
Infrared (IR) spectroscopy, 484, 494, 496–507
background on, 496
functional group identification, 496, 497, 498f
IR inactive vibration, 500
isomers distinguished by, 504
structure determination in, 505–507
vibration modes, 496
wavenumber scale, 496
Infrared (IR) spectrum
characteristics of, 497, 498f
fingerprint region, 497, 497f, 498f, 499
functional group region, 497, 497f, 498f, 499, 499f, 499t
Ingenol, 1060
Initiator, 1227, 1228, 1232, 1233
Inorganic compounds, 1
Inscribed polygon method for predicting aromaticity, 653–655, 654f
Insecticide, 243, 1052
Inspra. *See* Eplerenone
Insulin, 845, 1149, 1180, 1180f
Integral, NMR spectrum, 527–528
Intermolecular forces, 92–95
of aldehydes and ketones, 812, 813t
boiling point and, 96–98, 97f
in carboxylic acids, 723, 723f, 723t
dipole–dipole interactions, 94, 95t
hydrogen bonding, 94, 95t, 993
ion–ion interactions, 92, 95t
melting point and, 98–99
solubility and, 99–102, 99f, 101f
van der Waals forces, 92–94, 93f, 95t
International Union of Pure and Applied Chemistry, 126. *See also* IUPAC nomenclature
Intramolecular cyclization, of hydroxy aldehydes, 843, 846
Intramolecular hydrogen bonding, in β-dicarbonyl compounds, 917
Intramolecular malonic ester synthesis, 939
Intramolecular reactions
aldol reactions, 965–967, 966f
Robinson annulation, 974–978
electrocyclic ring closure, 1070
Friedel–Crafts reactions, 677–678, 677f
intramolecular Claisen (Diekmann reaction), 971–972
sigmatropic rearrangements, 1085–1090
Inversion of configuration
in alcohol reaction with HX, 347
in alkyl tosylate reactions, 353, 354
in S_N2 substitution reaction, 256–258, 257f, 273
Iodine, polarizability of, 93–94
Iodoform, 930
Iodoform test, 930
Iodomethane, polarizability and boiling point of, 96f, 97f
1-Iodo-1-methylcyclohexane, 299
Ion(s)
anions
acetate, 71, 71f
carbanion, 72, 210–211, 210f
cyclopentadienyl, 647–649, 654, 654f
definition of, 8
enolate, 22
naked, 251
radical, 454
salt formation, 12
solvation by hydrogen bonding, 250
bond formation by, 211
cations
carbocation. *See* Carbocation(s)
counterions, 59
cyclopentadienyl, 648
definition of, 8
radical, 485
salt formation, 12
solvation ion–dipole interactions, 250, 251, 275
spectator ions, 59
tropylium, 649, 654, 654f
counterions, 59
polyatomic, 17
spectator ions, 59
transport across cell membranes, 107–108, 108f
Ion–dipole interactions
cation solvation by, 250, 251, 275
description of, 99, 99f
Ionic bonding, 11–12
Ionic compounds
boiling points of, 96
formation of, 11–12
intermolecular forces, 92, 95t
melting points of, 98
solubility of, 99, 99f, 101f
Ionic intermediates, 576
Ionic polymerization, 1231–1233, 1232f
Ion–ion interactions, 92, 95t
Ionophores, 107–108, 108f
IR spectroscopy. *See* Infrared (IR) spectroscopy
Iso- (prefix), 127
Isoamyl acetate, 871
Isobutane, 122
p-Isobutylacetophenone, 703
p-Isobutylbenzaldehyde, 948
Isobutyl chloride, 241f
Isobutylene, 1232f
Isobutyl group, 127
Isocomene, 414
Isocyanate, 1240
Isoelectric point (p*I*), for amino acids, 744, 1152, 1152t
Isoleucine
isoelectric point for, 1152t
pK_a values for, 1152t
structure of, 1150f, 1151
Isomers
constitutional. *See* Constitutional isomers
definition of, 18, 169
infrared (IR) spectroscopy of, 504
Lewis structures, 18
ortho and para, 694–695
resonance structures compared, 20
stereoisomers. *See* Stereoisomers
types of, 189, 189f
Isoniazid, 1035
Isooctane, 155, 205, 215
Isopentane, 123, 134
Isopentenyl diphosphate, 1210, 1212, 1214
Isophorone, 987
Isoprene, 602, 627, 1237, 1253
Isoprene unit, 1208–1210, 1209t
Isopropyl alcohol, 328
Isopropylamine, 370, 991
Isopropylbenzene
oxidation to benzoic acid, 701
synthesis from benzene, 703
Isopropylcyclopentane, 794

Isopropyl group, 127
3-Isopropyl-4-methylcyclohexanone, 811
Isopropyl methyl ether, 335
Isopropyl 2-methylpentanoate, 868
Isoproterenol, 801
Isopulegone, 513
Isotactic polymer, 1235–1236
Isotopes, 8, 9f
of bromine, 489
of carbon, 8, 9f, 492t
of chlorine, 488
definition of, 8
masses of common, 492t
of nitrogen, 11, 492t
of oxygen, 492t
Isotretinoin, 854
IUPAC nomenclature
of alcohols, 327, 327f, 328
of aldehydes, 809, 810f
of alkanes, 128–134, 130f, 133f, 134f
of alkenes, 376–377
of alkyl halides, 240–241, 241f
of alkynes, 418–419
of benzene derivatives, 634–636
of carboxylic acids, 720, 722
of cycloalkanes, 132–134, 133f, 134f
description of, 126
of epoxides, 329–330
of ethers, 328–329
of ketones, 810–811, 812f

J

Jack-o'-lantern mushroom, 942
Januvia. *See* Sitagliptin
cis-Jasmone, 453
Johnson, W. S., 966
Jojoba, 1196
Joule (J), 43
Juvenile hormones, 778, 778f, 1044
mimics of, 778

K

Kavain, 379
Keflex. *See* Cephalexin
Kekulé, August, 631
Kekulé structures, 631, 632
Kelsey, Frances Oldham, 177
Keratins, 1149
α-keratins, 1182, 1182f
Kerosene, composition of hydrocarbons in, 136
Ketal, 837
Ketamine, 200
Ketene, 54
Keto–enol tautomers, 427–429
β-Keto esters
as active methylene compounds, 962
conversion to ketones, 940
pK_a, 922t
synthesis of
Claisen reaction, 967–971, 967f
Michael reaction, 974
D-Ketohexoses, 1108, 1108f
Ketones. *See also* Carbonyl compounds
aldol reactions, 955–967
boiling point of, 813t
carbohydrates, 845–846
in crossed Claisen reactions, 969–970
fragmentation pattern in mass spectrum, 491
functional group in, 91t
hydration of, 835–837
kinetics of hydrate formation, 836–837
thermodynamics of hydrate formation, 835–836
interesting examples, 816
iodoform test of, 930
IR spectra of, 502, 813–814, 814f
melting point of, 813t
NMR spectra of, 815
nomenclature, 810–811, 812
common names, 811, 812f
IUPAC system, 810–811, 812f
nucleophilic addition reactions, 756, 761, 807–846
carbanion addition, 822–823
cyanide addition, 823–824
hydride addition, 821–822
mechanism of, 819–820
nucleophiles in, 820, 821f
primary amine addition, 830–832, 834f
secondary amine addition, 833–834, 834f
physical properties, 812, 813t
pK_a, 922t
protecting groups for, 841–842
reactions of
aldol reactions, 955–967
with amines, 1015
at α carbon, 818–819
at carbonyl carbon, 818, 819
crossed Claisen reactions, 969–970
halogenation at α carbon, 928–932, 931f
hydration, 835–837
nucleophilic addition reactions, 756, 807–846
with organometallic reagents, 775–778, 777f, 778f, 822–823
reactivity of, 756
reduction of, 821–822
to alcohols, 759, 760, 761
of aryl ketones to alkyl benzenes, 702–703
reductive amination to amines, 1002–1005
to secondary alcohols, 450
solubility of, 813t
structure of, 754, 808
synthesis of, 816–818
acetotacetic ester synthesis, 936, 940–943
alcohol oxidation, 466, 467
Friedel–Crafts acylation, 667f, 672, 702–703, 817
hydration of alkynes, 427–429, 817
hydroboration–oxidation of alkynes, 430–431
hydrolysis of acetals, 840–841
hydrolysis of imines and enamines, 834
oxidation of secondary alcohols, 817
oxidative cleavage of alkenes, 463–464, 817
reactions of acid chlorides with organocuprates, 817
unreactivity to nucleophilic substitution, 758
unsymmetrical, alkylation of, 934–935
Wittig reaction, 825–830
Ketoprofen, 74, 199
Ketoses
D-ketose family, 1108, 1108f
structure, 1100
Keto tautomers, 899, 917–918
Kevlar, 1239, 1253
Kiliani–Fischer synthesis, 1123, 1124–1125
Kinetic enolates, 925, 926, 933, 934, 963
Kinetic product, in electrophilic addition reactions of conjugated dienes, 608–610, 609f
Kinetic resolution, of amino acids using enzymes, 1158
Kinetics
definition of, 216, 224
E1 elimination reactions, 301, 303t
E2 elimination reactions, 295, 298t
first-order, 227
rate equations, 226–227
second-order, 226
S_N1 substitution reactions, 262, 266t
S_N2 substitution reactions, 254, 260t

L

Lactams, 861, 1239
β-Lactam(s), 861, 872, 891–892
β-Lactam family of antibiotics, 483, 505
Lactase, 229, 229f, 1098, 1130
Lactate dehydrogenase, 766
Lactic acid, 30, 725, 765, 766
copolymerization with glycolic acid, 1239
optical activity of, 191
specific rotation of, 193
Lactide, 1246
Lactols, 842
Lactone(s), 861, 883
Lactose, 845, 1098, 1130
breakdown of, 229, 229f
Lactose intolerance, 1098, 1130
Laetrile, 825
Lanolin, 1196
Lanosterol, 1216f, 1217
Lard, 384
Latanoprost, 727
Latex, 1237, 1238
Laurencia cartilaginea, 243
Lauric acid, 1197t
Lavandulol, 780
l (levorotatory) compounds, 191, 1105
LDA. *See* Lithium diisopropylamide (LDA)
LDL particles (low density lipoproteins), 896
L-Dopa (levodopa), 7, 48, 200, 1190
LDPE (low-density polyethylene), 582, 1229, 1248t
Leaving group
of alcohols, 337, 344–347, 349–352, 354
of carbonyl compounds, 754, 756, 757–758
of carboxylic acid derivatives, 861, 863, 863t, 873–874
in E1 elimination reactions, 302, 303t
in E2 elimination reactions, 297, 298t
in nucleophilic acyl substitution reactions, 861, 873–874
in nucleophilic substitution reactions, 245, 246–248, 256–257, 274–275
good, 246–248, 247t
periodic trends in ability, 247
poor, 247t
reaction rate and, 274
weak bases, 246–248
in terpene biosynthesis, 1210–1213
Le Châtelier's principle, 340, 1115
Lecithin, 1201, 1202f
Length, units used to report wavelength, 494
Leprosy, 166, 177
Letrozole, 897
Leucine, 200
isoelectric point for, 1152t
pK_a values for, 1152t
structure of, 1150f
Leukotrienes, 1205, 1206f, 1206t
biological activity of, 362
leukotriene A_4, 362
leukotriene C_4, 362, 590
synthesis of, 362
Levonorgestrel, 421
Levorotatory (*l*) compounds, 191, 1105
Lewis acid, 77–79
alkenes as, 388
borane as, 401
carbocation as, 388
catalyst, 347
Lewis acid–base reactions, 77–79, 245. *See also* Nucleophilic substitution reactions
electrophilic addition, 388
S_N1 substitution reactions, 263
Lewis base, 77–79
nucleophile as, 248
tetrahydrofuran (THF) as, 401
Lewis structures, 13–18
of acyclic alkanes, 121–122
of benzene, 632
condensed formula conversion to, 29–30
drawing of, 13–15
formal charge, 16–18, 18t
isomers, 18
molecular shape determination, 24–28
multiple bonds in, 15–16
octet rule exceptions, 18–19
resonance structures, 19–24
Lexan, 1226f, 1241, 1247
Ligands, in palladium-catalyzed reactions, 1046
Light
polarized, 190
speed of, 494
Lightning, 463
Limonene, 54, 464, 1213
(*R*)-limonene, 381f
Linalool, 780
Linalyl diphosphate, 1213
Linamarin, 824–825
Lindlar catalyst, 453, 455f
Linear molecule, 25, 26, 28t, 47
alkynes, 417
Linen, 893, 893f
Linezolid, 914
Linoleic acid, 578, 1197, 1197t
as essential fatty acid, 382
melting point, 383t
as omega-3 fatty acid, 383
structure, 382t, 383f
Linolenic acid, 479, 1197, 1197t
as essential fatty acid, 382
melting point, 383t
sources of, 382
structure, 382t, 383f
Lipases, 888
Lipid bilayer, 106–107, 106f, 108f, 1201–1202, 1203

Lipids, 156–158, 382–384, 1194–1224
bonding in, 1195
definition of, 156
eicosanoids, 1205–1207, 1206f, 1206t
energy in, 158, 1200
examples of, 157, 157f, 1195f
fat-soluble vitamins, 1204, 1204f, 1205f
hydrolysis of, 887–889, 1196
hydrolyzable, 1196
metabolism of, 1200
nonhydrolyzable, 1196
origin of word, 1195
oxidation of, 577–578, 578f
phospholipids. *See* Phospholipids
solubility of, 156, 1195
steroids. *See* Steroids
structure of, 157f
terpenes, 1208–1214, 1209f, 1209t, 1211f
triacylglycerols. *See* Triacylglycerols
unsaturated, oxidation of, 577–578, 578f
waxes, 1196
Lipitor. *See* Atorvastatin
Lipoprotein, 896, 896f
Lipoxygenase, 362, 1205
Lisinopril, 182
Lithium
electronegativity value of, 772
valence electrons of, 12
Lithium acetylide, 773, 777
Lithium aluminum hydride ($LiAlH_4$), 760–762, 766, 770t
as reducing agent, 446
reduction of aldehydes and ketones, 821
reduction of alkyl halides, 455–456, 456f
reduction of a nitrile, 900
reduction of epoxides, 455–456, 456f
reduction of nitriles to primary amines, 1001
Lithium diisopropylamide (LDA), 933, 963
enolate formation with, 923, 925–926
pK_a, 923t
preparation of, 924
Lithium dimethylcuprate, 1055
Lithium fluoride, 12
Lithium tri-*sec*-butylborohydride (L-selectride), 805
Lithium tri-*tert*-butoxyaluminum hydride, 766, 767, 768, 770t
(–)-Littorine, 953
Living polymerization, 1233
Local anesthetic, 703, 715
Local mediators, 1205
Log, 64
London forces, 92. *See also* van der Waals forces
Lone pairs
in aromatic heterocycles, 644–646
Brønsted–Lowry bases and, 59–60, 59f
in carbanions, 211
on heteroatoms, 34, 87, 109
in hydrogen bonding, 94
in Lewis structures, 15–16
of negatively charged carbon atoms, 33
number of, 33
in resonance structures, 20, 21, 23, 71, 597, 598
second-row elements and, 13
Long, Dr. Crawford, 333
Loratadine, 638f
Low density lipoproteins (LDLs), 896
Low-density polyethylene (LDPE), 1229, 1248t
Lowest unoccupied molecular orbital (LUMO), 652, 1073, 1079
LSD, 932
intramolecular Friedel–Crafts acylation in the synthesis of, 677, 677f
structure of, 998
synthesis of, 677, 677f
LUMO (lowest unoccupied molecular orbital), 652, 1073, 1079
Lupinine, 1041
Lycopene, 602, 620, 620f, 1222
Lycra. *See* Spandex
Lynen, Feodor, 1216
Lysergic acid, 629
Lysergic acid diethyl amide. *See* LSD
Lysine, 752
abbreviation for, 742t
ionizable side chain of, 1151, 1152t
isoelectric point for, 1152t
pK_a values for, 1152t
structure of, 1150f
Lysozyme, 1178, 1178f
D-Lyxose, 1106, 1107f, 1124

M

Magnesium, electronegativity value of, 772
Magnesium monoperoxyphthalate (MMPP), 457f
Magnetic field, 515–518, 543
Magnetic resonance imaging (MRI), 547–548, 548f
Mahimahi, 646
Ma huang, 174, 200
Ma'ilione, 243
Malaria, 299
Maleic acid, 119, 613
Maleic anhydride, 613f
Malonic acid, 85, 722
Malonic ester synthesis, 936–940
intramolecular, 939
retrosynthetic analysis of, 939–940
steps in, 937–938
Maltose, 858, 1130
Mandelic acid, 203, 734
Manganese, in oxidizing agents, 457
Mannose
in Fischer proof, 1127–1128
D-mannose, 1107, 1107f, 1124
Haworth projections of, 1111–1112
Manoalide, 1209
Margarine, 450–451
Marine environment, organic chemistry in, 4–6, 5f
Markovnikov addition of water, 427
Markovnikov's rule, 389–391, 390f, 393t, 424, 425, 429, 606, 1231
Mass number, 8
Mass spectrometer
features of, 484
high-resolution, 492
schematic of, 484f
Mass spectrometry (MS)
of alkyl halides, 488–489, 488f, 489f
of amines, 994, 994f
analysis of unknowns using molecular ion, 486–488
base peak, 485
of biomolecules, 494
definition of, 484
electrospray ionization (ESI), 494
features of, 484–486
fragmentation in, 485, 489–491, 490f
gas chromatography and, 492–494, 493f
high-resolution, 492
M peak, 485, 488–489
M + 1 peak, 486
M + 2 peak, 488–489
Mass spectrum, 485
Mass-to-charge (*m*/*z*) ratio, 484f, 485
Mauveine, 1028
Maytansine, 1067
MDMA (3,4-methylenedioxymethamphetamine), 1039
Mefloquine, 203
Melamine, 1257
Melanin, 620
Melatonin, 910
Melmac, 1257
Melting point
of alcohols, 331t
of aldehydes and ketones, 813t
of alkanes, 136, 137t
of alkenes, 380, 382, 383t
of alkyl halides, 242t
of alkynes, 419
of amines, 993t
of carboxylic acids, 723t
definition of, 98
of enantiomers, 192, 192t
of epoxides, 331t
of ethers, 331t
of fats, 394, 1197–1198
of fatty acids, 382, 383t
intermolecular forces and, 98–99
of monosaccharides, 1108
of oils, 394, 1197–1198
of racemic mixtures, 192, 192t
of triacylglycerols, 451f
Membrane proteins, 1149
Menthol, 53, 115, 1208
Menthone, 115
Meperidine, 989
Mercapto group, 90t
Mercury, in Clemmensen reduction, 702
Merrifield, R. Bruce, 1173
Merrifield method, of peptide synthesis, 1173–1175
Mescaline, 997, 1039
Mesityl oxide, 805
Meso compounds, 185–186
achiral compounds, 186, 188, 398, 398f, 613, 1054
carbene addition and, 1054
disubstituted cycloalkanes, 188
from epoxidation of alkene, 459
plane of symmetry, 186
Mestranol, 115, 803
Meta (prefix), 634
Metabolite, 164
Meta director, 682, 683, 684, 686, 689, 690f, 692, 694, 699, 704
Metal–carbenes, 1058
Metal catalyst, 228, 447
Metal hydride reagents
reducing agents, 446, 760–762, 766–770, 770t
reduction of aldehydes and ketones, 760–762
reduction of nitrile, 900
Metals
as catalysts, 228, 447
in oxidizing agent, 457
Metathesis, 1056–1060, 1057f, 1059f
derivation of word, 1056
drawing products of, 1057, 1057f
mechanism, 1058
ring-closing (RCM), 1059–1060, 1059f
Met-enkephalin, 872
Meth- (prefix), 127
Methamphetamine, 997, 1003, 1003f
Methanal. *See* Formaldehyde
Methanamine. *See* Methylamine
Methane
bonding in, 35–36, 36f
combustion of, 155
description, 2
halogenation of, 562, 562f
Lewis structure, 14
mass spectrum of, 485–486
molecular formula, 121, 122, 125t
molecular shape of, 26–27
in natural gas, 135
oxidation of, 445, 445f
pK_a of, 64, 66, 67
structure of, 121
temporary dipole, 93
whole-number mass of, 485
Methanesulfonic acid, 741, 872
Methanethiol, 135
Methanol
ether formation by addition to alkenes, 395
hybrid orbitals in, 38
Lewis structure, 15
oxidation of, 470–471
as polar protic solvent, 250f
structure of, 332f
toxicity of, 331f, 332f
Methionine
abbreviation for, 742t
isoelectric point for, 1152t
pK_a values for, 1152t
structure of, 1150f
synthesis of, 1155f
Methoprene, 778
Methoxide, as Brønsted–Lowry base, 59f
p-Methoxybenzoic acid, 737
Methoxychlor, 244
Methoxycyclohexane, conformations of, 218
Methoxy group, 329
Methoxy methyl ether, 853
Methyl acetate
formation of, 253–254
NMR spectrum of, 545, 546, 546f
structure of, 860
Methyl acrylate, 613f
Methyl α-D-glucopyranoside, 1117, 1121f
Methylamine, 991
as Brønsted–Lowry base, 59f
electrostatic potential plot of, 990, 990f
N-Methylaniline, NMR spectrum of, 995, 995f
p-Methylaniline, 698
basicity of, 1009
electrostatic potential plot of, 1010f
Methyl anthranilate, 910
Methylation, of SAM, 261
N-Methylbenzamide, 867t
Methylbenzene, 634. *See also* Toluene
Methyl benzoate, synthesis of, 882
(*R*)-α-Methylbenzylamine, 1156–1158
2-Methyl-1,3-butadiene, 602, 1237
2-Methylbutane, 98, 123, 134, 586
2-Methylbutanenitrile, structure of, 867f
2-Methyl-2-butanol, 338
2-Methylbutanoyl chloride, structure of, 864
(*R*)-α-Methylbutyrophenone, 443

2-Methyl-CBS-oxazaborolidine, 763
Methyl chloride, electrostatic potential plot for, 46, 46f
7-Methyl-1,3,5-cycloheptatriene, 660
3-Methylcycloheptene, 377f
Methylcyclohexane, 133, 149, 150f
2-Methyl-1,3-cyclohexanedione, 975
3-Methylcyclohexanol, 327f
  cis-3-methylcyclohexanol, 354
trans-4-Methylcyclohexanol, 273
2-Methylcyclohexanone, 429, 963–964
  alkylation of, 934–935
  enolates formed from, 925
1-Methylcyclohexene, 793, 1045
3-Methylcyclohexene, 176
5-Methyl-1,3-cyclopentadiene, 660
2-Methylcyclopentanamine, in Hofmann reaction, 1018
Methylcyclopentane, 176
2-Methylcyclopentanecarboxamide, structure of, 865
(3*R*)-3-Methylcyclopentanone, 822–823
1-Methylcyclopentene, 377f
Methylene, 1055
α-Methylene-γ-butyrolactone, 936
Methylene chloride, 242f
Methylenecyclohexane, 379f, 829
Methylene group, 124, 379
Methyl ester, 1171
3-Methylfentanyl, 488
Methyl group, 128
  angular, 1214–1215
  as electron-donating group, 682
  inductive effect of, 678
  as ortho, para director, 682, 687, 692–693
Methyl halides
  coupling reaction with organocuprates, 1044
  S_N2 substitution reactions, 258, 272
6-Methyl-6-hepten-2-ol, 377
2-Methylhexanoic acid, synthesis of, 940
5-Methyl-3-hexanol, 327
5-Methyl-2-hexanone, 497, 498f
5-Methyl-4-hexen-1-yne, 419f
Methyl 5-hydroxyhexanoate, 841
N-Methylisopropylamine, 991
Methyl ketones, 427
  halogenation of, 930
  synthesis in acetoacetic ester synthesis, 936, 940–943
Methyllithium, 772
Methylmagnesium bromide, 772
Methylmagnesium chloride, 781
Methyl 2-methylbutanoate, 871
N-Methylmorpholine *N*-oxide (NMO), 462–463
Methyl orange, 1027, 1029
3-Methylpentanal, 810f
4-Methyl-1-pentanamine, 992
2-Methylpentane, 170f
3-Methylpentane, 170f
4-Methyl-1,4-pentanediol, 781–783, 782f
2-Methyl-3-pentanone, 812f
3-Methyl-2-pentanone, 811
3-Methyl-2-pentene, 378
  (2*E*)-3-methyl-2-pentene, 378
  (2*Z*)-3-methyl-2-pentene, 378
4-Methyl-3-penten-2-one, 812
1-Methyl-4-phenyl-4-propionoxypiperidine, 488
N-Methyl-2-propanamine, 991
2-Methylpropane, 122
2-Methyl-1-propanol, 279
2-Methylpropene, 716, 1055, 1232f
2-Methylpropene oxide, 1254
2-[4-(2-Methylpropyl)phenyl]propanoic acid, 126
4-Methylpyridine, 987
Methyl *trans*-chrysanthemate, 1065
Methyltriphenylphosphonium bromide, 827
β-Methylvaleraldehyde, 810f
Methyl vinyl ketone, 613f, 975
Metoprolol, 83
Mevalonic acid, 164
Micelles, 105f
Michael acceptor, 973
Michael reaction, 972–974, 974f
Mifepristone, 421
Mineral oil, 164
Mirror images, 167, 170–173, 184
Miscibility, 100
Misoprostol, 1207
Mixed aldol reaction. *See* Crossed aldol reactions
m-Methylaniline, 698
MMPP (magnesium monoperoxyphthalate), 457f
Molecular formula
  of acyclic alkanes, 121, 125, 125t
  of alkenes, 374
  of alkyl halides, 239
  of alkynes, 417
  of amines, 994
  of butane, 125t
  of carbohydrates, 1099f
  of cycloalkanes, 121, 125
  of decane, 125t
  of eicosane, 125t
  of ethane, 122, 125t
  of heptane, 125t
  of hexane, 125t
  of methane, 121, 122, 125t
  of nonane, 125t
  of octane, 125t
  of pentane, 125t
  of propane, 122, 125t
Molecular ion, 485, 486–488
Molecular orbitals (MOs), 650–653, 651f, 652f
  antibonding, 651, 651f, 652f, 653
  bonding, 651, 651f, 652–655, 652f, 654f
  of 1,3-butadiene, 1072–1073, 1073f
  degenerate, 652
  of ethylene, 1072, 1072f
  of 1,3,5-hexatriene, 1074, 1074f
  highest occupied MO (HOMO), 652
  lowest unoccupied MO (LUMO), 652
  patterns for cyclic, completely conjugated systems, 654f
  prediction/determination of relative energies of, 653–654, 654f
Molecular orbital (MO) theory, 650, 1072
Molecular recognition, 333
Molecular shape
  bent, 27, 47
  determining
    bond angle, 24–28
    bond length, 25, 25t
  four groups around an atom, 25, 26–28, 28t, 42t
  linear, 25, 26, 28t, 47
  tetrahedral, 25, 26–27, 28t
  three groups around an atom, 25, 28t, 42t
  trigonal planar, 25, 26, 28t
  trigonal pyramid, 27
  two groups around an atom, 25, 26, 28t, 42t
Molecules
  definition of, 12
  polarity of, 47, 47f
Molina, Mario, 573
Molozonide, 463
Molybdenum, 1056
Monensin, 414, 845
Monohalogenation, 562
Monomers, 1226–1227
Monosaccharides, 1100–1129
  D-aldoses, family of, 1106–1107, 1107f
  common names of, 1100, 1106
  constitutional isomers of, 1100
  conversion to esters, 1119–1120
  conversion to ethers, 1119–1120
  cyclic forms, 1109–1115
    anomers, 1110–1115, 1114f
    chair form, 1114
    drawing glucose as a cyclic hemiacetal, 1109–1110, 1111f
    furanoses, 1114–1115
    Haworth projections, 1110, 1111–1113
    three-dimensional representations for D-glucose, 1113, 1114f
  determining structure of unknown, 1125–1126
  examples of, 1100
  Fischer projection formulas of, 1101, 1103f
  Fischer proof of glucose structure, 1126–1129, 1127f
  glycosides
    formation, 1115–1116
    hydrolysis, 1117
    naturally occurring, 1118
  isomers (D and L) of, 1105
  D-ketoses, family of, 1108, 1108f
  melting point of, 1108
  physical properties of, 1108
  reactions at carbonyl group, 1120–1126
    addition or removal of one carbon, 1123–1126
    Kiliani–Fischer synthesis, 1123, 1124–1125
    oxidation, 1121–1122, 1121f
    reduction, 1120
    Wohl degradation, 1123–124
  reactions at hydroxy groups, 1119–1120
  solubility of, 1108, 1120
  stereogenic centers in, 1101–1110
    D and L designations, 1105
    multiple, 1103
  structure of, 1100
  sweetness of, 1108
Monosodium glutamate (MSG), specific rotation of, 193
Morphine, 59–60, 510, 593, 748, 880, 995
Morton, Dr. William, 333
Motrin. *See* Ibuprofen
M peak, in mass spectrum, 485, 488–489
M + 1 peak, in mass spectrum, 486
M + 2 peak, in mass spectrum, 488–489
MPPP, 488
MRI (magnetic resonance imaging), 547–548, 548f
MS. *See* Mass spectrometry (MS)
MSG (monosodium glutamate), specific rotation of, 193
MTBE. *See tert*-Butyl methyl ether (MTBE)
Multiple bond
  in condensed structures, 29–30
  Lewis structures, 15–16
  position of, 20, 24
Multiplet, NMR spectrum, 531, 531t, 534, 535f
α-Multistriatin, 473, 473f
Muscalure, 286, 480
Muscone, 762f
Mushroom
  jack-o'-lantern, 942
  Psilocybe, 998
Musk deer, 762
Mutarotation, 1110, 1116, 1130
Mycomycin, 203
Myelin sheath, 1203
Myoglobin, 1148, 1184, 1184f
Myrcene, 53, 479, 1208, 1209f
Myristic acid, 1197t

N

Nabumetone, 943, 980
NADH (nicotinamide adenine dinucleotide), 765–766
NAG (*N*-acetyl-D-glucosamine), 897, 1134–1135
Nandrolone, 1218
Naphthalene, 637, 644, 714
1-Naphthol, 370
Naprosyn. *See* Naproxen
Naproxen, 81, 195, 934
Natta, Giulio, 1236
Natural gas, 135
Natural product, 279
NBS (*N*-bromosuccinimide), 399
Nelfinavir, 638f
Neopentane
  melting point of, 98
  structure, 123
  van der Waals forces, 93, 93f
Neoprene, 1238
Neral, 113, 812, 1222
Nerol, 415
Nerolidol, 317
Neryl diphosphate, 1213, 1222
Neuroprotectin D1, 602
Neurotoxin, 5, 6, 89
Neurotransmitter
  acetylcholine, 895
  dopamine, 997–998, 997f
  serotonin, 998
Neutrons, 8
Newman projection, 138–139, 139f, 140f, 141f
Niacin, 103
Nickel, as catalyst, 228
Nicotinamide adenine dinucleotide (NADH), 765–766
Nicotine, 56, 262, 285, 995, 996f, 1012
Niphatoxin B, 433, 433f
Nitration
  of benzene, 667f, 670–671, 694
  electrophilic aromatic substitution reactions, 667f, 670–671, 693
Nitric oxide, as radical, 559, 574
Nitriles, 860, 897–901
  acidity of, 921
  addition of organometallic reagents, 901
  dipole–dipole interactions of, 868
  hydrolysis of, 898–899, 1155
  infrared (IR) spectra of, 503
  IR spectra of, 869
  NMR spectra of, 870
  nomenclature, 867, 867f, 867t
  physical properties, 868
  pK_a of, 921, 922t
  reduction of, 898, 900–901
  reduction to primary amines, 1001
  structure and bonding of, 861, 864, 897
  synthesis of, 897
Nitrite preservatives, 271–272

p-Nitroaniline
basicity of, 1009
electrostatic potential plot of, 1010f
Nitrobenzene, 667f, 670, 671, 682, 688, 703
p-Nitrobenzoic acid, 736
Nitrogen
in aromatic heterocycles, 644–647, 646f
bonding, 13f, 18t
common nucleophiles, 252t
infrared (IR) absorptions in nitrogen-containing compounds, 503
isotopes, 11, 492t
mass of, 492t
Nitrogen heterocycles, 992
Nitrogen–nitrogen double bond, 1026
Nitrogen rule, 487
Nitro group
as electron-withdrawing group, 682, 695–696
in Friedel–Crafts reactions, 691
as meta director, 682, 689, 692, 694, 704
reduction of, 703–704, 1001
Nitronium ion, 670
o-Nitrophenol, 634
p-Nitrophenol, 695
Nitrosamines
in foods, 271–272
formation of, 271
N-nitrosamine from primary amines, 1020
N-nitrosamine from secondary amines, 1021
N-Nitrosodimethylamine, 271
Nitrosonium ion, 1020–1021
N-Nitrosopyrrolidine, 271
o-Nitrotoluene, synthesis from benzene, 694–695
p-Nitrotoluene, 692
Nitrous acid, reaction of amines with, 1020–1021
NMO (*N*-methylmorpholine *N*-oxide), 462–463
NMR. *See* Nuclear magnetic resonance (NMR) spectroscopy
NMR spectrometers, 516–517, 516f
Noble gases, stability of, 11
Node of electron density, 10
Nomenclature, A-3–6. *See also* Common names; IUPAC nomenclature
of acid chlorides, 864, 867t
of alcohols, 327–328, 327f
of aldehydes, 809–810, 810f, 812
of alkanes, 125–135
acyclic alkanes, 128–132
common names, 134–135, 135f
cycloalkanes, 132–134
IUPAC system, 128–134, 130f
substituents, 127
of alkenes, 376–379
of alkyl halides, 240–241, 241f
of alkyl substituents that contain branching, A-3–4
of alkynes, 418–419
of amides, 866, 867t
of amines, 991–993
of anhydrides, 864, 867t
benzene derivatives, 634–636
of bicyclic compounds, A-5–6
of carboxylic acids, 720–722, 721t, 722f
E, Z system, 378–379
of epoxides, 329–330
of esters, 865, 867t
of ethers, 328–329
generic name, 126
of ketones, 810–811, 812, 812f
of monosaccharides, 1100, 1106
of nitriles, 867, 867f, 867t
of polyfunctional compounds, A-4–5
systematic name, 126
trade name, 126
Nomex, 1253
Nonactin, 107, 108
Nonane
constitutional isomers of, 125t
molecular formula, 125t
Nonbonded interactions. *See* Intermolecular forces
Nonbonding (unshared) electrons, 13
Noncovalent interactions. *See* Intermolecular forces
Nonnucleophilic bases, 249
Nonpolar bond, 45
Nonpolar molecule
description of, 47, 47f
solubility of, 99
Nonreducing sugars, 1121, 1121f, 1131
Nonsteroidal anti-inflammatory drugs (NSAIDs), 1207
Noradrenaline (norepinephrine)
structure of, 997
synthesis of, 261, 261f
Norethindrone, 102, 200, 420, 420f, 1218
Novadex. *See* Tamoxifen
Novocain. *See* Procaine
Noyori, Ryoji, 1159
NSAIDs (nonsteroidal anti-inflammatory drugs), 1207
Nuclear magnetic resonance (NMR) spectroscopy, 484, 494, 514–557
basis of, 515–517
^{13}C (carbon), 515, 543–547. *See also* Carbon NMR
^{1}H (proton), 515, 517–543. *See also* Proton NMR
medical uses of, 547–548, 548f
nuclear spin in, 515–516
reference signal, 517, 543
signal versus peak, 530
spectrometers, 516–517, 516f
variables in, 516
Nucleophiles, 90, 248–252
acetylide anions as, 423
addition to carbonyl groups, 820, 821f
alkyl halide substitution reactions with, 244
ambident, 924
amines as, 989, 1014–1016
attack of electron-deficient atoms by, 248
biological, 271
carbanions as, 210, 211
common, table of, 252t
enolates as, 924, 928
enols of, 919
hydroxide, in alcohol synthesis, 335
Lewis base, 78
meaning of term, 78
negatively charged, 252t
neutral, 252t
opening of epoxide rings with strong, 357–359
organometallic reagents as, 771, 772, 774–775
pi (π) bonds and, 87, 108–109
reactivity of, 108–109
strength, 249–252
strong, 273
in substitution reactions, 245–246, 273–274. *See also* Nucleophilic substitution reactions
weak, 273
Nucleophile strength. *See* Nucleophilicity
Nucleophilic acyl substitution reactions, 757, 872–892, A-12
biological, 895–897, 896f
examples of, 876
general reaction of, 916
leaving groups in, 861
mechanism of, 873–874
polyester synthesis, 1239–1240
reactions of acid chlorides, 876–878, 892t
reactions of amides, 890–892, 892t
reactions of anhydrides, 878–880, 892t
reactions of carboxylic acids, 880–885, 880f, 892t
conversion to acid chlorides, 880f, 881
conversion to amides, 880f, 883–885
conversion to cyclic anhydrides, 880f, 881
conversion to esters, 880f, 882–883
reactions of esters, 885–889, 888f, 892t
reactivity of carboxylic acids and derivatives in, 874–875
summary of reactions, 892, 892t
Nucleophilic addition reactions
aldehydes and ketones, 756, 761, 807–846, A-13
aldol reactions. *See* Aldol reactions
of carbonyl compounds, 916
Michael reaction, 973
organometallic reagents with aldehydes and ketones, 775–777, 777f
polyurethane synthesis, 1240
α,β-unsaturated carbonyl compounds, 788–791
Nucleophilic aromatic substitution, 695–699
by addition–elimination, 695–697
by elimination–addition, 697–699
Nucleophilicity
basicity compared to, 249, 250, 251
periodic trends in, 249, 250, 251
S_N1 versus S_N2 substitution reactions, 273–274
solvent effects, 250–252
polar aprotic solvents, 251, 251f
polar protic solvents, 250, 250f
steric effects and, 249
Nucleophilic substitution reactions, A-12
acetylide anion reactions with alkyl halides, 431–432
adrenaline synthesis, 261–262, 261f
of alcohols, 336–337, 345–354, 355f
alcohol synthesis by, 334–335
aldehyde formation by, 767
of alkyl halides, 245–280
amine formation by, 998–1001
bimolecular, 253–254
of carbonyl compounds, 756, 757–758, 916
Claisen reaction, 967–971, 967f
components of, 245
crown ether use in, 333, 333f
epoxide ring-opening reactions, 357–361
equilibrium and, 248
ethers with strong acids, 355–356
ether synthesis by, 334–335
features of, 245–246
first-order rate equation, 253, 254
leaving groups in, 245, 246–248, 247t, 256–257, 274–275
mechanisms, 252–280
distinguishing between S_N1 and S_N2, 272–276, 272f, 276t
one-step, 253, 254–255, 260t
order of bond breaking and bond making, 252–253, 262
S_N1, 262–272, 263f, 264f, 266t, 271f
S_N2, 254–262, 255f, 257f, 258f, 259f, 260f, 260t, 261f, 278t
two-step, 253, 254, 262–263, 266t
nucleophile strength (nucleophilicity), 249–252, 273–274
organic synthesis by, 278–280, 278t
in polycarbonate synthesis, 1241
rate-determining step in, 253, 254
second-order rate equation, 253, 254
solvent effects on, 250–252, 251f, 275, 276t
unimolecular, 254, 262
vinyl halides and, 277
Nucleotides, 110, 111f
Nucleus, atomic, 8
Nylon
history of, 893
nylon 6, 1239, 1249
nylon 6,6, 893, 1226f, 1227, 1238, 1245, 1245f
synthesis of, 893, 1238–1239

O

-o (suffix), 240
Occidentalol, 629
(*E*)-Ocimene, 293
Octane
constitutional isomers of, 125t
gasoline and, 88, 101
molecular formula, 125t
naming, 128–130
Octanenitrile, infrared (IR) spectrum of, 503
Octane rating, of gasoline, 88
(2*E*,4*Z*,6*E*)-2,4,6-Octatriene, 1075, 1077, 1078, 1079
4-Octene, 413
Octet rule
described, 11
exceptions to, 18–19
Octinoxate, 33, 887, 985
Octylamine, infrared (IR) spectrum of, 503
Octyl salicylate, 887
1-Octyne, 773
Odor(s)
of acetone, 815
of acid chlorides, 876
of aldehydes, 816, 816f
of amines, 995
of caraway, 196
of esters, 871
of spearmint, 196
Ofloxacin, 1037
OH proton, NMR spectra, 538–539, 539f
-oic acid (suffix), 720, 866
Oil(s), 384
crude, 135–136, 135f
degree of unsaturation, 450–451

essential, 1208
fatty acid composition, 1198, 1198t
fish, 1198
hardening, 1199
hydrogenation of, 450–452, 451f, 1199
insolubility of, 136
melting points of, 384, 1197–1198
mineral, 164
oxidation of, 577
partial hydrogenation of, 451, 451f
rancid, 1199
unsaturated, 384
vegetable, 887, 889, 1198, 1199
Oil of ginger, 381f
Oil refinery, 135f
Oil spill, 136
-ol (suffix), 327
Olefin metathesis, 1056–1060, 1057f, 1059f
Olefins, 373. *See also* Alkenes
Oleic acid, 372, 505, 1197t
melting point, 383t
structure, 110, 383f, 383t
triacylglycerol formation, 110
Olestra, 888–889
Olfactory receptors, 196, 196f
Olive oil, 384
Omega carbon, 721
Omega-3 fatty acids, 383, 384
-one (suffix), 810
-onitrile (suffix), 866, 867t
Open arrow, 434
Ophrys sphegodes, 122
Opium, 880
Opsin, 832, 832f
Optical activity, 190–191
of achiral compounds, 190
of chiral compounds, 191
dextrorotatory (*d*) and levorotatory (*l*) compounds, 191
enantiomeric excess, 192–193
of racemic mixtures, 191
specific rotation, 192
Optical purity, 192–193
Orajel. *See* Benzocaine
Oral contraceptives, 416, 420–421, 420f
Orbitals. *See also* Hybrid orbitals; Molecular orbitals (MOs); *specific orbitals*
description, 9–10
number of electrons in, 10
Orbital symmetry
cycloadditions and, 1082
of electrocyclic reactions, 1075–1076
sigmatropic rearrangements and, 1086–1087
Order, of a rate equation, 226
Organic chemistry
definition of, 1
importance of, 1, 2f
in marine environment, 4–6, 5f
Organic halides. *See also* Alkyl halides
coupling reaction with organocuprate reagents, 1043–1045
coupling with alkenes (Heck reaction), 1043, 1050–1052
coupling with organoboron reagents (Suzuki reaction), 1043, 1046–1049
Organic molecules
aromatic compounds, 630–664
reactions of, 665–717
common features of, 4
drawing structures of, 3, 29–34
condensed structures, 29–30, 29f, 30f
skeletal structures, 31–34, 32f
examples of, 2–4
grouping by functional group, 88
naming, 126
shape. *See* Molecular shape
solubility of, 100–101
Organic reactions, 205–237. *See also specific types of reactions*
acid–base, 60–62, 65–66
arrows used in describing, 211–212, 211t
asymmetric, 471
bimolecular, 226
bond breaking and bond making, 209–212, 210f
bond dissociation energy, 212–215, 213t
catalysts, 228, 228f
endergonic, 219
endothermic, 212–213
energy diagrams for, 219–224, 221f, 222f, 224f
energy of activation, 220–225, 221f, 224f, 228, 228f
enthalpy change in, 212–215, 218–219
entropy change in, 218–219
enzymes in, 229, 229f
equations for, 206, 206f
equilibrium constants for, 216–218, 217f, 217t
exergonic, 219
exothermic, 212–213, 215
free energy changes in, 216–219, 217f, 217t
general types, A-12–13
kinetics of, 224–227
learning details of, 406–407
mechanisms of. *See* Reaction mechanism
multistep, 224, 226, 227
oxidation and reduction reactions, 154–155, 155f
polar, 210, 210f
radical, 210, 210f
rate of. *See* Reaction rate
sequential, 206
thermodynamics of, 216–218, 217f, 217t
types of, 207–208. *See also specific types of reactions*
unimolecular, 227
Organic synthesis
alkenes in, 407–408
of aspirin, 279, 279f
carbon–carbon bond-forming reactions in, 1042–1068
definition of, 278
halogenation reactions, 570
halohydrin use in, 401
by nucleophilic substitution reaction, 278–280, 278t
reactions with organometallic reagents, 792–795
retrosynthetic analysis, 434–437
sodium borohydride reductions used in, 762f
Organoaluminum compounds, 1236
Organoborane, 429, 430, 431
definition of, 402
in Suzuki reaction, 1043, 1047–1049
synthesis of, 1047
Organocopper reagents. *See* Organocuprate reagents
Organocuprate reagents, 772
coupling reactions of, 1043–1045
general features of, 1043–1044
hydrocarbon synthesis in, 1045
stereospecificity of, 1044
preparation of, 773
reactions with α,β-unsaturated carbonyl compounds, 791
reactions with acid chlorides, 785
Organolithium reagents, 772
addition to nitriles, 901
in anionic polymerization, 1232
arylborane synthesis, 1047
in ethynylestradiol synthesis, 777, 777f
in lithium diisopropylamide preparation, 923
preparation of, 772
reactions
with aldehydes and ketones, 775, 822
as base, 773–774
with esters and acid chlorides, 784–785
with α,β-unsaturated carbonyl compounds, 790
Organomagnesium reagents, 772
Organometallic reagents, 771–792. *See also specific reagents*
acetylide anions, 773
definition of, 771
organic synthesis with, 792–795
preparation of, 772–773
protecting groups and, 781–783, 782f
reactions
with acid chlorides, 784–786
with aldehydes, 775–777, 822–823
as base, 771, 773–774
with carbon dioxide, 787
with carbonyl compounds, 775–778, 781–783, 782f
with carboxylic acid derivatives, 783–786
with epoxides, 787–788
with esters, 783–785
with ketones, 775–778, 777f, 778f, 822–823
as nucleophile, 771, 772, 774–775
rapid acid–base, 781
summary of, 791–792
with α,β-unsaturated carbonyl compounds, 788–791
Organopalladium compounds, 1046, 1048, 1052
Organophosphorus reagent, 826–827
Organosodium reagents, 773
Ortho (prefix), 634
Ortho, para activator, 682, 684
Ortho, para deactivator, 682
Ortho, para director, 682–683, 686, 687–688, 690f, 692–695, 1024
-ose (suffix), 1100
Oseltamivir, 91, 371, 907
Osmium tetroxide
as oxidizing agent, 457
in syn dihydroxylation, 462–463
Osprey, 288
Oxalic acid, 722, 725
Oxaphosphetane, 827
Oxazaborolidine, 763
Oxidation, 155f, 444–482
of alcohols, 457f, 466–471
of aldoses, 1121–1122
of alkanes, 154–156
of alkenes, 445f, 457f, 463–465
of alkyl benzenes, 701–702
of alkylborane, 404–405
of alkynes, 445f, 457f, 465–466
of carbonyl compounds, 758–759, 771
carboxylic acid synthesis
from alkyl benzenes, 728
from alkynes, 728
from primary alcohols, 728
definition of, 154, 445, 758
dihydroxylation, 461–463
anti, 461, 462
syn, 461, 462–463
energy released by, 215
epoxidation, 457f, 458–461
Sharpless, 471–473
stereochemistry of, 458–459
in synthesis of disparlure, 459–461, 460f
of ethanol, 470–471
of fatty acids, 888
general scheme for, 445f
green chemistry, 469–470
hydroboration–oxidation reactions, 386f, 401–406, 402f, 403f, 405f, 405t, 429–430
of hydrocarbons, 445, 445f
of lipids, 158
oxidative cleavage
of alkenes, 463–465
of alkynes, 465–466
of polycyclic aromatic hydrocarbons (PAHs), 363
reduction, relationship to, 445
of substituted benzenes, 701–702
of unsaturated fatty acids, 1199
of unsaturated lipids, 577–578, 578f
Oxidation and reduction reactions, 154–155, 155f
Oxidative addition
in Heck reaction, 1052
in palladium-catalyzed reactions, 1046, 1048, 1052
in Suzuki reactions, 1048
Oxidative cleavage
of alkenes, 463–465
of alkynes, 465–466, 728
Oxide, 330
Oxidized state, 154
Oxidizing agents, 456–457. *See also specific agents*
NAD^+, 766
peroxyacids, 456, 457f
Oxime, 1123
Oximene, 479
Oxiranes, 325, 329, 330. *See also* Epoxide(s)
6-Oxoheptanal, 983
-oxy (suffix), 329
Oxycodone, 510
Oxy-Cope rearrangements, 1088–1089
Oxygen
bonding, 13f, 18t
common nucleophiles, 252t
in condensed structures, 30
formal charge, 18t
infrared (IR) absorptions in oxygen-containing compounds, 502
isotopes of, 492t
mass of, 492t
as radical scavenger, 561
Oxytocin, 862, 1163, 1164f, 1180
-oyl (suffix), 812
Ozone, 470
destruction of atmospheric, 243, 573–574, 574f
as oxidizing agent, 456, 463–466
production of, 463
synthesis of, 573
Ozonide, 463, 465
Ozonolysis, 463–464

P

PABA (*para*-aminobenzoic acid), 621, 714, 1030–1031
Padimate O, 621
PAHs. *See* Polycyclic aromatic hydrocarbons (PAHs)
Pain reliever, 943. *See also* Analgesics
Palau'amine, 514, 540
Palladium-catalyzed reactions, 228
alkene reduction, 447
alkyne reduction, 453, 455f
general features of, 1046
Heck reaction, 1043, 1050–1052
hydrogenation of aldehydes and ketones, 761
oxidative addition in, 1046, 1048, 1052
in peptide synthesis, 1171–1172
reductive elimination in, 1046, 1048, 1052
Suzuki reactions, 1043, 1047–1049
Palmitic acid, 1197, 1197t
Palmitoleic acid, 1197t
Palm oil, 1198
Palytoxin, 324
Pantothenic acid, 104
Para (prefix), 634
Para red, 1029
Parent ion, 485. *See also* Molecular ion
Parent name, 126
Parkinson's disease, treatment of, 7, 48, 49, 997f, 998
Paroxetine, 83, 335
Parts per million (ppm), 517
Patchouli alcohol, 345f, 1222
PCB (polychlorinated biphenyl), 101
PCC (pyridinium chlorochromate), 457, 466
Peanut butter, 450, 451
PEG (polyethylene glycol), 1234
Penicillamine, 1188
Penicillin(s), 872, 891–892
discovery of, 483
penicillin G, 113, 165, 483, 505
Pentacycloanammoxic acid methyl ester, 1094
Pentadecane, 125t
1,4-Pentadiene, 594–595, 595f, 605
(3*E*)-1,3-Pentadiene, hydrogenation of, 605
Pentalene, 658
Pentamethyl ether, 1119
2-Pentanamine, in E2 elimination reaction, 1019, 1019f
Pentane, 486–487, 605
boiling point, 96
constitutional isomers of, 125t
melting point of, 98
molecular formula, 125t
structure, 123
van der Waals forces, 93, 93f, 95
2,4-Pentanedione, 917, 921, 945, 946
3-Pentanol, 779
2-Pentanone
mass spectrum of, 491
preparation from an acid chloride and an organocuprate reagent, 786
3-Pentanone, boiling point of, 96, 97f
1-Pentene, 486–487
2-Pentylcinnamaldehyde, 961
1-Pentyne, 486–487
Peptide bonds, 1160, 1162–1163
s-cis conformation, 1162
s-trans conformation, 1162–1163
planar geometry of, 1162–1163
Peptides, 871–872, 1160–1175
constitutional isomers, 1161
interesting examples, 1163–1164, 1164f
N- and C-terminal amino acids, 1161
peptide bond in, 1160, 1162–1163
sequencing, 1165
amino acid analysis, 1165
Edman degradation, 1165–1166
partial hydrolysis of peptide, 1167–1168, 1167t
simple, 1160–1162
synthesis of, 1168–1175
automated, 1173–1175
protecting groups in, 1169–1173
solid phase technique, 1173–1175
Percent *s*-character, 44, 72
bond length and, 603
effect on basicity of amines, 1012
hybrid orbital in alkenes, 294
infrared (IR) absorption and, 500
Percent transmittance, 497
Perfume, 453
Pericyclic reactions, 1069–1097
defined, 1070
rules for, 1090, 1090t
types, 1070–1071
cycloaddition reactions, 1081–1085
electrocyclic reactions, 1075–1081
sigmatropic rearrangements, 1085–1090
Period, in periodic table, 9
Periodic table, 8–11
bond length trends, 25
element location and bonding type, 11
of elements common in organic chemistry, 9f
first-row elements, 9f, 10
organization of, 9
second-row elements, 9f, 10–11
bonding of, 13
exceptions to octet rule, 19
shape arrangements, 25
third-row elements, 19
trends
acidity, 67–69
in bond dissociation energies, 214
electronegativity, 45, 45f
in leaving group ability, 247
nucleophilicity, 249, 250, 251
Periplanone B, 506, 964, 964f, 1069, 1222
Perkin, William Henry, 1028–1029
Perlon. *See* Nylon, Nylon 6
Peroxide, as radical initiator, 560
Peroxyacetic acid, 457f, 458
Peroxyacids
in epoxidation, 458–460
as oxidizing agents, 457f
Peroxy radical, 577, 578f, 1228
Pesticide, 243
PET. *See* Polyethylene terephthalate (PET)
Petroleum, 120, 135–136, 135f
ethylene preparation from, 380
as feedstock of polymer synthesis, 1245
Ph- (abbreviation), 635
PHAs (polyhydroxyalkanoates), 1249–1250
PHB (polyhydroxybutyrate), 1249
PHBV (polyhydroxyvalerate), 1249
α-Phellandrene, 1209f
Phenanthrene, 644, 659, 664
Phenol(s), 634
acidity of, 731, 733f
as antioxidants, 579
in aspirin synthesis, 279, 279f
Bakelite preparation from, 1243–1244, 1244f
benzene conversion to, 164
formation from anisole, 356
homolysis reaction, 237
hydroxy group of, 325
naming, 635
pK_a of, 731, 733f
polyhalogenation of, 690
synthesis from aryl diazonium salts, 1022
Phenoxide, 732, 732f, 733f
Phentermine, 82
Phenylacetaldehyde, 810f, 919
Phenylacetic acid, 984
Phenylalanine
abbreviation for, 742t
isoelectric point for, 1152t
N-acetyl, 1160
pK_a values for, 1152t
structure of, 1150f
synthesis of, 1154, 1160
Phenylcyclohexane
conformations of, 218
phenyl group in, 88, 89
Phenylethanal, 810f
2-Phenylethylamine, 1004
derivatives of, 997–998
in Hofmann elimination reaction, 1017
Phenyl group, 88, 89, 89t, 635
Phenyl isothiocyanate, 1165–1166
(1*Z*,3*E*)-1-Phenyl-1,3-octadiene, 1049
2-Phenylpropanoic acid, 204
1-Phenyl-1-propanol, 287
N-Phenylthiohydantoin (PTH), 1165–1166, 1193
N-Phenylthiourea, 1166
Pheromones, 121, 122, 459–461, 460f, 473, 473f, 878, 964, 964f, 1042, 1049
Phomallenic acid C, 438
Phosgene, 1241
Phosphatidylcholine, 1201
Phosphatidylethanolamine, 1201
Phosphine, in palladium-catalyzed reactions, 1046
Phosphoacylglycerols, 1201–1202, 1202f, 1203f
Phosphodiester, 1201, 1202, 1203, 1203f
Phospholipids, 117
in cell membranes, 106–108, 106f, 107f, 108f, 1201–1203
phosphoacylglycerols, 1201–1202, 1202f, 1203f
sphingomyelins, 1203, 1203f
structure of, 106, 106f, 1201
Phosphoric acid, 1201
Phosphoric acid diester, 1201
Phosphorus, octet rule exceptions in, 19
Phosphorus oxychloride, dehydration of alcohols using, 344, 345f
Phosphorus tribromide, conversion of alcohols to alkyl halides with, 349, 350, 350t
Photochemical electrocyclic reactions, 1079–1080
Photons, 495–496
Photosynthesis, 332, 332f, 1099
Phthalic acid, 702
Phthalimide, 1000
Phylloquinone, 103
Physical properties. *See* Boiling point; Melting point; Solubility
Pi* (π*) antibonding molecular orbital, 651, 651f
Pi (π) bond, 40, 40f, 41, 42f, 42t, 43
in alkene double bond, 291
in alkenes, 373, 374, 385–388, 407
in alkynes, 310, 311f, 417–418, 422, 423f
in aromatic compounds, 88, 631, 632
of benzyne, 699
breakage in addition reactions, 208, 373, 385–388, 386f, 394, 395, 396, 398, 407
bromination as test for, 395
Brønsted–Lowry bases and, 59–60, 59f
in carbonyl group, 90, 754–755, 756
in conjugated allyl carbocation, 596
in cycloaddition reactions, 1071, 1081–1084, 1085t
degrees of unsaturation and, 374, 449–450
delocalized, 605
in electrocyclic reactions, 1070, 1075, 1077–1090, 1080t
formation in elimination reactions, 207, 289–290, 301, 304, 310, 311f
in functional groups, 87, 108–109
in Lewis base, 77, 79
radical reactions with, 561, 584
in resonance structure, 71
in sigmatropic rearrangements, 1071, 1085–1088
strength, 373
Pi (π) bonding molecular orbital, 651, 651f
Picometer (pm), 25
Pi (π) electrons
in aromatic compounds, 636, 640, 641–642, 642t, 645–653
in benzene, 632, 633, 666
Hückel's rule and, 641–642, 642t, 650–653, 657, 658
in NMR spectroscopy, 525–526, 526t
Pinacol, 371
Pinacolone, 371
α-Pinene, 1222
Piperidine
basicity of, 1012, 1013t
structure, 992
Pitavastatin, 987
Pitocin. *See* Oxytocin
Pivalic acid, 64
pK_a values, 63–72, A-1–2
acid strength and, 63–64
of amines, 1005, 1007–1008, 1013t
of amino acids, 1151, 1152, 1152t
of carbonyl compounds, 920, 921t, 922t
definition, 63
of leaving groups in nucleophilic substitution reactions, 247
logarithmic scale of, 64
of selected organic compounds, 63t
of strong acids, 74
of strong bases, 75
PLA (polylactic acid), 894
Planar carbocation, 392, 1116–1117
Planar double bond, 392, 397, 402, 404
Planar molecule
benzene, 632–633
Hückel's rule, 641
Planar radical, 571–572
Plan B, 421
Plane of symmetry, 172–173
in disubstituted cycloalkanes, 188
of meso compound, 186
Plane-polarized light, 190
Plaque, atherosclerotic, 896, 896f
Plastic, polyethylene, 89
Plasticizers, 101, 1244

Platinum, as catalyst, 228
Plavix, 182. *See also* Clopidogrel
β-Pleated sheet, 1177–1178, 1177f, 1178f, 1179f, 1181f
Poison ivy, 738
Polar aprotic solvents, 251, 251f, 275, 276t, 297, 298t, 925
Polar bond
  carbon–halogen, 244, 244f
  description of, 46–47, 47f
Polarimeter, 190
Polarity, of carboxylic acids, 730
Polarizability
  boiling point and, 96, 97f
  inductive effects on substituted benzenes, 678
  van der Waals forces and, 94
Polarized light, 190–191
Polar molecule
  description, 47, 47f
  dipole–dipole interactions between, 94
  solubility of, 99
Polar protic solvents, 250, 250f, 275, 276t, 303t, 926
Polar reactions, 210, 210f
Poly(acrylic acid), 583, 1250
Polyacrylonitrile, 1232f
Polyalkylation, 691
Polyamides, 893, 1238–1239
PolyAspirin, 1256
Polyatomic ion, 17
Polycarbonates, 1241
Polychlorinated biphenyl (PCB), 101
Polycyclic aromatic hydrocarbons (PAHs), 363, 637, 637f, 644
Polyenes, 601, 602–603
  ultraviolet absorption, 620–621
Poly(ester amide), 1256
Polyesters, 894, 1239–1240
Polyethers, 333, 1234
Poly(ethyl acrylate), 590
Poly(ethyl α-cyanoacrylate), 1232f
Polyethylene, 89, 380, 381f, 582, 591, 1226f, 1229–1230, 1236
Poly(ethylene glycol) (PEG), 116, 1234
Polyethylene terephthalate (PET), 894, 1225, 1227f, 1239–1240, 1248, 1248t
Polyfunctional compounds, nomenclature of, A-4–5
Polyhalogenation, 690
Polyhydroxyalkanoates (PHAs), 1249–1250
Polyhydroxybutyrate (PHB), 1249
Polyhydroxyvalerate (PHBV), 1249
Polyisobutylene, 590, 1232f
Poly(lactic acid) (PLA), 894, 1246
Polymerization, 582–585
  anionic, 1232–1233, 1232f
   of epoxides, 1234–1235
  cationic, 1231–1232, 1232f
  chain branching in, 1229–1230
  coordination, 1236
  definition of, 582, 1226
  feedstock for, 1245
  head-to-tail, 585
  ionic, 1231–1233, 1232f
  living, 1233
  radical, 584–585, 1228–1229, 1229f
  Ziegler–Natta, 1235–1236
Polymers, 582–585, 1225–1257
  alternating, 1233
  amorphous regions of, 1243–1244
  atatic, 1235–1236
  "Big Six," 1247–1248, 1248t
  biodegradable, 1249–1250
  chain-growth, 1226, 1227–1234
  in consumer products, 1226, 1226f
  copolymers, 1233–1234
  crystalline regions of, 1243–1244
  definition of, 167, 1226
  derivation of word, 1226
  green synthesis of, 1244–1247, 1245f, 1246f
  insoluble, 1173
  isotactic, 1235–1236
  in medicine and dentistry, 583t
  molecular weights of, 1227
  natural and synthetic fibers, 892f, 893–894
  nylon, 893–894, 1226f, 1227, 1238–1239, 1245, 1245f, 1249
  physical properties of, 1243–1244
  polyesters, 894
  random, 1233
  recycling of, 1225, 1247–1249, 1248t
  shorthand representation of, 1227, 1227f
  step-growth, 1227, 1238–1242
  stereochemistry of, 1235–1236
  structure of, 1226, 1243–1244
  syndiotactic, 1235–1236
  synthetic, 1225–1257. *See also* Synthetic polymers
Poly(methyl methacrylate) (PMMA), 590
Poly (prefix), 1232f
Polypropylene, 583t, 1248t
Polysaccharides, 1132–1134
  cellulose, 1132–1133
  glycogen, 1134
  starch, 1133–1134
Polystyrene, 101, 381f, 558, 584, 591, 1227f, 1248t
Polystyrene derivative, 1174
Polytetrafluoroethylene (Teflon), 583t
Poly(trimethylene terephthalate) (PTT), 1246, 1246f
Polytulipalin, 984
Polyurethanes, 1240
Poly(vinyl acetate), 381f, 584, 1232f
Poly(vinyl alcohol), 1255
Poly(vinyl butyral), 1255
Poly(vinyl chloride) (PVC), 116, 243, 381f, 583t, 1226, 1244, 1248t
p orbitals
  description, 9–10
  hybridization of, 35–43, 36f–38f, 40f, 42f, 42t
  hyperconjuation, 268
  overlap of, 594–595, 600–601, 604, 633, 633f, 640, 650, 651
   molecular orbits and, 1072–1074, 1072f–1074f
  2*p* orbitals, 10, 35–37, 37f
   in alkenes, 291
   in alkynes, 417
Potassium dichromate, 457, 466, 467, 468, 469f
Potassium hydroxide, in dehydrohalogenation reactions, 290t
Potassium iodide, 12, 1023
Potassium permanganate ($KMnO_4$)
  as oxidizing agent, 457, 701–702, 705, 771
  in syn dihydroxylation, 462
Potassium peroxymonosulfate, 470
Potassium propanoate, 722f
Potassium sorbate, 726
Potassium *tert*-butoxide, 249, 290, 290t
Precor. *See* Methoprene
Prednisone, 816
Prefix, 126
  cis, 377–378
  cyclo-, 125, 132
  D-, 1105
  deoxy, 1136
  di-, 130, 328
  E, 377–378
  epoxy, 329
  eth-, 127
  iso-, 127
  L-, 1105
  meta-, 634
  meth-, 127
  ortho-, 634
  para-, 634
  R, 178–182, 187, 1102, 1105
  S, 178–182, 187, 1102, 1105
  sec-, 127
  tert-, 127
  tetra-, 130
  trans, 377–378
  tri-, 130
  Z, 378–379
Pregabalin, 113
Preparations, 728
Prepolymer, 1241–1242, 1242f
Preservatives, 271–272
Primary (1°) alcohols, 406
  classification as, 325
  conversion to alkyl halides with HX, 345–347, 350t
  conversion to alkyl halides with phosphorus tribromide, 350, 350t
  conversion to alkyl halides with thionyl chloride, 349, 350t
  dehydration by E2 mechanism, 340
  hydrogen bonding extent, 330
  from nucleophilic addition to aldehyde, 767
  oxidation to carboxylic acids, 466, 467–468, 728
  from reactions of aldehydes with organometallic reagents, 774–775
  from reduction of acid chlorides, 766–767
  from reduction of aldehydes, 450, 759, 760, 761
  from reduction of carboxylic acid derivatives, 759
  from reduction of carboxylic acids, 769
  from reduction of esters, 766–767
  from reduction of monosaccharides, 1120
Primary (1°) alkyl halides
  acetylide anion reactions with, 431–432
  classification as, 239
  E2 elimination reactions, 297, 298, 312f
  example of, 239f
  S_N2 substitution reactions, 258, 272, 272f, 312f
  synthesis of, 345
Primary (1°) amides, 861, 866, 868, 869, 877, 879, 885, 898
Primary (1°) amines
  addition to aldehydes and ketones, 830–832, 832f, 834f
  amino acids, 1151
  from direct nucleophilic substitution, 999–1000
  Gabriel synthesis, 1000–1001
  IR spectra of, 994, 994f
  nomenclature, 991
  reactions with acid chlorides and anhydrides, 1015
  reactions with aldehydes and ketones, 1015
  reactions with nitrous acid, 1020–1021
  from reduction of amides, 1001
  from reduction of nitriles, 1001
  from reduction of nitro compounds, 1001
  structure of, 989
  synthesis from reduction of nitriles, 900
Primary carbon (1°), 123–124
Primary hydrogen (1°), 123–124
Primary structure, of proteins, 1175, 1181f
Pristane, 158
Procaine, 638f
Procyclidine, 802
Progesterone
  analogs of, 420
  function in body, 1218t
  structure of, 420, 1195f, 1218t
  synthesis of, 966, 966f
Progestins, 1217
Proline, 751
  isoelectric point for, 1152t
  pK_a values for, 1152t
  structure of, 1150f, 1151
Prontosil, 1030
Propanal
  aldol reaction of, 957, 960
  enolate formation from, 920
  IR spectrum of, 813, 813f
  NMR spectra of, 815, 815f
  Wittig reaction, 827
Propanamide
  boiling point of, 97
  infrared (IR) spectrum of, 503
2-Propanamine, 991
Propane
  bromination of, 567, 568f
  chlorination of, 566–567, 569, 569f
  molecular formula of, 122, 125t
  naming, 127
  Newman projection, 139f
  as propellant, 573
  structure of, 122
  torsional energy of, 141
Propanedioic acid, 722
1,3-Propanediol, 1246, 1246f
1,2,3-Propanetriol, 328
Propanil, 1039
Propanoic acid, NMR spectra of, 725f
Propanol, 75
1-Propanol
  conversion to butanenitrile, 351
  IR spectrum of, 497
  NMR spectrum of, 546, 546f
2-Propanol, 332f
Proparacaine, 715, 1041
Propene
  borane addition to, 403
  hydrohalogenation, 389
  monomers in polymerization, 583t
  radical halogenation, 580–581
  synthesis from propylamine, 1017
2-Propen-1-ol, 377
Propionic acid, structure of, 721t
Propiophenone, 764
  halogenation of, 929–930
Propoxyphene, 174
Propranolol, 370
Propylamine, conversion to propene, 1017
Propylbenzene, 237, 703

Propyl group, 127
Prostacyclins, 1205, 1206f, 1206t
Prostaglandins, 157, 157f, 224, 1205–1207
analogues of, 120, 727, 1207
inhibitors of synthesis, 1207
PGE_1, 1207
PGE_2, 1206
$PGF_{2\alpha}$, 157, 157f, 233, 318, 415, 592, 726–727, 1195f, 1206f
PGG_2, 592, 727, 1205, 1206f
PGI_2, 1205, 1206f
synthesis of, 726–727, 1205, 1206f
Prosthetic group, 1183
Protecting groups, 781–783
acetals as, 841–842
amide for amines, 1016, 1016f
in amino acid synthesis, 1169–1173
general strategy for using, 782f
Proteins, 1160, 1175–1185. *See also* Peptides
amide linkages in, 871, 889–890
conjugated, 1183
fibrous, 1182
folding, 114
globular, 1182
important examples, 1182–1185, 1182f, 1183f, 1184f
membrane, 1149
natural fibers, 893, 893f
stability of, 890
structure, 1175–1181
primary, 1175, 1181f
quaternary, 1181, 1181f
secondary, 1176–1179, 1177f, 1178f, 1179f, 1181f
tertiary, 1179–1180, 1181f
subunits, 1181
Protic solvents, polar, 250, 250f, 275, 276t, 303t, 926
Proton acceptor, 59
Protonation
in acid-catalyzed ester hydrolysis, 885, 886
of alcohols, 337, 339, 340, 342, 343, 346, 347, 348
in aldehyde/ketone nucleophilic addition reactions, 819–820
of carboxylic acids, 729
of epoxides, 359
of ethers, 356
in glycoside formation, 1116
in glycoside hydrolysis, 1117
in nucleophilic addition to aldehydes and ketones, 756, 761
in tautomerization, 428–429, 918
Proton donor, 59
Proton NMR, 515, 517–543
of aldehydes, 815, 815f
of amines, 995, 995f
of aromatic compounds, 643
of benzene derivatives, 539–540, 540f, 636, 636t
of carboxylic acid derivatives, 870
of carboxylic acids, 724, 725f
characteristic absorptions, A-10–11
chemical shift
equation for, 518
predicting values of, 524–525
protons on benzene rings, 525, 526t
protons on carbon–carbon double bonds, 526, 526t
protons on carbon–carbon triple bonds, 526, 526t
scale, 517
values for common proton types, 524t
coupled protons, 531
of cyclohexane conformations, 539
general principles
chemical shifts, 517–518
downfield signals, 517–518
reference signal, 517
scale, 517
signal intensity, 517
upfield signals, 517–518
identification of an unknown, 541–543
integrals, 527–528
intensity of signals, 527–529
of ketones, 815
number of signals, 518–522, 519f
enantiotopic and diastereotopic protons, 520–522
equivalent protons in alkenes and cycloalkanes, 520
general principles, 518–519
OH proton, 538–539, 539f
position of signals, 522–525
chemical shift values, 524–525, 524t
shielding and deshielding effects, 522–524, 523f, 526t, 527f
regions of spectra, 526, 527f
spin–spin splitting, 529–538
in alkenes, 536–538, 537f, 538f
common patterns of, 532t
complex examples of, 533–536
how a doublet arises, 530
how a triplet arises, 530–531
overview of, 529–530
rules and examples, 531–533, 531t
Protons
description of, 8
relative acidity of, determining, 73–74
Proton transfer reaction
aspirin and, 76
description of, 60–62
Proventil. *See* Albuterol
Proximity effect, 609
Prozac, 3, 195, 260, 260f. *See also* Fluoxetine
D-Pscicose, 1108f
Pseudoephedrine, 69, 200, 1005, 1039
Psilocin, 998
Psilocybe mushroom, 998
PTH (*N*-phenylthiohydantoin), 1165–1166
PTT. *See* Poly(trimethylene terephthalate)
Puffer fish, 5, 5f, 611, 611f
Purine, 658, 1137
Putrescine, 995
PVC. *See* Poly(vinyl chloride)
Pyran, 1109
Pyranose ring, 1109, 1129
Pyrethrin I, 113, 1052, 1065
Pyridine, 75, 384, 645, 716, 876
alcohol conversion to alkyl tosylates in, 352, 354, 355f
basicity of, 1011–1012, 1013t
conversion of alcohols to alkyl halides, 349
conversion of monosaccharide to ester using, 1120
dehydration of alcohols using, 344, 345f
electrostatic potential plot of, 645, 646f
structure of, 992
Pyridinium chlorochromate (PCC), 457, 466
Pyrimidine, 1137
α-Pyrone, 659
Pyroxidine (vitamin B_6), 116
Pyrrole, 645–646, 659, 660, 716
basicity of, 1011, 1013t
electrostatic potential plot of, 646, 646f
structure of, 992
Pyrrolidine, structure of, 992
Pyruvic acid, 766

Q

Qinghao, 405
Quantum, 494
Quartet, NMR spectrum, 531t, 532t, 538
Quaternary ammonium salt. *See also* Ammonium salt
in Hofmann elimination reaction, 1016–1017
synthesis of, 999
Quaternary carbon (4°), 123–124
Quaternary structure, of proteins, 1181, 1181f
Quiana, 1253
Quinapril, 285
Quinine, 202
as natural alkaloid, 995
source of, 299
structure of, 647, 1014
synthesis of, 298, 299f, 932, 932f
Quinoline, 453, 717
o-Quinone, 1097
Quintet, NMR spectrum, 531t
Quinuclidine, 287

R

R (prefix), 178–182, 187
Racemic mixture (racemate), 191–192, 191t
of alcohols from hydroboration–oxidation of alkenes, 404
alkene halogenation, 397
of alkyl chlorides, 347
of amino acids, separation of, 1155–1158, 1156f
in carbene addition, 1054
in enolate alkylation, 934
from epoxidation of alkenes, 459, 461
in epoxide ring-opening reactions, 358
formation by hydrohalogenation, 391–392
halogenation reactions and, 397, 571–572
in hydride reduction of ketones, 762–763
in organometallic reagent reactions, 777
S_N1 substitution reactions and, 264–265, 264f
Racemization
at α carbon of carbonyl compounds, 927
definition of, 264
in S_N1 substitution reactions, 264–265, 264f
Radiation
electromagnetic, 494–495, 495f
infrared, 496
RF (radiofrequency), 515–516, 547–548
ultraviolet, 620–621
Radical(s)
bond formation from, 211
classification of, 559
definition of, 559
as electrophile, 211
as reactive intermediate, 210–211, 210f
resonance-stabilized, 576, 577
stability of, 559–560, 560f
Radical anion, 454
Radical cation, 485, 489
Radical inhibitor, 561
Radical initiator, 560
Radical intermediates, 559, 576, 580
Radical polymerization, 1228–1229, 1229f
Radical reactions, 210, 210f, 558–592. *See also specific reactions*
of alkanes, 562–572
of alkenes, 561, 579–582
applications of
antioxidants, 578–579
oxidation of unsaturated lipids, 577–578, 578f
ozone destruction by CFCs, 573, 574f
carbon–hydrogen bond, reaction of radical with, 561
double bonds, addition to, 561, 579–582
general features of, 560–561
halogenation at allylic carbon, 574–577
bromination, 575–577
product mixtures in, 576–577
halogenation of alkanes, 562–572
of achiral starting material, 570t, 571
bromination, 566–568, 568f
of chiral starting material, 570t, 571–572
chlorination, 563–567, 565f, 568f, 569–572, 569f
energy changes during, 565, 565f
mechanism of, 563–565
in organic synthesis, 570
stereochemistry of, 570–572, 570t
halogenation of alkyl benzenes, 699–701
inhibitors of, 561
polymerization, 582–585, 583t
two radicals reacting with each other, 561
Radical scavenger, 561
Radical substitution reaction, 562, A-12
Randomness, entropy as measure of, 218
Rate constant (*k*), 226
Rate-determining step
in chlorination of ethane, 565, 565f
E1 elimination reactions, 302, 303
electrophilic additions, 388, 388f, 394
in halogenation reactions, 565, 568–569
bromination, 568
chlorination, 569
halogenation of alkenes, 397
in multistep mechanisms, 224, 227
in nucleophilic substitution reactions, 253, 254
rate equation for, 226
S_N1 substitution reactions, 270
Rate equation, 226–227
first-order, 227, 253, 254
for nucleophilic substitution reactions, 253–254
second-order, 226, 253, 254
Rate law, 226–227
RCM (ring-closing metathesis), 1059–1060, 1059f
Reaction arrow, 206, 211t
curved, 210, 211t
double, 211t
Reaction coordinate, 220, 221f, 222f, 224f

Reaction mechanism
bond cleavage, 209
bond formation, 211
concerted, 209
definition of, 209
energy diagram for a two-step, 222–224, 224f
rate equations and, 226–227
stepwise, 209, 222–224, 227
Reaction rate
carbocation stability and, 268
catalysts and, 228, 228f
concentration effect on, 225, 226–227
of endothermic reactions, 221f, 269–270
energy of activation (E_a) and, 225
of exothermic reactions, 221f, 270
nucleophilic substitution reactions, 268, 270–271, 271f, 273–275
rate-determining step, 224, 227
temperature effect on, 225
Reactions. *See* Organic reactions
Reactive intermediate
carbanion, 210–211, 210f
carbocation, 210–211, 210f, 262–263, 264, 343
description of, 209
radicals, 210–211, 210f
synthetic intermediate compared, 408
in two-step reaction mechanism, 223
Reactivity, functional groups and, 108–109
Reagent, 206, 206f
Rebaudioside A, 1118
Receptors, olfactory, 196f
Recycling of polymers, 1225, 1247–1249, 1248t
Red seaweed (*Asparagopsis taxiformis*), 238
Reduced state, 154
Reducing agents, 446. *See also specific agents*
chiral, 763
metal hydride reagents, 446, 760–762, 766–770, 770t
NADH, 765–766
Reducing sugars, 1121, 1121f, 1130
Reduction, 154–155, 155f, 444–482
of acid chlorides and esters, 766–768
of alkenes, 445, 445f, 447–450
of alkyl halides, 455–456, 456f
of alkynes, 445, 445f, 452–455, 455f
to alkanes, 445f, 452–453, 455f
to cis alkene, 452, 453, 455f
to trans alkene, 452, 454–455, 455f
of amides to amines, 769, 1001
of aryl ketones to alkyl benzenes, 702–703
asymmetric, 763
of carbonyl compounds, 758–770
biological, 765–766
carboxylic acids and derivatives, 766–770
by catalytic hydrogenation, 761
enantioselective, 763–766, 764f
with metal hydride reagents, 760–762, 762f, 770t
stereochemistry of, 762–763
of the carbonyl group of monosaccharides, 1120
Clemmensen, 702
definition of, 154, 445, 758
dissolving metal, 446, 454
of epoxides, 455–456, 456f
general scheme for, 445f
of hydrocarbons, 445, 445f
hydrogenation, 447–452
of ketones to amines, 1002–1005
of nitriles, 898, 900–901, 1001
of nitro groups, 703–704
oxidation, relationship to, 445
of polar C–X sigma (σ) bonds, 455–456
of substituted benzenes, 702–704
of triple bonds, 452–455, 455f
Wolff–Kishner, 702
Reductive amination, of aldehydes and ketones to amines, 1002–1005
Reductive elimination
in Heck reaction, 1052
in palladium-catalyzed reactions, 1046, 1048, 1052
in Suzuki reactions, 1048
Refining, 135–136, 135f
Refrigerant, 243
Regioselectivity
of alcohol dehydrations, 338
of E1 elimination reactions, 303
of E2 elimination reactions, 299, 306, 307
of electrophilic addition of hydrogen halides, 389
of epoxide ring-opening reactions, 359–360
of halohydrin formation, 399–400, 400t
of Hofmann elimination, 1018
of hydroboration, 403, 405t
Reserpine, 914, 1083
Resolution, 194
of amino acids, 1155–1158, 1156f
Resolving agent, 1156
Resonance, 19–24
of allylic carbocations, 596–597, 596f
allyl type, 597–599
benzene, 632
examples of, 597–599
theory principles, 20
usage of term, 596
Resonance delocalization, 71
Resonance effects
on acidity, 70–71, 71f, 73f
on basicity of amines, 1013t
electron-donating, 679–681
electron-withdrawing, 679–681
on substituted benzenes, 679–681
Resonance hybrid, 19, 23–24, 96
of benzene, 632
drawing, 24
electron delocalization, hybridization, and geometry, 600–601
major and minor contributors, 23–24
major contributor to, 599–600
minor contributors to, 599–600
Resonance stabilization, of carboxylic acids, 731–732, 732f, 733f
Resonance-stabilized allyl carbocation, 596–597, 596f, 597f
Resonance-stabilized carbocation, 425, 428, 596–597, 596f, 597f, 606–607, 609
in electrophilic aromatic substitution reaction, 667, 669
in glycoside formation, 1116
in glycoside hydrolysis, 1117
Resonance-stabilized radical, 576, 577
Resonance structures, 19–24, 596–601
of acetate, 731, 733f
acidity and, 70–71
of allyl radical, 574–575
of benzylic radical, 699
of carboxylic acid derivatives, 862
cations with positive charge adjacent to lone pair, 598
conjugated allyl carbocation, 596–597
of conjugated dienes, 604–605
double bond
conjugated, 598
major contributor, 599–600, 604
minor contributors, 599–600, 604
with one atom more electronegative than the other, 598, 599
drawing, 20–23
of enolates, 919
of enols, 919
IR spectrum and, 814
isomers compared to, 20
of naphthalene, 644
of phenoxide, 732, 732f, 733f
stability of, 599–600
of substituted benzenes, 679–680
three atom allyl system, 597, 599
of α,β-unsaturated carbonyl compound, 972
of Wittig reagent, 826
Resveratrol, 590
Retention of configuration
in chlorination, 572
in conversion of alcohols to alkyl tosylates, 352, 354
in oxidation of alkylborane, 404
in S_N2 substitution reaction, 256
Retention time, in gas chromatography, 492
Retinal, 832, 832f
11-*cis*-Retinal, 379
Retinol, 102–103
Retro Diels–Alder reaction, 617
Retrosynthetic analysis, 408, 434–437
in acetoacetic ester synthesis, 941–942
in benzene derivative synthesis, 1024–1025
of Diels–Alder product, 616–617
of disparlure, 459–460
of Grignard products, 778–781
of Heck reaction, 1051
in malonic acid synthesis, 939–940
organometallic reagent reactions, 793–795
in phenylethylamine preparation, 1004
in substituted benzene syntheses, 704, 705–707
synthesis of *m*-bromoaniline from benzene, 704
using aldol reaction, 959–960
Wittig reaction, 828–829
RF radiation, 515–516, 547–548
R group, 87, 127
identity in S_N1 substitution reactions, 266, 266t
identity in S_N2 substitution reactions, 258–259, 260t
Rhodium, 1159
Rhodopsin, 832, 832f
Ribbon diagrams, 1178
α-D-Ribofuranose, 1114, 1135
β-D-Ribofuranose, 1114
Ribonucleosides, 1136
Ribonucleotides, 1137
D-Ribose, 1106, 1107f, 1114, 1136
D-Ribulose, 1108f
Rimantadine, 1005
Ring-closing metathesis (RCM), 1059–1060, 1059f
Ring expansion reactions, 966
Ring-flipping, 147–148, 148f, 152
Ring formation
in aldol reaction, 966, 966f
in Robinson annulation, 974–978
Ring strain, 814
RNA, 1137, 1138, 1138f
Robinson, Sir Robert, 974
Robinson annulation, 974–978
Rocaltrol. *See* Calcitriol
Rofecoxib, 984, 1207
Rosuvastatin, 980
Rotation
around carbon–carbon bonds, 137–138
barrier to, 143
restricted, 292–293, 292f, 374t
Row, in periodic table, 9
Rowland, F. Sherwood, 573
RU 486, 421
Rubber, 1226f, 1237–1238, 1237f
Rubbing alcohol, 332f
Ruthenium, 1056

S

S (prefix), 178–182, 187
Saccharin, 1131, 1132f
Safflower oil, 384
Safrole, 841, 1039
Salicin, 76f, 726, 1118
Salicylamide, 910
Salicylates, 76
Salicylic acid, 726, 908, 1256
Salmeterol, 361, 361f, 764f, 805
Salsolinol, 854
Salts
Brønsted–Lowry bases and, 59
of carboxylic acids, 726
formation of, 12
negatively charged nucleophile, 245
SAM (*S*-adenosylmethionine), 204, 260, 261
Samuelsson, Bengt, 727
Sand bee, 122
Sandmeyer reaction, 1022
Santalbic acid, 418
Saponification, 886, 889
Saponins, 104
Saquinavir, 203
Saran, 1234
Saturated fats, 383
Saturated fatty acid, 372, 382
Saturated hydrocarbons, 121
Saytzeff rule, 299
SBR (styrene–butadiene rubber), polymerization of, 1234
Sch38516, 1059f
s-character, of hybrid orbitals, 72
Schiff base, 830
Schrock, Richard, 1056
s-cis conformation, 602, 612
Scombroid fish poisoning, 646
Scopolamine, 988
Seashells, chiral helical, 173
Seaweed, 238, 243
Sebacic acid, 1256
sec- (prefix), 127
Secondary (2°) alcohols, 406
classification as, 325
conversion to alkyl halides with HX, 345–348, 350t
conversion to alkyl halides with phosphorus tribromide, 350, 350t
conversion to alkyl halides with thionyl chloride, 349, 350t
dehydration by E1 mechanism, 339–340
hydrogen bonding extent, 330
oxidation to ketones, 466, 467
from reactions of aldehydes with organometallic reagents, 774–775
from reduction of ketones, 450, 759, 760, 761

Secondary (2°) alkyl halides
acetylide anion reactions with, 432
classification as, 239
E1 elimination reactions, 303, 313f
E2 elimination reactions, 297, 313f
example of, 239f
S_N1 substitution reactions, 266, 272, 272f, 313f
S_N2 substitution reactions, 258, 272, 272f, 313f
synthesis of, 345
Secondary (2°) amides, 861, 866, 868–869, 877, 879, 885
Secondary (2°) amines
addition to aldehydes and ketones, 833–834, 834f
from direct nucleophilic substitution, 999
IR spectra of, 994, 994f
nomenclature, 991–992
proline, 1151
reactions with acid chlorides and anhydrides, 1015
reactions with aldehydes and ketones, 1015
reactions with nitrous acid, 1021
from reduction of amides, 1001
structure of, 989
Secondary carbon (2°), 123–124
Secondary hydrogen (2°), 123–124
Secondary structure, of proteins, 1176–1179, 1177f, 1178f, 1179f, 1181f
Second-order kinetics, 226
of E2 elimination reactions, 295
in nucleophilic substitution reactions, 253–254
Second-order rate equation, 226, 253, 254
Selective serotonin reuptake inhibitors (SSRIs), 998
Separation, of amino acids, 1155–1158
Separatory funnel, 738, 738f
Septet, NMR spectrum, 531t, 534
Serevent. *See* Salmeterol
Serine
abbreviation for, 742t
isoelectric point for, 1152t
pK_a values for, 1152t
structure of, 1150f
Serotonin, 910, 998
Sertraline, 638f, 665, 678
β-Sesquiphellandrene, 612
Sex hormones, 1217, 1218, 1218t. *See also specific hormones*
Sex pheromone, 964, 964f, 1042, 1049
Sextet, NMR spectrum, 531t, 535f
Shark liver oil, 158
Sharpless, K. Barry, 471
Sharpless epoxidation, 471–473, 1159
Sharpless reagent, 471, 472
Shell, of electrons, 9–10
Shielding effects, in NMR, 522–524, 523f, 526t, 527f
1,2-Shifts, 341–343
Shikimic acid, 91
Sickle cell anemia, 1185
Sickle cell hemoglobin, 1184–1185
Side chain, of amino acid, 1149, 1151, 1152t
Sigma (σ) bond, 34, 36, 39–43, 40f, 42f, 42t
in alkanes, 88
in alkenes, 291, 373
in alkynes, 417–418
breakage in addition reactions, 208
carbon–oxygen, 325
in cycloaddition reactions, 1071, 1081
in electrocyclic reactions, 1070, 1075, 1076, 1077
formation in addition reactions, 385, 386f, 387
formation in elimination reactions, 207
functional groups that contain C–Z σ bonds, 89, 90t
hyperconjuation, 267–268
inductive effect and, 69, 267
length in conjugated dienes, 603–604
radical reactions with, 560, 561
reduction of polar C–X bonds, 455–456
rotation around, 137–138
in sigmatropic rearrangements, 1071, 1085–1088
in substitution reactions, 207, 252
Sigmatropic rearrangement, 1085–1090
Claisen rearrangement, 1089–1090
Cope rearrangement, 1088–1089
description of, 1071
orbital symmetry and, 1086–1087
Woodward–Hoffmann rules for, 1087t
Sildenafil, 638f
Silent Spring, 243
Silk, 893, 893f
binding of dyes to, 1029
structure of, 1178, 1179f
Silver(I) oxide, 1119
in aqueous ammonium hydroxide, 771
as oxidizing agent, 457
Silyl ether, 782
Simmons, H. E., 1055
Simmons–Smith reaction, 1055–1056
Simmons–Smith reagent, 1056
Simvastatin, 177, 603, 603f, 1217, 1217f
Sinemat, 48
α-Sinensal, 755
Singlet, NMR spectrum, 529, 531t, 533, 538
Sirenin, 1065
Sitagliptin, 647
Six-membered ring, synthesis of
in aldol reaction, 966, 966f
in Dieckmann reaction, 971–972
in Robinson annulation, 975–978
Skeletal structures, 31–34, 32f
with charged carbon atoms, 33–34
interpreting, 31, 32f
Smith, R. D., 1055
S_N1 substitution reactions, 262–272
alcohol conversion to alkyl halide, 346–348
alkyl halide identity in, 272, 272f
applications of, 271–272
carbocation stability, 266–268
Hammond postulate and, 268–271
hyperconjugation and, 267–268
inductive effects and, 267
E1 elimination reaction compared, 304–305, 311–315, 312f–313f
E2 elimination reaction compared, 311–315, 312f–313f
energy diagram for, 263, 263f, 271f
ethers with strong acids, 355–356
features of, 262
kinetics of, 262, 266t
leaving group in, 265, 274–275
nucleophile strength in, 273–274
racemization in, 264–265, 264f
rate-determining step, 270
R group in, 266, 266t
S_N2 reactions compared, 272–276, 272f, 276t, 311–315, 312f–313f
solvent effects on, 275
stereochemistry, 264–265, 264f, 266t
transition state in, 263, 263f, 274
two-step mechanism for, 262–263, 266t
as unimolecular, 254, 262
S_N2 substitution reactions, 254–262
in acetoacetate ester synthesis, 941
acetylide anion reactions with alkyl halides, 431–433
acetylide anion reaction with epoxides, 434
alcohol conversion to alkyl halide
with HX, 346–347
with phosphorus tribromide, 350
with thionyl chloride, 349
alcohol synthesis from alkyl halides, 334–335
alkyl halide identity in, 272, 272f
alkyl halide with ammonia or amine, 999–1000
alkyl tosylate reactions, 353–354
applications of, 260–262, 260f, 261f
in automated peptide synthesis, 1174
backside attack in, 256–257, 273
direct enolate alkylation, 933
E1 elimination reactions compared, 311–315, 312f–313f
E2 elimination reactions compared, 311–315, 312f–313f
energy diagrams for, 255, 255f, 259f
epoxide ring opening reactions, 357–358
epoxide synthesis from halohydrin, 336
epoxy resin synthesis, 1241
ethers with strong acids, 355–356
ether synthesis from alkyl halides, 334–335
features of, 254, 260t
frontside attack in, 256
of α-halo acids with ammonia, 1152–1153, 1155f
of α-halo carbonyl compounds, 932, 932f
kinetics of, 254, 260t
leaving group in, 256–257, 274–275
in malonic ester synthesis, 938
nitrile synthesis, 897
nucleophile strength in, 273–274
one-step mechanism for, 254–255, 260t
organic synthesis, 278, 278t, 280
reduction of alkyl halides, 456, 456f
reduction of epoxides, 456, 456f
R group in, 258–259, 260t
S_N1 reactions compared, 272–276, 272f, 276t, 311–315, 312f–313f
solvent effects on, 275
stereochemistry of, 256–258, 257f, 260t
steric hindrance and, 258–259, 258f, 260t
transition state, 255, 255f, 257–259, 257f, 274
Soap, 104–105, 105f, 886, 889
Sodium, in dissolving metal reductions, 446, 454
Sodium acetate, 99, 722f
Sodium amide, for alkyne synthesis by dehydrohalogenation, 310, 311f
Sodium benzoate, 726, 739
Sodium bisulfite, 462
Sodium borohydride, 446, 760–762, 762f, 770t, 821, 1120
Sodium chloride, 12, 96, 98
Sodium cyanoborohydride, for reductive amination of aldehydes and ketones, 1002, 1003
Sodium dichromate, 457, 466
Sodium ethoxide, 290t, 335
Sodium hydroxide
in dehydrohalogenation reactions, 290, 290t
use in extraction procedure, 738–739, 740f
Sodium hypochlorite, 470
Sodium iodide, 1023
Sodium methoxide, 290t, 335
Sodium nitrite, 271–272
Sodium salicylate, 726
Soft coral (*Capnella imbricata*), 433
Solanine, 1118
Solid phase technique, of amino acid synthesis, 1173–1175
Solubility, 99–102, 101f
of alcohols, 331t
of aldehydes and ketones, 813t
of alkanes, 136, 137t
of alkenes, 380
of alkynes, 419
of amines, 993t
of carboxylic acids, 723t
definition of, 99
of epoxides, 331t
of ethers, 331t
intermolecular forces and, 99–102, 99f
"like dissolves like," 99
of lipids, 156, 1195
of monosaccharides, 1108, 1120
soap and, 104–105, 105f
of vitamins, 102–104
Solute, 99
Solvent effects, on nucleophilic substitution reactions, 250–252, 250f, 251f, 275, 276t
Solvents, 99
alkyl halides, 242
in E1 elimination reactions, 303t
in E2 elimination reactions, 297, 298t
for extraction procedure, 737–739, 738–740, 738f, 739f, 740f
liquid, 206
nonpolar, 99
nucleophilicity and, 250–252, 275
organic, 99, 100
polar, 99
polar aprotic, 251, 251f, 275, 276t, 297, 298t, 925
polar protic, 250, 250f, 275, 275t, 276t, 303t, 926
s orbitals
description, 9–10
hybridization of, 34–43, 36f–37f, 40f, 42f, 42t
1*s* orbital, 10, 34
2*s* orbital, 10, 35–36, 37f
Sorbitol, 187, 1120
D-Sorbose, 1108f
Sorona, 1246, 1246f
Spam, 271
Spandex, 1240
Spearmint, odor of, 196
Specific rotation, 192
Spectator ions, 59
Spectrometer, NMR, 516–517, 516f
Spectroscopy, 485
Spermaceti wax, 1196
Spermine, 989
SPF rating (sun protection factor), 621
Sphingomyelins, 1203, 1203f
Sphingosine, 1203
sp hybrid orbitals, 35–37, 37f, 41, 42f, 42t
in alkynes, 417, 418, 422, 423
percent *s*-character, 44, 72

sp^2 hybrid orbitals, 35–37, 37f, 39, 40, 40f, 42t, 268, 277, 325, 380
in alkenes, 291, 294
of alkenes, 373
of alkyl halides, 239, 239f
in aromatic heterocycles, 645–646, 646f
of benzene, 633
of benzyne, 699
carbon radical, 559
carboxy group, 719
percent *s*-character, 44, 72
sp^3 hybrid orbitals, 35–39, 36f, 38f, 42t, 325, 326, 380
in acyclic alkanes, 121
in alkenes, 294
of alkyl halides, 239, 239f, 277
in nucleophilic substitution reactions, 245–246, 252–277
percent *s*-character, 44, 72
Spiriva. *See* Tiotropium bromide
Spiro ring system, A–6
Splenda. *See* Sucralose
Squalene, 164, 479, 1209f, 1210, 1211f, 1212, 1216, 1216f, 1217
Squalene oxide, 1216f, 1217
Stachyose, 1146
Staggered conformation, 138–144, 139f, 140f, 141f, 143f, 306, 306f
Stanozolol, 663, 1218
Starch
hydrolysis of, 167, 168f, 332, 332f, 1134
structure of, 167, 168f, 169f, 1133–1134
Stearic acid, 372, 1197, 1197t
melting point, 383t
structure, 382f, 383t
Stearidonic acid, 383, 477
Step-growth polymers, 1227, 1238–1242
epoxy resins, 1241–1242, 1242f
polyamides, 1238–1239
polycarbonates, 1241
polyesters, 1239–1240
polyurethanes, 1240
Stepwise reaction, 209
Stereocenter. *See* Stereogenic centers
Stereochemistry, 136, 166–204
of addition reactions, 386, 391–393, 393f, 393t
of carbonyl reduction, 762–763
chemical properties of enantiomers, 195–196
chiral and achiral molecules, 170–173, 173f
diastereomers, 183–184, 185f, 194, 194f
of Diels–Alder reaction, 613–614
of dienophiles, 613–614
of dihydroxylation, 461–463
of disubstituted cycloalkanes, 187–188
of E2 elimination reactions, 305–309, 306f
of electrocyclic reactions, 1075–1076
of electrophilic addition reactions, 391–393, 393t
of enolate alkylation, 934
of epoxidation, 458–459
of halogenation, 396–398
of halogenation reactions, 570–572, 570t
of halohydrin formation, 399–400, 400t
of hydroboration–oxidation reactions, 402, 404, 405t
meso compounds, 185–186, 186f
organometallic reagent reactions with carbonyl compounds, 777
physical properties of stereoisomers, 190–194, 192t, 194f
polymer, 1235–1236
of sigmatropic rearrangements, 1086
of S_N2 subsitution reactions, 256–258, 257f, 260t
of S_N1 substitution reactions, 264–265, 264f, 266t
of starch and cellulose, 167–169, 168f, 169f
stereogenic centers. *see* Stereogenic centers
Stereogenic centers, 173–187
in amines, 990–991
in amino acids, 742, 1149, 1151
on carbon atoms not part of ring, 173–175
in cyclic compounds, 176–177
definition of, 171
in diastereomers, 183–184
drawing enantiomers, 175, 175f
enantiotopic and diastereotopic protons, 520–522
formation from hydrohalogenation, 391, 392
halogenation reactions and, 570–572
inversion of configuration around, 256–258, 257f
labeling with *R* or *S*, 178–182, 179f, 181f, 187
in meso compounds, 185–186
in monosaccharides, 1101–1110
number in a molecule, 172
priority assignment, 178–182, 179f
retention of configuration around, 256
tetrahedral, 172, 173, 175, 176, 186
Stereoisomers, 18. *See also* Enantiomers
in alkenes, 374t
chemical properties of, 195–196
cis, 151–154
configuration of, 170
of conjugated dienes, 601–602
constitutional isomers compared, 170f
of cycloalkanes, 151–154
definition of, 151
from dehydrohalogenation, 300
diastereomers, 183–184, 185f, 194, 194f
disubstituted cycloalkanes, 187–188
enantiomers, 172
of monosaccharides, 1103–1107, 1106f
nomenclature for alkenes, 377–379
number of, maximum, 183
physical properties of, 190–194, 192t, 194f
starch and cellulose, 167–169
trans, 151–154
Stereoselective reaction
alkyne reduction to a cis alkene, 453
dissolving metal reduction of alkyne, 455
of E2 elimination reactions, 300
Stereospecific reactions
carbene addition, 1054
coupling reactions with organocuprates, 1044
definition of, 397
epoxidation, 458
halogenation of alkenes, 397
Heck reaction, 1050
Simmons–Smith reaction, 1056
Suzuki reaction, 1047
Steric effects, nucleophilicity and, 249
Steric hindrance, 249
in alcohols, 330
in hydroboration reactions, 403
S_N2 substitution reactions and, 258–259, 258f, 260t
Steric strain, 142, 143t, 145, 249
Steroids, 1214–1219
adrenal cortical, 1217, 1219
anabolic, 1218
cholesterol. *See* Cholesterol
sex hormones, 1217, 1218, 1218t
structure of, 1214–1215, 1215f
synthesis in Diels–Alder reaction, 618
Stone, Reverend Edmund, 76f
Strain
angle, 144–146, 326, 327
Baeyer strain theory, 144
energy increase with, 141
steric, 142, 143t, 249
torsional, 140–141, 143t, 144, 145, 146
s-trans conformation, 602, 612
Strecker synthesis, 1154–1155, 1155f
Structural isomers. *See* Constitutional isomers
Strychnine, 1158
Styrene, 558, 584, 701, 1057, 1057f
polymerization of, 1227f, 1228, 1230, 1234
structure of, 1227f, 1229f
Styrene–butadiene rubber (SBR), polymerization of, 1234
Substituents, naming, 127, 634–635
naming aromatic rings as, 635
Substitution reactions, A–12
alcohols, 336–337, 346–350
allylic, 576
of aromatic compounds
of benzene, 666–678
electrophilic, 666–695
nucleophilic, 695–699
of substituted benzenes, 678–695
of aryl diazonium salts, 1022–1026
of benzene, 631, 640
at α-carbon of carbonyl compounds, 915–953
description of, 207
electrophilic aromatic. *See* Electrophilic aromatic substitution reactions
Heck reaction, 1043, 1050–1052
nucleophilic, 245–280
radical, 562
Substrate, 229, 229f
Succinic acid, 722
Succinimide, 576
Sucralose, 1131, 1132f
Sucrose, 115, 1131, 1131f
olestra synthesis from, 888–889
stereogenic centers, 177
structure of, 164, 1131f
Sudafed, 69. *See also* Pseudoephedrine
Suffix, 126
-adiene, 376
-al, 809
-aldehyde, 810
-amide, 866, 867t
-amine, 991–992
-ane, 124, 127, 128, 132, 135, 376
-ate, 722, 865, 867t
-carbaldehyde, 809
-carbonyl chloride, 864, 867t
-carboxylic acid, 864
-dioic acid, 722
-diol, 328
-ene, 376
-enol, A–5
-enone, A–5
-enyne, A–5
-ic acid, 721, 864, 866, 867
-ide, –241
-ine, 240–241
-o, 240
-oic acid, 720, 866
-ol, 327
-one, 810
-onitrile, 866, 867t
-ose, 1100
-oxy, 329
-oyl, 812
-yl, 127, 329, 812
-yl chloride, 864, 867, 867t
-ylic acid, 866
-yne, 418
Sugars. *See also* Carbohydrates
amino, 1134–1135
nonreducing, 1121, 1121f, 1131
reducing, 1121, 1121f, 1130
simple. *See* Monosaccharides
Sulfa drugs, 1030–1031
Sulfamethoxazole, 1031f
Sulfanilamide, 1030–1031
Sulfide (functional group), 90t
Sulfisoxazole, 1031f
Sulfonate anion, 741
Sulfonation
of benzene, 667f, 670, 671
electrophilic aromatic substitution reaction, 667f, 670, 671
Sulfonic acids, 741
Sulfur
common nucleophiles, 252t
in fossil fuels, 74
octet rule exceptions in, 19
Sulfuric acid, 19, 74
dehydration of alcohols in, 338–343, 341f
in epoxide ring-opening reactions, 359, 360
in nitration and sulfonation reactions of benzene, 670–671
Sulfur nucleophile, 362
Sulfur oxides, 74
Sulfur trioxide, 671
Sulfur ylides, 854, 1065
Sunscreen, 33, 620–621, 714
Supercoil, 1182, 1182f
Superhelix, 1182–1183
Suprafacial bond formation, 1082
Suprafacial rearrangement, 1086–1087, 1087t, 1088
Surface area
boiling point and, 96, 97f
van der Waals forces and, 93, 93f
Suzuki, Akira, 1050
Suzuki reaction, 1042, 1043, 1046–1049, 1049f
Sweeteners, artificial, 1131, 1132f, 1164
Sweetness, of monosaccharides, 1108
Sweet'n Low. *See* Saccharin
Symbol, atomic, 8
Symmetrical anhydrides, 861, 865
Symmetry
melting points and, 98
plane of, 172–173, 186, 188
Syn additions, 386, 392, 393t, 402, 404, 447, 452, 458, 460f, 461, 462–463, 1054
Syndiotactic polymer, 1235–1236
Syn periplanar geometry, 305, 306f
Synthetic intermediate, 408
Synthetic polymers, 582–584, 1225–1257
amorphous regions of, 1243–1244
atatic, 1235–1236

"Big Six," 1247–1248, 1248t
biodegradable, 1249–1250
chain-growth, 1226, 1227–1234
in consumer products, 1226, 1226f
crystalline regions of, 1243–1244
disposal of, 1247–1249
green synthesis of, 1244–1247, 1245f, 1246f
isotactic, 1235–1236
molecular weights of, 1227
nylon, 893–894
physical properties of, 1243–1244
plasticizer addition to, 1244
polyesters, 894
recycling of, 1225, 1247–1249, 1248t
shorthand representation of, 1227, 1227f
step-growth, 1227, 1238–1242
stereochemistry of, 1235–1236
structure of, 1226, 1243–1244
syndiotactic, 1235–1236
thermoplastics, 1243
thermosetting, 1243
Systematic name, 126. *See also* IUPAC nomenclature
of amines, 991–992

T

2,4,5-T (2,4,5-Trichlorophenoxyacetic acid herbicide), 670f
Tacrine, 1014
Tagamet. *See* Cimetidine
D-Tagatose, 1108f
Talose
D-talose, 1107f, 1124
Wohl degradation, 1124
Tamiflu, 91
Tamoxifen, 915, 935
Target compound, 435
Tartaric acid, stereoisomers of, 194, 194f
Tautomerization
in acid, 428, 918
of amides, 898–899
in base, 918
of carbonyl compounds, 898–899, 917–918, 929
mechanism of, 918
in sigmatropic rearrangements, 1088–1089
Tautomers
definition of, 427
enol, 427–429, 899, 917–918
keto, 427–429, 899, 917–918
Taxol, 177
TBDMS (*tert*-butyldimethylsilyl ether), 782, 783
Teflon, 243. *See also* Polytetrafluoroethylene (Teflon)
Telfairine, 240
Temperature, reaction rate and, 225
Teratogen, 176, 177
Terephthalic acid, 894, 1225, 1227f, 1239, 1256
Terpenes, 1208–1214
biosynthesis of, 1210–1213, 1211f
classes of, 1209t
examples of, 1209f
locating isoprene units in, 1208–1210, 1209f
rubber, 1237
α-Terpinene, 1214
α-Terpineol, 415, 1213
tert- (prefix), 127
Tertiary (3°) alcohols
classification as, 325
conversion to alkyl halides with HX, 345–348, 350t
dehydration by E1 mechanism, 339–340
hydrogen bonding extent, 330
from reaction of esters and acid chlorides with organometallic reagents, 783–785
from reaction of ketones with organometallic reagents, 774–775
Tertiary (3°) alkyl halides
acetylide anion reaction with, 432
classification as, 239
E1 elimination reactions, 303, 304, 312f
E2 elimination reactions, 297, 298, 312f
example of, 239f
S_N1 substitution reactions, 264, 266, 272, 272f, 312f
synthesis of, 345, 348
Tertiary (3°) amides, 861, 866, 877, 879, 885, 921
Tertiary (3°) amines
from direct nucleophilic substitution, 999
IR spectra of, 994, 994f
nomenclature, 991–992
from reduction of amides, 1001
structure of, 989
Tertiary carbon (3°), 123–124
Tertiary hydrogen (3°), 123–124
Tertiary structure, of proteins, 1179–1180, 1181f
Testosterone, 1218t
Tetra- (prefix), 130
Tetrabutylammonium fluoride, 782
Tetrachloromethane, 242
Tetradecane, 125t
Tetrafluoroethylene, monomers in polymerization, 583t
Tetrahalide, 426
Tetrahedral arrangement, 25, 26–27, 28t
Tetrahedral geometry, of acyclic alkanes, 121–122
Tetrahedral oxygen, 326
Tetrahedral stereogenic center, 172, 173, 176, 185, 186
Tetrahedrane, 145
Tetrahydrocannabinol (THC), 116
mass spectrum of, 492, 493f
structure of, 74
Tetrahydrofuran (THF), 118, 329, 662, 923, 924–926, 933, 934
complexed with borane, 401
as solvent, 251f, 355
Tetrahydrogestrinone, 1218
α-Tetralone, 677
Tetramethyl α-D-glucopyranose, 1121f
Tetramethylsilane (TMS), 517, 518, 543
Tetravalent carbon, 4, 27
Tetrodotoxin, 5, 5f, 611, 611f
Thalidomide, 166, 176–177
THC. *See* Tetrahydrocannabinol (THC)
Thermodynamic enolates, 925, 926, 934, 935
Thermodynamic product, in electrophilic addition reactions of conjugated dienes, 608–610, 609f
Thermodynamics, 215–218, 217f, 217t
of hydrate formation, 835–836
Thermoplastics, 1243
Thermosetting polymers, 1243
THF. *See* Tetrahydrofuran (THF)
Thiazolinone, 1166, 1193
Thioester, 895–896
Thiol (functional group), 90t
Thionyl chloride
conversion of alcohols to alkyl halides with, 349
conversion of carboxylic acids to acid chlorides, 880f, 881
Three-dimensional representation, of acyclic alkanes, 121–122
Threonine, 751
isoelectric point for, 1152t
pK_a values for, 1152t
structure of, 1150f, 1151
Threose
D-threose, 1106, 1106f, 1107f
L-threose, 1106, 1106f
Thrombin, 1149
Thromboxanes, 1205, 1206f, 1206t
Thymine, 1137, 1138f
Thymol, 550, 662
Ticlopidine, 854
Tiotropium bromide, 334
Titanium(IV) isopropoxide, 471
Toads (*Bufo*), 998
Tobacco, 637f
Tobramycin, 1135
Tollens reagent, 771, 1121
Toluene, 115, 494
in BTX mixture, 637
electrophilic aromatic substitution reaction, 682, 687
oxidation to benzoic acid, 701
structure of, 634
synthesis by Friedel–Crafts alkylation, 705
Toluene 2,6-diisocyanate, 1240
p-Toluenesulfonate. *See* Tosylate
p-Toluenesulfonic acid (TsOH), 74, 741, 837
dehydration of alcohols to alkenes in, 338, 344, 345f
p-Toluenesulfonyl chloride (TsCl), 352, 354, 355f
p-Toluidine, 1009, 1010f
Torsional energy, 140–141
Torsional strain, 140–141, 143t, 144, 145, 146
Tosic acid, 741
Tosylate, 352–354, 355f
Tosyl group, 352, 741
TPA (thermal polyaspartate), 1250
Trabectedin, 5, 5f
Trade name, 126
trans (prefix), 377–378
Trans diaxial geometry, 306–308, 307f
Trans dihalide, 426
Trans fats, 451–452
Trans geometry
alkenes, 374, 374t, 377–378, 392, 395
cycloalkenes, 374
Trans isomers
of 2-butene, 292–293, 292f, 294
of cycloalkanes, 151–154
definition of, 151, 292
of disubstituted cycloalkanes, 188
Transition state
definition of, 220
drawing structure of, 221
of E1 elimination reactions, 302, 302f
of E2 elimination reactions, 295–296, 295f, 297, 300, 305
in electrophilic addition, 388, 388f
endothermic reaction, 260–270, 269f
in energy diagrams, 220–224, 224f
exothermic reaction, 269, 270, 270f
four-centered, 402
in halogenation reactions, 565f, 567, 568f, 569, 569f
Hammond postulate and, 269–271, 269f, 270f, 271f, 568
S_N1 substitution reactions, 263, 263f, 274
S_N2 substitution reactions, 255, 255f, 257–259, 259f, 274
in two-step reactions, 222–224, 224f
Trans protons, 536, 537f
Tri- (prefix), 130
Triacylglycerols, 1197–1200
combustion of, 1200
common fatty acids in, 1197t
degrees of unsaturation in, 450–451
energy storage in, 1200
fats and oils, 384
formation of, 110
hydrogenation of, 450–452, 451f, 1199
hydrolysis of, 382, 888, 889, 1199
melting point, 382, 383t, 1197–1198
mixed, 1197
olestra as a substitute for, 888
oxidation of, 577, 578f, 1199
saponification of, 889
saturated, 887, 888f, 1197–1199, 1197t, 1198f
simple, 1197
structure of, 382, 887, 888f, 1195f, 1197–1198, 1197t, 1198f, 1203f
unsaturated, 1197–1199, 1197t, 1198f
Trialkylborane, 402, 402f
Triarylphosphine, 1050
1,3,5-Tribromobenzene, synthesis of, 1023–1024, 1024f
Tributyltin hydride, 592
Trichlorofluoromethane, 3, 573
Trichloromethane, 242
2,4,5-Trichlorophenoxyacetic acid herbicide (2,4,5-T), 670f
Tricyclohexylphosphine, 1046
Tridecane, 125t
Trienes, 376
Triethylamine, 75, 287, 991, 1050
1,2,4-Triethylcyclopentane, 134f
Trifluoroacetic acid, for removal of Boc protecting group, 1170
2,2,2-Trifluoroethanol, 69–70, 70f
Trifluoromethanesulfonic acid, 741
Trigonal planar carbocation, 264
Trigonal planar double bond, 291
Trigonal planar molecule, 25, 26, 28t
carbon radical, 559
carbonyl group, 754–755
carboxy group, 719
Trigonal pyramidal, 27, 989
Trihalomethanes, 1053
Trimethylamine, 990, 990f, 995
Trimethyl borate, 1047
2,5,5-Trimethylcyclohexanecarboxylic acid, 720
1,2,2-Trimethylcyclohexanol, 370
2,5,5-Trimethylcyclohexanol, 327f
2,3,5-Trimethyl-2-hexene, 376
2,2,4-Trimethylpentane, combustion of, 155
2,3,5-Trimethyl-4-propylheptane, 130f
Triols, 328
Tripeptide, 1160, 1173
Triphenylene, 664
Triphenylmethyl radical, 592
Triphenylphosphine, 826, 1046, 1048
Triphenylphosphine oxide, 825, 827
Triple bonds
in alkynes, 88, 89t, 417–418
of benzyne, 698–699
bond length and bond strength, 43, 44t

components of carbon–carbon, 41
as functional group, 88, 89t
Lewis structure, 16
NMR spectra of, 526, 526t, 527f
reduction of, 452–455, 455f
Triple helix, of collagen, 1183, 1183f
Triplet, NMR spectrum, 529, 530–531, 531t, 532t, 535f, 538
Tri(*o*-tolyl)phosphine, 1046, 1052
Triynes, 418
Tropylium cation, 649, 654, 654f
Truvia. *See* Rebaudioside A
Trypsin, 1167, 1167t
Tryptophan, 752
isoelectric point for, 1152t
pK_a values for, 1152t
structure of, 1150f
TsCl (*p*-toluenesulfonyl chloride), 352, 354, 355f
TsOH. *See* *p*-Toluenesulfonic acid (TsOH)
Tuberculosis, 260
Tulipalin A, 984
Tungsten, 1056
ar-Turmerone, 964
Twistoflex, 638, 638f
Two-electron bond, 12, 14
Two-step reaction mechanism, 222–224, 224f, 227
Tylenol. *See* Acetaminophen
Tyrian purple, 1028
Tyrosine
isoelectric point for, 1152t
pK_a values for, 1152t
structure of, 1150f
Tyvek, 1248

U

Ultraviolet light
absorption by conjugated dienes, 619–621, 620f
skin damage from, 620–621
Undecane, 121, 125t
Unimolecular elimination. *See* E1 elimination reactions
Unimolecular reaction
elimination reactions, 294, 301
in nucleophilic substitution reactions, 254, 262
organic reactions, 227
Unknown
analysis using mass spectrometry, 486–488
using ^{1}H NMR to identify an, 541–543
α,β-Unsaturated carbonyl compounds, 788–791
1,2-addition to, 789–791
1,4-addition to, 789–791
in Michael reaction, 972–974, 974f
resonance structures, 973
in Robinson annulation, 974–978
synthesis of
in dehydration of aldol product, 958–959, 961, 963f
from α-halo carbonyl compounds, 932
Unsaturated fatty acid. *See* Fatty acids, unsaturated
Unsaturation, degrees of
in alkenes, 449–450
benzene, 631, 632
calculation of, 374–376, 449–450
hydrogenation data and, 449–450
in triacylglycerols, 450–451
Unsaturation, in alkynes, 417
Uracil, 1137, 1138f
Urethanes, 1240
Urushiols, 738

V

Valdecoxib, 1207
Valence bond theory, 650
Valence electrons, 11–13, 18t, 35
Valence shell electron pair repulsion (VSEPR) theory, 25
Valeric acid, structure of, 721t
Valine
isoelectric point for, 1152t
pK_a values for, 1152t
structure of, 1150f
Valinomycin, 107
Valium. *See* Diazepam
Valproic acid, 83
Vancomycin, 118
van der Waals forces, 92–94, 93f, 95t
in alkanes, 136
surface area and, 93, 93f
Vane, John, 727
Vanillin, 32, 550, 816f
Vanilloids, 4
Vasopressin, 1163, 1164f, 1180
Vegetable oil, 887, 889
partial hydrogenation of, 451, 451f
Venlafaxine, 781
Ventolin. *See* Albuterol
β-Vetivone, 950, 953, 982
Viagra. *See* Sildenafil
Vibration of bonds, infrared spectroscopy and, 496, 498–500, 498f
Vicia faba, 7
Vicinal dibromide, 421, 422
Vicinal dihalides, 310, 395, 421–422
Vinegar, 725
Vinyl acetate
NMR spectrum of, 537–538, 538f
polymerization of, 1229, 1232f
structure of, 1229f
Vinylboranes, 1047, 1049
Vinyl bromide, 1047, 1049
Vinyl carbanion, 455
Vinyl carbocation, 424, 425, 428
Vinyl chloride, 55
monomers in polymerization, 583t
polymerization of, 1226, 1234
structure of, 1226, 1229f
1-Vinylcyclohexene, 379f
Vinyl group, 379
Vinyl halides, 239, 239f, 277
coupling reactions with
alkene, 1050–1051
organoborane, 1047
organocuprates, 1044
reactivity of, 674
synthesis in hydrohalogenation of alkynes, 424–425
Vinylidene chloride, polymerization of, 1234
Vinyl iodide, 1050
Vioxx. *See* Rofecoxib
Viracept. *See* Nelfinavir
Vitamin(s), 102–104
definition of, 102, 1204
fat-soluble, 102, 156, 1204, 1205f
origin of term, 102
water soluble, 102, 103
Vitamin A, 102–103, 345f
β-carotene conversion to, 103
deficiency, 102, 1204f
electrostatic potential plot of, 1204, 1205f
role in the body, 1204f
solubility, 102–103
sources, 1204, 1204f
structure, 102, 292, 1204f, 1209
Vitamin B_3, 103
Vitamin B_5, 104
Vitamin B_6, 48–49
Vitamin C, 590
Vitamin C (ascorbic acid), 86, 914
solubility of, 103
sources of, 103
structure of, 103, 871
Vitamin D_3, 603, 1080
deficiency, 1204f
role in the body, 1204f
sources of, 1204
structure of, 292, 1204f
Vitamin E, 116
as antioxidant, 578–579
deficiency, 1204f
electrostatic potential plot of, 1204, 1205f
as radical scavenger, 561
role in the body, 1204f
sources of, 1204
structure of, 578, 1204f
Vitamin K (phylloquinone), 103
deficiency, 1204f
role in the body, 1204f
sources of, 1204
structure of, 1204f
VSEPR (valence shell electron pair repulsion) theory, 25
Vulcanization, 1237, 1237f

W

Wald, George, 832
Walden, Dr. Paul, 256
Walden inversion, 256
Wang resin, 1192
Warfarin, 752
Water
as achiral molecule, 171
electrophilic addition of, 394–395, 405–406
electrostatic potential plot for, 47f
hybrid orbitals in, 38, 38f
hydration of alkynes, 423f, 427–429
hydrogen bonding, 94
as Lewis base, 77–78
Markovnikov addition of, 427
molecular shape of, 27–28
nucleophilicity of, 273
pK_a of, 63t, 66, 67
as polar molecule, 47
removing from reaction mixture using Dean–Stark trap, 837, 838f
as solvent, 99–101, 250, 250f, 275, 738, 738f
Wavelength
definition of, 494
electromagnetic spectrum and, 494–495, 495f
length units for, 494
Wavenumber, 496, 497
Waxes, 157, 157f, 1196
Wedges, 151, 1103
Wellbutrin. *See* Bupropion
Williamson ether synthesis, 334, 335
Willow tree, 76, 76f
Wittig reaction, 825–830
mechanism of, 827
retrosynthetic analysis using, 828–829
Wittig reagent, 825–830
Wittig, Georg, 825
Wohl degradation, 1123–1124
Wolff–Kishner reduction, 702
Wood alcohol, 332f. *See also* Methanol
Woodward, R. B., 1071
Woodward–Hoffmann rules
for cycloaddition reactions, 1084–1085, 1085t
for electrocyclic reactions, 1080, 1083t
for sigmatropic rearrangements, 1087t
Wool
binding of dyes to, 1029
structure of, 893, 893f

X

Xalatan. *See* Latanoprost
X-ray crystallography, 1126
m-Xylene, 693
p-Xylene, 494, 587, 637
D-Xylose, 1106, 1107f
D-Xylulose, 1108f

Y

-yl (suffix), 127, 329, 812
-yl chloride (suffix), 864, 867, 867t
-ylic acid (suffix), 866
Ylide, 826
-yne (suffix), 418

Z

Z (prefix), 378–379
Zaitsev rule, 299–301, 303, 307, 338, 1018
Z configuration, of double bonds, 382, 1237–1238
Zidovudine, 4. *See also* AZT (azidodeoxythymidine)
Ziegler, Karl, 1236
Ziegler–Natta catalysts, 1236, 1237
Ziegler–Natta polymerization, 1235–1236
Zigzag skeletal structures, 144
Zileuton, 362
Zinc
in Clemmensen reduction, 702
conversion of ozonide to carbonyl compounds, 463
Zinc chloride, 347
Zinc–copper couple, 1055–1056
Zingerone, 51
Zingiberene, 381f, 479, 612, 1209f
Zocor. *See* Simvastatin
Zoloft. *See* Sertraline
Zolpidem, 662
Zuclomiphene, 411
Zwitterion, 743, 1151
Zyban. *See* Bupropion
Zyflor. *See* Zileuton

Common Abbreviations, Arrows, and Symbols

Abbreviations

Ac	acetyl, CH_3CO-
BBN	9-borabicyclo[3.3.1]nonane
BINAP	2,2'-bis(diphenylphosphino)-1,1'-binaphthyl
Boc	*tert*-butoxycarbonyl, $(CH_3)_3COCO-$
bp	boiling point
Bu	butyl, $CH_3CH_2CH_2CH_2-$
CBS reagent	Corey–Bakshi–Shibata reagent
DBN	1,5-diazabicyclo[4.3.0]non-5-ene
DBU	1,8-diazabicyclo[5.4.0]undec-7-ene
DCC	dicyclohexylcarbodiimide
DET	diethyl tartrate
DIBAL-H	diisobutylaluminum hydride, $[(CH_3)_2CHCH_2]_2AlH$
DMF	dimethylformamide, $HCON(CH_3)_2$
DMSO	dimethyl sulfoxide, $(CH_3)_2S=O$
ee	enantiomeric excess
Et	ethyl, CH_3CH_2-
Fmoc	9-fluorenylmethoxycarbonyl
HMPA	hexamethylphosphoramide, $[(CH_3)_2N]_3P=O$
HOMO	highest occupied molecular orbital
IR	infrared
LDA	lithium diisopropylamide, $LiN[CH(CH_3)_2]_2$
LUMO	lowest unoccupied molecular orbital
m-	meta
mCPBA	*m*-chloroperoxybenzoic acid
Me	methyl, CH_3-
MO	molecular orbital
mp	melting point
MS	mass spectrometry
MW	molecular weight
NBS	*N*-bromosuccinimide
NMO	*N*-methylmorpholine *N*-oxide
NMR	nuclear magnetic resonance
o-	ortho
p-	para
PCC	pyridinium chlorochromate
Ph	phenyl, C_6H_5-
ppm	parts per million
Pr	propyl, $CH_3CH_2CH_2-$
RCM	ring-closing metathesis
ROMP	ring-opening metathesis polymerization
TBDMS	*tert*-butyldimethylsilyl
THF	tetrahydrofuran
TMS	tetramethylsilane, $(CH_3)_4Si$
Ts	tosyl, *p*-toluenesulfonyl, $CH_3C_6H_4SO_2-$
TsOH	*p*-toluenesulfonic acid, $CH_3C_6H_4SO_3H$
UV	ultraviolet

Arrows

$\longrightarrow$	reaction arrow
$\rightleftharpoons$	equilibrium arrows
$\longleftrightarrow$	double-headed arrow, used between resonance structures
$\curvearrowright$	full-headed curved arrow, showing the movement of an electron pair
$\frown$	half-headed curved arrow (fishhook), showing the movement of an electron
$\Longrightarrow$	retrosynthetic arrow
$\not\longrightarrow$	no reaction

Symbols

$+\!\!\!\longrightarrow$	dipole
$h\nu$	light
Δ	heat
δ^+	partial positive charge
δ^-	partial negative charge
λ	wavelength
ν	frequency
$\tilde{\nu}$	wavenumber
HA	Brønsted–Lowry acid
B:	Brønsted–Lowry base
$:Nu^-$	nucleophile
E^+	electrophile
X	halogen
◀	bond oriented forward
'''''	bond oriented behind
- - -	partial bond
$[\;\;]^\ddagger$	transition state
[O]	oxidation
[H]	reduction

Common Element Colors Used in Molecular Art

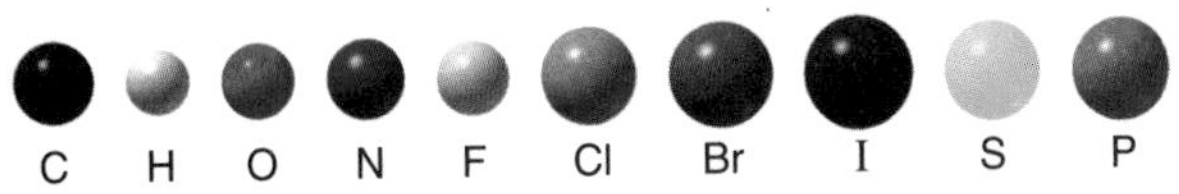
C
H
O
N
F
Cl
Br
I
S
P